# RHS
# PLANT
# FINDER
# 1999-2000

# RHS
# PLANT FINDER
# 1999-2000

DEVISED BY CHRIS PHILIP

COMPILED BY THE
ROYAL HORTICULTURAL SOCIETY

EDITED BY TONY LORD
WITH THE BOTANISTS
OF THE RHS GARDEN WISLEY

DORLING KINDERSLEY
LONDON • NEW YORK • SYDNEY

A DORLING KINDERSLEY BOOK

Published by
Dorling Kindersley Ltd
9 Henrietta Street
LONDON WC2E 8PS
www.dk.com

British Library Cataloguing Publication Data.
A Catalogue record for this book is available from the British Library.

ISBN 0 7513 0668-1
ISSN 0961-2599

Compiled by
The Royal Horticultural Society
80 Vincent Square
London
SW1P 2PE
Registered charity no: 222879
www.rhs.org.uk

Illustrations by Murdo Culver
Maps by Alan Cooper

Printed and bound in Italy by Legoprint

The Compiler and the Editors of the *RHS Plant Finder* have taken every care, in the time available,
to check all the information supplied to them by the nurseries concerned. Nevertheless, in a work of this
kind, containing as it does hundreds of thousand of separate computer encodings, errors and omissions
will, inevitably, occur. Neither the RHS, the Publisher nor the Editors can accept responsibility for
any consequences that may arise from such errors.

If you find mistakes we hope that you will let us know so that the matter can be corrected in the next edition.

**Front cover photographs clockwise from top left:** *Aster novae-angliae* 'Andenken an Alma Pötschke', *Allium rosenbachianum, Mutisia decurrens, Actinidia kolomikta, Adenophora bulleyana, Paeonia officinalis* 'Rubra Plena', *Helenium* 'Butterpat', *Meconopsis grandis*. **Spine:** *Camellia japonica* 'Elegans'. **Back cover photographs clockwise from top right:** *Aconitum lycoctonum* subsp. *vulparia, Aquilegia vulgaris* var. *stellata* 'Nora Barlow', *Adonis amurensis* 'Flore Pleno', *Alstroemeria hookeri, Anemone coronaria* 'Mister Fokker', *Beaufortia sparsa, Acacia baileyana, Camellia japonica* 'Elegans', *Crocus malyi, Agave victoriae-reginae*

# CONTENTS

SYMBOLS AND ABBREVIATIONS
*page 6*

PREFACE
*page 7*

INTRODUCTION *page 8*
Available from the Compiler *page 8*
• *Application for entry* • *Plants last listed
in earlier editions* • *Back copies*
• *List of nurseries for plants with more
than 30 suppliers* • *The* RHS Plant Finder
*on CD-Rom*
Acknowledgments *page 9*

PLANTS *page 10*

HOW TO USE THE
PLANT DIRECTORY *page 12*
How to find your Plant
Additional Plant Name Information
in the Directory
Supplementary Keys to the Directory

THE PLANT DIRECTORY *page 16*

SUPPLEMENTARY KEYS TO
THE DIRECTORY *page 755*
Nomenclature Notes *page 755*
Collectors' References *page 761*
Classification of Genera *page 764*
Reverse Synonyms *page 768*

THE NAMING OF PLANTS *page 773*
Bibliography *page 778*
International Plant Finders *page 791*

NURSERIES *page 793*

HOW TO USE THE
NURSERY LISTINGS *page 793*

NURSERY DETAILS BY CODE *page 796*

SPECIALIST NURSERIES *page 910*

NURSERY INDEX BY NAME *page 912*

MAPS *page 920*

DISPLAY ADVERTISEMENTS *page 932*

# SYMBOLS AND ABBREVIATIONS

## SYMBOLS APPEARING TO THE LEFT OF THE NAME

*  Name not validated. Not listed in the appropriate International Registration Authority checklist nor in works cited in the Bibliography. For fuller discussion see The Naming of Plants on p.773

I  Invalid name. See *International Code of Botanical Nomenclature 1994* and *International Code of Nomenclature for Cultivated Plants 1995*. For fuller discussion see The Naming of Plants on p.773

N  Refer to Nomenclature Notes on p.755

¶  New plant entry in this edition (or reinstated, having been last listed in an earlier edition)

♦  New or amended synonym or cross-reference included for the first time this year

§  Plant listed elsewhere in the Plant Directory under a synonym

x  Hybrid genus

+  Graft hybrid genus

## SYMBOLS APPEARING TO THE RIGHT OF THE NAME

✿  National Council for the Conservation of Plants and Gardens (NCCPG) Plant Collection exists for all or part of this genus. Provisional collections appear in brackets. Full details of the NCCPG Plant Collections are contained in the *National Plant Collections™ Directory 1999* available from: NCCPG, The Stable Courtyard, RHS Garden Wisley, Woking, Surrey GU23 6QP

♀  The Royal Horticultural Society's Award of Garden Merit, see p.15.

®  Registered Trade Mark

™  Trade Mark

(d)  double-flowered

(F)  Fruit

(f)  female

(m)  male

(v)  variegated plant, see p.15

For abbreviations relating to individual genera see **Classification of Genera** p.764.
For **Collectors' References** see p.761.
For symbols used in the **Nurseries** section see the reverse of the card insert

*Please, never use an old edition*

## SYMBOLS AND ABBREVIATIONS USED AS PART OF THE NAME

x  hybrid species
aff.  affinis (allied to)
cl.  clone
cv(s)  cultivar(s)
f.  forma (botanical form)
g.  grex
sp.  species
subsp.  subspecies
subvar.  subvarietas (botanical subvariety)
var.  varietas (botanical variety

## GEOGRAPHICAL KEY TO CODES

The first letter of each nursery code represents the area of the country in which the nursery is situated.

C  **South West England**
Avon, Devon, Dorset, Channel Isles, Cornwall, Isles of Scilly, Somerset & Wiltshire.

E  **Eastern England**
Cambridgeshire, Essex, Lincolnshire, Norfolk & Suffolk.

G  **Scotland**
Borders, Central, Dumfries & Galloway, Fife, Grampian, Highlands, Inverness, Orkney, Strathclyde, Shetland.

I  **Northern Ireland & Republic of Ireland.**

L  **London area**
Bedfordshire, Berkshire, Buckinghamshire, Hertfordshire, London, Middlesex, Surrey.

M  **Midlands**
Cheshire, Derbyshire, Isle of Man, Leicestershire, Northamptonshire, Nottinghamshire, Oxfordshire, Rutland, Staffordshire, Warwickshire, West Midlands.

N  **Northern England**
Cleveland, Cumbria, Durham, East Yorkshire, Greater Manchester, Humberside, Lancashire, Merseyside, Northumberland, North Yorkshire, South Yorkshire, Tyne & Wear, West Yorkshire.

S  **Southern England**
East Sussex, Hampshire, Isle of Wight, Kent, West Sussex.

W  **Wales and Western England**
All Welsh counties, Gloucestershire, Herefordshire, Shropshire and Worcestershire.

X  **Abroad**

# PREFACE

In this, the third edition of the *RHS Plant Finder* to be produced by the Society and published by Dorling Kindersley, regular users will notice that we have made a number of changes to the book. This is the first year in which we have reviewed its contents since the Society took over responsibility for its compilation from the late Chris Philip, the originator of *The Plant Finder*. Over the past three years we have gained experience in producing the book using our Horticultural Database at the RHS Garden Wisley and last year time was set aside to discuss the contents and how they might best be simplified and improved.

The book naturally forms two main sections: PLANTS and NURSERIES which we have sought to make clearer in this edition. All the information relating to the Plant Directory is now grouped together and separated from Nurseries by a card insert. Nomenclature Notes, Classification of Genera, Collectors' References, Reverse Synonyms, the Naming of Plants and the Bibliography will all be found after the Plant Directory and preceding the card insert for Nurseries. We believe this will make the Plant Directory and its cross-references – the essence of the book – both easier to follow and to find, as it is now placed immediately after the Introduction from p.11.

In this edition, a key change is the integration of what was formerly known as Plant Deletions into the main Plant Directory. Against the appropriate plant name, instead of nursery codes, you will find the phrase 'last listed', together with a year, e.g. '1997'. This indicates that the plant was last listed in the 1997-98 edition of the book.

The nursery indexes have been simplified by combining the Code-Nursery Index, Additional Nursery Index, Seed Suppliers, Cactus and Succulent Suppliers and Orchid Suppliers into one main listing called Nursery Details by Code in which every nursery now has a unique code. A further innovation, the Specialist Nurseries listing, has been included to help the reader find suppliers not only of seed, cacti, succulents and orchids but of 14 other plant groups as well.

Many users of the *RHS Plant Finder* find the maps at the back of invaluable assistance in planning visits to nurseries. In this edition, new Ordnance Survey grid references will make it even easier to locate the nurseries you wish to visit.

As always, we are indebted to the nurseries who supply their catalogues and plant information every year. We would especially like to welcome the 90 new nurseries whose details are listed for the first time. A new system of electronically updating nursery lists was trialled this year and our thanks go to all those nurseries that took part. This system has eased their task of submitting their entry and has enabled us to include more plants in the Plant Directory.

We must also thank Dorling Kindersley for providing a new style for the text, in particular for the new layout for Nursery Details by Code. The changes in type, style and layout should all add to the accessibility of the book and I look forward to using it as, I hope, will you.


**Gordon Rae**
Director General
The Royal Horticultural Society

# INTRODUCTION

The *RHS Plant Finder* exists to put enthusiastic gardeners in touch with suppliers of plants, many of them unusual. The book is divided into two related sections – PLANTS and NURSERIES. PLANTS includes an A–Z Plant Directory of some 70,000 plant names, against which are listed a series of nursery codes. These codes point the reader to the full nursery details contained in the NURSERIES section towards the back of the book. The *RHS Plant Finder* is comprehensively up-dated every year and provides the plant lover with the richest source of suppliers known to us, whether you are looking for plants locally, shopping from your armchair or touring the country in search of the rare and unusual.

Simply because a nursery is listed against a given plant, it does not necessarily follow that the plant will be in stock throughout the year.

TO AVOID DISAPPOINTMENT, WE SUGGEST THAT YOU ALWAYS:

Check with the nursery before visiting or ordering and always use the current edition of the book.

## AVAILABLE FROM THE COMPILER

### APPLICATION FOR ENTRY

Nurseries appearing in the *RHS Plant Finder* for the first time this year are printed in bold type in the Nursery Index by Name starting on p.912.

If any other nursery wishes to be considered for inclusion in the next edition of the *RHS Plant Finder* (2000-01), please write for details to the Compiler at the address below. The closing date for new entries will be 31 January 2000.

### PLANTS LAST LISTED IN EARLIER EDITIONS

*Previously known as Plant Deletions*
Plants cease to be listed for a variety of reasons but those listed in one or other of the last three editions are named in the Plant Directory, together with the date they were last listed. For more information turn to 'How to Use the Plant Directory' on p.12.

A booklet of the 18,000 or so plants last listed in earlier editions, and for which we currently have no known supplier, is available from the Compiler. Please send three £1 stamps.

### BACK COPIES

For those who wish to find previously listed plants, back editions of the *RHS Plant Finder* are still available at £6.00 (incl. p&p) from the Compiler.

### LISTS OF NURSERIES FOR PLANTS WITH MORE THAN 30 SUPPLIERS

To prevent the *RHS Plant Finder* from becoming still larger, if more than 30 nurseries offer the same plant we cease to print the nursery codes and instead list the plant as having 'more than 30 suppliers'. This is detailed more fully in 'How to Use the Plant Directory' on p.12.

If any readers have difficulty in finding such a plant, we will be pleased to send a full list of all the nurseries that we have on file as stockists. All such enquiries must include the full name of the plant being sought, as shown in the *RHS Plant Finder*, together with an A5 size SAE.

The above may all be obtained from:
**The Compiler,**
*RHS Plant Finder,*
**RHS Garden Wisley,**
**Woking,**
**Surrey  GU23 6QB**

### THE RHS PLANT FINDER ON CD-ROM

The *RHS Plant Finder* is available in an electronic format as part of the *RHS Plant Finder CD-ROM*. It is available from **RHS Enterprises Ltd, RHS Garden Wisley, Woking, Surrey, GU23 6QB.**

# ACKNOWLEDGMENTS

Generating the *RHS Plant Finder* from *BG-BASE*™ has required concentrated, steady and meticulous work throughout the last year from all involved. Plant Finder Compiler Clare Burgh, assisted by June Skinner, has added many more nursery codes and has co-ordinated the complex job of compiling nursery information and plant lists with astonishing proficiency. Our team has again benefited enormously from the efforts of Dr Kerry Walter of *BG-BASE* Inc. and Niki Simpson, Database Administrator. Dr Andrew Sier, Senior Database Administrator, has kept the database operational and assisted with name editing. I continue to check names in the *RHS Plant Finder*, especially each year's new entries, and all our efforts are supervised by the Society's Head of Botany, Dr Simon Thornton-Wood. I could not wish for more efficient and helpful colleagues. All who use the *RHS Plant Finder* owe them thanks and I am particularly grateful to them all for making the job of editing so much easier.

For the compilation of this edition, I am once more indebted to my colleagues on the RHS Advisory Panel on Nomenclature and Taxonomy: Chris Brickell, Susyn Andrews, James Compton, Stephen Jury, Sabina Knees, Alan Leslie, Simon Thornton-Wood, Piers Trehane and Adrian Whiteley, along with Mike Grant, Diana Miller and Janet Cubey, all of whom have provided much valuable guidance during the past year. Scores of nurseries have sent helpful information about asterisked plants which has proved immensely useful in verifying some of the most obscure names, as well as suggested corrections to existing entries. Though there has not been time to enter all these comments and corrections onto our database (work on new entries has had to take priority), all information received will be checked and recorded in time for our next edition. However, I have had to reject about 40 per cent of the suggested corrections because they contravene the Codes of Nomenclature for reasons covered in the Nomenclature Notes on p.755. I am grateful, too, to our regular correspondents, particularly Jennifer Hewitt for so thoroughly checking iris entries and to the RHS International Registrars.

| | |
|---|---|
| *Artemisia* | Dr J.D. Twibell ('94) |
| Bamboos | D. McClintock ('90-'94) |
| *Bougainvillea* | S. Read ('94) |
| *Camellia* | T.J. Savige, International Registrar, NSW, Australia ('93 & '96) |
| *Cimicifuga* | J. Compton ('94) |
| *Cistus* | R. Page ('97 & '99) |
| Conifers | J. Lewis, International Registrar, RHS Wisley ('93) |
| | H.J. Welch, World Conifer Data Pool ('90-'93) |
| | P. Trehane, International Registrar, RHS Wisley ('94 & '99) |
| *Cotoneaster* | Jeanette Fryer, NCCPG Collection Holder ('91-'92) |
| *Cyclamen* | Dr C. Grey-Wilson ('94) |
| *Dahlia* | R. Hedge, RHS Wisley ('96-'99) |
| *Delphinium* | Dr A.C. Leslie, International Registrar, RHS Wisley ('93, '97-'99) |
| *Dianthus* | Dr A.C. Leslie, International Registrar, RHS Wisley ('91-'99) |
| *Gesneriaceae* | J.D. Dates, International Registrar ('94) |
| *Gladiolus* | F.N. Franks ('92) |
| Heathers | D. McClintock ('92) |
| *Hebe* | Mrs J. Hewitt ('94-'99) |
| *Hedera* | P.Q. Rose & Mrs H. Key ('91 & '93) |
| | Alison Rutherford ('92-'94) |
| *Hypericum* | Dr N.K.B. Robson ('94-'97) |
| *Ilex* | Ms S. Andrews ('92-'98) |
| *Iris* | Mrs J. Hewitt ('95-'99) |
| *Jovibarba* & *Sempervivum* | P.J. Mitchell, International Registrar, Sempervivum Society ('91-'93 & '98) |
| *Lavandula* | Ms S. Andrews ('92-'99) |
| *Lilium* | Dr A.C. Leslie, International Registrar, RHS Wisley ('91-'99) |
| *Liriope* | Dr P.R. Fantz ('99) |
| *Narcissus* | Mrs S. Kington, International Registrar, RHS ('91-'99) |
| *Ophiopogon* | Dr P.R. Fantz ('99) |
| *Pelargonium* | Mrs H. Key ('91-'95) |
| *Pelargonium* spp. | Mrs D. Miller ('93) |
| *Polemonium* | Mrs D. Nichol-Brown ('94) |
| *Rhododendron* | Dr A.C. Leslie, International Registrar, RHS Wisley ('91-'99) |
| *Salix* | Dr R.D. Meikle ('93) |
| *Salvia* | J. Compton ('92 & '94) |
| *Zauschneria* | P. Trehane ('94) |

To all these, as well as the many readers and nurseries who have also made comments and suggestions, we are, once again, sincerely grateful.

**Tony Lord**

# Plants

WHATEVER PLANT YOU ARE LOOKING FOR,
MAYBE AN OLD FAVOURITE OR A MORE UNUSUAL
CULTIVAR, SEARCH HERE FOR A LIST OF THE
SUPPLIERS THAT ARE CLOSEST TO YOU.

# HOW TO USE THE PLANT DIRECTORY

## NURSERY CODES

Look up the plant you require in the alphabetical
Plant Directory. Against each plant you will find
one or more four-letter codes, for example SLan,
each code representing one nursery offering that
plant. The first letter of each code indicates the
main area of the country in which the nursery is
situated, based on their county. For this
geographical key, refer to Symbols and
Abbreviations p.6 and the card insert at the
beginning of the NURSERIES section p.793.

Turn to the **Nursery Details by Code** starting on
p.796 where, in alphabetical order of codes, you
will find details of each nursery which offers the
plant in question. If you wish to visit any of these
nurseries you can find its location on one of the
maps (following p.920). Mail order only nurseries
are generally not indicated on the maps. For a fuller
explanation of how to use the nursery listings please
turn to p.793. Always check that the nursery you
select has the plant in stock before you set out.

## PLANTS WITH MORE THAN 30 SUPPLIERS

In some cases, against the plant name you will see
the term 'more than 30 suppliers' instead of a
nursery code. Clearly, if we were to include every
plant listed by all nurseries, the *RHS Plant Finder*
would become unmanageably bulky. We therefore
ask nurseries to restrict their entries to only those
plants that are not already well represented. As a
result, if more than 30 nurseries offer any plant the
Directory gives no nursery codes and the plant is
listed instead as having 'more than 30 suppliers'.
You should have little difficulty in locating these in
local nurseries or garden centres. However, if you
are unable to find such plants, we will be pleased to
send a full list of all the nurseries that we have on
file as stockists. Please see the Introduction on p.8
for details of how to obtain the lists.

*Please, never use an old edition*

## IF YOU HAVE DIFFICULTY FINDING YOUR PLANT

If you cannot immediately find the plant you seek,
look through the various species of the genus. You
may be using an incomplete name. The problem is
most likely to arise in very large genera such as *Phlox*
where there are a number of possible species, each
with a large number of cultivars. A search through
the whole genus may well bring success.

## CROSS-REFERENCES

It may be that the plant name you seek is a
synonym. Our intention is to list nursery codes only
against the correct botanical name; where you find a
synonym you will be cross-referred to the correct
name. Sometimes you may find that the correct
botanical name to which you have been referred is
not listed. This is because it was last listed more
than three years ago as explained below. Major new
cross-references and synonyms have been marked
with a ◆. This sign has only been used when the
genus, species or cultivar name has been altered, but
not for minor typographic or orthographic changes.

## PLANTS LAST LISTED IN EARLIER EDITIONS

*Previously known as Plant Deletions*
It may also be that the plant you are seeking has no
known suppliers and is thus not listed. In this
edition, plants that were last listed in one or other of
the three previous editions of the *RHS Plant Finder*,
in a separate index called Plant Deletions, are here
integrated into the Plant Directory. Against the
plant name, instead of nursery codes, you will see
the phrase 'last listed' together with a year e.g.
'1997'. This indicates that the plant was last listed in
the 1997-98 edition of the book. Plants which have
received the AGM but which are not offered by any
of the nurseries in the book, are also included in this
way irrespective of when they were last listed.

The loss of a plant name from the Directory may
arise for a number of reasons – the supplier may
have gone out of business, or may not have
responded to our latest questionnaire and has

therefore been removed from the book. Such plants may well be still available but we have no current knowledge of their whereabouts. Alternatively, some plants may have been misnamed by nurseries in previous editions, but are now appearing under their correct name.

To obtain a booklet of plants last listed in earlier editions please see the Introduction on p.8.

## Finding Fruit and Vegetables

If the plant name you are seeking is a fruit or vegetable, you will need to look it up by its botanical name, for which you may find the following list useful.

Almond              See *Prunus dulcis*
Añu                 See *Tropaeolum tuberosum*
Apple               See *Malus domestica*
Apple, Crab         See *Malus*
Apricot             See *Prunus armeniaca*
Artichoke, Globe    See *Cynara cardunculus* Scolymus Group
Artichoke, Jerusalem See *Helianthus tuberosus*
Avocado             See *Persea*
Banana              See *Musa*
Blackberry          See *Rubus fruticosus*
Blackcurrant        See *Ribes nigrum*
Blueberry           See *Vaccinium corymbosum*
Boysenberry         See *Rubus* Boysenberry
Bullace             See *Prunus insititia*
Butternut           See *Juglans cinerea*
Calamondin          See × *Citrofortunella*
Cape Gooseberry     See *Physalis*
Carambola           See *Averrhoa carambola*
Cardoon             See *Cynara cardunculus*
Cashew-nut          See *Anacardium occidentale*
Cherimoya           See *Annona cherimola*
Cherry, Duke        See *Prunus × gondouinii*
Cherry, Sour or Morello  See *Prunus cerasus*
Cherry, Sweet       See *Prunus avium*
Chestnut, Sweet     See *Castanea*
Citron              See *Citrus medica*
Cobnut              See *Corylus avellana*
Coconut             See *Cocos nucifera*
Coffee              See *Coffea*
Cranberry           See *Vaccinium macrocarpon, V. oxycoccos*
Custard Apple       See *Annona cherimola, A. reticulata*
Damson              See *Prunus insititia*
Date                See *Phoenix dactylifera*
Elderberry          See *Sambucus*
Fig                 See *Ficus carica*
Filbert             See *Corylus maxima*
Gooseberry          See *Ribes uva-crispa* var. *reclinatum*
Granadilla          See *Passiflora quadrangularis*

Granadilla, Purple  See *Passiflora edulis*
Granadilla, Sweet   See *Passiflora ligularis*
Granadilla, Yellow  See *Passiflora laurifolia*
Grape               See *Vitis*
Grapefruit          See *Citrus × paradisi*
Guava, Common       See *Psidium guajava*
Guava, Purple or Strawberry  See *Psidium littorale*
Hazelnut            See *Corylus*
Hickory, Shagbark   See *Carya ovata*
Hildaberry          See *Rubus* 'Hildaberry'
Horned Melon        See *Cucumis metulifer*
Jostaberry          See *Ribes × culverwellii* Jostaberry
Jujube              See *Ziziphus jujuba*
Kaffir Plum         See *Harpephyllum caffrum*
Kiwano              See *Cucumis metulifer*
Kiwi Fruit          See *Actinidia deliciosa*
Kumquat             See *Fortunella*
Lemon               See *Citrus limon*
Lime                See *Citrus aurantiifolia*
Loganberry          See *Rubus* Loganberry Group
Loquat              See *Eriobotrya japonica*
Mandarin            See *Citrus reticulata*
Mango               See *Mangifera indica*
Medlar              See *Mespilus germanica*
Mulberry            See *Morus*
Natal Plum          See *Carissa macrocarpa*
Nectarine           See *Prunus persica* var. *nectarina*
Nut, Cob            See *Corylus avellana*
Nut, Filbert        See *Corylus maxima*
Olive               See *Olea europaea*
Orange, Sour or Seville  See *Citrus aurantium*
Orange, Sweet       See *Citrus sinensis*
Passion Fruit       See *Passiflora*
Passion Fruit, Banana See *Passiflora mollissima*
Paw Paw             See *Carica papaya*
Peach               See *Prunus persica*
Pear                See *Pyrus communis*
Pear, Asian         See *Pyrus pyrifolia*
Pecan               See *Carya illinoinensis*
Pepino              See *Solanum muricatum*
Persimmon           See *Diospyros virginiana*
Persimmon, Japanese See *Diospyros kaki*
Pineapple Guava     See *Acca sellowiana*
Pinkcurrant         See *Ribes rubrum* (P)
Plum                See *Prunus domestica*
Pomegranate         See *Punica granatum*
Pummelo             See *Citrus maxima*
Rhubarb             See *Rheum × hybridum*
Quince              See *Cydonia*
Raspberry           See *Rubus idaeus*
Redcurrant          See *Ribes rubrum* (R)
Satsuma             See *Citrus unshiu*
Seakale             See *Crambe maritima*
Shaddock            See *Citrus maxima*

| | | | |
|---|---|---|---|
| Soursop | See *Annona muricata* | Tayberry | See *Rubus* Tayberry Group |
| Strawberry | See *Fragaria* | Tummelberry | See *Rubus* 'Tummelberry' |
| Sunberry | See *Rubus* 'Sunberry' | Ugli | See *Citrus* x *tangelo* 'Ugli' |
| Tamarillo | See *Cyphomandra betacea* | Veitchberry | See *Rubus* 'Veitchberry' |
| Tamarind | See *Tamarindus indica* | Walnut | See *Juglans* |
| Tangelo | See *Citrus* x *tangelo* | Whitecurrant | See *Ribes rubrum* (W) |
| Tangerine | See *Citrus reticulata* | Wineberry | See *Rubus phoenicolasius* |
| Tangor | See *Citrus* x *nobilis* | Worcesterberry | See *Ribes divaricatum* |
| | Tangor Group | Youngberry | See *Rubus* 'Youngberry' |

# ADDITIONAL PLANT NAME INFORMATION IN THE DIRECTORY

## DESCRIPTIVE TERMS

Terms which appear after the main part of the name, are shown in a smaller font to distinguish name parts that are cultivar authors, common names, collectors' codes and other descriptive terms. For example, *Penstemon* 'Sour Grapes' M. Fish, *Lobelia tupa* dark orange.

## TRADE DESIGNATIONS (SELLING NAMES) AND PLANT BREEDERS' RIGHTS

Plants granted protection under Plant Breeders' Rights (PBR) legislation, and those with high-volume international sales, are often given a code or nonsense name for registration purposes. Under the rules of the *International Code of Nomenclature for Cultivated Plants 1995* (ICNCP), such a name, established by a legal process, has to be regarded as the correct cultivar name for the plant.

Unfortunately, the names are often unpronounceable and usually meaningless so the plants are given other names designed to attract sales when they are released. These are often referred to as selling names but are officially termed trade designations. Also, when a cultivar name is translated into a language other than that in which it was published, the translation is regarded as a trade designation in the same way as a PBR selling name. The name in its original language is the correct cultivar name.

While PBRs remain active it is a legal requirement for both names to appear on a label at point-of-sale. The reason for this may not appear obvious until it is realised that there is potentially no limit to the number of trade designations for any one plant. In reality, most plants are sold under only one trade designation, but some, especially roses, are sold under a number of names, particularly when cultivars are introduced to other countries. Usually, the registered or original cultivar name is the only way to ensure that the same plant is not bought unwittingly under two or more different trade designations. Although the use of trade designations goes against the principle that a cultivar should have only one correct name, the ICNCP has had to accommodate them, and the *RHS Plant Finder* follows its recommendations. These are always to quote the cultivar name and trade designation together and to style the trade designation in a different typeface, without single quotation marks. In this edition, the cultivar names of plants commonly known by trade designations have been added (where known) and cross-referred to the trade designation. In the regrettably increasing number of cases in which two or more different trade designations are used for the same cultivar, any additional trade designation is cross-referred to the one most widely listed.

In the Plant Directory, both cultivar names and trade designations are listed in alphabetical order, making plants easy to find using either name. **Example in** *Rosa*:

'Macpic'                     see *R.* Picasso='Macpic'
Picasso='Macpic'      EBls MAus MGan

We often receive queries as to whether certain varieties are the subject of Plant Breeders' Rights. Up to date information on all matters concerning PBR in the UK can be obtained from:
**Mrs J G H Lee**
**Plant Variety Rights Office, White House Lane, Huntingdon Road, Cambridge CB3 0LF**
Tel: (01223) 342350, Fax: (01223) 342386.

For details of plants which may be covered by Community Rights contact the Community Plant Variety Office (CPVO):
**Office Communautaire des Variétés Végétales, B.P. 2141, F-49021 Angers Cedex 02, France.**
Tel: 0033 (0)241 36 84 50
Fax: 0033 (0)241 36 84 60

## VARIEGATED PLANTS

Following a suggestion from the Variegated Plant Group of the Hardy Plant Society, we have added a (v) to those plants which are 'variegated' although this may not be apparent from their name.  The dividing line between variegation and less distinct colour marking is necessarily arbitrary and plants with light veins, pale, silver or dark zones or leaves flushed in paler colours are not shown as being variegated unless there is an absolutely sharp distinction between paler and darker zones.
For further details of the Variegated Plant Group, please write to
**Stephen Taffler,
18 Hayes End Manor,
South Pemberton,
Somerset TA13 5BE.**

## ✿ THE AWARD OF GARDEN MERIT

The Award of Garden Merit (AGM) is one of the highest accolades the Royal Horticultural Society can give to a garden plant and is of practical value for the ordinary gardener.  Every AGM plant should have the following qualities:
* outstanding excellence for garden decoration or use
* available in the trade
* of good constitution
* requiring neither highly specialist growing conditions nor care.

A complete and categorised listing of over 6,000 AGM plants is available as *AGM Plants 1999* from **RHS Enterprises Ltd, RHS Garden Wisley, Woking, Surrey, GU23 6QB. Tel:(01483) 211320**

# SUPPLEMENTARY KEYS TO THE PLANT DIRECTORY

## NOMENCLATURE NOTES

These refer to plants in the Directory that are marked with a 'N' to the left of the name.  The notes add further information to names which are complex or may be confusing.  They start on p.755.

## COLLECTORS' REFERENCES

Abbreviations (usually with numbers) following a plant name, refer to the collector(s) of the plant.  These abbreviations are expanded, with a collector's name or expedition title, in the section Collectors' References starting on p.761.

A collector's reference may indicate a new, as yet unnamed range of variation within a species; their inclusion in the *RHS Plant Finder* supports the book's role in sourcing unusual plants.

Since the adoption of the *Convention on Biological Diversity* in 1993, collectors are normally required to have prior consent for the acquisition and commercialisation of collected material.

## CLASSIFICATION OF GENERA

Genera including a large number of species or with many cultivars are often subdivided into groups, each based on a particular characteristic or combination of characteristics. Colour of flower or fruit and shape of flower are common examples, and with fruit, whether a cultivar is grown for culinary or dessert purposes. How such groups are named differs from genus to genus.

To help users of the *RHS Plant Finder* find exactly the plants they want, the majority of classifications used within cultivated genera are listed with codes, and each species or cultivar is marked with the appropriate code in brackets after its name in the Plant Directory. The codes relating to edible fruits are listed with the more specialised classifications; these apply across several genera. To find the explanation of each code, simply look it up under the genus concerned in the Classification of Genera on p.764.

## REVERSE SYNONYMS

It is likely that users of this book will come across names in certain genera which they did not expect to find. This may be because species have been transferred from another genus (or genera). In the list of Reverse Synonyms on p.768, the name on the left hand side is that of an accepted genus to which species have been transferred from the genus on the right. Sometimes all species will have been transferred, but in many cases only a few will be affected. Consulting Reverse Synonyms enables users to find the genera from which species have been transferred. If the right-hand genus is then found in the Plant Directory, the movements of species becomes clear through the cross-references in the nursery-code column.

# THE PLANT DIRECTORY

# A

**ABELIA** ✿ (Caprifoliaceae)
| | |
|---|---|
| ◆ 'Abghop' | See *A.* x *grandiflora* Hopleys = 'Abghop' |
| § *chinensis* R.Br. | CB&S CHan CPle EBee EHic EPfP MAsh SMer SPer SSta WAbe WFar WHCG WPat WSHC WWat |
| § - hort. | See *A.* x *grandiflora* |
| § Confetti = 'Conti' (v) | CAbP CB&S CBlo CChe CDoC COtt CRos EAst EBee ECle ELan LPan LRHS MAsh MCCP SPer SPla SSta WRHF WWeb |
| ◆ 'Conti' | See *A.* Confetti = 'Conti' |
| 'Edward Goucher' ♀ | CB&S CDoC CPle CWit EBee ELan ENot LPan MGos NFla SEND SPer WAbe WFar WPat WPyg WWal WWat WWeb |
| *engleriana* | CAbP CPle CSam EHic EPla MPla NOla SBid SEas WWat |
| *floribunda* ♀ | CB&S CDoC CFil CLan CPin CPle CTrw ELan IDee LHop MRav SEas SPer WAbe WBod WWat |
| *graebneriana* | Last listed 1997 |
| x *grandiflora* ♀ | More than 30 suppliers |
| - 'Aurea' | See *A.* x *grandiflora* 'Gold Spot' |
| - 'Compacta' | LRHS MAsh |
| ¶ - dwarf form | CDoC |
| § - 'Francis Mason' (v) ♀ | More than 30 suppliers |
| § - 'Gold Spot' | CB&S CBlo CDoC IOrc LHop MPla MWat SAga SBod SEas SOWG WPat WPyg WWeb |
| - 'Gold Strike' | See *A.* x *grandiflora* 'Gold Spot' |
| ◆ - 'Goldsport' | See *A.* x *grandiflora* 'Gold Spot' |
| § - Hopleys = 'Abghop' | LHop |
| ¶ - 'Panache' | CPle |
| - 'Prostrata' | EHic WWeb |
| ¶ - 'Sunrise' | CAbP ELan LRHS MAsh SPer SSta |
| I - 'Variegata' | See *A.* x *grandiflora* 'Francis Mason' |
| 'Panash' | CLyn |
| *rupestris* Lindley | See *A. chinensis* |
| - hort. | See *A.* x *grandiflora* |
| *schumannii* | CAbP CB&S CBot CFil CMCN CMHG CPle CSam EBee ELan ENot LHop MAsh MBri SDry SEas SLon SPer WAbe WBod WFar WHCG WPat WPyg WSHC WWat WGer |
| ¶ - 'Bumblebees' | EBee LRHS WWat |
| *spathulata* | CAbP CBot CFil CPle EHic LFis LHop SPla SSta WHCG WPat WSHC WWat |
| *triflora* | CAbP CBot CFil CPle EHic LFis LHop SPla SSta WHCG WPat WSHC WWat |
| *zanderi* | CTrw GQui |

**ABELIOPHYLLUM** (Oleaceae)
| | |
|---|---|
| *distichum* | CAbP CB&S CBot CDoC CMHG CPle EBee EBrP EBre ELan ENot LBre MAsh MBri MPla MRav SBre SEas SPer SPla SReu SSpi SSta WBod WHCG WSHC WWat WWeb WWin |
| - Roseum Group | CB&S CFil CPMA EBee EBrP EBre EHic ELan GBuc LBre LHop MAsh MPla MRav MUlv SAga SBre SEND SLon SPer SSpi WPGP |

**ABELMOSCHUS** (Malvaceae)
| | |
|---|---|
| § *manibot* | Last listed 1998 |

**ABIES** ✿ (Pinaceae)
| | |
|---|---|
| *alba* | CDul EBee LCon MBar |
| - 'Compacta' | CKen |
| - 'Green Spiral' | Last listed 1996 |
| - 'King's Dwarf' | CKen |
| - 'Microphylla' | CKen |
| - 'Pendula' | Last listed 1996 |
| - 'Schwarzwald' | Last listed 1998 |
| - 'Tortuosa' | CKen |
| *amabilis* | LCon WFro |
| - 'Spreading Star' | LCon MAsh |
| ¶ x *arnoldiana* | MBar |
| *balsamea* | CAgr |
| - var. *balsamea* | WFro |
| - Hudsonia Group ♀ | CDoC CFee CKen CMac EHul EPla GChr GNau IMGH IOrc LCon LLin MAsh MBar MBri MGos MOne NHed NMen SLim SLon SSmi WDin WWeb |
| - 'Nana' | CKen EBrP EBre EHul EOrn EWTr GRei LBee LBre LCon MAsh MBri MPla SBre SRms WDin WStI |
| - 'Piccolo' | CKen IMGH WGor |
| - 'Prostrata' | CBlo ECho |
| *borisii-regis* | Last listed 1997 |
| - 'Pendula' | CKen |
| *brachyphylla* dwarf | See *A. homolepis* 'Prostrata' |
| *bracteata* | ETen |
| *cephalonica* | ETen LCon |
| § - 'Meyer's Dwarf' | CDoC IMGH LCon LLin MAsh MBar SLim |
| I - 'Nana' | See *A. cephalonica* 'Meyer's Dwarf' |
| *chensiensis* | Last listed 1996 |
| *cilicica* | Last listed 1998 |
| *concolor* ♀ | CB&S CBlo CDoC CDul GChr GRei IOrc ISea LCon LPan MBal MBar NWea WFro |
| - 'Archer's Dwarf' | CKen MGos |
| § - 'Argentea' | Last listed 1996 |
| - 'Blue Spreader' | CKen MGos |
| - 'Candicans' | See *A. concolor* 'Argentea' |

| | |
|---|---|
| § - 'Compacta' ♀ | CDoC CKen EOrn IMGH LCon LLin LNet MAsh MBar MGos SLim |
| - 'Fagerhult' | CKen |
| - 'Gable's Weeping' | CKen |
| ♦ - 'Glauca' | See *A. concolor* Violacea Group |
| - 'Glauca Compacta' | See *A. concolor* 'Compacta' |
| - 'Hillier Broom' | See *A. concolor* 'Hillier's Dwarf' |
| § - 'Hillier's Dwarf' | CKen |
| - 'Husky Pup' | CKen |
| ¶ - (Lowiana Group) 'Creamy' | CKen |
| - 'Masonic Broom' | CKen |
| - 'Piggelmee' | CKen |
| * - 'Swift's Silver' | WBcn WFro |
| § - Violacea Group | CDoC LCon MAsh MBar |
| I - 'Violacea Prostrata' | Last listed 1998 |
| - 'Wattezii' | CKen LLin |
| - 'Wintergold' | LCon |
| *delavayi* | Last listed 1996 |
| - var. *delavayi* | Last listed 1997 |
| - - Fabri Group | See *A. fabri* |
| - 'Major Neishe' | CKen |
| - 'Nana Headfort' | See *A. fargesii* 'Headfort' |
| - SF 360 | ISea |
| - SF 656 | ISea |
| *ernesti* | See *A. recurvata* var. *ernestii* |
| § *fabri* | LCon |
| § *fargesii* 'Headfort' | CBlo LCon MBar |
| *firma* | NWea |
| ¶ *forrestii* var. *georgei* SF 519 | ISea |
| *fraseri* | CDoC GRei LCon MBal WFro WMou |
| - 'Kline's Nest' | CKen |
| *grandis* ♀ | CB&S CDoC CDul ENot GAri GChr GRei IIve IOrc LCon MBar NWea WDin WMou |
| - 'Compacta' | CKen |
| *holophylla* | LCon |
| *homolepis* | CDoC CDul LCon |
| § - 'Prostrata' | CKen |
| *kawakamii* | Last listed 1997 |
| *koreana* | More than 30 suppliers |
| - 'Aurea' | See *A. koreana* 'Flava' |
| - 'Blaue Zwo' | CKen |
| ¶ - 'Blauer Pfiff' | MGos SLim |
| - 'Cis' | CKen |
| - 'Compact Dwarf' | LCon LLin MBar MGos SSta WAbe |
| § - 'Flava' | CDoC CKen ECho GAri IMGH LCon LLin MAsh MBar MBri NHol SLim |
| ¶ - 'Gait' | CKen |
| - 'Golden Dream' | CKen |
| - 'Golden Wonder' | COtt |
| - 'Inverleith' | CKen |
| ¶ - 'Kohout' | CKen |
| - 'Luminetta' | CKen |
| - 'Nisbet' | ECho IMGH NHed |
| - 'Piccolo' | CKen |
| - 'Pinocchio' | CKen |
| I - 'Prostrata' | See *A. koreana* 'Prostrate Beauty' |
| § - 'Prostrate Beauty' | ECho EOrn IMGH LCon |
| - 'Silberkugel' | CKen |
| - 'Silberlocke' ♀ | CBlo CDoC CKen EBrP EBre GAri IOrc LBee LBre LCon LLin LPan MAsh MBar MBlu MBri MGos NHol SBre SLim SPer SSta |
| - 'Silberperl' | CKen |
| ¶ - 'Silberschmeltzer' | CDoC |
| - 'Silver Show' | CKen |
| - 'Starker's Dwarf' | CKen |
| * - 'Threave' | CKen |
| ¶ - 'Tundra' | CKen |
| * - 'Wittboldt' | CKen |
| *lasiocarpa* | Last listed 1996 |
| - var. *arizonica* | CLnd ETen LCon MBri SSta |
| - - 'Argentea' | NWea |
| - 'Arizonica Compacta' | CBlo CDoC CKen CMac EBrP EBre EHul IOrc LBee LBre LCon LLin LPan MAsh MBar MBri MGos NHol SBre SLim SMad |
| ¶ - 'Compacta' ♀ | IMGH |
| ¶ - 'Day Creek' | CKen |
| - 'Duflon' | CKen |
| ♦ - 'Glauca' | See *A. concolor* Violacea Group |
| - 'Green Globe' | CKen MBar NHol |
| - 'Kenwith Blue' | CKen |
| * - 'King's Blue' | CKen |
| ¶ - 'Mulligan's Dwarf' | CKen |
| I - 'Witch's Broom' | Last listed 1998 |
| *magnifica* | LCon LPan WFro |
| I - 'Nana' | CKen |
| *marocana* | See *A. pinsapo* var. *marocana* |
| *nobilis* | See *A. procera* |
| *nordmanniana* ♀ | CDoC CDul CMCN EHul GChr GRei LBuc LCon LPan MBal MBar MGos NWea SLim WDin WFro WGer WTro WWal |
| - 'Barabits' Compact' | MBar |
| - 'Barabits' Spreader' | CKen |
| ¶ - subsp. *equi-trojani* 'Archer' | CKen |
| - 'Golden Spreader' ♀ | CBlo CDoC CKen EBrP EBre EOrn IMGH LBee LBre LCon LLin MAsh MBar MBri MGos SBre SLim SPer SSta |
| - 'Jakobsen' | CKen |
| - 'Pendula' | LPan MBri |
| I - 'Reflexa' | Last listed 1996 |
| *numidica* | LPan |
| ¶ - 'Glauca' | CKen |
| I - 'Pendula' | Last listed 1998 |
| I - 'Prostrata' | LPan |
| *pindrow* | CLnd ETen WCoo |
| *pinsapo* | GChr LCon LPan MBar SEND |
| - 'Aurea' | CKen |
| I - 'Aurea Nana' ♀ | CKen |
| - 'Glauca' ♀ | CDoC CKen ELan IOrc LCon LPan MBar NHol WDin |
| - 'Hamondii' | CKen |
| I - 'Horstmann' | CKen LLin NHol |
| - 'Kelleriis' | LCon |
| § - var. *marocana* | Last listed 1997 |
| § *procera* ♀ | CDoC CDul EHul GAri GChr GRei LCon MBal MBar NWea STre WDin WGwG WMou WWal |
| - 'Blaue Hexe' | CKen |
| - 'Compacta' | See *A. procera* 'Prostrata' |
| - Glauca Group | CDoC CMac EBrP EBre IOrc LBre LCon LLin LPan MAsh MBar MBri MGos SBre SLim WGer |
| - 'Glauca Prostrata' | GAri IOrc LBee LPan MBar MGos |
| - 'Mount Hood' | Last listed 1998 |
| ¶ - 'Sherwoodii' | CKen |
| § *recurvata* var. *ernestii* | Last listed 1996 |
| *religiosa* | Last listed 1997 |
| ¶ Rosemoor form | CKen |
| *sibirica* | LCon |
| *spectabilis* | Last listed 1996 |
| *squamata* | Last listed 1998 |
| *veitchii* ♀ | CB&S CDul LCon MBar |
| - 'Hedergott' | CKen |
| - 'Heine' | CKen |
| I - 'Pendula' | CKen |

**ABROMEITIELLA** (Bromeliaceae)
*brevifolia* ♀                CFil

**ABROTANELLA** (Asteraceae)
sp.                           ECho

**ABRUS** (Papilionaceae)
*cantoniensis*                Last listed 1997
*precatorius*                 Last listed 1997

**ABUTILON** (Malvaceae)
'Alpha Glory'                 Last listed 1997
'Amiti'                       CCan
'Amsterdam'                   ERea
'Ashford Red' ♀               CCan IOrc LCns SOWG SRms
                              SYvo WWeb
'Bloomsbury Can-can'          LBlm
'Bloomsbury Rose'             LBlm
'Boule de Neige'              CBot ERea LCns LHil MBEx MBri
                              SOWG SYvo
'Canary Bird' ♀               CB&S CBot CGre CHal CPle ELan
                              ERea LBlm LCns LHil MBEx MBri
                              MLan SYvo WKif WWye
'Cannington Carol' (v) ♀      CCan ERea LBlm MBEx SBid WSan
'Cannington Peter' (v) ♀      CCan CHal LBlm MBEx
'Cannington Sally'            CCan
'Cannington Sonia' (v)        CCan ERea
'Cerise Queen'                CCan
'Cloth of Gold'               LCns SOWG
§ Feuerglocke = 'Firebell'    CSev LHop MBEx
♦ 'Firebell'                  See A. Feuerglocke = 'Firebell'
'Frances Elizabeth'           SOWG
'Glenroy Snowdrift'           MBal
*globosum*                    See A. x *hybridum*
'Golden Fleece'               ERea IBlr LCns
'Heather Bennington'          SOWG
'Henry Makepeace'             Last listed 1998
'Hinton Seedling'             CFil MBEx SBid
§ x *hybridum*                MBri
- 'Savitzii'                  See A. 'Savitzii'
¶ 'J. Morris'                 LRHS
'Kentish Belle' ♀             CAbb CB&S CFil CMHG CMac
                              CPle CSev CWit ECot ENot IOrc
                              NTow SBra SPer WWeb WWye
'Lemon Queen'                 Last listed 1996
'Louis Marignac'              CCan ERea LBlm MBEx
'Marion'                      SOWG
'Master Michael'              CMac ERea SBid
*megapotamicum* ♀             CB&S CBot CCan CMHG CPIN
                              CPle ECha ELan ENot EPla ERea
                              GQui MBal MGos MRav SBra SDix
                              SOWG SPer SRms SUsu WBod
                              WFar WHar WSHC WWat WWye
- 'Variegatum'                CAbb CB&S CBrm CFil CWit ECtt
                              ELan GQui IBlr IOrc LBlm MBEx
                              MBri SBod SBra SEas SOWG SRms
                              WFar WHar
- 'Wisley Red'                Last listed 1997
x *milleri* ♀                 CB&S CMac CRHN ELan ERea
                              IOrc SBra SMrm SVen WSHC
- 'Variegatum'                CB&S CCan CMHG CMac MBEx
                              SEND
'Nabob' ♀                     CCan CFil CGre CHal CWit ERea
                              LBlm LCns MBEx MBri MTis SBid
                              SLdr SOWG SYvo WWye
'Orange Glow' (v) ♀           Last listed 1995
'Orange King'                 CB&S
*otocarpum*                   Last listed 1998
'Patrick Synge'               CFil CMHG CPle CWit ERav ERea
                              GOrc LBlm LCns MBEx SOWG
                              SVen

'Peaches and Cream'           MBEx
§ *pictum*                    EHol ERea LBlm MBri
- 'Thompsonii' (v)            CHal ERea LBlm LCns MBEx
                              MLLN
'Pink Lady'                   CB&S ERea GQui
'Red Bells'                   CB&S GQui SVen
'Red Goblin'                  Last listed 1998
'Rotterdam'                   LCns MBEx SBid
§ 'Savitzii' (v)              CB&S CHal EPfP ERea MBEx
                              SOWG SRms SVen
*sellowianum* var.            ERea
  *marmoratum*
'Silver Belle'                LBlm
'Simcox White'                MHlr WSPU
'Souvenir de Bonn' (v) ♀      EHol ERea LBlm LCns MBEx MTis
                              NCut SBid SMrm
*striatum* hort.              See A. *pictum*
x *suntense*                  CB&S CMHG CMac CPle ELan
                              ERea LHop LHyd MBal NPer
                              SOWG SSta WEas
- 'Jermyns' ♀                 CB&S CEnd ECtt EPfP ERic LGre
                              MMil NEgg SMrm SSta WFar WPyg
- 'Ralph Gould'               ECGP
- 'Violetta'                  CEnd MAvo SSpi SSta
*theophrasti*                 MSal
*vitifolium*                  CB&S CBot CBrm CFil ECot ERea
                              IOrc ISea LHop NChi NEgg SChu
                              SPer SYvo WKif WWeb WWin
                              WWye
- var. *album*                CAbb CB&S CMHG EBee ECha
                              ELan ISea LHop LHyd MAvo MLan
                              SChu SEND SSpi SSta WFar WWye
- 'Ice Blue'                  CBot
¶ - 'Simcox White'            WEas
- 'Tennant's White' ♀         CAbP CBot CCan CEnd EPfP ERea
                              LGre SOWG WCot WCru
- 'Veronica Tennant' ♀        CEnd ERea GOrc LGre SLon
                              SMrm WPyg

**ACACIA** ✿ (Mimosaceae)
*acinacea*                    Last listed 1998
*alpina*                      MSag WCel
*armata*                      See A. *paradoxa*
*baileyana* ♀                 CB&S CDoC ECon ECot ELan
                              EMil ERea GQui LCns SBid SPar
                              SPlb
- 'Purpurea' ♀                CAbb CB&S CBos CEnd CGre
                              CTbh CWSG CWit EBee EMil EPfP
                              ERea GQui LHop MBlu SBid SPer
                              WCot WMul
§ *binervia*                  MSag
¶ *boormanii*                 WCel
*caffra*                      CTrC
*cardiophylla*                MSag
*catechu*                     MSal
*cultriformis*                ERea
*cyanophylla*                 See A. *saligna*
¶ *dawsonii*                  MSag
*dealbata* ♀                  More than 30 suppliers
- 'Gaulois Astier'            Last listed 1997
- 'Mirandole'                 Last listed 1997
- *prostrata*                 Last listed 1998
- 'Rêve d'Or'                 Last listed 1997
- *subalpina*                 LPan SArc WCel WGer WMul
*decora*                      MSag
*decurrens*                   CBrP
*dunnii*                      Last listed 1998
*erioloba*                    Last listed 1997
Exeter hybrid                 CGre
*farnesiana*                  Last listed 1998
*filicifolia*                 WCel
¶ *flexifolia*                WCel

| | |
|---|---|
| *floribunda* | Last listed 1998 |
| – 'Lisette' | ELan EPfP LCns LRHS |
| *frigescens* | WCel |
| *galpinii* | CTrC WMul |
| *gerrardii* | CTrC |
| *gillii* | Last listed 1996 |
| ◆ *glaucescens* | See *A. binervia* |
| *glaucoptera* | Last listed 1998 |
| ◆ *bowittii* | See *A. verniciflua* |
| *julibrissin* | See *Albizia julibrissin* |
| *juniperina* | See *A. ulicifolia* |
| *karroo* | CArn WMul |
| *kybeanensis* | CTrC WCel |
| *longifolia* | CAbb CB&S CBrP EOas MGos |
| | NPSI SPer SRms |
| *macradenia* | Last listed 1998 |
| *maidenii* | Last listed 1998 |
| *mearnsii* | CTrC MSag WCel WMul |
| *melanoxylon* | ISea LHil WCel WGer |
| *motteana* | ECot ERea |
| *mucronata* | CB&S |
| *obliquinervia* | WCel |
| *obtusifolia* | Last listed 1998 |
| § *paradoxa* | EHol LHop |
| – var. *angustifolia* | LBlm |
| *pendula* | Last listed 1998 |
| *podalyriifolia* | CAbb CBrP CFil |
| *polybotrya* hort. | See *A. glaucocarpa* |
| *pravissima* | CAbb CB&S CDoC CFil CGre |
| | CMFo CMHG CPle CTbh CTrC |
| | CWit ERea GQui LCns LHop LPan |
| | MBal SAPC SArc SBid WCel WMul |
| | WNor WPGP WPat |
| *pycnantha* | CBrP |
| *rebmanniana* | Last listed 1998 |
| *retinodes* ♀ | CAbb CB&S CBrP CDoC CGre |
| | CPle ELan EPfP ERea GQui IDee |
| | SEND SRms WMul |
| *riceana* | CB&S CTrC CTrG GLch GQui |
| *rivalis* | ERea |
| *rotundifolia* | CPle |
| *rubida* | LPan WMul WPat |
| *salicina* | MLan |
| § *saligna* | CPle |
| ¶ *senegal* | ELau |
| *sentis* | See *A. victoriae* |
| *sophorae* | MSag |
| ¶ *stricta* | MSag |
| *terminalis* | Last listed 1998 |
| *tortilis* | Last listed 1997 |
| *trinervis* | ERea |
| § *ulicifolia* | CGre CPle CTrG CWit |
| § *verniciflua* | MSag |
| *verticillata* | CPle CTrG |
| ¶ *vestita* | MSag WCel |
| § *victoriae* | ERea |
| ¶ *xanthopbloea* | WMul |

## ACAENA (Rosaceae)

| | |
|---|---|
| *adscendens* Vahl | See *A. magellanica* subsp. |
| | *laevigata* |
| – Margery Fish | See *A. affinis* |
| – hort. | See *A. magellanica* subsp. |
| | *magellanica, A. saccaticupula* |
| | 'Blue Haze' |
| – 'Glauca' | CMdw EMan LHop MBel NBir |
| | NFor |
| § *affinis* | ECha SDix |
| § *anserinifolia* Druce | ECha MRav NHol WPer WWin |
| § – hort. | See *A. novae-zelandiae* |

| | |
|---|---|
| *buchananii* | CTri EBee EGoo ENot EPot GTou |
| | MBar MBri MLLN NBro NFor |
| | NMGW SIng SRms SSmi WFar |
| | WHoo WLin WMer WPer WPyg |
| | WWhi |
| *caerulea* | See *A. caesiiglauca* |
| § *caesiiglauca* | CBar CNic CRow CTri GAbr GGar |
| | GTou MWat NFor NLon NSti SBla |
| | WCom WEas WPer |
| – CC 451 | MRPP |
| *fissistipula* | EHoe GAri GGar WHer |
| *glabra* | Last listed 1997 |
| *glaucophylla* | See *A. magellanica* subsp. |
| | *magellanica* |
| 'Greencourt Hybrid' | CLyd |
| *inermis* | CLyd EGar ELan EPot GTou MLLN |
| | SSmi WCom WPer |
| § *magellanica* subsp. | EHoe GAri GGar GTou WWin |
| *laevigata* | |
| – subsp. *magellanica* | ELan GTou WMer |
| *microphylla* ♀ | EBee EBrP EBre ECha ELan EMFP |
| | ESis GGar LBee LBre MBar MBri |
| | MWat NMen SBre SHFr SPlb SRms |
| | SSmi WCer WCla WEas WMoo |
| | WMow WPer |
| – Copper Carpet | See *A. microphylla* |
| | 'Kupferteppich' |
| – 'Glauca' | See *A. caesiiglauca* |
| § – 'Kupferteppich' | CLTr CRow EHoe GAbr GAri |
| | GGar MBri MBro MCLN MRav |
| | NCat NVic SIng WPat WPer WPyg |
| – var. *pallideolivacea* | CRow |
| – 'Pewter Carpet' | EGoo SIng WWat |
| – 'Pulchella' | EBrP EBre EMan LBre SBre |
| ¶ *minor* | GGar |
| *myriophylla* | CInt ECho EDAr MHar SGre WPer |
| § *novae-zelandiae* | CRow CTri GAri GTou SDix SIng |
| | SWat WPer |
| *ovalifolia* | CNic CRow EDAr EGoo GTou |
| | SLod |
| *pallida* | Last listed 1998 |
| 'Pewter' | See *A. saccaticupula* 'Blue Haze' |
| *pinnatifida* | ELan GTou NBro WPer |
| *profundeincisa* | See *A. anserinifolia* Druce |
| 'Purple Carpet' | See *A. microphylla* |
| | 'Kupferteppich' |
| *saccaticupula* | Last listed 1998 |
| § – 'Blue Haze' | CGle CLTr CLyd ECha EGoo ELan |
| | EPot GCHN GTou MBar MBro |
| | MLLN MWhi NPer SIng SPer SPlb |
| | SRms WFar WHoo WPer |
| *sanguisorbae* L.f. | See *A. anserinifolia* Druce |
| *sericea* | Last listed 1997 |
| *viridior* | See *A. anserinifolia* Druce |

## ACALYPHA (Euphorbiaceae)

| | |
|---|---|
| *bispaniolae* | ERea MBEx |
| *bispida* ♀ | MBri |
| *pendula* | See *A. reptans* |
| § *reptans* | CGen CHal LPVe |

## ACANTHOCALYX See MORINA

## ACANTHOLIMON (Plumbaginaceae)

| | |
|---|---|
| ¶ *acerosum* var. *acerosum* | NWCA |
| ¶ – var. *brachystachyum* | WLin |
| *androsaceum* | See *A. ulicinum* |
| *armenum* | NMen |
| ¶ *confertiflorum* | EHyt |
| *glumaceum* | MDHE MWat NMen SRms WPat |
| *bilariae* | Last listed 1998 |
| *bobenackeri* | WLin |

| | |
|---|---|
| *litvinovii* | Last listed 1996 |
| ¶ *trojanum* | WLin |
| § *ulicinum* | EHyt EPot NWCA |

## ACANTHOPANAX See ELEUTHEROCOCCUS

## ACANTHUS ✿ (Acanthaceae)

| | |
|---|---|
| *balcanicus* | See *A. hungaricus* |
| *caroli-alexandri* | Last listed 1997 |
| ¶ *dioscoridis* | EFou LGre |
| - var. *perringii* | CGle CHan CRDP SBla SIgm |
| | WCot WFar WSel WViv |
| ¶ - smooth-leaved | SIgm |
| *hirsutus* | EBee EMar LGre MMil SCro SIgm |
| | WCot |
| - JCA 109.700 | SBla |
| ¶ - f. *roseus* | SIgm WFar |
| - subsp. *syriacus* | CGle CLon LGre |
| JCA 106.500 | |
| § *hungaricus* | CArn CB&S CGle CHar CLon |
| | EBee ECGN EHal ELan EMan |
| | EMar EMon EPla GCal LFis MSte |
| | NLar NPSI SBla SPer SSoC SWat |
| | WCot WElm WFar |
| - AL&JS 90097YU | Last listed 1998 |
| *longifolius* | See *A. hungaricus* |
| *mollis* | More than 30 suppliers |
| - 'Fielding Gold' | EBee GCal WViv |
| ¶ - free-flowering form | GCal |
| - 'Hollard's Gold' | CRDP GBin LPio NDov SCob |
| | SWat WCot WViv |
| - Latifolius Group | CMGP EBee EFou EGar EPla MRav |
| | MSte MUlv NHol SChu SPer SRms |
| | WWal WWat |
| *spinosus* ♀ | More than 30 suppliers |
| - 'Lady Moore' | IBlr IHdy WCot WSPU |
| - Spinosissimus Group | CGle CMHG ECha EMan GCal |
| | LGre LPio MMil MRav SWat WCot |
| | WCru WFar |
| *syriacus* | EBee EMan GCal NLar NPro WViv |

## ACCA (Myrtaceae)

| | |
|---|---|
| *sellowiana* (F) | CArn CB&S CDoC CGre CHan |
| | CMHG CPle CSam CTrG EBee |
| | ELan EPla ERea GQui LCns LEdu |
| | LPan LSpr MCCP SOWG WBod |
| | WPat WSHC |
| - 'Apollo' (F) | ERea |
| - 'Coolidge' (F) | ERea LEdu |
| - 'Mammoth' (F) | CB&S ERea |
| - 'Triumph' (F) | CB&S ERea LEdu |
| - 'Variegata' (F) | CGre |

## ACER ✿ (Aceraceae)

| | |
|---|---|
| *acuminatum* | CMCN WNor |
| *albopurpurascens* | CMCN |
| *amplum* | CMCN WCwm WShe |
| *argutum* | CMCN SFur WCwm WNor |
| *barbinerve* | CPMA EPfP SFur WNor |
| *buergerianum* | CB&S CBlo CDul CGre CLnd |
| | CMCN CPMA ECrN GAri SSpi |
| | STre WCwm WNor WWat |
| - 'Goshiki-kaede' (v) | CPMA LNet |
| - 'Integrifolium' | See *A. buergerianum* |
| | 'Subintegrum' |
| - 'Naruto' | CMCN |
| § - 'Subintegrum' | CMCN |
| - 'Tanchô' | LNet |
| * - 'Variegatum' | CMCN |
| *caesium* | EPfP |
| *calcaratum* | CMCN |
| *campbellii* | CMCN LNet SFur |

| | |
|---|---|
| § - subsp. *flabellatum* | CGre CMCN |
| - - var. *yunnanense* | CFil CMCN |
| - - - SF 533 | ISea |
| - subsp. *sinense* | See *A. sinense* |
| - subsp. *wilsonii* | See *A. wilsonii* |
| *campestre* ♀ | CDoC CDul CKin CLnd CMCN |
| | CSam EBee EBrP EBre ECrN ENot |
| | GChr GRei IOrc LBre LBuc LHyr |
| | LPan MBri MGos NBee NWea |
| | SBre SPer SSta WDin WMou WNor |
| | WOrn WPyg |
| - 'Autumn Red' | Last listed 1996 |
| - 'Carnival' (v) | CB&S CBlo CDul CEnd CMCN |
| | CPMA ELan LNet LPan MAsh |
| | MBlu MBri MGos NHol SMad SPer |
| | SSoC WWeb |
| - 'Elsrijk' | CLnd |
| - 'Pendulum' | CBlo CEnd CTho |
| - 'Postelense' | CEnd CMCN CPMA LNet MBlu |
| | NBea SSpi |
| - 'Pulverulentum' (v) | CBlo CDoC CEnd CMCN CPMA |
| | LNet SMad SPer SSta |
| ¶ - 'Queen Elizabeth' | CDul |
| - 'Red Shine' | MGos |
| - 'Rockhampton Red Stem' | Last listed 1996 |
| - 'Royal Ruby' | CB&S CMCN CTho LNet NBea |
| | SSta |
| * - 'Ruby Glow' | CBlo CDoC CEnd |
| - 'Schwerinii' | CMCN |
| * - 'Weeping' | Last listed 1996 |
| - 'William Caldwell' | CTho |
| *capillipes* ♀ | CB&S CBlo CDul CMCN CTho |
| | EBee ECrN ELan ENot EPla ESis |
| | IOrc LPan MBar MBri MGos NBea |
| | SIgm SPer SSpi SSta WDin WFar |
| | WNor WPic WPyg WWat |
| - 'Candy Stripe' | SSpi SSta |
| - var. *morifolium* | See *A. morifolium* |
| * - 'Variegatum' | CEnd |
| *cappadocicum* | CBlo CMCN CSam GChr MLan |
| | WDin WNor WWes |
| - 'Aureum' ♀ | CAbP CB&S CBlo CDoC CDul |
| | CEnd CLnd CMCN CSam CTho |
| | EBee ELan ENot GChr IOrc LBuc |
| | LNet LPan MAsh MBlu MBri MGos |
| | MRav NBea SPer SRPl SSpi WDin |
| | WPyg |
| - var. *mono* | See *A. mono* |
| - 'Rubrum' ♀ | CBlo CDoC CDul CLnd CMCN |
| | ECrN ENot GChr IOrc LPan MAsh |
| | MBlu MGos MRav SPer WDin |
| - subsp. *sinicum* | CFil CMCN EPfP WWes |
| § - - var. *tricaudatum* | Last listed 1996 |
| I *carnea* 'Variegatum' | Last listed 1997 |
| *carpinifolium* | CLnd CMCN LNet MAsh SFur SSpi |
| | WGer WNor WWes |
| *catalpifolium* | See *A. longipes* subsp. |
| | *catalpifolium* |
| § *caudatifolium* | CMCN |
| - B&SWJ 3531 | WCru |
| § aff. *caudatifolium* | WHCr |
| CC 1744 | |
| § - CC 1927 | Last listed 1998 |
| § *caudatum* | SSpi |
| - subsp. *ukurunduense* | CMCN CPMA SFur WNor |
| *cinerascens* | CMCN |
| *cinnamomifolium* | See *A. coriaceifolium* |
| *circinatum* ♀ | CB&S CDul CMCN CPMA CSam |
| | CTho GChr LNet MLan NBea |
| | NHol SSpi SSta WDin WFro WNor |
| | WPat WWal WWat |
| - 'Little Gem' | CMCN LNet |

- 'Monroe'                     CMCN LNet
- NJM 94038                    Last listed 1998
*cissifolium*                  CB&S CDoC CFil CMCN WNor
x *conspicuum*                 CPMA
  'Elephant's Ear'
- 'Phoenix'                    CPMA CTho EPfP LNet MBlu
                    SMad SSpi
- 'Silver Cardinal'            See *A.* 'Silver Cardinal'
§ - 'Silver Vein'              CMCN CPMA EBee EBrP EBre
                    LBre LNet MBlu SBre SSpi WGer
                    WPGP
§ *cordatum*                   CMCN
§ *coriaceifolium*             CMCN WNor
x *coriaceum*                  Last listed 1996
*crataegifolium*               CMCN WNor
- 'Veitchii' (v)               CDoC CMCN CPMA EPfP LNet
                    SSpi SSta WBcn
*creticum*                     See *A. sempervirens*
*dasycarpum*                   See *A. saccharinum*
*davidii*                      CAbP CB&S CBlo CDoC CDul
                    CMCN CMHG EBee ECrN ENot
                    EWTr IOrc ISea MAsh MBal MBar
                    MGos MRav MWat NBea SPer
                    WBay WDin WFro WNor
- 'Ernest Wilson'              CB&S CBlo CMCN ELan MAsh
- 'George Forrest' ♀           CB&S CBlo CDul CMCN CTho
                    EBee EBrP EBre EPfP GChr LBre
                    LPan MAsh MBri MGos NBea
                    SBod SBre SEND WDin WOrn
- 'Karmen'                     MBri
- 'Rosalie'                    CLyn MBlu MBri
- 'Serpentine' ♀               CB&S CDoC CMCN CPMA CTho
                    EPfP IHar MAsh MBlu MBri NBee
                    SSpi
- 'Silver Vein'                See *A.* x *conspicuum* 'Silver Vein'
*diabolicum*                   CMCN
x *dieckii*                    Last listed 1996
*distylum*                     Last listed 1996
*divergens*                    CMCN
*elegantulum*                  CGre CMCN WFro WNor
*erianthum*                    CDul CLnd SSpi SSta WNor
*fabri*                        CMCN WNor
*flabellatum*                  See *A. campbellii* subsp.
                    *flabellatum*
§ *forrestii*                  CDoC CDul CMCN EPfP NBea
                    WNor
- 'Alice'                      CB&S CLyn CMCN CPMA LNet
                    MGos SMad SSpi SSta WBcn
¶ - PB 57173                   WPGP
- TW 348                       Last listed 1996
*franchetii*                   CMCN
§ x *freemanii*                CDoC IOrc
    Autumn Blaze®
    = 'Jeffersred'
- 'Autumn Fantasy'             MBlu
§ - 'Elegant'                  Last listed 1996
◆ - 'Jeffersred'               See *A.* x *freemanii* Autumn Blaze
                    = 'Jeffersred'
*fulvescens*                   See *A. longipes*
*ginnala*                      See *A. tataricum* subsp. *ginnala*
*giraldii*                     CMCN
*glabrum*                      CLnd CMCN WNor
- subsp. *douglasii*           CLyn CMCN
*globosum*                     See *A. platanoides* 'Globosum'
*grandidentatum*               See *A. saccharum* subsp.
                    *grandidentatum*
*griseum* ♀                    More than 30 suppliers
*grosseri*                     CB&S CDul CMCN CTri NEgg
                    WFro WLRN
- var. *hersii* ♀              CBlo CDoC CDul CLnd CTho
                    EBee ELan ENot MAsh MBal MBri
                    MRav NBea NWea SPer SRPl
                    WCwm WDin WGer WNor WOrn
                    WPyg WWat

*heldreichii*                  CLnd CMCN EPfP WShe
*henryi*                       CB&S CGre CLnd CMCN ENot
                    EPfP LNet MAsh SFur WCwm
                    WNor WWes WWoo
x *hillieri*                   CMCN
*hookeri*                      CMCN
*hyrcanum*                     CMCN
*japonicum*                    CDul CMCN GChr LNet MBal
                    MBar SSta WAbe WCoo WNor
                    WWat
§ - 'Aconitifolium' ♀          More than 30 suppliers
- 'Attaryi'                    CMCN
- 'Aureum'                     See *A. shirasawanum* 'Aureum'
- 'Ezo-no-momiji'              See *A. shirasawanum* 'Ezo-no-
                    momiji'
- 'Filicifolium'               See *A. japonicum* 'Aconitifolium'
- 'Green Cascade'              CEnd CMCN CPMA ECho WPat
* - 'King Copse'               SMur
- 'Laciniatum'                 See *A. japonicum* 'Aconitifolium'
- f. *microphyllum*            See *A. shirasawanum*
                    'Microphyllum'
- 'Ogurayama'                  See *A. shirasawanum*
                    'Ogurayama'
- 'Ô-isami'                    CMCN LNet
- 'Ô-taki'                     Last listed 1997
- 'Viride'                     Last listed 1996
- 'Vitifolium' ♀               CBlo CDoC CEnd CMCN CPMA
                    ELan EPfP IOrc LNet LPan MAsh
                    MBlu MBri NPSI SReu SSpi SSta
                    WWeb
*kawakamii*                    See *A. caudatifolium*
*laevigatum*                   CMCN
*lanceolatum*                  CMCN
*laxiflorum*                   CLnd CMCN SFur SSta
*lobelii* Bunge                See *A. turkestanicum*
- Tenore                       CLnd
§ *longipes*                   CMCN
§ - subsp. *catalpifolium*     CMCN
*macrophyllum*                 CFil CMCN EPfP ISea LHyd MBlu
                    SMad
- 'Kimballiae'                 CMCN
- NJM 94040                    Last listed 1998
- 'Seattle Sentinel'           CMCN
* - 'Variegatum'               CMCN
*mandschuricum*                CPMA EPfP MBlu SFur WNor
                    WWoo
§ *maximowiczianum*            CB&S CLnd CMCN CSam CTho
                    ELan GChr IOrc MBal SSpi SSta
                    WNor WPGP WWat WWes
*maximowiczii*                 CMCN NWea WNor
§ *metcalfii*                  WNor
*micranthum* ♀                 CMCN EPfP ESis SSpi WCoo
                    WGer WNor WWes
¶ *miyabei*                    SFur
§ *mono*                       CMCN EPfP MAsh
- 'Hoshiyadori' (v)            CMCN
- subsp. *mono*                WCwm WNor
- 'Shufu-nishiki'              CMCN
- var. *tricuspis*             See *A. cappadocicum* subsp.
                    *sinicum* var. *tricaudatum*
*monspessulanum*               CB&S CFil CMCN MAsh
§ *morifolium*                 CMCN
*morrisonense*                 See *A. caudatifolium*
*negundo*                      CBlo CDul CLnd CMCN ECrN
                    ENot EWTr NWea WNor WTro
- 'Argenteovariegatum'         See *A. negundo* 'Variegatum'
- 'Auratum'                    CBlo CMCN MBar WPat
- 'Aureovariegatum'            CB&S MBar
- subsp. *californicum*        SFur WNor
§ - 'Elegans' (v)              CBlo CDul CLnd CMCN COtt
                    EBrP EBre ENot LBre LPan SBre
                    SPer

| | |
|---|---|
| - 'Elegantissimum' | See *A. negundo* 'Elegans' |
| - 'Flamingo' (v) ♀ | More than 30 suppliers |
| - 'Kelly's Gold' | CB&S CBlo MGos |
| § - 'Variegatum' | CB&S CBlo CLnd EBee ENot LPan |
| | NBea NBee SPer WDin |
| - var. *violaceum* ♀ | CB&S CMCN WBcn |
| *nikoense* | See *A. maximowiczianum* |
| *nipponicum* | Last listed 1996 |
| *oblongum* | CDoC CMCN |
| § *obtusifolium* | CCHP CMCN |
| *okomotoanum* | CMCN |
| *oliverianum* | CLyn CMCN EPfP SFur WNor |
| *opalus* | CDul CMCN WCwm |
| - subsp. *obtusatum* | SSpi |
| *orientale* | See *A. sempervirens* |
| Pacific Sunset™ | MBri |
| *palmatum* | CDul CLan CMCN CMHG EBee |
| | ENot ESis GChr LNet MBal MBar |
| | MBro NBee SBrw SPar SPer SSpi |
| | SSta STre WAbe WCFE WCoo WFar |
| | WFro WHar WOrn WPat WWat |
| § - 'Aka Shigitatsusawa' | CMCN CMac CPMA LNet MAsh |
| - 'Akaji-nishiki' | See *A. truncatum* 'Akaji-nishiki' |
| ¶ - 'Akane' | LNet |
| - 'Akegarasu' | CMCN LNet |
| - 'Aoba-jo' | CPMA WWes |
| - 'Aoshime-no-uchi' | See *A. palmatum* 'Shinobugaoka' |
| - 'Aoyagi' | CMCN CPMA LNet WWes |
| § - 'Arakawa' | CMCN LNet |
| - 'Aratama' | CMCN WPat |
| ¶ - 'Ariadne' (v) | CPMA |
| - 'Asahi-zuru' (v) | CBlo CMCN CPMA EBee ECho |
| | LNet MGos NHol NPSI SSta WWes |
| - 'Atrolineare' | LNet |
| - f. *atropurpureum* | CB&S CDul EBrP EBre ELan ENot |
| | ESis GChr GRei LBre LHyd LNet |
| | MBal MBar MGos NBea NBee |
| | NWea SBod SBre SPer SReu WBod |
| | WDin WHil WOrn WPat WStI |
| | WWat WWeb |
| - 'Atropurpureum' | CDoC EBee NHol SBrw WFar |
| | WGwG WHar |
| - 'Atropurpureum | CBlo CMCN CMac MBri |
| Superbum' | |
| - 'Aureum' | CBlo CFil CMCN CPMA ELan EPfP |
| | LNet MBri SBod SSpi WPGP |
| - Autumn Glory Group | CPMA SSpi WWes |
| * - 'Autumn Red' | LPan |
| * - 'Autumn Showers' | CEnd |
| - 'Azuma-murasaki' | CMCN CPMA |
| ¶ - B&SWJ 4474 | WCru |
| * - 'Beni K Sport' | CPMA |
| - 'Beni-kagami' | CDul CEnd CMCN CPMA LNet |
| | MAsh MGos WWes |
| - 'Beni-kawa' | LNet |
| - 'Beni-komachi' | CB&S CFil CMCN CPMA ECho |
| | LNet WPGP WPat |
| - 'Beni-maiko' | CBlo CFil CMCN CPMA LNet |
| | MBri WPGP WPat WWeb WWes |
| - 'Beni-otake' | CB&S CMCN CPMA ECho LNet |
| | MGos |
| - 'Beni-schichihenge' (v) | CB&S CBlo CCHP CEnd CMCN |
| | CPMA ELan LNet MAsh NHol |
| | SMur SSta WPat |
| - 'Beni-shidare Variegated' | CMCN CPMA LNet |
| - 'Beni-shigitatsu-sawa' | See *A. palmatum* 'Aka |
| | Shigitatsusawa' |
| - 'Beni-tsukasa' (v) | CEnd CPMA LNet LPan LRHS SRPl |
| | SSpi WPat WWes |
| ¶ - 'Berry Dwarf' | WPat |
| - 'Bloodgood' ♀ | More than 30 suppliers |
| - 'Bonfire' | See *A. truncatum* 'Akaji-nishiki' |

| | |
|---|---|
| - 'Brocade' | CMCN WPat |
| - 'Burgundy Lace' ♀ | CB&S CBlo CDoC CEnd CMCN |
| | COtt CPMA EMil IOrc LNet MBlu |
| | MGos NHol WPat WPyg |
| - 'Butterfly' (v) ♀ | More than 30 suppliers |
| - 'Carminium' | See *A. palmatum* 'Corallinum' |
| - 'Chirimen-nishiki' (v) | CMCN LNet |
| - 'Chishio' | See *A. palmatum* 'Shishio' |
| - 'Chishio Improved' | See *A. palmatum* 'Shishio |
| | Improved' |
| - 'Chitoseyama' ♀ | CBlo CDul CEnd CMCN COtt |
| | CPMA CTho ELan LNet MBar |
| | MBri MGos SSpi SSta WPat WWeb |
| - 'Coonara Pygmy' | CMCN CPMA ECho LNet WPat |
| | WWes |
| - 'Coral Pink' | CPMA |
| § - 'Corallinum' | CBlo CEnd CMCN CPMA GOrc |
| | LNet LPan LRHS MGos SSpi WPat |
| N - var. *coreanum* | CMCN CSam WNor WWeb |
| ¶ - 'Crippsii' | EMil LRHS |
| - 'Deshôjô' | CB&S CBlo CMCN LNet LPan |
| | MAsh MBar MBlu MGos NHol |
| - var. *dissectum* ♀ | CDoC CEnd CTho EBee ENot |
| | IOrc LHyd MBar MBri MGos NBee |
| | NHol NWea SBod SBrw SReu |
| | SSoC WDin WFar WFro WNor |
| | WPat WPyg WStI WWat |
| - - 'Baldsmith' | CPMA |
| - - 'Crimson Queen' ♀ | CB&S CDoC CDul CEnd CMCN |
| | CPMA IOrc LNet LPan MAsh MBal |
| | MBar MBri MBro MGos NMoo |
| | SPer WFar WGer WNor WPat |
| | WPyg WStI |
| - - Dissectum | CB&S CPMA EBrP EBre ELan LBre |
| Atropurpureum | LHyd LNet LPan MBal MGos NBea |
| Group | NWea SBre SBrw SPer SReu SSpi |
| | SSta WBod WDin WFar WPat |
| | WWeb |
| - - 'Dissectum Flavescens' | CEnd CMCN CMac CPMA ISea |
| § - - 'Dissectum Nigrum' | CBlo CPMA CTri LNet MAsh |
| | MGos NBea NHol WLRN WPat |
| - - 'Dissectum | LNet |
| Palmatifidum' | |
| - - 'Dissectum Rubrifolium' | CMCN |
| § - - 'Dissectum Variegatum' | COtt CPMA EPfP LNet MAsh |
| | SMur SSta |
| - - Dissectum Viride Group | CB&S CDul CMCN CPMA ELan |
| | GRei ISea LNet MAsh MBro NBea |
| | SBrw SPer SPla SSta WBod WWeb |
| | LPan |
| - - 'Green Globe' | LPan |
| - - 'Green Mist' | CPMA |
| - - 'Inaba-shidare' ♀ | CB&S CDoC CEnd CMCN COtt |
| | CPMA EMil GRei IMGH LNet LPan |
| | LRHS MAsh MBar MBri MGos |
| | NHol SBod SPer SRPl SReu SSta |
| | WGer WPat WPyg |
| * - - 'Lionheart' | CPMA ECho LNet NPSI |
| - - 'Orangeola' | LNet WPat |
| - - 'Ornatum' | CDoC CMCN COtt CTri ECho |
| | IMGH LNet LRHS MBar MGos |
| | NBea SBrw SPer SSoC WFar WGer |
| | WHar |
| - - 'Sunset' | CMCN WPat |
| - - 'Eddisbury' | CPMA SSta WPat |
| - 'Effegi' | See *A. palmatum* 'Fireglow' |
| - 'Elegans' | EPfP |
| - 'Ever Red' | See *A. palmatum* var. *dissectum* |
| | 'Dissectum Nigrum' |
| - 'Filigree' (v) | CBlo CDoC CFil CMCN CPMA |
| | EPfP LNet MAsh MGos SSpi |
| | WPGP WPat |
| - 'Fior d'Arancio' | CPMA CEnd COtt |

§ - 'Fireglow'              CBlo CDoC CEnd CMCN COtt
                            CPMA EMil LPan MGos WPat
                            WWes
  - 'Fjellheim'             WPat
  - 'Frederici Guglielmi'   See *A. palmatum* var. *dissectum*
                            'Dissectum Variegatum'
  - 'Garnet' ♀             More than 30 suppliers
  - 'Goshiki-kotohime' (v)  CMCN CPMA WPat
  - 'Goshiki-shidare' (v)   CMCN LNet
  - 'Green Trompenburg'     CMCN LNet
§ - 'Hagoromo'              CDoC CPMA ECho LNet SPer
  - 'Hanami-nishiki'        CMCN CPMA
  - 'Harusame' (v)          CMCN LNet
  - 'Hazeroino' (v)         CMCN
  - var. *heptalobum*       CMCN
§ - 'Heptalobum Elegans'    CBlo CMCN CPMA LRHS SSpi
  - 'Heptalobum Elegans     See *A. palmatum* 'Hessei'
    Purpureum'
§ - 'Hessei'                CEnd CMCN LNet WPat
  - 'Higasayama' (v)        CB&S CDoC CFil CMCN COtt
                            CPMA LNet MGos NHol WPGP
                            WPat WWes
  - 'Hôgyoku'               CMCN CPMA
  - 'Ichigyôji'             CDul CEnd CMCN CPMA LRHS
                            MAsh WWeb
  - 'Improved Shishio'      See *A. palmatum* 'Shishio
                            Improved'
  - 'Inazuma'               CB&S CDoC CMCN ECho MGos
                            SBod
  - 'Jirô-shidare'          LNet LRHS SMur WWeb
  - 'Junihitoe'             See *A. shirasawanum* 'Junihitoe'
  - 'Kagero' (v)            CPMA
§ - 'Kagiri-nishiki' (v)    CDul CMCN CPMA LNet MGos
                            NHol SPer WNor WWeb
  - 'Kamagata'              CDoC CEnd CMCN CPMA EPfP
                            LRHS MAsh SSta WPat WWeb
  - 'Karaori-nishiki' (v)   CMCN LNet
  - 'Karasugawa' (v)        CMCN CPMA LNet
  - 'Kasagiyama'            CEnd CMCN COtt CPMA LRHS
                            WPat
  - 'Kasen-nishiki'         CPMA ECho
  - 'Kashima'               CMCN CPMA ECho WWes
  - 'Katsura'               CB&S CDoC CEnd CFil CMCN
                            COtt CPMA ELan LPan MAsh
                            MBlu MBri MGos NHol SPer SSpi
                            SSta WNor WPGP WWeb
  - 'Ki-hachijô'            CMCN CPMA
  - 'Kinran'                CMCN LNet LRHS WPat WWeb
  - 'Kinshi'                CEnd CMCN CPMA LNet LRHS
                            SSta WWeb WWes
  - 'Kiri-nishiki'          CMCN WPat
  - 'Kiyohime'              CDoC CMCN WPat
¶ - 'Komache-hime'          CPMA
¶ - 'Komon-nishiki' (v)     CPMA
  - 'Koshibori-nishiki'     CPMA
§ - 'Koshimino'             CPMA
  - 'Kotohime'              CMCN CPMA
  - 'Koto-ito-komachi'      ECho WPat
  - 'Koto-no-ito'           CMCN LNet
  - 'Kurui-jishi'           LNet WPat
  - 'Linearilobum' ♀       CMCN LHyd LNet MBlu NBea
                            NHol WNor WPat
  - 'Linearilobum          WNor
    Atropurpureum'
  - 'Little Princess'       See *A. palmatum* 'Mapi-no-
                            machihime'
  - 'Lutescens'             CMCN CPMA ECho
  - 'Maiko'                 CMCN ECho
  - 'Mama'                  CMCN
§ - 'Mapi-no-machihime'     CDoC CEnd CMCN CPMA ELan
                            LNet MAsh NHol SMur WPat
                            WWat WWeb WWes

¶ - 'Masamurasaki'          WPat
  - 'Masukagami' (v)        CEnd CPMA
  - 'Matsukaze'             CMCN COtt CPMA WWes
  - 'Mikawa-yatsubusa'      CMCN WPat
  - 'Mirte'                 LNet
¶ - 'Mizuho-beni'           CPMA
¶ - 'Mizu-kuguri'           CMCN
  - 'Momenshide'            WPat
¶ - 'Monzukushi'            CMCN
  - 'Moonfire'              CMCN CPMA ELan EPfP LNet
                            LRHS MAsh WWeb
  - 'Murasaki-kyohim'       CMCN CPMA ECho WPat
  - 'Mure-hibari'           CMCN
  - 'Murogawa'              CMCN
  - 'Nicholsonii'           CMCN LPan WPat
  - 'Nigrum'                CMCN LNet WPat
§ - 'Nishiki-gawa'          CMCN CPMA LNet
  - 'Nishiki-momiji'        Last listed 1998
  - 'Wada 'Nomurishidare'   SSpi
  - misapplied              See *A. palmatum* 'Shôjô-shidare'
    'Nomurishidare'
  - 'Nuresagi'              CMCN CPMA LNet
  - 'Ogon-sarasa'           CPMA
  - 'Ô-kagami'              CDoC CMCN CPMA ECho LNet
                            MBlu MBri SBod SSta
  - 'Okukuji-nishiki'       CBlo CPMA LNet
  - 'Okushimo'              CDoC CFil CMCN CPMA LNet
                            WPGP WPat
  - 'Omato'                 LNet
  - 'Omurayama'             CDoC CMCN CPMA EPfP LNet
                            LRHS MAsh MGos SSta WPat
                            WWeb WWes
§ - 'Ô-nishiki'             CMCN LNet
  - 'Orange Dream'          CMCN CPMA LNet LPan MAsh
                            MBri WWes
¶ - 'Oregon Sunset'         CMCN
  - 'Orido-nishiki' (v)     CEnd CMCN COtt CPMA ELan
                            EPfP LNet MAsh MBlu MGos
                            NBea NBee NPal SCoo SSta
  - 'Ôsakazuki' ♀          More than 30 suppliers
¶ - 'Ôshio-beni'            CPMA
  - 'Ôshû-beni'             CMCN
  - 'Ôshû-shidare'          CMCN CPMA WPat
  - 'Otome-zakura'          CMCN
  - 'Peaches and Cream' (v) CPMA
  - 'Pendulum Julian'       CMCN
  - 'Pine Bark Maple'       See *A. palmatum* 'Nishiki-gawa'
  - 'Pixie'                 CMCN CPMA
  - 'Red Dragon'            CB&S CDoC CPMA ECho LNet
                            MGos NPSI
  - 'Red Filigree Lace'     CMCN CPMA EPfP LNet MAsh
                            MBlu
  - 'Red Flash'             LPan
  - 'Red Pygmy' ♀          CB&S CBlo CDoC CEnd CMCN
                            COtt CPMA EMil GOrc LNet MBar
                            MBri MGos NBea NHol SPer SSta
                            WPat WWeb
  - 'Reticulatum'           See *A. palmatum* 'Shigitatsu-sawa'
  - 'Ribesifolium'          See *A. palmatum* 'Shishigashira'
  - 'Roseomarginatum'       See *A. palmatum* 'Kagiri-nishiki'
  - 'Rough Bark Maple'      See *A. palmatum* 'Arakawa'
  - 'Rubrum'                CMCN MBal
  - 'Rufescens'             CMCN
  - 'Ryuzu'                 CPMA
  - 'Sagara-nishiki' (v)    CMCN CPMA
  - 'Samidare'              CMCN CPMA
N - 'Sango-kaku' ♀         More than 30 suppliers
  - 'Saoshika'              CMCN CPMA
  - 'Sazanami'              CMCN CPMA WNor
  - 'Scolopendriifolium'    WPat
  - 'Seigen'                CMCN ECho

- 'Seiryû' ♀ — CAbP CB&S CDoC CEnd CMCN COtt CPMA ELan IMGH LNet LPan MBar MBri MGos NHol SBod SPer SSpi SSta WDin WFar WGer WNor WPat WWeb
- 'Sekimori' — CMCN CPMA SSta WWes
- 'Sekka-yatsubusa' — CMCN
- 'Senkaki' — See *A. palmatum* 'Sango-kaku'
- 'Septemlobum Elegans' — See *A. palmatum* 'Heptalobum Elegans'
- 'Septemlobum Purpureum' — See *A. palmatum* 'Hessei'
- 'Sessilifolium' dwarf — See *A. palmatum* 'Hagoromo'
- 'Sessilifolium' tall — See *A. palmatum* 'Koshimino'
- 'Shaina' — CB&S CMCN CPMA LNet LPan WPat WWeb
- 'Sherwood Flame' — CBlo CMCN CPMA LNet LRHS MBlu MBri MGos WPat
- 'Shichihenge' — Last listed 1996
¶ - 'Shidava Gold' — WPat
¶ - 'Shigarami' — CPMA
§ - 'Shigitatsu-sawa' (v) — CB&S CMCN CPMA EMil LPan MAsh MGos SSta
- 'Shigure-bato' — CMCN CPMA
¶ - 'Shigurezome' — CMCN
- 'Shikageori-nishiki' — Last listed 1998
- 'Shime-no-uchi' — CMCN LNet
- 'Shindeshôjô' — CDoC CEnd CMCN COtt CPMA ELan LNet LPan MAsh MBlu SBod SPer SPla SReu SSta WFoF WNor WPGP WPat WWeb
§ - 'Shinobugaoka' — CMCN CPMA LNet
- 'Shinonome' — CMCN COtt
§ - 'Shishigashira' — CDoC CMCN COtt CPMA LPan MBar MBri MGos SSta WPat
§ - 'Shishio' — CBlo CMCN COtt LHyd LNet MAsh SSpi
§ - 'Shishio Improved' — CFil CMCN CPMA LNet MBlu MGos SSta WPGP
- 'Shôjô' — CMCN
- 'Shôjô-nomura' — CEnd CMCN COtt
§ - 'Shôjô-shidare' — CEnd COtt ECho LRHS
- 'Skeeters' — WPat
- 'Stella Rossa' — CBlo CEnd CMCN COtt CPMA CSam MBlu WPat WWes
- 'Suminagashi' — CDoC CMCN COtt EMil LNet SMur SSta
- 'Takinogawa' — LRHS WWeb
- 'Tamahime' — CMCN
- 'Tamukeyama' — CMCN CPMA EMil SBod
- 'Tana' — CMCN CPMA
- 'Tatsuta-gawa' — Last listed 1996
¶ - 'Tiny Tim' — WPat
- 'Trompenburg' — CB&S CBlo CEnd CMCN COtt CPMA CTho ELan LNet LPan MAsh MBri MBro MGos NHol SBod SPer SPla SSpi SSta WPat WPyg WWeb
- 'Tsuchigumo' — CMCN CPMA ECho WWes
- 'Tsukubane' — CMCN
- 'Tsukushigata' — CMCN
- 'Tsuma-beni' — CMCN CPMA ELan EPfP LNet LRHS MAsh WPat WWeb
- 'Tsuma-gaki' — CMCN CPMA ECho
- 'Ukigumo' (v) — CB&S CEnd CMCN CPMA ELan LNet MGos NHol NPSI SBod SPer WPat
- 'Ukon' — CMCN
- 'Umegae' — CMCN CPMA
- 'Utsu-semi' — CMCN CPMA LNet
¶ - 'Vens Broom' — WPat
- 'Versicolor' (v) — CMCN CPMA LNet WWes

¶ - 'Vic Broom' — WPat
¶ - 'Vic Pink' — WPat
- 'Villa Taranto' — CDoC CEnd CMCN CPMA EPfP LNet LRHS MAsh MBlu MGos WPat
- 'Volubile' — CMCN ECho SMur
- 'Wabito' — CMCN
- 'Wada's Flame' — Last listed 1996
- 'Wakehurst Pink' (v) — CMCN
- 'Waterfall' — CMCN CPMA LNet MGos
- 'Wilson's Pink Dwarf' — CMCN ECho LNet
- 'Wou-nishiki' — See *A. palmatum* 'Ô-nishiki'
¶ - 'Yasemin' — CMCN
¶ - 'Yezo-nishiki' — MBri
- 'Yûgure' — MGos
*papilio* — See *A. caudatum*
*paxii* — CMCN
*pectinatum* — Last listed 1996
- subsp. *forrestii* — See *A. forrestii*
- 'Sirene' — CPMA MGos
- 'Sparkling' — MBri
*pensylvanicum* ♀ — CB&S CBlo CDul CMCN CSam CTho EBee ELan EPfP LPan MGos NBee NHol NWea SPer SSpi WDin WNor WOrn WWat WWeb
- 'Erythrocladum' ♀ — CDoC CEnd CMCN CPMA CTho LNet MBri MGos NBea NHol SMad SRPl SSpi SSta
*pentaphyllum* — CMCN LNet SSpi
*pictum* — See *A. mono*
*pilosum* var. *stenolobum* — CPMA MBlu SFur WWoo
*platanoides* ♀ — CBlo CDoC CKin CLnd CMCN ENot GChr GRei LBuc LHyr LPan MGos NWea SPer WDin WHar WMou WNor
- 'Cleveland' — CB&S ENot
- 'Columnare' — CDoC CMCN ENot EPfP IOrc LPan NBee WOrn
- 'Crimson King' ♀ — More than 30 suppliers
- 'Crimson Sentry' — CBlo CDoC CDul CEnd CLnd CMCN COtt EBee EBrP EBre ENot ERod LBre LBuc LNet MAsh MBri MGos SBre WHar WJas WLRN WOrn WWeb
- 'Cucullatum' — CMCN CTho
- 'Deborah' — CDul CLnd CTho LPan
- 'Dissectum' — CTho
- 'Drummondii' (v) ♀ — More than 30 suppliers
- 'Emerald Queen' — CDoC CLnd CMCN ENot EWTr WOrn
- 'Faassen's Black' — LPan
§ - 'Globosum' — CLnd CMCN ENot LPan MGos
- 'Goldsworth Purple' — CLnd CMCN SRPl
- 'Laciniatum' — CEnd CMCN ENot MAsh SLPl SPer
- 'Lorbergii' — See *A. platanoides* 'Palmatifidum'
- 'Olmsted' — ENot LNet
§ - 'Palmatifidum' — CSam
◆ - 'Prigo' — See *A. platanoides* Princeton Gold = 'Prigo'
§ - Princeton Gold = 'Prigo' — LPan MBri
- 'Pyramidale Nanum' — CTho
- 'Reitenbachii' — Last listed 1996
- 'Royal Red' — CBlo CDul CMCN ENot EWTr MGos
- 'Schwedleri' ♀ — CBlo CDul CLnd CMCN MGos NBee NWea
- 'Summershade' — CMCN
¶ - 'Tharandt' — CMCN
*pseudoplatanus* — CB&S CBlo CDul CKin CLnd CMCN CTri ENot GChr GRei LBuc LHyr LPan MBar MGos NWea WDin WHar WMou

| | |
|---|---|
| § - 'Atropurpureum' ♀ | CBlo CDoC CDul CLnd CTho ENot IOrc NBee NWea |
| - 'Brilliantissimum' ♀ | More than 30 suppliers |
| - 'Constant P.' | ENot |
| - 'Corstorphinense' | CMCN |
| - 'Erectum' | ENot WOrn |
| - 'Erythrocarpum' | CMCN |
| N - 'Leopoldii' (v) ♀ | CB&S CBlo CDoC CDul CLnd CMCN COtt CTho ECrN ELan ENot IOrc LPan MBar NBea SPer WOrn |
| - 'Negenia' | Last listed 1998 |
| - 'Nizetii' (v) | CMCN LRHS MBri |
| - 'Prinz Handjéry' | CB&S CBlo CDoC CDul CEnd CMCN CTri LNet LPan MAsh MBar MGos NWea SPer SSpi |
| - 'Simon-Louis Frères' (v) | CBlo CDul CEnd CLnd CMCN EBee EMui GChr LNet LPan MAsh MBri MGos MWat NBea WFoF WHar |
| N - 'Spaethii' hort. | See A. pseudoplatanus 'Atropurpureum' |
| - 'Spring Gold' | MGos |
| - f. variegatum | WCot |
| - 'Worley' ♀ | CB&S CBlo CDoC CDul CLnd CMCN COtt EBee ECrN ENot GChr IOrc NBea NWea SPer WDin WHar WOrn |
| pseudosieboldianum | CFil CMCN CPMA SSpi WFro WNor WPGP WWoo |
| - MSF 861 | Last listed 1998 |
| pubipalmatum | WNor |
| pycnanthum | CMCN |
| regelii | See A. pentapotamicum |
| robustum | WNor |
| rubescens | CLnd CSam SFur |
| rubrum | CAgr CB&S CBlo CDoC CDul CGre CLnd CMCN CTri EBee ECrN GCHN LHyr MGos MLan MWat NBea NBee NWea SPer WDin WNor WWat |
| - 'Armstrong' | Last listed 1997 |
| - 'Bowhall' | CMCN |
| - 'Columnare' | CMCN |
| ¶ - 'Elstead' | LNet |
| - 'Morgan' | CEnd |
| - October Glory® ♀ | CBlo CDoC CDul CEnd CMCN CMHG CSam CTho GChr IOrc LPan MAsh MBlu MBri SMad SSpi SSta WCwm WWeb |
| - Red Sunset | CDoC CEnd CMCN CTho EBee LPan MBlu MBri SMad SSpi SSta WCwm |
| - 'Schlesingeri' | CEnd CMCN MBlu |
| ¶ - 'Tilford' | SSta |
| § rufinerve ♀ | CB&S CBlo CDoC CDul CLnd CMCN CMHG CTho CTri ENot EPfP ESis GChr IOrc LPan MBri NBea NBee NWea SPer SSpi WDin WGer WNor WOrn WPyg WStI |
| - 'Albolimbatum' | See A. rufinerve 'Hatsuyuki' |
| - 'Albomarginatum' | See A. rufinerve 'Hatsuyuki' |
| ¶ - 'Erythrocladum' | CPMA |
| § - 'Hatsuyuki' (v) | CBlo CDoC CEnd CMCN CPMA ELan EPla SSpi |
| § saccharinum ♀ | CB&S CBlo CDul CLnd CMCN EBee ELan ENot EWTr GChr LHyr MGos MWat NBee NWea SPer SRPl SSpi WDin WFar WNor |
| - 'Born's Gracious' | IOrc |
| - 'Elegans' | See A. x freemanii 'Elegant' |
| - 'Fastigiatum' | See A. saccharinum f. pyramidale |

| | |
|---|---|
| - f. laciniatum | CMCN EBee ENot MBlu MGos WDin |
| - 'Laciniatum Wieri' | CLnd CMCN CTho MGos NBee |
| - f. lutescens | CDul CMCN CTho ENot MBlu |
| § - f. pyramidale | CBlo CDoC CLnd CMCN EBee ENot EPfP IOrc LPan |
| saccharum | CAgr CDoC CDul CLnd CMCN NWea WCwm WNor |
| - subsp. barbatum | See A. saccharum subsp. floridanum |
| § - subsp. floridanum | CMCN |
| § - subsp. grandidentatum | CMCN |
| - subsp. leucoderme | CMCN |
| - subsp. nigrum | CMCN |
| - - 'Temple's Upright' | CMCN LNet |
| - subsp. skutchii | CMCN |
| 'Scanlon' ♀ | CB&S CDul CEnd CMCN CTho WOrn |
| § sempervirens | CFil CMCN CPMA |
| serrulatum | CMCN |
| - CC 1891 | Last listed 1997 |
| § sbirasawanum | CDul CMCN WCoo WNor |
| § - 'Aureum' ♀ | More than 30 suppliers |
| § - 'Ezo-no-momiji' | CDul CMCN |
| § - 'Junihitoe' | WNor |
| § - 'Microphyllum' | CMCN LNet WNor |
| § - 'Ogurayama' | LNet |
| - 'Palmatifolium' | CBlo CMCN CPMA MGos WStI |
| - var. tenuifolium | CLyn WNor |
| sieboldianum | CLnd CMCN CTri ECho EPfP ESis SSpi WNor |
| - 'Kinugasayama' | Last listed 1996 |
| - 'Sode-no-uchi' | CMCN |
| sikkimense subsp. metcalfii | See A. metcalfii |
| § - 'Silver Cardinal' (v) | CB&S CEnd CPMA MGos SMad SSpi WWes |
| 'Silver Vein' | See A. x conspicuum 'Silver Vein' |
| § sinense | CMCN SFur WNor WWoo |
| - var. pubinerve | Last listed 1998 |
| sp. CC 1648 | Last listed 1997 |
| spicatum | CMCN WNor |
| stachyopbyllum | See A. tetramerum |
| § sterculiaceum | CMCN |
| syriacum | See A. obtusifolium |
| taronense | CMCN |
| tataricum | CAgr CMCN |
| § - subsp. ginnala ♀ | CAgr CB&S CBlo CDul CLnd CMCN CTho EBee ECrN ELan ENot EPla IOrc MBal MGos NBea WNor WWat |
| - - 'Durand Dwarf' | CMCN |
| * - - 'Fire' | LNet |
| - - 'Flame' | CBlo CLnd CPMA MGos WWoo |
| - subsp. semenowii | CMCN |
| tegmentosum | CMCN SFur WNor WWoo |
| - subsp. glaucorufinerve | See A. rufinerve |
| tenellum | Last listed 1997 |
| tenuifolium | CMCN |
| § tetramerum | GQui |
| thomsonii | Last listed 1998 |
| trautvetteri | CMCN WNor WTro |
| triflorum | CB&S CLnd CMCN CTho EPfP GChr IMGH SFur SSpi SSta WWat WWes |
| truncatum | CMCN WCwm WNor |
| - 'Akaji-nishiki' | MAsh WWeb |
| - 'Akikaze-nishiki' (v) | CPMA LNet SFur |
| tscbonoskii | CDoC CMCN GQui WWes |
| - subsp. koreanum | CDoC CPMA SFur WNor |
| § turkestanicum | CMCN |
| velutinum | CMCN |

| | |
|---|---|
| *villosum* | See *A. sterculiaceum* |
| § *wilsonii* | CMCN SFur WNor WShe |
| x *zoeschense* | CMCN |
| - 'Annae' | IOrc |

## ACERAS (Orchidaceae)
| | |
|---|---|
| ¶ *anthropophorum* | EFEx |

## ACERIPHYLLUM See MUKDENIA

## x ACHICODONIA (Gesneriaceae)
| | |
|---|---|
| § 'Cornell Gem' | NMos |

## ACHILLEA ✿ (Asteraceae)
| | |
|---|---|
| *abrotanoides* | EGoo ELan |
| *ageratifolia* ♀ | ECha LBee MBro MTho NLon |
| | NMen SRms SSca SSmi WByw |
| | WFar WLRN |
| - subsp. *ageratifolia* | Last listed 1998 |
| - - NS 692 | Last listed 1996 |
| § - subsp. *aizoon* | EGar WPer |
| ¶ - subsp. *serbica* | NBro |
| § *ageratum* | CArn CSev ELau GBar GPoy IIve |
| | LHol MChe MHer MSal SIde WHer |
| | WJek WOak WPer WWye |
| - 'W.B. Childs' | CGle CSpe ECha ELan GBuc LGre |
| | MArl MAvo MNrw MSte WEas |
| 'Alabaster' | CLon CRDP EFou EMon EPPr |
| | GBuc LGre LRHS MBel NPla |
| ♦ 'Anblo' | See *A.* Anthea = 'Anblo' |
| § Anthea = 'Anblo' | CHad CSpe CWit EBee EBrP EBre |
| | EMan GSki LBre LFis LGre MBro |
| | MCLN MLLN NLak NRoo SBre |
| | SMad SWat WFar WWat |
| § 'Apfelblüte' | CDoC CMGP CSli EAst EBee EBrP |
| | EBre ECtt EFou ELan EMan EWTr |
| | LBre LFis LHop MAvo MCLN |
| | MGrG MRav MTis NRoo SBre SPer |
| | SSpe SWat WFar WMer WMow |
| | WPer WRus |
| Appleblossom | See *A.* 'Apfelblüte' |
| *argentea* hort. | See *A. clavennae, A. umbellata* |
| - Lamarck | See *Tanacetum argenteum* |
| *aurea* | See *A. chrysocoma* |
| 'Bahama' | EBee GBuc NBro NFai |
| 'Bloodstone' | CSli EGar EMan EPPr GMac WBea |
| | WWhi |
| *brachyphylla* | EPot |
| *cartilaginea* | EAst EFou EGar LHop MTed WCot |
| | WFar WMaN WMoo |
| - 'Silver Spray' | EBee NLak SRCN WWhi |
| *chamaemelifolia* | WHil |
| § *chrysocoma* | ELan MWat NMen NRya NTow |
| | SSmi |
| - 'Grandiflora' | CHad CHar ECGN MGrG NGdn |
| | WLRN |
| § *clavennae* | CGle EPot GCHN GMaP LBee |
| | LPio MPla MWat NMen NRoo |
| | NTow SBla SIng SMer SRms WAbe |
| | WCot WFar WKif |
| *clypeolata* | GVic LPio NFla SRms |
| *coarctata* | NBir WElm WPer |
| 'Coronation Gold' ♀ | CBlo CDoC CWit EAst EFou ELan |
| | ENot EPfP LFis LGre MBri MCAu |
| | MCLN MMil MWat MWgw SMrm |
| | SPer WEas |
| 'Credo' | CGle CHad CMil CRDP CSev CSli |
| | EAst EBee EFou EMan EMon EPPr |
| | GBuc LGre MBel MCAu MCLN |
| | MHlr MLLN MRav MUlv MWgw |
| | SMad SWat WCot WElm WWhi |
| * 'Crimson King' | Last listed 1997 |

| | |
|---|---|
| 'Croftway' | SCro |
| *decolorans* | See *A. ageratum* |
| *erba-rotta* subsp. | EWTr NBro |
| *moschata* | |
| - subsp. *rupestris* | CMea MDHE SMer WPer |
| § 'Fanal' | More than 30 suppliers |
| 'Faust' | EFou |
| 'Feuerland' | CLon CSli CWit EBee ECha EFou |
| | EMan EMon EPPr GMac LFis |
| | MAvo MBro MCAu MCLN MLLN |
| | MRav SMad SSpe SUsu SWat WBea |
| | WCot WElm WFar WHoo WPer |
| | WWhi |
| *filipendulina* | NSti SWat |
| - 'Cloth of Gold' | More than 30 suppliers |
| - 'Gold Plate' ♀ | CDoC CHad EBrP EBre ECha ECtt |
| | EFou ELan LBre MBel MCLN |
| | MLan MMil MWgw NOrc NTow |
| | SBre SCro SMad SPer SRms WCot |
| | WEas |
| - 'Parker's Variety' | EGar EMil GBuc MBri MLan NOak |
| | SRCN WFar |
| Flowers of Sulphur | See *A.* 'Schwefelblüte' |
| 'Forncett Beauty' | EFou NBrk SChu WBea WWhi |
| 'Forncett Bride' | EFou |
| 'Forncett Candy' | CSli EFou |
| I 'Forncett Citrus' | EFou |
| 'Forncett Fletton' | CSli EFou EPPr LFis NBrk NCat |
| | NDov SCro SHel SUsu WBay WCot |
| | WViv |
| 'Forncett Ivory' | EFou NCat NLak |
| *fraasii* | SSvw WPer |
| *glaberrima* | WCot |
| *grandifolia* | CBos CBre CHan CPou CSam |
| | EBee EGle EMan EMon GCal IHdy |
| | LEdu LGre MSte NBro NSti NTow |
| | SMad SPer SSvw WBea WCot WFar |
| | WHer WWye |
| 'Great Expectations' | See *A.* 'Hoffnung' |
| 'Hartington White' | EMon GBuc MWgw |
| 'Hella Glashoff' | LGre NBrk SAga WCot |
| § 'Hoffnung' | CBlo CMGP EBrP EBre ECtt EFou |
| | EMan GSki LBre LHop NBrk SBre |
| | SCro SPer SSpe WEas WLRN WPer |
| | WWin |
| *holosericea* NS 747 | Last listed 1998 |
| 'Huteri' | CInt CLyd CNic CPea ECtt EGoo |
| | ELan EMNN EPot ESis GCHN |
| | GMaP LBee MBro MRav NCat |
| | NFor NLon NMen NNrd SChu |
| | SSmi WAbe WEas WFar WPer |
| | WWin |
| 'Inca Gold' | CSli EBee ECha EFou EGle EMan |
| | EPPr GBri MCLN SChu SUsu SWat |
| x *jaborneggii* | GCHN |
| 'Jambo' | Last listed 1998 |
| 'James Chapman' | Last listed 1997 |
| x *kellereri* | ELan MBro SAsh SSmi |
| 'Kempsey Buttermilk' | WBcn |
| x *kolbiana* | EMan LHop MWat NHol NMen |
| | NRoo SDys SRms SSmi WHoo |
| | WLin WPat WWin |
| § - 'Weston' | NRoo NTow |
| 'Lachsschönheit' | More than 30 suppliers |
| x *lewisii* | NMen |
| - 'King Edward' ♀ | CMHG CMea EBrP EBre ECha |
| | EFou ELan ERic ESis LBee LBre |
| | MTho NBir NMGW NRoo NTow |
| | SBla SBre SChu SSmi SWat WCom |
| | WFar WPer |
| 'Libella' | GBuc |
| ¶ 'Lucky Break' | SDix |

| | |
|---|---|
| 'Lusaka' | Last listed 1998 |
| *macrophylla* | EBee |
| 'Marmalade' | SMrm SUsu SWat |
| 'Martina' | CDoC CM&M CSli EBee EFou EGoo EHal EMan EMar EMon EPPr GBuc GNau MLLN NCat NOrc NTow SVil SWat |
| * 'McVities' | CSli EFou EPPr LFis SUsu SWat WCot WTin |
| *millefolium* | CArn CGle EEls ELau EWFC GBar GPoy LHol MHew NHex NLan NMir SIde WHbs WHer WOak WSel WWye |
| - 'Burgundy' | Last listed 1998 |
| ¶ - 'Carla Hussey' | MTed WFar |
| - 'Cerise Queen' | More than 30 suppliers |
| - 'Colorado' | CFri CM&M COlW CPou EWTr SPil SRCN |
| ¶ - dark red | CSli |
| - 'Fire King' | CHal |
| - 'Lansdorferglut' | LRHS MBri MRav MTed |
| - 'Lavender Beauty' | See A. *millefolium* 'Lilac Beauty' |
| § - 'Lilac Beauty' | CBlo CGle CSli CSpe ECha EFou EMan GLil MBel MRav SAga SUsu WBea WCot WElm WFar WHal WMaN WMer WWhi |
| * - 'Lilac Queen' | CMGP CSli MArl SWat |
| - 'Malmesbury' (v) | CNat |
| - 'Melanie' | WMer |
| - 'Paprika' | CBlo CPar CRDP CSli GBuc MAvo MBNS MBel MBri MCLN MCli MGrG MLLN NFai NHol SBod SMad SWat WBea WBro WByw WElm WHil WMaN WMow WPer WRus WWhi |
| - 'Prospero' | LFis MBro MSte NDov WBea WMaN |
| - 'Red Beauty' | CSli MTis SAga SMad SRms SWat WOve |
| - f.*rosea* | MBal NRoo |
| - 'Sammetriese' | EFou ELan EMon EPPr GBuc MAvo MSte SMad SUsu WCot WElm WHoo WMaN WPnP WPyg WRHF WWhi |
| - 'Sweet Harmony' | Last listed 1997 |
| - 'Tickled Pink' | WPer WRHF |
| - 'White Queen' | LWoo WMer WPer |
| ¶ 'Mondpagode' | EPPr LGre SAga |
| 'Moonlight' | MBro WHoo |
| 'Moonshine' ♀ | More than 30 suppliers |
| 'Moonwalker' | CBlo CSli EAst EBee EWTr LWoo MLLN SIde WFar WPer WRHF |
| 'Nakuru' | NCat |
| *nana* | Last listed 1996 |
| *nobilis* subsp.*neilreichii* | CMea CRDP CSpe EGoo EMar EMon EPPr LFis MLLN SAga SPer WCot WHal WOve |
| *odorata* | Last listed 1996 |
| 'Peach Queen' | Last listed 1996 |
| 'Peter Davis' | See *Hippolytia herderi* |
| *pindicola* subsp. *integrifolia* | CLyd EWes |
| *ptarmica* | CArn CKin ELau EWFC EWTr GBar Ilve LHol MChe MHew MSal NMir SIde SPer WGwy WWye |
| * - 'Ballerina' | NCat NDov NLar WRHF |
| - 'Boughton Beauty' | NLar |
| - Innocence | See A. *ptarmica* 'Unschuld' |
| - 'Major' | Last listed 1998 |
| - 'Nana Compacta' | ECha EFou EPPr MBri MCAu MHlr NDov NFor NRoo SMrm SUsu WCot |

| | |
|---|---|
| - 'Perry's White' | CBre EBee ECha EMon GCal GLil MHlr NCat WByw WCot WMaN WMer |
| - 'Stephanie Cohen' | CSpe CStr EFou GVic MAvo MLLN NDov WCot |
| N - The Pearl Group seed-raised (d) | More than 30 suppliers |
| - - 'Boule de Neige' (clonal) (d) | CBlo CHal EGoo LRHS MBri NDov NPer NSti SPer SPla WGwG WLRN WWal |
| N - - 'The Pearl' (clonal) (d) | EWTr NLon SRms WEas WFar WHer WMaN |
| § - 'Unschuld' | NBir |
| *pumila* | See A. *distans* subsp. *tanacetifolia* |
| Salmon Beauty = 'Lachsschönheit' | See A. 'Lachsschönheit' |
| 'Sandstone' | See A. 'Wesersandstein' |
| § 'Schwefelblüte' | ELan LFis NBir |
| 'Schwellenburg' | EBee EGle EPPr |
| *sibirica* | WElm |
| - AGS 1241 | CNic |
| - 'Kiku-san' | Last listed 1998 |
| 'Smiling Queen' | Last listed 1998 |
| 'Summer Glory' | SCro |
| Summer Pastels Group | CM&M EMan EMil GCHN MFir NArg NBus NFla NMir NOak NOrc NRoo SEas SRCN SRms SWat WLRN WPer WRha |
| 'Summerwine' | CSli ECha EFou EGle EGoo EMar EPPr GBri LGre MRav SAga SChu SCro SMad SUsu SWat WMaN WRus |
| I 'Taygetea' | CBot CGle CLyd CSam CSli ECha EFou ELan EMan LBlm MCAu MWat NSti SChu SDix SPer SUsu SWat WByw WCot WFar WKif WOve WPer WRus WSHC |
| 'Terracotta' | More than 30 suppliers |
| 'The Beacon' | See A. 'Fanal' |
| *tomentosa* ♀ | CHan CTri ECha ECtt EPfP LHop MBal NNrd SWat |
| § - 'Aurea' | CHal EBot ECtt ELan ELau LPVe MOne NBro NNrd SIde SRCN SRms WHil WPer WRos |
| - 'Maynard's Gold' | See A. *tomentosa* 'Aurea' |
| § *umbellata* | NTow |
| - NS 390 | Last listed 1997 |
| - 'Weston' | See A. x *kolbiana* 'Weston' |
| 'Walther Funcke' | CHad CLon CMdw CRDP CSpe EFou EGle EMil EPPr LFis LGre MBri MSCN MWat NPro SAga SMrm SUsu WCot |
| § 'Wesersandstein' | CSli EBee EFou EMan EMon EPPr GMac LFis MAvo MBri WCot WElm WMaN WMer WOve WWhi |
| 'Wilczekii' | NChi SBod SRms WViv |

## x ACHIMENANTHA (Gesneriaceae)

| | |
|---|---|
| 'Cerulean Mink' | See x *Smithicodonia* 'Cerulean Mink' |
| 'Dutch Treat' | NMos |
| 'Ginger Peachy' | NMos |
| 'Inferno' | NMos WDib |
| * 'Rose Bouquet' | NMos |
| 'Royal' | NMos |

## ACHIMENES (Gesneriaceae)

| | |
|---|---|
| 'Adelaide' | Last listed 1998 |
| 'Adèle Delahaute' | Last listed 1998 |
| 'Adonis Blue' | Last listed 1998 |
| 'Almandine' | NMos |

| | |
|---|---|
| 'Ambleside' | Last listed 1998 |
| 'Ambroise Verschaffelt' | LAma NMos |
| 'Ami Van Houtte' | NMos |
| 'Ann Marie' | NMos |
| 'Apricot Glow' | NMos |
| 'Aquamarine' | NMos |
| * 'Aries' | Last listed 1997 |
| 'Bassenthwaite' | NMos |
| 'Bea' | Last listed 1998 |
| *bella* | See *Eucodonia verticillata* |
| 'Bernice' | NMos |
| 'Blauer Planet' | NMos |
| 'Bloodstone' | NMos |
| 'Blue Gown' | NMos |
| 'Brilliant' | NMos |
| 'Butterfield Bronze' | NMos |
| 'Buttermere' | NMos |
| 'Camberwell Beauty' | NMos |
| 'Cameo Rose' | NMos |
| 'Cameo Triumph' | NMos |
| 'Camille Brozzoni' | NMos |
| *candida* | NMos |
| 'Carmine Queen' | NMos |
| 'Cascade Cockade' | NMos |
| 'Cascade Evening Glow' | NMos |
| 'Cascade Fairy Pink' | Last listed 1998 |
| 'Cascade Fashionable Pink' | NMos |
| 'Cascade Rosy Red' | NMos |
| 'Cascade Violet Night' | NMos |
| 'Cattleya' | LAma |
| 'Chalkhill Blue' | Last listed 1998 |
| 'Charm' | LAma NMos |
| 'Clouded Yellow' | NMos |
| 'Compact Great Rosy Red' | NMos |
| 'Coniston Water' | NMos |
| 'Copeland Boy' | NMos |
| 'Copeland Girl' | NMos |
| 'Coral Sunset' | NMos |
| 'Cornell Favourite 'A'' | NMos |
| 'Cornell Favourite 'B'' | NMos |
| 'Crimson Beauty' | NMos |
| 'Crimson Glory' | NMos |
| 'Crimson Tiger' | Last listed 1998 |
| 'Crummock Water' | NMos |
| 'Cupido' | NMos |
| 'Dentoniana' | Last listed 1998 |
| 'Derwentwater' | NMos |
| 'Dorothy' | NMos |
| 'Dot' | NMos |
| *dulcis* | NMos |
| 'Early Arnold' | NMos |
| *ebrenbergii* | See *Eucodonia ebrenbergii* |
| 'Elke Michelssen' | NMos |
| 'English Waltz' | NMos |
| *erecta* | WDib |
| 'Escheriana' | NMos |
| 'Flamenco' | NMos |
| 'Flamingo' | SDeJ |
| *flava* | NMos |
| 'Fritz Michelssen' | NMos |
| 'Gary John' | NMos |
| 'Gary/Jennifer' | NMos |
| 'Grape Wine' | NMos |
| 'Grasmere' | NMos |
| 'Harry Williams' | LAma |
| § 'Harveyi' | NMos |
| 'Haweswater' | NMos |
| 'Hilda Michelssen' | NMos WDib |
| 'Honey Gold' | NMos |
| 'Ida Michelssen' | NMos |
| 'India' | NMos |
| § 'Jaureguia Maxima' | NMos |

| | |
|---|---|
| 'Jennifer Goode' | NMos |
| 'Jewell Blue' | NMos |
| 'Johanna Michelssen' | NMos |
| 'Jubilee Gem' | NMos |
| 'Lakeland Lady' | NMos |
| 'Lavender Fancy' | Last listed 1998 |
| 'Little Beauty' | LAma NMos |
| 'Little Red Tiger' | NMos |
| *longiflora* | NMos |
| – 'Alba' | See *A.* 'Jaureguia Maxima' |
| – 'Major' | NMos |
| 'Magnificent' | NMos |
| 'Margaret White' | Last listed 1996 |
| 'Marie' | NMos |
| 'Masterpiece' | NMos |
| 'Maxima' | LAma |
| 'Menuett '80'' | NMos |
| 'Milton' | NMos |
| *misera* | NMos |
| 'Moonstone' | NMos |
| 'Old Rose Pink' | LAma NMos |
| 'Orange Queen' | NMos |
| 'Pally' | NMos |
| 'Panic Pink' | NMos |
| 'Patens Major' | NMos |
| 'Patricia' | Last listed 1998 |
| 'Paul Arnold' | NMos |
| 'Peach Blossom' | LAma NMos |
| 'Peach Glow' | NMos |
| 'Peacock' | Last listed 1998 |
| 'Pearly Queen' | NMos |
| 'Pendant Blue' | NMos |
| 'Pendant Purple' | NMos |
| 'Petticoat Pink' | NMos |
| 'Pink Beauty' | NMos |
| 'Pinocchio' | NMos |
| 'Prima Donna' | NMos |
| 'Pulcherrima' | LAma |
| 'Purple King' | NMos |
| 'Queen of Sheba' | Last listed 1998 |
| 'Quickstep' | NMos |
| 'Rachael' | NMos |
| 'Red Admiral' | NMos |
| 'Red Giant' | NMos |
| 'Red Imp' | Last listed 1998 |
| 'Red Top Hybrid' | NMos |
| 'Robin' | NMos |
| 'Rosenelfe' | NMos |
| 'Rosy Doll' | NMos |
| 'Rosy Frost' | NMos |
| 'Rydal Water' | NMos |
| 'Scafell' | NMos |
| * *selloana* | Last listed 1997 |
| 'Shirley Dwarf White' | NMos |
| 'Shirley Fireglow' | See *A.* 'Harveyi' |
| 'Show-off' | NMos |
| 'Silver Wedding' | NMos |
| 'Snow Princess' | SDeJ |
| Snow White | See *A.* 'Schneewittchen' |
| 'Sparkle' | NMos |
| 'Stan's Delight' | NMos WDib |
| 'Sue' | NMos |
| 'Tango' | NMos |
| 'Tantivvy' | Last listed 1998 |
| 'Tarantella' | NMos |
| 'Teresa' | NMos |
| 'Tiny Blue' | NMos |
| 'Topsy' | NMos |
| 'Troutbeck' | NMos |
| 'Ullswater' | NMos |
| 'Vanessa' | NMos |
| 'Viola Michelssen' | NMos |

| | |
|---|---|
| 'Violacea Semiplena' | NMos |
| 'Violetta' | Last listed 1996 |
| 'Vivid' | LAma NMos |
| 'Warren' | NMos |
| 'Wastwater' | NMos |
| 'Wetterflow's Triumph' | NMos |
| 'White Admiral' | NMos |
| 'White Rajah' | NMos |
| 'Wilma' | NMos |
| 'Windermere' | NMos |

## ACHLYS (Berberidaceae)

| | |
|---|---|
| *japonica* | WCru |
| *triphylla* | WCru |

## ACHNATHERUM See STIPA

## ACHYRANTHES (Amaranthaceae)

| | |
|---|---|
| ¶ *bidentata* | ELau IIve |

## ACIDANTHERA See GLADIOLUS

## ACINOS (Lamiaceae)

| | |
|---|---|
| § *alpinus* | CAgr EBee SBla SChu |
| - subsp. *meridionalis* | EGle NTow |
| § *arvensis* | CArn MBri MHer MSal |
| § *corsicus* | ESis LFis MBro NMen NWCA SIde SRCN WPat WWin |

## ACIPHYLLA (Apiaceae)

| | |
|---|---|
| *aurea* | EBee EPot GCal ITim MBal NHar SIgm WLin |
| - CC 464 | Last listed 1997 |
| *colensoi* | Last listed 1998 |
| * - *major* | Last listed 1997 |
| ¶ *crenulata* | EBee |
| *crosby-smithii* | Last listed 1997 |
| *dobsonii* | EBee EPot |
| *glaucescens* | MBal NHar |
| *hectoris* | EBee EPot |
| *horrida* | Last listed 1997 |
| *kirkii* | Last listed 1998 |
| 'Lomond' | SIgm |
| *lyallii* | Last listed 1998 |
| ¶ *maxima* | EBee |
| *monroi* | Last listed 1997 |
| *montana* | EBee |
| *pinnatifida* | GCal GCrs NHar |
| *procumbens* | Last listed 1996 |
| *scott-thomsonii* | EBee |
| *simplex* | EPot |
| *squarrosa* | ECou GCal SIgm |
| *subflabellata* | EBee ECou GCal NHar SIgm |

## ACNISTUS (Solanaceae)

| | |
|---|---|
| *australis* | See *Iochroma australe* |

## ACOELORRHAPHE (Arecaceae)

| | |
|---|---|
| *wrightii* | CBrP LPal |

## ACOKANTHERA (Apocynaceae)

| | |
|---|---|
| *spectabilis* | See *A. oblongifolia* |

## ACONITUM (✿) (Ranunculaceae)

| | |
|---|---|
| *alboviolaceum* | GCal |
| *anglicum* | See *A. napellus* subsp. *napellus* Anglicum Group |
| *anthora* | IHdy LPio NLar |
| *arcuatum* B&SWJ 864 | WCru |
| N *autumnale* | NBir |
| *bartlettii* B&SWJ 337 | WCru |
| 'Blue Sceptre' | EBrP EBre LBre NRoo SBre SRms |

| | |
|---|---|
| 'Bressingham Spire' ♀ | CMGP EBee EBrP EBre ECtt EFou ENot GAbr GMaP IHdy LBre LGre MBri MCAu MRav MWat MWgw NDea NOrc NPer NRoo SBre SChu SPer SRms WOld |
| x *cammarum* 'Bicolor' ♀ | More than 30 suppliers |
| - 'Grandiflorum Album' | LGre |
| § *carmichaelii* | CArn CBot CGle CLon EBee EFou EMan EWTr GAbr IBlr IHdy MBro MHlr MRav NChi NFla NFor NGdn NOrc NRoo SCro SRms WBod WHoo WRus |
| - 'Arendsii' | CMGP CMHG EBrP EBre ECGN ECha ECtt GMaP LBre LFis LRot MBri MBro MGrG MRav MSte NLar NRoo NTow SBre SChu SPer SPla SSoC SSvw WCot WEas WFar WOld WWye |
| - Wilsonii Group | CHad CHan CHar GGar LGre MBri MRav MSte NTow SAga SChu SSoC WFar WOve WPer WWin WWye |
| § - - 'Barker's Variety' | CPou CRow EFou EMan GBuc LGre MFir MHlr NHol NSti WCot WMer WRus |
| - - 'Kelmscott' ♀ | ECGN EGle EMon MSte MWgw SAga SBla SDix WByw WFar WRHF |
| ¶ - - 'Spätlese' | GCal |
| *cilicicum* | See *Eranthis hyemalis* Cilicica Group |
| *compactum* | See *A. napellus* subsp. *vulgare* |
| *deflexum* | Last listed 1998 |
| 'Eleonara' | CFir EFou EPfP GBuc LRHS MCli MRav WFar |
| *elliotii* | Last listed 1996 |
| *elwesii* | EBee GGar |
| *episcopale* | GCrs NDov WCru WFar |
| aff. *episcopale* CLD 1426 | GBuc LPio WCot WFar |
| *falconeri* | Last listed 1996 |
| ¶ *ferox* | EBee |
| *fischeri* hort. | See *A. carmichaelii* |
| *fukutomei* var. *formosanum* B&SWJ 3057 | WCru |
| *gymnandrum* | Last listed 1997 |
| § *hemsleyanum* | CBot CGle CHan CPlN CRow EBee ELan GAbr IBlr LGre LHol MFir MSCN MTho NSti SAga SMad SSoC WBrE WCot WCru WEas WHoo WOld WWhi WWye |
| - dark blue | CMea |
| - *latisectum* | IBlr |
| *heterophyllum* | Last listed 1996 |
| *hookeri* | Last listed 1996 |
| *hyemale* | See *Eranthis hyemalis* |
| 'Ivorine' | More than 30 suppliers |
| *japonicum* | EBee |
| *lamarckii* | See *A. lycoctonum* subsp. *neapolitanum* |
| *lycoctonum* | GCrs MCAu SRms SSoC |
| - 'Dark Eyes' | ECGN NBrk WCot |
| § - subsp. *lycoctonum* | CBlo MSal SRms |
| - subsp. *moldavicum* | Last listed 1998 |
| § - subsp. *neapolitanum* | CBlo CLon EAst EBee ECGN ELan EMFP EMan EPfP EWTr GCal MLLN NHol NLar NSti SWat WHil |
| § - subsp. *vulparia* | CArn EBee ECGN ECha ECtt EFou EGar GCal GPoy IHdy LHol MAvo MRav MSal NRoo WByw WCot WEas WLin WOld WWye |

| | |
|---|---|
| *napellus* | CArn CBlo CMHG CSpe EBee ECGN ECtt EFou EWFC GAbr GPoy LHol LLWP MBro MCLN MWat NFla SIde SRms SSoC SWat WHoo WOld WSel WShi WWhi WWye |
| - 'Albiflorus' | See *A. napellus* subsp. *vulgare* 'Albidum' |
| - 'Bergfürst' | EBee LGre LPio |
| - 'Blue Valley' | EBee EMar EPfP EWTr |
| - 'Carneum' | See *A. napellus* subsp. *vulgare* 'Carneum' |
| § - subsp. *napellus* Anglicum Group | CRow CSev EBee GBuc GSki IBlr MHlr MSal MSte NSti WCot WPen |
| - 'Rubellum' | CHan MCli NPri |
| - 'Sphere's Variety' | NOrc WPyg |
| - subsp. *tauricum* | Last listed 1998 |
| § - subsp. *vulgare* 'Albidum' | CMGP EAst EBee ECGN EFou EMan EMar ETen GSki LRHS MCLN MRav MTis NCat NFai NHol NLar NLon NPri NRoo NSti SCro SLon SPer SRob WByw WCot WHil WLRN WRus |
| § - - 'Carneum' | ECGN ELan EMon GMac MLLN MRav NRoo NSti WByw WCot WEas WHer WKif WLin WWin WWye |
| *neapolitanum* | See *A. lycoctonum* subsp. *neapolitanum* |
| 'Newry Blue' | CHad EBee ELan GBuc GSki IHdy MBri MCAu MRav MWll NHol SRms WFar WMer WPer WRHF |
| *orientale* hort. | See *A. lycoctonum* subsp. *vulparia* |
| ¶ *paniculatum* | EBee MBri |
| - 'Roseum' | LRHS MBNS SSvw |
| ¶ aff. *pendulum* KGB 762 | IDac |
| *pyrenaicum* | See *A. lycoctonum* subsp. *neapolitanum* |
| *ranunculifolius* | See *A. lycoctonum* subsp. *neapolitanum* |
| *sczukinii* | EMon WCru |
| ¶ *seoulense* B&SWJ 1005 | WCru |
| *septentrionale* | See *A. lycoctonum* subsp. *lycoctonum* |
| sp. ACE 1449 | GBuc |
| sp. B&SWJ 2652 from Sikkim, climbing | WCru |
| sp. B&SWJ 2954 from Nepal | WCru |
| 'Spark's Variety' ♀ | More than 30 suppliers |
| *spicatum* | EBee |
| 'Stainless Steel' | CBlo CFri CSpe GBri LGre LRHS MBri SCro WCot WViv |
| *stapfianum* B&L 12038 | Last listed 1997 |
| ¶ 'The Grim Reaper' | EMon |
| x *tubergenii* | See *Eranthis hyemalis* Tubergenii Group |
| *variegatum* | EBee |
| *volubile* hort. | See *A. hemsleyanum* |
| *vulparia* | See *A. lycoctonum* subsp. *vulparia* |

## ACONOGONON See PERSICARIA

## ACORUS ✿ (Araceae)

| | |
|---|---|
| *calamus* | CArn CRow CWat EHon ELau GPoy LPBA MCCP MHew MSal MSta NDea SWat SWyc WHer WMAq WWeb |
| - 'Argenteostriatus' (v) | CB&S CBen CHan CRow CWat ECha ECtt EHon EMFW GAbr GCal LHil LNor LPBA MBal MSta NDea NOrc SLon SWat SWyc WMAq WWye |
| - 'Purpureus' | Last listed 1998 |
| *gramineus* | CRow EMFW LPBA LRot MLan SWat WHer |
| - 'Hakuro-nishiki' (v) | CInt COtt CRow EOrn LWoo MCCP SCob SPla SVil WRHF |
| I - 'Licorice' | WBea WCot |
| - 'Masamune' (v) | EPla GBri GCal NPro WCot WLeb WSPU |
| N - 'Oborozuki' (v) | CRow EGle EPla NPro |
| N - 'Ogon' (v) | More than 30 suppliers |
| - 'Pusillus' | CRow EPPr EPla LHil NBro |
| - 'Variegatus' | More than 30 suppliers |
| - 'Yodo-no-yuki' (v) | CRow EPla |

## ACRADENIA (Rutaceae)

| | |
|---|---|
| *frankliniae* | CB&S CFil CMHG CPLG CPle CTrG GEil IBlr IDee SBid SSpi WSHC |

## ACRIDOCARPUS (Malpighiaceae)

| | |
|---|---|
| *natalitius* | CPIN |

## ACROCLADIUM See CALLIERGON

## ACTAEA (Ranunculaceae)

| | |
|---|---|
| ◆ *alba* | See *A. pachypoda*, *A. rubra* f. *neglecta* |
| ¶ *asiatica* | EBee GBin |
| - B&SWJ 616 | WCru |
| ◆ *erythrocarpa* | See *A. rubra* |
| § *pachypoda* ♀ | CBrd CLyd CPou CRow ECGN ECha EPar EPla GPoy GTou IBlr MFir MSal NLar WCot WMer WWye |
| ¶ - f. *rubrocarpa* | EBee |
| § *rubra* ♀ | More than 30 suppliers |
| - *alba* | See *A. pachypoda*, *A. rubra* f. *neglecta* |
| § - f. *neglecta* | CHan EBee GBuc IHdy SSpi WWat |
| § *spicata* | CRDP EBee GLil GPoy MSal MSte NLar NSti NWoo WCru |
| - var. *rubra* | See *A. rubra* |

## ACTINELLA (Asteraceae)

| | |
|---|---|
| *scaposa* | See *Tetraneuris scaposa* |

## ACTINIDIA ✿ (Actinidiaceae)

| | |
|---|---|
| *arguta* | CB&S CFil CPIN WPGP |
| - B&SWJ 569 | WCru |
| - 'Issai' (s-p/F) | CB&S EBee ERea LBuc LEdu MGos |
| - (m) | CB&S |
| ¶ - 'Weiki' | MGos |
| *callosa* | CPIN |
| ¶ - var. *ephippioidea* B&SWJ 1790 | WCru |
| ¶ - var. *formosana* B&SWJ 3806 | WCru |
| *chinensis* hort. | See *A. deliciosa* |
| § *deliciosa* | CGre CMac CWit ELan EMil ERom LHol MGos WSHC WStI |
| - (f/F) | NBea SPer WDin |
| - (m/F) | NBea SPer WDin |
| - 'Atlas' | MBri SDea |
| - 'Blake' (s-p/F) | Last listed 1998 |
| * - 'Boskoop' | SRPl |

- 'Hayward' (f/F)    CB&S CDoC CHad COtt CPlN
EBee EBrP EBre ELan EMil EMui
ERea IOrc ISea LBre LEdu MBri
MGos MWat NPal SBre SDea SSta
SSto WStI WWal
- 'Jenny' (s-p/F)    CMac LBuc LRHS MGos SDea
¶ - 'Solo'    CDoC
- 'Tomuri' (m)    CB&S CDoC CHad COtt CPlN
EBrP EBre ELan EMil EMui ERea
IOrc LBre MGos MWat NPal SBre
SDea SSta SSto WStI
*giraldii*    CMac
*kolomikta* ♀    More than 30 suppliers
*latifolia* B&SWJ 3563    WCru
*melanandra*    CAgr CPlN
*pilosula*    CFil CPlN GCal GOrc SLon WCru
WPGP WSHC
*polygama* (F)    CAgr CPlN LEdu WCru
*purpurea*    CPlN WCru
*rubricaulis* B&SWJ 3111    WCru
*rufa* B&SWJ 3525    WCru
sp. from China    WCru
*tetramera* B&SWJ 3664    WCru

## ADELOCARYUM See LINDELOFIA

## ADENOCARPUS (Papilionaceae)
¶ *decorticans*    CTrC
*foliolosus*    Last listed 1996

## ADENOPHORA ✿ (Campanulaceae)
¶ 'Afterglow'    CStr MAvo
* *asiatica*    WFar
*aurita*    CB&S CFir EBee MLLN NPla NSti
NWoo SWat WCot
*axilliflora*    Last listed 1997
*bulleyana*    CBrd EBee ECGN ELan EMan
EOld EWTr GBuc IBlr IHdy MLLN
MSCN NChi NLak NPri SSca SWat
WFar WHoo WLin WMoo WPer
* *campanulata*    WPer
*coelestis*    EBee SGre
- ACE 2455    EPot GBuc
*confusa*    CMdw EBee EGar EHal GAbr
LHop MLLN SSca WFar WHer
*coronopifolia*    Last listed 1997
*cymerae*    EBee
*divaricata*    Last listed 1997
*forrestii*    SBla WFar WMaN
- var. *bandeliana* KGB 86 Last listed 1998
*bimalayana*    EGle GBri GMac MNrw SAga
WCot WPer WRHF
*khasiana*    CBlo CFir CPea EBee GAbr MNrw
NFai NSti SCob SSca WCot WPrP
WRha WWin
*koreana*    EBee
*latifolia* hort.    See *A. pereskiifolia*
- Fischer    GBri NBir WElm
*liliifolia*    CHea ECtt EEls ELan EMan GAbr
GCal GMac NBro NCat NPer NSti
SCro SMrm SWat WCot WFar
WMaN WPer WPrP WPyg
§ *nikoensis*    EBee MNrw
* - *alba*    CGra
§ - var. *stenopbylla*    EHal
*nipponica*    See *A. nikoensis* var. *stenophylla*
§ *pereskiifolia*    CMGP EAst EBee EGar LIck MHlr
NBus WCot WElm WPer
- 'Alba'    Last listed 1997
- var. *heterotricha*    Last listed 1997
- *uryuensis*    Last listed 1997

*polyantha*    CGen CPea EBee GAbr GBuc
MLLN MNrw SRms SSca WPic
WPrP
*polymorpha*    See *A. nikoensis*
*potaninii*    CFir CHea EGle GBuc IHdy MGrG
MNrw NSti SBla SSca WFar WHal
WMoo WRHF WWhi
- 'Alba'    Last listed 1997
- lilac    Last listed 1997
* - 'Lilacina Flora Plena'    Last listed 1996
¶ - white    WHal
*remotiflora*    Last listed 1998
sp. Yunnan    Last listed 1997
*stricta*    EHal MLan WWeb
- subsp. *sessilifolia*    EBee GMac
*sublata*    EBee EGar WFar
*takedae*    Last listed 1997
- var. *bowozana*    NSti
*tasbiroi*    CElw CGen CLyd CNic EBee
GAbr GBri GBuc MBro MNrw
NBro SCob SCro SHel SIgm SWat
WHoo
*tripbylla*    GAbr WFar
- var. *bakusanensis*    CPou EBee
- var.*japonica*    Last listed 1997
- var. *puellaris*    Last listed 1997
*uehatae*    Last listed 1997
- B&SWJ 126    WCru

## ADENOSTYLES (Asteraceae)
*alpina*    See *Cacalia glabra*

## ADIANTUM ✿ (Adiantaceae)
*aetbiopicum*    WRic
§ *aleuticum* ♀    CCuc CFil CLAP CRDP EFer ELan
IOrc NBro NBus NHol NMar SBla
SCob WHal WPGP WRic WWat
- 'Laciniatum'    WRic
*capillus-veneris*    MWat WHil
- 'Banksianum'    NMar
- 'Cornubiense'    WRic
- 'Mairisii'    See *A.* x *mairisii*
- 'Pointonii'    NMar
*concinnum*    Last listed 1998
*cuneatum*    See *A. raddianum*
*diapbanum*    NMar
*edgewortbii*    NMar
*formosum*    WRic
*benslowianum*    NMar
¶ *bispidulum*    NMar SRms WRic
*jordanii*    CFil
§ x *mairisii* ♀    NMar
* *monocolor*    MBri
*pedatum* ♀    CFil CGle CLAP CRDP EBee EBrP
EBre ECha EFer ELan LBre LHil
MBal MBri MHlr NBus NHol SApp
SBre SChu SPer SSpi SWat WPGP
WWat
- var. *aleuticum*    See *A. pedatum* var. *subpumilum*
- Asiatic form    See *A. pedatum* 'Japonicum'
- 'Imbricatum'    ECha ETen NHar NHol NMar SBla
SRms
§ - 'Japonicum'    CBos CFil CLAP CMil CRDP ELan
MBri NBir NHol SEas SRms SSpi
WCot WCru WHal WRic
- 'Laciniatum'    CFil SRms
♦ - var. *minus*    See *A. aleuticum*
- 'Miss Sharples'    NMar SRms WCot WRic
- 'Roseum'    See *A. pedatum* 'Japonicum'
- var. *subpumilum*    See *A. aleuticum*
- - f. *minimum*    SCob SLon SRms
*peruvianum*    MBri

*pubescens*         MBri NMar
§ *raddianum* ♀     CFil CHal NMar
- 'Brilliantelse' ♀     MBri NMar
- 'Crested Majus'     NMar
- 'Crested Micropinnulum'     NMar
- 'Deflexum'     NMar
- 'Double Leaflet'     NMar
- 'Elegans'     NMar
- 'Feltham Beauty'     NMar
- 'Fragrans'     See *A. raddianum*
                  'Fragrantissimum'
§ - 'Fragrantissimum'     MBri NMar NOla
- 'Fritz Luthi' ♀     CHal MBri NMar
- 'Gracilis'     See *A. raddianum* 'Gracillimum'
§ - 'Gracillimum'     NMar
- 'Grandiceps'     NMar
- 'Gympie Gold'     NMar
- 'Kensington Gem' ♀     NMar
- 'Legrand Morgan'     NMar
- 'Legrandii'     NMar
- 'Micropinnulum'     NMar
- 'Pacific Maid'     NMar
- 'Pacottii'     NMar
- 'Triumph'     NMar
- 'Tuffy Tips'     NMar
- 'Variegated Pacottii'     NMar
- 'Variegated Tessellate'     NMar
- 'Victoria's Elegans'     NMar
- 'Weigandii'     NMar
*tenerum* 'Green Glory'     NMar
*venustum* ♀     CFil CGle CLAP CRDP EFer ELan
                  EMon EPot GCal MBal NBus
                  NHed NMar SBla SDix SIng SRms
                  SSpi SWat WCot WEas WFib
                  WPGP WRic
*whitei*     NMar

## ADLUMIA (Papaveraceae)
*fungosa*     CGle CPln CSpe EBrP EBre EHal
                  IHdy LBre MCCP MLLN NBur
                  NLar NSti SBre WCru WElm
                  WWeb

## ADONIS (Ranunculaceae)
*aestivalis*     Last listed 1997
*amurensis*     EPar EPot LAma WCot
- 'Flore Pleno' (d)     EBrP EBre EPar LBre MBri MTed
                  SBod SBre SPer WCot WFar
- 'Fukujukai'     ECha WFar
*annua*     EWFC MHew
*brevistyla*     EPot NSla NTow SBla WAbe
¶ *daburica*     WLin
*multiflora*     WCru
*pyrenaica*     Last listed 1998
¶ *sutchuenensis*     LAma
*vernalis*     EPar EWTr GPoy

## ADOXA (Adoxaceae)
*moschatellina*     CKin EWFC MTho WGwy WHer
                  WShi WWye

## AECHMEA (Bromeliaceae)
*caerulea*     See *A. lueddemanniana*
*chantinii* ♀     Last listed 1996
*fasciata* ♀     MBri
Foster's Favorite Group ♀     Last listed 1997
\* *fulgens* var. *discolor* ♀     Last listed 1990
*gamosepala*     Last listed 1997
\* 'Grand Prix'     Last listed 1996
*nudicaulis* ♀     Last listed 1995
*orlandiana* ♀     Last listed 1995
'Romero'     Last listed 1996

## AEGLE (Rutaceae)
*sepiaria*     See *Poncirus trifoliata*

## AEGOPODIUM (Apiaceae)
*podagraria* 'Bengt'     Last listed 1998
- 'Dangerous' (v)     CHid CNat WCHb
- 'Hullavington' (v)     Last listed 1997
- 'Variegatum'     More than 30 suppliers

## AEONIUM (Crassulaceae)
*arboreum* ♀     CAbb WHal WIvy WRos
\* - 'Arnold Schwarzkopff'     CAbb CBos CPLG ERea SAPC
                  SArc WIvy
- 'Atropurpureum' ♀     CWit EBee ERav ERea IBlr LHil
                  MBEx MBri MLan NPer SEND
                  WEas
\* - 'Magnificum'     LBlm SAPC SArc
- 'Variegatum'     LHil NPer
*balsamiferum*     CTbh LHil SArc WHal
♦ *barbatum*     See *A.* x *hybridum*
*canariense*     CAbb EBee LHil WHal
§ - var. *subplanum*     CTrC SVen
*cuneatum*     CTbh CTrC SAPC SVen
\* *decorum* 'Variegatum' (v)     Last listed 1998
'Dinner Plate'     Last listed 1998
x *domesticum*     See *Aichryson* x *domesticum*
*glandulosum*     SGre
*haworthii* ♀     CHal CTbh CTrC GAri LHil
- 'Variegatum'     Last listed 1998
*holochrysum*     IBlr
§ x *hybridum*     CCpl
*laxum*     SGre
¶ *lindleyi*     SChr
\* *manriqueorum*     CCpl
*nobile*     CAbb
*percarneum*     Last listed 1998
*simsii*     CHal CTbh SChr
*spathulatum*     SGre
*subplanum*     See *A. canariense* var. *subplanum*
*tabuliforme* ♀     Last listed 1998
*undulatum* ♀     Last listed 1998
*urbicum*     Last listed 1998
'Zwartkop' ♀     CTbh EGar EOas NPer WEas WHal
                  WRos

## AESCHYNANTHUS (Gesneriaceae)
'Big Apple'     WDib
Black Pagoda Group     WDib
'Fire Wheel'     WDib
*hildebrandii*     WDib
'Hot Flash'     WDib
*lobbianus*     See *A. radicans*
*longicalyx*     WDib
§ *longicaulis* ♀     WDib
*marmoratus*     See *A. longicaulis*
'Mira'     MBri
'Mona'     MBri
*parvifolius*     See *A. radicans*
I 'Pulobbia'     MBri
'Purple Star'     MBri
§ *radicans*     EBak MBri
- *lobbianus*     See *A. radicans*
'Rigel'     MBri
\* *rigidus*     Last listed 1997
*speciosus* ♀     CHal
- *rubens*     MBri
'Topaz'     MBri

## AESCULUS ✿ (Hippocastanaceae)
*arguta*     See *A. glabra* var. *arguta*
x *arnoldiana*     CDul CFil CMCN MAsh MBlu
                  WPGP

| | |
|---|---|
| *assamica* | WPGP |
| 'Autumn Splendor' | CLyn |
| § x *bushii* | CDul CFil CTho EBee WPGP |
| *californica* | CB&S CFil CMCN CSam CTho |
| | CTrw EPfP ERod LFis NPal SMad |
| | SSpi WPGP WWat |
| x *carnea* | CDul ELan GRei MBal MBar |
| - 'Aureomarginata' | ERod SMad |
| - 'Briotii' ♀ | More than 30 suppliers |
| - 'Marginata' (v) | CLyn |
| - 'Plantierensis' | CDul CTho ENot MBlu |
| * - 'Variegata' (v) | CDul CMCN LRHS MBlu |
| *chinensis* | MBlu |
| 'Dallimorei' (graft-chimaera) | EBee SMad |
| *discolor* 'Koehnei' | MBri |
| § *flava* ♀ | CFil CMCN CTho EBee ENot |
| | GChr MMea SPer SSpi WCwm |
| | WPGP |
| ♦ - x *pavia* | See *A.* x *hybrida* |
| - f.*vestita* | CDul MBlu |
| *georgiana* | See *A. sylvatica* |
| *glabra* | CDul CFil CLnd CMCN CTho |
| | WPGP |
| § - var. *arguta* | CFil CMCN WPGP |
| - 'October Red' | CFil MBlu WPGP |
| ♦ *glaucescens* | See *A.* x *neglecta* |
| *hippocastanum* ♀ | CB&S CBlo CDul CKin CLnd |
| | CTho EBee ECrN ELan ENot GChr |
| | GRei IOrc ISea LBuc LHyr LPan |
| | MAsh MBal MBar MBri MGos |
| | NBee NWea SPer WDin WFar |
| | WMou WOrn WStI |
| - 'Aureomarginata' (v) | Last listed 1998 |
| § - 'Baumannii' (d) ♀ | CBlo CDoC CDul CLnd COtt EBee |
| | ECrN ENot EPfP ERod EWTr |
| | GChr LPan MAsh MBlu MBri |
| | MGos NWea WDin WStI |
| - 'Digitata' | CDul |
| - 'Flore Pleno' | See *A. hippocastanum* |
| | 'Baumannii' |
| - 'Globosa' | See *A. hippocastanum* |
| | 'Umbraculifera' |
| - 'Hampton Court Gold' | CB&S CDul CEnd CMCN CTho |
| - 'Honiton Gold' | CTho |
| - 'Laciniata' | CDul CMCN ERod IDee MBlu |
| | SMad |
| - 'Pyramidalis' | Last listed 1998 |
| § - 'Umbraculifera' | SMad |
| - 'Wisselink' | CMCN MBlu SMad |
| § x *hybrida* | CFil SSpi WCwm WPGP |
| *indica* ♀ | CDul CLnd CMCN CSam CTho |
| | CTrw ELan ENot EOas IOrc MBlu |
| | MBri SLdr SPer SRPl SSpi WCwm |
| | WDin WPGP |
| - 'Sydney Pearce' | CEnd CFil CMCN IOrc MBlu |
| | MGos MMea SMad SSpi WPGP |
| x *marylandica* | CDul |
| x *mississippiensis* | See *A.* x *bushii* |
| x *mutabilis* 'Harbisonii' | Last listed 1998 |
| - 'Induta' | CFil MBlu MBri SMad SSpi WPGP |
| | WWes |
| § - 'Penduliflora' | CB&S CDul CEnd CFil CTho EPfP |
| | MBlu SMad |
| § x *neglecta* | CB&S CDul CLnd CMCN |
| ¶ - 'Autumn Fire' | CLyn SMad |
| - 'Erythroblastos' ♀ | CB&S CDoC CEnd CFil CLnd |
| | CMCN CPMA CTho EPfP ERod |
| | LNet MBlu SMad SSpi WPGP WPat |
| *parviflora* ♀ | CB&S CBlo CDul CFil CGre |
| | CMCN CTho EBee ELan ENot |
| | LNet LPan MBal MBlu MGos MUlv |
| | NFla SMad SPer SSpi WDin WPGP |
| | WWat |

| | |
|---|---|
| § *pavia* ♀ | CB&S CDul CFil CLnd CMCN |
| | CTho EPfP ISea SSpi WWoo |
| - 'Atrosanguinea' | CBlo CDul CEnd CFil CMCN |
| | ERod MAsh NPal SMad SSpi |
| | WPGP |
| - var. *discolor* 'Koehnei' | Last listed 1998 |
| - 'Penduliflora' | See *A.* x *mutabilis* 'Penduliflora' |
| - 'Rosea Nana' | CMCN MBlu |
| *splendens* | See *A. pavia* |
| § *sylvatica* | CFil CLnd CTho WPGP |
| *turbinata* | CB&S CLnd CMCN LBuc MBlu |
| | SMad WCwm WPGP |
| *wilsonii* | CB&S |
| ¶ x *woerlitzensis* | WCwm |

## AETHIONEMA (Brassicaceae)

| | |
|---|---|
| *armenum* | EBee ESis LIck MLan WLin |
| *caespitosum* | Last listed 1996 |
| *coridifolium* | EBee NBus WPer |
| § *euonomioides* | NTow |
| *graecum* | See *A. saxatile* |
| § *grandiflorum* ♀ | EBee NBro NSla NTow SBla SRms |
| | WPer |
| - Pulchellum Group ♀ | CLyd CNic EBee EPot MBro |
| | NMen NPri WWin |
| *iberideum* | EBee MOne MWat SRms |
| *oppositifolium* | CLyd CMea GTou MBro MWat |
| | NMen NNrd NWCA WHoo WPyg |
| ♦ *pulchellum* | See *A. grandiflorum* |
| ¶ *rotundifolium* | SIng |
| ¶ *schistosum* | EBee |
| 'Warley Rose' ♀ | CLyd ELan EPot LHop MBro |
| | MWat NFor NHol NMen NWCA |
| | SIng SRms WHoo WPat WPyg |
| | WWin |
| 'Warley Ruber' | CLyd CNic NBir NHol WAbe |

## AEXTOXICON (Aextoxicaceae)

| | |
|---|---|
| *punctatum* | CGre |

## AFROCARPUS (Podocarpaceae)

| | |
|---|---|
| *falcatus* | GCal |

## AGAPANTHUS ✿ (Alliaceae)

| | |
|---|---|
| 'Accebt' | Last listed 1997 |
| § *africanus* ♀ | CElw CStr EBee EPfP EWTr GSki |
| | IBlr LBlm MBNS NRog SAPC SArc |
| | SPar SWat WPer |
| * - 'Albus' ♀ | CB&S CDoC CHad EBee EMan |
| | EPfP GSki IBlr LFis MBNS SEND |
| | SPla WPer |
| 'Albatross' | ECha |
| * *alboroseus* | Last listed 1997 |
| * 'Albus' | CM&M |
| 'Apple Court' | Last listed 1996 |
| ¶ 'Arctic Star' | ERav |
| Ardernei hybrid | CBot CFil EBee ECha EWes GCal |
| | IBlr LGre MHlr MTed NCat SSpi |
| | WCot WOld |
| 'Baby Blue' | CLyd IBlr SApp |
| 'Ballyrogan' | IBlr |
| 'Ben Hope' | Last listed 1996 |
| 'Bethlehem Star' | ERav |
| 'Bicton Bell' | IBlr |
| ¶ 'Bicton Blue Bell' | CPin |
| 'Bicton Hybrid' | Last listed 1996 |
| 'Bleuet' | Last listed 1997 |
| 'Blue Baby' | CB&S LRHS |
| ¶ 'Blue Bird' | CPin EBee |
| 'Blue Companion' | IBlr |
| 'Blue Giant' | CBro EBee IBlr MTed NCut NRoo |
| | SPer SPla SRPl SWat WFar WPyg |

| | |
|---|---|
| 'Blue Globe' | EAst EBee EMan GMaP NCut SCro WWat |
| ¶ 'Blue Gown' | CPin |
| 'Blue Imp' | ECtt EHic GSki IBlr NHol |
| ¶ 'Blue Mercury' | IBlr |
| 'Blue Moon' | CBro CHad ECha IBlr SEND SLod |
| 'Blue Nile' | Last listed 1998 |
| 'Blue Skies' | CB&S CDoC EBee |
| 'Blue Star' | Last listed 1996 |
| 'Blue Triumphator' | CBlo EBee EPfP EWTr EWll IBlr LBow LFis MTed NCut WHil WMer |
| ¶ 'Blue Velvet' | CPin |
| 'Bressingham Blue' | CBlo CBro CTri EBee EBrP EBre GCal IBlr LBre MRav MSte SBre SSpe SWat |
| 'Bressingham Bounty' | EBrP EBre LBre SBre |
| 'Bressingham White' | CGle EBee EBrP EBre ECtt EFou GCHN LBre MBri MCLN MRav MTed NRoo SBre SSpe SWat WRus WWat |
| 'Buckingham Palace' | CFil EBee IBlr WPGP |
| ¶ Cambourne Hybrids | MBri |
| § campanulatus | CGle CRDP ElAn ERav GDra GSki ISea MHlr SCro SLon SWat WLRN |
| - var. albidus | CBos CHad CRDP EBee EBrP EBre ECha EFou ElAn EMan ENot IBlr LBre LHop MSte NFla NHol NRoo NVic SApp SBre SChu SPer SRPl SSpi WFar |
| - 'Albovittatus' | CLAP CSam ECho LGre SPlb |
| * - 'Albus Nanus' | Last listed 1998 |
| - bright blue | GCal |
| - 'Buckland' | IBlr |
| - 'Cobalt Blue' | ECha WCot |
| - 'Isis' | CBro CFir CTri EBrP EBre ECha GCHN IBlr IHdy LBre NRoo SBre |
| ¶ - 'Meibont' (v) | WCot |
| - 'Oxbridge' | IBlr |
| - Oxford blue | GBri IBlr |
| - subsp. patens ♀ | CPin GBri GBuc SApp SSpi SWat WHil |
| - - deep blue form | CFir IBlr |
| * - 'Premier' | IBlr |
| - 'Profusion' | ECha IBlr LBlm SSpi WFar |
| - 'Rosewarne' | CB&S GQui |
| - 'Slieve Donard Variety' | IBlr |
| * - 'Spokes' | IBlr |
| - variegated | ECha WOld |
| - Wedgwood blue | IBlr |
| - 'Wendy' | IBlr |
| - 'White Hope' | IBlr |
| ¶ - 'White Triumphator' | WCot |
| 'Castle of Mey' | CFil CPlt IBlr LGre LHyd MTho |
| caulescens ♀ | IBlr WCot |
| - subsp. angustifolius | IBlr |
| - subsp. caulescens | SWat |
| 'Cedric Morris' | ERav IBlr |
| 'Chandra' | IBlr LBlm |
| 'Charlie Morrell' | LHil |
| ¶ 'Cherry Holley' | CPin |
| coddii | SVen |
| comptonii | CFir CPou IBlr |
| - subsp. comptonii | SWat |
| - subsp. longitubus | EBee SWat |
| Danube | See A. 'Donau' |
| 'Delft' | IBlr |
| 'Density' | IBlr |
| § 'Donau' | EBee MTed SApp WRHF |
| dyeri | IBlr |
| ¶ 'Eve' | EBee |
| 'Evening Star' | ERav LRHS |
| ¶ 'Far Horizon' | CPin |
| 'Findlay's Blue' | WCot |
| * 'Gayle's Lilac' | WCot |
| giant hybrids | LBlm |
| 'Golden Rule' (v) | CFir CRow EBee IBlr LHil SSpi |
| ¶ 'Goliath' | ERav |
| § Headbourne hybrids | More than 30 suppliers |
| 'Holbrook' | CSam |
| 'Hydon Mist' | LHyd |
| ¶ 'Ice Blue Star' | ERav |
| inapertus | CFil CRDP SBla SWat WCot |
| - subsp. hollandii | CAvo GCal IBlr MSte SWat WCot |
| - subsp. inapertus | SWat |
| - subsp. intermedius | EBee GCal IBlr LBlm SWat |
| - subsp. pendulus | CHan CRow IBlr |
| ¶ Johannesberg hybrids | ECha |
| 'Kalmthout Blue' | EBee WWat |
| 'Kalmthout White' | MLan |
| * 'Kew White' | SDix |
| 'Kingston Blue' | CBos ECha IBlr WFar |
| ¶ 'Kobold' | EBee |
| 'Lady Moore' | IBlr LBlm SWas |
| ¶ 'Lady Wimborne' | CPin |
| ¶ 'Leighton Blue' | MBri |
| ¶ 'Lilac Bells' | CPin |
| ¶ 'Lilac Time' | CPin |
| 'Lilliput' | CAbb CB&S CBro CDoC CPlt CRow CSpe CVer EBee EBrP EBre ECtt ElAn ERav GCHN GMaP LBre LPio MRav NHol NRoo SBre SUsu WFar WRus WWat WWin |
| 'Loch Hope' ♀ | CFil CPin WCot |
| ¶ 'Mabel Grey' | CPin |
| ¶ 'Magnifico' | IBlr |
| * 'Marjorie' | CLCN |
| ¶ 'Midnight' | LRHS |
| 'Midnight Blue' | CGle ECha ElAn EPfP GCal IBlr LHil LPio SWas WFar WWeb |
| 'Midnight Star' | COtt EHic ERav MSte WCot |
| ¶ mixed giant hybrids | ERav |
| ¶ 'Mixed Whites' | ERav |
| 'Molly Howick' | Last listed 1998 |
| 'Moonstar' | LBlm |
| I 'Mooreanus' misapplied | GCal IBlr |
| 'Morning Star' | ERav |
| 'Norman Hadden' | IBlr |
| nutans | EBee IBlr WCot |
| - 'Albus' | GCal |
| ¶ pale form | SRms |
| Palmer's hybrids | See A. Headbourne hybrids |
| 'Penelope Palmer' | IBlr |
| 'Penny Slade' | Last listed 1998 |
| 'Peter Pan' | CB&S CElw CMil CRow CSWP CTrC EBee EFou GBuc LHop MRav NCut SPla WPyg WRHF WWat WWeb WWoo |
| 'Peter Pan' American | Last listed 1996 |
| 'Phantom' | CPin IBlr |
| 'Pinocchio' | CAbb LRHS NHol WWoo |
| 'Plas Merdyn Blue' | IBlr |
| 'Plas Merdyn White' | CFir IBlr |
| 'Podge Mill' | CLCN |
| 'Polar Ice' | CFir EBee EFou EHic IBlr MCCP NCut NHol WMer WPyg |
| praecox | CFil CLAP EBee ESis IBlr |
| - 'Bangor Blue' | IBlr |
| - 'Blue Formality' | IBlr |
| ¶ - 'Dwarf White' | WHil |
| - 'Flore Pleno' (d) | CLyd EBee ECha IBlr LGre SWas WCot WFar WOld |
| - subsp. floribundus | SWat |
| - - 'Saint Ivel' | Last listed 1998 |

- subsp. *maximus* 'Albus'　CPou EWTr IBlr SSpi
- 'Miniature Blue'　SWat
- subsp. *minimus*　GSki IBlr SWat
- - 'Adelaide'　SWat
¶ - - blue　SWat
- - 'Supreme'　IBlr
¶ - - white　SWat
- Mount Stewart form　IBlr
§ - subsp. *orientalis*　CBlo CHan EBee ERea EWTr GSki
　IBlr NPal SMad SWat WPic
- - var. *albiflorus*　CBro CPou ETub GSki LBow NPal
- subsp. *praecox*　IBlr
- - azure　SWat
- Slieve Donard form　IBlr
- 'Storms River'　SWat
- 'Variegatus' ♀　WSPU
- 'Vittatus' (v)　CHan WCot WFar
¶ 'Pride of Bicton'　CPin
'Profusion'　CBro
'Purple Cloud'　CAbb CB&S CDoC CLAP CRos
　CTrC ERea GSki IBlr LRHS SApp
　SMad SPla
¶ 'Queen Ann'　EBee
¶ 'Queen Elizabeth　EBee
　　The Queen Mother'
'Rhône'　EFou IBlr
¶ 'Rosemary'　EBee
'Rosewarne'　IBlr
'Royal Blue'　EBee ECtt EHic LPio MTed NHol
　SVil
'San Gabriel' (v)　EMon WCot
'Sandringham'　CFil IBlr WPGP
'Sapphire'　CB&S IBlr
¶ 'Silver Mist'　CPin
¶ 'Sky Rocket'　EBee
'Sky Star'　LBlm
'Snowball'　CB&S CLAP CPin SApp
* 'Snowdrop'　WCot
'Snowy Baby'　CRos
'Snowy Owl'　CLAP
'Spode'　Last listed 1996
'Storm Cloud' (d)　Last listed 1997
'Streamline'　CDoC EBee EMil IBro WCot
'Sunfield'　SApp WWeb
'Super Star'　Last listed 1996
'Tinkerbell' (v)　CAbb CB&S CBro CMil CRDP
　CRos CSWP EBee EMan EMil
　LRHS MDun MGrG MRav MTho
　SCob SPla WFar WMer
'Torbay'　IBlr LHil SBla
*umbellatus* Redouté　See *A. praecox* subsp. *orientalis*
'Underway'　GCal IBlr SSpi
'White Christmas'　ERea
'White Dwarf'　CBlo CHan ECha EFou LPio WFar
　WTre
'White Giant'　Last listed 1996
'White Ice'　CAbb CB&S CM&M EMil GQui
　SCro
'White Star'　Last listed 1996
'White Starlet'　Last listed 1996
'White Superior'　CSpe EBee EMan NCut SCro
　WWat
'White Umbrella'　Last listed 1998
¶ 'Windlebrooke'　ECha
'Windsor Castle'　IBlr
'Windsor Grey'　IBlr
'Wolga'　EBee EFou
¶ 'Woodcote Paleface'　LHil
¶ 'Yves Klein'　IBlr
'Zella Thomas'　LHyd

## AGAPETES (Ericaceae)

*buxifolia*　Last listed 1998
'Ludgvan Cross'　CGre MBal
*serpens* ♀　CGre MBal SLon
- 'Nepal Cream'　CGre MBal
- 'Scarlet Elf'　CGre SBid

## AGARISTA (Ericaceae)

§ *populifolia*　WWat

## AGASTACHE (Lamiaceae)

*anethiodora*　See *A. foeniculum*
*anisata*　See *A. foeniculum*
* *astromontana*　WPer
*barberi*　LGre
* - 'Tutti-frutti'　EBrP EBre EHrv EMan LBre SBre
'Blue Fortune'　EBee GBri SMad SOkh WFar
　WWeb
*breviflora*　EBee
camphor hyssop　EOHP
§ *cana*　CGle CM&M CPlt EBee ECoo
　EOHP LGre LWoo SRCN WCot
　WElm WFar WRos
- 'Cinnabar Rose'　WFar
¶ - 'Heather Queen'　EOHP
- variegated　Last listed 1996
*cusickii*　Last listed 1998
'Firebird'　More than 30 suppliers
§ *foeniculum*　CAgr CArn CGle CHan CSev ECha
　EFou ELan ELau EOHP EOld ERav
　EWTr GCHN GPoy LHol LHop
　MCAu MChe MRav NFai NFor
　NLon NSti SIde SPer SRms WGwG
　WPer WWye
- 'Alabaster'　CB&S CGle CHan ECha EGoo
　ELau WCom WWye
- 'Alba'　CBlo CBot EFou EWTr MLLN
　SHDw SIde WFar WRha
¶ - 'Fragrant Delight'　WElm
'Globe Trotter'　Last listed 1998
§ *mexicana*　CGle CSam CSev EBee LHop LIck
　MChe MHar NTow NWoo WCom
　WGwG WSan WWye
- 'Carille Carmine'　CLTr MLLN WPer
- 'Carminea'　Last listed 1996
- 'Champagne'　CGle GBri LIck MLLN SUsu SWat
　WPer WRus
- 'Mauve Beauty'　LHop SMrm WPer
¶ - pink　MBri
¶ - 'Rose Beauty'　SMrm
- 'Rosea'　See *A. cana*
aff. *mexicana* PC&H 153　Last listed 1998
*nepetoides*　CArn EBee MSal SPil WWye
¶ *occidentalis*　SIgm
¶ orange　EOHP
¶ *pallidiflora* var.　EBee
　*pallidiflora*
*pringlei*　EBee EMar LGre SWat WOut
*rugosa*　CAgr CArn CFir CSev EBee ELau
　EMan EOHP GBar GPoy LGre
　MLLN MSal NDov NPla SWat
　WCot WGwG WJek WPer WSel
　WWye
- 'Alba'　SGre
- 'Korean Zest' B&SWJ 735　EGoo EMar WCru
*rupestris*　LGre NTow WCot WKif
- JCA 1.025.050　Last listed 1998
*scrophulariifolia*　Last listed 1998
¶ 'Tangerine Dreams'　WCot
*urticifolia*　CArn EPfP LWoo MSal WOut
- 'Alba'　EGar EPfP EWll SWat WEas WPer

| | |
|---|---|
| *  - 'Alba Variegata' | Last listed 1996 |
| I  - 'Liquorice' | CSam |
|   - 'Liquorice Blue' | EBee EMan EMar GSki LRHS MLan MWgw NGdn NLar SChu SPer SWat WPer |
|   - 'Liquorice White' | CM&M CRDP CSam EBee EGar EMan GSki MWgw NLar SCro SPer SPil SWat WOve |
| *wrightii* | Last listed 1998 |

## AGATHAEA See FELICIA

## AGATHIS (Araucariaceae)
| | |
|---|---|
| *australis* | CFil CPLG |

## AGATHOSMA (Rutaceae)
| | |
|---|---|
| ¶ *crenulata* | ELau |
| ¶ *ovata* | SVen |
|   - 'Kleitijies Kraal' | Last listed 1997 |

## AGAVE ✿ (Agavaceae)
| | |
|---|---|
| *affinis* | See *A. sobria* |
| *americana* ♀ | CAbb CB&S CDoC CGre CTrC CWSG ECha ELau EOas GQui IBlr LCns LHil LPal LPan NPal SAPC SArc SMad WMul |
|   - 'Marginata' | CBrP CGre CHal CInt EOas IBlr LHop |
|   - 'Mediopicta' ♀ | CTbh LEdu SAPC SArc WEas |
| *  - 'Mediopicta Alba' ♀ | CBrP |
|   - 'Striata' (v) | Last listed 1998 |
|   - 'Variegata' ♀ | CAbb CB&S CDoC CMdw CTbh CTrC CWSG ECha ELau EWes GQui LCns LEdu MLLN NPal NPer SAPC SArc SChr SSoC SSto WCot WEas WMul |
| *angustifolia* | Last listed 1998 |
| ¶ *arizonica* | SChr |
| *attenuata* | SAPC SArc |
| *avellanidens* | See *A. sebastiana* |
| *bovicornuta* | Last listed 1996 |
| § *celsii* | CAbb CTbh SAPC SArc |
| ¶  - var. *albicans* | CCpl |
| *cerulata* | See *A. sobria* |
|   - subsp. *nelsonii* | CTbh |
| *chrysantha* | Last listed 1998 |
| *coarctata* | See *A. mitriformis* |
| *colorata* | Last listed 1998 |
| ¶ *deserti* | CCpl |
| ¶ *ferdinandi-regis* | SChr |
| *ferox* | CTbh CTrC |
| *filifera* ♀ | EOas SChr |
| *franzosinii* | Last listed 1996 |
| *gigantea* | See *Furcraea foetida* |
| ¶ *goldmaniana* | CCpl |
| ¶ *guadalajarana* 'Jalisco' | CCpl |
| ¶ *havardiana* | EOas |
| *lechuguilla* | SChr |
| ¶ *lophantha* | CCpl |
| *mitis* | See *A. celsii* |
| *neomexicana* | SIgm |
| ¶ *nizandensis* | CCpl |
| *palmeri* | EOas |
| *parryi* | CGre EGar EOas SChr SIgm |
|   - var. *couesii* | See *A. parryi* var. *parryi* |
|   - var. *huachucensis* | CBrP CCpl |
| §  - var. *parryi* | CTbh |
| ¶  - var. *truncata* | CCpl |
| *parviflora* ♀ | Last listed 1989 |
| *potatorum* ♀ | Last listed 1995 |
|   - var. *verschaffeltii* | CTbh CTrC |
| *salmiana* var. *ferox* | SAPC SArc |

| | |
|---|---|
| *schidigera* | CBrP CFir GCal |
| ¶ *schottii* | CTbh |
| § *sebastiana* | Last listed 1996 |
| *shawii* subsp. *goldmaniana* | Last listed 1996 |
| *sisalana* | CTrC |
| ¶ *striata* | CCpl |
| ¶ *stricta* ♀ | CCpl |
| ¶ *toumeyana* | CCpl SChr |
| *utahensis* | EOas SIgm WRos |
| ¶  - var. *discreta* | SChr |
|   - var. *eborispina* | Last listed 1996 |
|   - subsp. *kaibabensis* | Last listed 1996 |
| *victoriae-reginae* ♀ | CBrP CTbh EGar |
| *xylonacantha* | EOas |

## AGERATINA See EUPATORIUM

## AGLAONEMA (Araceae)
| | |
|---|---|
| § *crispum* | MBri |
| *  - 'Marie' | MBri |
|   'Malay Beauty' | MBri |
| *roebelinii* | See *A. crispum* |
|   'Silver Queen' ♀ | MBri |

## AGONIS (Myrtaceae)
| | |
|---|---|
| ¶ *flexuosa* | CB&S CTrC |
| *marginata* | Last listed 1998 |

## AGRIMONIA (Rosaceae)
| | |
|---|---|
| *eupatoria* | CArn CKin ELau EWFC GPoy IIve MChe MHew NMir SIde SWat WCHb WCla WGwy WHbs WHer WOak WWye |
| ¶  - 'Topas' | ELau |
| § *grandiflora* | EBee |
| *gryposepala* | EBee |
| *odorata* hort. | See *A. repens* |
|   - Miller | Last listed 1998 |
| ¶ *pilosa* | ELau IIve |
| ¶ *procera* | EWFC |
| § *repens* | GBar MSal WCHb |

## AGROPYRON (Poaceae)
| | |
|---|---|
| *glaucum* | See *Elymus hispidus* |
| *magellanicum* | See *Elymus magellanicus* |
| *pubiflorum* | See *Elymus magellanicus* |
| *scabrum* | See *Elymus scabrus* |

## AGROSTEMMA (Caryophyllaceae)
| | |
|---|---|
| *coronaria* | See *Lychnis coronaria* |
| *githago* | CJew EWFC MHew MMal MSal WCla WCot WHer WJek WOak |
|   - 'Purple Queen' | Last listed 1998 |

## AGROSTIS (Poaceae)
| | |
|---|---|
| *calamagrostis* | See *Calamagrostis epigejos* |
| *canina* 'Silver Needles' (v) | CBre CCuc CHor CInt EGle EGra EHoe EMan EMon EPPr EPla EPot EWes GCal MMil MMoz MWhi WElm |
| *karsensis* | See *A. stolonifera* |
| *nebulosa* | CInt LIck |
| § *stolonifera* | Last listed 1997 |

## AGROSTOCRINUM (Phormiaceae)
| | |
|---|---|
| *scabrum* | Last listed 1998 |

## AICHRYSON (Crassulaceae)
| | |
|---|---|
| § x *domesticum* | CHal CTrC |
| x  - 'Variegatum' ♀ | CHal EBak |

**AILANTHUS** (Simaroubaceae)
§ *altissima* ♀ — CB&S CDul CLnd EBee EBrP EBre ECrN EMil ENot EWTr IOrc LBre LPan MBlu MGos MPEx NBee SAPC SArc SBre SPer SRPl WDin WNor WStI
¶ - var. *sutchuenensis* — CFil
  *glandulosa* — See *A. altissima*

**AINSLIAEA** (Asteraceae)
¶ *acerifolia* B&SWJ 4795 — WCru

**AJANIA** (Asteraceae)
§ *pacifica* — CHal EBee ECtt ELan EMan EMar MRav MWgw NFai SPla SUsu WWal
  *tibetica* JJH 9308103 — NWCA
* *xylorhiza* JJH 95095 — EPot

**AJUGA** (Lamiaceae)
¶ *bombycina* — CCpl
  'Brockbankii' — Last listed 1998
  *chamaepitys* — Last listed 1998
  *genevensis* 'Alba' — Last listed 1998
  - 'Tottenham' — MCli
  *metallica* hort. — See *A. pyramidalis*
  'Monmotaro San' — EGar
¶ *orientalis* — WLin
§ *pyramidalis* — CFee ECha EGar EWTr LNor NBrk SCro WHer
  - 'Metallica Crispa' — CRDP EBee EWes MBro NHar NRya WHil WMer
  *reptans* — CJew CKin ECtt ELau EWFC GPoy LGro LHol LPBA MChe MHew MMal MSal NBrk NMir WGwy WRHF
  - 'Alba' — CArn CNic CRow CTri EBee EWTr GCal MNrw NBro NPla NPro NSti SRms SSvw WAlt WByw WCHb WFar WHil WLin WMer WPer WWeb WWye
  ¶ - 'Arctic Fox' (v) — CLAP GVic MLLN NWes WCot WGle WSpi
  - 'Argentea' — See *A. reptans* 'Variegata'
  § - 'Atropurpurea' ♀ — CB&S CRow ECha ELan ENot EPar EWTr LGro LPBA LSyl MBro MMal MWat MWgw NArg NEgg NFai NHol NLon NRoo SPer SPlb SRCN SRms WEas WFar WWat WWin
  - 'Braunherz' ♀ — More than 30 suppliers
  - 'Burgundy Glow' (v) ♀ — More than 30 suppliers
* - 'Burgundy Red' — Last listed 1998
  - 'Carol' — Last listed 1997
  § - 'Catlin's Giant' ♀ — More than 30 suppliers
  - 'Cavalier' — Last listed 1996
  - 'Delight' (v) — ECot ELan NNrd SBod WCHb WCer WEas
  - 'Grey Lady' — SUsu WCot
  - 'Harlequin' (v) — Last listed 1997
  - 'Julia' — EMon LNor
  - 'Jumbo' — See *A. reptans* 'Jungle Beauty'
  § - 'Jungle Beauty' — CRDP CRow CSev ECha ECtt EMan EOrc EPar EPla GCal NHol SLon WCer WCom WHen WHer WMow
  - 'Jungle Bronze' — Last listed 1996
  - 'Macrophylla' — See *A. reptans* 'Catlin's Giant'

  § - 'Multicolor' (v) — CArn CMCo CPri EAst EBee ELan EPar EPot LGro LNor LPBA MBar MLLN MMal MWat NArg NFai NFor SBod SPer SPlb SRPl SRms SSmi WCer WFar WHil WMow WPer
  - 'Palisander' — EBee GSki MTed NSti WShe
  I - 'Pat's Selection' — LNor NDov
  - 'Pink Elf' — CB&S CLyd CMCo CMHG CNic CRow CTri ELan EMan EOrc EWes LHop MRav NBro NLon NOak SHel SIng SUsu SWat WBea WCer WFar WHoo WMoo WPer WPyg
  - 'Pink Splendour' — CBre CTri EBee MGed NChi WCer
  - 'Pink Surprise' — CHad CHid CRow EBrP EBre ECha EHoe EMar EMon EPla EPri GBar LBre LRHS NChi NHol NRya SBre SCro SRPl SSvw WCHb WEas WFar
  - 'Pink Towers' — Last listed 1998
  - 'Purple Brocade' — CStr NLak WByw
  - 'Purple Torch' — EBee ECha EGar MBal MCli MHlr SLod WCHb WCer WEas WLin WMer WOut
  - 'Purpurea' — See *A. reptans* 'Atropurpurea'
  - 'Rainbow' — See *A. reptans* 'Multicolor'
  - 'Rosea' — CHal EBee NPro WHil
  - 'Schneekerze' — MCli
  - 'Silver Carpet' — Last listed 1996
  - 'Silver Shadow' — NLak NPro WCHb
  - 'Tricolor' — See *A. reptans* 'Multicolor'
  § - 'Variegata' — CPri CSpe EBrP EBre ECtt EHoe ELan EPar EWTr GDra LBre LGro LHop MLLN NEgg NRoo SBod SBre SPer SPlb SRms SSmi SWat WBea WCot WFar WHil WLin
  'Variegated Glacier' (v) — ELau

**AKEBIA** (Lardizabalaceae)
  *longeracemosa* — WCru
  B&SWJ 3606
  x *pentaphylla* — CPIN EMil EPfP ERea GQui LRHS MAsh SBra SPer
  *quinata* — More than 30 suppliers
  ¶ - B&SWJ 4425 — WCru
  - cream form — EPfP LRHS SBra SPer
  *trifoliata* — CBlo CPIN EPfP WSHC
  - B&SWJ 2829 — WCru
  ¶ - B&SWJ 5063 — WCru

**ALANGIUM** (Alangiaceae)
  *chinense* — CFil CMCN SLon WBcn WPGP
  *platanifolium* — CBot CFil CMCN EPla MBlu WPGP

**ALBIZIA** (Mimosaceae)
  *adianthifolia* — Last listed 1998
  *distachya* — See *Paraserianthes lophantha*
  *guachapele* — Last listed 1998
  § *julibrissin* — CArn CFil CHan CTho ISea MLan MWat WMul WPGP
  - f. *rosea* ♀ — CB&S CGre CMCN CPle CTrC EBee ELan GQui LPan MBri MCCP MTis SAPC SArc SDry SMad SOWG SPer WNor WSHC
  *lophantha* — See *Paraserianthes lophantha*

**ALBUCA** (Hyacinthaceae)
  *altissima* — EBee
  *aurea* — EBee
  *canadensis* — Last listed 1998

| | |
|---|---|
| *caudata* | Last listed 1998 |
| *cooperi* | EBee |
| *humilis* | EBee EPot ESis NMen NTow WAbe |
| *juncifolia* | Last listed 1998 |
| *nelsonii* | CAvo |
| *shawii* | EBee NSla SBla WAbe |
| ¶ *spiralis* | EBee |
| *tortuosa* S&SH 53 | CHan |
| *wakefieldii* | Last listed 1998 |

## ALCEA (Malvaceae)

| | |
|---|---|
| 'Arabian Nights' | SRCN WHer |
| 'Blackcurrant Whirl' | EBee WHer |
| § 'Double Moonlight' | SRCN |
| *ficifolia* | CGle EBee EMFP NBus NFai SSvw |
| - 'Golden Eye' | Last listed 1998 |
| *pallida* | EMan |
| - HH&K 284 | Last listed 1998 |
| § *rosea* | CGle LCot MRav MWgw WFar |
| ¶ - 'Black Beauty' | GBin |
| - Chater's Double Group (d) | CHad EBrP EBre ECtt EMan EPfP LBre MBri MTis NFor SBre SCoo SRms SRob WOve WRHF |
| - double apricot (d) | EBee WCot |
| ¶ - double white (d) | EBee EWTr |
| ¶ - double yellow | EBee |
| - forms | SPer WLRN |
| - 'Lemon Light' | EWTr WCom |
| - Majorette Group | ECtt |
| * - 'Negrite' | Last listed 1998 |
| - 'Nigra' | CArn CGle CHad CMil EGoo EMan EOld EOrc EWTr MBNS MCAu MHlr MNrw MSte MTis MWgw MWll NFor NGdn NPri SMad SPer SRCN SRob SSoC SSvw |
| - single | Last listed 1997 |
| - single pink | LCot |
| - single white | Last listed 1996 |
| - Summer Carnival Group | EMan SRms WGor |
| - yellow | Last listed 1998 |
| § *rugosa* | CGle CHad CMil CSam ECha ELan EMan EOrc MNrw MSte NCut SDix WCot WKif WOld WPGP WRus |
| ¶ - *alba* | WHil |
| - 'Caucasian Yellow' | Last listed 1996 |

## ALCHEMILLA ✿ (Rosaceae)

| | |
|---|---|
| § *abyssinica* | CGle CHid EHal EMar GAbr GBuc MBel NDov NWes WBro WCot WHen |
| N *alpina* | More than 30 suppliers |
| *aroanica* | EBee |
| *arvensis* | See *Aphanes arvensis* |
| *conjuncta* | More than 30 suppliers |
| *elisabethae* | ECGP EMon EPPr MGrG NBrk WCHb |
| *ellenbeckii* | CFee EBee EBrP EBre ELan EMon GCHN LBre LFis MBar MHar MLLN NChi NNrd NSti NWCA SBre SSca WCHb WEas WFar WHen WPer WWat |
| *epipsila* | MSte WPer |
| *erythropoda* ♀ | More than 30 suppliers |
| *faeroensis* | EGle LBee NChi NFor WPer WWat |
| - var. *pumila* | CLyd EBee LHop |
| *filicaulis* 'Minima' | CNat |
| § x *fulgens* | CArn CBlo CBod EPPr EWTr GAri LFis NRoo SMac WAbe WHen |
| *glaucescens* | CNat |
| *hoppeana* hort. | See *A. plicatula* |

| | |
|---|---|
| - Della Torre | Last listed 1996 |
| ¶ *iniquiformis* | EBee |
| *lapeyrousei* | EMon EPPr NChi SIng WPer |
| *mollis* ♀ | More than 30 suppliers |
| I - 'Auslese' | EBee LBuc LRHS NDov NRoo |
| * - 'Robusta' | EBee ECha EMan EPla MTho NBrk SEND SMad SPil SPlb SRPl SWat WFar WMoo |
| * - 'Senior' | GCal |
| - 'Variegata' | IBlr |
| *monticola* | WPer |
| 'Mr Poland's Variety' | See *A. venosa* |
| *pedata* | See *A. abyssinica* |
| *pentaphylla* | EBee |
| § *plicatula* | WPer |
| ¶ *potentilloides* | WLin |
| *psilomischa* | EBee EMon |
| *pumila* | EFou LRHS MGrG |
| *robusta* | Last listed 1997 |
| *saxatilis* | SPil WPer |
| * *siranines* | EFou ERav |
| *speciosa* | EBee SHel |
| N *splendens* | See *A.* x *fulgens* |
| § *venosa* | SCro SLod SPer WWat |
| aff. *venosa* | EPla |
| *vetteri* | EBee |
| *vulgaris* hort. | See *A. xanthochlora* |
| § *xanthochlora* | CAgr EBee EGol GGar GPoy MHew MSal NLar WBro WHer WPer |

## ALECTRYON (Sapindaceae)

| | |
|---|---|
| *excelsus* | Last listed 1998 |

## ALETRIS (Melanthiaceae)

| | |
|---|---|
| *farinosa* | Last listed 1996 |

## ALISMA (Alismataceae)

| | |
|---|---|
| *lanceolatum* | Last listed 1998 |
| *plantago-aquatica* | CBen CKin CRow EHon EMFW GBar LPBA MHew MSta NDea SWat WMAq WWeb |
| - var. *parviflorum* | CBen EMFW LPBA MSta SPlb SRms SWat WWeb |

## ALKANNA (Boraginaceae)

| | |
|---|---|
| *aucheriana* | Last listed 1997 |
| *orientalis* | Last listed 1998 |
| ¶ *tinctoria* | MSal |
| - HH&K 345 | CHan |

## ALLAGOPTERA (Arecaceae)

| | |
|---|---|
| *arenaria* | LPal |

## ALLAMANDA (Apocynaceae)

| | |
|---|---|
| § *blanchetii* | Last listed 1996 |
| *cathartica* | CPlN ECon ERea LChe MBri |
| - 'Birthe' | MBri |
| * - 'Chocolate Swirl' | Last listed 1998 |
| - 'Grandiflora' | CPlN |
| * - 'Hendersonii' ♀ | SOWG |
| - 'Stansill's Double' (d) | Last listed 1996 |
| - 'Williamsii' | Last listed 1998 |
| ¶ 'Halley's Comet' | LChe |
| ¶ 'Jamaican Sunset' | LChe |
| *neriifolia* | See *A. schottii* |
| § *schottii* ♀ | CPlN ECon SOWG |
| *violacea* | See *A. blanchetii* |

## ALLARDIA (Asteraceae)

| | |
|---|---|
| *glabra* | See *A. tridactylites* |

**ALLIARIA** (Brassicaceae)

| | |
|---|---|
| *petiolata* | CArn CKin CSev EWFC IIve WHbs WHer |

**ALLIUM** ✿ (Alliaceae)

| | |
|---|---|
| § *acuminatum* | EHyt GCHN NBir WCot |
| ◆ *aflatunense* hort. | See *A. hollandicum, A. stipitatum* |
| – Fedtschenko | EMon |
| *akaka* | ERos GCrs LBow |
| *albidum* | See *A. denudatum* |
| *albopilosum* | See *A. cristophii* |
| *altissimum* | LBow NRog |
| ¶ – 'Goliath' | EBee |
| *amabile* | See *A. mairei* var. *amabile* |
| *ambiguum* | See *A. roseum* var. *carneum* |
| *amethystinum* | EBee |
| *ampeloprasum* | CFil ECha WHer WPGP WShi |
| – var. *babingtonii* | CNat GPoy IIve ILis LRot MLLN WHer WShi |
| *amplectens* | GDra NRog |
| *anceps* | Last listed 1997 |
| § *angulosum* | CHan EBee LEdu LLWP MMil WCot |
| ¶ *anisopodium* | EBee |
| *atropurpureum* | CHad EBee ECha ELan EMon EPar LBow LEdu MLLN NRog SUsu WCot WRos |
| *aucheri* | CLAP |
| *azureum* | See *A. caeruleum* |
| 'Beau Regard' ♀ | LAma LBow NRog |
| *beesianum* hort. | See *A. cyaneum* |
| – W.W. Smith ♀ | CGle CLAP CLyd EBur EHyt ESis EWes MBal MBro NBir NRya NWCA WCot |
| ¶ *brevicaule* | EHyt |
| *bulgaricum* | See *Nectaroscordum siculum* subsp. *bulgaricum* |
| § *caeruleum* ♀ | More than 30 suppliers |
| – *azureum* | See *A. caeruleum* |
| *caesium* | EHyt |
| *callimischon* | CAvo CBro NRog NRya WLin |
| – subsp. *callimischon* | Last listed 1998 |
| – subsp. *haemostictum* | EHyt EPot LBow NRog SBla SIng |
| *campanulatum* | Last listed 1998 |
| ¶ *canadense* | CArn |
| *cardiostemon* | MBel |
| § *carinatum* | EBee GCHN |
| § – subsp. *pulchellum* ♀ | More than 30 suppliers |
| – – f. *album* | CAvo CBro CSWP CStr EBee ECha EMon EPar EPot ETub LBow LFis LLWP MBal MNrw NRog NSti NTow SIng SUsu WBea WPer WWin |
| – – 'Tubergen' | EBee ETub |
| *carolinianum* | GCrs |
| ¶ – CC 1935 | MRPP |
| – CC 322 | Last listed 1996 |
| *cepa* | CJew CMil EGar GBar |
| – Aggregatum Group | ELau GPoy ILis |
| – 'Perutile' | CArn GBar GPoy ILis LHol MCoo SIde |
| – Proliferum Group | CArn CSev ELau GBar GPoy ILis LEdu LHol MChe NWoo SIde WCHb WCer WHer WOak WSel |
| * – 'White Flower' | WCot |
| *cernuum* | More than 30 suppliers |
| – *album* | Last listed 1997 |
| – 'Hidcote' ♀ | CLAP EMon MCLN MHlr NPla WCot |
| – *roseum* | CLyd |
| *chamaemoly littorale* | Last listed 1998 |

| | |
|---|---|
| AB&S 4387 | |
| *cirrbosum* | See *A. carinatum* subsp. *pulchellum* |
| *cowanii* | See *A. neapolitanum* Cowanii Group |
| *crenulatum* | Last listed 1998 |
| § *cristophii* ♀ | More than 30 suppliers |
| *cupanii* | Last listed 1998 |
| – subsp. *hirtovaginatum* | Last listed 1997 |
| *cupuliferum* | Last listed 1998 |
| § *cyaneum* ♀ | CArn CAvo CBre CGle CGra CHan CHea CInt CLyd EHyt ERos GCrs LBee LBow NMen NNrd NRya NTow SRot SSca WBea WRus |
| *cyathophorum* | GCrs NRog |
| § – var. *farreri* | CArn CAvo CBre CBro CHea CLyd CNic ELan EPot ERos ESis GCHN GCrs GSki LBow LLWP MBal MBro MRav NChi NFor NLon NMen NNrd NRya WAbe |
| § *denudatum* | LBow SIng |
| *dichlamydeum* | CBro ERos LBow NRog |
| – JCA 11765 | Last listed 1998 |
| § *drummondii* | ECha |
| *elatum* | See *A. macleanii* |
| *ericetorum* | EBee ERos |
| *falcifolium* | NTow |
| – JCA 11625 | CLAP |
| *farreri* | See *A. cyathophorum* var. *farreri* |
| ¶ *fetisowii* | EBee |
| ¶ *fimbriatum* | EBee |
| – var. *abramsii* | Last listed 1997 |
| – var. *purdyi* | Last listed 1996 |
| 'Firmament' | CMil EBee EMon LBow |
| *fistulosum* | CArn CJew ELan ELau EPla GBar GPoy ILis LEdu MChe NBrk NFor SIde WCHb WCer WOak WPer WSel WWye |
| – red | Last listed 1996 |
| ¶ – 'Red Welsh' | IIve ILis |
| – 'Streaker' | Last listed 1997 |
| *flavum* ♀ | CArn CAvo CBro CGle CHad CHan CHea CLyd ECha ELan ELau EPar ETub LAma LBow LHop MCLN NRog NSti SRob SUsu WBea WCla WGor WPGP WPer |
| § – 'Blue Leaf' | EPot ERos LEdu NBir |
| ¶ – subsp. *flavum* | LEdu |
| – – var. *minus* HH&K 273 | CHan |
| – 'Glaucum' | See *A. flavum* 'Blue Leaf' |
| – 'Golden Showers' | MBNS |
| – var. *minus* | CNic ELan MTho NWCA SSca |
| – var. *nanum* | NTow |
| – subsp. *tauricum* | EBee |
| ¶ *forrestii* | GCrs |
| ¶ *galanthum* | EBee |
| *geyeri* | EBee EHyt WCot WLin |
| *giganteum* ♀ | CArn CB&S CBot CMea EBee ELan EMan EMon EOrc EPar EPot ETub LAma LBow LEdu MBri MLLN MRav NFor NLon NOrc NRog SBod SMad SPer SRms WBro WCot WFar WHoo |
| 'Gladiator' ♀ | CAvo CHar EBee EMan EMon LAma LBow MLLN NRog WSel |
| *glaucum* | See *A. senescens* subsp. *montanum* var. *glaucum* |
| 'Globemaster' ♀ | CBro CHar CMea CRDP ETub LAma LBow WBro |
| 'Globus' | EBee EPot |
| *goodingii* | CNic EHyt |

*griffithianum* — See *A. rubellum*
¶ *guttatum* subsp. *sardoum* EBee
¶ *haematochiton* WCot
*heldreichii* EBee
*hierochuntinum* S&L 79 Last listed 1998
'His Excellency' CBlo EBee ECho LBow LRHS
§ *hollandicum* ♀ CBro CFri CGle EBee ECha EMan
EPar EPfP LAma LBow MLLN
MNrw MWat NFai NOrc NRog
NSti SChu SUsu WHil WPer WSel
- 'Purple Sensation' ♀ More than 30 suppliers
- 'Purple Surprise' EBee LRHS
¶ *hookeri* ACE 2430 EPot
*humile* CLyd
*hyalinum* EHyt NRog
¶ - pink WCot
§ *insubricum* ♀ CHad CMea EHyt ERos GCrs
MS&S NBir
¶ 'Ivory Queen' EBee
*jajlae* See *A. rotundum* subsp. *jajlae*
*jepsonii* Last listed 1997
*jesdianum* CBro LBow MLLN
* - *album* EBee
- 'Michael Hoog' See *A. rosenbachianum* 'Michael Hoog'
- 'Purple King' CMil LBow
*kansuense* See *A. sikkimense*
*karataviense* ♀ CArn CAvo CBos CBro CGle CHea
CRDP ECha ELan EMon EOrc EPar
EPot LAma LBow MBri MRav
MTho MWat NBir NChi NNrd
NRog NSti SPer WFar WHil WHoo
WPGP WPer
*kharputense* LAma
¶ *ledebourianum* EBee
*libani* WPer WWye
*libonicum* Last listed 1996
*loratum* EPar
'Lucy Ball' EMon ETub LAma LBow MLLN
NRog
§ *macleanii* CArn EBee EMon EPar LAma
LBow NBrk NRog
*macranthum* CLyd EBee GCHN MSte NSti SWas
WLin
*macrochaetum* LAma
*mairei* CFee CInt EHyt ERos EWes GCHN
MBar MDHE NBus NMen NRya
SOkh WAbe
§ - var. *amabile* ERos MBal NCat NRya NTow
- - pink NBir
'Mars' CMea EBee LBow LRHS MLLN
*maximowiczii* ECho EWes SIng WThi
*moly* ♀ CArn CBro CGle CNic EBee ELan
EPar ETub GBuc IMGH LAma
LBow MBri MMal MRav MWat
NRog NRya NSti SIng SRms WBea
WCHb WCla WCot WPer WShi
WWin
- 'Jeannine' ♀ CBro EBee EPot LBow MLLN
MMal WBea WPGP
'Mont Blanc' ELan LBow
♦ *montanum* See *A. senescens* subsp. *montanum*
'Mount Everest' CAvo CBro CMea CMil EBee ETub
LBow LRHS WCot
*multibulbosum* See *A. nigrum*
*murrayanum* misapplied See *A. unifolium*
§ *narcissiflorum* Villars CLyd GCrs NMGW NMen NSla
NSti NWCA SIng
§ - hort. See *A. insubricum*
*neapolitanum* CAgr CArn CGle CLTr CM&M
EBee EGar EPar LAma LBow MBri
NRog NSti SRms WPer

§ - Cowanii Group CBro EBee IMGH MNrw WBea
WCot WLin WRHF WRos
- 'Grandiflorum' EPla MLLN MNrw NRog WBea
¶ *nevii* EBee
§ *nigrum* EBee EGar EMan EMon EPar
LAma LBow LEdu MLLN MNrw
MRav NBir NRog SRob WCot
*nutans* CBod EBee IIve LBow LEdu
SHDw WHal
*nuttallii* See *A. drummondii*
§ *obliquum* CHan ECha EHal GSki SBea SUsu
WCot WTin
*odorum* L. See *A. ramosum* L.
*oleraceum* WHer
*olympicum* MBro
- ES 13 MRPP
§ *oreophilum* ♀ CArn CAvo CBro CMdw EBee
ECha ECtt EHyt EPar GSki IMGH
LAma LBow MLLN NMGW NRog
SRms WBea WCla WCot WPer
WWye
- 'Agalik' LRHS
- 'Zwanenburg' ♀ CBro CMea EPot LBow NMen
NRog WBea
*orientale* EPot LAma
*ostrowskianum* See *A. oreophilum*
*pallens* CBre EBee ERav LBow MTho NBir
§ *paniculatum* CAvo CMea ECha EHyt EPot LEdu
MMil NRog
- subsp. *fuscum* Last listed 1998
*paradoxum* LRHS NBir NRog
- var. *normale* CRDP EHyt EMon LBow WCot
- PF 5085 Last listed 1998
*pedemontanum* See *A. narcissiflorum* Villars
*peninsulare* Last listed 1997
*perdulce* Last listed 1998
*polyastrum* GCHN
*porrum* 'Saint Victor' MHlr
*pulchellum* See *A. carinatum* subsp. *pulchellum*
¶ *pyrenaicum* CMea
¶ - hort. See *A. angulosum*
- Costa & Vayreda CAvo EBee ELan EMan
§ *ramosum* L. ELau LAma WPer
§ - Jacquin See *A. obliquum*
'Rien Poortvliet' CArn EBee LAma LBow NRog
* *romarovianum* EBee
*rosenbachianum* CArn CBro EHyt EMan EPar EPot
LAma MLLN NCat NRog
- 'Album' ECho EPar EPot LAma MLLN
NRog WCot
§ - 'Michael Hoog' EBee LBow
- 'Purple King' EBee LRHS
- 'Shing' EBee LRHS WIvy
*roseum* CArn CAvo CLTr CMea EBee ECtt
ELau EMon ERos LAma LBow
NRog WBea WPer
- *album* Last listed 1997
- B&S 396 Last listed 1998
§ - var. *bulbiferum* WCot
§ - var. *carneum* Last listed 1996
- 'Grandiflorum' See *A. roseum* var. *bulbiferum*
§ *rotundum* subsp. *jajlae* LLWP WPer
- subsp. *rotundum* Last listed 1998
*rubens* EBee
*sanbornii* var. *sanbornii* Last listed 1998
*sarawschanicum* Last listed 1997
*sativum* CArn EEls ELau SIde WJek WOak
WSel WWye
* - *aureum* GPoy
- var. *ophioscorodon* GPoy IIve ILis
- 'Printanor' CBod

| | |
|---|---|
| ¶ - 'Thermidrome' | CBod |
| ¶ *saxatile* | EBee |
| *scabriscapum* | Last listed 1998 |
| ¶ *schmitzii* | EMon |
| *schoenoprasum* | More than 30 suppliers |
| - 'Black Isle Blush' ♀ | GPoy |
| - 'Corsican White' | EMon |
| - fine-leaved | ELau IIve WRha |
| - 'Forescate' | CBod CM&M CPlt EBee ECha |
| | EFou ELau EPla EWes GCHN GCal |
| | LHol LNor MBal MBri MLLN NHol |
| | SSpe SSvw WBea WCHb WCot |
| ¶ - 'Grolau' | EOHP |
| - medium leaved | ELau |
| - 'Pink Perfection' ♀ | GPoy |
| - 'Polyphant' | CJew EBee WCHb WRha |
| - *roseum* | GBar |
| - 'Shepherds Crooks' | Last listed 1996 |
| - var. *sibiricum* | GBar GPoy MBri SDix WSel WShi |
| - 'Silver Chimes' | CMil SHDw |
| - 'Wallington White' | LHol MBro |
| - white | CMea CSWP ECha ELau GBar |
| | LEdu LGre MBro MSte NBir SIde |
| | SSvw WBea WCHb WCot WEas |
| | WHer WRha WWye |
| *schubertii* | CArn CAvo CB&S CBro CMea |
| | CMil EBee EMon EOrc EPar EPot |
| | ETub LAma LBow MBNS MBri |
| | MLLN MNrw NRog SMrm WAbe |
| | WCot |
| *scorodoprasum* | WCHb |
| - subsp. *jajlae* | See *A. rotundum* subsp. *jajlae* |
| *scorzonerifolium* | Last listed 1998 |
| var. *xericiense* | |
| *senescens* | CArn CTri ECGP ELan EPar ERos |
| | ESis GCHN LBow MRav NChi |
| | SRms SSpe SSvw WBea |
| ¶ - var. *calcareum* | CPLG |
| § - subsp. *montanum* | CLAP EGar EGoo ELan EPot ERav |
| | LEdu MBro NMen SDix SIng |
| | WAbe WCot |
| § - - var. *glaucum* | CBos CHad CHan CLyd CMea |
| | CPBP CStr EBrP EBre ECha EMan |
| | EPar ESis GCHN LBow LBre LEdu |
| | MBel MHlr NTow SBre SIng WCot |
| | WHer WPer WWye |
| - subsp. *senescens* | EMon MLLN SUsu |
| *sessiliflorum* | GCrs |
| *sibthorpianum* | See *A. paniculatum* |
| *siculum* | See *Nectaroscordum siculum* |
| § *sikkimense* | CHea CPlt EBee EHyt ERos GDra |
| | LFis MBro NMen NNrd NSla |
| | NTow NWCA SBea SBla WBea |
| | WCot WLRN WPer |
| - ACE 1363 | Last listed 1997 |
| *siskiyouense* | Last listed 1998 |
| sp. ACE 1745 | Last listed 1998 |
| *sphaerocephalon* | More than 30 suppliers |
| ¶ *splendens* | EBee |
| *stellatum* | EBee EHyt |
| *stellerianum* | GCHN WPer |
| - var. *kurilense* | Last listed 1997 |
| § *stipitatum* | EBee EMon LAma LBow MBro |
| | NRog WCot WHoo |
| - 'Album' | CBro EBee EMon LAma LBow |
| | NRog |
| ¶ - 'Glory of Pamir' | EBee |
| *stracheyi* | WCot |
| *strictum* | Last listed 1997 |
| *subhirsutum* | Last listed 1996 |
| ¶ *subvillosum* | WCot |
| *szovitsii* | Last listed 1998 |

| | |
|---|---|
| *tanguticum* | GCHN |
| *textile* | Last listed 1998 |
| *thunbergii* | CAvo CLTr CMea CNic EBee |
| | LBow NBir |
| ¶ - 'Nanum' | EPot |
| - 'Ozawa' | EHyt NMen SBla |
| *tibeticum* | See *A. sikkimense* |
| *togashii* | Last listed 1998 |
| * *tournefortii* | EBee |
| *tricoccum* | Last listed 1998 |
| *triquetrum* | CAvo CGle CLTr EBee ELan ERav |
| | GBar GGar IBlr ILis LAma LBow |
| | MMal NBir NRog SIng SLod WBea |
| | WCHb WCot WCru WHer WPer |
| | WPnP WShi WWin |
| *tuberosum* | CArn CAvo CBro CLyd CSev ECha |
| | EFou ELau EPar ERos GPoy ILis |
| | LEdu LHol MBri MChe MHew |
| | SIde WBea WCHb WCer WCot |
| | WOak WPer WWye |
| - purple/mauve | ELau |
| - variegated (v) | ELau EOHP |
| *turkestanicum* | EHyt |
| § *unifolium* | CAvo CBro CGle EBee EMan ETub |
| | LAma LBow LLWP MBri MLLN |
| | MNrw MRav NBir NCat NChi |
| | NRog NRoo NSti WBea WCla |
| | WFar WPer |
| *ursinum* | CArn CKin ETub EWFC GPoy |
| | LAma MHew MMal NMir NRog |
| | WGwy WHen WShi WWye |
| *validum* | Last listed 1998 |
| *victorialis* | Last listed 1998 |
| *vineale* | CArn MHew WHer WPer |
| *violaceum* | See *A. carinatum* |
| *virgunculae* | EHyt LBow SBla SWas WCot |
| *wallichii* | CLyd CPou EHyt EMon LAma |
| | NBir WTin |
| - B 445 | WLin |
| *zaprjagaevii* | EBee LEdu |
| *zebdanense* | LAma LBow MNrw |

## ALLOCASUARINA (Casuarinaceae)

| | |
|---|---|
| *crassa* | MSag |
| § *littoralis* | CGre MSag |
| *monilifera* | ECou |
| *nana* | Last listed 1998 |
| § *verticillata* | CTrC |

## ALNUS ✿ (Betulaceae)

| | |
|---|---|
| *cordata* ♀ | CB&S CBlo CDoC CDul CKin |
| | CLnd CMCN EBee ECrN ELan |
| | ENot EPfP GChr IOrc LBuc LHyr |
| | MGos NBee NRog NWea SPer |
| | SSta WDin WFar WMou WOrn |
| | WPic WStI WTro |
| - wild origin | Last listed 1998 |
| *crispa* | See *A. viridis* subsp. *crispa* |
| *firma* | CMCN |
| - var. *multinervis* | See *A. pendula* |
| - var. *sieboldiana* | See *A. sieboldiana* |
| *formosana* | Last listed 1996 |
| ♦ *fruticosa* | See *A. viridis* subsp. *fruticosa* |
| *glutinosa* | CB&S CBlo CDoC CDul CKin |
| | CLnd CSam ECrN ENot GChr |
| | GRei IOrc LBuc LHyr MGos NBee |
| | NRog NWea SHFr SPer WDin |
| | WMou WOrn WStI |
| - 'Aurea' | CDul CEnd CTho EBee MBlu SSpi |
| | WWat |
| - 'Imperialis' ♀ | CDoC CEnd CLnd CPMA CTho |
| | EBee ELan ENot EPfP GChr MAsh |
| | MBri MGos NBee NPSI SPer SSpi |
| | WDin WWat |

- f.*incisa* — ELan
- 'Laciniata' — CDoC CDul CLnd CTho IOrc MBlu
- 'Pyramidalis' — CTho
¶ - 'Razzmatazz' (v) — CPMA
*hirsuta* — CMCN
*incana* — CBlo CDoC CKin CLnd CMCN ECrN ENot GRei IOrc LBuc MBar MGos NRog NWea SPer WDin WMou WOrn
- 'Aurea' — CB&S CDul CLnd COtt CTho EBee ECrN ELan ENot IOrc LPan MBar MBlu MBri MGos SPer WDin WOrn
§ - subsp. *incana* — WCwm
- 'Laciniata' — CDul CTho ENot WDin
- 'Pendula' — Last listed 1998
- subsp. *tenuifolia* — See *A. incana* subsp. *incana*
*japonica* — Last listed 1998
*jorullensis* — Last listed 1996
¶ *lanata* — CMCN
*maritima* — Last listed 1998
*maximowiczii* — CMCN
- AGSJ 334 — SSta
*nepalensis* — WCwm WFro
*nitida* — CFil CGre CMCN
♦ *oregana* — See *A. rubra*
*rhombifolia* — Last listed 1998
§ *rubra* — CBlo CDoC CDul CKin CLnd CMCN CTho ELan ENot GAri GChr GRei IOrc LBuc NWea WDin WMou
♦ - 'Pinnatifida' — See *A. rubra* f. *pinnatisecta*
§ - f. *pinnatisecta* — CTho MBlu
§ *rugosa* — CMCN
*serrulata* — See *A. rugosa*
§ *sieboldiana* — CGre
♦ *sinuata* — See *A. viridis* subsp. *sinuata*
x *spaethii* ♀ — CDoC CDul CTho IOrc MCoo SRPl
*subcordata* — CLnd
*tenuifolia* — See *A. incana* subsp. *incana*
*viridis* — CAgr CMCN GAri NOla
- subsp. *crispa* var. *mollis* — CMCN
§ - subsp. *sinuata* — CAgr CMCN WPic

## ALOCASIA (✿) (Araceae)

x *amazonica* ♀ — ERea MBri MNew
¶ x - 'Polly' — MNew
¶ 'Aquino' — MNew
¶ x *argyraea* — MNew
¶ 'Black Velvet' — MNew
¶ 'Black Widow' — MNew
¶ 'Crinkles' — MNew
¶ *cucullata* — MNew WMul
¶ *culionensis* — MNew
¶ *cuprea* — MNew
- 'Blackie' — Last listed 1998
- 'Greenback' — Last listed 1998
¶ 'Elaine' — MNew
*gageana* — MNew WMul
¶ 'Green Shield' — MNew
¶ 'Green Velvet' — MNew
¶ *guttata* var. *imperialis* — MNew
¶ 'Hilo Beauty' — MNew
¶ *lancifolia* — MNew
¶ *longiloba* — MNew
*lowii* var. *veitchii* — See *A. veitchii*
*macrorrhiza* — EOas MNew WMul
- 'Jungle Gold' — WMul
¶ - 'Lutea' — MNew
¶ - 'Variegata' — MNew

¶ *maximiliana* — MNew
¶ *micholitziana* — MNew
¶ 'Mindanao' — MNew
*nigra* — See *A. plumbea* 'Nigra'
¶ *odora* — MNew
¶ *plumbea* — MNew
§ - 'Nigra' — MNew WMul
¶ - white — MNew
¶ *porphyroneura* — MNew
¶ *portei* — MNew
¶ 'Portora' — MNew
¶ 'Quilted Dreams' — MNew
¶ *sanderiana* 'Nobilis' — MNew
x *sedenii* — MNew
¶ 'Tigrina Suberba' — MNew
§ 'Uhinkii' — WMul
§ *veitchii* — Last listed 1998
¶ *watsoniana* — MNew
¶ *wentii* — MNew
I *whinkii* — See *A.* 'Uhinkii'
¶ 'White Knight' — MNew
¶ *zebrina* — MNew
¶ - 'Reticulata' — MNew

## ALOE (Aloaceae)

*arborescens* — CAbb CTrC MBro WCot
*aristata* ♀ — CHal EOas LBlm MBri MBro SAPC SArc WHer
*bakeri* ♀ — Last listed 1995
*barbadensis* — See *A. vera*
¶ *boylei* — CCpl
*brevifolia* — CTbh EOas SArc
*broomii* — CTrC EOas
*camperi* 'Maculata' — CTrC MBri
*ciliaris* — ERea
¶ *cooperi* — CAbb
*dichotoma* — CAbb GBin
¶ *ecklonis* — CCpl CTrC
*erinacea* — Last listed 1997
*ferox* — CTrC EOas
¶ *gracilis* — CCpl
¶ *grandidentata* — CCpl CTrF
¶ *greatheadii* var. *davyana* — CCpl
*humilis* — IBlr
¶ *jacksonii* — CCpl
*karasbergensis* — Last listed 1998
*melanacantha* ♀ — Last listed 1995
¶ *mitriformis* — CCpl CTrF SEND
¶ *pachygaster* — CCpl
¶ *parvibracteata* — CTrF
*plicatilis* — CTrC EOas
¶ *pluridens* — CTrF
¶ *polyphylla* — EOas
*pratensis* — CFir CTrC
*rauhii* ♀ — Last listed 1995
¶ *reitzii* — CCpl
*saponaria* — Last listed 1998
*somaliensis* ♀ — Last listed 1995
*striata* — Last listed 1998
*striatula* — CFil CTrC EOas IBlr SAPC SArc SBid SChr
- var. *caesia* — IBlr
¶ *succotrina* — CTrF
*variegata* ♀ — Last listed 1994
¶ *veitchii* — CTrC
§ *vera* ♀ — CArn ECon ELau EOHP EOas ERea GPoy ILis LChe LHol LPJP MSal NPer SIde SRCN WCot WHer WOak
'Walmsley's Blue' — MBri

## ALOINOPSIS (Aizoaceae)
*lueckhoffii*                  Last listed 1997

## ALONSOA (Scrophulariaceae)
*acutifolia*                   Last listed 1997
- *candida*                    Last listed 1998
- coral                        GPin LIck
*linearis*                     LCot
*meridionalis*                 NCut
\* - 'Salmon Beauty'            Last listed 1997
'Pink Beauty'                  ELan
¶ *unilabiata*                 CSpe
*warscewiczii* ♀              EBee ELan ERea SAga WWin
- pale form                    See *A. warscewiczii* 'Peachy-keen'
§ - 'Peachy-keen'              CSpe ECtt EMan NLak SAga

## ALOPECURUS (Poaceae)
*alpinus*                      CCuc CInt EHoe EMon LRHS
- subsp.*glaucus*              CBrm EHoe ETen MWhi
*lanatus*                      CInt NRya
*pratensis*                    CKin NOrc
- 'Aureovariegatus'            More than 30 suppliers
N - 'Aureus'                   CMGP ECha EGra EPot GAbr
                               GBin MBal MRav MUlv MWhi
                               NArg NBro NSti NVic SCob SSto
                               WByw WLin WPer WRHF WWin
- 'No Overtaking'              EMon

## ALOPHIA (Iridaceae)
¶ *drummondii*                 ERos
*lahue*                        See *Herbertia lahue*

## ALOYSIA (Verbenaceae)
*chamaedrifolia*               CPle
*citriodora*                   See *A. triphylla*
§ *triphylla* ♀               More than 30 suppliers

## ALPINIA (Zingiberaceae)
*formosana*                    EOas WMul
¶ *galanga*                    GPoy
*japonica*                     EOas MSal
*luteocarpa*                   Last listed 1998
*purpurata*                    Last listed 1996
*speciosa*                     See *A. zerumbet*
§ *vittata* (v)                Last listed 1996
§ *zerumbet*                   GPoy
- 'Variegata' (v)              WMul

## ALSOBIA See EPISCIA

## ALSTROEMERIA ✿ (Alstroemeriaceae)
'Aimi'                         COtt EBee MBri SBai WViv
*angustifolia* P&W 6574        Last listed 1998
'Apollo' ♀                    COtt LRHS MGrG SBai WViv
*aurantiaca*                   See *A. aurea*
§ *aurea*                      CGle CGre ELan EMar EPfP EWTr
                               EWoo LBlm MRav MUlv NCat
                               NFla NLar NMGW NSti SBla SDys
                               SRms SWot
- 'Cally Fire'                 GCal WCot
- 'Dover Orange'               CB&S CDoC CGle CHad CTri
                               EHic EMan MCLN SMrm SRPl
¶ - 'Golden Bob'               ELan
¶ - 'Lutea'                    SPer
- 'Orange King'                CBlo ENot EPfP MTed MUlv NLar
                               SCoo SDeJ
*brasiliensis*                 CGle CLAP CMil GCal NLon NPSI
                               WCot
¶ 'Bridesmaid'                 LIck
'Charm'                        EBee LRHS
'Coronet' ♀                   COtt EBee SBai WViv

'Dayspring Delight' (v)        CLAP
§ Diana, Princess of           SSmt
    Wales = 'Stablaco'
*diluta*                       Last listed 1996
- subsp.*diluta*               Last listed 1998
Doctor Salter's hybrids        ECGP EFou EHal MNrw SRms
¶ 'Evening Song'               MBri SBai WViv
¶ *exserens*                   SBla
¶ - F&W 7207                   WCot
- JCA 14415                    Last listed 1998
¶ 'Firefly'                    MBri SBai WViv
'Fortune'                      LRHS
*garaventae*                   Last listed 1998
§ H.R.H. Princess              SSmt
    Alexandra =
    'Zelblanca'
§ H.R.H. Princess              SSmt
    Alice = 'Staverpi'
*haemantha*                    CLAP
¶ - 'Rosea'                    EBee WCot
I 'Hatch Hybrid'               Last listed 1997
'Hawera'                       WCot
Hawera Seedlings               GCal
*hookeri*                      MTho SIgm
'Inca Charm'                   WWeb
'Inca Gold'                    WWeb
Inca hybrids                   CB&S
'Inca Salsa'                   WWeb
'Inca Spice'                   WWeb
'Inca Sunset'                  WWeb
¶ *ligtu* hybrid, variegated   CRDP
*ligtu* hybrids ♀             CAvo CB&S CDoC CGle CHor
                               CPou CTri ECha ELan EMan EPfP
                               ERav ETub LHop MCAu MNrw
                               MWgw NFor NPer NVic SDeJ
                               SPer SRms SWas WBod WBro
                               WFar
¶ *ligtu* var.*ligtu*          COtt EBee SBai SPla WViv
¶ 'Little Eleanor'             COtt EBee SBai SPla WViv
¶ 'Little Miss Charlotte'      CB&S COtt MBri SBai WViv
¶ 'Little Miss Lucy'           CB&S COtt SBai WViv
¶ 'Little Miss Matilda'        CB&S COtt MBri SBai WViv
¶ 'Little Miss Rosanna'        COtt SBai WViv
¶ 'Little Miss Teresa'         CB&S EBee MBri
*magnifica*                    Last listed 1996
¶ - subsp.*maxima*             SIgm
- RB 94012                     Last listed 1998
Manon                          See *A.* Princess Marie-Louise =
                               'Zelanon'
Margaret = 'Stacova'           Last listed 1997
Marie-Louise                   See *A.* Princess Marie-Louise =
                               'Zelanon'
'Marina'                       LRHS SBai SPla WViv
¶ 'Marissa'                    EBee LIck MBri SBai WViv
'Mars'                         LRHS
Meyer hybrids                  MLLN MTho
'Orange Gem' ♀                COtt LRHS SBai WViv
'Orange Glory' ♀             COtt EBee LRHS SBai SPla WViv
*pallida*                      CBro SIgm SSpi
- F&W 7241                     Last listed 1997
- JCA 12407                    Last listed 1998
- JCA 14335                    Last listed 1998
- JJA 12497                    Last listed 1996
*patagonica* P&W 6226          NTow
§ *paupercula*                 CSev
*pelegrina*                    MTho WCot
- 'Alba'                       ELan MRav
¶ - var.*humilis*              WCot
- 'Rosea'                      ELan
'Pink Perfection'              LRHS MGrG
*presliana* subsp.             CPou
    *australis*
- subsp.*australis*            SSpi
    JCA 12590

| | | |
|---|---|---|
| - subsp. *presliana* | EBee SBla | |
| - RB 94103 | WCot | |
| Princess Alice | See *A.* H.R.H. Princess Alice = 'Staverpi' | |
| Princess Angela = 'Staprila' | COtt LIck SSmt | |
| § Princess Beatrix = 'Stadoran' | SSmt | |
| § Princess Carmina = 'Stasilva' ♀ | SSmt | |
| § Princess Caroline = 'Staroko' ♀ | SSmt | |
| § Princess Charlotte = 'Staprizsa' | SSmt | |
| Princess Elizabeth | See *A.* Queen Elizabeth The Queen Mother = 'Stamoli' | |
| Princess Emily = 'Staprimil' | SSmt | |
| § Princess Frederika = 'Stabronza' | SSmt | |
| § Princess Grace = 'Starodo' ♀ | SSmt | |
| § Princess Ileana = 'Stalvir' | SSmt | |
| § Princess Juliana = 'Staterpa' ♀ | SSmt | |
| ¶ Princess Margarita | LIck | |
| § Princess Marie-Louise = 'Zelanon' | SSmt | |
| * Princess Marilene | COtt EBee SSmt | |
| § Princess Mira = 'Stapripur' ♀ | SSmt | |
| § Princess Monica = 'Staprimon' | COtt EBee SSmt | |
| * Princess Morana | COtt SSmt | |
| Princess Paola | COtt SSmt | |
| Princess Ragna | See *A.* Princess Stephanie = 'Stapirag' | |
| § Princess Sarah = 'Stalicamp' | SSmt | |
| § Princess Sissi = 'Staprisis' | COtt SSmt | |
| § Princess Sophia = 'Stajello' | SSmt | |
| § Princess Stephanie = 'Stapirag' | COtt SSmt | |
| § Princess Victoria = 'Regina' | SSmt | |
| Princess Zsa Zsa | See *A.* Princess Charlotte = 'Staprizsa' | |
| *pseudospatbulata* | EBee | |
| - RB 94010 | WCot | |
| § *psittacina* | CBos CBro CGle CHad CHan CPlt CRDP EBee EHrv ELan EPar ERav ERic ERos EWoo GCal LHop MSte NTow SIgm SSoC SSpi WCot WFar WPGP WRus WSHC | |
| - variegated | CLAP CMil CRDP CSpe EBee EGar ELan EMon EPPr MGrG MRav NPla SIgm WCot | |
| *pulchella* Sims | See *A. psittacina* | |
| *pulchra* | SIgm | |
| - BC&W 4751 | Last listed 1998 | |
| - BC&W 4762 | Last listed 1998 | |
| 'Purple Joy' | Last listed 1996 | |
| *pygmaea* | EHyt MTho | |
| § Queen Elizabeth The Queen Mother = 'Stamoli' | LIck SPla SSmt | |
| 'Red Beauty' | EBee LIck LRHS MBri MGrG NBir NCat SBai SPla WViv | |
| 'Red Elf' | LRHS MBri SBai WViv | |
| ♦ 'Regina' | See *A.* Princess Victoria = 'Regina' | |
| *revoluta* JCA 14378 | Last listed 1998 | |
| 'Rosy Wings' | Last listed 1996 | |
| 'Selina' | EBee SBai SPla WViv WCot | |
| short purple | WCot | |
| *simsii* | Last listed 1998 | |
| 'Solent Arrow' | Last listed 1997 | |
| 'Solent Candy' | WFar | |
| 'Solent Crest' ♀ | WFar | |
| ¶ 'Solent Dawn' | WFar | |
| 'Solent Glow' | Last listed 1997 | |
| 'Solent Haze' | Last listed 1998 | |
| 'Solent Mist' | Last listed 1997 | |
| ¶ 'Solent Pride' | WFar | |
| 'Solent Rose' ♀ | Last listed 1998 | |
| 'Solent Wings' | Last listed 1997 | |
| 'Sovereign' | Last listed 1996 | |
| sp. F&W 7975 | Last listed 1998 | |
| *spatbulata* RB 94015 | WCot | |
| 'Spring Delight' | Last listed 1998 | |
| ♦ 'Stablaco' | See *A.* Diana, Princess of Wales = 'Stablaco' | |
| ♦ 'Stabronza' | See *A.* Princess Frederika = 'Stabronza' | |
| ♦ 'Stadoran' | See *A.* Princess Beatrix = 'Stadoran' | |
| ♦ 'Stajello' | See *A.* Princess Sophia = 'Stajello' | |
| ♦ 'Stalicamp' | See *A.* Princess Sarah = 'Stalicamp' | |
| ♦ 'Stalvir' | See *A.* Princess Ileana = 'Stalvir' | |
| ♦ 'Stamoli' | See *A.* Queen Elizabeth The Queen Mother = 'Stamoli' | |
| ♦ 'Stapirag' | See *A.* Princess Stephanie = 'Stapirag' | |
| ♦ 'Staprimon' | See *A.* Princess Monica = 'Staprimon' | |
| ♦ 'Stapripur' | See *A.* Princess Mira = 'Stapripur' | |
| ♦ 'Staprisis' | See *A.* Princess Sissi = 'Staprisis' | |
| ♦ 'Staprizsa' | See *A.* Princess Charlotte = 'Staprizsa' | |
| ♦ 'Starodo' | See *A.* Princess Grace = 'Starodo' | |
| ♦ 'Staroko' | See *A.* Princess Caroline = 'Staroko' | |
| ♦ 'Stasilva' | See *A.* Princess Carmina = 'Stasilva' | |
| ♦ 'Staterpa' | See *A.* Princess Juliana = 'Staterpa' | |
| ♦ 'Staverpi' | See *A.* H.R.H. Princess Alice = 'Staverpi' | |
| 'Sunstar' | Last listed 1998 | |
| ¶ 'Tessa' | MBri SBai WViv | |
| *umbellata* F&W 8497 | Last listed 1998 | |
| - JCA 14348 | Last listed 1998 | |
| I 'Vanitas' | Last listed 1996 | |
| 'Verona' | Last listed 1998 | |
| *versicolor* | Last listed 1996 | |
| ¶ - F&W 8721 | SIgm | |
| *violacea* | See *A. paupercula* | |
| 'White Apollo' | EBee MBri SPla | |
| 'White Knight' | Last listed 1996 | |
| ¶ 'Yagana' | GVic | |
| 'Yellow Friendship' ♀ | COtt EBee LIck LRHS MBri SBai SPla WLRN WViv | |
| Yellow King | See *A.* Princess Sophia = 'Stajello' | |
| ¶ 'Yellow Queen' | WFar | |
| ♦ 'Zelanon' | See *A.* Princess Marie-Louise = 'Zelanon' | |
| ♦ 'Zelblanca' | See *A.* H.R.H. Princess Alexandra = 'Zelblanca' | |

**ALTERNANTHERA** (Amaranthaceae)
*lehmannii*                 Last listed 1998

**ALTHAEA** (Malvaceae)
*armeniaca*                 EEls GBuc NCat
*cannabina*                 CRDP EBee GBri GCal MAvo
                            MBro MFir MHlr NFor SOkh WCot
                            WHoo WOld WPGP WPen WWat
                            WWhi
*officinalis*               CArn CHan CKin CSev ECoo ELan
                            ELau EWFC EWTr GBar GPoy ILis
                            LHol LHop MChe MHew MMil
                            MPEx MSal NDea NFai SIde
                            WGwy WOak WPer WWye
- *alba*                    EBee EGar EWTr LCot MCLN
                            NLar WHer
§ - 'Romney Marsh'          CStr EWll GCal MRav SMad WCot
                            WSHC
*rosea*                     See *Alcea rosea*
*rugosostellulata*          See *Alcea rugosa*

**ALTINGIA** (Hamamelidaceae)
*chinensis*                 CMCN

**ALYOGYNE** (Malvaceae)
*hakeifolia*                CSpe ECou ERea
§ *huegelii*                CAbb EDAr EMan LCns LHil LRHS
                            MBEx SYvo
- 'Santa Cruz'             CBos CSpe EOrc ERea LHop
                            SMrm SOWG SSoC

**ALYSSOIDES** (Brassicaceae)
*utriculata*                CHor CNic ELan LIck MBNS NPri
                            NTow WCot WPer WWin
- var. *graeca*            Last listed 1998

**ALYSSUM** (Brassicaceae)
*argenteum* hort.           See *A. murale*
*caespitosum*               NWCA
¶ *corningii*               WLin
*corymbosum*                See *Aurinia corymbosa*
*cuneifolium*               Last listed 1998
- var. *pirinicum*          Last listed 1998
*gemonense*                 See *Aurinia petraea*
*idaeum*                    LBee
*markgrafii*                CLyd WCom
*moellendorfianum*          Last listed 1996
*montanum*                  CArn ECha EGar ELan GAbr
                            MWat SPlb SRms
§ - 'Berggold'              CB&S CTri EMan EPfP GChr
                            GMaP LBee LPVe NPri NRoo
                            WLRN
- Mountain Gold            See *A. montanum* 'Berggold'
§ *murale*                  EGar
*oxycarpum*                 CLyd EHyt EPot NMen SBla WAbe
*petraeum*                  See *Aurinia petraea*
*propinquum*                Last listed 1997
*pulvinare*                 CInt WAbe
*purpureum*                 Last listed 1998
*pyrenaicum*                NWCA
*repens*                    Last listed 1997
*saxatile*                  See *Aurinia saxatilis*
*serpyllifolium*            CLyd ESis MOne NWCA
*sphacioticum*              Last listed 1996
*spinosum*                  CMea MBro WAbe WFar
§ - 'Roseum' ♀             CNic ECha ELan EPot ESis LBee
                            LHop LSpr MPla MWat NHol
                            NMen NRoo NWCA SBla WAbe
                            WCot WLin WPat WPer WWin
¶ - 'Strawberries and Cream' NDov WAbe
*stribrnyi*                 Last listed 1998

*tenium*                    Last listed 1996
*tortuosum*                 CLyd MOne
*wulfenianum*               LIck NTow NWCA

**AMANA** See TULIPA

x **AMARCRINUM** (Amaryllidaceae)
*memoria-corsii*            Last listed 1998
- 'Howardii'               LPio WCot

x **AMARINE** (Amaryllidaceae)
'Fletcheri'                Last listed 1998
*tubergenii*                Last listed 1997
- 'Zwanenburg'             CAvo

x **AMARYGIA** (Amaryllidaceae)
*parkeri*                   Last listed 1998
§ - 'Alba'                  CAvo

**AMARYLLIS** (Amaryllidaceae)
§ *belladonna*              CB&S CBro CFil CSpe EPar ERav
                            ETub LAma LBow MBri MUlv
                            NRog SDeJ SSpi WCot WGer
                            WWat
- 'Johannesburg'           CAvo EMon WCot
- 'Kimberley'              EMon
- 'Major'                  CAvo
- 'Pallida'                See *A. belladonna* 'Elata'
- 'Parkeri Alba'           See x *Amarygia parkeri* 'Alba'
- 'Purpurea'               EBee ETub WCot

**AMBROSIA** (Asteraceae)
*mexicana*                  Last listed 1997

**AMBROSINA** (Araceae)
*bassii* S&L 315            Last listed 1998

**AMELANCHIER** ✿ (Rosaceae)
*alnifolia*                 CAgr CDul CPle EBee EPla
§ - var. *pumila*           CPle GBin GSki LHop MBal MPla
                            MSte NHol SSta WAbe WDin
                            WNor
- 'Smokey'                 CBlo
* *alpina*                  EHyt
*arborea*                   WNor
*bartramiana*               CTho SSta
*canadensis*                More than 30 suppliers
- 'Micropetala'            NHol
*florida*                   See *A. alnifolia* var. *semi-
                            integrifolia*
x *grandiflora*             CEnd
'Autumn Brilliance'
- 'Ballerina' ♀            CB&S CBlo CDoC CDul CEnd
                            CMCN CPMA CTho ELan ENot
                            LNet LPan MAsh MBri MGos
                            MRav MWat NBee SLon SPer SPla
                            SRPl SSta WDin WHCG WPat
                            WWat WWeb
- 'Robin Hill'             LPan MGos SMad
- 'Rubescens'              CEnd CPMA MRav
*laevis*                    CB&S CDul CTho MBal SPer
*lamarckii* ♀               More than 30 suppliers
*lucida*                    SSta
I *ovalis* 'Edelweiss'      CBlo CEnd COtt CPMA LRHS
                            MBri MGos SBid SMad SMur
♦ *pumila*                  See *A. alnifolia* var. *pumila*
*rotundifolia* 'Helvetia'   CDoC CEnd MBri WEas
'Snowflake'                CBlo CEnd COtt CPMA LRHS SBid
                            SSta
*spicata*                   Last listed 1998

**AMIANTHUM** (Melianthaceae)
*muscitoxicum* — Last listed 1998

**AMICIA** (Papilionaceae)
*zygomeris* — CAbb CBot CMdw CPle EBee GBuc GCal GNau LHil SBid SMrm SSoC SUsu WEas WWye

**AMMI** (Apiaceae)
*majus* — MSal
*visnaga* — CSpe ELau IIve MSal

**AMMOBIUM** (Asteraceae)
*alatum* — WBrE

**AMMOCHARIS** (Amaryllidaceae)
*coranica* — Last listed 1997

**AMMOPHILA** (Poaceae)
*arenaria* — GQui

**AMOMUM** (Zingiberaceae)
*cardamomum* — See *A. compactum*
§ *compactum* — Last listed 1996

**AMOMYRTUS** (Myrtaceae)
§ *luma* — CDoC CGre CLan CPle CTbh CTrG CTrw EPfP ISea SArc WBod WPic WWat

**AMORPHA** (Papilionaceae)
*canescens* — CB&S CBlo CFai CPle EPfP MWhi NSti SBid SEND
*fruticosa* — CAgr CB&S CFil CPle IOrc MNrw SHFr SLon

**AMORPHOPHALLUS** (Araceae)
*bulbifer* — LAma MDun WCru WMul
¶ *corrugatus* B&SWJ 5244 — WCru
*kiusianus* — CFil
*rivierei* — GCal LBlo WMul

**AMPELOCALAMUS** (Poaceae)
¶ *scandens* — CFil EPla ISta WPGP

**AMPELODESMOS** (Poaceae)
*mauritanicus* — CBrm COIW EHoe EMan GBin LRHS MCCP WLRN

**AMPELOPSIS** ✿ (Vitaceae)
*aconitifolia* — CPlN
*arborea* — CPlN
*bodinieri* — CPlN
*brevipedunculata* — See *A. glandulosa* var. *brevipedunculata*
*chaffanjonii* — CPlN SMur
§ *glandulosa* var. *brevipedunculata* — CB&S GAri SPer WDin WWat
  - var. *brevipedunculata* B&SWJ 1094 — WCru
  - - f. *citrulloides* B&SWJ 1173 — WCru
§ - - 'Elegans' (v) — More than 30 suppliers
  - - 'Tricolor' — See *A. glandulosa* var. *brevipedunculata* 'Elegans'
  - var. *hancei* B&SWJ 1793 — WCru
  - - B&SWJ 3855 — WCru
  - var. *heterophylla* B&SWJ 667 — WCru
* - var. *maximowiczii* — CPlN
*henryana* — See *Parthenocissus henryana*

*megalophylla* — CB&S CBot CGre CPlN EBee EHal EPfP ETen SPer WBcn WCru WNor WOVN WWat
*orientalis* — CPlN
*sempervirens* hort. — See *Cissus striata*
*sinica* — WCru
sp. Taiwan B&SWJ 1173 — Last listed 1997
*thunbergii* — CPlN
  - B&SWJ 1863 — WCru
*tricuspidata* 'Veitchii' — See *Parthenocissus tricuspidata* 'Veitchii'

**AMPHICOME** See INCARVILLEA

**AMSONIA** (Apocynaceae)
*ciliata* — CFir ECGN LFis LGre SMrm SWas WFar WMer WPer
*eastwoodiana* — EBee
¶ *hubrichtii* — EBee SIgm
*illustris* — LRHS MSte SMac WTin
*jonesii* — EBee WFar
§ *orientalis* ♀ — CHad CHea CMil CVer EBee ECha EFou EMan EPar ERea LGre LHop LSpr MBri MCAu MHar MRav SCro SMrm SUsu SWas WFar WOld WRHF WWin
*tabernaemontana* — CFir CHad CHan CLyd EBee ECGN ELan EMan EMil EWTr GBuc LGre MMil MNrw NDov SAga SIgm SOkh SRms SWas WCot WMer WPer
* - *galacticifolia* — EBee
  - var. *salicifolia* — ECha EOrc GSki MSte
*tomentosa* — EBee

**AMYGDALUS** See PRUNUS

**ANACAMPTIS** (Orchidaceae)
*pyramidalis* — EFEx SWes

**ANACARDIUM** (Anacardiaceae)
*occidentale* (F) — LBlo

**ANACYCLUS** (Asteraceae)
*pyrethrum* — GPoy
  - var. *depressus* — CGle EBrP EBre ELan EMNN EMar ESis GMaP GTou LBre LHop NFor NHol NMen NVic NWCA SBla SBre SIng SRms WFar WHoo WLin WPer WWin
  - var. *depressus* 'Golden Gnome' — MBNS MSCN
  - - 'Silberkissen' — Last listed 1997

**ANAGALLIS** (Primulaceae)
*alternifolia* var. *repens* — SSca
*arvensis* — EWFC MSal WEas WHbs
  - var. *caerulea* — EWFC
*foemina* — MSal
*linifolia* — See *A. monellii* subsp. *linifolia*
§ *monellii* ♀ — CNic ELan EPot SBla SMrm SRms SUsu WCla WCom WWin
§ - subsp. *linifolia* — EHyt
  - red — Last listed 1996
  - 'Sunrise' — CPBP MTho SUsu
  - 'Skylover' — EMan MSCN
*tenella* — EWFC
  - 'Studland' ♀ — EPot NMen NWCA SBla WAbe

**ANANAS** (Bromeliaceae)
¶ *comosus* — ECon
  - var. *variegatus* — MBri

**ANAPHALIS** (Asteraceae)

| | |
|---|---|
| *alpicola* | EPot NMen SGre |
| *margaritacea* | ECtt EMon EOld GBin GCHN GMaP MBri MLLN NBro NOak NSti SPar SRms SSca SSpe WBea WByw WFar |
| § - var. *cinnamomea* | CGle CHan ELan EMon WEas |
| § - 'Neuschnee' | CTri LFis MGed MWgw NArg NHol NMir NPri SPla WBea WPer WRHF |
| - New Snow | See *A. margaritacea* 'Neuschnee' |
| § - var. *yedoensis* ♀ | CBre CTri ECha ECot EFou EGle EPar MWat NLak SDix SPer WBrE WLRN |
| § *nepalensis* | Last listed 1996 |
| - B&SWJ 1634 | Last listed 1998 |
| § - var. *monocephala* | CGle ELan EMon MCAu MWat NSti SRms |
| - - CC&McK 550 | Last listed 1997 |
| *nubigena* | See *A. nepalensis* var. *monocephala* |
| *sinica* subsp. *morii* | Last listed 1998 |
| ¶ sp. ACE 1503 | WCot |
| ¶ sp. ACE 1832 | WCot |
| *triplinervis* ♀ | CGle EBee EFou ELan ENot GMaP MBrN MLLN MRav MWgw NBro NFla NFor NSti NVic SPer SRms SSpe SWat WByw WEas WFar WHoo WMow WRus WWin |
| ¶ - CC 1620 | WCot |
| - var. *intermedia* | See *A. nepalensis* |
| § - 'Sommerschnee' ♀ | EBee EBrP EBre ECha ECot ECtt EFou EHal LBre MBri MCLN MTis MWgw NFor NLon SAga SBre SChu SLon SPer WBea WElm WMow WPer WWal |
| - Summer Snow | See *A. triplinervis* 'Sommerschnee' |
| *yedoensis* | See *A. margaritacea* var. *yedoensis* |

**ANARRHINUM** (Scrophulariaceae)

| | |
|---|---|
| *bellidifolium* | EBee LIck NCut NPri |

**ANCHUSA** (Boraginaceae)

| | |
|---|---|
| *angustissima* | See *A. leptophylla* subsp. *incana* |
| *arvensis* | MHew |
| § *azurea* | NCut NOrc WPer |
| - 'Blue Angel' | CBlo EMan EWll GMaP |
| - 'Dropmore' | CBlo CMdw CTri EBee EPfP MWgw NBus NLon NOrc NPer SIde SRms SWat WOve WPer |
| ¶ - ES 33 | MRPP |
| - 'Feltham Pride' | CBot GMaP MLan NLon NPer NRoo SRms WElm WHoo WOve WPer WPyg |
| - 'Kingfisher Blue' | Last listed 1998 |
| - 'Little John' | COtt ECot SAga SRms |
| - 'Loddon Royalist' ♀ | More than 30 suppliers |
| - 'Morning Glory' | Last listed 1998 |
| - 'Opal' | CGle EBee ECot EMan LHop MCAu MMil MWat NRoo SApp SChu SMrm SPla WElm WLRN |
| - 'Royal Blue' | MLan |
| *barrelieri* | MLLN |
| *caespitosa* hort. | See *A. leptophylla* subsp. *incana* |
| *capensis* | EBee |
| *cespitosa* Lamarck ♀ | ELan EPot EWes SBla SIng |
| *italica* | See *A. azurea* |
| *laxiflora* | See *Borago pygmaea* |
| § *leptophylla* subsp. *incana* | CRDP EBee EMFP EMan EMar GBri LRHS WCot WRha |

| | |
|---|---|
| *myosotidiflora* | See *Brunnera macrophylla* |
| *officinalis* | CArn EWTr MHew MSal SIde |
| *sempervirens* | See *Pentaglottis sempervirens* |
| *undulata* | EBee SIgm |

**ANDROCYMBIUM** (Colchicaceae)

| | |
|---|---|
| *europaeum* MS 510 | Last listed 1998 |
| *gramineum* SB&L 26 | Last listed 1998 |
| *punicum* S&L 325 | Last listed 1998 |
| *rechingeri* | Last listed 1998 |

**ANDROMEDA** (Ericaceae)

| | |
|---|---|
| *glaucophylla* | IOrc MBar SBrw |
| *polifolia* | CMHG CSam EMil EPla GCrs IOrc SBrw WBod WDin WFar |
| - 'Alba' | ELan GChr MAsh MBal MBar MBro MDun MGos MPla MRav NHar NHol SBod SPer SPlb WAbe WLin WPat WPyg WWin |
| - 'Blue Ice' | EPfP LRHS MAsh SPer SSpi SSta |
| - 'Compacta' ♀ | CHor EMil EPot GCHN GCrs IMGH MAsh MBal MBar MBri MGos MPla NHar NHol NMen SPer SReu SRms WPat WPyg WSHC WWin |
| * - 'Compacta Alba' ♀ | Last listed 1992 |
| - 'Grandiflora' | ELan ITim LRHS MAsh MBal MBri MDun MGos SBod SPer |
| - 'Hayachine' | EPot |
| - 'Kirigamine' | ELan MAsh MBal MBri MGos NHol WPat WPyg |
| - 'Macrophylla' ♀ | EPot GCrs GDra ITim MBal MBro NHar NHed NHol SIng SSta WAbe WPat WPyg |
| - 'Major' | MBal |
| - 'Minima' | MBal |
| - 'Nana' | ELan EPot LNet MAsh MGos NMen SPer STre WAbe WLRN WStI WWat WWeb |
| - 'Nikko' | CBlo GBuc MAsh MBal MGos NHol SPer WPat WPyg |
| - 'Red Winter' | CBlo CRos LRHS |
| - 'Shibutsu' | GAri MGos MPla SSta |

**ANDROPOGON** (Poaceae)

| | |
|---|---|
| *gerardii* | CBrm COIW EBee ECGN EHoe EMon EPPr GBin LGre LRHS WPer |
| *ischaemum* | See *Bothriochloa ischaemum* |
| *saccharoides* | Last listed 1997 |
| *scoparius* | See *Schizachyrium scoparium* |

**ANDROSACE** (Primulaceae)

| | |
|---|---|
| *albana* | CLyd EWes NWCA |
| *armeniaca* var. *macrantha* | NWCA |
| *axillaris* ACE 1060 | EHyt WAbe |
| *barbulata* | CMea CNic EHyt GCHN |
| *bisulca* var. *aurata* | Last listed 1996 |
| ACE 1750 | |
| *bulleyana* | WAbe WLin |
| - ACE 2198 | EPot |
| *cantabrica* | EHyt |
| *carnea* | CLyd GCHN GCrs MNrw NHar NMen WCla |
| - *alba* | CNic LBee MBro NHar NWCA WLin |
| - 'Andorra' | WAbe |
| - subsp. *brigantiaca* | CElw CLyd EHyt GTou MBro NHar NMen NRoo NRya NSla WAbe WHoo |
| - - Myer's form | Last listed 1996 |
| - var. *halleri* | See *A. carnea* subsp. *rosea* |

| | |
|---|---|
| – subsp. *laggeri* ♀ | ECho EPot GCrs GTou NHar NSla WPat |
| – x *pyrenaica* | CGra EHyt EPot GCHN NHar NMen WAbe |
| § – subsp. *rosea* ♀ | GDra NTow NWCA WCla |
| ¶ – – x *carnea* subsp. *laggeri* | NHol WLin |
| *ciliata* | CGra GTou NTow WAbe |
| *cylindrica* | CGra CPBP EPot GCHN GCrs GTou NHar NMen SBla WFar WLin |
| – x *hirtella* | EHyt GTou NHar NMen NWCA SIng WAbe |
| *delavayi* | NWCA |
| *foliosa* | Last listed 1997 |
| *geraniifolia* | CPLG EBee ECha GCHN IHdy WAbe WCru |
| – ex CC&McK 109 | MRPP |
| *globifera* | NHar NMen WAbe |
| *hausmannii* | GCHN GTou |
| *hedraeantha* | CLyd EPot MWat WAbe WLin |
| x *beeri* | Last listed 1997 |
| – 'Alba' | EHyt GCHN |
| *helvetica* | Last listed 1996 |
| *himalaica* | EHyt |
| *hirtella* | EPot GCHN GTou MRPP NHar NTow |
| *jacquemontii* | See *A. villosa* var. *jacquemontii* |
| *lactea* | CNic GCHN GTou MHar |
| § *lactiflora* | Last listed 1998 |
| § *laevigata* | WAbe |
| – var. *ciliolata* | GTou SIng WLin |
| – – NNS 94-38 | MRPP |
| – 'Gothenburg' AM | WPat |
| § – var. *laevigata* 'Packwood' | CGra |
| *lanuginosa* ♀ | CLyd CPBP EHyt EPot GCrs LBee MBro MOne MWat NMen NWCA SBla SDys WAbe WWin |
| – compact form | EPot |
| – 'Leichtlinii' | Last listed 1998 |
| – 'Wisley Variety' | SIgm |
| *lehmannii* EMAK 951 | Last listed 1996 |
| *limprichtii* | See *A. sarmentosa* var. *watkinsii* |
| x *marpensis* | EHyt EPot |
| *mathildae* | EHyt GTou NMen NNrd NTow NWCA WHoo |
| – x *carnea* | NMen |
| *microphylla* | See *A. mucronifolia* Watt |
| *mollis* | See *A. sarmentosa* var. *yunnanensis* |
| § *montana* | CGra NWCA WLin |
| *mucronifolia* hort. | See *A. sempervivoides* |
| *mucronifolia* Schacht's form | EHyt |
| § *mucronifolia* Watt | EPot GTou |
| – CHP&W 296 | NWCA |
| – x *sempervivoides* | EHyt EPot MRPP |
| – SEP 284 | EHyt |
| *muscoidea* | EPot MRPP NWCA WAbe |
| – C&R 188 | GTou |
| – f. *longiscapa* | NWCA |
| – f. *muscoidea* | Last listed 1997 |
| – Schacht's form | CLyd CPBP EHyt SIgm |
| – SEP 132 | Last listed 1998 |
| § *nivalis* | NTow |
| *primuloides* Duby | See *A. studiosorum* |
| – hort. | See *A. sarmentosa* |
| – white form | Last listed 1998 |
| *pubescens* | EPot GCHN SBla SIng WLin |
| *pyrenaica* | EHyt GCHN GTou ITim NHar NMen NTow SBla WAbe |
| *rigida* ACE 2336 | EPot |
| – KGB 168 | EPot |
| *robusta* | Last listed 1998 |
| – var. *breviscapa* | CPBP GCrs NWCA |
| *rotundifolia* | GCHN GTou IMGH WCru |
| – 'Elegans' | Last listed 1996 |
| *salicifolia* | See *A. lactiflora* |
| § *sarmentosa* ♀ | EHyt ELan GTou IMGH ITim LBee MBro MWat NMen NNrd SRms SSmi WAbe WCla WEas WHoo WPyg |
| – 'Brilliant' | Last listed 1997 |
| – CC 407 | MRPP |
| – 'Chumbyi' | ESis MBro MOne MRPP NHol NTow NWCA SBla SIng SRms WPat |
| – *monstrosa* | Last listed 1996 |
| § – 'Salmon's Variety' | CMea CTri SIgm |
| – 'Sherriff's' | EPot GCHN GCrs MBro MOne NHar NTow SBla SIgm SIng SRms WLin |
| § – var. *watkinsii* | CLyd EPot MBro NHar NMen SIng WLin |
| § – var. *yunnanensis* | CPBP EPot SIgm SIng |
| § *sempervivoides* ♀ | CLyd ECha EHyt ELan GCHN GCrs GDra LBee MBro NHar NHed NHol NMen NWCA SBla SIgm SIng SRms WHoo WLin WPat WPyg WWin |
| – scented form | MBro |
| ¶ – 'Susan Joan' | EHyt WAbe |
| *septentrionalis* 'Stardust' | Last listed 1996 |
| *sericea* | NWCA |
| sp. CD&R 2477 | WCru |
| *spinulifera* | Last listed 1997 |
| *strigillosa* | Last listed 1996 |
| § *studiosorum* | GCHN NCat |
| * – *alba* | Last listed 1998 |
| – 'Doksa' | EHyt EPot GCrs WAbe |
| *tapete* | WAbe |
| – ACE 1725 | Last listed 1998 |
| * *tridentata* | Last listed 1996 |
| *vandellii* | CGra CPBP EHyt EPot GCHN GTou NWCA |
| *villosa* | Last listed 1998 |
| – var. *arachnoidea* | Last listed 1998 |
| – – 'Superba' | NMen |
| * – var. *congesta* | EHyt |
| § – var. *jacquemontii* | EHyt NHar NMen NTow NWCA SBla SIgm |
| – – lilac form | EPot |
| – – pink | EPot |
| – subsp. *taurica* | CLyd EPot |
| – – 'Palandoken' | MRPP |
| *vitaliana* | See *Vitaliana primuliflora* |
| *watkinsii* | See *A. sarmentosa* var. *watkinsii* |
| *yargongensis* ACE 1722 | EPot |

## ANDRYALA (Asteraceae)

| | |
|---|---|
| *agardhii* | NHol NMen NNrd NTow NWCA SSca WPat |
| *lanata* | See *Hieracium lanatum* |

## ANEMARRHENA (Asphodelaceae)

| | |
|---|---|
| *asphodeloides* | EBee MSal WCot |

## ANEMIA (Schizaeaceae)

| | |
|---|---|
| *phyllitidis* | NMar |

## ANEMONE ✿ (Ranunculaceae)

| | |
|---|---|
| *altaica* | GAbr SRms WAbe WCot |
| *apennina* ♀ | CLAP EPar SCro SRms SWas WCot WTin |

| | |
|---|---|
| - var. *albiflora* | EBee EPot ERos |
| - double form | SWas |
| - 'Petrovac' CE&H 538 | EPot |
| ¶ *baicalensis* | EHic NSti |
| *baldensis* | CGle ECho GAbr LBee LHop NMen NOak SRms WCom |
| ¶ *barbulata* | SIng |
| *biarmiensis* | See *A. narcissiflora* subsp. *biarmiensis* |
| *blanda* ♀ | EBrP EBre EOrc LAma LBre LHop MBri MBro NChi NFla NRog SBre SChu WBea WBro WCot WFar WPat WPer WShi |
| - blue | CAvo CBro CMea CTri ElAn EMar EPar EPfP EPot ETub GAbr LAma MBri MBro MHlr NLon NRoo SRms WFar |
| - 'Blue Shades' | WPGP |
| - 'Blue Star' | Last listed 1996 |
| - 'Charmer' | CMea EPar EPot MBNS MNrw NMen |
| - 'Ingramii' ♀ | EMan EPar GBri LAma MBal NRog SRms WPat |
| - 'Ingramii' CE&H 626 | Last listed 1997 |
| - 'Pink Star' | CBro EPot LAma MBNS NBir NRog SRms |
| - 'Radar' ♀ | CBro CLAP EPar EPot LAma MNrw NBir NRog SRms |
| - var. *rosea* ♀ | CAvo ELan LAma MLLN WFar WPer |
| - 'Violet Star' | CBro EPot NLon |
| - 'White Splendour' ♀ | CAvo CBro CGle CMea ECha ELan EMar EOrc EPar EPot ETub GAbr LAma LFis MBro MNrw NChi NLon NMen NRog SChu SRms WCot WHil WPGP WPer WRus |
| *canadensis* | CElw CHar CNic CSpe EBee ECGP MBrN MNrw MTis NBur NSti NWoo WCot WElm WRos WSan |
| *caroliniana* | CGle CLyd EBrP EBre EPot ESis GAbr GBuc GCrs LBre NOak NRoo SBre |
| ¶ *caucasica* | EPot |
| *cernua* | Last listed 1996 |
| *coronaria* | EPot SRms |
| - 'Blue Moon' | Last listed 1996 |
| - 'Creagh Castle' | Last listed 1997 |
| - De Caen Group | LAma NRog WFar |
| § - - 'Die Braut' | CGle MNrw NRog |
| - - 'His Excellency' | See *A. coronaria* (De Caen Group) 'Hollandia' |
| § - - 'Hollandia' | EPot MNrw SAga |
| - - 'Mister Fokker' | EPot ETub LAma MNrw NRog |
| - - The Bride | See *A. coronaria* (De Caen Group) 'Die Braut' |
| - - 'The Governor' | GSki MNrw NRog SAga |
| ¶ - 'Jerusalem' | WFar |
| - (Mona Lisa Group) 'Sylphide' | EPot MNrw NRog WCot |
| - MS 783 | Last listed 1998 |
| - MS&CL 613 | Last listed 1998 |
| ¶ - Saint Bridgid Group (d) | LAma MBri NRog SDeJ WFar |
| - - 'Lord Lieutenant' (d) | MNrw NBir NBur NOak NRog |
| - - 'Mount Everest' (d) | MNrw NBir SUsu WCot |
| - - 'The Admiral' (d) | ETub MNrw NBir NRog |
| - Saint Piran Group | SDeJ |
| *crinita* | NChi SMrm |
| *cylindrica* | CFir CGle CSWP GAbr MHar MNrw |
| *decapetala* | GCal |
| *demissa* | Last listed 1997 |
| *drummondii* | CHar EBee GAbr GLch MBrN NChi NPri WAbe WCla WSan |
| *elongata* B&SWJ 2975 | WCru |
| *fasciculata* | See *A. narcissiflora* |
| *flaccida* | CBro CRDP EBee EPot LGre LHop SIng WCot WCru WFar |
| x *fulgens* | ECha NWCA SIgm SRms |
| - 'Annulata Grandiflora' | Last listed 1998 |
| - 'Multipetala' | NRog |
| - Saint Bavo Group | CBro ECGP |
| *globosa* | See *A. multifida* |
| 'Guernica' | ECho GBuc |
| *hepatica* | See *Hepatica nobilis* |
| § *hortensis* | CMil SBla WCot WWat |
| - *alba* | Last listed 1998 |
| - subsp. *heldreichii* | WThi |
| ¶ - JCA 161.003 | IDac |
| - MS 958 | Last listed 1998 |
| § *hupehensis* | CBlo CBot EBee LFis NOrc WBod WCot WFar |
| § - 'Bowles' Pink' ♀ | CBlo CMil CRDP MBro MWat WCot WCru WHoo WMaN WPGP |
| ♦ - 'Crispa' | See *A.* x *hybrida* 'Lady Gilmour' |
| - 'Eugenie' | CGle CMil CStr EBee EMan LRHS NCat SSca |
| - 'Hadspen Abundance' ♀ | More than 30 suppliers |
| § - var. *japonica* | CGle CPou EGar GCal NFor NPla WCru WEas |
| ¶ - - 'Bodnant Burgundy' | LRHS |
| § - - 'Bressingham Glow' | CBel CMHG EBee EBrP EBre ECtt ELan EOrc EPot LBre LHop MCAu MCLN MLLN MMil MNrw NHol NOrc NRoo NSti NVic SBre SLon SPer SPlb SUsu WAbb WFar WOld WWal |
| § - - 'Pamina' ♀ | CAvo CGle CHea CMil CRDP EBee ECGN EFou EGar GCal GMac LFis LGre MBri MHlr MRav MSCN NFai NPri NSti NTow SHar WCot WCru WElm WFar WHoo WOld WPyg WRus |
| - - Prince Henry | See *A. hupehensis* var. *japonica* 'Prinz Heinrich' |
| § - - 'Prinz Heinrich' ♀ | More than 30 suppliers |
| § - - 'Rotkäppchen' | CLon GCal MRav NBrk |
| - 'Praecox' | CBel CMea EBee EWTr GBri LHop MBNS MBri MCLN NGdn NHol NRoo NSti SChu SCro SLod WAbb WCot WCru WHal WWal WWin |
| ♦ - 'September Charm' | See *A.* x *hybrida* 'September Charm' |
| - 'Splendens' | CBlo CMHG EAst EBee EMan LSyl MBri NCut NHol NPla SPer SSca WAbb WBro WFar WHal WPyg WRHF |
| ¶ - 'Superba' | SBla WKif |
| § x *hybrida* | CAvo CBos CGle EPar LEdu MBro NChi NOak SChu SPla SRms WAbe WCru WFar WHil WHoo WOld WRHF |
| - 'Alba Dura' | Last listed 1996 |
| - 'Alba' hort. (UK) | See *A.* x *hybrida* 'Honorine Jobert' |
| - 'Alba' hort. (USA) | See *A.* x *hybrida* 'Lady Ardilaun' |
| - 'Andrea Atkinson' | EAst EBee EGar EHal EMan MBri MBro NHol NPri NSti SChu WHoo WLRN |
| - 'Bowles' Pink' | See *A. hupehensis* 'Bowles' Pink' |
| - 'Bressingham Glow' | See *A. hupehensis* var. *japonica* 'Bressingham Glow' |
| - 'Coupe d'Argent' | EGar NRoo |
| - 'Elegans' ♀ | EFou EGar MRav SWat |

§ - 'Géante des Blanches' ♀ CBlo CBos CLon CMil EBee ECtt EGar GMac MBro NRoo WHoo
§ - 'Honorine Jobert' ♀ More than 30 suppliers
§ - 'Königin Charlotte' ♀ More than 30 suppliers
  - 'Kriemhilde' GCal GMac
§ - 'Lady Gilmour' CAvo CBel CBos CFai CRDP EBee EHic GCal MCCP NEgg NHol NPri NSti SMad WCot WCru WOve WViv
  - 'Loreley' CBlo CMea EAst EBee EMan GCal MBNS MCLN MWat NCut NTow SMad SPer WCot
  - 'Luise Uhink' CBlo CGle CHor CPou NBir SSpi WEas
§ - 'Margarete' CBlo CBos CElw CPar CPou ECtt EHol MAvo NBir SChu SCro SLod WCru WHoo WMoo
  - 'Max Vogel' LGre MTed WBcn
  - 'Monterosa' CGle CMil CPou EBee EBrP EBre EHrv EWes GCal LBre MBal NBir NCut NHol SBre SRms WCot WCru WFar WKif
◆ - 'Pamina' See *A. hupehensis* var. *japonica* 'Pamina'
  - Prince Henry See *A. hupehensis* var. *japonica* 'Prinz Heinrich'
  - 'Prinz Heinrich' See *A. hupehensis* var. *japonica* 'Prinz Heinrich'
  - 'Profusion' NCut WCot WOld WPyg WRus
  - Queen Charlotte See *A.* x *hybrida* 'Königin Charlotte'
  - 'Richard Ahrens' CBos CDoC EBee EGle EMan LGre LHop MBel MBri NHol NOrc NRoo SCro SMrm SRCN SSpe SWas SWat WAbe WCot WCru WFar WWal
  - 'Rosenschale' CBos GCal MBal MBri NRoo WCru WFar WOld
◆ - 'Rotkäppchen' See *A. hupehensis* var. *japonica* 'Rotkäppchen'
§ - 'September Charm' ♀ CB&S CHar EBee ECha EFou EHrv ELan EOrc EPfP LHop MBel MBri MCAu MNrw MWgw NLar NLon NOak NSti NTow SCob SPer SSoC SWat WCru WPyg WWal
  - 'Serenade' EBee EFou MBri NBir NCut NHol SSvw SVil WWat
* - 'Thomas Ahrens' Last listed 1997
◆ - Tourbillon See *A.* x *hybrida* 'Whirlwind'
§ - 'Whirlwind' More than 30 suppliers
  - 'White Queen' See *A.* x *hybrida* 'Géante des Blanches'
  - Wirbelwind See *A.* x *hybrida* 'Whirlwind'
◆ *japonica* See *A.* x *hybrida*, *A. hupehensis*
  x *lesseri* CGle CLyd ECha ELan EPri ESis GCrs GMac LHop MBri MBro NMen NSti NWoo SBla SIgm SMad SPer SRms WBea WCru WFar WHoo WPat WWin
  *leveillei* CHar CMil CRDP EBee ELan GAbr LGre MFir MHar MLLN SIgm WAbe WCot WCru WSan WSpi
§ x *lipsiensis* CAvo CBos CBro CHad CLon CPlt CRDP EBee ECha EHyt EPar EPot ERos GCHN LGre MRav MTho NTow NWCA SIgm SSvw SUsu SWas WAbe WCru WFar WHal WLin WSan
  - 'Pallida' ♀ CPlt CRDP ERos GCrs NPar NRar WAbe WCot WRus
N *magellanica* hort. See *A. multifida*
§ *multifida* More than 30 suppliers

  - var.*globosa* WWhi
  - 'Major' CFir CLyd CRDP EAst MBro MMal NHol NLon NWCA SBla WCot WHil
  - f.*polysepala* EBee GAbr
  - red CFir EBee MBNS MRav NFor NLon NRoo NSla WHil WShe
* - 'Rubra' EAst NHed
§ *narcissiflora* EMFP GSki LSyl NHar SSpi WCom WCot
  - *citrina* Last listed 1998
  *nemorosa* ♀ CAvo CBro CElw CGle CKin EOld EPar EPot ETub EWFC IMGH LAma LBow LSyl MBal MSal NHar NHol SCob SIng SRms SSpi WFar WMer WShi
N - 'Alba Plena' (d) CAvo CBro CHea CSWP EBee ECha ELan EPot ERos ETub GMac IMGH MTho NMGW NRoo NTow SIng SUsu WAbb WCot WCru WEas WRus
  - 'Allenii' ♀ CBro CHea CLAP CSpe EBee ECha EHyt EPar EPot ERos LGre LSyl MBal MRav NHar NMen NPar NRya NTow SIgm SIng SSpi SWas WAbe WCot WCru WPGP
  - 'Amy Doncaster' SCro WCot
  - 'Atrocaerulea' EPar EPot GBuc IBlr NHol NOla
  - 'Blue Beauty' CLAP EPot ERos GBuc IBlr MBal NMen WAbe WCru
  - 'Blue Bonnet' CElw GBuc WCot
  - 'Blue Eyes' (d) CLAP CRDP EGle IBlr SIgm SUsu
  - 'Blue Queen' EPot
  - 'Bowles' Purple' EBee EPar EPot IBlr NHar NPar NRar NRya NTow SIgm WAbe WCot WCru WFar WIvy
¶ - 'Bracteata' NDov
  - 'Bracteata Pleniflora' (d) ECha EPot GBuc IBlr LHop MBal MBro NWoo WAbe WCru WFar
  - 'Buckland' IBlr
  - 'Caerulea' EPot
  - 'Cedric's Pink' EGle IBlr WCot WCru
  - 'Currey's Pink' See *A. nemorosa* 'Lismore Pink'
  - 'Danica' MBal
  - 'Dee Day' CLAP GBuc NPar SWas WAbe
  - 'Flore Pleno' (d) EBrP EBre EHic EHyt EOrc EPar LBre MBal MBro NRar SBre WAbe WMaN WPGP
  - forms Last listed 1998
  - 'Green Fingers' EPot GBuc LGre SUsu SWas WCot WCru WIvy
  - 'Hannah Gubbay' CLAP CRDP EPar IBlr MBal WAbe
  - 'Hilda' CLAP EPar EPot GBuc MBal NHed NMen NRya NTow WAbe
  - 'Knightshayes Vestal' (d) MRav WCot WIvy
  - 'Lady Doneraile' CLAP ECha NTow WCru
  - 'Leeds' Variety' ♀ CRDP EGle EPot LGre MTho NHar NHol
  - 'Lychette' CAvo EGle EPar EPot IBlr LGre MBal WAbe WCru
  - 'Monstrosa' EBee EPar EPot WCot
  - 'Parlez Vous' CMil SWas
  - 'Pentre Pink' EGle IBlr MTho WAbe WCru WIvy
¶ - 'Picos Pink' SWas
  - pink CPlt EPot LGre WCru
  - x *ranunculoides* See *A.* x *lipsiensis*
  - 'Robinsoniana' ♀ More than 30 suppliers
  - 'Rosea' CGle EPot LAma NRar WAbe WCru
  - 'Royal Blue' CBos CLAP CMea CMil CNic CRDP EBee ECha EPar EPot GBuc LAma NHol NMen SUsu WAbe WCru WFar WTin

| | |
|---|---|
| - 'Vestal' ♀ | CElw CGle CLAP CMea CRDP EBee EBrP EBre EHyt EPar EPot ERos GBuc IBlr LBre LGre NFla NMGW NMen NRya SBre WSan WShi |
| - 'Virescens' ♀ | CMea NPar NRar SWas WAbe WIvy |
| - 'Viridiflora' | CMil CRDP EBee LGre MCCP MRav MTho NSti SSpi SUsu WCot WCru WFar |
| ¶ - 'Westwell Pink' | SIgm |
| - 'Wilks' Giant' | Last listed 1998 |
| - 'Wilks' White' | CLAP EGle EPar EPot MBal NOla |
| - 'Wyatt's Pink' | CAvo CBos CLAP LGre WAbe |
| *obtusiloba* | CRDP GCrs GDra GTou IMGH MTho NHar SBla SRms WAbe |
| - *alba* | CRDP GDra LSyl NHar NHol NMen SBla WAbe |
| *palmata* | CPou EBee GAbr WAbe WCru |
| - 'Alba' | Last listed 1998 |
| - MS 413 | Last listed 1998 |
| *parviflora* | CHea EHal GAbr MHar |
| *patens* | See *Pulsatilla patens* |
| *pavonina* | EBee ECha ERos MTho SBla SSca SWas WCom |
| *polyanthes* | GTou WThi |
| ¶ *pseudoaltaica* | WCru |
| ¶ - L 2084 blue | SBla |
| ¶ - L 2085 white | SBla |
| ¶ - purple | WThi |
| ¶ - white | WThi |
| *pulsatilla* | See *Pulsatilla vulgaris* |
| *raddeana* | Last listed 1996 |
| *ranunculoides* ♀ | CAvo CBro CElw CMHG CRDP EBee EHyt EPar EPot ERos ETub IMGH LAma MTho NHar NHol NMen NRya NSti NTow SIng SSpi SUsu SWas WCru WEas WShi |
| - 'Pleniflora' (d) | CAvo CHea CLAP CRDP ECha EPar EPot MHlr MRav WCot WIvy |
| ¶ *richardsonii* | CPla |
| ♦ *riparia* | See *A. virginiana* var. *alba* |
| *rivularis* | More than 30 suppliers |
| - CLD 573 | WLin |
| *rupicola* | MHar NBir |
| x *seemannii* | See *A.* x *lipsiensis* |
| * *sherriffii* | Last listed 1997 |
| ¶ sp. B&SWJ 1452 | WCru |
| sp. from China PLW12/93 | WCot |
| *stellata* | See *A. hortensis* |
| *sulphurea* | See *Pulsatilla alpina* subsp. *apiifolia* |
| *sylvestris* | More than 30 suppliers |
| § - 'Elise Fellmann' (d) | CLAP CRDP LGre WCot |
| - 'Flore Pleno' | See *A. sylvestris* 'Elise Fellmann' |
| - 'Macrantha' | CLAP CRDP EAst EBee MHlr SAga SMrm SSpi SWas WCot WRus |
| *tetrasepala* | Last listed 1998 |
| § *tomentosa* | CBel CGle CMGP EBee ECha EOld GMac NRoo SCro SMrm SRms SWat WEas WGwG WRha WWal WWhi |
| - 'Robustissima' | CBos CGle EBee EFou EGra EHic ENot MBri MTis MWgw NHol NSti SPer SPla WAbb WFar WMer |
| *trifolia* | CRDP EBee ECha EHyt EPot ERos GAbr MBal NMen SUsu WCot |
| - pink | Last listed 1996 |
| ¶ - 'Semiplena' (d) | WCot |
| *trullifolia* | CPlt CRDP GCrs NHar SBla |
| - *alba* | GTou WAbe |
| - blue form | GTou |

| | |
|---|---|
| - SBEC 797 | NTow |
| *vernalis* | See *Pulsatilla vernalis* |
| *virginiana* | CFir EBee EHal GBin MSte NChi |
| § - var. *alba* | MHar |
| § *vitifolia* DC. | CBos |
| - B&SWJ 1452 | NChi |
| - B&SWJ 2320 | WCru |
| - CC&McK 43 | CGle |
| § - hort. | See *A. tomentosa* |

## ANEMONELLA (Ranunculaceae)

| | |
|---|---|
| *thalictroides* | CElw CFir CGra CLAP CRDP EFEx EPar IMGH LAma NHar NMen NTow SBla SWas WAbe WCot WCru WFar WLin WWat |
| - 'Alba Plena' (d) | NHar |
| - 'Amelia' | GCrs NPar |
| - 'Betty Blake' | GCrs |
| - 'Cameo' | EFEx GCrs MS&S WCot |
| - 'Double Green' | EFEx |
| - double pink (d) | NHar SBla |
| - 'Full Double White' | EFEx |
| - 'Green Hurricane' | EFEx |
| - 'Oscar Schoaf' (d) | NHar |
| - pink | CLAP CRDP EPar GBuc LPio |
| - semi-double white (d) | CLAP CRDP EPar NRya SBla WCot |

## ANEMONOPSIS (Ranunculaceae)

| | |
|---|---|
| *macrophylla* | CBro CRDP ECha GCal GNau IHdy LGre MNrw MTho NLar NTow SMad SSpi WCot WCru WEas WOld |

## ANEMOPAEGMA (Bignoniaceae)

| | |
|---|---|
| *chamberlaynii* | CPIN |

## ANEMOPSIS (Saururaceae)

| | |
|---|---|
| *californica* | CRDP |

## ANETHUM (Apiaceae)

| | |
|---|---|
| *graveolens* | CArn EOHP GPoy LHol MChe MHew MMal SIde WCer WPer WSel WWye |
| - 'Dukat' | CJew CSev ELau GPoy MChe WGwG |
| - 'Fern Leaved' | CBod WJek |
| - 'Sowa' | EOHP |

## ANGELICA (Apiaceae)

| | |
|---|---|
| *acutiloba* | SIgm |
| - JCA via P.Kelaidis | IDac |
| *archangelica* | CArn CGle CSev ECha EEls ELan ELau GAbr GPoy LHol MBri MChe MHew NBid NBro NFai SChu SIde SWat WHbs WOak WOve WPer WWye |
| - 'Corinne Tremaine' | Last listed 1998 |
| ¶ *arguta* | EBee WCot |
| *atropurpurea* | CBot CHad CSpe EBee EGar EWll LGre MLLN MNrw MSal MSte NLar SWat WCHb WElm |
| *curtisii* | See *A. triquinata* |
| *gigas* | More than 30 suppliers |
| ¶ - B&SWJ 4170 | WCru |
| ¶ *grayi* | WCot |
| * *hispanica* | CSpe EBee LLew MLLN NSti SMad SSca WElm WLin |
| *montana* | See *A. sylvestris* |
| *pachycarpa* | CRDP EBee EFou EMan EOHP LPio SDix SIgm SWat WCot |
| *pinnata* | Last listed 1996 |
| ¶ *polymorpha sinensis* | EOHP |

¶ *razulii* — EBee
*saxatilis* — EBee IIve
§ *sylvestris* — CArn CKin EWFC GBar MSal SWat WCHb WGwy WHer
\* - 'Purpurea' — CBos CMea CSpe LHol MHer WCot
*taiwaniana* — EBee NBur SWat
§ *triquinata* — Last listed 1996
'Vicar's Mead' — IBlr

## ANGELONIA (Scrophulariaceae)
*gardneri* — CSpe LHil
sp. — Last listed 1998
'Stella Gem' — LFis LRHS MBEx

## ANIGOZANTHOS (Haemodoraceae)
'Bush Ranger' — Last listed 1998
*flavidus* — CB&S CHan EOHP MBri SOWG WCot
- green — Last listed 1996
- red — SSoC
- yellow — LHil WBrE
*humilis* ♀ — Last listed 1998
*manglesii* ♀ — CTrC MLan WBrE WPer
- 'Bush Dawn' — Last listed 1998
*preissii* — Last listed 1996

## ANISACANTHUS (Acanthaceae)
*wrightii* — Last listed 1998

## ANISODONTEA (Malvaceae)
§ *capensis* — CB&S CBar CChe ELan ERea IBlr LHil LHop MAsh MBEx MBNS NBir NBrk SChu SMrm SOWG SRms SVen WBod WEas
¶ - 'Tara's Pink' — LGre LHop MAsh
*elegans* — CSpe
*huegelii* — See *Alyogyne huegelii*
§ x *hypomadara* — CMHG CSev ECtt NPer SEas SMad
(Sprague) Bates — SRms WPer WRus
§ - hort. — See *A. capensis*
*julii* — MCCP WSan
*malvastroides* — CSev LHil LHop MBEx
*scabrosa* — CAbb CChe EMil SAga SBid

## ANISOTOME (Apiaceae)
*cauticola* — SIgm WLin
*haastii* — SIgm WAbe WLin
*imbricata* — GDra
*latifolia* — Last listed 1997
*pilifera* — Last listed 1998

## ANNONA (Annonaceae)
*cherimola* (F) — CTrG LBlo
*muricata* (F) — LBlo
¶ *reticulata* (F) — WMul
*squamosa* (F) — LBlo

## ANODA (Malvaceae)
*cristata* — Last listed 1996
- 'Opal Cup' — EMon

## ANOIGANTHUS See CYRTANTHUS

## ANOMALESIA See GLADIOLUS

## ANOMATHECA (Iridaceae)
*cruenta* — See *A. laxa*
§ *laxa* — CInt CMHG CVer ECha ELan EPot ERos IMGH LBee LGre MNrw MTho NMen SDix SHel SRms SSpi WAbe WCla WFar WPat WPer WWin

- var. *alba* — ELan EPot ERos LBee LGre MHar MTho NMen SSpi WAbe WBor WWeb
- *alba-maculata* — CPea
- Blue Form — Last listed 1996
- 'Joan Evans' — CElw CNic ELan EPot ERos NMen SRms WAbe
- redspot — Last listed 1998
\* *moisii* — Last listed 1996
*viridis* — CPou LBow MHar MNrw NMGW

## ANOPTERUS (Escalloniaceae)
*glandulosus* — IBlr WCru

## ANREDERA (Basellaceae)
§ *cordifolia* — CPlN CRHN LBow WCot WPer

## ANTENNARIA (Asteraceae)
*aprica* — See *A. parvifolia*
*dioica* — CTri ELan GCHN GPoy MBro NBus SRms WCla WFar WLow WPyg WWye
- 'Alba' — EHoe GAbr NRya WFar
- 'Alex Duguid' — CPlt EHyt GCrs LBee SBla WAbe
- 'Aprica' — See *A. parvifolia*
§ - var. *hyperborea* — LGro SSmi
- 'Minima' — EPot GCrs MBro MPla MWat NBro NHar NMen NNrd SIng WAbe
- 'Nyewoods Variety' — CNic EPot GDra NTow
- red — SIng
♦ - var. *rosea* — See *A. rosea*
\* - 'Rubra' — CTri ECha GAri MBro NMen NNrd SBla SHel SSmi WAbe WHen
- *tomentosa* — See *A. dioica* var. *hyperborea*
*macrophylla* hort. — See *A. microphylla*
§ *microphylla* — EHoe EMNN ESis LGro MBar NHar NHol NLon NMen NRya NWCA SDys SIng SRms SSmi WBea WEas WPat WPer
- 'Plena' (d) — SRms
*neglecta* var. *gaspensis* — SIng
§ *parvifolia* — CLyd CNic CTri ESis GCHN GDra MBar MPla NHar WAbe WCla WMoo WPer
- var. *rosea* — See *A. microphylla*
*plantaginifolia* — WCot
§ *rosea* ♀ — NVic SPlb

## ANTHEMIS (Asteraceae)
*aizoon* — See *Achillea ageratifolia* subsp. *aizoon*
*arvensis* — Last listed 1997
N 'Beauty of Grallagh' — CBre GCal GMac LFis MAvo MHlr NCat NGdn NRoo SHel SOkh WCot WMow
*biebersteinii* — See *A. marschalliana* subsp. *biebersteiniana*
♦ 'Blomit' — See *A. Susanna Mitchell* = 'Blomit'
*carpatica* — CGle GCHN MCCP NBro SIgm
- 'Karpatenschnee' — GMaP
*cretica* — Last listed 1998
§ - subsp. *cretica* — CLyd
- - NS 754 — NWCA
'Eva' — LRHS NCat NDov WEas WOld
*frutescens* — See *Argyranthemum frutescens*
N 'Grallagh Gold' — CGle CHea CLon CMil EBee ECha EGar EMon EOrc EWes LHop MBri MSCN MWat NCat NFla NPer SMrm SRPl WBea WEas WFar WMer WOld
§ *marschalliana* — ECha EPot ESis LBee NOak SSmi SSvw WPer

§ - subsp. *biebersteiniana* CHea
   *montana* See *A. cretica* subsp. *cretica*
   *nobilis* See *Chamaemelum nobile*
   *punctata* subsp. More than 30 suppliers
    *cupaniana* ♀
   - subsp. *cupaniana* 'Nana' EMon NPer
   *rudolphiana* See *A. marschalliana*
   *sachokiana* EBee
   *sancti-johannis* CGle EBee EGar EGoo EMar EWTr
     MBri MGed NArg NOak NPer
     NVic SMad SPer SRms WBea
     WElm WPer
¶ 'Sauce Béarnaise' EMon
§ Susanna Mitchell = EBrP EBre LBre LFis MArl MGrG
   'Blomit' NFla NHaw SAga SBre SMrm
   'Tetworth' CStr EBee ECha ELan EMar EMon
     EPPr GBuc LHop MAvo MMil
     MSte NGdn NLak SChu WFar
   *tinctoria* CArn CGle EBee ELan ELau EMon
     EWFC GMac GPoy LHol MChe
     MHew MMal NEgg NFor NLon
     NPer SIde WAbe WBea WByw
     WJek WOak WWye
   - 'Alba' CGle EBee ECGN ECha EMar
     GCal LFis LGre MAvo NRoo
     NWoo SChu SHar WAbe WHen
     WLRN WPer
* - 'Compacta' EFou EWes SMrm
   - dwarf form LRHS SUsu WCot
   - 'E.C. Buxton' More than 30 suppliers
   - 'Gold Mound' Last listed 1997
   - 'Grallagh Gold' See *A.* 'Grallagh Gold'
   - 'Kelwayi' CGle CHor EAst EBee ECtt EMar
     EWTr GCHN MBNS MTis NBro
     NFai NPer SHel SLon SPer SPla
     SRms WBea WFar WHen WOve
     WPer
   - 'Lemon Maid' EPPr SChu SUsu
♦ - 'Pride of Grallagh' See *A.* 'Beauty of Grallagh'
   - 'Sauce Hollandaise' More than 30 suppliers
¶ - subsp. *tinctoria* NCat
   - 'Wargrave Variety' More than 30 suppliers
   *triumfettii* NPer
   *tuberculata* NChi NRoo SBla SIng

## ANTHERICUM (Anthericaceae)
   *algeriense* See *A. liliago* var. *major*
   *baeticum* EBee ERos
* *bovei* Last listed 1998
* *fistulosum* EBee
   *liliago* More than 30 suppliers
§ - var. *major* ♀ CAvo EBee ECha GDra IBlr LGre
     SSpi WCot
   *ramosum* CAvo EBee ECGN ECha ELan
     EMan EPot ERos EWes GBin GDra
     LGre MBrN MBro MLLN NBid
     NBir NWCA SHel SIng SMrm
     SWas WAbe WCla WCot WPer
   - JCA 166.300 WLin
   - *plumosum* See *Trichopetalum plumosum*
¶ *saundersiae* WCot

## ANTHOCERCIS (Solanaceae)
   *littorea* Last listed 1998

## ANTHOLYZA (Iridaceae)
   *coccinea* See *Crocosmia paniculata*
   *crocosmioides* See *Crocosmia latifolia*
   *paniculata* See *Crocosmia paniculata*
¶ *ringens* CPLG

## ANTHOXANTHUM (Poaceae)
   *odoratum* CArn CJew CKin GBar GPoy

## ANTHRISCUS (Apiaceae)
   *cerefolium* CArn CJew CSev EOHP GPoy ILis
     LHol MChe MHew MMal SIde
     SLod WGwG WHbs WJek WOak
     WPer WSel WWye
   - 'D'Hiver de Bruxelles' Last listed 1998
   *sylvestris* Last listed 1997
¶ - 'Broadleas Blush' CNat
   - 'Hullavington' (v) CNat
   - 'Moonlit Night' EHoe
   - 'Ravenswing' More than 30 suppliers

## ANTHURIUM (Araceae)
   *amazonicum* MBri
   *andraeanum* MBri
   - 'Acropolis' MBri
   - 'Rose' See *A.* x *ferrierense* 'Roseum'
   *cordatum* See *A. leuconeurum*
   'Flamingo' MBri
   *scherzerianum* MBri
   - 'Rosemarie' MBri

## ANTHYLLIS (Papilionaceae)
   *cytisoides* Last listed 1998
   *hermanniae* CHan WAbe
   - 'Compacta' See *A. hermanniae* 'Minor'
§ - 'Minor' EPot NMen NSla SBla WLin
   *montana* ELan
   - subsp. *atropurpurea* LRHS
   - 'Rubra' ♀ CInt ECho EGle EPot LBee NFor
     NMen WWin
   - 'Rubra Compacta' Last listed 1996
   *vulneraria* CFee CGen CKin CMil EWFC
     GTou MChe MWat NMir NPri
     SSpi SUsu WBea WCla WHer WPer
   - var. *coccinea* CLyd CMil CNic CSpe EBee EGar
     EMar MBro MNrw MSCN MSte
     MTho NMen NSla NTow NWCA
     SUsu WAbe WBea WCom WElm
   - var. *iberica* CHan
* - 'Peach' CSpe

## ANTIGONON (Polygonaceae)
   *leptopus* CPIN LChe
   - 'Album' CPIN

## ANTIRRHINUM (Scrophulariaceae)
   *asarina* See *Asarina procumbens*
   *barrellieri* Last listed 1996
   *braun-blanquetii* CNic CPea EBee EMan GGar LRot
     MCAu MLLN MOne SAga WCot
     WWin
   'Bridesmaid' MBEx
   'Deep Pink' MBEx
   *glutinosum* See *A. hispanicum* subsp.
     *hispanicum*
§ *hispanicum* CGle NBir SBla WCla
   - 'Avalanche' CHal EMan MBEx MLan SCoo
     WLRN
§ - subsp. *hispanicum* CMea CSam CSpe CVer EDAr
    *roseum* ELan NTow WKif WOld
   *majus* 'Black Prince' CHad SAga
   - subsp. *linkianum* WOld
   - subsp. *majus* EWll
   - 'Taff's White' (v) CSpe EHol LGre SAga
   *molle* CHan CSpe EBee EHyt ELan EOrc
     GCal MSte MTho NBir NPer
     NWCA SRCN SUsu WCru WPyg

| | |
|---|---|
| - pink | CLyd CSWP EOrc GCal MSte MTho SOkh WCru |
| ¶ 'Pink Candelabra' | LFis |
| 'Powys Pride' (v) | EWll SAga WHer WSan |
| *pulverulentum* | CSam ESis LGre LHop MArl WKif |
| *sempervirens* | ESis SBla SOkh WAbe WPat |
| *siculum* | EBee |
| 'Starlight' | MBEx |
| 'Sugar Buttons' | MBEx |
| 'Summer Eyes' | MBEx |
| ¶ 'Torbay Rock' | EWll |
| 'White Monarch' | Last listed 1997 |

## APHANES (Rosaceae)
| | |
|---|---|
| § *arvensis* | MSal WWye |

## APHELANDRA (Acanthaceae)
| | |
|---|---|
| *alexandri* | Last listed 1997 |
| *squarrosa* | CHal MBri |
| - 'Dania' (v) | MBri |

## APHYLLANTHES (Aphyllanthaceae)
| | |
|---|---|
| *monspeliensis* | CFee ECho SBla |

## APIOS (Papilionaceae)
| | |
|---|---|
| § *americana* | CHan CPlN EMon LEdu WCot WCru WSHC |
| *tuberosa* | See *A. americana* |

## APIUM (Apiaceae)
| | |
|---|---|
| *graveolens* | CArn CBod ELau EOHP EWFC GPoy Ilve MHer MSal SIde WJek |
| ¶ - (Secalinum Group) 'Zwolsche Krul' | MMal |
| *nodiflorum* | Last listed 1997 |
| *prostratum* | Last listed 1997 |

## APOCYNUM (Apocynaceae)
| | |
|---|---|
| *androsaemifolium* | Last listed 1998 |
| *cannabinum* | CArn GPoy MSal WWye |

## APONOGETON (Aponogetonaceae)
| | |
|---|---|
| *distachyos* | CBen CRDP CRow CWat EHon ELan EMFW LPBA MBal MSta NDea SLon SWat SWyc WWeb |
| *krausseanus* | See *A. desertorum* |

## APTENIA (Aizoaceae)
| | |
|---|---|
| *cordifolia* | CSev NPer SChr SEND WRos |
| - 'Variegata' | LHil MRav SHFr |

## AQUILEGIA ✿ (Ranunculaceae)
| | |
|---|---|
| *akitensis* hort. | See *A. flabellata, flabellata* var. *pumila* |
| ¶ 'Alaska' | LEur |
| * *alba variegata* | WEas |
| *alpina* | CBot CMea EBee ECtt ELan ELau EWTr GAbr GCHN GTou LEur LSyl MLan MSCN MWll NFor SPer SRPl SRms WCla WFar WHen WOve WPer WStl WWin |
| - 'Alba' | CBlo ELan LEur MLLN MWll NLon NOak |
| ¶ - 'Carl Ziepke' | LEur |
| - German form | Last listed 1996 |
| - 'Hensol Harebell' | See *A.* 'Hensol Harebell' |
| 'Alpine Blue' | Last listed 1998 |
| *amaliae* | See *A. ottonis* subsp. *amaliae* |
| * *anemoniflora* | NEgg |
| *aragonensis* | See *A. pyrenaica* |
| § *atrata* | CGle CPou EBee EGar EMan GCHN GSki LEur NOak SRms WPer WRos |

| | |
|---|---|
| *atrovinosa* | GNau LEur |
| *aurea* Janka | CLTr EBee LEur |
| - misapplied | See *A. vulgaris* golden-leaved |
| *baicalensis* | See *A. vulgaris* Baicalensis Group |
| 'Ballerina' | CMil EBee GMac MLLN NCut NFai WHer |
| *barnebyi* | CMea CMil CPou EBee EHyt GAbr GBin LEur MLLN NSti NWCA SIgm |
| *bernardii* | NOak |
| *bertolonii* ♀ | CFee CGle EHyt EMNN GCrs GTou LEur LHop MBro NHar NMen NOak NRoo SBla SRms SSmi WHoo WPat WPyg |
| - *alba* | LEur NWCA |
| Biedermeier Group | CM&M EMil GAbr LPVe MBNS NOrc SRob WPer |
| 'Blue Berry' | CMHG EBee MBro NHar WLin WPat |
| 'Blue Bonnet' | CM&M CMGP EGar |
| 'Blue Jay' (Songbird Series) | CFai LEur NPri |
| 'Blue Jewel' | Last listed 1998 |
| § 'Blue Star' (Star Series) | EBee ECtt EFou ERic GCHN WElm WPer |
| ¶ 'Branching Red' | LEur |
| *brevicalcarata* | CHar CMil EBee GBin LEur NPri |
| *buergeriana* | CLTr CPou EBee GAbr GBin GGar LEur MCCP WPer |
| - f. *flavescens* | NLak |
| - var. *oxysepala* | See *A. oxysepala* |
| ¶ 'Bunting' (Songbird Series) | LEur NRoo |
| *canadensis* ♀ | CFri CGle CMHG EBee ECGN EHyt ELan GSki LEur MBal MLLN NBir NBro NOak NSti SRms WCru WOve WPer |
| - 'Corbett' | GBuc WHil |
| - 'Nana' | CInt EHal GAri MHar MSte |
| 'Cardinal' (Songbird Series) | CFai LEur NRoo |
| *cazorlensis* | See *A. pyrenaica* subsp. *cazorlensis* |
| 'Celestial Blue' | ELan |
| *chaplinei* | EBee EPot LEur |
| *chrysantha* | CFri CHea EBrP EBre ECGN EWTr GAbr GBin GCHN LBre LEur MHlr MLLN NBus NHar NOak NPri SBre SChu SPla SRms WBrE WCot WCru WOve WPer WRus |
| - var. *chaplinei* | CBot NBir |
| ¶ - 'Flore Pleno' (d) | EBee EWTr LEur |
| - 'Yellow Queen' | CSpe EBee EFou EPfP LEur NCut SSvw WElm WHil |
| *clematiflora* | See *A. vulgaris* var. *stellata* |
| *coerulea* ♀ | CGle EMan EWTr GAbr GCHN NCat SIgm SRms |
| ¶ - ex RMRP 940134 | LEur |
| - 'Mrs Nicholls' | EPar MBri WMer |
| - var. *ochroleuca* | GCHN |
| - var. *pinetorum* | Last listed 1997 |
| ¶ 'Colorado' (Swan Series) | EMar LEur |
| 'Cream Edge' | Last listed 1998 |
| 'Crimson Star' | CBlo CHea CLTr EBrP EBre EOld EPfP EWTr LBre LEur MLLN NBus SBre SPer SVil |
| *desertorum* | ESis LEur NTow |
| *discolor* | CMea GSki GTou LEur LHop MBro NHed NMen NRoo NWCA SUsu WPat |
| 'Dorothy' | LCTD LHop |
| 'Double Chocolate' | Last listed 1998 |
| 'Double Quilled Purple' | CMil |
| Double Rubies (d) | SCro |
| § 'Dove' (Songbird Series) | CFai EWll LCTD LEur NArg NRoo SWat |

I 'Dragonfly' CB&S CM&M EPfP GAbr GAri GMaP LNor MBri NMir NOak WFar WPer
¶ 'Dwarf Fairyland' NArg
'Eastgrove' WEas
*ecalcarata* See *Semiaquilegia ecalcarata*
*einseleana* GSki LEur WHer
*elegantula* GAbr LEur
 – JJA 11390 Last listed 1998
*eximia* SBla
¶ 'Firecracker' LEur
'Firewheel' CMil LRot MAvo NCut NFai WUnu
§ *flabellata* ♀ CGle CMil CTri GAri GCHN GGar LEur MBro NMen WPat WPer
§ – f.*alba* CBot CTri ELan EPla GCHN GGar LEur NWCA SRms WEas
 – 'Blue Angel' CB&S LEur WPer WWeb
¶ – Cameo Series NRoo WRos
 – Cameo Series mixed EWll
¶ – 'Cameo Blue and White' NCut NLar
  (Cameo Series)
¶ – 'Cameo Blue' LEur
  (Cameo Series)
¶ – 'Cameo Blush' NCut
  (Cameo Series)
¶ – 'Cameo Pink and White' NCut NLar
  (Cameo Series)
¶ – 'Cameo Pink' LEur
  (Cameo Series)
¶ – 'Cameo White' LEur NCut
  (Cameo Series)
 – double white (d) Last listed 1996
 – 'Jewel' ECho WHil
 – 'Ministar' CHor CM&M ESis GSki LEur MBNS MBro MRav NMir NOak NRoo NVic SRms SRot SSpe WFar WHil WHoo WPer WPyg WWin
 – 'Nana Alba' See *A. flabellata* var. *pumila* f. *alba*
§ – var.*pumila* ♀ ECha EHyt EPot GAbr GDra GTou LEur LHop MBal MTho NNrd NOak NRoo SBla SIng SRms WAbe WCla WCru WFar WPer
§ – – f.*alba* ♀ CBot CGle ECha ESis GAbr GDra LEur LHop MBNS MBal MSte NBus NRoo SIng SRms WCru WWin
¶ – – 'Flora Pleno' WLin
 – – f.*kurilensis* CGle GDra MSte WCla
 – – 'Silver Edge' CMil CPla MNrw NFai NLar NPro WBea WCot WPrP
* – – 'Snowflakes' Last listed 1997
 – soft pink LEur
* – 'White Angel' MLan NHol NPro WPer WWeb
*flavescens* SIgm WPer
 – var. *miniana* IDac
§ – var. *rubicunda* EBee
*formosa* CBot CLon EWTr GCHN GGar NChi NPri NRoo NWCA SBla SIng WCru WHoo WLin WPer
¶ – ex NNS 9343 LEur
¶ – var. *formosa* LEur
 – x *longissima* Last listed 1996
¶ – var. *pauciflora* LEur
¶ – var. *truncata* CGle CRDP EBee GBuc LEur MLLN WCru
 – var. *wawawensis* IDac LEur
  RMRP 950136
§ *fragrans* CArn CFri CGle CHar CInt CPou EBee ECGN EHyt GAbr GBin GCHN GCrs LEur LSyl MBro MCLN MLLN MTho NLak NOak NSti NWes SIng STes WHoo WMaN WOve WRha WWat

* – 'Alba' WPat
 – ex CC&MR 96 Last listed 1997
 – ex KBE 48 Last listed 1997
¶ – white LEur
*glandulosa* CMHG EBee ITim LEur NRoo SUsu WEas
*glauca* See *A. fragrans*
§ 'Goldfinch' (Songbird Series) CBot EWll LEur NRoo
'Graeme's Green' NFai
*grata* EWll GCHN LEur LGre NBur SChu WCot WPGP
§ 'Hensol Harebell' ♀ CGle CPou CSWP EBee LEur MBro NBus SPer SRms SSpe WHoo WPyg
*hinckleyana* See *A. chrysantha* var. *hinckleyana*
*hirsutissima* See *A. viscosa* subsp. *hirsutissima*
¶ 'Ice Blue' WPrP
'Irish Elegance' EGoo
*japonica* See *A. flabellata* var. *pumila*
Jewel hybrids CSpe EMNN NRoo WPer
*jonesii* LEur
 – x *saximontana* Last listed 1998
*karelinii* Last listed 1996
*kitaibelii* EBee LEur
'Koralle' CLTr GBin LEur
'Kristall' EPri LEur MWll NOak STes WHil WMer WPen
*kuhistanica* Last listed 1998
*kurdistanica* Last listed 1996
*laramiensis* CGra CLyd CPBP EBee EPot LEur NWCA WAbe
* 'Lavender and White' CFai
  (Songbird Series)
*longissima* CBel CGle CHar CMea CSam ECGN EHic GAbr GBri GBuc LCTD LEur LSyl MBro MLLN MTho SBla SMac WCla WEas WHoo WLin
 – 'Alba' WEas
¶ long-spurred hybrid, white LEur
¶ 'Lovebird' LEur
Lowdham strain Last listed 1996
'Magpie' CLTr CM&M CSam CSpe EWll NBir NOak SChu WCot
x *maruyamana* Last listed 1996
'Maxi Star' Last listed 1996
McKana Group EAst EBrP EBre ELan ENot GAbr GCHN GMaP LBre LHop MAvo NFor NGdn NLon NOak NRoo NVic SBre SPer SPlb SRms WBea WPer
*melange pygmaea* Last listed 1997
* 'Mellow Yellow' CHan CKel CPla ECGP GBuc LEur MBNS MLLN MSCN MWll NCut SIgm WBea WPer WPrP WViv
*micrantha* ESis GCHN LEur
aff. *micrantha* Last listed 1998
  JCA 1.061.350
*microphylla* Last listed 1996
*moorcroftiana* CPou NLak
 – CC 1371 CPLG MRPP
 – CC 1414 Last listed 1997
Mrs Scott-Elliot hybrids CBlo EHol EMan EWTr GAbr LEur LIck LNor MBri MLan SLon SPer WFar
Music Series ♀ CHor NOak SMrm SRms WByw
¶ 'Music Pink and White' LEur
  (Music Series)
¶ 'Music Red and White' LEur
  (Music Series)

'Music White' (Music Series) LEur
*nevadensis* — See *A. vulgaris* subsp. *nevadensis*
*nigricans* — See *A. atrata*
*nivalis* — CPBP LEur SBla
¶ 'Nuthatch' (Songbird Series) EMar
¶ 'Olympia' red and gold — LEur
§ *olympica* — EBee EMan EWes GAbr LEur LGre MLLN WCot WPer
'Orange Flaming Red' — LHop
*ottonis* — LEur LHop
§ - subsp. *amaliae* — SSca WLin
§ *oxysepala* — CBos CGle CMil EBee EWll GCal GMac LEur NBus NSti SAga SMac WLin
'Petticoats' — NFla
'Phyll's Bonnet' — GCal
'Pink Bonnet' — GCal
'Pink Jewel' — CMHG
*pubescens* — EBee LEur WLin
*pubiflora* — GCHN
- CC&MR 96 — WLin
¶ 'Purple Emperor' — WWeb
§ *pyrenaica* — CLTr CTri EBee LEur NHar NTow WCla
§ - subsp. *cazorlensis* — GCHN
'Quilled Violets' — CMil NWes
'Red Hobbit' — CB&S CSpe GBin LEur NOrc WWeb
§ 'Red Star' (Star Series) — EBee ECtt EFou ERic GCHN LEur NBus NOak WHil WMow WPer WRus
¶ 'Redwing' — LEur
§ 'Robin' (Songbird Series) — CBot CFai LCTD LEur NArg NPri NRoo SWat
*rockii* — GAbr SHut
- CLD 0437 — Last listed 1997
- KGB 176 — Last listed 1997
'Roman Bronze' — CPla EAst EBee EMan GBin LEur MCCP MCLN MLLN MWrn NCut NOak NPro SPla STes WUnu WViv WWhi
* 'Rose Red' — Last listed 1997
♦ *rubicunda* — See *A. flavescens* var. *rubicunda*
*saximontana* — EHyt GCHN GTou LEur NMen NWCA
§ 'Schneekönigin' — ELan GCHN LEur MTis NOak NWes WHen WPer WViv
*scopulorum* — CLyd EBee LEur NWCA
- subsp. *perplexans* — Last listed 1998
* *secundiflora* — Last listed 1998
*shockleyi* — CPou EBee GBuc LEur MLan NTow NWCA SIng
*sibirica* — EBee LEur WPer
'Silver Queen' — WRus
¶ 'Simone's White' — EBee LEur
*skinneri* — CBel CMil GAbr GBin GSki IHdy LEur LGre MCLN NBus NLak NRya SCro STes WBea WCru WHil WPrP WRha
Snow Queen — See *A.* 'Schneekönigin'
Songbird Series — MLLN NPri SWat WLRN
¶ sp. CDC&C 253 from Korea — LEur
sp. from Zigana Pass, Turkey — Last listed 1996
*stellata* — See *A. vulgaris* var. *stellata*
'Stoulton Blue' — WSPU
'Sunburst Ruby' — CHar CMil CPla LEur MAvo MCCP MWrn NOak NPro WPrP
'Sweet Lemon Drops' — CPla
¶ 'Sweet Surprise' — NCut
*thalictrifolia* — CLTr GBuc LEur LGre SBla WCot

- JCA 174.400 — NHol WCot WLin
*transsilvanica* — Last listed 1998
*triternata* — CMil LEur NCut NWCA SIgm
*turczaninovii* — LEur
*viridiflora* — CBot CGle CHar CMea CRDP CStr CTri EBee EHyt ELan EWTr GBuc GCHN LEur MTho NHar NHol NRoo NSti NTow SBea SBla SMac SMad WCot WEas WFar WPat WPer
*vulgaris* — CArn CMHG EWTr GAbr GPoy LEur LHol LLWP MCAu MChe MHew MMal NBro SPlb WGwG WMow WOak WPer WShi WWye
- 'Adelaide Addison' — CGle CPlt ECha ELan GBri GBuc MAvo NFai NWes SWas WEas WFar WMer WRha WViv WWeb
- var. *alba* — CArn CLTr CMea EMan LLWP MCAu SEND WByw
- 'Anne Calder' — Last listed 1996
- 'Aureovariegata' — See *A. vulgaris* Vervaeneana Group
§ - Baicalensis Group — GCHN NRya
- 'Blue Star' — See *A.* 'Blue Star' (Star Series)
* - 'Cap de Rossiter' — CRow
- 'Christa Barlow' — CB&S
- *clematiflora* — See *A. vulgaris* var. *stellata*
¶ - 'Dorothy Rose' — LEur
- 'Double Pleat' (d) — WHer
- 'Double Pleat' blue/white — EBee EWll WHil WPer
- 'Double Pleat' pink/white — EBee WHil WPer
- 'Dove' — See *A.* 'Dove' (Songbird Series)
- var. *flore-pleno* (d) — CLTr EHic LLWP WByw WHen WPer
- - black (d) — WCot
- - blue — WCot
- - 'Burgundy' (d) — CMil
- - pale blue — NSti
- - pink — GGar
- - 'Powder Blue' — Last listed 1998
- - purple (d) — Last listed 1997
- - red (d) — GGar
- - white (d) — GAbr LGre NOak SWas
- from Brno, Czech Republic — Last listed 1996
- from Rize, Turkey — Last listed 1996
- 'Gisela Powell' — Last listed 1996
- 'Gold Finch' — See *A.* 'Goldfinch' (Songbird Series)
§ - golden-leaved — CMea ECho
- 'Grandmother's Garden' — EWll LRHS
- 'Granny's Gold' — CMHG LRHS MBri
- 'Heidi' — CBot EBee EWll LEur NCut NEgg SVil WPer
- f. *inversa* — LEur
- 'Jane Hollow' — CMil CPou CRow EBee MLLN NCut
- 'Magda' — WRha
- 'Magpie' — See *A. vulgaris* 'William Guiness'
- 'Michael Strominger' — LEur MNrw WPer
- 'Miss Coventry' — Last listed 1997
- 'Mrs Fincham' — LEur
- Munstead White — See *A. vulgaris* 'Nivea'
§ - 'Nivea' ♀ — CBel CBot CGle CHad CMil CPou CSam EAst ECha ELan GAbr LEur MBro MCLN MNrw NChi NFai NRoo SBla WCla WHoo
- Olympica Group — See *A. olympica*
- 'Patricia Zavros' — Last listed 1998
- 'Pink Spurless' — See *A. vulgaris* var. *stellata* pink
¶ - 'Pink Storm' — MNrw
- Pom Pom Series — CMil MCCP

| | |
|---|---|
| - 'Pom Pom Crimson' | CMil NBro WCot WPrP |
| (Pom Pom Series) | |
| - 'Pom Pom Rose' | Last listed 1998 |
| (Pom Pom Series) | |
| - 'Pom Pom Violet' | CMil NCut WPrP |
| (Pom Pom Series) | |
| - 'Pom Pom White' | CLTr |
| (Pom Pom Series) | |
| - 'Primivera' | CFri |
| ¶ - 'Purple Emperor' | MBri |
| - 'Red Star' | See A. 'Red Star' (Star Series) |
| - 'Robin' | See A. 'Robin' (Songbird Series) |
| - 'Rose Barlow' | GCal SVil WHen WViv |
| - 'Ruth Steer' | Last listed 1996 |
| - scented | Last listed 1998 |
| - 'Silver Edge' | ELan GBri WBea |
| - 'Slaty Grey' | LEur |
| - 'Snowdust' | EHoe |
| § - var. stellata | CGle CHid EBee ELan GCHN GMaP LEur MBNS MTis NBro NFai NRoo WCot WPer WWat WWin |
| ¶ - - 'Belhaven Blue' | EGoo |
| - - 'Bicolor Barlow' (d) | GCal WViv |
| - - 'Black Barlow' (d) | CHad EGoo EWll GCal GMaP LRot NCut NOrc SCro WViv WWeb |
| - - 'Blue Barlow' (d) | GCal GMaP NCut SPla SUsu SVil WPer WPrP WViv |
| - - double | Last listed 1998 |
| - - double blue | CMil |
| ¶ - - 'Firewheel' | LEur |
| ¶ - - 'Green Barlow' | WViv |
| - - 'Greenapples' | CFri CLTr CMil EBee LEur LHop MAvo MCCP MLLN NPro NRya NSti SMac WCot WHen WHer WPrP |
| ¶ - - 'Iceberg' | CMil LEur MAvo NPro WPrP |
| - - 'Melton Rapids' | EWll WBea |
| - - 'Nora Barlow' (d) ♀ | More than 30 suppliers |
| § - - pink | GBin LEur NSti |
| ¶ - - purple | LEur |
| - - red | LLWP |
| - - 'Royal Purple' | CMil MAvo MWrn NBro STes WPrP |
| - - 'Ruby Port' | CM&M CMGP EHic EMan GCal GMac LEur LGre MBri MCLN MNrw MTis NBus NChi SLod SRCN WHen WRus WWhi |
| - - 'Sunlight White' | EWll LEur SWat WMaN WPer |
| § - - white | CGle CLTr CMil GCHN LEur LHop NBro WFar WHal |
| - 'Strawberry Ice Cream' | EBee GBri MUlv NBro NCut WElm |
| - tall form | Last listed 1996 |
| - 'The Bride' | CBlo EBee LEur MBro |
| - variegated foliage | See A. vulgaris Vervaeneana Group |
| - Vervaeneana Group (v) | More than 30 suppliers |
| - - double white (d) | CHad |
| - - 'Graeme Iddon' | GBuc LGre MBri MLLN NBrk NFai NMGW |
| - - 'Woodside' | See A. vulgaris Vervaeneana Group |
| - - 'Woodside Blue' | EGoo NCut |
| ¶ - - 'Woodside White' | NBir NCut |
| - 'Warwick' | Last listed 1996 |
| - 'Westfaeld' | MNrw MTed NDov NOak |
| - 'White Barlow' | GCal SCro WViv |
| * - 'White Bonnets' | SRos |
| - 'White Spurless' | See A. vulgaris var. stellata white |
| - 'White Star' | See A. 'White Star' (Star Series) |
| § - 'William Guiness' | More than 30 suppliers |

| | |
|---|---|
| ¶ - 'William Guiness Doubles' | MCCP |
| - 'Wishy Washy' | Last listed 1998 |
| white | Last listed 1998 |
| § 'White Star' (Star Series) | EBee ECtt EFou ERic EWTr GAbr GCHN LEur LSyl NBus SPer WHil WPer |
| ¶ 'White Swan' | CMil LEur |
| yabeana | CHid GBin LEur WPrP |
| 'Yellow Star' (Star Series) | LEur |

## ARABIS (Brassicaceae)

| | |
|---|---|
| albida | See A. alpina subsp. caucasica |
| alpina | CB&S SPlb |
| § - subsp. caucasica | WFar |
| - - 'Corfe Castle' | Last listed 1997 |
| § - - 'Flore Pleno' (d) ♀ | CHad CHan CTri ECha ECtt ELan EOrc GAbr LGro LHop MFir MTho NChi NFla NRoo NVic SBod SRms WByw WCot WEas WFar WWin |
| ¶ - - 'Gillian Sharman' (v) | NCat |
| - - 'Goldsplash' (v) | Last listed 1998 |
| - - 'Pink Pearl' | NPri WFar |
| - - 'Pinkie' | EMNN |
| * - - rosea | CHal MRav NBir SRms WFar WMoo |
| § - - 'Schneehaube' ♀ | CHor ECtt EMNN MBNS MBar NMir NOrc NRoo SRms WLRN WPer |
| - - 'Snow White' | Last listed 1996 |
| - - Snowcap | See A. alpina subsp. caucasica 'Schneehaube' |
| - - 'Snowdrop' | MRav NPri SMer WFar |
| - - 'Variegata' | CBot ECha EGoo EHoe ELan EPot ERic LBee LHop MBri MTho NFor NLon NRoo NVic SRms WByw WCot WEas WFar WPat WWin |
| androsacea | EPot GTou MRPP NTow WLRN |
| x arendsii 'Compinkie' | ECtt NRoo SRms WLRN |
| - 'La Fraicheur' | Last listed 1997 |
| - 'Rosabella' (v) | ECha LHop MBNS |
| - 'Rose Frost' | Last listed 1997 |
| aubrietoides | CLyd |
| blepharophylla | EPfP GAbr MWat NTow WCot |
| § - 'Frühlingszauber' ♀ | CB&S CInt CPea CTri GDra LPVe MOne MWat NNrd SIde SRms WFar WGor WGwG |
| - Spring Charm | See A. blepharophylla 'Frühlingszauber' |
| bryoides | EPot GTou LBee MDHE NTow |
| - olympica | Last listed 1997 |
| caucasica | See A. alpina subsp. caucasica |
| * 'Cloth of Gold' | Last listed 1997 |
| ¶ collina subsp. rosea | WUnu |
| cypria | Last listed 1998 |
| ferdinandi-coburgi | EGar EPot MGed MPla MRav NBro NBus SRms WCla WEas WWin |
| - 'Aureovariegata' | CTri EHoe LGro NLon |
| - 'Old Gold' | CNic EPot ESis LBee LHop MBar MPla MRav NEgg NHar NNrd NRoo NVic SBla SChu SHel SRms SSmi WCla WEas WFar WHoo WMoo WPat WWin |
| - 'Variegata' | See A. procurrens 'Variegata' |
| glabra | WPer |
| x kellereri | NMen NTow |
| microphylla | Last listed 1996 |
| muralis | See A. collina |
| 'Pink Snow' | Last listed 1996 |

§ *procurrens* 'Variegata' ♀ — ECha ELan ESis EWes GTou LBee LHop MBal MBar MTho MWat NFor NHar NHol NRoo NWCA SBla SHFr SHel SPlb SRms SSmi WCla WFar

*rosea* — See *A. collina*

§ *scabra* — CNat

Snow Cap — See *A. alpina* subsp. *caucasica* 'Schneehaube'

*soyeri* — Last listed 1996

- subsp. *jacquinii* — See *A. soyeri* subsp. *coriacea*

¶ sp. double white — CFee

*stricta* — See *A. scabra*

x *sturii* — NTow

x *suendermannii* — Last listed 1998

## ARACHNIODES (Dryopteridaceae)

*aristata* — WRic

*simplicior* — NMar WCot WRic

- C&L 236 — Last listed 1996

*standishii* — Last listed 1997

## ARAIOSTEGIA (Davalliaceae)

*pseudocystopteris* — SSpi

## ARALIA ✿ (Araliaceae)

*armata* B&SWJ 3137 — WCru

*bipinnata* — CFil WPGP

*cachemirica* — CHad EBee EWes GCal MBro NLar SDix WHoo WTin

*californica* — GCal GPoy LGre MSal NLar SIgm SLon SMrm

*chinensis* hort. — See *A. elata*

- L. — CB&S CMCN CSam MBNS MSal SRCN

*continentalis* — CHan GCal

- CC 1035 — Last listed 1997

*cordata* — CPle EBee EWes GAbr GCal NLar

*decaisneana* B&SWJ 3588 — WCru

¶ - CC 1925 — CPLG

§ *elata* ♀ — CBrm CDoC CDul CLnd CPle EBee ELan ENot EOas GChr IOrc LEdu LNet LPan MBal MBlu NBea NBee NFla NFor SArc SEas SPer SSpi WDin WNor WPGP WPic

- 'Albomarginata' — See *A. elata* 'Variegata'

- 'Aureovariegata' — CB&S CDoC ELan ENot IOrc LNet MBri WDin WPyg

- 'Silver Umbrella' — Last listed 1996

§ - 'Variegata' ♀ — CB&S CBot CDoC EMil ENot IOrc LNet MBlu MBri NBea NMoo SMad SRPl WDin WPat WPyg

¶ *nudicaulis* — EBee

*racemosa* — EBee ELau GCal GPoy LEdu MLLN MNrw MSal MSte NLar SRms

*sieboldii* de Vriese — See *Fatsia japonica*

*spinosa* — WHer

## ARAUCARIA (Araucariaceae)

*angustifolia* — Last listed 1998

§ *araucana* — More than 30 suppliers

*cookii* — See *A. columnaris*

♦ *excelsa* (Lamb.) R. Br. — See *A. columnaris*

♦ - hort. — See *A. heterophylla*

§ *heterophylla* ♀ — MBri WNor

*imbricata* — See *A. araucana*

## ARAUJIA (Asclepiadaceae)

*grandiflora* — Last listed 1998

*graveolens* — CPIN

*sericifera* — CB&S CFri CMHG CMac CPIN CRHN EMil ERea GQui MGos SLon SSpi WSHC

## ARBUTUS ✿ (Ericaceae)

*andrachne* — CDul CFil ISea SSpi

x *andrachnoides* ♀ — CAbP CB&S CFil CGre CMHG CPMA ELan IOrc LHop LNet LPan MBal SAPC SArc SBid SBrw SPer SReu SSpi SSta WHCG WPGP WWat WWeb

*canariensis* — Last listed 1998

*glandulosa* — See *Arctostaphylos glandulosa*

'Marina' — CAbP CFil CPMA CRos ELan MAsh SBid SMad SReu SSpi SSta WPGP WPat WWeb

*menziesii* ♀ — CFil CMCN CPMA EPfP EWes LNet MBal SLon SMad SSpi WPGP WWat

- NJM 94046 — Last listed 1998

*unedo* ♀ — More than 30 suppliers

- 'Compacta' — CB&S CBlo CDoC EBrP EBre LBre LPan MAsh MGos SBre

- 'Elfin King' — LRHS SSpi SSta

- 'Quercifolia' — MBal SSta WPat WPyg

- f. *rubra* ♀ — CB&S CBlo CDoC CMHG EBee EBrP EBre EHal ELan IOrc LBre LHop LNet MBal MBri MGos MHlr SBre SBrw SPar SPer SReu SSpi SSta WBod WFar WPat WPyg

*xalapensis* — Last listed 1997

## ARCHONTOPHOENIX (Arecaceae)

*alexandrae* — CRoM LPal

*cunninghamiana* ♀ — CBrP CRoM LPal

## ARCTANTHEMUM (Asteraceae)

§ *arcticum* — EFou MSte NBrk

¶ - 'Roseum' — EFou

- 'Schwefelglanz' — EFou WCot

## ARCTERICA See PIERIS

## ARCTIUM (Asteraceae)

*lappa* — CArn CKin GPoy IIve MChe MSal NHex SIde WHer

*minus* — CKin EWFC MSal

*pubens* — CKin

¶ *tomentosum* — IIve

## ARCTOSTAPHYLOS (Ericaceae)

* *californica* — MBal

§ *glandulosa* — SArc

*manzanita* — Last listed 1998

x *media* 'Snow Camp' — MBal

- 'Wood's Red' — GEil MBal MBar MGos SBrw WFar

*myrtifolia* — GAri MBar

*nevadensis* — MBal MBar SReu SSta

* - var. *coloradensis* — Last listed 1997

*nummularia* — MBal

*patula* — SMad

*stanfordiana* C&H 105 — GGGa

*uva-ursi* — CArn EBee ENot GPoy IOrc MBal MBar MGos MPla NFor SBod SBrw SEas SLon SPer SSta WBod WGer

- 'Massachusetts' — ELan GQui LRHS MAsh SMur SReu SSta

- 'Point Reyes' — SBrw SSto

- 'Snowcap' — MAsh

- 'Vancouver Jade' — CDoC CEnd EPfP GChr MAsh MBar MGos NHol SBrw SReu SSta

* - 'Variegata' — Last listed 1998

**ARCTOTIS** (Asteraceae)
*grandiflora*                  Last listed 1996
x **hybrida** 'African Sunrise' MBEx
   - 'Apricot'                  LHop MBEx MSte SMer SMrm
                               WEas
   - 'Bacchus'                  MBEx
   - 'China Rose'               SMrm SUsu
   - 'Flame' ♀                  CBar CHad CPlt CSpe LHop MBEx
                               MLan MSte NPla SAga SChu SMrm
                               SUsu WEas
¶  - 'Harlequin'               CBrm
   - 'Irene'                    Last listed 1996
*  - 'Mahogany' ♀              MSte SMrm SUsu
   - 'Midday Sun'               Last listed 1997
   - orange                     Last listed 1996
   - 'Pink'                     SChu
*  - 'Raspberry'               Last listed 1998
   - 'Red Devil'                SMrm WLRN
   - 'Red Magic' ♀             MBEx
   - 'Rosita'                   MBEx
   - 'Tangerine'                Last listed 1997
   - 'Terracotta'               MSte
   - 'Torch'                    MBEx
¶  - white                     EWTr
   - 'Wine'                     CBar EWTr LHop MBEx MSte
                               WEas WLRN
   - 'Yellow'                   MBEx
   'Prostrate Raspberry'        Last listed 1997

**ARDISIA** (Myrsinaceae)
*crenata*                      MBri
¶ **maclurei** B&SWJ 3772      WCru

**ARECA** (Arecaceae)
*catechu*                      MBri
*concinna*                     LPal

**ARECASTRUM** See SYAGRUS

**ARENARIA** (Caryophyllaceae)
*aggregata* subsp.             SIng
*erinacea*
*alfacarensis*                 See *A. lithops*
*balearica*                    CInt CLyd CNic ELan EPar GCHN
                               LBee MRPP SIng SRms WCom
*bertolonii*                   LBee
*caespitosa*                   See *Minuartia verna* subsp.
                               *caespitosa*
*festucoides*                  GCrs GTou WLRN
*grandiflora*                  ESis
*hookeri*                      NWCA
   - subsp. *desertorum*       WLin
   - var. *desertorum*         Last listed 1997
      NNS 93-53
*kingii*                       Last listed 1997
*ledebouriana*                 MWat NWCA
§ *lithops*                    Last listed 1996
*magellanica*                  See *Colobanthus quitensis*
*montana* ♀                    CGle ECha ECtt EHyt ELan EMNN
                               EPar GCHN GMaP LFis LGre MArl
                               MBrN MHlr NFor NMen NVic
                               SPlb SRCN SRms WAbe WCot
                               WEas WFar WPer WWeb WWhi
                               WWin
*nevadensis*                   Last listed 1998
*norvegica*                    CNat
   - subsp. *anglica*          Last listed 1998
*obtusiloba*                   See *Minuartia obtusiloba*
*pinifolia*                    See *Minuartia circassica*
*procera*                      Last listed 1996
   - subsp. *glabra*           NMen

*pseudacantholimon*           Last listed 1998
*pulvinata*                    See *A. lithops*
*pungens*                      Last listed 1998
*purpurascens*                 CInt CLyd EHyt EMNN ESis NMen
                               NRoo NSla NWCA SRms WHoo
   - 'Elliott's Variety'       NHol WPat
*recurva*                      See *Minuartia recurva*
*roseiflora* ACE 1526          EHyt
♦ *rubella*                    See *Minuartia rubella*
   sp. ex CC 1363              MRPP
*tetraquetra*                  CPBP EGle GCrs IMGH NMen
                               NWCA
§  - subsp. *amabilis*         EHyt EPot NHar NNrd NSla NTow
                               SIng WAbe WLin
   - var. *granatensis*        See *A. tetraquetra* subsp.
                               *amabilis*
*tmolea*                       NMen
*verna*                        See *Minuartia verna*·

**ARENGA** (Arecaceae)
*engleri*                      LPal

**ARGEMONE** (Papaveraceae)
*grandiflora*                  ELan SYvo
*mexicana*                     ELan WHer WWin
*ochroleuca*                   Last listed 1998

**ARGYLIA** (Bignoniaceae)
*adscendens*                   Last listed 1997

**ARGYRANTHEMUM** ✿ (Asteraceae)
   'Anastasia'                 CCan LIck MBEx
   'Apricot Surprise'          See *A.* 'Peach Cheeks'
   'Beauty of Nice'            WEas
§  'Blizzard' (d)              CB&S CCan CHal EPri LIck LLWP
                               MBEx SMer
   'Bofinger'                  LIck
   Boston Yellow daisy         See *A. callichrysum*
   'Bridesmaid'                CCan
   *broussonetii*              CCan LIck
   'Butterfly'                 LIck SVil
§ *callichrysum*               LIck
§  - 'Etoile d'Or'             LIck MBEx
   - 'Penny'                   MBEx
   - 'Prado'                   CB&S ECtt LIck
   - Yellow Star               See *A. callichrysum* 'Etoile d'Or'
   'Camilla Ponticella'        CCan LIck
   *canariense* hort.          See *A. frutescens* subsp. *canariae*
¶  - 'Saimi'                   CPin
   'Champagne'                 CCan LIck MBEx
   'Cheek's Peach'             See *A.* 'Peach Cheeks'
   'Chelsea Princess'          Last listed 1997
*  *compactum*                 LIck
   'Comtesse de Chambord'      LHil LIck
   'Cornish Gold' ♀            LFis LIck
   *coronopifolium*            CCan LIck MBEx
   'Donington Hero' ♀          LIck
   double cream (d)            CCan LHil LIck
   double white (d)            CHal LIck NHaw SCro
   double yellow (d)           Last listed 1996
   'Edelweiss' (d)             CCan ECtt LHil LIck MBEx WEas
                               WHen
   'Flamingo'                  See *Rhodanthemum gayanum*
§ *foeniculaceum* hort.        CTri ELan GMac LBlm WEas
                               WHen WKif
   - pink                      See *A.* 'Petite Pink'
§  - (Willd.) Webb & Sch.Bip.  CHal
§  - 'Royal Haze' ♀            CCan CLTr CSev LIck NPer SLon
                               SMer SUsu
   'Frosty'                    CCan LIck

§ *frutescens* — ECtt ELan EMan LBlm LHil LIck NFai NLon WEas
\* - 'Album Plenum' (d) — SEND
§ - subsp. *canariae* ♀ — CCan CHal LIck MBEx
§ - subsp. *frutescens* — Last listed 1997
- x *maderense* — LHil
- subsp. *succulentum* — CCan LIck MBEx
   'Margaret Lynch'
'Fuji Sund0ance' — CCan LIck
'George' — Last listed 1998
'Gill's Pink' — CElw ECtt LHil LIck LLWP MBEx WCot
'Golden Treasure' — CCan LIck
§ *gracile* — LHil WEas
- 'Chelsea Girl' ♀ — CB&S CCan CInt CLTr ECtt LIck MArl MBEx MSte SYvo
¶ 'Harvest Snow' — LIck MBNS
¶ 'Hopleys Double Cream' (d) LIck
'Hopleys Double Yellow' (d) LHil
§ 'Jamaica Primrose' ♀ — CB&S CBar CBot CCan CSev ELan ERic GMac LHop LIck MBEx MHar LHaw SCro SDys SHFr SRms WBod WEas WHen WPnn
'Jamaica Snowstorm' — See *A.* 'Snow Storm'
'Lemon Chiffon' — CCan LIck
¶ 'Lemon Delight' — LIck WWol
'Lemon Meringue' (d) — ECtt LIck MBEx NHaw SMer
¶ 'Lemon Soufflé' — LIck
'Levada Cream' ♀ — LIck
'Leyton Treasure' — MBEx
'Lilliput' — LIck
§ *maderense* ♀ — CCan CHal CLTr CSam IBlr LBlm LHil LIck MBEx MSte SCro SUsu WEas WPer
- pale form — LIck
'Mary Cheek' (d) ♀ — CCan LHil LIck MBEx MBNS WWol
'Mary Wootton' (d) — CCan ECtt ELan LIck MBEx NGdn
*mawii* — See *Rhodanthemum gayanum*
'Mike's Pink' — LIck MBEx
'Mini-snowflake' — See *A.* 'Blizzard'
'Mini-star Yellow' — Last listed 1997
§ 'Mrs F. Sander' (d) — ECtt LIck MBEx
'Nevada Cream' — See *A.* 'Qinta White'
*ochroleucum* — See *A. maderense*
§ 'Peach Cheeks' (d) — CB&S CHal LIck MBEx MSte NFai NHaw SAGa SRms
§ 'Petite Pink' ♀ — CB&S EAst ECtt EMan EPri GMac LIck MBEx MSte NHaw SMer SRms WEas WHen
'Pink Australian' (d) — CLTr CPin LHil LIck MBEx MBNS
'Pink Break' — CCan CHal LIck
I 'Pink Dahlia' — Last listed 1998
'Pink Delight' — See *A.* 'Petite Pink'
'Pink Pixie' — CCan LIck
'Powder Puff' (d) — CCan CLTr ECtt LIck MBEx MRav NFai NHaw SCro
¶ prostrate double pink — LIck
§ 'Qinta White' (d) ♀ — CCan ECtt LHil LIck MBEx WEas
'Rising Sun' — CCan LIck
'Rollason's Red' — MBEx
¶ 'Rosa Dwarf' — LIck
'Rosali' (d) — Last listed 1996
'Royal Haze' — See *A. foeniculaceum* Webb 'Royal Haze'
'Royal Yellow' — LIck
'Saute' — CCan LIck
'Silver Leaf' — LIck WLRN
'Silver Queen' — See *A. foeniculaceum* hort.
single pink — CLTr LHil LIck
§ 'Snow Storm' ♀ — CB&S CBar EAst LIck NFai NHaw WHer

'Snowflake' (d) — ECtt LHil MBEx MSte NPer WHen
♦ 'Snowflake' misapplied — See *A.* 'Mrs F. Sander'
'Starlight' — CCan LIck
'Stydd Rose' — Last listed 1996
'Sugar Baby' — CHal WLRN
'Sugar 'n' Ice' — MBEx
¶ 'Summer Angel' — CHal
¶ 'Summer Melody' — CSpe
'Summer Pink' — CHal MBEx WLRN
'Tenerife' — LIck MSte
'Tony Holmes' — CCan LIck
'Vancouver' (d) ♀ — CB&S CBot CCan CSpe ELan GMac LHil LHop LIck MBEx MBNS NGdn NHaw SChu SRms WEas WHen
\* 'Vera' — LIck
'Wellwood Park' — CCan ECtt LIck MBEx
¶ 'Weymouth Pink' — LIck
'Weymouth Surprise' — CCan LIck
'White Spider' — LIck MNrw
'Whiteknights' ♀ — Last listed 1995
¶ 'Yellow Australian' (d) — LIck

## ARGYREIA (Convolvulaceae)
*nervosa* — CPIN

## ARGYROCYTISUS See CYTISUS

## ARISAEMA (Araceae)
*amurense* — CCuc CFil CFir CLAP EPot GCal GDra NHar NHol SSpi WFar WPGP
- B&SWJ 762 — WCru
- B&SWJ 947 — WCru
¶ - subsp. *robustum* — WCru
  B&SWJ 1186
¶ - subsp. *serratum* — WCru
  B&SWJ 711
¶ *angustatum* var. — LAma
*amurense*
- var. *peninsulae* — LAma WCru
  B&SWJ 841
¶ - - f. *variegatum* — WCru
  B&SWJ 4321
¶ - var. *serratum* — LAma
¶ *auriculatum* — LAma
¶ *bathycoleum* — LAma WCru
*brevipes* — LAma WCru
*candidissimum* ♀ — CAvo CBro CFil CFir CHan CLAP CRDP EBee EHyt EPar EPot ETub GCal GCrs LAma NHar NHol SBla SSpi SWas WCot WCru WHal Wlvy
¶ - green — LAma
¶ - white — LAma
*ciliatum* — CRDP LAma MHlr SBla SSpi WCot
- CT 369 — CFil SWas WCru
*concinnum* — EPot LAma WCot WCru
*consanguineum* — CBro CFil CGle EPot ETub LAma SSpi WCru WPGP
- B&SWJ 071 — WCru
- CLD 1519 — Last listed 1997
*costatum* — CFil EPot GBuc LAma WCru WPGP
¶ *dilatatum* — LAma WCru
*dracontium* — CArn CLAP EBot EPot LAma WCru
¶ *du-bois-reymondiae* — LAma WCru
¶ *echinatum* — EPot
*elephas* — EPot LAma WCru
*erubescens* — EPot LAma WCru
*exappendiculatum* — CFil EPar EPot WCot WCru WPGP
¶ *fargesii* — CLAP EPot LAma WCru

| | |
|---|---|
| *flavum* | CBro CFil CLAP EHyt EPot GCal GCrs LAma NMen SIng SSpi WCot WCru WPGP |
| - CC 1782 | Last listed 1998 |
| - subsp. *intermedium* | Last listed 1997 |
| ¶ - tall form | CLAP |
| *formosanum* | LAma |
| - B&SWJ 280 | WCru |
| - B&SWJ 390 | CPou |
| - var. *bicolorifolium* | WCru |
|   B&SWJ 3528 | |
| - f. *stenophyllum* | WCru |
|   B&SWJ 1477 | |
| ¶ *franchetianum* | EPot WCot WCru |
| *fraternum* | Last listed 1997 |
| *galeatum* | EPot LAma WCru |
| *griffithii* | EPot LAma NHol SSON SSpi WCru |
| - var. *pradhanii* | Last listed 1996 |
| *helleborifolium* | See *A. tortuosum* |
| *heterophyllum* | WCru |
|   B&SWJ 2028 | |
| ¶ *inkiangense* | LAma |
| *intermedium* | EPot LAma WCru |
| - var. *biflagellatum* | Last listed 1998 |
| - - HWJCM 161 | WCru |
| *iyoanum* | WThi |
| *jacquemontii* | CAvo CBro CFil CLAP EHyt EPot GBuc GCrs LAma WCot WCru |
| - B&SWJ 2719 | WCru |
| - form | WCru |
| - SEP 263 | Last listed 1996 |
| *japonicum* | See *A. serratum* |
| *kiusbianum* | CFil EFEx WCru WThi |
| *lingyunense* | EPot LAma WCru |
| ¶ *lobatum* | LAma WCru |
| ¶ *maximowiczii* | WThi |
| § *nepenthoides* | CBro EPot LAma NHol WCru |
| ¶ - B&SWJ 2614b | WCru |
| *ochraceum* | See *A. nepenthoides* |
| * *ochresia* | EPot |
| ¶ *ostiolatum* | EPot |
| ¶ *ovale* | CLAP |
| *polyphyllum* B&SWJ 3904 | WCru |
| *propinquum* | EPot LAma WCru |
| ¶ *purpureogaleatum* | LAma |
| *quinatum* | Last listed 1997 |
| - f. *pusillum* | Last listed 1997 |
| - f. *zebrinum* | Last listed 1997 |
| *rhizomatum* | LAma |
| *rhombiforme* | LAma WCru |
| *ringens* (Thunb.) Schott | EFEx LAma NHol WCot WCru WPGP WThi |
| - f. *glaucescens* | WThi |
| - f. *praecox* B&SWJ 1515 | WCru |
| - f. *sieboldii* B&SWJ 551 | WCru |
| - hort. | See *A. robustum* |
| § *robustum* | CFil SSpi WPGP |
| - B&SWJ 711 | WCru |
| *saxatile* | LAma WCru |
| § *sazensoo* | WCru |
| § *serratum* | CFil LAma SSpi WCru |
| - GG 89394 | NHol |
| - GG 89399 | NHol |
| - GG 89404 | NHol |
| § *sikokianum* | CFil EFEx EPot ETub GCrs LAma SSpi WCru WPGP WThi |
| ¶ - var. *serratum* | WCru |
| ¶ - variegated | WCru |
| *sp.* CLD 12482* | Last listed 1998 |
| *speciosum* | EPot LAma NHol SSpi WCru |
| - B&SWJ 2403 | WCru |
| - var. *mirabile* | WCru |
|   B&SWJ 2712 | |

| | |
|---|---|
| * - var. *sikkimense* | LAma |
| *taiwanense* | CFil |
| - B&SWJ 269 | WCru |
| - B&SWJ 356 | CPou |
| - var. *brevipedunculatum* | WCru |
|   B&SWJ 1859 | |
| - f. *cinereum* B&SWJ 1912 | WCru |
| ¶ *tashiroi* | WThi |
| *ternatipartitum* | WCru WThi |
| *thunbergii* | EFEx WThi |
| ¶ - subsp. *autumnale* | WCru |
|   B&SWJ 1425 | |
| ¶ - subsp. *thunbergii* | WCru |
| - subsp. *urashima* | CLAP EFEx LAma SSpi WCru WThi |
| § *tortuosum* | CBro CFil CLAP ECha EPar EPot LAma MBal NHol NTow SBla WCru |
| - CC 1452 | CPou |
| - (high alt.form) | WCru |
|   B&SWJ 2386 | |
| - (low alt. form) | WCru |
|   B&SWJ 2298 | |
| *tosaense* | WThi |
| ¶ - GG 91224 | WCru |
| *triphyllum* | CFil CLAP EBot EPar EPot LAma MSal NMen SLod SSpi SUsu SWas WCru WPGP |
| - var. *atrorubens* | WPGP |
| *utile* | See *A. verrucosum* var. *utile* |
| *verrucosum* | EPot LAma WCru |
| § - var. *utile* | EPot LAma |
| - - HWJCM 161 | WCru |
| * *vulgare* var. *typicum* | WCot |
| ¶ *yamatense* | WThi |
| ¶ - subsp. *sugimotoi* | WCru |
| ¶ *yunnanense* | LAma |
| *zanlanscianense* | Last listed 1998 |

## ARISUM (Araceae)

| | |
|---|---|
| *proboscideum* | More than 30 suppliers |
| - MS 958 | EMar |
| *vulgare* | CRDP |
| - subsp. *simorrhinum* | Last listed 1998 |
|   SF 396/347 | |
| - subsp. *vulgare* JRM 1396 | Last listed 1998 |

## ARISTEA (Iridaceae)

| | |
|---|---|
| *africana* | SWat |
| *confusa* | SWat |
| *ecklonii* | CFil CHan CPLG CPou CTrC GSki LFis SLod SWat WCot WPer WWin |
| *ensifolia* | ELan EMon SWat |
| - S&SH 88 | CHan |
| *grandis* | WCot |
| *lugens* | SWat |
| *macrocarpa* | EBee SWat |
| *major* | CAbb GSki SWat |
| - pink | CGre |
| ¶ sp. JCA 15812 | SSpi |
| *spiralis* | SWat |
| *woodii* | SWat |

## ARISTIDA (Poaceae)

| | |
|---|---|
| *purpurea* | Last listed 1997 |

## ARISTOLOCHIA (✿) (Aristolochiaceae)

| | |
|---|---|
| *baetica* | CPlN WCru |
| *californica* | CPlN |
| *chrysops* | CPlN |
| *clematitis* | CArn CPlN GPoy MHew MSal NHex WCru WWye |

| | |
|---|---|
| *debilis* | CPlN |
| *durior* | See *A. macrophylla* |
| *elegans* | See *A. littoralis* |
| *fimbriata* | CPlN |
| *gigantea* | CPlN LChe |
| *grandiflora* | CPlN |
| ¶ *griffithii* B&SWJ 2118 | WCru |
| *heterophylla* B&SWJ 3109 | WCru |
| *kaempferi* | CPlN |
|   - B&SWJ 293 | WCru |
| § *labiata* | CPlN |
| § *littoralis* ♀ | CPlN SOWG |
| ¶ *longa* subsp. *paucinervis* | WCot |
| § *macrophylla* | CB&S CBot CPlN EBee ELan EPla ETen GOrc LEdu NFla NPal SBra SSoC WCru |
| *mansburiensis* | CPlN |
|   - B&SWJ 962 | WCru |
| *paucinervis* SF 235 | Last listed 1998 |
| *peruviana* | CPlN |
| *pistolochia* | CPlN |
| *ringens* Link & Otto | See *A. labiata* |
|   - Vahl | CPlN |
| *rotunda* | CPlN |
| *sempervirens* | CPlN |
| *sipho* | See *A. macrophylla* |
| *tagala* | CPlN WMul |
| *tomentosa* | CFil CPlN SSta WCru |
| *trilobata* | CPlN |
| *watsonii* | CPlN |

## ARISTOTELIA (Elaeocarpaceae)

| | |
|---|---|
| § *chilensis* | Last listed 1998 |
|   - 'Variegata' | CAbb CB&S CCHP CHan CPle EBee MMil WEas WLRN WPyg |
| *fruticosa* | Last listed 1998 |
|   - (f) | ECou |
|   - (m) | ECou |
| *macqui* | See *A. chilensis* |
| *peduncularis* | Last listed 1997 |
| *serrata* | ECou |

## ARMERIA (Plumbaginaceae)

| | |
|---|---|
| § *alliacea* | ECha GBar WPer |
|   - f. *leucantha* | NBro SRms WMoo |
| § *alpina* | MWat |
| Bee's hybrids | WMoo |
| 'Bee's Ruby' ♀ | MBri WMer WPer WWye |
| *caespitosa* | See *A. juniperifolia* |
| *formosa* hybrids | CTri ELan EMan EWTr IBlr LFis MNrw NMir SIde WRha |
| § *girardii* | NNrd |
| § *juniperifolia* ♀ | CPlt EBrP EBre ECtt EHyt ELan EMNN ESis LBee LBre LHop MPla MTho NMen NNrd NRoo NTow NVic NWCA SBla SBre SRms WCla WWin |
|   - 'Alba' | CMea ELan MPla NHar NMen NPri NRoo NRya SRms WAbe WWin |
|   - 'Beechwood' | LBee SBla SSmi |
|   - 'Bevan's Variety' ♀ | CPla EBrP EBre ECha ELan GCrs LBre MBro MNrw MWat NHar NHol NMen NNrd NRoo NRya SBre SIng SRms SRot SSmi WAbe WPat WPyg |
|   - dark form | EWes GDra WAbe |
| ¶   - dwarf spiny form | EDAr |
|   - rose | EPot |
|   - spiny dwarf form | EPot |
| *leucocephala* | Last listed 1996 |

| | |
|---|---|
| § *maritima* | CArn CKin CRow EBrP EBre EWTr LBee LBre LHol MBar MMal MRav NArg NCat NFor NMen SBre SIde WBea WCFE WOak |
|   - 'Alba' | More than 30 suppliers |
|   - subsp. *alpina* | See *A. alpina* |
|   - 'Bloodstone' | CB&S CTri ECot ELan LBee MWat SIng |
|   - 'Corsica' | CMea CTri ECha EPot IMGH MHar MOne NBir NRya SMer WFar |
|   - Düsseldorf Pride | See *A. maritima* 'Düsseldorfer Stolz' |
| §   - 'Düsseldorfer Stolz' | CPBP EBrP EBre ECha ELan LBre LNor MBri MBro NHar NMen NNrd NPro NRoo SBre WBea WHen WPat WWye |
|   - 'Glory of Holland' | EPot |
|   - 'Laucheana' | CBod NOak WHoo WMoo WPyg |
| *   - 'Pink Lusitanica' | WPer |
|   - 'Ruby Glow' | CTri GAri NMen |
|   - 'Snowball' | NOak |
|   - 'Splendens' | EMNN EMil EPfP ESis GCHN LFis MLan MMal MOne MPla MWgw NHar NMir NRya NVic WFar WMow WPer WWin |
|   - 'Vindictive' ♀ | CB&S CMea CTri EPfP LGro MBal |
| 'Nifty Thrifty' (v) | CBod CMea ECGP EWes NMen NPro NRoo SCoo SPlb SRot WHen WPat WWeb |
| 'Ornament' | ECtt LFis NRoo WCot WFar WHen |
| *plantaginea* | See *A. alliacea* |
| *pseudarmeria* | EBee ELan MLan MNrw WEas |
| *rumelica* | EWes |
| *setacea* | See *A. girardii* |
| sp. from Patagonia | Last listed 1997 |
| *tweedyi* | CLyd GTou NRoo NWCA |
| * *variegata* 'Stephen Taffler' | LFis |
| *vulgaris* | See *A. maritima* |
| *welwitschii* | SRms |

## ARMORACIA (Brassicaceae)

| | |
|---|---|
| § *rusticana* | CArn CSev ELau GPoy ILis LHol MBri MSal NPri SIde WCer WGwy WHer WJek WMow WOak WSel WWye |
|   - 'Horwood' | WCHb |
|   - 'Variegata' | CSev EBee EGoo ELau EMar EMon GBar GCal LFis LHol LHop NSti NWes SCob SMad SPla WCHb WCot WLRN |

## ARNEBIA (Boraginaceae)

| | |
|---|---|
| *densiflora* | Last listed 1997 |
| *echioides* | See *A. pulchra* |
| *longiflora* | See *A. pulchra* |
| § *pulchra* | Last listed 1998 |

## ARNICA (Asteraceae)

| | |
|---|---|
| *angustifolia* subsp. alpina | SRms |
|   - subsp. *iljinii* | NBir |
| *chamissonis* | CHan CSev EBee ELau GBar LHol MNrw MSal SIde WJek WPer WRha WWye |
| *cordifolia* | Last listed 1997 |
| *frigida* | Last listed 1998 |
| *lessingii* | EBee MChR |
| *longifolia* | EBee |
| *montana* | CArn EOHP GPoy GTou MChe MSal NSti SRms SWat WJek WPer WWye |

| | |
|---|---|
| - yellow | MLan |
| ***nevadensis*** | EBee |
| ***sachalinensis*** | EBee |

## ARONIA (Rosaceae)

| | |
|---|---|
| ***arbutifolia*** | CB&S CGre CPle CTri EPfP EPla |
| | GBin IOrc MBal MBlu MWhi SBid |
| | SLdr SLon WAbe WDin WWat |
| - 'Erecta' | CDul EBee EBrP EBre EHic ELan |
| | EPfP GChr LBre LHop MBlu MUlv |
| | SAga SBre SLPl SRms SSpi WWat |
| * ***flexuosa*** | SOWG |
| ***melanocarpa*** | CB&S CMCN CMHG CSam EBrP |
| | EBre EHic ELan EPla LBre MAsh |
| | MBar MBlu MRav NHol SBid SBre |
| | SSpi WCwm WDin WHCG WWat |
| - 'Autumn Magic' | CAbP CBlo CFai CSam EPfP LRHS |
| | MBlu NPSl SPer WBod WRHF |
| ¶ - 'Red Viking' | NPSl |
| - 'Viking' | EBee EHal LBuc MUlv WLRN |
| | WShe WWes |
| x ***prunifolia*** | CAgr CB&S CDoC CMHG CPle |
| | EPla NHol SBid SPer WHCG WWat |
| - 'Brilliant' | COtt MCoo MUlv SPer SRPl WBcn |
| | WWat |

## ARRHENATHERUM (Poaceae)

| | |
|---|---|
| ¶ ***elatius*** subsp. ***bulbosum*** | EPGN |
| - - 'Variegatum' | More than 30 suppliers |

## ARTEMISIA ✿ (Asteraceae)

| | |
|---|---|
| § ***abrotanum*** ♀ | More than 30 suppliers |
| * - 'Variegata' | EWll WShe |
| ***absinthium*** | CArn CSev EEls ELau EWFC EWTr |
| | GPoy LHol MBar MChe MLLN |
| | MWgw NFor NSti SIde SPer SWat |
| | WCer WHbs WOak WPer WWye |
| - 'Corinne Tremaine' (v) | WHer |
| - 'Huntingdon' | CHad |
| - 'Lambrook Giant' | EEls |
| - 'Lambrook Mist' ♀ | COtt CSev EBee ECha EEls ELan |
| | ELau EMar EPPr EPfP GBri MAvo |
| | MBel MCAu MRav NPla NRoo |
| | NSti NWoo SCob SWat WJek |
| | WLRN WRus WWat WWeb |
| - 'Lambrook Silver' ♀ | CArn CB&S CGle CHan CSam |
| | CSev EBrP EBre ECha EEls ELan |
| | EMan GBar LBre LFis LHop NBro |
| | NFai NFor NRoo SBre SPer SSvw |
| | SWat WDin WEas WOve WPer |
| | WRus WWin |
| - 'Silver Ghost' | EEls |
| * - 'Variegata' | WJek |
| ***afra*** | EEls |
| § ***alba*** | CSWP CSev EEls EMan EMon |
| | GBar GPoy ILis LHol NLon NSti |
| | SIde SMad WCer WMow WPer |
| | WRha |
| § - 'Canescens' ♀ | CGle CHan CLTr CSev EBee ECha |
| | EEls EFou EOrc MBri MCLN |
| | MNrw MRav MTis MWgw NTow |
| | SBla SChu SDix SEas SMrm SPer |
| | SSpe WCot WFar WHCG WMer |
| | WPer WWat |
| ***annua*** | CArn EEls MSal SIde WWye |
| ***arborescens*** | CArn CDul CGle CMHG CTri |
| | ECha EEls ENot MGed NFai NSti |
| | SDry SPer WDin WHer WMoo |
| - 'Brass Band' | See A. 'Powis Castle' |
| - 'Faith Raven' | CArn EEls GBuc NFai NLon SRPl |
| | WHer WMer WRus |
| - 'Porquerolles' | EEls |

| | |
|---|---|
| ***arctica*** | EEls |
| ***argyi*** | EEls |
| § ***armeniaca*** | EEls WWin |
| ***assoana*** | See A. caucasica |
| ***atrata*** | EEls |
| ***brachyloba*** | MLLN WCHb |
| ***brachyphylla*** | ELau |
| ***caerulescens*** | See Seriphidium caerulescens |
| ***californica*** | EEls |
| ***campestris*** | Last listed 1996 |
| - subsp. ***borealis*** | CJew EEls MChe WCer WRha |
| | WSel |
| - subsp. ***campestris*** | EEls |
| - subsp. ***maritima*** | EEls |
| - - Welsh form | EEls |
| ***camphorata*** | See A. alba |
| ***cana*** | See Seriphidium canum |
| ***canariensis*** | See A. thuscula |
| ***canescens*** hort. | See A. alba 'Canescens' |
| - Willd. | See A. armeniaca |
| ***capillaris*** | EBee EEls SMrm |
| § ***caucasica*** ♀ | CGle CPBP EBrP EBre EEls ELau |
| | EWes GCHN LBre LGro MBrN |
| | MRav NDov NNrd SBre SIng |
| | SRms SRot WCHb WEas WPer |
| | WWat |
| - ***caucasica*** | EEls ESis WFar |
| ***chamaemelifolia*** | CArn EEls EGar GBar LHol NTow |
| | SIde WPer WWye |
| ***cretacea*** | See Seriphidium nutans |
| ♦ ***discolor*** Dougl. ex Besser | See A. michauxiana |
| ***douglasiana*** | EEls |
| - 'Valerie Finnis' | See A. ludoviciana 'Valerie Finnis' |
| ***dracunculus*** | CArn CGle CHad CSev ECha EEls |
| | ELan ELau GAbr GBar GPoy LHol |
| | MBar MChe MMal MRav NFor |
| | NRoo SCob SIde WCer WEas |
| | WFar WOak WPer WSel WWye |
| - ***dracunculoides*** | CArn EEls GBar NPri WGwG |
| ***eriantha*** | EEls |
| ***ferganensis*** | See Seriphidium ferganense |
| ***filifolia*** | EEls |
| ♦ ***fragrans*** Willd. | See Seriphidium fragrans |
| ***frigida*** ♀ | EEls GBar ILis NRoo WEas WHCG |
| ***glacialis*** | ECha EEls EGar NBur NOla |
| ***gmelinii*** | EEls IIve |
| ***gnaphalodes*** | See A. ludoviciana |
| ***gorgonum*** | EEls |
| ***gracilis*** | See A. scoparia |
| N ***granatensis*** hort. | MSte |
| ***herba-alba*** | EEls |
| ¶ 'Jim Russell' | CElw LGre |
| ***kawakamii*** B&SWJ 088 | CFee EEls WCru |
| ***kitadakensis*** | EEls |
| - 'Guizhou' | See A. lactiflora Guizhou Group |
| ***laciniata*** | EEls |
| ***lactiflora*** ♀ | CGle CHan ECha ECtt EEls EFou |
| | ELan EMon EPar EWTr MLLN |
| | MRav NFor NLon NSti SDix |
| | SPer SRms WFar WWye |
| - dark form | See A. lactiflora Guizhou Group |
| § - Guizhou Group | More than 30 suppliers |
| - ***purpurea*** | See A. lactiflora Guizhou Group |
| - 'Rosenschleier' | EFou EMon LGre SRCN |
| - 'Variegata' | See A. vulgaris 'Variegata' |
| ***lagocephala*** | WCot |
| ***lanata*** Willd. | See A. caucasica |
| ***laxa*** | See A. umbelliformis |
| § ***ludoviciana*** | CGle CHan CM&M EBee EEls |
| | ELan ELau EOld GCHN GOrc |
| | LBlm MBrN MWat NFor NLon |
| | NOak NOrc SEas SIde SRCN |
| | SRms WOve WWin WWye |

♦ - var. *latifolia* — See *A. ludoviciana* subsp. *ludoviciana* var. *latiloba*

¶ - var. *latiloba* NNS 96-20 — MRPP

¶ - subsp. *ludoviciana* var. *incompta* — ECha EEls NFai WCot WHer

§ - - var. *latiloba* — CHor EBee EEls EHoe GBuc LBlm LHop MBro MRav NBro NOak NRoo NSti WByw WCot WHoo WMer WPer

¶ - subsp. *mexicana* var. *albula* — EBee EEls WFar

- 'Silver Queen' ♀ — More than 30 suppliers

N - 'Valerie Finnis' ♀ — More than 30 suppliers

¶ *manshurica* — WCot

*maritima* — See *Seriphidium maritimum*

§ *michauxiana* — EBee

*molinieri* — CSev EEls

*mutellina* — See *A. umbelliformis*

*niitakayamensis* — EEls GBar WWat

*nitida* — EEls

*nova* — See *Seriphidium novum*

*nutans* — See *Seriphidium nutans*

*palmeri* A.Gray — See *Seriphidium palmeri*

- hort. — See *A. ludoviciana*

*pamirica* — EEls

aff. *parviflora* CLD 1531 — EEls EMon

*pedemontana* — See *A. caucasica*

*pontica* ♀ — CArn CGle EBee ECha EEls EHoe ELan EOrc GMaP GPoy LBlm LHol MBNS MCAu MRav MWgw NBro NFor NSti SDix SIde SPer SSvw WEas WFar WHer WHil WPer WWin WWye

N 'Powis Castle' ♀ — More than 30 suppliers

*princeps* — EEls

*procera* — See *A. abrotanum*

*pursbiana* — See *A. ludoviciana*

*pycnocephala* — EEls SMad
'David's Choice'

¶ *ramosa* — EEls

*rupestris* — Last listed 1996

*rutifolia* — EEls

*schmidtiana* ♀ — ECha ECot EEls EFou EGar EMan EPot LHop MAvo MNrw MWat NOrc SIng SOkh SRms WOve

- 'Nana' ♀ — More than 30 suppliers

§ *scoparia* — EEls

*selengensis* — EEls

*sieberi* — EEls

sp. Guiz 137 — See *A. lactiflora* Guizhou Group

*splendens* hort. — See *A. alba* 'Canescens'

- Willd. — EBrP EBre ELan LBre LGre NSti SBre WEas

*stelleriana* — CGle ECha EEls GMaP LFis LHop MBEx MBel MCAu MTho NBro NFla NFor NSti SHel SPer SRms SSvw WCot WEas WHoo WPer

N - 'Boughton Silver' — CArn CHad CLyd CPlt EBee EEls EFou EGoo EHoe ELan GAbr GBri GMaP LGre MRav MSCN NRoo NSti NTow WFar WMer WOve WPer WWal WWat WWye

N - 'Mori' — See *A. stelleriana* 'Boughton Silver'

- 'Nana' — ECha EEls EMan

- 'Prostata' — See *A. stelleriana* 'Boughton Silver'

- 'Silver Brocade' — See *A. stelleriana* 'Boughton Silver'

*taurica* — EEls

§ *thuscula* — EEls

*tridentata* — See *Seriphidium tridentatum*

§ *umbelliformis* — EEls GBar MHar

*vallesiaca* — See *Seriphidium vallesiacum*

*verlotiorum* — EEls GBar

* *versicolor* — NLon

*vulgaris* — CArn CJew EEls ELau EWFC GPoy LHol MChe SIde WHbs WHer WOak WWye

- 'Byrne's Variegated' — EMar EMon

- 'Cragg-Barber Eye' (v) — EBee EGar MAvo NPro WAlt WCHb WCot WHer WRha

- 'Crispa' — ELau

¶ - 'Obelisk' — EFou

¶ - 'Oriental Limelight' — CSpe EBee LWoo MBri NPri NRoo WSpi WWoo

- 'Peddar's Gold' (v) — EPPr EWes

§ - 'Variegata' — CBre CWit EBee EEls ERav GBar GLil LFis LHol NBir NSti SLod SMad WAlt WBea WCHb WCot WFar WHer WHil WOak WPer WRha

¶ - 'Woolaston' (v) — WAlt

* × *wurzellii* — EEls

## ARTHROPODIUM (Anthericaceae)

*candidum* — CBot CHan CRow ECha ECou EPPr EPla EPot GBin IMGH NCat NWCA SBea SUsu WAbe WEas WHal WPer WRos

- *maculatum* — CInt WElm

- *purpureum* — CAbb CB&S CMea ELan EPPr GBri GCal LHil LRot SCob SPer SSoC WCot WFar WPrP WWin

*cirratum* — CAbb CHan ECou EPPr ERea GBri LHil MLan SVen WHal WMul

- 'Matapouri Bay' — CB&S CDoC

*milleflorum* — ECou NWoo

## ARUM (Araceae)

§ *besserianum* — Last listed 1998

§ *concinnatum* — CFil CLAP EBee EMon EPot EWes LAma SChr SSpi WCot WPGP

¶ - subsp. *albispathum* — WCot

*conophalloides* — See *A. rupicola* var. *rupicola*

*cornutum* — See *Sauromatum venosum*

*creticum* — CBot CBro CFir CHan ECha EMan EPar IBlr LPio MMil MRav MTho NLar NTow SAga SSpi SWas WCot WPGP

- FCC form — CLAP SBla WCot

- yellow — NBir NPar WFar WIvy

*cyrenaicum* — EHyt WCot

*detruncatum* var. *detruncatum* — See *A. rupicola* var. *rupicola*

§ *dioscoridis* — CLAP EPot MTho NRog WCot

- var. *dioscoridis* — Last listed 1997

- JCA 195.157 — WCot

- var. *liepoldtii* — See *A. dioscoridis*

¶ - var. *luscbanii* JCA 195200 — EMon

- var. *smitbii* — See *A. dioscoridis*

*dracunculus* — See *Dracunculus vulgaris*

*elongatum* — Last listed 1998

¶ *bygrophilum* — EMon

*idaeum* — CLAP SSpi

*italicum* — CGle CTri EBee EWTr LAma MBri MTho NLar NRog SEND SWat WAbe WByw WCot WFar WShi

- subsp. *albispathum* — CFil EMon EPot LAma NRog WCot WPGP

- black spotted form — EHyt WFar

¶ - 'Cyclops' EAF 7701 — CHid EBee MNrw WCot

- 'Green Marble' — SBla WFar

| | |
|---|---|
| - subsp. *italicum* | EPla SAWi |
| - - 'Bill Baker' | EMon |
| § - - 'Marmoratum' ♀ | More than 30 suppliers |
| ¶ - - 'Tiny' | GCal |
| § - - 'White Winter' | CAvo CRDP EMon GBuc WCot WRus WSPU |
| - 'Nancy Lindsay' | EMon |
| - subsp. *neglectum* | CBos CHad CLAP CRDP EBee EMon NCat WCot WHal WWeb |
| 'Chameleon' | |
| - NL 1234 | CLAP |
| - 'Pictum' | See *A. italicum* subsp. *italicum* 'Marmoratum' |
| - 'Spotted Jack' | MNrw WCot |
| *korolkowii* | NRog |
| *maculatum* | CArn CKin EOld EPar EPot EWFC GPoy LAma LSyl MMal MRav MSal NHex WHer WShi WWye |
| - 'Painted Lady' | WCot |
| - 'Pleddel' | MRav WCot |
| * - 'Variegatum' | GPoy |
| 'Miss Janay Hall' | WCot |
| *nickelii* | See *A. concinnatum* |
| § *nigrum* | EMon WCot |
| *orientale* | EHyt EPot NTow |
| - subsp. *alpinum* | CFil WPGP |
| - subsp. *besserianum* | See *A. besserianum* |
| - subsp. *sintenisii* | Last listed 1997 |
| *palaestinum* | WCot |
| *petteri* hort. | See *A. nigrum* |
| *pictum* | CAvo CLAP CRDP LAma LRHS NRog WCot WIvy |
| - ACL 321/78 | EMon |
| - CL 28 | Last listed 1998 |
| - 'Taff's Form' | See *A. italicum* subsp. *italicum* 'White Winter' |
| *purpureospathum* | SBla WCot |
| *rupicola* | Last listed 1996 |
| § - var. *rupicola* | Last listed 1996 |
| - var. *virescens* | Last listed 1996 |
| * *sintenisii* | WCot |

## ARUNCUS ✿ (Rosaceae)

| | |
|---|---|
| *aethusifolius* | More than 30 suppliers |
| *asiaticus* | EBee |
| ¶ *dioicus* | EPfP EWTr MBel NGdn SPlb SRPl WCot |
| - Child of Two Worlds | See *A. dioicus* 'Zweiweltenkind' |
| - 'Glasnevin' | CRow CSev ECha ECtt EGol EMan EPla LFis MBri MRav NDov NHol WMer |
| - var. *kamtschaticus* | NHol |
| - - AGSJ 238 | NHol |
| - - AGSJ 59 | Last listed 1996 |
| - 'Kneiffii' | CB&S CBot CGle CHad CRow EBee ECha EGol ELan GCal LHop LSyl MBri MWgw NDea NFor NHol NOak NOrc NSti SPer SPlb SRms SSoC SSpi WFar WMer WRus WWat |
| § - (m) ♀ | More than 30 suppliers |
| § - 'Zweiweltenkind' | CBrm ECGN EMan GSki MBro MCli WCot WMer WPer |
| *plumosus* | See *A. dioicus* |
| sp. AGSJ 214 | NHol |
| sp. CLD 718 | Last listed 1996 |
| *sylvestris* | See *A. dioicus* |

## ARUNDINARIA ✿ (Poaceae - Bambusoideae)

| | |
|---|---|
| *amabilis* | See *Pseudosasa amabilis* |
| *anceps* | See *Yushania anceps* |
| *angustifolia* | See *Pleioblastus chino* f. *angustifolius* |

| | |
|---|---|
| *auricoma* | See *Pleioblastus auricomus* |
| *chino* | See *Pleioblastus chino* |
| *disticha* | See *Pleioblastus pygmaeus* var. *distichus* |
| *falconeri* | See *Himalayacalamus falconeri* |
| *fangiana* | EPla |
| *fargesii* | See *Bashania fargesii* |
| *fastuosa* | See *Semiarundinaria fastuosa* |
| *fortunei* | See *Pleioblastus variegatus* |
| *funghomii* | See *Schizostachyum funghomii* |
| *gigantea* | EPla SDry WJun |
| *hindsii* | See *Pleioblastus hindsii* hort. |
| *hookeriana* hort. | See *Himalayacalamus falconeri* 'Damarapa' |
| - Munro | See *Himalayacalamus hookerianus* |
| *humilis* | See *Pleioblastus humilis* |
| *japonica* | See *Pseudosasa japonica* |
| *jaunsarensis* | See *Yushania anceps* |
| *maling* | See *Yushania maling* |
| *marmorea* | See *Chimonobambusa marmorea* |
| *murieliae* | See *Fargesia murieliae* |
| *nitida* | See *Fargesia nitida* |
| *oedogonata* | See *Clavinodum oedogonatum* |
| *palmata* | See *Sasa palmata* |
| *pumila* | See *Pleioblastus humilis* var. *pumilus* |
| *pygmaea* | See *Pleioblastus pygmaeus* |
| *quadrangularis* | See *Chimonobambusa quadrangularis* |
| *simonii* | See *Pleioblastus simonii* |
| *spathiflora* | See *Thamnocalamus spathiflorus* |
| § *tecta* | EPla SDry |
| *tessellata* | See *Thamnocalamus tessellatus* |
| *vagans* | See *Sasaella ramosa* |
| *variegata* | See *Pleioblastus variegatus* |
| *veitchii* | See *Sasa veitchii* |
| *viridistriata* | See *Pleioblastus auricomus* |
| 'Wang Tsai' | See *Bambusa multiplex* 'Fernleaf' |

## ARUNDO (Poaceae)

| | |
|---|---|
| *donax* | CFil CInt CPla CRow ECha EFul EPla EWes GLch LBlm LPBA LPan MBlu MUlv SAPC SApp SArc SDix SMad SSoC WGer WHal WMul |
| - 'Macrophylla' | CRow EPla LEdu LPJP |
| - 'Variegata' | See *A. donax* var. *versicolor* |
| § - var. *versicolor* (v) | CBen CBot CFil CInt CRDP CRow CWit EBee ECha EFul EPla EWes LEdu LHop LPBA LPJP LPan MBEx MMoz NMoo NPal SAPC SArc SMad SPer SSoC WCot WMul |
| *pliniana* | CRow LEdu |

## ASARINA (Scrophulariaceae)

| | |
|---|---|
| *antirrhiniflora* | See *Maurandella antirrhiniflora* |
| *barclayana* | See *Maurandya barclayana* |
| *erubescens* | See *Lophospermum erubescens* |
| *hispanica* | See *Antirrhinum hispanicum* |
| *lophantha* | See *Lophospermum erubescens* |
| *lophospermum* | See *Lophospermum erubescens* |
| § *procumbens* | CGle EBee ECha ELan GAbr GDra GTou IMGH MBal MTho NFor NHex NWCA SBea SHFr SHel SLod SRCN SRms SSpi WCla WCot WFar WGwG WHer WLin WPer WWin |
| - 'Alba' | SRms |
| *purpusii* | See *Maurandya purpusii* |

| | |
|---|---|
| ◆ *scandens* | See *Lophospermum scandens* |
| ◆ 'Victoria Falls' | See *Maurandya* 'Victoria Falls' |

## ASARUM ✿ (Aristolochiaceae)

| | |
|---|---|
| *albomaculatum* | |
| B&SWJ 1726 | WCru |
| *arifolium* | CLAP EPar |
| *asaroides* | WThi |
| ¶ *asperum* | WThi |
| * *campaniforme* | LAma WCru |
| *canadense* | CArn EBee EPot GPoy MSal WCru |
| *caudatum* | CHan CLAP CRow EGar EHyt EPla |
| | LHop NBro NLar NSti NWCA |
| | SRms WCot WCru WFar |
| *caudigerum* | LAma |
| - B&SWJ 1517 | WCru |
| *caulescens* | CLAP LAma WCru WThi |
| *chinense* | WCru |
| ¶ *costatum* | WThi |
| *debile* | LAma WCru |
| ¶ *delavayi* | LAma WCru |
| *epigynum* B&SWJ 3443 | WCru |
| ¶ - 'Silver Web' B&SWJ 3442 | WCru |
| *europaeum* | More than 30 suppliers |
| ¶ *forbesii* | WCru |
| *hartwegii* | CLAP CRDP EHyt EMan EPar EPot |
| | ERos WCru |
| *heterophyllum* | WThi |
| *hexalobum* | WCot WThi |
| *hirsutisepalum* | WThi |
| *infrapurpureum* | WCru |
| B&SWJ 1994 | |
| ¶ *kiusianum* | WThi |
| ¶ *kumageanum* | WCot |
| *lemmonii* | EBee EGar WCru |
| *leptophyllum* B&SWJ 1983 | WCru |
| ¶ *macranthum* | WCru |
| - B&SWJ 1691 | WCru |
| *maculatum* B&SWJ 1114 | WCru |
| *magnificum* | LAma WCru |
| *maximum* | LAma WCot WCru WThi |
| ¶ *megacalyx* | WCot |
| *minamitanianum* | WThi |
| ¶ *nipponicum* | WCot WThi |
| ¶ *rigescens* | WThi |
| *sakawanum* | WThi |
| *shuttleworthii* | CLAP WCot WCru |
| - 'Callaway' | WCot |
| *sieboldii* | CLAP |
| *splendens* | LAma SBla WCot WCru WThi |
| *stellatum* | WThi |
| *subglobosum* | WThi |
| *taipingshanianum* | WCru |
| B&SWJ 1688 | |
| *takaoi* | WThi |

## ASCLEPIAS (Asclepiadaceae)

| | |
|---|---|
| 'Cinderella' | CSev EBee LBuc NCut SIgm |
| | WOve WPnP WWin |
| *curassavica* | CHal CSev SHFr WMul |
| § *fascicularis* | SIgm |
| *fasciculata* | See *A. fascicularis* |
| *fruticosa* | See *Gomphocarpus fruticosus* |
| *incarnata* | CAgr CHan CInt CMea CSev ELan |
| | MRav MSal MUlv SPer WPer |
| - 'Alba' | Last listed 1996 |
| - 'Ice Ballet' | CMGP CSev EBee EFou EWll MMil |
| | MTis SIgm SWat WRus WWin |
| ¶ - 'Soulmate' | EPfP EWll |
| - 'White Superior' | Last listed 1997 |
| *physocarpa* | See *Gomphocarpus physocarpus* |
| *purpurascens* | CArn SRCN |

| | |
|---|---|
| *rotundifolia* | Last listed 1998 |
| *speciosa* | CAgr EBee |
| *syriaca* | CAgr CArn CGen EBee MLLN |
| | MSte SHFr WPer |
| *tuberosa* | CAgr CArn CB&S EBee ELau |
| | EMan GPoy MHer MNrw MRav |
| | MSal NCut NLak SCob WPer |
| | WWin |
| - Gay Butterflies Group | CInt MLan |
| ¶ - 'Hello Yellow' | EBee |
| ¶ *verticillata* | SIgm |

## ASIMINA (Annonaceae)

| | |
|---|---|
| *triloba* | CAgr LEdu WNor |

## ASKIDIOSPERMA (Restionaceae)

| | |
|---|---|
| ¶ *chartaceum* | CCpl |
| *esterhuyseniae* | CTrC WNor |
| ¶ *paniculatum* | LHil |

## ASPARAGUS (Asparagaceae)

| | |
|---|---|
| *asparagoides* ♀ | CPlN ERea |
| § - 'Myrtifolius' | CHal |
| *cochinchinensis* | ELau WCru |
| B&SWJ 3425 | |
| *densiflorus* 'Myersii' ♀ | CHal ERea LHil MBri SRms |
| - Sprengeri Group ♀ | CHal MBri SRms |
| *falcatus* | ERea MBri SEND |
| *officinalis* | ERea SEND |
| - 'Backlim' | EMui |
| ¶ - 'Butler' | SDea |
| ¶ - 'Cito' (m) | SDea |
| ¶ - 'Dariano' | SDea |
| - 'Franklim' | EMui MRav |
| *plumosus* | See *A. setaceus* |
| *pseudoscaber* | EBee WCot |
| 'Spitzenschleier' | |
| ¶ *schoberioides* | GCal |
| § *setaceus* ♀ | CHal MBri |
| - 'Nanus' | LPVe |
| - 'Pyramidalis' | MBri SRms |
| sp. B&SWJ 871 | WCru |
| *verticillatus* | GCal SRms |

## ASPERULA (Rubiaceae)

| | |
|---|---|
| § *arcadiensis* ♀ | EHyt ELan EPot NWCA SIng SRms |
| - JCA 210.100 | NTow |
| *aristata* subsp. *scabra* | ECha ELan EMar EMon |
| - subsp. *thessala* | See *A. sintenisii* |
| *cyanchica* | MHew |
| *daphneola* | CPBP ECho EHyt EWes SBla SIng |
| *gussonei* | CMea EDAr EMNN EPot ESis LBee |
| | MBro MWat NHed NMen NWCA |
| | SBla SRms SSmi WAbe WLin WPat |
| *hexaphylla* | Last listed 1998 |
| *hirta* | CMea EHyt |
| ¶ *lilaciflora* | IMGH NWCA SIng SSmi |
| - var. *caespitosa* | See *A. lilaciflora* subsp. *lilaciflora* |
| § - subsp. *lilaciflora* | CPBP ELan EPot ESis NMen WWin |
| *nitida* | ECho NNrd |
| - subsp. *puberula* | See *A. sintenisii* |
| *odorata* | See *Galium odoratum* |
| § *perpusilla* | Last listed 1996 |
| § *sintenisii* ♀ | CPBP EPot LBee MBro NMen |
| | NTow NWCA SBla SIng SSmi |
| | WAbe WHoo |
| ¶ *suavis* | WLin |
| ¶ *suberosa* Sibth & Sm | CPBP ECho |
| ¶ - hort. | See *A. arcadiensis* |
| *taurina* subsp. *caucasica* | CPLG EOrc MBro NSti WCHb |
| | WCot |
| *taygetea* NS 723 | NWCA |

*tinctoria* — CArn GBar GPoy LHol MChe MHew MSal SIde SRms WCHb WSel

## ASPHODELINE (Asphodelaceae)
§ *brevicaulis* — Last listed 1997
* *flava* — WCot
*liburnica* — CBro EBee ECGN ECGP ECha ELan EMan EMar ERos GAbr MBel MBro MRav MWat SAga SEND SSpi SUsu WCot WFar WGwG WPer
§ *lutea* — More than 30 suppliers
§ - 'Gelbkerze' — MNrw
- Yellow Candle — See *A. lutea* 'Gelbkerze'
¶ *rigidifolia* — EBee
*taurica* — ECGN EMan WPer

## ASPHODELUS (Asphodelaceae)
*acaulis* — EWoo SIgm SWas WLin
- SF 37 — Last listed 1998
§ *aestivus* — EBee SWat WCot WPer
*albus* — CArn CBlo CBot EBee ECha EWTr LGre MWll NBid NPri SRms WCot WPer
- subsp. *albus* — Last listed 1997
*brevicaulis* — See *Asphodeline brevicaulis*
*cerasiferus* — See *A. ramosus*
*fistulosus* — ECGN EMar NBir SAga WCot WPer WWin
*lusitanicus* — See *A. ramosus*
*luteus* — See *Asphodeline lutea*
*microcarpus* — See *A. aestivus*
§ *ramosus* — EBee ECGN ECGP EHal EMan MNrw MTho WCot WPer

## ASPIDISTRA (Convallariaceae)
*elatior* ♀ — CHal EBak ERav IBlr LHil MBri NPal NRog SAPC SArc SCob SMad SRms WCot
- 'Milky Way' — WCot
- 'Variegata' ♀ — CHal GCal IBlr LBlm MTho NBir WCot WViv
*lurida* — IBlr
- 'Irish Mist' — IBlr

## ASPLENIUM ✿ (Aspleniaceae)
*adiantum-nigrum* — NHar SPer SRms
§ *aethiopicum* — EBee
*alternans* — See *A. dalhousieae*
§ *australasicum* — WRic
  f.*robinsonii*
*bulbiferum* ♀ — ECon LCns NMar
*canariense* — NMar
§ *ceterach* — SRms
*dareoides* — GDra IMGH NMar
*flabellifolium* — WRic
*fontanum* — NHar
*forisiense* — Last listed 1998
*furcatum* Thunberg — See *A. aethiopicum*
*monanthes* — WRic
*nidus* ♀ — MBri
*oblongifolium* — Last listed 1998
*platyneuron* — CFil
*robinsonii* — See *A. australasicum* f. *robinsonii*
*ruta-muraria* — EFer SRms
§ *scolopendrium* ♀ — More than 30 suppliers
- var. *americanum* — WRic
- 'Angustatum' — CBlo CLAP CMil EBee LHil MBri NHar NHol SPla SSoC WHil
¶ - 'Capitatum' — SRms

* - 'Circinatum' — CFil CRow WPGP
- 'Conglomeratum' — SRms
¶ - *cornutum abruptum* — NMar
- Crispum Group — CCuc CFil CLAP CRDP CRow EBrP EBre ECha EFer ELan EMon LBre MBri MHlr NBus NHar NHol SBre SRms WFib WPGP
- 'Crispum Bolton's Nobile' ♀ — CFil NBro NMar WEas WFib WPGP WRic
* - Crispum Cristatum Group — CLAP
- Crispum Fimbriatum Group — GQui
¶ - - 'Drummondiae' — WRic
- (Crispum Group) 'Golden Queen' — CRow WRic
- Cristatum Group — CFil CLAP CRDP CRow EBee ELan EMar EMon IOrc MBal MBri MRav NBus NHar NHed NHol NMar SPer SRms SSoC SWat WCot WFib WGor WRic
- Fimbriatum Group — WRic
- 'Furcatum' — CLAP EBee EMar SMad
- 'Kaye's Lacerated' ♀ — CLAP CRow EFer EGol ELan EMon NHar NHed NHol NMar SChu WFib WRic
- Laceratum Group — SRms
- Marginatum Group — CFil EMon NMar SWat WPGP
- - 'Irregulare' — CRDP NHar NHol SChu SRms WFib
- 'Muricatum' — CLAP CRDP NMar SChu WFib WRic
- 'Ramocristatum' — CRow NMar
- Ramomarginatum Group — CLAP EFer ELan EMon SRms WRic
- 'Sagittatocristatum' — CFil WPGP
- 'Spirale' — Last listed 1997
- Undulatum Group — CLAP EBee EFou EGol NBus NHar NMar SRms SSpi SWat WRic
- Undulatum Cristatum Group — MBri NHed WRic
*septentrionale* — Last listed 1997
*terrestre* — SRms
*trichomanes* ♀ — CCuc CFil CHea CLAP EBee EBrP EBre EFer EFou ELan EMon GGar LBre MBal MBri MLan NHar NHed NHol NMar SBre SIng SLon SRms WFib WPGP WRic
- Cristatum Group — SRms
¶ - Grandiceps Group — EFer
- Incisum Group — CLAP EFer EMon IOrc NHar NHol NOrc SMad SRPl WCot WFib
¶ - 'Incisum Moule' — WRic
- 'Ramocristatum' — WRic
¶ - 'Stuart Williams' — WRic
*viride* — SRms

## ASTARTEA (Myrtaceae)
*fascicularis* — CPLG CTrC SOWG

## ASTELIA (Asteliaceae)
*banksii* — CB&S CSpe EMil WAbe
§ *chathamica* ♀ — CAbb CB&S CDoC CFee CFil CHan CSWP CSev CTrC ERea GCal LHop MBEx NPSI SAPC SArc SDry SMad WAbe WCot WCru WRus
- 'Silver Spear' — See *A. chathamica*
*cunninghamii* — See *A. solandri*
*fragrans* — CFil ECou
*graminea* — ECou

| | |
|---|---|
| *graminifolia* | See *Collospermum microspermum* |
| *grandis* | IBlr LEdu |
| *nervosa* | CAbb CFil ECou IBlr LEdu SAPC SArc SVen WPGP |
| *nivicola* | IBlr |
| - 'Red Gem' | CBos IBlr LEdu |
| § *solandri* | CFil LEdu LHil |

## ASTER ✿ (Asteraceae)

| | |
|---|---|
| *acris* | See *A. sedifolius* |
| *ageratoides* | See *A. trinervius* subsp. *ageratoides* |
| § *albescens* | CGre CPin CPle EPla GOrc ISea MBal WSHC |
| - AIC337 | WCot |
| *alpigenus* | Last listed 1998 |
| *alpinus* ♀ | EBrP EBre EHyt EMNN GCHN LBre MNrw MPla NMen SBla SBre SIng SRms WFar WPer WStI WWin |
| - var. *albus* | EPfP EWTr GCHN MPla MWll NPri SIng WPer |
| - Dark Beauty | See *A. alpinus* 'Dunkle Schöne' |
| - var. *dolomiticus* | Last listed 1998 |
| § - 'Dunkle Schöne' | NFai NOak SRms WPer |
| ¶ - 'Goliath' | MAvo |
| - 'Happy End' | CM&M EMil MAvo NFai NOak NPri SRms WCot |
| - 'Märchenland' | Last listed 1998 |
| - 'Trimix' | ESis LFis NArg NBir NMir NVic SRms WFar |
| - violet | WPer |
| - 'White Beauty' | NFai SRms |
| *amelloides* | See *Felicia amelloides* |
| *amellus* | EBot NFor NLon |
| - 'Blue King' | EFou LFis Llck MBri MCAu MLLN NFai WCot |
| - 'Breslau' | MTed |
| - 'Brilliant' | EBee ECtt EFou EMan EPPr LFis MBri MLLN MRav MWat NRoo SMer SMrm SPer WMer WOld WWin |
| - 'Butzemann' | EFou |
| - 'Doktor Otto Petschek' | WFar WMer WViv |
| - Empress | See *A. amellus* 'Glücksfund' |
| ¶ - 'Forncett Flourish' | EFou |
| - 'Framfieldii' ♀ | WFar WOld |
| § - 'Glücksfund' | Last listed 1998 |
| - 'Grunder' | EFou WOld |
| - 'Jacqueline Genebrier' ♀ | CHar CMil EPPr SChu SMrm SPla SUsu SWas WOld |
| ¶ - 'Joseph Lakin' | EFou |
| - 'King George' ♀ | CDoC CMHG EBee EBrP EBre EFou ELan EPPr ERou GMaP LBre MBel MCAu MRav MWat NRoo SBre SChu SPer SPla SRms SWat WCot WEas WFar WHoo WLin WOld WWal |
| - 'Kobold' | WFar WOld |
| - 'Lac de Genève' | EMil LFis WCot WFar WOld |
| - 'Lady Hindlip' | MTed WEas |
| * - 'Mary Ann Neil' | LFis |
| - 'Moerheim Gem' | EFou WEas WOld |
| - 'Mrs Ralph Woods' | WOld |
| - 'Nocturne' | EPPr ERou LFis NBrk SMrm WCot WOld |
| - 'Peach Blossom' | MCAu WCot |
| - 'Pink Pearl' | WFar WViv |
| - Pink Zenith | See *A. amellus* 'Rosa Erfüllung' |
| § - 'Rosa Erfüllung' | CDoC CPlt EBee EBrP EBre ECtt EFou ELan ERic ERou GMaP LBre MCAu MLLN MRav NFor NRoo SBla SBre SChu SPer SPla SSpe WAbe WCot WEas WHoo WOld WPer WRus |
| ¶ - 'Rotfeuer' | EFou |
| - 'Rudolph Goethe' | EMil EPri Llck MLLN MRav MUlv MWhi NFla NVic WCot WEas WFar WMer WMoo WOld |
| - 'Schöne von Ronsdorf' | LBuc |
| - 'September Glow' | ECha EFou EGle EHal SPla |
| - 'Sonia' | ECha EFou EGle LFis MBri MCAu NFla WFar WMer WOld |
| - 'Sonora' | LGre WOld |
| - 'Sternkugel' | NBrk WOld |
| - 'Ultramarine' | EFou WFar |
| - 'Vanity' | GBuc WOld |
| § - 'Veilchenkönigin' ♀ | More than 30 suppliers |
| N - Violet Queen | See *A. amellus* 'Veilchenkönigin' |
| - 'Weltfriede' | WOld |
| - 'Anja's Choice' | EMon LGre WOld WPrP |
| *asper* | See *A. bakerianus* |
| *asperulus* | LGre SUsu |
| § *bakerianus* | CMGP EBee NOak WFar WPer |
| 'Barbara Worl' | SAsh |
| *bellidiastrum* | Last listed 1996 |
| *capensis* 'Variegatus' | See *Felicia amelloides* variegata |
| § *carolinianus* | WOld |
| 'Cha-Cha' | Last listed 1998 |
| 'Climax' | CBre EBee ECha GBuc GCal GMac LBlm MRav MUlv NSti SPer WCot WOld |
| *coelestis* | See *Felicia amelloides* |
| *coloradoensis* | NSla |
| * 'Connecticut Snow Fleure' | WHil |
| 'Coombe Fishacre' ♀ | CGle EFou ERou GCal LFis LGre MBel MBri MBro MMil MRav MUlv NFai SAga SHel SPla SSvw WByw WCot WEas WFar WOld WOve |
| *cordifolius* | WFar |
| - 'Aldebaran' | NBrk |
| - 'Chieftain' ♀ | LGre MTed WCot WIvy WOld |
| - 'Elegans' | EFou EGar MBri NSti WCot WIvy WOld |
| - 'Ideal' | EFou WOld WPer WRus |
| - 'Little Carlow' | See *A.* 'Little Carlow' (*cordifolius* hybrid) |
| - 'Little Dorrit' | See *A.* 'Little Dorrit' (*cordifolius* hybrid) |
| - 'Photograph' | See *A.* 'Photograph' |
| - 'Silver Queen' | WHil WOld |
| - 'Silver Spray' | EFou EHic EMan ERou GMaP GMac LGre MBro MLLN MWat NBro WEas WHoo WMer WOld WPer WPyg |
| - 'Sweet Lavender' ♀ | ERou GMac LFis NBrk WOld |
| *corymbosus* | See *A. divaricatus* |
| § 'Dark Pink Star' | WOld |
| ♦ 'Deep Pink Star' | See *A.* 'Dark Pink Star' |
| *delavayi* | EBee SUsu |
| - CLD 0494 | Last listed 1997 |
| *diffusus* | See *A. lateriflorus* |
| *diplostephioides* | CMil SSpi |
| § *divaricatus* | More than 30 suppliers |
| N *dumosus* | SHel WPer |
| *eatonii* | EBee |
| ¶ 'Edo-murasaki' | WCot |
| *ericoides* | CBrm CGle CSam ERav SIng WWin |
| - 'Blue Star' ♀ | CM&M EFou EGar EWTr GBuc MBel MLLN NBrk NFai NSti SChu SHel SPer WCot WOld |
| - 'Blue Wonder' | CGle EOrc NBrk |
| - 'Brimstone' ♀ | EBee EPPr MRav SHel WOld |
| - 'Cinderella' | CHor CVer EGar EHal EPPr GBuc GMac NFla NRoo NSti SPla WCot WOld |

| | |
|---|---|
| ¶ - 'Cirylle' | EFou |
| - 'Constance' | NBrk WOld |
| * - 'Dainty' | Last listed 1997 |
| - 'Enchantress' | ERou |
| - 'Erlkönig' | EBee EFou EHic EMan EPPr GAbr LHop MMil MSte MWgw SChu SSpe SWat WOld WPer WWin |
| - 'Esther' | CGle CHea ECha EFou EGle ELan EMan EMou EOrc EPri ERou LFis MSte NBrk NSti SDix WOld |
| - 'Golden Spray' ♀ | EBee EFou MCAu NFai NSti SHel WFar WMer WOld |
| - 'Herbstmyrte' | EWTr GBuc MLLN |
| - 'Hon. Edith Gibbs' | GMac |
| - 'Hon. Vicary Gibbs' | See A. 'Hon. Vicary Gibbs' (ericoides hybrid) |
| - 'Kaytie Fisher' | LFis |
| - 'Maidenhood' | WBcn WOld |
| - 'Monte Cassino' | See A. pringlei 'Monte Cassino' |
| - 'Pink Cloud' ♀ | CGle CHan CHor COlW CVer EFou ERou LFis LHop MBro MCAu MRav MSte NFai NRoo SChu SCou SPer SPla SWat WCot WFar WHoo WOld WPer WPyg WWin |
| - f. prostratus | EMon EPot ERav LRHS SCro WFar |
| § - - 'Snow Flurry' | CStr ECha EFou EMan EPPr MAvo MHlr MLLN MNrw NBrk SCob SUsu WCot WOld WRus |
| - 'Rosy Veil' | CBre GMac NBrk NGdn WByw WCot WIvy WOld |
| ¶ - 'Ruth McConnell' | NSti |
| - 'Schneegitter' | EHic MLLN MSte |
| ¶ - 'Schneetanne' | EWTr |
| - 'Sulphurea' | MWat |
| - 'White Heather' | CVer EGar GMac MBro MHlr NFai WByw WCot WEas WIvy WOld WPyg WRHF |
| - 'Yvette Richardson' | MSte WOld |
| ¶ 'Fanny's Fall' | EBee NDov |
| farreri | GCHN NBro NLar SSpi |
| ¶ - 'Blue Moon' | WCom |
| § flaccidus | WCot |
| foliaceus | EBee NTow |
| - var. cusickii | Last listed 1997 |
| x frikartii | EAst EBrP EBre EFou ELan EPar ERou GCHN LBre LHop MBro MRav NFla SBla SBre SChu SPer SRms SSoC WByw WEas WOld WPer WWin |
| - 'Eiger' | NBrk WOld |
| - 'Flora's Delight' | EBrP EBre EFou EMan ERou LBre MRav NRoo SBre WOld |
| - 'Jungfrau' | MTed NCut SCob WOld |
| N - 'Mönch' ♀ | More than 30 suppliers |
| - Wonder of Stafa | See A. x frikartii 'Wunder von Stäfa' |
| § - 'Wunder von Stäfa' ♀ | CEnd CMGP EBee EMan EMar GBuc GMaP GMac LFis LHop MAvo MBNS MBri MUlv NLak NSti SChu SCob WLRN WLin WOld |
| ¶ glebnii | WCot |
| ¶ 'Hama-otome' | WCot |
| 'Herfstweelde' | CMil EFou EGar EMon GBuc LGre MBri MBro MSte SHel SLod SUsu SWas WFar WOld |
| x herveyi | EBee EMan EMon EPPr LGre SAga WOld |
| himalaicus | GCHN GTou SRms |
| - BM&W 12 | Last listed 1996 |
| - CC&McK 145 | GCHN MRPP NWCA |
| - EMAK 0952 | Last listed 1996 |
| 'Hittlemaar' | EBee EPPr WCot |
| § 'Hon. Vicary Gibbs' (ericoides hybrid) | CBre CHea EBee LFis MSte NBrk WCot WOld |
| hybridus luteus | See x Solidaster luteus |
| § 'Kylie' ♀ | CBre EMon GBuc LFis MBro MSte NBrk SCro WCot WFar WHoo WOld WPrP WTin |
| laevis | EMon MSte SWas |
| - 'Arcturus' | CFir CLTr EGar LBlm MBri MLLN MMil MTed NSti SSvw WCot |
| - 'Blauhügel' | GCal |
| - 'Calliope' | CHan CSam EBee ECha EMan GCal IHdy LGre LPio MBNS MBro MGed MHlr MLLN MMil MSte MTed NOak SAga SMrm SUsu SWas WCot WEas WFar WIvy WKif WLin WOld |
| - var. geyeri | MNrw |
| ¶ lanceolatus Willd. | WCot |
| ¶ - Kuntze | See Haplopappus lanceolatus |
| - 'Edwin Beckett' | LFis NBrk WOld |
| § lateriflorus | CGle EBee ERav ESis MNes MRav MWat WMaN WOld WPer |
| - 'Bleke Bet' | WCot WOld |
| - 'Buck's Fizz' | EFou ELan NLar SPla WOld |
| - 'Daisy Bush' | Last listed 1997 |
| - 'Datschii' | WFar |
| - 'Delight' | MLLN WCot |
| - 'Horizontalis' ♀ | More than 30 suppliers |
| ¶ - 'Jan' | WCot WOld |
| - 'Lady in Black' | CBos CBot CBre CElw CHid CLTr CSpe EBee EFou LGre MSte MTed NSti SAga SMrm SSvw SWas WCot WOld |
| - 'Lovely' | EFou EMan LFis MBro MLLN NOak WOld |
| - 'Prince' | More than 30 suppliers |
| ¶ - 'Rubrifolius' | MBel |
| likiangensis | See A. asteroides |
| linariifolius | EBee |
| § linosyris | EHal LFis MSte NLar SPer WCot WHer WMer WOld |
| - 'Goldilocks' | See A. linosyris |
| § 'Little Carlow' (cordifolius hybrid) ♀ | More than 30 suppliers |
| § 'Little Dorrit' (cordifolius hybrid) | CBre GMac MBro MLLN NBro NOak NWes WCot WOld |
| ¶ maackii | EBee |
| macrophyllus | CFee CPou ELan EMon MBel NSti SPer WOld |
| - 'Albus' | EMon EPPr WIvy WOld |
| - 'Twilight' | CGle CMea EBee EFou EGle EMan EOrc EPPr EPla GCal GMac LLWP MBro MLLN MSte SUsu WCot WFar WIvy WOld WRHF |
| mongolicus | See Kalimeris mongolica |
| natalensis | See Felicia rosulata |
| ¶ novae-angliae | ELau |
| - 'Andenken an Alma Pötschke' ♀ | More than 30 suppliers |
| - 'Andenken an Paul Gerbe' | WMer |
| - Autumn Snow | See A. novae-angliae 'Herbstschnee' |
| - 'Barr's Blue' | EFou MBNS MCAu MSte MTed MWat NFla NSti WFar WMer WOld |
| - 'Barr's Pink' | CBre EFou LFis MCAu MRav MWat NFla SHel WEas WFar WMer WOld WPer WPyg |
| - 'Barr's Violet' | NFor NLon SRms WCot WOld WPer WTin |

¶ - 'Bishop Colenso'    EFou
   - 'Christopher Harbutt'    ERou WOld
   - 'Crimson Beauty'    EGar GMac MWat WOld
   - 'Festival'    Last listed 1998
   - 'Forncett Jewel'    Last listed 1997
   - 'Harrington's Pink' ♀    More than 30 suppliers
§ - 'Herbstschnee'    CGle EBrP EBre EFou EMon ERou
                  GCHN LBre MAvo MBel MCAu
                  MRav MWat NFai NFla NFor
                  NRoo NSti NVic SBre SChu SEas
                  SHel SPer SSpe WCot WFar WOld
                  WPer
   - 'Lachsglut'    EFou
   - 'Lou Williams'    WOld
   - 'Lye End Beauty'    CPou EBee EMon MAvo MFir
                  MRav MSte MUlv MWat NFor
                  NLon SChu WCot WOld
   - mixed    Last listed 1998
   - 'Mrs S.T.Wright'    EFou EGar EGle EMon ERou LFis
                  MBrN WByw WFar WOld
* - 'Mrs S.W. Stern'    WOld
   - 'Pink Parfait'    WCot WOld
   - 'Pink Victor'    CTri EPPr NFai NLar SEND
¶ - 'Primrose Upward'    WCot
   - 'Purple Cloud'    EMon EPPr ERou GMac LHop
                  MWat WPrP
   - 'Purple Dome'    EBrP EBre EFou ELan EMon LBre
                  MBri MBro MCAu MNrw NRoo
                  SBre SEND SSpe SSvw SUsu WCot
                  WFar WOld WPrP
   - 'Quinton Menzies'    WCom WOld
   - 'Red Cloud'    EFou NFai
   - 'Rosa Sieger'    CBre CPlt EBrP EBre EFou EMon
                  LBre MHlr SBre SChu SUsu WMer
                  WOld WViv
   - 'Rose Williams'    WOld
   - 'Roter Stern'    Last listed 1998
   - 'Rubinschatz'    WOld
   - 'Rudelsburg'    Last listed 1998
   - 'Sayer's Croft'    EFou EGle EMon MBri MWat
                  WCot WOld
   - September Ruby    See *A. novae-angliae*
                  'Septemberrubin'
§ - 'Septemberrubin'    CBlo CMea ECtt EMon ERou
                  LHop MRav MSte NFai SChu SUsu
                  WByw WCot WEas WFar WHoo
                  WOld WPyg WWin
   - 'Treasure'    CBre CLTr EBee EFou WFar WOld
   - 'Violetta'    CBre EFou EMon LGre MAvo
                  MSte MTed NFai WOld WPrP
   - 'W. Bowman'    Last listed 1998
   *novi-belgii*    SEas WHer
N - 'Ada Ballard'    CBlo CVer EBee EMan ENot ERou
                  GCHN MBel SLon SPer WLRN
                  WOld WWal
   - 'Albanian'    CElw WOld
   - 'Alderman Vokes'    ERou WOld
   - 'Alex Norman'    ERou NOla WOld
   - 'Algar's Pride'    ERou MUlv NBro WOld
   - 'Alice Haslam'    CBlo CM&M CMGP ECtt EFou
                  EOld EPPr GBri MBri MFir MWgw
                  NOrc NPri SSpe WByw WLRN
                  WMow WOld WOve WPer WRHF
   - 'Alpenglow'    WOld
   - 'Anita Ballard'    WOld
   - 'Anita Webb'    ERou GBri NBir NOak WOld
   - 'Anneke'    EPfP WGor
   - Antwerp Pearl    See *A. novi-belgii* 'Antwerpse
                  Parel'
   - 'Apollo'    CB&S NBus NPri
   - 'Apple Blossom'    SHel WOld
   - 'Arctic'    ERou WBcn WOld

   - 'Audrey'    CMGP ECtt EFou ERou GCHN
                  GMaP MBNS MBri MLLN MWgw
                  NBro NLak NOrc SChu SEas SMer
                  SUsu WByw WCot WMer WOld
                  WWal
   - 'Autumn Beauty'    WOld
   - 'Autumn Days'    WOld
   - 'Autumn Glory'    CSam ERou WOld
   - 'Autumn Rose'    CHea WOld
   - 'Baby Climax'    WOld
   - 'Beauty of Colwall'    WOld
   - 'Beechwood Challenger'    ERou MOne WMer WOld
   - 'Beechwood Charm'    WOld
   - 'Beechwood Rival'    WMer
   - 'Beechwood Supreme'    ERou WOld
   - 'Bewunderung'    NBro WOld
   - 'Blandie'    CBlo CHea CTri EFou ERou MSte
                  MWat NBro SHel WLRN WOld
   - Blaue Lagune =    CBlo MBri WOld
      'Blue Lagoon'
   - 'Blauglut'    EFou NBro WOld
   - 'Blue Baby'    LHop WPer
   - 'Blue Bouquet'    ERou SRms WByw WOld
   - 'Blue Boy'    CHea WOld
   - 'Blue Danube'    WOld
   - 'Blue Eyes'    ERou EWTr LGre NOak WOld
   - 'Blue Gown'    EGar ERou GCal MUlv WOld
   - 'Blue Patrol'    ERou NOak WOld
   - 'Blue Radiance'    WOld
   - 'Blue Whirl'    ERou NBro WOld
   - 'Bonanza'    WOld
   - 'Boningale Blue'    MTed WOld
   - 'Boningale White'    ERou MAvo WOld
   - 'Bridesmaid'    SHel WOld
   - 'Brightest and Best'    NBrk WOld
   - 'Caborn Pink'    LLWP
   - 'Cameo'    WOld
   - 'Cantab'    WBcn WOld
   - 'Cantonese Queen'    EMon
   - 'Carlingcott'    ERou MOne NOak WOld
   - 'Carnival'    CBlo CM&M EBee EFou ERou
                  MBri MUlv NHaw NOrc SHel SPer
                  SSpe WOld
   - 'Cecily'    NBro SGre WLin WOld
   - 'Charles Wilson'    WOld
   - 'Chatterbox'    ECtt MBri MRav MWat SChu SRms
                  WOld
   - 'Chelwood'    WOld
   - 'Chequers'    CBlo CBrm CDoC CM&M EBee
                  ECot EMan ERou NLon WGor
                  WLRN WOld
   - 'Christina'    See *A. novi-belgii* 'Kristina'
   - 'Christine Soanes'    EFou WOld
   - 'Cliff Lewis'    ERou NBro WOld
   - 'Climax Albus'    See *A.* 'White Climax'
   - 'Cloudy Blue'    CElw WOld
   - 'Colonel F.R. Durham'    ERou MBro WMer
   - 'Coombe Delight'    ERou
   - 'Coombe Gladys'    ERou WOld
   - 'Coombe Joy'    ERou NOak WLRN WOld
   - 'Coombe Margaret'    MLLN WOld
   - 'Coombe Pink'    ERou
   - 'Coombe Queen'    WOld
   - 'Coombe Radiance'    ERou WOld
   - 'Coombe Ronald'    ERou MWat WOld
   - 'Coombe Rosemary'    ECtt EPPr ERou MBri MUlv NLar
                  NOak WOld WRHF
   - 'Coombe Violet'    LGre MWat WOld
   - 'Countess of Dudley'    WOld WPer
   - 'Court Herald'    WOld
   - 'Crimson Brocade'    CTri ELan ENot EPfP ERou MBri
                  MRav MWat SHel SPer WMer
                  WOld WWhi

| Name | Codes |
|---|---|
| - 'Dandy' | CBlo EBee ECot ELan EMar MBro NGdn SChu SEas WByw WOld WWal |
| - 'Daniela' | CHea EFou SGre WOld |
| - 'Daphne Anne' | WOld |
| - 'Dauerblau' | WOld |
| - 'Davey's True Blue' | CTri EBee EFou EMan ERou WLRN WOld WWal |
| - 'David Murray' | WOld |
| - 'Dazzler' | WOld |
| - 'Destiny' | WOld |
| - 'Diana' | CNic ERou NBro WOld |
| - 'Diana Watts' | ERou WOld |
| - 'Dietgard' | SGre WOld |
| - 'Dolly' | NBir WOld |
| - 'Dusky Maid' | MBri SHel WOld |
| - 'Elizabeth' | CElw WOld |
| - 'Elizabeth Bright' | WOld |
| - 'Elizabeth Hutton' | WOld |
| - 'Elsie Dale' | SHel WOld |
| - 'Elta' | WOld |
| - 'Erica' | CElw MWat WOld |
| - 'Ernest Ballard' | ERou WOld |
| - 'Eva' | WOld |
| - 'Eventide' | CB&S CElw CTri ENot ERou MBro NOak SPer WLRN WOld WRHF |
| - 'F.M. Simpson' | ERou WElm |
| - 'Fair Lady' | ERou MWat WOld |
| - 'Faith' | WOld |
| - 'Farrington' | WOld |
| - 'Fellowship' | CB&S CElw CFir CMGP CPar EFou ENot ERou GCHN MUlv MWat SEas SPer SRms WCot WEas WOld WWal |
| - 'Flamingo' | Last listed 1996 |
| - 'Fontaine' | WOld |
| - 'Freda Ballard' | EBee EPPr ERou GCHN MWat WLRN WOld WWal |
| ¶ - 'Freya' | WOld |
| - 'Fuldatal' | EFou SHel WOld |
| ¶ - 'Gayborder Blue' | WOld |
| - 'Gayborder Royal' | CFir ERou MOne SHel WOld |
| - 'Gayborder Splendour' | Last listed 1998 |
| - 'Glory of Colwall' | WOld |
| - 'Goliath' | WOld |
| - 'Grey Lady' | WOld |
| - 'Guardsman' | ERou MBri MUlv WOld |
| - 'Gulliver' | WOld |
| - 'Gurney Slade' | ERou MBri WOld |
| - 'Guy Ballard' | ERou |
| - 'Harrison's Blue' | ERou LGre WOld WPer |
| - 'Heinz Richard' | CBlo CM&M ECha EFou LHop MBri MUlv NBir NGdn SChu WLRN WOld |
| - 'Helen' | WOld |
| - 'Helen Ballard' | CHea CStr ERou NBrk WOld |
| ¶ - 'Herbstgruss vom Bresserhof' | EWTr MBro |
| - 'Herbstpurzel' | SGre WGor WMer |
| - 'Hilda Ballard' | ERou WOld |
| - 'Ilse Brensell' | WOld |
| - 'Irene' | WOld |
| - 'Isabel Allen' | WOld |
| - 'Janet McMullen' | Last listed 1998 |
| - 'Janet Watts' | ERou NBro WOld |
| - 'Jean' | MTed MWat SHel WOld |
| - 'Jean Gyte' | WOld |
| - 'Jenny' | CDoC EBrP EBre ECtt EFou EMar GCHN GMaP LBre LHop MBri MBro MRav MWat NBir NBro SBre SPer SRms SUsu WByw WEas WOld WWin |
| - 'Jollity' | WOld |
| - 'Judith' | MTed |
| - 'Julia' | WOld |
| - 'Karminkuppel' | WOld |
| - 'Kassel' | MBro |
| - 'King of the Belgians' | WOld |
| - 'King's College' | CElw MBri WOld |
| § - 'Kristina' | CDoC EBrP EBre ECha ECtt EFou ERou LBre LLWP MBro MCLN MOne MUlv NBrk NBur SBre SChu SSpe WCot WLin WOld WRHF |
| - 'Lady Evelyn Drummond' | WOld |
| - 'Lady Frances' | WOld |
| - 'Lady in Blue' | CDoC EBee ECtt ELan ENot EOld EPla GCHN MBNS MWat NMir NVic SEas SPer SRms SSpe SUsu SWat WByw WCot WFar WHil WMow WOld WPer WWal WWin |
| - 'Lady Paget' | WOld |
| - 'Lassie' | CHea ERou LFis MLLN MWat WOld |
| - 'Lavanda' | WLRN |
| - 'Lavender Dream' | WOld |
| - 'Lawrence Chiswell' | LGre SHel WOld |
| - 'Lilac Time' | WByw WLin WOld |
| - 'Lisa Dawn' | WOld |
| - 'Little Boy Blue' | CB&S ERou NBus WMer WOld |
| - 'Little Man in Blue' | WOld |
| - 'Little Pink Beauty' | EBee ECtt EFou ELan ERou GCHN GChr LHop MBNS MBri MRav NFai NMir NVic SAga SEas SHel SPer SRPl SSpe SUsu SWat WMow WOld WWal WWin |
| - 'Little Pink Lady' | ERou WLin WOld |
| - 'Little Pink Pyramid' | LLWP SRms |
| - 'Little Red Boy' | CB&S CBlo ERou MBel WOld |
| - 'Little Treasure' | WOld |
| - 'Lucy' | WOld |
| - 'Mabel Reeves' | Last listed 1997 |
| - 'Madge Cato' | MOne NOak WOld |
| - 'Malvern Castle' | ERou |
| - 'Mammoth' | WOld |
| - 'Margaret Rose' | NOrc NPla WLRN WOld |
| - 'Margery Bennett' | ERou GBri NOak WOld |
| - 'Marie Ann Neil' | Last listed 1997 |
| - 'Marie Ballard' | CB&S CDoC CElw CHea CSam CTri ENot ERou GMaP MAvo MBri MFir MWat NBro NLon NOrc SEas SHel SPer SRms WEas WOld WPer |
| - 'Marie's Pretty Please' | WOld |
| - 'Marjorie' | SEas WOld |
| - 'Marjory Ballard' | WOld |
| - 'Martonie' | WOld WPer |
| - 'Mary Ann Neil' | WOld |
| - 'Mary Deane' | CHea WOld WPer |
| ¶ - 'Mauve Magic' | MBri |
| - 'Melbourne Belle' | MUlv NOak WOld |
| - 'Melbourne Magnet' | CHea ERou WOld |
| - 'Michael Watts' | ERou WOld |
| - 'Mistress Quickly' | CPou CTri ERou MBel MBri NOak SHel WBro WOld |
| - 'Mount Everest' | ERou WMer WOld WPer |
| - 'Mrs Leo Hunter' | NOak WOld |
| - 'Newton's Pink' | CTri |
| - 'Niobe' | ELan WMer |
| - 'Nobilis' | WOld |
| - 'Norman's Jubilee' | ERou MTed NBir WOld |
| - 'Norton Fayre' | Last listed 1997 |
| - 'Nursteed Charm' | WOld |
| - 'Oktoberschneekuppel' | ERou MBri NBro |

- 'Orlando' — ERou WCot WOld
- 'Pacific Amarant' — SRos
- 'Pamela' — ERou WOld
- 'Patricia Ballard' — CBlo CTri ERou LFis MWat NBro NLak NLon SMer SPer SSpe WLRN WLin WOld WPer
- 'Peace' — WOld
- 'Percy Thrower' — CMGP ERou WEas WLRN WOld
- 'Peter Chiswell' — MBri WOld
- 'Peter Harrison' — GMaP GMac MOne NBir NBrk NBro WOld WPer
- 'Peter Pan' — EBee NBus WOld
- 'Picture' — WOld
- 'Pink Buttons' — Last listed 1996
- 'Pink Gown' — WOld
- 'Pink Lace' — ERou MBNS MBro MLLN WByw WOld WPer
- 'Pink Pyramid' — SRms WOld
- 'Plenty' — ERou MBri WOld
- 'Porzellan' — CDoC CMGP EMar
- 'Pride of Colwall' — ERou MWat NOla
- 'Priory Blush' — CHea ERou NBrk NOak WLRN WOld
- 'Professor Anton Kippenberg' — CBlo EFou EMan EPPr ERou GCHN GMaP GMac LBlm MBri NBro NFai NPri SPer WOld WWhi
- 'Prosperity' — ERou NOak WOld
* - 'Prunella' — ERou WOld
- 'Purple Dome' — ECha LFis WBcn WHoo WOld
- 'Queen Mary' — ERou WMer WOld
- 'Queen of Colwall' — WOld
- 'Ralph Picton' — WOld
- 'Raspberry Ripple' — CBlo CDoC CPar ECot EMar ERou EWes NPla SEas WLRN WOld WRha
I - 'Rector' — See *A. novi-belgii* 'The Rector'
- 'Red Robin' — MWat
- 'Red Sunset' — CB&S ERou MBro SRms WOld
* - 'Reitlinstal' — Last listed 1997
¶ - 'Rembrandt' — CDoC
- 'Remembrance' — EFou MBri WOld WWhi
- 'Reverend Vincent Dale' — WOld
- 'Richness' — ERou LGre NOak SHel WOld
- 'Robin Adair' — WOld
- 'Roland Smith' — WOld
- 'Rose Bonnet' — CMGP EFou ENot MMil MWat SChu SPlb WLRN
- 'Rose Bouquet' — WOld
- 'Rosebud' — CBlo ELan SEas WEas WOld
- 'Rosemarie Sallmann' — Last listed 1998
- 'Rosenwichtel' — CDoC EFou EMar GAri MCLN NLar SAga WLRN WOld
- 'Royal Blue' — WMer
- 'Royal Ruby' — ECtt WBcn WOld
- 'Royal Velvet' — ENot ERou WOld
- 'Rozika' — EFou WOld
- 'Rufus' — ERou NOak WOld
- 'Sailor Boy' — EFou ERou LFis WLRN WOld
- 'Saint Egwyn' — WOld
- 'Sam Banham' — ERou NBro
- 'Sandford White Swan' — CVer ERou LLWP MBel MBri WPer
- 'Sandford's Purple' — Last listed 1997
- 'Sarah Ballard' — ERou MWat WOld
§ - 'Schneekissen' — ECtt EGoo EHal EMan EMar EPla GMaP LHop NPri NTow SAga SEND SMer SPer WLRN WOld WWal
- 'Schöne von Dietlikon' — EFou NOak WLRN WMer WOld
- 'Schoolgirl' — ERou MBri WOld
- 'Sheena' — ERou MBri MUlv WOld
- Snow Cushion — See *A. novi-belgii* 'Schneekissen'
- 'Snowdrift' — EBee WOld

- 'Snowsprite' — CB&S ELan EMan MWat NBro NOrc SWat WOld WWal
- 'Sonata' — EBee ERou GMaP NLon NOak SHel SPer WOld
- 'Sophia' — ERou NOak WOld
- 'Starlight' — ENot ERou LWoo MBNS WMow WOld WRHF
- 'Steinebrück' — WOld
- 'Sterling Silver' — CElw ERou NOak WByw WOld
- 'Storm Clouds' — EFou LFis
- 'Sunset' — WOld
- 'Sweet Briar' — CElw WOld
- 'Tapestry' — WBcn WOld
- 'Terry's Pride' — WOld
- 'The Archbishop' — WOld
- 'The Bishop' — ERou WOld
- 'The Cardinal' — ERou WOld
- 'The Choristers' — CVer WOld
- 'The Dean' — ERou NHaw WOld
§ - 'The Rector' — WOld
- 'The Sexton' — ERou WOld
- 'Thundercloud' — SHel WOld
- 'Timsbury' — WOld
- 'Tony' — WOld
- 'Tosca' — LFis
- 'Tovarich' — GMac NBrk WOld
- 'Triumph' — Last listed 1997
- 'Trudi Ann' — EFou NBir WOld
- 'Twinkle' — NBro WOld
- 'Victor' — MBal WOld
- 'Violet Lady' — ERou MBro WOld
- 'Violetta' — CB&S
- 'Waterperry' — MWat
- 'Weisse Wunder' — EFou WOld
- 'White Ladies' — CBlo CDoC EBee ECtt EFou ERou GAri GMaP LLWP MUlv MWat NOrc SHel SMer SPer WLRN WWal
- 'White Swan' — CPou EMon EPPr LGre NOak WCot WEas WOld WPrP
- 'White Wings' — WOld
- 'Winston S. Churchill' — CTri EBee ELan ENot ERou GMaP MWat NLon NOrc NSti SEas SHel SPer SPlb SSpe WMoo WOld WPnP

*oblongifolius* — WOld
¶ - 'Fanny's Aster' — WOld
'Ochtendgloren' (*pringlei* hybrid) ♀ — CPlt EBee EBrP EBre EFou EGle EMon EPPr GBuc LBre LGre MBri MSte MTed SAga SBre WCot WFar WHil WMaN WOld
¶ 'Octoberlight' — EMon
*pappei* — See *Felicia amoena*
'Pearl Star' — WOld
*petiolatus* — See *Felicia petiolata*
§ 'Photograph' ♀ — MBri MWat NBrk WFar WOld
§ *pilosus* var. *demotus* ♀ — EBee EGar EMon EPPr EWes MLLN MRav MSte SCro SDys SHel SMrm SPla WCot WFar WRus
'Pink Cassino' — CMil EFou GMac LGre MBri MHlr MRav MWgw NPri NRoo NSti NWoo WCot WFar WOld
'Plowden's Pink' — WOld
'Poollicht' — EFou
§ *pringlei* 'Monte Cassino' ♀ — More than 30 suppliers
I - 'Phoebe' — WCot
- 'Pink Cushion' — Last listed 1998
§ *ptarmicoides* — CBlo CFee CM&M EBee EFou EMon MBrN MHlr MLLN WCot WEas WOld WPer
♦ *purdomii* — See *A. flaccidus*

| | |
|---|---|
| *pyrenaeus* 'Lutetia' | CDoC CHea EBee ECha EFou EGar EMan EOrc EPPr GCal GMac MBri MMil MSte NLar SHel SUsu WCot WFar WOld WOve |
| *radula* | EBee EGar EHal EMan EMon EPPr GCal NBrk NSti SUsu WCot WOld |
| 'Ringdove' (*ericoides* hybrid) ♀ | CBlo CBre CMGP EBee ERou MMil MWat MWgw NSti SPla WCot WEas WLRN WOld |
| 'Rosa Star' | SHel WOld |
| *rotundifolius* 'Variegatus' | See *Felicia amelloides* variegated |
| * *sativus atrocaeruleus* | Last listed 1998 |
| ¶ *scaber* | CPLG |
| *scandens* | See *A. carolinianus* |
| *schreberi* | CHea WCot |
| § *sedifolius* | CHea EBee ELan EMan LFis MSte MWat SDix SUsu WCot WEas WFar WOld WPer |
| - 'Nanus' | CHan ECha EFou ERou LFis MBri MBro MLLN NBir NFai NLar NSti SMrm WByw WCot WFar WOld |
| ◆ - 'Snow Flurries' | See *A. ericoides* f. *prostratus* 'Snow Flurry' |
| *shortii* | Last listed 1996 |
| § *sibiricus* | WOld |
| 'Snow Star' | SHel WOld |
| sp. CC&McK 145 | Last listed 1997 |
| *spathulifolius* | Last listed 1997 |
| *spectabilis* | CLyd WOld |
| *stracheyi* | NTow |
| *subspicatus* | WPer |
| ¶ *tataricus* | WOld |
| - 'Jindai' | WCot |
| *thomsonii* 'Nanus' | CGle CLyd CSam EBee EBrP EBre GCHN LBre LFis LGre MBro NNrd NRoo SBla SBre SPer WCot WEas WFar WHoo WOld WSHC |
| *tibeticus* | See *A. flaccidus* |
| § *tongolensis* | EBee EPfP MLLN SAga SEas SIgm SRms WCot WFar WWin |
| - 'Berggarten' | CHar EBrP EBre LBre LFis MBri MCli MMil NHaw NRoo SBla SBre SCro SUsu WAbe WFar WMer |
| - 'Dunkleviolette' | GBuc NBro SRms |
| - 'Lavender Star' | CBlo EFou GBuc SRms |
| - 'Leuchtenburg' | ERou WCot |
| - 'Napsbury' | CBlo EHic ERou MCli |
| - 'Sternschnuppe' | Last listed 1998 |
| - Summer Greeting | See *A. tongolensis* 'Sommergrüss' |
| - 'Wartburgstern' | CDoC CMdW CMil EBee EGar EMan EPfP LFis MBri MCli NGdn NPri SPla WFar WGwG WLRN WPer WWal |
| *tradescantii* L. | CGle CLTr EBee ECha EFou ELan EMan MBNS MFir MWgw NOak NSti SCou SHel SMad WEas WOld |
| - hort. | See *A. pilosus* var. *demotus* |
| ¶ *trinervius* subsp. *ageratoides* 'Asran' | SSvw |
| *tripolium* | WHer |
| *turbinellus* hort. ♀ | CPlt EBee ECGN EFou EMon GBuc GMac LGre MBNS MBro MHlr NBrk NTow SChu SDix SMrm WCot WFar WHer WHoo WOld |
| *umbellatus* | CBre CLTr EMon EPPr NSti SRms WCot WOld WPrP |
| *vablii* | EBee ECou GAbr WPer |
| *vimineus* Lamarck | See *A. lateriflorus* |
| - 'Ptarmicoides' | See *A. ptarmicoides* |
| § 'White Climax' | EFou MTed MUlv WCot WOld |
| *yunnanensis* | Last listed 1996 |

| | |
|---|---|
| 'Yvonne' | CBre EBee |

## ASTERANTHERA (Gesneriaceae)
| | |
|---|---|
| *ovata* | CAbb CDoC CFil CGre CPlN GGGa GGar GOrc MBal SBid WAbe WCru WGwG WSHC WWal WWat |

## ASTERISCUS (Asteraceae)
| | |
|---|---|
| 'Gold Coin' | See *A. maritimus* |
| * 'Golden Dollar' | NPri |
| § *maritimus* | EHic LIck |
| § *spinosus* | Last listed 1996 |

## ASTEROMOEA (Asteraceae)
| | |
|---|---|
| *mongolica* | See *Kalimeris mongolica* |
| ◆ *pinnatifida* | See *Kalimeris pinnatifida* |

## ASTEROPYRUM (Ranunculaceae)
| | |
|---|---|
| * *cavaleriei* | WCru |

## ASTILBE ✿ (Saxifragaceae)
| | |
|---|---|
| ¶ 'America' | MDun |
| 'Aphrodite' | |
| (*simplicifolia* hybrid) | CCuc CMCo CPlt EAst EGol ENot GAbr LFis MBri NFla NHol NMir NPro NRoo SChu SPla SSpi WGor |
| x *arendsii* | CPea MBro NFor WPer |
| - 'Amethyst' | CBlo CCuc CHor CMGP CMHG CTri EBee EGol MCli NFai NRoo SEas SMer SPer WHil |
| - 'Anita Pfeifer' | CMHG LRHS MBri WPnP |
| - 'Bergkristall' | CCuc CMHG EMil |
| § - 'Brautschleier' ♀ | CB&S CMHG CTri ECtt EFou EGol ENot EPfP GCHN MWat NCut NFai SMer |
| - 'Bressingham Beauty' | CCuc CDoC CMHG EBee EBrP EBre ECtt EHon ELan ENot EPar ERic EWTr GCHN GMaP LBre LSyl MBri MCLN MRav NFla NHol NRoo NSti SBre SEas SPer SSpe |
| - Bridal Veil | See *A.* x *arendsii* 'Brautschleier' |
| - 'Bumalda' | CFir CMCo COtt GCHN MBri NHed WFar WWat |
| - 'Cattleya' | CCuc CMHG EFou WFar WGor |
| * - 'Cattleya Dunkel' | CMHG |
| - 'Ceres' | CCuc CMHG MWat NHol |
| § - 'Diamant' | CHor CMHG EAst LFis MBri NGdn SEas WFar |
| - Diamond | See *A.* x *arendsii* 'Diamant' |
| - 'Drayton Glory' | See *A.* x *rosea* 'Peach Blossom' |
| ◆ - 'Eliblo' | See *A.* x *arendsii* Elizabeth Bloom = 'Eliblo' |
| § - Elizabeth Bloom = 'Eliblo' | ERic GCHN GSki MCLN NGdn SVil WHil |
| ◆ - 'Ellie' | See *A.* x *arendsii* 'Ellie van Veen' |
| § - 'Ellie van Veen' | CCuc EPGN LRHS MBri |
| - 'Erica' | CBlo CHor CMHG CTri EWTr MBri MDun MRav |
| - 'Fanal' ♀ | More than 30 suppliers |
| § - 'Federsee' | CB&S CMGP CMHG ECha ELan ENot LHop SPer WFar WLRN |
| § - 'Feuer' | CB&S CCuc CMGP CMHG CSam ECha ELan EPfP GCHN NHol NVic SPer SPla |
| - Fire | See *A.* x *arendsii* 'Feuer' |
| - 'Gertrud Brix' | CB&S CCuc EPar NGdn WMer WRus |
| ◆ - 'Gladstone' | See *A.* 'W.E. Gladstone' (japonica hybrid) |
| - 'Gloria' | CCuc CMHG CTri LPBA MBri NCut |

| | Name | Suppliers |
|---|---|---|
| § | - 'Gloria Purpurea' | CBlo CCuc CHor CMHG ECha LRHS MBri MDun MTed NHol |
| | - Glow | See *A.* x *arendsii* 'Glut' |
| § | - 'Glut' | CMHG MBri NHol NPri SRms |
| | - 'Granat' | CCuc CDoC CHor CMHG MBal MCli WLRN WWin |
| | - 'Grete Püngel' | EGol LRHS MBri MLLN WMer |
| | - 'Harmony' | CMHG |
| | - Hyacinth | See *A.* x *arendsii* 'Hyacinth' |
| § | - 'Hyazinth' | CDoC CFai CMHG EGol EHic ELan EWTr GAbr MCli NFai NHol WWal |
| | - 'Irrlicht' | CB&S CCuc CGle EBee EHon ELan EPla LHop LPBA MBal MBri NDea SEas SPer SWat |
| | - 'Kvele' | CMHG MBri WFar WViv |
| § | - 'Lachskönigin' | CMHG MWat |
| | - 'Lilli Goos' | Last listed 1996 |
| | - 'Mont Blanc' | Last listed 1998 |
| | - 'Obergärtner Jürgens' | EBee EMan EPGN GNau NCut SAga |
| | - 'Paul Gaärder' | CMHG |
| | - 'Pink Curtsy' | Last listed 1998 |
| | - Pink Pearl | See *A.* x *arendsii* 'Rosa Perle' |
| ♦ | - 'Queen of Holland' | See *A.* 'Queen of Holland' (japonica hybrid) |
| | - Red Light | See *A.* x *arendsii* 'Rotlicht' |
| § | - 'Rosa Perle' | CCuc CMHG ECha NHol |
| § | - 'Rotlicht' | CCuc CPlt ECot EHic MBri NPro NSti WFar WGor |
| | - Salmon Queen | See *A.* x *arendsii* 'Lachskönigin' |
| | - 'Sarma' | MBri |
| | - 'Snowdrift' | CCuc EBrP EBre ECha EFou EGol EPGN EPla GAri LBre MBNS MCli NFor NLon NOak NOrc NPro NRoo SBre SWat WHil |
| | - 'Solferino' | CMHG |
| ♦ | - 'Spartan' | See *A.* x *arendsii* 'Rotlicht' |
| | - 'Spinell' | CBlo MWat |
| | - 'Venus' | CCuc CSam ECha ECtt EFou EGol MBel NHol NOrc NVic SPer SSpe SWat WFar WViv |
| | - 'Walküre' | CMHG |
| ♦ | - 'Washington' | See *A.* 'Washington' (japonica hybrid) |
| § | - 'Weisse Gloria' | CCuc CMHG EBee ECha EPar LPBA NMGW NSti SLod SPla |
| | - 'Weisse Perle' | Last listed 1998 |
| | - White Gloria | See *A.* x *arendsii* 'Weisse Gloria' |
| | - 'White Queen' | GChr NHol NWoo |
| | - 'William Reeves' | CCuc CMHG MFir NHol |
| | - 'Zuster Theresa' | MBri |
| | *astilboides* | CHan NHol WCot |
| | 'Atrorosea' (*simplicifolia* hybrid) | ECha MBri SRms |
| ¶ | 'Avalanche' | EPGN |
| | 'Betsy Cuperus' (*thunbergii* hybrid) | CMHG EFou MCAu MCli NCut |
| | 'Bonn' (*japonica* hybrid) | CB&S EPar LPBA SRms WRus |
| | 'Bremen' (*japonica* hybrid) | CMHG LPBA |
| § | 'Bronce Elegans' (*simplicifolia* hybrid) ♀ | CB&S CMGP COtt EAst ECha EFou EPar GSki MBNS MBal MGrG NFla NHar NHol NMir NOrc SChu SPer WBea WFar WHoo WWat |
| * | 'Carmine King' | Last listed 1997 |
| | 'Carnea' (*simplicifolia* hybrid) | Last listed 1997 |
| ♦ | 'Catherine Deneuve' | See *A.* x *arendsii* 'Federsee' |
| | 'Cherry Ripe' | See *A.* x *arendsii* 'Feuer' |
| | *chinensis* | CMHG IBlr MMal NCut |
| | - var. *davidii* | CMHG |
| | - 'Finale' | CCuc GLil NHol SPer SRms WEas WFar WWat |
| | - 'Frankentroll' | CMHG |
| | - 'Intermezzo' | EBee GMaP |
| § | - var. *pumila* ♀ | More than 30 suppliers |
| | - - 'Serenade' | CCuc LBuc MBri WFar |
| ¶ | - 'Purperkerze' | MBri |
| | - 'Purple Glory' | CMHG |
| | - 'Spätsommer' | CMHG |
| ¶ | - var. *taquetii* | NSti |
| | - - Purple Lance | See *A. chinensis* var. *taquetii* 'Purpurlanze' |
| § | - - 'Purpurlanze' | CMCo CMHG ECha EFou EMan GCHN LGre MBri MRav NBir NCat NDov NPla NPro WCot WFar WMer WMow WWin |
| § | - - 'Superba' ♀ | CCuc CGle CMHG CRow EBee ECha ECoo ELan ENot GCHN MLLN MNrw MSte NCut NDea NFai NFor NHol NSti NVic SDix SPer SRms WEas WOld |
| | - 'Veronica Klose' | LRHS MBri NLar NPro |
| | - 'Visions' | CCuc MBri NPro WFar |
| | Cologne | See *A.* 'Köln' (japonica hybrid) |
| ♦ | 'Crimson Feather' | See *A.* x *arendsii* 'Gloria Purpurea' |
| | x *crispa* | IBlr |
| | - 'Gnom' | CMCo NHar |
| | - 'Lilliput' | CMGP EBee NHar NLar NPro SRPl |
| § | - 'Perkeo' ♀ | More than 30 suppliers |
| ♦ | - 'Peter Pan' | See *A.* x *crispa* 'Perkeo' |
| | - 'Snow Queen' | NHar NMen NPro WFar |
| | 'Darwin's Dream' | EBee MBri |
| | 'Darwin's Surprise' | Last listed 1997 |
| | 'Deutschland' (*japonica* hybrid) | CB&S CMHG ELan EPGN EWTr GCHN LSyl MBNS MBri MCLN MGrG MRav NBir NFor NHol NLon NVic SEas SMad SPer SPla SRms SSoC SSpi SWat WEas WHoo WWal WWin |
| | 'Dunkellachs' (*simplicifolia* hybrid) | CBlo CCuc CM&M EBee MBel MBri MDun SPla WAbe WMer WViv |
| | 'Düsseldorf' (*japonica* hybrid) | CCuc CMGP CMHG GGar MBri SPer SSea WRus |
| ¶ | 'Dutch Treat' (v) | CMea |
| * | 'Elisabeth' | EPGN |
| | 'Emden' (*japonica* hybrid) | MWat |
| | 'Etna' (*japonica* hybrid) | CB&S CCuc CMHG EGle GBri GHCN MBal NCut SRms WRus |
| | 'Europa' (*japonica* hybrid) | CBlo CCuc EBee EMil EPGN LPBA MBal NCut NFai NOak SMad SSoC SSpe |
| | *glaberrima* | EPPr EPar |
| | - var. *saxatilis* ♀ | CCuc CRow ELan GAri GCHN IMGH MBal MBro NOak NRoo NRya NSla NWoo SSmi WAbe WHal WOve WPrP |
| | - *saxosa* | See *A.* 'Saxosa' |
| * | - - *minor* | Last listed 1998 |
| | 'Glenroy Elf' | MBal |
| | *grandis* | CMHG SSca |
| | 'Hennie Graafland' (*simplicifolia* hybrid) | CB&S CMCo COtt EFou EGol MBNS |
| | 'Inshriach Pink'CCuc (*simplicifolia* hybrid) | CMHG EFou EGol EHoe ELan EPla EWTr GCHN GChr GCrs GDra MBri NBir NHar NHol NMen NNrd NOak NPla WCot WFar WHal |
| | 'Jo Ophorst' (*davidii* hybrid) | CCuc CMHG ECha GCHN LPBA MBel MRav NGdn SPer WLRN WWal |

'Koblenz' (*japonica* hybrid) CCuc MBri
§ 'Köln' (*japonica* hybrid)    EMil LPBA NFai
   ***koreana***    WCot
   'Koster'    LPBA
   'Kriemhilde'    Last listed 1998
   'Lady Digby'    LPBA
\* ***lilacina***    MBro
   'Maggie Daley'    COtt EBee EPGN
   'Mainz' (*japonica* hybrid)    EMil GCHN
   ***microphylla***    CCuc CMHG NHol
   - pink    CMHG NHol
   'Moerheimii'    CMHG
   (*thunbergii* hybrid)
   'Montgomery'    CCuc CHor ECha MBri NFai
   (*pitardii* x *japonica*)    NGdn NHol
   'Möwe' (*japonica* hybrid)    Last listed 1996
   Ostrich Plume    See *A.* 'Straussenfeder'
      (*thunbergii* hybrid)
   'Peaches and Cream'    MBri MRav
   'Peter Barrow'    SIng SRms
   (*glaberrima* hybrid)
   'Professor van der Wielen'    CCuc CGle CMHG EAst EFou
   (*thunbergii* hybrid)    EGle EMan GCHN GCal GGar
      MCAu MCli MSte SDix SMer SPer
      SRms SSpi WWat
   ***pumila***    See *A. chinensis* var. *pumila*
\* 'Queen'    LPBA
§ 'Queen of Holland'    MCli
   (*japonica* hybrid)
\* 'Red Admiral'    NFor NLon
   'Red Sentinel'    CB&S CCuc EFou EPGN EPar
   (*japonica* hybrid)    GCHN MCli NHar NHol NOrc
      SPla
   'Rheinland'    CCuc EGol EPGN EPfP GCHN
   (*japonica* hybrid) ♀    LPBA MBro NArg SLon SMad SSea
      WEas WHoo WRus
   ***rivularis***    CFil CMHG WPGP
§ x ***rosea*** 'Peach Blossom'    CB&S CCuc CM&M EMan EPGN
      EPar EWTr GCHN MBal MBel
      MBro MGrG NArg NBir NFai NHol
      NSti SEas SHel SRPl WFar WHoo
      WMer
¶ - 'Queen Alexandra'    SPla
   'Rosea'    CCuc NHol WFar
   (*simplicifolia* hybrid)
¶ Rosemary Bloom =    EBee
   'Rosblo'
§ 'Saxosa'    EPot ESis GGar NMGW SPla
\* 'Saxosa' x ***glaberrima***    Last listed 1997
\* 'Showstar'    LRHS NCut
   ***simplicifolia*** ♀    CGle CRow NHar NMen WEas
      WFar
   - 'Alba'    GGar NHol
   - Bronze Elegance    See *A.* 'Bronce Elegans'
      (*simplicifolia* hybrid)
   - 'Darwin's Snow Sprite'    EBee LRHS MBri NHol NPri
   - x ***glaberrima***    GDra NHar
¶ - 'Jacqueline'    EBee LBuc NCut
\* - 'Nana Alba'    NPro
   - 'Praecox Alba'    CBlo CCuc ECha MCli NFla NHol
      WLin
   - 'Sheila Haxton'    Last listed 1996
   sp. CLD 1559    Last listed 1997
   'Sprite'    CB&S CCuc CMCo CMHG CRow
   (*simplicifolia* hybrid) ♀    ECha EGol ELan EMNN EPot GDra
      GHCN MBal MBar MBri MGrG
      MWat NDea NFor NHar NHol
      NMen NRoo NSti SPer SPla SPlb
      WEas WFar WWal
§ 'Straussenfeder'    CCuc CM&M CMCo CMGP
   (*thunbergii* hybrid) ♀    CMHG CTri EAst EBee EFou EPla
      GCHN GCal GHCN GMaP MCAu
      MCli NHol SSpi WLRN WPnP
      WViv

   'Superba'    See *A. chinensis* var. *taquetii*
      'Superba'
   ***thunbergii***    Last listed 1998
   'Vesuvius'    CB&S CBlo CCuc CHor LSyl MBel
   (*japonica* hybrid)    MDun MGrG NCut NFai NSti
§ 'W.E. Gladstone'    CBlo CMea EAst GCHN GHCN
   (*japonica* hybrid)    MSte NHol NPla WGor WMer
      WWeb
§ 'Washington'    EPGN MCli WMer
   (*japonica* hybrid)
   'Willie Buchanan'    More than 30 suppliers
   (*simplicifolia* hybrid)
¶ 'Wisley Form'    CPla
   'Yakushima'    GCHN
\* ***yakusimanum*** pink    Last listed 1998

## ASTILBOIDES (Saxifragaceae)
§ ***tabularis***    CGle CHad CRow EAst ECha
      EGol ELan EWTr GAbr GMaP
      MBro MCli MRav NDea NHol
      NLar NSti NVic SMac SSoC SWat
      WCot WFar WHoo WWat WWhi

## ASTRAGALUS (Papilionaceae)
   ***alopecuroides***    EMan
   ***alpinus***    Last listed 1998
   ***arnotianus***    Last listed 1997
   ***arnottii*** JCA 14169    CPBP
   ***centralpinus***    Last listed 1998
   ***cicer***    WCot
   ***danicus***    Last listed 1998
   ***detritalis***    Last listed 1998
   ***falcatus***    EBee
   ***glycyphyllos***    CAgr EMan IIve MSal WWye
§ ***massiliensis***    Last listed 1998
   ***membranaceus***    ELau IIve MSal
   ***odoratus***    Last listed 1997
   ***penduliflorus***    Last listed 1996
   ***purpureus***    Last listed 1996
   ***purshii***    Last listed 1998
   ***tragacantha*** hort.    See *A. massiliensis*
   ***utahensis***    EHyt
§ ***whitneyi*** var. ***confusus***    Last listed 1998
\* - var. ***lenophyllus***    Last listed 1997
      NNS 93-98
♦ - var. ***sonneanus***    See *A. whitneyi* var. *confusus*

## ASTRANTHIUM (Asteraceae)
   ***beamanii***    Last listed 1997

## ASTRANTIA (Apiaceae)
   ***bavarica***    EBee GCal WCot
   ***carniolica***    EMon EOld
   - *major*    See *A. major*
   - var. *rubra*    See *A. major rubra*
   - 'Variegata'    See *A. major* 'Sunningdale
      Variegated'
   ***belleborifolia*** hort.    See *A. maxima*
§ ***major***    More than 30 suppliers
   - alba    CMHG CRow ECGN ECha EFou
      EGol LLWP MRav NBir NCat
      NGdn NPer WMoo
   - subsp. ***biebersteinii***    EBee EMon NBir
   - 'Buckland'    ECha GBuc LGre MTed MTho
      SIgm SSpe SSpi SWas WHal WLin
      WMoo WPnP
   - 'Canneman'    CLon EMon EWes NSti WCot
   - 'Claret'    CBos CLAP CRDP ECha EMon
      EOld EPPr LGre MBro SAga SWas
      SWat WCot WPnP WRus
   - 'Elmblut'    EMon
   - 'Hadspen Blood'    More than 30 suppliers

| | |
|---|---|
| - 'Hillview Red' | CElw |
| - subsp. *involucrata* | CLon EBee GCHN MBro NHol NVic SCro SWat WFar |
| - - 'Barrister' | CFil CSam EBee GBuc SSpi WFar WPGP |
| - - 'Margery Fish' | See *A. major* subsp. *involucrata* 'Shaggy' |
| - - 'Moira Reid' | GBri WRus |
| § - - 'Shaggy' ♀ | More than 30 suppliers |
| - 'Lars' | CBot CBro COlW CPar EAst EBee EFou EGol EMan EMon EPPr EPar MBri MCAu MLLN NFai NHol NOak NPri NWes SMad SPer SSoC WElm WFar WHoo WRus WWat |
| - 'Lars' seedlings | CSpe GCal MBel |
| - 'Maureen' | NOak |
| - 'Primadonna' | CFri CSam EBee EGol EHrv EMan MBNS MSte MTis NCut NLar NWes SCro SIgm WFar WHil WMer WMoo WPer WRha WWat WWeb |
| - 'Roma' | LGre SWas |
| - *rosea* | More than 30 suppliers |
| - 'Rosensinfonie' | EBee EOld GLil MCli MLLN MWrn NCut WMer WMoo WPyg WViv |
| § - *rubra* | More than 30 suppliers |
| - 'Ruby Cloud' | EHrv MBro WHoo |
| - 'Ruby Wedding' | CBlo CGle CLon EBrP EBre EHrv EOld GBuc LBre LGre MRav MTho MWrn NCot NFor SBla SBre SWas WCot WFar WMer |
| ¶ - 'Starburst' | NCot |
| § - 'Sunningdale Variegated' ♀ | More than 30 suppliers |
| - 'Titoki Point' | WCot |
| - 'Variegata' | See *A. major* 'Sunningdale Variegated' |
| § *maxima* ♀ | More than 30 suppliers |
| - 'Mark Fenwick' | NBir |
| *minor* | SRms WCru |
| 'Rainbow' | NLar |
| *rubra* | See *A. major rubra* |

## ASYNEUMA (Campanulaceae)

| | |
|---|---|
| *canescens* | EBee EMan LFis MLLN NFai SSca WCot WWin |
| *limonifolium* | Last listed 1996 |
| ¶ - subsp. *pestalozzae* | EHyt |
| *lobelioides* | SIng |
| *pulvinatum* | CPBP EHyt SIng WAbe |
| - Mac&W 5880 | EPot NNrd |
| *trichostegium* | EPot |

## ASYSTASIA (Acanthaceae)

| | |
|---|---|
| *bella* | See *Mackaya bella* |
| § *gangetica* | CSev LHil SYvo |
| *violacea* | See *A. gangetica* |

## ATHAMANTA (Apiaceae)

| | |
|---|---|
| *macedonica* | Last listed 1996 |
| ¶ - subsp. *arachnoidea* | EBee NChi |
| - - JCA 224105 | IDac |
| *turbith* | LGre SIgm |
| - subsp. *haynaldii* | NTow |
| *vestina* JCA 224300 | IDac SIgm SSpi |

## ATHANASIA (Asteraceae)

| | |
|---|---|
| ¶ *parviflora* | CPLG |

## ATHEROSPERMA (Monimiaceae)

| | |
|---|---|
| *moschatum* | CB&S CGre CPLG WSHC WWat |

## ATHROTAXIS (Taxodiaceae)

| | |
|---|---|
| *cupressoides* | GAri MBar WCwm |
| *laxifolia* | CDoC MBar WCwm |
| *selaginoides* | CDoC CTrG EPot WCwm |

## ATHYRIUM ✿ (Woodsiaceae)

| | |
|---|---|
| *filix-femina* ♀ | More than 30 suppliers |
| * - *congestum cristatum* | WFib |
| - 'Corymbiferum' | GQui LSyl NHar NMar SRms |
| ¶ - 'Crispum Grandiceps Kaye' | SRms |
| - Cristatum Group | CCuc CLAP EFer ELan EMon NHol SCob SWat WFib WRic |
| § - Cruciatum Group | CRDP CRow EBee EGol ELan EMar EMon GAri NHar NHol SLon SRms WFib WRic |
| - 'Fieldii' | CCuc CLAP CRow EFer NHar NHol SChu SRms WFib |
| - 'Frizelliae' ♀ | CBar CCuc CMil CRDP EBee EBrP EBre EFer ELan EMon IOrc LBre LHil MBri MLan NHar NHed NHol NMar NOrc SBre SChu SCob SMad SPla SRms WFib WGor WRic WWat |
| - 'Frizelliae Capitatum' | CCuc CRow NMar WFib |
| ¶ - 'Frizelliae Cristatum' | SRms |
| - 'Grandiceps' | EBee NHar NMar SRms |
| - 'Minutissimum' | CCuc CFil CPlt CRDP EBee ECha EFou EGol EHon ELan EMon GCHN LPBA NMar SCob WFib WPGP |
| - 'Percristatum' | EMon |
| - Plumosum Group | CFil CLAP GQui NMar WFib |
| - 'Plumosum Axminster' | CFil CRDP WRic |
| - 'Plumosum Cristatum' | NMar |
| - 'Plumosum Percristatum' | GQui NMar |
| - Ramocristatum Group | NMar |
| ¶ - 'Rotstiel' | CLAP MBri MSCN |
| - 'Setigerum Cristatum' | NMar WRic |
| * - *superbum* 'Druery' | WFib |
| - 'Vernoniae' ♀ | CLAP EBee EFer ELan EMon MBri WRic |
| - 'Vernoniae Cristatum' | EMon GBin MBal NHol NMar SPer WFib |
| - Victoriae Group & cl. | See *A. filix-femina* Cruciatum Group |
| ¶ *flexile* | WRic |
| *goeringianum* 'Pictum' | See *A. niponicum* var. *pictum* |
| *niponicum* | CCuc SLdr |
| - crested | ELan |
| - f. *metallicum* | See *A. niponicum* var. *pictum* |
| § - var. *pictum* ♀ | More than 30 suppliers |
| - - crested | Last listed 1998 |
| * - - 'Cristatoflabellatum' | CLAP EMon |
| *otophorum* ♀ | CRDP EMon NHol NMar SChu SRms WRic |
| - var. *okanum* | CBos CFil CLAP EBee ELan EMar GNau LHil MBri NBus NHar NHol WAbe WCot |
| *proliferum* | See *Diplazium proliferum* |
| *strigulosum* | Last listed 1996 |
| *vidalii* | CFil CLAP MBri WRic |

## ATRACTYLODES (Asteraceae)

| | |
|---|---|
| *japonica* | EFEx |
| *macrocephala* | EFEx GPoy |

## ATRAGENE See CLEMATIS

## ATRIPLEX (Chenopodiaceae)

| | |
|---|---|
| *canescens* | CAgr WDin |

| | |
|---|---|
| ***halimus*** | CAgr CB&S CBot CGle CHan ECha EHoe ENot GOrc MRav NBir NBrk NLar SLon SPer SSto SWat WCot WDin WHCG WHer |
| ***hortensis*** | MChe |
| - gold-leaved | MLan WCot WJek |
| - var. ***rubra*** | CArn CGle CHad CRDP ELan EOHP LHol MChe MGed NChi NWes SDys SIde WCHb WCot WEas WHer WJek WKif WOak WWye |
| ***portulacoides*** | See *Halimione portulacoides* |

## ATROPA (Solanaceae)

| | |
|---|---|
| ***bella-donna*** | CArn GBar GPoy IIve MSal WWye |
| - var. ***lutea*** | EMon MSal |
| ***mandragora*** | See *Mandragora officinarum* |

## ATROPANTHE (Solanaceae)

| | |
|---|---|
| § ***sinensis*** | MSal |

## AUBRIETA ✿ (Brassicaceae)

| | |
|---|---|
| ***albomarginata*** | See *A.* 'Argenteovariegata' |
| 'Alida Vahli' | Last listed 1996 |
| 'Alix Brett' | CPBP EBrP EBre EDAr ELan LBee LBre NEgg NPer SAga SBre |
| 'April Joy' | ECot EDAr ELan SRms |
| § 'Argenteovariegata' | CSpe ELan LHop NRoo SAga SBla SIgm SRms WAbe WPyg WWeb |
| 'Astolat' (v) | GCHN LBee MOne NSla SAga SBla SRms WAbe WEas WPat |
| § 'Aureovariegata' | EBrP EBre EGle ELan LBre MPla NFla NPer NRoo SBla SBre SIng WAbe WFar |
| 'Belisha Beacon' | ECtt EMNN LBee MBri |
| Bengal hybrids | ERic GAbr NFla WGor |
| Blaue Schönheit | See *A.* 'Blue Beauty' |
| 'Blue Cascade' | ECtt EPfP LPVe MPla SPlb WGor WShe |
| 'Blue Emperor' | WMer |
| 'Blue Gown' | NEgg |
| 'Blue King' | WMer |
| * 'Blue Mist' | Last listed 1997 |
| § 'Bob Saunders' (d) | CMea CTri EBrP EBre ECtt ELan LBee LBre LHop SBre |
| ¶ 'Bonfire' | ECho |
| * 'Bonsul' | Last listed 1997 |
| 'Bordeaux' | WMer |
| 'Bressingham Pink' (d) | CMea CNic CTri EBrP EBre ECtt ELan LBre LHop SBre |
| 'Bressingham Red' | EBrP EBre LBre SBre WMer |
| ***canescens*** | EPot NTow |
| 'Carnival' | See *A.* 'Hartswood Purple' |
| ¶ Cascade Series mixed | WFar |
| § ***columnae macrostyla*** | Last listed 1998 |
| 'Cumulus' | Last listed 1996 |
| * ***deltoidea*** 'Gloria' | WPat |
| - 'Nana Variegata' | CPBP EPot MPla MTho WGor |
| - ***rosea*** | Last listed 1998 |
| - 'Tauricola' | WMer WPyg |
| - 'Tauricola Variegata' | Last listed 1997 |
| - Variegata Group | ECtt EPot ESis LHop MTho NMen NSla SIng WFar WPat |
| 'Doctor Mules' ♀ | CTri EBrP EBre LBee LBre NEgg SBre SIng SMer SRms WPat |
| 'Doctor Mules Variegata' | LGro NEgg |
| ¶ Double Stock-flowered Group pink | MTed |
| 'Dream' | ECtt SIng |
| 'Elsa Lancaster' | EHyt EMNN EPot EWes GCrs NMen NSla |
| 'Fire King' | WMer |
| § 'Frühlingszauber' | SRms WGor |
| 'Gloriosa' | NEgg SIng |
| 'Godstone' | EWes |
| 'Golden Carpet' | SIng |
| 'Golden King' | See *A.* 'Aureovariegata' |
| ***gracilis*** | Last listed 1998 |
| § - subsp. ***scardica*** | NTow SSca |
| * 'Graeca' | Last listed 1997 |
| 'Graeca Superba' | Last listed 1998 |
| 'Greencourt Purple' | ELan EMNN GAbr MOne MWat SIng |
| 'Gurgedyke' | ECho ELan SIng SRms |
| 'Hartswood' | SIng |
| § 'Hartswood Purple' | Last listed 1997 |
| 'Hendersonii' | SRms |
| 'Ina den Ouden' | WMer |
| 'J.S. Baker' | SRms |
| 'Joan Allen' | Last listed 1998 |
| 'Joy' (d) | EMNN SIng |
| 'Lavender Gem' | Last listed 1998 |
| 'Leichtlinii' | NPri WPyg |
| 'Lemon and Lime' | LBee |
| 'Lilac Cascade' | Last listed 1997 |
| 'Little Gem' | Last listed 1998 |
| 'Lodge Crave' | SIng |
| ***macedonica*** | EPot |
| 'Magician' | ECtt |
| 'Mars' | SRms |
| 'Mary Poppins' | Last listed 1998 |
| 'Maurice Prichard' | ECtt EMNN |
| 'Mrs Lloyd Edwards' | ECtt |
| 'Mrs Rodewald' | CMea EMNN NEgg SRms |
| 'Novalis Blue' ♀ | SRms WLRN |
| 'Oakington Lavender' | ECho ELan LHop |
| ***parviflora*** | Last listed 1998 |
| 'Pennine Glory' | Last listed 1997 |
| 'Pennine Heather' | Last listed 1997 |
| 'Pike's Variegated' | EWes SRms |
| ***pinardii*** | EHyt |
| 'Prichard's A1' | WMer WPyg |
| 'Purity' | NPri SPla |
| 'Purple Cascade' | ECtt EMNN EPfP GCHN MPla SCoo SPlb SRms WFar WGor |
| 'Purple Charm' | SRms |
| ¶ 'Purple Emperor' | SIng |
| 'Red Carpet' | EBrP EBre ELan EMNN EPot LBre LGro MPla NEgg SBre SChu SIng SRms WWin |
| 'Red Carpet Variegated' | Last listed 1997 |
| 'Red Cascade' | ECtt EMNN GCHN MPla SCoo SPlb |
| 'Red Dyke' | SIng |
| * 'Red King' | Last listed 1998 |
| 'Riverslea' | SIng |
| 'Rosanna Miles' | SIng |
| 'Rose Queen' | CMea LBee SMrm |
| * 'Rosea Plena' | Last listed 1996 |
| 'Rosea Splendens' | MPla |
| 'Royal Blue' (Royal Series) | NNrd NRoo |
| 'Royal Red' (Royal Series) | ESis NPri NRoo SRms WFar WGor |
| 'Royal Violet' (Royal Series) | NPri NRoo WPer |
| ¶ 'Sauerland' | MTed |
| ***scardica*** subsp. ***scardica*** | See *A. gracilis* subsp. *scardica* |
| 'Schloss Eckberg' | WMer |
| 'Schofield's Double' | See *A.* 'Bob Saunders' |
| 'Silberrand' | ECha ECtt EDAr NSla |
| Spring Charm = 'Frühlingszauber' | See *A.* 'Frühlingszauber' |
| ***thessala*** | Last listed 1998 |
| 'Toby Saunders' | ECho |
| 'Triumphante' | CTri |
| 'Wanda' | ECho ELan SIng |

| | |
|---|---|
| 'Whitewell Gem' | NNrd SRms |

## AUCUBA ✿ (Aucubaceae)

| | |
|---|---|
| *japonica* (m) | CB&S CBlo CDoC ELan SReu |
| ¶ - (f) | CDul |
| ¶ - 'Angelon' | IHar |
| - 'Crassifolia' (m) | CHig MBal SAPC SArc |
| - 'Crotonifolia' (f/v) ♀ | CB&S CDoC EBee EBrP EBre ENot |
| | EPla LBre LPan MAsh MBal MBar |
| | MBri MGos MRav NBee NWea |
| | SBre SDix SPer SRPl WDin WHar |
| | WStI |
| - 'Gold Dust' (f/v) | CLan MAsh WWeb |
| - 'Gold Splash' | CBlo |
| - 'Golden King' (m/v) | CB&S CBlo CDoC CTrw EBee |
| | EHic ENot EPfP LNet MAsh MGos |
| | MUlv MWat SPla |
| - 'Golden Spangles' (v) | CB&S CBlo CDoC EBee ECot |
| | MBal |
| - 'Goldstrike' (v) | CBlo CDoC EHoe LNet |
| - 'Hillieri' (f) | CLan |
| ¶ - 'Lance Leaf' (m/v) | SLon WCru |
| - 'Latiomaculata' (v) | Last listed 1998 |
| - f.*longifolia* ♀ | CHig CMac SAPC SArc SDix WCru |
| - 'Maculata' | See *A. japonica* 'Variegata' |
| * - 'Marmorata' | LRHS |
| - 'Nana Rotundifolia' (f) | EPla MUlv |
| - 'Picturata' (m/v) | CB&S CBlo CPin EBee ENot EPfP |
| | MBal SAga SBid SPer WFar |
| - 'Rozannie' (f/m) | CB&S CBlo CDoC EAst ELan ENot |
| | EPla MAsh MBal MBlu MBri MGos |
| | MLan MRav MUlv MWat NBee |
| | NFla SAga SMad SPer SPla SReu |
| | WDin WStI |
| - 'Salicifolia' (f) | EBee ENot EPla MBri SLon SPer |
| | WBcn |
| - 'Speckles' | GSki |
| - 'Sulphurea Marginata' (f/v) | CB&S CDoC EHic EPla MBri SAga |
| | SBid SPer WBcn WBod WGwG |
| | WWal |
| § - 'Variegata' (f/v) | More than 30 suppliers |
| - Windsor form | EPla LRHS MAsh MBri |
| - 'Wykehurst' (v) | Last listed 1998 |

## AULAX (Proteaceae)

| | |
|---|---|
| ¶ *cancellata* | CTrC |

## AURINIA (Brassicaceae)

| | |
|---|---|
| § *corymbosa* | Last listed 1998 |
| § *petraea* | Last listed 1996 |
| § *saxatilis* ♀ | EBrP EBre GAbr LBre MBar MWat |
| | SBre SIng WFar |
| - 'Citrina' ♀ | CHal ECha ECtt EGar GMaP |
| | IMGH MPla MWat SDix SRms |
| | WCom WPyg |
| - 'Compacta' | CTri EBrP EBre ECtt ENot LBre |
| | MBro NFor NLon SBre WHoo |
| - 'Dudley Nevill' | EMan GAbr MSCN MWat SBla |
| | WFar WFoF |
| - 'Dudley Nevill Variegated' | EBrP EBre EGar EWes GAbr LBre |
| | NBir NRoo SBre WAbe WFar |
| - 'Flore Pleno' (d) | NRoo WCot WEas |
| - Gold Ball | See *A. saxatilis* 'Goldkugel' |
| - 'Gold Dust' | ECtt LGro MOne MWat SRms |
| - 'Golden Queen' | CDoC ECtt |
| § - 'Goldkugel' | ELan EMNN LBee NVic SRms |
| | WLRN |
| - 'Silver Queen' | ELan NRoo WEas |
| - 'Variegata' | SIng |

## AUSTROCEDRUS (Cupressaceae)

| | |
|---|---|
| § *chilensis* | CDoC CGre CKen CMCN LCon |
| | MBal |

## AVENA (Poaceae)

| | |
|---|---|
| *candida* | See *Helictotrichon sempervirens* |
| *sterilis* | Last listed 1998 |

## AVENULA See HELICTOTRICHON

## AVERRHOA (Geraniaceae)

| | |
|---|---|
| *carambola* (F) | LBlo |

## AYAPANA See EUPATORIUM

## AZARA ✿ (Flacourtiaceae)

| | |
|---|---|
| ¶ *alpina* | CFil |
| - G&P 5015 | WPGP |
| - SF 4583 | Last listed 1997 |
| *dentata* | CB&S CFil CGre CMac CPle CTrw |
| | ERea MBal WPGP WSHC |
| - 'Variegata' | CCHP ERea LRHS SBid |
| * *integerrima* | GQui |
| *integrifolia* | CFil SLon SPan WPGP |
| - 'Variegata' | CFil |
| *lanceolata* | CB&S CFil CHan CMCN CPle CTri |
| | EPfP IOrc ISea SPer WGer WPGP |
| | WPic WTro WWat |
| ¶ - G 3502 | WPGP |
| *microphylla* ♀ | CB&S CBrm CChe CDul CFil |
| | CGre CMCN CMHG CPle EBee |
| | EPla IOrc ISea MBal NSti SArc |
| | SBra SBrw SDry SSpi WBod WFar |
| | WPGP WSHC WWat |
| - 'Variegata' | CAbb CB&S CDoC CFil CGre |
| | CMac CPle EBee EHoe EPfP EPla |
| | GQui IOrc ISea LHop MBal MLan |
| | SBid SBrw SPan SSpi STre WCru |
| | WFar WGer WPGP WSHC WWat |
| N *paraguayensis* | CPin CPle GAri |
| * *patagonica* | Last listed 1997 |
| *petiolaris* | CFil CHan CPle EPfP NFla SPan |
| | WGer WPic |
| - G&P 5026 | WPGP |
| *serrata* | CDul CFil CHan CMCN CPle CTrC |
| | CTri EBee EPla GOrc ISea NTow |
| | SBrw SDix SMad SPer SRms SSta |
| | WBod WBor WCru WDin WFar |
| | WGer WHar WLRN WPyg WWat |
| - 'Patagonica' | ISea |
| sp. from Chile | CGre |
| *uruguayensis* | CFil CGre WPGP |

## AZOLLA (Azollaceae)

| | |
|---|---|
| *caroliniana* auct. | |
| non Willd. | See *A. mexicana* |
| - Willd. | See *A. filiculoides* |
| § *filiculoides* | CBen CRow ECoo EHon EMFW |
| | LPBA MSta NArg SCoo SRms SWat |
| | SWyc WStI |
| § *mexicana* | SWat WWeb |

## AZORELLA (Apiaceae)

| | |
|---|---|
| ¶ *compacta* | SIgm |
| *filamentosa* | ECou |
| *glebaria* A.Gray | See *Bolax gummifera* |
| - hort. | See *A. trifurcata* |
| *gummifera* | See *Bolax gummifera* |
| *lycopodioides* | GCHN |
| § *trifurcata* | CPar CTri ELan EPfP EPot GAbr |
| | GAri GTou NRoo SDys SIgm SIng |
| | SRms SSmi WAbe WByw WPer |
| - 'Nana' | CNic GGar MBro MTho MWat |
| | NHol NMen NNrd SDys SSmi |
| | WPat |

## AZORINA (Campanulaceae)

| | |
|---|---|
| § *vidalii* | CBot CSpe ERea SAPC SArc SVen WPer |
| - 'Rosea' | EMan |

# B

## BABIANA (Iridaceae)

| | |
|---|---|
| *ambigua* | Last listed 1998 |
| *angustifolia* | CGrW |
| 'Blue Gem' | CGrW LBow |
| *cedarbergensis* | Last listed 1998 |
| *disticha* | See *B. plicata* |
| *dregei* | Last listed 1998 |
| *ecklonii* | Last listed 1998 |
| hybrids | CGrW LBow |
| 'Laura' | Last listed 1998 |
| *nana* | Last listed 1998 |
| *odorata* | CGrW |
| ¶ *patula* | LBow |
| § *plicata* | CGrW |
| *pulchra* | LBow |
| *pygmaea* | Last listed 1998 |
| *rubrocyanea* | Last listed 1998 |
| *scabrifolia* | Last listed 1998 |
| *secunda* | Last listed 1998 |
| *striata* | Last listed 1998 |
| *stricta* | CGrW CSut |
| - 'Purple Star' | CGrW CPLG |
| - 'Tubergen's Blue' | CGrW |
| *tubulosa* | CGrW |
| *villosa* | CGrW |
| *villosula* | Last listed 1998 |
| 'White King' | Last listed 1998 |
| 'Zwanenburg's Glory' | CGrW |

## BACCHARIS (Asteraceae)

| | |
|---|---|
| *genistelloides* | SMad WCot |
| *glomeruliflora* | CPle |
| *halimifolia* | CPle GBin GQui SEND |
| - 'Twin Peaks' | SDry |
| *magellanica* | ECou |
| *patagonica* | CBlo LGre LSpr SAPC SAga SArc WBod WKif WPen |
| ¶ 'Sea Foam' ex RB 94142 | LLew NFla WSan |

## BACOPA (Scrophulariaceae)

| | |
|---|---|
| ¶ *caroliniana* | EOHP |
| ◆ 'Snowflake' | See *Sutera cordata* 'Snowflake' |

## BAECKEA (Myrtaceae)

| | |
|---|---|
| *camphorosmae* | Last listed 1998 |
| *gunniana* | MSag |
| *virgata* | CPLG CTrC |

## BAHIA (Asteraceae)

| | |
|---|---|
| *ambrosioides* | SVen |

## BAILLONIA (Verbenaceae)

| | |
|---|---|
| *juncea* | CPle WSHC |

## BALBISIA (Geraniaceae)

| | |
|---|---|
| *peduncularis* | SHFr WSan |

## BALDELLIA (Alismataceae)

| | |
|---|---|
| *ranunculoides* | CRow |
| - f. *repens* | CRDP EMan |

## BALLOTA (Lamiaceae)

| | |
|---|---|
| *acetabulosa* | CHan ECGP ECha EFou EGoo EHal EMan MBel NTow SDix SPar WCom WCot WWat WWeb |
| 'All Hallows Green' | CFee CGle EAst EBee ECtt EFou EGoo GBuc LHop MBri MCLN NDov NGdn NSti SChu SRPl WHen WWat |
| *hirsuta* | CGle CHan |
| *nigra* | CArn EBee MChe MHew MSal NLak SIde WHer WWye |
| § - 'Archer's Variegated' (v) | CHan CHar EGar EMan EMar EWes GBri MBel MGrG MLLN MSCN NFla NLak SAga SIde WCot WRus WSan |
| - 'Intakes White' | MInt |
| - 'Variegata' | See *B. nigra* 'Archer's Variegated' |
| - 'Zanzibar' (v) | EMon MBel |
| *pseudodictamnus* ♀ | More than 30 suppliers |

## BALSAMITA See TANACETUM

## BALSAMORHIZA (Asteraceae)

| | |
|---|---|
| *sagittata* | EMan |

## BAMBUSA ✿ (Poaceae - Bambusoideae)

| | |
|---|---|
| * *eutuldoides* | CB&S |
| *glaucescens* | See *B. multiplex* |
| * *gracillima* | CB&S COtt EPla |
| § *multiplex* | EFul LJus |
| - 'Alphonse Karr' | CB&S COtt EPla ISta SCob SDry WGer |
| - 'Chinese Goddess' | See *B. multiplex* var. *riviereorum* |
| § - 'Fernleaf' | CB&S COtt CTrC EFul EPla ISta LJus SCob SDry WGer |
| - 'Wang Tsai' | See *B. multiplex* 'Fernleaf' |
| *oldhamii* | Last listed 1997 |
| *pubescens* | See *Dendrocalamus strictus* |
| *textilis* | WJun |
| *tuldoides* | Last listed 1998 |
| *ventricosa* | ISta LJus SDry |
| *vulgaris* | Last listed 1997 |
| - 'Vittata' | Last listed 1997 |
| - 'Wamin' | Last listed 1997 |

## BANISTERIOPSIS (Malpighiaceae)

| | |
|---|---|
| *caapi* | Last listed 1998 |

## BANKSIA (Proteaceae)

| | |
|---|---|
| *aspleniifolia* | MSag |
| ¶ *baxteri* | CCpl |
| *burdettii* | Last listed 1997 |
| ¶ *caleyi* | CCpl CTrC |
| ¶ *canei* | CCpl |
| *coccinea* | Last listed 1998 |
| ¶ *conferta* | CTrC |
| *ericifolia* | CTrC SOWG |
| ¶ - var. *macrantha* | MSag |
| *grandis* | CTrC SOWG |
| *hookeriana* | Last listed 1998 |
| *integrifolia* | CB&S CPLG CTrC GQui |
| *marginata* | CTrC ECou |
| ¶ *media* | CCpl |
| *ornata* | Last listed 1998 |
| ¶ *praemorsa* red | CCpl |
| *quercifolia* | CGre |
| *robur* | Last listed 1998 |
| *saxicola* | MSag |
| *serrata* | SOWG |
| ¶ *serratifolia* | CPla |
| *speciosa* | Last listed 1998 |

*spinulosa* CTrC
- var. *collina* CCpl CTrC
¶ - var. *cunninghamii* CCpl
- var. *spinulosa* Last listed 1998

## BAPTISIA (Papilionaceae)
*arachnifera* Last listed 1997
*australis* ♀ More than 30 suppliers
- dark blue form Last listed 1997
- 'Exaltata' ELan GBuc LHop
§ *bracteata* SIgm
§ *lactea* CMdw CPle EBee ELan EWTr
MAvo NBir WCot
*leucantha* See *B. lactea*
*leucophaea* See *B. bracteata*
*megacarpa* Last listed 1997
*pendula* ECGN EMan NLar SIgm
*tinctoria* CPle MSal WPyg WThi

## BARBAREA (Brassicaceae)
*praecox* See *B. verna*
*rupicola* WPer
§ *verna* CArn GPoy SIde WHer WWye
*vulgaris* 'Variegata' CArn CGle CHal EBee ECha EHoe
ELan GAbr MFir MSCN NBro
NHex NOak NSti SDys SWat WBea
WByw WCHb WCot WMoo WOve
WSan WWye

## BARLERIA (Acanthaceae)
*cristata* Last listed 1997
* - *rosea* Last listed 1997
*greenii* Last listed 1997
*obtusa* Last listed 1998
- pink Last listed 1997
*repens* Last listed 1998
- 'Blue Prince' Last listed 1997
- 'Rosea' Last listed 1997
*suberecta* See *Dicliptera suberecta*

## BARTLETTINA See EUPATORIUM

## BASHANIA (Poaceae - Bambusoideae)
§ *fargesii* EPla ISta IJus SEND WJun
I *qingchengshanensis* CFil EPla

## BASSIA (Chenopodiaceae)
*scoparia* MSal
- f. *trichophylla* ♀ LPVe

## BASUTICA (Thymelaeaceae)
aff. *aberrans* JJ&JH 940178 NWCA

## BAUHINIA (Papilionaceae)
*alba* See *B. variegata*
*corymbosa* CPiN LCns SOWG
*galpinii* CPiN
*glabra* CPiN
*monandra* SOWG WMul
*natalensis* CSpe
*vahlii* CPiN
§ *variegata* MPEx WMul

## BEAUFORTIA (Myrtaceae)
*micrantha* SOWG
*orbifolia* SOWG
*sparsa* CTrC MSag SOWG

## BEAUMONTIA (Apocynaceae)
*grandiflora* CPiN LChe SOWG

## BEAUVERDIA See LEUCOCORYNE

## BECCARIOPHOENIX (Arecaceae)
*madagascariensis* LPal

## BECKMANNIA (Poaceae)
*eruciformis* Last listed 1997

## BEDFORDIA (Asteraceae)
*salicina* ECou

## BEGONIA ✿ (Begoniaceae)
'Abel Carrière' CHal ER&R
*acerifolia* See *B. vitifolia*
*acida* ER&R
*aconitifolia* ER&R
*acutifolia* ER&R
'Aladdin' ER&R
*albopicta* (C) CHal EBak ER&R
- 'Rosea' CHal WDib
'Allan Langdon' (T) CBla
'Alleryi' (C) ER&R
*alnifolia* ER&R
'Alto Scharff' ♀ ER&R
'Alzasco' (C) ER&R
*ampla* ER&R
'Amy' (T) CBla
*angularis* See *B. stipulacea*
'Anita Roseanna' (C) ER&R
'Anna Christine' (C) ER&R
'Anniversary' (T) CBla
'Apollo' (T) CBla
'Apricot Delight' (T) CBla
'Aquarius' ER&R
'Argentea' (R) EBak MBri
x *argenteoguttata* (C) CHal ER&R
'Aries' ER&R
'Arthur Mallet' ER&R
'Aruba' ER&R
'Autumn Glow' (T) ER&R
¶ 'Aya' (C) WDib
'Baby Perfection' WDib
'Bahamas' ER&R
'Barbara Ann' (C) ER&R
'Barclay Griffiths' ER&R
'Beatrice Haddrell' CHal ER&R WDib
* *benichoma* WDib
¶ 'Benitochiba' (R) ER&R
'Bernat Klein' (T) CBla
'Bertinii' (T) Last listed 1996
'Bess' ER&R
'Bessie Buxton' ER&R
'Bethlehem Star' ER&R WDib
§ 'Bettina Rothschild' (R) CHal ER&R WDib
'Beverly Jean' ER&R
'Billie Langdon' (T) CBla
'Black Knight' CHal
¶ 'Blanc de Neige' ER&R
'Bokit' ER&R WDib
'Bonaire' CHal
'Boomer' (C) ER&R
'Bouton de Rose' (T) NRog SDeJ
*bowerae* CHal ER&R
§ - var. *nigramarga* ER&R
¶ 'Boy Friend' ER&R
*bracteosa* ER&R
*brevirimosa* ER&R
'Brown Twist' WDib
'Bunchii' ER&R
'Burgundy Velvet' ER&R WDib
'Burle Marx' ♀ CHal ER&R LChe WDib

| | |
|---|---|
| 'Bush Baby' | CHal |
| 'Buttermilk' (T) | CBla |
| 'Calico Kew' | ER&R |
| 'Calla Queen' (S) | ER&R |
| 'Camelliiflora' (T) | NRog |
| 'Can-can' (R) | See *B.* 'Herzog von Sagan' |
| 'Can-can' (T) | CBla |
| 'Carol Mac' | ER&R |
| 'Carol Wilkins of Ballarat' (T) | CBla |
| 'Carolina Moon' (R) | ER&R |
| *carolineifolia* | LHil WDib |
| *carrieae* | ER&R |
| ♦ x *carrierei* | See *B.* Semperflorens Cultorum Group |
| 'Cathedral' | ER&R WDib |
| 'Chantilly Lace' | CHal ER&R |
| ¶ 'Charles Chevalier' | ER&R |
| 'Charles Jaros' | ER&R |
| 'Charm' (S) | CHal ER&R WDib |
| ¶ 'Cherry Feast' | NPri |
| ¶ 'Chocolate Box' | ER&R |
| ¶ 'Chocolate Chip' | ER&R |
| 'Christmas Candy' | ER&R WDib |
| 'Chumash' | ER&R |
| 'Clara' (R) | MBri |
| 'Cleopatra' ♀ | CHal ER&R MRav WDib |
| 'Clifton' | ER&R |
| *coccifera* | Last listed 1997 |
| *coccinea* (C) | ER&R WDib |
| *compta* | See *B. stipulacea* |
| 'Comte de Lesseps' (C) | WDib |
| *conchifolia* var. *rubrimacula* | ER&R |
| 'Concord' | ER&R |
| 'Connee Boswell' | ER&R WDib |
| *convolvulacea* | ER&R |
| *cooperi* | ER&R |
| * 'Coppelia' | CBla |
| x *corallina* | EBak |
| § - 'Lucerna' (C) | CHal EBak ER&R NPal |
| - 'Lucerna Amazon' (C) | CHal IBlr |
| 'Corbeille de Feu' | CHal ER&R |
| 'Cowardly Lion' (R) | ER&R |
| 'Crestabruchii' | ER&R |
| 'Crimson Cascade' | CBla |
| * 'Crystal Cascade' | CBla |
| *cubensis* | ER&R |
| *cucullata* | CHal ER&R |
| 'Curly Locks' (S) | CHal |
| ¶ 'Dancin' Fred' | ER&R |
| 'Dancing Girl' | ER&R |
| 'Dannebo' | MBri |
| 'D'Artagnan' | ER&R |
| 'Dawnal Meyer' (C) | ER&R WDib |
| ¶ 'De Elegans' | ER&R |
| 'Decker's Select' | ER&R |
| *decora* | ER&R |
| *deliciosa* | ER&R |
| 'Dewdrop' (R) | ER&R WDib |
| *diadema* | ER&R |
| 'Di-anna' (C) | ER&R |
| *dichotoma* | ER&R |
| *dichroa* (C) | ER&R |
| 'Di-erna' (C) | ER&R |
| *dietrichiana* hort. | See *B. echinosepala* 'Dietrichiana' |
| - Irmsch. | ER&R |
| 'Digswelliana' | ER&R |
| *discolor* | See *B. grandis* subsp. *evansiana* |
| ¶ 'Don Miller' | ER&R |
| ¶ 'Doublet Pink' | ER&R |
| ¶ 'Doublet Red' | ER&R |
| ¶ 'Doublet White' | ER&R |
| *dregei* (T) | ER&R |
| 'Druryi' | ER&R |
| 'Dwarf Houghtonii' | ER&R |
| * 'Ebony' (C) | CHal ER&R |
| *echinosepala* | ER&R |
| 'Edinburgh Brevirimosa' | ER&R |
| *egregia* | ER&R |
| 'Elaine' | ER&R |
| § 'Elaine Wilkerson' | ER&R |
| 'Elaine's Baby' | See *B.* 'Elaine Wilkerson' |
| 'Elda' | ER&R |
| 'Elda Haring' (R) | ER&R |
| 'Elizabeth Hayden' | ER&R |
| 'Elsie M. Frey' | ER&R |
| 'Emerald Giant' (R) | ER&R WDib |
| 'Emma Watson' | CHal ER&R |
| 'Enchantment' | ER&R |
| 'Enech' | ER&R |
| 'English Knight' | ER&R |
| 'English Lace' | ER&R |
| *epipsila* | ER&R |
| x *erythrophylla* 'Bunchii' | ER&R |
| § - 'Helix' | CHal ER&R |
| 'Essie Hunt' | ER&R |
| 'Esther Albertine' (C) ♀ | CHal ER&R |
| 'Evening Star' | ER&R |
| 'Exotica' | ER&R |
| 'Fairy' | ER&R |
| 'Fairylight' (T) | CBla |
| *feastii* 'Helix' | See *B.* x *erythrophylla* 'Helix' |
| *fernando-costae* | ER&R |
| 'Festiva' (T) | CBla |
| § 'Feuerkönigin' (S) | ER&R |
| 'Filigree' | ER&R |
| *fimbriata* | Last listed 1996 |
| 'Fire Flush' | See *B.* 'Bettina Rothschild' |
| 'Firedance' (T) | CBla |
| 'Fireworks' (R) | ER&R WDib |
| 'Five and Dime' | ER&R |
| Flaming Queen | See *B.* 'Feuerkönigin' |
| 'Flamingo' | ER&R |
| ¶ 'Flamingo Queen' | ER&R |
| 'Flo'Belle Moseley' (C) | ER&R WDib |
| 'Florence Carrell' | ER&R |
| 'Florence Rita' (C) | ER&R |
| *foliosa* | CHal ER&R WDib |
| - var. *amplifolia* | CHal ER&R |
| § - var. *miniata* 'Rosea' | CDoC CHal |
| 'Fred Bedson' | ER&R |
| *friburgensis* | ER&R |
| 'Frosty' (T) | WDib |
| 'Frosty Fairyland' | ER&R |
| 'Fuchsifoliosa' | ER&R |
| *fuchsioides* ♀ | CDoC EBak ER&R GPin LIck MArl NPri SYvo WDib WEas |
| - 'Rosea' | See *B. foliosa* var. *miniata* 'Rosea' |
| 'Full Moon' (T) | CBla |
| 'Fuscomaculata' | ER&R |
| *gehrtii* | ER&R |
| *glabra* | ER&R |
| *glaucophylla* | See *B. radicans* |
| 'Gloire de Lorraine' | Last listed 1996 |
| 'Gloire de Sceaux' | ER&R |
| *goegoensis* | ER&R |
| 'Gold Cascade' | CBla |
| 'Gold Doubloon' (T) | CBla |
| 'Goldilocks' (T) | CBla |
| 'Good 'n' Plenty' | ER&R |
| ¶ 'Granada' | ER&R |

| | |
|---|---|
| § *grandis* subsp. *evansiana* | CGle CHal EBee ELan EMon EOas ER&R GCal EEdu LHil MBEx MLLN MSte MTho NPla SDix SMad SSpi WCot WCru WHen |
| - subsp. *evansiana* | CHal EBee EMon ER&R GCal |
| var. *alba* | LBlm LHil MBEx MSte MTho SMad SSpi WCot |
| - - 'Claret Jug' | CHan EMon |
| - 'Maria' | EBee |
| - 'Simsii' | CHan WFar |
| * 'Great Beverly' | ER&R |
| 'Grey Feather' | ER&R |
| *griffithii* | See *B. annulata* |
| 'Gustav Lind' (S) | CHal ER&R MBEx SSad |
| 'Guy Savard' (C) | WDib |
| 'Gypsy Maiden' (T) | CBla |
| *haageana* | See *B. scharffii* |
| * 'Happy Heart' | ER&R |
| * 'Harry's Beard' | ER&R |
| *hatacoa* | ER&R |
| - silver | ER&R |
| - spotted | ER&R |
| 'Helen Teupel' (R) | ER&R WDib |
| 'Her Majesty' (R) | ER&R |
| § 'Herzog von Sagan' (T) | ER&R |
| *hispida* var. *cucullifera* | ER&R |
| 'Holmes Chapel' | ER&R |
| *homonyma* (T) | ER&R |
| 'Honeysuckle' (C) | ER&R |
| *hydrocotylifolia* | ER&R |
| *hypolipara* | ER&R |
| ¶ *imperialis* | ER&R |
| *incarnata* (C) | ER&R |
| - 'Metallica' | Last listed 1998 |
| 'Ingramii' | ER&R |
| ¶ *integerrima* | CEqu |
| 'Interlaken' (C) | ER&R |
| 'Irene Nuss' (C) ♀ | ER&R |
| 'Ivy Ever' | ER&R |
| 'Jean Blair' (T) | CBla |
| 'Jelly Roll Morton' | ER&R |
| 'Joe Hayden' | ER&R |
| 'John Tonkin' (C) | ER&R |
| ¶ 'Jumbo Jeans' | ER&R |
| ¶ 'Jumbo Jet' (C) | ER&R |
| 'Kagaribi' (C) | ER&R |
| *kellermanii* (C) | ER&R |
| ¶ 'Kentwood' (C) | ER&R |
| *kenworthyae* | ER&R |
| *kingiana* | WDib |
| * 'Krakatoa' | CBla |
| 'La Paloma' (C) | WDib |
| 'Lady Carol' | CHal |
| 'Lady Clare' | ER&R |
| * 'Lady France' | ER&R MBri |
| 'Lady Snow' | CHal |
| 'Lana' (C) | ER&R |
| * 'Lancelot' | CBla |
| 'Lawrence H. Fewkes' | ER&R |
| *leathermaniae* (C) | ER&R |
| 'Lenore Olivier' (C) | ER&R |
| 'Leopard' | ER&R MBri |
| 'Lexington' | ER&R |
| 'Libor' (C) | ER&R |
| 'Lime Swirl' | ER&R |
| *limmingheana* | See *B. radicans* |
| 'Linda Harley' | ER&R |
| 'Linda Myatt' | ER&R |
| *lindeniana* | ER&R |
| *listada* ♀ | CHal ER&R MBri WDib |
| 'Lithuania' | ER&R |
| 'Little Brother Montgomery' | CHal ER&R WDib |
| 'Little Darling' | ER&R |
| 'Lois Burks' (C) | ER&R WDib |
| 'Loma Alta' | ER&R |
| 'Looking Glass' (C) | ER&R WDib |
| 'Lospe-tu' | ER&R |
| 'Lou Anne' | CBla |
| 'Lubbergei' (C) | ER&R |
| 'Lucerna' | See *B.* x *corallina* 'Lucerna' |
| 'Lulu Bower' (C) | ER&R |
| *luxurians* | ER&R SYvo |
| - 'Ziesenhenne' | ER&R |
| 'Mabel Corwin' | ER&R |
| *macdougallii* | CHal WDib |
| var. *purpurea* | |
| *macrocarpa* | ER&R |
| 'Mac's Gold' | ER&R |
| *maculata* ♀ | ER&R |
| - 'Wightii' (C) | CHal CSpe ER&R WDib |
| 'Mad Hatter' | ER&R |
| 'Madame Butterfly' (C) | ER&R |
| 'Magic Carpet' | ER&R |
| 'Magic Lace' | ER&R |
| 'Majesty' (T) | CBla |
| *manicata* | ER&R WDib |
| 'Maphil' | MBri |
| * 'Mardi Gras' | CBla |
| 'Margaritae' | ER&R |
| 'Marmaduke' | CHal WDib |
| 'Marmorata' (T) | NRog |
| 'Martha Floro' (C) | ER&R |
| ¶ 'Martin Johnson' (R) | WDib |
| 'Martin's Mystery' | ER&R |
| *masoniana* ♀ | CHal ER&R EREa WDib |
| I 'Matador' (T) | CBla |
| * 'Maurice Amey' | ER&R |
| *mazae* | ER&R |
| 'Medora' (C) | ER&R |
| * 'Melissa' (T) | CBla |
| 'Merry Christmas' (R) ♀ | ER&R |
| *metachroa* | ER&R |
| *metallica* ♀ | CHal ER&R |
| 'Midnight Sun' | ER&R |
| 'Midnight Twister' | ER&R |
| 'Mikado' (R) | ER&R |
| 'Mirage' ♀ | ER&R |
| *mollicaulis* | ER&R |
| 'Moon Maid' | ER&R |
| * 'Moulin Rouge' | CBla |
| 'Mr Steve' (T) | CBla |
| 'Mrs Hashimoto' (C) | ER&R |
| *multinervia* | ER&R |
| 'Munchkin' ♀ | ER&R WDib |
| * 'Mystic' | ER&R |
| 'Mystique' | ER&R |
| *natalensis* (T) | ER&R |
| 'Nell Gwynne' (T) | CBla |
| 'Nelly Bly' | ER&R |
| *nelumbifolia* | ER&R |
| *nigramarga* | See *B. bowerae* var. *nigramarga* |
| 'Nokomis' (C) | ER&R |
| 'Norah Bedson' | ER&R |
| 'Northern Lights' (S) | ER&R |
| *obscura* | ER&R |
| 'Obsession' | ER&R |
| 'Odorata Alba' | ER&R |
| *olbia* Kerchove | ER&R |
| 'Old Gold' (T) | ER&R |
| 'Oliver Twist' | ER&R |
| 'Ophelia' (T) | CBla |
| 'Orange Cascade' (T) | CBla |
| 'Orange Dainty' | ER&R |
| 'Orange Rubra' (C) ♀ | CHal ER&R |

| | |
|---|---|
| 'Orpha C. Fox' (C) | ER&R |
| 'Orrell' (C) | ER&R |
| ¶ 'Othello' | ER&R |
| 'Panasoffkee' | ER&R |
| 'Panther' | ER&R |
| 'Papillon' (T) | ER&R |
| * 'Parilis' | ER&R |
| *partita* | ER&R |
| 'Passing Storm' | ER&R |
| 'Patricia Ogdon' | ER&R |
| 'Paul Harley' | ER&R |
| 'Paul-bee' | ER&R |
| *paulensis* | ER&R |
| *pearcei* | ER&R |
| 'Peggy Stevens' (C) | ER&R |
| * 'Penelope Jane' | ER&R |
| 'Persephone' (T) | CBla |
| 'Piccolo' | ER&R |
| 'Pickobeth' (C) | ER&R |
| 'Picotee' (T) | CSut NRog |
| 'Pinafore' (C) ♀ | ER&R |
| 'Pink Champagne' (R) | CBla |
| 'Pink Nacre' | CHal ER&R |
| 'Pink Parade' (C) | ER&R |
| 'Pink Spot Lucerne' (C) | ER&R |
| *plagioneura* | ER&R |
| *polyantha* | ER&R |
| *popenoei* | ER&R |
| 'Président Carnot' (C) | ER&R |
| 'Preussen' | ER&R |
| 'Primrose' (T) | CBla |
| 'Princess of Hanover' (R) | ER&R |
| *procumbens* | See *B. radicans* |
| *pustulata* 'Argentea' | ER&R |
| 'Queen Olympus' | ER&R WDib |
| 'Quinebaug' | ER&R |
| § *radicans* ♀ | CHal ER&R MBri |
| 'Raquel Wood' | ER&R |
| 'Raspberry Swirl' (R) ♀ | CHal ER&R WDib |
| ¶ *ravenii* B&SWJ 1954 | WCru |
| 'Raymond George Nelson' ♀ | ER&R |
| * 'Razzmatazz' | WDib |
| 'Red Berry' (R) | ER&R |
| 'Red Planet' | ER&R WDib |
| 'Red Reign' | ER&R |
| ¶ 'Red Robin' | WDib |
| 'Red Spider' | ER&R |
| ¶ 'Regal Minuet' (R) | WDib |
| 'Regalia' | ER&R |
| *rex* | MBri |
| 'Richard Robinson' | ER&R |
| 'Richmondensis' | ER&R LHil |
| 'Ricinifolia' | ER&R |
| 'Ricky Minter' ♀ | ER&R |
| *roxburghii* | ER&R |
| 'Roy Hartley' (T) | CBla |
| 'Royal Lustre' | ER&R |
| 'Royalty' (T) | CBla |
| 'Saber Dance' (R) | ER&R |
| 'Sachsen' | ER&R |
| *salicifolia* (C) | ER&R |
| *sanguinea* | ER&R |
| 'Scarlet Pimpernel' (T) | CBla |
| 'Scarlett O'Hara' (T) | CBla ER&R |
| 'Sceptre' (T) | CBla |
| *scharffiana* | ER&R |
| § *scharffii* | CHal EBak ER&R LChe |
| 'Scherzo' | CHal ER&R |
| 'Sea Coral' (T) | CBla |
| ◆ *semperflorens* hort. | See *B.* Semperflorens Cultorum Group |
| § Semperflorens Cultorum Group | MBri |
| - double (d) | CHal |
| 'Serlis' | ER&R |
| *serratipetala* | CHal EBak ER&R MBri |
| * *sheperdii* | CHal WDib |
| 'Silver Cloud' | ER&R WDib |
| * 'Silver Dawn' | ER&R |
| 'Silver Jewell' | WDib |
| 'Silver Mist' (C) | ER&R |
| 'Silver Points' | ER&R |
| 'Silver Sweet' (R) | ER&R |
| 'Silver Wings' | ER&R |
| ¶ *sinensis* | WCot |
| * 'Sir Charles' | ER&R |
| 'Sir John Falstaff' | ER&R |
| Skeezar Group | ER&R |
| - 'Brown Lake' | ER&R |
| 'Snowcap' (S) | ER&R WDib |
| *solananthera* ♀ | CHal ER&R LCns WDib |
| *sonderiana* | ERea |
| 'Sophie Cecile' (C) ♀ | CHal ER&R |
| 'Speculata' (R) | ER&R |
| 'Spellbound' | ER&R WDib |
| 'Spindrift' | ER&R |
| 'Spotches' | ER&R |
| § *stipulacea* | CHal ER&R |
| § - 'Bat Wings' | Last listed 1998 |
| *subvillosa* (S) | ER&R |
| 'Sugar Candy' (T) | CBla |
| *sutherlandii* ♀ | CAvo CHal EBak ER&R ERea ERos LHil MBri NBir NPer SDix SMrm SYvo WCot WDib WHer |
| - 'Papaya' | CSpe |
| 'Swan Song' | ER&R |
| 'Sweet Dreams' (T) | CBla |
| 'Sweet Magic' | CHal ER&R |
| 'Swirly Top' (C) | ER&R |
| 'Switzerland' | Last listed 1998 |
| 'Sylvan Triumph' (C) | ER&R |
| 'Tahiti' (T) | CBla |
| 'Tapestry' (R) | ER&R |
| * *taya* | WDib |
| 'Tea Rose' | ER&R |
| *teuscheri* (C) | ER&R |
| 'Texastar' | ER&R WDib |
| 'The Wiz' | ER&R |
| *thelmae* | ER&R |
| 'Thrush' (R) | Last listed 1998 |
| 'Thunderclap' | CHal ER&R |
| 'Thurstonii' ♀ | CHal ER&R |
| 'Tiger Paws' ♀ | CHal ER&R MBri |
| 'Tingley Mallet' (C) | ER&R |
| 'Tiny Bright' (R) | ER&R |
| 'Tiny Gem' | ER&R |
| 'Tom Ment' (C) | ER&R |
| 'Tom Ment II' (C) | ER&R |
| 'Tondelayo' (R) | ER&R |
| * 'Tribute' | ER&R |
| *tripartita* (T) | ER&R |
| 'Trout' (C) | Last listed 1997 |
| 'Two Face' | ER&R WDib |
| *ulmifolia* | ER&R |
| *undulata* (C) | CHal ER&R |
| 'Universe' | ER&R |
| *venosa* | CHal ER&R |
| 'Venus' | CHal ER&R |
| x *verschaffeltii* | ER&R |
| 'Vesuvius' | WDib |
| 'Viaudii' | ER&R |
| 'Viau-Scharff' | ER&R |
| § *vitifolia* | ER&R |

'Weltoniensis'                         ER&R
'Weltoniensis Alba' (T)                ER&R
*  'White Cascade'                     ER&R
'Witch Craft' (R)                      ER&R
'Withlacoochee'                        ER&R WDib
*wollnyi*                               ER&R
'Wood Nymph' (R)                       ER&R
'Yellow Sweety' (T)                    CBla
'Zuensis'                              ER&R
'Zulu' (T)                             CBla

## BELAMCANDA (Iridaceae)

*chinensis*                             CAbb CBot CBro EBee EGoo
                                       EMan GPoy LHop Llck MAvo
                                       MBNS MHar MLLN MSal NTow
                                       WElm WPer WWye
- 'Dwarf Orange'                       WCot
- 'Hello Yellow'                       MSte
* - 'Pumila Campbellii'                Last listed 1998
* - 'Yellow Bird'                      WCot

## BELLEVALIA (Hyacinthaceae)

*brevipedicellata* MS 746              Last listed 1998
*dubia*                                 WCot
*forniculata*                           GTou WCot
- JCA 227.770                          Last listed 1996
*gracilis*                              Last listed 1998
*backelii* MS 439                       Last listed 1998
*kurdistanica*                          WCot
*longistyla*                            Last listed 1998
*maura* SF 387                          Last listed 1998
*nivalis* CL 101                        Last listed 1998
§ *paradoxa*                            EHyt EPar ERos NRog SUsu WCot
*pycnantha* hort.                       See *B. paradoxa*
*romana*                                EHyt MTho NRog SHut WHil
- JCA 523                              Last listed 1998
*sessiliflora*                          Last listed 1998
sp. PD 20493                           Last listed 1998

## BELLIS (Asteraceae)

*perennis*                              CKin EWFC MHew
- 'Alba Plena' (d)                     ECho ELan
- 'Alice'                              CGle CLTr WSan
- 'Annie'                              CGle
- 'Aucubifolia' (v)                    Last listed 1998
- 'Capel Ulo'                          MAvo
- 'Dawn Raider'                        Last listed 1997
- 'Dresden China' ♀                    CElw CLTr ELan GAbr MAvo
                                       MTho SIng WAlt WOut WRus
§ - 'Habanera White With              NBrk
     Red Tips' (Habanera Series)
- Hen and Chicken                      See *B. perennis* 'Prolifera'
¶ - 'Jocelyn Castle' (d)               WAlt
- 'Lipstick' (Habanera Series) See *B. perennis* 'Habanera White
                                       With Red Tips' (Habanera Series)
- 'Miniskirt'                          WAlt
- 'Miss Mason'                         CGle GAbr NOla NPro SIng WRus
- 'Monstrosa'                          NVic
- 'Odd Bod'                            CNat WAlt
- 'Parkinson's Great White'            CLTr GAbr
- 'Pomponette' ♀                       NVic
§ - 'Prolifera'                        CBos GAbr WAlt
- 'Rob Roy' ♀                          CBos CGle
- 'Robert'                             CLTr GAbr
¶ - 'Rusher Rose'                      EPfP
- 'Single Blue'                        See *B. rotundifolia* 'Caerulescens'
- 'Stafford Pink'                      GAbr
- 'Super Enorma'                       Last listed 1997
*rotundifolia*                          CInt
§ - 'Caerulescens'                     CNic CSev ELan GAbr MTho NBir
                                       NBro NMGW NMen WPat

## BELLIUM (Asteraceae)

*bellidioides*                          NHol WAbe
*crassifolium canescens*                CInt WPer
*minutum*                               CNic ESis MMil MTho NPro
                                       NTow

## BELOPERONE See JUSTICIA

## BENSONIELLA (Saxifragaceae)

*oregona*                               EBee EMon LRHS NCat WCru

## BERBERIDOPSIS (Flacourtiaceae)

¶ *beckleri*                           CFil ISea
*corallina*                             More than 30 suppliers

## BERBERIS ✿ (Berberidaceae)

*aggregata*                             CAgr EPla MBal MNrw NBir SEas
                                       SPer SRms
*amurensis* 'Flamboyant'                WBcn
¶ - var. *latifolia* B&SWJ 4353        WCru
x *antoniana*                           LRHS MBri
*aquifolium*                            See *Mahonia aquifolium*
- 'Fascicularis'                       See *Mahonia* x *wagneri*
                                       'Pinnacle'
N *aristata*                            CAgr CArn CMCN LEdu SMrm
                                       SMur
*atrocarpa*                             CPle
*bealei*                                See *Mahonia japonica* Bealei
                                       Group
*bergmanniae*                           SLPl
*brevipedunculata* Bean                 See *B. prattii*
x *bristolensis*                        EPla LRHS MBri SLon SPla SRms
¶ *buchananii*                         WCwm
     var. *tawangensis*
*buxifolia*                             CBlo CPle MBal SCob WCFE
- 'Nana' hort.                         See *B. buxifolia* 'Pygmaea'
N - 'Pygmaea'                          CAbP CCHP CDoC CTri EBee
                                       ELan EMil ENot MBNS MBal MBar
                                       MBri MPla MRav NHol SPer STre
                                       WFar WPyg WStI
*calliantha* ♀                         CBlo CChe CPle WWat
*candidula*                             EBee EBrP EBre ENot IOrc LBre
                                       MBal MBar NFla NFor NHol SBre
                                       SLon SPer WDin WGwG WStI
                                       WWal WWat
- 'Jytte'                              See *B.* 'Jytte'
x *carminea* 'Barbarossa'               SPer
- 'Buccaneer'                          ENot EPfP SBod
- 'Pirate King'                        CBlo ENot MBal MBri MRav SEas
                                       SPer
¶ *chilensis*                          WPic
*chitria*                               Last listed 1998
*chrysosphaera*                         WWat
§ *concinna*                           GCrs IMGH
*congestiflora*                         CPle
*coryi*                                 See *B. wilsoniae* var.
                                       *subcaulialata*
*coxii*                                 GBin NTow WCwm
*darwinii* ♀                           More than 30 suppliers
*dictyophylla* ♀                       CFil CPMA CPle ELan EPfP MBri
                                       MGos SLon SPer SPla SSpi WCwm
                                       WGer WSHC
*dulcis* 'Nana'                         See *B. buxifolia* 'Pygmaea'
*empetrifolia*                          CPle NFor NLon SIng
- JCA 14165                            IDac
*erythroclada*                          See *B. concinna*
x *frikartii* 'Amstelveen' ♀           CBlo CDoC CSam EBee EBrP EBre
                                       EHic ELan ENot EPfP LBre MBNS
                                       SBre SCob WFar WGor
- 'Telstar' ♀                          CDoC EBee EHic ENot LBuc MBal
                                       MBri MRav NPro SCob WStI

¶ *gagnepainii* — NLon SLPl WGwG
¶ - hort. — See *B. gagnepainii* var. *lanceifolia*
 - 'Fernspray' — EPla MBri MRav SBod SRms WBod
§ - var. *lanceifolia* — CB&S CTri EBee ENot EPla IOrc MBar MGos MWhi NFor NHol NWea SPer WFar WHCG WWal
 - 'Purpure' — See *B.* x *interposita* 'Wallich's Purple'
 'Georgei' — CCHP CMHG WBcn
 *glaucocarpa* — ELan EPfP EPla LRHS WPat
 'Goldilocks' ♀ — CAbP CFil CMHG CPMA EPfP MBlu MBri WBcn WGer
¶ *bookeri* — CB&S
 - var. *latifolia* — See *B. manipurana*
 x *hybridogagnepainii* 'Chenaultii' — CBlo ELan SPer
 - 'Robin Hood' — Last listed 1996
 *hypokerina* — Last listed 1998
¶ *insignis* — WWat
 - subsp. *insignis* var. *insignis* B&SWJ 2432 — WCru
 *integerrima* — Last listed 1998
§ x *interposita* — CBlo CDoC EBee EHic ENot MBal MBar SPer WLRN WStI
 'Wallich's Purple'
 *jamesiana* — GAbr SLon
 *julianae* — CB&S CDoC CSam EBee ELan ENot EPla GChr IOrc MBal MBar MBri MGos MRav NBee NFla NFor NLon NWea SHFr SLPl SPer WDin WFar WHCG WHar WSHC
 - 'Mary Poppins' — LRHS MBri
§ 'Jytte' — MWhi
 *kawakamii* — SLPl
 *knightii* — See *B. manipurana*
 *koreana* — CFil CMCN CSam ECtt EPla GBin NFla WWes
 - 'Red Tears' — Last listed 1997
 *lempergiana* — CMCN CPle
 *linearifolia* — WPat
 - 'Orange King' — CAbP CB&S CDoC EBee ELan ENot MAsh MGos NBee NHol SIgm SPer SSta WDin WHar WPat WPyg WStI
 'Little Favourite' — See *B. thunbergii* 'Atropurpurea Nana'
 x *lologensis* — IMGH IOrc MGos WDin
 - 'Apricot Queen' ♀ — CAbP CB&S MAsh MBal MBri NBee NEgg SPer SSta WDin WPyg WStI WWeb
 - 'Mystery Fire' — CAbP CBlo CDoC COtt ECtt IOrc MAsh MBar MBlu MBri MGos NBee NEgg NMoo SCoo SPla WHar
 - 'Stapehill' — CB&S CCHP CSam ELan ENot EPfP LRHS MAsh MBri SSpi WBcn
 *lycium* — CAgr CPle WHCr
 - CC 1729 — CPLG MRPP
 *macrosepala* var. *macrosepala* B&SWJ 2124 — WCru
§ *manipurana* — CGre EBee ENot
 x *media* Park Jewel — See *B.* x *media* 'Parkjuweel'
§ - 'Parkjuweel' ♀ — CB&S CBlo EBee EHal EHic ENot EPfP MRav SRms WLRN WWeb
 - 'Red Jewel' ♀ — CBlo CChe CDoC EBrP EBre EPfP EPla LBre MBri MGos MWat SBre SEas SPer WFar WWal WWeb
 *morrisonensis* — CFil CPle WCom WPGP
 x *ottawensis* — GRei WStI
 - 'Auricoma' — MAsh MGos WShe
 - 'Decora' — Last listed 1998

N - f. *purpurea* — EBee MBri MGos NCut NFla SBod WDin WHar
§ - 'Silver Miles' (v) — EHoe ELan EPfP LHop LNet MBel MBri MCCP MRav SLon WFar WPat
N - 'Superba' ♀ — CB&S CBlo CChe CDoC CSam CTri EBee ELan ENot GOrc LHop MBal MBar MGos NBee NFor NHol NLon NRoo SPer SPla SRms SSoC WBod WDin WFar WGwG WHar
§ *panlanensis* — ENot MBar
 *patagonica* — NLon
 *poiretii* — CPle
 *polyantha* hort. — See *B. prattii*
 - Hemsley — Last listed 1998
§ *prattii* — CMHG MBri MWat
 *pruinosa* — CFil CPle
 'Red Tears' — CBlo CPMA CSam EHic MBlu MBri MGos MLan SPer WGwG WHCG WWes
 *replicata* — Last listed 1998
 'Rubrostilla' ♀ — EPla NLon
¶ x *rubrostilla* 'Cherry Ripe' — CMac
 - 'Wisley' — LRHS
 *sanguinea* hort. — See *B. panlanensis*
 *sargentiana* — CPle ENot NFor NLon SLPl SLon WTro
 *sherriffii* — WCwm
 *sieboldii* — LRHS WPat WPyg WWat
 sp. B&L 12060 — EPla
 sp. ACE 2237 — EPot
 sp. C&S 1571 — Last listed 1998
 sp. C&S 1651 — Last listed 1998
 x *stenophylla* ♀ — CB&S CChe CDoC EBee ELan ENot GChr GRei ISea LBuc MBar MBri MGos MLan MWat NHed NHol NLon NWea SPer SRPl WBod WDin WFar WHar WWin
 - 'Autumnalis' — CBlo SCob
 - 'Claret Cascade' — CBlo EBee EHal EHic ELan EPfP MAsh MBri MGos SEas SPer WBod WFar WGwG
 - 'Coccinea' — EPla MGos
 - 'Corallina Compacta' ♀ — CFee ELan EPot ESis LHop MAsh MBal MBlu MBro MPla NHol SChu SIng SRms WAbe WPat WPyg
 - 'Cornish Cream' — See *B.* x *stenophylla* 'Lemon Queen'
 - 'Crawley Gem' — CBlo CMHG LNet MBar MBri MGos MPla WFar WLRN WStI
 - Cream Showers™ — See *B.* x *stenophylla* 'Lemon Queen'
 - 'Etna' — MAsh
 - 'Irwinii' — CBlo CMHG CTri ENot IOrc MBar MBri MGos NHol SCob SLon SPer WDin WFar
N - 'Lemon Queen' — SEas SPer SSto
 - 'Nana' — EPla SRms
 - 'Pink Pearl' — CMHG LBuc LRHS MBri MGos
 *taliensis* — CPle
 *temolaica* — CFil CPMA ELan EPfP MBlu MBri SPla SSpi SSta WAbe WDin WPat WWat
 - SF 95186 — ISea
 *thunbergii* ♀ — CBlo CDoC CTri ENot GChr GRei LBuc MBal NWea SMer SPer SPlb WDin WFar WStI
 - f. *atropurpurea* — CB&S CPle EAst EBrP EBre ENot GRei LBre LBuc LGro MBal MBar MBri MGos MWat NFor NWea SBre SPer SRCN WBod WDin WFar WWin

§ - 'Atropurpurea Nana' ♀ | More than 30 suppliers
- 'Atropurpurea Superba' | See *B.* x *ottawensis* 'Superba'
- 'Aurea' | More than 30 suppliers
- 'Bagatelle' ♀ | CBlo CDoC COtt EBee EBrP EBre ECtt ELan EMil ENot EPot ESis IOrc LBre MAsh MBar MBri MGos MPla MRav MTis NBee NHar SBre SPer WDin WPat WPyg
- 'Bonanza Gold' | CAbP CB&S CBlo CDoC COtt EBee ELan EPfP LRHS MAsh SMur WSpi WWeb
¶ - 'Carmen' | MGos
- 'Carpetbagger' | IOrc WHar
- 'Crimson Pygmy' | See *B. thunbergii* 'Atropurpurea Nana'
- 'Dart's Purple' | MAsh MBri WFar
- 'Dart's Red Lady' | CBlo CBot CPMA EBee EBrP EBre ECtt EHal ELan ENot EPla ESis IOrc LBre MAsh MBri MPla MRav NRoo SBre SPer SPla WFar WPat
- 'Erecta' | ENot MBar MGos MRav NCut SCob WDin
- 'Golden Ring' | CChe CDoC EBee ECtt EHoe ELan EMil EPla LHop MBNS MBar MBri MGos NHol NRoo SChu SEND SPer SPla WDin WHCG WHar WPat WPyg WSHC
- 'Green Carpet' | CBlo EBrP EBre EHic ENot IOrc LBre MBal MBar MBlu SBre SLon SPer
- 'Green Mantle' | See *B. thunbergii* 'Kelleriis'
- 'Green Marble' | See *B. thunbergii* 'Kelleriis'
- 'Green Ornament' | MWat NCut SPer
¶ - 'Green Ring' | EWTr
- 'Harlequin' (v) | More than 30 suppliers
- 'Helmond Pillar' | CMHG EBee EBrP EBre EHoe ELan EMil ENot IOrc LBre MBar MBlu MBri MGos MRav MTis NBee NRoo SBre SCob SLon SMad SPer WDin WFar WPat WPyg WSHC
§ - 'Kelleriis' | CBlo CDoC EHic EPfP EPla GOrc MBar MBel MGos SBod SRms WFar WRHF WStl WWeb
- 'Kobold' | CBlo CHan ENot ESis MAsh MBar MBri MGos MPla NHol SEas SPer SPla WFar WLRN WPat WPyg
- 'Pink Attraction' | CBlo
- 'Pink Queen' (v) | CBlo EBee ENot EPfP MAsh MGos WHar WPat WWeb
- 'Pow-wow' | CB&S MGos MMil MTis SMur WBcn
- 'Red Chief' ♀ | CMHG EBee EBrP EBre ECtt EGra ELan ENot EPla LBre LHop MBal MGos MRav MWat NHol SBre SChu SCob SLon SPer SPla SRPl WDin WFar WHCG WHar WPat WStl
- 'Red King' | EHol MRav WDin
- 'Red Pillar' | CB&S CBlo CChe CDoC CLan CPle EBrP EBre EHoe ELan LBre MAsh MBal MBar MBlu MBri MGos MWat NBee NHed NHol SBre SPla WAbe WDin WFar WPat WStl WWeb
- 'Red Rocket' | EMil MGos
- 'Rose Glow' (v) ♀ | More than 30 suppliers
- 'Silver Beauty' (v) | CB&S CBlo CMHG CSam EBee EHal ELan MGos MPla SBod WHCG WWeb
- 'Silver Mile' | See *B.* x *ottawensis* 'Silver Miles'
* - 'Silver Queen' | CBlo CHor

- 'Somerset' | WWat
* - 'Tricolor' (v) | EHic EHoe WFar WPat WPyg WSHC
- 'Vermilion' | Last listed 1996
*tsangpoensis* | SLPl
*valdiviana* | CFil EPfP SSpi WPGP
*veitchii* | SLPl
*verruculosa* ♀ | CB&S CLan EAst EBee ENot GChr LHop MBal MBar MGos MPla NFor NHol NWea SPer SPla SRms WBod WCFE WDin WFar WGwG WWal WWat WWeb
*vulgaris* | CArn GPoy MSal
- 'Atropurpurea' | CAgr
*wallichiana* B&SWJ 2432 | Last listed 1997
*wardii* | CB&S
*wilsoniae* ♀ | CB&S CBlo CFil CLan CPle EBee EBrP EBre ELan ENot EPla GChr IOrc LBre MBar MWat MWhi NLon NWea SBre SPer WDin WFar
- ACE 2462 | EHyt
- blue | LRHS MBri WFar WGer
- 'Graciella' | EPla LRHS MBri NPro
- var. *guhtzunica* | EPla EWes
¶ - L 650 | WPGP
- var. *parvifolia* | CPle

## BERCHEMIA (Rhamnaceae)
*racemosa* | CPiN WSHC
*scandens* | CPiN

## BERGENIA ✿ (Saxifragaceae)
'Abendglocken' | CDoC CMil EBee ECha EHic EPla LFis LGro LRHS MBri MTis MWat NHol NPla NSti SChu WFar WWoo
§ 'Abendglut' | More than 30 suppliers
*acanthifolia* | See *B.* x *spathulata*
'Admiral' | ECha EGle EPla SCob
¶ *afghanica* | IHdy
'Apple Court White' | Last listed 1998
'Baby Doll' | COtt EBee EBrP EBre ECha EFou EPla GSki LBre LHop MAvo MCAu MUlv NBir NHol NOrc NPer NPro NRoo NSti SBre SCob WBro WCot WRus WWeb
§ 'Ballawley' ♀ | ECha EPla IBlr IHdy MCAu NDea SSpi SWat
N Ballawley hybrids | CMGP EPar LGro MUlv NHol NSti SDix SPer SWat WBro WCot WWoo
'BartPar' | LGro MUlv NHol
   *B. purpurascens* | CPlt ECha EGle EPPr EPla IHdy
'Beethoven' | NBir NPar SSpi SWat WCot
Bell Tower | See *B.* 'Glockenturm'
'Bizet' | MTed SSpi
¶ 'Borodin' | SCob
'Brahms' | SCob
'Bressingham Bountiful' | SCob SPer WCot
'Bressingham Ruby' | CTri EBrP EBre EFou EGar ENot EPla GAri LBre MCAu MHlr MRav MTed MUlv NBir NRoo SBre
'Bressingham Salmon' | CHar CMil EBee ELan GMaP MBri MRav NHol SCob SPer WCot WMer
'Bressingham White' ♀ | CTri EBrP EBre ECha ECtt EFou ELan EOrc EWTr LBre MBri MCAu MRav MUlv NDea NFai NGdn NHol NRoo SBre SCob SPer WBro WCot WRus WWat WWin
'Britten' | CMil LPio MBal

| | |
|---|---|
| *ciliata* | CFee CHan CLAP CMil ECGN ECha GCal IHdy LEdu MBal MRav NBir NLar NSti SDix SLon SPer SSpi SUsu WCot WEas WPGP WPer |
| - x *crassifolia* | See *B.* x *schmidtii* |
| - *ficifolia* | Last listed 1998 |
| - f.*ligulata* | CCuc CLAP EBee ECha LEdu MChR MWgw NBir NSti SCob SSpi WCot WPer |
| - - B&SWJ 2693 | WCru |
| ¶ - - 'Wilton' | WCot |
| ¶ 'Claire Maxine' | GCal |
| *cordifolia* | CB&S CGle CMHG EGoo EHon ELan ENot EOld EPla GAbr GCal GChr LSyl MBal MFir MMal NDea NFai NFor NLar SHel SPer SPlb SRPl WCot WFar WMow WPer WStI |
| - 'Purpurea' ♀ | CB&S CDoC EBee ECha ELan ENot EPla LBuc LGro MBNS MBri MCLN MRav NBir SDix SPer SRms WWal |
| - 'Redstart' | CBlo NOak |
| - 'Tubby Andrews' (v) | CRDP GBri MBel NEgg NLar NPro |
| ¶ - 'Winterglut' | GMaP |
| *crassifolia* | CB&S CGle EPla SRms SSca WByw |
| - 'Autumn Red' | ECha EPla |
| - DF 90028 | EMon |
| - 'Orbicularis' | See *B.* x *schmidtii* |
| - var.*pacifica* | CFil EBee WPGP WWoo |
| ¶ 'Croesus' | IHdy |
| * *cyanea* | WCot |
| 'David' | EMon |
| *delavayi* | See *B. purpurascens* var. *delavayi* |
| 'Delbees' | See *B.* 'Ballawley' |
| *emeiensis* | SBla SWas |
| 'Eric Smith' | CLAP ECha EPar EPla GAbr GCal IHdy WCot |
| 'Eric's Best' | Last listed 1998 |
| ¶ 'Eroica' | ECha EPla |
| 'Evening Glow' | See *B.* 'Abendglut' |
| ¶ 'Frau Holle' | EFou |
| § 'Glockenturm' | GCal |
| JCA mixed red clones | CNic |
| 'Jo Watanabe' | ECha EPla |
| 'Lambrook' | See *B.* 'Margery Fish' |
| § 'Margery Fish' | ECha EPla SPer SPla |
| *milesii* | See *B. stracheyi* |
| § 'Morgenröte' ♀ | CB&S CMGP ECha MBNS MBri MCLN NDea NHol NSti SAga SPer SPla SRms SWat |
| Morning Red | See *B.* 'Morgenröte' |
| 'Mrs Crawford' | ECha EPla SCob |
| 'Oeschberg' | Last listed 1998 |
| 'Opal' | ECha EPla |
| 'Perfect' | EFou |
| 'Profusion' | IHdy MCAu SPer |
| 'Pugsley's Pink' | CBlo CMil ECha EPla LHop LPio WLRN |
| 'Pugsley's Purple' | Last listed 1997 |
| ¶ aff.*purparascens* ACE 2175 | WCot |
| § *purpurascens* ♀ | EPla ERav GDra GSki LSyl MBal MBro NHol SDix SPer WByw WCot WPyg WWin |
| - 'Ballawley' | See *B.* 'Ballawley' |
| § - var.*delavayi* | MBri NVic SRms |
| - - CLD 1366 | EMon SRms WPer |
| ¶ - from Helen Dillon | ECha |
| - hybrid | Last listed 1997 |
| 'Purpurglocken' | EPla GCal |

| | |
|---|---|
| 'Red Beauty' | CBlo |
| 'Rosette' | LPio NFai |
| 'Rosi Klose' | CGle ECha EFou EMon EPPr EPla EWes GCal MBel MBri MRav NRoo NTow |
| 'Rotblum' | EAst ECtt GBin GMaP LFis LNor NCut NGdn NOrc NPri NVic WFar WPer |
| § x *schmidtii* ♀ | EBee EWll NBir NFla NOla SDix WCot |
| 'Schneekissen' | EBee EGle MRav SLon SWat WLRN |
| § 'Schneekönigin' | CGle ECha EPla LPio MRav WGer |
| § 'Silberlicht' ♀ | More than 30 suppliers |
| Silverlight | See *B.* 'Silberlicht' |
| Snow Queen | See *B.* 'Schneekönigin' |
| 'Snowblush' | MBal SSpi |
| § *stracheyi* | CFee ECha EGoo SApp SCob SDix WEas WPyg |
| - Alba Group | CGle CRDP EBee ECha EMan EPfP GCal LHop MBel NDea NSti NWoo SCob SWas WLRN |
| - KBE 151 | NHol |
| - KBE 209 | NHol |
| - red | Last listed 1996 |
| 'Sunningdale' | CB&S CDoC CMGP EBee ECha EFou ELan EMan EPPr EPar EPla GMaP MCAu MLLN MRav NBir NFla SChu SCob SPer SRPl SSpi WMer |
| * 'Winter Fairy' | Last listed 1998 |
| 'Wintermärchen' | CM&M CMGP CMHG EBee ECha ECtt ELan EPPr EPfP EPla ERav MBri MCli MSte NHol NSti SAga SHel SPla SSea WRus WWeb |
| 'Winterzauber' | MTed |

## BERGERANTHUS (Aizoaceae)
| | |
|---|---|
| ¶ *scapiger* | SDys |

## BERKHEYA (Asteraceae)
| | |
|---|---|
| *cuneata* | Last listed 1998 |
| *macrocephala* | EMon WCot WMer |
| *maritima* | Last listed 1998 |
| ¶ *multijuga* | EBee GLch WHil |

## BERLANDIERA (Asteraceae)
| | |
|---|---|
| *lyrata* | EMon GCal |

## BERNEUXIA (Diapensiaceae)
| | |
|---|---|
| ¶ *thibetica* | IBlr |

## BERULA (Apiaceae)
| | |
|---|---|
| *erecta* | EHon |

## BERZELIA (Bruniaceae)
| | |
|---|---|
| *lanuginosa* | CTrC |

## BESCHORNERIA (Agavaceae)
| | |
|---|---|
| *septentrionalis* | WCot |
| *tubiflora* | CFil EOas LEdu |
| *yuccoides* ♀ | CB&S CFil CTrC IBlr LHil MSte SAPC SArc SChr SSpi WMul |

## BESSERA (Alliaceae)
| | |
|---|---|
| *elegans* | ETub WCot |

## BETA (Chenopodiaceae)
| | |
|---|---|
| *trigyna* | EMon |
| *vulgaris* | WHer |
| - 'Bull's Blood' | Last listed 1996 |

## BETONICA See STACHYS

**BETULA** ✿ (Betulaceae)

| | |
|---|---|
| *alba* L. | See *B. pendula* |
| *albosinensis* ♀ | CB&S CBlo CDul CGre CMCN CSam EBee ELan GAri GChr NWea WCwm WDin WFro WNor WOrn WWoo |
| - 'Bowling Green' | CTho |
| - 'China Ruby' | MAsh MBri |
| - 'Chinese Garden' | CTho |
| - Clone F | CTho |
| - 'Conyngham' | CTho |
| ♦ - misapplied F 19505 | See *B. utilis* F 19505 |
| - 'Kenneth Ashburner' | CTho |
| - var. *septentrionalis* ♀ | CDoC CEnd CLnd CTho ENot LNet MAsh MBlu MBri MRav SPer SSpi SSta WPGP WWat |
| - W 4106 | Last listed 1998 |
| § *alleghaniensis* | CDul CGre CMCN CSam IOrc MBal |
| *alnoides* | WNor |
| *apoiensis* | CGre SSta |
| *austrosinensis* | WNor |
| ♦ *borealis* | See *B. pumila* |
| § x *caerulea* | CTho WWat |
| *caerulea-grandis* | See *B.* x *caerulea* |
| *chichibuensis* | EPla |
| *chinensis* | CMCN SMad WNor |
| - S016 | WHCr |
| ♦ *cordifolia* | See *B. papyrifera* var. *cordifolia* |
| *costata* Trautvetter | CDoC CLnd CTho EBee ELan ENot WDin WFro WOrn |
| ¶ - 'Fincham Cream' | EPfP |
| *davurica* | CBlo CMCN WCoo WNor WWoo |
| - 'Maurice Foster' | CTho |
| - 'Stone Farm' | CTho |
| *delavayi* B&L 12260 | Last listed 1997 |
| ♦ - subsp. *calcicola* | See *B. calcicola* |
| *ermanii* | CB&S CDoC CDul CGre CLnd CMCN CMHG COtt CSam CTho EBee ELan ENot IOrc LPan MBal MBlu MBri MGos MRav NBea NWea SPer STre WDin WGer WNor WOrn |
| ¶ - from Hokkaido, Japan | CSam |
| § - 'Grayswood Hill' ♀ | CEnd CTho MBal MBri MGos SPer SSpi SSta STre WWat |
| - 'Hakkoda Orange' | CTho |
| - var. *saitoana* | CFil |
| subvar. *genuina* | |
| * - var. *subcordata* | CSam |
| 'Fetisowii' | CDul CLnd CTho MBlu SSta |
| ♦ *fontinalis* | See *B. occidentalis* |
| *forrestii* Yu 10561 | Last listed 1997 |
| *fruticosa* | See *B. humilis* |
| ♦ *glandulifera* | See *B. pumila* |
| ¶ *glandulosa* | WLin |
| *globispica* | Last listed 1997 |
| ♦ *gmelinii* | See *B. ovalifolia* |
| *grossa* | CDul CLnd CMCN GAri |
| 'Hergest' | CBlo COtt EPfP MAsh MBri MGos WHCr |
| § *humilis* | CLnd CMCN GQui |
| 'Inverleith' | See *B. utilis* var. *jacquemontii* 'Inverleith' |
| *jacquemontii* | See *B. utilis* var. *jacquemontii* |
| ♦ *kamtschatica* | See *B. humilis* |
| § *kenaica* | CTho |
| ♦ x *kusmisscheffii* | See *B. pubescens* var. *kusmisscheffii* |

| | |
|---|---|
| *lenta* | CFil CLnd CMCN MBal SBir |
| § - subsp. *uber* | CMCN SBir |
| *litvinovii* | Last listed 1997 |
| *luminifera* | CBrd CDul |
| *lutea* | See *B. alleghaniensis* |
| § *mandshurica* | CLnd EBee EWes GChr WFro |
| var. *japonica* | WShe WWoo |
| ¶ - var. *japonica* 'Whitespire Senior' | CDoC ELan MBlu |
| *maximowicziana* | CB&S CLnd CMCN CTho GAri MBal SLPl SSta WFro WNor WPic |
| § *medwedewii* ♀ | CDul CFil CLnd CTho EPfP EPla GAri SSta WAbe WPGP WWat |
| - from Winkworth | CTho |
| - 'Gold Bark' | Last listed 1997 |
| ♦ *megrelica* | See *B. medwedewii* |
| § *michauxii* | MBro MDun NHol WAbe WPat WPyg |
| x *minor* | Last listed 1998 |
| *nana* | CBlo ELan ESis IOrc MBal MBar MPla MWhi NSla SIng SMac SRms SSta STre WPer |
| - 'Glengarry' | EPot GAri GBin WDin |
| ♦ - var. *michauxii* | See *B. michauxii* |
| § *neoalaskana* | WNor |
| *nigra* ♀ | CB&S CBlo CDoC CDul CGre CLnd CMCN CTho ENot GChr IOrc LPan MAsh MBal NWea SMad SPer SSta WDin WFro WGer WNor |
| - 'Heritage' | CDoC CDul CEnd EBee ENot LPan MBlu MBri SSpi SSta WWat |
| - Wakehurst form | EPfP |
| § *occidentalis* | MAsh |
| *papyrifera* | CB&S CBlo CDul CLnd CMCN CSam ECrN ELan ENot GChr IOrc LBuc LPan MAsh MBal MBar MGos MRav MWhi NBee NWea SPer SSta WCoo WDin WFar WNor WOrn WWat |
| - var. *commutata* | Last listed 1997 |
| ♦ - subsp. *humilis* | See *B. neoalaskana* |
| ♦ - var. *kenaica* | See *B. kenaica* |
| ♦ - 'Occidentalis' | See *B. occidentalis* |
| - 'Saint George' | CTho WWat |
| - 'Vancouver' | CTho |
| § *pendula* ♀ | More than 30 suppliers |
| - f. *crispa* | See *B. pendula* 'Laciniata' |
| N - 'Dalecarlica' hort. | See *B. pendula* 'Laciniata' |
| - 'Fastigiata' | CBlo CDoC CDul CEnd CLnd CTho EBee EBrP EBre ELan ENot GChr LBre LPan MGos SBre SPer WOrn |
| * - 'Golden Beauty' | CEnd |
| - 'Golden Cloud' | CLnd IOrc |
| - 'Gracilis' | CTho EMil |
| - 'Laciniata' ♀ | CB&S CBlo CDoC CDul CLnd CTho EBee ENot EWTr GChr GRei IOrc LPan MAsh MBar MBri MGos MRav NBea NBee NWea SPer SSpi SSta WBay WDin WMou WPyg WWes |
| - var. *pendula* 'Dissecta' | Last listed 1996 |
| - 'Purpurea' | CBlo CLnd CTho EBee EBrP EBre ECrN ELan ENot IOrc LBre LPan MBal MBar MBlu MGos NBea SBre SPer SSpi WDin |
| - 'Tristis' ♀ | CB&S CBlo CDoC CDul CEnd CLnd CTho CTri EBee ECrN EMil ENot GChr IOrc LPan MBal MBar MGos NBea NWea SPer SSpi SSta WDin WFar WMou WOrn WPyg |

| | |
|---|---|
| - 'Youngii' ♀ | More than 30 suppliers |
| **platyphylla** | CMCN GAri WFro |
| ♦ - var. **japonica** | See *B. mandshurica* var. *japonica* |
| ♦ - var. **kamtschatica** | See *B. mandshurica* var. *japonica* |
| ♦ - (Regel) V.N. Voroschilov subsp. **kamtschatica** | See *B. mandshurica* var. *japonica* |
| ♦ - var. **subcordata** | See *B. papyrifera* var. *subcordata* |
| **populifolia** | CFil CMCN GAri WPic |
| **potaninii** | Last listed 1998 |
| § **pubescens** | CDul CKin CLnd GChr IOrc ISea LHyr LNet I.Pan MBal NWea SLPl WDin WFar WMou |
| - 'Arnold Brembo' | CTho |
| ♦ - subsp. **carpatica** | See *B. pubescens* var. *glabrata* |
| ♦ - - var. **murithii** | See *B. pubescens* var. *glabrata* |
| ♦ - subsp. **celtiberica** | See *B. pubescens* var. *pubescens* |
| ♦ - subsp. **czerepanovii** | See *B. pubescens* var. *pumila* |
| ♦ - subsp. **tortuosa** | See *B. pubescens* var. *pumila* |
| § **pumila** | Last listed 1998 |
| **raddeana** | CFil WNor WPGP |
| - 'Hugh McAllister' | CTho |
| **resinifera** Britton | See *B. neoalaskana* |
| **saposhnikovii** | Last listed 1997 |
| **schmidtii** | WCoo |
| 'Snow Queen' | CBlo CDul CEnd COtt EPfP GRei IMGH LBuc MAsh MBri MGos SCoo SMer |
| **szechuanica** | Last listed 1998 |
| - 'Liuba White' | CTho |
| **tatewakiana** | See *B. ovalifolia* |
| **tianschanica** | WNor WShe |
| 'Trost's Dwarf' | CBlo EHal GQui IOrc MGos NHar SPer WPyg |
| ♦ **uber** | See *B. lenta* subsp. *uber* |
| x **utahensis** | Last listed 1998 |
| **utilis** | CBlo CLnd CMCN CMHG CTho EMil ENot LNet MAsh MBal MBar MRav NBee SPer SSta WDin WFro WNor WOrn |
| - BL&M 100 | CTho |
| - CC 1409 | Last listed 1997 |
| - DB 319 | Last listed 1998 |
| § - F 19505 | CTho |
| - 'Fascination' | SPer SRPl SSpi |
| - 'Forrest's Blush' | MAsh MBri |
| - 'Gregory Birch' | Last listed 1997 |
| N - var. **jacquemontii** | More than 30 suppliers |
| - - 'Doorenbos' ♀ | CDoC CLnd LPan MBlu MGos NBee NEgg SPer SSta |
| - - 'Grayswood Ghost' | CBlo CEnd CTho EBee EPfP SPer SRPl SSpi SSta WWat |
| - - 'Inverleith' | CEnd EBee MBri SSpi WWat |
| - - 'Jermyns' ♀ | CDul CLnd CTho ECot EPfP LNet MBlu SPer SRPl SSpi SSta WWat |
| - - 'Silver Shadow' ♀ | CLnd CTho EPfP MBlu MBri SPer SSpi SSta WWat |
| - - wild origin | Last listed 1998 |
| - 'Knightshayes' | CTho |
| - McB 1257 | CTho |
| ¶ - 'Moonbeam' | SSpi |
| - var. **occidentalis** 'Kyelang' | CTho |
| - var. **prattii** | CEnd CGre CTho |
| - 'Ramdang River' | CTho MBlu |
| - S&L 5380 | Last listed 1997 |
| - 'Schilling' | MBri |
| - SF 48 | ISea |
| - 'Silver Queen' | SSpi |
| ¶ - 'Trinity College' | SRPl SSpi |
| **verrucosa** | See *B. pendula* |

## BIARUM (Araceae)

| | |
|---|---|
| **arundanum** | Last listed 1998 |
| **bovei** S&L 132 | Last listed 1998 |
| **carduchorum** | GCrs |
| **carratracense** SF 233 | Last listed 1998 |
| **davisii** | CLAP EHyt GCrs LAma LRHS |
| - subsp. **davisii** MS 785/735 | Last listed 1998 |
| - subsp. **marmarisense** | Last listed 1998 |
| **dispar** AB&S 4455 | Last listed 1998 |
| - S&L 295 | Last listed 1998 |
| **ditschianum** | WCot |
| **eximium** FF 1024 | Last listed 1998 |
| - PD 26644 | Last listed 1998 |
| **ochridense** | WCot |
| - M&T 4629 | Last listed 1998 |
| **pyrami** PB | Last listed 1998 |
| - S&L 584 | Last listed 1998 |
| **spruneri** S&L 229 | Last listed 1998 |
| **tenuifolium** | CLAP EPot LAma SSpi WCot |
| - AB&S 4356 | Last listed 1998 |
| - subsp. **idomenaeum** MS 758 | Last listed 1998 |

## BIDENS (Asteraceae)

| | |
|---|---|
| **atrosanguinea** | See *Cosmos atrosanguineus* |
| **aurea** | CGle ECtt EMan LIck NFai SAga SCoo |
| **cernua** | MSal |
| **ferulifolia** ♀ | CLTr CSev ECtt LHil LHop MBEx MFir NPer SChu SMer SMrm SYvo |
| - 'Golden Goddess' | Last listed 1996 |
| * 'Goldie' | NPri |
| **heterophylla** | CHan CMil CStr EBee EWes LHil MGrG SAga SBla SChu SLod SMrm SUsu WFar |
| - CD&R 1230 | CHan |
| - cream | CHan MSte |
| - 'Hannay's Lemon Drop' | CHan CStr |
| **humilis** | See *B. triplinervia* var. *macrantha* |
| **integrifolia** | SMad WCot |
| **ostruthioides** | MBEx |
| ¶ **pilosa** | EBee |
| **polylepis** | Last listed 1998 |
| sp. CD&R 1515 | CGle CHan CLAP |
| **tripartita** | EWFC MSal |
| § **triplinervia** var. **macrantha** | Last listed 1996 |

## BIGNONIA (Bignoniaceae)

| | |
|---|---|
| **capreolata** | CPIN EHol EPfP GOrc SBra SSta WCru WSHC |
| **lindleyana** | See *Clytostoma callistegioides* |
| **unguis-cati** | See *Macfadyena unguis-cati* |

## BILDERDYKIA See FALLOPIA

## BILLARDIERA (Pittosporaceae)

| | |
|---|---|
| **bicolor** | CPIN MSag |
| * **cordata** | Last listed 1997 |
| **cymosa** | SOWG |
| **erubescens** | Last listed 1997 |
| **longiflora** ♀ | More than 30 suppliers |
| - 'Cherry Berry' | CGre CPIN EBee ECou ELan ICrw LHop LRHS MAsh SBra |
| - **fructu-albo** | CGre CPIN CPle EBee ELan EWes GOrc LPio MBal SBra SPan SPer |
| - red berried | CPle CSam |
| **scandens** | CPIN ECou |

## BILLBERGIA (Bromeliaceae)

| | |
|---|---|
| ¶ *decora* | GBin |
| *nutans* | CHal CMdw EBak EOas GBin IBlr LBlm LCns MBri SAPC SArc SRms SVen |
| * – 'Variegata' | LHil |
| *pyramidalis* | Last listed 1998 |
| var. *striata* (v) | |
| *saundersii* | See *B. chlorosticta* |
| x *windii* ♀ | CHal EBak ECon LCns SRms |

## BISCUTELLA (Brassicaceae)

| | |
|---|---|
| *frutescens* | WWin |

## BISMARCKIA (Arecaceae)

| | |
|---|---|
| *nobilis* | LPal |

## BISTORTA See PERSICARIA

## BIXA (Bixaceae)

| | |
|---|---|
| *orellana* | ELau MPEx MSal |

## BLANDFORDIA (Blandfordiaceae)

| | |
|---|---|
| *grandiflora* | Last listed 1998 |
| *punicea* | SIgm |

## BLECHNUM (Blechnaceae)

| | |
|---|---|
| *alpinum* | See *B. penna-marina* subsp. *alpinum* |
| *auriculatum* | Last listed 1996 |
| *brasiliense* | WRic |
| *cartilagineum* | CFil CRDP WRic |
| N *chilense* ♀ | CCuc CFil CRow EMon IBlr LBlm LEdu LSyl MBal SAPC SArc SChu SDix SLod SSpi WPGP WRic |
| *colensoi* | WRic |
| *discolor* | NMar WRic |
| *fluviatile* | NMar WRic |
| *gibbum* | MBri WRic |
| § *glandulosum* | NMar |
| *indicum* | WRic |
| *magellanicum* misapplied | See *B. chilense* |
| *minus* | NMar WRic |
| – x *wattsii* | WRic |
| *moorei* | NMar WRic |
| *nudum* | CFil CRDP CTrC WPGP WRic |
| ¶ *occidentale* | WRic |
| – *nanum* | See *B. glandulosum* |
| *patersonii* | WRic |
| *penna-marina* ♀ | CBro CCuc CFil EFer EMon EPar GGar LEdu MBal MBri NHar NMar NRya NVic SChu SDix SIng SRms SSpi WAbe WEas WPGP WRic |
| § – subsp. *alpinum* | CFil NMar WPGP |
| – 'Cristatum' | CCuc CFil EFer EMon GDra MBal NHar WPGP WRic |
| *spicant* ♀ | More than 30 suppliers |
| – 'Cristatum' | WRic |
| – 'Heterophyllum' | Last listed 1998 |
| – *incisum* | See *B. spicant* 'Rickard's Serrate' |
| § – 'Rickard's Serrate' | WRic |
| – Serratum Group | CFil |
| N *tabulare* (Thunb.) Kuhn ♀ | See *B. chilense* |
| – misapplied | |
| *vulcanicum* | Last listed 1998 |

## BLETILLA ✿ (Orchidaceae)

| | |
|---|---|
| Brigantes g. | EEve EPot SWes |
| * – 'Moonlight' | EEve |
| Coritani g. | EEve EPot LAma SWes WCot |
| *formosana* | EEve EPot LAma SWes |

| | |
|---|---|
| * – *alba* | EEve EPot SWes |
| *byacinthina* | See *B. striata* |
| *ochracea* | EEve EPot LAma SWes WCot |
| Penway Dragon g. | EEve EPot SWes |
| * Penway Imperial g. | EEve EPot SWes |
| Penway Paris g. | EEve EPot SWes |
| Penway Princess g. | EEve EPot SWes |
| Penway Rainbow g. | EEve EPot SWes |
| * Penway Rose g. | EEve EPot SWes |
| Penway Starshine g. | EEve EPot SWes |
| Penway Sunset g. | EEve EPot SWes WCot |
| § *striata* | EBee EBrP EBre ERea ERos IBlr LAma LBre LEdu LHop MBri MCli MSal NHol NRog SBre SCob SIng SLon SStn SWes WCot WFar |
| – *alba* | See *B. striata* var. *japonica* f. *gebina* |
| – 'Albostriata' | ELan IBlr LAma NHol NRog SWes WCot |
| – var. *japonica* | EEve EPot |
| § – – f. *gebina* | IBlr LAma NHol NRog SSpi SWes WCot WFar |
| – – – variegated | EPot SWes |
| *szetschuanica* | EEve EPot LAma SWes |
| 'Yokohama' | EEve EPot LAma SWes |

## BLOOMERIA (Alliaceae)

| | |
|---|---|
| *crocea* | SSpi |
| – var. *aurea* JCA 13091 | Last listed 1996 |

## BOCCONIA (Papaveraceae)

| | |
|---|---|
| *cordata* | See *Macleaya cordata* |
| *microcarpa* | See *Macleaya microcarpa* |

## BOEHMERIA (Urticaceae)

| | |
|---|---|
| *biloba* | WCot |

## BOENNINGHAUSENIA (Rutaceae)

| | |
|---|---|
| *albiflora* | IHdy WCot |
| – B&SWJ 1479 | WCru WTin |
| – S&SH 108 | CHan |
| ¶ *japonica* B&SWJ 4876 | WCru |

## BOLAX (Apiaceae)

| | |
|---|---|
| *glebaria* | See *Azorella trifurcata* |
| § *gummifera* | EPot GNor ITim NWCA WAbe |

## BOLBOSCHOENUS (Cyperaceae)

| | |
|---|---|
| § *maritimus* | LPBA |

## BOLTONIA (Asteraceae)

| | |
|---|---|
| *asteroides* | CBlo CFee CGle CHan CSam CSev EBee ECoo EHal EMon GMac MCAu NBrk NBro NSti SLon SWat WLRN WPrP WRHF |
| – var. *latisquama* | CGle CHan CHea CVer EHic GMaP GMac LRHS MBel MBrN MRav MSte MWat SMad SPer SSvw WCot WFar WHal |
| – – 'Nana' | CBre CSev EBee EMan EPPr GBuc MBro MLLN MRav MWgw NBid NBrk NBro NFai NPri WMoo WPer WPrP |
| – 'Pink Beauty' | Last listed 1998 |
| ¶ – var. *recognita* | EMon |
| – 'Snowbank' | ELan EMan MBel MCli |
| *incisa* | See *Kalimeris incisa* |

## BOLUSANTHUS (Papilionaceae)

| | |
|---|---|
| *speciosus* | Last listed 1997 |

**BOMAREA** (Alstroemeriaceae)
| | |
|---|---|
| *caldasii* ♀ | CPIN CRHN ERea SOWG SSpi WBor WCot |
| *edulis* | ERea |
| *hirtella* | CPIN CRHN SSpi WIvy |
| ¶ – JCA 13676 | WCot |
| *ovata* | ERea |
| *patacocensis* | Last listed 1998 |
| *sasilla* | Last listed 1996 |
| ¶ sp. RCB/Eq A-5 | WCot |
| ¶ sp. RCB/Eq C-1 | WCot |
| ¶ sp. RCB/Eq X-2 | WCot |

**BONGARDIA** (Berberidaceae)
| | |
|---|---|
| *chrysogonum* | EHyt LRHS NRog |

**BOOPHANE** (Amaryllidaceae)
| | |
|---|---|
| *disticha* | Last listed 1997 |
| *guttata* | Last listed 1997 |

**BORAGO** ✿ (Boraginaceae)
| | |
|---|---|
| *alba* | CJew EOHP MChe WCHb WGwG WRos |
| *laxiflora* | See *B. pygmaea* |
| *officinalis* | CArn CSev ELau GPoy LHol MBri MChe MHew MMal NFai SIde WGwG WHer WOak WPer WSel WWye |
| – 'Alba' | CBre CGle CSev ELau EMon ILis MMal NChi NCot NHex WCHb WHer WJek WPer WRha |
| * – 'Bill Archer' (v) | CNat GVic |
| – 'Variegata' (v) | EMon |
| § *pygmaea* | CArn CHid CSev CSpe ELan EMan ERav LHop MFir MHar MHer MHew MTho NChi NLar NSti NTow SChu STes SWat WCHb WOak WPrP WWin WWye |

**BORINDA** (Poaceae)
| | |
|---|---|
| *albocerea* | CFil EPla |

**BORNMUELLERA** (Brassicaceae)
| | |
|---|---|
| *tymphaea* | Last listed 1998 |

**BORONIA** (Rutaceae)
| | |
|---|---|
| 'Heaven Scent' | CB&S |
| *heterophylla* | CB&S CMHG ECon ERea SAga |
| *megastigma* | CB&S MSag |
| – brown | Last listed 1998 |
| – 'Brown Meg' | CB&S |
| 'Southern Star' | Last listed 1998 |

**BOTHRIOCHLOA** (Poaceae)
| | |
|---|---|
| § *bladhii* | EPPr |
| *caucasica* | See *B. bladhii* |
| § *ischaemum* | CInt EBee EGar EHoe EPPr EWes LEdu MCCP |

**BOTRYOSTEGE** See ELLIOTTIA

**BOUGAINVILLEA** (Nyctaginaceae)
| | |
|---|---|
| 'Ailsa Lambe' | See *B.* (Spectoperuviana Group) 'Mary Palmer' |
| * 'Alabama Sunset' | CWDa |
| 'Albo d'Ora' | Last listed 1996 |
| 'Alexandra' | LChe MBri |
| 'Amethyst' | ERea MBri |
| ◆ 'Apple Blossom' | See *B.* 'Elizabeth Doxey' |
| 'Asia' | ERea |
| ◆ 'Audrey Grey' (x *buttiana*) | See *B.* 'Elizabeth Doxey' |
| ◆ 'Aurantiaca' | See *B.* 'Lindleyana' |
| 'Aussie Gold' | See *B.* 'Carson's Gold' |
| 'Barbara Karst' | CWDa ERea |
| 'Begum Sikander' | CWDa |
| 'Betty Lavers' | ERea |
| § 'Blondie' | CWDa |
| 'Brasiliensis' | See *B. spectabilis* 'Lateritia' |
| 'Bridal Bouquet' | See *B.* x *buttiana* 'Cherry Blossom' |
| 'Brilliance' | CWDa ERea |
| ◆ 'Brilliant' misapplied | See *B.* 'Raspberry Ice' |
| x *buttiana* 'Afterglow' | CWDa |
| ◆ – 'Audrey Grey' | See *B.* 'Elizabeth Doxey' |
| § – 'Cherry Blossom' (d) | CWDa ERea LCns |
| ¶ – 'Daphne Mason' | ERea |
| § – 'Enid Lancaster' | ECon ERea |
| ◆ – 'Golden Glow' | See *B.* x *buttiana* 'Enid Lancaster' |
| § – 'Golden McLean' | CWDa |
| § – 'Jamaica Red' | ERea |
| ¶ – 'Killie Campbell' ♀ | ERea LChe MBri |
| ◆ – 'Lady Mary Baring' | See *B.* 'Lady Mary Baring' |
| § – 'Louise Wathen' | CWDa ECon LCns |
| § – 'Mahara' (d) | CWDa ERea SOWG |
| ◆ – 'Mahara Double Red' | See *B.* x *buttiana* 'Mahara' |
| ◆ – 'Mahara Off-white' | See *B.* x *buttiana* 'Cherry Blossom' |
| ◆ – 'Mahara Pink' | See *B.* 'Los Banos Beauty' |
| § – 'Mardi Gras' (v) | CWDa ERea |
| § – 'Mrs Butt' ♀ | CWDa ERea |
| § – 'Mrs McLean' | ERea |
| § – 'Poultonii' | ERea |
| – 'Poultonii Variegata' | Last listed 1998 |
| § – 'Poulton's Special' ♀ | ERea LChe |
| § – 'Rainbow Gold' | ERea |
| § – 'Rosenka' | CWDa ERea |
| § – 'Roseville's Delight' (d) | ERea LCns |
| § – 'Scarlet Glory' | ERea |
| § – Texas Dawn | ERea |
| * 'California Gold' | See *B.* x *buttiana* 'Enid Lancaster' |
| § Camarillo Fiesta™ (*spectabilis* hybrid) | CWDa ERea SOWG |
| 'Captain Caisy' | CWDa ERea |
| § 'Carson's Gold' (d) | CWDa |
| 'Cherry Blossom' | See *B.* x *buttiana* 'Cherry Blossom' |
| § 'Chiang Mai Beauty' | ERea |
| 'Coconut Ice' (v) | CWDa LCns SOWG |
| 'Crimson Lake' misapplied | See *B.* x *buttiana* 'Mrs Butt' |
| 'Dania' | MBri |
| 'Danica Rouge' | Last listed 1998 |
| 'Dauphine' | See *B.* 'Los Banos Beauty' |
| 'David Lemmer' | CWDa ERea |
| 'Delicate' | See *B.* 'Blondie' |
| 'Dixie' | ERea |
| § 'Doctor David Barry' | CWDa ERea |
| 'Donyo' | CWDa ERea LCns |
| 'Double Yellow' | See *B.* 'Carson's Gold' |
| 'Durban' | See *B. glabra* 'Jane Snook' |
| § 'Elizabeth Angus' | CWDa ERea |
| § 'Elizabeth Doxey' | CB&S ERea |
| 'Elizabeth' (*spectabilis* hybrid) | ERea |
| * 'Elsbet' | CWDa |
| 'Enchantment' | See *B.* 'Mary Palmer's Enchantment' |
| 'Fair Lady' | See *B.* 'Blondie' |
| 'Flamingo Pink' | See *B.* 'Chiang Mai Beauty' |
| 'Floribunda' | CWDa |
| 'Gillian Greensmith' | ERea |
| *glabra* ♀ | CB&S CPIN ERea LCns MBri WMul |
| – A | ERea |

| | | |
|---|---|---|
| ♦ | - 'Doctor David Barry' | See *B.* 'Doctor David Barry' |
| ♦ | - 'Elizabeth Angus' | See *B.* 'Elizabeth Angus' |
| § | - 'Harrissii' (v) | CWDa ERea MBri |
| § | - 'Jane Snook' | CWDa ERea |
| ♦ | - 'Jennifer Fernie' | See *B.* 'Jennifer Fernie' |
| § | - 'Magnifica' | ERea |
| § | - 'Pride of Singapore' | ERea |
| § | - 'Sanderiana' | ERea LPan NRog |
| | 'Gladys Hepburn' | ERea |
| | 'Gloucester Royal' | CWDa |
| * | 'Glowing Flame' | CWDa |
| ♦ | 'Golden Doubloon' | See *B.* x *buttiana* 'Roseville's Delight' (d) |
| | 'Golden Glow' (x *buttiana*) | See *B.* x *buttiana* 'Enid Lancaster' |
| I | 'Golden MacLean' | See *B.* x *buttiana* 'Golden McLean' |
| * | 'Golden Tango' | CWDa |
| * | 'Granada' | LChe |
| | 'Harlequin' | See *B.* (Spectoperuviana Group) 'Thimma' |
| | 'Harrissii' (*glabra*) | See *B. glabra* 'Harrissii' |
| ♦ | 'Hawaiian Scarlet' | See *B.* 'San Diego Red' |
| | 'Helen Johnson' | See *B.* 'Temple Fire' |
| | 'Hugh Evans' | See *B.* 'Blondie' |
| | 'Indian Flame' | See *B.* 'Partha' |
| ¶ | 'Isabel Greensmith' | CWDa ERea LCns |
| * | 'Jamaica Gold' | LChe |
| | 'Jamaica Orange' | CWDa ERea |
| | 'Jamaica Red' | See *B.* x *buttiana* 'Jamaica Red' |
| | 'James Walker' | ERea |
| | 'Jane Snook' | See *B. glabra* 'Jane Snook' |
| § | 'Jennifer Fernie' | ERea |
| | 'Juanita Hatten' | CWDa ERea |
| | 'Kauai Royal' | See *B.* 'Elizabeth Angus' |
| | 'Klong Fire' | See *B.* x *buttiana* 'Mahara' |
| | 'La Jolla' | ERea |
| | 'Lady Mary Baring' | ERea LCns SOWG |
| | 'Lavender Girl' | CWDa ERea |
| | 'Lemmer's Special' | See *B.* 'Partha' |
| | 'Limberlost Beauty' | See *B.* x *buttiana* 'Cherry Blossom' |
| § | 'Lindleyana' | CB&S |
| | 'Little Caroline' | CWDa |
| ♦ | 'Lord Willingdon' misapplied | See *B.* 'Pixie' |
| § | 'Los Banos Beauty' (d) | CWDa ERea |
| I | 'Louis Wathen' | See *B.* x *buttiana* 'Louise Wathen' |
| | 'Magnifica' (*glabra*) | See *B. glabra* 'Magnifica' |
| | 'Magnifica Traillii' | See *B. glabra* 'Magnifica' |
| | 'Mahara Double Red' (x *buttiana*) | See *B.* x *buttiana* 'Mahara' |
| | 'Mahara Off-white' (x *buttiana*) | See *B.* x *buttiana* 'Cherry Blossom' |
| ♦ | 'Mahara Orange' (x *buttiana*) | See *B.* x *buttiana* 'Roseville's Delight' |
| | 'Mahara Pink' (x *buttiana*) | See *B.* 'Los Banos Beauty' |
| | 'Mahara White' | See *B.* x *buttiana* 'Cherry Blossom' |
| ♦ | 'Manila Magic Red' | See *B.* x *buttiana* 'Mahara' |
| | 'Mardi Gras' (x *buttiana*) | See *B.* x *buttiana* 'Mardi Gras' |
| § | 'Mary Palmer's Enchantment' | CWDa ERea |
| | 'Meriol Fitzpatrick' | ERea |
| * | 'Michael Lemmer' | CWDa |
| ♦ | 'Mini-Thai' | See *B.* 'Pixie' |
| * | 'Mischief' | CWDa |
| § | 'Miss Manila' | CWDa ERea |
| | 'Mrs Butt' (x *buttiana*) | See *B.* x *buttiana* 'Mrs Butt' |
| | 'Mrs Butt Variegated' (x *buttiana*) | See *B.* x *buttiana* 'Mrs Butt Variegated' |
| | 'Mrs Helen McLean' (x *buttiana*) | See *B.* x *buttiana* 'Mrs McLean' |
| | 'Mrs McLean' (x *buttiana*) | See *B.* x *buttiana* 'Mrs McLean' |
| | 'Natalii Group' | CWDa ERea |
| | 'Nina Mitton' | CWDa ERea |
| | 'Ninja Turtle' (v) | Last listed 1997 |
| * | 'Orange Cotton' | LCns |
| | 'Orange Glow' | See *B.* Camarillo Fiesta (*spectabilis* hybrid) |
| | 'Orange King' | See *B.* x *buttiana* 'Louise Wathen' |
| | 'Orange Stripe' (v) | ERea |
| | 'Pagoda Pink' | See *B.* 'Los Banos Beauty' |
| § | 'Partha' | CWDa |
| | 'Pearl' | Last listed 1997 |
| | 'Penelope' | See *B.* 'Mary Palmer's Enchantment' |
| | pink | ECon |
| | 'Pink Champagne' | See *B.* 'Los Banos Beauty' |
| | 'Pink Clusters' | CWDa ERea |
| § | 'Pixie' | ERea |
| | 'Poultonii' | See *B.* x *buttiana* 'Poultonii' |
| | 'Poultonii Special' (x *buttiana*) | See *B.* x *buttiana* 'Poulton's Special' |
| | 'Pride of Singapore' | See *B. glabra* 'Pride of Singapore' |
| | 'Princess Mahara' | See *B.* x *buttiana* 'Mahara' |
| | 'Purple Robe' | CWDa ERea |
| | 'Rainbow Gold' | See *B.* x *buttiana* 'Rainbow Gold' |
| | 'Ralph Sander' | LCns |
| § | 'Raspberry Ice' (v) | ERea LCns SOWG WMul |
| | 'Ratana Orange' | Last listed 1997 |
| | 'Ratana Red' | Last listed 1997 |
| | 'Red Diamond' | ERea |
| | 'Red Fantasy' (v) | Last listed 1997 |
| | 'Red Glory' | CWDa ERea |
| * | 'Reggae Gold' | CWDa |
| | 'Robyn's Glory' | See *B.* x *buttiana* Texas Dawn |
| | 'Rose Parme' | ERea |
| | 'Rosenka' | See *B.* x *buttiana* 'Rosenka' |
| | 'Royal Purple' | CWDa ERea |
| | 'Rubyana' | CWDa ERea LChe LCns SOWG |
| § | 'San Diego Red' | CB&S ECon ERea GQui LCns SOWG |
| | 'Sanderiana' | See *B. glabra* 'Sanderiana' |
| | 'Sanderiana Variegata' | See *B. glabra* 'Harrissii' |
| ♦ | 'Scarlet Glory' | See *B.* x *buttiana* 'Scarlet Glory' |
| ♦ | Scarlett O'Hara | See *B.* 'San Diego Red' |
| | 'Singapore Pink' | See *B.* 'Doctor David Barry' |
| | 'Singapore White' | CWDa ERea |
| ♦ | 'Smartipants' | See *B.* 'Pixie' |
| | 'Snow Cap' | See *B.* (Spectoperuviana Group) 'Mary Palmer' |
| ♦ | *spectabilis* 'Variegata' | See *B. spectabilis* variegated |
| § | - variegated | Last listed 1998 |
| | - 'Wallflower' | CWDa |
| § | Spectoperuviana Group (v) | ERea |
| | - 'Makris' | Last listed 1997 |
| § | - 'Mary Palmer' | CWDa |
| § | - 'Mrs H.C. Buck' | CWDa ERea LCns |
| | 'Summer Snow' | CWDa |
| | Surprise | See *B.* (Spectoperuviana Group) 'Mary Palmer' |
| | 'Tango' | See *B.* 'Miss Manila' |
| * | 'Tango Supreme' | CWDa |
| § | 'Temple Fire' | ERea SOWG |
| ♦ | 'Thai Gold' | See *B.* x *buttiana* 'Roseville's Delight' |
| * | 'Tom Thumb' | CWDa |
| * | 'Tropical Bouquet' | CWDa |
| | 'Tropical Rainbow' | See *B.* 'Raspberry Ice' |
| * | 'Turkish Delight' | CWDa ECon LChe LCns |
| | 'Variegata' (*glabra*) | See *B. glabra* 'Harrissii' |
| | 'Variegata' (*spectabilis*) | See *B. spectabilis* variegated |
| | 'Vera Blakeman' | CWDa ECon ERea LCns |
| | 'Vicky' | See *B.* (Spectoperuviana Group) 'Thimma' |

'Wac Campbell' (d) CWDa
'Weeping Beauty' ERea
* 'White Cascade' CWDa
'White Empress' Last listed 1996

## BOUSSINGAULTIA (Basellaceae)
**baselloides** Hook. See *Anredera cordifolia*

## BOUTELOUA (Poaceae)
**curtipendula** EMon
§ **gracilis** CBrm CCuc CInt EBee ECGN
MCCP MLLN MMal MMoz NSti
SLod SPla SUsu WPer

## BOUVARDIA (Rubiaceae)
x **domestica** Last listed 1996
**longiflora** ERea LChe SOWG
**triphylla** See *B. ternifolia*

## BOWENIA (Boweniaceae)
**serrulata** CBrP LPal
**spectabilis** CBrP

## BOWIEA (Hyacinthaceae)
**volubilis** CHal CPlN

## BOWKERIA (Scrophulariaceae)
**citrina** CGre CPle
**gerrardiana** CGre CPle

## BOYKINIA (Saxifragaceae)
**aconitifolia** EBee EHal ELan GTou LFis MGrG
MLLN MRav NLar NRya SSpi
WCot WCru WMoo WPrP
**elata** See *B. occidentalis*
**heucheriformis** See *B. jamesii*
§ **jamesii** CGra CMCo GCrs MBro NNrd
NTow NWCA SIng WAbe WLin
¶ **major** WCru
§ **occidentalis** GGar NLar WCru
**rotundifolia** ELan GBin GBuc NSti SLon WCru
– JLS 86269LACA EMon
**tellimoides** See *Peltoboykinia tellimoides*

## BRACHYCHILUM See HEDYCHIUM

## BRACHYCHITON (Sterculiaceae)
**acerifolius** Last listed 1998
¶ **bidwillii** MSag
**populneus** Last listed 1997

## BRACHYGLOTTIS ✿ (Asteraceae)
§ **bidwillii** CB&S CDoC SDry WAbe WCru
§ **buchananii** GEil SDry WSHC
¶ – 'Silver Shadow' GRei
§ **compacta** CSam EBee ECha ECou EPfP
MAsh MPla MWgw SDry SPer
WEas
¶ – x **monroi** ECou
'Drysdale' CPle EPfP LRHS MAsh MBri MRav
MTed SDry SLon SPan SPla WWat
§ (Dunedin Group) CPle EGoo ELan EPla MBal SDry
'Moira Reid' (v) WEas WSHC
§ – 'Sunshine' ♀ CChe CDoC CDul EAst EBee
EGoo ELan ENot EWTr IBlr LGro
LHop MBal MGos NBee NPer SPer
SPla SPlb SRms WAbe WFar WHen
WTro
§ **elaeagnifolia** ISea
¶ 'Frosty' ECou
N **greyi** CTrG EBee EHol GRei ISea MBar
NLon NRoo WEas WWin

§ **huntii** CPle SPer
§ **kirkii** Last listed 1998
N **laxifolia** SIng
§ 'Leonard Cockayne' SPer
§ **monroi** ♀ CChe CSam EAst EBee ECou
EHoe EHol ELan IBlr IOrc LHop
MAsh MBal MBar MLLN MRav
NLon SCoo SMer SPan SPar SPer
WAbe WEas WTro WWat
– 'Clarence' ECou
**repanda** CPle CTrG
– x **greyi** CDoC CPle LHil SAPC SArc
– 'Purpurea' Last listed 1998
§ **rotundifolia** CDoC CPle EGoo EPfP IBlr MBlu
WCru WEas
¶ 'Silver Waves' ECou
§ **spedenii** CFee GCrs GTou
I 'Sunshine Improved' WSPU
'Sunshine Variegated' See *B.* (Dunedin Group) 'Moira Reid'

## BRACHYLAENA (Asteraceae)
**discolor** Last listed 1997

## BRACHYPODIUM (Poaceae)
**phoenicoides** Last listed 1997
**pinnatum** EHoe EPPr
**sylvaticum** CKin WPer

## BRACHYSCOME (Asteraceae)
'Blue Mist' GPin WLRN -
'Harmony' LHil
**iberidifolia** ELan
'Lemon Mist' GPin
**melanocarpa** CSpe
**multifida** EMan MBri
**nivalis** var. **alpina** See *B. tadgellii*
'Pink Mist' GPin LHil
**rigidula** ECou MDHE NMen
'Strawberry Mousse' LHil NPri
§ **tadgellii** IMGH MTPN
'Tinkerbell' CBar WLRN

## BRACHYSTACHYUM (Poaceae - Bambusoideae)
**densiflorum** SDry

## BRACTEANTHA (Asteraceae)
**acuminata** DC. See *B. subundulata*
**bracteata** 'Dargan Hill CMHG CSev MBEx SRms WEas
Monarch'
– 'Skynet' GMac MBEx
§ 'Coco' CMHG EBee MHlr SMrm WCot
WEas

## BRAHEA (Arecaceae)
**aculeata** LPal
**armata** CBrP CRoM CTrC EOas LPal NPal
SAPC SArc
**brandegeei** LPal
**edulis** CRoM CTrC LPal

## BRASSAIA See SCHEFFLERA

## BRASSICA (Brassicaceae)
**japonica** See *B. juncea* var. *crispifolia*
§ **juncea** var. **crispifolia** CArn WJek
**oleracea** WHer
* – **botrytis aparagoides** CAgr
* **rapa** var. **japonica** WJek
* – var. **purpurea** WJek

## BRASSIOPHOENIX (Arecaceae)
*schumannii*    LPal

## BRAVOA (Agavaceae)
*geminiflora*    See *Polianthes geminiflora*

## BRAYA (Brassicaceae)
*alpina*    Last listed 1996

## BREYNIA (Euphorbiaceae)
¶ *nivosa*    ECon
¶ - 'Rosea Picta'    ECon

## X BRIGANDRA (Gesneriaceae)
*calliantha*    NTow
- 'Tinneys Rose'    GCrs

## BRIGGSIA (Gesneriaceae)
*aurantiaca*    GCrs
*muscicola*    Last listed 1997

## BRIMEURA (Hyacinthaceae)
§ *amethystina*    CAvo EBot ERos WCot
- 'Alba'    CAvo EBot ERos NMen NRog
§ *fastigiata*    EHyt ERos

## BRIZA (Poaceae)
*maxima*    CJew CRDP EPla LIck NSti WByw
    WHal WHer WRos WWye
- from Rhodes    SApp
*media*    More than 30 suppliers
- Elatior Group    Last listed 1997
- 'Limouzi'    EMan EMon EPPr GCal LGre LRHS
    SApp SOkh
* - 'Luz'    NCat
*minor*    Last listed 1996
sp. from Chile    EPPr EWes
¶ *triloba*    CInt

## BRODIAEA (Alliaceae)
§ *californica*    CLAP CNic ERos
- var. *leptandra*    CLAP WCot
*capitata*    See *Dichelostemma pulchellum*
*coronaria* subsp. *rosea*    Last listed 1998
'Corrina'    See *Triteleia* 'Corrina'
* *crocea* var. *aurea*    WCot
*elegans*    Last listed 1998
*ida-maia*    See *Dichelostemma ida-maia*
*jolonensis*    Last listed 1997
*laxa*    See *Triteleia laxa*
*leptandra*    Last listed 1997
§ *minor*    WCot
*peduncularis*    See *Triteleia peduncularis*
*purdyi*    See *B. minor*
*stellaris*    EHyt
*terrestris*    Last listed 1997
*volubilis*    Last listed 1997

## BROMUS (Poaceae)
*catharticus*    See *B. unioloides*
*inermis* 'Skinner's Gold' (v) EBee EGar EHoe EMan EMon
    EPPr EPla EWes EWsh MAvo
    MMoz
*macrostachys*    See *B. lanceolatus*
*morrisonensis* B&SWJ 294 Last listed 1998
*ramosus*    CKin EHoe EPPr
§ *unioloides*    Last listed 1997

## BROUSSONETIA (Moraceae)
*papyrifera*    CAgr CB&S CFil CMCN ELan IDee
    LEdu LPan MLan MPEx SLon
    SMad SPer WPGP
- 'Laciniata'    SMad

## BROWALLIA (Solanaceae)
*speciosa* 'Major'    MBri
- 'Silver Bells'    MBri

## BRUGMANSIA (Solanaceae)
§ *arborea*    CArn LLew NPal SRms
*aurea*    Last listed 1998
- 'Golden Queen'    ERea LLew MBEx
x *candida*    EBak ERea LLew
- x *aurea*    LLew
- 'Blush'    ERea
- 'Ecuador Pink'    ERea
§ - 'Grand Marnier' ♀    CBot CMdw ECon ECot ELan
    ERea LLew MBri SOWG SSoC
    SVen WCot WEas WKif
§ - 'Knightii' (d) ♀    CBot CHal CSev EBak ECon ELan
    EPfP ERea LLew MBEx SOWG
    WCot
- pink    Last listed 1997
- 'Plena'    See *B.* x *candida* 'Knightii'
- 'Primrose'    ERea
§ - 'Variegata'    ERea
§ *chlorantha*    Last listed 1997
x *flava*    LLew
hybrids    Last listed 1997
§ x *insignis*    SEND
* - 'Orange'    Last listed 1998
§ - pink    EPfP
* 'La Fleur Lilas'    Last listed 1996
¶ 'Margaret Lewington'    LLew
*meteloides*    See *Datura inoxia*
'Panache'    CBot
* pink    LIck
*rosei*    See *B. sanguinea* subsp.
    *sanguinea* 'Flava'
§ *sanguinea* ♀    EBak ERea LLew MBEx MBri
    SOWG SSoC SVen WCot WHer
- 'Golden Queen'    Last listed 1997
- 'Rosea'    See *B.* x *insignis* pink
§ - subsp. *sanguinea* 'Flava'    MBri SYvo
§ *suaveolens* ♀    ELan ERea LLew NPal
* - hybrid pink    LLew
* - hybrid white    Last listed 1998
¶ - 'Myles Challis'    LLew
- *rosea*    See *B.* x *insignis* pink
- 'Variegata'    ERea
- x *versicolor*    See *B.* x *insignis*
- yellow    Last listed 1996
♦ 'Variegata Sunset'    See *B.* x *candida* 'Variegata'
§ *versicolor* Lagerh.    ERea LPan MBEx SOWG
§ - hort.    See *B. arborea*
yellow    LIck
* 'Yellow Trumpet'    EPfP

## BRUNFELSIA (Solanaceae)
*americana*    LChe SYvo
*calycina*    See *B. pauciflora*
*eximia*    See *B. pauciflora*
*jamaicensis*    CSpe
*latifolia*    ECon
§ *pauciflora* ♀    ELan MBri SYvo
- 'Floribunda'    LChe LCns SOWG
- 'Macrantha'    LCns SOWG
*undulata*    LChe

## BRUNIA (Bruniaceae)
¶ *albiflora*    CTrC

## BRUNNERA (Boraginaceae)
§ *macrophylla* ♀    More than 30 suppliers
- 'Alba'    See *B. macrophylla* 'Betty
    Bowring'

§ - Aluminium Spot = 'Langtrees' — More than 30 suppliers

§ - 'Betty Bowring' — CElw CHad CLAP CRDP CRow ECha GBuc MTed SWas WFar WHal

§ - 'Dawson's White' (v) — CBot CGle CLAP EBee ECha ELan EPar GCal LHop MAvo MBri MCAu MCLN MRav MTho MWat NChi NLar NRoo NSti SCob SPer SSpi WCot WHil WRus WWat

- 'Gordano Gold' — More than 30 suppliers
- 'Hadspen Cream' (v) ♀ — More than 30 suppliers
- 'Langford Hewitt' — CLAP
♦ - 'Langtrees' — See *B. macrophylla* Aluminium Spot = 'Langtrees'
- 'Variegata' — See *B. macrophylla* 'Dawson's White'

## x BRUNSCRINUM (Amaryllidaceae)
'Dorothy Hannibel' — Last listed 1998

## BRUNSVIGIA (Amaryllidaceae)
*grandiflora* — Last listed 1997
*gregaria* — Last listed 1997
*berrei* — Last listed 1996
*multiflora* — See *B. orientalis*
*natalensis* — Last listed 1996
§ *orientalis* — Last listed 1998
*radulosa* — Last listed 1998
*rosea* 'Minor' — See *Amaryllis belladonna*

## BRYANTHUS (Ericaceae)
*gmelinii* — Last listed 1996

## BRYONIA (Cucurbitaceae)
*dioica* — EWFC GPoy MHew MSal

## BRYOPHYLLUM See KALANCHOE

## BRYUM (Sphagnaceae)
*truncorum* — Last listed 1996

## BUCHLOE (Poaceae)
*dactyloides* — Last listed 1997

## BUDDLEJA ✿ (Buddlejaceae)
§ *abbreviata* — Last listed 1996
*agathosma* — CBot CFil CHan CPle WEas WHar WPen WSHC
¶ *albiflora* — SLon
*alternifolia* ♀ — More than 30 suppliers
- 'Argentea' — CBot CDoC CPMA CPle ELan ERav EREa MBNS MBro MHar MRav NFla NSti SPer SPla SSpi WCot WHCG WPat WSHC WWat
*asiatica* ♀ — CBot CBrm CPlN CPle ECon EREa LCns SBid SLon
- B&SWJ 2679 — WCru
*auriculata* — CAbb CB&S CBlo CBot CCHP CDoC CGre CHan CLTr CMCN CPle CWit EREa GQui LHil NSti SBid SDix SOWG SPer WCru WHCG
*australis* — CPle
*brevifolia* — See *B. abbreviata*
* 'Butterfly Ball' — SLon WBcn WPer
*caryopteridifolia* — EHal EHol ENot SBid SLon
*colvilei* — CAbb CB&S CDoC CFil CHan CPle CTrw CWit ENot EPfP MBal WAbe WCot WEas WSpi
¶ - B&SWJ 2121 — WCru
- C&S 1577 — Last listed 1998

- 'Kewensis' — CBot CGre IBlr ISea MBlu SLon WCru WPGP WSHC
*cordata* — CPle
*coriacea* — SLon
§ *crispa* — CB&S CBot CDoC CPle ECha ELan ERav IMGH LBlm SBid SBra SDry SOWG SPer SSpi SSta WAbe WCot WFar WHCG WKif WPGP WSHC WSpi WWat
- L 1544 — CFil NHex WPGP
*crotonoides amplexicaulis* — SLon
*curviflora* — CPle
*davidii* — CArn CKin MBro NWea SHFr STre WDin
- 'African Queen' — SPer SRPl
- var. *alba* — NSti
- 'Black Knight' ♀ — More than 30 suppliers
- 'Blue Horizon' — GCHN MHar MHlr SEND SLon WCot WMoo WRHF
- 'Border Beauty' — EHic SEas
- 'Calanadrina' — Last listed 1996
§ - 'Charming' — MBri WMoo WSHC
- 'Dartmoor' ♀ — More than 30 suppliers
- 'Dart's Blue Butterfly' — MBri SRPl
- 'Dart's Ornamental White' — CBlo EBee MBri
- 'Dart's Papillon Blue' — SLPl
- 'Dart's Purple Rain' — CBlo MBri
¶ - 'Dubonnet' — SLon
- 'Empire Blue' ♀ — CB&S CDoC EBee ECtt ELan ENot EWTr GChr GOrc MAsh MBal MRav MWat NBee NPer NWea SPer SPlb WBod WDin WGwG WMow WPyg WStI WWeb
- 'Fascinating' — CBlo CTri MAsh NPer SBod WMow
- 'Flaming Violet' — SLon
- 'Fortune' — Last listed 1998
- 'Glasnevin Blue' — CTri NSti SDix SMrm SPer
- 'Golden Sunset' — Last listed 1997
- 'Gonglepod' — ELan SLon
- 'Harlequin' (v) — More than 30 suppliers
- 'Ile de France' — CB&S CBlo EHic MGos MWat NWea SRms WWeb
- 'Les Kneale' — MBal
§ - Masquerade = 'Notbud' — CBlo CDoC EHic ENot EPfP MGos MGrG NRoo SLon WGor WLRN WStI WWes
§ - 'Nanho Blue' — CB&S CDoC CMHG CPle EBee EBrP EBre ECtt ELan ENot EWTr IOrc LBre LBuc LHop MAsh MBar MGos NFla NFor SBod SBre SEas SPla WBod WDin WFar WHar WSHC WWeb
- 'Nanho Petite Indigo' — See *B. davidii* 'Nanho Blue'
- 'Nanho Petite Purple' — See *B. davidii* 'Nanho Purple'
§ - 'Nanho Purple' — CDoC CHar CMHG EBee EGoo ELan ENot GAri GChr MAsh MBar MBel MBri NRoo SLon SPer WHar WSHC
- var. *nanhoensis* — CBlo CPle GCHN MWat MWhi SEND SIde SIgm SPer WHCG
- - *alba* — CBlo CChe ELan EPfP LFis LHop MBar MLan MMil SPan SPer SRPl SRms WWat
- - blue — LHil MBri SLon SPer SRPl WEas WMow WWat
¶ - - purple — CPLG
♦ - 'Notbud' — See *B. davidii* Masquerade = 'Notbud'
- 'Orchid Beauty' — CBlo MBNS MLan NCut
- 'Peace' — CChe EBee EHic ENot EPfP NPer SPer

| | |
|---|---|
| - Petite Indigo™ | See *B. davidii* 'Nanho Blue' |
| - Petite Plum™ | See *B. davidii* 'Nanho Purple' |
| - 'Pink Beauty' | CLTr WHCG WWat |
| - 'Pink Charming' | See *B. davidii* 'Charming' |
| ¶ - 'Pink Pearl' | SLon |
| * - 'Pixie Blue' | MAsh NCut WWeb |
| - 'Pixie Red' | CLyn MAsh NCut SLon WShe WWeb |
| * - 'Pixie White' | CLyn MAsh MBNS NCut WShe WWeb |
| - 'Purple Prince' | CB&S EHic NCut |
| - 'Purple Rain' | Last listed 1998 |
| - 'Royal Purple' | Last listed 1997 |
| - 'Royal Red' ♀ | More than 30 suppliers |
| ¶ - Santana = 'Thia' (v) | COtt LRHS WWeb |
| ¶ - 'Silver Butterfly' | WWeb |
| - 'Summer Beauty' | CBlo MBri MGos NPro WWeb |
| ¶ - 'Variegata' | SMrm |
| - 'Variegated Royal Red' | CBlo |
| ¶ - 'White Ball' | MBNS SLon |
| - 'White Bouquet' | CBlo EAst EBee GOrc GRei MBal MBel MPla MWat NRoo NWea SBod SEND SEas SMer SPer SReu WLRN WWeb |
| ¶ - 'White Butterfly' | SLon |
| - 'White Cloud' | EPar GQui IOrc SRms WGwG |
| - 'White Harlequin' (v) | CLTr CRow LHop SLon WCot WEas WWat |
| - 'White Perfection' | Last listed 1997 |
| - 'White Profusion' ♀ | CB&S CSam EBee ECtt ELan EWTr GCHN GChr LFis MBal MBar MGos MHlr NBee NBrk NFla NFor NWea WBod WDin WEas WFar WHCG WHar WPyg WStl WWin |
| ¶ - 'White Wings' | SLon |
| § *delavayi* | CMil CPle ERea SPan WCru |
| *fallowiana* misapplied | See *B.* 'West Hill' |
| - Balf. f. | CB&S CPle LRHS NFor NLon SPla SReu |
| ¶ - ACE 2481 | WAbe |
| - var. *alba* ♀ | CBlo CBot CDoC CMHG CPle EBee ELan ENot ERav LHop MBel MRav NSti SBid SLon SPer SPla SRPl SSta WAbe WCru WEas WPGP WSHC WWat |
| - CLD 1109 | CFil WPGP |
| *farreri* | CBot CPle MSte SOWG WBod |
| *forrestii* | CBot CPle WCru |
| ¶ - KR 2737 | WCru |
| *globosa* ♀ | More than 30 suppliers |
| - 'Cannington Gold' | CBlo |
| - 'Lemon Ball' | SMad |
| *heliophila* | See *B. delavayi* |
| *indica* | SLon |
| *japonica* | CPle |
| * 'Lady Curzon' | WRHF |
| x *lewisiana* | CPle |
| - x *asiatica* | Last listed 1996 |
| - 'Margaret Pike' | CBot SOWG |
| ¶ *limitanea* | SLon |
| *lindleyana* | CB&S CBot CFil CGre CHan CMCN CPin CPle EBee ELan EPla ERea MRav MTis NSti SBid SChu SOWG SPan SPer SPla SSpi WCru WFar WHCG WPGP WSHC WWeb |
| 'Lochinch' ♀ | More than 30 suppliers |
| ¶ *longifolia* | CChe |
| *loricata* | CAbb CBot CGre CHan CPle CStr ERea GQui MSte SOWG |
| - CD&R 190 | EPla |
| *macrostachya* | CFil CPle |
| - SBEC 360 | NHex WPGP |

| | |
|---|---|
| § *madagascariensis* | CB&S CPlN CPle CTbh LBlm SOWG WWat |
| *myriantha* | GQui SPan |
| ¶ *nappii* | SLon |
| ¶ *nepalensis* | CPLG |
| *nicodemia* | See *B. madagascariensis* |
| *nivea* | CBot CMCN CPle EHic MHar SBid SOWG SPan WCom |
| ¶ - pink | SLon |
| - var. *yunnanensis* | CPle MSte |
| aff. *nivea* L 860 | WPGP |
| *officinalis* | CBot CDoC CPle ERea LFis |
| *paniculata* | SLon |
| *parvifolia* MPF 148 | WPGP |
| ¶ *pichinchensis* | CFil |
| ¶ x *pikei* | SDys |
| § - 'Hever' | CHal CPle GQui SPer |
| - 'Pink Delight' ♀ | More than 30 suppliers |
| *pterocaulis* | CGre |
| *saligna* | CGre CPle CTrC SLon |
| *salviifolia* | CAbb CBot CFil CGre CPle CSWP CSam CTbh EGar ELan GQui SBid SDry SIgm SPan SPer WCot WHer WLRN WMul |
| - Burtt 6139 | WPGP |
| ¶ - white | CDoC |
| ¶ sp. ACE 2522 | WAbe |
| sp. TS&BC 94062 | Last listed 1997 |
| sp. TS&BC 94287 | Last listed 1997 |
| sp. TS&BC 94408 | Last listed 1997 |
| *stenostachya* | CPle |
| *sterniana* | See *B. crispa* |
| *tibetica* | See *B. crispa* |
| *tubiflora* | CBot ERea SLon SOWG |
| *venenifera* B&SWJ 895 | WCru |
| § 'West Hill' | SLon |
| x *weyeriana* | CBlo CLTr CSam CStr ECtt EOrc EPar GOrc LBlm MAsh MNrw MTis MWat NBir NSti SBod SEas SPlb WBea WEas WFar WHCG WPyg WSHC |
| * - 'Flight's Fancy' | EPla EWes |
| - 'Golden Glow' | CB&S CBlo CChe CDoC CHan CMil CTri EAst EHic GCHN MBri MPla NFor NLon SHel SLon SPla WPyg WSel WTro WWeb WWin |
| - 'Lady de Ramsey' | SEND WPer |
| - 'Moonlight' | CPle CRow EAst EHal SCob WCom WSel |
| - 'Sungold' ♀ | CPle EBee ELan IOrc MBal MBel MBlu MCCP MGos MLLN NFla SLon SPer WCot WHar WMow |
| - 'Trewithen' | CB&S |
| * - 'Variegata' | CPMA |

## BUGLOSSOIDES (Boraginaceae)

| | |
|---|---|
| § *purpurocaerulea* | CKin CMHG CRDP EBee ECha EEls ELan EMan EMar MAvo MBro MHew MSal MSte NChi WCot WEas WFar WOld WRHF WWin WWye |

## BULBINE (Asphodelaceae)

| | |
|---|---|
| *alooides* S&SH 74 | Last listed 1996 |
| *bulbosa* | SAga |
| *caulescens* | See *B. frutescens* |
| § *frutescens* | CAvo CPea CSev EWll LHil MWhi WCot WHal WWin |
| - yellow | LHil |
| *semibarbata* | EBee EGar NBro WPer |

## BULBINELLA (Asphodelaceae)

| | |
|---|---|
| *angustifolia* | WCot |
| ¶ *cauda-felis* | WCot |
| ¶ *eburnifolia* | WCot |
| *floribunda* | Last listed 1998 |
| *hookeri* | CRDP ECou EPPr GAbr GCrs GDra GGar ITim LBee MFir MTho NHar NHed SRms SYvo WCot WPer |
| *nutans* var. *nutans* | EEls |
| *rossii* | WLin |

## BULBINOPSIS See BULBINE

## BULBOCODIUM (Colchicaceae)

| | |
|---|---|
| *vernum* | CAvo EHyt EPot ERos ETub GCrs LAma MBri MNrw NRog WAbe |

## BUNIUM (Apiaceae)

| | |
|---|---|
| ¶ *bulbocastanum* | LEdu |

## BUPHTHALMUM (Asteraceae)

| | |
|---|---|
| § *salicifolium* | CSam CSev EBee ELan EPfP GMaP MBri MCli NBro NFla NGdn NOrc NTow SMac SPer SRms SWat WCot WMer WPer |
| – 'Alpengold' | ECha NVic SIgm |
| – 'Dora' | EMan NLak SUsu WCot WWal |
| – Golden Beauty | See *B. salicifolium* 'Golden Wonder' |
| ¶ – 'Sunwheel' | EFou EWll NPri WRHF |
| *speciosum* | See *Telekia speciosa* |

## BUPLEURUM (Apiaceae)

| | |
|---|---|
| *angulosum* | CFil CLon CLyd CNic CRDP LGre SIgm SMrm SWas WCru WFar WPGP |
| – copper | See *B. longifolium* |
| *barceloi* | SIgm |
| *falcatum* | CGle CLTr CLyd ECGP ECha ELau MBro MLLN MWgw NBro NFla NSti SChu SMrm WFar WWat |
| *fruticosum* | CB&S CBot CFil CHan CPle ECGP ELan ICrw LRHS MHar SBid SBla SChu SCob SIgm SPer SRPl SSpi WCot WCru WEas WKif WPGP WPat WSHC WSpi WStI WWat |
| ' *griffithii* | MSal |
| *komarovianum* | Last listed 1998 |
| § *longifolium* | CHan CRDP EBee ECha GBin GGar NSti SWas WCot WCru WWhi |
| ' – *roseum* | Last listed 1996 |
| *longiradiatum* B&SWJ 729 | WCru |
| *multinerve* | Last listed 1998 |
| *ranunculoides* | EBee SMrm |
| *rotundifolium* | EWFC MSal SMrm WPGP |
| *salicifolium* | CFil SIgm WCot |
| *spinosum* | SIgm WCru |
| *stellatum* | GGar LBee |
| *tenue* B&SWJ 2973 | WCru |

## BURCHARDIA (Colchicaceae)

| | |
|---|---|
| *umbellata* | Last listed 1998 |

## BURSARIA (Pittosporaceae)

| | |
|---|---|
| *spinosa* | CPle ECou GQui MSag SLon |

## BUTIA (Arecaceae)

| | |
|---|---|
| *capitata* | CBrP CRoM CTbh CTrC EOas LPJP LPal NPal SAPC SArc SEND WMul |
| ¶ *yatay* | CRoM |

## BUTOMUS (Butomaceae)

| | |
|---|---|
| *umbellatus* ♀ | CBen CRow CWat ECha ECoo ECtt EHon EMFW LPBA MSta NDea NVic SLon SRms SWat SWyc WFar WMAq WShi |
| – 'Rosenrot' | CRow SWyc |
| – 'Schneeweisschen' | CRow SWyc |

## BUXUS ✿ (Buxaceae)

| | |
|---|---|
| *aurea* 'Marginata' | See *B. sempervirens* 'Marginata' |
| *balearica* | CGre EPla SDry SLan WSHC WWat |
| *bodinieri* | EPla SLan WWat |
| – 'David's Gold' | WEas WSHC |
| *glomerata* | SLan |
| * 'Golden Frimley' | LHop |
| 'Green Gem' | EHic EPla LEar NHar NHol SLan |
| 'Green Mountain' | SLan |
| 'Green Velvet' | EHic LPan NHol SLan WWeb |
| *harlandii* hort. | EPla GAri LEar SIng SLan SRiv |
| – hort. 'Richard' | SLan STre |
| *henryi* | SLan |
| *japonica* 'Nana' | See *B. microphylla* |
| *jaucoensis* | SLan |
| ¶ *leonii* | SLan |
| *macowanii* | SLan |
| *macrophylla* | See *B. sinica* var. *insularis* |
| 'Winter | |
| 'Asiatic Winter' | Gem' |
| § *microphylla* | CBlo CSWP EHic GDra LHol LPan NHol SIde SIng SLan STre |
| § – 'Compacta' | CFil SLan SRiv WPGP |
| – 'Curly Locks' | EPla GAri NHol SLan |
| – 'Faulkner' | CChe CDoC EBee EMil ENot EPla ERea LEar LHop MBlu MBri MUlv NFla NHol SLan SRiv WBcn WLRN WWeb |
| – 'Grace Hendrick Phillips' | SLan |
| – 'Green Pillow' | CLTr NHol SLan SRiv |
| – 'Helen Whiting' | SLan |
| – var. *insularis* | See *B. sinica* var. *insularis* |
| – var. *japonica* | SLan |
| – – 'Aurea' | Last listed 1997 |
| – – 'Gold Dust' | SLan |
| – – 'Green Jade' | SLan |
| – – 'Morris Dwarf' | SLan |
| – – 'Morris Midget' | EHic NHol SLan |
| – – 'National' | SLan |
| – – 'Variegata' | Last listed 1998 |
| – – f. *yakushima* | SLan |
| – 'John Baldwin' | SLan SRiv WBcn |
| – var. *koreana* | See *B. sinica* var. *insularis* |
| – var. *riparia* | See *B. riparia* |
| – var. *sinica* | See *B. sinica* |
| ◆ – 'Winter Gem' | See *B. sinica* var. *insularis* 'Winter Gem' |
| 'Newport Blue' | See *B. sempervirens* 'Newport Blue' |
| § *riparia* | EPla SLan |
| * *rugulosa* var. *intermedia* | SLan |
| *sempervirens* ♀ | More than 30 suppliers |
| § – 'Angustifolia' | EPla NHol SLan SMad |
| – 'Argentea' | See *B. sempervirens* 'Argenteovariegata' |
| § – 'Argenteovariegata' | CBlo EPfP MBal MRav SLan WBay WBcn WFar WSHC |
| – 'Aurea' | See *B. sempervirens* 'Aureovariegata' |
| – 'Aurea Maculata' | See *B. sempervirens* 'Aureovariegata' |
| – 'Aurea Marginata' | See *B. sempervirens* 'Marginata' |

| | |
|---|---|
| – 'Aurea Pendula' (v) | EPla GAbr SLan SLon WWye |
| § – 'Aureovariegata' | CArn CB&S CLTr EBee EHic EPfP EWTr GAbr ISea MBar MGos MMal MRav MWat NCut NHol NSti SChu SIng SLan SPar SPer SRiv WDin WFar WJek WLRN WMoo WWeb WWye |
| – 'Blauer Heinz' | CSev EMil LEar MBri MTed SLan |
| § – 'Blue Cone' | CDoC EHic GBin LEar NHol |
| – 'Blue Spire' | See *B. sempervirens* 'Blue Cone' |
| – clipped ball | Last listed 1997 |
| – clipped pyramid | Last listed 1997 |
| § – 'Elegantissima' (v) ♀ | More than 30 suppliers |
| – 'Gold Tip' | See *B. sempervirens* 'Notata' |
| § – 'Graham Blandy' | EHic LEar LPan NHol SLan SRiv WBcn |
| ♦ – 'Greenpeace' | See *B. sempervirens* 'Graham Blandy' |
| – 'Handsworthiensis' | EBee EMil LEar SEND SLan SPer |
| – 'Handsworthii' | CBlo CTri ERea NWea SRms |
| – subsp. *byrcana* | SLan |
| – 'Ickworth Giant' | SLan |
| – 'Inverewe' | SLan |
| – 'Japonica Aurea' | See *B. sempervirens* 'Latifolia Maculata' |
| – 'Kensington Gardens' | SLan |
| I – 'Kingsville' | See *B. microphylla* 'Compacta' |
| ♦ – 'Kingsville Dwarf' | See *B. microphylla* 'Compacta' |
| – 'Lace' | NHol NSti SLan |
| § – 'Langley Beauty' | SLan WBcn |
| I – 'Langley Pendula' | See *B. sempervirens* 'Langley Beauty' |
| – 'Latifolia' | See *B. sempervirens* 'Bullata' |
| – 'Latifolia Macrophylla' | GAbr SEas SLan SLon |
| § – 'Latifolia Maculata' ♀ | CAbP CChe CHan EPla GDra LEar MBal MPla NHol NPer NRoo SEas SLan SRiv STre |
| * – 'Latifolia Pendula' | SLan |
| – 'Longifolia' | See *B. sempervirens* 'Angustifolia' |
| § – 'Marginata' | ECtt EPla GCHN LHop MRav NHol NSti SHFr SLan SLon SRPl WHar WOak WStI |
| – 'Memorial' | EHic GAbr LGre NHol SLan |
| – 'Myosotidifolia' | CFil CMHG EPla NHar NPro SLan WWat |
| – 'Myrtifolia' | CBot EPla NHar NHol SLan |
| § – 'Newport Blue' | MTed |
| § – 'Notata' (v) | CSWP ERea GAbr MAsh SBrw SHel WGor WWal |
| – 'Parasol' | SLan |
| – 'Pendula' | CGre CMHG EHic EPla SLan SLon SMad |
| I – 'Pendula Esveld' | Last listed 1998 |
| – 'Prostrata' | EHic NHol SLan |
| – 'Pyramidalis' | EHic GAbr NBee SLan SMad SRPl |
| – 'Rosmarinifolia' | MRav SLan |
| – 'Rotundifolia' | CLnd NFla SIde SLan WDin |
| – 'Salicifolia Elata' | SLan |
| – 'Silver Beauty' (v) | CB&S EMil MGos |
| – 'Silver Variegated' | See *B. sempervirens* 'Elegantissima' |
| – 'Suffruticosa' ♀ | More than 30 suppliers |
| I – 'Suffruticosa Blue' | NHol SVil |
| – 'Suffruticosa Variegata' | CB&S EOHP ERea SRms |
| * – 'Tropical Garden' | Last listed 1996 |
| – 'Vardar Valley' | EHic NHar NPro SLan |
| – 'Variegata' | EPfP SLon |
| – 'Waterfall' | SLan |
| § *sinica* | SLan |
| § – var. *insularis* | EPla |
| – – 'Filigree' | EPla NHol SLan |
| – – 'Justin Brouwers' | CSev SLan SRiv |
| – – 'Pincushion' | SLan |
| – – 'Tide Hill' | SLan |
| – – 'Winter Beauty' | Last listed 1997 |
| § – – 'Winter Gem' | CLyn EHic ENot MRav NHol SLPl SLan |
| *wallichiana* | CFil EPla SLan WPGP WWat |

# C

## CACALIA (Asteraceae)

| | |
|---|---|
| ¶ *atriplicifolia* | GVic |
| ¶ *firma* B&SWJ 4650 | WCru |
| § *glabra* | EBee |

## CACCINIA (Boraginaceae)

| | |
|---|---|
| ¶ *macrantha* | IHdy |
| ¶ *macranthera* | EBee |
| var. *crassifolia* | |

## CAESALPINIA (Caesalpiniaceae)

| | |
|---|---|
| ¶ *decapetala* S&SH 380 | CHan |
| *gilliesii* | CBot CFai NPSI SOWG |
| *pulcherrima* | LChe |
| – f.*flava* | LChe |

## CAIOPHORA (Loasaceae)

| | |
|---|---|
| *acuminata* | Last listed 1998 |
| *coronata* | Last listed 1998 |
| *borrida* | Last listed 1996 |
| § *lateritia* | WCot |
| *prietea* | Last listed 1998 |

## CALADENIA (Orchidaceae)

| | |
|---|---|
| Fairy Floss g. | SWes |
| ¶ *latifolia* | SWes |
| *menziesii* | SWes |

## CALADIUM (Araceae)

| | |
|---|---|
| § *bicolor* (v) | MBri |
| x *hortulanum* | See *C. bicolor* |
| § *lindenii* (v) | MBri |

## CALAMAGROSTIS (Poaceae)

| | |
|---|---|
| N x *acutiflora* 'Karl Foerster' | CLon EBee ECGN ECha EHoe EPPr EPla GAbr GCal GOrn LGre MMoz NSti SApp SCob SDix SMer SPer WWat WWye |
| x *acutiflora* 'Overdam' (v) | More than 30 suppliers |
| ¶ – 'Stricta' | EPPr |
| § *arundinacea* | More than 30 suppliers |
| – 'Autumn Tints' | ECou |
| – 'Gold Hue' | EPla |
| § *brachytricha* | CBrm CHan CHar CKno EBee ECGN ECha EGle EPPr EPla EWes GBin GOrn LEdu LGre SAsh SMrm WHal |
| ¶ *emodensis* | SApp |
| § *epigejos* | EMan EPPr GBin NHol |
| – CLD 1325 | EPla |
| ¶ *varia* | EHoe |

## CALAMINTHA ✿ (Lamiaceae)

| | |
|---|---|
| *alpina* | See *Acinos alpinus* |
| *clinopodium* | See *Clinopodium vulgare* |
| *cretica* | CLyd EMon GBar LHop MGrG MHew MTho WOut WPer WWye |
| – *variegata* | WEas |
| 'Gottfried Klein' | MRav |
| § *grandiflora* | More than 30 suppliers |

- 'Variegata' CBrm CGle CMil CRow EEls ELan
EMan EMon LFis LHop MBro
MGrG SCob SCro SWat WBea
WByw WCHb WFar WHer WHoo
WMaN WRus
¶ *megalantha* EMon
§ *nepeta* CAgr CArn CLon EAst EBee ECha
ECoo EWFC LGre MCAu MCLN
MFir MGrG MPEx MRav MSte
MWgw NBir NBro SBla SWat
WEas WFar WHal WPer WWin
WWye
- subsp.*glandulosa* WHoo
ACL 1050/90
- - 'White Cloud' CGle CHea CSpe EBrP EBre
ECGN ECha EFou GBuc LBre
LGre MBro MCAu MCLN MSte
NTow SBre SLod WHoo WMaN
WRus WWye
- 'Gottfried Kuehn' MCAu MRav
§ - subsp.*nepeta* CGle CHan CSev EBee ECGN
EFou ELan EMon EWTr GBar
GMac LHop MBri MPla MTho
NFla NOak NSti SHel SPer SRPl
SUsu WCHb WHoo WMer WRus
WSHC WWat WWhi
- - 'Blue Cloud' CGle CHan CHea CHor ECGN
ECha EFou LGre MCAu NTow
SAga SHel SLod SUsu SWat WCot
WMaN WRus WWye
*nepetoides* See *C. nepeta* subsp. *nepeta*
¶ *officinalis* SRCN
§ *sylvatica* CAgr NLar SRCN WCla
- subsp.*ascendens* MHew MLLN NCat
- HH&K 163 CHan
*vulgaris* See *Clinopodium vulgare*

## CALAMOVILFA (Poaceae)
*longifolia* Last listed 1997

## CALANDRINIA (Portulacaceae)
*caespitosa* Last listed 1998
*dianthoides* Last listed 1996
*grandiflora* ELan MBNS MLLN SAga WAbe
WWin
*megarhiza* See *Claytonia megarhiza*
'Neon' Last listed 1996
*sericea* Last listed 1998
- *alba* Last listed 1998
*sibirica* See *Claytonia sibirica*
*umbellata* MBNS NPri NWCA SBla WPer
WWin WWye
* - *amarantha* Last listed 1998

## CALANTHE (Orchidaceae)
*amamiana* EFEx
*arisanenesis* EFEx
*aristulifera* EFEx LAma
*bicolor* See *C. discolor* var. *flava*
*biloba* LAma
*brevicornu* LAma
*caudatilabella* EFEx
*chloroleuca* LAma
*discolor* EFEx LAma SWes WCot
§ - var.*flava* CLAP LAma
¶ Grouville g. SStn
*hamata* EFEx
*herbacea* LAma
Hizen g. Last listed 1997
Ishi-zuchi g. Last listed 1997
*japonica* EFEx
¶ Kozu g. WCot

¶ Kozu hybrids WThi
*mannii* EFEx LAma
*masuca* LAma
*nipponica* EFEx LAma
*puberula* LAma
*reflexa* EFEx LAma WCot
¶ Saint Aubin g. SStn
Satsuma g. Last listed 1997
§ *sieboldii* EFEx LAma SWes WCot
¶ - Takane hybrids WThi
*striata* See *C. sieboldii*
*tokunoshimensis* EFEx
*tricarinata* EFEx LAma SWes WCot
¶ *vestita* SStn

## CALATHEA (Marantaceae)
*albertii* MBri
*albicans* See *C. micans*
§ *bella* Last listed 1996
*burle-marxii* Last listed 1996
*crocata* MBri
'Exotica' MBri
'Greystar' MBri
*kegeljanii* See *C. bella*
§ *lancifolia* ♀ Last listed 1990
*lietzei* MBri
- 'Greenstar' MBri
§ *majestica* MBri
*makoyana* ♀ CHal MBri
* 'Mavi Queen' MBri
*metallica* MBri
* 'Misto' MBri
*oppenheimiana* See *Ctenanthe oppenheimiana*
*orbiculata* See *C. truncata*
*ornata* See *C. majestica*
*picturata* 'Argentea' MBri
- 'Vandenheckei' MBri
*roseopicta* MBri
§ *truncata* MBri
*veitchiana* MBri
*warscewiczii* MBri
'Wavestar' MBri
*zebrina* ♀ MBri

## CALCEOLARIA (Scrophulariaceae)
*acutifolia* See *C. polyrhiza*
*alba* CPla MSCN WCot WElm WLin
- RB 94025 Last listed 1996
*arachnoidea* NWCA NWoo WWhi
x *banksii* EBee GQui LBlm MFir WCot
*bicolor* WCot
§ *biflora* CLyd ELan GDra GTou MBal
MMal WPat
- 'Goldcrest Amber' GMaP WPer
'Camden Hero' CLyn MBEx WWat
*chelidonioides* MTho
x *clibranii* MBEx
*crenatiflora* NWoo
*cymbiflora* Last listed 1998
¶ *ericoides* EBee
- JCA 13818 Last listed 1998
*falklandica* NWCA SIng SRms SSca WPer
WWin
*fiebrigiana* Last listed 1998
*filicaulis* Last listed 1998
*fothergillii* GVic NArg NMen
'Goldcrest' ECtt EPfP NPri
¶ 'Hall's Spotted' NWCA
*helianthemoides* Last listed 1998
JCA 13911
*hirsuta* Last listed 1998
'Hort's Variety' Last listed 1998

*byssopifolia* JCA 13648    Last listed 1998
§ *integrifolia* ♀    CB&S ELan EMar EMon ERav
LBlm MBal MFir NRog SAga SChu
SLon SPer SRms WAbe WWat
- var. *angustifolia* ♀    SDry
- bronze    SPer WAbe
¶ - 'Sunshine' ♀    CChe
'John Innes'    EBur ECho ELan ESis NWCA
WCot
'Kentish Hero'    CB&S CElw CHal ELan EOrc LBlm
LHil MBEx NPer SChu WCot
*lagunae-blancae*    Last listed 1998
*lanigera*    Last listed 1998
*mendocina*    Last listed 1998
*mexicana*    SHFr
*nivalis* JCA 13888    Last listed 1998
aff. *pavonii*    LHil
*perfoliata* JCA 13736    Last listed 1998
*pinifolia*    CPBP
- JCA 14450    IDac
*pinnata*    Last listed 1998
*plantaginea*    See *C. biflora*
§ *polyrhiza*    ECho ELan LEur MBal NNrd NRoo
NRya NWCA WCla
*purpurea*    Last listed 1998
*rugosa*    See *C. integrifolia*
*scabiosifolia*    See *C. tripartita*
sp. ex P&W 6276    Last listed 1998
sp. JCA 14128    Last listed 1998
sp. JCA 14172    Last listed 1998
'Stamford Park'    MBEx
*tenella*    ECtt ELan EPot NHar NMen NTow
WAbe
§ *tripartita*    Last listed 1998
*uniflora* var. *darwinii*    ECho GTou NMen SIng
*volckmannii*    Last listed 1998
'Walter Shrimpton'    EDAr EPot EWes NWCA SIng

## CALDCLUVIA (Cunoniaceae)
*paniculata*    Last listed 1998

## CALEA (Asteraceae)
*zacatechichi*    Last listed 1998

## CALENDULA (Asteraceae)
'Fiesta Gitana' ♀    WJek
*officinalis*    CArn CJew ELau EWTr GPoy LHol
MChe MHew MMal MSal SIde
WHbs WHer WJek WOak WRha
WSel WWye
- 'Prolifera'    WHer
- 'Variegata'    MSal

## CALLA (Araceae)
*aethiopica*    See *Zantedeschia aethiopica*
*palustris*    CBen CRow CWat ECoo EHon
GAri GGar LPBA MCCP MSta
NDea SLon SWat SWyc WMAq
WWeb

## CALLIANDRA (Mimosaceae)
*brevipes*    See *C. selloi*
* *emarginata minima*    SOWG
§ *selloi*    WMul

## CALLIANTHEMUM (Ranunculaceae)
*anemonoides*    GCrs NHar WAbe
*coriandrifolium*    Last listed 1998
¶ *kernerianum*    GCrs

## CALLICARPA (Verbenaceae)
*americana* var. *lactea*    Last listed 1997

*bodinieri*    NBir
- var. *giraldii*    GBin MHlr MRav NFla SSta WDin
WWeb
- - 'Profusion' ♀    More than 30 suppliers
*cathayana*    Last listed 1997
*dichotoma*    CBlo CPle CTrG GSki MNes WCru
WSHC WWat WWin
*japonica*    SPan
- 'Leucocarpa'    CB&S CBlo CPle EHic EPfP MRav
SBid SMac SPer WBcn WWat
¶ *kwangtungensis*    CMCN

## CALLICOMA (Cunoniaceae)
*serratifolia*    MSag

## CALLIERGON (Sphagnaceae)
*giganteum*    Last listed 1996

## CALLIRHOE (Malvaceae)
*digitata*    EBee
*involucrata*    EBee EMan MAvo NWCA SMad
*triangulata*    MAvo

## CALLISIA (Commelinaceae)
*elegans* ♀    CHal
§ *navicularis*    CHal CInt
*repens*    CHal MBri

## CALLISTEMON ✿ (Myrtaceae)
*brachyandrus*    Last listed 1998
'Burning Bush'    CB&S LBlm SOWG
*chisholmii*    SOWG
*citrinus*    CPle ECot ECou ERav ERom GOrc
GSki ISea NPer SOWG SPer SUsu
WGwG WHar WWal WWin
♦ - 'Albus'    See *C.* 'White Anzac'
- 'Canberra'    SOWG
- 'Firebrand'    LRHS SMur WWeb
¶ - 'Horse Paddock'    SOWG
- 'Mauve Mist'    CB&S CTrC LBlm LRHS NPal
SOWG SSta
¶ - 'Reeve's Pink'    SOWG
¶ - 'Sockeye'    SOWG
- 'Splendens' ♀    CB&S CBrm CDoC CMac CTrC
EBrP EBre ELan EMil GQui IOrc
LBre LHil NPal SAga SBra SBre
SDry SHFr SOWG SReu SSta
WBod WStI WWat
- 'Yellow Queen'    CB&S
*coccineus*    CGre
*comboynensis*    SOWG
¶ 'Dawson River Weeper'    SOWG
*flavescens*    SOWG
*flavovirens*    SOWG
*glaucus*    See *C. speciosus*
'Kings Park Special'    EHol SOWG
♦ *laevis* hort.    See *C. rugulosus*
*lanceolatus*    CGre
*linearifolius*    Last listed 1998
*linearis* ♀    CBlo CHan CMac CTrC CTri ECou
EHic ELan IOrc LHil MBal SBrw
SEas SLon SOWG SPlb SRms SSpi
WNor
*macropunctatus*    CGre MSag SOWG SPlb
*pachyphyllus*    CGre SOWG
- var. *viridis*    Last listed 1998
*pallidus*    CGre CMHG CMac CPle CWit
ELan EPfP GLch IDee SOWG SPan
SPer SSta
- lilac    Last listed 1998
*paludosus*    See *C. sieberi*
- pink form    Last listed 1998

| | |
|---|---|
| * *pearsonii* | SOWG |
| 'Perth Pink' | CB&S CTrC GSki SBid SOWG |
| *phoeniceus* | MSag SOWG |
| *pinifolius* | CGre SOWG |
| - green form | LLew |
| ¶ - red | MSag |
| ¶ - yellow | MSag |
| *pityoides* | CGre ECou MSag SOWG WAbe |
| - alpine form | Last listed 1998 |
| - from Brown's Swamp, Australia | ECou |
| *polandii* | SOWG |
| *recurvus* | Last listed 1998 |
| 'Red Clusters' | CB&S ELan ERea GSki LRHS SMur SOWG |
| *rigidus* | CB&S CBlo CChe CDoC CLan CMHG CMac CTri CTrw EBrP EBre ELan EMil EOas GSki ISea LBre MBlu MGos MLan SBre SBrw SOWG SSoC WBod WCru WWeb |
| 'Royal Sceptre' | Last listed 1998 |
| § *rugulosus* | LRHS SOWG |
| *salignus* ♀ | CDoC CPlN CTrC CTri GSki IOrc ISea LEur MBal MCCP SLod SOWG SPer SSoC WGwG WSHC |
| - 'Ruber' | MSag |
| § *sieberi* ♀ | CGre CMHG CTrC ECou EPfP GSki ISea LEur NBir SOWG SSpi |
| § *speciosus* | CTrC SMur SOWG SPan WLRN |
| *subulatus* | CDoC ECou MBal MCCP NCut SAPC SArc SOWG |
| *teretifolius* | MSag SOWG |
| *viminalis* | EHic GLch SOWG SPlb |
| - 'Captain Cook' ♀ | ECou ERea LCns LRHS SOWG |
| - 'Hannah Ray' | NPer SOWG |
| ¶ - 'Harkness' | SOWG |
| - 'Little John' | CB&S CWSG LRHS SBid SOWG |
| - 'Malawi Giant' | SOWG |
| - 'Violaceus' | CHan |
| *viridiflorus* | CGre CPea CPle ECou GQui IBlr LEur MCCP NCut SOWG SRCN WWat |
| § 'White Anzac' | GCHN SOWG |

## CALLITRICHE (Callitrichaceae)

| | |
|---|---|
| *autumnalis* | See *C. hermaphroditica* |
| § *hermaphroditica* | EMFW SAWi |
| § *palustris* | CBen ECoo EHon SWyc |
| *verna* | See *C. palustris* |

## CALLITRIS (Cupressaceae)

| | |
|---|---|
| *monticola* | Last listed 1998 |
| *oblonga* | CGre ECou |
| *rhomboidea* | CGre ECou |

## CALLUNA ✿ (Ericaceae)

| | |
|---|---|
| *vulgaris* | CKin MGos MMal |
| - 'Adrie' | Last listed 1998 |
| - 'Alba Argentea' | Last listed 1998 |
| - 'Alba Aurea' | ECho MBar |
| - 'Alba Carlton' | Last listed 1998 |
| - 'Alba Dumosa' | Last listed 1998 |
| - 'Alba Elata' | CNCN ECho MBar |
| - 'Alba Elegans' | Last listed 1998 |
| - 'Alba Elongata' | See *C. vulgaris* 'Mair's Variety' |
| - 'Alba Erecta' | Last listed 1998 |
| - 'Alba Jae' | MBar |
| - 'Alba Minor' | Last listed 1998 |
| - 'Alba Multiflora' | Last listed 1998 |
| - 'Alba Pilosa' | Last listed 1998 |
| § - 'Alba Plena' (d) | CMac CNCN ECho MBar WStI |
| - 'Alba Praecox' | Last listed 1998 |
| - 'Alba Pumila' | MBar |
| § - 'Alba Rigida' | CNCN MBar |
| - 'Alec Martin' (d) | Last listed 1998 |
| - 'Alex Warwick' | Last listed 1998 |
| - 'Alexandra' | LRHS NHol SCoo |
| - 'Alicia' | ECho LRHS |
| - 'Alieke' | Last listed 1998 |
| - 'Alison Yates' | MBar |
| - 'Allegretto' | Last listed 1998 |
| - 'Allegro' ♀ | CNCN GAri MBar MOke NHol SBod WStI |
| - 'Alportii' | CMac GDra MBar MOke WStI |
| - 'Alportii Praecox' | CNCN ECho MBar |
| - 'Alys Sutcliffe' | Last listed 1998 |
| - 'Amanda Wain' | ECho |
| - 'Amethyst' | ECho NHol |
| - 'Amilto' | CNCN ECho NHol |
| - 'Amy' | Last listed 1998 |
| - 'Andrew Proudley' | MBar |
| - 'Anette' | ECho LRHS NHol SCoo |
| - 'Angela Wain' | ECho |
| - 'Anna' | Last listed 1998 |
| - 'Annabel' (d) | Last listed 1998 |
| - 'Anne Dobbin' | Last listed 1998 |
| - 'Anneke' | Last listed 1998 |
| - 'Annemarie' (d) ♀ | CMac CNCN EBrP EBre ENot GChr LBre MGos NHol SBod SBre SCoo |
| - 'Anthony Davis' ♀ | CNCN MBar MOke NHol SBod |
| - 'Anthony Wain' | Last listed 1998 |
| - 'Anton' | Last listed 1998 |
| - 'Apollo' | Last listed 1998 |
| - 'Applecross' (d) | CNCN |
| - 'Arabella' | NHol |
| - 'Argentea' | MBar |
| - 'Ariadne' | Last listed 1998 |
| - 'Arina' | CNCN ECho MBri MOke |
| - 'Arran Gold' | CNCN MBar |
| - 'Ashgarth Amber' | Last listed 1998 |
| - 'Ashgarth Amethyst' | Last listed 1998 |
| - 'Ashgarth Shell Pink' | Last listed 1998 |
| - 'Asterix' | Last listed 1998 |
| - 'Atalanta' | Last listed 1998 |
| - 'Atholl Gold' | CMac |
| - 'August Beauty' | CNCN ECho MOke |
| - 'Aurea' | CNCN ECho |
| - 'Autumn Glow' | ECho |
| - 'Baby Ben' | CNCN |
| - 'Barbara Fleur' | Last listed 1998 |
| - 'Barja' | Last listed 1998 |
| - 'Barnett Anley' | CNCN ECho |
| - 'Battle of Arnhem' ♀ | CNCN MBar |
| - 'Beechwood Crimson' | CNCN |
| - 'Ben Nevis' | Last listed 1998 |
| - 'Beoley Crimson' | CNCN GAri GDra MBar MGos |
| - 'Beoley Gold' ♀ | CB&S CNCN CTri EBrP EBre GChr LBre MBar MBri MGos MOke NHol SBod SBre WStI |
| - 'Beoley Silver' | CNCN |
| - 'Bernadette' | Last listed 1998 |
| - 'Betty Baum' | Last listed 1998 |
| - 'Blazeaway' | CMac CNCN CTri GDra MBar MBri NHar NHol SBod WStI |
| - 'Blueness' | Last listed 1998 |
| - 'Bognie' | CNCN |
| - 'Bonfire Brilliance' | CNCN MBar NHar SBod |
| - 'Boreray' | CNCN |
| - 'Boskoop' | CMac CNCN EBrP EBre LBre MBar MBri NHol SBod SBre |
| - 'Bradford' | Last listed 1998 |
| - 'Braemar' | CNCN |
| - 'Braeriach' | Last listed 1998 |

- 'Branchy Anne'          Last listed 1998
- 'Bray Head'             CNCN MBar
- 'Brightness'            Last listed 1998
- 'Brita Elisabeth' (d)   Last listed 1998
- 'Bud Lyle'              Last listed 1998
- 'Bunsall'               CMac CNCN
- 'Buxton Snowdrift'      Last listed 1998
- 'C.W. Nix'              CNCN ECho MBar
- 'Caerketton White'      ECho GChr
- 'Caleb Threlkeld'       ECho NHol
- 'Calf of Man'           Last listed 1998
- 'Californian Midge'     CNCN GAri MBar MGos NHol
- 'Cape Wrath'            Last listed 1996
- 'Carl Röders' (d)       Last listed 1998
- 'Carmen'                ECho
- 'Carngold'              Last listed 1998
- 'Carole Chapman'        MBar MGos
- 'Carolyn'               Last listed 1998
- 'Catherine Anne'        Last listed 1998
- 'Celtic Gold'           Last listed 1998
- 'Chindit'               Last listed 1998
- 'Christina'             Last listed 1998
- 'Cilcennin Common'      Last listed 1998
- 'Citronella'            Last listed 1998
- 'Clare Carpet'          Last listed 1998
- 'Coby'                  Last listed 1998
- 'Coccinea'              CMac ECho MBar
- 'Colette'               Last listed 1998
- 'Con Brio'              CNCN LRHS
- 'Copper Glow'           Last listed 1998
- 'Coral Island'          MBar MGos
- 'Corrie's White'        Last listed 1998
- 'Cottswood Gold'        Last listed 1998
- 'County Wicklow' (d) ♀  CNCN CTri EBrP EBre GChr LBre
                          MBar MBri MGos MOke NHar
                          NHol SBod SBre
- 'Craig Rossie'          Last listed 1998
- 'Crail Orange'          Last listed 1998
- 'Cramond' (d)           CNCN ECho GDra MBar
- 'Cream Steving'         ECho
- 'Crimson Glory'         CNCN MBar NHed WStI
- 'Crimson Sunset'        CNCN WStI
- 'Crowborough Beacon'    Last listed 1998
- 'Cuprea'                CNCN EOrn GDra MBar MBri
                          MOke NHol SBod WStI
- 'Cuprea Select'         Last listed 1998
- 'Dainty Bess'           CNCN MBar NHol SBod WStI
- 'Dark Beauty' (d)       CNCN EBrP EBre EOrn LBre
                          MGos NHed NHol SBre WStI
- 'Dark Star' (d) ♀       CMac CNCN EBrP EBre LBre
                          MBar MGos MOke NHar NHol
                          SBre SCoo
- 'Darkness' ♀            CB&S CNCN CTri EOrn MBar
                          MBri MGos MOke NHar NHol
                          SBod SCoo WStI
- 'Darleyensis'           Last listed 1998
- 'Dart's Amethyst'       Last listed 1998
- 'Dart's Beauty'         Last listed 1998
- 'Dart's Brilliant'      Last listed 1998
- 'Dart's Flamboyant'     CNCN
- 'Dart's Gold'           ECho MBar NHar NRoo
- 'Dart's Hedgehog'       ECho
- 'Dart's Parakeet'       CNCN
- 'Dart's Parrot'         ECho NHar
- 'Dart's Silver Rocket'  Last listed 1998
- 'Dart's Squirrel'       Last listed 1998
- 'David Eason'           CNCN ECho
- 'David Hagenaars'       Last listed 1998
- 'David Hutton'          MBar
- 'David Platt' (d)       Last listed 1998
- 'Denny Pratt'           Last listed 1998
- 'Desiree'               Last listed 1998

- 'Devon' (d)             Last listed 1998
- 'Diana'                 Last listed 1998
- 'Dickson's Blazes'      Last listed 1998
- 'Dirry'                 CNCN
- 'Doctor Murray's White' See C. vulgaris 'Mullardoch'
- 'Doris Rushworth'       Last listed 1998
- 'Drum-ra'               GDra MBar SRms
- 'Dunkeld White'         Last listed 1998
- 'Dunnet Lime'           SPlb
- 'Dunnydeer'             Last listed 1998
- 'Dunwood'               MBar
§ - 'Durfordii'           ECho
- 'E.F. Brown'            CNCN
- 'E. Hoare'              MBar
- 'Easter-bonfire'        CNCN NHol
- 'Eckart Miessner'       Last listed 1998
- 'Edith Godbolt'         CNCN
- 'Elaine'                ECho
- 'Elegant Pearl'         MBar SBod
- 'Elegantissima'         CNCN MOke
- 'Elegantissima Lilac'   Last listed 1998
- 'Elegantissima Walter   See C. vulgaris 'Walter Ingwersen'
  Ingwersen'
- 'Elkstone'              CNCN MBar
- 'Ellen'                 Last listed 1998
- 'Else Frye' (d)         Last listed 1998
- 'Elsie Purnell' (d) ♀   CNCN MBar MGos MOke NHol
                          SBod WStI
- 'Emerald Jock'          SBod
- 'Emma Louise Tuke'      ECho
- 'Eric Easton'           Last listed 1998
- 'Eskdale Gold'          Last listed 1998
- 'Fairy'                 CMac CNCN MOke
- 'Falling Star'          Last listed 1998
- 'Feuerwerk'             Last listed 1998
§ - 'Finale' ♀            CNCN MBar
- 'Findling'              Last listed 1998
- 'Fire King'             MBar
- 'Firebreak'             ECho MBar
- 'Firefly' ♀             CBrm CMac CNCN EBrP EBre
                          EOrn LBre MBar MBri MOke
                          NHar NRoo SBod SBre WStI
- 'Firestar'              Last listed 1998
- 'Flamingo'              CNCN EBrP EBre LBre MBar MBri
                          MOke NHar NHol SBre
- 'Flatling'              NHol
- 'Flore Pleno' (d)       MBar
- 'Floriferous'           Last listed 1998
- 'Florrie Spicer'        Last listed 1998
- 'Fokko' (d)             Last listed 1998
- 'Fortyniner Gold'       Last listed 1998
- 'Foxhollow Wanderer'    CNCN MBar MOke
- 'Foxii'                 Last listed 1998
- 'Foxii Floribunda'      ECho MBar
- 'Foxii Lett's Form'     See C. vulgaris 'Velvet Dome',
                          'Mousehole'
- 'Foxii Nana'            CNCN MBar NHar NHed NHol
                          SBod
- 'Foya'                  Last listed 1998
- 'Fred J. Chapple'       CNCN MBar MBri MOke SBod
                          WStI
- 'Fréjus'                Last listed 1998
- 'French Grey'           CNCN
- 'Fritz Kircher'         NHol
- 'Gerda'                 Last listed 1998
- 'Ginkels Glorie'        Last listed 1998
- 'Glasa'                 Last listed 1998
- 'Glen Mashie'           Last listed 1998
- 'Glencoe' (d)           MBar MBri MOke NHar
- 'Glendoick Silver'      Last listed 1998
- 'Glenfiddich'           CNCN MBar
- 'Glenlivet'             MBar

| | |
|---|---|
| - 'Glenmorangie' | MBar |
| - 'Gnome Pink' | Last listed 1998 |
| - 'Gold Charm' | Last listed 1998 |
| - 'Gold Finch' | Last listed 1998 |
| - 'Gold Flame' | LRHS MBar SBod |
| - 'Gold Hamilton' (d) | ECho NHol |
| - 'Gold Haze' ♀ | CB&S CMac CNCN EBrP EBre |
| | LBre MBar MBri MOke NHol SBod |
| | SBre SCoo WStI |
| - 'Gold Knight' | ECho EOrn LRHS MBar SBod |
| - 'Gold Kup' | MBar |
| - 'Gold Mist' | ECho LRHS NHed |
| - 'Gold Spronk' | Last listed 1998 |
| - 'Goldcarmen' | ECho |
| - 'Golden Blazeaway' | ECho |
| - 'Golden Carpet' | CB&S CNCN EOrn MBar MBri |
| | MGos MOke NHar NHed NHol |
| | SRms WStI |
| - 'Golden Dew' | Last listed 1998 |
| - 'Golden Dream' (d) | Last listed 1998 |
| - 'Golden Feather' | CNCN MBar MGos SBod |
| - 'Golden Fleece' | CNCN |
| - 'Golden Max' | NHar |
| - 'Golden Rivulet' | LRHS MBar |
| - 'Golden Turret' | CNCN ECho |
| - 'Golden Wonder' (d) | ECho |
| - 'Goldsworth Crimson' | ECho |
| - 'Goldsworth Crimson | CNCN MBar |
| Variegated' | |
| - 'Grasmeriensis' | MBar |
| - 'Great Comp' | MBar |
| - 'Grey Carpet' | CNCN MBar SBod |
| - 'Grijsje' | Last listed 1998 |
| - 'Grizzly' | Last listed 1998 |
| - 'Grönsinka' | Last listed 1998 |
| - 'Guinea Gold' | CNCN ECho MBar MBri |
| § - 'H.E. Beale' (d) | CB&S CNCN CTri EBrP EBre |
| | GDra LBre MBar MBri MGos |
| | MOke NHar NHed NHol SBod |
| | SBre |
| - 'Hamlet Green' | CNCN MBar |
| - 'Hammondii' | CNCN SBod WStI |
| - 'Hammondii Aureifolia' | CNCN EBrP EBre GAri LBre MBar |
| | MBri MOke SBre |
| - 'Hammondii Rubrifolia' | CNCN MBar MBri MOke NHar |
| - 'Harlekin' | Last listed 1998 |
| - 'Harry Gibbon' (d) | Last listed 1998 |
| - 'Harten's Findling' | Last listed 1998 |
| - 'Hatjes Herbstfeuer' (d) | Last listed 1998 |
| - 'Hayesensis' | Last listed 1998 |
| - 'Heidberg' | Last listed 1998 |
| - 'Heidepracht' | Last listed 1998 |
| - 'Heidesinfonie' | Last listed 1998 |
| - 'Heideteppich' | Last listed 1998 |
| - 'Heidezwerg' | Last listed 1998 |
| - 'Helen Gill' | Last listed 1998 |
| - 'Herbert Mitchell' | Last listed 1998 |
| - 'Hester' | Last listed 1998 |
| - 'Hetty' | Last listed 1998 |
| - 'Hibernica' | MBar |
| - 'Hiemalis' | MBar |
| - 'Hiemalis Southcote' | See C. vulgaris 'Durfordii' |
| - 'Highland Cream' | CNCN SDys |
| - 'Highland Rose' | CNCN ECho |
| - 'Highland Spring' | SDys |
| - 'Hilda Turberfield' | Last listed 1998 |
| - 'Hillbrook Orange' | MBar |
| - 'Hillbrook Sparkler' | Last listed 1998 |
| - 'Hinton White' | Last listed 1998 |
| - f. *hirsuta* | Last listed 1997 |
| - 'Hirsuta Albiflora' | Last listed 1998 |
| - 'Hirsuta Typica' | CNCN ECho |

| | |
|---|---|
| - 'Hirta' | CNCN MBar SBod |
| - 'Hollandia' | Last listed 1998 |
| - 'Holstein' | Last listed 1998 |
| - 'Hookstone' | MBar |
| - 'Hoyerhagen' | Last listed 1998 |
| § - 'Hugh Nicholson' | CNCN NHar |
| - 'Humpty Dumpty' | ECho NHol |
| - 'Hypnoides' | Last listed 1998 |
| - 'Ide's Double' (d) | SBod |
| - 'Inchcolm' | Last listed 1998 |
| - 'Ineke' | CNCN MBar |
| - 'Ingrid Bouter' (d) | Last listed 1998 |
| - 'Inshriach Bronze' | CNCN MBar SBod |
| - 'Iris van Leyen' | CNCN ECho LRHS |
| - 'Islay Mist' | Last listed 1998 |
| - 'Isobel Frye' | MBar |
| - 'Isobel Hughes' (d) | MBar |
| - 'J.H. Hamilton' (d) ♀ | CB&S CNCN CTri GDra MBar |
| | MBri MGos NHol SBod SRms WStI |
| - 'Jan' | Last listed 1998 |
| - 'Jan Dekker' | CNCN LRHS NHol SBod |
| - 'Janice Chapman' | ECho MBar |
| - 'Japanese White' | Last listed 1998 |
| - 'Jenny' | Last listed 1998 |
| - 'Jill' | Last listed 1998 |
| - 'Jimmy Dyce' (d) ♀ | SBod |
| - 'Joan Sparkes' (d) | CNCN MBar WStI |
| - 'Jochen' | Last listed 1998 |
| - 'John F. Letts' | CNCN MBar MGos SBod SRms |
| | WStI |
| - 'Johnson's Variety' | CNCN ECho MBar |
| - 'Josefine' | Last listed 1998 |
| - 'Joseph's Coat' | Last listed 1998 |
| - 'Joy Vanstone' ♀ | CMac CNCN MBar MBri MGos |
| | MOke NHol |
| - 'Julia' | CNCN |
| - 'Julie Ann Platt' | Last listed 1998 |
| - 'Julie Gill' | Last listed 1997 |
| - 'Karin Blum' | Last listed 1998 |
| - 'Kermit' | Last listed 1998 |
| - 'Kerstin' | CNCN ECho LRHS NHol |
| - 'Kinlochruel' (d) ♀ | CMac CNCN GChr GDra MBar |
| | MBri MGos MOke NHar NHol |
| | SBod SRms |
| - 'Kirby White' | CNCN MBar MBri NHed NHol |
| - 'Kirsty Anderson' | MOke |
| - 'Kit Hill' | MBar |
| - 'Kuphaldtii' | MBar |
| - 'Kuppendorf' | Last listed 1998 |
| - 'Kynance' | CNCN MBar |
| - 'Lady Maithe' | Last listed 1998 |
| - 'Lambstails' | MBar MGos |
| - 'L'Ancresse' | Last listed 1998 |
| - 'Late Crimson Gold' | Last listed 1998 |
| - 'Lemon Gem' | Last listed 1998 |
| - 'Lemon Queen' | Last listed 1998 |
| - 'Leprechaun' | ECho |
| - 'Leslie Slinger' | CNCN LRHS MBar |
| - 'Lewis Lilac' | Last listed 1998 |
| - 'Liebestraum' | Last listed 1998 |
| - 'Lime Glade' | CNCN ECho |
| - 'Limelight' | Last listed 1998 |
| - 'Llanbedrog Pride' (d) | CNCN MBar |
| - 'Loch Turret' | CNCN EOrn MBar MBri MOke |
| - 'Loch-na-Seil' | MBar |
| - 'London Pride' | Last listed 1998 |
| - 'Long White' | CNCN ECho MBar |
| - 'Lüneberg Heath' | Last listed 1998 |
| - 'Lyle's Late White' | CNCN |
| - 'Lyle's Surprise' | MBar |
| - 'Lyndon Proudley' | Last listed 1998 |
| § - 'Mair's Variety' ♀ | CNCN GDra MBar SBod |

- 'Mallard'                     Last listed 1998
- 'Manitoba'                    Last listed 1998
- 'Marie'                       Last listed 1998
- 'Marion Blum'                 MBar
- 'Marleen'                     CNCN MBar NHol SBod
- 'Marlies'                     NHol
- 'Martha Hermann'             Last listed 1998
- 'Masquerade'                 MBar
- 'Matita'                      Last listed 1998
- 'Mauvelyn'                    Last listed 1998
- 'Mazurka'                     Last listed 1998
- 'Melanie'                     ECho NHol
- 'Mick Jamieson' (d)          Last listed 1998
- 'Mies'                        Last listed 1998
- 'Minima'                      MBar
- 'Minima Smith's Variety'     MBar
- 'Mini-öxabäck'               Last listed 1998
- 'Minty'                       Last listed 1998
- 'Mirelle'                     CNCN
- 'Miss Muffet'                 NHol
- 'Molecule'                    MBar
- 'Monika' (d)                  Last listed 1998
- 'Moon Glow'                   Last listed 1998
§ - 'Mousehole'                 CNCN MBar MGos MOke NHol
- 'Mousehole Compact'          See C. vulgaris 'Mousehole'
- 'Mrs Alf'                     Last listed 1998
- 'Mrs E.Wilson' (d)           Last listed 1998
- 'Mrs Neil Collins'           Last listed 1998
- 'Mrs Pat'                     CNCN GAri MBar MOke NHol
- 'Mrs Ronald Gray'            CNCN MBar
- 'Mullach Mor'                 Last listed 1998
§ - 'Mullardoch'                MBar
- 'Mullion' ♀                   CNCN MBar MOke
- 'Multicolor'                  CB&S CNCN EOrn MBar MOke
                                NHed NHol SBod SRms
- 'Murielle Dobson'            MBar
§ - 'My Dream' (d)              CNCN MBar NHol SCoo
- 'Nana'                        Last listed 1997
- 'Nana Compacta'              CNCN ESis MBar MOke SRms
- 'Natasja'                     Last listed 1998
- 'Naturpark'                   MBar
- 'Nico'                        Last listed 1998
- 'Nordlicht'                   Last listed 1998
- 'October White'              CNCN
- 'Oiseval'                     Last listed 1998
- 'Old Rose'                    Last listed 1998
- 'Olive Turner'                ECho
- 'Olympic Gold'               Last listed 1998
- 'Orange and Gold'            ECho
- 'Orange Carpet'              Last listed 1998
- 'Orange Max'                  Last listed 1998
- 'Orange Queen' ♀             CNCN MBar SBod
- 'Oxabäck'                     MBar
- 'Oxshott Common'             CNCN GQui MBar
- 'Pallida'                     ECho
- 'Parsons' Gold'              Last listed 1998
- 'Parsons' Grey Selected'     Last listed 1998
- 'Pat's Gold'                  Last listed 1998
- 'Peace'                       Last listed 1998
- 'Pearl Drop'                  MBar
- 'Penhale'                     Last listed 1998
- 'Penny Bun'                   Last listed 1998
- 'Pepper and Salt'            See C. vulgaris 'Hugh Nicholson'
- 'Perestrojka'                 ECho NHol
- 'Peter Sparkes' (d)          CB&S CMac CNCN EOrn GDra
                                MBar MBri MGos MOke NHar
                                NHol SBod SRms
- 'Petra'                       Last listed 1998
- 'Pewter Plate'                MBar
- 'Pink Beale'                  See C. vulgaris 'H.E. Beale'
- 'Pink Dream' (d)             Last listed 1998
- 'Pink Gown'                   CNCN

- 'Plantarium'                  Last listed 1998
- 'Platt's Surprise' (d)       Last listed 1998
- 'Prizewinner'                 CNCN
- 'Prostrata Flagelliformis'   Last listed 1998
- 'Prostrate Orange'           CNCN MBar
- 'Punch's Dessert'            Last listed 1998
- 'Pygmaea'                     MBar
- 'Pyramidalis'                 ECho
- 'Pyrenaica'                   MBar
- 'R.A. McEwan'                Last listed 1998
- 'Radnor' (d) ♀               CNCN MBar MGos MOke NHar
                                SBod
- 'Radnor Gold' (d)            MBar
- 'Ralph Purnell'              CNCN MBar NHar SBod
- 'Ralph Purnell Select'       Last listed 1998
- 'Ralph's Pearl'              Last listed 1998
- 'Ralph's Red'                Last listed 1998
- 'Randall's Crimson'          Last listed 1998
- 'Rannoch'                     Last listed 1998
- 'Red Carpet'                  CNCN MBar MOke
- 'Red Favorit' (d)            CNCN LRHS SBod
- 'Red Fred'                    MGos NHol SCoo
- 'Red Haze'                    CBrm CMac CNCN MBar MOke
                                NHol SBod WStI
- 'Red Max'                     Last listed 1998
- Red October                   See C. vulgaris 'Roter Oktober'
- 'Red Pimpernel'              CNCN
- 'Red Rug'                     Last listed 1998
- 'Red Star' (d) ♀             CMac CNCN LRHS MBar MOke
                                NHol
- 'Red Wings'                   Last listed 1998
- 'Redbud'                      CNCN ECho
- 'Reini'                       CNCN ECho NHol
- 'Rica'                        Last listed 1998
- 'Richard Cooper'             MBar
- 'Rieanne'                     Last listed 1998
- 'Rigida Prostrata'           See C. vulgaris 'Alba Rigida'
- 'Rivington'                   Last listed 1998
- 'Robber Knight'              ECho
- 'Robert Chapman' ♀           CB&S CBrm CMac CNCN EBrP
                                EBre EOrn GChr LBre MBar MBri
                                MGos MOke NHar NHol SBod
                                SBre
- 'Rock Spray'                  Last listed 1998
- 'Roland Haagen' ♀            MBar MOke NHar
- 'Roma'                        ECho MBar
- 'Romina'                      CNCN ECho NHol
- 'Ronas Hill'                  CNCN GDra
- 'Roodkapje'                   Last listed 1998
- 'Rosalind'                    CNCN MBar MOke NHol
- 'Rosalind, Crastock Heath'   Last listed 1998
I - 'Rosalind, Crastock Heath   Last listed 1997
    Variety'
- 'Rosalind, Underwood's'      ECho LRHS
- 'Rosea'                       Last listed 1998
- 'Ross Hutton'                 Last listed 1998
- 'Roswitha'                    ECho
§ - 'Roter Oktober'             Last listed 1996
- 'Rotfuchs'                    Last listed 1998
- 'Ruby Slinger'                CNCN MBar SBod
- 'Rusty Triumph'              SBod
- 'Ruth Sparkes' (d)           CMac CNCN MBar MOke NHol
                                SBod
- Saint Kilda Group            Last listed 1997
- 'Saint Nick'                  CNCN MBar
- 'Salland'                     Last listed 1998
- 'Sally Anne Proudley'        CNCN MBar
- 'Salmon Leap'                 CNCN MBar NHol
- 'Sam Hewitt'                  Last listed 1998
- 'Sampford Sunset'            CSam
- 'Sandhammaren'              Last listed 1998
- 'Sandwood Bay'               Last listed 1998

- 'Sarah Platt' (d)    ECho
- 'Scaynes Hill'    Last listed 1998
- 'Schurig's Sensation' (d)    CNCN EBrP EBre GAri LBre MBar
   MBri MOke NHar SBod SBre
- 'Scotch Mist'    Last listed 1998
- 'Sedloňov'    Last listed 1998
- 'September Pink'    Last listed 1998
- 'Serlei'    MBar MOke
- 'Serlei Aurea' ♀    CNCN MBar SBod
- 'Serlei Grandiflora'    MBar
I - 'Serlei Lavender'    ECho
- 'Serlei Purpurea'    Last listed 1998
- 'Serlei Rubra'    Last listed 1998
- 'Sesam'    Last listed 1998
- 'Shirley'    CMac MBar
- 'Silver Cloud'    CMac CNCN MBar
- 'Silver Fox'    ECho
- 'Silver King'    CNCN MBar
- 'Silver Knight'    CNCN EBrP EBre EOrn LBre MBar
   MBri MGos MOke NHar NHol
   NRoo SBod SBre SPlb WStI
- 'Silver Queen' ♀    CNCN EBrP EBre LBre MBar MBri
   MOke NHar NHol SBod SBre
   SRms
- 'Silver Rose' ♀    CNCN MBar
- 'Silver Sandra'    Last listed 1998
- 'Silver Spire'    CNCN MBar
- 'Silver Stream'    MBar SBod
- 'Sir Anthony Hopkins'    ECho
- 'Sir John Charrington' ♀    CB&S CMac CNCN EBrP EBre
   EOrn GDra LBre MBar MBri MGos
   MOke NHol SBod SBre WStI
- 'Sirsson'    MBar MBri
- 'Sister Anne' ♀    CNCN EBrP EBre LBre MBri MGos
   MOke NHed NHol SBod SBre
   SRms
- 'Skipper'    ECho MBar
- 'Snowball'    See C. vulgaris 'My Dream'
- 'Snowflake'    Last listed 1998
- 'Soay'    MBar SBod
- 'Sonja' (d)    CNCN
- 'Sonning' (d)    Last listed 1998
- 'Sonny Boy'    Last listed 1998
- 'Spicata'    Last listed 1998
- 'Spicata Aurea'    CNCN MBar
- 'Spider'    ECho
- 'Spitfire'    CNCN MBar NHol WStI
- 'Spook'    Last listed 1998
- 'Spring Cream' ♀    CNCN EBrP EBre LBre MBar MBri
   MGos MOke NHar NHol SBod
   SBre WStI
- 'Spring Glow'    CMac CNCN MBar MBri MOke
   NHar SBod
- 'Spring Torch'    CB&S CNCN EBrP EBre EOrn
   GDra LBre MBar MBri MGos
   MOke NHar NHol NRoo SBod
   SBre SCoo WStI
- 'Springbank'    MBar
- 'Stag's Horn'    Last listed 1998
- 'Stefanie'    Last listed 1998
- 'Stranger'    Last listed 1998
- 'Strawberry Delight' (d)    CB&S NHol
- 'Summer Elegance'    Last listed 1998
- 'Summer Gold'    Last listed 1996
- 'Summer Orange'    CNCN MBar NHol
- 'Sunningdale'    See C. vulgaris 'Finale'
- 'Sunrise'    CNCN MBar MGos MOke NHol
   SBod WStI
- 'Sunset' ♀    CBrm CNCN EBrP EBre GDra
   LBre MBar NHol SBod SBre SRms
   WStI
- 'Sunset Glow'    Last listed 1998

- 'Talisker'    ECho
- 'Tenella'    Last listed 1998
- 'Tenuis'    CNCN ECho MBar
- 'Terrick's Orange'    Last listed 1998
- 'The Pygmy'    Last listed 1998
- 'Tib' (d) ♀    CB&S CMac CNCN MBar MBri
   MGos MOke NHed SBod SRms
   WStI
- 'Tino'    Last listed 1998
- 'Tom Thumb'    MBar
- 'Tomentosa Alba'    Last listed 1998
- 'Tom's Fancy'    Last listed 1998
- 'Torogay'    Last listed 1998
- 'Torulosa'    Last listed 1998
- 'Tremans'    Last listed 1998
- 'Tricolorifolia'    CNCN NHol SBod
- 'Underwoodii' ♀    ECho MBar
§ - 'Velvet Dome'    MBar SBod
- 'Velvet Fascination'    CNCN ECho LRHS MBar MGos
   NHol
- 'Violet Bamford'    Last listed 1998
- 'Visser's Fancy'    Last listed 1998
§ - 'Walter Ingwersen'    Last listed 1998
- 'Westerlee Gold'    Last listed 1998
- 'Westerlee Green'    Last listed 1998
- 'Westphalia'    Last listed 1998
◆ - 'White Bouquet'    See C. vulgaris 'Alba Plena'
- 'White Carpet'    MBar
- 'White Coral' (d)    ECho MGos SDys
- 'White Gold'    Last listed 1998
- 'White Gown'    GDra
- 'White Lawn' ♀    CNCN EOrn MBar MGos NHed
   NHol SRms
- 'White Mite'    ECho MBar
- 'White Princess'    See C. vulgaris 'White Queen'
§ - 'White Queen'    MBar
- 'White Star' (d)    LRHS
- 'Whiteness'    CNCN SDys
- 'Wickwar Flame' ♀    CB&S CBrm CMac CNCN EBrP
   EBre EOrn GDra LBre MBar MBri
   MGos MOke NHar NHol NRoo
   SBod SBre WGwG WStI
- 'Wingates Gem'    Last listed 1998
- 'Wingates Gold'    Last listed 1998
- 'Winter Chocolate'    CNCN MBar MBri MGos MOke
   NHed NHol SBod WStI
- 'Winter Fire'    Last listed 1998
- 'Winter Red'    Last listed 1998
- 'Wollmers Weisse' (d)    Last listed 1998
- 'Wood Close'    Last listed 1998
- 'Yellow Basket'    Last listed 1998
- 'Yellow Dome'    CNCN
- 'Yellow One'    Last listed 1998
- 'Yvette's Gold'    Last listed 1998
- 'Yvette's Silver'    Last listed 1998
- 'Yvonne Clare'    Last listed 1998

## CALOCEDRUS (Cupressaceae)

§ **decurrens** ♀    CB&S CDoC CDul CMac CTri
   EBrP EBre EHul ENot EOrn EPfP
   IOrc LBre LCon LPan MBal MBar
   MBlu MBri MGos NWea SBre
   SLim SPer SSta WFro WWat
- 'Aureovariegata' (v)    CBlo CDoC CKen IOrc LCon LLin
   LNet LPan MAsh MBar MBlu MBri
   NHol SLim
- 'Berrima Gold'    CKen EPfP
§ - 'Depressa'    CKen
- 'Intricata'    CKen
- 'Nana'    See C. decurrens 'Depressa'
- 'Pillar'    CKen LRHS MBri

## CALOCEPHALUS (Asteraceae)

*brownii*     See *Leucophyta brownii*

## CALOCHORTUS (Liliaceae)

| | |
|---|---|
| *albus* | EHyt EPot |
|  – J&JA 13053 | Last listed 1996 |
|  – var. *rubellus* | EHyt EPot GCrs LAma |
| *amabilis* | EPot |
| *ambiguus* | Last listed 1996 |
| *amoenus* | WCot WLin |
| *apiculatus* | EPot |
| *argillosus* | EPot |
| *barbatus* | EHyt EPot NWCA |
|  – var. *chihuahuaensis* | Last listed 1997 |
| *bruneaunis* | Last listed 1998 |
| ¶ *caeruleus* | EPot |
| *clavatus* | EPot |
|  – var. *avius* | EPot |
| *concolor* | EPot |
| *eurycarpus* | See *C. nitidus* |
| *excavatus* | EPot |
| *exilis* | Last listed 1996 |
| ¶ *greenei* | EPot |
| ¶ *gunnisonii* | EHyt |
| *howellii* | Last listed 1998 |
| *kennedyi* | Last listed 1997 |
| ¶  – JA 9312 | EHyt |
| *leichtlinii* | EPot |
| *luteus* | EHyt EPot LAma WLin |
| *  – 'Golden Orb' | GCrs WAbe WBea |
| *macrocarpus* | Last listed 1998 |
| *monophyllus* | Last listed 1997 |
| § *nitidus* | EPot |
| *obispoensis* | Last listed 1997 |
| ¶ *palmeri* | EPot |
| *plummerae* JA 94-104 | EHyt |
| *pulchellus* | Last listed 1998 |
| *splendens* | EPot LAma |
| ¶ *striatus* | EPot |
|  – JA 93-21 | EHyt |
| *superbus* | EPot GCrs |
| *tolmiei* | Last listed 1998 |
| *umbellatus* | Last listed 1997 |
| ¶ *umpquaensis* | GCrs |
| *uniflorus* | EHyt EPot GCrs WCot |
| *venustus* | EDAr EHyt EPot LAma WLin |
|  – Cuddy Valley reds | Last listed 1996 |
|  – J&JA 13288 | Last listed 1996 |
| *vestae* | EHyt WLin |

## CALOMERIA (Asteraceae)

§ *amaranthoides*     LHol WJek

## CALONYCTION See IPOMOEA

## CALOPHACA (Papilionaceae)

*grandiflora*     Last listed 1998

## CALOPOGON (Orchidaceae)

¶ *tuberosus*     SSpi

## CALOSCORDUM (Alliaceae)

§ *neriniflorum*     EBee EBur EHyt WAbe

## CALOTHAMNUS (Myrtaceae)

| | |
|---|---|
| *blepharospermus* | SOWG |
| *gilesii* | SOWG |
| *homolophyllus* | SOWG |
| ¶ *pinifolius* | CCpl |
| *quadrifidus* | SOWG |
| *rupestris* | MSag SOWG |
| *sanguineus* | SOWG |
| *validus* | SOWG |

## CALOTROPIS (Asclepiadaceae)

*gigantea*     Last listed 1998

## CALPURNIA (Papilionaceae)

*aurea*     Last listed 1997

## CALTHA ✿ (Ranunculaceae)

| | |
|---|---|
| 'Auenwald' | CLAP CRDP CRow |
| 'Honeydew' | CLAP CRDP CRow EBee GBuc NCat |
| *howellii* | WLin |
| *introloba* | SWat |
| *laeta* | See *C. palustris* var. *palustris* |
| *leptosepala* | CLAP CRow |
|  – NNS 9420 | EPot |
| *natans* | CRow |
| *palustris* ♀ | CBen CFee CGle CKin CMHG CRDP CRow CWat EBee EHon EPot ERos EWFC GPoy LFis LPBA MCLN MSCN MSta NDea NMir SWat SWyc WByw WFar WMAq WShi WWeb |
|  – var. *alba* | More than 30 suppliers |
|  – 'Flore Pleno' (d) ♀ | CBen CGle CRow EBrP EBre ECha EHon ELan LBre LHop LPBA LSyl MBal MBri MSta NChi NDea NFai NFor NGdn NHar NSti SBre SPer SRms SWat SWyc WByw WWeb |
|  – var. *himalensis* | GCrs NTow |
|  – 'Marilyn' | CLAP CRDP NCat |
|  – 'Multiplex' (d) | COtt WViv |
| §  – var. *palustris* | CBen CBre CRDP CRow ECha EHon ELan EMFW EMon EPar GAri GGar LPBA MSta NDea SLon SPer SSpi SWat WFar |
|  – – 'Plena' (d) | CRow CSam CWat ENot EPfP WCot WMAq WWat |
|  – var. *radicans* | CRow EMFW GCrs SSpi |
|  – 'Semiplena' (d) | EMon |
|  – 'Stagnalis' | CRow SWyc |
|  – 'Tyermannii' | CRow |
|  – 'Wheatfen' | Last listed 1997 |
| ¶ *polypetala* Hochst. | CLAP EBee EMFW |
| ¶  – hort. | See *C. palustris* var. *palustris* |
| *sagittata* | CRow |
| ¶  – JCA 2.198.200 | SSpi |
| ¶ *scaposa* ACE 2139 | EPot |
| 'Susan' | CRow |

## CALYCANTHUS (Calycanthaceae)

| | |
|---|---|
| ¶ *chinensis* | SRPl |
| ◆ *fertilis* | See *C. floridus* var. *glaucus* |
| ◆  – 'Purpureus' | See *C. floridus* var. *glaucus* 'Purpureus' |
| *floridus* | CArn CB&S CBlo CFil CMCN CPMA CPle EBee ELan ENot IOrc LHol MBNS MBlu MUlv MWhi SPan SPer WLRN WWat WWin |
| §  – var. *glaucus* | CFil EBee EPfP LBuc MBlu SPer WSHC |
| §  – – 'Purpureus' | MBlu NEgg |
|  – var. *laevigatus* | See *C. floridus* var. *glaucus* |
| *occidentalis* | CAgr CB&S CCHP CFil CGre CMCN CPle EMil LRHS MBlu SIgm SSpi WPGP |

## CALYDOREA (Iridaceae)

| | |
|---|---|
| *speciosa* | See *C. xiphioides* |
| § *xiphioides* | Last listed 1996 |

**CALYPSO** (Orchidaceae)

*bulbosa*                     Last listed 1997

**CALYPTRIDIUM** (Portulacaceae)
*umbellatum*                  See *Spraguea umbellata*

**CALYSTEGIA** (Convolvulaceae)
  *collina* subsp.*venusta*   WCot
§ *hederacea*                 CPlN CSpe EBee ECha ELan EMon
 ·  'Flore Pleno' (d)       EOrc EPar GMac LFis LHop MTho
                     NSti SMad WCot WHer WWin
  *japonica* 'Flore Pleno'  See *C. hederacea* 'Flore Pleno'
  *macrostegia* subsp.     WCot
    *cyclostegia*
  *pulchra*                 WCru
  *silvatica* 'Incarnata'   EBee EMon EOrc
  *tuguriorum*             Last listed 1997

**CAMASSIA** (Hyacinthaceae)
  *cusickii*                CAvo CBro CHad CHea CMea
                     EBee EBrP EBre ECha ELan EMan
                     EMon EOld EPar EPot GMaP
                     LAma LBow LBre MBri MNrw
                     MTho NBir NFai NRog NSti SBre
                     WCot
  *esculenta*              See *C. quamash*
  *fraseri*                See *C. scilloides*
  *leichtlinii* hort.      See *C. leichtlinii* subsp. *suksdorfii*
N - 'Alba' hort.              See *C. leichtlinii* subsp. *leichtlinii*
* - 'Alba Plena'              Last listed 1998
  - 'Blauwe Donau'         See *C. leichtlinii* subsp. *suksdorfii*
                     'Blauwe Donau'
  - Blue Danube           See *C. leichtlinii* subsp. *suksdorfii*
                     'Blauwe Donau'
  - 'Electra'             ECha LPio MRav SWas
§ - subsp.*leichtlinii* ♀     CAvo CBro CHad CHea CLAP
                     CMea CMil ELan EMan EMon EPar
                     EPfP EPot GBri GMaP ISea LAma
                     MGed MNrw MRav MWll NCat
                     NPer SRPl SRms WCot WFar
                     WHoo WShi
N - 'Plena' (d)               ECha WCot
  - 'Semiplena' (d)       CAvo CBro CFai CLAP CMea CMil
                     CRDP EBee EMon EPar LPio
                     MBNS
§ - subsp.*suksdorfii*        CAvo EPar ETub GBuc LBow NCat
                     NRoo SAga SPer
§ - - 'Blauwe Donau'         LAma LBow LRHS MGed
  - - Caerulea Group      CBro CHad CMdw CMea CMil
                     CRDP EBee ELan EMan EMon
                     EOld EPar EPfP ISea LAma MNrw
                     MUlv NRog SUsu WAbb WCot
                     WHoo WPGP
§ *quamash*                   CAvo CBro CLAP CSpe EBee ECha
                     ELan EMon EPar ETub GSki LAma
                     LBow LEdu MBri MTho NBir
                     NRog SMad SPar SRms WBea
                     WByw WFar WLin WShi WWeb
  - 'Blue Melody'         CBro CMea CMil EBee LRHS WHil
  - subsp.*linearis*       NHol
  - 'Orion'               CBro CLAP CMea CSWP EMon
                     GBuc MAvo WCot
§ *scilloides*                MBri WCot

**CAMELLIA** ♣ (Theaceae)
  'Arbutus Gum' (*reticulata*   Last listed 1996
    x *japonica*)
  'Auburn White'          See *C. japonica* 'Mrs Bertha A.
                     Harms'
  'Autumnal White'        Last listed 1996
  'Baby Face'             See *C. reticulata* 'Tongzimian'

  'Barbara Clark'         CDoC MGos SCog
    (*saluenensis*
    x *reticulata*)
  'Barbara Hillier' (*reticulata*   CTre SStn
    x *japonica*)
  'Barchi'                See *C. japonica* 'Contessa
                     Samailoff'
  'Bertha Harms Blush'    See *C. japonica* 'Mrs Bertha A.
                     Harms'
¶ 'Betty Ridley' (hybrid)     SStn
  'Black Lace'            CDoC CTrh EBee MAsh MBal
    (*reticulata* x *williamsii*)   MBri SCog SLdr SPer SStn WLRN
  'Bonnie Marie' (hybrid)  CTre SCog SStn
  *caudata*               Last listed 1996
  'Chandleri'             Last listed 1996
  'China Lady' (*reticulata*   Last listed 1997
    x *granthamiana*)
  'Christmas Daffodil'    CTrh
    (*japonica* hybrid)
  *chrysantha*            See *C. nitidissima* var.
                     *nitidissima*
¶ 'Cinnamon Cindy' (hybrid)   CDoC
  'Contessa Lavinia Maggi'  See *C. japonica* 'Lavinia Maggi'
  'Cornish Clay'          ISea
  'Cornish Snow' (*japonica*   CB&S CDoC CGre COtt CSam
    x *cuspidata*) ♀       CTre CTrh GGGa IOrc ISea LNet
                     MBal SBrw SPer SReu SSpi SStn
                     WBod WCwm WWat
  'Cornish Spring'        CB&S CDoC COtt CPin CTre
                     CTrh
    (*japonica* x *cuspidata*) ♀ EPfP WBcn WLRN WWat
  'Corsica'               Last listed 1998
  *crapnelliana*          CGre
  *cuspidata*             CGre CTre CTrh
  'Czar'                  See *C. japonica* 'The Czar'
  'Dawn'                  See *C. x vernalis* 'Ginryû'
  'Debut' (*reticulata*    Last listed 1996
    x *japonica*)
  'Delia Williams'        See *C. x williamsii* 'Citation'
  'Diamond Head' (*japonica*   CB&S
    x *reticulata*)
  'Doctor Clifford Parks'  CDoC CTre SCog
    (*reticulata* x *japonica*) ♀
  'Donckelaeri'           See *C. japonica* 'Masayoshi'
¶ 'Dorothy James' (hybrid)    SStn
  'Dream Girl' (*sasanqua*   Last listed 1996
    x *reticulata*)
  'Eclipsis'              See *C. japonica* 'Press's Eclipse'
  'El Dorado' (*pitardii*   CTrh ECle
    x *japonica*)
  'Elizabeth Bolitho'     Last listed 1996
  'Extravaganza' (*japonica*   CB&S CTrh SBod SCog SStn
    hybrid)
  'Fairy Wand' (hybrid)   CB&S CDoC
  'Faustina Lechi'        See *C. japonica* 'Faustina'
  'Felice Harris' (*sasanqua*   SCog
    x *reticulata*)
  'First Flush' (*cuspidata*   Last listed 1997
    x *saluenensis*)
* 'Fishtail White'            Last listed 1997
  'Flower Girl' (*sasanqua*   Last listed 1996
    x *reticulata*)
  'Forty-niner' (*reticulata*   CB&S CDoC SCog
    x *japonica*) ♀
  'Fragrant Pink' (*rusticana*   CTrh
    x *lutchuensis*)
  'Francie L' (*saluenensis*   CDoC CGre CTre CTrh SSta
    x *reticulata*)
  *fraterna*              Last listed 1996
  'Frau Minna Seidel'     See *C. japonica* 'Otome'
  'Freedom Bell' (hybrid) ♀  CB&S CDoC CTre CTrh GGGa
                     ISea MAsh MBri SBrw SCog SStn

'Gay Baby' (hybrid)                CB&S MGos
'Grace Caple'                      Last listed 1996
  (*pitardii* x *japonica*)
*granthamiana*                     Last listed 1997
*grijsii*                          CTrh
*hiemalis* 'Chansonette'           SCog SLdr
§ - 'Dazzler'                      CDoC CTre CTrh SCog SStn
§ *hiemalis* 'Kanjirô'             CTrh SCog
- 'Shôwa-no-sakae'                 SCog
- 'Sparkling Burgundy'             CB&S CTre LHyd SCog SStn
¶ 'Hooker' hybrid                  CDoC
'Howard Asper' (*reticulata*       Last listed 1997
  x *japonica*)
'Imbricata Rubra'                  See *C. japonica* 'Imbricata'
'Innovation' (x *williamsii*       CB&S CDoC CTre ISea MGos SStn
  x *reticulata*)
'Inspiration' (*reticulata*        CB&S CDoC CGre CMHG CMac
  x *saluenensis*) ♀      CTre CTrh EPfP GGGa ISea LHyd
                          MAsh MBri MGos SBod SBrw
                          SCog SLdr SSpi SStn WBod
*japonica* 'Aaron's Ruby'          CB&S CDoC COtt CTre SStn
- 'Ada Pieper'                     CTrh
- 'Adelina Patti'                  CB&S CDoC CTre CTrh SCog SStn
                          WCwm
- 'Adolphe Audusson' ♀             More than 30 suppliers
- 'Adolphe Audusson                CB&S
  Special'
§ - 'Akashigata' ♀                 CDoC CTre CTrw ENot EPfP
                          MWat SMad SReu SSta SStn
§ - 'Akebono'                      CTrw
- 'Alba Plena'                     CDoC CGre CMac CTre CTrh
                          ENot IOrc LNet MGos SBod SCog
                          SPer SStn
- 'Alba Simplex'                   CB&S CGre CMac CTre CTrh
                          ELan EPfP IOrc LNet MBal SBod
                          SCog SPer SSta SStn WStI
§ - 'Albertii'                     WBod
- 'Alex Blackadder'                Last listed 1996
- 'Alexander Hunter' ♀             CTre LHyd MAsh SBod SStn
- 'Alice Wood'                     Last listed 1998
§ - 'Althaeiflora'                 CB&S CDoC CGre CTre SStn
- 'Ama-no-gawa'                    Last listed 1997
- 'Anemoniflora'                   CB&S CDoC CTre ELan SBod SLdr
                          SPer
- 'Angel'                          CB&S CTre SCog SStn
- 'Angela Cocchi'                  Last listed 1998
- 'Ann Sothern'                    CTrh
- 'Annie Wylam'                    CTrh SCog
§ - 'Apollo'                       CB&S CDoC CSam CTrG CTrh
                          EPfP MAsh MGos SBrw SPer SStn
                          WBcn WBod
§ - 'Apple Blossom' ♀              CGre CMac ELan LRHS MBal SStn
- 'Arabella'                       Last listed 1997
♦ - 'Arajishii'                    See *C. rusticana* 'Arajishi'
* - 'Augustine Supreme'            CMac
- 'Augusto Leal de Gouveia         CB&S CTre SStn
  Pinto'
- 'Australis'                      CTrh
- 'Ave Maria'                      CTrh
- 'Azurea'                         CGre
- 'Baby Sis'                       CB&S
- 'Ballet Dancer' ♀                CDoC SCog SLdr SPla SStn WBcn
                          WGwG
- 'Barbara Woodroof'               Last listed 1997
- 'Baron Gomer'                    See *C. japonica* 'Comte de
                          Gomer'
- 'Baronne Leguay'                 LRHS SStn
¶ - 'Beau Harp'                    SStn WBod
¶ - 'Bella Romana'                 SStn WBod
- 'Belle of the Ball'              Last listed 1996
¶ - 'Benidaikagura'                SStn
¶ - 'Benihassaku'                  SStn

- 'Benten' (v)                     CTrw
- 'Berenice Boddy' ♀               CB&S CTrh SStn
¶ - 'Berenice Perfection'          SStn
¶ - 'Bertha Raressi'               WBod
- 'Betty Foy Sanders'              CTrh
- 'Betty Sheffield'                CDoC CGre COtt CTre MGos
                          SBod SCog
- 'Betty Sheffield Blush'          Last listed 1998
- 'Betty Sheffield Coral'          Last listed 1997
¶ - 'Betty Sheffield Pink'         SStn
- 'Betty Sheffield Supreme'        CB&S CDoC CGre LRHS SCog
- 'Betty Sheffield White'          Last listed 1997
- 'Bienville'                      Last listed 1997
¶ - 'Billie McCaskill'             SStn
- 'Blackburnia'                    See *C. japonica* 'Althaeiflora'
- 'Blaze of Glory'                 CDoC CGre CTrh WBcn
§ - 'Blood of China'               CB&S CDoC COtt MAsh SBod
                          SPer SStn WBod WCwm
- 'Bob Hope' ♀                     CB&S CDoC CGre CTre CTrh
                          ECle SCog SStn
- 'Bob's Tinsie' ♀                 CDoC CGre CTre CTrw ECle
                          SCog
§ - 'Bokuhan'                      CGre CTre SStn
- 'Bonomiana'                      Last listed 1998
- 'Brushfield's Yellow'            CB&S CDoC CGre CMHG COtt
                          MBal MGos SPer SSta SStn
- 'Bryan Wright'                   Last listed 1996
- 'Burgundy Gem'                   Last listed 1996
- 'Bush Hill Beauty'               See *C. japonica* 'Lady de
                          Saumarez'
§ - 'C.M. Hovey' ♀                 CMHG CMac CTrh EPfP MAsh
                          MBal MNes SStn WBcn WGwG
- 'C.M. Wilson' ♀                  CMac CTre SCog SStn
- 'Caleb Cope'                     Last listed 1996
N - 'Campbellii'                   WBod
- 'Campsii Alba'                   WStI
- 'Can Can'                        CB&S CDoC SCog
- 'Canon Boscawen'                 CTrG
- 'Cara Mia'                       CB&S CTre SStn
¶ - 'Cardinal Variegated'          SStn
- 'Cardinal's Cap'                 CGre
- 'Carolyn Tuttle'                 Last listed 1997
- 'Carter's Sunburst' ♀            CB&S CDoC CTrh EPfP SStn
- 'Cécile Brunazzi'                SCog
- 'Chandleri Elegans'              See *C. japonica* 'Elegans'
¶ - 'Charlie Bettes'               SStn
- 'Charlotte de Rothschild'        CTrh CTri MBri
- 'Charming Betty'                 See *C. japonica* 'Funny Face
                          Betty'
- 'Cheerio'                        Last listed 1997
- 'Cheryll Lynn'                   CTrh SStn WBod
¶ - 'Christmas Beauty'             MAsh WBod
- 'Cinderella'                     CDoC CTre SCog SStn
- 'Clarise Carleton'               CTre CTrh
¶ - 'Clarissa'                     SStn
- 'Colonel Firey'                  See *C. japonica* 'C.M. Hovey'
- 'Colonial Dame'                  Last listed 1997
- 'Commander Mulroy'               CTrh SStn WBcn
- 'Compton's Brow'                 See *C. japonica* 'Gauntlettii'
§ - 'Comte de Gomer'               CGre ELan EPfP SLdr SSta WBcn
- 'Conrad Hilton'                  Last listed 1997
- 'Conspicua'                      CB&S
§ - 'Coquettii' ♀                  CB&S CDoC CTre
¶ - 'Coral Pink Lotus'             SStn
¶ - 'Coral Queen'                  SStn
- 'Countess of Orkney'             CTre WBcn
- 'Daikagura'                      Last listed 1997
- 'Dainty'                         CB&S
- 'Daitairin'                      See *C. japonica* 'Dewatairin'
- 'Daphne du Maurier'              Last listed 1996
- 'Dear Jenny'                     CB&S CTrG CTre SCog
- 'Debbie'                         WGwG

| | | |
|---|---|---|
| | - 'Debutante' | CB&S CGre CMac CTre CTrh LHyd MAsh MBri SStn WBcn |
| ¶ | - 'Deep Secret' | CDoC |
| | - 'Desire' | CB&S CDoC CMHG CTrh ECle SCog |
| | - 'Devonia' | CB&S EPfP LHyd MBal |
| § | - 'Dewatairin' | CMac SStn WBod |
| | - 'Dixie Knight' | CDoC SLdr SSta |
| | - 'Dobreei' | CMac WBod WGer WWal |
| | - 'Doctor Burnside' | CB&S CMHG CTrh SCog SStn |
| | - 'Doctor Tinsley' ♀ | CDoC CGre CTrh SStn WBcn |
| | - 'Dona Herzilia de Freitas Magalhaes' | CB&S CTre SSta SStn WBcn |
| ¶ | - 'Dona Jane Andresson' | SStn |
| ♦ | - 'Donckelarii' | See C. japonica 'Masayoshi' |
| | - 'Donnan's Dream' | CTrh |
| | - 'Double Rose' (d) | Last listed 1998 |
| | - 'Doutor Balthazar de Mello' | Last listed 1997 |
| | - 'Drama Girl' ♀ | CB&S CDoC CGre CTre CTrw IOrc MBal SBod SStn WBod |
| | - 'Duc de Bretagne' | Last listed 1997 |
| | - 'Duchesse Decazes' | CB&S COtt CTre SStn |
| ¶ | - 'Duchesse Decazes Pink' | SStn |
| | - 'Effendee' | See C. sasanqua 'Rosea Plena' |
| ¶ | - 'Eleanor Grant' | SStn |
| | - 'Eleanor Hagood' | CB&S CGre WBcn |
| § | - 'Elegans' ♀ | CB&S CDoC CGre CHig CMac CTre ENot IOrc LHyd MBal MWat SBod SBrw SCog SLdr SPer SReu SSta SStn WBcn |
| | - 'Elegans Champagne' | CTrh SCog WBcn |
| | - 'Elegans Splendor' | CTre WBcn |
| | - 'Elegans Supreme' | CGre CTre SStn |
| ♦ | - 'Elegant Beauty' | See C. x williamsii 'Elegant Beauty' |
| | - 'Elisabeth' | Last listed 1998 |
| | - 'Elizabeth Arden' | CTre |
| | - 'Elizabeth Dowd' | CB&S SCog |
| | - 'Elizabeth Hawkins' | CTre CTrh EBee WLRN |
| | - 'Ella Drayton' | SCog |
| | - 'Ellen Sampson' | Last listed 1998 |
| ¶ | - 'Emmett Barnes' | SStn |
| ¶ | - 'Emmett Pfingstl'™ (v) | SStn WBcn |
| | - 'Emperor of Russia' | CB&S CDoC ELan MAsh SStn WBod |
| | - 'Erin Farmer' | CB&S SCog |
| ¶ | - 'Eugene Bolen' | SStn |
| ¶ | - 'Eugène Lizé' | SStn |
| ¶ | - 'Evelyn' | SStn |
| | - 'Eximia' | WBod |
| ¶ | - 'Extravaganza Pink' | SStn |
| ¶ | - 'Faith' | SStn |
| ¶ | - 'Fashionata' | SStn |
| | - 'Fatima' | CTre |
| § | - 'Faustina' | Last listed 1997 |
| ¶ | - 'Feast Perfection' | CDoC |
| § | - 'Fimbriata' | SStn |
| | - 'Fimbriata Alba' | See C. japonica 'Fimbriata' |
| | - 'Finlandia Variegated' | Last listed 1998 |
| | - 'Fire Dance' | CTrh |
| | - 'Fire Falls' | Last listed 1998 |
| | - 'Flame' | CB&S CDoC |
| § | - 'Fleur Dipater' | SStn |
| ¶ | - 'Flowerwood' | SStn |
| | - 'Forest Green' | ELan LRHS MAsh SBrw SCog |
| | - 'Frans van Damme' | SStn |
| ¶ | - 'Fred Sander' | EBee SStn |
| | - 'Frosty Morn' | CB&S |
| § | - 'Funny Face Betty' | Last listed 1996 |
| | - 'Furo-an' | MAsh SStn |
| § | - 'Gauntlettii' | SStn |
| | - 'Gay Chieftain' | WBod |
| ¶ | - 'Geisha Girl' | CDoC SStn |
| ¶ | - 'Général Lamoricière' | MAsh |
| | - 'Giardino Franchetti' | CGre CMHG |
| § | - 'Gigantea' | SStn |
| § | - 'Gigantea Red' | IOrc |
| ¶ | - 'Giuditta Rosani' | CDoC |
| | - 'Gladys Wannamaker' | Last listed 1998 |
| | - 'Glen 40' | See C. japonica 'Coquettii' |
| | - 'Gloire de Nantes' ♀ | CB&S CGre MNes SStn WBcn |
| * | - 'Golden Wedding' | Last listed 1998 |
| | - 'Goshoguruma' | WBod |
| | - 'Grace Bunton' | CB&S CDoC |
| | - 'Granada' | SCog |
| | - 'Grand Prix' ♀ | CDoC CTrh CTrw SLdr SSta SStn WBod |
| | - 'Grand Slam' ♀ | CB&S CDoC CMac CTre CTrh ISea MAsh SStn WBcn |
| ¶ | - 'Grand Sultan' | SStn |
| ¶ | - 'Great Eastern' | CDoC WBod |
| | - 'Guest of Honor' | CB&S COtt |
| | - 'Guilio Nuccio' ♀ | CB&S CDoC CTrG CTre MGos SCog SPer SStn |
| ¶ | - 'Gus Menard' | SStn |
| | - 'Gwenneth Morey' | CB&S CTre EPfP MAsh SStn |
| ¶ | - 'H.A. Downing' | SStn |
| § | - 'Hagoromo' ♀ | CDoC CGre ELan ENot EPfP MBal SStn WBcn WWat |
| | - 'Hakurakuten' ♀ | CDoC CTre CTrh EHol ISea SBod SCog SStn WBod |
| | - 'Hanafûki' | CDoC CTre SStn WBod |
| | - 'Hanatachibana' | SStn WBcn |
| | - 'Hassaku' | See C. japonica 'Hassaku-shibori' |
| | - 'Hatsuzakura' | See C. japonica 'Dewatairin' |
| | - 'Hawaii' | CB&S CMac CTre CTrh SCog SStn |
| ¶ | - 'Henry Turnbull' | SStn |
| | - Herme | See C. japonica 'Hikarugenji' |
| | - 'High Hat' | CB&S LHyd SLdr SStn WBod |
| § | - 'Hikarugenji' | CDoC |
| ¶ | - 'Hime-otome' | SStn |
| | - 'Hinomaru' | CMac |
| | - 'Holly Bright' | CTrh |
| § | - 'Imbricata' | CTre ENot MGos SCog |
| | - 'Imbricata Alba' | SBrw SCog SSta SStn |
| | - 'In the Pink' | Last listed 1998 |
| | - 'Italiana Vera' | Last listed 1998 |
| | - 'J.J.Whitfield' | CMac SStn |
| | - 'Jack Jones Scented' | CMHG |
| | - 'Janet Waterhouse' | CB&S SCog SStn WWat |
| § | - 'Japonica Variegata' | CGre CMHG WBcn |
| | - 'Jean Clere' | MGos SStn WBcn |
| | - 'Jean Lyne' | Last listed 1997 |
| | - 'Jingle Bells' | Last listed 1998 |
| | - 'Joseph Pfingstl' | CDoC CGre CTre MAsh SLdr SStn WBod LHyd |
| | - 'Joshua E.Youtz' | LHyd |
| ¶ | - 'Jovey Carlyon' (hybrid) | CDoC |
| | - 'Joy Sander' | See C. japonica 'Apple Blossom' |
| § | - 'Julia Drayton' | Last listed 1998 |
| | - 'Julia France' | CB&S |
| | - 'Juno' | CB&S |
| | - 'Jupiter' ♀ | CB&S CDoC CMac CTre CTrh CTri CTrw EPfP ISea LHyd LNet MAsh MBal MGos SCog SMad SStn WBod |
| | - 'Just Darling' | Last listed 1996 |
| ¶ | - 'Just Sue' | CDoC |
| ¶ | - 'Justine Heurtin' | SStn |
| | - 'K. Sawada' | Last listed 1997 |
| ¶ | - 'Katherine Nuccio' | SStn |
| | - 'Katie' | Last listed 1998 |
| ¶ | - 'Kay Truesdale' | SStn |

| | | |
|---|---|---|
| | - 'Kellingtoniana' | See *C. japonica* 'Gigantea' |
| | - 'Kenny' | CB&S |
| | - 'Kewpie Doll' | CDoC CTrh SCog |
| | - 'Kick-off' | CB&S CTrh SStn |
| | - 'Kimberley' | CB&S EPfP SCog WBcn WBod WLRN |
| | - 'King's Ransom' | CDoC CMac LHyd WBod |
| § | - 'Kingyo-tsubaki' | CGre SSta |
| ♦ | - 'Kinsekai' | See *C. rusticana* 'Kinsekai' |
| | - 'Kitty' | SBid SCog |
| | - 'Kitty Berry' | CTrh SStn |
| ¶ | - 'Kokinran' | SStn |
| § | - 'Konronkoku' ♀ | CDoC SCog SStn WBcn |
| | - 'Kouron-jura' | See *C. japonica* 'Konronkoku' |
| | - 'Kramer's Beauty' | ECle SCog |
| | - 'Kramer's Supreme' | CB&S CDoC CGre CTrG LNet MBal MGos SBod SBrw SCog SStn WLRN |
| § | - 'Kumasaka' | WBod |
| ♦ | - 'La Graciola' | See *C. japonica* 'Odoratissima' |
| ¶ | - 'La Pace' | SStn |
| ¶ | - 'La Pace Rubra' | SStn |
| | - 'Lady Campbell' | SStn |
| | - Lady Clare | See *C. japonica* 'Akashigata' |
| § | - 'Lady de Saumarez' ♀ | CDoC LNet SBod SStn |
| | - 'Lady de Saumarez' white | CGre |
| | - 'Lady Erma' | CB&S |
| | - 'Lady Loch' | CTre CTrh MGos SCog SStn |
| | - 'Lady Marion' | See *C. japonica* 'Kumasaka' |
| | - 'Lady McCulloch' | Last listed 1997 |
| | - 'Lady Vansittart' | CB&S CDoC CSam CTrG CTre EBee ELan ENot ISea LHyd LNet MAsh MBal SBod SBrw SCog SPer SStn WBcn WBod |
| § | - 'Lady Vansittart Pink' | MGos SBod SLdr |
| | - 'Lady Vansittart Red' | See *C. japonica* 'Lady Vansittart Pink' |
| ♦ | - 'Lady Vansittart Shell' | See *C. japonica* 'Yours Truly' |
| | - 'Lanarth' | CTre |
| | - 'Latifolia' | CTre |
| | - 'Laurie Bray' | CGre |
| § | - 'Lavinia Maggi' ♀ | CDoC CGre CTrG CTre CTrh ELan IOrc LHyd MAsh MBri MGos SBod SBrw SCog SPer SReu SRms SSta SStn |
| | - 'Lavinia Maggi Rosea' | SCog SStn |
| | - 'L'Avvenire' | Last listed 1997 |
| § | - 'Le Lys' | SStn |
| | - 'Lemon Drop' | CTrh |
| | - 'Lily Pons' | CTrh |
| | - 'Lipstick' | CTrh |
| | - 'Little Bit' | CB&S CDoC CTrh SSta |
| | - 'Little Bo Peep' | CTrh |
| | - 'Little Red Riding Hood' | CB&S |
| | - 'Little Slam' | CB&S |
| | - 'Look-away' | Last listed 1997 |
| I | - 'Lotus' | See *C. japonica* 'Gauntlettii' |
| | - Lotus | See *C. japonica* 'Gauntlettii' |
| | - 'Lovelight' | CTrh SCog |
| | - 'Lucy Hester' | CTre MBal |
| | - 'Lulu Belle' | SCog |
| | - 'Ma Belle' | SCog |
| ¶ | - 'Mabel Blackwell' | SStn |
| | - 'Madame Charles Blard' | Last listed 1998 |
| ¶ | - 'Madame de Cannart d'Hamale' | SStn |
| | - 'Madame de Strekaloff' | CMac SStn |
| | - 'Madame Lebois' | CB&S SStn |
| | - 'Madame Lourmand' | Last listed 1998 |
| | - 'Madame Martin Cachet' | SCog |
| | - 'Madge Miller' | CTre ELan |
| | - 'Magic City' | Last listed 1997 |
| | - 'Magnoliiflora' | See *C. japonica* 'Hagoromo' |
| | - 'Magnoliiflora Alba' | See *C. japonica* 'Miyakodori' |
| | - 'Maiden's Blush' | CMac SCog |
| ¶ | - 'Man Size' | CDoC ECle |
| | - 'Margaret Davis' | CDoC ECle SStn |
| | - 'Margaret Davis Picotee' | CB&S CGre CMHG CTrh CTrw MGos SCog SSta WBcn |
| ¶ | - 'Margaret Rose' | SStn |
| ¶ | - 'Margaret Short' | MAsh |
| | - 'Margarete Hertrich' | Last listed 1997 |
| | - 'Margherita Coleoni' | CB&S SBod SBrw SStn WBcn WBod |
| | - 'Marguérite Gouillon' | ISea SStn |
| ¶ | - 'Marian Mitchell' | SStn |
| | - 'Mariana' | CTrh SSta |
| | - 'Marie Bracey' | CB&S SStn |
| | - 'Marinka' | CB&S |
| | - 'Mariottii Rubra' | Last listed 1997 |
| | - 'Marjorie Magnificent' | CDoC LRHS MAsh |
| | - 'Mark Alan' | CTrh |
| | - 'Maroon and Gold' | CDoC WBcn |
| | - 'Mars' ♀ | CB&S CDoC CTre MWat SBrw SLdr SStn |
| | - 'Martha Brice' | Last listed 1996 |
| | - 'Mary Costa' | CB&S CGre CTrh |
| | - 'Mary J. Wheeler' | CTrw |
| § | - 'Masayoshi' ♀ | CDoC CMac IOrc LHyd LNet SStn |
| ¶ | - 'Masquerade' | SStn |
| ¶ | - 'Masterpiece' | SStn |
| § | - 'Mathotiana' | CTrw MBal |
| | - 'Mathotiana Alba' ♀ | CB&S CDoC CMac MBal SBid SPer SReu SSta SStn |
| | - 'Mathotiana Purple King' | See *C. japonica* 'Julia Drayton' |
| § | - 'Mathotiana Rosea' | CB&S CMac CTre LNet SBod SBrw SPer SStn WBod |
| | - 'Mathotiana Supreme' | CDoC SStn |
| | - 'Matterhorn' | CTrh WBcn |
| | - 'Mattie Cole' | CDoC CGre CTre SStn |
| | - 'Mattie O'Reilly' | CTre |
| | - 'Melody Lane' | Last listed 1997 |
| | - 'Mercury' ♀ | CB&S CDoC CMac COtt GGGa MWat SPer WBod |
| | - 'Mercury Variegated' | CMHG |
| | - 'Midnight' | CB&S CDoC CGre CMHG MAsh SCog SStn |
| | - 'Midnight Magic' | Last listed 1998 |
| | - 'Midnight Serenade' | CDoC CTrh MAsh SStn |
| | - 'Midsummer's Day' | CB&S |
| § | - 'Mikenjaku' | ENot LNet SBrw SStn WBod |
| ¶ | - 'Minnie Maddern Fiske' | SStn |
| | - 'Miss Charleston' ♀ | CB&S SStn |
| ¶ | - 'Miss Lyla' | SStn |
| | - 'Miss Universe' | CGre CTrh |
| | - 'Mississippi Beauty' | CTrh |
| § | - 'Miyakodori' | EPfP |
| | - 'Momiji-gari' | Last listed 1997 |
| ¶ | - 'Mona Lisa' | SStn |
| | - 'Monsieur Faucillon' | CB&S |
| | - 'Monstruosa Rubra' | See *C. japonica* 'Gigantea Red' |
| | - 'Monte Carlo' | CDoC |
| | - 'Moonlight Bay' | Last listed 1997 |
| | - 'Moonlight Sonata' | Last listed 1996 |
| | - 'Morning Glow' | WBod |
| | - 'Moshe Dayan' | EBee |
| § | - 'Mrs Bertha A. Harms' | CGre |
| | - 'Mrs D.W. Davis' ♀ | CB&S CGre CTrw SStn |
| ¶ | - 'Mrs Tingley' | SStn |
| I | - 'Mutabilis' | WBcn |
| | - 'Nagasaki' | See *C. japonica* 'Mikenjaku' |
| | - 'Nigra' | See *C. japonica* 'Konronkoku' |

- 'Nobilissima'  CB&S CDoC CMac CTre CTrh CTri ENot ISea MAsh MWat SBid SBod SBrw SCog SPer SSta SStn WBcn WBod WWeb
- 'Nuccio's Cameo'  CDoC CTrh
- 'Nuccio's Gem' ♀  CDoC ELan LHyd SCog SSta SStn
- 'Nuccio's Jewel' ♀  CB&S CDoC COtt CTre CTrh MGos SCog SPer WBcn
- 'Nuccio's Pearl'  CB&S SCog WBcn
§ - 'Odoratissima'  CTrG WBod
- 'Onetia Holland'  CB&S CDoC CTre CTrw SLdr
§ - 'O-niji'  MBal
¶ - 'Onore Del Monte'  WBod
- 'Optima Rosea'  CB&S ENot
§ - 'Otome'  SBrw WBod
- 'Painted Lady'  Last listed 1997
- 'Paolina'  Last listed 1997
- 'Paolina Maggi'  CDoC ECle SCog SStn
- 'Patricia Ann'  CTrh
¶ - 'Paulette Goddard'  SStn
- 'Pauline Winchester'  Last listed 1997
- 'Paul's Apollo'  See *C. japonica* 'Apollo'
- 'Peachblossom'  See *C. japonica* 'Fleur Dipater'
¶ - 'Pearl Harbor'  SStn
- 'Pensacola Red'  Last listed 1998
- 'Pink Champagne'  CTre SBod WBod
- 'Pink Clouds'  Last listed 1997
¶ - 'Pink Pagoda'  SStn
- 'Pink Perfection'  See *C. japonica* 'Otome'
- 'Pink Star'  WBod
- 'Pirate's Gold' (v)  Last listed 1997
- 'Platipetala'  Last listed 1996
- 'Pompone'  Last listed 1997
- 'Pope Pius IX'  See *C. japonica* 'Prince Eugène Napoléon'
- 'Powder Puff'  CTre
- 'Preston Rose'  CB&S CDoC CTre ISea MBal SStn WBcn
- 'Pride of Descanso'  See *C. japonica* 'Yukibotan'
- 'Primavera'  CTrh SStn
♦ - 'Prince Albert'  See *C. japonica* 'Albertii'
§ - 'Prince Eugène Napoléon'  SStn
¶ - 'Prince of Orange'  SStn
- 'Princess Baciocchi'  CB&S
- 'Princess du Mahe'  CMac
- 'Professor Sargent'  Last listed 19.97
- 'Purity'  See *C. japonica* 'Shiragiku'
- 'Purple Emperor'  See *C. japonica* 'Julia Drayton'
- 'R.L.Wheeler' ♀  CB&S CDoC CGre CTre CTrw MAsh MBal SCog WBod
- 'Rafia'  CDoC SLdr SSta
- 'Rainbow'  See *C. japonica* 'O-niji'
¶ - 'Red Cardinal'  SStn
- 'Red Dandy'  CDoC SStn
- 'Red Ensign'  Last listed 1997
¶ - 'Reg Ragland'  CDoC SStn
♦ - 'Reigyoku'  See *C. rusticana* 'Reigyoku'
¶ - 'Robert Strauss'  SStn
- 'Roger Hall'  SCog
- 'Rôgetsu'  CB&S CGre SStn WBod
- 'Roman Soldier'  CB&S
- 'Rose Dawn'  WBod
¶ - 'Roza Harrison'  LHyd
♦ - 'Rubescens Major' ♀  CB&S CGre ISea LHyd SStn
- 'Ruddigore'  CTrh
- 'Sabrina'  Last listed 1997
¶ - 'Saint André'  CMac WLRN
¶ - 'Sally Harrell'  SStn
- 'San Dimas'  CDoC CTrh SLdr WBcn
- 'Sarah Frost'  Last listed 1996
- 'Saturnia'  CDoC COtt MAsh
¶ - 'Sawada's Dream'  SStn

- 'Scented Red'  CDoC WWat
- 'Scentsation' ♀  CMHG COtt CTre SCog
- 'Sea Foam'  Last listed 1996
- 'Sea Gull'  CTrh SStn
- 'Seiji'  CMac
- 'Serenade'  CMHG MAsh
- 'Shin-akebono'  See *C. japonica* 'Akebono'
¶ - 'Shiro Chan'  SStn
- 'Shirobotan'  EPfP GQui SCog SPla WBod
♦ - 'Shiro-daikagura'  See *C. rusticana* 'Shiro-daikagura'
- 'Sierra Spring'  Last listed 1997
- 'Silver Anniversary'  CB&S CMHG CTrh ELan GQui MAsh MGos SBod SCog SLdr SReu SSta SStn
- 'Silver Ruffles'  SStn
¶ - 'Silver Triumph'  SStn
- 'Silver Waves'  Last listed 1997
¶ - 'Simeon'  CDoC
- 'Snow Goose'  Last listed 1997
- 'Snowflake'  WBod
¶ - 'Snowman'  SStn
- 'Souvenir de Bahuaud-Litou' ♀  CB&S CGre CTre SBid SCog SStn WBod WWat
- 'Spencer's Pink'  CB&S CTre CTrw LRHS SStn
¶ - 'Spring Fever'  SStn
- 'Spring Formal'  Last listed 1998
- 'Spring Sonnet'  Last listed 1997
¶ - 'Strawberry Blonde'  CDoC
- 'Strawberry Swirl'  Last listed 1997
- 'Sweet Delight'  Last listed 1996
¶ - 'Sweetheart'  CDoC
¶ - 'Sylva'  CPin SStn
- 'Sylvia'  CMac LRHS WBod
¶ - 'Takayama'  SStn
- 'Tammia'  CB&S COtt
¶ - 'Tarô'an'  CDoC
¶ - 'Temple Incense'  CB&S
¶ - 'Teresa Ragland'  SStn
- 'Teringa'  CDoC CTre
§ - 'The Czar'  CB&S CTre CTrw ISea
- 'The Mikado'  CDoC CGre CTre SCog
- 'The Pilgrim'  Last listed 1997
- 'Thomas Cornelius Cole'  CTre
¶ - 'Tick Tock Blush'  CDoC
¶ - 'Tickled Pink'  CDoC
- 'Tiffany'  CB&S CDoC CTre LHyd LNet SSta SStn
- 'Tinker Bell'  CB&S CGre
- 'Tinker Toy'  CTrh
- 'Tom Thumb'  CMHG CTrh SRms SStn
- 'Tomorrow'  CB&S CDoC CTre CTrw EBee MAsh WBod
- 'Tomorrow Park Hill'  SStn
§ - 'Tomorrow Variegated'  CDoC
- 'Tomorrow's Dawn'  CB&S SStn
¶ - 'Touchdown'  SStn
- 'Tregye'  CB&S
- 'Trewithen White'  CSam
§ - 'Tricolor' ♀  CB&S CDoC CGre CMHG CMac CTrh ENot IOrc MAsh SBrw SCog SPer SStn WGwG
- 'Tricolor Red'  See *C. japonica* 'Lady de Saumarez'
- 'Tricolor Superba'  Last listed 1997
¶ - 'Twilight'  SStn
- 'Valtevareda'  CGre WBod
- 'Victor de Bisschop'  See *C. japonica* 'Le Lÿs'
- 'Victor Emmanuel'  See *C. japonica* 'Blood of China'
- 'Ville de Nantes'  CB&S CDoC SSta WBcn
¶ - 'Ville de Nantes Red'  SStn
- 'Virginia Carlyon'  CB&S CDoC CTre
- 'Virginia Robinson'  SStn

¶ - 'Virgin's Blush'  SStn
- 'Vittorio Emanuele II'  CTrh
- 'Warrior'  CDoC COtt CTre SStn
¶ - 'White Giant'  CDoC
- 'White Nun'  SCog SStn
- 'White Swan'  CB&S CMac COtt CTre MAsh SStn
- 'White Tulip'  CGre
- 'Wilamina'  CTrh
- 'Wildfire'  SStn
- 'William Bartlett'  CTrh
- 'William Honey'  CTrh
- 'Woodville Red'  Last listed 1997
- 'Yoibijin'  See C. japonica 'Suibijin'
§ - 'Yours Truly'  CB&S CMac CTre CTrh LHyd SBod SCog WBcn
§ - 'Yukibotan'  Last listed 1997
- 'Yukimi-guruma'  WBod
§ - 'Yukishiro'  CTrw
- 'Zoraide Vanzi'  WBod
  'Jury's Charity'  See C. × williamsii 'Charity'
♦ 'Jury's Yellow'  See C. × williamsii 'Jury's Yellow'
  kissi  CGre CTrh
♦ 'Kôgyoku'  See C. sasanqua 'Kôgyoku'
  'Lasca Beauty' (reticulata × japonica) ♀  Last listed 1997
♦ 'Lavender Queen'  See C. sasanqua 'Lavender Queen'
  'Leonard Messel' (reticulata × williamsii) ♀  CB&S CDoC CGre CMHG CTre CTrh ENot GGGa LHyd MBal MGos SBod SBrw SCog SMad SPer SReu SStn WBod WCwm WStI
  'Lila Naff' (reticulata hybrid)  CTre
  lutchuensis  CTrh
  'Madame Victor de Bisschop'  See C. japonica 'Le Lys'
  'Magnolia Queen'  See C. japonica 'Priscilla Brooks'
§ maliflora (d)  CB&S
  'Mandalay Queen' (reticulata hybrid) ♀  Last listed 1994
* 'Marjorie Miller'  Last listed 1996
¶ 'Night Rider' (hybrid)  CDoC
  'Nijinski' (reticulata hybrid) CDoC ISea
§ nitidissima var. nitidissima  Last listed 1997
  oleifera  CSam CTre CTrh SCog SStn WWat
  'Pink Spangles'  See C. japonica 'Mathotiana Rosea'
  'Polar Ice' (oleifera hybrid)  CDoC SCog
  'Portuense'  See C. japonica 'Japonica Variegata'
  'Quintessence' (japonica × lutchuensis)  SCog
  reticulata  CGre CTre
¶ - 'Arch of Triumph' ♀  CTrG
- 'Brilliant Butterfly'  Last listed 1996
- 'Captain Rawes' ♀  CB&S CMac CTre
- 'Flore Pleno'  See C. reticulata 'Songzilin'
¶ - 'Mary Williams'  CB&S
- 'Ming Temple'  CTre
- 'Nuccio's Ruby'  Last listed 1997
- 'William Hertrich'  CB&S CGre CTre
  'Robert Fortune'  See C. reticulata 'Songzilin'
  rosiflora  CTre
  'Royalty' (japonica × reticulata)  CB&S CTrG CTre
§ rusticana 'Arajishi'  CB&S CDoC CMac COtt CTre SCoo SStn WBod WLRN WWal
§ - 'Kinsekai' (v)  SStn
§ - 'Reigyoku' (v)  SStn
§ - 'Shiro-daikagura'  WBod

- 'Salonica'  See C. × williamsii 'Shimna'
  saluenensis  CGre CTre CTrh WBod
- 'Apple Blossom'  See C. 'Shôwa-wabisuke' (Wabisuke)
- 'Baronesa de Soutelinho'  Last listed 1997
- 'Exbury Trumpet'  CTre
- × japonica  See C. × williamsii
- 'Trewithen Red'  CTrw
- 'William's Lavender'  WBod
  'Salutation' (saluenensis × reticulata)  CB&S CDoC CGre CSam CTre ISea SStn
  sasanqua  CSam ISea
I - 'Alba'  SCog
I - 'Apple Blossom'  Last listed 1998
- 'Ben'  Last listed 1998
- 'Bert Jones'  Last listed 1996
- 'Bettie Patricia'  SCog
¶ - 'Cotton Candy'  CDoC
- 'Crimson King' ♀  CGre GQui MBal SBod SCog WBod
♦ - 'Dazzler'  See C. hiemalis 'Dazzler'
- 'Flamingo'  See C. sasanqua 'Fukuzutsumi'
- 'Flore Pleno'  See C. maliflora
- 'Fragrans'  Last listed 1996
- 'Fuji-no-mine'  CTrh
§ - 'Fukuzutsumi'  CB&S CBrm CDoC COtt LHyd SBod SBrw SCog SStn WCwm
- 'Gay Sue'  CTrh
- 'Hugh Evans'  CB&S CDoC COtt CTre CTrh LHyd SBrw SCog SSta SStn
- 'Jean May'  CB&S CDoC COtt CTre SBod SCog SSta SStn
- 'Kenkyô'  SCog SSta SStn
§ - 'Kôgyoku'  SStn
§ - 'Lavender Queen'  SStn
- 'Little Liane'  SCog
- 'Little Pearl'  CTrh
- 'Lucinda'  SCog
- 'Mignonne'  CTrh
- 'Mine-no-yuki'  SCog
- 'Momozono-nishiki'  Last listed 1996
- 'Narumigata' ♀  CB&S CDoC CMac COtt CTrw EBee LHyd MAsh MBal MBlu SBod SCog SLdr SSta SStn WBod WCwm WSHC
- 'Navajo'  CTrh
- 'Nodami-ushiro'  CTrh
- 'Nyewoods'  CMac
¶ - 'Papaver'  SStn
- 'Paradise Blush'  SCog
- 'Paradise Glow'  SCog
- 'Paradise Hilda'  SCog
- 'Paradise Pearl'  SCog
- 'Paradise Petite'  SCog
- 'Paradise Venessa'  SCog
- 'Peach Blossom'  CB&S
- 'Plantation Pink'  ECle SBrw SCog SPer
- 'Rainbow'  CTrh ISea SCog SSta SStn
- 'Rosea'  SSta SStn
§ - 'Rosea Plena'  CB&S CMac CTre CTrw
- 'Sasanqua Rubra'  CMac
- 'Sasanqua Variegata'  SSta SStn WWat
¶ - 'Setsugekka'  SStn
- 'Shishigashira'  CTrh
- 'Snowflake'  SSta SStn
- 'Tanya'  CTrh
  'Satan's Robe' (reticulata hybrid)  CDoC CTre
  'Scentuous' (japonica × lutchuensis)  CTrh SCog WBcn
  'Show Girl' (sasanqua × reticulata)  CDoC CTre CTrh SBod SCog WBod

§ *sinensis* — CGre CTre GPoy
'Snow Flurry' (*oleifera* hybrid) — CDoC SCog
'Splendens' — See *C. japonica* 'Coccinea'
'Spring Festival' (*cuspidata* hybrid) ♀ — CDoC CHig CMHG CTrh MGos SPer
'Spring Mist' (*japonica* x *lutchuensis*) — CMHG CTrh
'Stella Polare' — See *C. japonica* 'Etoile Polaire'
¶ 'Strawberry Parfait' — ECle
'Swan Lake' (hybrid) — SCog
*taliensis* — CB&S CGre CTre
¶ 'Tarōkaja' (Wabisuke) — SStn
*thea* — See *C. sinensis*
'Tinsie' — See *C. japonica* 'Bokuhan'
'Tôkô' — See *C. sasanqua* 'Azuma-beni'
'Tom Knudsen' (*reticulata* x *japonica*) — CTre CTrh EPfP SBrw
'Tomorrow Supreme' — See *C. japonica* 'Tomorrow Variegated'
*transnokoensis* — CTre CTrh
'Tricolor Sieboldii' — See *C. japonica* 'Tricolor'
'Tristrem Carlyon' (*reticulata* hybrid) ♀ — CB&S CDoC CTrG CTre LRHS WBod
*tsai* ♀ — CGre CTrh
'Usu-ôtome' — See *C. japonica* 'Otome'
'Valley Knudsen' (*saluenensis* x *reticulata*) — Last listed 1997
*vernalis* 'Hiryû' — SCog SStn
- 'Kyô-nishiki' — SCog
- 'Yuletide' — SCog
'Waterloo' — See *C. japonica* 'Etherington White'
§ x *williamsii* — CGre
- 'Anemone Frill' — Last listed 1998
- 'Anticipation' ♀ — CB&S CDoC CGre CMHG CSam CTre CTrh CTrw EBee ENot EPfP GGGa GOrc IOrc ISea LHyd MAsh MBri MGos SBod SBrw SCog SPer SSpi WBcn
- 'Anticipation Variegated' — SCog
- 'Ballet Queen' — CB&S CDoC MGos
- 'Ballet Queen Variegated' — CDoC SCog SSta
- 'Bartley Number Five' — CMac
- 'Beatrice Michael' — CB&S CMac CTre SStn
- 'Bow Bells' — CDoC CGre CMac CTre CTrh LHyd SCog WWat
- 'Bowen Bryant' ♀ — CGre CTre CTrh CTrw GGGa SCog
- 'Bridal Gown' — Last listed 1997
- 'Brigadoon' ♀ — CDoC CMHG CTre CTrh CTri CTrw EPfP GGGa IOrc LHyd MAsh MBal MBri MGos SCog WBod WWal
- 'Burncoose' — CB&S
- 'Burncoose Apple Blossom' — CB&S
- 'C.F. Coates' — CTre MNes SSta
- 'Caerhays' — CB&S CTre
¶ - 'Carnation' — MAsh
- 'Carolyn Williams' — CB&S
- 'Celebration' — CB&S
§ - 'Charity' — Last listed 1998
¶ - 'Charlean' — SStn
- 'Charles Colbert' — CTrh
- 'Charles Michael' — CB&S CGre SStn
¶ - 'Charles Puddle' — WBod
- 'China Clay' ♀ — CB&S CDoC CSam CTrG CTre LHyd SBod SCog WWal
§ - 'Citation' — CB&S CGre CMac CTrw WBod
- 'Clarrie Fawcett' — CDoC CTre

- 'Contribution' — CTrh
- 'Crinkles' — CGre
- 'Daintiness' ♀ — CB&S CDoC CTre CTrh SCog SPer SStn
- 'Dark Nite' — CMHG CPin
- 'Debbie' ♀ — More than 30 suppliers
- 'Debbie's Carnation' — Last listed 1998
- 'Donation' ♀ — More than 30 suppliers
- 'Dream Boat' — CB&S
¶ - 'Dresden China' — CDoC
- 'E.G. Waterhouse' — CB&S CDoC CGre CMHG CTrh CTri CTrw EPfP GChr MAsh MBal SBod SCog SSta SStn WBcn WBod WCwm WWeb
- 'E.T.R. Carlyon' ♀ — CB&S CDoC CTre EPfP MBal
§ - 'Elegant Beauty' — CB&S CGre CTrG CTre CTrh CTrw MBal SBod SBrw SCog SPer WCwm WGwG
- 'Elizabeth Anderson' — CTrh
¶ - 'Elizabeth de Rothschild' — SStn
- 'Ellamine' — CB&S
- 'Elsie Jury' ♀ — CB&S CDoC CGre CMac CSam CTrw GQui IOrc LHyd MBal MGos SBod SCog SPer SStn WBcn WGwG WWal
- 'Empire Rose' — Last listed 1997
- 'Exaltation' — CB&S
- 'Francis Hanger' — CB&S CDoC CSam CTre CTrh CTrw IOrc LHyd MBal SBod SCog SSpi SStn WGwG WWal
¶ - 'Free Style' — SStn
- 'Galaxie' ♀ — CB&S CTrh EPfP ISea
- 'Garden Glory' — CTre CTrh
- 'Gay Time' — CTre
- 'George Blandford' ♀ — CB&S CMHG CMac CTre
- 'Glenn's Orbit' ♀ — CB&S CDoC CGre CTre CTrw WBcn
- 'Golden Spangles' (v) — CB&S CDoC CGre CMac CTrG CTre CTrh ELan GOrc IOrc LHyd MBal MBri MGos MNes SPer SReu SSta SStn WBcn
- 'Grand Jury' — CB&S CTre MGos SStn
- 'Gwavas' — CB&S CDoC CTre MAsh
- 'Hilo' — CTrw
- 'Hiraethlyn' ♀ — CB&S CTre LHyd SStn WBod
- 'Hope' — CTrh
- 'J.C. Williams' ♀ — CB&S CGre CMac CSam CTre CTrw ENot IOrc ISea LHyd MBal SBod SCog SPer SSpi SStn WCwm
¶ - 'Jean Claris' — CDoC
- 'Jenefer Carlyon' ♀ — CB&S CTre LRHS
- 'Jill Totty' — CTrh
- 'Joan Trehane' ♀ — CTrw
- 'Joyful Bells' — Last listed 1997
- 'Jubilation' — Last listed 1998
- 'Julia Hamiter' ♀ — CB&S CGre CTrw SStn
§ - 'Jury's Yellow' — CB&S CTrh CTrw ECle ELan EPfP GOrc GQui IOrc LHyd MAsh MBri MGos SBod SCog SPer SSta SStn WBcn WWat
- 'Laura Boscawen' — CTrG CTrh
- 'Les Jury' — SCog
- 'Margaret Waterhouse' — COtt CTre
- 'Mary Christian' ♀ — CB&S COtt CTre EPfP LBuc LHyd SStn WBod
- 'Mary Jobson' — CB&S CDoC CTre SStn WWat
- 'Mary Larcom' — CPin CTre
- 'Mary Phoebe Taylor' — CB&S CDoC CTre CTrh CTrw SBod SCog WBod
- 'Mildred Veitch' — CGre CTre
- 'Mirage' — CTrh SStn
- 'Mona Jury' — Last listed 1998

| | |
|---|---|
| - 'Monica Dance' | CB&S |
| - 'Muskoka' ♀ | CB&S CTrh ISea SStn WCwm |
| - 'New Venture' | CB&S |
| - 'November Pink' | CB&S CTre EHol |
| - 'Opal Princess' | SCog |
| - 'Parkside' | CTre |
| - 'Phillippa Forward' | CB&S CMac |
| ¶ - 'Red Dahlia' | SStn |
| - 'Rendezvous' | CDoC SLdr |
| - 'Rose Court' | WBod |
| - 'Rose Holland' | Last listed 1996 |
| - 'Rose Parade' ♀ | CTrh MAsh |
| - 'Rose Quartz' | Last listed 1998 |
| - 'Rosemary Williams' | CB&S CTre CTrw |
| - 'Ruby Bells' | CMHG |
| - 'Ruby Wedding' | CTrh GQui SCog |
| - 'Saint Ewe' ♀ | CB&S CDoC CGre CTrG CTre |
| | CTrh CTri CTrw MBal MBri MGos |
| | SBod SBrw SCog SPer SStn WBod |
| - 'Saint Michael' ♀ | CB&S |
| - 'Sayonara' | CTre CTrh SCog |
| - 'Senorita' | CTrh LHyd |
| - 'Taylor's Perfection' | CTrw |
| - 'The Duchess of | CTre |
| Cornwall' | |
| - 'Tiptoe' ♀ | CTrh SStn |
| - 'Tregrehan' | COtt |
| ¶ - 'Twinkle Star' | CDoC |
| - 'Water Lily' ♀ | CB&S CDoC CTre CTrh CTrw |
| | EPfP MGos SStn WBcn |
| - 'Wilber Foss' | CB&S CDoC CGre CTre CTrh |
| | CTrw SStn |
| - 'William Carlyon' | CB&S CTre MBal |
| - 'Wood Nymph' | CTre ISea MBal |
| - 'Yesterday' | CTre MAsh SMur |
| ¶ - 'Winter's Fire' (hybrid) | CDoC |
| 'Winter's Interlude' | SCog |
| (oleifera x sinensis) | |
| ¶ - 'Winter's Toughie' | |
| (C. ?oleifera x sasanqua) | CDoC SCog |
| 'Winton' (cuspidata | CB&S CDoC SStn WWat |
| x saluenensis) | |
| 'Yukihaki' | See C. japonica 'Yukishiro' |

## CAMISSONIA See OENOTHERA

## CAMPANULA ✿ (Campanulaceae)

| | |
|---|---|
| adsurgens | Last listed 1997 |
| aizoides | Last listed 1997 |
| alaskana | See C. rotundifolia var. alaskana |
| § alliariifolia | More than 30 suppliers |
| - 'Ivory Bells' | See C. alliariifolia |
| allionii | See C. alpestris |
| § alpestris | GTou NMen SIgm |
| - 'Grandiflora' | Last listed 1998 |
| - JCA 250500 | SBla |
| - 'Rosea' | MTPN |
| alpina | GAbr WLin |
| - var. bucegiensis | Last listed 1996 |
| - subsp. orbelica | See C. orbelica |
| americana | Last listed 1997 |
| anchusiflora | NWCA |
| andrewsii | Last listed 1997 |
| - subsp. andrewsii | Last listed 1997 |
| - subsp. birsutula | Last listed 1996 |
| ¶ argaea | NBur |
| argyrotricha | Last listed 1998 |
| - CC&McK 477 | NTow |
| arvatica ♀ | CLyd EPot GCHN LBee MRPP |
| | NHar NNrd NRya NTow SIng |
| | SSmi WLin WPat |

| | |
|---|---|
| - 'Alba' | CGra CLyd EPot LBee NTow |
| | WAbe WLin WPat |
| - x cochleariifolia | WBea |
| atlantis | Last listed 1997 |
| aucheri | EBur GAbr NBur |
| autraniana | Last listed 1997 |
| 'Avalon' | SAsh |
| § 'Balchiniana' (v) | WEas |
| barbata | CSam EBee ELan GAbr GCHN |
| | GDra GTou LHop MSte NWCA |
| | SUsu WAbe WCla WMoo WPer |
| - var. alba | EBee ELan GAbr |
| ¶ baumgartenii | EBee |
| bellidifolia | NBir |
| bertolae | Last listed 1997 |
| § betulifolia ♀ | CGra CSam ECtt EHyt EMon |
| | GCHN GDra MBro NHar NHol |
| | NLon NMGW NNrd NTow WHoo |
| | WLin WPat |
| - JCA 252.005 | SBla |
| - x troegerae | Last listed 1997 |
| biebersteiniana | Last listed 1997 |
| 'Birch Hybrid' ♀ | CMHG ELan EMNN ESis GCHN |
| | GDra LBee MBal MBro NBur NHar |
| | NRoo SCro SIng WCom WFar |
| | WPyg |
| § bluemelii | Last listed 1998 |
| bononiensis | EBee EHal EMon NBrk SRms |
| | WOld |
| ¶ bornmuelleri | EHyt |
| 'Bumblebee' | CGra |
| 'Burghaltii' ♀ | More than 30 suppliers |
| § buseri | Last listed 1997 |
| caespitosa | See C. cespitosa |
| calaminthifolia | CGra EBur WAbe |
| § carnica | MSte |
| carpatha | MRPP SBla |
| carpatica ♀ | CGle EWTr GAri GDra MBar MBri |
| | NBro NChi NLon SIng SRms SWat |
| | WMoo WWin |
| - f. alba | CGle EWTr LPVe MBro NFor SIng |
| | SWat |
| - - 'Bressingham White' | CBlo EBrP EBre GAri GCHN GDra |
| | LBre SBla SBre WHoo |
| - - 'Snowdrift' | Last listed 1998 |
| § - - 'Weisse Clips' | CPri EBee ECtt ELan EMNN EPar |
| | ERav ESis GTou LHop MPla NFla |
| | NMen NRoo NVic SPer SPla SRPl |
| | SRms WFar WPer |
| § - 'Blaue Clips' | EBee ECtt ELan EMNN EPar ESis |
| | GTou MBNS MPla NFla NMen |
| | NRoo NVic SPer SPla SRms WFar |
| | WGwG WPer |
| ¶ - blue | SPlb |
| ¶ - 'Blue and White Uniform' | WElm |
| - Blue Clips | See C. carpatica 'Blaue Clips' |
| - 'Blue Moonlight' | EBrP EBre EBur LBre NRoo SBre |
| | SMer |
| - 'Caerulea' | CB&S |
| - 'Chewton Joy' | CLyd EBrP EBre EPPr GAri GCHN |
| | LBre MBro NRoo SBre WLin |
| - 'Ditton Blue' | GDra |
| - dwarf form | EPot |
| - 'Harvest Moon' | Last listed 1997 |
| - 'Karpatenkrone' | EBee |
| - 'Kathy' | GBuc SAsh |
| - 'Lavender' | Last listed 1997 |
| ¶ - 'Mattock's Double' (d) | WCot |
| ¶ - 'Maureen Haddon' | EBrP EBre GAri GCHN LBre NRoo |
| | NWCA SBre |
| ◆ - 'Molly Pinsent' | See C. 'Molly Pinsent' |
| - 'Mrs V. Frère' | Last listed 1997 |

¶ - 'Queen of Sheba' | NBur
- 'Queen of Somerville' | NBur NNrd NWoo
- 'Riverslea' | Last listed 1997
- 'Suzie' | EWes SBla
- var. *turbinata* | EBee GDra MTho NSla SRms WPer
- - f. *alba* | Last listed 1998
- - - 'Hannah' | EBrP EBre GCHN GDra LBre SBre
- - - 'Snowsprite' | Last listed 1997
§ - - 'Craven Bells' | Last listed 1997
- - 'Georg Arends' | CLyd SAsh
- - 'Isabel' | GCHN LRHS
- - 'Jewel' | LBee LRHS SIng SSmi
- - 'Karl Foerster' | CTri EBrP EBre GBuc GCHN LBre MTho NNrd NRoo SBre SMer WFar WHoo
- - 'Pallida' | GDra SSmi
- - 'Wheatley Violet' | CLyd GCHN LBee SBla WCom
- White Clips | See *C. carpatica* f. *alba* 'Weisse Clips'
§ *cashmeriana* | CGen EBur EHyt GCHN NTow NWCA
¶ *celsii* | NBur
- subsp. *carystea* | Last listed 1996
¶ *cenisia* | SIng
*cephallenica* | See *C. garganica* subsp. *cephallenica*
*cervicaria* | Last listed 1997
§ *cespitosa* | EHyt
§ *chamissonis* | EHyt GAbr GBuc NNrd NSla WPat
§ - 'Major' | CPBP EMNN EPot EWes MBro NMGW NOla
- 'Oyobeni' | MOne NHar SUsu WLin
§ - 'Superba' ♀ | EBur EGle ELan GDra IMGH MBal MTho NMen NSla NTow SAga SSmi
*chorubensis* | CGra EHyt
§ *cochleariifolia* ♀ | CLyd CPBP CSpe ELan EMNN ESis EWTr GCHN GTou MBal MBro MFir MTho MWat NHar NRoo SIng SSvw WAbe WCla WFar WHoo WPer WWhi WWin
- var. *alba* | CMea CSpe CVer EMNN EPot GCHN MBal MBro MWat NChi NHar NMen NNrd NRya SBla SRms SSmi WAbe WCla WHoo WPer
- - 'Bavaria White' | NHar
- - 'White Baby' | EPfP NPri SCob
- 'Bavaria Blue' | NHar
¶ - 'Blue Baby' (Baby Series) | SCob
- 'Blue Tit' | EPot GBuc
- 'Cambridge Blue' | EBrP EBre GCHN LBre NMen SBre SSmi WAbe
- 'Elizabeth Oliver' (d) | More than 30 suppliers
- 'Flore Pleno' (d) | ECtt NMen NNrd WRHF
- 'Miss Willmott' | CBrd EBur MTho NBir NTow
- 'Oakington Blue' | CTri MBro SRms
- var. *pallida* | SRms
- - 'Miranda' | WIvy
- - 'Silver Chimes' | MBro
¶ - 'R.B. Loder' (d) | SUsu
- - 'Temple Bells' | MBro
- - 'Tubby' | CInt CLyd CMea CPlt CRDP GCHN MTho SAga SRms
- 'Warleyensis' | See *C. x haylodgensis* 'Warley White'
*collina* | CTri GBri MBro NBur NHar NPri SIgm WHoo WPer WPyg
*colorata* | Last listed 1996
'Constellation' | MDHE NCat
*coriacea* JCA 253.800 | Last listed 1997

'Covadonga' | CLyd CMea CPBP MBro MDHE SIng
◆ 'Craven Bells' | See *C. carpatica* var. *turbinata* 'Craven Bells'
*crispa* JCA 253.901 | Last listed 1997
*dasyantha* | See *C. chamissonis*
*divaricata* | Last listed 1997
'E.K. Toogood' | CBre CElw CPBP EBee ECtt EMNN MAvo MDHE MWat NBro NFai NHar NHol NNrd SBla SCro SMac SRms WRHF
*elatines* | NNrd NOak
- var. *elatinoides* | WMoo
- - JCA 254.300 | Last listed 1998
§ 'Elizabeth' | More than 30 suppliers
*ephesia* | Last listed 1997
*erinus* | Last listed 1997
*eriocarpa* | See *C. latifolia* 'Eriocarpa'
*excisa* | LBee NPri
§ 'Faichem Lilac' | EBee MTis NChi NPro WCot WPer WSan
*fenestrellata* | MDHE MTho NBro SRms SSmi WAbe
- subsp. *fenestrellata* | Last listed 1997
§ - subsp. *istriaca* | Last listed 1997
*finitima* | See *C. betulifolia*
*foliosa* | WCot WPer
*formanekiana* ♀ | CHar CSam EBur MLLN NWCA WLin WSan
*fragilis* | CPBP EBur ELan WPer
- subsp. *cavolinii* | EHyt
- 'Hirsuta' | Last listed 1997
- x *isophylla* | Last listed 1996
'G.F. Wilson' ♀ | EBee EBur EGle MBal
*garganica* ♀ | ESis GAbr MBro MRav NFla NFor NHar NLon NMen NRoo WFar WMaN WMoo WPer
- 'Aurea' | See *C. garganica* 'Dickson's Gold'
- 'Blue Diamond' | ELan EMNN ESis LHop NBur SAga SCro SIng WAbe WLRN
§ - subsp. *cephallenica* | CLyd MDHE NBro NHol NNrd
§ - 'Dickson's Gold' | More than 30 suppliers
- 'Hirsuta' | SRms
◆ - subsp. *istriaca* | See *C. fenestrellata* subsp. *istriaca*
¶ - 'Major' | EWTr SRms
- 'W.H. Paine' ♀ | CInt CLyd EBrP EBre ECho LBre NSla SBre SIng WHoo
*gieseckiana* | Last listed 1997
§ 'Glandore' | NCat NMen
*glomerata* | CBot CKin GTou MBNS MBal MBrN MFir NBro NFai NLan NMir NRya SIgm SOkh SSoC WBea WByw WFar WGwG WMoo WOve WWin
- var. *acaulis* | CNic EBee EMNN EOld GCHN MBNS MBro NArg NOak NTow SEas SPla SSca WFar WHil WHoo WMoo WPer WPyg WWin
- var. *alba* | CB&S EBee ELan EMon GMaP LNor MBal MBri MBro MNrw MRav MUlv MWat NBro NFai SChu SPer SPla SSvw SWat WFar WHil WHoo WMaN WMoo WOve WPer
§ - - 'Alba Nana' | CLyd NPro
§ - - 'Schneekrone' | EBee ECha EFou EWTr MCli MGrG NBrk NFor NLon NOak NRoo WBea WFar
- - 'White Barn' | ECha NBrk NOak
- 'Caroline' | EBee EMil MGed MRav SCro SOkh SPer SSvw WCot WHal WHil

- Crown of Snow See *C. glomerata* var. *alba* 'Schneekrone'
- var. ***daburica*** CHan CTri EWTr MCLN MOne NLar NOak WBea WMoo WOut WPer
- 'Joan Elliott' EBee ECha GBuc MRav MWat NBrk SChu
♦ - 'Nana Alba' See *C. glomerata* var. *alba* 'Alba Nana'
- 'Purple Pixie' Last listed 1998
- 'Superba' ♀ More than 30 suppliers
***grossekii*** GBuc MNrw
***grossheimii*** Last listed 1996
***hagielia*** Last listed 1997
***hakkiarica*** Last listed 1996
'Hallii' CNic ESis MBro MPla NRoo NWCA WPat
***hawkinsiana*** CPBP
- JCA 256002 Last listed 1998
x ***haylodgensis*** sensu stricto hort. See *C.* x *haylodgensis* 'Plena'
§ - 'Marion Fisher' (d) MBro WHoo
§ - 'Plena' (d) CElw EBee ELan EPot ESis GMac LBee LHop MBal MBro NBro NHar NRoo SBla SIng SRms SSmi WAbe WEas WHoo WKif WPyg
§ - 'Warley White' (d) CNic EBur ELan EPot NNrd
- 'Yvonne' EDAr NNrd SIng WFar WLRN WPer
***hemschinica*** Last listed 1997
'Hemswell Starlight' CLyd NMen NPro
***hercegovina*** NTow
- 'Nana' CGra CPBP NNrd SBla WAbe
¶ ***herminii*** EHyt
***heterophylla*** Last listed 1997
***hierosolymitana*** Last listed 1997
¶ 'Hilltop Snow' CGra
***iconia*** Last listed 1997
§ ***incurva*** CGle CPou EBee EBur ELan GAbr GBin GBuc MAvo MMil MNrw MRPP MTho MTis NBrk NBro NFla NLak NOak WBea WByw WElm WPer WUnu
- *alba* WPer
- 'Blue Ice' LFis WWin
- JCA 256.800 Last listed 1998
x ***innesii*** See *C.* 'John Innes'
***isophylla*** ♀ MBri SIng SRms WEas
- 'Alba' ♀ SIng WEas
- 'Flore Pleno' (d) EBur
- 'Mayi' ♀ CSpe
♦ - 'Mayi' misapplied See *C.* 'Balchiniana'
- 'Variegata' See *C.* 'Balchiniana'
***jaubertiana*** CGra EHyt
'Joe Elliott' ♀ CPBP EWes SBla WCom
§ 'John Innes' CLyd MGed
***justiniana*** Last listed 1997
***kemulariae*** ESis GCHN MAvo WPer
- *alba* IDac MAvo
'Kent Belle' More than 30 suppliers
***kladniana*** Last listed 1997
***kolenatiana*** GCHN
***laciniata*** Last listed 1998
***lactiflora*** More than 30 suppliers
N - 'Alba' ♀ MAvo STes
- *alba* See *C. lactiflora* white
- 'Blue Avalanche' CBos EHal SMrm
- 'Blue Cross' COtt EFou GMac NLar NRoo WCot
- 'Loddon Anna' ♀ More than 30 suppliers

- 'Pouffe' CDoC EBee ECha EFou ELan GMac MBro MGrG MRav NBro NFla NGdn NRoo SCro SPer SPla SWat WHoo WPyg WRus WWin
- 'Prichard's Variety' ♀ More than 30 suppliers
¶ - 'Senior' EFou
¶ - 'Splash' MGrG
¶ - 'Superba' ♀ WCot
- 'Violet' EBee SWat WPer
§ - white CBot EBee ECha EFou MBro NBir NBrk SPer SPla WHoo WOld WOut WPer
- 'White Pouffe' CSpe EBee EBrP EBre EFou EHal ELan EOrc GAbr GMaP GMac LBre MBro MCAu MRav NLar SBre SMer SOkh SPer SPla SWat WByw WFar WHoo WPyg WRus
***lanata*** GAbr SSca WBea WUnu
***lasiocarpa*** CPBP EBur WFar
- 'Talkeetna' Last listed 1998
§ ***latifolia*** CAgr CArn CKin CSev EBee ECha EFou EWTr GAbr LEdu MCLN MWgw NChi NFla NFor NMir NOrc NTow NVic SPer WCer WCla WEas WFar WLin WMoo WWat
* - 'Amethyst' CFri
- 'Brantwood' CBos CGle CMil EBee EBrP EBre ECoo EMan EMar LBre MBel MFir MSte MWat NBrk NHol NOak NPro SBla SBre SChu SCro SMer SPer SSpe WCot WWin
§ - 'Eriocarpa' CHan MWrn NBur
- 'Gloaming' LRHS MBri WCot
¶ - 'Lavender' NBur
- var. ***macrantha*** EBrP EBre EFou EWTr GAbr GLil LBre LFis LHop MCli MNrw MSCN MSte NSti SBre SSvw WBea WCot WHoo WMoo WPer WRus WWat WWye
- - *alba* CBos CM&M CMil EBee ECtt EMan EPri LGre LHop MRav NHol SPla WCot WPer WPyg WWat
- 'Roger Wood' Last listed 1997
- white CGle CHan EBrP EBre ECha LBre MBro MCLN MRav MSte NTow SBre SPer SSpi WEas WHoo WRus NDov NRoo
- 'White Ladies' 
§ ***latiloba*** CBre CGle CMHG LGro MBro MFir MUlv NChi NWoo WByw WCot WEas WHoo WWin
- 'Alba' ♀ CBre CElw CGle CHar CVer EFou EHal ELan GAbr GCal GMac NChi WAbe WEas WLin WMaN
- 'Hidcote Amethyst' ♀ CElw CHad CHan CSpe EBee EFou ELan GAbr GCal GMac LGre MBel MBri MBro MGrG NBir SUsu WCot WEas WFar WHoo WKif WLin WMaN WOld
- 'Highcliffe Variety' ♀ CMGP EBee ECGN ECha EFou EMan EPfP LFis MBel MBri MCLN MRav NSti SChu SPla SSpe SSpi WCot WEas WKif WLRN WOld WRHF
* - 'Highdown' MLLN WFar
- 'Percy Piper' ♀ CHea CSam EBee EHal ELan GBri GMac MBri MCAu MNrw MRav MSCN NBrk NBro NFor NSti WByw WFar WHil WLin
- 'Splash' MAvo WCot
***lingulata*** EBee
***linifolia*** See *C. carnica*

*longestyla*                     Last listed 1997
'Lynchmere'                      EWes MBro NTow
*lyrata*                         Last listed 1997
*makaschvilii*                   Last listed 1998
*marchesettii*                   EBee
♦ 'Marion Fisher'               See *C.* x *haylodgensis* 'Marion
                                 Fisher'
§ *medium* 'Calycanthema' ♀      Last listed 1997
♦ - 'Cup and Saucer'            See *C. medium* 'Calycanthema'
*mirabilis*                      Last listed 1997
'Mist Maiden'                    CFee CLyd CMHG CPBP GAri
                                 NNrd NTow SIng WFar
*modesta*                        Last listed 1996
*moesiaca*                       EWTr SGre
*mollis*                         Last listed 1997
- var. *gibraltarica*            EHyt NTow
¶ *morettiana*                   NMen SIng
*muralis*                        See *C. portenschlagiana*
*myrtifolia*                     NWCA
¶ 'Mystery'                      EFou
*nitida*                         See *C. persicifolia* var. *planiflora*
- var. *planiflora*              See *C. persicifolia* var. *planiflora*
'Norman Grove'                   CLyd EGle EPot LBee
*oblongifolioides*               Last listed 1997
*ochroleuca*                     CBel CMea CRDP EAst EBee EFou
                                 EGar GAbr GCal MCLN NLak
                                 SCro SWat WBea WCot WHal
                                 WUnu
*olympica* Boissier              Last listed 1998
- hort.                          See *C. rotundifolia* 'Olympica'
§ *orbelica*                     Last listed 1997
*oreadum*                        Last listed 1997
*orphanidea*                     Last listed 1997
*ossetica*                       See *Symphyandra ossetica*
*pallida*                        Last listed 1997
- subsp. *tibetica*              See *C. cashmeriana*
¶ *parryi*                       IDac
♦ *parviflora* Lam.             See *C. sibirica*
*patula*                         CBrm GBin LSyl MHew NLar SGre
                                 WCla
- subsp. *abietina*              Last listed 1997
'Paul Furse'                     EPPr MTed NSti WHil WLin WWin
*pelviformis*                    MNrw
*peregrina*                      EBee
*persicifolia*                   More than 30 suppliers
- *alba*                         More than 30 suppliers
§ - 'Alba Coronata' (d)          CFir CMil CStr EBrP EBre EMon
                                 EPPr GBri LBre MBal MBro MCAu
                                 NBir NBrk NRoo SBre SPer WEas
                                 WFar WRus
- 'Alba Plena'                   See *C. persicifolia* 'Alba Coronata'
- 'Bennett's Blue' (d)           EBee EOrc LFis MTed MUlv
¶ - 'Best China'                 MAvo
- blue                           EMan EOrc MMal MRav NCut
                                 SPlb WEas WFar
- 'Blue Bell'                    CBlo
- 'Blue Bloomers' (d)            EBee EMon EWes GBri MAvo
                                 WCot WRHF
- blue cup-in-cup (d)            CMil WLin WRus
- 'Boule de Neige' (d)           CHea CHid CLon LFis NBrk
                                 NMGW NOak NRya WCot WEas
- 'Caerulea Coronata'            See *C. persicifolia* 'Coronata'
* - 'Caerulea Plena' (d)        ELan MBNS WEas
- 'Capel Ulo' (v)                WHer
- 'Carillon'                     GBri NBrk WCot
§ - 'Chettle Charm'              More than 30 suppliers
* - 'China Blue'                Last listed 1996
§ - 'Coronata' (d)               CHea EHal MDun MRav WShe
N - cup and saucer white (d)     CBlo CElw CLyd ELan MMHG
                                 NBrk WByw WHil WPer
- double blue (d)                CLon CSWP EOrc MBal MBel
                                 NBro NFai SUsu WByw WCot
                                 WEas WRHF WRus

- double powder blue (d)         Last listed 1998
- double white (d)               EBee ELan NChi SUsu WMoo
                                 WRus
- 'Eastgrove Blue'               NWes
- 'Fleur de Neige' (d) ♀         CGle CMea CPlt CSam MBel MBro
                                 MLLN NOak NRoo SWat WHoo
                                 WLin WPyg WRus
- 'Flore Pleno' (d)              NBir
- 'Frances' (d)                  CHar CLAP EBee EMon GBri
                                 MAvo MRav SWat WCot WLin
                                 WMaN
- 'Frank Lawley' (d)             EBrP EBre EFou LBre NRoo SBre
♦ - 'Gawen'                     See *C. persicifolia* 'Hampstead
                                 White'
- 'George Chiswell'              See *C. persicifolia* 'Chettle
                                 Charm'
- 'Grandiflora'                  Last listed 1996
- 'Grandiflora Alba'             GBuc SSca
¶ - 'Grandiflora Caerulea'       CMGP EBee NLar
§ - 'Hampstead White' (d)        CElw CGle CLon CMil ECha EEls
                                 EPar GBri GMac LFis LGre MBri
                                 MCAu MCLN MRav NBir NBro
                                 NRoo SChu SUsu WCot WEas
                                 WHer WHoo WLin WPen WRHF
                                 WWin
- 'Hetty'                        See *C. persicifolia* 'Hampstead
                                 White'
- Irish double white (d)         EMon WCot
- 'Moerheimii' (d)               EBee EOrc EPar MBel NBir NDov
                                 WHal WIvy WWin
- var. *nitida*                  See *C. persicifolia* var. *planiflora*
- 'Peach Bells'                  MBNS NOak
- 'Perry's Boy Blue'             NPer
♦ - 'Pike's Supremo'            See *C.* 'Pike's Supremo'
§ - var. *planiflora*            CPBP CSpe EBee GTou NHar
                                 NTow WAbe
§ - - f. *alba*                  WAbe WSan WWin
- 'Pride of Exmouth' (d)         CGle CHar CHea CPou CSam
                                 EBee ELan EMon GMac LHop
                                 LLWP MArl MBro MRav NFor
                                 NLon NOak NVic WCot WFar
                                 WHoo WLin
- subsp. *sessiliflora*          See *C. latiloba*
¶ - 'Snowdrift'                  EBee SRms
- 'Telham Beauty'                CDoC CHea CKel COtt EBee
                                 EFou ELan EPri EWTr LHop LRot
                                 MFir MRav SAga SMad SMer
                                 SMrm SPer SRCN SRms WBea
                                 WCot WMoo WPer WRus WWat
- 'Wedgwood'                     MBal
N - 'White Cup and Saucer'       NBrk NCat WFar WRus WWhi
    (d)
- 'White Queen' (d)              CMGP EFou NCat NFai WEas
- 'Wortham Belle' (d)            CGle CSev EBee EMan EPri ERic
                                 GBri GCal LFis LHop MAvo MBel
                                 MCAu MCLN MMil NCat NRoo
                                 NSti SChu SCoo SPer SSpi SWat
                                 WGle WHil WLRN WMoo WMow
                                 WRus WWal
*petraea*                        Last listed 1997
*petrophila*                     CLyd
§ 'Pike's Supremo' (d)           LHop NBir
*pilosa*                         See *C. chamissonis*
*piperi*                         CGra NWCA SBla
- 'Marmot Pass'                  Last listed 1998
- 'Townsend Ridge'               CGra
¶ - 'Townsend Violet'            CGra
*planiflora*                     See *C. persicifolia* var. *planiflora*
§ *portenschlagiana* ♀          CAgr CElw ELan ENot EPar GAbr
                                 LGro MHar MMal MWat NBro
                                 NHed NRoo NRya NVic SBla SDix
                                 SPer SRms SSmi WAbe WCot WEas
                                 WFar WMoo WPyg WWin

| | |
|---|---|
| - 'Lieselotte' | GBuc MDHE |
| - 'Major' | CMCo GMaP SRms WFar |
| - 'Resholdt's Variety' | CMea CSam EBee EBrP EBre EFou |
| | ELan EPla GCHN LBee LBre NCat |
| | SBre SUsu WLRN WPer |
| **poscharskyana** | More than 30 suppliers |
| - 'Blauranke' | EWes GAri GCHN MDHE NRoo |
| - 'Blue Gown' | GMaP WWeb |
| - 'E.H. Frost' | CBre ECtt EMNN EMou ESis EWTr |
| | LHop LNor MBro MPla MWat |
| | NBro NCat NHol NNrd NRya |
| | SCro SIng SRms SSmi WBea WFar |
| | WPer |
| - 'Glandore' | See *C.* 'Glandore' |
| - 'Lilacina' | EPPr NDov SCro SHel SIng WThi |
| - 'Lisduggan' | CBre CFri CGle EBrP EBre EBur |
| | ESis EWes GAbr GMaP LBre MBal |
| | MBro MWat NBro NCat NChi SBla |
| | SBre SRms SUsu WAbe WBea |
| | WCom WCot WFar WPer WPyg |
| | WWin |
| - 'Stella' ♀ | EBrP EBre ECha EMNN ENot EPPr |
| | ESis GCHN GChr LBre MAvo |
| | MRav NBro NCat NRoo NVic SBre |
| | SChu SDix SIng WCom WFar |
| | WPyg |
| - variegated | EHoe IBlr |
| ¶ - white | WFar |
| **primulifolia** | CFri CPou ECoo ELan GAbr GBuc |
| | LFis MBro MMil MNrw MTis |
| | MWrn NFai NFla SMac SPer SSca |
| | WPer WPrP WPyg WSan WWeb |
| | WWin |
| - 'Blue Spires' | EBee LRHS MBri NPro |
| ¶ - 'Priory' | CHan |
| x **pseudoraineri** | EBee EBur EHyt ELan EWes NMen |
| | NNrd SSmi |
| **pulla** | CLyd CPlt CRDP EBur EHyt ELan |
| | EMNN EPot ESis MBro MTho NFla |
| | NHar NMGW NMen SSmi WAbe |
| | WFar WPat WPer |
| - alba | CInt CPBP CPlt CRDP EBur EHyt |
| | ELan EMNN EPot LBee MBro |
| | NHar NHol NMGW NNrd WAbe |
| | WPat |
| x **pulloides** | CLyd EBrP EBre LBee LBre NMen |
| | SBre SSmi |
| **punctata** | CBot CMHG CMil CSpe EBee |
| | ECoo EFou GCHN LFis LPio MBel |
| | MBro MFir NBrk NBro NHar NSti |
| | SMac WCla WCot WEas WFar |
| | WLin WMoo WPer WWin |
| - f.*albiflora* | CHan LHop MBri MBro MLLN |
| | MOne NMen SCro SSvw SUsu |
| | WFar WWin |
| - - 'Nana Alba' | CLon CMil EBee EHyt GBin GCal |
| | GMac NCut WCot WMoo |
| I - 'Beetroot' | EMon |
| - var. **bondoensis** | CHar CPea EBee MBel MNrw |
| | NLar NSti SAga WBea WCot WLin |
| | WMoo WUnu |
| ¶ - - white | WUnu |
| - f.**impunctata** | Last listed 1997 |
| ¶ - 'Milly' | EMon |
| * - 'Nana' | Last listed 1997 |
| - 'Pallida' | Last listed 1997 |
| - 'Rosea' | CGle LPio MBri SRms WHil WSan |
| - f.**rubriflora** | More than 30 suppliers |
| ♦ - var. **takesimana** | See *C. takesimana* |
| - 'White Hose-in-hose' | SBla 6Far |
| - wine red form | CStr MAvo |
| * 'Purple Dwarf' | Last listed 1998 |

| | |
|---|---|
| **pusilla** | See *C. cochleariifolia* |
| **pyramidalis** | CBot CMGP CSpe EBee EPfP |
| | EWTr LIck NLak NOrc SSca |
| | WByw WPer |
| - alba | CM&M CMGP CSpe EBee EWTr |
| | LPio MCAu SIde SSca WPer |
| x **pyraversi** | Last listed 1997 |
| **raddeana** | CRDP GCHN MBro NBus NLar |
| | SCro SSmi WFar |
| **raineri** ♀ | CFee CPBP EPot MBro NMen |
| | NOak NTow NWCA SBla WPat |
| | WPyg |
| * - alba | Last listed 1997 |
| - 'Nettleton Gold' | EPot |
| **ramosissima** | Last listed 1997 |
| § **rapunculoides** | CAgr CArn CBrm CHan EBee |
| | EGoo GAbr LRot MCli MLLN NPri |
| | SMac SWat SWea WHer WOut |
| | WPer |
| - 'Alba' | CStr EMon MAvo |
| **rapunculus** | ILis LFis MGed |
| 'Rearsby Belle' | Last listed 1998 |
| **recurva** | See *C. incurva* |
| ¶ **reiseri** | EBee NBur |
| **retrorsa** | Last listed 1997 |
| **rhomboidalis** Gorter | See *C. rapunculoides* |
| **rigidipila** | Last listed 1997 |
| **rotundifolia** | CArn CKin CNic EWTr MHew |
| | NChi NMir NNrd NRoo NSti SIde |
| | SPlb SRms SSvw WBea WCla |
| | WElm WGwy WJek WOak WOve |
| | WPer |
| § - var. **alaskana** | NWCA |
| - var. **alba** | EBee MBro NChi WHoo WPyg |
| - 'Caerulea Plena' | See *C. rotundifolia* 'Flore Pleno' |
| § - 'Flore Pleno' (d) | Last listed 1996 |
| - forms | MBro |
| - 'Jotunheimen' | CGra EHyt |
| § - 'Olympica' | CInt EBee EBur EPfP GAbr GCHN |
| | LFis MBNS MHar NPri SEas WFar |
| - 'Superba' | SCro |
| **rupestris** | CBot CPBP EBur |
| **rupicola** | Last listed 1997 |
| - JCA 262.400 | SBla |
| **samarkandensis** | Last listed 1997 |
| 'Sarastro' | CLAP EBee EFou EMon LGre |
| | MAvo |
| **sarmatica** | CGle CHan CHea EBee ECoo |
| | GAbr GBuc LCot NFla NOak NSti |
| | SRCN SRms WMaN WPer |
| **sartorii** | CPBP EBur ELan WWin |
| **saxatilis** ♀ | Last listed 1997 |
| ¶ - subsp. **saxatilis** | NBur |
| **saxifraga** | EBur EHyt EPot GCHN SIgm |
| **scabrella** | NWCA |
| * **scardica** | Last listed 1997 |
| **scheuchzeri** | NNrd |
| **sclerotricha** | Last listed 1997 |
| **scouleri** | NWCA |
| **serrata** | Last listed 1997 |
| **shetleri** | CGra EHyt |
| § **sibirica** | LFis WPer |
| - subsp. **taurica** | Last listed 1997 |
| ¶ - white | NLar |
| ¶ **siegizmundii** | NBur |
| 'Southern Seedling' | Last listed 1997 |
| sp. ex Furze | Last listed 1996 |
| sp. from Iran | CElw EMon |
| sp. from Morocco | CGra |
| sp. JCA 6872 | Last listed 1997 |
| sp. JCA 8363 | Last listed 1997 |
| sp. JJH 918638 | Last listed 1997 |

| | |
|---|---|
| *sparsa* | Last listed 1997 |
| *spathulata* | Last listed 1997 |
| - subsp. *spathulata* | NNrd |
| - subsp. *spruneriana* | Last listed 1997 |
| ¶ *speciosa* | EBee |
| ¶ *spicata* | MNrw |
| *sporadum* | Last listed 1998 |
| 'Stansfieldii' | CPBP EBur EPot NMen NNrd WPat |
| *stevenii* | CGra EBee |
| - subsp. *beauverdiana* | Last listed 1997 |
| *sulphurea* | Last listed 1997 |
| 'Swannbles' | CPou NCat WCot |
| § *takesimana* | More than 30 suppliers |
| * - *alba* | EBee LPio LSyl MAvo NBur NCut NFla WCot WIvy WRus WUnu |
| - dark form | LFis |
| - 'Elizabeth' | See *C.* 'Elizabeth' |
| *teucrioides* | EHyt |
| *thessala* | CSWP |
| *thyrsoides* | GDra GTou ITim MNrw NWCA WBea WCla WHal WPer |
| - subsp. *carniolica* | NChi |
| *tommasiniana* ♀ | CGra EHyt LBee SAsh WAbe |
| *topaliana* | Last listed 1998 |
| - subsp. *cordifolia* | Last listed 1997 |
| *trachelium* | CGle CKin ECoo EOrc GAbr LHop MBNS MHew MNrw MRav NLan SCou SIde SSca WByw WCla WCot WFar WHer WPer |
| - var. *alba* | CGle CPea EBee GAbr LFis LSyl MFir MNrw NPar SCou SSca STes WCot WFar WMaN WMoo WPer WWal WWhi |
| - 'Alba Flore Pleno' (d) | CBos CFir CGle CHar CHea CLon CPou ECha EFou EMan LGre LHop LPio MBel SMac WBro WByw WCot WFar WGle WHoo WMaN WRus WSan |
| - 'Bernice' (d) | More than 30 suppliers |
| ♦ - 'Faichem Lilac' | See *C.* 'Faichem Lilac' |
| - lilac-blue | CBlo NCut NOrc |
| *transsilvanica* | Last listed 1997 |
| *trautvetteri* | Last listed 1997 |
| *trichocalycina* | Last listed 1997 |
| *tridentata* | NTow WLin WPer |
| *troegerae* | EPot LBee LRHS SBla WLin |
| *tubulosa* | See *C. buseri* |
| 'Tymonsii' | CPBP EBur ECho EHyt ELan ESis LBee NBir NNrd |
| *uniflora* | Last listed 1997 |
| 'Van-Houttei' | CBos CElw CHan CHar CMil CPlt CStr EMan EMon GCal LGre MBro MSte NBrk SUsu WCot WFar WPer |
| *versicolor* | LFis WCot |
| - G&K 3347 | EMon |
| - NS 745 | NWCA |
| ¶ 'Victor Cohen' | EPot |
| *vidalii* | See *Azorina vidalii* |
| *waldsteiniana* | CPBP EPot LBee NTow SSmi WFar |
| - JCA 266.000 | MBro |
| 'Warley White' | See *C.* x *haylodgensis* 'Warley White' |
| 'Warleyensis' | See *C.* x *haylodgensis* 'Warley White' |
| x *wockei* 'Puck' | CPBP EBee EBur EHyt EPot ESis LBee MBro NHar NMen NSla NWCA SSmi WPat |
| *xylocarpa* | Last listed 1997 |
| *zoysii* | CGra LRHS SIng |

## CAMPANULA x SYMPHYANDRA
(Campanulaceae)

| | |
|---|---|
| *C.* sp. x *S.* sp. | EBee GMac |

## CAMPANUMOEA See CODONOPSIS

## CAMPSIS (Bignoniaceae)

| | |
|---|---|
| * *atrosanguinea* | LRHS |
| *grandiflora* | CB&S CPIN EBee EBrP EBre EHic ELan ENot EPfP GSki IMGH LBre MGos SBre WCFE |
| *radicans* | CArn CB&S CBot CDoC CMac CPIN CRHN EBee ELan EOld EWTr GQui LPan MGrG MNrw MWat NBea NFla SLon SPer SPlb SYvo WDin |
| - 'Flamenco' | CB&S CBlo CDoC CPIN EBee EHic ELan GOrc GQui GSki IOrc LHop NBea SBra WBro WCru |
| § - f. *flava* ♀ | CDoC CMac CPIN EBee ELan IMGH IOrc LHol LHop MAsh MBri MCCP MGos MWat NBea NPal NSti SBra SPer SSoC SSta WBro WSHC |
| - 'Yellow Trumpet' | See *C. radicans* f. *flava* |
| * x *tagliabuana* 'Flamenco' | MAsh |
| - 'Madame Galen' ♀ | More than 30 suppliers |

## CAMPTOSORUS See ASPLENIUM

## CAMPTOTHECA (Cornaceae)

| | |
|---|---|
| *acuminata* | ISea |

## CAMPYLANDRA See TUPISTRA

## CANANGA (Annonaceae)

| | |
|---|---|
| *odorata* | ERea |

## CANARINA (Campanulaceae)

| | |
|---|---|
| *canariensis* ♀ | CPIN CPle |

## CANDOLLEA Labill. See HIBBERTIA

## CANNA ✿ (Cannaceae)

| | |
|---|---|
| 'Adams Orange' | Last listed 1998 |
| ¶ 'Aida' | MBEx |
| ¶ *altensteinii* | LBlo |
| 'Angele Martin' | MBEx |
| 'Argentina' | Last listed 1998 |
| 'Assaut' | LLew LPio MBEx SVen |
| 'Australia' | MBEx |
| 'Black Knight' | EBee GBuc LAma LPio MBEx |
| ¶ *brasiliensis* | EOas |
| - 'Rosea' | MBEx WMul |
| 'Brillant' | NCut |
| ¶ 'Cerise Davenport' | CFir MBEx |
| 'Champion' | MBEx |
| ¶ 'Cherry Red' | MBEx |
| 'China Lady' | Last listed 1996 |
| 'Chinese Coral' | LHil MBEx |
| ¶ 'City of Portland' | NCut |
| 'Cleopatra' | MBEx |
| *coccinea* | LBlo MBEx |
| ¶ 'Côte d'Or' | MBEx |
| ¶ cream speckled | LBlo |
| 'Creamy White' | Last listed 1998 |
| Crozy hybrids | Last listed 1998 |
| 'Délibáb' | Last listed 1997 |
| 'Di Bartolo' | LPio MBEx |
| 'Durban' (v) | CFil CSpe LBlo LHil LPJP MBEx MHlr WCot WMul |

¶ *edulis* — LBlo
  x *ehemanii* — CGre SVen
  - x *iridiflora* — LHil WMul
  'En Avant' — MBEx
  'Endeavour' — CFil LLew LPJP MBEx MSta WMAq WMul WPGP
  'Erebus' — MBEx MSta WMAq
  'Étoile du Feu' — MBEx
  'Extase' — MBEx
  Firebird — See *C.* 'Oiseau de Feu'
*flaccida* — Last listed 1996
¶ 'Florence Vaughan' — MBEx
  'General Eisenhower' — MBEx
  x *generalis* — CB&S
*glauca* — MBEx SDix
  'Gnom' — MBEx
  'Golden Lucifer' — LAma MBri MRav SAga
  'Heinrich Seidel' — MBEx
  'Hercule' — MBEx
  hybrids — LBow
§ *indica* — CB&S CSev EFul ERav LBlm LHil LPio MBEx SAPC SArc SYvo
  - x *generalis* — Last listed 1996
  - 'Purpurea' — CFil ECha ERav LBlm LEdu LHil MBEx SDix SLon WMul WPGP WPic
  'Ingeborg' — NCut
  'Intrigue' — MBEx
*iridiflora* — CSev CWit EOas MBEx SAPC SArc SDix
  'Jivago' — MBEx
  'King Hakon' — MBEx
I 'King Humbert' (blood-red) — LBlo SYvo
  King Humbert (orange-red) — See *C.* 'Roi Humbert'
  'King Midas' — LBlo MBEx SVen
  'Königin Charlotte' — MBEx
¶ 'La Bohème' — NCut
¶ 'La Gloire' — MBEx
  'Lafayette' — LBlo
  'Lesotho Lill' — CHad LHil
  'Libération' — MBEx
  'Louis Cayeux' — MBEx
¶ 'Louise Cottin' — ETub
  'Lucifer' — CSpe EOas MBEx NCut SYvo
*lutea* — LBlm WCot
  'Malawiensis Variegata' — See *C.* 'Striata'
  'Melanie' — Last listed 1998
  'Meyerbeer' — MBEx
¶ 'Mrs Oklahoma' — MBEx
  'Mrs Tim Taylor' — MBEx
*musifolia* — LBlo LHil LLew LPJP MBEx SDix WMul
¶ 'Mystique' — MBEx
¶ 'Nectarine' — MBEx
§ 'Oiseau de Feu' — MBri SVen
  'Oiseau d'Or' — LHil MBEx
¶ 'Orange Beauty' — MBEx SVen
  'Orange Perfection' — CFir MBEx
  'Orchid' — LAma MBEx MBri
  'Panache' — CFil MBEx
  'Perkeo' — LHil MBEx
  'Picadore' — MBEx
  'Picasso' — EBee LAma MBEx SYvo
¶ 'Pink Paradise' — LHil
  'Pink Sunburst' — MBEx WCot
  'President' — LAma LHil LPio MBEx MBri NCut SAga
  'Pretoria' — See *C.* 'Striata'
  'Primrose Yellow' — Last listed 1997
* 'Pringle Bay' (v) — LBlo
  'Professor Lorentz' — CFil LBlo MBEx WPGP
  'Ra' — LLew MBEx MSta WMAq

  'Richard Wallace' — EBee LPio MBEx NCut
§ 'Roi Humbert' — LHil MBEx NCut SVen
  'Roi Soleil' — CFil MBEx WPGP
  'Roitelet' — Last listed 1998
  'Rosemond Coles' — MBEx
  'Saladin' — MBEx
  'Salmon' — Last listed 1997
  'Sémaphore' — MBEx
  'Shenandoah' — MBEx
  'Singapore Girl' — MBEx
§ *speciosa* — LBlo
  'Strasbourg' — MBEx
§ 'Striata' (v) — CFil CSev CSpe EOas LBlo LHil LPJP MBEx MSta SVen WCot WHal WMul WSPU
  'Striped Beauty' (v) — LHil MBEx
  'Stuttgart' (v) — MBEx
  'Talisman' — MBEx
  'Taney' — MSta WMAq
  'Tango' — Last listed 1998
  'Taroudant' — MBEx
  'Tashkent Red' — CHad LHil
  'Tirol' — LHil MBEx SVen
  'Tropical Rose' — LBlo LHil WMul
¶ 'Tropical Rose' red — LBlo
¶ Tropicanna = 'Phasion' — COtt WCot
* 'Variegata' (v) — LAma NCut
  'Verdi' — LHil MBEx
*warscewiczii* — CBos LBlo MBEx WMul
  'Wyoming' — CHad EBee EOas LAma LBlo LHil LLew LPio LWoo MBEx MBNS MTis NCut SArc SYvo
  'Yellow Humbert' — CSev LAma LHil

## CANTUA (Polemoniaceae)
*buxifolia* — CB&S CFee CFil CPle ERea GQui LCns LHil SIgm SMad SOWG

## CAPSICUM (Solanaceae)
*annuum* — MBri
* - 'Janne' — MBri

## CARAGANA (Papilionaceae)
*arborescens* — CBlo CDul ENot EPfP GChr IOrc MBar MCoo MWhi SRCN WDin WStI WWat
  - 'Lorbergii' ♀ — CDoC CEnd CLnd IOrc MBlu SEas WFoF
  - 'Pendula' — CBlo CLnd EBee ElAn ENot EPfP GRei MAsh MBar MBlu NBee NEgg SPer WDin WStI
  - 'Walker' — CB&S CBlo CDoC CDul COtt EBee EBrP EBre EMil IOrc LBre LPan MAsh MBar MBlu MBri MGos SBre SMad SPer WOrn WStI
*aurantiaca* — MBar
*brevispina* — CHan SRms
*franchetiana* — Last listed 1998
*frutex* 'Globosa' — SPer
*jubata* — SMad
*microphylla* — SMad WNor

## CARDAMINE ✿ (Brassicaceae)
*alba* — WEas
*asarifolia* L. — WCru
  - hort. — See *Pachyphragma macrophyllum*
*bulbifera* — CHan CLAP CRDP IBlr NDov NRya NWoo SIng WCot WCru
¶ *diphylla* — WCot
*enneaphyllos* — IBlr SSpi WCot WCru WRHF
*glanduligera* — CElw EBee SWas

§ *heptaphylla* — CLAP ELan EPar GBri GNau IBlr MBri MRav SSpi SWat WCru WHoo
- Guincho form — CFir IBlr
- white — CPlt GMaP WCot
§ *kitaibelii* — CLAP EPar GAbr IBlr NHol SSpi WCru
*laciniata* — SWat WCot WCru
*latifolia* Vahl — See *C. raphanifolia*
*macrophylla* — CLAP COtt EBee SDys SSpi SWas SWat WCot WCru WFar WIvy
§ *microphylla* — CLAP EHyt GCrs IMGH WCot
x *paxiana* — Last listed 1997
§ *pentaphyllos* — CGle EBee ECha ELan EMar EPar EPla ERos GAbr GCrs GNau MBri MRav NSti SIgm SSpi WCot WCru
- bright pink form — CLAP
*pratensis* — CArn CKin CRow EMan EWFC MHew MMal NDea NMir NOrc SIde SWat WCla WGwy WHbs WHer WShi
- 'Edith' (d) — CGle CLAP CMil CRow EPPr GAri GBuc MNrw NChi NLon SWat
- 'Flore Pleno' (d) ♀ — CBre CFee CGle CRow CSpe CVer EBee ECha GAbr MCLN MNrw MRav MTho NBro NLar NSti SUsu SWat WAlt WCla WCot WEas WFar WHoo WMer WRus
- 'William' (d) — CGle CMea CVer EPPr GBuc MNrw NLon WFar WPrP
*quinquefolia* — CElw CGle CLAP EBee EPar NCat SCro SDys SUsu SWas WCot WCru WFar WHal WRha WWye
§ *raphanifolia* — CBre CGle CRow CVer EBee ECha EMan EOrc GAbr GBuc GCal GGar IBlr MFir MRav NBro NCat NChi NVic SSpi SWat WBor WCru
*trifolia* — CGle CRDP EBee ECha EPar ERos GAbr GCal GMaP LBee MBar MSCN NBro NChi NFor NLon NRya NVic SWat WCot WCru WFar WHal WHer WHil WWye
* - *digitata* — MTho
*waldsteinii* — CLon EBee EGle SSpi SWas WCot WCru WHal WTin

## CARDIANDRA (Hydrangeaceae)
*formosana* B&SWJ 2005 — WCru

## CARDIOCRINUM (Liliaceae)
*cordatum* — Last listed 1998
- var. *glehnii* — CFil WPGP
*giganteum* ♀ — CB&S CBot CBro CFil EBee EBot EBrP EBre EPar ETub GGGa IBlr LAma LBre LSyl MAvo MBal MBlu MRav MWll SAga SBre SMad SSoC SSpi WCru WHer WPGP
- var. *yunnanense* — CFil GGGa IBlr SSpi WCru WPGP

## CARDIOSPERMUM (Sapindaceae)
*grandiflorum* — CPIN
*halicacabum* — Last listed 1996

## CARDUNCELLUS (Asteraceae)
*rhaponticoides* — Last listed 1996

## CARDUUS (Asteraceae)
*benedictus* — See *Cnicus benedictus*
*nutans* — Last listed 1996

## CAREX (Cyperaceae)
*acutiformis* — Last listed 1997

*albida* — CCuc CInt EBee EGle EHoe EPPr EPla EWes GOrn MBal SCob
*appressa* — SApp
*arenaria* — Last listed 1997
*atrata* — CCuc CHar EHoe EMar EMon EPPr EPla ESis MAvo
*aurea* — Last listed 1997
*baccans* — EPla GCal
*berggrenii* — More than 30 suppliers
*binervis* — Last listed 1998
*boottiana* — EPPr EWes GGar
*brunnea* — EHoe EPPr EWes
- 'Variegata' — CCuc EHoe EPla GGar SCob WCot WLeb
*buchananii* — More than 30 suppliers
- 'Viridis' — CB&S EHoe ELan EPPr EPla WHer WWoo
*caryophyllea* 'The Beatles' — CCuc CMea EBee EGoo EHoe EPPr EPla ESis MCCP MMoz NBro NHar NHol
*comans* — CCuc CKel EBee EFul EHoe ELan EMon EOld EPPr EPar EPla GCHN GCal GGar GOrn IBlr LHil MBal NBro NHol NOak SCob SHel SMad
- bronze — More than 30 suppliers
- 'Frosted Curls' — More than 30 suppliers
* - 'Small Red' — MAsh MMoz
§ *conica* — LHil LHop MBri SPer
- 'Hime-kan-suge' — See *C. conica* 'Snowline'
§ - 'Snowline' (v) — More than 30 suppliers
*crinata* — Last listed 1997
*crus-corvi* — EBee EPPr
* *cyperus* — Last listed 1996
*dallii* — ECou EWes
*demissa* — CCuc CInt EBee EHoe EPPr GBin WWye
*depauperata* — CCuc EHoe EMon EPla WWye
*digitata* — WWye
*dipsacea* — CElw CRow ECou EHoe EMon EWsh GBri GCal GOrn MAvo MBel MBrN MLLN MNrw MWhi NChi NHed NWCA WHal WPer WPrP WWye
*dissita* — CInt
*divulsa* — GBin
- subsp. *leersii dolichostachya* — Last listed 1997
'Kaga-nishiki' (v) — EBee EMon GBin MAvo MMoz SApp WCot
§ *elata* 'Aurea' (v) ♀ — More than 30 suppliers
- 'Bowles' Golden' — See *C. elata* 'Aurea'
- 'Knightshayes' — MMoz WCot
* - 'Everbright' (v) — CB&S
'Evergold' — See *C. oshimensis* 'Evergold'
*ferruginea* — GBin
*firma* — NNrd
- 'Variegata' — CLyd EHyt EPar EPot MAsh MDHE MTho MWat NHar NMen NTow NWCA SChu SIng SRot SSmi WAbe WRus
§ *flacca* — CBrm EHoe EPPr GBin MSCN
- 'Bias' (v) — CKin CNat EMon EPPr MMoz NSti WCot
§ - subsp. *flacca* — EWes MMoz NHol SApp
*flaccosperma* — SApp
* *flagellaris* 'Cyperacea' — CInt
*flagellifera* — More than 30 suppliers
- 'Rapunzel' — Last listed 1997
*flava* — EHoe SBea
*forsteri* — See *C. pseudocyperus*
*fortunei* 'Variegata' — See *C. morrowii* 'Variegata'

| | |
|---|---|
| *fraseri* | EHoe GBin |
| *fuscula* | Last listed 1997 |
| *glauca* Bosc. ex Boott | Last listed 1998 |
| - Scopoli | See *C. flacca* subsp. *flacca* |
| *grayi* | CElw CHan CInt EGar EHoe EMar |
| | EMon EPla GCal MCCP MTho |
| | WCot WPer WWye |
| § *hachijoensis* | EMon EPPr EPla LRHS |
| ¶ 'Happy Wanderer' | SLPl |
| 'Hime-kan-suge' | See *C. conica* |
| *hirta* | CKin EPPr |
| *hispida* | GLch GVic WWye |
| *hordeistichos* | Last listed 1998 |
| *humilis* 'Hexe' | Last listed 1997 |
| § 'Ice Dance' | SApp WCot |
| *intumescens* | Last listed 1998 |
| *kaloides* | CVer EBee EHoe EWes |
| ♦ 'Kan-suge' | See *C. morrowii* |
| 'Little Red' | EPla |
| *lurida* | EPGN GBin MCCP |
| *macloviana* | CInt EBee EPPr |
| *montana* | EPPr |
| § *morrowii* | GCHN WHil |
| § - hort. | See *C. oshimensis* , *C. hachijoensis* |
| § - Boott | IBlr MWhi NSti WPyg |
| - 'Evergold' | See *C. oshimensis* 'Evergold' |
| - 'Fisher's Form' (v) | CBrd CCuc CFil CHan CInt EBee |
| | EFou EHoe EPPr EPla GCHN LHil |
| | LHop MBri MMoz MRav MUlv |
| | NHar NHol NMir SApp SCob |
| | WBro WCot WPGP WPer WWat |
| | WWye |
| - 'Gilt' | EMon EPPr LRHS MAvo |
| ♦ - 'Ice Dance' | See *C.* 'Ice Dance' |
| - 'Nana Variegata' | NBir NWoo WPGP |
| N - 'Variegata' | More than 30 suppliers |
| *muricata* | CKin |
| *muskingumensis* | CB&S CBrm CCuc CInt CVer |
| | EBee ECGN EGar EHoe EMar |
| | EMon EPPr EPla GBin LGre LHil |
| | NBro NFai NHol NSti SApp SDix |
| | SMad SPan SRms SUsu WHil WPer |
| | WWye |
| - 'Oehme' | CBel CHar EMon EPPr EPla GBin |
| | SApp SUsu WCot WLeb |
| - 'Silberstreif' | EMon |
| - 'Small Red' | Last listed 1998 |
| - 'Wachtposten' | GCal MFir |
| *nigra* | CKin EHon EWFC GAbr GSki |
| ¶ - 'On-line' | WPrP |
| - subsp. *tornata* | Last listed 1998 |
| - variegated | EPPr EPla GBin MAvo MMoz |
| | WCot |
| *obnupta* | EBee |
| *ornithopoda* | EPot |
| - 'Aurea' | See *C. ornithopoda* 'Variegata' |
| - 'Variegata' | CCuc CKel CSam EBee EBrP EBre |
| | ECtt EHoe EPar EPla ESis GCHN |
| | LBre LHil MBal MBrN MBro MMoz |
| | MWhi NBro NHar NHol SBre |
| | SCob SSmi WCot WFar WRus |
| | WWat WWye |
| § *oshimensis* | IBlr |
| § - 'Evergold' (v) ♀ | More than 30 suppliers |
| - 'Variegata' | NBir SCob |
| *otrubae* | CKin |
| *ovalis* | CKin |
| *pallescens* | GBin WWye |
| - 'Wood's Edge' (v) | CNat MAvo |
| *panicea* | EHoe EMar EPPr EPla MMoz SApp |
| *paniculata* | Last listed 1997 |

| | |
|---|---|
| *pauciflora* | EPPr |
| *pendula* | More than 30 suppliers |
| - 'Moonraker' | CBot CFil CHar EPla LEdu SApp |
| | WLeb |
| *petriei* | CCuc CSam CVer CWSG EAst |
| | EBee ECha ECoo EHoe ELan EPPr |
| | EPot EWsh GAbr GAri GOrn LHil |
| | LLWP MBNS MHlr MMoz MSCN |
| | NHed NPSl NVic SPla SSoC WCot |
| | WFar WPer |
| ¶ - dwarf form | EWes |
| *phyllocephala* | EHoe WCot |
| - 'Sparkler' (v) | CInt EAst EBee EHoe EPPr GBin |
| | LEdu MAvo MBri MCCP MSCN |
| | NChi NCut SApp SCob SMad |
| | WCot |
| *pilulifera* | EBee EHoe EPPr EPot IBlr LRHS |
| 'Tinney's Princess' (v) | LWoo MCCP NHol |
| *plantaginea* | CFil CHan EGar EHoe EMar EMon |
| | EPPr EPla GBin SCob WCot WFar |
| | WPGP |
| § *pseudocyperus* | CInt CKin ECGN EGar EHoe |
| | EHon EPPr EPla EWFC GBin |
| | GCHN MLLN MNrw MSCN MSta |
| | SBea SRms SWyc WLeb WPer |
| | WWye |
| *pulicaris* | CKin |
| *reinii* | EBee |
| *remota* | CKin EPPr GBin WWye |
| *riparia* | EMFW EPPr LPBA MWhi WShi |
| | WWeb |
| - 'Bowles' Golden' | See *C. elata* 'Aurea' |
| - 'Variegata' | More than 30 suppliers |
| * *saxatilis* 'Variegata' | CInt EMon |
| *secta* | ECou EHal EHoe EPPr GOrn |
| | MNrw NLak |
| - var. *tenuiculmis* | CCuc EHoe EMon EOld EPPr EPla |
| | EWsh GBin LRHS MAvo MWhi |
| | NHol |
| *siderosticha* | CFil EPla EPot GAri WPGP WPer |
| - 'Kisokaido' (v) | EMon |
| - 'Shima-nishiki' (v) | EMon WCot |
| - 'Variegata' | More than 30 suppliers |
| 'Silver Sceptre' | CMHG CMil EBee EMon EPPr EPla |
| | LRHS MBri MCCP MMoz NFai |
| | NHed NHol NLak NPla NPro |
| | NRoo NSti SApp SBea SCob SSto |
| | WCot WLeb WWat |
| sp. from Uganda | GCal LEdu |
| sp. from Wellington, New Zealand | EWes |
| *spicata* | Last listed 1996 |
| *spissa* | MNrw |
| *stenocarpa* | EBee |
| *stricta* Lamarck | EPPr EPla |
| - Goodenough | See *C. elata* |
| - 'Bowles' Golden' | See *C. elata* 'Aurea' |
| *sylvatica* | CKin ECGN MBrN WWye |
| *testacea* | More than 30 suppliers |
| - 'Old Gold' | LRot SMer SPlb WFar |
| *texensis* | EPPr MMoz SApp |
| *trifida* | CInt EBee ECou EHoe EPla EWsh |
| | GAbr GCHN GCal MBel MNrw |
| | MUlv MWhi SCob SPla WCot |
| | WLeb WWye |
| *uncifolia* | ECou |
| *vulpina* | CKin EPPr SBea |

## CARICA (Caricaceae)

| | |
|---|---|
| *papaya* (F) | Last listed 1998 |

## CARISSA (Apocynaceae)

| | |
|---|---|
| *bispinosa* | Last listed 1998 |
| *grandiflora* | See *C. macrocarpa* |
| § *macrocarpa* (F) | CSpe ECon ERea LCns |

## CARLINA (Asteraceae)

| | |
|---|---|
| *acanthifolia* | EHyt MAvo SIgm WCot WGle |
| - subsp. *cyanara* | NWCA |
| JJA 274.101 | |
| *acaulis* | CM&M ELan EPfP MBel NSti |
| | NWCA SRms SSpi WEas WElm |
| | WPer WPyg |
| - bronze | ECGN EMan GCal NChi |
| - var. *caulescens* | See *C. acaulis* subsp. *simplex* |
| § - subsp. *simplex* | EBee ECGN ECGP ECha ERic |
| | GBuc GMaP MBri MHar NPri |
| | NRoo SIgm SMad WCot WFar |
| | WPer |
| - - bronze | MAvo NSla |
| *corymbosa* | Last listed 1997 |
| *vulgaris* | CKin EWFC WPer |
| - 'Silver Star' | Last listed 1998 |

## CARMICHAELIA (Papilionaceae)

| | |
|---|---|
| ¶ 'Abundance' | ECou |
| ¶ 'Angie' | ECou |
| ¶ *angustata* 'Buller' | ECou |
| *appressa* | ECou |
| - 'Ellesmere' | ECou |
| § *arborea* | ECou |
| ¶ - 'Grand' | ECou |
| *arenaria* | Last listed 1998 |
| *astonii* | ECou |
| ¶ - 'Ben More' | ECou |
| ¶ - 'Chalk Ridge' | ECou |
| ¶ *australis* | ECou |
| ¶ - Aligera Group | SVen |
| ¶ - 'Bright Eyes' | ECou |
| ¶ - 'Cunningham' | ECou |
| ¶ - Flagelliformis Group | ECou SVen |
| ¶ - 'Mahurangi' | ECou |
| ¶ - Ovata Group | ECou |
| ¶ - 'Solander' | ECou |
| ¶ 'Charm' | ECou |
| ¶ 'Clifford Bay' | ECou |
| *corrugata* | ECou |
| ¶ 'Culverden' | ECou |
| *curta* | ECou |
| *enysii* | CTri ITim MBro |
| - AGS 27 | Last listed 1998 |
| - 'Pringle' | Last listed 1998 |
| *exsul* | ECou |
| ¶ *fieldii* 'Westhaven' | ECou |
| ¶ *flagelliformis* 'Roro' | ECou |
| *glabrata* | CPLG CPle MBlu |
| ¶ 'Hay and Honey' | ECou |
| ¶ *juncea* Nigrans Group | ECou |
| *kirkii* | ECou |
| - x *astonii* | Last listed 1998 |
| - hybrid | Last listed 1998 |
| ¶ 'Lilac Haze' | ECou |
| *monroi* | ECou |
| ¶ - 'Rangitata' | ECou |
| ¶ - 'Tekapo' | ECou |
| ¶ *nana* | ECou |
| ¶ - 'Desert Road' | ECou |
| ¶ - 'Pringle' | ECou |
| ¶ - 'Waitaki' | ECou |
| ¶ *nigrans* 'Wanaka' | ECou |
| *odorata* | ECou SVen |
| - Angustata Group | ECou |

| | |
|---|---|
| ¶ - 'Green Dwarf' | ECou |
| ¶ - 'Lakeside' | ECou |
| ¶ - 'Riverside' | ECou |
| ¶ *ovata* 'Calf Creek' | ECou |
| 'Parson's Tiny' | ECou |
| *petriei* | ECou SMad |
| ¶ - 'Aviemore' | ECou |
| ¶ - 'Lindis' | ECou |
| ¶ - 'Pukaki' | ECou |
| ¶ - Virgata Group | ECou |
| ¶ 'Porter's Pass' | ECou |
| *robusta* | Last listed 1998 |
| ¶ 'Spangle' | ECou |
| *suteri* | Last listed 1997 |
| ¶ 'Tangle' | ECou |
| *uniflora* | ECou |
| ¶ - 'Bealey' | ECou |
| *violacea* | Last listed 1997 |
| ¶ 'Weka' | ECou |
| *williamsii* | ECou |
| ¶ 'Yellow Eyes' | ECou |

## CARMICHAELIA x CORALLOSPARTIUM
See x CORALIA

## x CARMISPARTIUM (Papilionaceae)

| | |
|---|---|
| *astens* | See x *C. hutchinsii* |
| § *hutchinsii* | ECou |
| - 'County Park' | ECou |
| ¶ - 'Pink Beauty' | ECou |

## CARPENTERIA (Hydrangeaceae)

| | |
|---|---|
| *californica* ♀ | CBot CDoC CPMA ELan ENot |
| | EPfP EWTr GQui IOrc LHop LNet |
| | MAsh MBri MGos MRav MWhi |
| | SPer SReu SSpi SSta WHCG WHar |
| | WPat WSHC WWat |
| - 'Bodnant' | LRHS |
| - 'Elizabeth' | CPMA LRHS MBri SPla SSpi |
| | WWeb |
| - 'Ladhams' Variety' | CB&S CPMA EBee WSPU |

## CARPINUS ✿ (Corylaceae)

| | |
|---|---|
| *betulus* ♀ | More than 30 suppliers |
| - 'Columnaris' | CLnd CTho MBri |
| * - 'Columnaris Nana' | CMCN |
| § - 'Fastigiata' ♀ | More than 30 suppliers |
| - 'Frans Fontaine' | CDul CMCN CTho IOrc MBlu |
| | SSta |
| - 'Horizontalis' | CMCN |
| - 'Incisa' | GAri |
| - 'Pendula' | CDul CTho EBee EBrP EBre GAri |
| | LBre SBre |
| - 'Purpurea' | CDul ENot |
| - 'Pyramidalis' | See *C. betulus* 'Fastigiata' |
| *caroliniana* | CLnd CMCN SMad WNor WWoo |
| *caucasica* | Last listed 1997 |
| * *comptoniifolia* | Last listed 1998 |
| *cordata* | CMCN WCwm WDin |
| *coreana* | CDul CMCN CTho SFur WNor |
| | WWoo |
| *fargesii* | See *C. laxiflora* var. |
| | *macrostachya* |
| *henryana* | WDin |
| *japonica* | CDul CEnd CMCN EPfP LBuc |
| | MBlu SFur WWoo |
| *laxiflora* | CMCN GAri SMad SSpi WNor |
| § - var. *macrostachya* | CBlo CDoC CEnd WNor |
| *mollicoma* | WWoo |
| *omeiensis* | WWoo |
| *orientalis* | CMCN GAri WNor |
| *polyneura* | CMCN EPfP WNor |

| | |
|---|---|
| *schisiensis* | WCwm |
| x *schuschaensis* | Last listed 1997 |
| *tschonoskii* | CMCN |
| *turczaninowii* | CDul CMCN WDin WNor WShe WWoo |
| *viminea* | CMCN EPfP WNor |

## CARPOBROTUS (Aizoaceae)

| | |
|---|---|
| § *edulis* | CAgr CTrC EOas IBlr SAPC SArc SChr SEND WHer |
| *muirii* | CTrC EOas |
| ¶ *quadrifidus* | EOas |
| *sauerae* | CTrC EOas |

## CARPODETUS (Escalloniaceae)

| | |
|---|---|
| *serratus* | Last listed 1997 |

## CARTHAMUS (Asteraceae)

| | |
|---|---|
| *tinctorius* | MChe MSal |

## CARUM (Apiaceae)

| | |
|---|---|
| *carvi* | CArn CJew ELau GPoy IIve LHol MChe MHew NVic SIde WHer WJek WOak WPer WSel WWye |
| *copticum* | MSal |
| *petroselinum* | See *Petroselinum crispum* |

## CARYA ✿ (Juglandaceae)

| | |
|---|---|
| *aquatica* | Last listed 1996 |
| . *cordiformis* ♀ | CMCN |
| *glabra* | Last listed 1998 |
| N *illinoinensis* | CMCN |
| *laciniosa* | Last listed 1996 |
| ¶ - 'Henry' (F) | CAgr |
| ¶ - 'Stephens' (F) | CAgr |
| *myristiciformis* | CMCN |
| *ovata* ♀ | CAgr CMCN LEdu MBlu SSpi |
| *pallida* | Last listed 1996 |
| *texana* | Last listed 1996 |
| *tomentosa* | Last listed 1997 |

## CARYOPTERIS ✿ (Verbenaceae)

| | |
|---|---|
| * x *bungei* | WElm |
| x *clandonensis* | CB&S CBot CSam CTrw EBee ELan ENot GRei LHop MAsh MWat NBir SHel WBod WDin WFar WHCG WHar WSHC WStI WWat WWin WWye |
| - 'Arthur Simmonds' | CBlo EBee ECha EHal EHic EPfP LFis LHop MBal SPer SPlb WGor |
| - 'Dark Night' | CHar MBri WBcn |
| - 'Ferndown' | CArn CChe CDoC EBee EBrP EBre ELan EMil EWTr GOrc LBre LFis LHop MAsh MUlv SBre SPer SPla SReu SRms SSpi WFar WSHC WWeb |
| - 'First Choice' | CAbP CRos ELan LRHS MAsh MWat SChu SMad SMrm SPer SUsu WBcn WRus |
| - 'Heavenly Blue' ♀ | More than 30 suppliers |
| - 'Kew Blue' | CB&S CBot CDoC CLTr CSpe EAst EBee EBrP EBre ELan EMil ENot LBre MGos NFla NSti SBre SEas SLon SPer SPla SSta WGwG WHar WPyg WSHC WStI WWat WWeb WWye |
| - 'Longwood Blue' | GCal LRHS MAsh WBcn WWeb |
| * - 'Newleaze' | LHop |
| * - 'Pershore' | LRHS MBri MHlr MTis WCFE WSPU |
| - 'Worcester Gold' | More than 30 suppliers |
| * 'Dark Prince' | Last listed 1998 |

| | |
|---|---|
| *divaricata* | CFil CPle EBee EMon WPGP |
| ¶ - 'Electrum' | EMon |
| ¶ - 'Jade Shades' | EMon |
| - variegated (v) | Last listed 1998 |
| § *incana* | CPle EBrP EBre ELan ERav LBre LFis LHop MSte MUlv MWhi SBre SPer SPla WCot WSHC |
| - pink form | LRHS |
| - weeping form | EHic GBuc GCal LFis SBid SMrm SPan SRms |
| *mastacanthus* | See *C. incana* |
| *odorata* | Last listed 1998 |

## CARYOTA (Arecaceae)

| | |
|---|---|
| 'Hymalaya' | LPal |
| *mitis* | LPal |
| *obtusa* | LPal |
| *ochlandra* | LPal |
| *ophiopellis* | LPal |
| *urens* | LPal |

## CASSANDRA See CHAMAEDAPHNE

## CASSIA (Caesalpiniaceae)

| | |
|---|---|
| *corymbosa* Lam. | See *Senna corymbosa* (Lam.) Irwin & Barneby |
| § *javanica* | MSag |
| ♦ *marilandica* | See *Senna marilandica* |
| ♦ *nodosa* | See *C. javanica* |
| *obtusifolia* | See *Senna obtusifolia* |
| ♦ *siamea* | See *Senna siamea* |

## CASSINIA (Asteraceae)

| | |
|---|---|
| *aculeata* | Last listed 1998 |
| *aureonitens* | Last listed 1998 |
| *leptophylla* | CDoC SPer |
| - subsp. *fulvida* | CB&S ECou EHoe EMil GOrc GTou IOrc MBar MBlu MPla NFor SAga SPer STre WBcn WTro |
| - subsp. *vauvilliersii* | CDoC NFor NLon SPer |
| - - var. *albida* | CB&S CHan EGoo EPfP SPer WBod WGer |
| - - CC 570 | NWCA |
| - - 'Silberschmelze' | SOWG |
| N *retorta* | CDoC ECou NLon |
| - yellow | Last listed 1998 |
| 'Ward Silver' | CBot ECou EWes GSki MBel NFor SPan |

## CASSINIA x HELICHRYSUM (Asteraceae)

| | |
|---|---|
| * *C.* sp. x *H.* sp. | WKif WPen WSHC |

## CASSIOPE ✿ (Ericaceae)

| | |
|---|---|
| * 'Askival' | ITim |
| 'Askival Arctic Fox' | GCrs |
| ♦ 'Askival Freebird' | See *C.* Freebird Group |
| 'Askival Snowbird' | GCrs |
| ♦ 'Askival Snow-wreath' | See *C.* Snow-wreath Group |
| 'Askival Stormbird' | GCrs |
| 'Badenoch' | ECho EPot GAri GDra LRHS MBal NHar NHed WAbe |
| 'Bearsden' | CMHG GAri GDra MBal MBar NHar NRya WPat WPyg |
| 'Edinburgh' ♀ | CMHG EPfP EPot GAbr GChr GDra MBal MBar MBro NHar NHed NHol NMen WAbe WPat WPyg |
| § Freebird Group | GCrs |
| 'George Taylor' | WAbe |
| 'Inverleith' | Last listed 1996 |
| 'Kathleen Dryden' | GDra MBal |

*lycopodioides* ♀ — EPot GCrs GDra GTou IMGH MBal MBar MGos NHar NHol WAbe
- 'Beatrice Lilley' — ELan EPot GAri GChr GTou MBal MBar NHar NHed NHol WAbe WPat WPyg
- var. *crista-pilosa* — Last listed 1996
- var. *globularis* — Last listed 1996
¶ - 'Jim Lever' — WAbe
- *minima* — Last listed 1996
- 'Rokujô' — EPot GCrs NHol
'Medusa' — GDra GTou LRHS MBal NHar NHol WPat WPyg
*mertensiana* — ECho GTou MBal MBar NHed NMen SRPl
- 'California Pink' — Last listed 1998
¶ - var. *californica* — WAbe
- dwarf form — MBal
- var. *gracilis* — CMHG ELan LRHS MGos NHar NHol
- - - dwarf form — EPot
'Muirhead' ♀ — CMHG EPot GDra GTou IMGH MBal MBar NHar NHed NHol NMen NRya SRms WAbe WPat WPyg
'Randle Cooke' ♀ — CMHG ELan EPot EWes GChr GCrs GDra GTou MBal MBar MBro NHar NHed NHol SRms WAbe WPat WPyg
*selaginoides* — Last listed 1996
- LS&E 13284 — GAri WAbe
- McB 1124 — Last listed 1996
§ Snow-wreath Group — GCrs
§ *stelleriana* — Last listed 1998
*tetragona* — EPfP GTou LRHS MBal MBar SRms
- var. *saximontana* — EPot MBal NHol
*wardii* — Last listed 1998
- x *fastigiata* Askival Strain — Last listed 1998

## CASTANEA ✿ (Fagaceae)
'Layeroka' (F) — CAgr LEdu
* 'Marigoule' — Last listed 1997
*mollissima* — CMCN GAri WWoo
x *neglecta* — CTho
*sativa* ♀ — CB&S CDoC CKin CLnd ECrN ENot EWTr GChr GRei IOrc LBuc LHyr LPan MAsh MBar MBri MGos MWat NBee NRog NWea SPer WDin WFar WHar WMou WOrn WStI WWes
§ - 'Albomarginata' — CBlo CDoC CDul CTho EBee EBrP EBre IMGH LBre MBlu MBri MGos NBea NBee SBre SMad SPer WWeb WWes
- 'Anny's Red' — MBlu
- 'Anny's Summer Red' — CDul
- 'Argenteovariegata' — See *C. sativa* 'Albomarginata'
- 'Aspleniifolia' — CB&S CDoC CDul MBlu WPGP
- 'Aureomarginata' — See *C. sativa* 'Variegata'
- 'Bournette' (F) — Last listed 1998
* - 'Corkscrew' — Last listed 1997
* - 'Doré de Lyon' — Last listed 1997
- 'Glabra' — MAsh
- 'Marron de Lyon' (F) — CEnd CTho EMui MBlu MCoo
§ - 'Variegata' — CAbP CB&S CFil CMCN COtt CTho ELan EMil EPfP LPan MAsh
- 'Vincent van Gogh' — SMad
¶ *seguinii* — CAgr LEdu
'Simpson' — CAgr LEdu

## CASTANOPSIS (Fagaceae)
*cuspidata* — CMCN

## CASUARINA (Casuarinaceae)
*cunninghamiana* — CTrC
*equisetifolia* — CGre CTrC
*glauca* — CPle
*littoralis* — See *Allocasuarina littoralis*
*stricta* — See *Allocasuarina verticillata*

## CATALPA ✿ (Bignoniaceae)
*bignonioides* ♀ — CB&S CBlo CBot CDoC CDul CLnd CMCN CTho ECrN ELan ENot EWTr IOrc LHyr LPan MBri MBro MCCP MWat MWhi NBee NPal NWea SPer WBod WDin WNor WWat
- 'Aurea' ♀ — More than 30 suppliers
- 'Nana' — Last listed 1997
- 'Purpurea' — See *C.* x *erubescens* 'Purpurea'
- 'Variegata' — EBee EPfP LNet LRHS MBro NHol SSta WPat WPyg
*bungei* — LPan WNor
- 'Purpurea' — ELan
x *erubescens* — LPan
§ - 'Purpurea' ♀ — CB&S CBlo CBot CDoC CDul CEnd CLnd CTho EBee EBrP EBre EMil EPla IOrc LBre MAsh MBlu MBro SBre SPer SSoC SSta WGer WPat WPyg
*fargesii* — CFil CLnd
- f. *duclouxii* — CB&S CFil WPGP
*ovata* — CAgr CBlo CGre CMCN LEdu SFur
*speciosa* — CB&S CLnd CMCN LRHS SPer
- 'Pulverulenta' (v) — CB&S CDoC CEnd CMCN

## CATANANCHE (Asteraceae)
*caerulea* — More than 30 suppliers
- 'Alba' — CGle CPou EBee ECha EPar EWTr LIck NBir NPri NRoo SIgm SPer SSvw WBea WMow WOld WPer WWhi
- 'Bicolor' — CHan CM&M CSev EBee EMan EWTr LFis MNrw NFai NRoo SLon SUsu WElm WHer WHoo WMaN WPnP WWal
- 'Major' ♀ — ENot EWTr MWat SRms WEas
* - 'Stargazer' — Last listed 1998
*caespitosa* — SBla

## CATAPODIUM (Poaceae)
§ *rigidum* — Last listed 1997

## CATHA (Celastraceae)
*edulis* — Last listed 1998

## CATHARANTHUS (Apocynaceae)
*roseus* ♀ — GPoy MBri
- Ocellatus Group — MBri

## CATOPSIS (Bromeliaceae)
*berteroana* — WMEx

## CAULOPHYLLUM (Berberidaceae)
*thalictroides* — CArn CRDP EBee LRHS MSal WCot WThi
¶ - subsp. *robustum* — WCru

## CAUTLEYA (Zingiberaceae)
§ *gracilis* — WCot
*lutea* — See *C. gracilis*
*spicata* — IBlr WCru
- 'Robusta' — CRDP EMan GCal NCat SMad SSoC

## CAYRATIA (Vitaceae)

| | |
|---|---|
| *japonica* | CPlN |
| - B&SWJ 570 | WCru |

## CEANOTHUS ✿ (Rhamnaceae)

| | |
|---|---|
| 'A.T. Johnson' | CBlo EBee EGra ENot EOld LNet MAsh NFai SPer SRPl SRms SSoC WGwG WWal |
| *americanus* | CArn CPle MSal |
| - 'Fincham' | CKno |
| *arboreus* | SAPC SArc |
| - 'Owlswood Blue' | LRHS |
| - 'Trewithen Blue' ♀ | More than 30 suppliers |
| 'Autumnal Blue' ♀ | More than 30 suppliers |
| *azureus* | See *C. coeruleus* |
| 'Basil Fox' | LRHS |
| 'Blue Boy' | Last listed 1997 |
| 'Blue Buttons' | LRHS |
| * 'Blue Carpet' | Last listed 1998 |
| 'Blue Cushion' | CB&S CBlo CDoC CLan ECtt EHic LHop MGos SEas WAbe |
| 'Blue Jeans' | CAbP CBlo CPle EBee LRHS MAsh SBid SPan SPla WAbe |
| 'Blue Mist' | Last listed 1997 |
| * 'Blue Moon' | LRHS WWeb |
| * 'Blue Mound' ♀ | CDoC CLan CTrw EBee EBrP EBre EMil ENot EWTr LBre MGos MRav NFor NHol NLon SBre SPer SPla SReu SSpi WRHF WSHC WWal WWat WWeb |
| * 'Blue Star' | LHop |
| * 'Borne Again' (v) | WBcn |
| 'Burkwoodii' ♀ | CB&S CDoC CMac CTri EBrP EBre EWTr IOrc LBre MAsh MBal MBri MGos SBre SPer SRPl SReu WFar WWal |
| 'Burtonensis' | Last listed 1997 |
| 'Cascade' ♀ | CB&S CLan EAst EBee ELan ENot IOrc LNet MAsh MBri MGos MWat NFla NFor SLon SPer SRPl WAbe WBod WHCG WSHC WStI |
| § *coeruleus* | Last listed 1996 |
| 'Comtesse de Paris' | See *C. x delileanus* 'Comtesse de Paris' |
| 'Concha' | More than 30 suppliers |
| *crassifolius* var. *planus* | Last listed 1998 |
| * - 'Plenus' | SBid |
| § *cuneatus* var. *rigidus* | CPle SBid SDry SRms WAbe WSHC WWeb |
| - var. *rigidus* 'Snowball' | EBee ELan EPfP GSki LRHS MAsh MGos SPan SSto WBcn |
| *cyaneus* | CGre CPle |
| 'Cynthia Postan' | CAbP CMHG CPle CSam CWSG EBee EBrP EBre EPfP GOrc ISea LBre LRHS MAsh MBlu MWat SBre SPan WAbe WPat |
| 'Dark Star' | CBlo CChe CDoC CMHG CTbh CWSG EPfP EWll GOrc MAsh SAga SOWG SReu SSta |
| 'Delight' ♀ | CBlo EBee ELan EPla IOrc MGos NFla SBid SPer SSoC WAbe WBod WFar WWat |
| ¶ x *delileanus* | CKno |
| § - 'Comtesse de Paris' | CKno MRav WBcn |
| - 'Gloire de Versailles' ♀ | CB&S CBot CChe CDoC CKno CMac CPle CSam ELan ENot EWTr IOrc ISea MAsh MBri MGos MRav NBee NBrk SPer WDin WFar WGwG WPyg WSHC WWeb WWin |
| - 'Henri Desfossé' | CBlo CKno CPle ELan MRav SBid SOWG SPer WDin WKif |
| - 'Indigo' | CKno NFla |
| - 'Topaze' ♀ | CB&S CBlo CKno CPle ELan EMil ENot EPfP EWTr ISea MRav SAga SBid SLon SOWG WHar WKif |
| *dentatus* hort. | See *C. x lobbianus* |
| - Torrey & A.Gray | ELan ENot GRei IOrc MAsh MBal MGos SChu SPer WPyg |
| - var. *floribundus* | ELan LRHS |
| - 'Prostratus' | MBal |
| * - 'Superbus' | EBee |
| *depressus* | Last listed 1996 |
| ♦ 'Diamond Heights' | See *C. griseus* var. *horizontalis* 'Diamond Heights' |
| 'Dignity' | WWeb |
| *divergens* | CPle SBid |
| 'Edinburgh' ♀ | CBlo CMHG EPfP MAsh NCut SBid WBod WWeb |
| 'Edward Stevens' | Last listed 1997 |
| * 'Elan' | Last listed 1997 |
| 'Eleanor Taylor' | LRHS |
| 'Fallen Skies' | CAbP LRHS MAsh WWeb |
| *fendleri* | Last listed 1996 |
| *foliosus* | CPle |
| - var. *austromontanus* | CB&S CTrw EBee EHic SPan |
| 'Frosty Blue' | COtt LRHS |
| 'Gentian Plume' | LRHS MAsh SMad |
| * 'Gloire Porrectus' | Last listed 1997 |
| *gloriosus* | CFai CPle EWes IOrc SAga SBid SDry WSHC WWat |
| - 'Anchor Bay' | COtt EBee ELan EPfP LRHS MAsh SCob SLon SOWG SPan WWeb |
| - 'Emily Brown' | CB&S |
| *griseus* var. *horizontalis* | Last listed 1996 |
| § - var. *horizontalis* | LRHS MAsh NOla SPer WWeb |
| 'Diamond Heights' (v) | |
| - - 'Hurricane Point' | CB&S WFar |
| - - 'Yankee Point' | CB&S CBlo CChe CDoC CMHG CMac EBee EMil LHop LNet MAsh MBel MBri MGos MRav NFai SEas SPer WAbe WDin WWeb |
| - 'Santa Ana' | Last listed 1997 |
| *hearstiorum* | CPle LRHS |
| *impressus* | CB&S CBlo CLan CMHG CPle EBee ELan EMil ENot GOrc MAsh MBal MRav NBur SEas SPer SPla SSoC WAbe WEas WFar WPyg WWeb |
| *integerrimus* | Last listed 1998 |
| var. *macrothyrsus* | |
| N 'Italian Skies' ♀ | CB&S CBlo CChe CDoC CLan CMHG CMac CSam EBee EHal ELan EMil LHop MAsh MBri MGos MRav SAga SEas SLon SPer WBod WGwG WWeb |
| 'Joyce Coulter' | CB&S EMil |
| 'Julia Phelps' | CMHG CWSG SRPl WEas WSPU |
| 'Ken Taylor' | CRos LRHS MAsh |
| § x *lobbianus* | CB&S CBrm CDoC CTri EBee ERic EWTr MRav NHol NSti SPlb |
| - 'Russellianus' | CAbP MGos WSPU |
| *maritimus* 'Point Sierra' | Last listed 1997 |
| 'Mary Lake' | Last listed 1997 |
| x *mendocinensis* | Last listed 1998 |
| *oliganthus* | Last listed 1998 |
| § - var. *sorediatus* | Last listed 1998 |
| x *pallidus* | CFai WBcn |
| - 'Golden Elan' | CKno WBcn |
| - 'Marie Simon' | CB&S CBlo CBot CChe CKno CPle ELan EMil EPfP GEil LHop MBel MBri MRav NFla NFor NLon SEas SMad SPer SRms WBod WFar WKif WPyg WSHC WWeb |

- 'Marie Simon Variegated'  CPMA
  (v)
- 'Perle Rose'  CB&S CBlo CKno CMac CPle IOrc
  MAsh MTis SOWG SPer SPla WKif
  WSHC
*papillosus*  CMac CPle SBid
- var. *roweanus*  CMac CPle GAri WEas WWat
- x *thyrsiflorus*  Last listed 1996
'Percy Picton'  Last listed 1997
'Pershore Zanzibar' (v)  LRHS MGos SCoo WOVN WSPU
'Picnic Day'  Last listed 1997
'Pin Cushion'  CFai CWSG EBee EPfP LRHS
  MAsh SPla WFoF WPat WSPU
  WWat
*prostratus*  GSki LBuc MAsh SDry WAbe WEas
  WWin
'Puget Blue' ♀  CB&S CBlo CDoC CLan CMac
  CPle CTbh EBee EBrP EBre ELan
  EMil GAbr LBre LHop MAsh MBri
  MGos MPla MWat SBre SDix SPer
  SReu SSpi SSta WBod WDin WKif
  WSHC
*purpureus*  CPle EHic LBuc WWeb
*ramulosus*  LRHS
'Ray Hartman'  SMad SSoC WBcn
x *regius*  Last listed 1996
*repens*  See *C. thyrsiflorus* var. *repens*
♦ *rigidus*  See *C. cuneatus* var. *rigidus*
'Sierra Blue'  WRHF
'Snow Flurries'  CB&S CBlo EAst EHal EHic EHol
  EMil EPfP MBel SEND SPan WAbe
  WFar WGwG WWat WWeb
♦ *sorediatus*  See *C. oliganthus* var. *sorediatus*
'Southmead' ♀  CBlo CDoC CTri EBee ECtt EHic
  EMil EWTr GBuc IOrc ISea MAsh
  MBel MBri MGos NCut NFla
  WBod WHCG WPat WWat
*spinosus*  Last listed 1998
'Thundercloud'  Last listed 1997
*thyrsiflorus*  CB&S CBlo CMac CTri ELan LNet
  LRHS MAsh MBal MBri MTis NFai
  NHol SArc SRms WDin WFar
  WHar
- 'Millerton Point'  CBlo CChe CPle CWSG EBee
  ELan EMil LRHS MAsh MBlu MBro
  SBid SPla WWeb
§ - var. *repens* ♀  More than 30 suppliers
- 'Skylark'  CBlo CDoC CMHG CPle CRos
  CTbh EBee EHic ELan LHop
  MAsh MBri SBid SBra SDix SLon
  SReu SSta SVil WFar WWat WWeb
¶ 'Tilden Park'  LRHS
* 'Underway'  WWat
x *veitchianus*  CB&S CBlo CDoC CMac CSam
  EBee ENot GChr LNet MAsh MBar
  NHol SBid SEas SPer SSta WWeb
*verrucosus*  Last listed 1998
'White Cascade'  SPan

## CEDRELA (Meliaceae)
*sinensis*  See *Toona sinensis*

## CEDRONELLA (Lamiaceae)
§ *canariensis*  CArn CGle CInt CSev GPoy IBlr
  IIve ILis LHol MChe MHer MMal
  MSal NHex SIde SOWG SWat
  WCer WHer WOak WPer WWye
*mexicana*  See *Agastache mexicana*
*triphylla*  See *C. canariensis*

## CEDRUS (Pinaceae)
*atlantica*  CDoC CDul CGre EHul LCon
  MBar NWea SLim SPar WDin
  WMou WWal
- 'Aurea'  CDoC CMac LCon LLin LPan
  MAsh MBar MGos SSta WDin
  WHar
- 'Fastigiata'  CDoC CMac EHul LCon LPan
  MBar MBri MGos SLim
- Glauca Group ♀  More than 30 suppliers
¶ - - 'Saphir Nymphe'  CKen
¶ - - 'Silberspitz'  CKen
¶ - 'Glauca Fastigiata'  CKen
- 'Glauca Pendula'  CDoC CKen EHul EOrn IMGH
  IOrc LCon LNet LPan MBar MBri
  MGos NBee SLim SMad SSta
  WGer WOrn WWes
¶ - 'Pendula'  CDul CMac GAri NBee
*brevifolia* ♀  CDoC ECho GAri LCon MBar
  MBri MGos
¶ - 'Epstein'  LCon MBar
¶ - 'Hillier Compact'  CKen
¶ - 'Kenwith'  CKen
*deodara* ♀  CDoC CDul CMac CSam EHul
  ENot EWTr GRei IOrc LBee LCon
  LHyr MBal MBar MBri MGos
  NBee NWea SLim SPer STre WAbe
  WDin WFar WMou WPyg WWat
  WWeb
¶ - 'Albospica' (v)  LCon
- 'Argentea'  MBar MGos NHol
- 'Aurea' ♀  CDoC CDul EHul EOrn IMGH
  ISea LBee LCon LLin LPan MAsh
  MBar MBri MGos SLim WDin
  WFro WOrn
I - 'Aurea Pendula'  Last listed 1997
- 'Blue Dwarf'  CKen LCon LLin MAsh NHol
* - 'Blue Mountain Broom'  CKen
- 'Blue Triumph'  LPan
- 'Cream Puff'  ECho LCon LLin MAsh MBar
  MGos
- 'Feelin' Blue'  CDoC CKen COtt CSli EBrP EBre
  EPla IMGH LBee LBre LCon LLin
  LPan MAsh MBar MBri MGos
  NHol SBre SCoo SLim WDin WStI
  WWeb
- 'Gold Cone'  MGos
- 'Gold Mound'  CKen GAri LCon
- 'Golden Horizon'  CDoC CKen CMac EBrP EBre
  EHul EOrn IMGH IOrc LBee LBre
  LCon LLin LPan MAsh MBar MBri
  MGos NHed NHol SBre SLim SPer
  WDin WPyg WWeb
- 'Karl Fuchs'  CDoC EBrP EBre ETen LBre LRHS
  MAsh MBri NMoo SBre WGor
- 'Kashmir'  CSli
¶ - 'Kelly Gold'  CDoC MBri
- 'Klondyke'  LCon
- 'Lime Glow'  CKen
- 'MacPenny's Seedling'  Last listed 1997
- 'Mountain Beauty'  CKen
- 'Nana'  CKen
- 'Nivea'  CKen
- 'Pendula'  CDoC EHul LPan MBar MGos
  MWat WGor WStI
- 'Pygmy'  CKen
- 'Robusta'  Last listed 1996
- 'Roman Candle'  CSli ECho EOrn
- 'Scott'  CKen
- 'Silver Mist'  CKen
- 'Verticillata Glauca'  Last listed 1997

| | |
|---|---|
| * 'Home Park' | CKen |
| *libani* | CDoC CDul CLnd CMCN CTri |
| | GChr LLin LPan LRHS MAsh NBee |
| | SFam WPGP WWat WWeb |
| - subsp. *libani* ♀ | CDoC CMac EHul ENot IOrc |
| | LCon MBar MBri MLan NWea |
| | SLim WDin WFro WMou WNor |
| | WWat |
| - - 'Comte de Dijon' | EHul LCon LLin SLim |
| - - 'De Creffe' | Last listed 1996 |
| - - Nana Group | CKen ECho LCon |
| - - 'Sargentii' | CDoC CKen CMac EHul EOrn |
| | IMGH LCon LLin MAsh MBal |
| | MBar MBri MGos SLim SSta |
| - - 'Taurus' | MBar NHol |

## CELASTRUS (Celastraceae)

| | |
|---|---|
| *angulatus* | CPIN |
| *loeseneri* (f) | Last listed 1996 |
| - (m) | Last listed 1996 |
| *orbiculatus* | CB&S CDoC CMac CPIN EBee |
| | ELan EMil GBin GEil MPla MRav |
| | NPal NSti SLon SPer SRPl SReu |
| | SSta WBod WFar WGwG WSHC |
| - 'Diana' (f) | ELan NBea SSta |
| - 'Hercules' (m) | ELan NBea |
| - Hermaphrodite Group ♀ | CBrm CSam EHic EPla GOrc GSki |
| | MCCP MGrG NHol SBra SDix |
| | SPan SSpi WTro WWat WWeb |
| - JLS 88018WI | Last listed 1997 |
| - var. *papillosus* | WCru |
| B&SWJ 591 | |
| - var. *punctatus* | WCru |
| B&SWJ 1931 | |
| *scandens* | CMac CPIN ELan IMGH MSal |
| | SMur |
| - (f) | Last listed 1996 |
| - (m) | Last listed 1996 |
| sp. KR 1269 | Last listed 1996 |

## CELMISIA ✿ (Asteraceae)

| | |
|---|---|
| *adamsii* | IBlr |
| *allanii* | GCrs IBlr |
| *alpina* | GAbr IBlr NHol |
| - large form | IBlr |
| *angustifolia* | EPot GCrs GNor IBlr IMGH |
| - silver form | IBlr |
| *argentea* | EPot EWes GCrs GNor GTou IBlr |
| | IMGH NHar NHed WAbe |
| *asteliifolia* | IBlr |
| Ballyrogan hybrids | IBlr |
| *bellidioides* | EPot EWes GCrs IBlr NEgg NHar |
| | NHol NMen NWCA WAbe |
| *bonplandii* | IBlr |
| *brevifolia* | GNor IBlr |
| * *ceracophyllus* | Last listed 1996 |
| *coriacea* | GCal IBlr MDun NFor NHar |
| - 'Harry Bryce' | IBlr |
| *dallii* | IBlr |
| *densiflora* | GCrs GMaP IBlr |
| ¶ - silver-leaved | IBlr |
| *discolor* | IBlr |
| ¶ *durietzii* | IBlr |
| 'Edrom' | Last listed 1998 |
| *glandulosa* | IBlr |
| *gracilenta* | GCrs IBlr NSla |
| - CC 563 | NWCA |
| - forms | IBlr |
| *graminifolia* | IBlr |
| ¶ *baastii* | IBlr |
| *bectorii* | IBlr ITim |
| *bolosericea* | IBlr |

| | |
|---|---|
| *bookeri* | GCal IBlr |
| *incana* | GCrs IBlr |
| Inshriach hybrids | IBlr MBal |
| ¶ *insignis* | IBlr |
| Jury hybrids | IBlr |
| *lindsayi* | Last listed 1997 |
| *longifolia* | GNor SSpi |
| - large form | IBlr |
| - small form | IBlr |
| *lyallii* | Last listed 1996 |
| *mackaui* | IBlr |
| *monroi* | IBlr |
| *morganii* | IBlr |
| *prorepens* | IBlr |
| ¶ *ramulosa* | GNor SIng |
| § - var. *tuberculata* | GCrs GTou IBlr ITim WAbe |
| *saxifraga* | IBlr |
| *semicordata* | EPot NHar NSla |
| ¶ - subsp. *aurigans* | EPot |
| - 'David Shackleton' | IBlr |
| - subsp. *stricta* | GCrs IBlr |
| * *sericifolia* | IBlr |
| *sericophylla* | IBlr |
| - large form | IBlr |
| *sessiliflora* | EPot GAri GTou IBlr IMGH ITim |
| - 'Mount Potts' | IBlr |
| *spectabilis* | EPot IBlr MDun NEgg NHar WAbe |
| | WCot |
| - var. *angustifolia* | IBlr |
| - subsp. *magnifica* | GAri IBlr |
| * - *major* | Last listed 1996 |
| *traversii* | EPot IBlr NHar |
| *verbascifolia* | IBlr |
| *viscosa* | IBlr |
| § *walkeri* | EPot GCrs GTou IBlr |
| *webbiana* | See *C. walkeri* |

## CELOSIA (Amaranthaceae)

| | |
|---|---|
| *argentea* var. *cristata* | MBri |
| - - Plumosa Group | MBri |

## CELSIA See VERBASCUM

## CELSIOVERBASCUM See VERBASCUM

## CELTIS (Ulmaceae)

| | |
|---|---|
| *africana* | CGre |
| *aurantiaca* | Last listed 1998 |
| *australis* | CB&S CDul LPan SRCN SSpi SSta |
| *biondii* | Last listed 1996 |
| *bungeana* | Last listed 1996 |
| *caucasica* | Last listed 1997 |
| *glabrata* | Last listed 1996 |
| ¶ *jessoensis* | CMCN |
| *julianae* | WCwm WNor |
| *laevigata* | Last listed 1997 |
| *occidentalis* | CPle ELan EPfP LRHS SSta |
| - var. *pumila* | WNor |
| *reticulata* | Last listed 1996 |
| *sinensis* | CMCN CPle WNor |
| *tetrandra* | Last listed 1996 |
| *tournefortii* | CMCN |

## CENOLOPHIUM (Apiaceae)

| | |
|---|---|
| *denudatum* | SDix SIgm |

## CENTAUREA (Asteraceae)

| | |
|---|---|
| ¶ *alba* | EBee |
| - HH&K 228A | CHan |
| *argentea* | CBot |
| *atropurpurea* | ECGN NLar NSti |
| *bella* | More than 30 suppliers |

| | |
|---|---|
| *benoistii* | CHad CHan ECGN EMar SIgm WCot |
| 'Blue Dreams' | CSpe EMon MGrG MLLN SUsu |
| *cana* | See *C. triumfettii* subsp. *cana* |
| *candidissima* Lamarck | See *C. rutifolia* |
| - hort. | See *C. cineraria* |
| *cheiranthifolia* | ECha EMon GCal WFar |
| § - var. *purpurascens* | EMon MAvo |
| § *cineraria* | MBEx MHlr SRms WCot WEas |
| - subsp. *cineraria* ♀ | Last listed 1997 |
| *cyanus* | EWFC MHew MMal MPEx NArg WFar WJek |
| *cynaroides* | See *Leuzea centauroides* |
| *dealbata* | CBot CKel ECtt EOld EWTr GAbr MBNS MBro MFir MMal NArg NBro NFai NMir NOak NOrc NRoo SCro WByw WFar WHoo WOve WPer WWin |
| - 'Steenbergii' | CGle CHor CM&M CPou CRDP EBee EBrP EBre ELan EWTr GCal LBre MBel MCAu NChi NMGW NOak NPer NSti SBre SOkh SPer SSpe WAbb WCot WFar WHoo |
| *debeauxii* subsp. *nemoralis* | Last listed 1998 |
| ¶ *declinata* | NLon |
| *drabifolia* | Last listed 1997 |
| ¶ - subsp. *austro-occidentalis* | WLin |
| *fischeri* | See *C. cheiranthifolia* var. *purpurascens* |
| *glastifolia* | EMon GCal MLLN WCot WGwy |
| *gymnocarpa* | See *C. cineraria* |
| *hypoleuca* 'John Coutts' | More than 30 suppliers |
| *jacea* | CGen ECGN WCot |
| *kerneriana* subsp. *kerneriana* HH&K 297 | CHan |
| ¶ *kotschyana* | EBee |
| *macrocephala* | More than 30 suppliers |
| *marschalliana* HH&K 271 | CHan |
| - HH&K 276 | Last listed 1998 |
| *montana* | CBre EBee ELan EWFC EWTr GAbr MBro MCAu MCLN MFir NBro NLar NOak NOrc NRoo NVic SHel SPer SPlb SRms SSvw SWat WFar WHen WOak WOve WPer WStl WWin WWye |
| - *alba* | More than 30 suppliers |
| § - *carnea* | CBre CElw CMea EBee ECha MAvo NChi NFla WHal WRus WWin |
| - 'Gold Bullion' | EBee EGar EMon EPla MAvo NBir WBcn |
| - 'Grandiflora' | LRHS MBri |
| * - 'Lady Flora Hastings' | CBot CElw CSam EBee GMac MAvo MTed |
| - 'Ochroleuca' | CElw EBee EGoo EMon MLLN SOkh SWat |
| - 'Parham' | CMGP CPou CSev EBee EMan GCal LFis LLWP MBel MBro MCLN NPla NRoo NSti SChu SHel SMrm SPer SPla SSpe SSvw SWat WLRN |
| ¶ - 'Purple Prose' | EMon |
| ¶ - *purpurea* | MRav |
| - *rosea* | See *C. montana carnea* |
| * - *violacea* | IBlr |
| - 'Violetta' | CPou NBir WCot |
| *nervosa* | See *C. uniflora* subsp. *nervosa* |
| *nigra* | CArn CKin EWFC EWTr MHew MOne NLan NMir SBea SRob WCla WJek |
| - var. *alba* | CArn |
| - subsp. *rivularis* | ECha |
| *orientalis* | ECha LGre NBro NLar SIgm SSvw WPer WRha |
| *ornata* | Last listed 1998 |
| *pannonica* subsp. *pannonica* HH&K 259 | CHan |
| *parilica* NS 699 | NWCA |
| *phrygia* | EBee GBuc MGed MNrw SUsu WFar WRos |
| *pulcherrima* | CBot ECha EGle MHar MLLN NChi NOak SIgm SUsu WByw WCot WPer |
| 'Pulchra Major' | See *Leuzea centauroides* |
| *rhapontica* | See *Leuzea rhapontica* |
| *rigidifolia* | SMer |
| ¶ *rothrockii* | EWTr |
| *rupestris* | LGre |
| *ruthenica* | SIgm WCot |
| § *rutifolia* | Last listed 1997 |
| *salonitana* | CElw EMon WCot |
| *scabiosa* | CArn CKin CPea ECoo EHal EWFC EWTr MChe MNrw MWhi NLan SIde WCla WGwy WJek WPer |
| - f. *albiflora* | CNat EMan WCot |
| - 'Nell Hill' | CNat |
| *seridis* subsp. *maritima* | Last listed 1997 |
| *simplicicaulis* | CHan CInt CMea CNic CPlt CRDP GAbr MAvo MBel MBro MFir MHlr MTho NChi NRoo SIgm SRms WCot WEas WHoo WPer WWhi |
| *solstitialis* subsp. *solstitialis* HH&K 179 | Last listed 1998 |
| ¶ *thracica* | WCot |
| § *triumfettii* subsp. *cana* 'Rosea' | CNic CPea CRDP NNrd WWin |
| - subsp. *stricta* | ECoo EMar EMon EPPr GBuc LWoo MCCP MSte NMGW NTow |
| - - from Macedonia | LFis |
| § *uniflora* subsp. *nervosa* | CSam EMan NBro SGre WBea WPer WRha |

**CENTAURIUM** (Gentianaceae)

| | |
|---|---|
| *chloodes* | See *C. confertum* |
| § *confertum* | MNrw |
| *erythraea* | CArn EWFC GPoy MChe MHew MSal SIde WCla WWye |
| *scilloides* | CInt MBro MTho NFor NHol NMen NWCA WAbe WCla WHoo WWin |

**CENTELLA** (Apiaceae)

| | |
|---|---|
| § *asiatica* | CArn EOHP ILis MSal |

**CENTRADENIA** (Melastomataceae)

| | |
|---|---|
| *inaequilateralis* 'Cascade' | CHal CInt CLTr ECtt EMan GPin LHil LPVe MBri NFai WCot WLRN |
| *rosea* | See *C. inaequilateralis* |

**CENTRANTHUS** (Valerianaceae)

| | |
|---|---|
| § *ruber* | More than 30 suppliers |
| § - 'Albus' | More than 30 suppliers |
| - *atrococcineus* | ECha SPer WPer |
| - var. *coccineus* | CB&S CDoC CLTr EBee EGoo ELan ENot EPfP GAbr LGre LIck MCAu MRav MWat NFai NPri SEND SMrm SRPl WCot |
| ¶ - mauve | LGre |
| ¶ - 'Pretty Betsy' | NPri |
| * - 'Roseus' | NCut |

¶ 'White Cloud' WRHF

## CEPHALANTHERA (Orchidaceae)
*falcata* EFEx
*longibracteata* EFEx

## CEPHALANTHUS (Rubiaceae)
*occidentalis* CB&S CBlo CPMA CPle EBee EHic
EMil LFis MBNS MBlu MBro MPla
SPer SSta WCot WPat

## CEPHALARIA (Dipsacaceae)
§ *alpina* CBar CElw CGle EBee ECha EMan
EMar GCHN MNrw NFla NHed
NLar NNrd NTow SIng SMer
SOkh SRms SWat WCot WFar
WLin WPer
- 'Nana' CMil NMen NWCA WPyg
*ambrosioides* MLLN
¶ *dipsacoides* EHal EMon LGre
*flava* EBee LFis
¶ *galpiniana* subsp. EBee
*simplicior*
§ *gigantea* More than 30 suppliers
* *graeca* EBee
*leucantha* CHea COlW EBot EGar EWTr
GAbr GBuc MBel MLLN NLar
WBea WElm WWhi
*litvinovii* EMon
¶ *natalensis* EBee
*radiata* EBee
¶ sp. from Nepal 2800m CSam
*tatarica* See *C. gigantea*
¶ *tchihatchewii* IHdy SHut
*uralensis* EMon

## CEPHALIPTERUM (Asteraceae)
*drummondii* Last listed 1998

## CEPHALOPHYLLUM (Aizoaceae)
¶ *alstonii* CCpl

## CEPHALOTAXUS (Cephalotaxaceae)
*fortunei* CAgr CGre SLon
- 'Prostrate Spreader' Last listed 1996
¶ *harringtonia* ECho LEdu LLin MRav SMur
- var. *drupacea* CMCN LCon
- 'Fastigiata' CB&S CDoC CKen EHul EOrn
ETen LCon LPan MBar MBri SLim
SSmi WGer
- 'Gimborn's Pillow' MBar
- 'Korean Gold' CKen
- 'Nana' Last listed 1996
¶ - 'Prostrata' MBar

## CEPHALOTUS (Cephalotaceae)
*follicularis* CSWC EAnd EEls GTro WMEx

## CERASTIUM (Caryophyllaceae)
*alpinum* CMea ELan SRms
- var. *lanatum* CPBP EGoo EWes NTow NWCA
WPer
*candidissimum* EWes
*theophrasti* Last listed 1998
*tomentosum* CHal CTri EFer ELan EWTr IMGH
LGro NFor NPri NVic SPlb WCer
WFar WLRN WPer
- var. *columnae* CBlo EBrP EBre ECha ECho EHoe
EPfP EWes LBre MHlr SBre SRms
WCot
- 'Silberteppich' EGoo LFis

## CERATONIA (Caesalpiniaceae)
*siliqua* CFil MSal

## CERATOPHYLLUM (Ceratophyllaceae)
*demersum* CBen CRow EHon EMFW NDea
SAWi SWat SWyc

## CERATOSTIGMA ✿ (Plumbaginaceae)
*abyssinicum* ELan ERav
*griffithii* More than 30 suppliers
- 'Album' CPle
- SF 149/150 ISea
¶ *minus* CPLG
- SF 95001 Last listed 1996
§ *plumbaginoides* ♀ More than 30 suppliers
*ulicinum* Last listed 1998
*willmottianum* ♀ More than 30 suppliers
- Forest Blue = 'Lice' CAbP EBee ELan ENot MAsh
SCoo SPer SPla SReu WWeb

## CERATOTHECA (Pedaliaceae)
*triloba* SUsu SWat

## CERCIDIPHYLLUM ✿ (Cercidiphyllaceae)
*japonicum* ♀ More than 30 suppliers
¶ - 'Boyd's Dwarf' SSta
- 'Heronswood Globe' CPMA
- f. *pendulum* CBlo CDul CEnd CFil CMCN
CPMA EBee ELan EPfP LBuc LPan
MAsh MBlu MBri NBea SSpi
WWes
◆ - Red Fox See *C. japonicum* 'Rotfuchs'
§ - 'Rotfuchs' CB&S CEnd CMCN CPMA LRHS
MBlu MDun SMad SSpi WCot
WGer WPGP
- 'Ruby' CPMA
*magnificum* ♀ CEnd CFil CMCN EPfP MBlu SSpi
WCru
- Og 95.144 CFil WPGP
¶ - Og 95.111 CDoC
CERCIS (Caesalpiniaceae) CAgr CB&S CMCN EMil LEdu
*canadensis* MCCP MGos SPer WHCG WNor
WPat WWes
- 'Forest Pansy' ♀ CAbP CB&S CDul CEnd CMCN
COtt CPMA EBee ELan EMil LHop
LNet LPan MBlu MBri MDun
MGos NBea SCoo SMad SPer SRPl
SSta WDin WHar WPat
* - 'Gigantea' MBlu
§ - var. *occidentalis* CAgr SOWG
¶ - 'Royal White' EPfP
- 'Rubye Atkinson' MBlu
*chinensis* MCCP NPSI SPer WWoo
- f. *alba* Last listed 1997
- 'Avondale' CEnd CPMA EBee EMil LNet MBlu
MGos
◆ *occidentalis* See *C. canadensis* var.
*occidentalis*
*reniformis* 'Texas White' CPMA
*siliquastrum* ♀ CB&S CBot CCHP CDul CLnd
CMCN CTho EBee ELan ENot
EPla ERom IOrc LHop LNet LPan
MAsh MBar MBri MGos MWat
SOWG SPer SReu SSta WDin WFro
WPat WWat
- f. *albida* CB&S CBlo CBot CDoC CLnd
CTho EPfP LPan SPer WWeb

## CERCOCARPUS (Rosaceae)
*breviflorus* See *C. montanus* var.
*paucidentatus*

¶ *ledifolius*                  CPLG

## CERINTHE (Boraginaceae)
*glabra*                        CPea EMan SRms WWye
¶ 'Kiwi Blue'                   CHar
*major*                         EWll SRCN WEas WSan
- 'Purpurascens'               More than 30 suppliers

## CEROPEGIA (Asclepiadaceae)
*africana*                      CPIN
*ampliata*                      CPIN
*barklyi*                       CHal
*lanceolata*                    See *C. longifolia*
*linearis* subsp. *woodii* ♀    CHal IBlr MBri SRms
* - subsp. *woodii* 'Variegata' CInt
§ *longifolia*                  Last listed 1998
*pubescens* B&SWJ 2531          WCru
*radicans*                      CPIN
*stapeliiformis* ♀             Last listed 1998

## CEROXYLON (Arecaceae)
*alpinum*                       LPJP LPal
*quindiuense*                   Last listed 1997
*utile*                         Last listed 1997
*ventricosum*                   LPal

## CESTRUM (Solanaceae)
*aurantiacum*                   CB&S CPIN CPle EREa IDee LHil
*auriculatum*                   SOWG
x *cultum*                      CPle
*diurnum*                       Last listed 1996
§ *elegans* ♀                  CDoC CHal ECon LCns LHil
                                MBEx SOWG WMul
- 'Penlee'                     LHil
*fasciculatum*                  CB&S CPle GQui LHil SOWG
'Newellii' ♀                   CAbb CB&S CHan CMHG CSev
                                CTbh EBak ECon ELan EREa
                                ERom GQui LCns LLew MBal
                                NPSI SIgm SOWG SYvo WMul
                                WSHC
*nocturnum*                     CB&S CPIN CPle EBak ECon ELan
                                EOHP EREa LBlm LHil LLew MSal
                                SOWG SYvo WMul
*parqui* ♀                     CAbb CDoC CGre CMHG CPle
                                ECha ECon ELan EREa LHil LHop
                                SDix SLon SOWG SUsu SYvo
                                WCot WKif WOld WPen WSHC
* - 'Cretian Purple'           Last listed 1997
- hybrid                       LHil
*psittacinum*                   CGre CPle
*purpureum*                     See *C. elegans*
*roseum*                        ECon
- 'Ilnacullin'                 CB&S CDoC CGre EHol EREa
* *splendens*                  SOWG
♦ *violaceum* misapplied       See *Iochroma cyaneum* 'Trebah'
- pale blue                    Last listed 1997
♦ - misapplied
  'Woodcote White'             See *Iochroma cyaneum*
                                'Woodcote White'

## CHAENACTIS (Asteraceae)
*ramosa*                        MRPP

## CHAENOMELES (Rosaceae)
x *californica*                 CAgr
- 'Enchantress'                Last listed 1997
*cathayensis*                   CAgr CTho EMon EPla LEdu
                                WBcn
¶ 'James Pilger'               GAbr
§ *japonica*                    CAgr ENot GOrc GRei MBal MBar
                                NEgg NFor SEND WDin
- f. *alba*                    Last listed 1997

- var. *alpina*                MPla
- 'Orange Beauty'              Last listed 1997
- 'Sargentii'                  CB&S CBlo CFai CMac COtt EHic
                                NBee NEgg
¶ 'John Pilger'                LEdu NPro SPan
*lagenaria*                      See *C. speciosa*
*maulei*                        See *C. japonica*
*sinensis*                      See *Pseudocydonia sinensis*
§ *speciosa*                    CSam MBal MBar NFla NFor
                                NWea WNor
- 'Apple Blossom'              See *C. speciosa* 'Moerloosei'
- 'Aurora'                     LRHS MBri
- 'Cardinalis'                 CGre
- 'Choshan'                    See *C.* x *superba* 'Yaegaki'
- 'Contorta'                   EPfP EPla WCot
- 'Falconnet Charlet' (d)     MRav WWal
- 'Geisha Girl'               CB&S CBlo CChe CDoC CEnd
                                CMac EAst EBee EBrP EBre ECtt
                                ESis LBre LHop MAsh MBri MCCP
                                MGos MRav NPSI SAga SBre SPer
                                SPla SRms WFar WPyg WWat
                                WWeb
- 'Grayshott Salmon'          CLyn MCCP NHol NPla NPro
                                SPan
- 'Knap Hill Radiance'        CBlo
§ - 'Moerloosei' ♀            CDoC CPMA CSam EAst EBee
                                ELan ENot GOrc IMGH MAsh
                                MBri MPla MRav NPSI NSti SPer
                                SPla SSta WDin WGwG WMoo
                                WWal WWat WWeb
- 'Nivalis'                    More than 30 suppliers
- 'Phylis Moore' (d)          Last listed 1996
- 'Port Eliot'                MBal WBcn WWeb
¶ - 'Rosea Plena' (d)         WBcn
- 'Rosemoor Seedling'         GAri
- 'Rubra Grandiflora'         CBlo MGos
- 'Simonii' (d)               CB&S CBlo EBee EHic EHol ENot
                                ISea MBal MBri MGos MRav NFla
                                NWea SEND SPer WWat
- 'Snow'                       CChe CSam ISea MBal MPla MRav
                                MWat SEas SPla SRms WLRN WStI
- 'Umbilicata'                ENot MRav SPer SRms WWes
- 'Yukigoten'                 WBcn
x *superba*                     NFor
- 'Boule de Feu'              CTri ECtt
- 'Cameo' (d)                 CBot CChe EAst EPfP MBri SEas
                                SLPl WLRN WWat
- 'Clementine'                CBlo
- 'Coral Sea'                 NFor NLon
- 'Crimson and Gold' ♀       More than 30 suppliers
- 'Elly Mossel'              CB&S CBlo CMac WLRN
- 'Ernst Finken'             WSPU
- 'Etna'                      CBlo EHic NCut
- 'Fire Dance'               CBlo CMac EBee ECtt EGra ENot
                                EOld MAsh NBee NHol SEas SPer
                                WLRN
- 'Hever Castle'             MPla
- 'Hollandia'                CBlo MGos NEgg SRms WRHF
- 'Issai White'              LRHS MBri
- 'Jet Trail'                CB&S CBlo EAst EBee EHic ELan
                                ENot MBri MCCP MGos MRav
                                NPro
- 'Knap Hill Scarlet' ♀      CBlo CDoC EBee EBrP EBre ECot
                                ENot EPfP IOrc LBre LHop SBre
                                SEND SPer SRms STre WBod
                                WDin WStI WTro WWat
- 'Lemon and Lime'           CLyn EBee ELan ENot MGos
                                MRav NSti SPer WBcn
- 'Nicoline' ♀               CB&S CBlo CDoC EBee EHic
                                ENot EPfP GRei MBri MWat NEgg
                                SBra WDin WStI
- 'Ohio Red'                 WBod WTro

| - 'Pink Lady' ♀ | More than 30 suppliers |
| - 'Red Trail' | EBee ENot MRav |
| - 'Rowallane' ♀ | CBlo EBee ELan ENot EPfP GAri MBal MRav MWat NFla SEas SPer WLRN |
| - 'Texas Scarlet' | MBri |
| - 'Tortuosa' | CBlo EHic GOrc SPan WWat |
| ¶ - 'Vermilion' | MBNS |
| § - 'Yaegaki' (d) | Last listed 1997 |

## CHAENORHINUM (Scrophulariaceae)

| *glareosum* | WCla |
| § *origanifolium* | CNic CPBP ESis Llck NWCA SPlb WCru WRHF WWin |
| - 'Blue Dream' | CSpe EMan GBri LRHS MDHE MGed MNrw NPri SCob SCro WElm WFar WPer WWal |

## CHAEROPHYLLUM (Apiaceae)

| *hirsutum* | CRow ELan NBrk |
| - 'Roseum' | More than 30 suppliers |

## CHAMAEBATIARIA (Rosaceae)

| *millefolium* | Last listed 1996 |

## CHAMAECRISTA (Caesalpiniaceae)

| *nictitans* | Last listed 1996 |

## CHAMAECYPARIS ✿ (Cupressaceae)

| *formosensis* | CKen |
| *funebris* | See *Cupressus funebris* |
| *lawsoniana* | CDul EHul GAri GChr GRei MBar NWea WDin WMou |
| - 'Albospica' (v) | CMac EHul MBal MBar MWat SBod WFar |
| - 'Albospica Nana' | See *C. lawsoniana* 'Nana Albospica' |
| - 'Albovariegata' (v) | ECho EHul EOrn LBee MBar SRms |
| - 'Albrechii' | ENot |
| - 'Allumii Aurea' | See *C. lawsoniana* 'Alumigold' |
| - 'Allumii Magnificent' | CB&S MAsh WWeb |
| § - 'Alumigold' | CB&S CDoC CKen CSli GPin LCon MAsh MBal MBar MGos SBod SLim SPer WGwG WStl WWal WWeb |
| - 'Alumii' | CDoC CMac CTri EHul ENot GChr GRei MBal MBar MGos NWea SLim SMer SPer WStl |
| - 'Argentea' | See *C. lawsoniana* 'Argenteovariegata' |
| § - 'Argenteovariegata' (v) | CMac LCon SLim |
| ¶ - 'Aurea' | CDul |
| I - 'Aurea Compacta' | ECho |
| - 'Aurea Densa' ♀ | CBlo CKen CMac CNic CSli CTri EHul EOrn GAri LCon MAsh MBar MGos SBod SSmi STre |
| - 'Aureovariegata' | MBal MBar WBcn |
| § - 'Barabits' Globe' | MBar MWat |
| ¶ - 'Barry's Gold' | EOrn |
| § - 'Bleu Nantais' | CBrm CKen CMac CTri EHul EOrn LBee LCon LLin LNet MAsh MBal MBar MGos MPla MWat SBod SLim SSmi WCFE WWal |
| - 'Blom' | CKen EHul LRHS MBri |
| - 'Blue Gem' | LBee NHol |
| § - 'Blue Gown' | CBlo CTri EHul GRei LBee MBar MGos SRms |
| § - 'Blue Jacket' | MBar |
| - 'Blue Nantais' | See *C. lawsoniana* 'Bleu Nantais' |
| - 'Blue Surprise' | CKen EHoe EHul EOrn EPla LCon LLin MAsh MBal MBar MPla NPro WFar WWal |
| - 'Bowleri' | Last listed 1997 |
| - 'Brégéon' | CKen |
| - 'Broomhill Gold' | CBrm CDoC CMac CSli EBrP EBre EHul ENot LBre LCon LLin LNet MAsh MBal MBar MBri MGos MPla MWat NHol SBod SBre SLim SPer WDin WWal WWeb |
| - 'Buckland Gem' | WLRN |
| * - 'Burkwood's Blue' | MBar |
| - 'Caudata' | CKen MBar WBcn |
| - 'Chantry Gold' | CBlo CKen EHul SLim |
| § - 'Chilworth Silver' ♀ | EBrP EBre EHul EOrn EPot EWTr LBee LBre MAsh MBar MBri MGos MPla SBod SBre SLim SPer SRms WDin WFar WGwG WStl WWal |
| - 'Chingii' | EHul |
| - 'Columnaris' | CB&S CDoC CMac EBrP EBre ENot EPfP GRei IOrc LBee LBre MBal MBar MBri MGos MOke NBee NWea SBre SLim WFar |
| - 'Columnaris Aurea' | See *C. lawsoniana* 'Golden Spire' |
| N - 'Columnaris Glauca' | EBrP EBre EHul EOrn GChr LBre LCon LPan MAsh MGos MPla MWat SBod SBre SPer WDin WFar WStl WWeb |
| ¶ - 'Crawford's Compact' | CMac |
| - 'Cream Crackers' | EHul |
| - 'Croftway' | EHul SRms |
| - 'Delorme' | Last listed 1998 |
| - 'Dik's Weeping' | SMad |
| ¶ - 'Dorset Gold' | CMac |
| ¶ - 'Dow's Gem' | LCon |
| - 'Drummondii' | Last listed 1998 |
| - 'Duncanii' | EHul MBal |
| - 'Dutch Gold' | EHul GAri MAsh |
| - 'Dwarf Blue' | See *C. lawsoniana* 'Pick's Dwarf Blue' |
| - 'Eclipse' | CKen |
| N - 'Elegantissima' | CKen CMac |
| - 'Ellwoodii' ♀ | CB&S CChe CMac EBrP EBre EHul ENot EPfP EPot GChr GRei LBre LCon LLin MBal MBar MGos MPla MWat NEgg NRoo NWea SBod SBre SLim SPer WCFE WDin WFar |
| - 'Ellwood's Empire' | EHul MBri |
| - 'Ellwood's Gold' ♀ | CB&S CDoC CMHG CMac EBrP EBre EHul ENot EPfP EPot GRei LBee LBre LCon LLin MBal MBar MBri MGos MOke MPla MWat NRoo NWea SBod SBre SPer WDin WFar WGwG |
| - 'Ellwood's Gold Pillar' | CDoC EHul EOrn LBee LLin MAsh MBri MGos NHol SLim SSmi SVil WGwG WLRN WPat |
| § - 'Ellwood's Nymph' | CBlo CKen CNic CSli EOrn MBar SLim WGor WWeb |
| - Ellwood's Pillar | More than 30 suppliers |
| - 'Ellwood's Pygmy' | CMac ECho MBar NHol |
| - 'Ellwood's Silver' | MAsh WFar WGor |
| * - 'Ellwood's Treasure' | WCFE |
| - 'Ellwood's Variegata' | See *C. lawsoniana* 'Ellwood's White' |
| § - 'Ellwood's White' (v) | CBlo CBrm CKen CMac CSli EHul EOrn GPin MBal MBar MBri WFar |
| ¶ - 'Ellwood's Silver Threads' | CMac |
| I - 'Emerald' | CKen MBar MBri NHol |
| - 'Emerald Spire' | CBlo CDoC CMac CTri MAsh NHol |
| - 'Empire' | CBlo |
| - 'Erecta Aurea' | CSli ECho EHul LBee MAsh SBod |
| - 'Erecta Filiformis' | MBar |

| | | |
|---|---|---|
| § | – 'Erecta Viridis' | CB&S CDoC CMac CTrG CTri LCon MBal MBar MPla MWat NEgg NWea SBod WDin WFar WStl |
| | – 'Ericoides' | EHul |
| | – 'Erika' | MBar |
| | – 'Fantail' | Last listed 1998 |
| | – 'Filiformis Compacta' | EHul |
| | – 'Fleckellwood' | CSli EHul GPin LLin MAsh MBar MGos MPla SBod SLim SMer WLRN WStl WWal |
| | – 'Fletcheri' ♀ | CB&S CMac EHul ENot LBee LCon MAsh MBar MGos MPla NBee NWea SBod SLim SPer WDin WFar WStl |
| | – 'Fletcheri Aurea' | See *C. lawsoniana* 'Yellow Transparent' |
| | – 'Fletcheri Nana' | CBlo |
| | – "Fletcher's White" | ECho EHul MBar MBri WBcn |
| | – 'Forsteckensis' | CKen CNic CSli EHul EOrn ESis LLin MBar MGos MOne NWea SLim SRms SSmi WFar WGwG WWal |
| I | – 'Forsteckensis Aurea' | CBlo |
| | – 'Fraseri' | CMac LCon MBar NWea WDin |
| | – "Gail's Gold" | CKen |
| | – 'Gilt Edge' | CKen |
| | – 'Gimbornii' ♀ | CDoC CMac EBrP EBre EHul EOrn GChr LBee LBre LCon LLin MAsh MBar MBri MPla SBod SBre SLim SRms WAbe WCFE |
| ¶ | – 'Glauca' | CDul |
| | – 'Glauca Spek' | See *C. lawsoniana* 'Spek' |
| ¶ | – 'Globosa' | MGos |
| | – 'Globus' | See *C. lawsoniana* 'Barabits' Globe' |
| | – 'Gnome' | CDoC CMac CNic EHul EOrn EPot ESis GAri MBal MBar MGos MPla NHol SBod SLim SPer WAbe |
| | – 'Gold Flake' | CBlo MBar MBri MGos |
| | – 'Gold Splash' | CBlo CKen GPin MBar |
| | – 'Golden Guinea' | Last listed 1998 |
| | – 'Golden King' | MAsh MBar SRms |
| § | – 'Golden Pot' | CBrm CDoC CKen CMac CSli EHul EOrn LBee LCon MBar MGos MOke MPla MWat NRoo SBod SMer WAbe WGwG WWal WWeb |
| § | – 'Golden Queen' | CKen CMHG EHul |
| | – 'Golden Showers' | CKen EHul |
| § | – 'Golden Spire' | LRHS MAsh MBar MBri MGos SBod |
| | – 'Golden Triumph' | CBlo EHul |
| | – 'Golden Wonder' | CDoC CMac CSli EHul IOrc LBee LBuc LCon LNet MAsh MBal MBar MGos NWea SRms WFar WStl |
| | – 'Goldfinger' | CKen NHol |
| | – "Grant's Gold" | EHul |
| | – 'Grayswood Feather' | CDoC CKen CTri EHul LBee LCon MAsh MBar MBri MGos MPla SLim SMer WWeb |
| | – 'Grayswood Gold' | CBlo CKen EHul EOrn LBee LLin MAsh MBar MGos MPla SSto |
| | – 'Grayswood Pillar' ♀ | CBlo CKen CMac EHul EOrn LBee LCon MBal MBar MGos |
| * | – 'Grayswood Spire' | CMac |
| | – 'Green Globe' | CBlo CDoC CKen CNic CSli EBrP EBre EHul EOrn EPot LBee LBre LCon LLin MAsh MBar MBri MPla NHol SBod SBre WAbe WDin |
| § | – 'Green Hedger' ♀ | CMac EHul ENot GRei LBuc MBar SBod SRms WFar |
| § | – 'Green Pillar' | CBrm CKen CTri EGra GAri IOrc LBee MAsh MBal MBar MGos MWat |
| | – 'Green Spire' | See *C. lawsoniana* 'Green Pillar' |
| | – 'Green Wall' | Last listed 1998 |
| ¶ | – 'Greycone' | CKen LBee |
| | – 'Hillieri' | MBar |
| | – "Hogger's Blue Gown" | See *C. lawsoniana* 'Blue Gown' |
| * | – "Hogger's Gold" | CBlo |
| | – "Howarth's Gold" | GAri MBri |
| * | – 'Imbricata' | MBlu |
| | – 'Imbricata Pendula' | CKen SMad |
| | – 'Intertexta' ♀ | CMHG EHul LCon WBcn WCwm |
| | – 'Ivonne' | EHul MGos |
| | – "Jackman's Green Hedger" | See *C. lawsoniana* 'Green Hedger' |
| | – "Jackman's Variety" | See *C. lawsoniana* 'Green Pillar' |
| | – 'Kelleriis Gold' | EHul LPan MBar |
| | – 'Killiney Gold' | Last listed 1998 |
| | – 'Kilmacurragh' ♀ | CMac ENot GRei LLin MAsh MBal MBar MGos NWea SPer WCwm |
| | – 'Kilworth Column' | CBlo LLin MGos |
| ¶ | – 'Kingswood' | MBri |
| | – 'Knowefieldensis' | CMac EHul LLin MAsh WBcn |
| § | – 'Lane' ♀ | CDoC CMac CSli EHul ENot EPfP LCon MAsh MBal MBar MGos NWea WFar |
| | – 'Lanei' | See *C. lawsoniana* 'Lane' |
| | – 'Lanei Aurea' | See *C. lawsoniana* 'Lane' |
| | – 'Lemon Flame' | NHol |
| | – 'Lemon Pillar' | CBlo |
| | – 'Lemon Queen' | CBlo EHul LBee LCon LRHS NBee |
| | – 'Limelight' | CKen EHul EPot MGos |
| | – 'Little Spire' | CDoC CMHG EBrP EBre EOrn EPla LBee LBre LCon LLin MAsh MBar MBri MGos MPla NHol SBre SLim WGor WWal |
| | – 'Lombartsii' | EHul WFar |
| | – 'Lutea' ♀ | CMac EHul LCon MBal MGos SBod SPer |
| § | – 'Lutea Nana' ♀ | CBlo CKen CMac EHul MAsh MBar MGos MOne WGwG WLRN |
| § | – 'Lutea Smithii' | EHul MBar NWea |
| | – 'Luteocompacta' | CKen LBee LRHS MGos |
| | – 'Lycopodioides' | EHul MBar SSmi |
| * | – "MacPenny's Gold" | CMac |
| | – 'Magnifica Aurea' | Last listed 1997 |
| | – 'Milford Blue Jacket' | See *C. lawsoniana* 'Blue Jacket' |
| § | – 'Minima' | MBar SRms WCFE |
| ◆ | – 'Minima Argentea' | See *C. lawsoniana* 'Nana Argentea' |
| | – 'Minima Aurea' ♀ | More than 30 suppliers |
| I | – 'Minima Densa' | See *C. lawsoniana* 'Minima' |
| | – 'Minima Glauca' ♀ | More than 30 suppliers |
| | – 'Moonlight' | CBlo MBar MGos MPla |
| | – 'Nana' | CMac MBar |
| § | – 'Nana Albospica' (v) | CKen EHul EOrn LBee LCon LLin MAsh MBal MBar MGos MPla NPro SLim SPla WFar WGwG WStl WWal |
| § | – 'Nana Argentea' | CKen CMac CSli ECho EHul EOrn EPfP GPin WGor |
| | – 'Nana Lutea' | See *C. lawsoniana* 'Lutea Nana' |
| | – 'New Silver' | CBlo |
| | – 'Nidiformis' | CBlo EHul LBee MBal MBar NWea SRms |
| | – 'Nivea' | Last listed 1996 |
| | – 'Nyewoods' | See *C. lawsoniana* 'Chilworth Silver' |
| | – 'Nymph' | See *C. lawsoniana* 'Ellwood's Nymph' |
| | – 'Parsons' | Last listed 1996 |

| | |
|---|---|
| - 'Pearl Nova' | CBlo |
| § - 'Pelt's Blue' ♀ | CBlo CDoC CKen CSli EHul LBee LCon MAsh MBar MBri MGos NBee SCoo SLim SMer WLRN |
| - 'Pembury Blue' ♀ | More than 30 suppliers |
| - 'Pendula' | LCon LLin MBar |
| § - 'Pick's Dwarf Blue' | CBlo EHul MBar MBri NHol |
| - Pot of Gold™ | See *C. lawsoniana* 'Golden Pot' |
| - 'Pottenii' | CDoC CMac CSli EHul IOrc LBee LCon MAsh MBal MBar MGos MPla MWat NBee NWea SBod SPer WDin WFar WStl |
| - 'Pygmaea Argentea' (v) ♀ | More than 30 suppliers |
| - 'Pygmy' | CBlo CNic CSli EHul ESis GAri MBar MOne MPla SLim WLRN |
| - 'Pyramidalis Lutea' | CKen |
| I - 'Reid's Own Number One' | Last listed 1997 |
| - 'Rijnhof' | EHul GAri LLin WBcn |
| ¶ - 'Rogersii' | EOrn MBar SRms WFar |
| - 'Romana' | ENot MAsh MBri |
| - 'Royal Gold' | CSli ECho EHul EOrn |
| - 'Silver Queen' (v) | CKen GChr GRei MBal MBar NWea WBcn |
| - 'Silver Threads' (v) | CMac CSli EBrP EBre EHul ENot EOrn EPla LBee LBre LCon LLin MAsh MBar MBri MGos MPla MWat SBre SLim WStl WWeb |
| - 'Silver Tip' (v) | EHul GPin SLim |
| - 'Smithii' Dallimore & Jackson | See *C. lawsoniana* 'Lutea Smithii' |
| - 'Snow Flurry' (v) | EHul |
| - 'Snow White' (v) | CDoC EBrP EBre EHul EPla LBee LBre LCon LLin MAsh MBar MBri MGos MPla NHol SBre SLim SPla WGor WWeb |
| - 'Somerset' | CBlo CMac MBar |
| § - 'Spek' | CB&S MBar |
| - 'Springtime' | CDoC EHul EOrn LCon MAsh MBri SLim WGor WWeb |
| - 'Stardust' ♀ | CChe CDoC CMac CSli EHul ENot GRei IOrc LCon LPan MAsh MBar MBri MGos MPla MWat NHol NRoo SBod SLim SPer WDin |
| - 'Stewartii' | CMac CTri ENot GChr MBal MBar MGos MPla NWea SBod SMer SPer WStl |
| - 'Stilton Cheese' | MBar |
| * - 'Summer Cream' | EHul |
| - 'Summer Snow' (v) | CB&S CDoC EHoe EHul ENot IOrc LBee LLin MAsh MBal MBar MBri MGos MPla SBod SLim SPla SRms WFar WGwG WStl WWal WWeb |
| - 'Summerford Spire' | Last listed 1996 |
| - 'Sunkist' | CKen MAsh WFar |
| ¶ - 'Sylvia's Gold' | EOrn |
| ¶ - 'Tamariscifolia' ♀ | CDoC EHul LCon MBal MBar SBod WDin WFar WGwG WLRN WStl WWal |
| - 'Temple's White' | CKen |
| - 'Tharandtensis Caesia' | EOrn LCon MBar SLon WFar |
| - 'Tilford' | EHul |
| - 'Treasure' (v) | CKen CSli EBrP EBre EHoe EHul EOrn EPla LBee LBre LCon LLin MAsh MBar MBri MGos NHol SBre SLim WGor |
| - 'Triomf van Boskoop' | MBar |
| - 'Van Pelt's Blue' | See *C. lawsoniana* 'Pelt's Blue' |
| - 'Versicolor' (v) | MBar |
| - 'Westermannii' (v) | CMac EHul LCon MBal SBod SLim SPer |

| | |
|---|---|
| - 'White Spot' (v) | CDoC CKen CSli EBrP EBre EHul LBee LBre LCon MBal MBar MBri MGos SBre SLim WStl WWal |
| - 'Winston Churchill' | CBlo LCon MAsh MBar MGos MPla SBod SPer |
| - 'Wisselii' ♀ | CDoC CKen CMac CTrG EHul ENot GChr LBee LCon LLin MAsh MBar NWea SBod SPer SRms WCFE WDin |
| - 'Wisselii Nana' | CKen EHul |
| - 'Wissel's Saguaro' | CKen LRHS MAsh |
| - 'Witzeliana' | CBlo ECho EOrn GPin MAsh MBar MBri MGos WGer WGor |
| - 'Wyevale Silver' | MBar |
| - 'Yellow Cascade' | ECho GPin MOne |
| - 'Yellow Queen' | See *C. lawsoniana* 'Golden Queen' |
| - 'Yellow Success' | See *C. lawsoniana* 'Golden Queen' |
| § - 'Yellow Transparent' | CDoC CMac CSli CTri LCon MBar MGos SBod SLim SPer WGor |
| - 'Yvonne' | CBlo EPla LCon LRHS MAsh MBar MBri NHol SLim SPla WWeb |
| **leylandii** | See x *Cupressocyparis leylandii* |
| **nootkatensis** | MBar SMer |
| - 'Aurea' | MAsh |
| - 'Aureovariegata' (v) | EHul SLim WBcn |
| - 'Compacta' | CBlo CTri MBar |
| - 'Glauca' | LCon MBar |
| - 'Gracilis' | EHul |
| - 'Jubilee' | SMad |
| - 'Lutea' | CMHG CMac CTri LCon MBal MBar NWea SLim |
| - 'Nidifera' | MBar WCwm |
| - 'Pendula' ♀ | CDoC EBrP EBre ENot EOrn IOrc LBre LCon LLin LNet LPan MAsh MBal MBar MBri MGos NBee NWea SBre SLim SMad SPer WCwm WDin WGer |
| I - 'Pendula Speech House' | WCwm |
| - 'Variegata' (v) | MBar SLim WBcn |
| **obtusa** 'Albospica' (v) | ECho EHul |
| - 'Albovariegata' (v) | CKen |
| - 'Aurea' | CDoC |
| I - 'Aureovariegata' | See *C. obtusa* 'Opaal' |
| - 'Aurora' | CKen EOrn LCon |
| * - 'Autumn Gold' | MBar |
| - 'Bambi' | CKen EOrn MGos |
| - 'Barkenny' | CKen |
| - 'Bartley' | CKen EPot |
| - 'Bassett' | CKen |
| - 'Bess' | CKen |
| - 'Caespitosa' | CKen EPot |
| - 'Chabo-yadori' | CBlo CDoC EHul EOrn LCon LLin MAsh MBal MBar MGos NHol SBod SLim WStl |
| - 'Chilworth' | CKen LCon MBar MGos |
| - 'Chima-anihiba' | CKen |
| - 'Chirimen' | CKen |
| ¶ - 'Clarke's Seedling' | MGos |
| - 'Confucius' | CBlo EHul NHol |
| - 'Contorta' | EOrn EPot LCon MBar |
| § - 'Coralliformis' | CMac ECho EOrn LLin MBal MBar NHol NPoe SMur WGwG |
| § - 'Crippsii' ♀ | CB&S CDoC CKen CMHG CMac EHul EOrn LCon MAsh MBal MBar MGos NHol SBod SLim SPla |
| - 'Crippsii Aurea' | See *C. obtusa* 'Crippsii' |
| - 'Dainty Doll' | CKen EOrn |
| - 'Densa' | See *C. obtusa* 'Nana Densa' |
| ¶ - 'Drath' | CBlo CDoC MBar WBcn |
| - 'Elf' | CKen |

| | | |
|---|---|---|
| - | 'Ellie B' | CKen EOrn |
| - | 'Ericoides' | CKen ECho EOrn GPin |
| - | 'Erika' | ECho EOrn GPin MPla WBcn |
| - | 'Fernspray Gold' | CBlo CDoC CKen CMac CSli CTri EHul ENot EOrn LCon LLin MAsh MBar MPla NHol SBod SLim WWeb |
| - | 'Flabelliformis' | CKen |
| - | 'Gimborn Beauty' | MGos |
| - | 'Golden Fairy' | CKen EOrn |
| - | 'Golden Filament' (v) | CKen |
| - | 'Golden Nymph' | CKen CSli EOrn MGos |
| - | 'Golden Sprite' | EBrP EBre EPot LBre MGos SBre |
| - | 'Goldilocks' | ECho EHul WAbe |
| - | 'Gracilis Aurea' | CKen |
| - | 'Graciosa' | See C. obtusa 'Loenik' |
| - | 'Hage' | CKen EOrn EPot LCon MGos MPla |
| - | 'Hypnoides Nana' | CKen EOrn |
| - | 'Intermedia' | CKen EOrn EPot MGos |
| - | 'Ivan's Column' | CKen |
| - | 'Juniperoides' | CKen EOrn |
| - | 'Juniperoides Compacta' | CKen EPot |
| - | 'Kamarachiba' | CKen SLim WBcn |
| - | 'Kanaamihiba' | MAsh MBar |
| - | 'Konijn' | EHul EOrn WLRN |
| - | 'Kosteri' | CDoC CKen CMac EBrP EBre EHul EOrn EPot ESis LBee LBre LCon LLin MBar MGos MPla NHed SBre SIng SLim WStI |
| - | 'Laxa' | LCon |
| ¶ - | 'Leprechaun' | LCon |
| - | 'Little Markey' | CKen EOrn |
| § - | 'Loenik' | EOrn MBar NHol |
| - | 'Lycopodioides' | EOrn EPot |
| ¶ - | 'Lycopodioides Aurea' | SLim |
| - | 'Marian' | CKen |
| § - | 'Mariesii' (v) | CKen CSli EOrn LCon MAsh |
| - | 'Minima' | CKen MGos |
| - | 'Nana' ♀ | CBlo CKen CMac EPot GAri LBee LCon MBar MGos MPla NHol SIng SSmi |
| - | 'Nana Albospica' | ECho |
| - | 'Nana Aurea' ♀ | CDoC CMac CSli EBrP EBre EHul EOrn EPot GPin LBre LLin MAsh MBar MGos MWat NHol NPro NWea SBre SIgm SIng SMer WStI WWeb |
| - | 'Nana Compacta' | EOrn LCon |
| § - | 'Nana Densa' | CKen CMac |
| - | 'Nana Gracilis' ♀ | More than 30 suppliers |
| I - | 'Nana Gracilis Aurea' | EHul SMur |
| I - | 'Nana Lutea' | CBlo CDoC CKen CSli EBrP EBre EHul EOrn EPfP EPla ESis LBee LBre LCon LLin MAsh MBar MBri MGos MPla NHed NHol NRoo SBod SBre SLim SPla SSmi WGer |
| - | 'Nana Pyramidalis' | CBlo |
| - | 'Nana Rigida' | See C. obtusa 'Rigid Dwarf' |
| - | 'Nana Variegata' | See C. obtusa 'Mariesii' |
| § - | 'Opaal' (v) | MBar WBcn |
| - | 'Pygmaea' | EBrP EBre EHul ENot EOrn EPot ESis LBre LCon LLin MAsh MBal MBar MGos MPla SBod SBre SLim SPla WWal |
| - | 'Pygmaea Aurescens' | MBar SIng |
| - | 'Reis Dwarf' | Last listed 1997 |
| - | 'Repens' | EOrn WBcn |
| § - | 'Rigid Dwarf' | CKen EHul EOrn EPot IMGH LBee LCon LRHS MBar WLRN |
| * - | 'Saint Andrew' | CKen |
| - | 'Snowflake' (v) | CKen EOrn MGos WBcn WGor |
| - | 'Snowkist' (v) | CKen |
| - | 'Spiralis' | CKen MBar |
| - | 'Stoneham' | CKen EPot LCon MBar |
| - | 'Tempelhof' | CKen EHul EOrn LCon LLin MAsh MBar MGos MPla NHed SBod SLim SMer SPla WStI WWeb |
| - | 'Tetragona Aurea' ♀ | CB&S CMac EGra EHul EOrn EPot GPin IMGH LCon MBar MGos SBod SLim WGer |
| - | 'Tonia' (v) | CBlo CDoC CKen EHul EOrn ESis MAsh MBri NHol SLim WLRN |
| ♦ - | 'Torulosa' | See C. obtusa 'Coralliformis' |
| ¶ - | 'Tsatsumi Gold' | CKen |
| ¶ - | 'Verdon' | MAsh |
| - | 'Watchi' | Last listed 1997 |
| - | 'Wissel' | CKen EOrn |
| - | 'Yellowtip' (v) | CKen EHul LCon MAsh MBar MGos |
| **pisifera** | | CSli GAri |
| - | 'Aurea Nana' misapplied | See C. pisifera 'Strathmore' |
| - | 'Avenue' | CBlo EHul LCon LLin MPla NHol |
| - | 'Baby Blue' | LCon SLim |
| ¶ - | 'Blue Globe' | CKen EOrn |
| - | 'Blue Tower' | CBlo |
| - | 'Boulevard' ♀ | More than 30 suppliers |
| - | 'Compacta' | ECho EOrn MLan NHed |
| - | 'Compacta Variegata' | ECho EHul EOrn MBar NHed |
| - | 'Curly Tops' | CKen LCon MGos SLim WBcn |
| - | 'Devon Cream' | LBee LLin MAsh MBar MPla NHol SBod WWeb |
| - | 'Filifera' | CBlo CMac EBrP EBre LBre MBal MBar SBod SBre SLim SLon WFar |
| - | 'Filifera Aurea' ♀ | CGre CKen CMac EBrP EBre EHul EOrn LBee LBre LCon LLin LNet MAsh MBal MBar MBri NBee NWea SBod SBre SRms WDin WFar |
| - | 'Filifera Aureovariegata' (v) | CMac CSli EBrP EBre EHul GAri LBre LLin MBal MBar SBre SLim |
| - | 'Filifera Nana' | CDoC EBrP EBre EHul EOrn LBre LCon MBal MBar MBri MOne MWat NHed SBre SPer STre WDin WFar |
| I - | 'Filifera Sungold' | See C. pisifera 'Sungold' |
| ¶ - | 'Fuiri-tsukomo' | CKen |
| * - | 'Gold Cascade' | MGos |
| - | 'Gold Cushion' | CKen |
| - | 'Gold Dust' | See C. pisifera 'Plumosa Aurea' |
| - | 'Gold Spangle' | EHul EOrn MBar MGos SBod WFar |
| - | 'Golden Mop' ♀ | CKen EHul LCon MAsh WAbe |
| - | 'Hime-himuro' | CKen |
| - | 'Hime-sawara' | CKen EOrn EPot |
| * - | 'Minima Aurea' | CKen |
| - | 'Nana' | CKen EBrP EBre EHul EPfP GAri GPin IOrc LBre LLin MAsh MBal MBar MWat NHed NHol SBod SBre SMer WFar |
| I - | 'Nana Albovariegata' | CBlo CDoC EOrn MBar MBri NPro SBod SSmi |
| § - | 'Nana Aureovariegata' | CDoC CMac CSli EHul ESis IMGH IOrc LBee LCon MAsh MBal MBar MBri MPla MWat NHed NHol SBod SLim SPer SSmi WFar WWal |
| I - | 'Nana Compacta' | CMac SRms |
| - | 'Nana Variegata' | CSli ECho LBee MAsh MBar MGos SLim |
| I - | 'Parslorii' | CKen |
| - | 'Pici' | CKen |
| - | 'Plumosa' | MBal SRms |
| - | 'Plumosa Albopicta' (v) | MBal MBar SBod |
| § - | 'Plumosa Aurea' | CKen EHul MAsh MBal MBar NWea WDin WFar |

| | | |
|---|---|---|
| - | 'Plumosa Aurea Compacta' | CBlo CKen CMac GAri LCon MPla NHed |
| I - | 'Plumosa Aurea Compacta Variegata' | CMac |
| - | 'Plumosa Aurea Nana' | CBlo CDoC ENot MAsh MBal MBar MGos MPla NBee NHed WGwG WWal |
| I - | 'Plumosa Aurea Nana Compacta' | CMac SBod |
| - | 'Plumosa Aurescens' | CMac |
| § - | 'Plumosa Compressa' | CDoC CKen CSli EHul EOrn ESis LBee LCon MBar MGos NHed SLim WGor WGwG |
| - | 'Plumosa Densa' | See C. pisifera 'Plumosa Compressa' |
| - | 'Plumosa Flavescens' | CDoC EHul GPin LLin MBar MPla NHed |
| I - | 'Plumosa Juniperoides' | CKen EBrP EBre EHul EOrn LBre MAsh MBar MOne MPla SBre |
| - | 'Plumosa Purple Dome' | See C. pisifera 'Purple Dome' |
| I - | 'Plumosa Pygmaea' | ECho MGos MLan WGor |
| § - | 'Plumosa Rogersii' | CDoC EHul EOrn MBar MGos MPla SBod |
| § - | 'Purple Dome' | CSli EHul EOrn MBar MGos SBod WLRN |
| - | 'Rogersii' | See C. pisifera 'Plumosa Rogersii' |
| - | 'Silver and Gold' (v) | CBlo CSli EHul MBar |
| - | 'Silver Lode' (v) | CKen EOrn |
| - | 'Snow' (v) | CKen CMac EOrn GAri MBal MBar MPla SBod SIng SMer WDin |
| - | 'Snowflake' | CKen EHul |
| ¶ - | 'Spaan's Cannon Ball' | CKen |
| - | 'Spindrift' | Last listed 1998 |
| § - | 'Squarrosa' | GAri MBal MBar NWea WDin WFar WGor |
| N - | 'Squarrosa Argentea' | MBal |
| - | 'Squarrosa Dumosa' | CKen CSli EHul MBar |
| - | 'Squarrosa Intermedia' | EHul LLin MBar MGos |
| I - | 'Squarrosa Lombarts' | CMac CSli EBrP EBre EHul EOrn LBee LBre LCon LLin MBar MPla MWat NHed NPro SBod SBre SSmi WGwG |
| - | 'Squarrosa Lutea' | CKen MAsh MBar NPro |
| - | 'Squarrosa Sulphurea' | CDoC CMac CSli EBrP EBre EHul EOrn EPfP LBee LBre LCon LLin MAsh MBal MBar MPla NBee SBod SBre SLim SPer WDin WFar WWal |
| - | 'Squarrosa Veitchii' | See C. pisifera 'Squarrosa' |
| § - | 'Strathmore' | CKen EHul LLin MAsh MBar NHol SPla WWal |
| § - | 'Sungold' | CDoC CKen CSli CTri EGra EHul ENot LCon LLin MAsh MBar MBri MPla SBod SLim WAbe |
| - | 'Tama-himuro' | CKen LLin MGos SLim |
| - | 'White Beauty' (v) | CKen |
| * - | 'White Brocade' | CMac |
| - | 'White Pygmy' | EOrn EPot MAsh |
| **thyoides** | | Last listed 1996 |
| - | 'Andelyensis' ♀ | CBlo CDoC CMac EHul EOrn GAri LLin MAsh MBal MBar MPla NHol |
| - | 'Andelyensis Nana' ♀ | CKen WPyg |
| - | 'Aurea' | EHul MBar WBcn |
| - | 'Conica' | CKen CSli MAsh |
| - | 'Ericoides' ♀ | CBlo CDoC CKen CMac CSam CSli CTri EHul EOrn LBee LLin MAsh MBal MBar MWat NHed SBod SPer WDin WFar WGwG WPyg WWal |
| § - | 'Glauca' | EOrn |
| § - | 'Kewensis' | See C. thyoides 'Glauca' |

| | | |
|---|---|---|
| - | 'Purple Heather' | LRHS SMur |
| - | 'Red Star' | See C. thyoides 'Rubicon' |
| § - | 'Rubicon' | CBlo CKen CMac CSli EBrP EBre EHul EOrn EPla ESis LBee LBre LCon LLin MAsh MBar MGos MPla NHed SBod SBre SLim SPla WFar WGer |
| - | 'Schumaker's Blue Dwarf' | EPla WBcn |
| - | 'Top Point' | CKen EOrn LCon SLim |
| - | 'Variegata' (v) | ECho EHul MBar |

## CHAMAECYTISUS (Papilionaceae)

| | | |
|---|---|---|
| § | **albus** | ENot GQui SDix SPer WDin WStI |
| | danubialis HH&K 327 | CHan |
| | glaber | Last listed 1997 |
| § | **hirsutus** | CFil CHan SBid WLin WPGP |
| ♦ - | **demissus** | See C. polytrichus |
| ¶ - | subsp. **hirsutissimus** | WLin |
| § | **polytrichus** ♀ | EPot MHar WLin |
| | proliferus | Last listed 1998 |
| § | **purpureus** | CABP EBee EBrP EBre ELan IOrc LBre LHop MBal MBar MBri MGos MPla MRav SBre SPer SRPl WAbe WDin WFar WPat |
| - | f. **albus** | EPfP MBar MPla SPer WBcn |
| § - | 'Atropurpureus' ♀ | ENot MPla NFla NHol SPer |
| - | 'Incarnatus' | See C. purpureus 'Atropurpureus' |
| | pygmaeus C&W 3818 | Last listed 1998 |
| § | **supinus** | EBee LHop MNrw SHFr SRms |

## CHAMAEDAPHNE (Ericaceae)

| | | |
|---|---|---|
| § | **calyculata** | CB&S GEil LRHS SPer WSHC |
| - | 'Nana' | CMHG EHic MBal MBar MGos MPla SRPl |

## CHAMAEDOREA (Arecaceae)

| | | |
|---|---|---|
| ¶ | **cataractarum** | CBrP |
| | costaricana | Last listed 1997 |
| | **elegans** ♀ | LPal MBri |
| | erumpens | See C. seifrizii |
| | linearis | LPal |
| | metallica Cook ♀ | LPal |
| - | hort. | See C. microspadix |
| § | **microspadix** | CRoM LPJP LPal |
| | radicalis | CBrP LPJP LPal |
| § | **seifrizii** ♀ | LPal |

## CHAMAELIRIUM (Melanthiaceae)

| | | |
|---|---|---|
| | **luteum** | WThi |

## CHAMAEMELUM (Asteraceae)

| | | |
|---|---|---|
| § | **nobile** | CArn CBrm CSev ELau GBar GPoy LHol MBar MBri MMal NNrd NRoo SIde SPlb SRms WJek WOak WPer WSel WWye |
| - | 'Flore Pleno' (d) | More than 30 suppliers |
| - | 'Treneague' | CArn CBre CBrm CSev ELan ELau EOHP GAbr GPoy LHol LMor MAvo MBri NFor NHol NLon NRoo NSti SIde SIng SRms WFar WHal WHer WJek WOak WPer WSel WWat WWye |

## CHAMAENERION See EPILOBIUM

## CHAMAEPERICLYMENUM See CORNUS

## CHAMAEROPS (Arecaceae)

| | | |
|---|---|---|
| | **excelsa** Thunberg | See Rhapis excelsa |
| - | hort. | See Trachycarpus fortunei |

*humilis* ♀ | CAbb CB&S CBrP CFil CRoM
 | CTbh CTrC CWSG EOas GOrc
 | IOrc LHil LPJP LPal MCCP NMoo
 | NPal NRog SAPC SArc SDry SEND
 | SPar WGer WMul WPGP WPic
- 'Cerifera' | CBrP LPal
- silver back | NPal

## CHAMAESCILLA (Anthericaceae)
*corymbosa* | Last listed 1998

## CHAMAESPARTIUM See GENISTA

## CHAMBEYRONIA (Arecaceae)
*macrocarpa* | CBrP LPal

## CHAMELAUCIUM (Myrtaceae)
*uncinatum* | ECon LRHS

## CHARA (Charophyceae)
*vulgaris* | SAWi

## CHASMANTHE (Iridaceae)
*aethiopica* | CPou MBel
*bicolor* | CPou SMrm
*floribunda* | LBow
- var. *duckittii* | Last listed 1998

## CHASMANTHIUM (Poaceae)
§ *latifolium* | More than 30 suppliers

## CHEILANTHES (Adiantaceae)
*alabamensis* | Last listed 1996
*bonariensis* | Last listed 1996
¶ *distans* | WRic
*eatonii* | Last listed 1997
*feei* | Last listed 1998
*hirta* var. *ellisiana* | Last listed 1996
*kaulfussii* | Last listed 1996
*lanosa* | SRms
*lendigera* | Last listed 1996
§ *nivea* | Last listed 1998
*pulchella* | Last listed 1996
*tomentosa* | LHil WRic

## CHEIRANTHUS See ERYSIMUM

## CHELIDONIUM (Papaveraceae)
*japonicum* | See *Hylomecon japonica*
*majus* | CArn CFri CKin CRow ELau
 | EWFC GPoy MChe MHew MSal
 | NHex SIde WCHb WHer WRHF
 | WShi WWye
- 'Bowles' Variety' | EBee
- 'Flore Pleno' (d) | CBre CGle CRow ECoo ELan
 | GBar GCHN NBrk NBro NSti
 | WCHb WCot WHer WOve
- var. *laciniatum* | CInt EMon GBar NSti WCHb
 | WRha
- 'Laciniatum Flore Pleno' | CRow EBee EMar IBlr NBro WCot
 (d) | WPer

## CHELONE (Scrophulariaceae)
*barbata* | See *Penstemon barbatus*
§ *glabra* | More than 30 suppliers
*lyonii* | ETen NCut NLar SHFr WShi
*obliqua* | More than 30 suppliers
- var. *alba* | See *C. glabra*
- *rosea* | LRHS

## CHELONOPSIS (Lamiaceae)
*moschata* | EBee ECha EMan

## CHENOPODIUM (Chenopodiaceae)
*ambrosioides* | WJek
*bonus-henricus* | CArn ELau GAbr GBar GPoy ILis
 | MChe SIde WCHb WHer WOak
 | WPer WSel WWye
*botrys* | MSal

## CHIASTOPHYLLUM (Crassulaceae)
§ *oppositifolium* ♀ | CGle ECha ELan EPar ESis GCHN
 | MBal MBar MBro MFir MMal
 | MRav MWat NRoo NWCA SHel
 | SIng SMer SPlb SRms SSmi WAbe
 | WCot WEas WFar WHoo WWin
 | WWye
- 'Frosted Jade' | See *C. oppositifolium* 'Jim's Pride'
§ - 'Jim's Pride' (v) | CHar CRow EAst EDAr EMon ESis
 | EWes GMaP LBee LHop MAvo
 | MHlr MRav NArg NMGW NMen
 | NPer NVic SCob SIng SLod SRms
 | SRot WAbe WCot WFar WRHF
 | WRus WWin WWye
*simplicifolium* | See *C. oppositifolium*

## CHILIOTRICHUM (Asteraceae)
*diffusum* | CPle ECou EHic GChr GDra GEil
 | GOrc GSki IDee IMGH MBlu
 | SMad SPer
¶ - 'Siska' | EBee IMGH

## CHILOPSIS (Bignoniaceae)
*linearis* | Last listed 1998

## CHIMAPHILA (Pyrolaceae)
*maculata* | Last listed 1997
*umbellata* | Last listed 1997

## CHIMONANTHUS (Calycanthaceae)
*fragrans* | See *C. praecox*
*nitens* | CMCN
§ *praecox* | More than 30 suppliers
- 'Grandiflorus' ♀ | CEnd ENot
- var. *luteus* ♀ | CBlo CEnd CPMA ENot EPfP
 | LRHS WWeb
- 'Mangetsu' | SSta
- 'Trenython' | CEnd CPMA SSta
*yunnanensis* | CGre EPfP
*zhejiangensis* | EPfP

## CHIMONOBAMBUSA (Poaceae)
*falcata* | See *Drepanostachyum falcatum*
*hookeriana* hort. | See *Himalayacalamus falconeri*
 | 'Damarapa'
*macrophylla* | EPla SDry
 f. *intermedia* |
§ *marmorea* | CFil EOas EPla ISta LJus MMoz
 | MUlv SDry WBay WJun WPGP
- 'Variegata' | CFil EFul EPla ISta LJus MTed
 | SDry WBay WJun WPGP
§ *quadrangularis* | CFil EFul EPla ERod GAri ISta LJus
 | SDry WBay WJun WPGP
¶ - f. *nagaminea* | EPla
- 'Svow' (v) | EPla ISta SDry
§ *tumidissinoda* | EPla ISta NDov SDry

## CHIOGENES See GAULTHERIA

## CHIONANTHUS (Oleaceae)
*retusus* | CMCN EPfP MBlu WWat
*virginicus* | CB&S CBlo CDoC CEnd CFil
 | CMCN CPMA ELan EPfP IOrc
 | MBlu MBri MPla NFla SMad SSpi
 | SSta WDin WHCG WWat

## CHIONOCHLOA (Poaceae)

| | |
|---|---|
| *conspicua* | CDoC CElw CFil CHan EWes GAbr GAri MBal MFir NBir WLRN WPGP |
| – 'Rubra' | See *C. rubra* |
| *flavescens* | GBin GSki |
| *flavicans* | EBee MBel |
| § *rubra* | CElw CFil EBee EHoe EMon EPPr EPla EWes LEdu MMoz SApp SCob WCot WPGP |

## CHIONODOXA ✿ (Hyacinthaceae)

| | |
|---|---|
| *cretica* | See *C. nana* |
| § *forbesii* | CBro EPar EPot SRms WPer WShi |
| – 'Alba' | ECho EPar LAma NRog |
| – 'Blue Giant' | EPot LRHS |
| – 'Pink Giant' | CAvo CBro ELan EPar EPot ETub LAma NEgg WCot |
| – 'Rosea' | EPar LAma NRog |
| § – Siehei Group ♀ | CBro |
| *gigantea* | See *C. luciliae* Gigantea Group |
| *luciliae* Boiss. ♀ | CAvo CBro EPar EPot ETub LAma MBal MBri NRog |
| § – Gigantea Group | ELan EPar EPot ETub LAma NEgg NRog SRms |
| – 'Alba' | EPar EPot GCrs |
| *luciliae* hort. | See *C. forbesii* |
| * *mariesii* | LAma |
| § *nana* | EHyt |
| *sardensis* ♀ | CAvo CBro EPar EPot LAma MBNS MBal NEgg NRog WPer |
| *siehei* | See *C. forbesii* Siehei Group |
| *tmolusi* | See *C. forbesii* 'Tmoli' |

## CHIONOGRAPHIS (Liliaceae)

| | |
|---|---|
| *japonica* | EFEx |

## CHIONOHEBE (Scrophulariaceae)

| | |
|---|---|
| *armstrongii* | EPot ITim |
| *densifolia* | ECou EPot GCrs NHed WPat |
| *pulvinaris* | CPBP GCrs ITim NHar NSla WAbe |

## x CHIONOSCILLA (Hyacinthaceae)

| | |
|---|---|
| § *allenii* | LAma |

## CHIRITA (Gesneriaceae)

| | |
|---|---|
| ¶ *linearifolia* | WDib |
| *sinensis* ♀ | CHal WDib |

## CHIRONIA (Gentianaceae)

| | |
|---|---|
| *baccifera* | Last listed 1997 |

## CHLIDANTHUS (Amaryllidaceae)

| | |
|---|---|
| *fragrans* | NRog WCot |

## CHLORANTHUS (Chloranthaceae)

| | |
|---|---|
| ¶ *fortunei* | SBla WCru |
| ¶ *japonicus* | SWas WCru WThi |
| *oldhamii* B&SWJ 2019 | WCru |
| *serratus* | WCru |

## CHLOROPHYTUM (Anthericaceae)

| | |
|---|---|
| *comosum* 'Mandanum' (v) | CHal |
| – 'Variegatum' ♀ | CHal LChe MBri SRms |
| – 'Vittatum' (v) ♀ | SRms |
| § *laxum* 'Bichetii' (v) | WCot |
| – 'Variegatum' | See *C. laxum* 'Bichetii' |
| § *majus* | WCot |
| *nepalense* B&SWJ 2393 | WCru |

## CHOISYA (Rutaceae)

| | |
|---|---|
| 'Aztec Pearl' ♀ | More than 30 suppliers |
| *dumosa* var. *arizonica* | SDry |
| ¶ – var. *mollis* | SLon |
| *ternata* ♀ | More than 30 suppliers |
| § – Moonshine = 'Walchoi' | LRHS |
| – Moonsleeper | See *C. ternata* Sundance = 'Lich' |
| § – Sundance = 'Lich' ♀ | More than 30 suppliers |
| ◆ – 'Walchoi' | See *C. ternata* Moonshine = 'Walchoi' |

## CHONDROPETALUM (Restionaceae)

| | |
|---|---|
| ¶ *mucronatum* | CCpl |
| *tectorum* | CAbb CTrC IDac WMul WNor |

## CHONDROSUM (Poaceae)

| | |
|---|---|
| *gracile* | See *Bouteloua gracilis* |

## CHORDOSPARTIUM (Papilionaceae)

| | |
|---|---|
| *muritai* | ECou |
| ¶ – 'Huia Gilpen' | ECou |
| ¶ – 'Ron Feron' | ECou |
| ¶ – 'Wayne Nichols' | ECou |
| *stevensonii* | CPle ECou EPfP SBid WHer |
| – 'Duncan' | ECou |
| – 'Kiwi' | ECou |
| – 'Miller' | ECou |

## CHORIZEMA (Papilionaceae)

| | |
|---|---|
| *cordatum* ♀ | CPIN |
| *dicksonii* | Last listed 1998 |
| *diversifolium* | CPIN ERea |
| *ilicifolium* | CAbb CB&S CPIN CSPN CWSG ERea GQui SBid SBra |

## CHRYSALIDOCARPUS (Arecaceae)

| | |
|---|---|
| *lutescens* | See *Dypsis lutescens* |

## CHRYSANTHEMOPSIS See RHODANTHEMUM

## CHRYSANTHEMUM (Asteraceae)

| | |
|---|---|
| 'Adorn' (22d) | MCol |
| 'Agnes Ann' (29K) | MCol |
| ¶ 'Aimee Jane' (24b) | MCol |
| 'Alan Rowe' (5a) | Last listed 1997 |
| 'Albert Broadhurst' (24b) | NHal |
| 'Albert's Yellow' (29Rub) | MCol MMil |
| 'Alexis' (5a) | Last listed 1997 |
| 'Alfreton Cream' (5b) | Last listed 1996 |
| 'Aline' (29K) | Last listed 1997 |
| 'Alison' (29c) | LRHS |
| 'Alison Kirk' (23b) | NHal |
| 'Allouise' (25b) ♀ | MCol NHal |
| 'Allure' (22d) | Last listed 1997 |
| *alpinum* | See *Leucanthemopsis alpina* |
| 'Amber Enbee Wedding' (29d) ♀ | Last listed 1997 |
| 'Amber Yvonne Arnaud' (24b) ♀ | Last listed 1995 |
| 'American Beauty' (5b) | Last listed 1998 |
| 'Amy Shoesmith' (15a) | MCol |
| 'Anastasia' (28) | CElw CHid CLTr ECtt EMan EPPr GMac LHop MCol MHlr MMil MRav NBrk NFai NSti SEas SPla SRms SUsu WCot WEas WFar WPer WRHF WWin |
| N 'Anastasia Variegated' (28) | CSam MBel NSti WCot WHer |
| 'Anastasia White' (28) | WCot WIvy |
| 'Angelic' (28) | MCol |
| 'Angora' (25b) ♀ | MCol |

'Anja's Bouquet' — Last listed 1998
'Ann Brook' (23b) — Last listed 1997
'Anna Marie' (18c) ♀ — MCol
'Annapurna' (3b) — Last listed 1997
'Anne' (29K) — Last listed 1997
'Anne, Lady Brocket' — CLTr EFou EMon GBuc MBel MNrw NBrk WCot WMaN
'Apollo' (29K) — EFou EMon EWll LRHS SMer
'Apricot' (29Rub) — EBrP EBre ECtt EFou EPPr LBre MFir MRav SBre SMad SSoC SSvw WCot
'Apricot Alexis' (5a) — Last listed 1997
'Apricot Cassandra' (5b) — Last listed 1996
'Apricot Chessington' (25a) — NHal
'Apricot Chivenor' (9c) — NHal
'Apricot Courtier' (24a) — NHal
'Apricot Enbee Wedding' (29d) — Last listed 1996
'Apricot Margaret' (29c) ♀ — MCol
'Archie Benson' (3b) — Last listed 1998
'Arctic' (9c) — MCol
'Arctic Beauty' (4b) — Last listed 1996
*arcticum* L. — See *Arctanthemum arcticum*
*argenteum* — See *Tanacetum argenteum*
'Audrey Shoesmith' (3a) — Last listed 1997
'Aunt Millicent' (29K) — MCol
'Aurora' (4a) — Last listed 1996
'Autumn Days' (25b) — MCol NHal
'Autumn Sonata' — Last listed 1997
'Babs' (28) — MMil
'Baden Locke' (24b) — Last listed 1997
'Bagley Cream' (3b) — MCol
'Bagley Glow' (4b) — MCol
'Bagley Pink' (14b) — MCol
'Balcombe Perfection' (5a) — MCol NHal WWol
*balsamita* — See *Tanacetum balsamita*
¶ 'Barbara Ward' (7b) — MCol
Barbara = 'Yobarbara' (22) — EPfP MCol NHal WLRN
'Beacon' (5a) ♀ — NHal
'Belair' (9c) — MCol
'Belle' (29K) — LRHS
'Beppie' (29e) — MCol
'Bernadette Wade' (25b) — WWol
'Bertos' — Last listed 1997
'Bessie Rowe' (25a) — MCol
'Betty' (29K) — MCol
'Betty Wiggins' (25b) — MCol
'Bill Bye' (1) — NHal
'Bill Sands' (3a) — Last listed 1996
'Bill Wade' (25a) — MCol
'Black Magic' (24b) — MCol
'Bob Dear' (25a) — MCol
'Bonnie Jean' (9d) — Last listed 1997
'Bo-peep' (28) — MCol
Bravo = 'Yobravo' (22c) ♀ — EPfP MCol
* 'Breitner's Supreme' — MCAu WCot
'Brenda Rowe' (5a) — MCol
'Brendon' (9c) — Last listed 1996
'Brierton Celebration' (7b) — Last listed 1996
'Brietner' (24b) — MCol MNrw
'Bright Eye' (28) — MCol WPer
'Bright Golden Princess Anne' (4b) — Last listed 1997
'Brightness' (29K) — NFai SChu SUsu WEas
'Broadacre' (7a) — MCol
'Broadway Mandy' (29c) — NHal
¶ 'Bronze Beauty' — WFar
'Bronze Belair' (9c) — MCol
'Bronze Bornholm' (14b) — MCol
'Bronze Cassandra' (5b) ♀ — NHal
'Bronze Dee Gem' (29c) — NHal

§ 'Bronze Elegance' (28b) — CLTr CM&M CSam EFou ELan EMan EMon LLWP MLLN NGdn NSti SIng SPer SPla SRms SUsu WAbe WEas WIvy WMaN WWat
'Bronze Elite' (29d) — Last listed 1997
'Bronze Enbee Wedding' (29d) ♀ — MCol NHal
'Bronze Fairy' (28a) — MCol
¶ 'Bronze John Wingfield' (14b) — NHal
'Bronze John Wingfield' (24b) — Last listed 1997
'Bronze Margaret' (29c) ♀ — MCol NHal
'Bronze Maria' (18a) — MCol
'Bronze Matlock' (24b) — NHal
'Bronze Max Riley' (23b) — NHal WWol
'Bronze Mayford Perfection' (5a) ♀ — MCol NHal
'Bronze Mei-kyo' — See *C.* 'Bronze Elegance'
'Bronze Pamela' — See *C.* 'Pamela'
'Bronze Pennine Goal' (29c) — Last listed 1998
¶ 'Bronze Yvonne Arnaud' (24b) — MCol
'Bronzetti' — Last listed 1997
'Brown Eyes' (29K) — WWin
'Bruera' (24a) — NHal
'Bryan Kirk' (4b) — NHal WWol
§ 'Buff Margaret' (29c) — Last listed 1997
'Buff Peter Rowe' (23b) — NHal
'Bullfinch' (12a) — Last listed 1998
'Bunty' (28) — LRHS
¶ 'Butter Milk' (25c) — MCol
'Cameo' (28a) ♀ — MCol WIvy
'Candid' (15b) — MCol
¶ 'Candlewick Limelight' (29d) ♀ — MCol
'Candylite' (14b) — MCol
'Cappa' (9a) — Last listed 1996
'Carlene Welby' (25b) — NHal
'Carmine Blush' — EFou WCot
'Caroline Barclay' (14a) — WWol
I 'Cassandra' (5b) — NHal
¶ 'Challenger' (25b) — MCol
'Charles Tandy' (5a) — Last listed 1997
'Charles Wood' (25a) — Last listed 1997
'Cheddar' (13a) — MCol
¶ 'Cherry Chessington' (25a) — NHal
'Cherry Dynasty' (14a) — Last listed 1996
'Cherry Enbee Wedding' (29d) — WWol
'Cherry Margaret' (29c) — NHal
'Chessington' (25a) — MCol NHal
'Chester Globe' (23b) — NHal
'Chesterfield' (15b) — WWol
'Chestnut Talbot Parade' (29c) ♀ — NHal
'Chivenor' (9c) — MCol NHal
'Christine' (28) — Last listed 1996
'Christine Hall' (25a) — MCol
'Christmas Wine' (5a) — Last listed 1996
'Christopher Lawson' (24a) — NHal
*cinerariifolium* — See *Tanacetum cinerariifolium*
I 'Citrus' (8) — EFou
'Clara Curtis' (29Rub) — More than 30 suppliers
'Clare Dobson' (25b) — Last listed 1997
'Clare Louise' (24b) — Last listed 1997
'Claudia' (24c) — MCol
*clusii* — See *Tanacetum corymbosum* subsp. *clusii*
*coccineum* — See *Tanacetum coccineum*
'Colossus' (24a) — MCol NHal

'Columbine' (29K)   Last listed 1997
'Copper Margaret' (29c)   Last listed 1998
'Copper Nob' (29K)   Last listed 1998
'Cornetto' (25b)   MCol NHal
'Corngold' (5b)   NHal
*corymbosum*   See *Tanacetum corymbosum*
'Cossack' (2)   Last listed 1998
'Cottage Apricot'   CHea EWoo GMac LHop MBNS
    SMrm SUsu WCot WEas WRHF
'Cottage Pink'   See *C.* 'Emperor of China'
¶ 'Cottingham' (25a)   MCol
'Courtier' (24a)   NHal
'Cream Elegance' (9c)   NHal
'Cream John Hughes' (3b)   NHal
'Cream Margaret' (29c) ♀   NHal
'Cream Pauline White' (15a)   Last listed 1997
'Cream Pennine Serene'   Last listed 1996
    (29d)
'Cream Pennine Thrill' (29)   Last listed 1996
'Cream West Bromwich'   Last listed 1997
    (14a)
'Creamist' (25b) ♀   MCol
'Cricket' (25b)   MCol
'Crimson Yvonne Arnaud'   MCol
    (24b) ♀
'Cropthorne'   Last listed 1996
'Cygnet' (24b)   Last listed 1996
'Dana' (25b) ♀   NHal
'Daniel Cooper' (29Rub)   MCol
'Danielle' (29d)   MCol
* 'Daphne'   Last listed 1997
'Dark Corfu'   Last listed 1996
¶ Dark Triumph =   WLRN
    'Dark Yotri' (22)
'David Shoesmith' (25a)   MCol
¶ 'Dawn Jackson' (29d)   MCol
'Deane Dainty' (9f) ♀   MCol
'Deane Joy' (9a)   Last listed 1996
'Deane Snow' (9a)   Last listed 1996
'Debbie' (29K)   Last listed 1997
Debonair =   EPfP MCol NHal WLRN
    'Yodebo' (22c) ♀
'Dee Candy' (29c)   NHal
'Dee Crimson' (29c)   NHal
'Dee Gem' (29c) ♀   NHal
'Dee Pink' (29c)   Last listed 1997
'Denise' (28) ♀   MCol WLRN
'Dennis Fletcher' (25a)   Last listed 1998
'Derek Bircumshaw' (28a)   MCol
'Deva Glow' (25a)   MCol NHal
'Diamond Wedding' (25a)   Last listed 1996
§ 'Doctor Tom Parr' (28)   CGle EFou ELan EMon LGre MBel
    MFir NBrk SUsu
'Domingo' (4b)   WWol
Donna = 'Yodon' (22f)   MCol
'Doreen Burton' (25b)   MCol
'Doreen Hall' (15a)   MCol
'Doreen Statham' (4b)   NHal WWol
'Doris' (29K)   Last listed 1997
'Dorothy Stone' (25b)   NHal
'Dorridge Beauty' (24a)   NHal WWol
'Dorridge Bolero' (24a)   Last listed 1998
'Dorridge Celebration' (3b)   WWol
'Dorridge Crystal' (24a)   NHal WWol
'Dorridge Dawn' (4b)   Last listed 1998
'Dorridge Flair' (3b)   NHal
'Dorridge Gem' (24b)   Last listed 1996
'Dorridge King' (4b)   Last listed 1998
'Dorridge Velvet' (4b)   NHal
'Dorridge Vulcan' (23b)   WWol
'Dragon' (9c)   NHal
'Duchess of Edinburgh'   CGle CPlt CSam EBrP EBre ECtt

(29Rub)   ELan EMon GMac LBre LGre
    MBNS MBri MCol MFir SBre SEas
    SSpe SSvw WEas WMaN WPyg
    WRHF
'Dulverton' (24c)   Last listed 1997
'Early Bird' (24b) ♀   MCol
'Eastleigh' (24b) ♀   Last listed 1995
'Ed Hodgson' (25a)   MCol NHal
'Edelgard'   WMaN
'Edelweiss' (29K)   EFou LWoo
'Egret' (23b)   Last listed 1998
'Elegance' (9c)   MCol NHal
'Elizabeth Burton' (5a)   Last listed 1996
'Elizabeth Lawson' (3a)   NHal
'Elizabeth Shoesmith' (1)   NHal
'Ellen' (29c)   NHal
'Embleton' (24a)   Last listed 1996
'Emily Peace' (25a)   Last listed 1997
Emily = 'Yoemily' (22) ♀   MCol
'Emma Lou' (23a)   MCol NHal
§ 'Emperor of China' (29Rub)   CGle CSam EBee ECha EFou EMar
    GCal GMac LGre MBel MCol
    MNrw MRav MSte NBrk NFai
    NFor NLon SChu SMad SSvw SUsu
    WEas WFar WHoo WMaN WRus
'Enbee Dell' (29d)   MCol
'Enbee Frill' (29d)   MCol
'Enbee Sunray' (29d)   EFou
'Enbee Wedding' (29d) ♀   MCol NHal WWol
'Encore'   Last listed 1998
'Ermine' (23a)   MCol NHal
¶ 'Eston Fancy' (5a)   NHal
'Evelyn Bush' (25a)   MCol
'Eye Level' (5a)   NHal
'Fairway' (15a)   NHal
'Fairweather' (3b)   MCol
'Fairy' (28)   MCol
'Fairy Rose' (4b)   LRHS MCol
'Felicity' (15b)   Last listed 1998
'Fellbacher Wein' (29K)   EFou
'Feu de l'Automne'   EFou
'Fieldfare' (22)   NHal
Fiery Barbara =   WLRN
    'Fiery Yobarbara' (22c)
'Flame Enbee Wedding'   MCol
    (29d)
'Flamingo' (9f)   Last listed 1998
§ 'Fleet Margaret' (29c) ♀   Last listed 1998
'Flo Cooper' (25a) ♀   Last listed 1989
'Flying Saucer' (6a)   MCol
*foeniculaceum*   See *Argyranthemum*
    *foeniculaceum* (Willd.) Webb &
    Sch.Bip.
'Formcast' (24a)   Last listed 1996
'Fortune' (24b)   Last listed 1996
'Foxdown' (24b)   MCol
'Foxy Valerie' (22c)   Last listed 1998
¶ 'Frances Jeavons'   EBee
¶ 'Fred Brocklehurst' (25a)   MCol
'Fred Shoesmith' (5a)   MCol WWol
'Frederick Thompson' (15b)   Last listed 1996
'Fresha' (25a)   Last listed 1998
Frolic = 'Yofrolic' (22)   MCol WLRN
*frutescens*   See *Argyranthemum frutescens*
'Fulfen' (24b)   NHal
'Gala Princess' (24b)   Last listed 1997
'Galaxy' (9d) ♀   MCol NHal
'Gambit' (24a)   NHal
'Gary Scothern' (25b)   Last listed 1997
'Gay Anne' (4b)   Last listed 1997
'Gazelle' (23a)   MCol
'Geordie' (25b)   MCol

| | | |
|---|---|---|
| | 'George Griffiths' (24b) ♀ | NHal |
| | 'Gerry Tull' (29d) | NHal |
| | 'Gertrude' (19c) | MCol |
| | 'Gigantic' (1) | NHal |
| I | 'Ginger' (22c) | WLRN |
| | 'Gingernut' (5b) | MCol NHal |
| | 'Gladys' (24b) | EBee ELan EWoo |
| ¶ | 'Gloria' (29K) | MCol |
| | 'Gloria' (25a) | Last listed 1997 |
| | Glowing Lynn = | WLRN |
| | 'Glowing Yolynn' (22) | |
| | 'Gold Chessington' (25a) | Last listed 1998 |
| | 'Gold Enbee Frill' (29d) | Last listed 1997 |
| | 'Gold Enbee Wedding' (29d) ♀ | NHal WWol |
| | 'Gold Foil' (5a) | NHal |
| | 'Gold Margaret' | See C. 'Golden Margaret' |
| | 'Golden Allouise' (25b) | Last listed 1996 |
| | 'Golden Anemone' (29K) | Last listed 1997 |
| | 'Golden Angora' (25b) | MCol |
| | 'Golden Cassandra' (5b) ♀ | NHal |
| | 'Golden Courtier' (24a) | MCol |
| | 'Golden Creamist' (25b) ♀ | MCol |
| | 'Golden Elegance' (5a) | NHal |
| ¶ | 'Golden Greenheart' | EFou |
| | 'Golden Honeyball' (15b) | MCol |
| | 'Golden Ivy Garland' (5b) | MCol |
| | 'Golden Lady' (3b) | Last listed 1996 |
| § | 'Golden Margaret' (29c) ♀ | MCol NHal |
| | 'Golden Mayford Perfection' (5a) ♀ | MCol NHal |
| | 'Golden Orfe' (29c) | Last listed 1996 |
| | 'Golden Pamela' (29c) | NHal |
| | 'Golden Pixton' (25b) | MCol |
| | 'Golden Plover' (22) | NHal |
| | 'Golden Saskia' (7b) | MCol |
| | 'Golden Seal' (7b) | EMon GBuc MCol NBrk |
| | 'Golden Shoesmith Salmon' (4a) ♀ | Last listed 1987 |
| | 'Golden Taffeta' (9c) | Last listed 1997 |
| | 'Golden Treasure' (28a) | MCol WWol |
| | 'Golden Wedding' (29K) | MCol |
| | 'Goldengreenheart' | WCot |
| | 'Goldmine' (22c) ♀ | Last listed 1995 |
| | 'Goodlife Sombrero' (29a) ♀ | NHal |
| | 'Grace Fraser' (15b) | WWol |
| | 'Grace Riley' (24a) | MCol |
| | 'Grandchild' (29c) | LRHS MCol |
| § | grandiflorum | MNrw SRms |
| | 'Green Satin' (5b) | WWol |
| | 'Grenadier' (24b) | MCol |
| | 'Grenadine' (22c) ♀ | NHal |
| | 'Halloween' (4b) | Last listed 1997 |
| | 'Handford Pink' (29K) | Last listed 1997 |
| | 'Happy Geel' | Last listed 1997 |
| | haradjanii | See Tanacetum haradjanii |
| | 'Hardwick Bronze' (29c) | Last listed 1996 |
| | 'Hardwick Lemon' (29c) | Last listed 1996 |
| | 'Hardwick Primrose' (29c) | Last listed 1996 |
| | 'Hardwick Yellow' (19b) | Last listed 1996 |
| | 'Harold Lawson' (5a) | NHal |
| | 'Harry Gee' (1) | Last listed 1996 |
| | 'Harry James' (25a) | Last listed 1996 |
| * | 'Harry Lawson' | Last listed 1996 |
| | 'Harry Wilson' (3b) | NHal |
| | 'Harry Woolman' (3b) | NHal |
| | Harvest Emily = | MCol |
| | 'Harvest Yoemily' (22c) | |
| | 'Harvey' (29K) | MCol |
| | 'Hayley Griffin' (25a) | NHal |
| * | 'Hazel' (29K) | LRHS |
| | 'Hazel Macintosh' (5a) | NHal |

| | | |
|---|---|---|
| | 'Hazy Days' (25b) | NHal |
| | 'Heather James' (3b) | MCol NHal |
| ¶ | Heather = 'Yoheather' (22) | WLRN |
| | 'Hedgerow' (7b) | MCol |
| | 'Heide' (29c) ♀ | MCol NHal |
| | 'Hekla' (30) | MCol |
| | 'Helen' (29K) | Last listed 1997 |
| | 'Hesketh Crystal' (5b) | Last listed 1996 |
| | 'Hesketh Knight' (5b) | NHal |
| | Holly = 'Yoholly' (22b) ♀ | MCol WLRN |
| | 'Honey' (25b) | EMan LRHS SMer |
| ¶ | 'Honey Enbee Wedding' (29d) | NHal |
| | 'Honeyball' (25b) | MCol |
| | 'Horace Martin' | LRHS |
| | 'Horningsea Pink' (19d) | ECGP EPPr |
| | hosmariense | See Rhodanthemum hosmariense |
| | 'Ian' (29K) | Last listed 1997 |
| | 'Illusion' | Last listed 1996 |
| | 'Imp' (28) | MCol |
| | 'Innocence' (29Rub) | CGle CSam EBee EFou EHal ELan EMon GMac LGre MBel MNrw MRav NFai NGdn NSti SEas SPla |
| | 'Irene' (29K) | CElw |
| | 'Ivy Garland' (5b) | MCol |
| | 'Jan Wardle' (5a) | Last listed 1996 |
| | 'Janice' (7a) | Last listed 1997 |
| | 'Janice Shreeve' (24a) | MCol |
| | 'Jante Wells' (28) | EMon MBel MCol MFir WEas |
| | japonense | Last listed 1996 |
| | var. ashizuriense | |
| | Jennifer = | WLRN |
| | 'Yojennifer' (22c) | |
| | 'Jessica' (29c) | Last listed 1997 |
| | 'Jessie Cooper' | See C. 'Mrs Jessie Cooper' |
| | 'Jimmy Motram' (1) | NHal |
| | 'Joan' (25b) | LRHS |
| | 'John Cory' (3b) | NHal |
| | 'John Harrison' (25b) | MCol NHal |
| | 'John Hughes' (3b) | MCol NHal |
| | 'John Lewis' (24b) | Last listed 1997 |
| | 'John Murray' | Last listed 1996 |
| | 'John Riley' (14a) | Last listed 1997 |
| | 'John Wingfield' (14b) | NHal |
| | 'Julia' (28) | CLTr EFou |
| | 'Julie Lagravère' (28) | EFou EMon GBuc MBel |
| | 'June Buglass' (3b) | Last listed 1998 |
| | 'June Rose' (24b) | NHal |
| | 'June Wakley' (25b) | Last listed 1997 |
| | 'Karen Riley' (25a) | Last listed 1997 |
| | 'Kay Woolman' (3b) | NHal |
| | 'Ken Lyons' (7b) | MCol |
| | 'Keystone' (25b) | MCol |
| | 'Kimberley Marie' (15b) | NHal |
| | 'Kingfisher' (12a) | Last listed 1996 |
| | x koreanum | See C. grandiflorum |
| | 'Lady in Pink' (29Rub) | GBuc |
| | 'Lakelanders' (3b) | NHal WWol |
| | 'Lantern' (15b) | Last listed 1998 |
| | 'Laser' (24b) | NHal WWol |
| | 'Laurie' (22c) | WLRN |
| | 'Leading Lady' (25b) | WWol |
| | 'Legend' (22) | NHal |
| | 'Lemon Blanket' (29K) | Last listed 1996 |
| | 'Lemon Hawaii' (9c) | Last listed 1996 |
| ¶ | 'Lemon Heide' (29c) | MCol |
| | 'Lemon Margaret' (29c) ♀ | NHal |
| | leucanthemum | See Leucanthemum vulgare |
| | 'Lilian Hoek' (29c) | MCol |
| | 'Lilian Jackson' (7b) | MCol |
| | 'Lilian Shoesmith' (5b) | Last listed 1997 |

| | |
|---|---|
| Linda = 'Lindayo' (22c) | MCol WLRN WWol |
| 'Lindie' | EFou |
| 'L'Innocence' (29K) | WMaN |
| Lisa = 'Yolisa' (22c) | MCol |
| 'Little Dorrit' (29K) | LRHS MBNS MCol |
| 'Liverpool Festival' (23b) | MCol |
| 'Long Island Beauty' (6b) ♀ | MCol |
| 'Long Life' (25b) | MCol |
| 'Lorna Wood' (13b) | NHal |
| 'Louise' (25b) | LRHS |
| 'Louise Park' (24a) | NHal |
| 'Lucida' (29c) | Last listed 1996 |
| 'Lucy Simpson' (29K) | MCol MMil WMaN |
| 'Lundy' (2) | NHal |
| 'Lyndale' (25b) | MCol |
| 'Lynmal's Choice' (13b) | Last listed 1998 |
| Lynn = 'Yolynn' (22) | NHal WLRN |
| *macrophyllum* | See *Tanacetum macrophyllum* |
| 'Mac's Delight' (25b) | MCol |
| 'Madeleine' (29c) ♀ | Last listed 1998 |
| 'Malcolm Perkins' (25a) | NHal |
| 'Mancetta Bride' (29a) ♀ | Last listed 1995 |
| ¶ 'Mancetta Comet' (29a) | NHal |
| 'Mandarin' (5b) | CGle EFou |
| *maresii* | See *Rhodanthemum hosmariense* |
| 'Margaret' (29c) ♀ | MCol NHal |
| 'Margaret Patricia' (24b) | Last listed 1996 |
| 'Maria' (28a) | MCol |
| 'Mariann' (12a) | Last listed 1998 |
| 'Marie Brunton' (15a) | Last listed 1997 |
| 'Marion' (25a) | Last listed 1998 |
| 'Marlene Jones' (25b) | Last listed 1996 |
| 'Martha' | LRHS MBNS |
| 'Martin Riley' (23b) | MCol |
| 'Martina' (24b) | Last listed 1996 |
| 'Mary' (29K) | MCol WMaN |
| 'Mary Stevenson' (25b) | MCol |
| 'Mary Stoker' (29Rub) | More than 30 suppliers |
| 'Mason's Bronze' (7b) | MCol |
| 'Matlock' (24b) | MCol NHal |
| 'Matthew Woolman' (4a) | Last listed 1997 |
| 'Maudie Hodgson' (24b) | Last listed 1996 |
| 'Maureen' (29K) | Last listed 1997 |
| 'Mauve Gem' (29K) | Last listed 1997 |
| 'Mavis' (28a) ♀ | MCol |
| *mawii* | See *Rhodanthemum gayanum* |
| 'Max Riley' (23b) ♀ | NHal |
| *maximowiczii* | EMon |
| *maximum* Ramond | See *Leucanthemum maximum* (Ramond) DC |
| - hort. | See *Leucanthemum* x *superbum* |
| 'May Shoesmith' (5a) | NHal |
| 'Mayford Perfection' (5a) ♀ | MCol NHal |
| ¶ 'Medallion' (9c) | MCol |
| 'Megan' (22d) | WLRN |
| 'Megan Woolman' (3b) | WWol |
| 'Mei-kyo' (28b) | CGle CHar CM&M CMea ECtt EFou ELan EMon MBel MLLN MRav NFai SIng SPer SPla SRms SSea SUsu WAbe WEas WFar WWat |
| 'Membury' (24b) ♀ | MCol NHal |
| 'Michelle Walker' (24b) | Last listed 1996 |
| 'Minaret' (3b) | WWol |
| 'Minstrel Boy' (3b) | MCol |
| 'Mirage' (22b) ♀ | Last listed 1997 |
| 'Miss Prim' (24b) | MCol |
| 'Moira' (29K) | LRHS |
| 'Molly Lambert' (5a) | NHal |
| 'Moonlight' (29K) | Last listed 1997 |
| 'Morning Star' (12a) | Last listed 1998 |
| 'Mottram Barleycorn' (29d) | Last listed 1997 |
| 'Mottram Minstrel' (29d) | MCol |
| 'Mottram Sentinel' (29d) | MCol |
| 'Mottram Twotone' (29d) | MCol |
| § 'Mrs Jessie Cooper' (29Rub) | ECGP EFou ELan EMon MHlr MNrw MSte NBir NBrk SChu SEas WCot WHoo WLRN |
| 'Muriel Vipas' (25b) | Last listed 1996 |
| 'Music' (23b) | MCol NHal |
| 'My Love' (7a) | MCol |
| 'Myss Madi' (29c) ♀ | NHal |
| 'Myss Rosie' (29c) | Last listed 1997 |
| 'Myssy Angie' (29c) ♀ | Last listed 1995 |
| *naktongense* | See *C. zawadskii* var. *latilobum* |
| 'Nancy Perry' (29Rub) | CElw CSam ELan EMon LWoo MCol MRav SChu SEas |
| § *nankingense* | EMon WFar |
| 'Nantyderry Sunshine' (28b) ♀ | CMea EFou MAvo MHlr MNrw MWgw SIng SMrm SPla SUsu WAbe WCot WEas WMaN WPen WPer WPrP WRha WWat |
| 'Naomi' (22f) | Last listed 1997 |
| ¶ 'Naru' (9c) | NHal |
| 'Nathalie' (19c) ♀ | Last listed 1995 |
| 'National Celebration' (25a) | MCol NHal WWol |
| 'Nell Gwyn' (29Rub) | NHal |
| Nicole = 'Yonicole' (22c) | MCol NHal WLRN |
| *nipponicum* | See *Nipponanthemum nipponicum* |
| 'Nora Brook' (25b) ♀ | Last listed 1987 |
| ¶ 'Nudazzler' (9d) | MCol |
| ¶ 'Nurobin' (9d) | MCol |
| ¶ 'Nurosemary' (9d) ♀ | MCol NHal |
| 'Ogmore Vale' (12a) | Last listed 1996 |
| 'Old Cottage Yellow' | Last listed 1998 |
| 'Orange Allouise' (25b) | MCol NHal |
| 'Orange Corfu' (9a) | Last listed 1998 |
| 'Orange Enbee Wedding' (29d) | NHal |
| 'Orange Fairway' (15b) | NHal |
| 'Orangeade' (24b) | MCol |
| 'Orno' (29b) ♀ | Last listed 1996 |
| 'Overbury' | Last listed 1996 |
| *pacificum* | See *Ajania pacifica* |
| 'Packwell' (24b) | Last listed 1997 |
| § 'Pamela' (29c) | NHal |
| 'Panache' (5a) | MCol |
| ¶ 'Parkfield Tigger' (29c) | NHal |
| *parthenium* | See *Tanacetum parthenium* |
| 'Pat' (6b) | Last listed 1996 |
| 'Pat Davison' (25b) | NHal |
| 'Patricia' (29c) | Last listed 1996 |
| 'Patricia Millar' (14b) | NHal |
| 'Paul Boissier' (29Rub) | CGle EFou ELan EMon LGre MBel MBro MHlr NSti SUsu WCot WEas WHoo |
| 'Pauline White' (15a) | NHal |
| 'Pavilion' (25a) | Last listed 1996 |
| 'Payton Blaze' (29c) | MCol |
| 'Payton Dale' (29c) ♀ | MCol NHal |
| 'Payton Lady' (29c) | MCol |
| 'Payton Pixie' (29c) | Last listed 1997 |
| 'Payton Prince' (29c) ♀ | Last listed 1995 |
| 'Payton Snow' (29c) | MCol NHal |
| 'Peach Allouise' (25b) ♀ | NHal |
| 'Peach Cassandra' (5b) | MCol |
| 'Peach Courtier' (24a) | NHal |
| 'Peach Enbee Wedding' (29d) ♀ | MCol |
| 'Peach Margaret' | See *C.* 'Salmon Margaret' |
| ¶ Peachy Lynn = 'Peachy Yolynn' (22c) | WLRN |
| 'Pearl Celebration' (24a) | NHal WWol |
| 'Peggy' (28a) | Last listed 1997 |

| | |
|---|---|
| 'Pelsall Imperial' (3a) | Last listed 1998 |
| 'Pennine Alfie' (29f) ♀ | Last listed 1989 |
| 'Pennine Autumn' (29c) | MCol |
| 'Pennine Bouquet' (29e) | WWol |
| 'Pennine Bride' (29c) | Last listed 1996 |
| 'Pennine Calypso' (29b) ♀ | Last listed 1993 |
| 'Pennine Canary' (29c) ♀ | Last listed 1998 |
| 'Pennine Charm' (29b) | Last listed 1998 |
| 'Pennine Cheer' (29c) | Last listed 1998 |
| 'Pennine Claret' (29c) | Last listed 1998 |
| 'Pennine Clarion' (29c) | Last listed 1996 |
| 'Pennine Click' (29c) | Last listed 1998 |
| 'Pennine Club' (29d) ♀ | NHal WWol |
| 'Pennine Coffee' (29c) | WWol |
| 'Pennine Colt' (29d) | WWol |
| 'Pennine Crystal' (29c) | MCol |
| 'Pennine Cupid' (29c) | Last listed 1996 |
| 'Pennine Dancer' (29d) | Last listed 1998 |
| 'Pennine Dart' (29d) | NHal WWol |
| 'Pennine Dell' (29d) | MCol |
| 'Pennine Digger' (29c) | Last listed 1998 |
| 'Pennine Eagle' (29c) | NHal |
| 'Pennine Fizz' (29d) | Last listed 1997 |
| 'Pennine Flute' (29f) ♀ | Last listed 1992 |
| 'Pennine Gambol' (29a) ♀ | Last listed 1993 |
| 'Pennine Gift' (29c) | MCol NHal |
| 'Pennine Ginger' (29c) ♀ | NHal |
| 'Pennine Gipsy' (29c) | Last listed 1998 |
| 'Pennine Glory' (29c) ♀ | MCol NHal |
| 'Pennine Goal' (29c) ♀ | Last listed 1998 |
| 'Pennine Hannah' (29d) | Last listed 1997 |
| 'Pennine Hayley' (29d) | Last listed 1998 |
| 'Pennine Jade' (29d) ♀ | Last listed 1998 |
| 'Pennine Jessie' (29d) | NHal |
| 'Pennine Jude' (29a) ♀ | Last listed 1993 |
| 'Pennine Lace' (29f) ♀ | Last listed 1995 |
| 'Pennine Lotus' (29c) ♀ | Last listed 1992 |
| 'Pennine Magic' (29c) ♀ | Last listed 1993 |
| 'Pennine Magnet' (29a) ♀ | NHal |
| 'Pennine Marie' (29a) ♀ | MCol NHal |
| 'Pennine Oriel' (29a) ♀ | MCol NHal |
| 'Pennine Pageant' (29d) | NHal |
| 'Pennine Panda' (29d) | NHal |
| 'Pennine Phyllis' (29b) ♀ | Last listed 1992 |
| 'Pennine Pink' (29c) | Last listed 1996 |
| 'Pennine Polo' (29d) | MCol NHal |
| 'Pennine Posy' (29f) | WWol |
| 'Pennine Pride' (29d) | Last listed 1997 |
| 'Pennine Punch' (29a) | Last listed 1997 |
| 'Pennine Purple' (29c) | MCol |
| 'Pennine Ranger' (29d) | NHal |
| 'Pennine Ray' (29d) | Last listed 1997 |
| 'Pennine Ritz' (29d) | Last listed 1997 |
| 'Pennine Robe' (29c) | Last listed 1996 |
| 'Pennine Romeo' (19c) | NHal |
| 'Pennine Saffron' (29c) | NHal |
| 'Pennine Sally' (29c) | Last listed 1998 |
| 'Pennine Serene' (29d) | Last listed 1996 |
| 'Pennine Signal' (29d) ♀ | Last listed 1993 |
| 'Pennine Silver' (29c) ♀ | Last listed 1992 |
| 'Pennine Ski' (29c) | MCol |
| 'Pennine Slumber' (29c) | Last listed 1998 |
| 'Pennine Soldier' (29d) ♀ | NHal |
| 'Pennine Sparkle' (29f) | Last listed 1997 |
| 'Pennine Splash' (29d) | NHal |
| 'Pennine Sprite' (29d) | Last listed 1997 |
| 'Pennine Sun' (29d) ♀ | Last listed 1996 |
| 'Pennine Swan' (29c) | MCol NHal |
| 'Pennine Sweetheart' (29c) ♀ | Last listed 1990 |
| 'Pennine Swing' (29d) | NHal |
| 'Pennine Tango' (29d) ♀ | Last listed 1996 |
| 'Pennine Thrill' (29d) | Last listed 1996 |
| 'Pennine Twinkle' (29a) ♀ | Last listed 1994 |
| 'Pennine Waltz' (29c) | Last listed 1996 |
| 'Pennine Wax' (29) | Last listed 1996 |
| 'Pennine Whistle' (29f) ♀ | Last listed 1994 |
| 'Pennine Wine' (29c) | Last listed 1998 |
| 'Percy Salter' (24b) | MCol |
| 'Perry's Peach' | MAvo MNrw NPer |
| 'Peter Fraser' (14b) | Last listed 1998 |
| 'Peter Pan' (24b) | Last listed 1998 |
| 'Peter Rowe' (23b) | MCol NHal |
| 'Peter Sare' (29d) | EBrP EBre GMac LBre SBre |
| 'Peter White' (23a) | MCol |
| 'Peterkin' | CHea EBrP EBre ECtt EMar EMon GMac LBre SBre |
| 'Phil Houghton' (1) | WWol |
| 'Phillip McNamara' (3b) | WWol |
| 'Piecas' | Last listed 1997 |
| 'Pink Champagne' (4b) | Last listed 1997 |
| 'Pink Chempak Rose' (14b) | Last listed 1996 |
| 'Pink Duke' (1) | NHal |
| 'Pink Favorite' (5b) | MCol |
| 'Pink Gin' (9c) ♀ | Last listed 1996 |
| 'Pink Honeysuckle Time' | Last listed 1998 |
| 'Pink Ice' (5b) | MCol WRha |
| 'Pink John Wingfield' (24b) | NHal |
| 'Pink Margaret' (29c) ♀ | NHal |
| 'Pink Nu Rosemary' (9d) ♀ | MCol |
| 'Pink Overture' (15b) | MCol |
| 'Pink Pennine Cheer' (29c) | Last listed 1998 |
| 'Pink Progression' | ECtt GMac NBir NBrk |
| 'Pink Sands' (9d) | Last listed 1996 |
| 'Pink Windermere' (24a) | Last listed 1996 |
| 'Pink World of Sport' (25a) | Last listed 1997 |
| 'Pixton' (25b) | MCol |
| 'Playmate' (29K) | MCol |
| 'Polar Gem' (3a) | MCol NHal |
| 'Polaris' (9c) | Last listed 1997 |
| 'Pomander' (25b) | Last listed 1996 |
| 'Poppet' (28a) ♀ | Last listed 1987 |
| 'Pot Black' (14b) | Last listed 1998 |
| *praeteritum* | See *Tanacetum praeteritum* |
| 'Primrose Alison Kirk' (23b) | MCol NHal |
| 'Primrose Allouise' (24b) ♀ | NHal |
| 'Primrose Anemone' (29K) | Last listed 1997 |
| 'Primrose Angora' (25b) | MCol |
| 'Primrose Bill Wade' (25a) | NHal |
| 'Primrose Chessington' (25a) | NHal |
| 'Primrose Courtier' | See *C.* 'Yellow Courtier' |
| 'Primrose Cricket' (25b) | MCol |
| 'Primrose Dorothy Stone' (25b) | NHal |
| ¶ 'Primrose Dorridge Crystal' (24a) | NHal |
| 'Primrose Enbee Wedding' (29d) | NHal |
| 'Primrose Ermine' (23a) | NHal |
| 'Primrose John Hughes' (3b) | NHal |
| 'Primrose Margaret' | See *C.* 'Buff Margaret' |
| 'Primrose Mayford Perfection' (5a) ♀ | MCol NHal |
| 'Primrose Pennine Oriel' (29a) | Last listed 1997 |
| 'Primrose Sam Vinter' (5a) | Last listed 1996 |
| 'Primrose Tennis' (25b) | Last listed 1996 |
| 'Primrose West Bromwich' (14a) | NHal |
| ¶ 'Prince Bishop' (25a) | NHal |
| 'Princess' (29K) | LRHS |
| 'Princess Anne' (4b) | MCol |

| | |
|---|---|
| 'Promise' (25a) | MCol NHal |
| *ptarmiciflorum* | See *Tanacetum ptarmiciflorum* |
| 'Purleigh White' (28b) | EFou MAvo SIng SPla WAbe WCot WMaN |
| 'Purple Fairie' (28b) | MCol |
| 'Purple Gerrie Hoek' | Last listed 1996 |
| 'Purple Glow' (5a) | NHal |
| 'Purple Margaret' (29c) | NHal |
| 'Purple Pennine Wine' (29c) ♀ | Last listed 1992 |
| 'Purple Wessex Charm' (29d) | Last listed 1997 |
| 'Queenswood' (5b) | MCol |
| 'Quill Elegance' (9f) | MCol |
| 'Rachel Knowles' (25a) | MCol NHal |
| Radiant Lynn = 'Radiant Yolynn' (22c) | MCol NHal WLRN |
| ¶ Raquel = 'Yoraquel' (22c) | MCol |
| 'Rayonnante' (11) | MCol |
| 'Red Balcombe Perfection' (5a) | NHal WWol |
| 'Red Carlene Welby' (25b) | Last listed 1998 |
| 'Red Chempak Rose' (14b) | Last listed 1997 |
| 'Red Claudia' (29c) | Last listed 1997 |
| 'Red Early Bird' (24b) | MCol |
| 'Red Eye Level' (5a) | Last listed 1997 |
| 'Red Formcast' (24a) | NHal |
| 'Red Galaxy' (9d) | NHal |
| 'Red Gambit' (24a) | NHal |
| 'Red Hoek' (29c) | Last listed 1996 |
| 'Red Margaret' | Last listed 1996 |
| 'Red Mayford Perfection' (5a) | MCol |
| 'Red Pamela' (29c) | NHal |
| ¶ 'Red Payton Dale' (29c) | MCol |
| ¶ 'Red Pennine Gift' (29c) | NHal |
| 'Red Pennine Jade' (29d) ♀ | Last listed 1992 |
| 'Red Pheasant' | Last listed 1997 |
| 'Red Rosita' (29c) | MCol |
| 'Red Shirley Model' (3a) | NHal |
| 'Red Shoesmith Salmon' (4a) | Last listed 1997 |
| 'Red Wendy' (29c) ♀ | MCol NHal |
| 'Red Windermere' (24a) | Last listed 1996 |
| 'Redall' (4c) | MCol |
| 'Regal Mist' (25b) | MCol |
| 'Regalia' (24b) ♀ | MCol |
| 'Remarkable' (30) | MCol NHal |
| 'Resilient' (4b) ♀ | Last listed 1991 |
| 'Riley's Dynasty' (14a) | NHal |
| 'Robeam' (9c) ♀ | Last listed 1998 |
| Robin = 'Yorobin' (22c) | MCol NHal WLRN WWol |
| 'Roblaze' (9c) | NHal |
| 'Roger Kirby' (15a) | Last listed 1998 |
| 'Rolass' (9c) | NHal |
| 'Romano Mauve' | Last listed 1997 |
| 'Romantika' | EFou |
| 'Romany' (2) | WEas |
| 'Romark' (9c) | MCol |
| 'Rose Broadway Mandy' (29c) | MCol |
| 'Rose Enbee Wedding' (29d) | MCol NHal WWol |
| 'Rose Mayford Perfection' (5a) ♀ | MCol NHal |
| 'Rose Patricia Millar' (14b) | NHal |
| 'Rose Windermere' (24a) | Last listed 1996 |
| 'Rosedew' (25a) ♀ | Last listed 1987 |
| ¶ 'Rosepink Debonair' | WLRN |
| *roseum* | See *Tanacetum coccineum* |
| 'Rosita' (28b) | MCol |
| 'Roswan' (9c) | NHal |
| 'Roy Coopland' (5b) ♀ | Last listed 1997 |
| 'Royal Cardinal' (9c) | MCol |
| 'Royal Command' (29Rub) | EMon NBro WCot |

| | |
|---|---|
| 'Royal Hawaii' (9c) | Last listed 1996 |
| Royal Lynn = 'Royal Yolynn' (22c) | MCol WLRN |
| 'Rozette' | Last listed 1997 |
| *rubellum* | See *C. zawadskii* |
| 'Ruby Enbee Wedding' (29d) ♀ | NHal WWol |
| 'Ruby Mound' (29K) | CMdw EFou LGre MCol MHlr WEas |
| 'Ruby Raynor' (29Rub) | MCol |
| 'Rumpelstilzchen' | CElw CMea EBee EMan EMar EPPr MAvo MNrw WPer |
| 'Russet Gown' | EBee |
| 'Rybronze' (9d) | NHal |
| 'Ryfinch' (9d) | MCol |
| 'Ryflare' (9c) | Last listed 1997 |
| 'Ryflash' (9d) | MCol |
| 'Rylands Gem' (24b) | MCol |
| 'Rylands Victor' (23c) | MCol |
| 'Rynoon' (9d) ♀ | MCol |
| ¶ 'Ryred' | MCol |
| 'Rystar' (9d) ♀ | Last listed 1991 |
| 'Rytorch' (9d) | MCol |
| 'Salmon Cassandra' (5b) ♀ | Last listed 1997 |
| 'Salmon Enbee Wedding' (29d) ♀ | NHal |
| 'Salmon Fairie' (28a) ♀ | MCol |
| § 'Salmon Margaret' (29c) ♀ | MCol NHal |
| 'Salmon Nu Rosemary' (9d) ♀ | Last listed 1996 |
| 'Salmon Pauline White' (15a) | Last listed 1997 |
| 'Salmon Pennine Gambol' (29a) ♀ | Last listed 1992 |
| 'Salmon Pennine Wine' (29c) ♀ | Last listed 1992 |
| 'Salmon Rylands Gem' (24b) | MCol |
| 'Salmon Susan Rowe' (24b) | MCol |
| 'Salmon Talbot Parade' (29c) ♀ | Last listed 1995 |
| 'Salmon Venice' (24b) | Last listed 1997 |
| 'Salmon Woolley Pride' (24b) | Last listed 1996 |
| 'Salurose' | Last listed 1997 |
| 'Sam Vinter' (5a) | MCol NHal |
| 'Sandy' (30) | MCol |
| Sarah = 'Yosar' (22f) | WLRN |
| 'Sarah's Yellow' | CSam |
| 'Saskia' (7b) | MCol |
| 'Satin Pink Gin' (9c) ♀ | Last listed 1996 |
| ¶ 'Scarlet Medallion' (9c) | MCol |
| 'Scottie' (24b) | NHal |
| 'Sea Urchin' (29c) | MCol |
| 'Seashell' (28b) | MCol |
| 'Seatons Flirt' (3b) | Last listed 1998 |
| 'Setron' | Last listed 1998 |
| 'Sheila' (29K) | Last listed 1997 |
| ¶ Shelley = 'Yoshelley' (22b) | WLRN |
| 'Shining Light' (29K) | MCol |
| 'Shirley' (25b) | Last listed 1997 |
| 'Shoesmith's Salmon' (4a) ♀ | Last listed 1995 |
| 'Simon Mills' (2) | NHal |
| 'Snowbound' (29K) | Last listed 1997 |
| 'Snowdon' (5b/9c) ♀ | Last listed 1987 |
| Soft Lynn = 'Soft Yolynn' (22c) | NHal WLRN |
| 'Solarama' (9e) | NHal |
| 'Sonnenschein' | LHop WHen |
| 'Sonya' (29K) | Last listed 1997 |
| Sophia = 'Yosophia' (22c) | WLRN |
| 'Southway Sacy' (29d) | Last listed 1996 |
| 'Southway Sanguine' (29d) | NHal |
| ¶ 'Southway Sonar' (29d) | NHal |
| 'Southway Sovereign' (29d) | Last listed 1996 |

| | |
|---|---|
| 'Southway Stomp' (29d) | NHal |
| 'Southway Sure' (29d) ♀ | NHal |
| 'Sparta' (9c) | NHal |
| 'Spartan Crest' | Last listed 1996 |
| 'Spartan Fire' | Last listed 1996 |
| 'Spartan Glory' (25b) | WWol |
| 'Spartan Legend' (29c) | Last listed 1996 |
| 'Spartan Leo' (29c) | Last listed 1996 |
| 'Spartan Magic' (29d) | Last listed 1998 |
| 'Spartan Moon' (25b) | WWol |
| 'Spartan Pearl' | Last listed 1996 |
| 'Spartan Rose' (29c) | Last listed 1998 |
| 'Spartan Royal' | Last listed 1996 |
| 'Spartan Sunrise' (29c) | Last listed 1996 |
| 'Spartan Torch' | WWol |
| 'Spartan White' (29c) | Last listed 1998 |
| 'Spencer's Cottage' (13b) | MCol |
| * 'Spoons' | SCro SHel |
| 'Stan's Choice' (29K) | MCol |
| 'Stardust' (24b) | MCol |
| 'Starlet' (29K) | LRHS MCol |
| ¶ 'Stella' | EFou |
| 'Stockton' (3b) | NHal |
| 'Stoke Festival' (25b) | MCol |
| 'Stuart Jackson' (25a) | Last listed 1998 |
| 'Stuart Lawson' (5b) | Last listed 1996 |
| Stunning Lynn = | WLRN |
|   'Stunning Yolynn' (22c) | |
| 'Sun Spider' (30) | Last listed 1997 |
| 'Sun Valley' (5a) | Last listed 1997 |
| 'Sunbeam' (28) | EBrP EBre ECtt EFou LBre SBre |
| 'Suncharm Bronze' (22a) | Last listed 1997 |
| 'Suncharm Pink' (22a) | Last listed 1997 |
| 'Suncharm Red' (22a) | Last listed 1997 |
| 'Suncharm White' (22a) | Last listed 1996 |
| 'Suncharm Yellow' (22a) | Last listed 1997 |
| 'Sundora' (22d) | NHal WLRN |
| 'Sunflash' (5b/12a) | Last listed 1996 |
| 'Sunflight' (25b) | MCol |
| 'Sunny Denise' (22) | WLRN |
| Sunny Linda = | WLRN WWol |
|   'Sunny Lindayo' (22c) | |
| 'Susan Dobson' (25b) | Last listed 1996 |
| 'Susan Rowe' (24b) | MCol |
| 'Sussex County' (15a) | Last listed 1996 |
| 'Sutton White' (25a) | WWol |
| 'Suzanne Marie' (24a) | MCol |
| 'Swalwell' (25b) ♀ | Last listed 1995 |
| 'Taffeta' (9c) | MCol NHal |
| 'Talbot Bolero' (29c) | MCol NHal |
| 'Talbot Bouquet' (29a) ♀ | Last listed 1995 |
| 'Talbot Parade' (29c) ♀ | MCol NHal |
| 'Tang' (12a) | Last listed 1998 |
| 'Tapestry Rose' | CGle CMea EMon MMil NBrk |
| 'Tapis Blanc' | Last listed 1997 |
| ¶ Target = 'Yotarget' (22) | MCol NHal WLRN |
| 'Tennis' (25b) | Last listed 1996 |
| 'Terry Ball' (29c) | Last listed 1996 |
| 'Thacker's Joy' (24a) | Last listed 1996 |
| 'The Favourite' (5b) | MCol |
| 'Thoroughbred' (24a) | NHal WWol |
| 'Tickled Pink' (29K) | Last listed 1997 |
| 'Tim Woolman' (25a) | Last listed 1996 |
| 'Toledo' (25a) | WWol |
| 'Tom Blackshaw' (25b) | NHal |
| 'Tom Parr' | See C. 'Doctor Tom Parr' |
| 'Tom Snowball' (3b) | NHal |
| 'Tommy Trout' (28) | MCol |
| 'Tone Gambol' (29a) | MCol |
| 'Tone Sail' (29a) | MCol |
| 'Topsy' (29K) | Last listed 1997 |
| 'Tracy Waller' (24b) | NHal |
| 'Triumph' (22) | NHal |
| 'Tundra' (4a) | NHal |
| *uliginosum* | See *Leucanthemella serotina* |
| 'Universiade' (25a) | NHal |
| 'Vagabond Prince' | CSam MBro WHoo |
| 'Valerie' (10) | Last listed 1998 |
| 'Vanity Pink' (7b) | MCol |
| 'Vanity Primrose' (7b) | MCol |
| 'Vedova' (6a) | Last listed 1996 |
| 'Venice' (24b) | NHal |
| 'Venus' (29K) | CBlo LRHS MBro |
| 'Vera Smith' (3b) | MCol |
| 'Veria' | Last listed 1997 |
| 'Victor Rowe' (5b) ♀ | MCol |
| 'Virginia' (29K) | Last listed 1997 |
| 'Vrenelli' | EFou |
| 'Wedding Day' (29K) | CElw CStr EMan EMon GBuc |
| | LGre MBro MFir MMil NFor SRms |
| | SUsu WCot WHoo WMaN WOve |
| | WRus |
| 'Wedding Sunshine' (29K) | LRHS MMil WCot |
| ♦ *welwitschii* | See *Xanthophthalmum segetum* |
| 'Wembley' (24b) | Last listed 1998 |
| 'Wendy' (29c) ♀ | MCol NHal |
| 'Wendy Tench' (29d) | Last listed 1997 |
| 'Wessex Dawn' (29d) | MCol |
| 'Wessex Eclipse' (29c) | MCol NHal |
| 'Wessex Ivory' (29d) | MCol |
| 'Wessex Shell' (29d) ♀ | Last listed 1990 |
| 'Wessex Solo' (29d) | Last listed 1996 |
| 'Wessex Sunshine' (29d) | MCol |
| 'Wessex Tang' (29d) ♀ | Last listed 1995 |
| 'West Bromwich' (14a) | NHal |
| § *weyrichii* | EBrP EBre ELan LBre LFis LHop |
| | MAvo MTho NHol NMen NNrd |
| | NWCA SBla SBre SRms SSmi |
| | WAbe |
| 'White Allouise' (25b) ♀ | NHal |
| 'White Beppie' (29e) | MCol |
| 'White Bouquet' (28) | MCol WWol |
| 'White Cassandra' (5b) | NHal |
| 'White Enbee Wedding' (29d) | Last listed 1997 |
| 'White Fairweather' (3b) | Last listed 1998 |
| 'White Fiji' (9c) | Last listed 1996 |
| 'White Gem' (25b) | Last listed 1997 |
| 'White Gerrie Hoek' (29c) | Last listed 1996 |
| 'White Gloss' (29K) | LRHS SMer |
| 'White Margaret' (29c) ♀ | MCol NHal WWol |
| ¶ 'White Nurosemary' (9d) | NHal |
| 'White Rachel Knowles' (25a) | NHal |
| 'White Rayonnante' (11) | MCol |
| 'White Sands' (9a) ♀ | MCol |
| 'White Skylark' (22) | NHal |
| 'White Sonja' (29c) | MCol |
| 'White Spider' (10a) | MCol |
| 'White Taffeta' (9c) | MCol NHal |
| 'White Tower' | Last listed 1998 |
| ¶ 'William Florentine' (5a) | NHal |
| 'Win' (9c) | NHal |
| 'Winchcombe' (29c) | Last listed 1996 |
| 'Windermere' (24a) | NHal |
| ¶ 'Wine Carlene Welby' (25b) | NHal |
| 'Winnie Bramley' (23a) | WWol |
| 'Winning's Red' (29Rub) | EMon NBro SMad WWin |
| 'Winter Queen' (5b) | NHal |
| 'Woolley Globe' (25b) | MCol WWol |
| 'Woolley Pride' (14b) | Last listed 1996 |
| 'Woolman's Century' (1) | Last listed 1996 |
| 'Woolman's Perfecta' (3a) | Last listed 1997 |
| 'Woolman's Prince' (3a) | WWol |
| 'Woolman's Star' (3a) | NHal |
| 'Woolmans Venture' (4b) | NHal |

'World of Sport' (25a)          Last listed 1997
'Yellow Alfreton Cream' (5b)    Last listed 1997
'Yellow Allison Kirk' (23b)     NHal
'Yellow Allouise' (25b)         NHal
'Yellow Beppie' (29e)           MCol
§ 'Yellow Courtier' (24a)       NHal WWol
'Yellow Danielle' (29d)         MCol
'Yellow Egret' (23b)            Last listed 1996
'Yellow Ellen' (29c)            NHal
'Yellow Flying Saucer' (6a)     MCol
'Yellow Fred Shoesmith' (5a)    Last listed 1998
'Yellow Galaxy' (9d) ♀          MCol
'Yellow Gingernut' (25b)        MCol NHal
'Yellow Hammer' (12a)           Last listed 1997
'Yellow Hazy Days' (25b)        NHal
'Yellow Heather James' (3b)     MCol
'Yellow Heide' (29c) ♀          MCol NHal
'Yellow John Hughes' (3b) ♀     MCol NHal
'Yellow John Wingfield' (14b)   MCol NHal
'Yellow Lilian Hoek' (29c)      MCol
'Yellow Margaret' (29c) ♀       MCol NHal
'Yellow Margaret Riley' (25b)   Last listed 1996
'Yellow May Shoesmith' (5a)     NHal
'Yellow Mayford                 MCol NHal
  Perfection' (5a) ♀
'Yellow Megan Woolman'          WWol
  (3b)
'Yellow Pennine Oriel'          MCol NHal
  (29a) ♀
'Yellow Percy Salter' (24b)     MCol
'Yellow Phil Houghton' (1)      WWol
'Yellow Pinocchio' (29c)        Last listed 1996
'Yellow Plover' (22)            NHal
* 'Yellow Pom' (28)             LRHS
'Yellow Resilient' (5b) ♀       Last listed 1991
'Yellow Roswan' (9c)            NHal
'Yellow Sands' (9d)             MCol
'Yellow Spider' (10a)           MCol
* 'Yellow Stardust' (24b)       MCol
¶ 'Yellow Starlet' (29K)        MCol
'Yellow Taffeta' (9c)           MCol
'Yellow Talbot Parade' (29c)    NHal
'Yellow Tennis' (25b)           Last listed 1996
¶ Yellow Triumph =              WLRN
  'Yellow Yotri' (22)
'Yellow Whitby' (5b)            MCol
§ yezoense ♀                    ELan EMan EMon MBel NFai SPla
                                WCot WEas
  - 'Roseum'                    MBel MNrw
  'Yvonne Arnaud' (24b) ♀       MCol
§ zawadskii                     WFar WHer WPyg
§ - var. latilobum              Last listed 1996
  Zesty Barbara =               WLRN
  'Zesty Yobarbara' (22c)

## CHRYSOCOMA (Asteraceae)
ciliata JJH 9401633             NWCA
coma-aurea                      Last listed 1998

## CHRYSOGONUM (Asteraceae)
australe                        Last listed 1997
virginianum                     CHal CMea CRDP EBee ECha
                                EMan EMar EPla MRav SCob SPer
                                WFar

## CHRYSOPOGON (Poaceae)
gryllus                         EMon LRHS

## CHRYSOPSIS (Asteraceae)
villosa                         See Heterotheca villosa

## CHRYSOSPLENIUM (Saxifragaceae)
alternifolium                   EMan
davidianum                      CBre CGle EBee ECha EMan EPar
                                EPot LSpr NBir NSla SMac WCot
                                WCru WGer WGwy WHil WWat
- SBEC 231                      NHol NWoo
oppositifolium                  EMNN GAri GDra GGar WCla
                                WHer WShi

## CHRYSOTHEMIS (Gesneriaceae)
pulchella ♀                     CHal

## CHUSQUEA ✿ (Poaceae - Bambusoideae)
argentina                       ISta
culeou ♀                        CDoC CEnd CFil CGre EFul EOas
                                EPfP EPla IOrc ISta LJus MMoz
                                MNes MWht SArc SDry SSta WBay
                                WJun WNor WPGP
- 'Breviglumis'                 See C. culeou 'Tenuis'
§ - 'Tenuis'                    EPla ERod ISta LJus SDry
liebmannii                      Last listed 1998
montana                         CFil EPla ISta WPGP
nigricans                       ISta
quila                           CFil ISta SDry WPGP
ramosissima                     CFil SDry
valdiviensis                    ISta

## CIBOTIUM (Dicksoniaceae)
barometz                        Last listed 1996
glaucum                         Last listed 1998
schiedei                        Last listed 1996

## CICERBITA (Asteraceae)
§ alpina                        GAbr NBid NHex NLar
macrorrhiza B&SWJ 2970          WCot WCru
plumieri                        MAvo WCot
- 'Blott'                       LSpr WCot
¶ sp. B&SWJ 5162                WCru

## CICHORIUM (Asteraceae)
intybus                         More than 30 suppliers
- f. album                      CGle CPou CRDP EAst EBee ECha
                                ECoo EMan EMon LHol LHop
                                MAvo MCAu MRav MSte NSti
                                SChu SRPl SWat WCHb WCot
- 'Roseum'                      CGle CJew CPou CRDP CSpe EAst
                                EBee ECGP ECha ECoo ECot ELan
                                EMan EMon GBri LHol LHop
                                MAvo MCAu MRav NRoo SChu
                                SPer SWat WCHb WCot WWal
                                WWin
'Rosso di Verona'               Last listed 1996
spinosum                        Last listed 1997

## CIMICIFUGA ✿ (Ranunculaceae)
acerina                         See C. japonica
§ americana                     MSal SRms
arizonica                       SBla
cordifolia Pursh                See C. americana
- (DC.) Torrey & A.Gray         See C. rubifolia
dahurica                        CHan EBee GAbr GCal MCli MSal
                                SWat WCru
elata                           EBee WCru
foetida                         GPoy
¶ - B&SWJ 2966                  WCru
frigida B&SWJ 2657              WCru
§ japonica                      CHan CLAP CRow GAbr GCal
                                LFis LGre NDov WCot WRus

*racemosa* ♀ — CArn CBos CRow CSam EAst EBee EBrP EBre EGol ELan GCal GPoy IHdy LBre LFis LHol MBal MCAu MSal NDea NPSI NSti NWoo SBre SPer WByw WCot WFar
- var. *cordifolia* — See *C. rubifolia*
* - 'Purple Torch' — WEas
- 'Purpurea' — See *C. simplex* var. *simplex* Atropurpurea Group
I *ramosa* — See *C. simplex* var. *simplex* 'Prichard's Giant'
§ *rubifolia* — CHan EBee GMaP LGre MBel MSal NCut WCru WWat
*simplex* — CBot CFil CMea EWTr IHdy LHol MBri SPer SWat WCot WCru WWat
- var. *matsumurae* — CBos CFil CHan CRow ECha EPar 'Elstead' ♀ — GCal LGre MRav SSpi
- - 'Frau Herms' — ECha LGre MRav
- - 'White Pearl' — More than 30 suppliers
- 'Scimitar' — LGre
- 'Silver Axe' — GCal
§ - var. *simplex* — More than 30 suppliers Atropurpurea Group
- - 'Brunette' — CFir CLAP CPar EBee GBin GNau LGre MCAu MCLN MTis NRoo SMad SVil SWat WCot
§ - - 'Prichard's Giant' — CHan CPlt EBee GAri GBuc GCal LGre MBri MLLN MRav WFar
sp. B&SWJ 343 — Last listed 1998
* *taiwanensis* B&SWJ 3413 — WCru
¶ *yezoensis* — LGre
*yunnanensis* ACE 1880 — GBuc

## CINERARIA (Asteraceae)
*maritima* — See *Senecio cineraria*

## CINNAMOMUM (Lauraceae)
*camphora* — CB&S CFil CTrG ERea GQui

## CIONURA (Asclepiadaceae)
§ *erecta* — CPlN
*oreophila* — CPlN GCal SMur

## CIRCAEA (Onagraceae)
*lutetiana* — CKin EWFC MHew MSal WHer WShi
- 'Caveat Emptor' (v) — EMon WCot

## CIRSIUM (Asteraceae)
*acaule* — CKin
* *atro roseum* — SWat
*diacantha* — See *Ptilostemon diacantha*
*dissectum* — Last listed 1998
*eriophorum* — Last listed 1998
¶ *erisithales* — EBee
*helenioides* — See *C. heterophyllum*
§ *heterophyllum* — ECGN WCot
*japonicum* — Last listed 1998
'Early Rose Beauty'
* - 'Pink Beauty' — CSpe EMar EWTr WElm WFar WRos
- 'Rose Beauty' — ELan EMar EWTr MBri MCAu WElm WFar WRos
- 'Strawberry Ripple' — Last listed 1996
- 'White Beauty' — Last listed 1996
*oleraceum* — NLar

*palustre* — Last listed 1998
*rivulare* 'Atropurpureum' — CElw CGle CMCo CPlt CSev EBee ELan EMon LGre MAvo MGrG MTed NBid NBir NTow SSpi WByw WCHb WCot WEas WMer WPGP
¶ *ugoense* — EBee
*vulgare* — CKin
- variegated — WAlt
- white form — WAlt

## CISSUS (Vitaceae)
*adenopoda* — CPlN
*antarctica* ♀ — MBri
*discolor* — CHal
*hypoglauca* — Last listed 1998
*pedata* B&SWJ 2371 — WCru
*rhombifolia* ♀ — MBri
- 'Ellen Danica' ♀ — CHal MBri
§ *striata* — CB&S CDoC CPlN CSPN CTrC EBee EMil IMGH LRHS MBel SBra SLon WCot WCru WSHC WWat

## CISTUS ✿ (Cistaceae)
x *aguilarii* — CChe CSam CTri EBee SIgm WGer WOve WSHC
- 'Maculatus' ♀ — CB&S CBot CDoC CHar CLTr EBee EBrP EBre ELan EOld GEil LBre LGre MBri MWgw NFai SBre SDry SDys SEas SLPl SLdr SPer WAbe WGer WHCG WKif WWeb WWin
*albanicus* — See *C. sintenisii*
*albidus* — CArn CFil EGoo MLLN NTow SDry SPan SSpi WHer
*algarvensis* — See *Halimium ocymoides*
'Ann Baker' — LGre MBri NOla SLPl SPan
'Anne Palmer' — CDoC CHor NBrk WAbe
*atriplicifolius* — See *Halimium atriplicifolium*
'Barnsley Pink' — See *C.* 'Grayswood Pink'
◆ 'Blanche' — See *C. ladanifer* 'Blanche'
'Candy Stripe' (v) — GBri MCCP MMHG NPro SPer WRHF WWeb
x *canescens* — WAbe
- f. *albus* — LGre MBri NSti SIgm SPan WAbe WGer WHCG
'Chelsea Bonnet' — CFai CPlt EBee EHic MSte SBid SIgm SPan SRPl SUsu SVen WAbe WPen
'Chelsea Pink' — See *C.* 'Grayswood Pink'
§ *clusii* — CHar MAsh
*coeris* — See *C.* x *hybridus*
x *corbariensis* — See *C.* x *hybridus*
*creticus* — CDoC MBel SPan
§ - subsp. *creticus* — CMHG EGoo ELan GBin GEil LGre MBNS MBel MSte SPer WAbe WGer WWin
- - f. *albus* — MBel
§ - - - 'Tania Compton' — LGre SPan
§ - subsp. *incanus* — LGre MNrw WHCG
x *crispatus* 'Warley Rose' — CLon EGoo MBri NSti SIgm WAbe
*crispus* hort. — See *C.* x *pulverulentus*
- L. — CHan ECha GOrc LGre NFor SIgm SPan WAbe WEas WGer WWeb
- 'Prostratus' — See *C. crispus* L.
- 'Sunset' — See *C.* x *pulverulentus* 'Sunset'
§ x *cyprius* ♀ — CDoC CSpe EAst ECtt ELan ENot LHil LHop MBel MGos MRav MWat MWhi NBrk NSti SDix SEND SLPl SRms WBod WDin WFar WGer WPnn WWeb

- 'Albiflorus' — WBcn
◆ - 'Tania Compton' — See *C. creticus* subsp. *creticus* f. *albus* 'Tania Compton'
§ x *dansereaui* — CHan CHar CMHG CSam EBee ELan ENot IOrc LGre MRav MSte NSti SPer WAbe WPat WPyg WWat
- 'Albiflorus' — Last listed 1998
- 'Decumbens' ♀ — More than 30 suppliers
- 'Jenkyn Place' — MBri NOla SLPl SPan SUsu
§ - 'Portmeirion' — WAbe
'Elma' ♀ — CDoC CMHG ELan EPfP LGre MAsh SDry SIgm SPan SPla WAbe WGer WHCG WPGP
§ x *florentinus* Lamarck — CLTr EBee IOrc MMil NCut NFor SChu WSHC
§ - hort. — See *x Halimiocistus* 'Ingwersenii'
¶ - 'Fontfroide' — SPan
*formosus* — See *Halimium lasianthum*
Golden Treasure — EBee EPfP GRei LRHS MAsh
= 'Nepond' (v) — MGos SMur SPer SPla
§ 'Grayswood Pink' — CDoC CMHG EBee ELan EPla GCal GMac GOrc MAsh MBri MGos MLLN MSte NSti SCoo SEND SIgm SMrm SOkh SRms SSoC WAbe WGer WHCG
*halimifolius* — See *Halimium halimifolium*
◆ *hirsutus* Lam. 1786 — See *C. inflatus*
◆ - var. *psilosepalus* — See *C. inflatus*
§ x *hybridus* ♀ — More than 30 suppliers
*incanus* — See *C. creticus* subsp. *incanus*
- subsp. *creticus* — See *C. creticus* subsp. *creticus*
- subsp. *incanus* — See *C. creticus* subsp. *incanus*
§ *inflatus* — CPle NWoo SDry SEND SRms WAbe WHar WHer
*ingwerseniana* — See *x Halimiocistus* 'Ingwersenii'
¶ 'Jessamy Beauty' — SLPl SPan
¶ 'Jessamy Bride' — SLPl
¶ 'John Hardy' — SPan
*ladanifer* hort. — See *C.* x *cyprius*
*ladanifer* L. ♀ — CB&S CFil CTri ECha ELan IMGH IOrc MBal MBel MLan MRav NChi NFor NLon NSti SChu SPan SPer SPla WEas WFar WHar WSHC WWye
- var. *albiflorus* — CB&S SPan SSpi
§ - 'Blanche' — LGre LRHS SIgm WKif WPGP
§ - 'Paladin' — LGre WAbe
- Palhinhae Group — See *C. ladanifer* var. *sulcatus*
- 'Pat' — CGre ELan EPfP
§ - var. *sulcatus* ♀ — CFai CLTr LGre MSte SDry WAbe WCot
*lasianthus* — See *Halimium lasianthum*
*laurifolius* ♀ — CFil EBee ENot EPfP ESis LPio MBal MGos MLan MNrw NBir NChi NSti SLPl SLon SPer WEas WHar WWal WWat
x *laxus* 'Snow Queen' — See *C.* x *laxus* 'Snow White'
§ - 'Snow White' — CAbP CDoC CHan EAst EBee ELan LGre LHop MAsh MBel MBri MSte NBur NLon NPer NPro NSti SAga SChu SLon SPan SPer SPla SSpi WKif WWeb
¶ x *ledon* — SLPl SUsu
*libanotis* — CSam ELan MAsh NFor
'Little Gem' — MAsh MBri SPan
x *longifolius* — See *C.* x *nigricans*
N x *loretii* Rouy & Fouc. — See *C.* x *stenophyllus*
N - hort. — See *C.* x *dansereaui*
x *lusitanicus* Maund. — See *C.* x *dansereaui*
'Merrist Wood Cream' — See *x Halimiocistus wintonensis* 'Merrist Wood Cream'

*monspeliensis* — CHan CPle EPfP GOrc LPio MAsh SPan SPer SSpi
- CMBS 62 — WPGP
§ x *nigricans* — EBee MWhi SPan SRPl
¶ x *oblongifolius* — NOla
'Barr Common'
x *obtusifolius* Sweet — CInt EHic ELan EPfP EWes MBel NLon SMer
- hort. — See *C.* x *nigricans*
*ochreatus* — See *C. symphytifolius* subsp. *leucophyllus*
*ocymoides* — See *Halimium ocymoides*
*osbeckiifolius* — SSpi
◆ 'Paladin' — See *C. ladanifer* 'Paladin'
*palhinhae* — See *C. ladanifer* var. *sulcatus*
*parviflorus* hort. — See *C.* 'Grayswood Pink'
- Lamarck — CBot ECha LGre LHol LHop NSti SChu SPer WSHC
'Peggy Sammons' ♀ — CBot CDoC CHar CLTr EBee EBrP EBre ECha ELan EWTr GEil IMGH IOrc LBre LHop MBri MRav NBrk NSti SBre SIgm SPan SPer SSoC WBod WCot WHar WPyg WSHC WWat
¶ x *platysepalus* — LGre SUsu
*populifolius* — CMHG ECha EHic SPer SSta WAbe
- var. *lasiocalyx* — See *C. populifolius* subsp. *major*
§ - subsp. *major* ♀ — CPle EPfP IOrc LGre SBid SMrm SPan
◆ *psilosepalus* — See *C. inflatus*
§ x *pulverulentus* ♀ — CHan CTri EPfP MBel SChu SCro WDin WLRN WSHC
§ - 'Sunset' — More than 30 suppliers
- 'Warley Rose' — See *C.* x *crispatus* 'Warley Rose'
N x *purpureus* ♀ — More than 30 suppliers
- 'Alan Fradd' — CBlo EBee EHic ENot GMac MAsh MBri MGos MGrG MTis MWgw NBrk NHaw SAga SCoo SCro SEND SLod SMrm SPan SPla WGer WGwG WWal
- 'Betty Taudevin' — See *C.* x *purpureus*
*rosmarinifolius* — See *C. clusii*
*sabucii* — See *x Halimiocistus sabucii*
*salviifolius* — CArn CB&S CHan CPle CSam EMil SPan SRCN SSpi WHCG WLRN WWeb
- 'Avalanche' — MRav WAbe
- x *monspeliensis* — See *C.* x *florentinus*
- 'Prostratus' — ELan LGre LRHS NPro SRPl WHCG WWat
'Silver Pink' — More than 30 suppliers
◆ 'Silver Pink' misapplied — See *C.* 'Grayswood Pink'
§ *sintenisii* — GCHN
x *skanbergii* ♀ — More than 30 suppliers
§ 'Snow Fire' — LGre LRHS MAsh MBri SIgm SLPl SPan SSpi SUsu WGer
'Snowflake' — See *C.* 'Snow Fire'
§ x *stenophyllus* — EBee LGre NSti SPan SUsu WKif
'Stripey' — SVen
*symphytifolius* — SSpi WPGP WPic
§ - subsp. *leucophyllus* — CFil SSpi
¶ - - MSF 98.019 — WPGP
◆ 'Tania Compton' — See *C. creticus* subsp. *creticus* f. *albus* 'Tania Compton'
'Thornfield White' — Last listed 1998
*tomentosus* — See *Helianthemum nummularium* subsp. *tomentosum*
x *verguinii* — LGre LHop SDix SIgm SPan
◆ - var. *albiflorus* — See *C.* x *dansereaui* 'Portmeirion'
◆ *villosus* — See *C. creticus* subsp. *creticus*
*wintonensis* — See *x Halimiocistus wintonensis*

## CITHAREXYLUM (Verbenaceae)

| | |
|---|---|
| *quadrangulare* Jacquin | See *C. spinosum* |
| § *spinosum* | CPLG CPle |

## x CITROFORTUNELLA (Rutaceae)

| | |
|---|---|
| § *floridana* | CGOG |
| - 'Eustis' (F) | ECon ERea SCit |
| - 'Lakeland' (F) | ERea |
| Lemonquat (F) | SCit |
| Limequat | See x *C. floridana* |
| § *microcarpa* (F) ♀ | CAgr CGOG EHol EPfP ERea ETub LCns LHol MBri SCit |
| § - 'Tiger' (v/F) | CB&S ECon EHol EPfP ERea LCns SCit |
| - 'Variegata' | See x *C. microcarpa* 'Tiger' |
| *mitis* | See x *C. microcarpa* |
| Procimequat (F) | SCit |
| *reticulata* (F) | SCit |
| *swinglei* 'Tavares' (F) | ERea |

## x CITRONCIRUS (Rutaceae)

| | |
|---|---|
| Citremon | CAgr LEdu |
| 'Swingle' (F) | SCit |
| *webberi* 'Benton' | SCit |
| - 'C-32' | CAgr LEdu |
| - 'C-35' | CAgr |
| - 'Carrizo' | CAgr SCit |
| - 'Rusk' | LEdu SCit |
| - 'Troyer' | CAgr LEdu |

## CITRONELLA (Icacinaceae)

| | |
|---|---|
| § *gongonha* | Last listed 1997 |
| *mucronata* | See *C. gongonha* |

## CITRUS ✿ (Rutaceae)

| | |
|---|---|
| *amblycarpa* Djeruk lime (F) | ERea |
| *aurantiifolia* (F) | SCit |
| - 'Indian Lime' x *limon* (F) | ERea |
| - 'La Valette' x *limon* (F) | ECon EPfP ERea |
| *aurantium* (F) | SCit |
| - 'Aber's Narrowleaf' (F) | SCit |
| - 'Bigaradier Apepu' | SCit |
| - 'Bittersweet' (F) | SCit |
| - 'Bouquet de Fleurs' | CGOG ERea SCit |
| - 'Bouquetier de Nice' | LChe |
| - 'Bouquetier de Nice à Fleurs Doubles' (d) | SCit |
| - 'Gou-tou Cheng' (F) | SCit |
| - var. *myrtifolia* 'Chinotto' (F) | CGOG ERea SCit |
| - 'Sauvage' (F) | SCit |
| - 'Seville' (F) | CGOG ERea |
| - 'Smooth Flat Seville' (F) | SCit |
| - 'Willowleaf' (F) | SCit |
| *bergamia* Bergamot | CGOG ERea |
| - 'Fantastico' | SCit |
| Calamondin | See x *Citrofortunella microcarpa* |
| *deliciosa* | See *C.* x *nobilis* |
| Ichang Lemon (F) | CAgr LEdu |
| *ichangensis* (F) | SCit |
| *jambhiri* 'Milam' | SCit |
| - Red Rough Lemon (F) | SCit |
| - Rough Lemon (F) | SCit |
| - Schaub Rough Lemon (F) | SCit |
| *japonica* | See *Fortunella japonica* |
| *junos* | CAgr LEdu |
| *kinokuni* | SCit |
| Kumquat | See *Fortunella margarita* |
| *latifolia* 'Bearss' (F) | CGOG ERea |
| - 'Tahiti' (F) | ECon ERea LChe LCns |
| * x *latipes* | Last listed 1997 |

| | |
|---|---|
| *limettoides* (F) | SCit |
| *limon* (F) | LPan |
| - 'Eureka Variegated' (F) | CGOG SCit |
| - 'Fino' (F) | CGOG SCit |
| § - 'Garey's Eureka' (F) | ERea LCns |
| - 'Imperial' (F) | ERea |
| - 'Lemonade' (F) | ERea SCit |
| - 'Lisbon' (F) | ERea |
| - 'Quatre Saisons' | See *C. limon* 'Garey's Eureka' |
| - x *sinensis* | See *C.* x *meyeri* |
| ¶ - 'Toscana' | EPfP |
| - 'Variegata' (F) | ERea |
| - 'Verna' (F) | CGOG SCit |
| - 'Villa Franca' (F) | ERea |
| - 'Yen Ben' (F) | SCit |
| x *limonia* 'Rangpur' (F) | ERea |
| *macrophylla* | SCit |
| *madurensis* | See *Fortunella japonica* |
| *maxima* (F) | ERea SCit |
| *medica* (F) | SCit |
| ◆ - 'Cidro Digitado' | See *C. medica* var. *digitata* |
| § - var. *digitata* (F) | CGOG ERea SCit |
| - 'Ethrog' (F) | ECon ERea SCit |
| ◆ - var. *sarcodactylis* | See *C. medica* var. *digitata* |
| x *meyeri* 'Meyer' (F) | CB&S CGOG ECon EHol EPfP ERea GTwe LCns LHol LHop SCit SPer |
| *microcarpa* Philippine Lime | See x *Citrofortunella microcarpa* |
| *mitis* | See x *Citrofortunella microcarpa* |
| *natsudaidai* | SCit |
| § x *nobilis* (F) | LPan |
| - 'Blida' (F) | ERea SCit |
| - 'Ellendale' (F) | SCit |
| - 'Murcott' (F) | ERea SCit |
| - Ortanique Group (F) | CGOG ECon EPfP SCit |
| - 'Silver Hill Owari' (F) | ERea |
| - Tangor Group (F) | ERea |
| x *paradisi* (F) | LPan |
| - 'Foster' (F) | ERea |
| - 'Golden Special' (F) | ERea |
| ¶ - 'Marsh' (F) | CGOG |
| - 'Navel' (F) | SCit |
| - 'Red Blush' (F) | CGOG |
| - 'Star Ruby' (F) | CGOG ECon ERea LCns SCit |
| - 'Wheeny' (F) | SCit |
| *pennivesiculata* (F) | SCit |
| 'Ponderosa' (F) | CGOG ERea LChe SCit |
| *reshni* Cleopatra Mandarin (F) | SCit |
| ¶ *reticulata* (F) | LBlo |
| - 'Arrufatina' (F) | CGOG |
| - 'Dancy' (F) | SCit |
| - 'Fina' (F) | SCit |
| - 'Hernandina' (F) | CGOG SCit |
| - Mandarin Group (F) | Last listed 1996 |
| - - 'Clementine' (F) | ERea LCns LHol |
| - - 'Comun' (F) | CGOG |
| - - 'De Nules' (F) | CGOG ECon SCit |
| - - 'Encore' (F) | ERea |
| - - 'Fortune' (F) | CGOG ECon SCit |
| - - 'Tomatera' (F) | CGOG |
| - 'Marisol' (F) | CGOG SCit |
| - 'Nour' (F) | CGOG SCit |
| ◆ - 'Nova' | See *C.* x *tangelo* 'Nova' |
| - 'Orogrande' | CGOG |
| - x *paradisi* | See *C.* x *tangelo* |
| - Satsuma Group | See *C. unshiu* |
| ◆ - 'Suntina' | See *C.* x *tangelo* 'Nova' |
| *sinensis* (F) | ERea LBlo LPan SAPC SArc |
| - 'Egg' (F) | ERea |
| - 'Embiguo' (F) | ERea |
| - 'Harwood Late' (F) | ERea |
| - 'Jaffa' | See *C. sinensis* 'Shamouti' |

| | |
|---|---|
| - 'Lane Late' (F) | CGOG SCit |
| - 'Malta Blood' (F) | ECon ERea |
| - 'Midknight' (F) | ERea |
| - 'Moro Blood' (F) | ERea SCit |
| - 'Navelate' (F) | CGOG SCit |
| - 'Navelina' (F) | CGOG ECon ERea SCit |
| - 'Newhall' (F) | CGOG LChe SCit |
| - 'Parson Brown' (F) | ERea |
| - 'Prata' (F) | ERea |
| - 'Ruby' (F) | ERea |
| - 'Saint Michael' (F) | ERea |
| - 'Salustiana' (F) | CGOG SCit |
| - 'Sanguinelli' (F) | CGOG ERea LChe SCit |
| § - 'Shamouti' (F) | ERea |
| - 'Succari' (F) | SCit |
| - 'Tarocco' (F) | SCit |
| - 'Thomson' (F) | ERea |
| - 'Valencia' (F) | ECot ERea |
| - 'Valencia Late' (F) | CGOG ECon ERea LChe SCit |
| - 'Washington' (F) | CGOG ERea GTwe LHol SCit |
| *tachibana* | SCit |
| x *tangelo* 'Mapo' (F) | Last listed 1996 |
| - 'Minneola' (F) | CGOG SCit |
| - 'Nocatee' (F) | SCit |
| § - 'Nova' (F) | CGOG SCit |
| - 'Orlando' (F) | SCit |
| - 'Samson' (F) | SCit |
| - 'Seminole' (F) | ERea |
| - 'Ugli' (F) | SCit |
| § *unshiu* (F) | ERea |
| ¶ - 'Clausellina' (F) | CGOG ECon ERea |
| - 'Hashimoto' (F) | CGOG SCit |
| ¶ - 'Okitsu' (F) | CGOG SCit |
| ¶ - 'Owari' (F) | CGOG SCit |
| *volkameriana* | ERea SCit |

## CLADIUM (Cyperaceae)

| | |
|---|---|
| *mariscus* | EWFC |

## CLADOTHAMNUS (Ericaceae)

| | |
|---|---|
| § *pyroliflorus* | SSta |

## CLADOTHAMNUS See ELLIOTTIA

## CLADRASTIS (Papilionaceae)

| | |
|---|---|
| *kentukea* ♀ | CArn CB&S CLnd CMCN CPle ELan EPfP MBlu NBea NPal SPer SSpi WCoo WDin WNor WWat |
| ¶ *sinensis* | SSpi WWat |

## CLARKIA (Onagraceae)

| | |
|---|---|
| *breweri* | Last listed 1996 |
| *concinna* | Last listed 1998 |
| * *repens* | CSpe |

## CLAVINODUM (Poaceae - Bambusoideae)

| | |
|---|---|
| § *oedogonatum* | EPla SDry |

## CLAYTONIA (Portulacaceae)

| | |
|---|---|
| *alsinoides* | See *C. sibirica* |
| *australasica* | See *Neopaxia australasica* |
| *caespitosa* | Last listed 1997 |
| *caroliniana* | LAma NRog |
| § *megarhiza* var. *nivalis* | GDra MAsh NTow NWCA |
| § *nevadensis* | EMar |
| *parvifolia* | See *Naiocrene parvifolia* |
| § *perfoliata* | CAgr CArn EWFC GPoy ILis WCHb WHer |
| § *sibirica* | CAgr CArn CNic CRow CSpe ECoo EEls EMan NBus SDys WHen WPer WRHF WWye |
| - 'Alba' | NBid WCot |

| | |
|---|---|
| *virginica* | EBee EPot LAma MBro NRog |

## CLEMATIS ✿ (Ranunculaceae)

| | |
|---|---|
| 'Abundance' (Vt) | CDoC CPev CRHN CSCl CSPN ERob ESCh ETho GMac IOrc LHol LPri MBri NBea NHol NTay SBra SChu SDix WSHC WTre WWeb |
| 'Acton Pride' | Last listed 1996 |
| 'Ada Sari' (L) | Last listed 1998 |
| *addisonii* | CSCl ERob ESCh WTre |
| *aethusifolia* | CB&S CPIN CSCl CSPN ETen LPri MBri NTay SBra WTre |
| *afoliata* | CB&S CPev ECou ERob ESCh ETho WTre |
| ¶ 'Aino' (Vt) | ERob |
| 'Akaishi' | ERob ESCh NTay WTre |
| *akebioides* | CHan CPIN CSCl EBee NBrk SBra SPer WFar |
| - CLD 0601/12 | Last listed 1996 |
| 'Akemi' (L) | ERob WTre |
| 'Akeshina' | Last listed 1998 |
| § Alabast™ = 'Poulala' (Fl) | CBlo EBee EMil ERob ESCh ETho NTay WTre |
| 'Alba Luxurians' (Vt) ♀ | More than 30 suppliers |
| *albicoma* | CSCl |
| 'Albiflora' | CSPN |
| I 'Albina Plena' (A/d) | ESCh ETho NBrk SPla |
| 'Alice Fisk' (P) | CSCl ESCh LPri NBea NBrk NHaw NTay SBra WGor |
| 'Aljonushka' | CSCl EBee EBrP EBre ELan EOrc ERob ESCh ETho LBre LPri MBri MGos NBea NBrk NHaw NTay SBra SBre SMur SPer SPla WSHC WTre WWeb |
| 'Allanah' (J) | CRHN CSCl EBee ELan EPfP ERob ESCh ETho LPri MGos NBea NTay SBra SEas SPla WStI WTre |
| § *alpina* (A) ♀ | CMac CPev CSCl EWTr GDra GSki IOrc MBal MBar NEgg NMen NPer NRoo NSti SPlb WAbe WFar WWat |
| I - 'Alba Belsay' | Last listed 1996 |
| - 'Blush Queen' | Last listed 1996 |
| - 'Burford White' (A) | CSCl LPri NBrk |
| - 'Columbine' (A) | CPev EBee ENot EOrc ETho LPri MBar NBea NTay SBra SDix WTre WWeb |
| - 'Columbine White' | See *C. alpina* 'White Columbine' |
| - 'Constance' (A) | CBlo CSPN EPfP ESCh ETho GMac LPri MBri NSti NTay SBra SPer SRPl SRms WTre WWeb |
| - 'Foxy' (A) | EBee EPfP ERob ESCh ETho GMac LPri MBri NBrk NTay WTre |
| - 'Frances Rivis' (A) ♀ | More than 30 suppliers |
| - 'Frankie' (A) | CDoC CSPN EBee EBrP EBre ELan ERob ESCh ETho LBre MBri NTay SBra SBre WGor WTre WWeb |
| - 'Jacqueline du Pré' (A) | CHad CPev CSCl CSPN EBee EOrc ERob ESCh ETho GMac IHar LPri MBri MGos NBea NBrk NTay SBra SPer WTre WWat |
| - 'Jan Lindmark' | See *C. macropetala* 'Jan Lindmark' |
| - 'Linava' | Last listed 1996 |
| - 'Odorata' (A) | ERob ESCh ETho MGos NBea |
| § - 'Pamela Jackman' (A) | CDoC CSCl CSPN EAst EBee ELan ESCh GChr IHar IOrc LFis LPri MBri MGos NBea NHol NRoo NSti NTay SBra SDix SHFr SPer WTre WWeb |
| - 'Pink Flamingo' (A) | CBlo CMHG CSPN EBee EBrP EBre ELan ENot ERob ESCh ETho GMac LBre MBri NEgg NPri NSti NTay SBra SBre SMur WTre WWeb |

- 'Ria' — Last listed 1996
- 'Rosy Pagoda' (A) — CSPN EBee ELan EOrc EPfP ERob ESCh ETho LPri NBea NBir NRoo WTre
- 'Ruby' (A) — CMHG CMac CPev CSCl EBee ELan ESCh ETho GChr LHol LPri MBri MGos NBea NEgg NHol NSti SBra SChu SDix SPer SReu WSHC WTre WWeb
§ - subsp. *sibirica* (A) — CPev
¶ - - 'Riga' (A) — ERob WTre
§ - - 'White Moth' (A) — CBlo CMac CSCl CSPN ELan ESCh ETho IHar LPri MBri MGos NBrk NHol NTay SBra SPer SRms WSHC WTre
- 'Tage Lundell' — See C. 'Tage Lundell'
¶ - 'Violet Purple' (A) — ERob
§ - 'White Columbine' (A) ♀ — CRHN CSCl CSPN EPfP ERob ESCh ETho MBri MGos NBea SBra
- 'Willy' (A) — More than 30 suppliers
¶ 'Alpinist' (L) — ERob
'Ametistina' (A) — ERob
'André Devillers' — See C. 'Directeur André Devillers'
I 'Andromeda' (Fl) — ERob ESCh ETho NTay WTre
'Anita' (Ta) — CSCl EMil ERob ESCh ETho NTay SBra SPer WTre
'Anna' (P) — CSCl CSPN ERob ESCh NTay
¶ 'Anna German' — ERob
§ Anna Louise™ = — CSCl CSPN EBee ERob ESCh
  'Evithree' (P) — ETho LRHS MBri NTay WTre
'Annabel' (P) — ERob WTre
'Annamieke' (Ta) — CSCl ERob ESCh MGos NTay SBra WTre
* 'Anniversary' — LPri
¶ 'Anouchka' (L) — CSCl
* 'Anuska' — EBrP EBre LBre SBre
¶ 'Aotearoa' — ERob
*apiifolia* — CPev CSCl ERob ESCh NTay WTre
¶ - B&SWJ 4838 — WCru
- var. *biternata* GR 0008 — Last listed 1996
'Arabella' (D) — CBar CHad CHan CLAP CPev CPou CSCl CSPN EBee ERob ESCh ETho MBri MGrG NBea NBrk NHaw NTay SBra SMur SPla WSHC WTre WWat WWeb
§ Arctic Queen™ = — CB&S CSCl CSPN EBee EBrP EBre
  'Evitwo' (Fl) — ESCh ETho LBre LPri MBri NBea NTay SBre WBay WLRN WTre WWeb WWes
*aristata* — CPlN
*armandii* — More than 30 suppliers
- 'Apple Blossom' — CB&S CPev CPou CSCl CSPN EBee ERob ESCh ETho EWTr GQui IHar IOrc LBuc LPri LRHS MGos NBea NHol NPal NTay SBra SPer SReu SSoC SSta WStl WTre
- var. *biondiana* — ERob MNes SBla WTre
- 'Bowl of Beauty' — CSCl ERob ESCh MGos
- 'Jeffries' — CSPN LRHS
- 'Meyeniana' — CSCl ERob ESCh SPer WTre
- 'Snowdrift' — CB&S CPev CSCl CSam EBee EPfP ERob ESCh ETho LPri LRHS MGos NPal NTay SEas SPer SReu SRms WTre
¶ - Treasure's form — WTre
x *aromatica* — ERob ESCh ETho GMac LFis NBea NTay SBra WTre
'Asagasumi' (L) — ERob
'Asao' (P) — CLAP CRHN CSCl CSPN EAst EBee EBrP EBre ELan ERob ESCh ETho LBre LPri NBea NTay SBra SBre SPer SSoC WTre WWeb

'Ascotiensis' (J) ♀ — CPev CRHN CSCl CSPN EBee EBrP EBre ESCh ETho LBre LPri NBea NTay SBra SBre SDix SPer WStl WTre
'Ashitaka' — Last listed 1998
§ 'Aureolin' (Ta) ♀ — CSCl EBee EBrP EBre EPfP ERob ETho LBre MBar MGos NBrk NHol SBra SBre WTre
'Aurora Borealis' — Last listed 1998
*australis* — Last listed 1998
¶ Avalanche™ = 'Blaaval' — ERob LRHS NPri SBla
'Bagatelle' (P) — ESCh
'Barbara Dibley' (P) — CPev CSCl CTri EBee ERob ESCh LPri NBea NTay SBod SBra SDix WBod WTre
'Barbara Jackman' (P) — CPev CSCl CSPN CSam EBee ENot ERob ETho EWTr LPri MBar MBri NBea NTay SBra SDix SPer WFar WStl WTre
*barbellata* (A) — CSCl ERob
- 'Pruinina' — See C. 'Pruinina'
'Beata' (L) — Last listed 1998
'Beauty of Richmond' (L) — ESCh NBea SDix SPer WTre
'Beauty of Worcester' (Fl/L) — CLAP CPev CSCl CSPN EAst EBee EBrP EBre ELan ESCh ETho LBre LPri MAsh MBar NBea NEgg NHaw NTay SBra SBre SDix SPer WTre
'Bees' Jubilee' (P) ♀ — More than 30 suppliers
'Bella' (J) — ERob ESCh
'Belle Nantaise' (L) — CPev CSCl CSPN EBee EBrP EBre EPfP ERob ESCh ETho LBre LPri NBea NTay SBre WTre
'Belle of Woking' (Fl/P) — CPev CRHN CSCl CSPN EBee EBrP EBre ELan ERob ESCh ETho GMac LBre LPri MBar NBea NHaw NTay SBra SBre SDix SPer WGwG WTre
'Benedictus' (P) — Last listed 1997
'Bessie Watkinson' — WTre
'Betina' (A) — ERob ESCh ETho IHar LPri WTre
'Betty Corning' (VtxT) — CSCl CSPN EBee EBrP EBre EMil EOrc EPfP ERob ESCh ETho LBre LFis LPri NBea NBrk NTay SBra SBre SLon WBay WSHC WTre
'Betty Risdon' — ERob ETho NBea
'Big Horns' — Last listed 1998
§ 'Bill MacKenzie' (Ta) ♀ — More than 30 suppliers
'Black Madonna' (P) — ESCh
'Black Prince' — ELan EPfP ERob ESCh LPri NTay WTre
§ 'Blekitny Aniol' (J/Vt) — CRHN CSCl ERob ESCh ETho LPri MGrG NBrk NTay SBra WTre
Blue Angel — See C. 'Blekitny Aniol'
'Blue Belle' (Vt) — CBar CPou CRHN CSCl CSPN EBee ELan CSCl LPri MBri NBea NBrk NSti NTay SBra WTre WWat WWeb
'Blue Bird' (A/d) — CRHN CSCl EBee IOrc LPri NBea NHol SBod SBra SPer SPla SRms WTre
'Blue Boy' (D) — See C. x *eriostemon* 'Blue Boy'
'Blue Boy' (L/P) — See C. 'Elsa Späth'
'Blue Dancer' (A) — CAbP CBlo CSCl EBee ESCh ETho MBal MWat NEgg NTay WTre WWeb WWes
'Blue Gem' (L) — ERob ESCh NBrk NTay SBra WTre
§ Blue Moon™ = 'Evirin' — EBrP EBre ESCh ETho LBre LRHS NBea NPri SBre
Blue Rain = 'Sinij Dozhdj' (D) — ERob ESCh MBri WTre
'Blue Ravine' (P) — ERob ESCh ETho NTay WTre

x *bonstedtii* (H) — ESCh
- 'Côte d'Azur' (H) — NCut WTre
- 'Crépuscule' (H) — ERob ESCh MCli NCut SRms WCot WTre
'Boskoop Beauty' (PxL) — ERob NBrk
'Bracebridge Star' (L/P) — CSCl ERob ESCh SBra
*brachiata* — CSCl SBra
*brachyura* — ERob
¶ 'Bravo' (Ta) — ERob WTre
§ 'Brunette' (A) — ERob ESCh ETho LPri MBri MGos SBra WTre
*buchananiana* Finet & Gagnepain — See *C. rehderiana*
- DC. — CSCl WTre
- S&SH 373 — CHan
¶ 'Burford Bell' — ERob WTre
* 'Burford Princess' — ERob
'Burford Variety' (Ta) — ERob ESCh LPri NBea NTay WTre
'Burma Star' (P) — CLAP CPev ERob ESCh ETho
'C.W. Dowman' (P) — ERob
'Caddick's Cascade' — Last listed 1998
'Caerulea Luxurians' — Last listed 1997
* *calanthe* — Last listed 1997
*calycina* — See *C. cirrhosa*
*campaniflora* — CBot CHan CPev CPIN CSCl CSPN EBee EOrc EPla ERob ESCh ETho MWhi NBea NBrk NSti NWCA SBra SDix WTre
- 'Lisboa' — ERob ESCh ETho NBrk SBra WSHC WTre
- x *viticella* — Last listed 1996
¶ 'Campanulina Plena' (A) — ERob
'Candy Stripe' — CSCl ERob
'Capitaine Thuilleaux' — See *C*. 'Souvenir du Capitaine Thuilleaux'
'Cardinal Wyszynski' — See *C*. 'Kardynał Wyszyński'
¶ 'Carmen Rose' (A) — ERob
'Carmencita' — ERob GMac NBrk
'Carnaby' (L) — CDoC CSCl CSPN EAst EBee EBrP EBre ELan ENot ERob ESCh ETho LBre LPri MBar MBri NBea NHaw NTay SBod SBra SBre SRPl WTre WWeb
'Carnival Queen' — CSCl ERob NTay WTre
'Caroline' (J) — CPev CSCl ESCh ETho NBrk SBra
x *cartmanii* (Fo) — Last listed 1998
- 'Joe' (Fo) — CB&S CSCl EHyt ESCh ETho EWes GCrs ITim LPri MAsh MBri MGos MLan NBrk NHar NMen SAga SBra SMad SMrm WAbe WBay WHil WTre
- 'Joe' x 'Sharon' — Last listed 1996
- 'Moonbeam' (Fo) — ESCh MGos NBrk NTay SBla SIng SMrm WCot
'Cassiopeia' (PxL) — Last listed 1997
'Centre Attraction' — ESCh
'Chalcedony' (FlxL) — CPev CSCl ERob ESCh ETho LPri MGos NBrk NTay SBra WTre
'Charissima' (P) — CPev CSCl ERob ESCh ETho IHar LPri MBri NTay WTre
'Cherry Brandy' — Last listed 1996
*chiisanensis* — CB&S ERob ESCh SBra WCwm WTre
¶ - 'Lemon Bells' — LRHS
¶ - 'Love Child' — ERob ESCh WTre
*chinensis* hort. — See *C. terniflora*
- Retz — ERob WTre
'Christian Steven' (J) — Last listed 1998
*chrysantha* — Last listed 1997
- var. *paucidentata* — See *C. hilariae*
N *chrysocoma* Franchet — CHan CPev CSCl ELan ERob ETho LPri MBNS MBar NHol SBra SDix WCru WTre

- ACE 1093 — CPou
- B&L 12237 — NBea WTre
- B&L 12324 — Last listed 1996
- hybrid — CSCl ERob NTay
N *chrysocoma* hort. — See *C. montana* var. *sericea*
'Cicciolina' (Vt) — ERob
§ *cirrhosa* — CBot CPev CSCl ELan ESCh EWTr GSki LPri MGos NTay SArc SPer WTre
- var. *balearica* ♀ — More than 30 suppliers
- - forms — CPev WCru
- 'Freckles' ♀ — More than 30 suppliers
- 'Jingle Bells' — CSCl ERob ESCh ETho LFis LPri LRHS NBea NTay WTre
- 'Ourika Valley' — Last listed 1996
¶ - subsp. *semitriloba* — ERob
- 'Wisley Cream' — CB&S CSCl CSPN EBee EBrP EBre ECtt ELan ENot EOrc ESCh ETho LBre LPri MAsh MGrG NBea NHol NSti NTay SBra SBre SChu SPer SPla WBay WSHC WTre WWeb
*coactilis* — CSCl ERob
'Colette Deville' (J) — EPfP ERob ESCh NBea NBrk NTay
*columbiana* — CSCl LFis
- var. *columbiana* — Last listed 1998
§ - var. *tenuiloba* — Last listed 1998
¶ 'Columella' (A) — ERob
'Comtesse de Bouchaud' (J) ♀ — CDoC CMac CPev CSCl CSPN EAst EBee EBrP EBre ELan ENot ETho EWTr GRei LBre LPri MBar MBri NBea NEgg NHaw NRoo SBra SBre SDix SPer WTre
*connata* — CPIN ERob ESCh NBrk NWCA SBra WCru WTre
- HWJCM 132 — WCru
'Corona' (PxL) — CBlo CPev CSPN EAst EBee ELan ERob LPri MBar NBea NHaw NTay SBra WTre
'Corry' (Ta) — ERob ESCh NBrk WTre
'Countess of Lovelace' (P) — CLAP CSCl CSPN EBee EBrP EBre ELan ERob ESCh ETho ICrw LBre LPri MBar MGos MSte NBea NTay SBod SBra SBre SDix SPer WTre
County Park Group (Fo) — ECou
§ - 'Pixie' (Fo/m) — CSCl ECre ESCh IHar MGos WTre
'Crimson King' (L) — CTri ESCh MAsh NTay SBod SBra WGor WTre
§ *crispa* — CPIN CPou CSCl ERob NBea NTay SBra WSHC WTre
§ - 'Cylindrica' — CBlo CSCl NBrk
- hybrid — ERob
I - 'Rosea' — See *C. crispa* 'Cylindrica'
*cunninghamii* — See *C. parviflora*
'Cyanea' — EBee ERob ESCh ETho GMac LPri MBri NTay WTre
x *cylindrica* — CSCl CSPN ESCh NBrk NTay WTre
'Daniel Deronda' (P) ♀ — CPev CSCl CSPN EAst EBee EBrP EBre ECtt ELan ERob ESCh ETho EWTr LBre LPri MBri NBea NHol NTay SBod SBra SBre SDix SPer WTre WWeb
'Darlene' — Last listed 1996
'Dawn' (L/P) — CPev CSCl CSPN EBee ERob ESCh ETho LPri NBea NTay SBra SPer SPla WGwG WTre WWal
'Debutante' — ETho
'Denny's Double' (d) — ERob ESCh NBrk NTay WTre
*denticulata* — WCru
'Dilly Dilly' — Last listed 1996
*dioscoreifolia* — See *C. terniflora*

§ 'Directeur André Devillers' ERob
  (P)
'Doctor Label' — Last listed 1996
'Doctor Ruppel' (P) ♀ — CMac CPev CSCl CSPN EAst EBee
  EBrP EBre ELan EOld ESCh ETho
  EWTr LBre LPri MBar MBri MGos
  NBea NRoo SBod SBra SBre SDix
  SPer WSHC WTre
¶ 'Doggy' (Vt) — ERob
¶ 'Dominika' (J) — ERob ESCh
'Donna' — Last listed 1996
¶ 'Dorath' — ESCh
¶ 'Dorota' — ERob
'Dorothy Tolver' — CSCl ERob ESCh ETho
'Dorothy Walton' (J) — CBlo CRHN CSCl CSPN EBee
  ERob ESCh ETho LPri NBrk
  NHaw NTay SBra WTre
***douglasii*** — See *C. hirsutissima*
¶ 'Dr Lebel' — ERob
'Duchess of Albany' (T) ♀ — More than 30 suppliers
'Duchess of Edinburgh' — More than 30 suppliers
  (Fl)
'Duchess of Sutherland' — CPev CSCl CSPN ESCh LPri MAsh
  (Vt/d) — NBea NTay SBra SDix WTre
x ***durandii*** (D) ♀ — More than 30 suppliers
'Early Sensation' (Fo) — COtt CSCl ESCh ETho IHar LRHS
  MGos NBea NPro NTay WTre
'East Sunset' — Last listed 1996
'Ebba' — Last listed 1998
'Edith' (L) ♀ — CSCl CSPN EBee EBrP EBre ECtt
  ERob ESCh ETho LBre LPri MAsh
  NBea NBrk NTay SBra SBre WGor
  WGwG WTre
'Edomurasaki' (L) — CSCl CSPN EBee ERob ESCh LPri
  MBri NTay WTre
'Edouard Desfossé' (P) — CSCl ESCh ETho NTay WTre
'Edward Prichard' — ERob NBea NBrk WTre
¶ 'Eetika' (Vt) — ERob
¶ 'Ekstra' (J) — ERob ESCh
'Ellenbank White' — Last listed 1997
§ 'Elsa Späth' (L/P) ♀ — CB&S CPev CSCl CSPN EAst EBee
  EBrP EBre ELan ENot ERob ESCh
  ETho LBre LPri MBar MBri MGos
  NBea SBra SBre SDix SPer SRPl
  WMer WTre
'Elvan' (Vt) — CHan CPev CRHN CSCl ERob
  ESCh NBea NBrk NTay WSHC
  WTre
'Emajögi' (L) — Last listed 1997
'Emilia Plater' (Vt) — CSCl ERob ESCh ETho LPri MBri
  NBea SBra WGor WTre
'Empress of India' (P) — EBrP EBre ERob ESCh LBre LPri
  NTay SBre WTre
¶ 'Entel' (J) — ERob WTre
§ x ***eriostemon*** (D) — CSCl CSPN EBee EMar EOrc EPfP
  ESCh LFis MBNS MSte NBrk
  NHaw NHol SBra SPer SPla WCot
  WTre
§ - 'Blue Boy' (D) — EPfP ERob ESCh ETho LFis MBri
  MGos NBrk NHaw SBra WTre
§ - 'Hendersonii' (D) — CHad CLon CPev EAst EBee EBrP
  EBre ELan ERob ESCh ETho LBre
  LHop MRav NBea NBir NHol
  NTay SBra SBre SCro SDix SPer
  SWat WCot WLin WSHC WTre
  WWal
'Ernest Markham' (J/V) ♀ — More than 30 suppliers
'Esperanto' (J) — Last listed 1998
'Etiole de Malicorne' (P) — NTay
'Etoile de Malicorne' (P) — EBee ERob ESCh ETho NBea
  WGor WTre

'Etoile de Paris' (P) — CBlo CSCl ERob ESCh ETho NTay
  SBra WTre
¶ 'Etoile Nacrée' — CSCl ESCh
'Etoile Rose' (T) — CHan CLAP CPev CSCl CSPN EAst
  EBrP EBre ELan EOrc ERob ESCh
  ETho IOrc LBre LFis LPri NBea
  NTay SBra SBre SChu SDix SMur
  SPer WFar WSHC WTre WWat
'Etoile Violette' (Vt) ♀ — More than 30 suppliers
¶ 'Europa' — ERob
¶ Evening Star™ = 'Evista' — ETho NTay
♦ 'Evifive' — See *C.* Liberation = 'Evifive'
♦ 'Evifour' — See *C.* Royal Velvet = 'Evifour'
♦ 'Evijohill' — See *C.* Josephine = 'Evijohill'
♦ 'Evione' — See *C.* Sugar Candy = 'Evione'
♦ 'Evirin' — See *C.* Blue Moon = 'Evirin'
♦ 'Evisix' — See *C.* Petit Faucon = 'Evisix'
♦ 'Evithree' — See *C.* Anna Louise = 'Evithree'
♦ 'Evitwo' — See *C.* Arctic Queen = 'Evitwo'
¶ 'Eximia' (A) — ERob
'Fair Rosamond' (L/P) — CPev CSCl CSPN EBee EPfP ERob
  ESCh ETho LPri MBri NBea NTay
  SBod SBra SDix SPla WTre
'Fairy Queen' (L) — CSCl ERob ESCh LPri NTay SBra
***fargesii*** — See *C. potaninii*
x ***fargesioides*** — See *C.* 'Paul Farges'
'Farrago' — Last listed 1996
***fasciculiflora*** — CBot CGre CMHG CPIN CRHN
  CSCl ETen SLon SSpi WCru WTre
  WWat
  - L 657 — Last listed 1998
¶ ***fauriei*** — ERob
***finetiana*** hort. — See *C. indivisa*
  - L. — Last listed 1998
'Firefly' — ERob ESCh NTay
'Fireworks' (P) ♀ — COtt CSCl CSPN EAst EBee EBrP
  EBre ENot ESCh ETho LBre MBri
  MGos NBea NPri NTay SBra SBre
  WFoF WGor WStI WTre WWeb
'Flamingo' (L) — Last listed 1998
***flammula*** — More than 30 suppliers
* - ***rotundiflora*** — CSCl
  - 'Rubra Marginata' — See *C.* x *triternata*
    'Rubromarginata'
§ 'Floralia' (A/d) — CSCl CSPN EBee ELan EOrc ESCh
  LPri LRHS MBri NBea WTre
***florida*** — CSCl ETho
  - 'Bicolor' — See *C. florida* 'Sieboldii'
  - 'Flore Pleno' (d) — CPev CSCl CSPN EBrP EBre ELan
  EOrc ESCh ETho LBre NBea NHol
  NTay SBod SBra SBre SPer SPla
  SSoC WTre
§ - 'Sieboldii' — More than 30 suppliers
***foetida*** — CB&S ESCh WTre
***forrestii*** — See *C. napaulensis*
§ ***forsteri*** — CB&S CPIN CSCl CSPN CSam
  ERob ESCh ETho GSki LPri NBrk
  NTay SBod SBra WCru WSHC
  WTre WWat
  - x ***indivisa*** — WCru
'Four Star' (L) — LPri
¶ 'Frau Mikiko' (P) — ERob
***fremontii*** — Last listed 1996
¶ 'Fryderyk Chopin' — ERob ESCh WTre
'Fuji-musume' (L) — CSCl ERob ESCh ETho LPri SBra
  WTre
¶ 'Fujinami' (L) — ERob
***fusca*** Turczaninow — ERob WTre
  - hort. — See *C. japonica*
  - var. ***coreana*** f. ***umbrosa*** — WCru
    B&SWJ 700
  - dwarf form — Last listed 1998

§ - subsp. *fusca* — CSCl ESCh
 - var. *kamtschatica* — See *C. fusca* subsp. *fusca*
 - *koreana* — See *C. koreana*
 - var. *mandshurica* — CSCl
§ - var. *violacea* — CSCl EPfP ERob ESCh ETho NBea SBra WSHC WTre
 'G. Steffner' (A) — Last listed 1998
 'Gabriëlle' (P) — CSCl ERob ESCh WMer WTre
 'Général Sikorski' (L) ♀ — CMHG CMac CSCl CSPN CSam EAst EBee EBrP EBre ECtt ELan ESCh ETho LBre LPri MBri MGos NBea NHaw NTay SBra SBre SDix SPer WTre WWat
 *gentianoides* — CSCl CSPN ERob GCHN WAbe
¶ 'Georg' (A/d) — ERob
¶ 'Georg Ots' (J) — ERob
 'Gillian Blades' (P) ♀ — CSCl CSPN EAst EBee EBrP EBre ELan EPfP ERob ESCh ETho LBre MBri NBea NBrk NHaw NTay SBra SBre SSoC WTre
 'Gipsy Queen' (J) ♀ — More than 30 suppliers
 'Gladys Picard' (P) — ERob ESCh WTre
 *glauca* hort. — See *C. intricata*
 *glaucophylla* — CSCl
 *glycinoides* — GSki
 'Glynderek' (L) — ERob ESCh NTay SBra WTre
 'Golden Harvest' (Ta) — ERob ESCh MBri WTre
§ Golden Tiara® = 'Kugotia' (Ta) — CSCl EBee ESCh ETho LPri LRHS MAsh MGos NBea NTay WLRN WTre WWeb
¶ 'Gornoe Ozero' — ERob
 *gouriana* — ERob ESCh NTay WTre
 - subsp. *lishanensis* B&SWJ 292 — WCru
¶ 'Grace' (Ta) — ERob ETho WTre
 *gracilifolia* — ERob ESCh WTre
¶ 'Grandiflora Sanguinea' (Vt) — ERob
 'Grandiflora Sanguinea' Johnson — See *C.* 'Södertälje'
 *grata* Wallich — CPev ERob NBrk WTre
 - hort. — See *C. x jouiniana*
 - CC 1895 — WHCr
 'Gravetye Beauty' (T) — CHad CPev CSCl CSPN EAst EBee ELan EOrc ERob ESCh ETho LFis LHol LPri MBri NBea NRoo SBra SDix SMad SPer SReu SRms SSta WMer WSHC WTre WWat
 'Gravetye Seedling' (T) — Last listed 1997
 'Green Velvet' (Fo) — CSCl ECou
 *grewiiflora* B&SWJ 2956 — WCru
 'Guernsey' — Last listed 1997
 'Guernsey Cream' (P) — CBlo CSCl CSPN EBee EBrP EBre EMil ESCh ETho LBre LPri MBri NBea NTay SBra SBre WLRN WTre WWeb WWes
 'Guiding Star' — ERob NTay SBra
 'H.F.Young' (L/P) ♀ — More than 30 suppliers
 'Hagley Hybrid' (J) — More than 30 suppliers
¶ 'Hainton Ruby' (P) — ERob
 'Haku-ôkan' (L) — CPev CSCl CSPN EBee EBrP EBre ERob ESCh ETho LBre LPri MAsh NBea NTay SBod SBra SBre WTre WWeb
 'Halina Nell' (Fl) — Last listed 1996
 'Hanaguruma' (P) — ESCh ETho WBcn WTre
¶ 'Hanna' — ERob
 'Harlequin' — Last listed 1996
¶ 'Harmony' — ERob
 'Haru-no-hoshi' — Last listed 1997
 'Haruyama' — Last listed 1998
 Havering hybrids (Fo) — ECou
 'Heather Herschell' — CPev

 'Heirloom' — Last listed 1996
 'Helen Cropper' (P) — ERob ESCh ETho NBrk
 'Helios' (Ta) — CSCl EBee ENot EPfP ERob ESCh ETho IHar LPri MBri MGos NBea NBrk SBra WCot WTre
 'Helsingborg' (A) ♀ — CB&S CSCl CSPN EBee ELan ENot ERob ESCh ETho LPri MBri NBea NHol NSti NTay SBra SPla WTre WWes
 *hendersonii* Standley — See *C. x eriostemon*
 - Koch — See *C. x eriostemon* 'Hendersonii'
 'Henryi' ♀ — CPev CSCl CSPN EAst EBee EBrP EBre ELan ENot ERob ESCh ETho EWTr IOrc LBre LPri MBar MBri MLan NBea NTay SBra SBre SDix SPer WSHC WTre
 *henryi* var. *morii* B&SWJ 1668 — WCru
 *heracleifolia* (H) — CB&S CBot CPou CSCl ESCh GSki NLar NRoo WTre
¶ - 'Alan Bloom' (H) — NCat
¶ - B&SWJ 4560 (H) — WCru
¶ - B&SWJ 5073 (H) — WCru
N - 'Campanile' (H) — CPev CSCl ERob ESCh LPri NBea NBir NTay SDix
I - 'Cassandra' (H) — EFou
 - CC 612 (H) — Last listed 1996
N - 'Côte d'Azur' (H) — ESCh MCAu MTed NPla
 - var. *davidiana* (H) — CPev CPle NBea NHol SPla SRms WTre
 - - 'Wyevale' (H) ♀ — CHan CPev CSCl CSPN CStr EBee EBrP EBre ELan ERob ETho LBre LHop LPri MBri MRav NBea NTay SBla SBra SBre SCro SDix SPer SSoC WCot WEas WHil WTre WWye
 - 'Jaggards' (H) — Last listed 1997
¶ - 'New Love' (H) — ESCh
¶ - 'Purple Spider' (H) — CSCl
 - 'Roundway Blue Bird' (H) — CBot
 'Herbert Johnson' (P) — CPev ESCh ETho NBea NBrk SBra WTre
 *hexapetala* hort. — See *C. recta* subsp. *recta* var. *lasiosepala*
 - DC. — See *C. forsteri*
 'Hidcote Purple' (L) — Last listed 1998
 'Hikarugenji' — ERob ESCh ETho NTay
§ *hilariae* — CSCl EBee ERob ESCh NTay
§ *hirsutissima* — CSCl NOak
 - var. *scottii* — ERob
 'Honora' (P) — CSCl ESCh WTre
 *hookeriana* — WTre
 'Horn of Plenty' (L/P) ♀ — CSCl CSPN EBee ERob ESCh ETho NBea NPri NTay SBra WTre
 'Huldine' (Vt) — More than 30 suppliers
¶ 'Huvi' — ERob
§ 'Hybrida Sieboldii' (L) — CRHN CSCl CSPN EBee ERob ESCh ETho LPri NBea NBrk NTay SBra SPer WTre
 'Hythe Egret' — EHyt
 *ianthina* — See *C. fusca* var. *violacea*
° - var. *kuripoensis* — ERob
¶ 'Ideal' (L) — ERob
 'Ilka' (P) — Last listed 1997
 'Imperial' (P/d) — ERob ESCh WTre
§ *indivisa* — CPev CSCl EBee LPri LRHS SBra WTre
 - (f) — Last listed 1998
 - (m) — Last listed 1998
 - 'Fairy' (Fo) — ECou
§ - var. *lobata* — CSCl MGrG WTre

*integrifolia* — CPou CSCl ERob ESCh ETho LFis LHop LPri MBri MBro MGos MLLN MTho NFla NHol NLar NPer NRoo NSti SPer SRPl SRms SSoC WCot WCru WHoo WPer WTre

- 'Alba' — CBot CSCl ECtt ELan NHaw NTay SPer WSHC

§ - var. *albiflora* — CHad EBee ESCh ETho GBuc LPri MBel MBri NBea NBir NBrk SBra WCru WTre

- 'Amy' — ERob ESCh

\* - 'Cascade' — CSCl

\* - 'Finnis Form' — SChu

- 'Floris V' — ERob

- 'Hendersonii' Koch — See *C.* x *eriostemon* 'Hendersonii'

- 'Hendersonii' hort. — ERob ETho WTre

¶ - subsp. *integrifolia* — ERob
var. *latifolia*

- 'Lauren' — ERob

- 'Olgae' — CHad CLAP CPev CSCl CSPN EBee ESCh ETho LPri NBea NBrk NTay SBra WTre

- 'Pangbourne Pink' — CHad CLAP EBee ESCh ETho GBuc NBea NBrk NHaw NTay SBra WCru WSHC WTre

- 'Pastel Blue' — CPev ERob ESCh NBea

- 'Pastel Pink' — CPev ERob ESCh ETho

- 'Rosea' ♀ — CBot CHar CLon CM&M CPev CSCl CSPN EBee ELan ERob ESCh ETho LPri MBri MTho NBea NBrk NTay SPer SSoC WSHC WTre

- 'Tapestry' — CPev CSCl ERob NTay SBra WTre

- white — See *C. integrifolia* var. *albiflora*

§ *intricata* — CSCl CSPN ETen NSti WTre WWat

¶ - 'Harry Smith' — ERob

¶ 'Iola Fair' (P) — ESCh ETho

'Ishobel' (P) — CSCl ERob ESCh LPri NBrk

*ispabanica* — See *C. orientalis* L.

'Ivan Olsson' (PxL) — ERob ESCh LPri

'Jackmanii' ♀ — CB&S CMHG CMac CRHN CSCl CTri EBee EBrP EBre ENot EOld ERob ESCh ETho EWTr GRei IHar LBre NBea NEgg NRoo NWea SBod SBra SBre SPer SSoC WFar WTre WWeb

'Jackmanii Alba' (J) — CPev CSCl CSPN EAst EBee EBrP EBre ELan ERob ESCh ETho LBre LPri MBar NBea NBrk NTay SBra SBre SDix WTre

'Jackmanii Rubra' (J) — CPev CRHN CSCl ERob LPri MAsh NBea SBra WLRN WTre

N 'Jackmanii Superba' (J) — CChe CMac CPev CSCl CSPN EAst EBee EBrP EBre ECtt ELan ERob ETho GChr LBre LPri MBar MBri MGos NBea NTay SBra SBre SDix SPer SReu SSta WBod WTre

'Jacqueline' — LRHS

'James Mason' — CMHG CPev CSCl CSPN ESCh ETho NBea NTay WMer WTre

§ 'Jan Pawel II' (J) — CBlo CMHG CMac CSCl CSPN EBee EBrP EBre ELan ESCh ETho IHar LBre LPri NBea NTay SBra SBre SPer WTre

¶ Jánis Rupléns No. 1 — ERob

§ *japonica* — CPev CSCl ERob ETho NBea NBrk NHaw WTre

- var. *obvallata* — See *C. obvallata*

'Jashio' — Last listed 1998

¶ 'Jasper' — ERob WTre

'Jennifer Valentine' — Last listed 1998

¶ 'Jenny' — ERob

'Jenny Caddick' — ERob WTre

'Jim Hollis' (Fl) — ERob ESCh NTay WTre

'Joan Gray' — ERob

'Joan Picton' (P) — CSCl ESCh ETho LPri MAsh NBea NTay SBra WTre

'Joanna' (Fo) — Last listed 1997

'John Gould Veitch' (Fl) — ERob

\* 'John Gudmunsson' — ERob ESCh

'John Huxtable' (J) — CDoC CPev CRHN CSCl ERob ESCh ETho EWTr LPri MBri NBea NBrk NHaw NTay SBra SDix WGor WTre

John Paul II — See *C.* 'Jan Pawel II'

'John Warren' (L) — CSCl ERob ESCh ETho LPri NBea NTay SBod SBra SPer WTre WWeb

'Jorma' (J) — Last listed 1998

§ Josephine™ = 'Evijohill' — COtt ESCh ETho LPri LRHS MBNS NPri NTay WWeb

§ x *jouiniana* — EBee ERob ESCh GBuc GOrc MBal MBlu NHol SEas SPer WGwG WSHC WTre

§ - 'Mrs Robert Brydon' — CSCl EBee EPfP ERob ETho NBrk NFla NTay SBra SHel SPer WCot WTre

- 'Praecox' ♀ — CLAP CPev CRHN CSCl EAst EBee ECtt EFou EHal ELan EOrc EPla ESCh ETho GMac LPri MBar MBri NBea NBee NBir NHol NPro SBra SChu SDix SPer WCot WTre WWeb

¶ 'Jubileinyi 70' — ERob ESCh

¶ 'Kaaru' (Vt) — ERob

'Kacper' (L) — CSCl ESCh LPri NTay WTre

¶ 'Kaiu' — ERob

§ 'Kakio' (P) — CDoC CSCl EAst EBee ENot ERob ESCh ETho LPri MBri NBea NTay SBra SPer WLRN WTre

'Kaleidoscope' — Last listed 1998

¶ 'Kalina' (P) — ERob ESCh

¶ 'Kamilla' — ERob ESCh

§ 'Kardynał Wyszyński' (J) — CBlo CRHN CSCl EBee ESCh LPri MGos NBea NTay SBra WTre

¶ 'Kasmu' — ERob WTre

'Kasugayama' (L) — ERob WTre

'Katherine' — WMer

'Kathleen Dunford' (Fl) — CSCl ERob ESCh LPri MAsh NBea NHaw NTay SBra WMer WTre

'Kathleen Wheeler' (P) — CMac CPev ERob ESCh ETho LPri NBea NTay SBra SDix WTre

'Keith Richardson' (P) — CPev CSCl ESCh LPri NBea NBrk NTay SBra WTre

'Ken Donson' (L) ♀ — CBlo EBee EPfP ERob ESCh ETho MBri NBrk NTay SBod SBra

'Kermesina' (Vt) — CHad CPev CRHN CSam EBee EBrP EBre ELan ESCh ETho GChr GMac IHar LBre LHol LPri MBri NBea NHol NSti NTay SBra SBre SDix SPer SSta WSHC WTre WWat WWeb

¶ 'Kiev' (Vt) — ERob

'King Edward VII' (L) — CSPN EBee EPfP ERob ESCh ETho LPri LRHS NBea NBrk SBra WGor WStI WTre

'King George V' (L) — ERob ESCh NBrk SBra

'Kiri Te Kanawa' — CPev CSCl EPfP ERob ESCh ETho NBea NBrk NTay SBra WTre

*kirilovii* — CSCl ERob GSki

¶ 'Kirimäe' (P) — ERob

¶ 'Kjell' — ERob

¶ 'Klaara' (P) — ERob

¶ 'Kommerei' (Vt) — ERob

'Königskind' (P) — ERob ESCh NTay WTre

| | |
|---|---|
| ¶ 'Königskind Rosa' (P) | ERob |
| § *koreana* | CSCl ERob NBea NHol WHer WTre |
|   - 'Brunette' | See *C.* 'Brunette' |
| *  - *citra* | ERob ESCh |
|   - var.*fragrans* | CSCl |
|   - f.*lutea* | CSCl EHyt WTre |
| ¶  - 'Shiva' | ERob |
| 'Kosmiczeskaja Melodija' (J) | Last listed 1998 |
| ¶ 'Kuba' (P) | ERob |
| ♦ 'Kugotia' | See *C.* Golden Tiara = 'Kugotia' |
| 'Kyllus' (L) | ERob NTay |
| *ladakhiana* | CHan CPev CSCl EPfP ESCh ETho GQui NBea NBir NTay SBra WTre |
| 'Lady Betty Balfour' (J/Vt) | CPev CSCl CSPN EBee EBrP EBre ELan ERob ESCh ETho LBre LPri MBNS MBri NBea NHaw NTay SBra SBre SDix WFar WTre WWal |
| 'Lady Caroline Nevill' (L) | CPev CSCl EBee ERob ESCh ETho LPri NBea NTay SBra WTre |
| ¶ 'Lady Catherine' | ESCh |
| 'Lady in Red' | LPri |
| 'Lady Londesborough' (P) | CPev CSCl CSPN ELan ESCh ETho LPri NBea NBrk NTay SBra SDix WLRN WTre |
| 'Lady Northcliffe' (L) | CPev CSCl CTri ELan EPfP ERob ESCh ISea LPri MAsh NBea NTay SBra SDix SPer WTre |
| 'Ladybird Johnson' (T) | CPev CSCl ERob ESCh ETho NBrk SBra WTre |
| 'Lanuginosa Candida' | Last listed 1998 |
| *lasiandra* | CSCl ERob WTre |
| *lasiantha* | CSCl ESCh |
| 'Lasurstern' (P) ♀ | More than 30 suppliers |
| 'Laura' (L) | ERob ESCh WTre |
| 'Laura Denny' (P) | CSCl NBrk |
| 'Lavender Lace' | ERob WTre |
| 'Lawsoniana' (L) | CSCl CSPN EAst ESCh ETho LPri MAsh MBar NBea NBrk NTay SBra WTre |
| 'Lemon Chiffon' (P) | CSCl EBee ERob ETho NBea NBrk NTay SBra |
| § Liberation™ = 'Evifive' | EBee ERob ESCh ETho LPri MBri NTay SBra WTre |
| § *ligusticifolia* | CSCl EBee ERob GSki |
| 'Lilacina Floribunda' (L) | CSCl CSPN EBee ELan ESCh LPri MBNS MBar NBea NBrk NHaw NTay SBra WTre |
| 'Lilactime' | CBlo EBee ESCh LPri NBea |
| 'Lincoln Star' (P) | CMac CPev CRHN CSCl CSPN EAst EBee EBrP EBre ERob ESCh ETho LBre LPri MBar NBea NBrk NTay SBra SBre SDix SPer WTre |
| 'Lincolnshire Lady' | WPen |
| 'Little Joe' | Last listed 1998 |
| 'Little Nell' (Vt) | CPev CRHN CSCl CSPN EBee EBrP EBre ELan ERob ESCh ETho LBre LHol LPri NBea NBrk NHol NSti NTay SBod SBra SBre SDix SPer SSta WSHC WTre |
| 'Lord Herschell' | CPev |
| 'Lord Nevill' (P) ♀ | CMHG CPev CSCl EBrP EBre ESCh ETho IHar LBre LPri MBri NBea NTay SBod SBra SBre SDix WTre |
| 'Louise Rowe' (Fl) | CSCl EBee EBrP EBre ELan ERob ESCh ETho EWTr IHar LBre LPri MGos NBea NTay SBra SBre SPla WTre |
| ¶ 'Lucey' (J) | NTay |
| 'Lucie' (P) | ESCh NBea WTre |
| 'Lunar Lass' (Fo) | ECho EHyt ETho LBee WAbe WTre |
| 'Lunar Lass' x *foetida* | EBee ECou EPot GCHN |
| 'Luther Burbank' (J) | CSCl ERob ESCh NBea WTre |
| *macropetala* (A/d) | CB&S CPev CSCl EAst EBee ELan ENot ERob ESCh EWTr GChr GDra LHol LPri MBal MBar MGos MWat NBea NEgg SBod SDix WBod WTre WWat WWin |
|   - 'Alborosea' (A/d) | Last listed 1997 |
|   - 'Anders' (A/d) | Last listed 1997 |
|   - 'Ballerina' (A/d) | Last listed 1998 |
|   - 'Ballet Skirt' (A/d) | ERob ESCh ETho MGos WTre |
|   - 'Blue Lagoon' | See *C. macropetala* 'Lagoon' |
| §  - 'Chili' (A) | ERob ESCh NBrk NTay |
|   - 'Floralia' | See *C.* 'Floralia' |
|   - forms (A/d) | CPev |
|   - 'Harry Smith' | See *C. macropetala* 'Chili' |
| §  - 'Jan Lindmark' (A/d) | CSPN EBee EOrc ERob ESCh ETho MBri MGos NBea NBir NTay SBra SPla WGor WTre |
| §  - 'Lagoon' (A/d) | ECle ERob LRHS MBri NBea NBrk NSti SBra SMur WTre |
| *  - 'Lord Neville' | CRHN |
|   - hort. 'Maidwell Hall' (A/d) ♀ | CDoC CMac CSCl EBee EBrP EBre ERob ESCh ETho LBre LFis LPri MGos NBea NBrk NHol NRoo SBra SBre SChu SPer SPla WSHC WTre |
|   - 'Markham's Pink' (A/d) ♀ | More than 30 suppliers |
|   - 'Pauline' (A/d) | ERob ETho NBea NBrk SBra |
|   - 'Pearl Rose' (A/d) | ERob |
|   - 'Purple Spider' (A/d) | CSCl ERob ESCh ETho LRHS MBri NBea SBra WTre WWeb |
|   - 'Rödklokke' (A/d) | Last listed 1996 |
|   - 'Rosea' (A/d) | Last listed 1997 |
|   - 'Salmonea' (A/d) | Last listed 1997 |
|   - 'Snowbird' (A/d) | CPev ERob ESCh NBea NHol SBra WTre |
|   - 'Vicky' (A/d) | CSCl |
|   - 'Wesselton' (A/d) | CSCl ERob ESCh ETho NHol WTre |
|   - 'White Lady' (A/d) | CSCl ERob ESCh SBra SDix WTre |
|   - 'White Moth' | See *C. alpina* subsp. *sibirica* 'White Moth' |
|   - 'White Swan' | See *C.* 'White Swan' |
|   - 'White Wings' (A/d) | ESCh |
| 'Madame Baron Veillard' (J) | CMHG CPev CSCl CSPN EAst EBee EBrP EBre ESCh ETho IHar LBre LPri MBar MHlr NBea NBrk NTay SBra SBre SDix SRPl WTre |
| 'Madame Edouard André' (J) ♀ | CDoC CPev CRHN CSCl CTri EPfP ERob ESCh ETho LPri NBea NTay SBra SDix SPla WTre |
| 'Madame Grangé' (J) ♀ | CPev CRHN CSPN EBee ESCh ETho LPri NBea NBrk NHaw NTay SBod SBra SDix WTre |
| 'Madame Julia Correvon' (Vt) ♀ | More than 30 suppliers |
| 'Madame le Coultre' | See *C.* 'Marie Boisselot' |
| 'Madame van Houtte' (L) | ERob ESCh |
| ¶ 'Magnus Johnson' (A) | ERob |
| 'Majojo' (Fo) | CB&S ESCh |
| 'Mammut' (P) | ERob ESCh WTre |
| § *mandschurica* | CSCl ERob ETho GSki LEur NTay WTre |
|   - B&SWJ 1060 | WCru |
| *marata* | CSCl WTre |
|   - 'Temple Prince' (m) | Last listed 1997 |
|   - 'Temple Queen' (f) | Last listed 1997 |
| 'Marcel Moser' (P) | CPev ESCh NBrk NTay SBra SDix WTre |
| 'Margaret Hunt' (J) | CBlo CMHG CSCl CSPN ELan ERob ESCh ETho LPri NBea NBrk NHaw NTay SBra SPla WTre |
| 'Margaret Wood' (P) | ERob ESCh |

'Margot Koster' (Vt) — CDoC CRHN CSCl EBee EBrP EBre ESCh LBre LPri MBri NBea NHaw NTay SBra SBre WSHC WTre

§ 'Marie Boisselot' (L) ♀ — CB&S CGle CLAP CMac CPev CRHN CSCl CSPN EBee ELan ENot ERob ETho EWTr GChr GMac LPri MBar MBri MGos NBea NSti SBod SBra SChu SDix SPer WSHC WTre WWat

'Marie Louise Jensen' (J) — CSCl ESCh ETho NTay WTre

*marmoraria* ♀ — CPBP CSCl EPot GCrs GNor NHar SBla WAbe WCot WFar WLin

- x *cartmanii* 'Joe' — NHar
- hybrid — LBee LRHS NHar
- x *petriei* (f) — CSCl GCrs

¶ 'Marmori' — ERob
¶ 'Mary Claire' — ERob
§ 'Maskarad' (Vt) — CBlo CSPN EBee EBrP EBre ERob ESCh ETho LBre NBrk SBra SBre WLRN WTre WWeb

Masquerade (Vt) — See C. 'Maskarad' (Vt)
'Masquerade' (P) — MBri NTay SMur
¶ 'Matka Siedliska' (Fl) — ERob WTre
§ 'Matka Teresa' — ERob ESCh WTre
'Matthais' (PxL) — Last listed 1997
'Maureen' (L) — CPev CSCl CSPN EBee ESCh ETho LPri NBea SBra SDix WTre

*mauritiana* — CSCl ERob
*maximowicziana* — See C. *terniflora*
'Meeli' (J) — Last listed 1998
§ 'Mevrouv Oud' (P) — ESCh
¶ 'Mia' (P) — ERob
*microphylla* — ECou
'Miikla' (J) — ERob ESCh ETho WTre
¶ 'Mikelite' (P) — ERob
¶ 'Miniseelik' (J) — ERob
'Minister' (P) — ESCh
'Minuet' (Vt) ♀ — CHad CRHN CSCl CSPN EBee EBrP EBre ELan ERob ESCh ETho IOrc LBre LPri MBri NBea NHol NRoo NTay SBra SBre SChu SDix SPer WSHC WTre WWeb

'Miriam Markham' (J) — CPev ERob ESCh NBea NHaw WTre

'Miss Bateman' (P) ♀ — CDoC CMac CPev CSCl CSPN CSam EAst EBee EBrP EBre ECtt ELan ERob ESCh ETho EWTr LBre LPri MBar MBri MPla NBea SBod SBra SBre SDix SPer WSHC WTre

'Miss Crawshay' (P) — CPev CSCl EBee ERob ESCh NBea NHaw NTay SBra WTre

N *montana* — CB&S CPev CTrw EBee ENot ESCh EWTr GChr GRei LPri MBal MBar MGos MWat NBea NEgg NHol NRoo SBod SBra SDix SSta WAbe WFar WTre WWeb

- *alba* — See C. *montana*
- 'Alexander' — CBlo CDoC CPou CSCl CSPN ERob ESCh LPri MGos NTay SBra SRPl WCru WTre
* - 'Boughton Beauty' — WTre
- 'Fragrant Spring' — ERob ESCh ETho MGos NTay SBra WBcn WTre
- 'Gothenburg' — CSCl EBee EPfP ERob ESCh ETho NBea NTay SBra WTre WWes
- f.*grandiflora* ♀ — CChe CHad CMac EBee EBrP EBre ECtt ELan ENot ERob ESCh ETho EWTr GOrc ISea LBre LBuc LPri MBri NBea NTay SBra SBre SPer SReu WSHC WTre WWeb
§ - 'Hidcote' — ERob ESCh ETho SBra WTre

¶ - 'Jacqui' — ERob ESCh ETho LPri LRHS WWeb
* - 'Lilacina' — ESCh IHar WTre
- 'Mrs Margaret Jones' (d) — CSCl EHol ERob ESCh ETho NBrk NTay SBra SPla WCot WTre
- 'New Dawn' — CSCl ERob ESCh NTay SBra WTre
- 'Odorata' — CDoC CSCl EBee ELan EPfP ERob ETho GSki MGos NTay SBra WGor
* - 'Olga' — ESCh IHar
- 'Peveril' — CPev CSCl ERob ESCh ETho IHar NBea NBrk SBra
- 'Pleniflora' (d) — ESCh ETho MGos SBra WTre
- var. *rubens* ♀ — More than 30 suppliers
- - 'Broughton Star' (d) — CBlo CGre CHad CPou CRHN CSCl CSPN EBee ERob ESCh ETho EWTr GMac ISea LFis LPri MBri MGos NBea NHaw SBra WCot WTre WWeb
- - 'Continuity' — SBra SDix WSHC WTre
- - 'East Morning' — ESCh NBrk
- - 'Elizabeth' ♀ — More than 30 suppliers
- - 'Freda' ♀ — CRHN CSCl EBrP EBre ENot ERob ESCh ETho GMac IHar LBre LPri MBri MGos NBea NHol NRoo NSti NTay SBod SBra SBre SDix SMad SPer WCru WTre
- - 'Marjorie' (d) — More than 30 suppliers
- - 'Mayleen' — CBlo CHad CPou CSCl EBee EBrP EBre ESCh ETho LBre LPri MBri MGos NBea NTay SBra SBre SPer WPen WTre WWat WWeb
- - 'Odorata' — ESCh WTre
- - 'Picton's Variety' — CDoC CPev CSCl ETho LPri NBea NHol NTay SBra SPer SPla SRms WTre
- - 'Pink Perfection' — CDoC CSCl EAst EBee EBrP EBre ECtt ELan ERob ESCh ETho GOrc LBre LPri NBea NBrk NHaw NHol NTay SBra SBre SPer WStI WTre WWeb
§ - - 'Superba' — CBlo CMHG EBee ECtt
- 'Rubens Superba' — See C. *montana* var. *rubens* 'Superba'
- var. *rubens* 'Tetrarose' ♀ — More than 30 suppliers
- - 'Vera' — CSPN EBee ERob ESCh ETho GMac NBea NBir NBrk NTay SBra SEas SPla WCru WTre
- - 'Warwickshire Rose' — CHan CSCl EBee ESCh ETho NBea NBrk NHaw NHol NPro NTay SBra WCot WSHC WTre WWeb
§ - var. *sericea* ♀ — CBot CHan CPev CTri ERob ESCh LPri LRHS NBea NBrk NTay SBra SLon SRms WCru WFoF WHil WTre WWat WWeb
- 'Snow' — Last listed 1997
- 'Spooneri' — See C. *montana* var. *sericea*
- 'Veitch's Form' — CBot
- var. *wilsonii* — CLan CPev CSCl CSPN CSam EAst EBee EBrP EBre ELan ERob ESCh ETho LBre LHol LPri MBar MRav MWat NBea NTay SBra SBre SDix SPer WSHC WTre WWat WWeb

'Monte Cassino' (J) — CSCl ERob ESCh WTre
§ 'Moonlight' (P) — CPev CSCl ERob ESCh LPri NBea NBrk SBra WTre
'Moonman' (Fo) — EHyt ETho WTre
* 'Morning Cloud' — Last listed 1998
'Morning Glory' — Last listed 1996
'Mother Theresa' — See C. 'Matka Teresa'
'Mrs Bush' (L) — ERob ESCh LRHS NBea WTre WWes

'Mrs Cholmondeley' (L) ♀ More than 30 suppliers
'Mrs George Jackman' (P) ♀ CPev CSCl ERob ESCh ETho LPri MBri NBea NBrk NTay SBra WStI WTre
'Mrs Hope' (L) CPev ERob ESCh MAsh NBea NBrk NTay SBra WTre
'Mrs James Mason' CPev CSCl ESCh ETho NBea NHaw NTay SBra WTre
'Mrs N. Thompson' (P) CMac CPev CSCl CSPN EAst EBee EBrP EBre ELan ENot ERob ESCh ETho IHar LBre LPri MBar MBri NBea NHaw NTay SBod SBra SBre SDix SSoC SSta WTre
'Mrs Oud' See C. 'Mevrouw Oud'
'Mrs P.B. Truax' (P) CMHG CSCl CSPN ERob ESCh LPri NBea NRoo NTay SBra SDix WLRN WTre
'Mrs Robert Brydon' See C. x jouiniana 'Mrs Robert Brydon'
'Mrs Spencer Castle' (Vt) CPev CSCl ERob ESCh ETho LPri MAsh NBea NTay SBra WTre
'Mrs T. Lundell' ERob ESCh ETho NBea NBrk WTre
'Mukle' Last listed 1998
'Multi Blue' CB&S CRHN CSCl CSPN CSam CTri EAst EBee EBrP EBre ELan ENot ERob ESCh ETho IHar LBre LPri MBri MGos NBea NTay SBra SBre SMad SSoC WTre
'Muly' Last listed 1998
'Musa China' (L) Last listed 1998
'Myôjô' (P) CSCl CSPN ERob ESCh ETho LPri NTay WMer WTre
'Myôkô' (L) CBlo WMer
¶ 'Nadezhda' (P) ERob
§ napaulensis CB&S CPev CPlN CSCl EBee ERob ESCh IBlr LPri NBea SBra SHFr WCru WLRN WSHC WTre
'Natacha' (P) ERob ESCh WTre
¶ 'Negristka' LPri
'Negritjanka' (J) CSCl ERob ESCh ETho MBri WTre
¶ 'Negus' (J) ERob
'Nelly Moser' (L/P) ♀ More than 30 suppliers
'New Love' CSCl MGos
New Zealand hybrids ECou
'Nikolai Rubtsov' ERob ESCh ETho LPri NTay WTre
'Niobe' (J) ♀ More than 30 suppliers
'North Star' See C. 'Pôhjanael'
'Nuit de Chine' ERob ESCh
obscura CSCl
§ obvallata CSCl
§ occidentalis CSCl
 - var. dissecta EHyt
¶ - var. occidentalis CSCl
ochotensis CSCl ERob SDys WTre
ochroleuca WTre
'Olimpiada-80' (L) ESCh NTay SPla
* 'Opaline' CSCl
orientalis hort. See C. tibetana subsp. vernayi
 - 'Orange Peel' See C. tibetana subsp. vernayi 'Orange Peel'
 - 'Sherriffii' See C. tibetana subsp. vernayi LS&E 13342
orientalis L. EPfP EsCh GSki IMGH NChi NHol SBod SBra SReu WTre
 - 'Bill MacKenzie' See C. 'Bill MacKenzie'
 - var. daurica CHan
¶ - 'My Angel' ESCh MBri
 - var. orientalis CStr ERob ETho WTre
* - 'Rubromarginata' CPev
 - var. tenuifolia ERob ESCh
'Otto Froebel' (L) ESCh ETho NTay

'Paala' Last listed 1996
'Paddington' ERob ETho
'Pagoda' (PxVt) CDoC CPev CRHN CSCl CSPN EBee EOrc ESCh ETho LFis MBri NBea NHol NTay SBra SPla SRms WSHC WTre WWat
¶ 'Pamela' ESCh WTre
'Pamela Jackman' See C. alpina 'Pamela Jackman'
¶ 'Pamjat Serdtsa' ERob
paniculata Thunberg See C. terniflora
 - Gmelin See C. indivisa
◆ - 'Lobata' See C. indivisa var. lobata
* 'Paola' NTay
'Parasol' ERob WTre
◆ 'Parfar' See C. Patricia Ann Fretwell = 'Parfar'
§ parviflora ERob
 - x forsteri ESCh WTre
* 'Pastel Princess' ERob NTay
'Pat Ann' Last listed 1996
patens CSPN NBea WTre
 - Chinese form ERob ESCh
 - Japanese form ERob ESCh
§ Patricia Ann Fretwell CPev ERob LPri LRHS NBea = 'Parfar' WWeb
§ 'Paul Farges' CB&S CSCl CSPN EOrc ERob ETho LFis MBri NBrk NHol NTay SBra WTre WWeb
¶ 'Pendragon' ERob
'Pennell's Purity' (L) ESCh
'Percy Picton' (P) MAsh WTre
'Perle d'Azur' (J) ♀ More than 30 suppliers
'Perrin's Pride' (Vt) CSCl CSPN EBee ERob ESCh ETho NBrk NTay WGwG WMer WTre
¶ 'Peter Pan' (P) ERob
peterae CSCl ERob
¶ - var. trichocarpa ERob
§ Petit Faucon™ = 'Evisix' CBlo CSCl EBee EBrP EBre ECtt ERob ETho LBre LPri MBri NBea NTay SBra SBre WTre
petriei ECou EHyt ESCh NTow WTre
 - x cartmanii 'Joe' (Fo) Last listed 1996
 - x foetida ECou
 - x forsteri Last listed 1998
 - 'Limelight' (m) CSCl
 - x marmoraria GCHN
 - x parviflora Last listed 1997
 - 'Princess' (f) CSCl ECou
'Peveril Peach' CPev
'Peveril Pearl' (P) CPev CSCl CSPN EBee ERob ESCh ETho LPri NTay WWeb
'Peveril Pendant' CPev
phlebantha CPlN
I 'Phoenix' (P) ESCh
pierotii ERob WTre
¶ 'Piilu' (P) CSCl ERob ESCh WTre
'Pink Champagne' See C. 'Kakio'
'Pink Fantasy' (J) CPev CSCl CSPN CTri EBee EBrP EBre ERob ESCh ETho IHar LBre LPri MAsh MBar NBea NBrk NTay SBra SBre WTre WWeb
'Pink Pearl' NBrk
§ pitcheri CPev CPlN CSCl ERob ESCh NBrk NSti NTay WSHC WTre
* - 'Phil Mason' CSCl
¶ - x texensis 'Boulevard' CSCl
◆ 'Pixie' See C. (County Park Group) 'Pixie'
§ 'Pôhjanael' (J) ERob ESCh WTre
'Polish Spirit' (Vt) ♀ More than 30 suppliers
§ potaninii CSCl ELan MNrw NSti

§ - var. *potaninii* — CGle CHan CPev EPfP ERob ETen MGed NBea SDix SLon WHil
  - var. *souliei* — See *C. potaninii* var. *potaninii*
◆ 'Poulala' — See *C.* Alabast = 'Poulala'
◆ 'Poulvo' — See *C.* Vino = 'Poulvo'
  'Prairie River' (A) — ERob ETho WTre
¶ 'Pribaltika' (J) — ERob
  'Prince Charles' (J) — CHad CLAP CPou CSCl EBee EBrP EBre ELan ESCh ETho LBre LPri LRHS NBea NBir NHaw NRoo NTay SBra SBre SDix SPla WSHC WTre WWat
  'Prince Philip' (P) — ERob ESCh ETho SBra WTre
§ 'Princess Diana' (T) — CBlo CPev ERob ESCh ETho LRHS MGos NBrk SBra WTre WWat
  'Princess of Wales' (L) — CSCl ERob LPri LRHS MBri MGrG NBea SBra WSHC WTre
  'Prins Hendrik' (L/P) — CSCl ERob ESCh WGor WTre
¶ 'Propertius' (A) — ERob
  'Proteus' (Fl) — CPev CSCl CSPN EAst EBee EBrP EBre ELan ESCh ETho IHar LBre LPri MBNS NBea NTay SBra SBre SDix SPer SPla WSHC WTre WWeb
§ 'Pruinina' (A) — ERob WTre
  *psilandra* B&SWJ 3650 — WCru
¶ 'Purple Haze' — CRHN
  *quadribracteolata* — ECou EHyt
  'Queen Alexandra' (P) — ERob ESCh
  'Radiant' — Last listed 1996
¶ 'Radostj' (J) — ERob
¶ 'Rahvarinne' — ERob
  'Ramona' — See *C.* 'Hybrida Sieboldii'
  *ranunculoides* CD&R 2345 — WCru
  - KGB 111 — Last listed 1998
  *recta* — CFee CHad CHan CPev CSPN ERob ETho LHol LPri MBel MBro MLLN MNrw NBea NLar NOak NRoo NWCA SPer WByw WHil WHoo WPer WPyg WTre WWye
  - 'Grandiflora' — CSCl
  - 'Peveril' — CPev ERob ESCh NBrk
  - 'Purpurea' — More than 30 suppliers
§ - subsp. *recta* — CSCl ERob
    var. *lasiosepala*
* - 'Velvet Night' — CSpe EAst EBee GBin MBri MLLN MMil MTis SMad WTre
¶ 'Red Ballon' (Ta) — ERob
  'Red Cooler' — ERob ESCh WTre
¶ 'Red Pearl' (P) — ERob
§ *rebderiana* ♀ — More than 30 suppliers
¶ *reticulata* — ERob
  'Rhapsody' — CPev CSCl EPfP ERob ETho IHar LRHS MBri NBrk NHaw NTay SBra WSHC WTre
  'Richard Pennell' (P) ♀ — CMac CPev CSCl CSPN EBee ERob ESCh ETho LPri MBri NBea NBrk NTay SBra SDix WTre
¶ 'Rodomax' (A) — ESCh
¶ 'Roguchi' — LPri
  'Roko-Kolla' (J) — ERob ESCh ETho
  'Romantika' (J) — ERob ESCh ETho LPri SBra SPer
¶ 'Roogoja' (L) — ERob
  'Rose Supreme' — Last listed 1998
  'Rosie O'Grady' (A) — CSPN EBee ELan ESCh ETho IHar LPri MBar MGos NBea NHol NSti SBra SPer WTre
* 'Rosugyana' — Last listed 1998
  'Rouge Cardinal' (J) — More than 30 suppliers
  'Royal Velours' (Vt) ♀ — More than 30 suppliers
§ Royal Velvet™ = 'Evifour' — CSCl CSPN EBee ESCh ETho MBri NTay WTre WWeb

  'Royalty' (LxP) ♀ — CB&S CSCl CSPN EBee EBrP EBre ELan ERob ESCh ETho LBre LPri NBea NBir NTay SBra SBre SDix WBod WTre
  'Ruby Anniversary' — Last listed 1998
  'Ruby Glow' (L) — CSPN EPfP ERob ESCh NTay SBra WLRN WStl WTre WWeb
  'Ruby Lady' — LPri
  'Rüütel' (J) — ERob ESCh ETho NTay
¶ 'Saalomon' (J) — ERob
  'Sally Cadge' (P) — ERob
  'Samantha Denny' — ERob NBea NBrk NTay WTre
¶ 'Sander' (H) — ERob WTre
  'Saruga' — Last listed 1998
  'Satsukibare' — ERob ESCh WTre
  'Saturn' (Vt) — ECle ERob ESCh NBea SBra SPla WTre
  'Scartho Gem' (P) — CPev CSCl EBee ERob ESCh NBea NTay SBra WTre
  'Schneeglanz' (P) — Last listed 1998
  'Sealand Gem' (L) — CPev CSCl CSPN EAst EBee ESCh ETho NBea NHaw NTay SBod SBra WTre
  'Serebrjannyj Ruczejok' — Last listed 1998
  'Serenata' (J) — CSCl ERob LPri NBea NTay
  *serratifolia* — CHan CLon CPev CSCl CSPN ELan ESCh ETho LPri NSti NTay SDix SPer WTre
  'Sheila Thacker' — ETho
  'Sherriffii' (Ta) — ERob ESCh
  'Shogun' — Last listed 1998
  'Sho-un' (L) — CSCl ERob ESCh ETho
  'Sialia' (A/d) — ESCh
  *sibirica* — See *C. alpina* subsp. *sibirica*
  'Signe' (Vt) — ERob ESCh ETho WTre
  'Silver Lining' — Last listed 1998
  'Silver Moon' (L) ♀ — CSCl CSPN ERob ESCh ETho LPri MAsh NBea NPri NTay SBra WTre WWeb
  'Simi' — Last listed 1998
  *simsii* Britt. & A.Br. — See *C. pitcheri*
  - Sweet — See *C. crispa*
  'Sir Garnet Wolseley' (P) — ERob ESCh NBea NBrk NTay SBod SBra SDix WTre
  'Sir Trevor Lawrence' (T) — CPev CSCl CSPN EBee EBrP EBre ERob ESCh ETho LBre LFis LPri NBea NHol NTay SBod SBra SBre SDix SPer WTre
  'Sizaja Ptitsa' (I) — Last listed 1997
  *smilacifolia* — Last listed 1998
    subsp. *andersonii*
  'Snow Queen' — CB&S CBlo CLAP CSCl CSPN EBee EBrP EBre EPfP ESCh ETho LBre LPri MBri NBea NTay SBra SBre WTre WWeb
◆ 'Snowdrift' — See *C.* 'Paul Farges'
§ 'Södertälje' (Vt) — CRHN CSCl CSPN EBrP EBre ERob ESCh ETho LBre LPri NBea NTay SBra SBre WLRN WSHC WTre
¶ 'Solveig' (P) — ERob
  *songarica* — CBlo CSCl CSPN EBee ESCh LFis NBea NBrk NHol NTay SBra WSHC
  - var. *songarica* — ERob WTre
  - 'Sundance' — ERob WTre
  'Souvenir de J.L. Delbard' (P) — ERob ESCh NBea NBrk NTay SBra
§ 'Souvenir du Capitaine — CPev EAst EBee ESCh ETho LPri MBri NBea SBra SPer WTre
    Thuilleaux' (P)
  sp. B&L 12329 — Last listed 1996
  sp. B&SWJ 1243 — WCru
  sp. B&SWJ 1423 — Last listed 1996

| | |
|---|---|
| sp. B&SWJ 1668 | Last listed 1996 |
| sp. B&SWJ 292 | Last listed 1996 |
| sp. B&SWJ 599 | Last listed 1996 |
| sp. CC&McK 1011 | Last listed 1996 |
| sp. CC&McK 1099 | Last listed 1996 |
| sp. ACE 16807* | WCru |
| 'Special Occasions' | ESCh ETho NBea NTay WWeb |
| *spooneri* | See *C. montana* var. *sericea* |
| - 'Rosea' | See *C.* x *vedrariensis* 'Rosea' |
| 'Sputnik' (J) | EPfP ERob NTay WTre |
| *stans* | CHea CMdw CPou EBee EHal EOrc EPfP ERob ESCh ETho GSki LEur LRHS MCli NBea SIng SSca WTre |
| - 'Rusalka' | ERob WTre |
| 'Star Fish' (L) | ERob ESCh WTre |
| 'Star of India' (P/J) ♀ | CBlo CPev CRHN CSCl EBee EBrP EBre ERob ESCh ETho IHar LBre LPri MBri NBea NTay SBra SBre SDix WTre |
| ¶ 'Stasik' (J) | ERob |
| 'Strawberry Roan' (P) | NTay |
| § Sugar Candy™ = 'Evione' (P) | CB&S CBlo CSPN EBee EBrP EBre EMil ERob ESCh ETho LBre LPri MAsh MBri NPri NTay SBra SBre SRPl WTre WWeb WWes |
| Summer Snow | See *C.* 'Paul Farges' |
| 'Sunset' (J) | CSPN EBee ESCh ETho MAsh MBri NBea NTay SBra SMur WLRN |
| 'Susan Allsop' (L) | CPev ERob ESCh WTre |
| 'Sylvia Denny' (Fl) | CSPN EAst EBee EBrP EBre ELan ERob ESCh ETho IHar LBre LPri MBar MBri NBea NBrk NTay SBod SBra SBre SPer WTre |
| 'Sympathia' (L) | CSCl ERob ESCh ETho WTre |
| ¶ 'Syrena' (J) | ESCh |
| § 'Tage Lundell' (A) | CSPN EBee ECle ERob NBea NBrk NTay WTre |
| 'Tango' (T) | CRHN CSCl ERob ESCh ETho MBri NBrk SBra WTre |
| *tangutica* | More than 30 suppliers |
| - 'Aureolin' | See *C.* 'Aureolin' |
| - 'Bill MacKenzie' | See *C.* 'Bill MacKenzie' |
| - dwarf form | Last listed 1998 |
| - 'Gravetye Variety' | CBlo CSCl ERob ESCh NHol WTre |
| - 'Lambton Park' | CSCl EPfP ERob ESCh ETho LPri NBea NBrk NTay SBra SPla WTre |
| - var. *obtusiuscula* | Last listed 1998 |
| - 'Radar Love' | CMdw MWhi |
| - 'Warsaw' | Last listed 1996 |
| ¶ 'Tartu' (L) | ERob |
| *tashiroi* B&SWJ 1423 | WCru |
| 'Tateshina' (P) | Last listed 1998 |
| ¶ 'Teksa' (J) | ERob |
| ¶ 'Tentel' (J) | ERob |
| ◆ *tenuiloba* | See *C. columbiana* var. *tenuiloba* |
| § *terniflora* | CPev CSCl EBee EHol EPfP ESCh ETho LPri NBea NBrk NSti NTay SBra SPer SSpi |
| - Caddick's form | CHan |
| - var. *mandshurica* | See *C. mandschurica* |
| - var. *robusta* | See *C. terniflora* var. *terniflora* |
| § - var. *terniflora* | ERob ESCh WTre |
| 'Teshio' (Fl) | ERob ESCh ETho LPri SBra WTre |
| 'Tevia' | Last listed 1998 |
| *texensis* | CSCl CSPN NBea |
| § - 'The Princess of Wales' | See *C.* 'Princess Diana' |
| 'The Bride' (J) | CSCl ERob ESCh NBrk NHaw NTay SBra WTre |
| 'The Comet' | ERob LPri |
| * 'The First Lady' | ERob ESCh ETho WTre |
| 'The President' (P) ♀ | More than 30 suppliers |
| 'The Princess of Wales' | See *C.* 'Princess Diana' |
| 'The Vagabond' (P) | CSCl ELan ERob ETho LPri NBea NBrk NHaw NTay SBra WLRN WTre |
| *thunbergii* Steudel | See *C. hirsuta* |
| - hort. | See *C. terniflora* |
| ¶ 'Thyrislund' | ESCh WTre |
| ¶ Tibetan mix | ERob ESCh |
| § *tibetana* | CMac CPev CSCl CSPN ELan ETho MBal MBar MNrw NChi NTay SPer WSHC |
| § - subsp. *vernayi* ♀ | CMHG CNic CSCl EBee ERob MHlr MPla MSte NBea NSti SBra SPer WWin |
| - - CC&McK 193 | NWCA |
| - var. *laciniifolia* | ERob ESCh NHol WTre |
| § - - LS&E 13342 | CPev CSCl EPfP ERob ESCh NBea NBrk NHol SBra SDix SPer WTre |
| § - - 'Orange Peel' | CB&S CDoC EAst EBee ENot ERob ESCh ETho IOrc LBuc WTre |
| 'Titania' (PxL) | EPfP ERob |
| ¶ *tongluensis* HWJCM 076 | WCru |
| ¶ 'Treasure Trove' | ESCh MBri WTre |
| 'Trianon' (P) | CSCl ERob NBrk |
| § x *triternata* 'Rubromarginata' ♀ | CDoC CPev CRHN CSCl CSPN EAst EBee ELan EOrc ERob ESCh ETho LFis LPri MBri NBea NHol NRoo SBod SBra SDix SMur SPer SPla WCru WSHC WTre |
| * 'Tsuzuki' | ERob ESCh NBea SPla |
| ¶ *tubulosa* 'Alba' | ERob |
| ¶ 'Tuczka' (J) | ERob |
| 'Twilight' (J) | CSPN EBee ECle ESCh ETho MAsh NBea NTay SBra SPer WTre |
| 'Ulrique' (P) | ERob NTay |
| *uncinata* | CPev SDix |
| - B&SWJ 1893 | WCru |
| 'Valge Daam' (L) | Last listed 1998 |
| ¶ 'Vanessa' | ERob |
| 'Vanilla Cream' | ECou |
| x *vedrariensis* | NBrk SPer |
| - 'Dovedale' | CPev |
| ◆ - 'Hidcote' | See *C. montana* 'Hidcote' |
| - 'Highdown' | CSCl ERob LPri NBrk NHol SBra SPer WTre |
| § - 'Rosea' | CTrw ERob ESCh NBrk WSHC |
| *veitchiana* | ERob |
| ¶ 'Velutinea Purpurea' (J) | ESCh |
| 'Venosa Violacea' (Vt) ♀ | CRHN CSCl CSPN EBee ELan EOrc ERob ESCh ETho GMac LPri MBri NBea NHol NSti SBra SDix SPer WFar WSHC WTre WWeb |
| *vernayi* | See *C. tibetana* subsp. *vernayi* |
| 'Veronica's Choice' (L) | CPev CRHN CSCl EBee ELan ERob ESCh ETho MBri MGos NBea NHaw NTay SBra WTre |
| *versicolor* | CSCl ERob ESCh |
| *verticillaris* | See *C. occidentalis* |
| N 'Victoria' (J) | CPev CRHN CSCl EAst EBrP EBre ERob ESCh ETho LBre LPri NBea NHaw NTay SBra SBre SDix WTre |
| 'Ville de Lyon' (Vt) | More than 30 suppliers |
| § Vino™ = 'Poulvo' (J) | CBlo CSCl CSPN EBee ERob ESCh ETho ICrw IHar MBri NBea NTay WTre |
| * 'Viola' (J) | CSCl ECle ERob ESCh NBea NTay SPla WBcn WTre |
| 'Violet Charm' (L) | CBlo CSPN ERob ESCh ETho LPri NTay SBra WTre |
| 'Violet Elizabeth' (P) | CSCl ESCh NBrk NTay SBra WTre |
| ¶ 'Violetta' (P) | ERob |

| | |
|---|---|
| *viorna* | CPlN CSCl EBee ERob LPri MNrw NBea WSHC WTre |
| *virginiana* Hooker | See *C. ligusticifolia* |
| - hort. | See *C. vitalba* |
| § *vitalba* | CArn CJew CPev CSCl ERob ESch MBar MHer WGwy WHer WTre |
| *viticella* | CPev CSCl ERob ESCh ETho LHol LPri MBNS NBea SBra SDix WSHC WStI WTre WWat |
| - 'Brocade' | CPev |
| I - 'Danae' | ERob WTre |
| * - 'Foxtrot' | ERob WTre |
| - 'Mary Rose' (d) | CPev CSCl ERob SBra WTre |
| - 'Purpurea Plena Elegans' (d) ♀ | More than 30 suppliers |
| ¶ - 'Rosea' (Vt) | ERob |
| 'Viticella Rubra' (Vt) | ETho NBrk |
| ¶ 'Vivienne' | ESCh ETho |
| ¶ 'Vivienne Lawson' | ESCh NTay WTre |
| 'Voluceau' (Vt) | CPou CRHN CSCl CSPN EAst EBee ELan ERob ESCh NBea NTay SBra SPer WStI WTre |
| 'Vostok' (J) | ERob ESCh ETho WTre |
| 'Vyvyan Pennell' (Fl/P) ♀ | More than 30 suppliers |
| 'W.E. Gladstone' (L) | CPev CSCl EBee ENot ERob ESCh ETho LPri NBea NTay SBra SDix SPer WTre |
| 'W.S. Callick' (P) | CSCl ERob ESCh WTre |
| 'Wada's Primrose' (P) | CDoC CSCl CSPN EAst EBee EBrP EBre ELan ERob ESCh ETho IHar LBre LPri MBri NBea NEgg NRoo NTay SBra SBre SPer SPla WSHC WTre WWat |
| 'Walenburg' (Vt) | SBra |
| 'Walter Pennell' (Fl/P) | CPev ESCh ETho LPri NBea NTay SBra WGor WTre |
| 'Warszawska Nike' (J) | CLAP CRHN CSCl ELan EPfP ERob ESCh ETho IHar LPri MGos MSte NBea NTay SBra SPer WStI WTre |
| 'Western Virgin' | EBee ERob ESCh WTre |
| 'Westerplatte' (P) | ESCh NBea WTre |
| § 'White Swan' (A) | CSCl CSPN EBee ERob ESCh ETho LHol LPri MBri MGos NBea NHol NRoo NSti SBra SPer SPla SSoC WFoF WTre |
| 'White Tokyo' (A) | MGos |
| 'Wilhelmina Tull' (L) | CSCl ERob ESCh NBrk WTre |
| 'Will Goodwin' (L) ♀ | CB&S CSCl CSPN EAst EBee EBrP EBre ELan EPfP ERob ESCh ETho LBre LPri MBri NBea NBrk SBra SBre WStI WTre |
| 'William Kennett' (L) | CMHG CPev CSCl CSPN EAst EBee ELan ESCh ETho LPri MBNS MBar MBri MGos NBea NTay SBod SBra SDix SPer WTre |
| 'Wistaria Purple' (A) | NBrk |
| 'Wolga' (P) | Last listed 1998 |
| 'Xerxes' | See *C. 'Elsa Späth'* |
| 'Yellow Queen' | See *C. 'Moonlight'* |
| 'Yorkshire Pride' | Last listed 1998 |
| 'Yukiokomachi' (LxJ) | ERob ESCh WTre |
| ¶ 'Yukiokoshi' (Fl) | ERob |
| 'Yvette Houry' (L) | CSCl ERob ESCh NTay WMer WTre |
| 'Zato' | Last listed 1996 |
| ¶ 'Zingaro' (Vt) | ERob |
| ¶ 'Zolotoi Jubilei' (J) | ERob ESCh |

## CLEMATOPSIS (Ranunculaceae)

| | |
|---|---|
| *scabiosifolia* | WCot |

## CLEMENTSIA See RHODIOLA

## CLEOME (Capparaceae)

| | |
|---|---|
| *arborea* | Last listed 1997 |
| § *bassleriana* | MLan SMrm SWat WRos |
| sp. JCA 13931 | Last listed 1998 |
| *spinosa* hort. | See *C. bassleriana* |

## CLERODENDRON See CLERODENDRUM

## CLERODENDRUM (Verbenaceae)

| | |
|---|---|
| *bungei* ♀ | CAbb CB&S CBlo CBot CGre CHad CHan CPle CWit EBee ELan EPar ERea MAsh MBlu MRav SDix SMad SMur SPer SRPl SSpi SSta WBod WCot WWal WWat WWye |
| § *chinense* 'Pleniflorum' (d) | ERea WMul |
| *fragrans* var. *pleniflorum* | See *C. chinense* 'Pleniflorum' |
| *myricoides* 'Ugandense' | CPIN CSpe ECon ELan EPfP ERea LChe LCns SOWG WMul |
| *philippinum* | See *C. chinense* 'Pleniflorum' |
| ¶ *quadriloculare* | LChe |
| ¶ sp. SF 96243 | ISea |
| *speciosissimum* | LChe |
| x *speciosum* | CPIN LChe SOWG |
| *splendens* ♀ | LCns SOWG |
| *thomsoniae* ♀ | CPIN ELan LChe LCns MBri SOWG SYvo WMul |
| ¶ - 'Variegatum' | ECon |
| *trichotomum* | More than 30 suppliers |
| - 'Carnival' (v) | CFil ELan EPfP LRHS MAsh MBri SBrw SMur SSta WWeb |
| - var. *fargesii* ♀ | CAbb CB&S CBlo CBrm CPMA ELan IOrc LHol LHop MBNS MBlu MGos MRav NFla SIgm SPer SRPl SSpi WCot WEas WPat WPyg WWat |
| * - - 'Variegatum' | CPMA SPer WWes |

## CLETHRA (Clethraceae)

| | |
|---|---|
| *acuminata* | WWoo |
| *alnifolia* | CB&S CBlo CBot CBrm CDul CGre CMHG CTrG ELan GCHN GChr IOrc MBar NBee SPer SRPl SRms SSpi WBod WDin WFar WWat WWin WWye |
| - 'Alba' | Last listed 1998 |
| - 'Hummingbird' | LRHS SBrw |
| - 'Paniculata' ♀ | CDoC EHic EWTr MUlv WWat |
| - 'Pink Spire' | CB&S CWSG EBee EHic ELan EPfP EWTr MPla MRav MUlv SBrw SCoo WFar WLRN WPyg WStI WWat |
| - 'Rosea' | CBot CTri IMGH IOrc MBal MBar MBlu MGos SPer WSHC WWat |
| * - 'Ruby Spice' | CDoC LRHS MBri SBrw SPer |
| *arborea* | CB&S CFil CMHG CPle CTre |
| *barbinervis* ♀ | CB&S CFai CMCN EPfP IMGH MBel MBlu SPer WBod WSHC WWat |
| *delavayi* ♀ | CBrd GGGa GQui MBal SSpi |
| - C&H 7067 | GGGa |
| ¶ - CNW 815 | ISea |
| *fargesii* | MGos |
| *monostachya* | GGGa |

## CLEYERA (Theaceae)

| | |
|---|---|
| *fortunei* | See *C. japonica* 'Fortunei' |
| - 'Variegata' | See *C. japonica* 'Fortunei' |
| § *japonica* 'Fortunei' (v) | CDoC CFil CHal CMac WWat |
| - var. *japonica* | MBal |
| - 'Tricolor' (v) | Last listed 1996 |

## CLIANTHUS (Papilionaceae)
*formosus* — Last listed 1998
§ *puniceus* ♀ — CAbb CB&S CBrm CCHP CDoC CHan CMac CPlN CPle CTrw EBee ECou EMil EOas ERea LCns LHop MBal SBid SHFr SLon SOWG SPer SSoC WBrE WCru
§ - 'Albus' ♀ — CBot CCHP CTrw EBee ELan EMil ERea IOrc LCns LHop SBid SDry SDys SOWG SPer SSoC
- 'Flamingo' — See *C. puniceus* 'Roseus'
¶ - var. *maximus* — ECou
- 'Red Admiral' — See *C. puniceus*
- 'Red Cardinal' — See *C. puniceus*
§ - 'Roseus' — ELan EMil ERea LHop SPer
- 'White Heron' — See *C. puniceus* 'Albus'

## CLINOPODIUM (Lamiaceae)
*acinos* — See *Acinos arvensis*
*ascendens* — See *Calamintha sylvatica*
*calamintha* — See *Calamintha nepeta*
*grandiflorum* — See *Calamintha grandiflora*
§ *vulgare* — CArn CKin ECoo EOHP EWFC GBar MHer MHew NMir SIde WCla WHer

## CLINTONIA (Convallariaceae)
*andrewsiana* — CBro GDra GGGa SSpi WCru WThi
*borealis* — CBro EBee SWas WCru
*udensis* — WCru
*umbellulata* — WCru
*uniflora* — CBro SSpi WCru

## CLITORIA (Papilionaceae)
*mariana* — Last listed 1996
*ternatea* — Last listed 1996
- 'Blue Sails' — Last listed 1996

## CLIVIA ✿ (Amaryllidaceae)
*gardenii* — ERea
*miniata* ♀ — CB&S CHal SRms SYvo WCot
- var. *citrina* — Last listed 1997
- - 'New Dawn' — ERea
- hybrids — ERea LAma LHil MBri NPal SEND
- 'Striata' — ERea
*nobilis* — ERea

## CLUSIA (Clusiaceae)
*rosea* — See *C. major*

## CLYTOSTOMA (Bignoniaceae)
§ *callistegioides* — CPlN ERea

## CNEORUM (Cneoraceae)
*tricoccon* — CFil SRCN SSpi

## CNICUS (Asteraceae)
§ *benedictus* — CArn GPoy MSal SIde WHer WWye
*diacantha* — Last listed 1997

## COBAEA (Cobaeaceae)
*pringlei* CD&R 1323 — CHan
*scandens* ♀ — CPlN IBlr NFai SVen WPen
- f. *alba* ♀ — IBlr WPen
*trianea* — CPlN ERea

## COCCINIA (Cucurbitaceae)
¶ *rebmannii* — CFir

## COCCOTHRINAX (Arecaceae)
*crinita* — LPal

## COCCULUS (Menispermaceae)
*carolinus* — CPlN
§ *orbiculatus* — CPlN WCru
*trilobus* — See *C. orbiculatus*

## COCHLEARIA (Brassicaceae)
*armoracia* — See *Armoracia rusticana*
*glastifolia* — MSal NBur
*officinalis* — MHer MSal WHer

## COCOS (Arecaceae)
*nucifera* (F) — LPal
- 'Dwarf Golden Malay' — Last listed 1996
*plumosa* — See *Syagrus romanzoffiana*
*weddelliana* — See *Lytocaryum weddellianum*

## CODIAEUM ✿ (Euphorbiaceae)
*variegatum* var. *pictum*
'Gold Moon' (v) — MBri
- - 'Gold Sun' (v) — MBri
- - 'Goldfinger' (v) — MBri
- - 'Juliette' (v) — MBri
- - 'Louise' (v) — MBri
- - 'Mrs Iceton' (v) — MBri
- - 'Petra' (v) — MBri
- - 'Sunny Star' (v) — MBri

## CODONANTHE (Gesneriaceae)
*gracilis* — EBak WDib
*paula* — WDib

## x CODONATANTHUS (Gesneriaceae)
'Sunset' — WDib
'Tambourine' — MBri WDib

## CODONOPSIS (Campanulaceae)
¶ *affinis* HWJCM 70 — LEur WCru
*benthamii* — Last listed 1996
*bhutanica* — CMdw EBee GAri GCrs LEur MHar
*bulleyana* — EBee LEur MHar NLar NMen WSan
*cardiophylla* — EBee GDra LEur MHar MNrw WLin
*clematidea* — More than 30 suppliers
*convolvulacea* ♀ — CBlo CPlN EBee GBuc LEur MTho NHar NSla WCru WHoo
- 'Alba' — See *C. grey-wilsonii* 'Himal Snow'
¶ - ex J&JA 4220705 — LEur NWCA
- Forrest's form — See *C. forrestii* Diels
¶ *dicentrifolia* — EBee
- HWJCM 267 — LEur WCru
§ *forrestii* Diels — CNic EBee EHyt LEur NHar NTow WCru
§ - hort. — See *C. grey-wilsonii*
§ *grey-wilsonii* — CLAP EBee GCrs LEur NChi
§ - 'Himal Snow' — CLAP EHyt GCrs IMGH LEur NHar
*handeliana* — See *C. tubulosa*
§ *javanica* B&SWJ 380 — WCru
*kawakamii* — EBee LEur
- B&SWJ 1592 — WCru
§ *lanceolata* — CPlN CRDP EBee EHyt GAri LEur MCCP MGrG NChi NHar NLar
¶ - B&SWJ 562 — LEur WCru
*lancifolia* B&SWJ 3835 — LEur WCru
◆ *meleagris* misapplied — See *C. meleagris* hybrid
◆ - Diels — NHar

§ – hybrid    EBee LEur NChi
**mollis**    CBlo EBee GSki LEur NLar WCru
    WFar
**nepalensis** Grey-Wilson    See *C. grey-wilsonii*
**obtusa**    EBee LEur NChi
**ovata**    CBot CFir CGle CHid EBee ELan
    EPri GBuc GDra LEur LHop MTho
    NBro NChi NWCA SBla SIgm
    SRms SSca WCru WEas
**pilosula**    EBee GAri LEur MLLN MNrw
    MSal MTho NChi WCru
**rotundifolia**    CPlN EBee GBin LEur
§ – var. **angustifolia**    LEur NChi
¶ – CC 2015    MChR
**silvestris**    EBee LEur
sp. ACE 1687    Last listed 1997
**subsimplex**    LEur NChi
**tangshen** Oliver    CArn CGre CPlN GBuc GPoy
    MCCP MNrw MSal MTho NChi
    NSti SHFr WCru
– misapplied    See *C. rotundifolia* var.
    *angustifolia*
¶ **thalictrifolia** MECC 93    WCru
§ **tubulosa**    EBee LEur NCut
**ussuriensis**    See *C. lanceolata*
**vinciflora**    CFir LEur NChi SBla WCru
**viridiflora**    CLyd EBee LEur MHar WRha
– CLD 156    Last listed 1996
**viridis**    EHal
– S&L 4962    Last listed 1998

## COELOGLOSSUM (Orchidaceae)
¶ **viride**    EFEx

## COELOGLOSSUM x DACTYLORHIZA See x DACTYLOGLOSSUM

## COFFEA (Rubiaceae)
¶ **arabica**    LCns

## COIX (Poaceae)
**lacryma-jobi**    MSal

## COLCHICUM ✿ (Colchicaceae)
**agrippinum** ♀    CAvo CBro CFee EHyt EMon EPar
    EPot LAma MBal MRav NBir
    NMGW NRog WTin
**algeriense** AB&S 4353    Last listed 1998
**alpinum**    Last listed 1996
'Antares'    LAma
**atropurpureum**    CBro EBot EPot LAma
'Attlee'    EPot LAma LRHS
'Autumn Herald'    LAma LRHS
N 'Autumn Queen' ♀    CBro EPot LAma LRHS
§ **autumnale**    CArn CAvo CBro CFee EPot ETub
    GPoy LAma MBal NMGW NRya
    WAbe WShi
* – 'Albopilosum'    NBir
– 'Alboplenum'    CBro CSWP EPot ETub LAma
    NMGW
– 'Album'    CAvo CBro CSWP ECha EHyt EPar
    EPot ETub LAma MBal NBir WShi
¶ – 'Atropurpureum'    WShi
– var. **major**    See *C. byzantinum*
– var. **minor**    See *C. autumnale*
– 'Nancy Lindsay' ♀    CBro EPot NMGW
§ – 'Pleniflorum' (d)    CBro EPar EPot LAma
– 'Roseum Plenum'    See *C. autumnale* 'Pleniflorum'
**baytopiorum**    EHyt EPot
– PB 224    Last listed 1998
'Beaconsfield'    Last listed 1997
§ **bivonae**    CBro CLAP ECha LAma NMGW

§ **boissieri**    EHyt EPot
– S&L 468    Last listed 1998
**bornmuelleri** Freyn    CAvo CBro EPar EPot LAma
– hort.    See *C. speciosum* var.
    *bornmuelleri* hort.
**bowlesianum**    See *C. bivonae*
**burttii**    Last listed 1996
§ **byzantinum** ♀    CAvo CBro EBot EPar EPot LAma
    MBri NRog
– **album**    CBro EBot EPot
**chalcedonicum**    Last listed 1997
**cilicicum**    CBro EPot ETub LAma WAbe
– Bowles' form    Last listed 1997
– 'Purpureum'    LAma
'Conquest'    See *C.* 'Glory of Heemstede'
**corsicum**    EHyt EPar LAma WLin
**cupanii**    EHyt EPot
* – var. **cousturieri**    EHyt
– Glossophyllum Group    EPot
– MS 977    Last listed 1998
– var. **pulverulentum**    EPot
'Daendels'    LAma LRHS
**deserti-syriaci** SB&L 155    Last listed 1998
'Dick Trotter'    LAma LRHS
'Disraeli'    CBro LRHS
**doerfleri**    See *C. hungaricum*
'E.A. Bowles'    LAma
**fasciculare**    Last listed 1998
§ **giganteum**    EPot LAma
§ 'Glory of Heemstede'    ECha LAma
**hierosolymitanum**    LAma
§ **hungaricum**    CBro EHyt EPot LAma
– f. **albiflorum**    EHyt
'Huxley'    EPot
**illyricum**    See *C. giganteum*
'Jarka'    Last listed 1996
**kesselringii**    CLAP
**kotschyi**    LAma
**laetum** hort.    See *C. parnassicum*
'Lilac Wonder'    CBro ECha EHyt EPot ETub LAma
    MBri NMGW NRog NRoo WCot
**lingulatum**    NRog WTin
– S&L 217    Last listed 1998
'Little Woods'    Last listed 1997
§ **longiflorum**    LAma
**lusitanicum**    LAma
– HC 2273    Last listed 1998
**luteum**    EHyt LAma NRog
¶ – CC 2020    MChR
¶ **macedonicum**    GCrs
**macrophyllum**    LAma
– S&L 578    Last listed 1998
**micranthum**    LAma
– AB&S 4522    Last listed 1997
**neapolitanum**    See *C. longiflorum*
* – **macranthum**    Last listed 1998
**parlatoris**    Last listed 1998
– Rix 2127    Last listed 1998
§ **parnassicum**    CBro CLAP ECha EHyt EPot
**peloponnesiacum**    Last listed 1998
'Pink Goblet' ♀    CBro EHyt EPot LAma
**polyphyllum**    LAma
'Prinses Astrid'    LAma
**procurrens**    See *C. boissieri*
**psaridis**    Last listed 1996
– S&L 198    Last listed 1998
**pusillum**    EPot
– MS 803/833    Last listed 1998
'Rosy Dawn' ♀    CBro ECha EPot LAma
¶ **sfikasianum**    EHyt
**sibthorpii**    See *C. bivonae*

| | |
|---|---|
| *speciosum* ♀ | CAvo CBro EBrP EBre EPot ETub LAma LBre LEdu MBal NBir SBre WCot WShi |
| - 'Album' ♀ | CAvo CBro CFee ECha EHyt EPar LAma MBri NBir NMGW |
| - 'Atrorubens' | ECha GDra LAma |
| § - var. *bornmuelleri* hort. | EBee |
| - var. *illyricum* | See *C. giganteum* |
| - 'Maximum' | LAma |
| - 'Ordu' | Last listed 1996 |
| - 'Rubrum' | Last listed 1998 |
| ¶ *stevenii* | EHyt |
| - SB&L 120 | Last listed 1998 |
| *szovitsii* | EHyt EPot |
| *tenorei* ♀ | LAma NBir |
| 'The Giant' | CAvo CBro ECha EPot ETub LAma NMGW NRog |
| *troodii* ♀ | Last listed 1998 |
| *turcicum* | Last listed 1997 |
| *umbrosum* | Last listed 1998 |
| *variegatum* | CBro LAma |
| - S&L 594 | Last listed 1998 |
| 'Violet Queen' | CBro CFee EPot LAma |
| 'Waterlily' ♀ | CAvo CBro CLyd EBrP EBre ECha EPar EPot ETub LAma LBre MBal MBri NBir NMGW NRog SBre WAbe WCot |
| 'William Dykes' | EPot LAma |
| 'Zephyr' | LAma LRHS |

## COLEONEMA (Rutaceae)

| | |
|---|---|
| *album* | SAga WPat |
| *aspalathoides* | Last listed 1996 |
| *pulchrum* | CSpe CTrC ECre LHop |

## COLEUS See PLECTRANTHUS, SOLENOSTEMON

## COLLETIA (Rhamnaceae)

| | |
|---|---|
| *armata* | See *C. hystrix* |
| *cruciata* | See *C. paradoxa* |
| *ferox* | Last listed 1998 |
| § *hystrix* | CB&S CPle GBin GGar SAPC SArc SLon SMad SOWG |
| - 'Rosea' | CAbb CGre CPle SAPC SMur WSHC |
| § *paradoxa* | CB&S CCHP CGre CPle CTri EPla LEdu LPJP SAPC SArc SMad WWat |
| - x *spinosissima* | SMad |

## COLLINSIA (Scrophulariaceae)

| | |
|---|---|
| *bicolor* Benth. | See *C. heterophylla* |
| § *heterophylla* | Last listed 1997 |

## COLLINSONIA (Lamiaceae)

| | |
|---|---|
| *canadensis* | CArn EBee ELan ELau EMan MSal |

## COLLOMIA (Polemoniaceae)

| | |
|---|---|
| *biflora* | Last listed 1997 |
| *debilis* | EHyt NWCA |
| ♦ - var. *larsenii* | See *C. larsenii* |
| *grandiflora* | LCot |
| § *larsenii* | GTou |

## COLLOSPERMUM (Asteliaceae)

| | |
|---|---|
| § *microspermum* | IBlr |

## COLOBANTHUS (Caryophyllaceae)

| | |
|---|---|
| *acicularis* | EHyt |
| *apetalus* | Last listed 1998 |
| - var. *alpinus* | Last listed 1997 |
| *buchananii* | Last listed 1998 |

| | |
|---|---|
| *canaliculatus* | CPBP NTow |
| *muelleri* | Last listed 1997 |
| § *quitensis* | Last listed 1996 |
| sp. CC 465 | NWCA |

## COLOCASIA (Araceae)

| | |
|---|---|
| *antiquorum* | See *C. esculenta* |
| § *esculenta* ♀ | EOas WMul |
| ¶ - 'Black Magic' | WMul |
| - 'Fontanesii' | WMul |
| - 'Illustris' | Last listed 1998 |
| - 'Nigrescens' | WMul |

## COLQUHOUNIA (Lamiaceae)

| | |
|---|---|
| *coccinea* ♀ | CArn CHal CHan CWit EMil MBal MRav SIgm WCru WHer WSHC |
| - var. *mollis* | See *C. coccinea* var. *vestita* |
| § - var. *vestita* | CB&S CCHP CFai CFil CGre CPle CTrC EBee EPfP MSte NPSI SEND SLPl WPat |

## COLUMNEA (Gesneriaceae)

| | |
|---|---|
| 'Aladdin's Lamp' | CHal WDib |
| 'Apollo' | WDib |
| x *banksii* | CHal MBri WDib |
| 'Bold Venture' | WDib |
| * 'Bonfire' | WDib |
| § 'Broget Stavanger' (v) | WDib |
| 'Chanticleer' ♀ | CHal MBri WDib |
| I 'Firedragon' | WDib |
| 'Gavin Brown' | WDib |
| *gloriosa* | EBak |
| 'Heidi' | MBri |
| *hirta* ♀ | MBri WDib |
| - 'Variegata' | See *C.* 'Light Prince' |
| 'Inferno' | WDib |
| 'Katsura' | MBri SOWG WDib |
| I 'Kewensis Variegata' ♀ | MBri |
| § 'Light Prince' (v) | MBri WDib |
| 'Merkur' | WDib |
| *microphylla* 'Variegata' | MBri |
| I 'Midnight Lantern' | WDib |
| 'Rising Sun' | WDib |
| 'Robin' | WDib |
| *schiedeana* | CHal MBri WDib |
| 'Starburst' | Last listed 1998 |
| 'Stavanger' ♀ | CHal EBak MBri WDib |
| 'Stavanger Variegated' | See *C.* 'Broget Stavanger' |
| 'Winifred Brown' | WDib |
| Yellow Dragon Group | CHal |

## COLUTEA (Papilionaceae)

| | |
|---|---|
| *arborescens* | CAgr CArn CB&S CBlo EBee EBrP EBre ELan EMil ENot IBlr IOrc LBre MBlu MGos MPEx MSal MWhi NWea SBre SIde SPer SRCN WDin WHer WOve WWin |
| x *media* | CHad EMil MBel MBlu MNrw SRCN WBcn |
| - 'Copper Beauty' | CB&S CHan ELan EPfP GEil MGos SPer WPat |
| *orientalis* | Last listed 1998 |
| *persica* | SLPl SOWG |

## COMARUM See POTENTILLA

## COMBRETUM (Combretaceae)

| | |
|---|---|
| *erythrophyllum* | CGre |
| *paniculatum* | CPIN |

## COMMELINA (Commelinaceae)

| | |
|---|---|
| *coelestis* | See *C. tuberosa* Coelestis Group |

| | |
|---|---|
| *dianthifolia* | CFee CInt CRDP EMon GBuc GCal GCrs MTho NTow SSad WCot WPer |
| - 'Sapphirino' | EMon |
| *tuberosa* | CAvo EHic ELan EPfP GBuc MLan NSti SLod |
| - 'Alba' | CPea ELan EMon MLLN MSte NTow WHer WPer WWye |
| - 'Axminster Lilac' | WPer |
| § - Coelestis Group | CBrm CInt ECha EMan EMon ETub MLLN NFai SRms WFar WHer WPer WWin WWye |
| - 'Snowmelt' | MGrG |
| *virginica* hort. | See *C. erecta* |
| - L. | IBlr |

## COMMIPHORA (Burseraceae)
| | |
|---|---|
| ¶ *opobalsamum* | LEdu |

## COMPTONIA (Myricaceae)
| | |
|---|---|
| *peregrina* | CMac WCru |

## CONANTHERA (Tecophilaeaceae)
| | |
|---|---|
| *campanulata* | Last listed 1998 |

## CONICOSIA (Aizoaceae)
| | |
|---|---|
| ¶ *pugioniformis* | CTrF |

## CONIOGRAMME (Adiantaceae)
| | |
|---|---|
| *intermedia* | NMar |
| *japonica* | WRic |

## CONIOSELINUM (Apiaceae)
| | |
|---|---|
| *morrisonense* B&SWJ 173 | WCru |
| *schugnanicum* | EBee |

## CONIUM (Apiaceae)
| | |
|---|---|
| ¶ *maculatum* | |
| 'Golden Nemesis' | EMon |

## CONOCEPHALUM (Conocephalaceae)
| | |
|---|---|
| *supradecompositum* | Last listed 1996 |

## CONOPODIUM (Apiaceae)
| | |
|---|---|
| *majus* | CKin WShi |

## CONRADINA (Lamiaceae)
| | |
|---|---|
| *verticillata* | CFee |

## CONSOLIDA (Ranunculaceae)
| | |
|---|---|
| § *ajacis* | EWFC MSal |
| *ambigua* | See *C. ajacis* |
| *regalis* | ECoo |

## CONVALLARIA ✿ (Convallariaceae)
| | |
|---|---|
| *japonica* | See *Ophiopogon jaburan* |
| *keiskei* | CLAP |
| *majalis* ♀ | More than 30 suppliers |
| § - 'Albostriata' | CFil CLAP CRDP CRow EBee ECha ELan EPar MRav MTho NBir SDys SLod SSvw WCHb WCot WCru WEas WHer WPGP |
| - 'Berlin Giant' | EBee WCot |
| ¶ - 'Dorien' | EBee EFou |
| - 'Flore Pleno' (d) | EPar WCot |
| - 'Fortin's Giant' | CAvo CBro CLAP CMea CRDP CRow EGar ELan EPar EPla ERav LHop MRav NBrk WCot WPGP |
| * - 'Haldon Grange' | CBos EMon WCot |
| - 'Hardwick Hall' (v) | CAvo CLAP CRDP CRow ECha EHoe EPar EPla EPot NPar NRar WCot |

| | |
|---|---|
| - 'Hofheim' (v) | CRow |
| - 'Prolificans' | CAvo CBro CLAP CRDP CRow EMon EPar EPot ERos MRav SIng SSvw |
| - var. *rosea* | More than 30 suppliers |
| - 'Variegata' | CAvo CBlo CBos CRow EPar EPla ERav SMac |
| - 'Vic Pawlowski's Gold' (v) | CRow WCHb |
| *montana* | LRHS WThi |
| *transcaucasica* | WHer |

## CONVOLVULUS (Convolvulaceae)
| | |
|---|---|
| *althaeoides* | CBos CBot CFil CHad CMil CPle ECGP MAvo MHar MNes MNrw MTho SAga SBla SChu SHFr SMad SWas WAbb WCru WEas WHal WOld WWin |
| § - subsp. *tenuissimus* | CGle CSWP CSpe EBee EMar EPPr EWes LHop MBri MWat NTow SUsu WCot |
| *arvensis* | Last listed 1997 |
| *assyricus* | Last listed 1996 |
| § *boissieri* | CFir EHyt MTho NWCA SBla SIng WAbe |
| *cantabricus* | Last listed 1998 |
| *capensis* | Last listed 1996 |
| *chilensis* RB 94080 | Last listed 1998 |
| *cneorum* ♀ | More than 30 suppliers |
| *compactus* | Last listed 1996 |
| *elegantissimus* | See *C. althaeoides* subsp. *tenuissimus* |
| *incanus* | WCru |
| *lineatus* | CPBP EHyt ELan ESis LBee MBro MRPP MTho NMen NNrd NWCA SBla SIng SRot WAbe |
| *mauritanicus* | See *C. sabatius* |
| *nitidus* | See *C. boissieri* |
| *remotus* | Last listed 1998 |
| § *sabatius* ♀ | CB&S CGle CHad CHal CHar CSam ECha ECtt ELan ERea GCHN LHop MBEx SBla SDix SRCN SYvo WAbe WEas WOld WSHC WWat WWin |
| - dark form | CMHG CSpe ELan EMan LFis LHil LHop LIck LLWP MBEx MSte SMrm SUsu |

## COOPERANTHES See ZEPHYRANTHES

## COOPERIA See ZEPHYRANTHES

## COPERNICIA (Arecaceae)
| | |
|---|---|
| *alba* | LPal |
| *prunifera* | LPal |

## COPROSMA ✿ (Rubiaceae)
| | |
|---|---|
| ¶ *acerosa* 'Live Wire' (f) | ECou |
| *areolata* | ECou |
| ¶ *atropurpurea* (f) | ECou |
| - (m) | ECou |
| *baueri* | See *C. repens* |
| 'Beatson's Gold' (f/v) | CB&S CBot CChe CGre CHal CHan CLTr CMHG EMil ERea GEil GOrc GQui IOrc MBEx MPla NFai STre WHen WSHC |
| *billardierei* | See *C. quadrifida* |
| 'Blue Pearls' (f) | ECou |
| 'Brunette' (f) | ECou |
| § *brunnea* | ECou |
| ¶ - 'Blue Beauty' (f) | ECou |
| - (m) x *kirkii* | Last listed 1998 |
| ¶ - 'Violet Fleck' (f) | ECou |

¶ 'Bruno' (m)    ECou
  *cheesemanii* (f)    ECou
  - (m)    ECou
¶ - 'Hanmer Red' (f)    ECou
  - 'Mack' (m)    ECou MSag
  - 'Red Mack' (f)    ECou MSag
  'Chocolate Soldier' (m)    ECou
  'Coppershine'    CB&S ERea MBEx
  *crassifolia* (m) x *repens*    ECou
  x *cunninghamii* (f)    ECou
¶ - x *macrocarpa* (m)    ECou
  *depressa*    ECou
¶ - 'Orange Spread' (f)    ECou
¶ 'Evening Glow'    LHop
  *foetidissima* Forster    Last listed 1997
  'Green Girl' (f)    ECou
  'Hinerua' (f)    ECou
  'Indigo Lustre' (f)    ECou
  'Jewel' (f)    ECou
  x *kirkii* 'Kirkii' (f)    CInt ECou ERea STre
  - 'Kirkii Variegata' (f)    CB&S CBot CDoC CGre CTrC
     EBee ECou ERea GEil GQui LHop
     SEas SLon SOWG STre WBrE
     WSHC
  'Kiwi-gold' (v)    ECou ERea
  'Lemon Drops' (f)    ECou
  *linariifolia*    ECou
  *lucida* (f)    ECou
  - (m)    Last listed 1997
  *macrocarpa* (f)    ECou
  - (m)    ECou
  *nitida* (f)    ECou
  - (m)    ECou
  *parviflora* (m)    ECou
¶ - purple fruit (f)    ECou
¶ - red fruit (f)    ECou
¶ - white fruit (f)    ECou
¶ 'Pearl Drops' (f)    ECou
  'Pearl's Sister' (f)    ECou
  'Pearly Queen' (f)    ECou
  *petriei*    CLTr CNic ECou GLch SIng WAbe
  - AGS 50    Last listed 1998
  - 'Don' (m)    ECou
  - 'Lyn' (f)    ECou
¶ 'Pride'    CDoC
  *propinqua*    EPla SDry WSHC
  - (f)    ECou
  - (m)    ECou
¶ - var. *latiuscula* (m)    ECou
¶ - - (f)    ECou
  'Prostrata' (m)    ECou
¶ *pseudocuneata* (m)    ECou
  *pumila*    Last listed 1997
§ *quadrifida*    Last listed 1996
§ *repens*    CDoC LHil
§ - (f)    ECou
  - (m)    CB&S ECou SEND
  - 'Apricot Flush' (f)    ECou
  - 'Brownie' (f)    Last listed 1998
¶ - CC 543    CPLG
  - 'County Park Purple' (f)    ECou ERea
  - 'Exotica' (f/v)    ECou LHop
  - 'Marble King' (m/v)    ECou
  - 'Marble Queen' (m/v)    ECou LHil LHop SEND WLRN
  - 'Orangeade' (f)    ECou
  - 'Painter's Palette'    CB&S ECou
  - 'Picturata' (m/v)    ECou
  - 'Pink Splendour' (m/v)    CB&S CDoC ECou ERea LHop
¶ - 'Rangatiri' (f)    ECou
  - 'Silver Queen' (m/v)    ECou SVen
  - 'Variegata' (m)    ECou LHil MSag
  *rhamnoides*    Last listed 1997

  *rigida*    ECou
  *robusta*    ECou SDry
¶ - 'Cullen's Point' (f)    ECou
¶ - 'Sally Blunt' (f)    ECou
¶ - 'Steepdown' (f)    ECou
¶ - 'Tim Blunt' (m)    ECou
* - 'Variegata' (m)    ECou
¶ - 'William' (m)    ECou
  - 'Williamsii Variegata' (f/m)    LHop
¶ - 'Woodside' (f)    ECou
  *rotundifolia*    ECou
  'Roy's Red'    ECou
  *rugosa* (f)    ECou
I  'Snowberry' (f)    ECou
  *tenuifolia* (m)    ECou
  'Tuffet' (f)    Last listed 1997
  'Violet Drops' (f)    ECou
  *virescens*    ECou
  'Walter Brockie'    CGre CHal CLTr
  'White Lady' (f)    ECou
¶ 'Winter Bronze' (f)    ECou

## COPTIS (Ranunculaceae)

¶ *japonica* var. *dissecta*    WThi
  *quinquefolia*    WCru

## x CORALIA (Papilionaceae)

¶ 'County Park'    ECou
¶ 'Essex'    ECou
¶ 'Havering'    ECou

## CORALLOSPARTIUM (Papilionaceae)

  *crassicaule*    ECou

## CORDYLINE (Agavaceae)

  *australis* ♀    More than 30 suppliers
  - 'Albertii' (v) ♀    CB&S CTrC EHic ERea GQui LNet
     MBri SAPC SArc
* - 'Atropurpurea'    CB&S
* - 'Black Tower'    CB&S LRHS MAsh WGer
* - 'Coffee Cream'    CBrm CTor CTrC EBee IOrc LEdu
     LRHS MAsh MBlu NPal SPer SSto
     WGer
  - 'Pink Stripe' (v)    CAbb CB&S CDoC COtt CTor
     CTrC EBee ELan ERic IOrc ISea
     LRHS MAsh NPal SPla SSto WGer
     WPat WWeb
  - 'Purple Tower'    CB&S CBlo CDoC COtt CTor
     CTrC EBee EHic EMil IOrc LRHS
     MAsh SPla SSto WBod WLRN
     WPat WWeb
  - Purpurea Group    CB&S CBot CChe EAst EBee EBrP
     EBre ENot EOld ERea GOrc GQui
     IOrc ISea LBre NCut SBre SEND
     SMad SPer WFar WGer WStI
     WWeb
  - 'Red Star'    CAbb CB&S CBlo CDoC COtt
     CTor EAst EBee EHic ENot EWTr
     LHil MCCP MLan NHol SMer SPar
     WBod WCot WLRN WStI WWes
  - 'Sundance'    CB&S CBlo CDoC CEnd CTor
     CWit EAst EBee IOrc LEdu MBri
     MCCP NCut SMer SPla SRPl SSto
     SWat WCot WFar WPyg WStI
     WWeb WWes
* - 'Torbay Coffee Cream'    EHic
  - 'Torbay Dazzler' (v)    More than 30 suppliers
  - 'Torbay Green'    CTor
* - 'Torbay Razzle Dazzle'    CTor
  - 'Torbay Red'    CAbb CB&S CBrm CDoC COtt
     CSam CTor CTrC EBee ELan IOrc
     LPan MAsh MBlu MBri SEas SPla
     SSto WPat WWeb

| | |
|---|---|
| - 'Torbay Sunset' | CDoC COtt CTor ELan IOrc SSto |
| - 'Torbay Surprise' | CDoC CTor |
| - 'Variegata' | CBot |
| * **autumn** | NCut |
| **banksii** | ECou EOas EWes IHdy WLRN |
| **baueri** | Last listed 1997 |
| ¶ 'Dollar Princess' | EOld |
| **fruticosa** 'Atom' | MBri |
| - 'Baby Ti' (v) | MBri |
| - 'Calypso Queen' | MBri |
| - 'Kiwi' | MBri |
| - 'Orange Prince' | MBri |
| - 'Red Edge' | MBri |
| - 'Yellow King' | MBri |
| 'Green Goddess' | CB&S EOas |
| § **indivisa** | CBrP EBak IHdy MBri SAPC SPlb |
| | WGer WPGP |
| **kaspar** | LHil SAPC |
| **parryi** 'Purpurea' | NPal |
| § **stricta** | MBri |
| **terminalis** | See *C. fruticosa* |

## COREOPSIS ✿ (Asteraceae)

| | |
|---|---|
| **auriculata** Cutting Gold | See *C. auriculata* 'Schnittgold' |
| § -  'Schnittgold' | CBlo CMea CWit EOld LFis NCut |
| | NRoo SHel WPer |
| - 'Superba' | Last listed 1998 |
| 'Baby Gold' | EPfP LRHS |
| Baby Sun | See *C.* 'Sonnenkind' |
| 'Goldfink' | EBrP EBre ECha EMan GSki LBre |
| | MNrw MRav SBre SRms |
| **grandiflora** | EHal EWTr SRPl SWat WWeb |
| - 'Astolat' | CStr EMon NLak |
| - 'Badengold' | CB&S EBee EMil |
| I  - 'Calypso' (v) | MAsh WWeb |
| - 'Domino' | LHop LWoo NCut NOak SMrm |
| | WShe |
| - 'Early Sunrise' | CSam EBee ECtt EWTr GMaP |
| | MMal NFai NMir NPer SAga SMer |
| | WHen WHoo WPer WPyg WRHF |
| - Flying Saucers | LRHS SCoo |
| = 'Walcoreop' | |
| - 'Kelvin Harbutt' | CStr EMan |
| - 'Mayfield Giant' | CBlo EBee EFou EMan EWTr EWll |
| | MGrG MNrw MWat NFla NPri |
| | NVic SMer SRms SWat |
| § - 'Rotkehlchen' | Last listed 1997 |
| - Ruby Throat | See *C. grandiflora* 'Rotkehlchen' |
| - variegated | Last listed 1998 |
| **integrifolia** | EMon WCot |
| **lanceolata** | EBee EFou NSti |
| - 'Lichtstad' | Last listed 1997 |
| - 'Sterntaler' | CFir EBee EFou EMil EPar LWoo |
| | NOrc NRoo NTow WPer |
| ¶ **latifolia** | EBee |
| **maximilianii** | See *Helianthus maximilianii* |
| ¶ **palmata** | EMon WCot |
| ¶ **pubescens** | EBee |
| **rosea** | EGar MBel NLar NPro SRPl WFar |
| - 'American Dream' | CB&S CHor CRDP EBee ECtt ELan |
| | EMil EWTr LHop MCLN MCli |
| | MMil NBro NFai NRoo NTay SHel |
| | SMad SPer SRms WAbe WFar |
| | WMer WPyg WWin |
| - f. *leucantha* | CStr |
| - 'Nana' | SPla |
| § 'Sonnenkind' | ECtt EPar GMaP NBro |
| Sun Child | See *C.* 'Sonnenkind' |
| 'Sunburst' | CBlo CDoC COtt EOHP NFai |
| | NOak SRCN WOve WPer |

| | |
|---|---|
| 'Sunray' | CB&S CDoC EBee ECtt EOld EPar |
| | LPVe MBri MFir MNrw NFai |
| | NGdn NOak NOrc NRoo SIde |
| | SPlb SRCN SRms SSea WPer WWal |
| | WWeb WWye |
| **tinctoria** | MSal SIde |
| - var. *atkinsoniana* | WPer |
| **tripteris** | CGen CPou EGar EMon LGre |
| | SMrm SSvw WCot |
| **verticillata** | CMea CTri ECha ENot EOld LFis |
| | MBal MBrN MBro MFir MWat |
| | NFai NPer SDix SRPl SRms SSpe |
| | SWat WAbe WEas WHal WOld |
| | WPyg |
| - 'Alba' | Last listed 1998 |
| - 'Golden Gain' | CDoC EBee EBrP EBre EFou EMan |
| | EPla GBri GSki LBre LHop MArl |
| | MLLN MMil NCat NHol SBre |
| | WWal |
| - 'Golden Shower' | See *C. verticillata* 'Grandiflora' |
| § - 'Grandiflora' ♀ | CB&S CHor CSev EBee EBrP EBre |
| | EFou ELan GMaP LBre MBri |
| | MCLN MRav NCat NFor NHol |
| | NLon NOak NVic SBre SChu |
| | SMad SPer SPla SSpe WWal WWin |
| - 'Moonbeam' | More than 30 suppliers |
| - 'Rosea' | CHar |
| - 'Zagreb' | COtt CSev EBee EBrP EBre ECtt |
| | EMil ENot EPar EPla LBre LFis |
| | MBNS MBri MCLN MLLN MMil |
| | MSCN MUlv NHol NRoo NTay |
| | SBre SPla WFar WHil WMer |
| | WMow WOld |

## CORETHROGYNE (Asteraceae)

| | |
|---|---|
| **californica** | Last listed 1996 |

## CORIANDRUM (Apiaceae)

| | |
|---|---|
| **sativum** | CArn EOHP GPoy ILis LHol MChe |
| | MHew SIde WOak WPer WWye |
| - 'Cilantro' | CJew CSev GAbr WGwG WHer |
| - 'Leisure' | CBod CSev GPoy MMal NPri |
| - 'Morocco' | Last listed 1996 |
| - 'Santo' | ELau WJek |

## CORIARIA ✿ (Coriariaceae)

| | |
|---|---|
| **intermedia** B&SWJ 019 | WCru |
| **japonica** | CPle SVen WCru |
| - B&SWJ 2833 | WCru |
| **kingiana** | ECou WCru |
| § **microphylla** | WCru |
| **myrtifolia** | CFil CPle GCal GSki WCot WCru |
| | WWat |
| **nepalensis** | CPle GCal SLon WCru WWat |
| * 'Pictons' | Last listed 1996 |
| **ruscifolia** | WCru |
| ¶ - HCM 98178 | WCru |
| **sarmentosa** | GCal WCru |
| * **terminalis fructu-rubro** | Last listed 1997 |
| - var. *xanthocarpa* | CCHP CPle CTrG EBee GBuc |
| | GCal IBlr MBal NHol NPSI SSpi |
| | WCot WCru WGwG WWat |
| **thymifolia** | See *C. microphylla* |

## CORNUS ✿ (Cornaceae)

| | |
|---|---|
| **alba** | CDoC CKin CLnd CTri ENot |
| | GChr IOrc MBar MMal NWea |
| | SRms WDin WMou WStl WWat |
| * - 'Albovariegata' | ENot |
| - 'Argenteovariegata' | See *C. alba* 'Variegata' |

| | | |
|---|---|---|
| - 'Aurea' ♀ | CB&S CChe CDoC CDul CMCN EBee EBrP EBre ECtt EHoe ELan EPla IOrc LBre MAsh MBar MBri MRav NBee SBre SEas SPer SSpi WAbe WDin WFar WPat WWeb | |
| - 'Elegantissima' (v) ♀ | More than 30 suppliers | |
| - 'Gouchaultii' (v) | CB&S CBlo CDoC EBee EHic LPan MBar NPla SPer SRms WDin | |
| - 'Ivory Halo' | EBee EBrP EBre LBre MGos SBre | |
| - 'Kesselringii' | CAbP CB&S CDoC CDul EBee EBrP EBre EHoe EMil ENot EPla EWTr GChr IOrc LBre MBar MBel MBri MRav SBre SEas SMad SPer SPla WBod WDin WLeb WWat | |
| - 'Siberian Pearls' | CB&S COtt ELan MBlu MGos NEgg NMoo SSta | |
| § - 'Sibirica' ♀ | More than 30 suppliers | |
| - 'Sibirica Variegata' | CDoC EBee EBrP EBre EPla EWTr GOrc IOrc LBre LPan MAsh MBlu MBri MGos NBee NEgg SBre SSpi SSta WFar WPat WPyg WWeb | |
| - 'Spaethii' (v) ♀ | More than 30 suppliers | |
| § - 'Variegata' | CB&S CBlo SPer WWal WWin | |
| - 'Westonbirt' | See *C. alba* 'Sibirica' | |
| *alternifolia* | CBlo CMCN CMHG COtt CPMA ELan EWTr IOrc LPan SPer SSpi WWat | |
| § - 'Argentea' (v) ♀ | More than 30 suppliers | |
| - 'Variegata' | See *C. alternifolia* 'Argentea' | |
| *amomum* | CB&S EPla NHol WBcn WWat | |
| *angustata* | MBal SPer | |
| *angustifolia* | See *C. linifolia* | |
| § 'Ascona' | CPMA CRos ELan EPfP EWTr LNet LRHS MAsh MBri NBee SSpi SSta WWes | |
| *australis* | EPla | |
| *baileyi* | See *C. stolonifera* 'Baileyi' | |
| § *canadensis* ♀ | More than 30 suppliers | |
| *candidissima* | See *C. racemosa* | |
| *capitata* | CB&S CBar CDoC CGre CHan CPMA CTbh CTrG CTri IHdy IOrc SEND SSpi WAbe WCoo | |
| - ACE | WHCr | |
| - 'Rag Doll' (v) | CPMA | |
| *chinensis* | Last listed 1997 | |
| *controversa* | CB&S CBlo CDoC CDul CFee CMCN CPMA CSam CTho ELan EMil GChr IOrc LPan MBar MBlu NHed NPSI NWea SBrw SLPl SPer SReu SSpi SSta WCoo WDin WHar WPGP WWat | |
| - 'Pagoda' | CBlo CEnd CPMA MBlu SMur SSpi | |
| - 'Variegata' ♀ | CDoC CDul CLnd CSam CTho EBee ENot IMGH ISea MAsh MBar MGos NBee NPal SBrw SLon SPla SRPl WAbe WFoF WPGP WStI | |
| - 'Variegata' Frans type | CB&S CBot CEnd CPMA CRos EBrP EBre ELan EMil ERom IOrc LBre LNet LPan MBlu MBri MPla MWat SBre SPer SReu SSta WDin WHCG WPat WSHC WWat | |
| 'Eddie's White Wonder' ♀ | CB&S CDoC CEnd CFil CPMA CRos CTho ECho ELan ICrw IMGH IOrc LNet LPan MBal MBlu MBri MGos SBid SBrw SPer SRPl SReu SSpi SSta WAbe WDin WPat WPyg | |
| *florida* | CBlo CMCN EHic ELan EPfP GOrc IOrc ISea MBar SBrw SPer SRPl SReu SSta WLRN WNor WWat WWoo | |
| - 'Alba Plena' (d) | CPMA LPri | |
| - 'Apple Blossom' | CPMA | |
| ⌐ 'Cherokee Brave' | LRHS SSpi | |
| - 'Cherokee Chief' ♀ | CAbP CB&S CCHP CEnd COtt CPMA EPfP IMGH LPan MBel MGos WAbe | |
| - 'Cherokee Princess' | CPMA CRos ELan LPan LRHS SMur SSta | |
| - 'Clear Moon' | LPan | |
| - 'Cloud Nine' | CB&S CDoC COtt CPMA EMil LPan LRHS MBal SLdr SSpi | |
| * - 'Daniela' | Last listed 1998 | |
| - 'Daybreak' (v) | CEnd COtt CPMA LPan | |
| - 'First Lady' | CB&S CPMA ECho LPan SPer | |
| - 'Fragrant Cloud' | Last listed 1998 | |
| - 'G.H. Ford' | CPMA | |
| - 'Golden Nugget' | CPMA | |
| - 'Green Glow' (v) | CPMA | |
| - 'Junior Miss Variegated' (v) | CPMA | |
| - 'Moonglow' | CPMA | |
| - 'Pendula' | CPMA | |
| - 'Pink Flame' (v) | CPMA | |
| - 'Purple Glory' | CPMA | |
| - 'Rainbow' (v) | CAbP CB&S COtt CPMA ELan EPfP LPan MAsh MBri MGos NBee NEgg SPer SSta WAbe WDin | |
| - 'Red Giant' | CPMA CRos ELan EPfP LRHS SMur SSpi SSta | |
| - 'Royal Red' | CPMA | |
| - f. *rubra* | CB&S CBlo CDoC ELan EPfP LPan MGos NEgg SSta WAbe WGer WNor WPyg WWoo | |
| - 'Spring Song' | CPMA ECho MBri | |
| - 'Stoke's Pink' | CEnd COtt CPMA ECho LNet | |
| - 'Sunset' (v) | CEnd COtt CPMA MGos SPer WPat | |
| - 'Sweetwater' | CPMA | |
| - 'Tricolor' | See *C. florida* 'Welchii' | |
| § - 'Welchii' (v) | CEnd CPMA | |
| - 'White Cloud' | CPMA | |
| *foemina* | See *C. stricta* | |
| ¶ 'Greenlight' | WWeb | |
| *hemsleyi* | EPla WCoo | |
| § *hessei* | EPla MBro WPat WPyg WShe | |
| 'Kelsey's Dwarf' | See *C. stolonifera* 'Kelseyi' | |
| *kousa* | CB&S CDoC CDul CMCN CTho ECrN ELan EMil ERom ISea LNet MAsh MBal MBar MWat NFla NFor NLon SBrw SPer WAbe WCoo WDin WHCG WHar WStI WWat | |
| * - *angustifolia* | SSta | |
| - 'Beni-fuji' | CPMA | |
| ¶ - 'Boltincks Beauty' | LRHS SMad SSpi SSta | |
| - 'Bonfire' (v) | CPMA | |
| - var. *chinensis* ♀ | More than 30 suppliers | |
| - - 'Bodnant Form' | CEnd CPMA SPer | |
| - - 'China Girl' | CAbP CEnd COtt CPMA CRos ELan EWTr LPan MAsh MBlu MBri MGos SPer SSta WPyg | |
| - - 'Milky Way' | CPMA | |
| - - Spinners form | CPMA | |
| ¶ - 'Elizabeth Lustgarten' | SSpi SSta | |
| - 'Gold Star' (v) | CAbP CB&S CDoC CEnd COtt CPMA CTho ELan IOrc MAsh MBri MGos SPer SPla SSpi SSta WWeb | |
| - 'Greta's Gold' (v) | CPMA | |
| ¶ - 'Lustgarten Weeping' | LRHS SSpi | |
| - 'Madame Butterfly' | CEnd CPMA ELan LRHS MAsh SSpi | |
| ¶ - 'National' | CPMA | |
| * - 'Nicole' | CDoC LPan | |

- 'Radiant Rose' CPMA
- 'Rosea' CPMA CTho
- 'Satomi' ♀ CB&S CDoC CEnd CFil COtt
  CPMA ELan EWTr LNet LPan
  MAsh MBri MGos SLdr SPer SRPl
  SReu SSpi SSta WDin WPat
¶ - 'Schmetterling' CPMA
- 'Snowboy' (v) CB&S CEnd COtt CPMA LRHS
  NBee NEgg SPer
- 'Snowflake' CPMA
¶ - 'Southern Cross' CPMA
- 'Summmer Majesty' CPMA
- 'Sunsplash' (v) CPMA
- 'Temple Jewel' (v) CPMA LRHS
- 'Triple Crown' CPMA
- 'Tsukubanomine' CPMA
- 'Weaver's Weeping' CB&S COtt CPMA NEgg
§ *linifolia* Last listed 1996
*macrophylla* CMCN SMad WCwm
*mas* ♀ More than 30 suppliers
- 'Aurea' (v) CAbP CPMA ELan LPan MAsh
  MBri MCCP SPan SPer SSpi SSta
  WAbe WDin WPat WWat
§ - 'Aureoelegantissima' (v) CFil CPMA ELan LNet MBri MBro
  NHol SPer WPGP WPat WSHC
- 'Elegantissima' See *C. mas* 'Aureoelegantissima'
- 'Golden Glory' CB&S CPMA MBri
- 'Variegata' ♀ CB&S CBot CDoC CMCN CPMA
  EBee ELan IOrc LNet LPan MAsh
  MBri MGos NEgg NPal SBrw SSpi
  WDin WFar WPat WWat
N 'Norman Hadden' ♀ CAbP CBar CDoC CPMA CRos
  CSam CTho MBel SBid SBrw SHFr
  SPer SSpi SSta WAbe WPat WWat
*nuttallii* CB&S CDoC ELan GOrc LPan
  MBal MBro SSta WDin WNor
  WWat WWoo
- 'Ascona' See *C.* 'Ascona'
- 'Colrigo Giant' CPMA EWTr SSpi
- 'Gold Spot' (v) CB&S CBlo CPMA EPfP IOrc
  MGos SPer WWes
- 'Monarch' CB&S CPMA LPan SPer WWes
- 'North Star' CPMA CRos
- 'Portlemouth' CEnd CPMA LRHS
*obliqua* CFil WPGP
§ *occidentalis* EPla
*officinalis* CPMA EPfP LPan MBri WCwm
  WWat
'Ormonde' CPMA ECho SPer SSpi WWes
'Pink Blush' CPMA
¶ 'Porlock' ♀ EPfP WDin
*pubescens* See *C. occidentalis*
*pumila* NHol WDin
§ *racemosa* WWat
*rugosa* WNor
I x *rutgersiensis* 'Aurora' CPMA
§ - Celestial™ = 'Rutdan' CPMA
¶ - Constellation™ = 'Rutcan' CPMA
♦ - Galaxy™ See *C.* x *rutgersiensis* Celestial =
  'Rutdan'
- 'Ruth Ellen' CPMA
- 'Stellar Pink' CPMA
*sanguinea* CB&S CBlo CDoC CDul CKin
  CLnd CSam CTri EBrP EBre ENot
  GChr LBre LBuc MAsh MPEx
  NFor NLon NWea SBre WDin
  WGwG WHar WMou
- 'Compressa' See *C. hessei*
- 'Midwinter Fire' CB&S CBlo CDoC CEnd COtt
  EBee EBrP EBre ENot EPla ERic
  EWTr EWll LBre LBuc LNet LPan
  MBar MGos MRav MWat NHol
  SBre SBrw SMad SRPl SRms WFar
  WLRN WWeb

- 'Winter Beauty' CDoC CDul EMil IOrc LHop
  MBro NHol SEas WPat WPyg
  WWat
- 'Winter Flame' See *C. sanguinea* 'Winter Beauty'
¶ - 'Winter Flame Anny' NPSI
sp. CLD 613 EPla
*stolonifera* CArn EPla MGos
§ - 'Baileyi' CB&S
- 'Flaviramea' ♀ More than 30 suppliers
§ - 'Kelseyi' CB&S CBlo CWit EBee EPla ESis
  IOrc MBNS MBar MRav NPro
  SBod SLPl SPer SVil WLRN WWat
- Kelsey's Gold = 'Roseo' Last listed 1997
¶ - 'Sunshine' CSpe
§ - 'White Gold' (v) CAbP CBlo CPMA EBee ENot EPla
  IOrc LNet MBri MGos WBcn
  WWeb
- 'White Spot' See *C. stolonifera* 'White Gold'
§ *stricta* Last listed 1998
x *unalaschkensis* Last listed 1997
*walteri* CMCN WCwm

## COROKIA (Escalloniaceae)

*buddlejoides* CAbb CDoC CMHG CPle ECou
  MGrG SOWG WBod WCru WPic
  WTro
- var. *linearis* Last listed 1998
'Coppershine' CB&S
*cotoneaster* CAbP CHor CPle CTrw ECou
  ELan ENot EPot IGri MBlu MUlv
  NHol SDry SIgm SLon SPar SSta
  WBod WBrE WCot WFar WPat
  WSHC WWat WWes
- 'Little Prince' CB&S
- 'Ohau Scarlet' ECou
- 'Ohau Yellow' ECou
- 'Swale Stream' ECou
- 'Wanaka' ECou
*macrocarpa* CDoC CPle ISea SDix SPer WSHC
- x *buddlejoides* Last listed 1998
x *virgata* CAbP CB&S CMHG CPle CTrC
  ECou ELan IOrc ISea MBlu MCCP
  MWhi SAPC SArc SBrw SPer
  WLeb WSHC WTro WWal
- 'Bronze King' CDoC CMil CPle CWit SPer SVen
- 'Bronze Knight' MHar
- 'Bronze Lady' MBal
- 'Cheesemanii' ECou
- 'County Park Lemon' ECou SOWG
- 'County Park Purple' ECou
* - 'Dartonii' MBlu
* - 'Frosted Chocolate' CB&S
- 'Havering' ECou
- 'Pink Delight' CDoC EPfP
* - *purpurea* Last listed 1998
- 'Red Wonder' CBlo CMHG EBee ERea MHlr
  SAga SDry SEND SOWG WLeb
* - 'Sunsplash' CB&S
- 'Virgata' CChe ECou
- 'Yellow Wonder' CB&S CMHG EBee ECot ECou
  GEil SAga

## CORONILLA (Papilionaceae)

*cappadocica* See *C. orientalis*
*comosa* See *Hippocrepis comosa*
*emerus* See *Hippocrepis emerus*
*glauca* See *C. valentina* subsp. *glauca*
*globosa* SUsu
*minima* NTow SBla
§ *orientalis* NWCA WWin
- var. *orientalis* Last listed 1998

*valentina*    CMac CSPN CSam EMil LHop
MHlr SBra SDix SVen WCot

§ - subsp. *glauca* ♀    CB&S CBot CFee CGle CMac CPle
CSam CTri EBee ELan ENot ERea
IOrc MBal MWhi NTow SPer
SRCN SRms WAbe WHCG WPic

- - 'Citrina' ♀    CB&S CBot CDoC CHan CSam
CSpe ELan LGre LHop MLan NPer
SChu SPer SUsu SVil WAbe WCot
WHCG WKif WRus WSHC WSpi

\* - - 'Pygmaea'    WCot
- - 'Variegata'    More than 30 suppliers
§ *varia*    CAgr CStr NLar SRCN WViv
¶ - HH&K 334    CHan

## CORREA (Rutaceae)

*alba*    CDoC CSev ECou ERea MSag
SMur
- 'Pinkie'    ECou ERea LHop SOWG
*backhouseana* ♀    CAbb CB&S CHan CPle CTrG CTri
ECre ERea GCal GQui IOrc LCns
LHil LHop SAga SLon SOWG
WAbe WBod WCot WSHC
*baeuerlenii*    CMHG SOWG
*calycina*    ERea
*decumbens*    CPle ECon ECou GSki LCns SMur
SOWG WSHC
'Dusky Bells'    CDoC CHan CPle CSWP CWSG
ECou ERea LCns LHop SOWG
'Dusky Maid'    CAbb WAbe WLRN
'Harrisii'    See *C.* 'Mannii'
*lawrenceana*    CAbb CB&S CDoC CWSG GQui
SBid SEND WAbe WLRN
- *rosea*    Last listed 1998
§ 'Mannii' ♀    CHan CLTr CSam CSev ECou ERea
EWTr IOrc LHop MHlr MNes
SOWG SVen WAbe WSHC WWat
'Marian's Marvel'    CAbb CB&S CMHG ERea GQui
LCns LHil MSag SOWG SVen
WAbe WLRN
¶ 'Peachy Cream'    CDoC
*pulchella*    CB&S CDoC CGre CPle CTri ERea
GLch GQui LBlm MNes SAga
SOWG WAbe
§ *reflexa*    CB&S CPle ECou LBlm SOWG
- var. *reflexa*    Last listed 1998
- *virens*    WEas
- 'Yanakie'    CPle SOWG
*speciosa*    See *C. reflexa*
*viridiflora*    GQui

## CORTADERIA ✿ (Poaceae)

*argentea*    See *C. selloana*
§ *fulvida*    EBrP EBre EGar EWes IBlr IHdy
LBre SBre SMad
*richardii* hort.    See *C. fulvida*
§ - (Endlicher) Zotov    CHan EBrP EBre EFou EHoe ELan
EPla EWes GAri GGar IBlr LBre
MBal MUlv SAPC SArc SBre WCot
§ *selloana*    CB&S CTri ELan ENot EPfP LNet
MBar MMal MRav NArg NBee
NBir NFor SAPC SArc SPlb WStI
§ - 'Albolineata' (v)    CBrm CMil EHoe EWes SCob
SEND SMad SSto WLRN
§ - 'Aureolineata' (v) ♀    CB&S CBrm CDoC CMil EHoe
ELan ENot MAsh MBal MBri MGos
MMoz MRav SCob SEas SPer WFar
WLeb WLRN
- 'Gold Band'    See *C. selloana* 'Aureolineata'
- 'Monstrosa'    SMad
- 'Pink Feather'    CBlo EWsh MBNS MMal MWat
NEgg SRms WFar WLow WPyg
WStI

- 'Pumila' ♀    CB&S CCuc CDoC EBrP EBre ECtt
EHoe ELan ENot EPla GAbr LBre
MBNS MBal MBri MGos MMoz
MRav NEgg NFai SApp SBre SCob
SDix SEas SMad SPer SPla WFar
WStI
- 'Rendatleri'    CB&S CDoC EHoe ELan MAsh
MBal SCob SEND SEas SMad SPer
WLRN
- 'Roi des Roses'    CBlo
- 'Rosea'    GSki MBal MBar MGos NArg
- 'Silver Comet'    WWoo
- 'Silver Fountain'    ELan LRHS MAsh SPer
- 'Silver Stripe'    See *C. selloana* 'Albolineata'
- 'Sunningdale Silver' ♀    CB&S CDoC EBrP EBre
ECha ECtt EHoe ELan ENot LBre
MBal MBri MGos MUlv MWat SBre
SCob SEas SMad SPer WPyg
- 'White Feather'    CBlo ECtt WFar WLow
Toe Toe    See *C. richardii* (Endlicher) Zotov

## CORTUSA (Primulaceae)

*altaica*    GCal
*brotheri*    NWCA
- ex KBE 141    Last listed 1996
*matthioli*    CGle EBee EPfP GTou LBee MBal
MFir NMGW NMen NRya NTow
NWCA SRms WFar WWhi
- 'Alba'    ECGN EPPr MBal NHar NHed
NWCA SRms
- var. *congesta*    EBee
- subsp. *pekinensis*    CFir EBee GDra GLch GSki IMGH
LBee LSyl NDov NHar NMen
NRoo SRms WOve
- var. *yezoensis*    EHyt
¶ *turkestanica*    EBee WAbe

## CORYBAS (Orchidaceae)

*diemenicus*    SWes
*incurvus*    SWes

## CORYDALIS (Papaveraceae)

§ *aitchisonii*
   subsp. *aitchisonii*    Last listed 1997
*alexeenkoana*    CLAP EHyt EPot
- subsp. *vittae*    See *C. vittae*
\* *alta*    CPla
*ambigua* hort.    See *C. fumariifolia*
*ambigua* Cham. & Schldt.    ETub
*angustifolia*    EPot GCrs
\* *atrata*    Last listed 1996
*aurea*    Last listed 1996
¶ *blanda* subsp. *oxelmannii*    GCrs
- subsp. *parnassica*    EHyt EPot GCrs
¶ 'Blue Dragon'    MBNS
'Blue Panda'    See *C. flexuosa* 'Blue Panda'
*bracteata*    EHyt GCrs LRHS
- *alba*    Last listed 1997
- 'Marina'    Last listed 1998
*bulbosa* auct. non DC.    See *C. cava*
- (L.) DC.    See *C. solida*
*buschii*    EHyt GCrs IMGH SWas
*cashmeriana*    EHyt EPot GCrs GTou IMGH
NHar NHol NNrd SBla WAbe WIvy
- 'Kailash'    EHyt GBuc
*caucasica*    EHyt EPot GCrs GDra LAma
- var. *alba* misapplied    See *C. malkensis*
§ *cava* ♀    CGle EBot EPar EPot LAma WShi
- *albiflora*    EPar EPot SBla
*chaerophylla* B&SWJ 2951    WCru
*cheilanthifolia*    More than 30 suppliers
*chionophila*    Last listed 1998

| | |
|---|---|
| conorbiza | EHyt EPot |
| ¶ darwasica | GCrs |
| decipiens | See *C. solida* subsp. *incisa* |
| elata | More than 30 suppliers |
| - 'Blue Summit' | SBla |
| erdelii | GCrs |
| firouzii | EPot |
| flexuosa | CBar CFee CKel CMil CSpe EGle |
| | ELan EMar EMou LHop MArl MBel |
| | MBro MGrG MNrw MRPP MTho |
| | NNrd NWes SChu WAbe WRus |
| | WSHC WWin |
| ¶ - 'Balang Mist' | SWas |
| § - 'Blue Panda' | CBos EBee EHyt EPfP EWes GCrs |
| | LPio SSoC SSpi WAbe WCot |
| - CD&R 528 | CAvo CGle EHyt LGre MBro MRav |
| | NHar NRya SAga SIng WCot WCru |
| | WRHF |
| - 'China Blue' CD&R 528c | More than 30 suppliers |
| ¶ - 'Copperhead' | CCuc |
| - 'Nightshade' | CElw GAri GBuc MAvo MCCP |
| | NCot NDov SWat WCot WIvy |
| | WRHF WSpi |
| I - 'Norman's Seedling' | EPPr WCot WPGP |
| - 'Père David' CD&R 528b | More than 30 suppliers |
| - 'Purple Leaf' CD&R 528a | More than 30 suppliers |
| § fumariifolia | EPot LAma MTho NRog |
| glauca | See *C. sempervirens* |
| glaucescens | EHyt EPot GCrs |
| - 'Medeo' | GCrs |
| ¶ gracilis | EHyt |
| haussknechtii | EHyt GCrs |
| henrikii | EHyt EPot GCrs |
| ¶ heterocarpa | EBee |
| integra | GCrs |
| intermedia | EPot |
| * itacifolia | WCot |
| kashgarica | EPot |
| ¶ kusnetzovii | GCrs |
| ledebouriana | Last listed 1997 |
| * lindleyana | Last listed 1996 |
| linstowiana | CElw CLon EBee EHyt EMar EPPr |
| | IBlr LGre NCot |
| - CD&R 605 | CLAP |
| ludlowii | Last listed 1997 |
| § lutea | CB&S ELan EMar EWTr GBuc IBlr |
| | IMGH LGro MMal MTis NFai NPer |
| | NPri NRoo NVic SBea SEND SRms |
| | WBea WCot WHen WRha |
| macrocentra | Last listed 1997 |
| § malkensis ♀ | CLAP EHyt EPot GCrs NBir NTow |
| | WCot |
| ¶ nariniana white | EHyt |
| nevskii | See *C. aitchisonii* subsp. |
| | *aitchisonii* |
| nobilis | Last listed 1998 |
| nudicaulis | GCrs |
| ochotensis | NLar WCot |
| - B&SWJ 3138 | WCru |
| § ochroleuca | CRow EBee EMar EPot ESis EWTr |
| | MBro MCLN MTho MTis NCot |
| | WBro WCru WHal WRha |
| ophiocarpa | CGle CInt EBee EHoe ELan EMan |
| | EMar EWTr GAri GCal GGar IBlr |
| | LSyl NArg NFla SOkh WBea WCot |
| | WElm WFoF WOve WPrP |
| oppositifolia | |
| subsp. oppositifolia | GCrs |
| ¶ ornata | EHyt |
| paczoskii | EHyt EPot GCrs LRHS WAbe |
| - RS 12180 | Last listed 1996 |
| pallida B&SWJ 395 | WCru |
| parnassica | EHyt |
| paschei | EHyt |
| popovii | GCrs |
| pseudofumaria alba | See *C. ochroleuca* |
| pumila | EPot GCrs LRHS NTow |
| - alba | EPot |
| rosea | GBuc IBlr |
| ruksansii | EPot GCrs |
| rupestris | Last listed 1997 |
| § saxicola | EBee EPot |
| scandens | See *Dicentra scandens* |
| schanginii | CLAP EPot |
| - subsp. ainii | CLAP EHyt EPot GCrs |
| - subsp. schanginii | EHyt |
| scouleri | NBir WCot |
| § seisumsiana | GCrs |
| § sempervirens | CInt EWTr MLan NFai WBea |
| | WCot WCru WHer WPat WRos |
| | WSan WWin |
| - alba | ELan WFoF |
| - 'Rock Harlequin' | Last listed 1997 |
| smithiana | WFar WTin WUnu |
| - ACE 154 | CPBP EHyt EPot GBuc MRPP |
| | NCot NMen WCot |
| aff. smithiana CLD 385 | Last listed 1997 |
| § solida ♀ | CBro CElw CGle CMea CRDP |
| | EBee EHyt ELan EPar EPot GCrs |
| | IBlr LAma MHlr MMal MRPP NChi |
| | NFla NHar NMen NNrd NRog |
| | NRya SBea WAbe WCot WFar |
| | WShi |
| - BM 8499 | NHol |
| - subsp. densiflora | See *C. solida* subsp. *incisa* |
| - forms | EPot MRav |
| - from Penza | GCrs |
| - 'Harkov' | GCrs LRHS |
| - 'Ice Pink' | EPot |
| § - subsp. incisa | CMea EHyt EPot LRHS MNrw |
| | MTho |
| - MS 881 | Last listed 1998 |
| - PJC 214 | Last listed 1996 |
| * - 'Smokey Blue' | Last listed 1998 |
| - 'Soft Pink' | EPot |
| - subsp. solida | |
| 'Beth Evans' ♀ | CBro EHyt |
| ¶ - - 'Blue Pearl' | GCrs |
| - - 'Blushing Girl' | GCrs |
| ¶ - - 'Evening Shade' | GCrs |
| - - 'Highland Mist' | GCrs NHar |
| - - 'Prasil Sunset' | EHyt |
| - - 'Snowstorm' | Last listed 1997 |
| ¶ - - 'White Knight' | GCrs |
| - f. transsylvanica | CLAP EHyt EPot GCrs NBir NHar |
| | NMen NPar NRya SWat WAbe |
| | WCot |
| - - 'Dieter Schacht' | GCrs |
| - - 'George Baker' ♀ | CAvo CBro CRDP EHyt EPar EPot |
| | GCrs MTho NHar NMen SUsu |
| | SWas WCot |
| - - 'Lahovice' | GCrs |
| - - 'Nettleton Pink' | EPot |
| - 'White King' | Last listed 1997 |
| ¶ sp. from Sichuan, China | NCot |
| speciosa | Last listed 1997 |
| taliensis ACE 2443 | EPot GBin |
| tashiroi | Last listed 1996 |
| tauricola | EHyt EPot |
| thalictrifolia Franchet | See *C. saxicola* |
| tomentella | CPBP EPot |
| uniflora | GCrs |
| ¶ verticillaris | EHyt |
| § vittae | EHyt |

*wendelboi* — EPot GCrs
- subsp. *congesta*
  'Abant Wine' — EPot
*wilsonii* — CBot CLyd EDAr ESis GCHN GCal IBlr MTho NTow NWCA SBla WEas
*zetterlundii* — Last listed 1998

## CORYLOPSIS ✿ (Hamamelidaceae)

§ *glabrescens* — CPMA MBal SMur WNor
- var. *gotoana* — CMCN CPMA ELan EPfP SMur SPer SSpi SSta WWat
*himalayana* KR 990 — Last listed 1998
*pauciflora* ♀ — CB&S CDoC CEnd CPMA EBee EBrP EBre ELan EMil ENot IOrc LBre MAsh MBal MBel MBri MGos NBee SBre SPer SReu SSpi SSta WBod WPat WWat
*platypetala* — See *C. sinensis* var. *calvescens*
- var. *laevis* — See *C. sinensis* var. *calvescens*
*sinensis* — EMil SSta WShe
§ - var. *calvescens* — CB&S CPMA MBal
§ - - f. *veitchiana* ♀ — CBlo CPMA MBal SMur WWoo
- - - 'Purple Selection' — CPMA
§ - var. *sinensis* ♀ — CDoC CPMA CWit EAst EHic EPfP MBal SMad SPer SRPl SReu WAbe WWat
- - 'Spring Purple' — CAbP CPMA EPfP LHop MBri SBrw SPer SSpi SSta WWat
sp. from Chollipo, South Korea — Last listed 1997
*spicata* — CB&S CBlo CDoC CPMA ELan IMGH MBal MBlu MBri MPla SCoo SPer SRPl WBay WHCG
¶ - 'Chollipo' — LRHS
*veitchiana* — See *C. sinensis* var. *calvescens* f. *veitchiana*
*willmottiae* — See *C. sinensis* var. *sinensis*

## CORYLUS ✿ (Corylaceae)

*avellana* (F) — CDoC CKin CLnd CSam EBee EBrP EBre ECrN EMui ENot ERea EWTr GRei IOrc LBre LBuc LHyr MBal MBar MBri NBee NRog NWea SBre SKee SPer WDin WHar WMou WStI
- 'Aurea' — CBlo CEnd COtt CTho ELan ENot EPfP LBuc MAsh MBlu MBri MGos NHol SPer SPla SSta WDin WPyg
- 'Bollwylle' — See *C. maxima* 'Halle'sche Riesennuss'
- 'Contorta' ♀ — More than 30 suppliers
- 'Cosford Cob' (F) — CBlo CDoC CTho CTri EBrP EBre ERea GTwe LBre LBuc MBlu MBri MGos NRog SBre SDea SKee SPer WWal
§ - 'Fuscorubra' (F) — CDoC CMac IOrc MRav
§ - 'Heterophylla' — CEnd CTho SRPl WMou WWes
- 'Laciniata' — See *C. avellana* 'Heterophylla'
- 'Merveille de Bollwyller' — See *C. maxima* 'Halle'sche Riesennuss'
- 'Nottingham Prolific' — See *C. avellana* 'Pearson's Prolific'
§ - 'Pearson's Prolific' (F) — EBee ERea GTwe LBuc SDea
- 'Pendula' — MBlu WMou
- 'Purpurea' — See *C. avellana* 'Fuscorubra'
- 'Webb's Prize Cob' (F) — ERea GTwe IOrc LHol NRog SDea WMou
*colurna* ♀ — CAgr CBlo CDul CFil CLnd CMCN CTho ECrN ENot GChr IOrc LHyr MGos NBee NWea SKee SLPl SPer WDin WMou WOrn
- x *avellana* — See *C.* x *colurnoides*

* - 'Te Terra Red' — CEnd CMCN MBlu SMad WMou
- variegated — Last listed 1996
§ x *colurnoides* — Last listed 1998
*maxima* (F) — CDul CLnd EMui GTwe NWea SDea WDin
* - 'Annise Summer Red' — Last listed 1997
- 'Butler' (F) — CBlo ERea GTwe MBri SKee WPyg
- 'Ennis' (F) — ERea GTwe SDea SKee
- 'Fertile de Coutard' — See *C. maxima* 'White Filbert'
- 'Frizzled Filbert' (F) — EMil ERea
- 'Frühe van Frauendorf' — See *C. maxima* 'Red Filbert'
- 'Grote Lambertsnoot' — See *C. maxima* 'Kentish Cob'
¶ - 'Gunslebert' (F) — CBlo ERea GChr GTwe MBri SDea SKee WPyg
- Halle Giant — See *C. maxima* 'Halle'sche Riesennuss'
§ - 'Halle'sche Riesennuss' (F) — ERea GTwe LHol SKee
§ - 'Kentish Cob' (F) — CBlo CDoC CSam CTho EBrP EBre ERea GTwe IOrc LBre LBuc MBlu MGos NRog SBre SDea SFam SKee SRms WHar WPyg
- 'Lambert's Filbert' — See *C. maxima* 'Kentish Cob'
- 'Longue d'Espagne' — See *C. maxima* 'Kentish Cob'
- 'Monsieur de Bouweller' — See *C. maxima* 'Halle'sche Riesennuss'
- New Giant — See *C. maxima* 'Neue Riesennuss'
- 'Purple Filbert' — See *C. maxima* 'Purpurea'
§ - 'Purpurea' (F) ♀ — More than 30 suppliers
§ - 'Red Filbert' (F) — CBlo CEnd ERea GTwe IOrc MBlu MBri NRog SKee
- 'Red Zellernut' — See *C. maxima* 'Red Filbert'
- 'Spanish White' — See *C. maxima* 'White Filbert'
- 'Tonne de Giffon' (F) — Last listed 1997
§ - 'White Filbert' (F) — ERea GTwe NRog SKee WHar
- 'White Spanish Filbert' — See *C. maxima* 'White Filbert'
- 'Witpit Lambertsnoot' — See *C. maxima* 'White Filbert'
x *vilmorinii* — WMou

## CORYMBIUM (Asteraceae)

*africanum* — Last listed 1996

## CORYNEPHORUS (Poaceae)

*canescens* — EBee EHoe EMan EPla GBin MCCP MLLN

## CORYNOCARPUS (Corynocarpaceae)

*laevigatus* — ECou MBri
- 'Picturatus' — Last listed 1998
- 'Variegatus' — Last listed 1998

## COSMOS (Asteraceae)

§ *atrosanguineus* — More than 30 suppliers
* *bipinnatus* 'Sonata' ♀ — Last listed 1994

## COSTUS (Zingiberaceae)

*curvibracteatus* — Last listed 1996
§ *cuspidatus* — LChe
*igneus* — See *C. cuspidatus*
*malortieanus* — LChe
*speciosus* — ELau GPoy NRog WMul
- tetraploid — Last listed 1997
*spiralis* — LChe

## COTINUS (Anacardiaceae)

*americanus* — See *C. obovatus*
§ *coggygria* ♀ — CB&S CDoC CDul CMCN EBee EBrP EBre ELan ENot EWTr IOrc LBre LHop MBar MBri MRav MWat NBee NFor SBre SDix SPer WDin WGwG WHCG WHar WStI WWat WWes
- 'Foliis Purpureis' — See *C. coggygria* Rubrifolius Group

- 'Notcutt's Variety'  CBlo EBrE EBre ELan ENot LBre
MAsh MRav NSti SBre SPer WWes
- 'Pink Champagne'  CPMA
- Purpureus Group  ENot
- 'Red Beauty'  MBri
- 'Royal Purple' ♀  More than 30 suppliers
§ - Rubrifolius Group  CB&S MBal NFor SChu SDix SPer
SPla WHCG WWeb
- 'Velvet Cloak'  CBlo CPMA ELan EPfP MAsh
MGos MRav MTis SLon SPer SPla
SReu SSta WHCG WPat WPyg
'Flame' ♀  CBlo CPMA EBee EPfP IOrc MAsh
SPla SSta WPat WWat WWeb
'Grace' ♀  More than 30 suppliers
§ obovatus ♀  CGre CMCN CMHG CPMA CPle
EBee ENot EPfP MRav SPer SSpi
WWat WWes

## COTONEASTER ✿ (Rosaceae)

acuminatus  SRms WPGP
acutifolius var. laetevirens  See C. laetevirens
adpressus ♀  CBlo EPfP EPla GDra MGos NCut
NFor NHar NLon NWea
§ - 'Little Gem'  GAri MAsh MBri MPla NMen
SRms
- var. praecox  See C. nanshan
- 'Tom Thumb'  See C. adpressus 'Little Gem'
affinis  SRms
afghanicus CC 738  WLRN
albokermesinus  SRms
altaicus  SRms
ambiguus  SRms
amoenus  SLPl SRms
¶ - 'Fire Mountain'  NPro WFar
apiculatus  CSWP SRms
armenus  SRms
§ ascendens  SRms
assadii  SRms
assamensis  SRms
§ astrophoros  MBlu SIng SRms WBod
atropurpureus  SRms
§ - 'Variegatus' ♀  CBot CDul EBee EHoe ELan ENot
EPot GChr GRei IOrc LHop MBNS
MBal MBar MBri MGos NBee
NHol SPer SRms WRHF WSHC
WWal WWat WWin
bacillaris  SRms
boisianus  SRms
bradyi  SRms
§ bullatus ♀  CDul ELan ENot GRei MGos NFor
NLon NTow SEND SLon SPer
SRms WCwm WSHC WWat
- 'Firebird'  CBlo SPer SRms
- f. floribundus  See C. bullatus
- var. macrophyllus  See C. rehderi
buxifolius Wallich  EHic ESis SRms
ex Lindley
- blue-leaved  See C. lidjiangensis
- 'Brno'  SRms
- f. vellaeus  See C. astrophoros
calocarpus  SRms
cambricus  CNat SRms
canescens  SRms
§ cashmiriensis ♀  SRms
cavei  SRms
chailaricus  SRms
chengkangensis  SRms
cinerascens  SRms
§ cochleatus  CChe EBee EPot ESis EWTr GAri
GDra MBal MBar MGos MPla NFla
NLon NMen SReu SRms WEas
WRHF WWat

§ congestus  CFee EBee GRei IOrc MBal MBar
MBri MBro MGos MRav NFor
NLon NRoo SPer SPlb SRms WHar
WWat WWin
- 'Nanus'  CLyd CMHG CNic ELan EMil
EOrn ESis MAsh MBro MOne
MPla NHol NNrd SIng SPla SRms
WPat WPyg WWat
conspicuus  CB&S CSam SRms
- 'Decorus' ♀  CDoC CMHG EBee ELan ENot
GOrc GRei IOrc MBar MGos
MRav NFor NHol NLon NRoo
NWea SPer WDin WPyg WStI
WWes
- 'Flameburst'  MBal MBri
- 'Red Alert'  SRms
- 'Red Glory'  SRms
* - 'Winter Jewel'  CBlo
cooperi  SRms
crispii  SRms
aff. crispii  SRms
cuspidatus  SRms
N dammeri ♀  CBlo CChe CDul CMHG EBee
ELan ENot GRei ISea LBuc MBal
MBar MGos NBee NFor NWea
SIng SMac SPer SRPl SRms WBod
WDin WFar WHar WWat WWin
§ - 'Major'  CBlo NFla SPla WCFE
- 'Oakwood'  See C. radicans 'Eichholz'
- var. radicans Schneider  See C. radicans
◆ - - hort.  See C. dammeri 'Major'
- 'Streibs Findling'  See C. procumbens
dielsianus  NWea SPer SRms
- 'Rubens'  SRms
discolor  SRms
distichus  See C. nitidus
- var. tongolensis  See C. splendens
divaricatus  ENot EPla GRei SLon SPer SRms
WFar WWat
¶ 'Donald Lowndes'  SRPl
duthieanus  SRms
§ - 'Boer'  MAsh MBar MBri SRms WRHF
elegans  SRms
ellipticus  SRms
'Erlinda'  See C. x suecicus 'Erlinda'
'Falconeri'  SRms
fangianus  SRms
floccosus  CBlo EHal GOrc MBri NWea SPer
SRms WLRN WWat
forrestii  SRms
franchetii  CB&S CChe CDul EBee EBrP EBre
ELan EMil ERom EWTr GCHN
IOrc LBre LBuc LPan MBal MGos
MRav NFor NHol NLon NRoo
SPer SRms WDin WFar WGwG
WHar WStI
¶ - SF 96051  ISea
- var. sternianus  See C. sternianus
frigidus  CBlo GAri NWea SRms
§ - 'Cornubia' ♀  More than 30 suppliers
- 'Fructu Luteo'  IBlr SRms
- 'Notcutt's Variety'  ELan ENot WWes
- 'Saint Monica'  MBlu
- 'Sherpa'  Last listed 1997
froebelii  SRms
gamblei  SRms
gangbobaensis  SRms
giraldii  SRms
glabratus  SLPl SRms
glacialis  SRms
glaucophyllus  SEND SRms
- TW 332  Last listed 1997

| | |
|---|---|
| § *glomerulatus* | ESis MBar SRms |
| *goloskokovii* | SRms |
| *gracilis* | SRms |
| *griffithii* | SRms |
| *harrovianus* | EPla SLPl SRms |
| *barrysmithii* | SRms |
| *bebepbyllus* | SRms |
| *henryanus* | SRms |
| - 'Anne Cornwallis' | WBcn |
| § 'Herbstfeuer' | CBlo EBee ECtt EHol GRei MBal |
| | MGos MWat NFor NLon SRms |
| *bessei* | SRms |
| 'Highlight' (aff. *sheriffii*) | ECtt SRms |
| *hissaricus* | SRms |
| § *hjelmqvistii* | LBuc SRms WRHF |
| - 'Robustus' | See *C. hjelmqvistii* |
| - 'Rotundifolius' | See *C. hjelmqvistii* |
| *horizontalis* ♀ | More than 30 suppliers |
| - 'Tangstedt' | ENot |
| - 'Variegatus' | See *C. atropurpureus* 'Variegatus' |
| - var. *wilsonii* | See *C. ascendens* |
| *hsingshangensis* | SRms |
| *humifusus* | See *C. dammeri* |
| *hummelii* | SRms |
| 'Hybridus Pendulus' | See *C. salicifolius* 'Pendulus' |
| § *hylmoei* | SLPl SRms |
| *ignavus* | SLPl SRms |
| *ignescens* | SRms |
| *induratus* | SLPl SRms |
| *insculptus* | SRms |
| *insolitus* | SRms |
| *integerrimus* | NHol SRms |
| § *integrifolius* | CMHG EHic ELan EPfP EPla ESis |
| | LNet MAsh MBal MBar MWhi |
| | NHol NMen NRoo SRms STre |
| | WMoo WWat |
| *juranus* | SRms |
| *kitaibelii* | SRms |
| *kweitschoviensis* | SRms |
| *lacteus* ♀ | CBlo CTri EBee ELan ENot EPla |
| | IOrc LBuc LPan MGos MRav |
| | SEND SLon SPer SPla SRPl SRms |
| | WDin WFar WWat |
| - 'Golden Gate' | Last listed 1997 |
| ¶ - 'Variegatus' | CEnd |
| § *laetevirens* | SRms |
| *langei* | SRms |
| *laxiflorus* | SRms |
| § *lidjiangensis* | SRms WCot |
| § *linearifolius* | CLyd EHol SRms |
| *lucidus* | SRms |
| *ludlowii* | SRms |
| § *mairei* | SRms |
| - Yu 14144 | MBal |
| *marginatus* | SRms |
| *marquandii* | EPla SRms |
| *megalocarpus* | SRms |
| *meiophyllus* ♀ | SRms |
| *melanocarpus* | SRms |
| *melanotrichus* | See *C. cochleatus* |
| *microphyllus* Wallich | CChe CLan ELan ENot GRei IOrc |
| ex Lindley ♀ | ISea MBar MBri MGos NFor NWea |
| | SDix SPer SRms STre WBod WDin |
| | WWal WWat |
| - hort. | See *C. purpurascens* |
| - var. *cochleatus* (Franch.) | Rehd.  & Wils. See *C. cochleatus* |
| - - misapplied | See *C. cashmiriensis* |
| - 'Donard Gem' | See *C. astrophoros* |
| ¶ - KR 3407 | CDoC |
| - 'Teulon Porter' | See *C. astrophoros* |
| - var. *thymifolius* hort. | See *C. linearifolius* |
| - - (Lindl.)  Koehne | See *C. integrifolius* |

| | |
|---|---|
| *miniatus* | SRms |
| *mongolicus* | SRms |
| *monopyrenus* | SRms |
| * 'Mooncreeper' | CChe CDoC WRHF |
| *morrisonensis* | SRms |
| *moupinensis* | EBee SRms |
| *mucronatus* | SRms |
| *multiflorus* Bunge | NWea SRms |
| § *nanshan* | GRei NWea SRms WSPU |
| ♦ - 'Boer' | See *C. duthieanus* 'Boer' |
| *nepalensis* | SRms |
| *newryensis* | SRms |
| *niger* | SRms |
| *nitens* | SRms |
| *nitidifolius* | See *C. glomerulatus* |
| § *nitidus* | SRms |
| *nummularius* | SRms |
| *obscurus* | SRms |
| *oliganthus* | SRms |
| *otto-schwarzii* SF 636 | ISea |
| *ovatus* | SRms |
| *pannosus* | SLPl SRms WWat |
| *paradoxus* | SRms |
| *parkeri* | SRms |
| *peduncularis* | SRms |
| *pekinensis* | SRms |
| *permutatus* | SRms |
| *perpusillus* | GAri MBri SRms WFar |
| 'Pershore Coral' | MAsh MBri |
| *poluninii* | SRms |
| *polyanthemus* | SRms |
| *praecox* 'Boer' | See *C. duthieanus* 'Boer' |
| § *procumbens* | EPla ESis GAri MAsh NRoo SRms |
| - 'Queen of Carpets' | CBlo CDoC EBrP EBre ECtt EHic |
| | LBre MBri MGos MRav SBre SRms |
| - 'Seattle' | SRms |
| *prostratus* | SRms |
| - 'Arnold Forster' | SRms |
| *przewalskii* | SRms |
| *pseudoambiguus* | SRms |
| *pyrenaicus* | See *C. congestus* |
| *racemiflorus* | SRms |
| § *radicans* | SRms |
| § - 'Eichholz' | ECtt ENot EPfP MGos WWeb |
| § *rehderi* | SRms |
| *rokujdaisanensis* | SRms |
| *roseus* | SRms |
| 'Rothschildianus' | See *C. salicifolius* |
| | 'Rothschildianus' |
| *rotundifolius* | SLon SRms |
| 'Royal Beauty' | See *C.* x *suecicus* 'Coral Beauty' |
| *rugosus* | SRms |
| ¶ 'Saldam' | CB&S |
| *salicifolius* | CBlo CLnd EMil NFor SMad SRms |
| | WDin WFar |
| - Autumn Fire | See *C.* 'Herbstfeuer' |
| § - 'Avonbank' | CBlo CEnd MAsh WLRN WSPU |
| - 'Elstead' | SPer |
| - 'Exburyensis' | CB&S CBlo CDoC CDul CSam |
| | CTrw EBrP EBre LBre LNet MAsh |
| | MBri MGos MWat SBre SPer SRms |
| | WDin WFar WHCG WWat WWeb |
| | WWin |
| - 'Fructu Luteo' | MBri WWes |
| - 'Gnom' | CBlo GOrc LNet MAsh MBal MBar |
| | MBlu MBri MGos MRav NFor |
| | NLon NRoo SPer SRms WFar |
| | WWat |
| - 'Merriott Weeper' | CDoC WWat |
| - Park Carpet | See *C. salicifolius* 'Parkteppich' |
| § - 'Parkteppich' | CBlo NWea SPer |

| | |
|---|---|
| § - 'Pendulus' | CBlo CDoC EBee ELan GChr GRei IOrc LNet LPan MAsh MBal MBar MBri MGos MRav MWat NWea SPer SRPl SRms WHCG WHar WStI |
| - 'Red Flare' | SPer SRPl |
| - 'Repens' | CBlo CChe EHic EPfP MBal MTis NFor NLon NRoo NWea SPer SRms WFar |
| § - 'Rothschildianus' ♀ | CBlo CTri EBee EBrP EBre ECtt ELan EMil ENot GOrc LBre LHop MAsh MBal MBar MRav SBre SEas SPer SPla WMoo |
| - var. *rugosus* hort. | See *C. hylmoei* |
| - 'Scarlet Leader' | MBri |
| *salwinensis* | SLPl SRms |
| *sandakphuensis* | SRms |
| *saxatilis* | SRms |
| *scandinavicus* | SRms |
| *schantungensis* | SRms |
| *schlechtendalii* 'Blazovice' | SRms |
| - 'Brno' | SRms |
| *serotinus* Hutchinson | EPla SLPl SRms |
| - misapplied | See *C. meiophyllus* |
| *shansiensis* | MBri SRms |
| *sherriffii* | SRms |
| *sikangensis* | SLon SRms |
| *simonsii* ♀ | CChe CDoC EBee EBrP EBre ELan GChr IOrc LBre LBuc MBar MGos NBee NWea SBre SPer SRms WDin WFar WHar |
| *soczavianus* | SRms |
| § *splendens* ♀ | EBee SRms WWat |
| - 'Sabrina' | See *C. splendens* |
| *staintonii* | SRms |
| § *sternianus* ♀ | ENot EPfP MBar MBri SLPl SRms |
| - ACE 2200 | EPot |
| *suavis* | SRms |
| *subadpressus* | SRms |
| x *suecicus* 'Coral Beauty' | More than 30 suppliers |
| § - 'Erlinda' (v) | CEnd ELan MBar SMad SRms |
| - 'Jürgl' | SRms |
| - 'Skogholm' | CTri EBee EWTr GChr LPan MBal MBar MGos MWat NWea SPer SRms WDin WHar WStI WWin |
| *talgaricus* | SRms |
| *tengyuehensis* | SRms |
| *tomentellus* | SRms |
| *tomentosus* | SRms WWat |
| *transens* | SRms |
| *tripyrenus* | SRms |
| *turbinatus* | SRms |
| *turcomanicus* | SRms |
| *veitchii* | SRms |
| *vernae* | SRms |
| *verruculosus* | SRms |
| *vestitus* | SRms |
| *villosulus* | SRms |
| *vilmorinianus* | SRms |
| *wardii* W.W. Smith | CB&S IOrc NBee |
| - hort. | See *C. mairei* |
| x *watereri* | CBlo CDul CLnd EBee GChr LNet MAsh MGos NWea SPla WDin WWeb |
| - 'Avonbank' | See *C. salicifolius* 'Avonbank' |
| - 'Cornubia' | See *C. frigidus* 'Cornubia' |
| - 'Goscote' | MGos |
| - 'John Waterer' ♀ | EPfP MGos SRms WBod |
| - 'Pendulus' | See *C. salicifolius* 'Pendulus' |
| - 'Pink Champagne' | CAbP LRHS MAsh MBri SPer |
| *wilsonii* | SRms |
| *zabelii* | SRms |

| | |
|---|---|
| - 'Magyar' | SRms |

## COTULA (Asteraceae)

| | |
|---|---|
| *atrata* | See *Leptinella atrata* |
| - var. *dendyi* | See *Leptinella dendyi* |
| *coronopifolia* | CBen CSev CWat LPBA MSta NDea SWat SWyc WWeb |
| *goyenii* | See *Leptinella goyenii* |
| *hispida* | CInt CLyd CMHG ECtt EPot GAbr GCHN IMGH MBNS MBar MTho MWat NFor NHol NMen NPer NRya NWCA SBla SChu SIng SRms SSmi WAbe WCru WEas WFar WMow WPat WPer |
| *lineariloba* | CHea CPBP ECha EWes LBee |
| *minor* | See *Leptinella minor* |
| *pectinata* | See *Leptinella pectinata* |
| *perpusilla* | See *Leptinella pusilla* |
| ◆ 'Platt's Black' | See *Leptinella squalida* 'Platt's Black' |
| *potentilloides* | See *Leptinella potentillina* |
| *pyrethrifolia* | See *Leptinella pyrethrifolia* |
| *reptans* | See *Leptinella scariosa* |
| *rotundata* | See *Leptinella rotundata* |
| *scariosa* | See *Leptinella scariosa* |
| *sericea* | See *Leptinella albida* |
| *serrulata* | See *Leptinella serrulata* |
| sp. C&H 452 | MRPP NWCA |
| *squalida* | See *Leptinella squalida* |

## COTYLEDON (Crassulaceae)

| | |
|---|---|
| *chrysantha* | See *Rosularia chrysantha* |
| *gibbiflora* var. *metallica* | See *Echeveria gibbiflora* var. *metallica* |
| *oppositifolia* | See *Chiastophyllum oppositifolium* |
| *orbiculata* | LHil SDix WCot |
| ¶ - var. *oblonga* | CTrC SChr |
| - S&SH 40 | Last listed 1998 |
| * *pomedosa* | MBri |
| * - 'Variegata' | MBri |
| *simplicifolia* | See *Chiastophyllum oppositifolium* |
| *undulata* | WEas |

## COWANIA (Rosaceae)

| | |
|---|---|
| *stanburyana* | Last listed 1997 |

## COXELLA (Apiaceae)

| | |
|---|---|
| ¶ *dieffenbachii* | GCal |

## CRAIBIODENDRON (Ericaceae)

| | |
|---|---|
| *yunnanense* | MBal |

## CRAMBE (Brassicaceae)

| | |
|---|---|
| *abyssinica* | Last listed 1997 |
| *cordifolia* ♀ | More than 30 suppliers |
| ¶ *filiformis* | WCot |
| *koktebelica* | Last listed 1998 |
| *maritima* | CGle CSev EBee ECGP ECha EMan EMar ERav GPoy MAvo MLLN MSal MWgw NFor NSti SMad SPer SSoC SWat WCot WCru WHer WHow WMer WPer WWeb |
| - 'Lilywhite' | CAgr ILis WCot |
| *orientalis* | ECha MAvo WCot |
| ¶ *tatarica* | CArn EGar EMan MAvo NLar WCot WPer |
| ¶ - HH&K 236 | CHan |

## CRASPEDIA (Asteraceae)

| | |
|---|---|
| *globosa* | Last listed 1998 |

*lanata* — Last listed 1996
- var. *elongata* — Last listed 1998
*richea* — See *C. glauca*
*uniflora* — Last listed 1998

## CRASSULA (Crassulaceae)

*anomala* — SChr
*arborescens* — GAri SRms STre
*argentea* — See *C. ovata*
¶ *brachystachya* — EBee
*coccinea* — CTrC EDAr
*dejecta* x *coccinea* — Last listed 1998
*exilis* subsp. *cooperi* — Last listed 1996
*falcata* ♀ — IBlr LHil MBri WCot
* *galanthea* — Last listed 1998
§ *helmsii* — EHon EMFW NDea WMAq WWeb
*justi-corderoyi* — CHal
¶ *lactea* — CHal STre
¶ *lanceolata* — CCpl EBee
  subsp. *lanceolata*
§ *milfordiae* — CTri ELan MBar MOne MRPP
  MWat NBir SSmi WPer
- 'Silver Stars' — Last listed 1996
*monstrosa* — Last listed 1998
*muscosa* — STre
- 'Variegata' — Last listed 1997
¶ *natalensis* — CTrC
§ *ovata* ♀ — CHal EBak GBin MBri NPer
- 'Basutoland' — MPla
- 'Blue Bird' — GBin
* - 'Coral' — GBin
- 'Hummel's Sunset' (v) ♀ — CHal LHil
* - *nana* — STre
* - 'Riversii' — Last listed 1998
- 'Variegata' — CHal EBak
*pellucida* — CHal
  subsp. *marginalis*
* - subsp. *marginalis* — CHal
  'Variegata'
*peploides* — Last listed 1998
*perforata* — CHal
- 'Variegata' — CHal
*portulacea* — See *C. ovata*
*recurva* — See *C. helmsii*
*rupestris* ♀ — MBri
*rupicola* — GAri
§ *sarcocaulis* — CHal CTri ELan EOas EPot ESis
  GTou MHar MRPP MTho NMen
  NVic NWCA SIgm SIng SRms SRot
  SSmi STre WAbe WCot WEas
  WLow WPat WSHC WWin
- *alba* — CHal ELan SHFr SIng STre WPer
- 'Ken Aslet' — SIng STre
*schmidtii* — CHal EDAr MBri
*sedifolia* — See *C. milfordiae*
*sediformis* — See *C. milfordiae*
*socialis* — CHal
*tetragona* — Last listed 1998
* *tomentosa* 'Variegata' — LHil
¶ 'Très Bon' — STre
¶ *vaginata* — CTrF

## + CRATAEGOMESPILUS (Rosaceae)
'Jules d'Asnières' — Last listed 1996

## CRATAEGUS (Rosaceae)
*arnoldiana* — CAgr CEnd CLnd CTho SEND
  SLPl
'Autumn Glory' — CBlo CEnd CLnd EBee EBrP EBre
  LBre MGos SBre
*azarolus* — CAgr LEdu
- 'White Italian' (F) — Last listed 1998

*champlainensis* — CTho
¶ *chungtiensis* ACE 1624 — SSpi
N *coccinea* — NWea
*cordata* — See *C. phaenopyrum*
*crus-galli* hort. — See *C. persimilis* 'Prunifolia'
*crus-galli* L. — CBlo CDoC CLnd CTho LBuc
  MAsh SPer WDin WJas WMou
- var. *pyracanthifolia* — CTho
x *durobrivensis* — CLnd CTho WWat
*ellwangeriana* — Last listed 1998
*eriocarpa* — CLnd
*flabellata* — CEnd SSpi
*gemmosa* — CEnd CTho
x *grignonensis* — CB&S CDul CLnd ENot LBuc
  MAsh MCoo SPer WJas WPyg
¶ *jonesiae* — EPfP
§ *laciniata* — CBlo CDul CEnd CLnd CMCN
  EBee EPfP MAsh MCoo SLPl SSpi
  WJas WMou
§ *laevigata* — WMou
- 'Coccinea Plena' — See *C. laevigata* 'Paul's Scarlet'
- 'Crimson Cloud' — CBlo CDoC CEnd CLnd EBee
  ENot EPfP GChr MAsh MBri
  MGos MRav MWat SCoo SLon
  SPer WGor WJas WOrn WPyg
- 'Flore Pleno' — See *C. laevigata* 'Plena'
- 'Masekii' (d) — Last listed 1996
¶ - x *media* 'Gireoudii' — CCHP
- 'Mutabilis' — CTho
§ - 'Paul's Scarlet' (d) ♀ — More than 30 suppliers
- 'Pink Corkscrew' — CTho GAri MBlu
§ - 'Plena' (d) — CB&S CBlo CDoC CDul CTho
  EBee GChr GRei LPan MAsh MBri
  MWat NWea SFam SPer WDin
  WMou WOrn
- 'Punicea' — CBlo
- 'Rosea Flore Pleno' (d) ♀ — CB&S CBlo CDoC CDul CLnd
  CTho EBee EBrP EBre ELan ENot
  EWTr GRei LBre LPan MAsh MBar
  MBri MGos MWat NWea SBre
  SPer WDin WJas WStI
x *lavalleei* — CBlo CLnd CTri ENot EPfP GChr
  MAsh SPer SRPl WDin WOrn
- 'Carrierei' ♀ — CBlo CDoC CDul CSam CTho
  EPfP IOrc LPan MBri NWea SRPl
x *media* 'Gireoudii' (v) — CEnd CPMA LNet MBlu MGos
  WMou WPat
*mexicana* — See *C. pubescens* f. *stipulacea*
*mollis* — EPfP
*monogyna* — CB&S CDoC CKin CLnd CSam
  EBrP EBre ELan ENot EPfP GChr
  GRei LBre LBuc LHyr MBar MBri
  MGos NBee NWea SBre SPer SRPl
  WDin WMou
- 'Biflora' — CDul CEnd CTho MAsh MGos
  NWea WMou WSPU
- 'Compacta' — EPla MBlu
- 'Ferox' — CTho
- 'Flexuosa' — LNet
- 'Pendula Rosea' — Last listed 1996
- 'Stricta' — CDul CLnd CTho EBee ENot
  WOrn WSpi
- 'Variegata' — CDul EBee LNet WBcn WSPU
x *mordenensis* 'Toba' (d) — CBlo CDoC CDul CLnd CTho
¶ *opaca* (F) — CAgr
*orientalis* — See *C. laciniata*
*oxyacantha* — See *C. laevigata*
*pedicellata* — CDul CLnd CTho LPan
§ *persimilis* 'Prunifolia' ♀ — More than 30 suppliers
* - 'Prunifolia Splendens' — LPan
§ *phaenopyrum* — CDul CLnd CMCN CTho EPfP
  SLPl SSpi WMou

| | |
|---|---|
| *pinnatifida* | WWat |
| - var. *major* | CBlo CEnd |
| ¶ - - 'Big Golden Star' | CTho |
| * 'Praecox' | CBlo |
| *prunifolia* | See *C. persimilis* 'Prunifolia' |
| § *pubescens* f. *stipulacea* | CMCN |
| *punctata* | SLPl |
| *schraderiana* | CLnd CTho WJas |
| *succulenta* | |
| var. *macracantha* | Last listed 1997 |
| *tanacetifolia* | CLnd CTho MBlu SSpi |
| *wattiana* | CLnd CTho |

## x CRATAEMESPILUS (Rosaceae)

| | |
|---|---|
| *grandiflora* | CLnd CTho |

## CRAWFURDIA (Gentianaceae)

| | |
|---|---|
| *crawfurdioides* | Last listed 1996 |
| *speciosa* | Last listed 1997 |
| - B&SWJ 2102 | WCru |
| - HWJCM 135 | WCru |

## CREMANTHODIUM (Asteraceae)

| | |
|---|---|
| *arnicoides* | Last listed 1998 |
| *pinnatifidum* | Last listed 1996 |
| sp. ACE 1420 | Last listed 1996 |

## CRENULARIA See AETHIONEMA

## CREPIS (Asteraceae)

| | |
|---|---|
| *aurea* | EPar GAbr GGar IBlr |
| *incana* ♀ | CFee CGle CPla EBrP EBre ECha |
| | EMFP EMan EPar GBri LBre LGre |
| | LHop LLWP MAvo MTho NChi |
| | NHaw NSla SBre SDix SPer WAbe |
| | WCot WGer WPat WWin |
| *paludosa* | Last listed 1996 |
| ¶ *rubra* | WCot |
| ¶ *sibirica* | SHut |

## CRINITARIA See ASTER

## CRINODENDRON (Elaeocarpaceae)

| | |
|---|---|
| § *bookerianum* ♀ | More than 30 suppliers |
| *patagua* | CB&S CEnd CGre CLTr CPle |
| | CSam EPfP GQui LHop MBal SLon |
| | SPer SRPl WAbe WBod WPic |
| | WSHC |

## CRINUM (Amaryllidaceae)

| | |
|---|---|
| *amoenum* | Last listed 1998 |
| *aquaticum* | See *C. campanulatum* |
| § *bulbispermum* | CFil CFir ELan WPGP |
| - 'Album' | ECha EMan |
| *capense* | See *C. bulbispermum* |
| ¶ 'Ellen Bosanquet' | CFir |
| *moorei* | CAvo CFir LBlo NRog SChr |
| ¶ - f. *album* | WMul |
| *pedunculatum* R.Br. | Last listed 1998 |
| - hort. | See *C. asiaticum* var. *sinicum* |
| § x *powellii* ♀ | More than 30 suppliers |
| - 'Album' ♀ | CAvo CHan CPin ECha ELan |
| | EMan ERav EWes LAma LBow |
| | LPio MUlv NRog SPar SSpi WCot |
| | WCru WPic WViv |
| - 'Longifolium' | See *C. bulbispermum* |
| - 'Roseum' | See *C.* x *powellii* |
| *yemense* | Last listed 1998 |

## CRIOGENES See CYPRIPEDIUM

## CRITHMUM (Apiaceae)

| | |
|---|---|
| *maritimum* | CArn EBee GPoy MGrG MSal |
| | NLar SIgm WWye |

## CROCOSMIA ✿ (Iridaceae)

| | |
|---|---|
| 'Amberglow' | CElw CGle EWoo IBlr MBNS WFar |
| | WMer WRus |
| *aurea* | CAvo SIng SSpi WCot |
| - hort. | See *C.* x *crocosmiiflora* 'George |
| | Davison' Davison |
| - var. *aurea* | GCal IBlr |
| - var. *maculata* | IBlr |
| - var. *pauciflora* | IBlr |
| ¶ *bicolor* | WHil |
| ◆ 'Blos' | See *C.* Bressingham Beacon = |
| | 'Blos' |
| § Bressingham Beacon | CMHG EBee EBrP EBre IBlr LBre |
| = 'Blos' | NHol SBre SLod SLon SWat WBea |
| 'Bressingham Blaze' | CMHG EBrP EBre EGar GCal IBlr |
| | IHdy LBre MBri NOak NTay SBre |
| | WCot WWin |
| 'Carnival' | IBlr |
| N 'Citronella' misapplied | See *C.* 'Honey Angels' |
| ¶ 'Comet' | GBuc IBlr IBro MAvo |
| x *crocosmiiflora* | CLTr CTri ECha EGra EPla IBlr |
| | MBel MCli NCut NOrc NTay SWat |
| | WCHb WCot WFar WOld WShi |
| - 'A.E.Amos' | Last listed 1996 |
| ¶ - 'A.J.Hogan' | IBlr |
| ¶ - 'Apricot Queen' | IBlr |
| ¶ - 'Baby Barnaby' | CBos IBlr MUlv |
| - 'Babylon' | CBre CBro EBee IBlr LRHS MBri |
| | WFar WPer |
| - 'Brightest and Best' J.E. Fitt | Last listed 1996 |
| - 'Burford Bronze' | IBlr |
| - 'Canary Bird' | CBlo CBro CRow CSam GAbr |
| | GCHN GCal GMac IBlr NRoo |
| | WHil |
| - 'Carmin Brillant' | CAvo CBro CFil CLTr CMHG CRos |
| | CRow CSam EBrP EBre EGar GCal |
| | IBlr IBro LAma LBre LRHS MBri |
| | NHol NSti NTay SBre WCot WFar |
| | WOld |
| N - 'Citronella' J.E. Fitt | CBro CSam MHlr SCob WRha |
| - 'Constance' | CBre CBro CSam IBlr MBri NFai |
| | WCHb WFar WWoo |
| ¶ - 'Corten' | IBlr |
| § - 'Croesus' | CAvo GBri IBlr IBro NRoo WCot |
| | WHal |
| - 'Custard Cream' | EBee IBlr IBro MBri WCot |
| ¶ - 'Debutante' | CMil IBlr MCLN WCot WRus |
| - 'Dusky Maiden' | More than 30 suppliers |
| § - 'E.A. Bowles' | IBlr NRoo |
| - 'Eastern Promise' | CAvo CBre EBee IBlr |
| - 'Elegans' | CElw IBlr |
| § - 'Emily McKenzie' | More than 30 suppliers |
| - 'Firebrand' | IBlr MCLN WCot |
| - 'Flamethrower' | IBlr |
| § - 'George Davison' Davison | CBre CDoC CGle CM&M CPou |
| | CRow EBla ECha EMan EWTr |
| | GCal IBlr LEur MCCP MTis NBur |
| | NHol SCro WBro WCot WGle |
| | WHoo WLin |
| § - 'Gerbe d'Or' | CRow CSpe ECGP GBri GCal |
| | GMac IBlr IBro IHdy MAvo MBri |
| | MCLN NHol NRoo SOkh SSpe |
| | SUsu WCot WFar WHil WLin |
| | WOld WRus WViv |
| - 'Gloria' | IBlr |
| § - 'Golden Glory' | CSam EPar IBlr WCot |

- 'Golden Sheaf'    EGar GBri IBlr WBea
- 'Goldfinch'    IBlr IBro
- 'Hades'    IBlr
- 'Highlight'    IBlr
- 'His Majesty'    CBos CGle CLTr CMil CRDP
  CRow CSam CSpe EGar IBlr IBro
  LGre LRHS MAvo MBri NHol SAga
  WGer WOld WPer
§ - 'Jackanapes'    CAvo CBro CMil CRDP CRow
  EBee EGar GCal IBlr MBri NHol
  NRoo SRPl WBro WCot WHal
  WWeb WWhi
N - 'James Coey' J.E. Fitt    CBro CFee CFil CHad CRow CTrC
  ECha GCal IBlr LAma LHop MCLN
  NHol NOrc NRog SPer WFar WLin
  WOld
* - 'Jesse van Dyke'    IBlr
§ - 'Jessie'    EBee IBlr MBri WCot WPer
- 'Kiatschou'    CFil EBee ECha EGar IBlr SLod
- 'Lady Hamilton'    More than 30 suppliers
- 'Lady McKenzie'    See *C.* x *crocosmiiflora* 'Emily
  McKenzie'
- 'Lady Oxford'    CFil ECha EGar IBlr IBro WCot
- 'Lutea'    EGar EGra IBlr
- 'Marjorie'    CAvo WCot
- 'Mephistopheles'    IBlr
- 'Météore'    EBee NCut NOrc NPri
- 'Morning Light'    IBlr
§ - 'Mrs Geoffrey Howard'    CBos CGle CPlt CSam EGar GBri
  IBlr IBro IHdy LLew MAvo SUsu
  WCot WCru WPGP
- 'Mrs Morrison'    See *C.* x *crocosmiiflora* 'Mrs
  Geoffrey Howard'
- Newry seedling    See *C.* x *crocosmiiflora*
  'Prometheus'
- 'Nimbus'    GBri IBlr
§ - 'Norwich Canary'    More than 30 suppliers
¶ - 'Polo'    EBee
- 'Princess'    See *C.* x *crocosmiiflora* 'Red
  Knight'
- 'Princess Alexandra'    IBlr WCHb WMer WWoo
- 'Prolificans'    IBlr
§ - 'Prometheus'    IBlr
N - 'Queen Alexandra' J.E. Fitt    ECha EGar EHal IBlr IBro LAma
  LHop MAvo MLan NCut SWat
  WHal WPer
- 'Queen Charlotte'    IBlr
- 'Queen Mary II'    EBee IBlr SUsu
- 'Queen of Spain'    CRos IBlr IBro LRHS MLLN NTay
  NWes SCro SMad WHil WMer
- 'Red King'    EBee IBlr NPri
§ - 'Red Knight'    CAvo EBee IBlr IBro WCot WHil
- 'Rheingold'    See *C.* x *crocosmiiflora* 'Golden
  Glory'
¶ - 'Rose Queen'    IBlr
- 'Saracen'    EGar IBlr MAvo SSpi WCot WFar
  WPer
- 'Sir Matthew Wilson'    EGar EGra GBri IBlr
- 'Solfaterre' ♀    More than 30 suppliers
- 'Solfaterre Coleton    See *C.* x *crocosmiiflora* 'Gerbe
  Fishacre'    d'Or'
- 'Star of the East'    More than 30 suppliers
§ - 'Sulphurea'    CBos CPou CRos CRow CSam
  EBee EOrc GCal GGar IBlr LAma
  LHop MBel MBri MCLN NHol
  NRoo NWes SDix SOkh SPer
  WAbe WCot WEas WHal WHil
  WPer
- 'Sultan'    CBro CGle EGar IBlr LPio NCat
  WCot WFar WMaN WMer
* - 'Tiger'    IBlr
- 'Venus'    CBre EBee EGar EGra IBlr WLin

- 'Vesuvius' W. Pfitzer    IBlr MBri WFar
¶ - 'Voyager'    IBlr
- 'Culzean Peach'    GCal
- 'Darkleaf Apricot'    See *C.* x *crocosmiiflora* 'Gerbe
  d'Or'
- 'Eldorado'    See *C.* x *crocosmiiflora* 'E.A.
  Bowles'
- 'Emberglow'    More than 30 suppliers
¶ - 'Fandango'    IBlr
¶ - 'Festival Orange'    NCat
* - 'Feuerser'    EBee NHol
- 'Fire King' misapplied    See *C.* x *crocosmiiflora*
  'Jackanapes'
- 'Firebird'    CBlo GBuc IBlr MBri MUlv NHol
  NRoo SIgm SMer WBea WCot
- 'Fireglow'    CCuc IBlr WPer
¶ *fucata*    IBlr
¶ - plicate leaf form    IBlr
- 'George Davison' hort.    See *C.* x *crocosmiiflora* 'Golden
  Glory', 'Sulphurea'
- Golden Fleece Lemoine    See *C.* x *crocosmiiflora* 'Gerbe
  d'Or'
I 'Golden Fleece'    Last listed 1997
  M.Wickenden
N 'Honey Angels'    EGar MAvo MBel MLan NCut NSti
  NTow SCro SUsu WCot WPer
¶ 'Jennine'    WHil
- 'Jenny Bloom'    CAvo CFil EBee EBrP EBre EGar
  GCal LBre NBir NRoo NTay SBre
  WWoo
§ - 'Jupiter'    CAvo CBlo CBos CM&M EFou
  EGar IBlr NHol WHal WOld
- 'Kiaora'    IBlr
- 'Lady Wilson' hort.    See *C.* x *crocosmiiflora* 'Norwich
  Canary'
- 'Lana de Savary'    CRow EGar GBri IBlr WCot
- 'Late Cornish'    See *C.* x *crocosmiiflora* 'Queen
  Alexandra' J.E. Fitt
- 'Late Lucifer'    SDix
§ *latifolia*    IBlr
- 'Castle Ward Late'    CLAP CRow EGar GCal IBlr MSte
- 'Vulcan' T.Smith    IBlr
- 'Lord Nelson'    Last listed 1997
- 'Lucifer' ♀    More than 30 suppliers
¶ - 'Mandarin'    IBlr
§ - 'Marcotijn'    EBee EGar EWoo GCal IBlr MBel
  NCut NLon WGwG
- 'Mars'    CMil EGar EHal GBuc GCal IBlr
  IBro MBel NCut NFai NHol NTay
  SUsu WCHb WCot WFar WGer
  WOld WPer WWoo
§ *masoniorum* ♀    More than 30 suppliers
- 'Auricorn'    IBlr
- 'Dixter Flame'    IBlr SDix
- 'Fern Hill'    IBlr
- 'Flamenco'    IBlr IBro LRHS MBri MTed MUlv
- 'Minotaur'    IBlr
- red    IBlr
- Rowallane orange    IBlr
- 'Rowallane Yellow'    GBri GCHN IBlr LRHS MBri NHol
  NRoo WCot
*mathewsiana*    IBlr
aff. *mathewsiana*    IBlr
- 'Merryman'    WRus
- 'Mistral'    IBlr
- 'Mount Stewart'    See *C.* x *crocosmiiflora* 'Jessie'
- 'Mount Usher'    CAvo ECha EGar IBlr LRHS
- 'Mr Bedford'    See *C.* x *crocosmiiflora* 'Croesus'
◆ Old Hat    See *C.* 'Walberton Red'
- 'Orangeade'    GBri IBlr MAvo
* - 'Orangerot'    NCut

§ *paniculata* — CAvo CB&S CPou EMar GAbr IBlr MBal MUlv NHol NOrc NTow SAPC SChu WCot WPen WPyg WShi
- 'Major' — CTri
¶ - x *masoniorum* 'Shocking' — IBlr
- red — CSpe IBlr
\* - 'Ruby Velvet' — IBlr
aff. *paniculata* — IBlr
*pearsei* — IBlr
¶ 'Plaisir' — MBri WFar
*pottsii* — CAvo CFee CRow CSpe EGar EPla GBin IBlr LEur SLod WFar WHil
- CC 1077 — Last listed 1996
- CD&R 109 — CLAP CPou
- 'Culzean Pink' — EBrP EBre GBuc IBlr LBre SBre
- deep pink — IBlr
- 'Grandiflora' — IBlr
'Red Star' — NFai
*rosea* — See *Tritonia disticha* subsp. *rubrolucens*
'Rowden Bronze' — See *C.* x *crocosmiiflora* 'Gerbe d'Or'
'Rowden Chrome' — See *C.* x *crocosmiiflora* 'George Davison' Davison
'Saturn' — See *C.* 'Jupiter'
'Severn Sunrise' — More than 30 suppliers
'Short Red' — Last listed 1998
'Sonate' — NCut NHol NWes WPer
'Spitfire' — CAvo CBot CCuc CMil CRow CSam EBee ECha EGar GBuc IBlr MArl MBri MRav NRoo SChu SUsu SWat WByw WEas WFar WLRN WOld
'Tangerine Queen' — IBlr
'Vic's Yellow' — SMrm SSpe
\* 'Voyager' — CTrC NFai WWoo
I 'Vulcan' A.Bloom — CMil EBrP EBre EWoo IBlr LBre SBre WFar
§ 'Walberton Red' — SUsu
§ Walberton Yellow = 'Walcroy' — IBlr SSpi SWas
♦ 'Walcroy' — See *C.* Walberton Yellow = 'Walcroy'
'Zeal Giant' — IBlr
'Zeal Tan' — CElw IBlr
Zeal unnamed — IBlr

## CROCUS ✿ (Iridaceae)
*abantensis* — EHyt ERos
*adanensis* — EHyt ERos
'Advance' — CAvo CBro EPar EPot LAma NRog
§ *aerius* — LAma
- 'Cambridge' — EHyt
*alatavicus* — CBro EHyt EPot LRHS
*albiflorus* — See *C. vernus* subsp. *albiflorus*
§ *ancyrensis* — CAvo CBro EHyt EPar EPot ETub LAma NRog WShi
§ *angustifolius* ♀ — CAvo CBro EBot EBrP EBre EPot ERos LAma LBre MBNS NRog SBre
- 'Minor' — EPot LAma
*antalyensis* — EPot
*asturicus* — See *C. serotinus* subsp. *salzmannii*
*asumaniae* — EHyt EPot ERos LRHS
*aureus* — See *C. flavus* subsp. *flavus*
*banaticus* ♀ — CBro EHyt EPot ERos GCrs LAma NHol WCot
- *albus* — EHyt EPot ERos
*baytopiorum* — EHyt EPot
*biflorus* — LAma NRog
- subsp. *adamii* — CLAP ERos LAma

- subsp. *alexandri* — EPot ERos LAma MRPP NRog
§ - subsp. *biflorus* — ERos LAma
- - MS 984/957 — Last listed 1998
- subsp. *crewei* — ERos
- subsp. *isauricus* — EHyt LRHS
- subsp. *melantherus* — Last listed 1998
  S&L 226
- 'Miss Vain' — CAvo LAma
♦ - var. *parkinsonii* — See *C. biflorus* subsp. *biflorus* 'Parkinsonii'
- subsp. *pulchricolor* — LAma
- subsp. *tauri* — Last listed 1997
- subsp. *weldenii* — Last listed 1997
- - 'Albus' — ERos LAma LRHS
- - 'Fairy' — CAvo CBro EPot ERos LAma
'Big Boy' (*speciosus* x *pulchellus*) — EHyt
*biliottii* — See *C. aerius*
*boryi* ♀ — CAvo EHyt EPot LRHS
- CE&H 582 — Last listed 1998
- PJC 168 — Last listed 1997
- VHH 1546 — Last listed 1998
*cambessedesii* — CLAP ERos
- PB 91 — Last listed 1998
§ *cancellatus* subsp. *cancellatus* — EHyt EPot ERos LAma
- var. *cilicicus* — See *C. cancellatus* subsp. *cancellatus*
- subsp. *mazziaricus* — CNic EHyt ERos LRHS
- subsp. *pamphylicus* — ERos LRHS
*candidus* var. *subflavus* — See *C. olivieri* subsp. *olivieri*
*carpetanus* B&S 399 — Last listed 1996
§ *cartwrightianus* ♀ — CAvo CBro EHyt LAma LRHS
N - 'Albus' ♀ — CLAP EHyt EPot ERos
- CE&H 613 — Last listed 1997
- S&L 484 — Last listed 1998
*caspius* — Last listed 1998
- PF 5036 — Last listed 1996
*chrysanthus* ♀ — Last listed 1994
- 'Ard Schenk' — LAma MBNS
- 'Blue Bird' — EPar EPot LAma
- 'Blue Giant' — LAma
- 'Blue Pearl' ♀ — CAvo CBrm CBro CMea EPar EPot ETub LAma MBri NBir NRog WShi
- 'Blue Peter' — CBro LAma
- 'Brass Band' — CAvo LAma LRHS
- 'Canary Bird' — NRog
- 'Cream Beauty' ♀ — CAvo CBro EBrP EBre EPar EPot ETub EWal LAma LBre MBri NBir NRog SBre
- 'Dorothy' — EPot LAma NRog
- 'E.A. Bowles' ♀ — LAma
- 'E.P. Bowles' — CBro EPot LAma MBri NRog
- 'Elegance' — CBro LAma
- 'Eye-catcher' — EPot LAma
- var. *fuscotinctus* — CBro LAma MBri NRog WShi
- 'Gipsy Girl' — CBro EPot LAma MBri NRog
- 'Gladstone' — Last listed 1997
- 'Goldilocks' — CBro EPot ETub LAma
- 'Herald' — LAma
- 'Ladykiller' ♀ — CBro EBrP EBre EPar EPot LAma LBre MBri NRog SBre
- 'Moonlight' — CAvo CBro ETub LAma NRog
- 'Prins Claus' — CAvo EPot LAma WShi
- 'Prinses Beatrix' — EPot LAma NRog
- 'Romance' — EPot LAma
- 'Saturnus' — EPot LAma NRog
- 'Sky Blue' — LAma
- 'Skyline' — CAvo CBro EPot GCrs
- 'Snow Bunting' ♀ — CAvo CBro EPar EWal LAma NBir NRog
- 'Spring Pearl' — CBro LAma

| | |
|---|---|
| - 'Sunkist' | Last listed 1997 |
| - 'Uschak Orange' | Last listed 1997 |
| - 'Warley' | NRog |
| - 'White Beauty' | LAma |
| - 'White Triumphator' | EPot ETub LAma NBir NRog |
| - 'Zenith' | LAma |
| - 'Zwanenburg Bronze' ♀ | CAvo EBrP EBre EPar EPot EWal LAma LBre NRog SBre |
| 'Cloth of Gold' | See *C. angustifolius* |
| *clusii* | See *C. serotinus* subsp. *clusii* |
| *corsicus* ♀ | EHyt EPot ERos LAma |
| *cvijicii* | EPot |
| *cyprius* | Last listed 1997 |
| *dalmaticus* | EPot LAma |
| *danfordiae* | ERos LRHS |
| 'Dutch Yellow' | See *C.* x *luteus* 'Golden Yellow' |
| *etruscus* ♀ | CAvo ERos |
| - B&S 334 | Last listed 1998 |
| * - 'Rosalind' | EPot |
| - 'Zwanenburg' | EPot LAma WCot |
| *flavus* | See *C. flavus* subsp. *flavus* |
| § - subsp. *flavus* ♀ | EPot LAma |
| - M&T 4578 | Last listed 1998 |
| *fleischeri* | CMea EPot ERos LAma NMen |
| *gargaricus* | EPot ERos LRHS |
| - subsp. *herbertii* | Last listed 1997 |
| - *minor* JRM 3299/75 | Last listed 1996 |
| 'Golden Mammoth' | See *C.* x *luteus* 'Golden Yellow' |
| *goulimyi* ♀ | CAvo CBro EHyt EPar EPot ERos LAma MRPP WCot |
| - 'Albus' | See *C. goulimyi* 'Mani White' |
| - deep colour form | EHyt |
| - var. *leucanthus* | EHyt |
| § - 'Mani White' ♀ | EHyt |
| - S&L 197 | Last listed 1998 |
| 'Haarlem Gem' | LAma WCot |
| § *hadriaticus* ♀ | CAvo CLAP EHyt EPot ERos LAma LRHS |
| - B&M 8039 | Last listed 1997 |
| - BM 8124 | Last listed 1998 |
| - var. *chrysobelonicus* | See *C. hadriaticus* |
| - f. *hadriaticus* | Last listed 1996 |
| - f. *lilacinus* | EPot |
| *hermoneus* LB 1 | Last listed 1998 |
| *hyemalis* S&L 50 | Last listed 1998 |
| *imperati* ♀ | CNic ERos |
| - subsp. *imperati* | EHyt |
| - - 'De Jager' | CAvo EPot ETub LAma WCot |
| - - MS 965 | Last listed 1998 |
| - subsp. *suaveolens* | ERos LRHS |
| - - MS 962 | Last listed 1998 |
| ¶ x *jessoppiae* | EHyt ERos |
| *karduchorum* | CBro LAma NRog |
| *korolkowii* | EHyt EPar EPot ERos ETub LAma |
| - 'Agalik' | Last listed 1997 |
| - 'Dytiscus' | Last listed 1997 |
| - 'Golden Nugget' | EPot |
| - 'Kiss of Spring' | EPot |
| - 'Mountain Glory' | Last listed 1997 |
| - 'Varzob' | Last listed 1997 |
| - 'Yellow Princess' | EPot |
| - 'Yellow Tiger' | Last listed 1997 |
| *kosaninii* | ERos MPhe |
| *kotschyanus* ♀ | EHyt EPar |
| - 'Albus' | SRms |
| - subsp. *cappadocicus* ♀ | EHyt LRHS |
| - CM&W 2720 | Last listed 1998 |
| § - subsp. *kotschyanus* | CBro CLAP EPot LAma NRog WCot |
| - var. *leucopharynx* | ECha |
| *laevigatus* ♀ | CLAP |
| - CE&H 612 | Last listed 1998 |
| - 'Fontenayi' | CAvo CBro EPot ETub LAma LEdu |
| - form | LAma |
| - from Crete | EHyt LRHS |
| 'Large Yellow' | See *C.* x *luteus* 'Golden Yellow' |
| *lazicus* | See *C. scharojanii* |
| ¶ *ligusticus* | EPar |
| *longiflorus* ♀ | CAvo CBro EPot ERos |
| - MS 968/974/967 | EHyt |
| § x *luteus* 'Golden Yellow' ♀ | EPot ETub LAma MBNS |
| § - 'Stellaris' | EBot EPot ERos |
| *malyi* ♀ | CAvo CLAP EPot GCrs LRHS |
| - CE&H 519 | Last listed 1997 |
| 'Mammoth Yellow' | See *C.* x *luteus* 'Golden Yellow' |
| *medius* ♀ | CBro ECha EHyt EPot ERos LAma NMGW NRog WCot |
| *michelsonii* | Last listed 1996 |
| *minimus* | CBro CMea EHyt EPot ERos LAma |
| *nevadensis* AB&S 4415 | Last listed 1996 |
| - SB&L 62 | Last listed 1996 |
| *niveus* | CAvo CBro CLAP EHyt EPot ERos ETub LAma WCot |
| - blue | Last listed 1997 |
| - PJC 164 | Last listed 1997 |
| - S&L 194 | Last listed 1998 |
| *nudiflorus* | CAvo CBro CLAP EHyt EPot ERos LAma NHol |
| - MS 872 | Last listed 1998 |
| *ochroleucus* ♀ | CBro EBot EBrP EBre EHyt EPot ERos LAma LBre NRog SBre |
| *olivieri* | ERos LAma |
| - subsp. *balansae* | Last listed 1997 |
| - - 'Zwanenburg' | EPot ETub |
| - subsp. *istanbulensis* | EPot |
| § - subsp. *olivieri* | LAma |
| *oreocreticus* | EHyt |
| - PB 137 | Last listed 1998 |
| *pallasii* | LAma |
| ¶ - subsp. *pallasii* | ERos |
| *pelistericus* | EHyt EPot |
| *pestalozzae* | EPot ERos |
| - var. *caeruleus* | EHyt EPot ERos |
| *pulchellus* ♀ | EPot ERos ETub GCrs LAma WCot |
| ¶ - *albus* | EHyt |
| - CE&H 558 | Last listed 1997 |
| - M&T 4584 | Last listed 1998 |
| 'Purpureus' | See *C. vernus* 'Purpureus Grandiflorus' |
| *reticulatus* | CLAP EHyt MPhe |
| - subsp. *reticulatus* | EPot |
| *robertianus* ♀ | EHyt LRHS |
| *rujanensis* | Last listed 1997 |
| *sativus* | CArn CAvo CBod CBro ELan EOHP EPar EPot GPoy LAma LHol MBri MSal NRog |
| - var. *cartwrightianus* | See *C. cartwrightianus* |
| - var. *cashmirianus* | ETub |
| *scardicus* | EHyt EPot |
| - JCA Sar Planina 1985 | Last listed 1996 |
| *scepusiensis* | See *C. vernus* subsp. *vernus* var. *scepusiensis* |
| § *scharojanii* | EHyt EPot |
| - var. *flavus* | Last listed 1997 |
| § *serotinus* subsp. *clusii* ♀ | CBro EHyt EPot LAma |
| § - subsp. *salzmannii* | CBro EHyt EPar ERos LAma |
| - - AB&S 4326 | Last listed 1998 |
| - - 'Albus' | Last listed 1997 |
| - - MS 343 | Last listed 1998 |
| - - SF 218 | Last listed 1998 |
| *sibiricus* | See *C. sieberi* |
| § *sieberi* ♀ | EHyt EPot ERos LAma |
| - 'Albus' | CAvo CBro EPot LAma MBNS |
| - subsp. *atticus* | EPot LAma |

- 'Bowles' White'  See *C. sieberi* 'Albus'
- 'Firefly'  CBro EPot LAma NRog
- 'Hubert Edelsten' ♀  EHyt EPot ERos LAma
- f. *pallidus*  Last listed 1998
- subsp. *sublimis*  CBro EPot ERos ETub GCrs LAma
  'Tricolor' ♀  WCot
- 'Violet Queen'  CBro LAma MBri NRog
¶ sp. WM 9803 from Slovenia  MPhe
¶ sp. WM 9809 from Bosnia  MPhe
*speciosus* ♀  CAvo CBro EBrP EBre EPar ETub
  GCHN LAma LBre NMGW NRog
  SBre WHoo WShi
- 'Aitchisonii'  CBro LAma
- 'Albus' ♀  CBro ECha EPar EPot
- 'Artabir'  CAvo CBro EPot MRPP
- 'Cassiope'  EPot LAma
- 'Conqueror'  CBro ETub LAma
- subsp. *ilgazensis*  EPot
- 'Oxonian'  EMon EPar EPot LAma
x *stellaris*  See *C.* x *luteus* 'Stellaris'
*susianus*  See *C. angustifolius*
*suterianus*  See *C. olivieri* subsp. *olivieri*
*thomasii* B&S 364  Last listed 1998
- MS 978/982  Last listed 1998
*tommasinianus* ♀  CAvo CBro EPar EPot ETub LAma
  MBri MRav NMGW WShi
- f. *albus*  CBro EHyt EPot LAma LRHS
- 'Barr's Purple'  LAma
- 'Bobbo'  EHyt
- 'Eric Smith'  CAvo CLAP
- 'Lilac Beauty'  EPot LAma
- PF 6584  Last listed 1998
- var. *pictus*  EHyt LAma LRHS
- purple tips  Last listed 1997
- var. *roseus*  CBro CLAP EHyt EPot LAma
  MRPP
- 'Ruby Giant'  CAvo CBro CNic EPar EPot ETub
  LAma NRog WShi
- 'Whitewell Purple'  CAvo CBro EPot LAma MBri
  NMGW NRog
*tournefortii* ♀  CAvo CBro CLAP EHyt EPot ERos
  LAma
*vallicola*  EHyt
*veluchensis*  EPot
- JCA 354.002  CLAP
*veneris* PB 198  Last listed 1998
§ *vernus* subsp. *albiflorus*  EPot ERos LAma
- 'Enchantress'  EPot ETub LAma
- 'Flower Record'  EPot NBir
- 'Graecus'  EHyt EPot ERos
- 'Grand Maître'  LAma NRog
- 'Jeanne d'Arc'  CBrm CBro EPot ETub LAma NBir
  NRog
- 'King of the Blues'  LAma NRog
- 'Paulus Potter'  NRog
- 'Peter Pan'  NRog
- 'Pickwick'  EPot ETub LAma NBir NRog
§ - 'Purpureus Grandiflorus'  CBro EPot ETub LAma NRog
- 'Queen of the Blues'  CBro EPot NRog
- 'Remembrance'  EPot ETub GCrs LAma NBir NRog
- 'Sky Blue'  NRog
- 'Snowstorm'  LAma
- 'Striped Beauty'  LAma NRog
- 'Vanguard'  CBro EPot ETub LAma NRog
- subsp. *vernus*
  'Grandiflorus'  See *C. vernus* 'Purpureus
    Grandiflorus'
§ - - Heuffelianus Group  EHyt EPot
* - - *napolitanus*  ERos
§ - - var. *scepusiensis*  EHyt EPot ERos
- 'Victor Hugo'  NRog
- WM 9615 from E Slovenia  Last listed 1998

*versicolor*  EHyt
- 'Picturatus'  EBrP EBre EPot ERos ETub LAma
  LBre SBre
'Yellow Mammoth'  See *C.* x *luteus* 'Golden Yellow'
'Zephyr' ♀  CBro EPot ERos ETub ITim LAma
*zonatus*  See *C. kotschyanus* subsp.
  *kotschyanus*

## CROSSANDRA (Acanthaceae)
*infundibuliformis*  MBri

## CROTALARIA (Papilionaceae)
*capensis*  Last listed 1997
*cunninghamii*  Last listed 1998

## CROWEA (Rutaceae)
¶ *exalata* x *saligna*  CPLG

## CRUCIANELLA (Rubiaceae)
*stylosa*  See *Phuopsis stylosa*

## CRUCIATA (Rubiaceae)
§ *laevipes*  CKin EWFC NMir WGwy

## CRYPTANTHUS (Bromeliaceae)
*bivittatus* ♀  CHal
- 'Pink Starlight' (v) ♀  MBri
- 'Roseus Pictus'  CHal
*bromelioides*  MBri
- var. *tricolor* (v) ♀  Last listed 1990
*fosterianus* ♀  Last listed 1992
'It' (v) ♀  Last listed 1992
* 'Red Starlight' (v)  MBri
x *roseus* 'Le Rey'  MBri
- 'Marian Oppenheimer'  MBri
*zonatus* ♀  Last listed 1992

## CRYPTOCARYA (Lauraceae)
*alba*  CGre

## CRYPTOGRAMMA (Adiantaceae)
*crispa*  CCuc SRms WShe

## CRYPTOMERIA (Taxodiaceae)
*fortunei*  See *C. japonica* var. *sinensis*
*japonica* ♀  CDul GAri IOrc LCon MLan STre
  WFro WNor
¶ - Araucarioides Group  EHul
- 'Aritaki'  Last listed 1997
- 'Bandai-sugi' ♀  CBlo CDoC CKen CMac EHul
  EOrn ESis LCon LLin MBar MGos
  MOne NHed SLim SSmi STre WStI
- 'Barabits Gold'  MGos
- 'Compressa'  CBlo CDoC CKen CNic CSli EHul
  ESis LBee LCon LLin MBar MBri
  MGos MOne MPla SLim SSmi
  WGwG WLRN
§ - 'Cristata'  CDoC CMac ELan EOrn LCon
  LLin MBal MBar NPal SLon WWeb
* - 'Cristata Compacta'  EOrn
- Elegans Group  CB&S CBrm CDoC CHig CMac
  CTri EHul ELan ENot EOrn GRei
  IOrc LCon LLin LNet LPan MBal
  MBar MGos MUlv MWat SBod
  SLim SPer WDin WFar WPyg
  WWin
- 'Elegans Aurea'  CB&S CBlo CDoC CSli CTri EHul
  LCon LLin MBal MBar MBri MPla
  SBod SRms STre WDin WPyg
  WTro
- 'Elegans Compacta' ♀  CBlo CDoC CSli EHul EOrn IMGH
  LBee LCon MBNS MBar MBri
  MPla SLim WWeb

| | |
|---|---|
| - 'Elegans Nana' | CBlo LBee NFla SLim SRms |
| - 'Elegans Viridis' | CBlo SLim |
| - 'Globosa' | CDoC EOrn SRms |
| - 'Globosa Nana' ♀ | EHul ERom LBee LCon LLin LPan MBar NHed SLim WGor |
| ¶ - 'Golden Promise' | EOrn SLim |
| - 'Jindai-sugi' | CMac MBal MBar MPla NHed |
| - 'Kilmacurragh' | CKen EHul MBar SLim |
| ¶ - 'Knaptonensis' (v) | LLin |
| - 'Kohui Yatsubusa' | CKen |
| * - 'Konijn Yatsubusa' | CKen |
| - 'Koshiji-yatsubusa' | EOrn LCon MBar MBri |
| - 'Koshyi' | CKen |
| - 'Little Diamond' | CKen |
| - 'Littleworth Dwarf' | See C. japonica 'Littleworth Gnom' |
| § - 'Littleworth Gnom' | LCon |
| - 'Lobbii' | Last listed 1996 |
| - 'Lobbii Nana' hort. | See C. japonica 'Nana' |
| § - 'Mankichi-sugi' | CBlo |
| - 'Midare-sugi' | See C. japonica 'Viridis' |
| - 'Monstrosa' | MBar |
| - 'Monstrosa Nana' | See C. japonica 'Mankichi-sugi' |
| § - 'Nana' | CDoC CMac CTri EBrP EBre EGra EHul EOrn EPfP LBre LLin MBal MPla SBod SBre WLRN |
| - 'Pygmaea' | CBlo LCon MBar MGos SRms |
| - 'Rasen-sugi' | COtt GAri LCon SLim SMad |
| - 'Sekkan-sugi' | CB&S CBlo CSli EBrP EBre EHul EOrn EPla GAri IGri LBee LBre LCon LLin MAsh MBar MBri MGos MPla MUlv SAga SBre SLim SMad WPyg |
| - 'Sekka-sugi' | See C. japonica 'Cristata' |
| § - var. sinensis | CMCN LCon WPGP |
| * - - 'Vilmoriniana Compacta' | EOrn |
| § - 'Spiralis' | CDoC CGre CKen CMac EHul EOrn EPfP IOrc LBee LCon LLin MBal MBar MBri SLim SPer SSmi WFar WWeb |
| § - 'Spiraliter Falcata' | CBlo CDoC MBar |
| § - 'Tansu' | CBlo EHul EOrn LCon LLin MAsh MBar NHol SLim WFar |
| - 'Tenzan-sugi' | CKen |
| - 'Tilford Cream' | MAsh |
| - 'Tilford Gold' | EGra EHul EOrn GPin LLin MBar MGos NHed NHol WAbe WBcn |
| - 'Vilmorin Gold' | CKen EOrn MBri |
| - 'Vilmorin Variegated' | Last listed 1997 |
| - 'Vilmoriniana' ♀ | More than 30 suppliers |
| - 'Viminalis' | NHol |
| - 'Winter Bronze' | CKen |
| - 'Wogon' | See C. japonica 'Aurea' |
| - 'Yatsubusa' | See C. japonica 'Tansu' |
| ♦ - 'Yore-sugi' | See C. japonica 'Spiralis', 'Spiraliter Falcata' |
| - 'Yoshino' | CKen |
| sinensis | See C. japonica var. sinensis |

## CRYPTOTAENIA (Apiaceae)

| | |
|---|---|
| canadensis | MRav |
| japonica | CPou EGar LFis WHer WJek |
| - f. atropurpurea | CElw CGle CLTr CMea CPla CVer ECha ECoo EHoe EMan EMar EMon GCal LSpr MNrw NPer NRoo NWes SUsu WCHb WCot WEas |

## CTENANTHE (Marantaceae)

| | |
|---|---|
| § amabilis ♀ | CHal MBri |
| * 'Greystar' | MBri |
| lubbersiana ♀ | CHal MBri SRms |

| | |
|---|---|
| § oppenheimiana | MBri |
| - 'Tricolor' ♀ | Last listed 1990 |
| setosa | MBri |
| 'Stripe Star' | MBri |

## CTENIUM (Poaceae)

| | |
|---|---|
| concinnum | EBee |

## CUCUBALUS (Caryophyllaceae)

| | |
|---|---|
| baccifer | MNrw |

## CUCUMIS (Cucurbitaceae)

| | |
|---|---|
| metulifer (F) | Last listed 1998 |

## CUCURBITA (Cucurbitaceae)

| | |
|---|---|
| 'Cerrano' | Last listed 1998 |
| ficifolia | Last listed 1998 |

## CUDRANIA (Moraceae)

| | |
|---|---|
| tricuspidata | CAgr LEdu |

## CUMINUM (Apiaceae)

| | |
|---|---|
| cyminum | CArn SIde WGwG |

## CUNILA (Lamiaceae)

| | |
|---|---|
| ¶ origanoides | EOHP |

## CUNNINGHAMIA (Taxodiaceae)

| | |
|---|---|
| ¶ konishii | CDoC |
| § lanceolata | CB&S CDoC CGre CMCN LCon LLin MDun MPla MUlv SLim SMad SSta STre WNor |
| § - 'Bánó' | MPla SLim |
| - 'Compacta' | See C. lanceolata 'Bánó' |
| * - 'Coolwijn's Compact' | CKen |
| ¶ - 'Glauca' | SLim |
| - 'Little Leo' | CKen |
| - Og 911101 | Last listed 1997 |
| sinensis | See C. lanceolata |
| unicaniculata | See C. lanceolata |

## CUNONIA (Cunoniaceae)

| | |
|---|---|
| capensis | Last listed 1997 |

## CUPHEA (Lythraceae)

| | |
|---|---|
| caeciliae | CHal CLTr LHop MBEx |
| cyanaea | CMHG CSev ENot LHil LHop MBEx SDix SIgm SOWG SVen |
| ¶ hirtella | CMHG EBee LHop MBEx SDys SOWG |
| hyssopifolia ♀ | CFee CHal CPle CTre EMil GQui MBEx MBri SOWG SRms STre |
| - 'Alba' | CLTr LIck MBEx MLan NPri SOWG STre |
| - 'Riverdene Gold' | CHal CLTr MBEx |
| - 'Rob's Mauve' | CB&S |
| - 'Rosea' | LIck NPri |
| § ignea ♀ | CHal CLTr ELan MBEx MBri NPri SOWG SRms SYvo |
| - 'Variegata' | CHal EBee LHil MBEx SLod SOWG |
| ¶ lanceolata | CHad |
| llavea | See C. x purpurea |
| macrophylla | MBEx |
| miniata hort. | See C. x purpurea |
| platycentra | See C. ignea |
| § x purpurea | Last listed 1996 |
| violacea | Last listed 1998 |
| viscosissima | Last listed 1996 |

## x CUPRESSOCYPARIS ✿ (Cupressaceae)

| | |
|---|---|
| § *leylandii* | CB&S CChe CDoC CMac EBrP EBre EGra EHul ENot IOrc LBre LBuc LCon LHyr LPan MBal MBar MBri MGos SBod SBre SLim SPer WHar WMou WStI |
| § - 'Castlewellan' | CB&S CChe CDoC CDul CMac EBrP EBre EGra EHul ENot EPot ERom IOrc LBre LBuc LCon LHyr LPan MBal MBar MBri MGos MWat SBod SBre SLim SPer WFar WHar WMou |
| - 'Galway Gold' | See *x C. leylandii* 'Castlewellan' |
| - 'Golconda' | Last listed 1996 |
| - 'Gold Rider' ♀ | CDoC EHul IOrc LBee LPan MAsh MBar MBri MGos NMoo SLim SPer WHar WLRN |
| - 'Haggerston Grey' ♀ | Last listed 1992 |
| § - 'Harlequin' (v) | CMHG LCon MBar SLim WHar WWeb |
| * - 'Herculea' | LPan MGos WWeb |
| - 'Hyde Hall' | CTri EOrn EPla ESis LBee LCon SBod WAbe WLRN |
| * - 'Medownia' | Last listed 1998 |
| - 'Michellii' | Last listed 1997 |
| - 'Naylor's Blue' | CMac SEND |
| - 'New Ornament' | Last listed 1997 |
| - 'Olive's Green' | COtt EHul IOrc LCon LPan SCoo WHar |
| - 'Robinson's Gold' ♀ | CDul CMac EHul GAri GQui LBee LCon MBal MBar MGos NWea SBod SLim WFar WHar WStI |
| - 'Silver Dust' (v) | MBri NEgg SRms WFar |
| - 'Variegata' | See *x C. leylandii* 'Harlequin' |
| *notabilis* ♀ | WCwm |
| *ovensii* | EHul WCwm |

## CUPRESSUS (Cupressaceae)

| | |
|---|---|
| N *arizonica* var. *arizonica* | MBal |
| § - - 'Arctic' | CBlo LRHS MAsh MBri |
| ♦ - var. *bonita* | See *C. arizonica* var. *glabra* |
| - 'Conica Glauca' | ENot MBar |
| - var. *glabra* 'Aurea' | CBlo ECho EHul LCon MAsh MBar SLim SPer WGer |
| - - 'Blue Ice' | CB&S CBlo CDoC CMHG EHul EOrn LCon LLin MAsh MBar MBri SLim WGer |
| - - 'Compacta' | CKen |
| - - 'Conica' | CKen SBod WWat |
| I - - 'Fastigiata' | CB&S EHul LCon LPan MBar |
| * - - 'Lutea' | EOrn |
| - 'Pyramidalis' ♀ | CBlo CMac MAsh WCwm |
| I - 'Sulfurea' | CKen |
| *bakeri* | CMHG |
| *cashmeriana* ♀ | CB&S ERea LCon SIgm SLim WNor |
| *chengiana* | Last listed 1997 |
| *duclouxiana* | CMHG |
| *dupreziana* | WCwm |
| § *funebris* | CMCN |
| *glabra* | See *C. arizonica* var. *glabra* |
| - 'Arctic' | See *C. arizonica* var. *arizonica* 'Arctic' |
| *goveniana* | GAri MBar |
| ¶ - var. *abramsiana* | WCwm |
| *guadalupensis* | CMHG |
| *lusitanica* | WCwm |
| ¶ - var. *benthamii* 'Knightiana' | WCwm |
| ¶ - 'Brice's Weeping' | CKen |
| - 'Glauca Pendula' | CBlo CKen EPfP LCon MAsh MBri WCwm |

| | |
|---|---|
| - 'Pygmy' | CKen |
| *macrocarpa* | CDoC EHul GChr SEND |
| - 'Barnham Gold' | SBod SRms |
| - 'Compacta' | CKen |
| - 'Donard Gold' ♀ | CMac EOrn LCon MBal MBar |
| - 'Gold Spire' | Last listed 1996 |
| - 'Gold Spread' ♀ | CDoC ECho EHul EOrn LBee LCon LLin SLim WBcn WGer |
| - 'Goldcrest' ♀ | CB&S CDoC CMac EHul ENot EOrn IOrc LBee LCon LLin LPan MBal MBar MBri MGos MPla SBod SLim SPer WAbe WDin WFar WPyg |
| - 'Golden Cone' | CKen CMac MBal |
| - 'Golden Pillar' | CBlo CDoC CMac EHul EOrn LBee LCon LLin MAsh MBar MBri MWat SLim WDin WGer WLRN WPyg WWeb |
| - 'Greenstead Magnificent' | MAsh SLim |
| - 'Horizontalis Aurea' | CTri EHul MBar WBcn |
| - 'Lohbrunner' | CKen |
| - 'Lutea' | CB&S CDoC CMac ECho |
| - 'Pygmaea' | CKen |
| - 'Sulphur Cushion' | CKen |
| - 'Sulphurea' | See *C. macrocarpa* 'Crippsii' |
| - 'Wilma' | EHul EOrn LBee LCon MGos SCoo WBcn WWeb |
| - 'Woking' | CKen |
| *sempervirens* | CB&S CMCN EHul ERom GChr LEdu LLin |
| ¶ - 'Garda' | CDoC |
| ¶ - 'Green Pencil' | CKen WWat |
| - 'Pyramidalis' | See *C. sempervirens* Stricta Group |
| - var. *sempervirens* | See *C. sempervirens* Stricta Group |
| § - Stricta Group ♀ | CArn CMCN CSWP EHul EPfP GAri LCon LPan SAPC SArc |
| - 'Swane's Gold' ♀ | CDoC CKen CMHG EHul EOrn LBee LCon LLin MAsh MPla SLim |
| - 'Totem Pole' | CBlo CDoC CKen EHul EOrn EPfP SEND SLim WBcn WGor |

## CURCUMA (Zingiberaceae)

| | |
|---|---|
| ¶ *amada* | GPoy |
| ¶ *aromatica* | GPoy |
| ¶ *elata* | EOas |
| ¶ *longa* | GPoy |
| ¶ *petiolata* | EOas |
| *zedoaria* | GPoy LAma |

## CURTONUS See CROCOSMIA

## CUSSONIA (Araliaceae)

| | |
|---|---|
| *paniculata* | SIgm WMul |
| ¶ *spicata* | WMul |

## CYANANTHUS (Campanulaceae)

| | |
|---|---|
| § *chungdienensis* | Last listed 1998 |
| ¶ *delavayi* | WCru |
| - ACE 2449 | EHyt |
| *incanus* | Last listed 1997 |
| - ACE 1700 | Last listed 1996 |
| *inflatus* | Last listed 1998 |
| *integer* hort. | See *C. microphyllus* |
| - Wallich | Last listed 1997 |
| - 'Sherriff's Variety' | GDra NHar WAbe WLin |
| *lobatus* ♀ | CPla EHyt GBuc IMGH LBee SBla WCot |
| - 'Albus' | EHyt EPot EWes NHar SBla WAbe |
| - 'Dark Beauty' | NHar WCot |
| - dark form | EWes GDra WAbe |

| | |
|---|---|
| - giant form | EPot GCrs GDra GTou NHar SBla WAbe |
| - var. *insignis* | Last listed 1997 |
| - x *microphyllus* | EPot NWCA WAbe |
| *longiflorus* ACE 1963 | Last listed 1997 |
| *macrocalyx* | WAbe |
| § *microphyllus* ♀ | CPla EPot GDra GMaP WAbe |
| *sherriffii* | EHyt |
| sp.ACE 1813 | Last listed 1996 |
| *spathulifolius* | Last listed 1997 |
| - CLD 1492 | Last listed 1997 |
| I *zhongdienensis* | See *C. chungdienensis* |

## CYANELLA (Tecophilaeaceae)

| | |
|---|---|
| *capensis* | See *C. hyacinthoides* |
| *orchidiformis* | LBow |

## CYANOTIS (Commelinaceae)

| | |
|---|---|
| *somaliensis* ♀ | CHal |

## CYATHEA (Cyatheaceae)

| | |
|---|---|
| *albifrons* | Last listed 1997 |
| *australis* | EOas GQui LPal WMul WRic |
| *baileyana* | Last listed 1996 |
| *brownii* | EOas WRic |
| *celebica* | Last listed 1997 |
| *cooperi* | CB&S EOas WRic |
| * - 'Brentwood' | WRic |
| ¶ *cunninghamii* | EOas WRic |
| *dealbata* | CAbb CB&S CTrC GQui WRic |
| *dregei* | EOas WRic |
| *incisoserrata* | WRic |
| *intermedia* | Last listed 1997 |
| *lepifera* | WRic |
| *lunulata* | WRic |
| * 'Marleyi' | WRic |
| *medullaris* | CAbb CB&S CTrC EOas LBlo WMul WRic |
| *nova-caledoniae* | Last listed 1996 |
| *rebeccae* | Last listed 1997 |
| *robertsiana* | Last listed 1997 |
| *robusta* | Last listed 1996 |
| *smithii* | CAbb EOas WMul WRic |
| *tomentosissima* | EOas WRic |
| *woollsiana* | Last listed 1997 |

## CYATHODES (Epacridaceae)

| | |
|---|---|
| § *colensoi* | EPot MBal MBar MBri MPla NHar NHol SLon SSpi WAbe WBod WPat WWat |
| *empetrifolia* | EPot |
| *fasciculata* | See *Leucopogon fasciculatus* |
| *fraseri* | See *Leucopogon fraseri* |
| *juniperina* | ECou |
| § *parviflora* | Last listed 1998 |
| ¶ *parvifolia* | ECou |

## CYBISTETES (Amaryllidaceae)

| | |
|---|---|
| *longifolia* | Last listed 1998 |

## CYCAS (Cycadaceae)

| | |
|---|---|
| *cairnsiana* | Last listed 1997 |
| *circinalis* | LPal |
| *kennedyana* | See *C. papuana* |
| *media* | CRoM LPal |
| ¶ *panzihihuaensis* | LPal |
| § *papuana* | Last listed 1997 |
| *revoluta* ♀ | CAbb CB&S CBrP CTrC LCns LPal LPan MBri NPal SAPC SArc SEND SPar WMul WNor |
| ¶ - x *taitungensis* | CBrP |
| § *rumphii* | CBrP LPal |

| | |
|---|---|
| *siamensis* | LPal |
| *simplicipinna* | LPal |
| *taitungensis* | CBrP LPal |
| *thouarsii* | See *C. rumphii* |

## CYCLAMEN ✿ (Primulaceae)

| | |
|---|---|
| *africanum* | CBro CLCN EBee EBrP EBre EJWh EPot ITim LAma LBre MAsh SBre STil WAbe WCom WIvy |
| *balearicum* | CAvo CBro CLCN EBrP EBre EJWh EPot LAma LBre LCTD MAsh MBal SBre STil WCot |
| *cilicium* ♀ | CAvo CBro CLCN EBee EBrP EBre EHyt EJWh EPot ERos LAma LBow LBre MBal MBri MS&S MTho NMen SBla SBre SDeJ SSpi STil WCot WIvy WNor WPat WPyg WWat |
| - f. *album* | CAvo CBro CLCN EBrP EBre EHyt EJWh GCrs LAma LBre LCTD MAsh SBre STil |
| § *coum* ♀ | More than 30 suppliers |
| - var. *abchasicum* | See *C. coum* subsp. *caucasicum* |
| * - Blanchard's form pink-flowered | Last listed 1998 |
| - 'Broadleigh Silver' | LCTD |
| - BS 8927 | Last listed 1997 |
| - BSBE | STil |
| § - subsp. *caucasicum* | CBel EBee EPot ERos LAma SSpi STil |
| - subsp. *coum* | CBro MBal |
| - - f. *albissimum* | LCTD |
| - - - 'Golan Heights' | STil |
| - - 'Atkinsii' | CBro MBro |
| - - f. *coum* 'Crimson King' | SDeJ |
| - - - 'Dusky Maid' | LCTD |
| - - - 'Linnett Jewel' | LCTD |
| - - - 'Linnett Rose' | LCTD |
| - - - Nymans Group | EPot LCTD MAsh SBla |
| - - - Pewter Group ♀ | CMil ERos MAsh MTho NPar NRoo SSpi WIvy WPyg |
| - - - - bicoloured | EJWh |
| - - - - 'Blush' | STil |
| - - - 'Maurice Dryden' | CAvo CBro CGle GCrs LAma LCTD MAsh SSpi STil WAbe WIvy |
| - - - - red | CLCN LAma LCTD SWas WPat |
| - - - 'Tilebarn Elizabeth' | EHyt MAsh STil |
| - - - - white | Last listed 1997 |
| - - - plain-leaved red | STil |
| - - - 'Roseum' | CAvo CBel LAma LBow SDeJ STil SUsu WAbe |
| - - - Silver Group | CBro EBee LRHS NSla SSpi WAbe |
| - - - - bicolor | LCTD |
| - - - 'Heavy Metal' | LCTD |
| - - - - red | CAvo EBrP EBre EPot LBre MTho NHar SBre STil WHoo |
| - - - 'Silver Star' | LCTD |
| - - - 'Sterling Silver' | LCTD |
| - - - 'Turkish Princess' | Last listed 1998 |
| - - - 'Urfa' | EPot |
| - - magenta | Last listed 1996 |
| - - f. *pallidum* 'Album' | CAvo CBot EHyt EPot ERos ITim LAma MAsh NHol NRoo SDeJ SIng STil WAbe WHoo WNor WPat |
| - - - 'Marbled Moon' | LCTD STil |
| - dark pink | CAvo |
| - subsp. *elegans* | STil |
| - forms | LAma LCTD MBro MS&S WWat |
| - M&T 4051 | Last listed 1998 |
| - marbled leaf | WHoo |
| - 'Meaden's Crimson' | EPot LCTD |
| * - *merymana* | Last listed 1998 |

| | |
|---|---|
| - plain-leaved | EPot LCTD WAbe |
| - red | EBee |
| - scented | Last listed 1998 |
| - TK form | ERos |
| *creticum* | CBro CLCN EJWh LAma MAsh STil |
| - x *repandum* | See *C.* x *meiklei* |
| *cyprium* | CAvo CBro CLCN EBrP EBre EHyt EJWh EPot LAma LBre MAsh NSla SBla SBre STil WCot WIvy WPGP |
| - 'E.S.' | LCTD MAsh STil |
| *europaeum* | See *C. purpurascens* |
| ◆ *fatrense* | See *C. purpurascens* subsp. *purpurascens* from Fatra, Slovakia |
| *graecum* | CBro CFil CLCN EJWh EPot LAma MAsh MSpi STil WCot WIvy |
| - f. *album* | CAvo CBro EJWh LAma MAsh STil |
| - subsp. *anatolicum* | STil |
| § *hederifolium* ♀ | More than 30 suppliers |
| - x *africanum* | EHyt |
| - arrow-head form | Last listed 1997 |
| - var. *confusum* | MAsh STil |
| - forms | CSam LAma LCTD MS&S |
| - var. *hederifolium* | CAvo CBro CHea CLCN CSWP |
| f. *albiflorum* | EBee EPot ERos ETub GPoy LAma LBow LCTD MBar MBri MBro NHar NHol NRog NTow SBla SIng SSpi STil SUsu WAbe WCla WHoo WPat WWat |
| - - - Bowles' Apollo Group | CLCN CMil LCTD NPar WCom WCot |
| § - - - - 'Artemis' | STil WCot |
| ◆ - - - - 'White Bowles' Apollo' | See *C. hederifolium* var. *hederifolium* f. *albiflorum* (Bowles' Apollo Group) 'Artemis' |
| ¶ - - - 'Cotswold White' | WCot |
| ◆ - - - 'Nettleton Silver' | See *C. hederifolium* var. *hederifolium* f. *albiflorum* 'White Cloud' |
| - - - 'Perlenteppich' | GMaP LCTD NRoo |
| § - - - 'White Cloud' | EBee EPot MAsh STil WIvy |
| - f. *hederifolium* | CLAP ITim LCTD MAsh SBla SSpi |
| Bowles' Apollo Group | STil |
| - - - 'Coquette' | LCTD |
| - - - 'Fairy Rings' | LCTD MAsh |
| - - - 'Green Elf' | Last listed 1997 |
| - - - red | WPyg |
| - - - 'Rosenteppich' | GMaP LCTD |
| - - - 'Ruby Glow' | LCTD MAsh WCot |
| - - - 'Silver Cloud' | CBel CBro CLCN LCTD MAsh SSpi STil WAbe WCot WIvy |
| - - - 'Silver Shield' | LCTD |
| ¶ - - - 'Stargazer' | LCTD |
| ¶ - 'San Marino Silver' | LCTD |
| - scented | CLCN STil |
| - silver leaved | CAvo CMil EPot LCTD MAsh STil SUsu |
| x *hildebrandii* | WIvy |
| *ibericum* | See *C. coum* subsp. *caucasicum* |
| *intaminatum* | CBro CLCN CMea CPBP CSWP EHyt EJWh EPot ERos LAma MAsh NMen NSla NTow SBla STil WAbe WCom WIvy WPGP |
| - 'E.K. Balls' | Last listed 1996 |
| - EKB 628a | EPot |
| - patterned-leaved | EJWh LCTD STil |
| - pink flowered | STil |
| - plain-leaved | STil |
| - 'Silver Cloud' | Last listed 1996 |
| *latifolium* | See *C. persicum* |
| *libanoticum* ♀ | CAvo CBro CLCN EBrP EBre EHyt EJWh EPot ERos LAma LBre LCTD MAsh MBal SBla SBre STil WCom WCot |
| § x *meiklei* | CBro |
| *mirabile* ♀ | CAvo CBro CFee CLCN EBrP EBre EJWh EPot LAma LBre MAsh SBla SBre STil WAbe WIvy |
| - silver leaved | Last listed 1998 |
| - 'Tilebarn Anne' | STil |
| - 'Tilebarn Jan' | STil |
| - 'Tilebarn Nicholas' | MAsh STil |
| *neapolitanum* | See *C. hederifolium* |
| *orbiculatum* | See *C. coum* |
| *parviflorum* | EJWh EPot LAma NMen STil |
| *peloponnesiacum* | See *C. repandum* subsp. *peloponnesiacum* |
| § *persicum* | CBro CFil CLCN EJWh LAma MAsh STil WPGP |
| - CSE 90560 | STil |
| - var. *persicum* | STil |
| f. *puniceum* 'Tilebarn Karpathos' | |
| - RRL N8/65 | Last listed 1998 |
| - S&L 55 | Last listed 1998 |
| *pseudibericum* ♀ | CBro CLCN EBrP EBre EHyt EJWh EPot LAma LBre LCTD MAsh SBla SBre STil WIvy |
| - 'Roseum' | CLCN EHyt LCTD MAsh STil |
| - scented form | Last listed 1997 |
| § *purpurascens* ♀ | CBro CFil CLCN CMea EBrP EBre EJWh EPot LAma LBre MAsh MBro MS&S NMen NRoo SBla SBre SSpi STil WCot WHoo WIvy WPat WWat |
| - f. *album* | SBla |
| ◆ - var. *fatrense* | See *C. purpurascens* subsp. *purpurascens* from Fatra, Slovakia |
| - form | Last listed 1997 |
| - 'Lake Garda' | CFil MAsh SSpi WPGP |
| § - subsp. *purpurascens* from Fatra, Slovakia | EPot GCrs STil |
| - silver-leaved | LCTD |
| - silver-leaved from Limone, Italy | SBla SSpi |
| *repandum* | CAvo CBro CFil CLCN EBrP EBre EHyt EJWh ERos LAma LBre LCTD MAsh MBal SBla SBre SSpi STil SWas WHer WPGP WWat |
| - JCA 5157 | SSpi |
| § - subsp. *peloponnesiacum* ♀ | EJWh MAsh |
| - - var. *peloponnesiacum* | CBro CLCN LCTD SSpi STil |
| - - var. *vividum* | STil |
| - 'Pelops' misapplied | See *C. repandum* subsp. *peloponnesiacum* var. *peloponnesiacum* |
| - subsp. *repandum* f. *album* | CLCN EHyt EJWh MAsh SBla STil |
| - subsp. *rhodense* | CLCN LAma LCTD MAsh SSpi STil |
| - WM 9709 | MPhe |
| *rohlfsianum* | CBro CFil CLCN EJWh MAsh STil WPGP |
| x *saundersii* | CLCN EJWh STil |
| 'Super Puppet' | Last listed 1997 |
| *trochopteranthum* | CAvo CBro CLCN EHyt EJWh EPot LAma MAsh NRog SBla STil WAbe WCom WIvy |
| - 'Pink Swirl' | Last listed 1997 |
| - 'Red Devil' | Last listed 1997 |
| - 'Speckles' | Last listed 1996 |
| x *wellensiekii* | STil |

## CYCLANTHERA (Cucurbitaceae)
| | |
|---|---|
| *pedata* | CPlN |

## CYDISTA (Bignoniaceae)
| | |
|---|---|
| *aequinoctialis* | CPlN |

## CYDONIA ✿ (Rosaceae)
| | |
|---|---|
| *japonica* | See *Chaenomeles speciosa* |
| *oblonga* (F) | LHol |
| - 'Bereczcki' | See *C. oblonga* 'Vranja' |
| - 'Champion' (F) | GTwe SKee WJas |
| - 'Early Prolific' | Last listed 1997 |
| - 'Isfahan' | SKee |
| * - 'Le Bourgeaut' (F) | GTwe |
| * - 'Lescovacz' | MGos WJas |
| - 'Ludovic' | GTwe WJas |
| ♦ - 'Lusitanica' | See *C. oblonga* Portugal = 'Lusitanica' |
| - 'Meech's Prolific' (F) | CSam CTho EMui ERea GTwe MBlu MWat SDea SFam SKee |
| - pear shaped | CBlo CTri NRog |
| § - Portugal = 'Lusitanica' (F) | CBlo GTwe NRog SKee WJas |
| - 'Seibosa' (F) | SKee |
| ¶ - 'Shams' | SKee |
| § - 'Vranja' (F) ♀ | CDoC CEnd CMac CTho EBee EBrP EBre ERea GTwe LBre LBuc LEdu MBri MGos NRog SBre SDea SFam SKee SPer WDin WJas WMou |

## CYMBALARIA (Scrophulariaceae)
| | |
|---|---|
| *aequitriloba* | Last listed 1997 |
| - 'Alba' | GGar |
| § *hepaticifolia* | EDAr LBee NNrd WCru WPer |
| - 'Alba' | CNic |
| § *muralis* | CArn CKin EWFC EWTr GAbr MBar MWat NMir NPri WGor WHer WMow WRus |
| - 'Albiflora' | See *C. muralis* 'Pallidior' |
| § - 'Globosa Alba' | CHal EDAr EPot MDHE |
| - 'Globosa Rosea' | WCla |
| - 'Nana Alba' | CPea ELan GAbr MDHE MLan NNrd NPri NWCA WPer |
| § - 'Pallidior' | CMea ESis MAvo MBar MHar NHar NVic WRHF WWin |
| ¶ - 'Rosea' | WFar |
| § *pallida* | CMea LBee NHar NSla SBla SPlb WByw WCla WCru WFar WPer |
| - 'Alba' | LBee |
| § *pilosa* | ECtt EMNN GAbr NNrd NSti WLRN |
| - 'Alba' | Last listed 1998 |

## CYMBIDIUM ✿ (Orchidaceae)
| | |
|---|---|
| *ensifolium* 'Kwanyin Susin' | SWes |
| - var. *rubrigemmum* | SWes |
| - 'Tehku Susin' | SWes |
| ¶ *goeringii* | SWes |
| ¶ - 'Chun Chien' | SWes |
| * - var. *formosanum* | SWes |
| - 'Tow Tow Shang' | SWes |
| *kanran* | Last listed 1997 |
| *sinense* | SWes |
| * - var. *album* | Last listed 1998 |

## CYMBOPOGON (Poaceae)
| | |
|---|---|
| *citratus* | CArn CJew CSev ELau EOHP GPoy LHol MChe MSal NPri SHDw SIde WCHb WGwG WHer WJek |
| *martinii* | GPoy MSal |

| *nardus* | GPoy MSal |
|---|---|

## CYMOPHYLLUS (Cyperaceae)
| | |
|---|---|
| *fraseri* | EPla WCot |

## CYMOPTERUS (Apiaceae)
| | |
|---|---|
| ¶ *terebinthinus* | SIgm |

## CYNANCHUM (Asclepiadaceae)
| | |
|---|---|
| * *acuminatifolium* | Last listed 1998 |
| sp. B&SWJ 1924 | WCru |

## CYNARA (Asteraceae)
| | |
|---|---|
| § *baetica* subsp. *maroccana* | EBee |
| § *cardunculus* ♀ | More than 30 suppliers |
| - ACL 380/78 | EMon |
| - 'Cardy' | CBot EGoo EMan MLLN MWat SMrm WWhi |
| - dwarf form | SDix |
| - 'Florist Cardy' | MTis NLar NPSl |
| - New House Farm strain | MCoo |
| - Scolymus Group | CB&S CHad CJew EPfP ERav GCal GPoy ILis LHol MBri SMrm SPer WByw WHer WOak |
| ¶ - - 'Brittany Belle' | NFla |
| - - 'Green Globe' | CBod CBot CSev MWat NPSl NPer |
| - - 'Gros Camus de Bretagne' | WCot |
| - - 'Gros Vert de Lâon' | MHlr WCot |
| - - 'Large Green' | NLar |
| - - 'Purple Globe' | CArn NPSl |
| - - 'Violetto di Chioggia' | WHer |
| *hystrix* | See *C. baetica* subsp. *maroccana* |

## CYNODON (Poaceae)
| | |
|---|---|
| ¶ *aethiopicus* | EHoe |

## CYNOGLOSSUM (Boraginaceae)
| | |
|---|---|
| *amabile* ♀ | ELan MGed SRms |
| - 'Firmament' | SRms WCot |
| - f. *roseum* | Last listed 1998 |
| *creticum* | Last listed 1996 |
| *dioscoridis* | CBot CGle NLar WCom WPer WRha |
| *glochidiatum* | Last listed 1998 |
| *grande* | CFee EBee SCro |
| *hungaricum* | Last listed 1997 |
| *nervosum* | CBot CGle EAst EBee EBrP EBre ECha ECtt EFou EMil EPar LBre MCAu MRav MTis MWgw NChi NSti SBre SLon SPer SRms SWat WCHb WCot WWhi WWin |
| *officinale* | EWFC GBar MChe MHew MSal SIde WCHb WCer WHer |
| *wallichii* | CFee |
| *zeylanicum* | Last listed 1998 |

## CYNOSURUS (Poaceae)
| | |
|---|---|
| *cristatus* | CKin |

## CYPELLA (Iridaceae)
| | |
|---|---|
| *aquatilis* | MSta |
| § *coelestis* | EGar EHal WPer |
| *herbertii* | CGle LAma |
| *plumbea* | See *C. coelestis* |

## CYPERUS (Cyperaceae)
| | |
|---|---|
| § *albostriatus* | CHal MBri |
| - 'Nanus' | MMoz |
| *alternifolius* hort. | See *C. involucratus* |
| ♦ - 'Compactus' | See *C. involucratus* 'Nanus' |
| § *cyperoides* | MBri |
| *diffusus* hort. | See *C. albostriatus* |

§ *eragrostis*  CBrm CCuc CElw CHal CMil CRow ECha EHoe EPPr EPla NSti SDix SUsu SWat WAbb

*esculentus*  IBlr

*fuscus*  CCuc CElw CInt EPPr EPla NSti WHal

*glaber*  EMan

*haspan* hort.  See *C. papyrus* 'Nanus'

§ *involucratus* ♀  CBen CHal EBak EHon EMFW EOas ERea LCns MBri MSta SApp SArc SWat WFar WMul WWeb WWye

– 'Gracilis'  CCuc EBak MBri

§ – 'Nanus'  MSCN

*longus*  CBen CCuc CHan CRow CWat EBee EHoe EHon EMFW EPPr LPBA MHew MSta NDea NSti SMad SSoC SWat SWyc WHal WMAq WWeb WWye

*nanus*  Last listed 1998

*obtusiflorus* subsp. *sphaerocephalus*  Last listed 1998

*papyrus*  CInt ERea LCns LPan MBri MSta SAPC SArc SLdr SSoC SYvo WMul

§ – 'Nanus'  CInt ERea WMul

¶ *rotundus*  CStr EPGN

*sumula* hort.  See *C. cyperoides*

*ustulatus*  Last listed 1997

*vegetus*  See *C. eragrostis*

## CYPHOMANDRA (Solanaceae)

*betacea* (F)  GPoy LBlo WMul

– 'Goldmine' (F)  ERea

– 'Oratia Red' (F)  ERea

## CYPRIPEDIUM (Orchidaceae)

¶ *acaule*  CHdy

¶ – x *pubescens*  CHdy

¶ *Aki* g.  CHdy

¶ *Andrewsii* g.  CHdy

x *barbeyi*  Last listed 1998

*calceolus*  CHdy

– var. *parviflorum*  SWes

♦ – var. *pubescens*  See *C. pubescens*

¶ *candidum*  CHdy

– x *macranthos*  Last listed 1998

¶ *cordigerum* x *reginae*  CHdy

*debile*  EFEx

*Emil* g.  CHdy XFro

*flavum*  CHdy SWes

– red unspotted form  EFEx

* – var. *speciosum*  Last listed 1997

– yellow spotted form  EFEx

§ *formosanum*  CHdy EFEx LAma SSpi SWes

¶ – x *pubescens*  CHdy

*franchetii*  CHdy EFEx SWes

*Gisela* g.  XFro

*guttatum* var. *guttatum*  EFEx

– var. *yatabeanum*  See *C. yatabeanum*

*Hank Small* g.  Last listed 1997

*henryi*  CHdy EFEx

¶ *himalaicum*  EFEx

§ *japonicum*  CHdy EFEx LAma SWes

– var. *formosanum*  See *C. formosanum*

– var. *japonicum*  See *C. japonicum*

¶ *Karl Heinz* g.  CHdy

¶ *kentuckiense*  CHdy

¶ – x *reginae*  CHdy

*macranthos*  CHdy EFEx

* – var. *album*  CHdy

– dark pink form from Wou-long, China  Last listed 1998

– green-flowered  EFEx

– var. *hotei-atsumorianum*  CHdy EFEx

– light pink form from Man-chou, China  Last listed 1998

– var. *rebunense*  EFEx

– var. *speciosum*  CHdy EFEx

*margaritaceum*  CHdy EFEx SWes

*Maria* g.  Last listed 1998

¶ *montanum*  EFEx

¶ *parviflorum*  CHdy GCrs

– var. *makasin*  GCrs

*passerinum*  CHdy SWes

§ *pubescens*  CHdy GCrs LAma

¶ – Aitkin form  GCrs

¶ – dwarf form  GCrs

*reginae*  CHdy GCrs LAma

*segawae*  CHdy EFEx SWes

*tibeticum*  CHdy EFEx SWes

§ *yatabeanum*  CHdy EFEx

## CYRILLA (Cyrillaceae)

*racemiflora*  CPle SSpi

## CYRTANTHUS (Amaryllidaceae)

'Atalanta'  Last listed 1996

§ *brachyscyphus*  EBee SHFr WSPU

¶ *breviflorus*  SIgm

*clavatus*  Last listed 1997

§ *elatus* ♀  CAvo CBro CHal CSev CSpe EBot ERea LAma LBow MBri MCCP NChi NRog SCou SLon SRms SYvo WCot WHer

– 'Delicatus'  LBow

¶ *epiphyticus*  SIgm

*falcatus*  MLan

*flanaganii* S&SH 11  Last listed 1996

*luteus*  Last listed 1998

*mackenii*  NRog

– var. *cooperi*  Last listed 1998

*montanus*  Last listed 1997

*obliquus*  Last listed 1997

*obrienii*  Last listed 1997

*ochroleucus*  Last listed 1996

* – 'Stutterheim Variety'  WCot

*parviflorus*  See *C. brachyscyphus*

'Pink Diamond'  CBro

*purpureus*  See *C. elatus*

*sanguineus*  Last listed 1998

*smithiae*  Last listed 1997

'Snow White'  CBro

*speciosus*  See *C. elatus*

*spiralis*  Last listed 1997

*staadensis*  Last listed 1997

## CYRTOMIUM (Dryopteridaceae)

§ *caryotideum*  GQui NMar

§ *falcatum* ♀  CCuc CHal CRDP CTrC EBee EHic EMon MBri NMar NOrc SArc SRms SVen WRic WWat

– 'Butterfieldii'  EMon

– 'Rochfordianum'  CRow LBlm WFib

§ *fortunei* ♀  CFil CHal CHid EBee EFer EHic GBin IOrc NHar NHed NHol NMar SChu SRms WFib WRic

– var. *clivicola*  CBar NHar NHed WRic

*lonchitoides*  WRic

*macrophyllum*  CFil NMar

## CYRTOSTYLIS (Orchidaceae)

*reniformis*  Last listed 1998

*robusta*  Last listed 1998

## CYSTICAPNOS (Papaveraceae)

| | |
|---|---|
| ¶ *pruinosa* | CSpe |

## CYSTOPTERIS ✿ (Woodsiaceae)

| | |
|---|---|
| *alpina* | Last listed 1997 |
| *bulbifera* | CCuc CFil CLAP EFer EPot GQui NMar NVic WEas |
| *diaphana* | WRic |
| *dickieana* | CFil GAri NHar NMar NVic SRms WFib |
| *fragilis* | CCuc CFil EMon GQui MBal NBro NHed NMar SRms WRic |
| - 'Cristata' | CLAP |
| - var. *sempervirens* | WRic |
| *regia* | Last listed 1996 |
| ¶ *tennesseensis* | WRic |

## CYTISOPHYLLUM (Papilionaceae)

| | |
|---|---|
| § *sessilifolium* | Last listed 1998 |

## CYTISUS (Papilionaceae)

| | |
|---|---|
| *albus* Hacq. | See *Chamaecytisus albus* |
| - hort. | See *C. multiflorus* |
| 'Andreanus' | See *C. scoparius* f. *andreanus* |
| *ardoinoi* ♀ | GDra MBal MBro MPla WLin |
| *battandieri* ♀ | More than 30 suppliers |
| - 'Yellow Tail' ♀ | CEnd LRHS MBri MGos WSPU |
| x *beanii* ♀ | ELan ENot ESis MAsh MBal MBar MPla NFor SLon SPer SRms WDin |
| - 'Osiris' | EPfP |
| 'Boskoop Glory' | CBlo SPer |
| 'Boskoop Ruby' ♀ | CBlo CDoC EBee EGra EOld EPfP GSki NWoo SSoC WLRN |
| 'Burkwoodii' ♀ | CB&S CDoC EBee EHic ENot GCHN GChr MWhi NFla WFar WPyg WStI |
| 'Butterfly' | CB&S |
| 'C.E. Pearson' | Last listed 1996 |
| *canariensis* | See *Genista canariensis* |
| 'College Girl' | Last listed 1996 |
| 'Compact Crimson' | EBrP EBre ECle LBre SBre |
| 'Cottage' | EPot GDra IMGH MBro MPla NHol WAbe WBod WLin |
| 'Cottage Gold' | GSki MPla |
| 'Criterion' | NCut |
| 'Dainty' | WGwG |
| 'Dainty Maid' | CEnd |
| 'Daisy Hill' | CBlo |
| § *decumbens* | CBlo IOrc MAsh MBro NHar WLin WWin |
| ♦ *demissus* | See *Chamaecytisus polytrichus* |
| 'Dorothy Walpole' | CBlo CMHG |
| 'Dragonfly' | CBlo ELan IOrc |
| 'Dukaat' | EBee MAsh WLRN |
| 'Eastern Queen' | Last listed 1997 |
| 'Firefly' | CBlo EBee MBal |
| 'Fulgens' | CBlo ELan EPfP MAsh MBar SPer WLRN WWeb |
| 'Golden Cascade' | CB&S CBlo ELan GChr MWat WGwG WLRN WWeb |
| 'Golden Showers' | MBal |
| 'Golden Sunlight' | CBlo EGra ELan ENot WStI |
| 'Goldfinch' | CB&S CBlo CDoC CHar EBee EGra ENot MBri MWat SMer WAbe WWeb |
| *hirsutus* | See *Chamaecytisus hirsutus* |
| 'Hollandia' ♀ | CB&S CDoC EBee EBrP EBre EGra EWTr GCHN GChr LBre MBar MGos NFla SBre SPer WDin WStI WWeb WWin |
| x *kewensis* ♀ | More than 30 suppliers |
| - 'Niki' | CBlo CDoC MAsh MBri MGos MPla SPan SPer WGer |
| 'Killiney Red' | CBlo CChe EBee EGra ENot IOrc MBal MBri WRHF |
| 'Killiney Salmon' | CBlo CChe ENot MAsh SSoC |
| 'La Coquette' | CBlo CDoC CMHG EBee EGra MBar SPlb WLRN |
| 'Lena' ♀ | CDoC EBee EBrP EBre EGra EWTr GAri GOrc LBre MAsh MBar MBri MGos MTis NRoo SBre SRPl WBod WFar WStI WWeb |
| *leucanthus* | See *Chamaecytisus albus* |
| 'Lord Lambourne' | CBlo CChe NCut |
| 'Luna' ♀ | Last listed 1996 |
| *maderensis* | See *Genista maderensis* |
| 'Maria Burkwood' | CBlo |
| 'Miki' | Last listed 1996 |
| 'Minstead' ♀ | CBlo EBee EBrP EBre ECle ELan EPfP LBre MBal SBre SPer WAbe |
| *monspessulanus* | See *Genista monspessulana* |
| 'Moonlight' | EWTr SPer WGwG |
| 'Moyclare Pink' | CMHG MSte |
| 'Mrs Norman Henry' | Last listed 1996 |
| 'Muldean' | WWeb |
| § *multiflorus* ♀ | MBal SRms |
| - 'White Bouquet' | MBri SPan SPla |
| *nigrescens* | See *C. nigricans* |
| § *nigricans* | CFil CPle ENot SPer WPGP |
| - 'Cyni' | CB&S ELan EPfP GEil MAsh NFla SPer SSpi SSta |
| *nubigenus* | See *C. supranubius* |
| 'Palette' | ELan MBar SPer WRHF |
| 'Porlock' ♀ | CB&S CDoC CLan CSPN CTre CWSG CWit ELan SEND SPla WBod WWeb |
| x *praecox* | See *C.* x *praecox* 'Warminster' |
| - 'Albus' | CDoC EAst EBee EBrP EBre ELan ENot EWTr GCHN GRei IOrc LBre MAsh MBar MBri MGos MRav MWat NRoo SBre SEND SPer SPla SRPl WAbe WCFE WFar WHCG WWat |
| - 'Allgold' ♀ | CB&S CChe CDoC CMHG EBee EBrP EBre EGra ENot GRei LBre MAsh MBar MBri MPla MRav NRoo SBre SLon SPer SPla SReu SRms SSta WAbe WBod WDin WFar WGwG |
| - 'Canary Bird' | See *C.* x *praecox* 'Goldspeer' |
| - 'Frisia' | CB&S GAri MBar NFla WBod |
| § - 'Goldspeer' | CBlo ENot SEND |
| § - 'Warminster' ♀ | CChe CHar EAst EBee EGra ELan ENot EWTr GCHN GChr GDra GRei LHop MBal MBar MBri MGos MPla MRav MWat NFla NRoo NWea SPer SRms WAbe WWat WWin |
| 'Princess' | MBri MPla WBcn |
| *procumbens* | EPla LHop MBal |
| *purgans* | CBlo CPle MBal NLon |
| *purpureus* | See *Chamaecytisus purpureus* |
| *racemosus* hort. | See *Genista* x *spachiana* |
| 'Radiance' | Last listed 1996 |
| Red Favourite | See *C.* 'Roter Favorit' |
| 'Red Wings' | CBlo EGra GCHN MGos SPer WAbe WStI |
| § 'Roter Favorit' | CBlo MBar WGor |
| 'Royal Standard' | Last listed 1996 |
| *scoparius* | CAgr CArn CBlo CKin EBee ENot EWFC GChr GRei IIve LEdu MCoo NWea SRms WDin |

§ - f.*andreanus* ♀ — CBlo CDoC EBee EGra ENot GChr GRei MGos NFor NLon
- - 'Splendens' — CB&S CBlo WStI
- - 'Cornish Cream' ♀ — CB&S CBlo ECot EPfP SPer
- f.*indefessus* — Last listed 1996
§ - subsp. *maritimus* — GSki MBri MMHG MRav NLon SLPl WGer
- 'Pastel Delight' — Last listed 1998
- var.*prostratus* — See *C. scoparius* subsp. *maritimus*
*sessilifolius* — See *Cytisophyllum sessilifolium*
§ *striatus* — SSpi
'Sunset' — Last listed 1996
'Sunshine' — Last listed 1996
*supinus* — See *Chamaecytisus supinus*
'Windlesham Ruby' — CChe CDoC EGra EHic ELan EPfP GRei MAsh MBar MPla SMer SPer WDin WPyg WWeb
'Zeelandia' ♀ — CB&S CHar EBee EHic ENot EWTr MBar MRav SEND SMer SSoC WAbe WWeb

# D

**DABOECIA** ✿ (Ericaceae)
§ *cantabrica* — GAri MBal
§ - f.*alba* — CB&S CMac CNCN COCH ENot MBal MBar MBri MGos MOke NHol SBod WStI
- 'Alba Globosa' — MBar
\* - 'Arielle' — CB&S
- 'Atropurpurea' — CNCN COCH ENot MBal MGos MOke NHol WBod WStI
- 'Barbara Phillips' — MBar
- 'Bicolor' ♀ — CNCN COCH EPfP MBal MGos MOke NHar
- 'Blueless' — COCH
- f.*blumii* 'Pink Blum' — Last listed 1998
- - 'White Blum' — CNCN COCH ECho
- 'Bubbles' — Last listed 1998
- 'Celtic Star' — Last listed 1998
- 'Charles Nelson' (d) — MBar MOke
- 'Cherub' — Last listed 1998
- 'Cinderella' — CNCN MBar
- 'Cleggan' — Last listed 1998
- 'Clifden' — Last listed 1996
- 'Covadonga' — CNCN COCH MBar
- 'Creeping White' — Last listed 1998
- 'Cupido' — CNCN COCH
- 'David Moss' ♀ — CNCN MBal MBar SBod
- 'Donard Pink' — See *D. cantabrica* 'Pink'
- 'Early Bride' — COCH
- 'Eskdale Baron' — Last listed 1998
- 'Eskdale Blea' — Last listed 1998
- 'Eskdale Blonde' — Last listed 1998
- 'Glamour' — Last listed 1998
- 'Globosa Pink' — Last listed 1998
- 'Harlequin' — Last listed 1998
- 'Heather Yates' — MOke
I - 'Hookstone Pink' — Last listed 1996
- 'Hookstone Purple' — COCH MBar MGos MOke NHol
- 'Lilacina' — MBar
§ - 'Pink' — COCH MBar NMen SRms
- 'Pink Lady' — MBar
- 'Polifolia' — CNCN MOke SBod SRms
- 'Porter's Variety' — ECho MBar MOke NHar
- 'Praegerae' — CMac CNCN EPfP MBal MBar MGos NHol
- 'Purpurea' — ECho MBar

- 'Rainbow' (v) — CNCN MBar
- 'Rodeo' — Last listed 1998
- 'Rosea' — MBar
- subsp.*scotica* 'Bearsden' — MBar
- - 'Ben' — Last listed 1998
- - 'Cora' — CNCN MBar
- - 'Goscote' — MGos
- - 'Jack Drake' ♀ — CNCN GChr MBal MBar MBri MOke
- - 'Red Imp' — Last listed 1998
- - 'Robin' — Last listed 1998
- - 'Silverwells' ♀ — CNCN EPfP GChr MBar MBri NHar
- - 'Tabramhill' — CNCN MBar
- - 'William Buchanan' ♀ — CMac CNCN GChr MBal MBar MBri MGos MOke NHar NHol NMen SBod
- - - 'William Buchanan Gold' — CNCN MBar MBri
- - 'Snowdrift' — MBar
- 'Tinkerbell' — ECho
- 'Waley's Red' ♀ — COCH EPfP GQui MBar SDys
- 'White Carpet' — Last listed 1998
- 'Wijnie' — Last listed 1998
x *scotica* — See *D. cantabrica* subsp. *scotica* cultivars

**DACRYCARPUS** (Podocarpaceae)
§ *dacrydioides* — ECou
- 'Dark Delight' — ECou

**DACRYDIUM** (Podocarpaceae)
*bidwillii* — See *Halocarpus bidwillii*
*cupressinum* — ECou
*franklinii* — See *Lagarostrobos franklinii*
*laxifolium* — See *Lepidothamnus laxifolius*

**DACTYLIS** (Poaceae)
*glomerata* 'Variegata' — CCuc EGle EMan EMon ENot EPPr EPla IBlr MAvo MCCP MMoz NBro NCat NSti WCot

**DACTYLORHIZA** (Orchidaceae)
*aristata* — EFEx SWes
\* - x *fuchsii* — EFEx
\* - *punctata* — EFEx
x *braunii* — ECha IBlr
♦ *coccinea* — See *D. incarnata* subsp. *coccinea*
¶ *cordigera* — CHdy
§ *elata* ♀ — CEnd CHdy CLAP EPar GCrs IBlr LAma MDun SSpi
- 'Lydia' — CLAP GCrs
\* - *variegata* — IBlr
¶ *Eskimo Nell* g. — CHdy
¶ *Estella* g. (*elata* x *foliosa*) — EPot GCrs
*Florina* g. — Last listed 1997
   (*iberica* x *saccifera*)
§ *foliosa* ♀ — CBro CHdy ERos GCrs IBlr MBri MDun MNrw MTho NHar WCot WCru WOld
- x *romana* — Last listed 1996
¶ - x *saccifera* — CHdy EPot
§ *fuchsii* — CHdy EPot ERos GBuc GCrs MNrw NHar NRya SSpi SUsu WCru WHer WShi
\* - *alba* — Last listed 1998
¶ - 'Bressingham Bonus' — EHyt
- 'Cruickshank' — NHar
- x *purpurella* — See *D.* x *venusta*
¶ *Glendora* g. (*elata* x *incarnata*) — CHdy
x *grandis* — CHdy
hybrids — WCru

| | |
|---|---|
| *incarnata* | EPot GCrs LAma SPer SWes |
| - subsp. *cruenta* | Last listed 1997 |
| - × *foliosa* | Last listed 1996 |
| **Larissa g.** × *purpurella* | SWes |
| § *maculata* | CHdy CHid EPar EPot GCrs IBlr LAma NRog SPer SWyc WCru WHer WShi |
| - subsp. *ericetorum* | Last listed 1997 |
| ¶ - 'Strawberry Fields' | EPot |
| *maderensis* | See *D. foliosa* |
| ¶ **Madonna g.** (*majalis* × *sambucina*) | CHdy |
| § *majalis* | CHdy EPot LAma SPer SSpi SWes WCru |
| ¶ - *alba* | CHdy |
| ¶ - var. *bowmanii* | CHdy |
| ¶ - subsp. *occidentalis* | SWes |
| - subsp. *praetermissa* | See *D. praetermissa* |
| *mascula* | See *Orchis mascula* |
| ¶ *nieschalkiorum* | SWes |
| *pindica* | Last listed 1996 |
| § *praetermissa* | EPot GCrs SSpi |
| - subsp. *junialis* var. *junialis* | Last listed 1996 |
| *purpurella* | CHdy SPer SSpi |
| ¶ *saccifera* | CHdy |
| 'Tinney's Spotted' | NHar |
| ¶ *traunsteineri* | SWes |

## DAHLIA ✿ (Asteraceae)

| | |
|---|---|
| 'Abridge Bertie' (MinD) | Last listed 1996 |
| 'Abridge Natalie' (SWL) | Last listed 1997 |
| ¶ 'Akita' (Misc) | WAba |
| 'Alloway Cottage' (MD) | LAyl NHal |
| 'Alltami Cherry' (SBa) | Last listed 1997 |
| 'Alltami Classic' (MD) | NHal |
| 'Alltami Corsair' (MS-c) | LAyl NHal |
| 'Alltami Cosmic' (LD) | NHal |
| 'Almand's Climax' (GD) ♀ | LBut WAba |
| 'Alstergruss' (Col) | NRog |
| 'Alva's Doris' (SS-c) ♀ | LAyl |
| 'Alva's Supreme' (GD) | LBut NHal |
| 'Amaran Candyfloss' (SD) | NHal |
| 'Amaran Relish' (LD) | NHal |
| 'Amaran Royale' (MinD) | Last listed 1997 |
| 'Amber Banker' (MC) | Last listed 1996 |
| 'Amberglow' (MinBa) | LAyl NHal |
| ¶ 'Amberley Jean' (SD) | LAyl |
| ¶ 'Amberley Victoria' (MD) | LAyl |
| 'American Copper' (GD) | NHal |
| 'Amgard Delicate' (LD) | NHal |
| 'Amira' (SBa) | NHal |
| ¶ 'Amy Campbell' (MD) | NHal |
| * 'Anaïs' | Last listed 1997 |
| * 'Anatol' (LD) | CSut |
| 'Andrew Magson' (SS-c) ♀ | NHal |
| 'Andrew Mitchell' (MS-c) | NHal |
| * 'Andries Amber' (MinS-c) | LBut |
| 'Andries' Orange' (MinS-c) | LBut |
| 'Anglian Water' (MinD) | NHal |
| * 'Anniversary Ball' (MinBa) | LAyl |
| 'Apricot Beauty' (MS-c) | NHal |
| 'Apricot Jewel' (SD) | LAyl |
| 'Arabian Night' (SD) | CHad CLTr EAst EBee EMan LAma MBEx MHlr NDov NRog SDeJ SPer WCot WPen WSpi |
| 'Athalie' (SC) | GHCN |
| ¶ 'Aurwens Violet' (Pom) | NHal |
| 'Autumn Lustre' (SWL) ♀ | LAyl |
| 'Aylett's Dazzler' (MinD) ♀ | Last listed 1995 |
| 'B.J. Beauty' (MD) | LAyl NHal WAba |
| 'Banker' (MC) | Last listed 1996 |
| ¶ 'Barat Joy' (MD) | WAba |

| | |
|---|---|
| ¶ 'Barbarossa' (LD) | CSut |
| ¶ 'Barbarry Aegean' | WAba |
| 'Barbarry Ball' (SBa) | NHal |
| 'Barbarry Banker' (MinD) | LAyl NHal |
| ¶ 'Barbarry Choice' | WAba |
| 'Barbarry Epic' (SD) | Last listed 1996 |
| 'Barbarry Fern' (SD) | NHal |
| 'Barbarry Flag' (MinD) | NHal |
| 'Barbarry Gaiety' (MinD) | Last listed 1997 |
| 'Barbarry Gateway' (MinD) | Last listed 1997 |
| 'Barbarry Glamour' (SBa) | Last listed 1996 |
| 'Barbarry Ideal' (MinD) | Last listed 1998 |
| 'Barbarry Lavender' (MinD) | Last listed 1996 |
| 'Barbarry Majestic' (SBa) | NHal |
| ¶ 'Barbarry Oracle' (SD) | WAba |
| ¶ 'Barbarry Orange' (SD) | WAba |
| 'Barbarry Pinky' (SD) | Last listed 1997 |
| 'Barbarry Snowball' (MinBa) | LAyl |
| ¶ 'Barbarry Suffusion' (MinBa) | NHal |
| ¶ 'Barbarry Ticket' (SWL) | WAba |
| 'Barbarry Token' (SD) | NHal |
| 'Baret Joy' (LS-c) | NHal WAba |
| ¶ 'Bea' (SWL) | WAba |
| 'Bednall Beauty' (DwB) | CBos CGle CHad CLTr CMil CRDP CSpe EBee EWes LHil LHop MBEx MHlr SDys SMrm WCot |
| ¶ 'Ben Huston' (GD) | WAba |
| 'Berwick Wood' (MD) | NHal |
| 'Biddenham Fire' (SD) | Last listed 1998 |
| 'Biddenham Strawberry' (SD) | LAyl |
| 'Biddenham Sunset' (MS-c) | LAyl |
| 'Bill Homberg' (GD) | Last listed 1997 |
| 'Bishop of Llandaff' (Misc) ♀ | More than 30 suppliers |
| 'Black Diamond' (Ba) | CHad |
| 'Black Fire' (SD) | LAyl SMrm |
| 'Black Monarch' (GD) | NHal |
| ¶ 'Blewbury First' (MinD) | LBut |
| ¶ 'Blithe Spirit' (LD) | CSut |
| 'Bloom's Amy' (MinD) | NHal |
| 'Blue Beard' | CSut |
| 'Bonanza' (LD) | Last listed 1996 |
| 'Bonaventure' (GD) | NHal |
| 'Bonne Esperance' (Sin/Lil) | CInt LBut |
| 'Border Princess' (SC) | SDeJ |
| 'Bracken Ballerina' (SWL) | LAyl NHal WAba |
| 'Brackenhill Flame' (SD) | NHal |
| ¶ 'Brackenridge Ballerina' (SWL) | WAba |
| 'Brandaris' (MS-c) | LAyl |
| 'Brandysnap' (SD) ♀ | LAyl |
| ¶ 'Bridal Bouquet' (Col) | LAyl |
| 'Burnished Bronze' (Misc/DwB) ♀ | Last listed 1997 |
| 'Butterball' (MinD) ♀ | LAyl |
| 'Calgary' (SD) | Last listed 1997 |
| 'Cameo' (WL) | NHal |
| 'Candy Cane' (MinBa) | CSut WAba |
| 'Candy Cupid' (MinBa) | LBut NHal WAba |
| 'Candy Keene' (LS-c) | NHal |
| 'Carolina Moon' (SD) | LAyl NHal |
| 'Carstone Cobblers' (SBa) | NHal WAba |
| 'Carstone Ruby' (SD) | NHal |
| 'Carstone Sunbeam' (SD) | Last listed 1996 |
| 'Charlie Kenwood' (MinD) | Last listed 1996 |
| 'Charlie Two' (MD) | LAyl LBut NHal WAba |
| 'Cherry Wine' (SD) | LAyl |
| ¶ 'Cherwell Goldcrest' (SS-c) | LBut NHal |
| ¶ 'Chessy' (Sin/Lil) | LBut |
| 'Cheyenne' (SS-c) | NHal |
| 'Chimborazo' (Col) | LAyl |
| 'Christmas Carol' (Col) | NHal |
| 'Christopher Nickerson' (MS-c) ♀ | LAyl |

'Christopher Taylor' (SWL) NHal SMrm WAba
'Clair de Lune' (Col) ♀ LBut NHal
'Clarion' (MS-c) SDeJ
'Classic A1' (MC) LAyl
*coccinea* CFil CGle CPou EAst EBee SMad
WCot WPGP
- hybrids Last listed 1998
- var. *palmeri* CD&R 1367 Last listed 1996
¶ 'Color Spectacle' (LSD) CSut
'Connie Bartlam' (MD) NHal
'Conway' (SS-c) ♀ Last listed 1998
'Cornel' (SBa) LBut WAba
'Corona' (SS-c/DwB) LAyl NHal
* 'Corrine' WAba
'Corton Bess' (SD) Last listed 1997
'Cream Alva's' (GD) ♀ Last listed 1993
'Cream Beauty' (SWL) LBut
'Cream Delight' (SS-c) Last listed 1997
'Cryfield Bryn' (SS-c) NHal
'Cryfield Keene' (LS-c) NHal
'Crystal Ann' (MS-c) NHal
'Curiosity' (Col) LAyl LBut NHal
'Czardas' GCal
'Daddy's Choice' (SS-c) LAyl
'Dad's Delight' (MinD) Last listed 1998
'Daleko Jupiter' (GS-c) NHal WAba
'Dana Iris' (SS-c) ♀ Last listed 1998
'Dancing Queen' (S-c) Last listed 1997
'Dandy' See D. 'Harvest Dandy'
'Danjo Doc' (SD) NHal
¶ 'Danum Meteor' (GS-c) WAba
'Dark Splendour' (MC) Last listed 1998
'Davar Donna' (MS-c) ♀ Last listed 1995
'Davenport Anita' (MinD) Last listed 1998
'Davenport Honey' (MinD) NHal
'Davenport Lesley' (MinD) Last listed 1997
'Davenport Pride' (MS-c) Last listed 1996
'Davenport Sunlight' (MS-c) LAyl
'David Digweed' (SD) NHal
'David Howard' (MinD) ♀ CB&S CGle CHad EAst EBee EBrP
EBre ECle ELan EMan GCal LAyl
LBre LHil MMil NHal SBid SBre
SPla WCot WHil WLRN
'Dawn Sky' (SD) LAyl
'Daytona' (SD) CSut
'Dazzler' (MinD/DwB) LAyl
'Deborah's Kiwi' (SC) NHal
'Debra Anne Craven' (GS-c) NHal
'Doctor Caroline Rabbitt'
(SD) ♀ Last listed 1993
¶ 'Doktor Hans Ricken' (SD) WAba
'Doris Day' (SC) LAma LBut NHal NRog WAba
'Doris Knight' (SC) LBut
'Downham Royal' (MinBa) CSut
'Duet' (MD) LAma NRog
'Duncan' Last listed 1996
'Dusky Harmony' (SWL) LBut
'Earl Marc' (SC) LBut
'East Anglian' (SD) LAyl
'East Court' (Sin) SMrm
'Easter Sunday' (Col) LAyl SMrm
'Eastwood Moonlight' (MS-c) NHal WAba
¶ 'Edge of Gold' (GD) CSut
'Edinburgh' (SD) LAma NRog
'Elizabeth Hammett' (MinD) NHal WAba
¶ 'Ella Britton' (MinD) EBee EMan NDov
'Ellen Huston' (Sin/DwB) ♀ CHad EBee EMan LRHS MBri
NHal
'Elma E' (LD) NHal WAba
'Elmbrook Chieftain' (GD) Last listed 1998
'Emory Paul' (LD) Last listed 1997
'Ernie Pitt' (SD) Last listed 1998

'Esther' MBri
'Eveline' (SD) ETub SDeJ
'Evelyn Foster' (MD) NHal
'Evelyn Rumbold' (GD) Last listed 1996
'Evening Mail' (GS-c) ♀ Last listed 1995
'Exotic Dwarf' (Sin/Lil) NHal
'Explosion' (SS-c) NHal
'Ezau' (GD) CSut
'Fascination' (SWL/DwB) ♀ CBos LAyl MHlr MSCN NHal
SChu WCot
'Fashion Monger' (Col) NHal
'Fermain' (MinD) NHal
* 'Fernhill Suprise' (SD) LBut
¶ 'Fidalgo Magic' WAba
'Fidalgo Supreme' (MD) NHal
* 'Figaro White' Last listed 1997
'Figurine' (SWL) ♀ LAyl NHal
'Finchcocks' (SWL) ♀ LAyl
'Fiona Stewart' (SBa) GHCN
¶ 'Fire Mountain' (MinD) NHal
'Firebird' (Sin) NRog
'Flutterby' (SWL) Last listed 1998
* 'Fluttering' Last listed 1997
'Foreman's Jubilee' (GS-c) LAyl
'Formby Supreme' (MD) Last listed 1998
'Forncett Furnace' (B) GCal
'Freestyle' (SC) Last listed 1996
'Freya's Thalia' (Sin/Lil) ♀ LBut
'Frigoulet' CSut
* 'Friquolet' LAma
¶ 'Funny Face' (MC) WAba
'Fusion' (MD) CSut
'Gaiety' (SD/DwB) LAyl
'Gala Parade' (SD) NHal
'Garden Festival' (SWL) LAyl
'Garden Party' (MC) ♀ LAyl
'Gateshead Festival' (SD) LAyl NHal
'Gay Mini' (MinD) LBut
'Gay Princess' (SWL) LAyl
§ 'Geerling's Indian Summer' (MS-c) ♀ NHal
'Geerlings Queeny' (SC) ♀ Last listed 1995
'Gerrie Hoek' (SWL) LAma LBut NRog
¶ 'Gina Lombaert' (MS-c) WAba
¶ 'Glenbank Twinkle' (MinC) NHal
'Glorie van Heemstede' LAma LAyl LBut NHal NRog
SMrm
(SWL) ♀
'Go American' (GD) NHal
'Gold Crown' (LS-c) NRog
'Gold Diable' (SS-c) ♀ Last listed 1995
'Golden Emblem' (MD) SDeJ
'Golden Impact' (MS-c) NHal
¶ 'Golden Symbol' (MS-c) WAba
'Good Earth' (MC) LAma
'Good Hope' (MinD) Last listed 1997
'Good Intent' (LD) Last listed 1996
¶ 'Grand Prix' (GD) CSut
¶ 'Grand Willo' (Pom) WAba
'Grenadier' (SWL) EBee MHlr WCot
'Grenidor Pastelle' (MS-c) LAyl LBut NHal WAba
'Gypsy Boy' (LD) LAyl
¶ 'Halam Portia' WAba
'Hamari Accord' (LS-c) LAyl NHal WAba
'Hamari Bride' (MS-c) ♀ LAyl
'Hamari Girl' (GD) NHal
'Hamari Gold' (GD) ♀ NHal
'Hamari Katrina' (SC) LAyl WAba
'Hamari Rosé' (MinBa) ♀ LAyl NHal
'Hamari Sunshine' (LD) ♀ NHal
¶ 'Hamilton Lillian' (SD) ♀ WAba
¶ 'Hans Radi' WAba
'Hans Ricken' (SD) Last listed 1997

| | | | |
|---|---|---|---|
| * 'Haresbrook' | CMil EBee EHic WCot WSpi | 'Jo's Choice' (MinD) | LBut |
| * 'Hartenaas' (Col/DwB) | NRog | 'Karenglen' (MinD) ♀ | LBut NHal |
| 'Harvest Amanda' (Sin/Lil) ♀ | LBut | 'Kathleen's Alliance' (SC) ♀ | LAyl NHal |
| 'Harvest Brownie' (Sin/Lil) | LBut | 'Kathryn's Cupid' (MinBa) ♀ | GHCN LAyl NHal WAba |
| § 'Harvest Dandy' (Sin/Lil) | LBut | ¶ 'Katie Dahl' (MinD) | NHal |
| § 'Harvest Imp' (Sin/Lil) | LBut | 'Keith's Choice' (MD) | NHal WAba |
| § 'Harvest Inflammation' | LBut | ¶ 'Kelsea Carla' (SS-c) | NHal |
| (Sin/Lil) ♀ | | ¶ 'Keltie Peach' (MD) | NHal |
| § 'Harvest Red Dwarf' (Sin/Lil) | LBut | 'Kelvin Floodlight' (GD) | Last listed 1996 |
| § 'Harvest Samantha' | LBut NHal | 'Kenn Emerland' (MS-c) | LAma |
| (Sin/DwB) ♀ | | 'Kenora Canada' (MS-c) | NHal |
| § 'Harvest Tiny Tot' (Sin) ♀ | LBut NHal | 'Kenora Challenger' (LS-c) | NHal WAba |
| 'Hayley Jayne' (SC) | CSut NHal | 'Kenora Fireball' (MinBa) | NHal |
| 'Hazard' (MS-c) | LAma NRog | 'Kenora Moonbeam' (MD) | Last listed 1997 |
| I 'Hazel' (Sin/Lil) | Last listed 1997 | ¶ 'Kenora Petite' (MinS-c) | WAba |
| 'Henriette' (MC) | Last listed 1998 | 'Kenora Sunset' (MS-c) | LAyl NHal |
| 'Highgate Gold' (MS-c) | Last listed 1997 | 'Kenora Superb' (GS-c) | LAyl NHal |
| 'Hilda Clare' (Col) | Last listed 1997 | ¶ 'Kenora Valentine' (LD) ♀ | WAba |
| 'Hillcrest Albino' (SS-c) ♀ | Last listed 1998 | ¶ 'Kenora Wildfire' (GD) | WAba |
| 'Hillcrest Blaze' (SS-c) ♀ | Last listed 1995 | 'Ken's Coral' (SWL) | NHal |
| 'Hillcrest Desire' (SC) ♀ | NHal WAba | 'Key West' (LD) | Last listed 1996 |
| ¶ 'Hillcrest Divine' (MinD) | NHal | 'Kidd's Climax' (GD) ♀ | LBut NHal WAba |
| ¶ 'Hillcrest Heights' (LS-c) | WAba | 'Kimi' (O) | Last listed 1998 |
| 'Hillcrest Hillton' (LS-c) | NHal | 'Kim's Marc' (SC) | GHCN LBut |
| 'Hillcrest Royal' (MC) ♀ | LAyl NHal | 'Kiwi Gloria' (SC) | GHCN NHal WAba |
| 'Hillcrest Suffusion' (SD) | NHal | 'Klankstad Kerkrade' (SC) | LAyl |
| 'Hillcrest Ultra' (SD) | LAyl | ¶ 'Klondike' (MS-c) | CSut |
| 'Hindu Star' (MinBa) | Last listed 1996 | 'Kochelsee' (MinD) | LAma |
| 'Hit Parade' (MS-c) | CSut LAma NRog | 'Kotare Jackpot' (SS-c) | LAyl |
| 'Holland Festival' (GD) | Last listed 1996 | 'Kym Willo' (Pom) | LBut |
| 'Honey' (Anem/DwB) | CInt NRog | * 'Kyoto' | WAba |
| 'Honeymoon Dress' (SD) | LAyl NHal | 'La Cierva' (Col) | LBut NHal |
| 'House of Orange' (MD) | SDeJ | 'La Corbière' (DwBa) | Last listed 1997 |
| 'Hugh Mather' (MWL) | LAyl | 'Lady Kerkrade' (SC) | Last listed 1997 |
| 'Ice Cream Beauty' (SWL) ♀ | Last listed 1995 | 'Lady Linda' (SD) | GHCN LBut NHal WAba |
| 'Imp' | See *D.* 'Harvest Imp' | 'Lady Sunshine' (SS-c) | Last listed 1998 |
| ***imperialis*** (B) | GCal.MBEx WCot | 'L'Ancresse' (MinBa) | LAyl NHal |
| ¶ - 'Alba' (B) | EMon | * 'Laura's Choice' (SD) | LAyl |
| ¶ - pink double (B) | WCot | 'Lauren's Moonlight' (MS-c) | NHal |
| 'Inca Dambuster' (GS-c) | LBut NHal | 'Lavender Athalie' (SC) | LAyl |
| ¶ 'Inca Matchless' (MD) | WAba | ¶ 'Lemon' (Anem) | WAba |
| 'Inca Metropolitan' (LD) ♀ | Last listed 1987 | 'Lemon Cane' | CSut WAba |
| 'Inflammation' | See *D.* 'Harvest Inflammation' | 'Lemon Elegans' (SS-c) ♀ | GHCN LBut NHal |
| 'Inglebrook Jill' (Col) | LAyl NHal | * 'Lemon Puff' (Anem) | Last listed 1996 |
| 'Inland Dynasty' (GS-c) | Last listed 1996 | ¶ 'Lemon Zing' (MinBa) | NHal |
| 'Iris' (Pom) | LBut NHal | * 'Life Force' | Last listed 1998 |
| 'Jaldec Joker' (SC) ♀ | Last listed 1995 | 'Lilac Shadow' (S-c) | Last listed 1998 |
| ¶ 'Jamie' (SS-c) | LAyl | § 'Lilac Taratahi' (S-c) | LAyl |
| 'Jane Horton' (Col) | LBut | 'Lilac Time' (MD) | SDeJ |
| ¶ 'Jason' | WAba | 'Lilianne Ballego' (MinD) | NHal |
| 'Jean Fairs' (MinWL) | LBut | 'Linda's Chester' (SC) | LAyl LBut NHal |
| 'Jean McMillan' (SC) | NHal | 'Lismore Moonlight' (Pom) | NHal |
| 'Jeanette Carter' (MinD) ♀ | LAyl | 'Lismore Sunset' (Pom) | NHal |
| 'Jeanne d'Arc' | CSut | 'Lismore Willie' (SWL) | LAyl LBut |
| 'Jescot Jess' (MinD) | LBut | 'Little Dorrit' (Sin/Lil) ♀ | LBut |
| 'Jescot Julie' (O) | LAyl LBut | 'Little Dream' (S-c) | SDeJ |
| 'Jescot Lingold' (MinD) | CSut WAba | 'Little Sally' (Pom) | LAyl |
| 'Jessica' (S-c) | CSut NHal | 'Little Tiger' | NRog |
| 'Jessica Crutchfield' (SWL) ♀ | Last listed 1995 | ¶ 'Love's Dream' (SWL) | LAyl |
| 'Jessie G' (SBa) | NHal | ¶ 'Lynda Windsor' (Sin) | CRDP |
| 'Jessie Ross' (MinD/DwB) | Last listed 1998 | ¶ 'Madame Simone Stappers' | EBee MSCN |
| 'Jill Day' (SC) | LBut | (WL) | |
| * 'Jill's Blush' (MS-c) | Last listed 1997 | 'Madame Vera' (SD) | LBut |
| 'Jill's Delight' (MD) ♀ | LAyl | 'Maelstrom' (SD) | LAyl |
| 'Jim Branigan' (LS-c) | LAyl NHal | 'Majestic Kerkrade' (SC) | Last listed 1998 |
| 'Joan Beecham' (SWL) | LAyl | 'Majuba' (MD) | LAma NRog SDeJ |
| 'Jocondo' (GD) | LAyl NHal | 'Margaret Ann' (MinD) | LAyl LBut |
| 'Johann' (Pom) | LBut NHal | ¶ 'Margie' (MS-c) | WAba |
| 'John Prior' (SD) | NHal | 'Mariner's Light' (SS-c) ♀ | Last listed 1997 |
| 'John Street' (SWL) ♀ | LAyl LBut | 'Mark Damp' (LS-c) | NHal |
| 'Jomanda' (MinBa) | NHal | 'Mark Hardwick' (GD) | LAyl NHal |
| ¶ 'Jorja' (MS-c) | NHal | ¶ 'Mark Lockwood' (Pom) | WAba |

| | |
|---|---|
| 'Marlene Joy' (MS-c) | LAyl NHal WAba |
| 'Martin's Yellow' (Pom) | NHal |
| 'Mary Eveline' (Col) | NHal |
| ¶ 'Mary Hammett' (MinD) | WAba |
| 'Mary Layton' (Col) | NHal |
| 'Mary Pitt' (MinD) | LAyl NHal |
| ¶ 'Matilda Huston' | NHal |
| 'Maxine Bailey' (SD) | Last listed 1997 |
| *merckii* | CGle CHad EWes GBri GCal |
| | GMac LHil MBEx MNrw MTho |
| | NSti SIng WPer WRus WWin |
| - *alba* | CFil CHad MTho WPGP WPer |
| - compact | CBos CFil WPGP |
| ¶ - 'Edith Eddleman' | CFil |
| - gold-leaved | Last listed 1996 |
| - 'Hadspen Star' | Last listed 1996 |
| 'Meredith's Marion Smith' (SD) | NHal |
| 'Mi Wong' (Pom) | GHCN LAyl NHal |
| ¶ 'Mikado' (MD) | CSut |
| 'Mini' (Sin/Lil) | LBut |
| 'Minley Carol' (Pom) | LAyl NHal |
| 'Minley Iris' (Pom) | LBut |
| 'Minley Linda' (Pom) | LAyl LBut NHal |
| 'Mistill Contessa' (MinD) | NHal |
| 'Monk Marc' (SC) | LBut |
| 'Monkstown Diane' (SC) | LAyl NHal |
| 'Moonfire' (Misc) | CFir EBee EBrP EBre ECle LAyl |
| | LBre LHop MBEx MMil MSte MTis |
| | NGdn NHal SBre SSea SUsu WCot |
| | WHer WMer WWol |
| 'Moonlight' (SD) | MBri SBid |
| 'Moor Place' (Pom) | LAyl NHal WAba WCot |
| 'Morning Dew' (SC) | SDeJ |
| 'Morning Kiss' (LSD) | SDeJ |
| 'Mount Noddy' (Sin) | SMrm |
| 'Mrs McDonald Quill' (LD) | NHal |
| 'Murdoch' | CBos EAst EHic WCot WSpi |
| 'Murillo' | MBri NRog |
| 'My Love' (SS-c) | LAma NRog |
| ¶ 'Nagano' (MD) | CSut |
| 'Nargold' (MS-c) | NHal |
| 'Nationwide' (SD) ♀ | Last listed 1993 |
| 'Neal Gillson' (MD) | NHal |
| 'Nepos' (SWL) | LBut NHal |
| 'New Baby' (MinBa) | NRog |
| ¶ 'Nicola Jane' (Pom) | NHal |
| 'Nina Chester' (SD) | NHal WAba |
| ¶ 'Nonette' (MD) | WAba |
| 'Noreen' (Pom) | LAyl NHal |
| 'Oakwood Diamond' (SBa) | LBut |
| 'Omo' (Sin/Lil) ♀ | LBut |
| 'Orange Keith's Choice' (MD) | NHal |
| 'Orange Mullett' (MinD) ♀ | LAyl |
| ¶ 'Oreti Duke' (Pom) | LAyl |
| 'Orfeo' (MC) | LAma NRog |
| I 'Orion' (MD) | Last listed 1998 |
| 'Ornamental Rays' (SC) | LBut |
| ¶ 'Pablo' | WWol |
| ¶ 'Pacific Argyle' (SD) | NHal |
| ¶ 'Pacific Revival' (Pom) | NHal |
| * 'Park Fever' | Last listed 1997 |
| 'Park Princess' (DwB/SC) | LAma NHal SDeJ |
| 'Paul Chester' (SC) | NHal |
| ¶ 'Peace Pact' (SWL) | WAba |
| 'Peach Cupid' (MinBa) ♀ | LBut NHal WAba |
| 'Peachette' (Misc/Lil) ♀ | LBut |
| 'Pearl of Heemstede' (SD) ♀ | LAyl NHal |
| 'Pearl Sharowean' (MS-c) | WAba |
| ¶ 'Periton' (MinBa) | LAyl NHal |
| 'Phill's Pink' (SD) ♀ | Last listed 1995 |
| ¶ 'Pinelands' Morgenster' (S-c) | NHal |
| 'Pink Jupiter' (GS-c) | NHal |
| 'Pink Pastelle' (MS-c) ♀ | LAyl NHal |
| 'Pink Paul Chester' (SC) ♀ | Last listed 1995 |
| 'Pink Sensation' (SC) | LBut |
| 'Pink Shirley Alliance' (SC) | LAyl |
| * 'Pink Silvia' | Last listed 1997 |
| 'Pink Suffusion' (SD) | NHal |
| 'Pink Surprise' (LS-c) | SDeJ |
| 'Pink Symbol' (MS-c) | LAyl |
| *pinnata* soft yellow | CGle |
| 'Piper's Pink' (SS-c/DwB) ♀ | LAyl |
| I 'Pippa' (MinWL) | LBut |
| 'Plum Surprise' (Pom) | NHal |
| 'Polventon' (SD) | Last listed 1997 |
| 'Polventon Supreme' (SBa) | Last listed 1998 |
| 'Pomponnette' (Anem) | CSut |
| 'Pontiac' (SC) | LAyl |
| 'Pop Willo' (Pom) | GHCN NHal |
| ¶ 'Poppet' (MinD) | WAba |
| 'Porcelain' (SWL) ♀ | LBut NHal |
| 'Potgieter' (MinBa) | NRog |
| 'Preference' (SS-c) | LAma |
| 'Preston Park' (Sin/DwB) ♀ | LAyl NHal |
| 'Pretty Little Princess' (SS-c) ♀ | Last listed 1995 |
| 'Pride of Berlin' | See D. 'Stolze von Berlin' |
| 'Primrose Diane' (SD) | NHal WAba |
| 'Promotion' (MC) | SDeJ |
| 'Purple Gem' | NRog |
| * 'Quantum Leap' | WCot |
| 'Radfo' (SS-c) | GHCN NHal WAba |
| 'Raffles' (SD) | LAyl |
| 'Raiser's Pride' (MC) | NHal WAba |
| 'Rebecca Lynn' (MinD) | NHal |
| 'Red Balloon' (SBa) | NHal |
| 'Red Diamond' (MD) | NHal |
| 'Red Dwarf' | See D. 'Harvest Red Dwarf' |
| 'Red Velvet' (SWL) | LAyl LBut NHal |
| I 'Reedley' (SWL) | LBut |
| ¶ 'Regal Boy' | WAba |
| 'Reginald Keene' (LS-c) | NHal |
| ¶ 'Requiem' (SD) | WAba |
| 'Rhonda' (Pom) | LBut NHal |
| 'Rhonda Suzanne' (Pom) | LBut |
| 'Richard Marc' (SC) | LBut |
| ¶ 'Rip City' (MS-c) | CSut |
| 'Risca Miner' (SBa) | GHCN LBut WAba |
| ¶ 'Roberta' (LD) | WAba |
| ¶ 'Robin Hood' (SBa) | WAba |
| 'Rockliffe' (MinD) | NHal |
| 'Rokesly Mini' (MinC) ♀ | Last listed 1995 |
| 'Rosalie' (Pom) | Last listed 1996 |
| 'Rose Jupiter' (GS-c) | NHal |
| 'Rothesay Herald' (SD/DwB) | Last listed 1998 |
| 'Rothesay Reveller' (MD) | Last listed 1998 |
| ¶ 'Rothesay Robin' (SD) | WAba |
| 'Rotterdam' (MS-c) | SDeJ |
| I 'Roxy' | CMil EBee ECle LRHS NGdn NSti |
| | WCot WWeb |
| 'Royal Blush' (MinD) | Last listed 1997 |
| 'Ruby Wedding' (MinD) | NHal |
| 'Ruskin Belle' (MS-c) | Last listed 1998 |
| 'Ruskin Diane' (SD) | LBut NHal WAba |
| ¶ 'Ruskin Lilo' | WAba |
| * 'Ruskin Tangerine' (SBa) | LBut |
| ¶ 'Rustig' (MD) | WAba |
| 'Ryedale Rebecca' (GS-c) | Last listed 1997 |
| 'Safe Shot' (MD) | NRog |
| 'Saint Moritz' (SS-c) | Last listed 1997 |
| 'Salmon Athalie' (SC) | Last listed 1997 |
| 'Salmon Beauty' (D) | SDeJ |
| 'Salmon Keene' (LS-c) | NHal |

¶ 'Salmon Symbol' (MS-c)　WAba
　'Salsa' (Pom) ♀　NHal
¶ 'Sam Huston' (GD)　WAba
　'Samantha'　See *D.* 'Harvest Samantha'
　'Satellite' (MS-c)　SDeJ
　'Scarlet Kokarde' (MinD)　GHCN
¶ 'Scarlet Rotterdam' (MS-c)　WAba
¶ 'Scaur Swinton' (MD)　NHal
　'Scottish Relation' (SS-c) ♀　Last listed 1996
　'Scottish Rhapsody' (MS-c)　NHal
　'Seattle' (SD)　SCoo
¶ 'Seikemans Feueball'　WAba
　'Senzoe Ursula' (SD)　GHCN
　'Shandy' (SS-c)　LAyl NHal
　***sherffii***　CHad CHal MBEx MCCP MNrw
　- x ***coccinea***　CHad
　'Sherwood Standard' (MD)　NHal WAba
　'Sherwood Titan' (GD)　LAyl
　'Shirley Alliance' (SC)　LAyl
　'Shooting Star' (LS-c)　Last listed 1997
* 'Show and Tell'　Last listed 1997
　'Siemen Doorenbos' (Anem)　NRog
　'Silver City' (LD)　NHal
　'Silver Years'　SCoo
　'Small World' (Pom)　GHCN LAyl LBut NHal
　'Snowstorm' (MD)　LAma SDeJ
　'So Dainty' (MinS-c) ♀　LAyl WAba
　'Sonia'　Last listed 1998
* 'Spacemaker'　SDeJ
§ 'Stolze von Berlin' (MinBa)　NRog WAba
　'Stoneleigh Cherry' (Pom)　LAyl LBut
　'Suffolk Punch' (MD)　LAyl LBut SMrm
　'Suffolk Spectacular' (MD)　Last listed 1996
　'Suitzus Julie' (DwB)　NHal
¶ 'Summer Night' (SC)　NHal
　'Summer Night' (MC)　CHad CPlt
¶ 'Sunray Glint' (MS-c)　WAba
　'Superfine' (SC)　WAba
　'Swanvale' (SD)　NHal
　'Sweet Sensation' (MS-c)　NHal
　'Sweetheart' (SD)　CInt ETub
　'Sylvia's Desire' (SC)　NHal
　'Symbol' (MS-c)　Last listed 1996
　'Sympathy' (SWL)　NHal
¶ 'Tally Ho' (Sin)　LRHS MBri WCot WWeb
¶ 'Tender Moon' (SD)　LAyl
♦ 'Taratahi Lilac'　See *D.* 'Lilac Taratahi'
　'Thomas A. Edison' (MD)　CSut LAma
　'Tiny Tot'　See *D.* 'Harvest Tiny Tot'
　'Tommy Doc' (SS-c)　NHal WAba
　'Tomo' (SD)　NHal
　'Top Choice' (GS-c)　SDeJ
¶ 'Trelawny' (GD)　WAba
　'Trendy' (SD)　SDeJ
　'Trengrove Jill' (MD)　LAyl NHal
　'Trengrove Tauranga' (MD)　Last listed 1998
　'Trevelyn Kiwi' (S-c)　NHal
　'Tui Orange' (SS-c)　NHal WAba
¶ 'Union Jack' (Sin)　WAba
　'Vaguely Noble' (SBa)　NHal
　'Vazon Bay' (MinBa)　CSut
　'Vera's Elma' (LD)　NHal
　'Veritable' (MS-c)　SDeJ
　'Vicky Crutchfield' (SWL)　LAyl LBut
　'Walter Hardisty' (GD) ♀　Last listed 1988
　'Walter James' (SD)　Last listed 1997
　'Wanda's Capella' (GD)　LAyl NHal WAba
　'Wandy' (Pom) ♀　Last listed 1995
　'Warkton Willo' (Pom)　Last listed 1997
¶ 'Wendy's Place' (Pom)　LAyl
¶ 'Weston Nugget' (MinC)　WAba
¶ 'Whale's Rhonda' (Pom)　WAba

　'White Alva's' (GD) ♀　LAyl NHal
　'White Ballet' (SD) ♀　LAyl LBut NHal
　'White Kerkrade' (SC)　Last listed 1997
　'White Klankstad' (SC)　LAyl
　'White Linda' (SD)　NHal
　'White Moonlight' (MS-c)　LAyl LBut NHal WAba
　'White Perfection' (LD)　CSut SDeJ
　'White Polventon' (SBa)　NHal
　'White Swallow' (SS-c)　NHal
¶ 'Willo's Flecks' (Pom)　WAba
　'Willo's Surprise' (Pom)　NHal
¶ 'Willo's Violet' (Pom)　WAba
　'Winkie Colonel' (GD)　NHal
　'Winston Churchill' (MinD)　LBut
　'Winter Dawn' (SWL)　Last listed 1996
　'Wittemans Superba' (SS-c) ♀　LAyl NHal
¶ 'Wootton Cupid' (MinBa) ♀　LAyl LBut NHal
¶ 'Wootton Impact' (MS-c) ♀　LBut NHal
　'Worton Bluestreak' (SS-c)　LBut
　'Yellow Cheer' (SD/DwB)　SDeJ
¶ 'Yellow Hammer'　LAyl NHal SChu SMrm
　　(Sin/DwB) ♀
　'Yellow Impact' (MS-c)　NHal
　'Yellow Linda's Chester' (SC)　Last listed 1998
　'Yellow Spiky' (MS-c)　Last listed 1997
　'Yellow Star' (MS-c)　Last listed 1998
　'Yellow Symbol' (MS-c)　LBut
　'Yelno Enchantment' (SWL)　LAyl
　'Yelno Harmony' (SD) ♀　LBut
　'Yelno Velvena' (SWL)　LAyl
¶ 'York and Lancaster' (MD)　EMon
¶ 'Yorkie' (MS-c)　WAba
I 'Yvonne' (MWL)　NHal
　'Zorro' (GD) ♀　LAyl LBut NHal WAba

## DAIS (Thymelaeaceae)
¶ ***cotinifolia***　CPLG SIgm

## DAISWA See PARIS

## DALEA (Papilionaceae)
　***fremontii***　Last listed 1998
　***gattingeri***　Last listed 1996
　***purpurea***　WMoo

## DALECHAMPIA (Euphorbiaceae)
¶ ***dioscoreifolia***　CPlN

## DAMPIERA (Goodeniaceae)
　***diversifolia***　CSpe

## DANAE (Ruscaceae)
§ ***racemosa*** ♀　CB&S CFil EAst EBee EMon ENot
　　　GCal MRav MSte MTed NFla SAPC
　　　SArc SBid SDry SPer SRms SSpi
　　　SSta WBay WCot WSpi WWeb

## DAPHNE ✿ (Thymelaeaceae)
　***acutiloba***　CHan CPMA ERea LRHS MPla
　　　SBrw SSta WCru WWes
　***albowiana***　CFil CPMA MPla SSta WCru WPGP
　　　WPat WWat WWes
　***alpina***　CPMA EHyt NNrd SBla WAbe
　　　WCru
　***altaica***　CPMA
　'Anton Fahndrich'　SBla
　***arbuscula*** ♀　CPMA EPot SBla SIgm WPat
　- subsp. ***arbuscula***　SBla
　　f. ***albiflora***
　'Beauworth'　CPMA EHyt GCrs SBla SIgm SSta
　***bholua***　ERea GGGa LHop SBid SBrw SReu
　　　SSta WCru WRus WSpi WWat

| | |
|---|---|
| I – 'Alba' | CB&S CFil CPMA LRHS SBla SSta WCru WPGP |
| – 'Damon Ridge' | CPMA |
| – Darjeeling form | CFil CPMA CSam ELan EPfP SBid SBla SBrw SPla SSpi SSta WCru WPGP WPat WWat WWeb |
| – var. *glacialis* | WCru |
| – 'Gurkha' ♀ | CPMA SSta |
| – 'Jacqueline Postill' ♀ | CEnd CPMA EBee LRHS MAsh MBlu MBri MDun MGos SBla SMur SPer SSpi SSta WAbe WCru WGer WPat |
| ¶ – 'Peter Smithers' | SSta |
| – Waterhurst form | CPMA |
| *blagayana* | CBlo CFil CPMA EPot LHop MBal MGrG MPla SBla SIgm SRms WCru WPGP WWat |
| * – *nana* | ITim |
| 'Bramdean' | SBla |
| x *burkwoodii* ♀ | CB&S CBlo CBot CSam IOrc MBal SLon WCru WDin WGwG WRHF WWat |
| – 'Albert Burkwood' | CPMA NWea SBla |
| – 'Astrid' (v) | CB&S COtt CPMA ELan LHop LNet MBlu MGos SBrw SPer SSta WDin WPyg WWeb WWes |
| § – 'Carol Mackie' (v) | CBot CPMA LHop SBla SIgm SSta WWat |
| – 'G.K.Argles' | CBlo CFil CPMA EPfP LRHS SBid SBla SSta WCom WCru WPat WWes |
| – 'Gold Strike' (v) | CPMA |
| – 'Lavenirei' | CPMA |
| * – 'Moonlight' | LRHS WWeb |
| – 'Somerset' | More than 30 suppliers |
| § – 'Somerset Gold Edge' (v) | CPMA |
| § – 'Somerset Variegated' | CFil SBla WPGP |
| I – 'Variegata' | IMGH WPat |
| – 'Variegata' broad cream edge | See *D.* x *burkwoodii* 'Somerset Variegated' |
| – 'Variegata' broad gold edge | See *D.* x *burkwoodii* 'Somerset Gold Edge' |
| – 'Variegata' narrow gold edge | See *D.* x *burkwoodii* 'Carol Mackie' |
| *caucasica* | CPMA SBla |
| 'Cheriton' | CPMA GCrs SBla SSta |
| *cneorum* | CB&S CBlo CEnd CFil CPMA ELan ENot EPfP EWTr MBal MDun MGos NBee NEgg SBod SPer SReu SSoC SSta WPat WSpi WWat WWeb WWin |
| – f.*alba* | CPMA SBla |
| ¶ – var.*arbuscula* x *verlotii* | CPMA |
| ¶ – 'Blackthorn Triumph' | SBla |
| – 'Eximia' ♀ | CPMA EPot GCrs IOrc LNet MBel MGos SIng SRms WAbe WCru |
| ◆ – 'Grandiflora' | See *D.* x *napolitana* 'Maxima' |
| * – 'Poszta' | CPMA SBla SIgm WCru |
| – var.*pygmaea* | CPMA EPot SBla WPat |
| – – 'Alba' | CPMA SBla WPat |
| – 'Rose Glow' | CPMA |
| – 'Rubrum' | EPot |
| – 'Variegata' | CPMA EPot LHop MGos MMil NWCA SPer SReu SSta WAbe WSHC |
| ¶ – 'Velký Kosir' | CPMA SBla |
| *collina* | See *D. sericea* Collina Group |
| ¶ – x *petraea* | SSta |
| 'Fragrant Cloud' (aff. *acutiloba*) CD&R 626 | SBla |
| *genkwa* | CPMA SBla SBrw |
| *giraldii* | CPMA EPot GCrs SIgm SSpi WCru |

| | |
|---|---|
| x *hendersonii* | CPMA |
| – 'Appleblossom' | SBla |
| ¶ – 'Blackthorn Rose' | SBla |
| – CDB 11660 | SBla |
| – 'Ernst Hauser' | CPMA GCrs SBla |
| – 'Fritz Kummert' | SBla |
| – 'Rosebud' | SBla |
| x *houtteana* | CBot CPMA LRHS MPla NBir SSta WCru |
| x *hybrida* | CPMA SBla |
| *japonica* 'Striata' | See *D. odora* 'Aureomarginata' |
| *jasminea* | CPMA ECho SBla SIng WPat |
| – AM form | Last listed 1998 |
| *jezoensis* | CPMA |
| *juliae* | CPMA SBla |
| 'Kilmeston' | CPMA EHyt SBla |
| ¶ *kosaninii* | WLin |
| *laureola* | CPMA CSWP GPoy MBro MGos MPla NPer NSti SSta WSpi WWat WWye |
| – var. *cantabrica* | SChu |
| – 'Margaret Mathew' | EPot SBla |
| – subsp. *philippi* | CBlo CPMA EBee EPfP IMGH LHop MAsh MPla SBrw SChu SPer SSpi SSta WCru WPat WWat |
| 'Leila Haines' x *arbuscula* | CPMA SBla |
| *longilobata* | WCru WPat WWat |
| – 'Peter Moore' | CPMA |
| x *manteniana* | Last listed 1998 |
| – 'Manten' | CPMA SLon |
| 'Meon' | CPMA SBla |
| *mezereum* | CBlo CBot ENot EWFC GAbr GDra GPoy GRei ITim MBal MBar MBri MGrG MPla NFor NLon NNrd NRoo NWea SBrw SPer SReu SSoC SSta WDin WFar WHar WPat WWat WWeb |
| – f.*alba* | CFil GAbr IOrc LHop MBar MGrG MPla NChi NNrd SBla SEas SSta WAbe WCru WPGP WPat WPyg WTin WWat WWeb |
| – 'Bowles' Variety' | CBot CPMA EPot |
| – 'Grandiflora' | See *D. mezereum* var. *autumnalis* |
| – 'Rosea' | SRms |
| – var.*rubra* | CB&S CBlo CFil CPMA ELan EPfP IOrc LNet MGos NBee NFla SBod SPer SReu SSta WAbe WCru WDin WGer WWeb |
| – 'Variegata' | LHop |
| x *napolitana* ♀ | CHan CPMA LNet LRHS MGos SSta WWat |
| § – 'Maxima' | MGos |
| *odora* | CBlo CPMA CPle ERea GOrc LSpr MGos SBrw SChu SRms SSta WCru WSel |
| § – f.*alba* | CB&S CBlo ERea MGos SMrm SSta |
| § – 'Aureomarginata' | More than 30 suppliers |
| – 'Banana Split' | Last listed 1998 |
| – 'Clotted Cream' | CPMA |
| – var.*leucantha* | See *D. odora* f. *alba* |
| – 'Marginata' | See *D. odora* 'Aureomarginata' |
| – var.*rubra* | CPMA LRHS NPSl SBrw SSta |
| – 'Sakiwaka' | CPMA |
| – 'Walberton' (v) | LRHS |
| * – 'Zuiko-nishiki' | WCru |
| *oleoides* | CPMA GAbr GCrs IMGH LNet SBla |
| ¶ 'Perfume of Spring' | CPMA |
| *petraea* | EPot SBla |
| – 'Alba' | See *D. petraea* 'Tremalzo' |

|  |  |
|---|---|
| - 'Grandiflora' ♀ | EPot GCrs SBla WPat |
| § - 'Tremalzo' | SBla |
| *pontica* ♀ | CB&S CFil CPMA CPle EHyt ELan |
|  | EOHP LHop MPla SBrw SDix |
|  | SMad SSpi SUsu WCru WPat WWat |
| ¶ *pseudomezereum* | WCru |
| *retusa* | See *D. tangutica* Retusa Group |
| 'Richard's Choice' | CPMA |
| *rodriguezii* | Last listed 1998 |
| x *rollsdorfii* 'Arnold Cihlarz' | CPMA SBla |
| ¶ - 'Wilhelm Schacht' | CPMA SBla |
| 'Rosy Wave' | SBla |
| § *sericea* ♀ | CFil CPMA SBla SRms WCru |
| § - Collina Group | CPMA EPfP SMur SRms SSpi SSta |
|  | WWat |
| x *suendermannii* | SBla |
| *tangutica* ♀ | More than 30 suppliers |
| § - Retusa Group ♀ | CCHP CPMA EHyt EPot GAbr |
|  | GChr GRei LHop MBri MGos |
|  | MPla NRoo SBla SIgm SReu SRms |
|  | SSta SUsu WPyg |
| x *thauma* | SBla |
| - 'Aymon Correvon' | SBla |
| 'Tichborne' | CPMA SBla |
| 'Warnford' | Last listed 1996 |

## DAPHNIPHYLLUM (Daphniphyllaceae)

|  |  |
|---|---|
| *glaucescens* B&SWJ 4058 | WCru |
| *himalense* | CB&S CDoC CFil CPle EPfP EPla |
| var. *macropodum* | GCal IDee MBlu SAPC SArc SBid |
|  | SDix SLPl SMad SSpi SSta WPGP |
|  | WShe |
| - var. *macropodum* | WCru |
| B&SWJ 581 |  |
| *humile* B&SWJ 2898 | WCru |
| ¶ *teijsmannii* B&SWJ 3805 | WCru |

## DARLINGTONIA (Sarraceniaceae)

|  |  |
|---|---|
| *californica* ♀ | CFil CSWC EAnd EEls EFEx GTro |
|  | WMEx WPGP |

## DARMERA (Saxifragaceae)

|  |  |
|---|---|
| § *peltata* ♀ | More than 30 suppliers |
| - 'Nana' | ECha GNau MFir NHol NLar SWat |

## DASYLIRION (Agavaceae)

|  |  |
|---|---|
| § *acrotrichum* | SAPC SArc |
| *glaucophyllum* | Last listed 1997 |
| *gracile* Planchon | See *D. acrotrichum* |
| *longissimum* | CAbb |
| ¶ *texanum* | EOas |
| *wheeleri* | CAbb CRoM CTrC EOas |

## DASYPHYLLUM (Asteraceae)

|  |  |
|---|---|
| *diacanthoides* | CGre |

## DATISCA (Datiscaceae)

|  |  |
|---|---|
| *cannabina* | GCal SMrm WCot WPic |

## DATURA (Solanaceae)

|  |  |
|---|---|
| *arborea* | See *Brugmansia arborea* |
| *ceratocaula* | Last listed 1996 |
| *chlorantha* | See *Brugmansia chlorantha* |
| *cornigera* | See *Brugmansia arborea* |
| § *inoxia* | EBak ERea MSal SOWG SRCN |
|  | SVen SYvo |
| - 'Evening Fragrance' | SPar |
| - subsp. *inoxia* | Last listed 1998 |
| *metel* | ERea |
| - black | Last listed 1997 |
| * - 'Cherub' | GQui |
| * - 'La Fleur Lilas' | Last listed 1997 |

|  |  |
|---|---|
| *meteloides* | See *D. inoxia* |
| *rosea* | See *Brugmansia* x *insignis* pink |
| *rosei* | See *Brugmansia sanguinea* |
| *sanguinea* | See *Brugmansia sanguinea* |
| *stramonium* | CArn EWFC MHew MSal WHer |
| - var. *chalybaea* | MSal |
| *suaveolens* | See *Brugmansia suaveolens* |
| *versicolor* | See *Brugmansia versicolor* |
|  | Lagerh. |
| - 'Grand Marnier' | See *Brugmansia* x *candida* |
|  | 'Grand Marnier' |

## DAUCUS (Apiaceae)

|  |  |
|---|---|
| *carota* | CArn CKin EWFC IIve MHew |
|  | WGwy WHer |

## DAVALLIA ✿ (Davalliaceae)

|  |  |
|---|---|
| *canariensis* ♀ | CFil CGre |
| I *fejeensis* | See *D. solida* var. *fejeensis* |
| § *mariesii* ♀ | CFil MBri WCot WRic |
| - var. *stenolepis* | NMar |
| *pyxidata* | See *D. solida* var. *pyxidata* |
| § *solida* var. *fejeensis* | MBri |
| § - var. *pyxidata* | NMar |
| ¶ *tasmanii* | CFil |
| *trichomanoides* | NMar WRic |
| - var. *lorrainei* | NMar |

## DAVIDIA (Davidiaceae)

|  |  |
|---|---|
| *involucrata* ♀ | More than 30 suppliers |
| - var. *vilmoriniana* ♀ | CB&S CGre ELan EPfP LNet MAsh |
|  | MGos MWat NBee NFla NPal SPer |
|  | SRPl SSta |

## DEBREGEASIA (Urticaceae)

|  |  |
|---|---|
| *longifolia* | CPle |

## DECAISNEA (Lardizabalaceae)

|  |  |
|---|---|
| *fargesii* | CBrd CDoC CPle EBee ELan EPla |
|  | GOrc MBNS MBel MBlu MCCP |
|  | MDun MWhi NArg NPal NTow |
|  | SMad SPar SPer WBor WCoo |
|  | WDin WGer WWat |
| - 'Harlequin' (v) | Last listed 1997 |
| *insignis* | WNor |

## DECODON (Lythraceae)

|  |  |
|---|---|
| *verticillatus* | CHan EHon EMon |

## DECUMARIA (Saxifragaceae)

|  |  |
|---|---|
| *barbara* | CB&S CDoC CFil CGre CMac |
|  | CPlN CTrC EBee EMil EPfP EPla |
|  | GOrc SBra SLon SPer SSta WCru |
|  | WSHC WThi WWat |
| *sinensis* | CPlN EPfP SBra SSpi WSHC |

## DEGENIA (Brassicaceae)

|  |  |
|---|---|
| *velebitica* | NTow |

## DEINANTHE (Hydrangeaceae)

|  |  |
|---|---|
| *bifida* | WCru |
| ¶ - B&SWJ 5012 | WCru |
| *caerulea* | WCru |

## DELAIREA (Asteraceae)

|  |  |
|---|---|
| § *odorata* | WMul |

## DELONIX (Caesalpiniaceae)

|  |  |
|---|---|
| *regia* | LBlo SOWG |

## DELOSPERMA (Aizoaceae)

|  |  |
|---|---|
| § *aberdeenense* | WCot |

| | |
|---|---|
| * *album* | Last listed 1998 |
| *ashtonii* | EOas WPer |
| 'Basutoland' | See *D. nubigenum* |
| *congestum* | WCot |
| *cooperi* | CFai EOas NHol NTow SChr WPat |
| | WPer WPyg WWoo |
| ¶ *floribundum* | CTrC |
| *lineare* | NBir |
| *lydenburgense* | IBlr SChr |
| * *macei* | Last listed 1997 |
| *macellum* | EOas |
| *mariae* | Last listed 1997 |
| § *nubigenum* | CHal CTrC EDAr ELan EOas EPot |
| | GGar LBee LNor NHol NNrd SIng |
| | SSmi WHoo WPer WPyg WWin |
| *sutherlandii* | EDAr WCot WPyg |
| ¶ *uncinatum* | EOas |

## DELPHINIUM ✿ (Ranunculaceae)

| | |
|---|---|
| 'Abendleuchten' | LGre |
| 'After Midnight' | Last listed 1996 |
| 'Agnes Brookes' | ERou |
| *alabamicum* | Last listed 1998 |
| 'Alice Artindale' | CBos CHad CPlt EGle LGre MRav |
| | SAga SMrm WCom WSan |
| ¶ 'Alie Duyvensteyn' | EFou |
| *ambiguum* | See *Consolida ajacis* |
| *andesicola* | Last listed 1998 |
| ¶ 'Ann Kenrick' | MWoo |
| 'Ann Woodfield' | MWoo |
| 'Anne Page' | ERou |
| Astolat Group | CB&S CBot CDoC EBee EBrP EBre |
| | ELan EOld EWTr GAbr LBre LPVe |
| | LRot MBri MRav MWat NFla NFor |
| | NLon NPri NRoo SBre SPer SSoC |
| | WFar WHoo WSan |
| 'Atholl' | Last listed 1996 |
| 'Augenweide' | EFou |
| Avon strain | MWoo |
| 'Barbara Nason' | Last listed 1997 |
| *barbeyi* | Last listed 1998 |
| 'Basil Clitheroe' | Last listed 1998 |
| *beesianum* | Last listed 1998 |
| ¶ – ACE 1361 | EPot GBin |
| Belladonna Group | ELan SRPl |
| – 'Andenken an August | See *D.* (Belladonna Group) |
|    Koeneman' | 'Wendy' |
| – 'Atlantis' | EBee ECha EFou LGre MBri MTed |
| | WViv |
| – 'Balkleid' | EBee EFou |
| – 'Blue Shadow' | Last listed 1998 |
| – 'Capri' | Last listed 1998 |
| – 'Casa Blanca' | CBlo CGle EBee EFou LEur MMal |
| | MTis SIgm SPla SRPl WLRN |
| – 'Cliveden Beauty' | CBlo CGle EBee EFou EWTr GBri |
| | SIgm SMrm SPla WHoo WLRN |
| | WMer |
| I – 'Freedom' | LRHS |
| – 'Kleine Nachtmusik' | EFou |
| – 'Moerheimii' | EFou SPla WMer |
| – 'Peace' | EBrP EBre LBre NRoo SBre |
| – 'Piccolo' | EBee EFou SPla WViv |
| – 'Pink Sensation' | See *D.* x *ruysii* 'Pink Sensation' |
| – 'Völkerfrieden' | EBee EFou MBri MRav NPri NPro |
| | SPla WMer WRus |
| x *bellamosum* | CBlo CBot CMGP EBee EFou |
| | EWTr GBri MTis SMrm SPla |
| | WLRN WViv |
| 'Berghimmel' | Last listed 1998 |
| 'Beryl Burton' | ERou |
| 'Betty Baseley' | ERou |
| *bicolor* | Last listed 1998 |

| | |
|---|---|
| *biternatum* | Last listed 1996 |
| Black Knight Group | CB&S CDoC EBee EBrP EBre ECtt |
| | ELan EOld EWTr GAbr LBre MBri |
| | MCAu MRav MWat MWgw NFla |
| | NFor NMir NPri NRoo NVic SBre |
| | SPer SPlb SSoC WFar WRus |
| 'Blauwal' | LGre |
| Blue Bird Group | CB&S EBee ELan EPfP EWTr GAbr |
| | MBri MBro MCAu MRav NFor |
| | NLon NMir NPri NRoo NVic SPer |
| | WFar |
| 'Blue Butterfly' | See *D. grandiflorum* 'Blue |
| | Butterfly' |
| 'Blue Dawn' ♀ | CBla ERou |
| Blue Fountains Group | ELan EMan MBri NBee NOak SPer |
| | SRms WStI |
| Blue Heaven Group | Last listed 1997 |
| Blue Jade Group | CBla ERou |
| 'Blue Jay' | CB&S CMGP EBee EBrP EBre |
| | ENot EOld EWTr LBre MCAu NBir |
| | NLon NPri SBre WLRN |
| 'Blue Lagoon' | CBla |
| ¶ 'Blue Mirror' | MMal |
| 'Blue Nile' ♀ | CBla ERou MWoo |
| Blue Springs Group | NOrc WShe |
| 'Blue Tit' | CBla ERou MWat |
| 'Blue Triumph' | WPyg |
| 'Blue Triumphator' | Last listed 1998 |
| § *brachycentrum* | Last listed 1998 |
| 'Browne's Lavender' | Last listed 1997 |
| 'Bruce' ♀ | EFou ERou MWoo |
| *brunonianum* | SBla |
| *bulleyanum* | SIng |
| 'Butterball' | CBla |
| *californicum* | Last listed 1998 |
| Cameliard Group | CB&S CMGP EBee EBrP EBre ECtt |
| | ELan EMan GAbr LBre NCut |
| | NLon NPri SBre SPer SRPl WLRN |
| 'Can-can' | ERou |
| *cardinale* | CBot CGen EBee EWTr LEur |
| 'Carl Topping' | ERou |
| *carolinianum* | Last listed 1998 |
| ♦ – subsp. *virescens* | See *D. virescens* |
| *cashmerianum* | CBot EBee ELan EWes MTho |
| | NTow |
| – 'Gladys Hull' | Last listed 1998 |
| 'Cassius' ♀ | CBla ERou MWoo |
| *caucasicum* | See *D. speciosum* |
| 'Celebration' | Last listed 1997 |
| * 'Centurion Sky Blue' | CFai |
| *ceratophorum* | SIng WLin |
| ♦ *chamissonis* | See *D. brachycentrum* |
| *cheilanthum* | NFla |
| 'Chelsea Star' | CBla ERou WViv |
| ¶ 'Cherry Blossom' | NLon |
| 'Cherub' | CBla ERou MWoo |
| *chinense* | See *D. grandiflorum* |
| 'Christel' | EFou |
| 'Circe' | ERou |
| 'Clack's Choice' | ERou WViv |
| 'Claire' ♀ | MWoo |
| 'Clear Springs Lavender' | Last listed 1998 |
|    (Clear Springs Series) | |
| 'Clear Springs Mid Blue' | Last listed 1998 |
|    (Clear Springs Series) | |
| 'Clear Springs Rose Pink' | Last listed 1998 |
|    (Clear Springs Series) | |
| 'Clifford Lass' | MWoo |
| 'Clifford Pink' | CBla MWoo |
| 'Clifford Sky' | MWoo |
| Connecticut Yankees Group | CBlo CFri NOak SIgm |
| 'Conspicuous' ♀ | CBla ERou MWoo |

| | |
|---|---|
| 'Constance Rivett' ♀ | ERou |
| aff. *crassifolium* | WLin |
| 'Cream Cracker' | Last listed 1996 |
| 'Cressida' | ERou |
| 'Cristella' | ERou |
| 'Crown Jewel' | CBla EFou ERou |
| 'Cupid' | CBla ERou |
| 'Daily Express' | ERou |
| 'Darling Sue' | Last listed 1997 |
| 'David's Magnificent' | WEas |
| *decorum* | Last listed 1998 |
| *delavayi* | SIng |
| - CLD 895 | EHyt |
| * 'Delfy Blue' | WViv |
| 'Demavand' | ERou |
| 'Diana Grenfell' | Last listed 1996 |
| 'Dolly Bird' | CBla ERou |
| 'Dora Larkan' | Last listed 1997 |
| 'Dorothy Ash' | Last listed 1996 |
| 'Dreaming Spires' | SRms |
| 'Duchess of Portland' | ERou |
| 'Dunsdon Green' | Last listed 1996 |
| dwarf dark blue | LRHS |
| dwarf lavender | LRHS |
| dwarf pink | LRHS |
| dwarf sky blue | LRHS |
| 'Eamonn Andrews' | ERou |
| *elatum* | EWTr GCal SRms |
| 'Elisabeth Sahin' | Last listed 1996 |
| 'Elmfreude' | Last listed 1998 |
| 'Emily Hawkins' ♀ | ERou MWoo |
| 'Eva Gower' | ERou |
| 'Evita' | Last listed 1996 |
| *exaltatum* | CPou ECGN |
| 'F.W. Smith' | EFou WMer WPyg |
| 'Fanfare' ♀ | CBla ERou |
| 'Father Thames' | ERou |
| 'Faust' ♀ | CBla ERou MWat MWoo |
| 'Fenella' ♀ | CBla MWoo WCFE |
| 'Finsteraarhorn' | EFou |
| 'Florestan' | Last listed 1996 |
| 'Foxhill Eileen' | Last listed 1996 |
| 'Foxhill Lady' | Last listed 1996 |
| 'Foxhill Nina' | Last listed 1997 |
| 'Foxhill Oscar' | Last listed 1996 |
| 'Foxhill Pinta' | Last listed 1996 |
| 'Foxhill Roseanna' | Last listed 1996 |
| 'Fred Yule' | ERou |
| Galahad Group | CB&S CDoC EBee EBrP EBre EFou ELan ENot EWTr GAbr LBre LGre MBNS MBri MCAu MRav MWat NBir NFla NFor NLon NMir NPri NRoo NVic SBre SPer SPlb WFar |
| 'Garden Party' | CBla |
| 'Gemma' | MWoo |
| *geraniifolium* | NTow |
| ¶ *geyeri* | EBee |
| 'Gillian Dallas' ♀ | CBla ERou MWoo |
| 'Giotto' ♀ | Last listed 1995 |
| *glareosum* | EHyt |
| *glaucum* | Last listed 1998 |
| 'Gletscherwasser' | LGre |
| 'Gordon Forsyth' | CBla ERou MWoo |
| 'Gossamer' | Last listed 1998 |
| § *grandiflorum* | ESis EWTr NChi SMrm |
| ¶ - ACE 1606 | EHyt |
| ¶ - 'Azure Fairy' | SRms |
| § - 'Blauer Zwerg' | CGle EBee EPfP WRus |
| § - 'Blue Butterfly' | CBot CSpe EBrP EBre EBur EWTr LBre LHop MWgw NOrc SAga SBla SBre SCoo SPlb WElm WWin |

| | |
|---|---|
| - Blue Dwarf | See *D. grandiflorum* 'Blauer Zwerg' |
| * - 'Tom Pouce' | WHil |
| - 'White Butterfly' | Last listed 1996 |
| Guinevere Group | CB&S EBee EBrP EBre ECtt EMan EOld EWTr GAbr LBre LPVe MBri MRav MWat NBir NFor NLon NPri NRoo SBre SPer WFar WRHF WViv |
| 'Guy Langdon' | ERou |
| 'Harlekijn' | Last listed 1998 |
| 'Harmony' | ERou |
| *himalayae* | Last listed 1998 |
| 'Honey Bee' | Last listed 1997 |
| *hotulae* | EBee |
| *hybridum* | Last listed 1998 |
| 'Icecap' | Last listed 1997 |
| 'Iceman' | Last listed 1996 |
| Ivory Towers Group | ECtt |
| 'James Nuttall' | ECha |
| 'Jill Curley' | Last listed 1996 |
| 'Joyce Roffey' | ERou |
| 'Judy Knight' | ERou MWat |
| 'Kathleen Cooke' ♀ | Last listed 1997 |
| 'Kestrel' | ERou |
| King Arthur Group | CB&S CDoC EBee ECtt ELan ENot EPfP GAbr MBri MCAu MOne MRav MWat NFla NPri SPer WFar |
| 'Lady Guinevere' | ERou WPyg |
| 'Lady Hambleden' | See *D.* 'Patricia, Lady Hambleden' |
| § 'Langdon's Royal Flush' ♀ | CBla MWoo |
| 'Leonora' | ERou |
| *likiangense* | EHyt EPot WLin |
| * 'Lilac Arrow' | Last listed 1998 |
| 'Lilian Bassett' ♀ | ERou MWoo |
| 'Loch Katrine' | Last listed 1996 |
| 'Loch Leven' ♀ | CBla ERou MWoo |
| 'Loch Nevis' | Last listed 1997 |
| 'Loch Torridon' | Last listed 1996 |
| 'Lord Butler' ♀ | CBla |
| 'Lorna' | ERou |
| § *luteum* | CPBP NChi SBla SIgm |
| Magic Fountains Series | EBrP EBre EWTr LBre NCut NPri NRoo SBre SPlb WGor WRHF |
| 'Magic Fountains Sky Blue' (Magic Fountains Series) | Last listed 1998 |
| 'Margaret Farrand' | ERou |
| 'Marie Broan' | ERou |
| 'Max Euwe' | Last listed 1998 |
| *menziesii* | ERos NWCA |
| 'Michael Ayres' ♀ | CBla ERou MWoo |
| 'Micky' | Last listed 1998 |
| 'Mighty Atom' ♀ | CBla ERou MWoo |
| 'Min' ♀ | ERou MWoo |
| 'Molly Buchanan' | CBla ERou |
| *montanum* | Last listed 1998 |
| 'Moonbeam' | CBla |
| 'Morning Cloud' | ERou |
| 'Mother Teresa' | ERou |
| 'Mrs Newton Lees' | ERou WPyg |
| 'Mrs T. Carlile' | ERou |
| *multiplex* | Last listed 1998 |
| *muscosum* | Last listed 1998 |
| * 'Mystique' | CBla ERou |
| 'Nar' | Last listed 1998 |
| *nelsonii* | Last listed 1998 |
| New Century hybrids | CB&S EBrP EBre LBre SBre |
| 'Nicholas Woodfield' | MWoo |
| 'Nimrod' | CBla ERou |
| 'Nobility' | CBla ERou |
| *nudicaule* | CBot CGen EBee ELan EPfP ESis GBuc MBNS NRoo NWCA SRot WLin |

| | |
|---|---|
| - var. *luteum* | See *D. luteum* |
| *nuttallianum* | Last listed 1998 |
| *occidentale* | Last listed 1998 |
| 'Olive Poppleton' | CBla MWoo |
| 'Oliver' ♀ | ERou MWoo |
| * *orfordii* | EBee NWCA |
| 'Our Deb' ♀ | MWoo |
| *oxysepalum* | Last listed 1998 |
| Pacific hybrids | ENot EWTr NOak SRms WByw |
| * 'Pandora' | CBla |
| * 'Parade' | EFou |
| *parryi* | Last listed 1998 |
| 'Patricia Johnson' | ERou |
| Percival Group | LRHS NLon |
| 'Pericles' | CBla |
| ¶ 'Perlmutterbaum' | LGre |
| Pink Dream Group | Last listed 1997 |
| 'Pink Ruffles' | CBla ERou |
| *pogonanthum* | EBee |
| 'Polar Sun' | ERou |
| ¶ 'Princess Caroline' | CB&S |
| *przewalskii* | Last listed 1998 |
| ¶ *pseudograndiflorum* | EPot WLin |
| ACE 2243 | |
| 'Purity' | ERou |
| 'Purple Ruffles' | ERou |
| 'Purple Sky' | Last listed 1998 |
| 'Purple Triumph' | ERou |
| 'Purple Velvet' | CBla |
| *pylzowii* | CLyd EBee MBro NNrd |
| *pyramidatum* | Last listed 1998 |
| 'Pyramus' | ERou |
| ¶ 'Rakker' | WCot |
| 'Red Rocket' | CB&S |
| *requienii* | CBot EBee ERav MTho NBir WCot WEas WHer WOut |
| - variegated | Last listed 1997 |
| 'Romany' | Last listed 1996 |
| 'Rona' | Last listed 1997 |
| 'Rosemary Brock' ♀ | ERou MWoo |
| ¶ Round Table Mixture | CSam |
| 'Royal Copenhagen' | Last listed 1998 |
| 'Royal Flush' | See *D.* 'Langdon's Royal Flush' |
| 'Royal Velvet' | Last listed 1997 |
| ¶ 'Rubin' | LGre |
| 'Ruby' | CBla |
| § x *ruysii* 'Pink Sensation' | CBot EFou ERou GBri MTed NPri NRoo WHil WMer WPGP WPyg WRus |
| 'Sabrina' | CBla ERou |
| 'Samantha' | ERou |
| 'Sandpiper' ♀ | Last listed 1997 |
| 'Sarah Edwards' | Last listed 1997 |
| *scaposum* | Last listed 1998 |
| 'Schildknappe' | EFou LGre |
| 'Schönbuch' | EFou |
| *scopulorum* | Last listed 1998 |
| § *semibarbatum* | CBot CGen EWTr NPri SIgm |
| 'Sentinel' | ERou |
| 'Shimmer' | CBla ERou |
| 'Silver Jubilee' | ERou |
| 'Silver Moon' | ERou |
| 'Sky Beauty' | Last listed 1997 |
| * 'Sky Fantasie' | Last listed 1998 |
| 'Skyline' | CBla ERou |
| Snow White Group | NOak SRms |
| 'Snowdon' | Last listed 1998 |
| 'Solomon' | ERou |
| Southern Aristocrats Group | WGle WPyg |
| Southern Consort Group | CBlo WGle WPyg |
| Southern Countess Group ♀ | WGle |
| Southern Countrymen Group ♀ | Last listed 1996 |
| Southern Debutante Group | CBlo WGle WPyg |
| Southern Jesters Group | CBlo WGle WPyg |
| Southern Ladies Group | WPyg |
| Southern Maidens Group ♀ | WGle |
| Southern Minstrels Group | WGle |
| Southern Noblemen Group | Last listed 1996 |
| Southern Royals Group | CBlo WGle WPyg |
| sp. ACW | Last listed 1998 |
| sp. CC&McK 123 | Last listed 1996 |
| sp. CLD 349 | Last listed 1998 |
| sp. from Czech Republic | CGra |
| * 'Space Fantasy' | Last listed 1998 |
| § *speciosum* | EBee |
| 'Spindrift' ♀ | EFou |
| *stapeliosmum* | EBee WCru |
| B&SWJ 2954 | |
| *staphisagria* | EOHP MHew MSal |
| * - 'Variegatum' | Last listed 1998 |
| 'Strawberry Fair' | CBla EFou ERou MWat WViv |
| *suave* | Last listed 1998 |
| 'Summer Haze' | ERou |
| Summer Skies Group | CB&S CMGP EBee ECtt EMan EWTr MBri MCAu MWat MWgw NBir NFla NLon NPri NRoo SPer SRPl SSoC WFar |
| ¶ 'Summerfield Ariane' | MWoo |
| ¶ 'Summerfield Diana' | MWoo |
| 'Summerfield Miranda' ♀ | MWoo |
| 'Summerfield Oberon' | MWoo |
| 'Summerfield Viking' | MWoo |
| 'Sungleam' ♀ | CBla CFir EFou ERou EWTr MCAu MWat WRus |
| 'Sunkissed' | MWoo |
| 'Swan Lake' | ERou |
| *tatsienense* | CGen CLyd CMdw EHyt GDra MBro MTho NChi NWCA SIng SRms WHoo WLin WPyg |
| - 'Album' | EWes SRms |
| 'Tessa' | ERou |
| 'Thamesmead' ♀ | Last listed 1996 |
| 'Thelma Rowe' ♀ | Last listed 1991 |
| 'Thundercloud' | ERou |
| 'Tiddles' ♀ | CBla |
| 'Titania' | CBla |
| *trichophorum* | Last listed 1998 |
| *tricorne* | ERos GCrs LRHS |
| 'Turkish Delight' | CBla ERou WViv |
| *uliginosum* | Last listed 1998 |
| 'Vespers' | CBla ERou |
| *vestitum* | GCan |
| § *virescens* | Last listed 1998 |
| ♦ - subsp. *wootonii* | See *D. wootonii* |
| 'Walton Beauty' | MWoo |
| 'Walton Gemstone' ♀ | CBla MWoo |
| 'Watkin Samuel' | ERou |
| 'White Ruffles' | CBla |
| § *wootonii* | Last listed 1998 |
| *yunnanense* | Last listed 1998 |
| 'Yvonne' | EFou |
| *zalil* | See *D. semibarbatum* |
| Zeeland Series light blues ♀ | Last listed 1996 |

# DENDRANTHEMA ✿ (Asteraceae)

| | |
|---|---|
| cultivars | See *Chrysanthemum* |
| *nankingense* | See *Chrysanthemum nankingense* |
| *pacificum* | See *Ajania pacifica* |

## DENDRIOPOTERIUM See SANGUISORBA

## DENDROBENTHAMIA See CORNUS

## DENDROBIUM ✿ (Orchidaceae)
*moniliforme*                   SWes

## DENDROCALAMUS (Poaceae - Bambusoideae)
*giganteus*                     Last listed 1997
§ *strictus*                    Last listed 1997

## DENDROMECON (Papaveraceae)
*rigida*                        CB&S CFil EPfP GCal LRHS NRar
                                SBid SSoC SSpi SSta WPGP

## DENDROSERIS (Asteraceae)
*littoralis*                    Last listed 1998

## DENNSTAEDTIA (Dennstaedtiaceae)
*davallioides*                  WRic

## DENTARIA (Brassicaceae)
*californica*                   EBee EPar WCru
*digitata*                      See *Cardamine pentaphyllos*
*diphylla*                      EPar WCru
*microphylla*                   See *Cardamine microphylla*
*pinnata*                       See *Cardamine heptaphylla*
*polyphylla*                    See *Cardamine kitaibelii*

## DERMATOBOTRYS (Scrophulariaceae)
¶ *saundersii*                  LHil

## DERRIS (Papilionaceae)
*elliptica* ✿                  CPlN

## DERWENTIA See PARAHEBE

## DESCHAMPSIA (Poaceae)
*cespitosa*                     CKin CNat EPPr GMaP GOrn
                                MBar MBrN MHar MUlv MWhi
                                NArg NHol WCFE WPer
 - subsp. *alpina*              EHoe EMon EPPr LRHS
 - Bronze Veil                  See *D. cespitosa* 'Bronzeschleier'
§ - 'Bronzeschleier'           CHan EBrP EBre ECGN ECoo
                                EFou EHoe EMan EPla GBri
                                GCHN GCal GMaP IBlr LBre LGre
                                MCAu MCLN MSte NHol NSti
                                SBre SCob SMrm SPer SPla SUsu
                                WCot WRus WWat
 - 'Fairy's Joke'               See *D. cespitosa* var. *vivipara*
 - Gold Dust                    See *D. cespitosa* 'Goldstaub'
 - Golden Dew                   See *D. cespitosa* 'Goldtau'
 - Golden Pendant               See *D. cespitosa* 'Goldgehänge'
♦ - 'Golden Shower'            See *D. cespitosa* 'Goldgehänge'
 - Golden Veil                  See *D. cespitosa* 'Goldschleier'
§ - 'Goldgehänge'             CCuc ECtt EGar EHoe EMan
                                EMon EPPr EPfP EPla GCal IBlr
                                NHol NPro NSti SLPl
§ - 'Goldschleier'            CVer ECha EFou EHoe EMon EPPr
                                EPla EWsh GAri GBuc GCHN
                                GOrn IBlr LGre MCLN NHar
                                NOak SApp SCob SUsu
§ - 'Goldstaub'               EFou EPla WCot
§ - 'Goldtau'                 EBrP EBre ECGN ECha EHoe
                                EMon EPGN EPPr EPla ESis EWsh
                                GCHN GMaP LBre LGre LHil
                                MCLN MMoz MRav MTis NEgg
                                NHol NOrc SBre SCob SLPl SPla
                                SUsu
 - subsp. *paludosa*           EMon EPPr
 - var. *parviflora*           Last listed 1997

¶ - 'Tautrager'                 SMad
§ - var. *vivipara*            CVer EBee ECtt EHoe EMon EPPr
                                EPla LHil NBro NHol NSti SAsh
*flexuosa*                      CBrm CCuc CPea EHoe EMon
                                EPPr EPla MBri WPer
 - 'Peter David'                Last listed 1996
 - 'Tatra Gold'                 More than 30 suppliers
*media*                         Last listed 1997
 - bronze                       Last listed 1997
* 'Morning Dew'                ECoo WFar
*setacea* bronze               Last listed 1997

## DESFONTAINIA (Loganiaceae)
§ *spinosa* ♀                  More than 30 suppliers
 - 'Harold Comber'             CMac MBal WBod WCru
 - *hookeri*                    See *D. spinosa*

## DESMANTHUS (Mimosaceae)
*illinoensis*                   Last listed 1998
*leptolobus*                    Last listed 1998

## DESMAZERIA (Poaceae)
*rigida*                        See *Catapodium rigidum*

## DESMODIUM (Papilionaceae)
*callianthum*                   CMac CSam EPfP NPSI
*canadense*                     EBee
§ *elegans*                     CB&S CFil CMCN CPle ELan EPfP
                                GOrc SSpi WBod WSHC
*podocarpum* B&SWJ  1269       WCru
*praestans*                     See *D. yunnanense*
*styracifolium*                 Last listed 1997
*tiliifolium*                   See *D. elegans*
§ *yunnanense*                 CPle EPfP LRHS SBid WCru WSHC

## DEUTZIA ✿ (Hydrangeaceae)
*calycosa*                      CFil
 - 'Dali' SBEC  417            SDys WPGP
*chunii*                        See *D. ningpoensis*
*compacta*                      CFil CHan CHar WBod WPGP
                                WWat
 - 'Lavender Time'             CHar CPle EHic GSki MPla NSti
                                SEas SPan
*corymbosa*                     CFil
*crenata* 'Flore Pleno'        See *D. scabra* 'Plena'
 - var. *nakaiana*             SIng WCot
 - - 'Nikko'                   CB&S CPBP EBrP EBre EHyt EPla
                                ESis EWTr EWes GOrc LBre LHop
                                MAsh MBar MGos MPla SBre
                                WHCG WSHC WWeb WWin
§ - var. *pubescens*          CFil WPGP
x *elegantissima*             CBlo ENot ISea MRav NFla SReu
                                SRms
 - 'Fasciculata'              EHic EPfP SPer WWin
 - 'Rosealind' ♀             CB&S CBlo EBee EBrP EBre ECtt
                                ELan ENot EWTr IOrc LBre LHop
                                MBri MGrG MPla NBee NCut NFla
                                NLon SBre SPer SPla SReu SRms
                                SSpi SSta WKif WPyg WSHC
¶ *glabrata*                   WPGP
¶ - B&SWJ  617                 WCru
*glomeruliflora*               CFil
*gracilis*                      CBlo CDoC CHar CTri EBee GQui
                                MBal MBar MBel MPla MRav
                                MWat NBee SEas SLod SPer WBod
                                WDin WFar WGwG WHCG WStI
                                WWal WWat
¶ - 'Aurea'                    LBuc
 - 'Carminea'                 See *D.* x *rosea* 'Carminea'
§ - 'Marmorata'              CBlo CPMA WHCG WWes
 - 'Variegata'               See *D. gracilis* 'Marmorata'
*hookeriana*                    GGGa ISea WWat

| | |
|---|---|
| x *hybrida* 'Contraste' | CDoC MBri SPer |
| - 'Joconde' | ECtt EHic GSki MBri WFar WKif |
| - 'Magicien' | CBrm CCHP CDoC CHar CMHG |
| | CSam EBrP EBre ECtt ELan ENot |
| | EPla LBre MBal MBel NFla NHol |
| | SBre SEas SLon SPer SSta WFar |
| | WHCG WHar WPGP WPat |
| - 'Mont Rose' ♀ | More than 30 suppliers |
| - 'Perle Rose' | WLRN |
| x *kalmiiflora* | CB&S CMil EPla GQui MBar MBel |
| | MBri MGos MGrG MRav MWhi |
| | NFor SLPl SPer SRms WDin |
| x *lemoinei* | CBot |
| *longifolia* | CCHP CFil WPGP |
| - 'Veitchii' ♀ | CPle GQui MRav SMrm |
| § - 'Vilmoriniae' | MRav |
| x *magnifica* | CB&S CDoC ELan GEil GQui IOrc |
| | NFla SPan SRms WHCG WHar |
| | WStl WWeb WWin |
| - 'Rubra' | See *D.* 'Strawberry Fields' |
| *monbeigii* | ENot WWat |
| § *ningpoensis* | CB&S CCHP CEnd CFil CWSG |
| | EBee EHic NHol NSti SPan SPer |
| | SSta WPGP WWat |
| 'Pink Pompon' | See *D.* 'Rosea Plena' |
| ◆ *pubescens* | See *D. crenata* var. *pubescens* |
| *pulchra* | CFai CFil CHan CHar CPle EHal |
| | EHic GOrc NPro SBid SLon SPer |
| | SSpi WHCG WPGP WWat |
| - B&SWJ 3870 | WCru |
| *purpurascens* | WPyg |
| x *rosea* | CTrw EBee EGra ENot MBar MPla |
| | MWat NFla NLon SMer SRms |
| | WHCG WKif WStl WWin |
| - 'Campanulata' | ENot GSki |
| § - 'Carminea' ♀ | CB&S CChe GChr GRei MBal |
| | MHlr MRav SDix SPer SRms SSta |
| | WDin WFar WPyg |
| - 'Floribunda' | Last listed 1997 |
| § 'Rosea Plena' (d) | CCHP CDoC CHar EHic EPfP GSki |
| | MGos MGrG MPla SSta |
| *scabra* | EPla NPro WCru |
| § - 'Candidissima' (d) | CBlo CMHG GQui ISea MBri |
| | MRav SMer SPer WBod |
| - 'Codsall Pink' | CB&S EBee MGos MRav |
| § - 'Plena' (d) | CB&S CChe CPle ECtt ELan EPfP |
| | EWTr IMGH MRav NFla SPer |
| | WPyg WWal |
| - 'Pride of Rochester' (d) | EBee EBrP EBre EHic ENot GChr |
| | LBre MBar MRav SBre SLon SMad |
| | WDin WHar WLRN |
| - 'Punctata' (v) | CFai EHoe MWhi SRms WFar |
| - 'Variegata' | EPla NPro NSti WPGP WSHC |
| - 'Watereri' | Last listed 1996 |
| *schneideriana* | LRHS |
| *setchuenensis* | EPfP GGGa GQui SBid SSpi SSta |
| | WHCG WSHC |
| - var. *corymbiflora* ♀ | CB&S CBot CDoC CFil EPfP WBcn |
| | WKif WPGP WWat |
| sp. CC 1231 | Last listed 1997 |
| *staminea* | CFil WPGP |
| § 'Strawberry Fields' ♀ | CEnd CFai CFil CHar EAst EBee |
| | LRHS MAsh MBlu MBri MRav |
| | MTis NPro SBod SLon SPan WKif |
| | WLRN |
| *taiwanensis* | CFil WPGP |
| ¶ 'Tourbillon Rouge' | SRPl |
| x *wellsii* | See *D. scabra* 'Candidissima' |
| x *wilsonii* | SRms |

## DIANELLA (Phormiaceae)

| | |
|---|---|
| *caerulea* | ECou EGar ELan GBuc |

| | |
|---|---|
| - var. *petasmatodes* | LHil WCot |
| - 'Variegata' | See *D. tasmanica* 'Variegata' |
| ¶ *ensifolia* | CInt |
| *intermedia* | IBlr WCot WWat |
| - 'Variegata' | EPPr |
| *nigra* | CFil CPou ECou LBlm WCot |
| * - 'Variegata' | WCot |
| *revoluta* | ECou GLch IBlr LLew |
| - var. *revoluta* | Last listed 1996 |
| *tasmanica* | CElw CFee CFil CFir CGle CHan |
| | CRow ECou ECre GBuc GGar IBlr |
| | LBlm LEdu MHar SAga SArc SIgm |
| | SLod SSpi WWat |
| § - 'Variegata' | CB&S CFir CPou CRDP ECou |
| | ELan EPPr EWes GQui IBlr LEdu |
| | LHop NPSI WCot WOld |

## DIANTHUS ✿ (Caryophyllaceae)

| | |
|---|---|
| *acicularis* | EHyt |
| 'ACW 2116' | LBee WPer |
| 'Ada Florence' | Last listed 1998 |
| 'Admiral Crompton' (pf) | NPin |
| 'Admiral Lord Anson' (b) | WKin |
| 'Admiration' (b) | SHay |
| 'Afton Water' (b) | Last listed 1998 |
| 'Alan Hardy' (pf) | Last listed 1998 |
| 'Alan Titchmarsh' (p) | NPin NSti SBai WSpi |
| 'Albatross' (p) | SChu |
| 'Albert Portman' (p) | NCra |
| 'Albus' | Last listed 1996 |
| 'Aldridge Yellow' (b) | SAll |
| 'Alfriston' (b) ♀ | Last listed 1989 |
| 'Alice' (p) | EBee EMFP EPfP EWTr SAll SHay |
| 'Alice Forbes' (b) | SAll SHay |
| 'Alice Lever' (p) | WAbe |
| 'Alick Sparkes' (pf) | Last listed 1996 |
| § 'Allen's Ballerina' (p) | NCra |
| § 'Allen's Huntsman' (p) | CBlo |
| § 'Allen's Maria' (p) | CBlo NPla |
| 'Alloway Star' (p) | CStr EMFP |
| 'Allspice' (p) | CLTr CLyd CThr EGar EMFP MBro |
| | MRav NCra SChu SSvw WEas |
| | WHoo WPyg WWhi WWye |
| 'Allspice Sport' (p) | WKin |
| Allwoodii Alpinus Group (p) | CNic SRms |
| 'Allwood's Crimson' (pf) | Last listed 1997 |
| *alpinus* ♀ | CGle CLyd EMFP GTou LBee MBal |
| | NHol NMen NWCA SBla SIng |
| | SRms WHen WPer |
| - 'Adonis' | Last listed 1998 |
| - 'Albus' | CPBP EHyt LBee SBla WAbe |
| § - 'Joan's Blood' ♀ | EPot ESis LHop MBro NHar NMen |
| | SAga SBla WAbe WHoo WLRN |
| | WPyg |
| - 'Millstream Salmon' | EHyt |
| - 'Rax Alpe' | EPot NNrd |
| 'Alyson' (p) | SAll |
| * 'Amalfi' (pf) | SAll |
| 'Amarinth' (p) | EGar MNrw |
| ¶ 'Ambervale' (pf) | NPin |
| *amurensis* | CFri EBrP EBre EMon GCal LBre |
| | SBre SIgm WCla WPer |
| ¶ - 'Siberian Blue' | WRHF |
| *anatolicus* | CLyd CPBP CTri EGle ELan LBee |
| | MOne NHol WPer |
| 'Andrew' (p) | SHay |
| 'Angelo' (b) | SAll |
| 'Ann Franklin' (pf) ♀ | SBai |
| 'Ann Unitt' (pf) ♀ | Last listed 1998 |
| 'Annabelle' (p) | CLyd EMFP GMaP LRHS MMal |
| | SChu WCom |
| 'Annette' (pf) | EBee LFis NHol NRoo |

'Annie Claybourne' (pf) — NPin
'Anniversay' (p) — NPin SBai
*anomala* — Last listed 1997
¶ 'Antique' — WCot
'Apricot Sue' (pf) — SHay
'Archfield' — Last listed 1997
'Arctic Star' (p) — CMea EBee MBNS NHol NRoo
*arenarius* — CGen CMea CNic EMFP GCHN LPVe SHel SPlb WPer WWin
'Argus' — CMil WKin
Arizona (pf) — SAll
* 'Arlene' (b) — SAll
*armeria* ♀ — CKin ELan EWFC WHer WPer
'Arnhem Spirit' (pf) — Last listed 1998
*arpadianus* — MPla NHol
'Arthur' (p) — EMFP
'Arthur Leslie' (b) — SAll
§ x *arvernensis* (p) ♀ — CLyd CNic ECha EPot GAbr MBro MPla NRoo SAga
'Ashley' (p) — SAll
*atrorubens* — See *D. carthusianorum* Atrorubens Group
'Audrey Robinson' (pf) — NPin
'Audrey's Frilly' — WKin
'Aurora' (b) — SHay
'Autumn Tints' (b) — SAll
'Auvergne' — See *D.* x *arvernensis*
'Avon Dasset' — Last listed 1998
'Baby Treasure' (p) — CLyd NHol
'Badenia' (p) — CLyd LBee SBla SChu SIgm
'Bailey's Apricot' (pf) — Last listed 1997
¶ 'Bailey's Celebration' (p) — SBai
Bailey's Yellow Delight (p) — Last listed 1998
'Ballerina' (p) — SHay
'Barbara Evelyn' (pf) — NPin
*barbatus* — Last listed 1997
- *albus* — Last listed 1996
- Nigrescens Group ♀ — CBre CHad CHan CSpe LBlm LFis MHlr NDov SUsu WCot
I - 'Sooty' — EBee SSca WHer WUnu WWhi
- 'Wee Willie' — Last listed 1997
'Barleyfield Rose' (p) — CLyd EWes NHar
'Barlow' (p) — SHay
*basuticus* — Last listed 1998
- subsp. *basuticus* — CSpe
¶ - ECN 058 — IDac
'Bath's Pink' — GMac
§ 'Bat's Double Red' (p) — EGar EMFP LBlm NCra SSvw
'Beauty of Cambridge' (b) — SAll
'Beauty of Healey' (p) — CLTr EMFP
'Becka Falls' (p) — SHay SRms
'Becky Robinson' (p) ♀ — CThr SAga SAll SHay WWhi
'Bella' — CPBP
'Belle of Bookham' (b) — SAll
'Berlin Snow' — EPot ITim LBee SGre
'Bet Gilroy' (b) — SHay
'Betty Buckle' (p) — SChu
'Betty Day' (b) — SHay
'Betty Dee' (pf) — NPin
'Betty Morton' (p) ♀ — CLyd CPri EBee MBro NBus NCra NPri SBla SMrm SSvw WHoo WKif WLRN WPyg
'Betty Tucker' (b) — SHay
'Betty's Choice' (pf) — NPin
'Betty's Delight' (pf) — NPin
'Bibby's Cerise' (pf) — Last listed 1997
'Bill Smith' (pf) — Last listed 1997
'Binsey Red' (p) — EMFP WKin
Black and White Minstrels Group (p,a) — WKin
* 'Blue Carpet' — WPer
'Blue Hedgehog' — Last listed 1997

'Blue Hills' (p) — CLyd ECho ELan LBee MWat SChu
'Blue Ice' (b) — SAll SHay
'Blush' — See *D.* 'Souvenir de la Malmaison'
'Bobby' (p) — SAll
'Bobby Ames' (b) — SHay
'Bob's Highlight' (pf) — NPin
'Bombardier' (p) — EBrP EBre LBre SBre WIvy
'Bookham Fancy' (b) — SAll SHay
'Bookham Grand' (b) — SHay
'Bookham Lad' (b) — SAll
'Bookham Lass' (b) — Last listed 1998
'Bookham Perfume' (b) — SBai SHay
'Bookham Sprite' (b) — SAll SHay
'Bourboule' — See *D.* 'La Bourboule'
'Bovey Belle' (p) ♀ — CLTr CSam CThr EBrP EBre ECot LBre NCra NPin SBai SBre SMer WSpi
'Boydii' (p) — CLyd
'Bransgore' (p) — MBro WHoo WPyg
♦ 'Brecas' (pf) — See *D.* Dona = 'Brecas'
*brevicaulis* — NWCA
- *brevicaulis* — Last listed 1998
- Mac&W 5849 — Last listed 1998
'Brian Tumbler' (b) — SAll
'Bridal Veil' (p) — CLon CThr EMFP GAbr NCra SChu SSvw
'Bridesmaid' (p) — Last listed 1996
'Brigadier' (p) — MHar SRms WPer WWin
'Brilliant' — See *D. deltoides* 'Brilliant'
§ Brilliant Gipsy® = 'Stagispan' — SSmt
'Brilliant Star' (p) — CPBP NRoo WCot
'Brimstone' (b) — SHay
'Bruce Parker' (p) — Last listed 1998
'Brymos' (p) — Last listed 1996
'Brympton Red' (p) — CLon CLyd CThr ECha EFou EGar EMFP EOrc MRav NCra NSti SBla SChu SMrm WCom WEas WKif WWhi
'Bryony Lisa' (b) ♀ — Last listed 1995
§ 'Caesar's Mantle' (p) — WKin
*caesius* — See *D. gratianopolitanus*
- 'Compactus' — See *D. gratianopolitanus* 'Compactus Eydangeri'
*callizonus* — CLyd CPBP ESis LBee NWCA SIng
'Calypso' (pf) — SHay
'Calypso Star' (p) — EBee NRoo WCot
'Camelford' (p) — NCra WKin
'Camilla' (b) — CLyd CThr EGoo EMFP SSvw
'Can-can' (pf) — SHay
'Candy' (p) — See *D.* 'Sway Candy'
'Candy Clove' (b) — SAll SHay
'Cannup's Pride' (pf) — Last listed 1997
*capitatus* subsp. *andrzejowskianus* — Last listed 1998
'Carinda' (p) — SHay
'Carlotta' (p) — SHay
'Carmen' (b) — SHay
¶ 'Carmine Joy' — EBee
'Carmine Letitia Wyatt' (p) — Last listed 1998
'Caroline Bone' (b) — SHay
'Caroline Clove' (b) — SHay
'Carolyn Hardy' (pf) — Last listed 1997
*carthusianorum* — CHad CHan EGar EMFP EWTr GSki MNrw MSte SRCN SSvw WCot WPer
- subsp. *vaginatus* — Last listed 1998
*caryophyllus* — CArn CJew IIve MPEx SIde WOak
* 'Casper' (pf) — SAll
'Casser's Pink' (p) — GBuc MTho
'Catherine Glover' (b) — SAll SHay
* 'Catherine Tucker' — WEas
'Catherine's Choice' — See *D.* 'Rhian's Choice'

| | |
|---|---|
| *caucaseus* | EHyt |
| 'Cecil Wyatt' (p) | CThr EBee |
| § 'Cedric's Oldest' (p) | SChu WKin |
| 'Champagne' (pf) | SAll |
| ¶ 'Charcoal' | WCot |
| 'Charity' (p) | Last listed 1998 |
| 'Charles' (p) | SAll |
| 'Charles Edward' (p) | SAll SIng |
| 'Charles Musgrave' | See *D*. 'Musgrave's Pink' |
| 'Charlotte' | SAll |
| 'Charm' (b) | SHay |
| 'Chastity' (p) | EMFP GAbr GCHN GMaP MBro |
| | SBla SChu SSvw WHoo WPyg |
| Cheddar pink | See *D. gratianopolitanus* |
| 'Cherry Clove' (b) | SAll |
| 'Cherry Moon' | LRHS |
| 'Cherryripe' (p) | SHay |
| 'Cheryl' | See *D*. 'Houndspool Cheryl' |
| 'Chetwyn Doris' (p) | NPin SBai |
| *chinensis* (p,a) | MBri |
| 'Chris Crew' (b) ♀ | SBai |
| 'Christine Hough' (b) | SAll |
| 'Christopher' (p) | CBlo EBrP EBre GCHN LBre SAll |
| | SBre SHay |
| 'Christopher Tautz' (b) ♀ | Last listed 1995 |
| *cinnabarinus* | See *D. biflorus* |
| 'Circular Saw' (p) | CInt SChu |
| 'Clara' (pf) | NPin SHay |
| 'Clara's Flame' (pf) | Last listed 1998 |
| 'Clara's Lass' (pf) | NPin SHay |
| 'Clare' (p) | SAll SHay |
| 'Claret Joy' (p) ♀ | CThr EBrP EBre EMFP LBre NCra |
| | NPin SBai SBre SRms WSpi |
| 'Clarinda' (b) | SAll |
| 'Clifford Pink' | WKin |
| ¶ 'Clockface' | SIng |
| 'Clunie' (b) | SAll SHay |
| § 'Cockenzie Pink' (p) | CLTr CThr EMFP GAbr SAll SSvw |
| | WEas |
| 'Cocomo Sim' (pf) | Last listed 1998 |
| 'Colin's Shot Salmon' (pf) | Last listed 1997 |
| 'Constance' (p) | CBlo SAll |
| 'Constance Finnis' | See *D*. 'Fair Folly' |
| 'Consul' (b) | SAll |
| 'Copperhead' (b) | SHay |
| 'Cornish Snow' (p) | Last listed 1996 |
| 'Coronation Ruby' (p) ♀ | NPin SBai |
| 'Coste Budde' (p) | CLyd EMFP WEas WIvy WKin |
| 'Cranborne Seedling' (p) | WKin |
| 'Cranmere Pool' (p) ♀ | CMea CThr EBee EBrP EBre ELan |
| | LBre MBNS MCAu MWat NCra |
| | NPin NRoo SBai SBre SHay SMrm |
| | WSpi |
| 'Cream Lass' (pf) | NPin |
| 'Cream Sue' (pf) | SHay |
| 'Crimson Ace' (p) | SHay |
| 'Crimson Chance' | Last listed 1997 |
| 'Crimson Joy' (p) | EBee |
| 'Crimson Tempo' (pf) | SBai |
| 'Crimson Velvet' (b) | SHay |
| *crinitus* | SHFr |
| 'Crompton Bride' (pf) | Last listed 1998 |
| 'Crompton Classic' (pf) | NPin |
| 'Crompton Princess' (pf) | NPin |
| 'Crompton Wizard' (pf) | Last listed 1997 |
| 'Crossways' (p) | CLyd NHar |
| 'Crowley's Pink Sim' (pf) | Last listed 1997 |
| *cruentus* | MSte |
| 'Dad's Choice' (p) | SBai WSpi |
| 'Dad's Favourite' (p) | CGle CSam CThr ECha EMFP |
| | EOrc LBlm NCra SAll SChu SHay |
| | SRms WEas WHoo WWhi |

| | |
|---|---|
| 'Daily Mail' (p) | NCra NPin SBai SChu SMer WWhi |
| 'Dainty Clove' (b) | Last listed 1997 |
| 'Dainty Dame' (p) | CKel CMea CTri EBee EGoo ESis |
| | GMaP LBee MOne NBus NCra |
| | NHol NMen NRoo SAga SBla |
| | SChu SMrm WLRN WWoo |
| * 'Dainty Dance' | Last listed 1996 |
| 'Dainty Lady' (b) | SBai |
| 'Damask Superb' (p) | CLyd EMFP MBro WKin |
| 'Daphne' (p) | SAll |
| 'Dark Pierrot' (pf) ♀ | Last listed 1995 |
| 'Dark Tempo' (pf) | SBai |
| 'Darling' (b) | SAll |
| 'Dartington Double' (p) | NHol |
| 'Dartington Laced' | GAbr WKin |
| 'Dartmoor Forest' (p) | Last listed 1998 |
| 'David' (p) | CPri EPfP SAll SHay |
| 'David Saunders' (b) ♀ | SBai |
| 'Dawlish Charm' (p) | CThr SBai |
| 'Dawlish Joy' (p) | CThr EBee |
| 'Dawn' (b) | SAll SHay |
| * 'Dazzler' | MPla |
| 'Debi's Choice' (p) | Last listed 1997 |
| 'Deep Purple' (pf) | Last listed 1997 |
| Delphi (pf) | SBai |
| *deltoides* ♀ | CArn CSev ECha EPfP EWFC LHol |
| | MPla SPlb SRms WCla WFar WJek |
| | WOak |
| – 'Albus' | CFri CLyd CNic ECha EWTr GSki |
| | MBar MPla SPil SRms SWat WCla |
| | WPer WRos |
| – 'Bright Eyes' | CFri |
| § – 'Brilliant' | CSev GTou LPVe MNrw SRms |
| | SWat WGor WOve |
| – 'Broughty Blaze' | Last listed 1998 |
| – 'Dark Eyes' | EWes |
| – *degenii* | Last listed 1997 |
| – 'Erectus' | ELan EPfP NFla NLon |
| – Flashing Light | See *D. deltoides* 'Leuchtfunk' |
| § – 'Leuchtfunk' | CPri EBrP EBre EMNN GDra |
| | GTou LBre LGro MOne MTis NFla |
| | NHar NMir NVic SBre SHel SRms |
| | SWat WEas WFar WHen WPer |
| | WRos |
| – 'Microchip' | NHar SRms SSca WFar |
| ¶ – 'Nelli' (p) | SSvw |
| – red | Last listed 1996 |
| * – 'Red Eye' | MNrw |
| – *splendens* | EPfP |
| – 'Wisley Variety' | Last listed 1996 |
| 'Denis' (p) | CLyd ELan NPla SAll SBai WSpi |
| 'Desert Song' (b) | SAll |
| 'Desmond' | WRus |
| 'Devon Blossom' (p) ♀ | Last listed 1995 |
| 'Devon Blush' (p) | EBee EBrP EBre LBre LRHS SBre |
| 'Devon Charm' (p) | LRHS |
| 'Devon Cream' (p) | CThr EBee EBrP EBre EMFP LBre |
| | LRHS SBre SRms WLRN |
| 'Devon Dove' (p) ♀ | CMea CThr EBee EBrP EBre EPfP |
| | GMaP LBre LFis SBre SRms |
| 'Devon General' (p) ♀ | CThr CTri EBee EBrP EBre LBre |
| | LRHS SBre |
| 'Devon Glow' (p) ♀ | CLTr CThr EBrP EBre EMFP EPfP |
| | GMaP LBre SBre SRms WLRN |
| | WWeb |
| 'Devon Joy' (p) | CMea CThr EBee SRms |
| 'Devon Magic' (p) | CBlo EBee SRms |
| 'Devon Maid' (p) ♀ | CThr EBee |
| 'Devon Pearl' (p) | CBlo CThr EBee |
| 'Devon Pink Pearl' | Last listed 1996 |
| 'Devon Pride' (p) ♀ | EBrP EBre LBre SBre |
| ¶ 'Devon Violet' | NRoo |

| | |
|---|---|
| 'Devon Wizard' (p) ♀ | EBee EMFP NRoo SRms WLRN WWeb |
| 'Dewdrop' (p) | CInt CLyd CMea CSWP CTri EBee ECtt ESis GCHN LBee NBir NCra NGdn NHar NMen SAll SChu SMer SMrm SSvw WAbe WCom WFar WLRN WPer |
| 'Diana' | See D. Dona = 'Brecas' |
| 'Diane' (p) ♀ | CLyd CThr EBrP EBre ELan EMFP LBre LHop NCra NPin SAga SAll SBai SBre SHay WEas WPer WSpi WWal |
| * 'Diane Cape' | SAll |
| 'Dick Portman' (p) | Last listed 1998 |
| 'Diplomat' (b) | SAll |
| 'Doctor Archie Cameron' (b) | SHay |
| 'Doctor Ramsey' | CLyd |
| § Dona = 'Brecas' (pf) | SAll SBai |
| 'Dora' | LRHS |
| 'Doris' (p) ♀ | More than 30 suppliers |
| 'Doris Allwood' (pf) | NPin |
| 'Doris Elite' (p) | SAll |
| 'Doris Galbally' (b) | SBai |
| 'Doris Majestic' (p) | SAll |
| 'Doris Ruby' | See D. 'Houndspool Ruby' |
| 'Doris Supreme' (p) | SAll |
| 'Double Irish' | See D. 'Irish Pink' |
| 'Downs Cerise' (b) | SHay |
| ¶ drenovskianus | EHyt |
| § 'Dubarry' (p) | CLyd CTri EWes NLak SBla WGor WPer |
| ¶ 'Duchess of Fife' (p) | EWTr |
| 'Duchess of Westminster' (M) | WMal |
| * 'Duet' | SAll |
| 'Dunkirk' (b) | Last listed 1998 |
| 'Dunkirk Spirit' (pf) ♀ | Last listed 1998 |
| 'Dusky' (p) | NCra WKin |
| 'Dwarf Vienna' | CPri |
| 'E.J. Baldry' (b) | SHay |
| 'Earl of Essex' (p) | CThr EMFP NCra SAll SHay |
| 'Ebor II' (b) | SAll |
| 'Edan Lady' (pf) | Last listed 1996 |
| 'Edenside Scarlet' (b) | SHay |
| 'Edenside White' (b) | SAll |
| 'Edith Johnson' (pf) | Last listed 1996 |
| 'Edna' (p) | SAll |
| 'Edward' (p) | Last listed 1996 |
| * 'Eilat' | SAll |
| 'Eileen' (p) | SAll |
| 'Eileen Lever' (p) | SBla WAbe |
| 'Eileen Neal' (b) ♀ | Last listed 1989 |
| 'Eileen O'Connor' (b) ♀ | SBai |
| 'Elfin Star' (p) | NRoo |
| 'Elizabeth' (p) | CFee CGle CThr LHop |
| 'Elizabeth Jane' (p) | EMFP |
| 'Elizabeth Pink' | SMrm |
| 'Elizabethan' (p) | CSam SBla |
| * 'Elizabethan Pink' | CNic EGar |
| 'Ember Rose' | See D. 'Le Rêve' |
| 'Emile Paré' (p) | MTho SChu |
| 'Emperor' | See D. 'Bat's Double Red' |
| 'Enid Anderson' (p) | SChu |
| 'Enid Burgoyne' | WKin |
| eretmopetalus | Last listed 1998 |
| erinaceus | CMea EHyt EMNN EPot ESis GCHN GCrs GMaP GTou ITim LBee MBro MOne MPla NHar NMen NRoo NTow NWCA WAbe WPer WWin |
| - var. alpinus | CLyd EPot SIng |
| 'Erycina' (b) | SAll |
| 'Esperance' (pf) | Last listed 1996 |
| 'Ethel Hurford' | WHoo WKin |
| 'Eudoxia' (b) | SAll |
| 'Eva Humphries' (b) | SAll SBai SHay |
| 'Evening Star' (p) | EBee NRoo |
| 'Excelsior' (p) | CBlo CThr NFor NLon NSti |
| 'Exquisite' (b) | SAll |
| § 'Fair Folly' (p) | CThr NBus SChu SSvw WEas |
| 'Fair Lady' (p) | Last listed 1998 |
| 'Faith Raven' (p) | Last listed 1996 |
| 'Falcon' (pf) | SBai |
| 'Fanal' (p) | CLyd NBir |
| * 'Fancy Magic' (pf) | CBlo SAll |
| 'Farnham Rose' (p) | CLTr SChu |
| 'Fascination' (b) | Last listed 1996 |
| 'Fenbow Nutmeg Clove' (b) | SChu WKin WRha |
| 'Fettes Mount' (p) | CLTr GAbr NChi NSti WCot |
| 'Fiery Cross' (b) | SAll SHay |
| 'Fimbriatus' (p) | MBro WHoo WPyg |
| 'Fingo Clove' (b) | SAll |
| 'Fiona' (p) | SAll |
| 'Firecrest Rose' | Last listed 1998 |
| 'Firewitch' | Last listed 1996 |
| 'First Lady' (b) | SAll |
| 'Flame' (p) | SHay |
| 'Flame Sim' (pf) | SHay |
| 'Flanders' (b) ♀ | Last listed 1989 |
| 'Fleur' (p) | SAll |
| 'Forest Edge' (b) | SBai |
| 'Forest Glow' (b) | SAll |
| 'Forest Sprite' (b) | SAll SBai |
| 'Forest Treasure' (b) | SAll SBai |
| 'Forest Violet' (b) | SAll |
| 'Fortuna' (p) | SAll |
| 'Fountain's Abbey' (p) | EMFP NChi WIvy WKin |
| 'Fragrant Ann' (pf) ♀ | NPin SHay |
| 'Fragrant Phyllis' (pf) | NPin |
| 'Fragrant Rose' (pf) | NPin |
| * fragrantissimus | Last listed 1997 |
| 'Frances Isabel' (p) ♀ | NCra SAll |
| 'Frances King' (p) | Last listed 1998 |
| 'Frances Sellars' (b) | SHay |
| 'Frank's Frilly' (p) | CThr WKin |
| 'Freckles' (p) | CThr SHay |
| 'Freda' (p) | SAll |
| 'Freeland Crimson Clove' (b) | Last listed 1998 |
| 'French' | Last listed 1997 |
| freynii | CLyd EPPr EWes NHed SAga WLin |
| * 'Frilly' | Last listed 1997 |
| fringed pink | See D. superbus |
| furcatus | NWCA |
| 'Fusilier' (p) | CLyd CMea EBrP EBre EMFP GCrs LBre MBar NCra NPri NRoo SAga SAll SBre SChu WAbe WFar WPat WPer |
| 'G.J. Sim' (pf) | Last listed 1998 |
| 'G.W. Hayward' (b) | Last listed 1997 |
| 'Gail Tilsey' (b) | SHay |
| 'Galil' (pf) | SAll |
| 'Garland' (p) | CLyd CMea CTri WGor |
| 'Garnet' (p) | SChu |
| 'Gatekeeper' (p) | GCHN |
| 'Gaydena' (b) | SAll |
| 'George Allwood' (pf) | NPin |
| § Giant Gipsy® = 'Stagigi' | SSmt |
| giganteus | ECGN EMFP IBlr MNrw |
| 'Gingham Gown' (p) | NBir NBrk NLak NOla |
| 'Gipsy Clove' (b) | SHay |
| ♦ 'Gipsy King' | See D. Giant Gipsy = 'Stagigi' |
| ♦ 'Gipsy Maiden' | See D. Pastel Gipsy = 'Stagipast' |
| ♦ 'Gipsy Monarch' | See D. Brilliant Gipsy = 'Stagispan' |
| ♦ Gipsy Prince | See D. Smiling Gipsy = 'Staviolet' |
| ♦ Gipsy Queen | See D. Salmon Gipsy = 'Stadarpi' |

◆ Gipsy Rascal | See *D.* Rondo = 'Stagirond'
§ Gipsy Rogue® = 'Stagilon' | SSmt
*glacialis* | GMaP GTou NHar NHol NRya
- subsp.*gelidus* | CGra NMen
'Glebe Cottage White' | CGle CVer
'Gloriosa' (p) | Last listed 1996
'Glorious' (p) | SHay
'Gold Dust' | Last listed 1996
'Gold Fleck' | EBee EDAr LBee
'Golden Cross' (b) ♀ | SBai
'Golden Rain' (pf) | SHay
'Golden Sceptre' (b) ♀ | SBai
'Grandma Calvert' (p) | SAll
*graniticus* | WPer
'Gran's Favourite' (p) ♀ | CKel CLTr CMea EBee EBrP EBre
 | EMFP EWTr GMaP LBre LFis
 | MWat NPin SBai SBre SChu SHay
 | SRms WEas WWye
§ *gratianopolitanus* ♀ | CArn CLyd CTri EWTr GCHN
 | GTou LBee LEdu LHol MMal
 | MNrw MRav NBid NMen NOak
 | SIde SRms WAbe WPer WWye
- 'Corinne Tremaine' | Last listed 1998
- 'Emmen' (p) | Last listed 1998
- 'Fellerhexe' (d) | WEas
- 'Flore Pleno' (d) | EMFP MInt SSvw
* - 'Karlik' | CLyd
§ - 'Princess Charming' | SRms
- red | GAbr
- 'Rosenfeder' | WPer
- 'Splendens' | WPer
§ - 'Tiny Rubies' | ECho WAbe WFar
'Gravetye Gem' (b) | CLyd SRms WPyg
'Gravetye Gem' (p) | Last listed 1998
'Grenadier' (p) | ECho ELan
'Grey Dove' (b) ♀ | Last listed 1989
'Greytown' (b) | GAbr
'Gwendolen Read' (p) | SHay
'Gypsy Star' (p) | NRoo
*baematocalyx* | NWCA WAbe WPer
- 'Alpinus' | See *D. baematocalyx* subsp.
 | *pindicola*
§ - subsp.*pindicola* | CPBP EMFP NHol WPat
'Hannah Louise' (b) ♀ | SBai
'Harlequin' (p) | EBee ECtt EMFP WPer
'Harmony' (b) | SAll SHay
'Harry Wilcock' (pf) | Last listed 1998
'Havana' (pf) | SBai
'Haytor' | See *D.* 'Haytor White'
'Haytor Rock' (p) ♀ | CThr EBee EBrP EBre EPfP LBre
 | NCra SBre SHay
§ 'Haytor White' (p) ♀ | CSam CThr EBee EBrP EBre EMFP
 | EWTr GCHN LBre MHlr NCra
 | NPin SBai SBre SChu SHay SRms
 | WCot WEas WWhi
'Hazel Ruth' (b) ♀ | SBai
I 'Heath' (b) | Last listed 1996
'Heidi' (p) | EPfP SRms
'Helen' (p) | CThr SAll SHay WEas
'Helena Hitchcock' (p) | CThr
'Herbert's Pink' (p) | EMFP WKin
'Hereford Butter' | EBee WKin
'Hidcote' (p) | CLyd CTri EBee ELan EMFP MWat
 | NBus NMen NRoo SBla WLRN
 | WWin
'Hidcote Red' | ECho
* Highgates hybrid | CLyd
¶ 'Highland Fraser' (p) | GAbr MBro SAll SRms WEas
 | WHoo WKif WWin
¶ Highland hybrids | SSvw
'Highland Queen' (p) | WKin
'Hilda Scholes' (p) | NCra

* 'Hi-lite' (pf) | SAll
*hispanicus* | See *D. pungens*
'Hollycroft Fragrance' (p) | Last listed 1996
'Hope' (p) | CLyd EBee EMFP SChu
'Horsa' (b) | SHay
§ 'Houndspool Cheryl' (p) ♀ | CMea CPri EBee EMFP EPfP
 | GMaP NPin SRms WWeb
§ 'Houndspool Ruby' (p) ♀ | CLyd CSam CThr EMFP EPfP
 | EWTr MBNS MCAu MWat NOak
 | NPin SBai SMer WEas WSpi WWeb
'Howard Hitchcock' (b) ♀ | SBai
'Huntsman' | See *D.* 'Allen's Huntsman'
'Ian' (p) | CLTr CThr NPin SAll SBai SHay
 | WSpi
'Ibis' (b) | SHay
'Iceberg' (p) | Last listed 1996
'Icomb' (p) | CLyd CSam CTri SRms WHoo
 | WPer WPyg
'Imperial Clove' (b) | Last listed 1996
'Impulse' (pf) | SBai
'Ina' (p) | SRms
Incas (pf) | SBai
'Inchmery' (p) | CLTr CLyd CMil EBrP EBre EMFP
 | LBre NCra NFor NTow SAll SBre
 | SChu SHay SSvw WEas WHoo
 | WWhi
¶ 'India Star' (p) | EBee NRoo
Indios (pf) ♀ | SBai
'Inga Bowen' (p) | Last listed 1997
'Inglestone' (p) | CSam CTri NHar SBla WLin WPer
'Inshriach Dazzler' (p) ♀ | CInt CMea EBrP EBre GAbr
 | GCHN GCrs GDra ITim LBee LBre
 | LHop NHar NHed NHol NPri
 | NRoo SBla SBre SSvw WHal
'Inshriach Startler' (p) | CFee CMea
'Ipswich Crimson' (p) | Last listed 1996
'Ipswich Pink' (p) | LGro WElm
'Irene Della-Torré' (b) ♀ | SBai
'Ivonne Orange' (pf) | SBai
'J.M. Bibby' (p) | Last listed 1998
'Jacqueline Ann' (pf) ♀ | SHay
¶ 'James Portman' (p) | SBai
'Jane Austen' (p) | EBee NBrk NCra SChu WKin
 | WPer WWye
'Jane Coffey' (b) | SHay
'Janelle Welch' (pf) | Last listed 1998
'Janet Walker' (p) | Last listed 1997
*japonicus* | LCot
* 'Jenny Spillers' | Last listed 1997
'Jenny Wyatt' (p) | SHay
'Jess Hewins' (pf) | NPin
'Jessica' (pf) | SAll
¶ 'Jo Emma' (pf) | NPin
'Joan Randal' (pf) | SBai
'Joan Schofield' (p) | NHol NRoo
'Joan Siminson' (p) | WKin WWhi
'Joanne' (pf) | Last listed 1998
'Joanne's Highlight' (pf) | NPin
'Joan's Blood' | See *D. alpinus* 'Joan's Blood'
'Joe Vernon' (pf) | NPin
'John Ball' (p) | CLTr EMFP SSvw
'John Faulkner' (pf) ♀ | Last listed 1998
'John Gray' (p) | Last listed 1997
'John Grey' (p) | WKin
'John Partridge' (p) | SBai WSpi
'Joker' (pf) | Last listed 1997
'Joy' (p) ♀ | CThr EBee EBrP EBre EMFP EPfP
 | LBre NCra NPin SBai SBre SHay
 | SRms
'Judy' (p) | CLyd
'Julian' (p) | SAll
'Kathleen Hitchcock' (b) ♀ | SBai

| | |
|---|---|
| 'Kesteven Chambery' (p) | CLyd WPer |
| 'Kesteven Chamonix' (p) | WPer |
| 'Kesteven Kirkstead' (p) ♀ | CSWP |
| 'Kestor' (p) | NCra |
| 'King of the Blacks' (p,a) | CHad ELan MRav |
| *kitaibelii* | See *D. petraeus* subsp. *petraeus* |
| 'Kiwi Pretty' (p) | CThr |
| *knappii* | CGen CLyd CPou EGar ELan |
| | GCHN MLLN MNrw NChi NOak |
| | SAga SSca WCla WElm WPer |
| | WWin WWye |
| - 'Yellow Harmony' (p,a) | MMal NPri SBea WHer |
| ♦ 'Kosalamana' | See *D.* Salamanca = 'Kosalamana' |
| § 'La Bourboule' (p) ♀ | CSam ELan EMNN EPot GAbr |
| | LBee MBar MBro MPla MWat |
| | NHol NMen NRoo SBla SIng SRms |
| | SSmi WFar WLin WPat WPer |
| | WWin |
| 'La Bourboule Albus' (p) | CMea CTri EPot NMen SBla |
| | WCom WFar WPer WWin |
| 'Laced Hero' (p) | SChu WKin |
| laced hybrids | WCla |
| 'Laced Joy' (p) | CThr EMFP SAll SChu SHay SMer |
| 'Laced Monarch' (p) | CThr EBee EBrP EBre EMFP |
| | GCHN LBre MBro NPin SAga SAll |
| | SBai SBre SChu SPlb SRms SSvw |
| | WSpi |
| 'Laced Mrs Sinkins' (p) | SBai WSpi |
| 'Laced Prudence' | See *D.* 'Prudence' |
| 'Laced Romeo' (p) | EMFP SAll SChu SHay WEas |
| 'Laced Treasure' (p) | CLTr CThr SAll |
| 'Lady Granville' (p) | SSvw WKin |
| 'Lady Salisbury' (p) | EMFP SAsh WKin |
| § 'Lady Wharncliffe' (p) | CLTr CMil EMFP WKin |
| 'L'Amour' (b) | SAll |
| * 'Lancing' | EGoo |
| 'Lancing Lady' (b) | SAll |
| 'Lancing Monarch' (b) | SAll SHay |
| *langeanus* | SIng |
| - NS 255 | NWCA |
| 'Laura' (p) | SAll SHay |
| 'Lavender Clove' (b) | SAll SBai SHay |
| 'Lavender Lady' (pf) | NPin |
| 'Lawley's Red' (p) | WKin |
| 'Leiden' (b) | SAll SBai |
| 'Lemsii' (p) ♀ | EMFP GCHN MBal NMen NVic |
| | WHoo WPer WPyg WWye |
| 'Lena Sim' (pf) | Last listed 1998 |
| 'Leslie Rennison' (b) | SAll SHay |
| 'Letitia Wyatt' (p) ♀ | CMea CThr EBee LFis NCra NRoo |
| 'Leuchtkugel' | Last listed 1998 |
| Liberty® | SBai |
| 'Lightning' (pf) | SAll |
| 'Lilac Clove' (b) | Last listed 1998 |
| 'Lior' (pf) | SAll |
| 'Little Diane' (p) | Last listed 1997 |
| 'Little Jock' (p) | EBrP EBre ELan EMNN EPot |
| | GCHN LBee LBre LHop MBal |
| | MBar MRav MWat NCra NEgg |
| | NFla NHar NHol NRoo SAll SBla |
| | SBre SPlb SRms SSmi WEas WFar |
| | WWin |
| 'Little Miss Muffet' (p) | Last listed 1998 |
| 'Little Old Lady' | See *D.* 'Chelsea Pink' |
| 'Liz Rigby' (b) | Last listed 1997 |
| 'London Brocade' (p) | NBrk NCra SUsu WIvy WKin |
| 'London Delight' (p) | CThr NCra SHay |
| 'London Glow' (p) | CLTr CThr SAll WKin |
| * 'London Joy' | Last listed 1997 |
| 'London Lovely' (p) | CLTr CThr NCra SAll SSvw |
| 'London Poppet' (p) | CThr SAll WHoo |
| 'Lord Grey' (b) | Last listed 1996 |

| | |
|---|---|
| 'Louise's Choice' (p) ♀ | Last listed 1993 |
| 'Loveliness' (p) | CBre |
| *lumnitzeri* | EPot WPer |
| *lusitanicus* | Last listed 1997 |
| 'Lustre' (b) | SAll SHay |
| 'Mab' | WKin |
| 'Madame Dubarry' | See *D.* 'Dubarry' |
| 'Madonna' (p) | SBai SHay WKin |
| 'Maisie Neal' (b) ♀ | Last listed 1989 |
| Malaga (pf) ♀ | NPin SAll SBai |
| 'Mambo' (pf) | SAll SBai |
| 'Mandy' (p) | SAll |
| 'Manningtree Pink' | See *D.* 'Cedric's Oldest' |
| Manon (pf) | Last listed 1997 |
| 'Marcato' (pf) | SBai |
| 'Marg's Choice' (p) ♀ | EMFP |
| 'Maria' | See *D.* 'Allen's Maria' |
| 'Marmion' (M) | WMal |
| 'Mars' (p) | ELan GAbr NBus NHed SAll SChu |
| | WAbe WFar WWye |
| 'Marshwood Melody' (p) | CThr NCra SBai WSpi |
| 'Marshwood Mystery' (p) | CThr |
| 'Martin Nest' | Last listed 1996 |
| 'Mary Jane Birrel' (pf) | Last listed 1997 |
| 'Mary Simister' (b) | SAll |
| * 'Mary's Gilliflower' | EMFP |
| 'Master Stuart' (b) | SBai |
| 'Matador' (b) | SHay |
| 'Maudie Hinds' (b) | SBai |
| 'Maureen Lambert' (pf) | Last listed 1998 |
| 'Maybole' (b) | SAll SHay |
| 'Maythorne' (p) | SRms |
| 'Mendip Hills' (b) | SAll SHay |
| 'Mendlesham Belle' (p) | EMFP |
| 'Mendlesham Frilly' (p) | EMFP |
| 'Mendlesham Glow' (p) | EMFP |
| 'Mendlesham Maid' (p) | EMFP |
| 'Mendlesham Moll' (p) | EMFP |
| ¶ 'Mendlesham St Helens' (p) | EMFP |
| 'Mercury' (p) | SAll |
| 'Merlin Clove' (b) | SBai SHay |
| 'Messines Pink' (p) | SAll |
| 'Michael Saunders' (b) ♀ | SBai |
| 'Michelangelo' (pf) | Last listed 1997 |
| *microlepis* | CPBP ITim NMen NWCA WAbe |
| | WCot |
| - f. *albus* | NSla WAbe |
| - ED 791562 | Last listed 1998 |
| - 'Leuchtkugel' | EHyt EPot ITim WAbe |
| - var. *musalae* | CMea EHyt EPot NHar WLin |
| 'Mida' | See *D.* 'Melody' |
| 'Miss Sinkins' (p) | Last listed 1996 |
| * 'Misty Morn' | Last listed 1998 |
| * 'Molly Blake' | Last listed 1998 |
| * 'Momoko' (pf) | SAll |
| 'Monarch' (pf) | Last listed 1997 |
| 'Mondriaan' (pf) | CInt ELan |
| 'Monica Wyatt' (p) ♀ | CThr EBee EBrP EBre LBre LFis |
| | NCra NPin SAga SBai SBre SChu |
| | SRms |
| *monspessulanus* | NWCA WPer |
| 'Montrose Pink' | See *D.* 'Cockenzie Pink' |
| 'Moortown Plume' | WKin |
| ¶ 'Moulin Rouge' | EBee |
| 'Mrs Clark' | See *D.* 'Nellie Clark' |
| 'Mrs Elmhurst' (p) | NCra |
| 'Mrs Glumbly' | WKin |
| 'Mrs Holt' (p) | EMFP |
| 'Mrs Jackson' (p) | CLyd SAsh SBla |
| 'Mrs Macbride' (p) | WKin |
| 'Mrs N. Clark' | See *D.* 'Nellie Clark' |
| 'Mrs Perkins' (b) | SAll |

| | |
|---|---|
| 'Mrs Roxburgh' | WKin |
| 'Mrs Shaw' (p) | NCra |
| 'Mrs Sinkins' (p) | More than 30 suppliers |
| 'Munot' | EPfP |
| Murcia (pf) | SBai |
| 'Muriel Wilson' (pf) | Last listed 1996 |
| 'Murray's Laced Pink' (p) | WSPU |
| N 'Musgrave's Pink' (p) | CGle CLTr CLon CSam CThr ECha ELan EMFP LHop NCra SAll SChu SSvw WEas WHoo |
| 'Musgrave's White' | See *D.* 'Musgrave's Pink' |
| *myrtinervius* | CBar CLTr EHyt ITim NRoo NWCA WCla WPer |
| 'Mystery' (pf) | SAll |
| 'N.M. Goodall' (p) | LHop |
| 'Nan Bailey' (p) | NCra SBai |
| 'Nancy Lindsay' (p) | Last listed 1996 |
| * 'Napoleon' | SAll |
| 'Napoleon III' (p) | WKif |
| *nardiformis* | CLyd WPer |
| 'Natalie Saunders' (b) ♀ | SBai |
| 'Nautilus' (b) | SAll SHay |
| *neglectus* | See *D. pavonius* |
| § 'Nellie Clark' (p) | MBal MWat NMen SChu WPat |
| 'New Tempo' (pf) | SBai |
| 'Nichola Ann' (b) ♀ | SAll |
| 'Nicol' (pf) | Last listed 1998 |
| ¶ 'Night Star' (p) | CMea EBee |
| *nitidus* | NBir WPer |
| *nivalis* | NMen |
| *noeanus* | See *D. petraeus* subsp. *noeanus* |
| 'Nonsuch' (p) | EMFP NBrk |
| 'Norman Hayward' (b) | Last listed 1996 |
| 'Northland' (pf) | NPin |
| 'Nyewoods Cream' (p) | CInt CLyd CTri EBee EBrP EBre EMFP ESis LBee MBar MBro MPla MRav NCra NHar NHol NMen NRoo SBre SIng WPat WPer |
| 'Oakfield Clove' (b) | Last listed 1996 |
| § 'Oakington' (p) | CSam CTri EBrP EBre EMNN GCHN LBre MBal MRav MWat NCra SBre SChu SMer |
| 'Oakington Rose' | See *D.* 'Oakington' |
| ¶ 'Oakwood Erin Mitchell' (p) | NPin |
| 'Oakwood Gillian Garforth' (p) ♀ | NPin SBai |
| 'Oakwood Romance' (p) ♀ | NPin SBai |
| 'Oakwood Rose Parker' (p) | NPin |
| 'Oakwood Splendour' (p) ♀ | NPin |
| * 'Odino' | SAll |
| 'Old Blush' | See *D.* 'Souvenir de la Malmaison' |
| 'Old Clove Red' (b) | LFis |
| 'Old Crimson Clove' (b) | Last listed 1997 |
| 'Old Dutch Pink' (p) | CLTr CMil NCra SChu SSvw WKin |
| 'Old Fringed Pink' (p) | WKin |
| 'Old Fringed White' (p) | CLTr EMFP |
| 'Old Irish' (p) | WCot WKin |
| 'Old Mother Hubbard' (p) ♀ | CFee |
| 'Old Red Clove' (p) | WCot |
| § 'Old Square Eyes' (p) | CInt CLyd EOrc MNrw SAga SAll SBla SChu SSvw WEas |
| 'Old Velvet' (p) | CLTr EFou GCal SChu WKin |
| 'Oliver' (p) | SAll |
| * 'Olivia' (p) | SAll |
| 'Omagio' (pf) | SAll |
| * 'Ondina' (pf) | SAll |
| * 'Opera' | SAll |
| * 'Orange Magic' (pf) | SAll |
| 'Orange Maid' (b) | SAll |
| 'Orchid Beauty' (pf) | Last listed 1997 |
| 'Oscar' (b) | SAll |
| 'Osprey' (b) | SHay |

| | |
|---|---|
| 'Paddington' (p) | CThr EMFP NCra SChu WKin |
| 'Painted Beauty' (p) | CLTr CSam CThr EMFP NBir |
| 'Painted Lady' (p) | CThr EMon NHol SAll SChu WKin |
| 'Paisley Gem' (p) | CLTr CLon CThr NCra SChu WKif |
| *palinensis* B&SWJ 3770 | WCru |
| § Pastel Gipsy® = 'Stagipast' | SSmt |
| 'Patchwork' | Last listed 1997 |
| 'Patricia' (b) | SHay |
| 'Patricia Bell' | See *D. turkestanicus* 'Patricia Bell' |
| 'Paul' (p) | EBrP EBre LBre SBai SBre WSpi |
| 'Paul Hayward' (p) | SHay |
| § *pavonius* ♀ | EHyt EWes GTou NWCA SBla SIng WPer |
| - *roysii* | See *D.* 'Roysii' |
| Pax (pf) | SAll SBai |
| 'Peach' (p) | SHay |
| 'Pearl' | SAll |
| 'Perfect Clove' (b) | SHay |
| 'Peter Wood' (b) ♀ | Last listed 1989 |
| § *petraeus* | EWes NHol WPat |
| § - subsp. *noeanus* | CGra CPBP ESis WAbe WHal WPat WPer |
| ¶ - - *albus* | WLin |
| § - subsp. *petraeus* | NOak WPer |
| 'Petticoat Lace' (p) | EMFP SHay |
| 'Phantom' (b) | SHay |
| 'Pheasant's Eye' (p) | CLTr CLyd EMFP NCra SSvw WKin |
| 'Philip Archer' (b) | SHay |
| * 'Picton's Propeller' (p) | CMil GBuc |
| 'Picture' (b) | Last listed 1996 |
| ¶ Pierrot = 'Kobusa' (pf) ♀ | SBai |
| 'Pike's Pink' (p) ♀ | CKel CLyd CMea CSam EBee ELan GCHN LBee LFis LHop MBal MRav MWat NCra NEgg NHol NMen NNrd NRoo SAll SRPl SRms SSmi SSvw WAbe WEas WLin WWin |
| *pindicola* | See *D. haematocalyx* subsp. *pindicola* |
| *pinifolius* | Last listed 1998 |
| 'Pink Bizarre' (b) | SHay |
| 'Pink Calypso' | See *D.* 'Truly Yours' |
| 'Pink Damask' (p) | GAbr |
| 'Pink Devon Pearl' | Last listed 1996 |
| * 'Pink Dona' (p) | SAll SBai |
| 'Pink Doris' (pf) | NPin |
| * 'Pink Fringe' | NSla |
| 'Pink Jewel' (p) | CInt CLyd CMea CTri ECha ESis LBee NHol NMen SAll SChu SIng WEas |
| 'Pink Mist Sim' (pf) | Last listed 1997 |
| 'Pink Monica Wyatt' (p) | CThr EBee |
| 'Pink Mrs Sinkins' (p) | CLTr ECha EMFP GAri SAll SBai SChu WHoo |
| 'Pink Pearl' (p) | CBlo CThr EBee SAll WLRN |
| 'Pink Sim' (pf) | SAll |
| 'Pixie' (b) | CLyd EPot NHol |
| 'Pixie Star' (p) | EBee NRoo |
| *plumarius* | EBee MGed NMir SRms SSvw WByw WGor WGwG WMoo WPer |
| - 'Albiflorus' | SRms WPer |
| *pontederae* | NHed WPer |
| 'Portsdown Fancy' (b) | SHay |
| 'Portsdown Lass' (b) | Last listed 1998 |
| 'Portsdown Perfume' (b) | SHay |
| 'Prado' (pf) | SAll SBai |
| *preobrazbenskii* | SGre |
| 'Pretty' | EBee LHop |
| 'Pretty Lady' (p) | NRoo |
| 'Prince Charming' (p) | CSam ELan EMNN GAbr ITim NMen NPri NRoo SAga SRms WLRN WPer |

'Princess Charming' See D. gratianopolitanus 'Princess Charming'
'Princess of Wales' (M) WMal
'Priory Pink' (p) SAll
§ 'Prudence' (p) CThr NCra SAll WHoo
'Pudsey Prize' (p) EHyt
'Pummelchen' (p) ITim
'Purley King' (p) CThr
'Purple Frosted' (pf) Last listed 1997
'Purple Jenny' (p) SAll
'Purple Pacal' (pf) SBai
'Purple Pierrot' (pf) SBai
'Purple Rendez-vous' (pf) SAll
*pygmaeus* NBro NHed
 - B&SWJ 1510 NHol NPla
 - B&SWJ 3533 WCru
'Queen of Hearts' (p) CLyd EBrP EBre ESis LBre NBus SBre SMrm WPer WWye
§ 'Queen of Henri' (p) CLyd GMaP LBee MMil NCra NHol NNrd SBla SChu WFar
'Queen of Sheba' (p) CThr EMFP NCra SChu SSvw WKin
'Raby Castle' See D. 'Lord Chatham'
'Rachel' (p) CLyd
'Raeden Pink' (p) Last listed 1997
'Raggio di Sole' (pf) SAll SBai
'Rainbow Loveliness' (p,a) NBir SAll SSca WCla WHil
'Ralph Gould' (p) ECho
Ramona (pf) SBai
'Red and White' (p) WKin
'Red Denim' (p) SIng
'Red Emperor' (p) Last listed 1997
'Red Penny' (p) NCat SAsh WWin
* 'Red Rimon' (pf) SAll
'Red Velvet' CLyd CSWP LBee LRHS SAsh SMrm
'Red-edged Skyline' (pf) Last listed 1998
'Reiko' (pf) SAll
'Reine de Henri' See D. 'Queen of Henri'
'Rembrandt' (p) Last listed 1997
'Rendez-vous' (pf) SAll SBai
'Renoir' (b) SAll SHay
'Revell's Lady Wharncliffe' See D. 'Lady Wharncliffe'
§ 'Rhian's Choice' (p) ♀ Last listed 1996
'Riccardo' (b) ♀ SBai
'Richard Gibbs' (p) WWin
'Rimon' (pf) SAll
'Rivendell' (p) CPBP EHyt NHar NSla WAbe
'Robert' (p) SAll
'Robert Allwood' (pf) Last listed 1996
'Robert Baden-Powell' (b) SHay
'Roberta' (pf) SAll
* 'Robin Ritchie' WHoo WKin
'Robin Thain' (b) SAll SBai SHay
'Rodrigo' (pf) Last listed 1998
§ Rondo® = 'Stagirond' SSmt
'Ron's Joanne' (pf) SHay
'Roodkapje' (p) SSvw WKin
'Rosalind Linda' (pf) Last listed 1997
'Rose de Mai' (p) CBre CLTr CMil CSam CSev EBee EMFP LBlm LLWP NCra SAll SChu SMer SSvw WEas WHoo WLin
'Rose Joy' (p) ♀ CThr EBee EMFP EPfP NCra NPin SBai SHay SRms
'Rose Monica Wyatt' (p) ♀ CThr EBee
'Rose Perfection' (pf) SHay
'Rosealie' (p) SHay
'Royal Scot' (pf) ♀ Last listed 1998
'Royalty' (p) SHay
§ 'Roysii' (p) CLyd MPla WPer
'Rubin' (pf) WEas
'Ruby' See D. 'Houndspool Ruby'

'Ruby Doris' See D. 'Houndspool Ruby'
'Ruby Wedding' (p) GCHN
*rupicola* Last listed 1998
'Russling Robin' See D. 'Fair Maid of Kent'
'Sabra' (pf) Last listed 1996
'Sahara' (pf) SAll
'Saint Edith' (p) WKin
'Saint Nicholas' (p) EMFP WKin
'Saint Winifred' WKin
§ Salamanca = 'Kosalamana' SBai (pf)
'Sally Anne Hayward' (b) SHay
'Salmon Clove' (b) Last listed 1998
§ Salmon Gipsy® = 'Stadarpi' SSmt
'Sam Barlow' (p) CPri CThr EMFP GMaP NCra SAll SChu SHay SIng SSvw WWye
Sammy Last listed 1997
'Samuel Doby' (p) Last listed 1997
'Sandra Neal' (b) ♀ SBai
'Santa Claus' (b) SAll SHay
'Sappho' (b) Last listed 1997
'Scania' (pf) SHay
*scardicus* EHyt
'Scarlet Fragrance' (b) SHay
'Scarlet Joanne' (pf) NPin SHay
*scopulorum perplexans* NTow
*seguieri* GSki MNrw WPer
*serotinus* Last listed 1998
'Shaston' (b) Last listed 1998
'Shaston Scarletta' (b) SHay
'Shaston Superstar' (b) Last listed 1997
'Sheila's Choice' (p) ♀ Last listed 1993
'Shot Silk' (pf) NPin
'Show Aristocrat' (p) SAll
'Show Beauty' (p) Last listed 1998
'Show Portrait' (p) NFor
*simulans* EHyt EWes
'Sir Arthur Sim' (pf) Last listed 1998
'Sir Cedric Morris' See D. 'Cedric's Oldest'
'Sir David Scott' (p) Last listed 1997
* 'Six Hills' CLyd WPat
§ Smiling Gipsy® = 'Staviolet' SSmt
'Snow Clove' (b) SHay
'Snowbird' (pf) SAll
'Snowfire' SChu
'Snowshill Manor' (p) WPer
* 'Sofia' (p) SAll
'Solomon' (p) CThr EBee SSvw WKin
'Solway Hannah Scholes' (pf) Last listed 1998
'Solway Sovereign' (pf) Last listed 1996
'Solway Splash' (pf) Last listed 1997
'Solway Sunset' (pf) Last listed 1998
'Solway Surprise' (pf) NPin
'Solway Susan' (pf) Last listed 1998
'Solway Sweetheart' (pf) Last listed 1998
'Sops-in-wine' (p) CLTr CLon CSam CThr ECha EGar EMFP GCal GMac LNor MNrw NCra SAll SChu SHay WWhi
'Southmead' (p) Last listed 1998
§ 'Souvenir de la Malmaison' CMil WMal (M)
sp. B&SWJ 1414 Last listed 1998
sp. J Watson Last listed 1998
'Spangle' (b) SAll
'Spangled Star' (p) EBee NRoo
'Spencer Bickham' (p) EMFP EPot MNrw
'Spetchley' Last listed 1997
'Spindrift' (b) Last listed 1996
'Spinfield Happiness' (b) ♀ Last listed 1995
'Spring Beauty' (p) LPVe NBir NFla WHer
'Spring Star' (p) EBee NRoo
'Square Eyes' See D. 'Old Square Eyes'

| | |
|---|---|
| *squarrosus* | EGar EPot LBee NWCA SUsu |
| \* – *alpinus* | ECho |
| – 'Nanus' | CLyd CNic ELan EWes |
| 'Squeeks' (p) | SChu |
| 'Staccato' (pf) | SBai |
| ◆ 'Stadarpi' | See *D.* Salmon Gipsy = 'Stadarpi' |
| ◆ 'Stagigi' | See *D.* Giant Gipsy = 'Stagigi' |
| ◆ 'Stagilon' | See *D.* Gipsy Rogue = 'Stagilon' |
| ◆ 'Stagipast' | See *D.* Pastel Gipsy = 'Stagipast' |
| ◆ 'Stagirond' | See *D.* Rondo = 'Stagirond' |
| ◆ 'Stagispan' | See *D.* Brilliant Gipsy = 'Stagispan' |
| 'Stan Stroud' (b) | SHay |
| 'Startler' (p) | Last listed 1997 |
| ◆ 'Staviolet' | See *D.* Smiling Gipsy = 'Staviolet' |
| *sternbergii* | Last listed 1998 |
| – JJH 931078 | NWCA |
| 'Storm' (pf) | SBai |
| 'Strathspey' (b) | SAll SHay |
| 'Strawberries and Cream' (p) | CThr EAst EBee EBrP EBre EMFP |
| | EWTr LBre LHop NOrc NPin SBai |
| | SBre SHay |
| *strictus* var. *brachyanthus* | See *D. integer* subsp. |
| | *minutiflorus* |
| \* – *pulchellus* | EHyt |
| § *subacaulis* | EPot GAbr NHar NWCA |
| ¶ 'Sue Randall' (pf) | SBai |
| *suendermannii* | See *D. petraeus* |
| \* 'Sullom Voe' | Last listed 1998 |
| 'Sunray' (b) | SAll SHay |
| 'Sunstar' (b) | SAll SHay |
| § *superbus* | CGen MTho WCla WPer WWhi |
| | WWin WWye |
| – 'Crimsonia' | WPer |
| – var. *longicalycinus* | MNrw MSte |
| – – B&SWJ 3230 | Last listed 1998 |
| I – 'Primadonna' | WPer |
| \* – 'Rose' | WPer |
| – 'Snowdonia' | WPer |
| 'Susan' (p) | EMFP SAll |
| 'Susannah' (p) | SAll |
| \* 'Susan's Seedling' (p) | SAll |
| 'Swanlake' (p) | SHay |
| 'Swansdown' (p) | NFor |
| 'Sway Belle' (p) | CThr NCra NPla SBai WSpi |
| § 'Sway Candy' (p) | NCra |
| 'Sway Gem' (p) | SBai |
| 'Sway Joy' (p) | NCra SBai |
| 'Sway Lass' (p) | SBai |
| ¶ 'Sway Melody' (p) | SBai |
| 'Sway Mist' (p) | NCra |
| 'Sway Pearl' (p) | NCra NPin SBai |
| 'Sway Ripple' (p) | SBai |
| § 'Sway Sunset' (p) | SBai |
| ¶ 'Sweet Sophie' (pf) | NPin |
| 'Sweet Sue' (b) | SAll SHay |
| 'Sweetheart Abbey' (p) | CLon CLyd CThr EMFP NCra |
| | SChu SMer SSvw |
| *sylvestris* | EPot |
| ¶ – subsp. *tergestinus* | SSvw |
| – 'Uniflorus' | Last listed 1998 |
| 'Syston Beauty' (p) | WKin |
| 'Tamsin' (p) ♀ | EMFP MCAu SBla |
| 'Tamsin Fifield' (b) ♀ | Last listed 1995 |
| 'Tangerine Sim' (b) | Last listed 1997 |
| \* 'Tasty' (pf) | SAll |
| ¶ 'Tatra Bull's-eye' (p) | GCal |
| *tatsiense* | CFri |
| 'Tayside Red' (M) | WMal |
| 'Telstar' (pf) | Last listed 1997 |
| 'Tempo' (pf) | SBai |
| \* *tenerifa* | MBri |
| 'Terra' (pf) | Last listed 1998 |

| | |
|---|---|
| 'Terry Sutcliffe' (p) | WKin |
| 'Texas' (pf) | SAll |
| the Bloodie pink | See *D.* 'Caesar's Mantle' |
| 'Theo' (p) | SAll |
| 'Thomas' (p) | EFou NBrk SAll SChu WEas |
| 'Thomas Lee' (b) | SAll |
| 'Thora' (M) | WMal |
| 'Tinnington Secret Garden' | Last listed 1998 |
| 'Tiny Rubies' | See *D. gratianopolitanus* 'Tiny |
| | Rubies' |
| 'Toledo' (p) | EMFP |
| 'Tom Portman' (p) | Last listed 1997 |
| ¶ 'Tony's Choice' (pf) | NPin |
| 'Torino' (pf) | SAll |
| 'Tracy Barlow' (b) | SHay |
| 'Tracy Jardine' (pf) | Last listed 1998 |
| 'Treasure' (p) | SHay |
| 'Trevor' (p) | SAll |
| 'Trisha's Choice' (p) ♀ | Last listed 1993 |
| Tundra (pf) | SBai |
| *turkestanicus* | CLyd NBir |
| § – 'Patricia Bell' (p) | CSam |
| 'Tweedale Seedling' | GBuc |
| \* 'Tyrolean Trailing Carnations' | SAll |
| 'Uncle Teddy' (b) ♀ | SBai |
| *uniflorus* | Last listed 1998 |
| 'Unique' (p) | CLon EMFP MBro SSvw WHoo |
| | WIvy WKin |
| 'Ursula Le Grove' (p) | CLTr EMFP SChu SSvw WHoo |
| | WIvy WKin |
| 'V.E. Jubilation' (pf) ♀ | Last listed 1998 |
| 'Valda Wyatt' (p) ♀ | CThr EBee ELan EMFP EPfP EWTr |
| | GCHN LHop NCra NPin SAll SBai |
| | SChu SRms WSpi WWhi WWol |
| Valencia (pf) | SBai |
| Van Gogh (pf) | Last listed 1997 |
| 'Velvet and Lace' | Last listed 1997 |
| 'Vera Woodfield' (pf) | Last listed 1998 |
| 'Vermeer' | Last listed 1998 |
| 'Violet Carson' (b) | Last listed 1996 |
| 'Violet Clove' (b) | SHay |
| 'Visa' (pf) | SAll |
| 'W.A. Musgrave' | See *D.* 'Musgrave's Pink' |
| 'W.H. Brooks' (b) | SAll |
| 'Waithman Beauty' (p) | CLyd CMil CTri ECha GAbr MBar |
| | MBro MHar MPla NCra NRoo SAll |
| | WEas WHoo WPer WPyg WWye |
| 'Waithman's Jubilee' (p) | GCHN NBrk NCat SRms WLin |
| 'Warden Hybrid' (p) | CMea CTri EBee EMNN EPfP ESis |
| | GAbr MOne NCra NHol NRoo |
| | WAbe WLRN |
| 'Warrior' (b) | CBlo |
| 'Wedding Bells' (pf) | NPin |
| 'Weetwood Double' (p) | WPer |
| 'Welcome' (b) | SHay |
| *weyrichii* | NMen WPer |
| 'Whatfield Anona' (p) | CLyd EGle ELan SAll |
| 'Whatfield Beauty' | ECho ELan LRHS SAll |
| ¶ 'Whatfield Brilliant' (p) | CLyd LBee |
| 'Whatfield Can-can' | CInt CLyd CMea CPBP CPri EBee |
| | EMFP ESis LFis MOne NCra NHol |
| | NRoo SAll WAbe WWeb |
| 'Whatfield Cyclops' | CLyd CPBP EHyt EWes MBro |
| | MOne NCra SAll SChu WLRN |
| 'Whatfield Dawn' | ECho ELan NNrd SAll |
| 'Whatfield Dorothy Mann' (p) | CLyd ECho ELan SAll |
| 'Whatfield Fuchsia' (p) | SAll |
| 'Whatfield Gem' (p) | CInt CKel CLyd EBrP EBre ELan |
| | EMFP ESis GCal LBre MBro MOne |
| | MWgw NCra NHol NMen NRoo |
| | SAll SBre WFar WHoo WPer |

'Whatfield Joy' (p)    CLyd EBee ELan EPot ESis LBee
MOne NCra NHol NMen NPri
NRoo NTow SAll

'Whatfield Magenta' (p)    CLyd CPBP EGle ELan EPot ESis
LBee LRHS MOne NCra NHol
NNrd NRoo SAll SChu WAbe
WEas WLin

'Whatfield Mini' (p)    CLyd SAll SRms WPer
'Whatfield Miss' (p)    SAll
'Whatfield Misty Morn' (p)    ECho ELan
'Whatfield Peach' (p)    SAll
Whatfield pinks (p)    Last listed 1997
'Whatfield Polly Anne' (p)    Last listed 1996
'Whatfield Pom Pom' (p)    CLyd
'Whatfield Pretty Lady' (p)    ECho ELan SAll
'Whatfield Rose' (p)    ECho SAll
'Whatfield Ruby' (p)    CLyd EGle ELan EMFP LRHS SAll
WPer

'Whatfield Supergem' (p)    CLyd ECho ELan EPot SAll
'Whatfield White' (p)    CLyd ECho ELan LRHS SAll SRms
WGwG

'Whatfield White Moon' (p)    ECho
'Whatfield Wink'    EGle
'Whatfield Wisp' (p)    CLyd CM&M CPBP CTri EGle
ELan NBir NMen WCom WFar
WLRN

'White Barn' (p)    ECha
'White Joy' (p) ♀    EBee EMFP NOla
'White Ladies' (p)    CLyd CThr ELan EMFP ENot SAll
'White Liberty' (pf)    SBai
'White Lightning' (pf)    SAll
'White Sim' (pf)    Last listed 1997
'Whitecliff' (b)    SAll SHay
'Whitehill' (p) ♀    EPot NHol NMen NWCA NWoo
WPat WWin

'Whitesmith' (b) ♀    SAll
'Whitford Belle' (p)    SBai
'Widecombe Fair' (p) ♀    CLTr CMea CThr CTri EBee EBrP
EBre LBre NCra NPla SAll SBre
SRms

 * 'Wild Velvet' (p)    MMal
'William Brownhill' (p)    CMil EMFP SChu SMer
'William Sim' (pf)    Last listed 1997
'Winsome' (p)    SHay
'Woodfield's Jewel' (p)    Last listed 1998
'Yellow Dusty Sim' (pf)    Last listed 1997
'Yellow Rendez-Vous' (pf)    SBai
'Yorkshireman' (b)    SAll SHay
'Zebra' (b)    SAll SBai SHay
*zederbaueri*    NWCA SIng
'Zodiac' (pf)    Last listed 1997
'Zoe's Choice' (p) ♀    Last listed 1996

## DIAPENSIA (Diapensiaceae)

*lapponica* var. *obovata*    WAbe

## DIARRHENA (Poaceae)

*japonica*    Last listed 1997

## DIASCIA ✿ (Scrophulariaceae)

'Alys'    WPeH
*anastrepta*    CVer EGar MSCN WPer WWye
- HWEL 0219    NWCA
'Andrew'    WPeH
'Appleby Appleblossom'    CMea CRDP CStr EOrc EPot LLWP
MAvo MBEx MLLN SChu SIng
SSoC SSvw WRus

'Appleby Apricot'    EMar MAvo MBEx MSCN NDov
NGdn WHoo

'Apricot' hort.    See *D. barberae* 'Hopleys Apricot'
'April Fool'    LLWP MAvo WPeH
 * 'Aquarius'    SChu WPeH WPen

*barberae*    CInt EBrP EBre EHic ELan GAri
LBre LHop SBre SEas WOve

¶ - 'Belmore Beauty' (v)    CElw EGoo EMar LLWP MAvo
SUsu WByw WElm

- 'Blackthorn Apricot' ♀    More than 30 suppliers
§ - 'Fisher's Flora' ♀    CGle EPot LFis MBal NBro NHar
NMen WOve WWin WWye

§ - 'Hopleys Apricot'    CLTr ELan EPfP LHop MBEx
MLLN NBrk

- HWEL 037    NWCA
§ - 'Ruby Field' ♀    CB&S CGle ECha ELan EMNN
EWTr GCHN LHop MBNS MBri
NEgg NSti SBla SIng SLon SPer
SRPl SRms WEas WFar WHoo
WOld WRha WWeb

'Bloomsbury Ice'    Last listed 1998
'Blue Bonnet'    ECtt EHic EPot LHop MBEx SChu
WPeH

'Blush'    See *D. integerrima* 'Blush'
 * 'Chalgrave Beauty'    EMan
§ Coral Belle = 'Hecbel'    CHea CPBP CRDP CSpe EMan
EOrc EPot EWTr EWes GMac
LLWP MAvo MBEx MDHE MMil
NHar NLak NLon NPla NWes
SChu SMac SSoC SUsu SWas WEas
WFar WLRN WPer

'Coral Cloud'    Last listed 1996
*cordata* hort.    See *D. barberae* 'Fisher's Flora'
- × 'Lilac Belle'    SCoo SHFr
*cordifolia*    See *D. barberae* 'Fisher's Flora'
'Cotswold Beauty'    LFis
'Crûg Variegated'    CElw EPot MAvo MLLN SChu
WCot WCru WPat WPer

'Dainty Duet'    EOrc EWes MBEx MGed SChu
SUsu WPer

'Dark Eyes' ♀    SChu WPeH
*denticulata*    Last listed 1996
*elegans*    See *D. fetcaniensis* , *D. vigilis*
'Elizabeth' ♀    LFis NFai NHar NLon WPeH WPen
'Emma'    CMea EOrc LHop LLWP NBur
NHar NLon SChu SIng SUsu
WCom WPeH

*felthamii*    See *D. fetcaniensis*
§ *fetcaniensis*    CHan CLon CMHG CMea CSpe
LGre LHil LHop MBEx MBal NDov
NPer SChu SCro SIgm SIng SPer
WHal WMow WPer WWin

¶ - 'Pitlochrie Pink'    GRei
 * 'Fiona'    Last listed 1997
*flanaganii*    See *D. stachyoides* , *D. vigilis*
'Frilly' ♀    CRDP ECtt NBrk SChu WPeH
¶ 'Garden News'    WPeH
♦ - 'Hecbel'    See *D.* Coral Belle = 'Hecbel'
♦ - 'Hecsyd'    See *D.* Sydney Olympics =
'Hecsyd'

'Hector Harrison'    See *D.* 'Salmon Supreme'
'Hector's Hardy' ♀    EOrc GMaP LLWP SUsu WPeH
'Ice Cracker'    CLTr CSpe EHic EPot EWll LHop
MBEx NPri SAsh SIng WPeH

¶ 'Iceberg'    SIng
§ *integerrima* ♀    CHan CSam CSpe ECha ELan
EOrc LFis LGre LHil LLWP MBEx
MBNS MBro MFir NSti SChu SHel
SIgm SMrm SPla WCom

♦ - 'Alba'    See *D. integerrima* 'Blush'
§ - 'Blush'    CMil CSpe EGoo EMan EMar LHil
NHar NLak SMrm SUsu

- from Lesotho    GCal
- 'Harry Hay'    CGle
- 'Ivory Angel'    See *D. integerrima* 'Blush'
*integrifolia*    See *D. integerrima*

◆ 'Jack Elliott'　　　　　　See *D. vigilis* 'Jack Elliott' ex JE
　　　　　　　　　　　　　8955
'Jackpot'　　　　　　　　EPot MDHE WPeH
'Jacqueline's Joy'　　　　CGle CLyd CRDP EMan GMac
　　　　　　　　　　　　　MBEx NHar NHaw NNrd NPer
　　　　　　　　　　　　　NPla SAga SChu SMrm SSoC WFar
'Joyce's Choice' ♀　　　 CHar EOrc EPot EWes GCal LBee
　　　　　　　　　　　　　LGre LHop LLWP MBEx MBri
　　　　　　　　　　　　　MSCN NHaw NPla NPri NWes
　　　　　　　　　　　　　SAga SChu SMer SUsu WCot
　　　　　　　　　　　　　WLRN
'Kate'　　　　　　　　　　LHil MBEx NLak SChu SIng SMrm
　　　　　　　　　　　　　WCru WPeH
'Katherine Sharman' (v)　 CElw EMon EPPr MAvo WCom
　　　　　　　　　　　　　WWeb
'Lady Valerie' ♀　　　　 CLTr CRDP CSpe EWes GMac LHil
　　　　　　　　　　　　　LHop LLWP MBEx MBri MGed
　　　　　　　　　　　　　MLLN NHar NHaw NWes SLod
　　　　　　　　　　　　　SRPl SWas WPer WWin
'Lavender Bell'　　　　　 Last listed 1997
'Lilac Belle' ♀　　　　　 CB&S CLTr CRDP CVer ECtt ELan
　　　　　　　　　　　　　EWTr LHil LHop LLWP MBEx
　　　　　　　　　　　　　MMil NHar SChu SEas SLod SMrm
　　　　　　　　　　　　　WFar WPeH WWin
'Lilac Dream'　　　　　　LHop LLWP WPeH WWin
'Lilac Lace' (v)　　　　　NHar WPeH
'Lilac Mist' ♀　　　　　 CLTr LGre LLWP MBEx MLLN
　　　　　　　　　　　　　NBur NHar NLon NSti NWoo
　　　　　　　　　　　　　SChu SDix SLod SSoC WPen
'Lilac Queen'　　　　　　WEas
*lilacina*　　　　　　　　CLTr ECtt EMan GAri WPer WWye
'Little Charmer'　　　　　MBEx MBro WHoo WPeH
'Little Emma'　　　　　　WPeH
'Little Fiona'　　　　　　WPeH
'Louise'　　　　　　　　　CSpe EOrc EPot GBuc MDHE
　　　　　　　　　　　　　MRav NHar SMrm WPeH
'Lucy'　　　　　　　　　　CRDP EPot LLWP NHar WPeH
'Lucy' x *mollis*　　　　　SChu SDys SUsu WPeH
*megathura*　　　　　　 Last listed 1998
'Megavil'　　　　　　　　EPot
*mollis*　　　　　　　　　LLWP WPeH
'Orangeade'　　　　　　 LLWP SUsu WPeH
'Pale Face'　　　　　　　NHar WCom
*patens*　　　　　　　　 CLyd MBEx SAga
'Patio Wine'　　　　　　 Last listed 1998
'Paula'　　　　　　　　　LHil LHop
'Penlyn'　　　　　　　　　WPeH
*personata*　　　　　　　Last listed 1998
'Pink Queen'　　　　　　EWTr
'Pink Spires'　　　　　　Last listed 1997
'Pink Spot'　　　　　　　SAga SIng WPeH
* 'Pisces'　　　　　　　　SChu WPeH
* 'Pitlochrie Pink'　　　　Last listed 1997
¶ *purpurea*　　　　　　CPin
*racemulosa*　　　　　　WPeH
'Red Ace'　　　　　　　　CElw CSpe EPot EWTr MDHE
　　　　　　　　　　　　　SIng WPeH
'Red Start'　　　　　　　CPBP EHic EOrc LFis LHop LLWP
　　　　　　　　　　　　　MDHE MMil NHar NHaw NLak
　　　　　　　　　　　　　NPla SChu SIng SUsu SVil WFar
　　　　　　　　　　　　　WLRN WPeH WWeb WWin WWoo
*rigescens* ♀　　　　　　More than 30 suppliers
§ - 'Anne Rennie'　　　　SUsu
　- x *integerrima*　　　WLRN
　- x *lilacina*　　　　　EHic EMar MArl NCat NHol NLak
　　　　　　　　　　　　　SIgm
　- pale form　　　　　　See *D. rigescens* 'Anne Rennie'
'Ruby Field'　　　　　　 See *D. barberae* 'Ruby Field'
'Ruby's Pink'　　　　　　EOrc WPeH
'Rupert Lambert' ♀　　　CLTr EMon GBuc GCal GMac LHil
　　　　　　　　　　　　　LLWP MBEx MBro NHar NSti
　　　　　　　　　　　　　SChu SLod SUsu WHoo WLin
　　　　　　　　　　　　　WPat WPer WPyg

§ 'Salmon Supreme'　　　CB&S CGle CLTr CStr ECtt EHyt
　　　　　　　　　　　　　ELan EWTr GCal GMac LFis LGre
　　　　　　　　　　　　　LHil LHop LLWP MMil NHar SChu
　　　　　　　　　　　　　SHel SMrm SRms SUsu WEas
　　　　　　　　　　　　　WFar WPer WRus
'Selina's Choice'　　　　EPot GBuc SChu WPeH
§ *stachyoides*　　　　　EHal ELan LHop MBNS NDov
　　　　　　　　　　　　　NHaw NPer WPer
'Stella'　　　　　　　　　LHop
* 'Strawberry Sundae'　　Last listed 1998
'Super Salmon'　　　　　EPot
§ Sydney Olympics = 'Hecsyd'　EHic EPot LHil LLWP MLLN NHar
　　　　　　　　　　　　　NHaw WLRN WPer
*tugelensis*　　　　　　 CGle CLon WFar
'Twinkle' ♀　　　　　　　CLyd CPBP CPlt CRDP CSpe EMar
　　　　　　　　　　　　　EPot EWes GCal GMac LHil LLWP
　　　　　　　　　　　　　MBEx MLLN NBir NFai NHar
　　　　　　　　　　　　　NHol NNrd SAga SChu SEas
　　　　　　　　　　　　　WCom WCru WEas WPer WWin
* 'Twins Gully'　　　　　 GCal
* *variegata*　　　　　　SIng
§ *vigilis* ♀　　　　　　More than 30 suppliers
§ - 'Jack Elliott' ex JE 8955　CB&S CLTr CSev CSpe EBrP EBre
　　　　　　　　　　　　　EHic EWes ITim LBre LHop
　　　　　　　　　　　　　NHaw NHol SBre SHel SIde SWas
　　　　　　　　　　　　　WCFE WLRN WPer
'Wendy'　　　　　　　　　LHop WPeH
'White Cloud'　　　　　　LLWP SChu WPeH WSPU
'Woodcote'　　　　　　　LHil LLWP NLak

## DIASCIA x LINARIA   See NEMESIA *caerulea*

## DICENTRA ✿ (Papaveraceae)
'Adrian Bloom'　　　　　CDoC EBee EBrP EBre EPla EWTr
　　　　　　　　　　　　　LBre LRot MBNS MCLN MCli
　　　　　　　　　　　　　NArg NCat NOak NSti SBre SPer
　　　　　　　　　　　　　SPla
'Bacchanal'　　　　　　 More than 30 suppliers
'Boothman's Variety'　　See *D.* 'Stuart Boothman'
'Boothman's White'　　　WWeb
'Bountiful'　　　　　　　CGle CMHG CRow EBee GMaP
　　　　　　　　　　　　　LHop MBro MLLN MRav MTho
　　　　　　　　　　　　　NArg NFor NLon NRoo NSti SPer
　　　　　　　　　　　　　WMoo WRHF
'Brownie'　　　　　　　　GBuc MBel MCLN NCat NGdn
　　　　　　　　　　　　　NSti
*canadensis*　　　　　　EPot GBuc MSal MTho NSti WCot
　　　　　　　　　　　　　WThi
'Catforth Filigree'　　　NCat
'Cherub'　　　　　　　　Last listed 1996
*chrysantha*　　　　　　ECGN
'Coldham'　　　　　　　WCru WTin
*cucullaria*　　　　　　 CBos CRDP CRow CSWP EHyt
　　　　　　　　　　　　　EPar EPot ERos GBuc GCrs IMGH
　　　　　　　　　　　　　LGre MRav MTho NHar NMen
　　　　　　　　　　　　　NRya NSti NTow NWCA SWas
　　　　　　　　　　　　　WAbe WCot WCru WLin WThi
　- 'Pittsburg'　　　　　CBos EBee WCot
* 'Dark Stuart Boothman'　EWTr NOak
*eximia* (Ker-Gawl.) Torr.　EBee MTho MWat SWat
*eximia* hort.　　　　　 See *D. formosa*
　- 'Alba'　　　　　　　 See *D. eximia* 'Snowdrift'
§ - 'Snowdrift'　　　　　CLAP CLon CM&M CSpe CTri
　　　　　　　　　　　　　EBee ELan EPfP EWTr MBro
　　　　　　　　　　　　　MTho NWoo SCob SDys SRms
　　　　　　　　　　　　　SSpi WLin WMoo WPnP WWat
　　　　　　　　　　　　　WWeb
§ *formosa*　　　　　　 More than 30 suppliers
§ - *alba*　　　　　　　 CGle CHad CRow ECha ELan
　　　　　　　　　　　　　LGre MCAu MCLN NBir NBur
　　　　　　　　　　　　　NCot NFor NLon NOak NRoo
　　　　　　　　　　　　　NSti NVic SChu SCob SPer SRPl
　　　　　　　　　　　　　SRms WByw WFar WRus

| | |
|---|---|
| * - 'Aurora' | CHid EBee EFou MCLN MRav SCob |
| ¶ - dark form | WMoo |
| - 'Furse's Form' | EBee NCat NOak WCot |
| - subsp. *oregana* | CLAP CRow EPar GCal MBal NCat NChi NOak NRoo NSti WAbb WAbe WByw WCru WWin |
| - - 'Rosea' | MBel NChi NSti |
| ◆ 'Fusd' | See *D.* Snowflakes = 'Fusd' |
| 'Langtrees' ♀ | More than 30 suppliers |
| 'Luxuriant' ♀ | More than 30 suppliers |
| *macrantha* | CAvo CFil CGle CHad CRDP CRow ECha EPfP LGre MRav MTho SSpi WCru WPGP |
| *macrocapnos* | CB&S CFir CHan CPlN CRow EBee GQui IHdy LFis MTho SMrm WCot WCru WSHC WWeb |
| 'Pearl Drops' | More than 30 suppliers |
| *peregrina* | GCrs GTou WViv |
| § *scandens* | CGle CHar CMil CPlN CRHN CRow CSpe ELan EPfP GCal IHdy MCCP MSCN MTho NLar SLon SSpi SUsu WCru WSHC WWhi |
| - B&SWJ 2427 | WCru |
| 'Silver Smith' | CFil |
| § Snowflakes = 'Fusd' | CDoC EBrP EBre EWes GAbr GCHN LBre MCCP MRav MUlv NHaw NMen NRoo SBre WCer |
| *spectabilis* ♀ | More than 30 suppliers |
| - 'Alba' ♀ | More than 30 suppliers |
| - 'Goldheart' | CHad GBin GBri LRHS SPla WFar |
| 'Spring Morning' | CElw CGle CMHG CMil CRow CSam EGle IBlr NSti SChu SSpi WEas WRHF WRus |
| § 'Stuart Boothman' ♀ | More than 30 suppliers |
| *thalictrifolia* | See *D. scandens* |
| *torulosa* CLD 685 | Last listed 1996 |
| *uniflora* | Last listed 1996 |

## DICHELOSTEMMA (Alliaceae)

| | |
|---|---|
| *congestum* | CAvo EBee ERos LBow MNrw WCot |
| § *ida-maia* | CAvo EBee EPot ETub WLin |
| *multiflorum* | Last listed 1997 |
| § *pulchellum* | NTow |
| *volubile* | CPlN |

## DICHOPOGON (Anthericaceae)

| | |
|---|---|
| *strictus* | EBee |

## DICHOTOMANTHES (Rosaceae)

| | |
|---|---|
| *tristaniicarpa* | CFil SRms |

## DICHROA (Hydrangeaceae)

| | |
|---|---|
| *febrifuga* | CAbb CB&S CCHP CDoC CEnd CFil CGre CHan ERav EWes GBri GQui LBlm LCns LHop SBid SLon SOWG WCru WOVN WWat |
| *versicolor* | CPle |

## DICHROMENA (Cyperaceae)

| | |
|---|---|
| ◆ *colorata* | See *Rhynchospora colorata* |

## DICKSONIA ✿ (Dicksoniaceae)

| | |
|---|---|
| *antarctica* ♀ | CAbb CB&S CDoC CFil COtt CTbh CTrC CTre CTrw EOas EWes ISea LBlo LEdu LHil LPal LPan MCCP MLan NHol NMoo NPal SAPC SArc WFib WGer WMul WNor WRic WWeb |
| *brackenridgei* | Last listed 1997 |
| * *conjugata* | Last listed 1997 |

| | |
|---|---|
| *fibrosa* ♀ | CAbb CB&S EOas WMul WRic |
| *herbertii* | Last listed 1996 |
| * *juxtaposita* | Last listed 1997 |
| * *neorostbornii* | Last listed 1997 |
| *sellowiana* | EOas WRic |
| *squarrosa* ♀ | CAbb CB&S CTrC EOas EREa LBlo MLan SAPC WMul WRic |
| *youngiae* | WRic |

## DICLIPTERA (Acanthaceae)

| | |
|---|---|
| § *suberecta* | CB&S CHal EHol EREa LBlm LHop MBEx SIgm SOWG SUsu |

## DICRANOSTIGMA (Papaveraceae)

| | |
|---|---|
| *lactucoides* | EBee WLin |

## DICTAMNUS (Rutaceae)

| | |
|---|---|
| *albus* ♀ | CArn CB&S EBee EBrP EBre ECha EFou ELan GCal LBre LFis LGre LHop MBel MBri MCAu MRav MUlv NHol NSti SBre SChu SPer WEas WHoo WMer WWat WWye |
| § - var. *purpureus* ♀ | More than 30 suppliers |
| *fraxinella* | See *D. albus* var. *purpureus* |

## DICTYOLIMON (Plumbaginaceae)

| | |
|---|---|
| *macrorrhabdos* | Last listed 1998 |

## DICTYOSPERMA (Arecaceae)

| | |
|---|---|
| *album* | LPal MBri |

## DIDYMOCHLAENA (Dryopteridaceae)

| | |
|---|---|
| *lunulata* | See *D. truncatula* |
| § *truncatula* | CHal MBri |

## DIDYMOSPERMA (Arecaceae)

| | |
|---|---|
| *caudatum* | See *Arenga caudata* |

## DIERAMA (Iridaceae)

| | |
|---|---|
| *ambiguum* | Last listed 1996 |
| *argyreum* | CFil CPla EBee WPGP WSan |
| ¶ - JCA 3.140.400 | SSpi |
| 'Ariel' | IBlr |
| 'Black Knight' | IBlr |
| 'Blush' | IBlr |
| 'Candy Stripe' (v) | CPla CRow EWTr GBri MCCP SMad |
| *cooperi* | CHan IBlr |
| - 'White Form' S&SH 20 | CHan |
| 'Coral Pink' | Last listed 1996 |
| * 'Donard Legacy' | IBlr |
| § *dracomontanum* | CBro CElw CFil CGle CHan CLon CMHG CPou CRDP CRow CVer EBee ECGN GCal GLch IBlr LGre MHar NBir NRoo NWCA SBla SIgm SWat WAbe WCot WHil WHoo WRHF |
| - dwarf lilac | CM&M GCal |
| - dwarf pale pink | CM&M GCal |
| - dwarf pink | Last listed 1998 |
| *dubium* x *robustum* | EBee |
| *ensifolium* | See *D. pendulum* |
| *erectum* | EBee NBur WCot |
| ¶ *floriferum* | CBro |
| *grandiflorum* | IBlr |
| *igneum* | CFai CFil CFir CMea CMil EBee ECGP ELan GBri IBlr MAvo MLLN MNrw MTed NBur SMad SSca WAbe WHoo WPGP WSan WWin |
| - CD&R 278 | CHan CPou CRDP |
| *jucundum* | CHan GBri GBuc MLLN |
| *latifolium* | CHan CPla IBlr NBur WSan |

¶ *lepidum* JCA 3.952.800 | SSpi
*luteoalbidum* CD&R 1025 | Last listed 1996
¶ 'Mandarin' | IBlr
*medium* | CFil CLon EBee GSki LPio SMrm
| WAbe WPGP
'Milkmaid' | IBlr
¶ *mossii* | EBee
'Pamina' | IBlr
'Papagena' | IBlr
'Papageno' | IBlr
*pauciflorum* | CFil CFir CHan CHid CLon CMil
| CRDP CVer EBee ECGP LGre
| SIgm WAbe WCot
¶ – JCA 3.143.500 | SSpi
§ *pendulum* | CAvo CBen CBot CFee CMGP
| EBee EBrP EBre EFou ELan IBlr
| LBre LPio MFir MHar MNrw MRav
| NHol NRoo SBre SPer SWat WAbe
| WByw WGwG WHil WWal
¶ 'Pretty Flamingo' | IBlr
'Puck' | ECha GCal IBlr MRav
*pulcherrimum* | More than 30 suppliers
– var. *album* | ECha GBuc LPio MNrw
– 'Blackbird' | CM&M IBlr NOla SSoC
– x *dracomontanum* | Last listed 1998
– dwarf forms | GCal GSki WWhi
– forms | CRDP CRow IBlr NRoo WSan
– 'Pearly Queen' | CRow
– 'Peregrine' | WPGP
¶ – pink | NCut
– Slieve Donard hybrids | CFri EBrP EBre GBri GCal GMac
| LBre LHop SBre SRCN WRHF
*pumilum* (Baker)N.E.Br. | See *D. pendulum* var. *pumilum*
– hort. | See *D. dracomontanum*
'Queen of the Night' | IBlr
*reynoldsii* | EBee IBlr
*robustum* | CFil CHan GBri GLch IBlr WAbe
| WHil
– S&SH 49 | CHan
– S&SH 63 | CHan
– white S&SH 18 | CHan
¶ *sertum* | CBro
§ Slieve Donard hybrids | WSan
* 'Snowbells' | WWhi
¶ sp. CD&R 192 | CRow
¶ sp. CD&R 96 | WCot
sp. from Lesotho | EBee GCal
¶ sp. JCA 15555 | SSpi
sp. SH 85 | CHan
'Tamino' | IBlr
'Titania' | IBlr
*trichorhizum* | CHan WCot
'Tubular Bells' | IBlr
'Violet Ice' | IBlr
'Westminster Chimes' | IBlr

## DIERVILLA ✿ (Caprifoliaceae)

*lonicera* | CPle MTis SMac SPan WFar WWat
*middendorffiana* | See *Weigela middendorffiana*
*rivularis* | Last listed 1998
*sessilifolia* | CB&S CHar CPle CSpe EPar GOrc
| IMGH IOrc MBel SChu SLon
| WBod WCot WHCG WMow WRus
| WSHC WWin
– 'Butterfly' | MBri
x *splendens* | CDoC CMHG CPle EHoe ELan
| ENot EPla IOrc LHop MBNS MBar
| MPla MRav MUlv NArg NHol SEas
| SLPl SPer SSta WDin WTro

## DIETES (Iridaceae)
*bicolor* | CAbb CPin ERea

*grandiflora* | CPin CTrC EMan ERea LEdu
§ *iridioides* | CGle CSWP GBin LEdu MSte
| WPer

## DIGITALIS ✿ (Scrophulariaceae)
*ambigua* | See *D. grandiflora*
apricot hybrids | See *D. purpurea* 'Sutton's Apricot'
'Butterfingers' | LEur WCot
§ 'Butterfingers' x *ferruginea* | LEur
¶ 'Butterfingers' x *laevigata* | LEur
subsp. *laevigata*
¶ 'Butterfingers' x *obscura* | LEur
* *campanulata alba* | Last listed 1998
*cariensis* | EBee EBla LEur
*ciliata* | CFir CFri EBee ECGN ELan LEur
| MLLN NLak NOak SCou
¶ cream hybrids | EFou
*davisiana* | CBot CLon EBee EBla EWTr GAbr
| LEur NLak NOak SCou STes WCot
| WMoo WPGP WPer
*dubia* | CBot EBla EWTr LEur NBir SPil
| WBro WCHb WGor
¶ 'Electrum' | LEur
*eriostachya* | See *D. lutea*
*ferruginea* | More than 30 suppliers
– 'Gelber Herold' | CBot CLon EMan EPfP EWTr
| GMaP LEur LGre MSte NLar SMrm
| WGor WHil WWhi
– 'Gigantea' | CBot CPou EBee ECGN GCal LEur
| SCro SMrm SSoC WBea
¶ – x *grandiflora* | LEur
– var. *schischkinii* | EBee EBla EWTr GCal GNau LEur
| NArg NBur
♦ 'Flashing Spires' | See *D. lutea* 'Flashing Spires'
* *floribunda* | EBee
*fontanesii* | GMac NLak WBro WViv
'Frosty' | Last listed 1997
x *fulva* | EBee LEur MLLN NBir
'Glory of Roundway' | CBot CPlt LEur MRav NLak SOkh
| SWat WCot WSan WWeb
§ *grandiflora* ♀ | More than 30 suppliers
– 'Carillon' | CSam ECle EMar LEur MSte NLak
| NPri NPro SRob SSca WBro WGor
| WHil WPer
– 'Dropmore Yellow' | Last listed 1997
* – 'Dwarf Carillon' | ETen
– 'Temple Bells' | CBlo EBla EHic EMar GAbr LEur
| LSyl NLak SRPl SWat WPer
*heywoodii* | See *D. purpurea* subsp.
| *heywoodii*
'John Innes Tetra' | CHad CLon CMil CSam ECoo
| LEur LRHS MBNS SUsu SWat
| WGor WPer WRus WWin
*kishinskyi* | See *D. parviflora*
*laevigata* | CBot CHad CSam EBee EBla
| ECGN GAbr GMac LGre MSCN
| MSte NBro NChi SIgm SSoC
| WCHb WHer WPer
– subsp. *graeca* | CMdw EBee LEur MGed MLLN
| SSoC WGor
¶ – subsp. *laevigata* | LEur
¶ – – x *obscura* | LEur
*lamarckii* Ivanina | EBee LEur SIgm WPer
– hort. | See *D. lanata*
§ *lanata* ♀ | More than 30 suppliers
– HH&K 177 | CHan
– HH&K 178 | CHan
*leucophaea* | EMar
§ *lutea* | More than 30 suppliers
§ – subsp. *australis* | EBee LEur SHFr
– Brickell's form | CBel EBee LEur MSte
¶ – ex NS 676 | LEur

| | |
|---|---|
| § - 'Flashing Spires' (v) | CPla NPro WCot WSan |
| * - floribunda form | LEur |
| ¶ - subsp. *lutea* | LEur |
| - 'Yellow Medley' | LEur WCot |
| ¶ x *macedonica* from Macedonia | LEur |
| x *mertonensis* ♀ | More than 30 suppliers |
| *micrantha* | See *D. lutea* subsp. *australis* |
| 'Molten Ore' | ESis |
| *nervosa* | Last listed 1996 |
| *obscura* | CBot CFir CGle CLon CSam EBee ECtt ELan EWTr LEur LHop NOak SBla SIgm SSoC SSpi WCHb WElm WGor WHer WPer |
| - JCA 409.401 | Last listed 1996 |
| *orientalis* | See *D. grandiflora* |
| § *parviflora* | More than 30 suppliers |
| ¶ x *purpurascens* 'Aurora' | LEur |
| *purpurea* | CArn CKin EBrP EBre EFou ENot EWFC GPoy LBre LHol MMal NArg NFor NLan NMir NPri SBre SCou SIde SPlb SRCN WCla WGwG WOak WPer WWye |
| - f. *albiflora* | More than 30 suppliers |
| - - unspotted | LEur WAlt |
| - 'Campanulata' | Last listed 1996 |
| - 'Chedglow' (v) | CNat MAvo WCHb |
| * - 'Danby Lodge' | Last listed 1997 |
| * - 'Dwarf Red' | ECoo LEur WGor |
| - Excelsior Group | CB&S CBot CKel CTri EBrP EBre EMan GMaP LBre MBri MWat NFai NFla NMir NVic SBre SPer SRms WGor |
| ¶ - - primrose | LEur |
| ¶ - - (Suttons; Unwins) ♀ | CBrm MRav |
| ¶ - - white | LEur |
| - Foxy Group | CBlo CBot EGoo MBNS MRav NFai NRoo SRms SRob SWat WHen WPer |
| - Giant Spotted Group | COtt CSam ECGN EWTr SCoo WPer WRus |
| ¶ - - pink | LEur |
| ¶ - - purple | LEur |
| ¶ - - white | LEur |
| - Glittering Prizes Group | ECoo SWat |
| ¶ - - maroon | LEur |
| ¶ - - white | LEur |
| - Gloxinioides Group | EBee EPfP EWTr NRya SHFr SRPl WElm WUnu |
| - - 'The Shirley' ♀ | ECtt WGor |
| § - subsp. *beywoodii* | CBel CSam CSpe EGoo ELan EMar ESis GBuc LEur SPer SRob WCHb WCru WLRN WPer WWin |
| - 'Isabelina' | CBot LEur NLak WPer WViv |
| - subsp. *mariana* | EBee |
| - subsp. *nevadensis* | CBot LEur |
| ¶ - 'Pam's Choice' | CSpe |
| ¶ - peloric | WViv |
| ¶ - 'Primrose Carousel' | LEur NArg |
| § - 'Sutton's Apricot' ♀ | More than 30 suppliers |
| * - 'Sutton's Giant Primrose' | CBot |
| - white cen-type mutant | CNat |
| ¶ - 'Roundway Gold' | Last listed 1998 |
| *sibirica* | CFri CSam EBee EBla GBuc LEur MLLN NLak SCou WBro WPer |
| * *stewartii* | EBee |
| 'Strawberry Crush' | Last listed 1998 |
| *tbapsi* | CBot CSam EBee ECGN EOld ESis LEur MLLN NLak SBla WBro WCHb WPer WSel WUnu |
| ¶ - JCA 410.000 | EBee LEur |

| | |
|---|---|
| *trojana* | CLon CSam EBee GBuc LEur LFis MCli NLak NPri SCou SLod SUsu WEas WPer WWin |
| * *tuberosa* | LFis |
| ¶ Vesuvius hybrids | LEur |
| *viridiflora* | CFri CSam ECtt ESis EWTr GAbr LEur MBNS NBro NPri NSti SPil SSoC WBro WCHb WElm WHer WPer WWin |
| - HH&K 308 | CHan |

## DIGITALIS x ISOPLEXIS (Scrophulariaceae)

| | |
|---|---|
| ¶ *D. obscura* x *I. canariensis* | LEur |

## DIONAEA (Droseraceae)

| | |
|---|---|
| *muscipula* | CSWC EAnd WMEx |
| ¶ - 'Royal Red' | NCot |
| ¶ - 'Spider' | NCot |

## DIONYSIA (Primulaceae)

| | |
|---|---|
| 'Agnes' | Last listed 1998 |
| 'Annielle' | EHyt |
| *archibaldii* | Last listed 1997 |
| *aretioides* ♀ | EPot WAbe |
| - 'Gravetye' | ECho MRPP |
| - 'Paul Furse' | EHyt |
| - 'Phyllis Carter' | CPBP ECho EHyt EPot MRPP NMen |
| ¶ - 'Susan Hale' | EHyt |
| *curviflora* | EHyt EPot |
| - x *tapetodes* MK 2 | Last listed 1998 |
| *denticulata* | Last listed 1998 |
| 'Ewesley Epsilon' | EHyt |
| *involucrata* | CGra WAbe |
| 'Markus' | CGra EHyt |
| 'Monika' MK 8809/1 | CGra EHyt |
| * 'Nan Watson' | EHyt |
| *tapetodes* | Last listed 1998 |
| * - CGW No. 1 | Last listed 1998 |
| - ENF 5 | EHyt |
| - farinose form | ECho |
| - 'Peter Edwards' (Hewer 1164) | Last listed 1996 |
| ¶ - 'Sulphur' | EHyt |

## DIOON (Zamiaceae)

| | |
|---|---|
| *edule* | CBrP CRoM LPal |
| ¶ - var. *angustifolium* | CBrP |
| ¶ - var. *edule* | CTrC |
| *mejiae* | LPal |
| *rzedowskii* | LPal |
| *spinulosum* | CBrP LPal |

## DIOSCOREA (Dioscoreaceae)

| | |
|---|---|
| *batatas* | IIve MSal |
| *deltoidea* | WCru |
| *dregeana* | CPIN |
| *elephantipes* | CPIN |
| ¶ *nipponica* | IIve |
| *quinqueloba* | WCru |
| *villosa* | MSal |

## DIOSMA (Rutaceae)

| | |
|---|---|
| *ericoides* | LBuc SRms |
| - 'Pink Fountain' | WWeb |
| - 'Sunset Gold' | CCHP CInt LBuc SCoo WWeb |

## DIOSPHAERA (Campanulaceae)

| | |
|---|---|
| *asperuloides* | See *Trachelium asperuloides* |

## DIOSPYROS (Ebenaceae)

| | |
|---|---|
| *austroafricana* | Last listed 1998 |

| | |
|---|---|
| *duclouxii* | CFil SBid WPGP |
| *kaki* (F) | CAgr CGre CMCN LEdu LPan SSpi WDin |
| *lotus* | CAgr CB&S CFil CMCN LEdu LPan SSpi WPGP |
| ¶ *rhombifolia* | CFil |
| *virginiana* (F) | CAgr CB&S CMCN EPfP ICrw LEdu SSpi |

**DIPCADI** (Hyacinthaceae)

| | |
|---|---|
| *lividum* SF 1 | Last listed 1998 |
| *serotinum* | Last listed 1997 |

**DIPELTA** (Caprifoliaceae)

| | |
|---|---|
| *floribunda* | CBot CFil CPMA CPle EPfP LRHS MAsh SSpi WBod WPGP WWat |
| *ventricosa* | CFil CPMA CPle EPfP LRHS WPGP WWat |
| *yunnanensis* | CFil EPfP LRHS SPla WPGP |

**DIPHYLLEIA** (Berberidaceae)

| | |
|---|---|
| *cymosa* | CRDP EBee ECha EMan EOld EPar MSal WCru |
| ¶ *grayi* | WCru |
| ¶ *sinensis* | WCru |

**DIPIDAX** See ONIXOTIS

**DIPLACUS** See MIMULUS

**DIPLADENIA** See MANDEVILLA

**DIPLARCHE** (Ericaceae)

| | |
|---|---|
| ¶ *multiflora* | WAbe |

**DIPLARRHENA** (Iridaceae)

| | |
|---|---|
| ¶ Helen Dillon's form | EMan |
| § *latifolia* | CAvo CFil LBee SWas WAbe WCot |
| *moraea* | CDoC CFil CHan CHid EBee EMan EPla GCal GGar IBlr ILis LFis MTho SSpi WAbe WCot WHal WOld WPGP WWin |
| - *minor* | SWas |
| - 'Slieve Donard' | CLAP CRDP |
| - West Coast form | See *D. latifolia* |

**DIPLAZIUM** (Woodsiaceae)

| | |
|---|---|
| § *proliferum* | WRic |

**DIPLOTAXIS** (Brassicaceae)

| | |
|---|---|
| *tenuifolia* | Last listed 1997 |

**DIPOGON** (Papilionaceae)

| | |
|---|---|
| § *lignosus* | CPlN WCot |

**DIPSACUS** (Dipsacaceae)

| | |
|---|---|
| § *fullonum* | CArn CHal CKin CLTr COlW EWFC EWTr GCHN MChe MHew MUlv NBro NLan NMir SIde SSvw WBea WByw WCer WHer WOak WPer WWye |
| - subsp. *fullonum* | WJek |
| *inermis* | CHan EBee ECha GCan NBid NPSI WFar |
| - CC&McK 567 | GCHN |
| *laciniatus* | SRCN WMoo |
| *pilosus* | CKin EWFC |
| *sativus* | NHex |
| *sylvestris* | See *D. fullonum* |

**DIPTERACANTHUS** See RUELLIA

**DIPTERONIA** (Aceraceae)

| | |
|---|---|
| *sinensis* | CB&S CFil CMCN CSam MAsh SSpi WNor WShe |

**DISA** (Orchidaceae)

| | |
|---|---|
| *aurata* | GCrs |
| Diores g. | GCrs |
| x *kewensis* | GCrs SWes |
| 'Kirstenbosch Pride' | GCrs |
| *tripetaloides* | GCrs |
| *uniflora* | GCrs |

**DISANTHUS** (Hamamelidaceae)

| | |
|---|---|
| *cercidifolius* ♀ | CAbP CB&S CFil CPMA ELan EPfP ICrw IDee MAsh MBel MBlu MBri MGos NPal SPer SReu SSpi SSta WBod WDin WPat WWat |

**DISCARIA** (Rhamnaceae)

| | |
|---|---|
| *toumatou* | Last listed 1998 |

**DISELMA** (Cupressaceae)

| | |
|---|---|
| *archeri* | CKen CNic LCon MBar |

**DISPHYMA** (Aizoaceae)

| | |
|---|---|
| ¶ *crassifolium* | SChr |

**DISPOROPSIS** (Convallariaceae)

| | |
|---|---|
| *arisanensis* B&SWJ 1490 | WCru |
| *aspera* | WCru |
| ¶ *longifolia* B&SWJ 5284 | WCru |
| § *pernyi* | CAvo CHid CLAP CLon CRDP EBee ECha EMon EPar EPla LGre MBel MGrG NHar SCob SLod SSpi SWas WCot WCru WFar WHal |
| sp. from Philippines B&SWJ 3891 | WCru |

**DISPORUM** (Convallariaceae)

| | |
|---|---|
| *cantoniense* | WCot |
| - B&SWJ 1424 | WCru |
| ¶ - var. *cantoniense* f. *brunneum* B&SWJ 5290 | WCru |
| - var. *kawakamii* | Last listed 1998 |
| - var. *kawakamii* B&SWJ 350 | WCru |
| *flavens* | CFil CRDP EBee EBrP EBre EPPr EPar LBre LGre MUlv SBre SUsu SWas WCot WFar WPGP |
| - B&SWJ 872 | WCru |
| *hookeri* | EPar WCru |
| - var. *oreganum* | CBro CRow GTou IBlr WCru |
| *kawakamii* B&SWJ 350 | WCru |
| *lanuginosum* | CBro GCrs WCot WCru WThi |
| *lutescens* | WCru |
| *maculatum* | CLAP CRDP EPar LGre SMac SWas |
| ¶ *megalanthum* CD&R 2412b | SWas |
| *nantauense* B&SWJ 359 | WCru |
| *sessile* 'Variegatum' | More than 30 suppliers |
| *shimadae* B&SWJ 399 | WCru |
| *smilacinum* | EPar WCru |
| * - 'Aureovariegatum' | WCru |
| - B&SWJ 713 | WCru |
| *smithii* | CFil CRDP EBee EPar EPot ERos GCrs NBir NHar NMen NTow WCru WPGP WWat |
| sp. B&SWJ 872 | WCru |
| *taiwanense* B&SWJ 1513 | WCru |

*uniflorum*    WCru
- B&SWJ 651    WCru
*viridescens*    WCru

## DISSOTIS (Melastomataceae)
*canescens*    Last listed 1997

## DISTICTIS (Bignoniaceae)
*buccinatoria*    CPlN
'Mrs Rivers'    CPlN

## DISTYLIUM (Hamamelidaceae)
*myricoides*    CFil CMCN EPfP
*racemosum*    CB&S CFil CTre ELan EPfP GSki
   SReu SSta WSHC

## DIURANTHERA See CHLOROPHYTUM

## DIURIS (Orchidaceae)
*corymbosa* from    SWes
   South Australia
- from West Australia    SWes
¶ - yellow    SWes
*drummondii* 'Buttery'    SWes
¶ Earwig g.    SWes
*lanceolata*    SWes
*longifolia*    Last listed 1996
'Pioneer Big Ears'    SWes
*punctata* 'Old Vic'    SWes
*sulphurea* 'Golden Dragon'    SWes

## DIZYGOTHECA See SCHEFFLERA

## DOBINEA (Podoaceae)
*vulgaris* B&SWJ 2532    WCru

## DODECATHEON ✿ (Primulaceae)
*alpinum*    GCrs IMGH NHar NRya SRms
- JCA 11744    SBla
- JCA 9542    Last listed 1996
*amethystinum*    See *D. pulchellum*
*clevelandii*    NTow
- subsp. *insulare*    CNic LRHS NWCA
- subsp. *patulum*    LRHS
*conjugens*    EBee
- JCA 11133    CNic
*cusickii*    See *D. pulchellum* subsp. *cusickii*
*dentatum* ♀    CElw CNic CPBP CVer EPar IMGH
   LBee MBal MBro MPhe MTho
   NMen NSla NTow WAbe WFar
- subsp. *dentatum*    Last listed 1996
- subsp. *ellisiae*    GCrs MPhe NRya
*frigidum*    WAbe
§ *hendersonii* ♀    CBro EBee EPar MBal MPhe NPar
   SBla SRms
- 'Inverleith' ♀    Last listed 1995
- subsp. *parvifolium*    GNor
*integrifolium*    See *D. hendersonii*
§ *jeffreyi*    MBro MPhe NHar NMen NWCA
   WAbe WCla WViv
- 'Rotlicht'    NHar SRms
* x *lemoinei*    EPot WAbe
§ *meadia* ♀    More than 30 suppliers
- f. *album* ♀    CB&S CBro CCuc CLon CSWP
   CVer EBee ECha EFou ELan EOrc
   EPar GDra LAma LHop MLLN
   MTho NChi NHol NMen NRoo
   NRya NTow SPer SRms WWat
- from Cedar County    WAbe
* - 'Goliath'    Last listed 1997
- membranaceous    WAbe
- 'Millard's Clone'    EPar

- red shades    Last listed 1997
- 'Rose Farben'    Last listed 1996
- 'Splendidum' ♀    Last listed 1995
*pauciflorum* hort.    See *D. pulchellum*
- (Dur.)E. Greene    See *D. meadia*
*poeticum*    EHic MBro NTow
§ *pulchellum* ♀    CBro EBee EPar EPot GDra LBee
   MBal MBro MNrw NHar NMen
   NRya NWCA SBla WAbe
- *album*    Last listed 1997
§ - subsp. *cusickii*    LBee NWCA SRms
- subsp. *macrocarpum*    Last listed 1996
- subsp. *pulchellum*    CLon CMea CVer EBrP EBre EPot
   'Red Wings'    GDra LBre MBro NTow SBre
   WHoo WLin WPyg
- *radicatum*    See *D. pulchellum*
¶ - 'Sooke's Variety'    WAbe
*radicatum*    See *D. pulchellum*
*redolens*    EBee WAbe
¶ - NNS 95-224    MRPP
*tetrandrum*    See *D. jeffreyi*

## DODONAEA (Sapindaceae)
*humilis* (f)    Last listed 1997
- (m)    Last listed 1997
*viscosa*    CArn CMFo ECou IBlr LHil MSag
- subsp. *angustifolia*    Last listed 1998
- subsp. *cuneata*    Last listed 1998
- subsp. *linearis*    Last listed 1998
- 'Purpurea'    CAbb CB&S CDoC CGre CTrC
   EBee ECou EHic ERea LHop

## DOLICHOS (Papilionaceae)
*lablab*    See *Lablab purpureus*
*lignosus*    See *Dipogon lignosus*

## DOLICHOTHRIX (Asteraceae)
§ *ericoides*    WHer

## DOMBEYA (Sterculiaceae)
*burgessiae*    SOWG

## DONDIA See HACQUETIA

## DOODIA (Blechnaceae)
*aspera*    GQui NMar
§ *caudata*    NMar WRic
*heterophylla*    NMar
*media*    GQui NMar WRic
*mollis*    NMar
* *rubra*    NMar
*squarrosa*    See *D. caudata*

## DORONICUM ✿ (Asteraceae)
*austriacum*    EBee EPri MSCN NCat SMac SSca
   WCot
*carpetanum*    CSam
¶ *catactactarum*    EBee
*caucasicum*    See *D. orientale*
¶ *clusii*    GVic
§ *columnae*    EBee GDra
*cordatum*    See *D. columnae*
§ x *excelsum* 'Harpur Crewe'    CGle ELan MCAu MHlr MRav
   NPer NTow NVic WCot WEas
'Finesse'    CBlo EBee EPfP NOak SOkh SRms
   WMoo
§ 'Frühlingspracht' (d)    CRDP ENot GDra MInt NFla SRms
*grandiflorum*    EBee
¶ 'Little Leo'    LRHS WHil WWeb
'Miss Mason' ♀    MBNS MBri SPer
§ *orientale*    CBlo EMar ENot EPfP MOne
   MSCN NPla SEND SMac SWat
   WByw WMow WOve

| | |
|---|---|
| - 'Goldcut' | EWll NRoo SPla WLRN |
| - 'Goldzwerg' | Last listed 1996 |
| - 'Magnificum' | CSam EAst EBee EMan GMaP |
| | LPVe MFir MWat NArg NFai NFla |
| | NLon NMir NOak SMer SRms |
| | WBea WFar WPer WPyg WWal |
| | WWin |
| *pardalianches* | CMea ECha MHew MLLN SDys |
| | WByw WCot WRHF |
| *plantagineum* 'Excelsum' | See *D.* x *excelsum* 'Harpur Crewe' |
| 'Riedels Goldkranz' | GBuc MBri MWhi |
| Spring Beauty | See *D.* 'Frühlingspracht' |

## DORYANTHES (Agavaceae)
| | |
|---|---|
| *excelsa* | CTrC |
| *palmeri* | Last listed 1998 |

## DORYCNIUM See LOTUS

## DORYOPTERIS (Adiantaceae)
| | |
|---|---|
| *pedata* | MBri |

## DOUGLASIA (Primulaceae)
| | |
|---|---|
| *laevigata* | See *Androsace laevigata* |
| *montana* | See *Androsace montana* |
| *nivalis* | See *Androsace nivalis* |
| *vitaliana* | See *Vitaliana primuliflora* |

## DOVEA (Restionaceae)
| | |
|---|---|
| ¶ *macrocarpa* | CCpl |

## DOVYALIS (Flacourtiaceae)
| | |
|---|---|
| *caffra* (F) | LBlo |

## DOXANTHA See MACFADYENA

## DRABA (Brassicaceae)
| | |
|---|---|
| *acaulis* | EHyt |
| *aizoides* | EBrP EBre ECha ELan GCHN GCrs |
| | GDra LBre MOne MWat NRya |
| | SBre SIng SRms WCla WCom |
| | WLow WWin |
| - 'Compacta' | Last listed 1997 |
| *aizoon* | See *D. lasiocarpa* |
| *alticola* JJH 119.94 | EPot |
| § *aspera* | Last listed 1998 |
| *bertolonii* Nyman | See *D. aspera* |
| - Thell. | See *D. brachystemon* |
| - Boissier | See *D. loeseleurii* |
| *breweri* | Last listed 1996 |
| *bruniifolia* | EBrP EBre EBur EGle EWes LBre |
| | MTho NHed NWCA SBre SSmi |
| - subsp. *bruniifolia* | CGra |
| - subsp. *olympica* | Last listed 1996 |
| *bryoides* | See *D. rigida* var. *bryoides* |
| *cappadocica* | EHyt |
| *caucasica* | Last listed 1996 |
| *cinerea* | Last listed 1998 |
| *compacta* | See *D. lasiocarpa* Compacta |
| | Group |
| *cretica* | NMen |
| *cusickii* | CGra CPBP |
| *cuspidata* | EHal EPot |
| *daurica* | See *D. glabella* |
| *dedeana* | EWes |
| - subsp. *mawii* | NTow |
| *densifolia* | NTow |
| - JJA 11826 | NWCA |
| *dubia* | Last listed 1998 |
| *glacialis* var. *pectinata* | NTow |
| *haynaldii* | Last listed 1997 |
| *hispanica* | NMen |

| | |
|---|---|
| - subsp. *lebrunii* | Last listed 1998 |
| *hoppeana* | NWCA |
| *igarishii* | Last listed 1996 |
| *imbricata* | See *D. rigida* var. *imbricata* |
| § *incana* | MOne WPyg |
| § - Stylaris Group | Last listed 1998 |
| *incerta* | Last listed 1996 |
| *kitadakensis* | GCHN |
| § *lasiocarpa* | NArg |
| § - Compacta Group | Last listed 1996 |
| § *loeseleurii* | NPri |
| *lonchocarpa* | Last listed 1998 |
| *longisiliqua* ♀ | EHyt ITim NWCA SBla |
| - EMR 2551 | EPot |
| *magellanica* | Last listed 1998 |
| *mollissima* | CGra CLyd EHyt EPot GTou NHed |
| | NMen NWCA |
| *oligosperma* | CGra CPBP NWCA WLin |
| * - var. *hastere* | GCrs |
| - NNS 94-40 | MRPP |
| *oreades* CC&McK 804 | MRPP |
| ¶ *oreibata* | WLin |
| *ossetica* var. *racemosa* | WLin |
| *pamirica* | ITim |
| *parnassica* | GCHN |
| *paysonii* | CLyd |
| - var. *treleasei* | WAbe WLin |
| *polytricha* | EHyt GTou NHed NSla |
| *repens* | See *D. sibirica* |
| *rigida* | CMea MLan MOne MTho SIng |
| | SSmi |
| § - var. *bryoides* | CGra EHyt MBro NHar NWCA |
| - - HZ 82-97 | EHyt |
| - - JJH 960858 | Last listed 1998 |
| § - var. *imbricata* | CPBP EHyt MBro NHar NHol |
| | NTow SSmi WLin |
| - - f. *compacta* | EPot |
| ¶ - var. *rigida* | CNic |
| *rosularis* | EPot SIng WLin |
| *rupestris* | See *D. norvegica* |
| *sakuraii* | EDAr |
| x *salomonii* | EPot |
| *sauteri* | GCHN |
| *scardica* | See *D. lasiocarpa* |
| sp. ACE 1382 | Last listed 1996 |
| sp. CC 1911 | MRPP SGre |
| sp. F&W 8173 from Peru | Last listed 1997 |
| sp. from Mt Bross | Last listed 1996 |
| sp. JHH 9309139 | Last listed 1996 |
| *sphaeroides* | CGra |
| *streptocarpa* | Last listed 1998 |
| *stylaris* | See *D. incana* Stylaris Group |
| *talassica* | Last listed 1997 |
| * *thymbriphyrestus* | WLin |
| *ussuriensis* | WPer |
| *ventosa* | GTou NTow |
| ¶ *yunnanensis* | WLin |
| - ex JJH 90856 | Last listed 1997 |

## DRACAENA ✿ (Agavaceae)
| | |
|---|---|
| *cincta* 'Tricolor' (v) | Last listed 1996 |
| *congesta* | See *Cordyline stricta* |
| *draco* | ECre WMul |
| *fragrans* | MBri |
| - (Compacta Group) | MBri |
| 'Compacta Purpurea' | |
| - - 'Compacta Variegata' | MBri |
| - Deremensis Group | Last listed 1996 |
| - - 'Lemon Lime' (v) | MBri |
| - - 'Warneckei' (v) ♀ | MBri SRms |
| - - 'Yellow Stripe' (v) | MBri |
| * - *glauca* | MBri |

- 'Janet Craig'                MBri
- 'Massangeana' (v) ♀         MBri
*indivisa*                     See *Cordyline indivisa*
*marginata* (v) ♀            MBri
- 'Colorama' (v)              MBri
*reflexa* 'Variegata' ♀       Last listed 1995
*sanderiana* (v) ♀           MBri
\* *schrijveriana*             MBri
*steudneri*                    MBri
*stricta*                      See *Cordyline stricta*
*surculosa* 'Florida Beauty'  Last listed 1996
  (v)
- 'Wit' (v)                    Last listed 1996

## DRACOCEPHALUM (Lamiaceae)
*altaiense*                    See *D. imberbe*
*argunense*                    CMil CPBP CPlt CRDP LBee LFis
                               LGre NMen SAga SBla SCro SOkh
                               SRms SRot SSoC WCot WPat WPer
                               WWin
\* - 'Album'                   EBee
*botryoides*                   CPBP EBee NWCA
*calophyllum* ACE 1611        Last listed 1997
- var. *smithianum*           Last listed 1998
*canescens*                    See *Lallemantia canescens*
*forrestii*                    CLyd EPot ESis SBla SIng SMac
                               WCot
aff. *forrestii* ACE 2465     Last listed 1996
*grandiflorum*                 NLar SAga SUsu
*hemsleyanum*                  EBee WPat
§ *imberbe*                    EBee
*isabellae*                    EBee
*mairei*                       See *D. renatii*
*moldavica*                    MSal SIde WWye
*nutans*                       NLar WCot
*oblongifolium*                Last listed 1998
¶ *palmatum*                   IIve
aff. *paulsenii* JJH 9209334  Last listed 1997
*peregrinum*                   Last listed 1998
*prattii*                      See *Nepeta prattii*
§ *renatii*                    EBee MSal
*rupestre*                     EBee EPPr MBri
*ruyschianum*                  CPBP EMan EMon EPPr MLLN
                               NWCA NWoo WCot
*sibiricum*                    See *Nepeta sibirica*
sp. CLD 551                    Last listed 1996
¶ *tanguticum*                 NLar
*virginicum*                   See *Physostegia virginiana*
*wendelboi*                    CPea EBee GBri MLLN NBir NBus
                               WPat WPer WWin

## DRACUNCULUS (Araceae)
*canariensis*                  CAvo
- MS 934                      Last listed 1998
§ *vulgaris*                   CGle CHid CLAP EBee EBot EMon
                               EPar EPot LEdu MCCP MRav SDix
                               SEND SSoC WBor WCot WCru
                               WHal

## DRAPETES (Thymelaeaceae)
*dieffenbachii*                Last listed 1998
*lyallii*                      Last listed 1998

## DREGEA (Asclepiadaceae)
§ *sinensis*                   CB&S CBot CBrd CGre CPIN
                               CSam EBee ELan ERav ERea GQui
                               SBra SOWG WCot WSHC WWat
                               WWeb

## DREPANOSTACHYUM (Poaceae - Bambusoideae)
§ *falcatum*                   CTrC ISta LJus WBay WJun
♦ - hort.                     See *Himalayacalamus falconeri*

*bookerianum*                  See *Himalayacalamus*
                               *bookerianus*
§ *khasianum*                  ISta
§ *microphyllum*               EPla ISta SDry WJun

## DRIMIOPSIS (Hyacinthaceae)
*maculata*                     Last listed 1998

## DRIMYS (Winteraceae)
*aromatica*                    See *D. lanceolata*
*colorata*                     See *Pseudowintera colorata*
¶ *granatensis*                CFil
§ *lanceolata*                 More than 30 suppliers
- (f)                         ECou GEil SPer
- (m)                         CDoC ECou
¶ - 'Mount Wellington'        GCal
¶ - 'Suzette'                 MBlu
§ sp.                         CPla
*winteri*                      CAbb CAgr CB&S CDoC CFil CPle
                               CSam CTrG CTrw EPfP IOrc ISea
                               SArc SPer SRPl WBrE WCwm
                               WDin WSHC WWat
- var. *andina*               CFil CMHG EPfP GGGa SBid SSpi
                               WPGP
§ - var. *chilensis*          CFil CGre CLan ISea MBal WCru
                               WPGP
- 'Fastigiata'                LBlm
- Latifolia Group             See *D. winteri* var. *chilensis*

## DROSANTHEMUM (Aizoaceae)
¶ *bellum*                     EOas
¶ *bicolor*                    CCpl EOas
*floribundum*                  EOas WEas
*hispidum*                     CHal EBrP EBre ECtt ELan EOas
                               EPot IMGH LBre LHop MBro
                               MTho NMen NNrd NTow NWCA
                               SBre SChr SIng WPat WPyg
¶ *micans*                     CCpl EOas
*speciosum*                    EOas
\* *striatum*                  EOas
\* *sutherlandii*              EOas

## DROSERA (Droseraceae)
*adelae*                       EAnd WMEx
¶ *admirabilis*                NCot
*aliciae*                      EAnd WMEx
*andersoniana*                 EFEx
*anglica*                      CSWC WMEx
x *badgerupii*                 WMEx
  'Lake Badgerup'
'Beermullah'                   WMEx
*binata*                       GTro WMEx
§ - subsp. *dichotoma*        Last listed 1998
- 'Extrema'                   WMEx
- 'Multifida'                 WMEx
- T form                      EAnd
*browniana*                    EFEx
*bulbigena*                    EFEx
*bulbosa*                      WMEx
- subsp. *bulbosa*            EFEx
- subsp. *major*              EFEx
x *californica*                WMEx
  'California Sunset'
*capensis*                     EAnd GTro WMEx
- *alba*                      EAnd GTro WMEx
- narrow-leaved              WMEx
¶ - red form                  NCot
*capillaris*                   WMEx
*cuneifolia*                   WMEx
*dichotoma*                    See *D. binata* subsp. *dichotoma*
*dielsiana*                    WMEx
*dilatatopetiolaris*           Last listed 1996

| | |
|---|---|
| *erythrorrhiza* | WMEx |
| - subsp. *collina* | EFEx WMEx |
| - subsp. *erythrorrhiza* | EFEx |
| - *imbecilia* | EFEx |
| - subsp. *magna* | EFEx |
| - subsp. *squamosa* | EFEx |
| *falconeri* | Last listed 1996 |
| *filiformis* var. *filiformis* | EAnd WMEx |
| - var. *tracyi* | Last listed 1997 |
| *fulva* | Last listed 1996 |
| *gigantea* | EFEx WMEx |
| *graniticola* | EFEx |
| *hamiltonii* | WMEx |
| *heterophylla* | EFEx WMEx |
| *indica* | Last listed 1996 |
| *intermedia* | WMEx |
| - × *rotundifolia* | See *D.* × *beleziana* |
| *lanata* | Last listed 1996 |
| *loureirii* | EFEx |
| *macrantha* | EFEx WMEx |
| - subsp. *macrantha* | EFEx |
| *macrophylla macrophylla* | EFEx |
| - *prophylla* | EFEx |
| 'Marston Dragon' | WMEx |
| *menziesii* | Last listed 1997 |
| - subsp. *basifolia* | EFEx |
| - subsp. *menziesii* | EFEx |
| - subsp. *thysanosepala* | EFEx |
| *modesta* | EFEx |
| * *multifida* | GTro |
| *nitidula* | Last listed 1996 |
| *orbiculata* | EFEx WMEx |
| * *ordensis* | Last listed 1996 |
| *peltata* | EFEx WMEx |
| - subsp. *auriculata* | Last listed 1997 |
| *platypoda* | EFEx WMEx |
| *pulchella* | WMEx |
| - giant form | Last listed 1997 |
| - × *nitidula* | WMEx |
| *pygmaea* | Last listed 1996 |
| *ramellosa* | EFEx |
| *rosulata* | EFEx WMEx |
| *rotundifolia* | CSWC GBar WMEx |
| *salina* | EFEx |
| ¶ *scorpioides* | CSWC |
| *slackii* | WMEx |
| *spatulata* | WMEx |
| - Kansai | WMEx |
| - Kanto | WMEx |
| *stolonifera* | WMEx |
| - subsp. *compacta* | EFEx |
| - subsp. *humilis* | EFEx |
| - subsp. *porrecta* | EFEx |
| - subsp. *rupicola* | EFEx |
| - subsp. *stolonifera* | EFEx |
| *stricticaulis* | WMEx |
| *tubaestylus* | EFEx WMEx |
| *villosa* | Last listed 1997 |
| *zonaria* | EFEx WMEx |

## DRYANDRA (Proteaceae)

| | |
|---|---|
| *armata* | Last listed 1998 |
| * *aromatica* | Last listed 1998 |
| ¶ *formosa* | CCpl |
| *nivea* | Last listed 1997 |
| *nobilis* | Last listed 1997 |
| *praemorsa* | Last listed 1997 |
| *quercifolia* | MSag |

## DRYAS (Rosaceae)

| | |
|---|---|
| *drummondii* | EPot SBla WAbe |
| - 'Grandiflora' | Last listed 1998 |

| | |
|---|---|
| * - 'Grandiflora E.B.Anderson' | NHar |
| *grandis* | Last listed 1997 |
| § *integrifolia* | EPot GDra IMGH NHar NMGW WAbe WLin |
| - 'Greenland Green' | WAbe |
| *lanata* | See *D. octopetala* var. *argentea* |
| *octopetala* ♀ | CAgr CBar CGle CSam ELan ESis GCHN GDra GTou IMGH LHop MBal MBro MWat NChi NFla NFor NHar NLon NVic SBla SIng SRms WAbe WCot WEas WWin |
| - 'Minor' ♀ | LBee MBro NMen NWCA NWoo SRms WAbe WPyg |
| × *suendermannii* ♀ | CMHG EBrP EBre ELan EPfP GTou LBee LBre MBro NHol NMen NRoo NWCA SBre WAbe WPyg |
| *tenella* | See *D. integrifolia* |

## DRYOPTERIS ✿ (Dryopteridaceae)

| | |
|---|---|
| *aemula* | EFer |
| § *affinis* ♀ | CCuc CFil CLAP CRow EBee ECha EFou EHic EPar GGar LSyl MBal NHol NMar SCob SRms WFib WRic |
| § - subsp. *borreri* | EFer MBri NBus |
| ¶ - subsp. *cambrensis* | EFer |
| - 'Congesta' | CLAP SLon WFib WWat |
| - 'Congesta Cristata' | EBrP EBre LBre MBri NHar NHol SBre |
| - Crispa Group | EAst EBee GBin IOrc SCob SRPl |
| § - 'Crispa Gracilis' ♀ | CCuc CLAP CMil EBee EFer ELan EMon LHil MBri NBir NBus NLak SPer SPla SRms WAbe WRic |
| - 'Cristata' ♀ | More than 30 suppliers |
| - 'Cristata Angustata' ♀ | CLAP EBee EFer ELan EMon GBin IOrc NHed NHol NLak NMar SCob SRms WFib WPGP WRic |
| - 'Cristata Grandiceps Askew' | CCuc NMar WFib |
| - 'Linearis Cristata' | Last listed 1997 |
| - 'Pinderi' | CLAP EFou ELan MBri NOrc SCob WGor |
| - Polydactyla Group | GQui NMar |
| * - 'Polydactyla Mapplebeck' ♀ | CCuc CRDP CRow NHol SRms |
| - 'Revoluta' | Last listed 1996 |
| - 'Revolvens' | EFer SRms WRic |
| - 'Stableri' | EFer EMon GQui WFib |
| *aitoniana* | WRic |
| *atrata* hort. | See *D. cycadina* |
| *austriaca* hort. | See *D. dilatata* |
| *blanfordii* | CFil WPGP |
| *borreri* | See *D. affinis* subsp. *borreri* |
| *buschiana* | EBee |
| *carthusiana* | CBlo CFil CLAP EBee EFer NBus NHar SRms WPGP WRic |
| - 'Cristata' | NVic |
| - × *oreades* | Last listed 1996 |
| *clintoniana* | EBee WRic |
| × *complexa* 'Stablerae' | NMar WRic |
| ¶ *conjugata* | WRic |
| ¶ *corleyi* | WRic |
| *crassirhizoma* | Last listed 1998 |
| ¶ *crispifolia* | EFer |
| *cristata* | EBee WRic |
| § *cycadina* ♀ | CCuc CFil CLAP CRDP EBee EFer ELan EMar EMon GCal IOrc MCCP MDun NHol NMar SEas SMad SPla WFib WGor WRic WWat |
| *darjeelingensis* | WCru |
| *dickinsii* | EMon WRic |

§ *dilatata* ♀ — CBar CCuc CKin EBee ECha EFer ELan EMon MBal NHol NMar SCob SRms WFib WRic WWat
- 'Crispa Whiteside' ♀ — CFil CLAP CMil EBee EFer ELan EMon MBri MDun NBus NHar NHol NPla SCob WFib WHil WPGP WRic WWoo
- 'Grandiceps' — CLAP CMHG CRDP CRow EFer EMon MBri NHar NHol NVic SChu WFib WRic
- 'Jimmy Dyce' — Last listed 1996
¶ - 'Lepidota Crispa Cristata' — CLAP
- 'Lepidota Cristata' ♀ — CCuc CLAP CMHG CRDP EFer ELan EMon IOrc NHar NHol NMar SCob SRms WFib WRic
- 'Lepidota Grandiceps' — CLAP NMar
*erythrosora* ♀ — More than 30 suppliers
* - 'Prolifera' ♀ — CLAP CRDP EBee EFer EMon GCal GMaP MSte NBir NHar NHed NHol NPla WFib WRic
*expansa* — EMon
*filix-mas* ♀ — EBee EFou EPfP GMaP IIve LHil LPBA MCLN MDun MHlr NBus SRCN SRPl WShi WWat
- 'Barnesii' — CBlo CCuc CLAP EBee EFer MSte NHar NHed NMar SCob WRic
- 'Bollandiae' — WRic
* - 'Corymbifera Crispa' — EFer
- 'Crispa' — EHon NHol SCob WFib
♦ - 'Crispa Congesta' — See *D. affinis* 'Crispa Gracilis'
- 'Crispa Cristata' — CCuc CLAP CRDP EBee EBrP EBre EGol ELan EMon LBre LHop MBri MCLN NBus NFla NHed NHol NMar SBre SChu SCob SLon SMer SPla SRms SWat WFib WGor WHil WRic
- 'Crispatissima' — CCuc MDun
- 'Cristata' ♀ — CBar CCuc CFil CKin CRow EBrP EBre EFer EHon ELan IOrc LBre MBal NMar NOak NOrc SBre SChu SCob SPer SWat WFib WRic WWye
- Cristata Group — EFer NMar SCob SPer WFib WRic
- - 'Fred Jackson' — MLan NHol WFib
* - 'Cristata Grandiceps' — EFer
¶ - 'Cristata Jackson' — SPlb
- 'Cristata Martindale' — CRDP CRow GQui NHol NMar SRms WFib
- 'Decomposita' — Last listed 1996
- 'Depauperata' — CCuc CFil CLAP CRDP SChu WFib WPGP
¶ - 'Euxinensis' — CLAP
- 'Fluctuosa' — SRms
¶ - 'Furcans' — CLAP
¶ - Grandiceps Group — SCob
- 'Grandiceps Wills' ♀ — CRow EMon NHol NMar SChu WFib WRic
- 'Linearis' — CBar CMHG CRow EBee EFer EHon ELan EMar EMon IOrc MBri NBus SCob SRms
- 'Linearis Congesta' — CFil WPGP
- 'Linearis Cristata' — NMar WRic
- 'Linearis Polydactyla' — CLAP CMil EBee EHic IMGH MDun NFla NHar NLak NMar SCob SLdr SMad SPla WHil
- 'Multicristata' — NMar
- Polydactyla Group — GAri NMar SPer WFib
- 'Polydactyla Dadds' — IOrc MBri MLan WFib
*fragrans* — Last listed 1998
* *fructuosa* — Last listed 1997
*goldieana* — CLAP EBee GMaP LSyl NHar NMar SCob WFib WRic

*guanchica* — CFil
*hawaiiensis* — Last listed 1998
*hirtipes* — See *D. cycadina*
*hondoensis* — CFil
*lacera* — NHar
*lepidopoda* — Last listed 1998
*marginalis* — CLAP WRic
§ *nigropaleacea* — Last listed 1998
*odontoloma* — See *D. nigropaleacea*
*oreades* — SRms
*paleacea* — CLAP
*pallida* — CFil
*pseudomas* — See *D. affinis*
x *remota* — SRms WRic
*shiroumensis* — Last listed 1997
*sieboldii* — CCuc CFil CLAP EBee ELan MDun NHar NHol NMar SChu SRms WFib WPGP WRic
sp. from Emei Shan, China — WPGP
*stenolepis* — WRic
*stewartii* — NHar
x *tavelii* — IOrc
x *tokyoensis* — CLAP NHar WFib WRic
x *uliginosa* — WRic
*uniformis* — Last listed 1998
*wallichiana* ♀ — More than 30 suppliers

## DRYPIS (Caryophyllaceae)
*spinosa* — Last listed 1996

## DUCHESNEA (Rosaceae)
*chrysantha* — See *D. indica*
§ *indica* — CAgr CSWP EHic EMan GAbr IBlr MRav NHol NPri NSti SRms SSca WBor WCer WOak
¶ - CC 2007 — NDov
- 'Dingle Variegated' — Last listed 1997
§ - 'Harlequin' (v) — EMon GBar GBuc MCCP MNrw MTho NSti WRha
- 'Snowflakes' — CRow
- 'Taff's Silverline' (v) — Last listed 1998
- 'Variegata' — See *D. indica* 'Harlequin'

## DUDLEYA (Crassulaceae)
*cymosa* — NTow
- JCA 11777 — Last listed 1996
- subsp. *pumila* — NWCA WCot WLin
*farinosa* — IBlr
¶ - NNS 93-240 — IDac
*lanceolata* NNS 95230 — IDac
*pulverulenta* — Last listed 1997

## DUMASIA (Papilionaceae)
¶ *truncata* B&SWJ 4905 — WCru

## DUMORTIERA (Weisnerellaceae)
*hirsuta* — Last listed 1996

## DUNALIA (Solanaceae)
*australis* — See *Iochroma australe*
♦ - blue — See *Iochroma australe* 'Bill Evans'
♦ - white — See *Iochroma australe* 'Andean Snow'

## DURANTA (Verbenaceae)
§ *erecta* — CSpe
- 'Variegata' — Last listed 1998
*plumieri* — See *D. erecta*
*repens* — See *D. erecta*
* *stenostophylla* — CSpe

## DYCKIA (Bromeliaceae)

| | |
|---|---|
| *argentea* | See *Hechtia argentea* |
| *fosteriana* | Last listed 1996 |

## DYMONDIA (Asteraceae)

| | |
|---|---|
| *margaretae* | LRHS WAbe |

## DYPSIS (Arecaceae)

| | |
|---|---|
| § *decaryi* | CBrP LPal |
| *decipiens* | LPal |
| § *leptocheilos* | LPal |
| § *lutescens* ♀ | LPal MBri |
| *utilis* | LPal |

# E

## EBENUS (Papilionaceae)

| | |
|---|---|
| *cretica* | Last listed 1997 |

## ECBALLIUM (Cucurbitaceae)

| | |
|---|---|
| *elaterium* | MHew MSal WHer |

## ECCREMOCARPUS (Bignoniaceae)

| | |
|---|---|
| *ruber* | See *E. scaber* f. *carmineus* |
| *scaber* ♀ | CB&S CFri CPlN CRHN CTrC CTrG EBee ELan EMil ENot EWTr GAbr GCHN LIck MBri MNrw NChi NPer SPer SRms SUsu SYvo WBrE WBro WFar WWye |
| – f.*aureus* | CB&S CMHG EPfP MAsh NLar SDys SHFr |
| § – f.*carmineus* | CB&S CMHG CNic GCHN NLar WCru WElm WPyg |
| – f.*roseus* | CBot CGle EPfP MAsh WBro |

## ECHEVERIA ✿ (Crassulaceae)

| | |
|---|---|
| *affinis* | MBri |
| *agavoides* ♀ | MRav WBrE |
| * – 'Metallica' | MBri |
| * 'Black Knight' | LHil |
| * 'Black Prince' | NPer SGre |
| *derenbergii* ♀ | Last listed 1998 |
| ¶ 'Derosa' | LHil |
| * 'Duchess of Nuremberg' | Last listed 1998 |
| *elegans* ♀ | CHal EOas LHil MBri SAPC |
| § *gibbiflora* var.*metallica* ♀ | WEas |
| *glauca* Bak. | See *E. secunda* var. *glauca* |
| *harmsii* ♀ | CSWP LHil NTow WEas |
| * 'Harry Butterfield' | Last listed 1998 |
| * 'Imbricata' | Last listed 1998 |
| ¶ *nodulosa* | LHil |
| 'Paul Bunyon' | CHal |
| ¶ *peacockii* | EPfP |
| 'Perle von Nürnberg' ♀ | SGre |
| ¶ *prolifica* | CCpl |
| *pulvinata* ♀ | CHal |
| * – 'Frosty' | SGre |
| ¶ *secunda* | LHil |
| § – var.*glauca* | IBlr MHlr NBir SArc |
| * – – 'Gigantea' | NPer |
| *setosa* ♀ | Last listed 1998 |
| 'Warfield Wonder' ♀ | WEas |

## ECHINACEA ✿ (Asteraceae)

| | |
|---|---|
| *angustifolia* | CArn GPoy MSal WCot WHer WOak WWye |
| – 'Mecklenburg Select' | Last listed 1998 |

| | |
|---|---|
| *pallida* | CBot CMil EAst EGar ELan EMan GPoy LFis LHol MSal NCut NPri SMad SSoC WCot WMoo |
| *paradoxa* | CArn CPou EHrv EWTr MSal NChi SDys SMrm WCot |
| § *purpurea* | More than 30 suppliers |
| – Bressingham hybrids | EBrP EBre ELan LBre SBre SPer SPla WFar |
| – dark stemmed form | Last listed 1996 |
| – 'Green Edge' | Last listed 1998 |
| ¶ – 'Knee High' | COtt EHic NDov WCot |
| – 'Leuchtstern' | CHar CMdw ECGN EOld GSki MBel MWll NCut SMrm WLin WPer |
| – 'Magnus' | More than 30 suppliers |
| – 'Robert Bloom' | EHrv ENot LGre LHop SUsu WCot |
| – 'Rubinstern' | COtt EHic LGre NDov WCot |
| – 'The King' | Last listed 1997 |
| ¶ – 'Verbesserter Leuchtstern' | NLar |
| – 'White Lustre' | EBee EBrP EBre ECha LBre MUlv NWoo SBre WCot WMer |
| – 'White Swan' | More than 30 suppliers |
| *simulata* | Last listed 1998 |

## ECHINOPS (Asteraceae)

| | |
|---|---|
| *albus* | See *E.* 'Nivalis' |
| § *bannaticus* | EBee ERav EWTr LLWP MCAu SRms WCot |
| * – 'Albus' | EAst EPfP NSti |
| § – 'Blue Globe' | CHar EBee ECGN EHic EMan EOld GCal LFis MCli MMal NChi SCoo SIgm SSca WHil WLRN WPer WWal |
| – 'Taplow Blue' ♀ | CB&S CHad CSev EBee EBrP EBre EFou ELan LBre LHop MBNS MCLN MRav MUlv MWat NArg NCut NFla NPer SBre SCro SEND SLon SMad SPer SPla WLRN WMer WWeb |
| *chantavicus* | Last listed 1996 |
| ◆ *commutatus* | See *E. exaltatus* |
| § *exaltatus* | EBee MWgw NBir SLon |
| *giganteus* | Last listed 1996 |
| *maracandicus* | GCal WCot |
| *microcephalus* | EGar |
| – HH&K 285 | CHan |
| § 'Nivalis' | CBre EBee ECha EHic ELan EPla GAbr GCal MWgw SEND SPer |
| *oxyodontus* HH&K 145 | CHan |
| – HH&K 153 | Last listed 1998 |
| – HH&K 235 | Last listed 1998 |
| * *perringii* | GCal |
| *ritro* hort. | See *E. bannaticus* |
| § *ritro* L. ♀ | CB&S CHan ECha ECtt ELan ENot GCHN MArl MCLN NBro NCut NFai NFor NRoo NVic SEND SMac SPer SRms SSvw WEas WFar WOve WPer WWin |
| – 'Charlotte' | Last listed 1998 |
| – 'Moonstone' | CRow |
| – subsp.*ruthenicus* ♀ | EBee ECGP ELan EWTr EWll GBuc MRav WBro WPGP |
| – 'Veitch's Blue' | CDoC CHad CM&M CPlt EBee EFou EWTr GCal GLil MBri MCAu MCLN MCli MRav NCat NCut NLak SAga SPer SRPl SSpe WCot WLRN WMer WWeb |
| ◆ – 'Veitch's Blue' misapplied | See *E. ritro* L. |
| *sphaerocephalus* | CHan ECha ELan EMan EMon EWTr IBlr MHlr SIgm SSca WBea WByw WLRN WPer |

| - 'Arctic Glow' | CMil CPou EBee EFou EWTr GMaP GSki MBro MCLN MMHG MRav MSte NBro NChi NCut NFai NLar NPri SBea SCro SGre SPla SSvw WBay WBea WCot WHil WLRN WViv WWhi |
|---|---|
| *strigosus* | EBee |
| *tournefortii* | EGar |
| *tschimganicus* | EBee |

## ECHINOSPARTUM See GENISTA

## ECHIUM (Boraginaceae)

| ¶ *boissieri* | IHdy |
|---|---|
| § *candicans* | CAbb CSpe CTbh CTrC ECre EOas LHil MNrw SAPC SArc SVen |
| *fastuosum* | See *E. candicans* |
| *italicum* | NLar |
| * *nebrum* | GBri |
| *nervosum* | SGre |
| § *pininana* | CAbb CGre CHan CTbh CTrC EBee ECre ELan EOas EWes IHdy ISea NPal SAPC SArc SChr SRCN WCHb WHer |
| - x *wildpretii* | Last listed 1996 |
| *pinnifolium* | See *E. pininana* |
| *russicum* | CFir EBee ECGN LGre MAvo NLar SIgm |
| x *scilloniense* | SYvo |
| *simplex* | Last listed 1997 |
| sp. from Greece | WHer |
| * *virescens* | CTrC |
| *vulgare* | CArn CKin ECGN EEls ELan EOHP EWFC LHol MChe MHew MMal MSal NMir SIde WBrE WCHb WHer WJek WWye |
| ¶ - Drake's form | WElm |
| *webbii* | CGre CHan |
| *wildpretii* | CAbb CBot CTrC ECre IHdy SAPC SIgm WHer |

## EDGEWORTHIA (Thymelaeaceae)

| § *chrysantha* | CB&S CCHP CPMA EPfP LBuc LPan WSHC |
|---|---|
| - B&SWJ 1048 | WCru |
| - 'Rubra' | CPMA |
| *papyrifera* | See *E. chrysantha* |

## EDRAIANTHUS (Campanulaceae)

| *dalmaticus* | SBla |
|---|---|
| *dinaricus* | Last listed 1998 |
| *graminifolius* ♀ | CHea ECtt MOne NHar NHol NMen NWCA SRms SRot WFar WPer WWin |
| - *albus* | See *E. graminifolius* subsp. *niveus* |
| § - subsp. *niveus* | WHil |
| ¶ *parnassicus* | NMen |
| § *pumilio* ♀ | CNic EPot GMaP NHar NMen NTow SBla SIng SRms WAbe WLin |
| *serbicus* | Last listed 1998 |
| § *serpyllifolius* | Last listed 1998 |
| § - 'Major' | WAbe |

## EGERIA (Hydrocharitaceae)

| § *densa* | CBen SWyc |
|---|---|

## EHRETIA (Boraginaceae)

| § *acuminata* var. *obovata* | CGre |
|---|---|
| *dicksonii* | CFil SSpi WPGP |
| *ovalifolia* | See *E. acuminata* var. *obovata* |
| *thyrsiflora* | See *E. acuminata* var. *obovata* |

## EHRHARTA (Poaceae)

| *thunbergii* | EBee |
|---|---|

## EICHHORNIA (Pontederiaceae)

| 'Azure' | Last listed 1998 |
|---|---|
| *crassipes* | CBen CWat EMFW LPBA MSta NDea |
| - 'Major' | SAWi WWeb |

## ELAEAGNUS ✿ (Elaeagnaceae)

| *angustifolia* | CAgr CB&S CBlo CBot EBee ENot MBar MBlu MCoo MRav SPer SRPl SRms WDin WGer WWat |
|---|---|
| - Caspica Group | See *E.* 'Quicksilver' |
| *argentea* | See *E. commutata* |
| § *commutata* | CAgr CBot CDoC CMCN CPle EBee EHoe ENot EPar IMGH IOrc LHop MBlu MCoo MWhi NFor SLPl SMad SPer WRus WWat |
| x *ebbingei* | More than 30 suppliers |
| I - 'Aurea' | Last listed 1997 |
| - 'Coastal Gold' (v) | CAbP CB&S CBlo CDoC COtt EBee EMil ENot LBuc MAsh MBri MGos MUlv SReu SRms SSta WPat WStI WWes |
| - 'Gilt Edge' (v) ♀ | CB&S CDoC CLan CMHG EBee EHoe ELan ENot EWTr IOrc LHop LPan MBal MBri MGos MPla MRav MWat NHol SPer SPla SReu SSta WAbe WFar WHCG WHar WPat WStI WWeb |
| - 'Gold Splash' | CDoC CWSG MBri |
| - 'Limelight' (v) | More than 30 suppliers |
| - 'Salcombe Seedling' | LHop LRHS MBri MUlv |
| - 'Southern Seedling' | Last listed 1998 |
| *glabra* 'Reflexa' | See *E.* x *reflexa* |
| *macrophylla* | CLan CSam ENot NFor SDry WWat |
| *multiflora* | CAgr CDul LBuc LEdu SPer |
| - 'Gigantea' | ELan |
| *parvifolia* ♀ | ENot |
| *pungens* | ERom NBir |
| - 'Argenteovariegata' | See *E. pungens* 'Variegata' |
| - 'Aureovariegata' | See *E. pungens* 'Maculata' |
| - 'Dicksonii' (v) | CBlo CDoC LNet SLon SPer SRms SSpi WBcn |
| - 'Forest Gold' (v) | CAbP ELan LRHS MAsh |
| - 'Frederici' (v) | CB&S CBlo CDoC CMHG EHoe ELan EPla ERav MAsh MBal MBri MPla MRav NHol SCob SPer SSpi WAbe WHCG WPat WWat |
| - 'Goldrim' (v) | CBlo COtt GOrc MAsh MBri MGos SCob |
| § - 'Maculata' (v) ♀ | More than 30 suppliers |
| § - 'Variegata' | CB&S CBlo CDoC IOrc MBal MBri NBir SCob SPer SRPl WHCG WLRN |
| § 'Quicksilver' ♀ | CAgr CFil CHad CPMA CPle EBee ECha ECre ELan EWTr MAsh MPla MRav SEND SLon SMad SMur SPer SPla SSpi SSta SUsu WCru WEas WHCG WPGP WSHC WWat |
| § x *reflexa* | CB&S CFil WHCG WWat |
| *umbellata* | CAgr CDul CPle MBlu MCoo SPan SPer WHCG WWat |
| - *borealis* | CFil |

## ELATOSTEMA (Urticaceae)

| *repens* var. *pulchrum* ♀ | CHal MBri |
|---|---|
| - var. *repens* | CHal |

ELEGIA (Restionaceae)
¶ *caespitosa*               CTrC
  *capensis*                CFee CTrC WMul WNor
¶ *cuspidata*                CTrC
  *equisetacea*             CFee CTrC LHil WNor
  *fenestrata*              Last listed 1998
¶ *grandis*                 LHil
¶ *grandispicata*           LHil

ELEOCHARIS (Cyperaceae)
  *acicularis*              ELan EMFW NDea SWyc WWeb
  *palustris*               EMFW MSta SWyc

ELEPHANTOPUS (Asteraceae)
  *tomentosus*              Last listed 1997

ELETTARIA (Zingiberaceae)
  *cardamomum*              CArn ELau GPoy LBlm MBri MSal
                           WCot WJek WMul

ELEUTHEROCOCCUS (Araliaceae)
  *pictus*                  See *Kalopanax septemlobus*
  *senticosus*              GPoy
  *septemlobus*             See *Kalopanax septemlobus*
§ *sieboldianus*            MRav
  - 'Aureomarginatus'       Last listed 1998
§ - 'Variegatus'            CBot CHan EBee ELan EPfP ICrw
                           IHar IOrc MBlu MRav NPal WCot
                           WHer WSHC WWat

ELINGAMITA (Myrsinaceae)
  *johnsonii*               ECou

ELISENA (Amaryllidaceae)
  *longipetala*             See *Hymenocallis longipetala*

ELLIOTTIA (Ericaceae)
  *bracteata*               See *Tripetaleia bracteata*
  *pyroliflorus*            See *Cladothamnus pyroliflorus*
  *racemosa*                CTrG

ELLISIOPHYLLUM (Scrophulariaceae)
  *pinnatum* B&SWJ 197      WCru

ELMERA (Saxifragaceae)
  *racemosa*                Last listed 1998

ELODEA (Hydrocharitaceae)
  *canadensis*              CBen EHon EMFW SAWi SWat
                           SWyc
  *crispa*                  See *Lagarosiphon major*
  *densa*                   See *Egeria densa*

ELSHOLTZIA (Lamiaceae)
  *ciliata*                 Last listed 1998
  *fruticosa*               CArn WWye
  *stauntonii*              CArn CB&S CBot CFee ECha
                           EMan EOHP EPri GPoy IMGH
                           MTis SBid SLPl WSHC WWye
  - 'Alba'                  CBot LBuc NEgg

ELYMUS (Poaceae)
  *arenarius*               See *Leymus arenarius*
  *canadensis*              CBrm CCuc CKno EHoe WMoo
  - f. *glaucifolius*        GCal
  *cinereus*                EPPr
  *farctus*                 EPPr
  *giganteus*               See *Leymus racemosus*
  *glaucus* hort.           See *E. hispidus*

§ *hispidus*                CBrm CCuc CHan CInt EBee
                           ECoo EGoo EHoe EMan EPPr EPla
                           ESis EWTr LHop MBri MMoz
                           MUlv NHol NPSI SCob SOkh SPer
                           SUsu WHil WLin WPrP WWye
N *magellanicus*            More than 30 suppliers
§ *scabrus*                 LRHS SMrm
  *tenuis*                  CCuc CInt SMad
  *villosus* var. *arkansanus*   EPPr EPla

ELYTROPUS (Apocynaceae)
  *chilensis*               Last listed 1996

EMBOTHRIUM ✿ (Proteaceae)
  *coccineum*               CFil CTrG EPfP GOrc SDry
                           SReu WBrE WNor WPat WPyg
  - Lanceolatum Group       CEnd CGre ELan EPfP GOrc MBal
                           MDun NPal SBid SBrw SPer SSpi
                           SSta WPic WWat
  - - 'Inca Flame'          CDoC CEnd CFai COtt CPMA
                           CTrC CWSG ISea MDun NHed
                           SBrw SMur SSta WGer WPat WWat
* - - 'Inca King'           LRHS NOla
  - - 'Ñorquinco' ♀         CB&S IOrc LRHS MBal MBri
                           MDun WBod WCru WPyg
  - Longifolium Group-      CB&S IBlr IOrc ISea

EMILIA (Asteraceae)
  *javanica* hort.          See *E. coccinea*

EMINIUM (Araceae)
  *albertii*                LAma
  *rauwolffii*              Last listed 1996

EMMENOPTERYS (Rubiaceae)
  *henryi*                  CBrd CFil CLyn EPfP WPGP

EMPETRUM (Empetraceae)
  *luteum*                  MBar
  *nigrum*                  GAri GPoy MBal MBar SMur
  - 'Bernstein'             NHol
* - 'Gold'                  Last listed 1998
  - var. *japonicum*         GTou
  - 'Lucia'                 MGos
  *rubrum*                  WAbe
  - 'Tomentosum'            Last listed 1996
¶ sp. from Falklands        WWat

ENCELIOPSIS (Asteraceae)
  *argophylla*              Last listed 1998
  *covillei*                Last listed 1998

ENCEPHALARTOS (Zamiaceae)
  *natalensis*              LPal

ENCHYLAENA (Chenopodiaceae)
  *tomentosa*               Last listed 1998

ENDYMION See HYACINTHOIDES

ENKIANTHUS ✿ (Ericaceae)
  *campanulatus* ♀          More than 30 suppliers
  - var. *campanulatus*      CWSG ELan GGGa MBal SMur
    f. *albiflorus*          SPer SSpi
  - var. *palibinii*         CGre GAri GChr GGGa LRHS
                           MAsh MBal MGos NHol SSpi SSta
                           WBrE WNor WPat WWat
  - 'Red Bells'             CABP CBlo CDoC COtt CPMA
                           CWSG EBee EPfP GOrc MBri
                           MDun MGos NHed SPer SSpi SSta
                           SSto WWeb
  - var. *sikokianus*        CFai CWSG GAri GGGa

| | |
|---|---|
| * - 'Variegatus' | LRHS MAsh WWeb |
| *cernuus* var. *matsudae* | GAri |
| - f. *rubens* ♀ | CB&S GAri GGGa MAsh MBal |
| | SSpi SSta WDin WNor WWeb |
| *chinensis* | ELan EPfP GAri GGGa MAsh SSta |
| | WCwm WNor WWat |
| *deflexus* | CFil LRHS MAsh SSpi SSta WPGP |
| *perulatus* ♀ | CBrm CFil EMil EPfP GAri LRHS |
| | MBar SSpi SSta WWat WWes |

## ENSETE (Musaceae)
| | |
|---|---|
| § *ventricosum* | CAbb CBot CRoM EOas LBlo LCns |
| | LPal LPan SAPC SArc WMul |
| - 'Atropurpureum' | Last listed 1998 |
| § - 'Maurelii' | LCns SArc WMul |
| ♦ - 'Rubrum' | See *E. ventricosum* 'Maurelii' |

## ENTELEA (Tiliaceae)
| | |
|---|---|
| *arborescens* | CTrC ECou |

## ENTEROLOBIUM (Mimosaceae)
| | |
|---|---|
| ¶ *cyclocarpum* | WMul |

## EOMECON (Papaveraceae)
| | |
|---|---|
| *chionantha* | CHid CMCo CSam EBee EBrP |
| | EBre ECha EMar EPar EPla ERos |
| | GAbr GCal IBlr LBre LEdu MRav |
| | MUlv NSti SBre SCob SMad SSpi |
| | WCru WFar WHer WOld WWin |
| | WWye |

## EPACRIS (Epacridaceae)
| | |
|---|---|
| *paludosa* | GCrs GGGa IMGH |
| *petrophila* | GCrs GGGa WPat |
| - Baw Baw form | Last listed 1997 |

## EPHEDRA (Ephedraceae)
| | |
|---|---|
| *alte* | WCot |
| *americana* var. *andina* | SAPC SArc |
| *distachya* | GPoy NFor NLon WWye |
| *equisetina* | Last listed 1998 |
| - JJH 920912 | Last listed 1998 |
| - JJH 9308135 | NWCA |
| *fedtschenkoi* | EBee WIvy |
| *fragilis* | SDry |
| *gerardiana* | Last listed 1998 |
| ¶ - KR 0853 | EPla |
| - var. *sikkimensis* | EPla SDry WPer |
| *glauca* | Last listed 1996 |
| aff. *glauca* | Last listed 1996 |
| *intermedia* | Last listed 1996 |
| *likiangensis* | EBee |
| § *major* | SDry WHer |
| *minima* | MTPN NWCA |
| *monosperma* | Last listed 1998 |
| *nebrodensis* | See *E. major* |
| *nevadensis* | CArn GBin GPoy MSal |
| *przewalskii* | Last listed 1998 |
| *sinica* | MSal |
| *viridis* | CArn ELau GBin MSal |

## EPIDENDRUM (Orchidaceae)
| | |
|---|---|
| *criniferum* | Last listed 1997 |
| *radicans* | See *E. ibaguense* |

## EPIGAEA (Ericaceae)
| | |
|---|---|
| *asiatica* | MBal |
| *gaultherioides* | GCrs GGGa MBal |
| *repens* | MBal |

## EPILOBIUM (Onagraceae)
| | |
|---|---|
| § *angustifolium* | CGle CKin GBar NNrd SWat |
| | WHer |

| | |
|---|---|
| § - var. *album* | More than 30 suppliers |
| - 'Isobel' | CHea CSpe LFis MAvo MRav |
| | NHex WAbb WBay WCot |
| - f. *leucanthum* | See *E. angustifolium* var. *album* |
| - 'Stahl Rose' | CBot CHid CMea EBee EMar |
| | EMon EWes GCal LGre LPio MAvo |
| | NHex SOkh SWat WSHC |
| *californicum* Hausskneckt | See *Zauschneria californica* |
| | subsp. *angustifolia* |
| - hort. | See *Zauschneria californica* |
| *canum* | See *Zauschneria californica* |
| | subsp. *cana* |
| § *chlorifolium* | Last listed 1998 |
| - var. *kaikourense* | See *E. chlorifolium* |
| *crassum* | CPBP ESis GBuc MBNS NArg |
| | NWoo WBea WMoo WWin |
| § *dodonaei* | CGle EBee EMan LFis MLLN |
| | MTho WBea WCot WMoo WSHC |
| | WWin |
| *fleischeri* | CLyd CPou EBee EDAr MTho |
| | SAga WSHC |
| *garrettii* | See *Zauschneria californica* |
| | subsp. *garrettii* |
| N *glabellum* | CGle CHea CMea CSpe ELan |
| | EMan EMon ESis GMac LBee LGre |
| | LHop MWat NBir NMen SAga |
| | SUsu WAbe WEas WFar WOve |
| | WSpi WWhi WWin |
| - 'Sulphureum' | GMaP NChi |
| *hirsutum* | CKin EBee SWat WCla |
| - *album* | NSti WAlt |
| - 'Caerphilly Castle' (d) | WAlt |
| ¶ - 'Pistils at Dawn' | EMon |
| - *roseum* | WRha |
| - 'Well Creek' (v) | CElw ECha EMan EMar GVic LFis |
| | MAvo MCLN MLLN SWat WCot |
| | WOve WPer |
| *latifolium* | Last listed 1998 |
| *luteum* | WCla |
| *microphyllum* | See *Zauschneria californica* |
| | subsp. *cana* |
| *montanum* | Last listed 1998 |
| - variegated | Last listed 1998 |
| *obcordatum* | CLTr LHop NWCA SSca |
| *rosmarinifolium* | See *E. dodonaei* |
| * *spathulifolium* | LHop |
| ¶ x *subhirsutum* | WAlt |
| *tasmanicum* | CLyd |
| *tetragonum* | Last listed 1997 |
| *villosum* | See *Zauschneria californica* |
| | subsp. *mexicana* |
| *wilsonii* hort. | See *E. chlorifolium* |

## EPIMEDIUM ✿ (Berberidaceae)
| | |
|---|---|
| *acuminatum* | CBos CElw CFil CLAP CVer EBee |
| | EFEx GLil LEur LGre LPio SChu |
| | WAbe WPGP |
| - L 575 | CBos CLon CRDP EHrv MSte SBla |
| | SSpi WAbe WPnP |
| 'Akakage' | GLil |
| 'Akebono' | GLil |
| *alpinum* | CMGP EMon EPar GBuc LEur |
| | MBal NHol SMac SPer WMoo |
| Asiatic hybrids | SChu SWas |
| 'Beni-chidori' | GLil |
| 'Beni-kujaku' | GBuc GLil |
| ¶ 'Black Sea' | GLil |
| *brevicornu* Og 88010 | SBla |
| - f. *rotundatum* Og 82010 | SBla |
| x *cantabrigiense* | CBlo CVer ECtt EOrc EPla GCHN |
| | GLil LEur MBal MBri MBro MRav |
| | MUlv MWgw NHol NRoo SMac |
| | SPer WAbe WCot WCru WWeb |

| | |
|---|---|
| *cremeum* | See *E. grandiflorum* subsp. *koreanum* |
| *davidii* | CRDP EBee ECha GBri MBro MSte SSpi WAbe WFar WHal WPnP |
| - EMR 4125 | CElw CLAP EHrv SAga SBla |
| *diphyllum* | CBos CLTr CRDP EHrv EMon LGre NDov SAga SWas WHal |
| - dwarf white | GLil |
| *dolichostemon* | CBos LEur SBla WAbe |
| - Og 81010 | SBla |
| ¶ *ecalcaratum* Og 93082 | SBla |
| *elongatum* | Last listed 1998 |
| 'Enchantress' | CBos EBee ECha GBuc LEur NRoo SSpi SWas WAbe WHal |
| ¶ *fangii* | SSpi |
| - Og 81.007 | Last listed 1998 |
| ¶ *fargesii* | SBla |
| *flavum* Og 92036 | SBla |
| *franchetii* 'Brimstone Butterfly' Og 87.001 | SBla WAbe |
| 'Genpei' | GLil |
| § *grandiflorum* ♀ | More than 30 suppliers |
| - 'Album' | CLAP EPot IMGH |
| - var. *coelestre* | GLil |
| - 'Crimson Beauty' | CLAP CLTr ECha GBuc LEur LGre SAga SChu WCru WHal |
| - 'Elfenkönigin' | EBee LRHS WAbe |
| - 'Koji' | Last listed 1998 |
| § - subsp. *koreanum* | CFil CLAP CLon CPla CRDP EFEx GLil LGre MBro NDov NHar SBla WAbe WPGP |
| ¶ - 'La Rocaille' | SBla |
| - lilac seedling | CHad CPlt CRDP LGre WFar |
| - 'Lilacinum' | SBla |
| - 'Lilafee' | More than 30 suppliers |
| - 'Mount Kitadake' | GLil SSpi SWas WAbe |
| - 'Nanum' ♀ | CMil CRDP EBee EHrv EHyt EPot LGre NHar NMen NTow NWCA SBla SChu SWas WAbe WCru |
| ¶ - 'Nanum Freya' | SWas |
| ¶ - pink | EHrv |
| - 'Rose Queen' ♀ | More than 30 suppliers |
| § - 'Roseum' | CHid CLAP EBrP EBre GBri LBre LPio NDov NTow SBre WWeb |
| - 'Rubinkrone' | EBee EMar GBin GLil GNau NHol WOVN |
| - 'Shikinomai' | LEur SWas WAbe |
| - f. *violaceum* | CFir CLAP CLTr SBla SChu WAbe WPnP |
| - 'White Queen' ♀ | CFir CLon CRDP CVer EHrv GLil LGre NOak SBla SSpi SWas WAbe |
| ¶ *higoense* | LPio |
| 'Kaguyahime' | SBla WAbe |
| *latisepalum* Og 91002 | SBla |
| *leptorrhizum* | CLAP EMon GLil LEur LPio NBrk SBla WAbe |
| - Og Y 44 | CRDP EHyt SAga SSpi SWas |
| 'Little Shrimp' | CTri EBee LEur MBro WPat |
| *macranthum* | See *E. grandiflorum* |
| *membranaceum* | CBos WAbe |
| *ogisui* Og 91.001 | SBla WAbe |
| x *omeiense* | WBcn |
| ¶ - 'Stormcloud' Og 82002 | SBla |
| *pauciflorum* Og 92.123 | NHed SBla |
| x *perralchicum* ♀ | CBro EMon EPot GBuc GMaP MBal MBel NFla NRoo SChu SIng SLPl SSON SSpi WPGP WRus WSHC |
| - 'Frohnleiten' | More than 30 suppliers |
| - 'Wisley' | EHrv LEur MBro NDov SBla SOkh |
| *perralderianum* | CFil CSam EBee ELan ENot EPar LEur LGro MBal MBro MFir NHar SBla SCro SRPl SRms SSpi WAbe WCru WHen WLin WPnP WWin |

| | |
|---|---|
| - 'Weihenstephan' | Last listed 1997 |
| *pinnatum* | GMaP WHal |
| § - subsp. *colchicum* ♀ | More than 30 suppliers |
| - - L 321 | SBla |
| - *elegans* | See *E. pinnatum* subsp. *colchicum* |
| *platypetalum* Og 93085 | SBla |
| *pubescens* Og 91.003 | SBla |
| *pubigerum* | CBlo CLTr EBee ECha EGar EGle GAbr GLil GNau IMGH MBal MWgw NHol NPri SCob |
| *rhizomatosum* Og 92114 | SBla |
| x *rubrum* ♀ | More than 30 suppliers |
| *sagittatum* | EFEx GLil LPio |
| 'Sasaki' | GBuc GLil |
| *sempervirens* | SBla |
| *setosum* | CElw CFil ECha EHrv LEur MSte SMac SSpi SWas WAbe |
| 'Shiho' | GLil |
| 'Sohayaki' | GLil LPio |
| *stellulatum* 'Wudang Star' L 1193 | EHrv EWes WAbe |
| 'Sunset' | GLil |
| 'Tamabotan' | GBuc GLil WCot |
| x *versicolor* | CBlo LEur MBal |
| - 'Cupreum' | SSpi |
| - 'Neosulphureum' | CBro CLAP EMon SBla SSpi WHil WViv |
| - 'Sulphureum' ♀ | More than 30 suppliers |
| - 'Versicolor' | EHrv LGre NHar SBla |
| x *warleyense* | CBos CHan EBee ECha EFou EHyt ELan EPot GCHN GLil LFis LGre MBal MBro MUlv NHar SAga SBla SOkh WAbe WFar WHal WRus WWin |
| - 'Orangekönigin' | EPar GBuc LEur LPio MBel MCAu MMil NHol SLPl SPla WAbe WHil WPnP WWeb |
| *wushanense* 'Caramel' Og 92009 | SBla |
| x *youngianum* | CB&S EGle EPot |
| - 'Lilacinum' | See *E.* x *youngianum* 'Roseum' |
| - 'Merlin' | CBos CFir CPlt ECha EHrv EHyt EMar GLil SBla SChu WAbe |
| - 'Niveum' ♀ | More than 30 suppliers |
| § - 'Roseum' | CB&S CHid CLon CRDP EBee EFou EMan EMil EOrc EPar ERos GAbr GLil MBal MBri MUlv NHar NMen NPri NSti NTow SIng SMac SOkh SPer WAbe WLin WRHF WRus |
| - 'Typicum' | CLon WAbe |
| - white seedling | EHyt NMen |

## EPIPACTIS (Orchidaceae)

| | |
|---|---|
| *gigantea* | CAvo CBos CBro CFil CHdy ECha ELan EPar EPot ERos MBal MS&S MTho NHar SBla WAbe WCru |
| - 'Enchantment' | Last listed 1997 |
| - x *palustris* | Last listed 1997 |
| * - 'Serpentine Night' | IBlr |
| - x *veratrifolia* | See *E.* Lowland Legacy g. |
| *helleborine* | SSpi |
| § Lowland Legacy g. | Last listed 1997 |
| § Lowland Legacy g. 'Edelstein' | SWes |
| * - 'Frankfurt' | SWes |
| *palustris* | CHdy SWes WHer WShi |
| 'Renate' | SWes |
| * Sabine g. 'Frankfurt' | SWes |
| *thunbergii* | EFEx GCrs WThi |
| * *veratrifolia* 'Jerusalem' | Last listed 1997 |

## EPIPREMNUM (Araceae)
§ *aureum* ♀ — CHal EBak LBlo MBri
- 'Marble Queen' (v) — CHal
§ *pinnatum* — MBri
* - 'Aztec' ♀ — Last listed 1995

## EPISCIA (Gesneriaceae)
¶ 'Country Kitten' — CHal
¶ *cupreata* — CHal
§ *dianthiflora* — CHal MBri SRms WDib
'Iris August' — MBri
¶ 'Pink Panther' — CHal
* *primeria* — MBri
* 'San Miguel' — CHal MBri WDib

## EQUISETUM ✿ (Equisetaceae)
*arvense* — MSal
x *bowmanii* — CNat
*camtschatcense* — SMad
*giganteum* — CNat
*byemale* — CNat EPla MCCP SPlb WHal
§ - var. *affine* — CNat ELan EMon EPla
- var. *robustum* — See E. hyemale var. affine
*ramosissimum* — EMFW MCCP WWeb
  var. *japonicum*
*scirpoides* — CInt EMFW MCCP WHal WMAq
  WWeb
*sylvaticum* — CNat
¶ x *trachyodon* 'Bandit' — EMon

## ERAGROSTIS (Poaceae)
*abyssinica* — See E. tef
*capensis* — EBee EWes
*chloromelas* — CMHG
*curvula* — CElw CFil CInt CKno CSpe EBee
  ECGN ECha EHoe EMon EPPr
  GBin LGre MCCP NChi WCot
  WPic WWye
- S&SH 10 — CCuc CHan CRDP MSte NLak
§ *tef* — LIck
*trichodes* — GBin WPer

## ERANTHEMUM (Acanthaceae)
*pulchellum* — LHil

## ERANTHIS (Ranunculaceae)
§ *byemalis* ♀ — CBro CMea ELan EMon EPar EPot
  ETub EWFC LAma MBri MBro
  MHew MHlr NRog SRms WCot
  WMaN WRHF WShi
§ - Cilicica Group — CBro EMon EPar EPot ERav LAma
  NRog
§ - Tubergenii Group — EPot
- - 'Guinea Gold' ♀ — EHyt GCrs
*pinnatifida* — EFEx
¶ *stellata* — WCru

## ERCILLA (Phytolaccaceae)
*volubilis* — CAbb CFee CGre CPlN CPle
  CSam EBee ETen GOrc LHop SPer
  SVen WCot WCru WPic WSHC

## EREMAEA (Myrtaceae)
*beaufortioides* — SOWG
*pauciflora* — SOWG

## EREMOPHILA (Myoporaceae)
¶ *maculata* — CPLG

## EREMURUS (Asphodelaceae)
§ *aitchisonii* — LAma NRog SIgm

- 'Albus' — WCot
¶ 'Brimstone Beauty' — NRog
* 'Brutus' — CMea LAma MMHG
*bungei* — See E. stenophyllus subsp.
  stenophyllus
*elwesii* — See E. aitchisonii
¶ 'Emmy Ro' — LBow NRog
¶ 'Harmony' — LBow NRog
*bimalaicus* — CBot EBee ELan EMan EPar ETub
  EWTr LAma LBow MAvo NEgg
  NLar NRog SAga SCoo SPer WHil
  WPyg
¶ 'Image' — LBow NRog
x *isabellinus* 'Cleopatra' — CBot CHad CMea CSWP CSpe
  EBee EMon EWTr GCHN LAma
  LBow LPio LRHS MCli MLLN
  MMHG NHol NPSI NRog WCot
  WPGP
- 'Pinokkio' — EBee EMan ETub LAma NRog
  WPyg
- Ruiter hybrids — CBlo CSWP EAst EBee ECot ELan
  EMan EPar LAma MLLN MTis NFla
  NRog SCro SPer WBro WHil WViv
  WWat
- Shelford hybrids — CB&S CBlo CBro ELan LAma
  LBow MLLN MMHG MNrw NOak
  SDeJ WPen
¶ *lactiflorus* — SIgm
'Moneymaker' — EBee LAma LEdu NRog
'Oase' — ELan LBow NRog
'Obelisk' — CMea EBee EHic LBow LPio LRHS
  NPla NRog
¶ 'Paradiso' — EBee
¶ 'Rexona' — NRog
*robustus* — CB&S CBot EBee ELan EPar ETub
  EWTr LAma LBow LFis LPio NLar
  NRog SIgm SMad SPer WCot
  WPyg WWat
- pink — NPSI
¶ 'Roford' — NRog
'Romance' — EBee LBow LPio NRog
*stenophyllus* — CBro EWTr LEdu MGrG NFai
  NHol WHil WPGP WWeb
- subsp. *aurantiacus* — LFis
§ - subsp. *stenophyllus* — CHad CMea ELan EMan EOld EPar
  ETub EWTr LAma LBow MLLN
  MNrw NEgg NFla NFor NOak
  NRog SPer WCot WPyg

## ERIANTHUS See SACCHARUM

## ERICA ✿ (Ericaceae)
*arborea* — CNCN CTrG MBal SAPC SArc
  SLon
§ - 'Albert's Gold' ♀ — CB&S CMac CNCN CTrC EBrP
  EBre ELan EPfP GChr IOrc LBre
  MAsh MBal MBar MBri MOke
  NHol SAga SBod SBre SBrw SPer
  SPla
- var. *alpina* ♀ — CDoC CMac CNCN ENot IOrc
  MBal MBar MGos NHar NHol
  SBod SBrw SDys SPar SPer SReu
  SSta WWat
- 'Arbora Gold' — See E. arborea 'Albert's Gold'
- 'Arnold's Gold' — See E. arborea 'Albert's Gold'
- 'Estrella Gold' ♀ — CDoC CMac CNCN EBrP EBre
  ELan LBre MAsh MBal MBar MGos
  NHar NHol SBod SBre SBrw SPer
  SPla SSta SVil WStI
- 'Picos Pygmy' — SDys
- 'Spring Smile' — Last listed 1998
*australis* ♀ — CB&S ELan MBar

- 'Castellar Blush'            CNCN NHol
- 'Holehird'                   Last listed 1998
- 'Mr Robert' ♀               CNCN ELan EPfP LRHS MBar
                               SBod
- 'Riverslea' ♀               CNCN GAri IOrc MBal MBar
                               MOke NHol SBod SPer
*bauera*                       Last listed 1998
*canaliculata* ♀              CB&S CGre MBal SBod
*carnea* 'Accent'              Last listed 1998
- 'Adrienne Duncan' ♀         CNCN COCH MBar MBri MGos
                               MOke NHed NHol NRoo SBod
- 'Alan Coates'                CNCN COCH MBar
- 'Alba'                       COCH
- 'Altadena'                   CNCN COCH MBar
¶ - 'Amy Backhouse'            CMac
- 'Amy Doncaster'              See *E. carnea* 'Treasure Trove'
- 'Ann Sparkes' ♀             CMac CNCN COCH EBrP EBre
                               EOrn GChr LBre LGro MBar MBri
                               MGos MOke MWat NHol SBod
                               SBre SPla
- 'Atrorubra'                  CMac CNCN COCH MBar NHol
- 'Aurea'                      CB&S CMac CNCN COCH LGro
                               MBar MBri MOke MPla NHed
                               NHol SBod
- 'Barry Sellers'              COCH LRHS NHol
- 'Bell's Extra Special'       COCH ECho
- 'Beoley Pink'                CNCN COCH SBod
- 'C.J. Backhouse'             COCH
- 'Carnea'                     CNCN COCH MBar MOke NHol
- 'Catherine'                  Last listed 1998
- 'Cecilia M. Beale'           CNCN COCH MBar NHol
- 'Challenger' ♀              CNCN COCH EBrP EBre LBre
                               MBar MBri MGos NHol SBod SBre
- 'Christine Fletcher'         COCH
- 'Clare Wilkinson'            CNCN COCH
- 'David's Seedling'           COCH
- 'December Red'               CB&S CMac CNCN COCH EBrP
                               EBre EOrn LBre MBar MBri MOke
                               MWat NHol SBod SBre SPla
- 'Dommesmoen'                 Last listed 1998
- 'Early Red'                  COCH
- 'Eileen Porter'              CMac CNCN MBar
- 'Foxhollow' ♀               CMac CNCN COCH EBrP EBre
                               ENot GChr GDra LBre LGro MBar
                               MBri MGos MOke MPla MWat
                               NHar NHol SBod SBre
- 'Foxhollow Fairy'            CB&S CBrm CNCN COCH MBar
                               SRms
- 'Gelber Findling'            COCH
- 'Golden Starlet' ♀          CMac CNCN COCH EBrP EBre
                               EOrn LBre LGro MBar MGos NHol
                               SBre
- 'Gracilis'                   ECho MBar NHed NHol NHol
- 'Heathwood'                  CB&S CNCN COCH ENot MBar
                               NHol SBod SRms
- 'Hilletje'                   CNCN COCH NHol
- 'Ice Princess'               CNCN COCH NHol
- 'Isabell'                     CNCN LRHS
- 'Jack Stitt'                 COCH MBar
- 'James Backhouse'            CNCN COCH NHed NHol
- 'January Sun'                COCH EOrn NHol
- 'Jason Attwater'             Last listed 1998
- 'Jean'                       CNCN LRHS NHol
- 'Jennifer Anne'              CNCN COCH MBar
- 'John Kampa'                 CNCN COCH EOrn MBar NHol
                               NRoo
- 'John Pook'                  Last listed 1998
- 'King George'               CMac CNCN COCH CTri GChr
                               MBar MGos MWat NHar NHol
                               SBod SPla
- 'Kramer's Rubin'             Last listed 1996
- 'Lake Garda'                 COCH NHol

- 'Late Pink'                  COCH
- 'Lesley Sparkes'             COCH MBar
- 'Little Peter'               COCH
- 'Lohse's Rubin'              COCH ECho NHed
- 'Loughrigg' ♀               CMac CNCN COCH CTri EOrn
                               GDra MBar MGos MOke NHol
                               SBod WStl
- 'March Seedling'             CB&S CNCN COCH EBrP EBre
                               GDra LBre MBar MBri MGos
                               MOke MPla NHol SBod SBre WStl
- 'Margery Frearson'           Last listed 1998
- 'Martin'                     COCH
- 'Moonlight'                  Last listed 1998
- 'Mrs Sam Doncaster'          CNCN COCH ECho MBar SBod
- 'Myretoun Ruby' ♀          CB&S CMac CNCN COCH EBrP
                               EBre ENot GDra LBre LGro MBar
                               MBri MGos MOke MPla MWat
                               NHar NHed NHol NRoo SBod
                               SBre
- 'Nathalie'                   CNCN ECho LRHS
- 'Orient'                     COCH
- 'Pallida'                    COCH
- 'Pink Beauty'                See *E. carnea* 'Pink Pearl'
- 'Pink Cloud'                 CNCN COCH
- 'Pink Mist'                  COCH LRHS
§ - 'Pink Pearl'               CNCN COCH MBar
- 'Pink Spangles' ♀          CB&S CMac CNCN COCH EBrP
                               EBre GChr GDra LBre MBar MBri
                               MGos MOke MPla NHol NRoo
                               SBod SBre
- 'Pirbright Rose'             CNCN COCH ECho MGos MPla
                               SBod
- 'Polden Pride'               COCH
- 'Porter's Red'               COCH ECho LRHS MBar
- 'Praecox Rubra' ♀          CB&S CNCN COCH GDra LGro
                               MBar MGos MOke NHol
- 'Prince of Wales'            CNCN COCH ECho NHol
- 'Queen Mary'                 CNCN ECho SBod
- 'Queen of Spain'             CNCN COCH MBri MOke
- 'R.B. Cooke' ♀             CBrm CNCN COCH EOrn MBar
                               MBri SBod
- 'Red Rover'                  COCH
- 'Robert Jan'                 Last listed 1998
- 'Rosalie'                    CB&S CNCN LRHS NHol
- 'Rosalinde Schorn'           COCH NHol
- 'Rosantha'                   CNCN NHol
- 'Rosea'                      ECho
- 'Rosy Gem'                   CNCN ECho MBar
- 'Rosy Morn'                  COCH
- 'Rotes Juwel'                CNCN ECho LRHS
- 'Rubinteppich'               CNCN COCH SBod
- 'Rubra'                      Last listed 1998
- 'Ruby Glow'                  CNCN COCH CTri ENot MBar
                               MOke NHed NHol
- 'Scatterley'                 Last listed 1998
- 'Schatzalp'                  Last listed 1998
- 'Schneekuppe'                CNCN COCH NHol
- 'Schneesturm'                COCH
§ - 'Sherwood Creeping'        MBar
- 'Sherwoodii'                 See *E. carnea* 'Sherwood
                               Creeping'
- 'Smarts Heath'               CNCN COCH ECho NHol
- 'Snow Queen'                 CMac CNCN COCH MBar SBod
- 'Spring Cottage Crimson'     COCH MBar
- 'Spring Day'                 Last listed 1998
- 'Springwood Pink'            CBrm CMac CNCN COCH CTri
                               GDra LGro MBar MBri MGos
                               MOke MPla MWat NHol SBod
- 'Springwood White' ♀       CB&S CBrm CMac CNCN COCH
                               EBrP EBre ENot GDra LBre LGro
                               MBar MBri MGos MOke MPla
                               MWat NHar NHol SBod SBre

| | |
|---|---|
| - 'Startler' | COCH LRHS MBar NHol SBod SPla |
| - 'Sunshine Rambler' ♀ | CNCN COCH MBar MGos NHol SPla |
| - 'Thomas Kingscote' | CNCN COCH MBar |
| § - 'Treasure Trove' | CMac COCH NHol |
| - 'Tybesta Gold' | CNCN COCH NHol |
| - 'Urville' | See E. carnea 'Vivellii' |
| - 'Viking' | CNCN COCH NHol NRoo |
| § - 'Vivellii' ♀ | CMac CNCN COCH CTri EBrP EBre ENot GDra LBre MBar MBri MOke MPla MWat NHar NHed NHol SBod SBre |
| - 'Vivellii Aurea' | COCH |
| - 'Walter Reisert' | CNCN COCH |
| - 'Wanda' | COCH MBar |
| - 'Wentwood Red' | COCH |
| - 'Westwood Yellow' ♀ | CMac CNCN COCH EBrP EBre LBre LGro MBar MBri MGos NHar NHol SBod SBre SPla |
| - 'White Glow' | CMac ECho EOrn |
| - 'White March Seedling' | Last listed 1998 |
| - 'Whitehall' | LRHS NHol |
| - 'Winter Beauty' | CNCN COCH MOke MPla NHed NHol |
| - 'Winter Gold' | COCH |
| - 'Winter Melody' | Last listed 1998 |
| - 'Winter Rubin' | Last listed 1998 |
| - 'Winter Snow' | ECho |
| - 'Winter Sports' | Last listed 1996 |
| - 'Winterfreude' | NHol |
| - 'Wintersonne' | ECho LGro NHol |
| *ciliaris alba* | Last listed 1998 |
| - 'Aurea' | CMac CNCN MBar SRms |
| - 'Camla' | MBar |
| - 'Corfe Castle' ♀ | CNCN MBar |
| - 'David McClintock' ♀ | CNCN GChr MBar |
| - 'Egdon Heath' | Last listed 1996 |
| - 'Globosa' | ECho GChr |
| - 'Maweana' | Last listed 1998 |
| - 'Mrs C.H. Gill' ♀ | CMac CNCN GChr MGos |
| - 'Ram' | Last listed 1998 |
| - 'Rotundiflora' | Last listed 1998 |
| - 'Stapehill' | Last listed 1998 |
| - 'Stoborough' ♀ | CNCN MBar |
| - 'White Wings' | CNCN |
| - 'Wych' | Last listed 1998 |
| ¶ *cinerea* f.*alba* | CMac |
| - 'Alba Major' | CNCN ECho MBar |
| - 'Alba Minor' ♀ | CNCN EOrn MBar MBri MOke NHar NHol SBod |
| - 'Alette' | Last listed 1998 |
| - 'Alfred Bowerman' | Last listed 1998 |
| - 'Alice Anne Davies' | Last listed 1998 |
| - 'Angarrack' | Last listed 1998 |
| - 'Anja Blum' | Last listed 1998 |
| - 'Ann Berry' | CNCN MBar SBod |
| - 'Apple Blossom' | Last listed 1998 |
| - 'Apricot Charm' | CNCN MBar SBod |
| - 'Aquarel' | Last listed 1998 |
| - 'Ashdown Forest' | Last listed 1998 |
| - 'Ashgarth Garnet' | MBar |
| - 'Atrococcinea' | Last listed 1997 |
| - 'Atropurpurea' | CNCN ECho MBar NHed |
| - 'Atrorubens' | MBar NHar SRms |
| - 'Atrorubens, Daisy Hill' | Last listed 1998 |
| - 'Atrosanguinea' | CNCN MBar SBod |
| - 'Atrosanguinea Reuthe's Variety' | ECho |
| - 'Atrosanguinea Smith's Variety' | ECho |
| - 'Baylay's Variety' | MBar |
| - 'Blossom Time' | MBar |
| - 'Brick' | Last listed 1998 |
| - 'Bucklebury Red' | Last listed 1998 |
| - 'C.D. Eason' ♀ | CB&S CMac CNCN GDra MBar MBri MGos MOke NHol SBod |
| § - 'C.G. Best' ♀ | CMac CNCN MBar |
| - 'Cairn Valley' | Last listed 1998 |
| - 'Caldy Island' | MBar |
| - 'Carnea' | Last listed 1998 |
| - 'Carnea Underwood's Variety' | Last listed 1998 |
| - 'Celebration' | ECho |
| - 'Cevennes' ♀ | CMac CNCN MBar MGos MOke SBod |
| - 'Champs Hill' | Last listed 1998 |
| - 'Cindy' ♀ | CNCN MBar MOke NHol |
| - 'Coccinea' | CNCN ECho |
| - 'Colligan Bridge' | MBar |
| - 'Constance' | MBar |
| - 'Contrast' | LRHS MBar |
| - 'Daphne Maginess' | CNCN |
| - 'Discovery' | Last listed 1998 |
| - 'Doctor Small's Seedling' | Last listed 1998 |
| - 'Domino' | CNCN MBar MGos MOke |
| - 'Duncan Fraser' | CNCN ECho MBar |
| - 'Eden Valley' ♀ | CMac CNCN MBar MGos NHol SRms |
| - 'England' | ECho |
| - 'Felthorpe' | Last listed 1998 |
| - 'Fiddler's Gold' ♀ | CNCN GAri MBar MBri MOke NHar NHed NHol |
| - 'Flamingo' | Last listed 1998 |
| - 'Foxhollow Mahogany' | MBal MBar |
| - 'Frances' | Last listed 1998 |
| - 'Fred Corston' | Last listed 1998 |
| - 'G. Osmond' | MBar MOke |
| - 'Glasnevin Red' | MBar NHar |
| - 'Glencairn' | MBar NHol |
| - 'Godrevy' | Last listed 1998 |
| - 'Golden Charm' | CMac CNCN ECho GChr NHol |
| - 'Golden Drop' | CNCN EOrn GChr MBar MBri MGos MOke NHol SBod |
| - 'Golden Hue' ♀ | CB&S CMac CNCN MBar MOke NHed NHol |
| - 'Golden Sport' | ECho MGos NHar |
| - 'Golden Tee' | Last listed 1998 |
| - 'Graham Thomas' | See E. cinerea 'C.G. Best' |
| - 'Grandiflora' | MBar |
| - 'Guernsey Lime' | MBar |
| - 'Guernsey Pink' | Last listed 1998 |
| - 'Guernsey Plum' | Last listed 1998 |
| - 'Guernsey Purple' | Last listed 1998 |
| - 'Hardwick's Rose' | CNCN MBar |
| - 'Harry Fulcher' | CNCN MBri MGos MOke |
| - 'Heatherbank' | Last listed 1998 |
| - 'Heathfield' | Last listed 1998 |
| - 'Heidebrand' | MBar |
| - 'Hermann Dijkhuizen' | Last listed 1998 |
| - 'Honeymoon' | MBar |
| - 'Hookstone Lavender' | Last listed 1998 |
| - 'Hookstone White' ♀ | CNCN EBrP EBre GDra LBre MBar NHed SBre |
| - 'Hutton's Seedling' | Last listed 1998 |
| - 'Iberian Beauty' | Last listed 1998 |
| - 'Jack London' | CNCN |
| - 'Janet' | ECho MBar MGos |
| - 'Jersey Wonder' | Last listed 1998 |
| - 'Jim Hardy' | Last listed 1998 |
| - 'John Ardron' | Last listed 1998 |
| - 'John Eason' | Last listed 1998 |
| - 'Joseph Murphy' | CNCN MBar |
| - 'Joseph Rock' | Last listed 1998 |

| | |
|---|---|
| - 'Josephine Ross' | MBar |
| - 'Joyce Burfitt' | CNCN |
| - 'Jubilee' | ECho |
| - 'Katinka' | CNCN MBar NHol |
| - 'Kerry Cherry' | Last listed 1998 |
| - 'Knap Hill Pink' ♀ | CNCN ECho MBar |
| - 'Lady Skelton' | MBar |
| - 'Lavender Lady' | Last listed 1998 |
| - 'Lilac Time' | ECho MBar |
| - 'Lilacina' | ECho MBar MOke |
| - 'Lime Soda' | CMac CNCN MBri |
| - 'Lorna Anne Hutton' | Last listed 1998 |
| - 'Maginess Pink' | CNCN |
| - 'Marina' | Last listed 1998 |
| - 'Michael Hugo' | CNCN |
| - 'Miss Waters' | MBar |
| - 'Mrs Dill' | ECho MBar |
| - 'Mrs E.A. Mitchell' | CNCN LRHS MOke |
| - 'Mrs Ford' | MBar |
| - 'My Love' | CNCN MBar MBri MOke |
| - 'Nell' | MBar |
| - 'Nellie Dawson' | Last listed 1998 |
| - 'Newick Lilac' | MBar MOke |
| - 'Next Best' | MBar |
| - 'Novar' | Last listed 1998 |
| - 'Old Rose' | Last listed 1998 |
| - 'P.S. Patrick' ♀ | CNCN MBar |
| - 'Pallas' | Last listed 1998 |
| - 'Pallida' | Last listed 1998 |
| - 'Patricia Maginess' | CNCN |
| - 'Peñaz' | Last listed 1998 |
| - 'Pentreath' ♀ | CNCN MBar MBri MOke |
| - 'Pink Foam' | MBar |
| - 'Pink Ice' ♀ | CB&S CMac CNCN EBrP EBre GDra LBre MBar MBri MGos MOke NHar NHed NHol SBod SBre |
| - 'Plummer's Seedling' | MBar |
| - 'Prostrate Lavender' | Last listed 1998 |
| - 'Providence' | LRHS |
| - 'Purple Beauty' | CNCN MBar MGos MOke |
| - 'Purple Robe' | ECho LRHS |
| - 'Purple Spreader' | Last listed 1998 |
| - 'Purpurea' | Last listed 1998 |
| - 'Pygmaea' | MBar |
| - 'Red Pentreath' | Last listed 1998 |
| - 'Rijneveld' | Last listed 1998 |
| - 'Robert Michael' | Last listed 1998 |
| - 'Rock Pool' | MBar NHol |
| - 'Rock Ruth' | Last listed 1998 |
| - 'Romiley' | EOrn MBar MBri MOke |
| - 'Rosabella' | CNCN MBar |
| - 'Rose Queen' | ECho |
| - 'Rosea' | Last listed 1998 |
| * - 'Rosea Splendens' | Last listed 1998 |
| - 'Rozanne Waterer' | Last listed 1998 |
| - 'Ruby' | CMac CNCN MBar |
| - 'Sandpit Hill' | MBar |
| - 'Schizopetala' | CNCN MBar |
| - 'Sea Foam' | CNCN MBar |
| - 'Sherry' | CNCN MBar |
| - 'Smith's Lawn' | Last listed 1998 |
| - 'Snow Cream' | MBar |
| - 'Son of Cevennes' | MGos |
| - 'Spicata' | Last listed 1998 |
| - 'Splendens' | CNCN |
| - 'Startler' | CB&S MBri MOke |
| - 'Stephen Davis' ♀ | CNCN EBrP EBre LBre MBar MBri MOke NHol SBod SBre |
| - 'Steven Leitch' | ECho |
| * - 'Strawberry' | Last listed 1998 |
| - 'Sue Lloyd' | Last listed 1998 |

| | |
|---|---|
| - 'Summer Gold' | CNCN EBrP EBre ECho LBre LRHS NHed SBre |
| - 'Tilford' | Last listed 1998 |
| - 'Tom Waterer' | MBar |
| - 'Uschie Ziehmann' | Last listed 1998 |
| - 'Velvet Night' ♀ | CB&S CMac CNCN MBar MBri MOke NHar NHol SRms |
| - 'Victoria' | MBar |
| - 'Violetta' | CNCN |
| - 'Vivienne Patricia' | MBar |
| - 'W.G. Notley' | Last listed 1998 |
| - 'West End' | Last listed 1998 |
| - 'White Dale' | ECho MBar |
| - 'Windlebrooke' ♀ | CNCN MBar MGos NHol |
| - 'Wine' | Last listed 1998 |
| - 'Yvonne' | ECho |
| *cruenta* | Last listed 1998 |
| *curviflora* | Last listed 1998 |
| x *darleyensis* | CNCN COCH EBrP EBre LBre |
| 'Ada S. Collings' | MBar MPla NRoo SBod SBre SPla |
| - 'Alba' | See *E.* x *darleyensis* 'Silberschmelze' |
| - 'Archie Graham' | COCH |
| § - 'Arthur Johnson' ♀ | CB&S CMac CNCN COCH EBrP EBre LBre MBar MBri MGos MOke MPla NHol SBod SBre SPla SRms |
| - 'Cherry Stevens' | See *E.* x *darleyensis* 'Furzey' |
| § - 'Darley Dale' | CMac CNCN COCH EBrP EBre EOrn LBre MBar MBri MOke MPla NHol SBod SBre |
| - 'Dunreggan' | COCH |
| - 'Dunwood Splendour' | See *E.* x *darleyensis* 'Arthur Johnson' |
| - 'Epe' | COCH |
| - 'Erecta' | COCH |
| § - 'Furzey' ♀ | CB&S CMac CNCN COCH EOrn MBar MBri MGos MOke MPla NHar NHed NHol NRoo SBod SPla SRms |
| - 'George Rendall' | CB&S CMac CNCN COCH CTri MPla NHol WGwG |
| - 'Ghost Hills' ♀ | CBrm CNCN COCH EBrP EBre GDra LBre MBar MOke MPla NHol SBod SBre |
| - 'J.W. Porter' ♀ | CNCN COCH EOrn MBar MOke NHed SPla |
| § - 'Jack H. Brummage' | CMac CNCN COCH CTri EBrP EBre EOrn LBre MBar MBri MGos MOke MPla NHar NHol SBod SBre SPla |
| - 'James Smith' | COCH MBar |
| - 'Jenny Porter' ♀ | CMac CNCN COCH EOrn MBar MBri MOke |
| - 'Kramer's Rote' ♀ | CBrm CMac CNCN COCH CTri EBrP EBre EOrn LBre MBar MBri MGos MOke NHed NHol NRoo SBre SPla |
| - 'Margaret Porter' | CB&S CMac CNCN COCH MPla SBod |
| - 'Mary Helen' | CB&S CBrm CNCN COCH EOrn LRHS MGos NHol |
| - Molten Silver | See *E.* x *darleyensis* 'Silberschmelze' |
| - 'Mrs Parris' Red' | Last listed 1998 |
| - 'Norman R. Webster' | CNCN COCH |
| - 'Pink Perfection' | See *E.* x *darleyensis* 'Darley Dale' |
| § - 'Silberschmelze' | CB&S CNCN COCH CTri EBrP EBre EOrn GDra LBre MBar MBri MGos MOke NHed NHol SBod SBre SPla |
| * - 'Silver Bells' | CMac EOrn |

| | |
|---|---|
| - 'Spring Surprise' | CB&S |
| - 'W.G. Pine' | COCH |
| - 'White Glow' | CNCN COCH CTri EOrn NHol WGwG |
| - 'White Perfection' ♀ | CNCN COCH EBrP EBre EOrn LBre MBar MBri NHol NRoo SBre SPla WGwG |
| *discolor* | CGre |
| *doliiformis* | Last listed 1998 |
| § *erigena* | Last listed 1998 |
| - 'Alba' | CMac COCH MBar |
| - 'Brian Proudley' ♀ | CNCN COCH MBar |
| - 'Brightness' | CB&S CNCN COCH GChr MBar MBri MOke NHar NHed NHol SBod |
| - 'Coccinea' | COCH |
| - 'Ewan Jones' | CNCN COCH IOrc MBar |
| - 'Glauca' | COCH |
| - 'Golden Lady' ♀ | CMac CNCN COCH EOrn MBar MBri MGos MOke NHol SBod |
| - 'Hibernica' | Last listed 1998 |
| - 'Hibernica Alba' | MBar |
| - 'Irish Dusk' ♀ | CNCN COCH EBrP EBre LBre MBar MBri MGos MOke NHar NHol SBod SBre SPla SRms |
| - 'Irish Salmon' ♀ | CMac CNCN COCH EOrn GChr MBar NHed |
| - 'Irish Silver' | COCH MBar MBri |
| - 'Ivory' | COCH |
| - 'Maxima' | Last listed 1998 |
| - 'Mrs Parris' Lavender' | Last listed 1998 |
| - 'Mrs Parris' White' | Last listed 1998 |
| - 'Nana' | Last listed 1998 |
| - 'Nana Alba' | CNCN COCH MBar |
| - 'Nana Compacta' | Last listed 1998 |
| - 'Rosea' | ECho MBar |
| - 'Rosslare' | Last listed 1998 |
| - 'Rubra' | ECho NHed |
| - 'Rubra Compacta' | Last listed 1997 |
| - 'Superba' | CMac CNCN COCH MBar MGos MOke SBod |
| - 'W.T. Rackliff' ♀ | CB&S CNCN COCH EBrP EBre ENot EOrn LBre MBar MBri MGos MOke NHol SBre SPla SRms |
| - 'W.T. Rackliff Variegated' | Last listed 1998 |
| *fontana* | Last listed 1998 |
| *formosa* | CGre |
| *glomiflora* | CGre |
| *gracilis* | CGre ECho |
| x *griffithsii* | NHol |
| - 'Ashlea Gold' | Last listed 1998 |
| § - 'Heaven Scent' ♀ | CNCN COCH LRHS |
| § - 'Valerie Griffiths' | CBrm COCH LRHS MBar NHol SBod |
| 'Heaven Scent' | See *E.* x *griffithsii* 'Heaven Scent' |
| *bibernica* | See *E. erigena* |
| x *biemalis* | Last listed 1998 |
| - 'Dusky Maid' | Last listed 1996 |
| x *krameri* | SDys |
| *laeta* | Last listed 1997 |
| *lusitanica* ♀ | CB&S CMac CNCN COCH CTrG MAsh MBar NHol SBod |
| - 'George Hunt' | CNCN ELan LRHS NHol SBod SPer |
| * - 'Sheffield Park' | LRHS SPer |
| *mackayana* | Last listed 1998 |
| subsp. *andevalensis* | |
| - 'Ann D. Frearson' (d) | CNCN |
| - 'Doctor Ronald Gray' | CNCN MBar MBri MOke SBod |
| - 'Donegal' | Last listed 1998 |
| - 'Errigal Dusk' | Last listed 1998 |
| - 'Galicia' | CNCN |

| | |
|---|---|
| - 'Lawsoniana' | Last listed 1998 |
| - 'Maura' (d) ♀ | Last listed 1998 |
| - 'Plena' (d) | CNCN MBar MOke |
| - 'Shining Light' ♀ | SDys |
| - 'William M'Calla' | Last listed 1998 |
| *mammosa* | Last listed 1998 |
| *manipuliflora* | MBar |
| - 'Aldeburgh' | CNCN |
| § - 'Cascade' | Last listed 1998 |
| - 'Corfu' | COCH |
| - 'Don Richards' | COCH |
| - 'Elegant Spike' | Last listed 1998 |
| - 'Ian Cooper' | COCH |
| - 'Korcula' | COCH |
| - x *vagans* 'Valerie Griffiths' | See *E.* x *griffithsii* 'Valerie Griffiths' |
| - 'Waterfall' | See *E. manipuliflora* 'Cascade' |
| *mediterranea* | See *E. erigena* |
| *multiflora* 'Formentor' | Last listed 1998 |
| x *oldenburgensis* | SDys |
| 'Ammerland' | |
| - 'Oldenburg' | Last listed 1998 |
| *pageana* | Last listed 1998 |
| *patersonia* | Last listed 1997 |
| *plukenetii* | CGre |
| x *praegeri* | See *E.* x *stuartii* |
| *scoparia* subsp. *azorica* | Last listed 1998 |
| - subsp. *maderincola* | Last listed 1998 |
| 'Madeira Gold' | |
| § - subsp. *scoparia* 'Minima' | MBar |
| - - 'Pumila' | See *E. scoparia* subsp. *scoparia* 'Minima' |
| *sparsa* | CGre |
| *speciosa* | SBod |
| *sphaeroidea* | CGre |
| *spiculifolia* | EPot GChr ITim MBal MBar NHed |
| ¶ - 'Balkan Rose' | GCrs NHol |
| § x *stuartii* | MBar SBod |
| - 'Charles Stuart' | See *E.* x *stuartii* 'Stuartii' |
| - 'Connemara' | Last listed 1998 |
| - 'Irish Lemon' ♀ | CNCN MBar NHar NHol SBod |
| - 'Irish Orange' | CNCN MBar NHol SBod |
| - 'Nacung' | Last listed 1998 |
| - 'Pat Turpin' | Last listed 1998 |
| § - 'Stuartii' | CNCN |
| § *terminalis* ♀ | CMac CNCN COCH ENot IOrc MBar SBod SRms WPic |
| - *stricta* | See *E. terminalis* |
| - 'Thelma Woolner' | CNCN COCH MBar |
| *tetralix* | CKin SRms WCla |
| - 'Afternoon' | Last listed 1998 |
| - 'Alba' | Last listed 1998 |
| - 'Alba Mollis' ♀ | CMac CNCN ENot EOrn MBar MBri MOke NHar NHol SBod |
| - 'Alba Praecox' | Last listed 1998 |
| - 'Allendale Pink' | Last listed 1998 |
| - 'Ardy' | Last listed 1998 |
| - 'Bala' | CNCN |
| - 'Bartinney' | MBar |
| - 'Con Underwood' ♀ | CMac CNCN EBrP EBre EOrn GChr LBre MBar MBri MOke NHol SBod SBre SRms |
| - 'Curled Roundstone' | Last listed 1998 |
| - 'Dänemark' | Last listed 1998 |
| - 'Daphne Underwood' | Last listed 1998 |
| - 'Darleyensis' | Last listed 1998 |
| - 'Dee' | Last listed 1998 |
| - 'Delta' | MBar |
| - 'Foxhome' | MBar |
| - 'George Frazer' | Last listed 1998 |
| - 'Hailstones' | MBar |
| - 'Helma' | Last listed 1998 |

- 'Hookstone Pink'     CNCN MOke NHar
- 'Humoresque'         Last listed 1998
- 'Ken Underwood'      CNCN MBar
- 'L.E. Underwood'     MBar NHol
- 'Mary Grace'         Last listed 1998
- 'Melbury White'      CNCN MBar
- 'Morning Glow'       See E. x watsonii 'F.White'
- 'Pink Glow'          Last listed 1998
- 'Pink Pepper'        Last listed 1998
- 'Pink Star' ♀        CMac CNCN EBrP EBre LBre
                       MBar NHol SBre
- 'Rosea'              Last listed 1998
- 'Rubra'              Last listed 1998
§ - 'Ruby's Variety'   MBar
- 'Ruby's Velvet'      See E. tetralix 'Ruby's Variety'
- 'Ruth's Gold'        CMac CNCN MBar NHol
- 'Salmon Seedling'    Last listed 1998
- 'Silver Bells'       MBar
- 'Stardome'           Last listed 1998
- 'Swedish Yellow'     Last listed 1998
- 'Terschelling'       Last listed 1998
- 'Tina'               CNCN
- 'Trixie'             Last listed 1998
- 'White House'        Last listed 1998
umbellata              CNCN MBar
vagans 'Alba Nana'     See E. vagans 'Nana'
- 'Birch Glow' ♀       CNCN SBod
- 'Carnea'             Last listed 1998
- 'Charm'              Last listed 1998
- 'Chittendenii'       Last listed 1998
- 'Cornish Cream' ♀    CNCN GAri MBar NHol
- 'Cream'              CNCN MOke NHar
- 'Diana Hornibrook'   CNCN MBar MOke NHar
- 'Diana's Gold'       Last listed 1998
- 'Fiddlestone' ♀      CNCN MBar SBod
- 'French White'       CNCN MBar SBod
- 'George Underwood'   MBar
- 'Golden Triumph'     ECho MBar NHol
- 'Grandiflora'        CNCN MBNS MBar
- 'Holden Pink'        CNCN MOke NHar
- 'Hookstone Rosea'    MBar
- 'Ida M. Britten'     MBar
- 'J.C. Fletcher'      Last listed 1998
- 'Kevernensis Alba' ♀ MBar SBod SRms
- 'Leucantha'          Last listed 1998
- 'Lilacina'           CMac CNCN MBar
- 'Lyonesse' ♀         CB&S CMac CNCN EBrP EBre
                       ENot LBre MBar MBri MGos
                       MOke NHol NRoo SBod SBre
                       SRms
- 'Miss Waterer'       MBar
- 'Mrs D.F. Maxwell' ♀ CB&S CMac CNCN EBrP EBre
                       GChr LBre MBar MBri MGos
                       MOke NHar NHol SBod SBre
                       SRms
- 'Mrs Donaldson'      Last listed 1998
§ - 'Nana'             ECho MBar
- 'Pallida'            CNCN
- 'Peach Blossom'      MBar
- 'Pyrenees Pink'      CMac CNCN MBar MOke NHar
- 'Rosea'              ECho
- 'Rubra'              CNCN ECho MBal MBar
- 'Rubra Grandiflora'  Last listed 1997
- 'Saint Keverne'      CB&S CMac CNCN MBal MBar
                       MGos MOke NHar NHol NRoo
                       SBod
- 'Summertime'         CNCN MBar
- 'Valerie Proudley' ♀ CB&S CMac CNCN EBrP EBre
                       EOrn GDra LBre MBar MBri MGos
                       MOke MWat NHar NHol SBod
                       SBre SRms
- 'Valerie Smith'      Last listed 1998

- 'Viridiflora'        CNCN MBar
- 'White Giant'        Last listed 1998
- 'White Lady'         ECho MBar
- 'White Rocket'       CNCN MBar
- 'White Spire'        Last listed 1998
- 'Yellow John'        CNCN ECho
x veitchii             MBal
- 'Brockhill'          SDys
- 'Exeter' ♀           CNCN COCH EBee EPfP GAri
                       MAsh MBar NHol
- 'Gold Tips' ♀        CDoC CNCN CTrC MAsh MBal
                       MBar MBri MGos MOke NHar
- 'Pink Joy'           CNCN GAri MAsh MBal MBri
                       MOke NHar NHol SVil
versicolor             CGre
verticillata           SBod
viridescens            CGre
x watsonii 'Cherry Turpin' Last listed 1998
- 'Ciliaris Hybrida'   Last listed 1998
- 'Dawn' ♀             CNCN MBar MBri NHar SBod
- 'Dorothy Metheny'    Last listed 1998
§ - 'F.White'          MBar
- 'Gwen'               CNCN MBar
- 'H. Maxwell'         CNCN MBal
- 'Mary'               Last listed 1998
- 'Pink Pacific'       Last listed 1998
- 'Rachel'             MBal
- 'Truro'              Last listed 1998
x williamsii 'Cow-y-Jack' Last listed 1998
- 'David Coombe'       Last listed 1998
- 'Gold Button'        MBar
- 'Gwavas'             CNCN MBar SBod
- 'Ken Wilson'         SDys
- 'Lizard Downs'       Last listed 1998
- 'P.D. Williams' ♀    CNCN ECho MBal MBar

# ERIGERON ✿ (Asteraceae)
acer                   CKin EWFC WCla WHer
- var. debilis         Last listed 1998
- HH&K 269A            CHan
'Adria'                EBee GBuc MAvo MMil NLak
                       NRoo SPer
§ alpinus              EHol GCHN GTou LBee MOne
'Amity'                EBee EBrP EBre EFou GCHN LBre
                       SBre SMer
aphanactis NNS 93-249  Last listed 1997
argentatus             Last listed 1997
atticus                Last listed 1997
aurantiacus            EHol EPfP EWTr GMaP LHop
                       MBNS MCCP NBro NOak WCot
§ aureus               NWCA WAbe
§ - 'Canary Bird' ♀    CPBP EGle EPfP EWes NBir NHar
                       NMen SRot SWas WAbe WLin
* 'Azure Beauty'       CMGP EPfP LRHS NPro SHel
Azure Fairy            See E. 'Azurfee'
§ 'Azurfee'            ELan ERic GAbr GMaP MBNS
                       MCLN NFai NMir NOak NRoo
                       SMer SPer SPla WHen WMer WPer
                       WWin
'Birch Hybrid'         SIng
Black Sea              See E. 'Schwarzes Meer'
bloomeri               Last listed 1998
- NNS 92-108           Last listed 1997
'Blue Beauty'          NCut SRms
borealis               CSam GCHN
- Arctic form          Last listed 1996
'Charity'              CGle CMGP EBee EFou EGar
                       SLon SSpe SSvw WLRN
chrysopsidis           CPBP EPfP NWCA SIng WAbe
'Grand Ridge' ♀
compactus var. consimilis Last listed 1998
- var. consimilis NNS 93-252 Last listed 1998

| | |
|---|---|
| *compositus* | CGra GAbr GCHN ITim NWCA SRms WPer |
| § - var. *discoideus* | EBur NMen WPer |
| - var. *glabratus* | NWCA |
| - JCA 8911 | Last listed 1996 |
| ¶ - 'Mount Adams Dwarf' | WLin |
| - 'Rocky' | GMaP |
| * *daicus* | Last listed 1997 |
| Darkest of All | See *E.* 'Dunkelste Aller' |
| 'Dignity' | EBee EFou ELan GCHN LFis MWat NTow NVic SMer SPer SSpe SUsu WCot WEas WFar WViv |
| 'Dimity' | CGle ECha EHic EPPr GMac MBri NPla WAbe WWin |
| § 'Dunkelste Aller' ♀ | CGle CSev EAst EBee EBrP EBre EFou EGar ELan EMan ENot GCHN GMaP LBre MBri MCAu MRav MTis NFla NGdn NRoo SBre SPer SPla SRms WMer WMow WWin |
| *elegantulus* | NSla |
| * *epirocticus* | Last listed 1997 |
| * - NS 462 | NWCA |
| 'Felicity' | CElw EFou MBel SRms |
| 'Festivity' | Last listed 1996 |
| *flettii* | EBee GCHN WPer WWin |
| 'Foersters Liebling' ♀ | MBri MNrw MWat NFla NPla NRoo SHel WByw WCot WMer |
| *formosissimus* | EBee |
| 'Four Winds' | EBrP EBre ECtt ELan EMan ESis EWes GAbr LBre LHop MRav MUlv NGdn NMen SBre WMer WPer |
| from Big Horns | CGra |
| 'Gaiety' | Last listed 1996 |
| *glabellus yukonensis* | Last listed 1996 |
| *glaucus* | CAgr EBee EHol EWTr GMaP NCat NVic SMrm WBea WCot WLRN |
| - 'Albus' | CSev LBee LHop WMow WPer |
| - 'Elstead Pink' | CSev CTri EBee NFai SPla WEas WMow |
| - pink | NCat |
| * - 'Roger Raiche' | Last listed 1997 |
| - 'Roseus' | CB&S CHal NLon |
| *bowellii* | EBee ECha |
| § *karvinskianus* ♀ | More than 30 suppliers |
| *kennedyi alpigenus* | Last listed 1998 |
| NS 93-276 | |
| *leiomerus* | CLyd EFou EPot GCrs LBee NTow NWCA |
| *linearis* | NMen NWCA WPat |
| 'Mrs F.H. Beale' | EFou SCro |
| *mucronatus* | See *E. karvinskianus* |
| *multiradiatus* | EBee NLak |
| *nanus* | CLyd NWCA WPat WPer WPyg |
| *oreganus* | EBee |
| § *peregrinus* | NOak |
| § - subsp. *callianthemus* | Last listed 1997 |
| *philadelphicus* | CElw CGle NBir NBro |
| ¶ 'Pink Beauty' | NCut |
| Pink Jewel | See *E.* 'Rosa Juwel' |
| Pink Triumph | See *E.* 'Rosa Triumph' |
| *pinnatisectus* | NWCA WPer |
| *polymorphus* | Last listed 1998 |
| ◆ 'Profusion' | See *E. karvinskianus* |
| 'Prosperity' | CGle EFou |
| *pygmaeus* | Last listed 1998 |
| *pyrenaicus* Rouy | See *Aster pyrenaeus* |
| - hort. | See *E. alpinus* |

| | |
|---|---|
| 'Quakeress' | CBos CElw CGle CSam EBee EBrP EBre EFou EMan EMon GCHN GMac LBre MBel MRav MTis MUlv NBro NCat NRoo SBre SHel SMer SMrm SSpe WCot WFar WLin WRHF |
| § 'Rosa Juwel' | CM&M ENot ERic GAbr GCHN LHop LPVe MBNS NBir NBro NMir NOak NRoo SEND SMer SPla SRms WHen WMow WPer |
| § 'Rosa Triumph' | EFou MBel MCAu SPla |
| 'Rosenballett' | EBrP EBre GMac LBre MUlv NBrk SBre |
| *roseus* | Last listed 1997 |
| 'Rotes Meer' | ELan MAvo MBri NTow |
| *rotundifolius* 'Caerulescens' | See *Bellis rotundifolia* 'Caerulescens' |
| ◆ *salsuginosus* misapplied | See *Aster sibiricus*, *E. peregrinus* subsp. *callianthemus* |
| ◆ - (Richardson) A.Gray | See *E. peregrinus* |
| § 'Schneewittchen' | CGle CMGP EAst EBee EFou EGar ELan EMan GMac LHop LRHS MBel MCAu MMil MRav MWat MWgw NRoo NSti NVic SCro SPla WLRN WMow |
| 'Schöne Blaue' | NBro NPri NRoo |
| § 'Schwarzes Meer' | EFou EHal LHop MUlv NGdn NRoo SPla WCot WMer |
| ¶ *scopulinus* | EHyt LBee |
| 'Serenity' | Last listed 1997 |
| *simplex* | MWat NMen NNrd NSla NTow |
| 'Sincerity' | Last listed 1996 |
| ¶ 'Snow Queen' | WFar |
| Snow White | See *E.* 'Schneewittchen' |
| 'Sommerabend' | MTed |
| 'Sommerneuschnee' | ECha NPri SHel |
| sp. dwarf from Idaho, USA | Last listed 1998 |
| sp. from Bald Mountains | NWCA |
| * 'Spanish Daisy' | EAst GPin |
| *speciosus* | EBee SMer SSvw |
| ¶ - var. *macranthus* | SIgm WLin |
| 'Strahlenmeer' | EBee LRHS WLRN |
| * *strictus* from Ireland | Last listed 1997 |
| *trifidus* | See *E. compositus* var. *discoideus* |
| *tweedyi* | NBro |
| *uncialis* var. *conjugans* | CGra |
| *uniflorus* | NNrd |
| 'Unity' | MWat |
| *vagus* | WWin |
| - JCA 8911 | MRPP |
| 'White Quakeress' | CElw GBuc LHil MCLN NRoo SLod SOkh WRHF |
| 'Wuppertal' | CBlo EBee EGar EMan LRHS SSvw WLRN |
| *yukonensis* | CLyd |

# ERINACEA (Papilionaceae)

| | |
|---|---|
| § *anthyllis* ♀ | SIng |
| *pungens* | See *E. anthyllis* |

# ERINUS (Scrophulariaceae)

| | |
|---|---|
| *alpinus* ♀ | CMHG CMea EBot ECtt ELan ESis EWFC GTou MBal MBro MPla MRPP MWat NBro NFor NHol NRoo SIng SRms WAbe WCla WEas WFar WPer WPyg WWin |
| - var. *albus* | CBot CLyd CNic GTou MBro MPla NMen NWCA SRms WAbe WCla WHoo WPer WPyg |
| - 'Dr Hähnle' | CNic EBrP EBre ECGP LBre MMal NMen SBre SRms WHoo WPyg |
| - 'Mrs Charles Boyle' ♀ | MBro WHoo WPyg |

\* *olivana*  EWes

## ERIOBOTRYA (Rosaceae)
*deflexa*  CFil
*japonica* (F) ♀  CAbb CB&S CBot CDoC CFil
 CGre CMCN ERea ERom GQui
 LBlo LPan MRav NPal SArc SDry
 SLon SPer SSta WHer WMul WNor
 WPGP WSHC WWat
- 'Benlehr' (F)  Last listed 1998
- 'Mrs Cookson' (F)  Last listed 1998

## ERIOCAPITELLA See ANEMONE

## ERIOCEPHALUS (Asteraceae)
*africanus*  WJek

## ERIOGONUM (Polygonaceae)
*argophyllum*  Last listed 1996
*breedlovei*  Last listed 1996
¶ - var. *breedlovei*  CGra
*brevicaule* var. *nanum*  NWCA
¶ *cespitosum*  CPBP NTow NWCA SIgm SIng
♦ - subsp. *douglasii*  See E. douglasii
- NNS 94-44  MRPP
¶ *compositum*  SIgm WLin
 var. *leianthum*
*croceum*  Last listed 1997
§ *douglasii*  CGra WLin
¶ - NNS 95-238  MRPP
*flavum*  WPer
*giganteum*  Last listed 1998
♦ *heracleoides* var. *minus*  See E. umbellatum var. minus
*jamesii*  WPat WPyg
¶ *kennedyi* var. *alpigenum*  CGra WLin
¶ - var. *austromontanum*  NTow
*libertini*  WLin
*lobbii* var. *lobbii*  Last listed 1998
*ochrocephalum*  Last listed 1998
*ovalifolium*  NTow NWCA SIgm
- var. *depressum* NNS 94-47 Last listed 1998
- var. *nivale*  Last listed 1996
*panguicense alpestre*  Last listed 1998
*pauciflorum*  Last listed 1997
 subsp. *nebraskense*
*rosense*  EHyt
*saxatile*  Last listed 1998
*siskiyouense*  Last listed 1997
¶ *subalpinum*  EPot
¶ *thymoides*  CGra
*umbellatum*  ECha EPot NTow SIng
♦ - var. *haussknechtii*  See E. umbellatum var.
 polyanthum
- var. *humistratum*  SIgm WLin
§ - var. *minus*  WLin
§ - var. *polyanthum*  WLin
- var. *porteri*  NWCA WLin
- var. *subalpinum*  Last listed 1997
- var. *torreyanum*  CMea EPot MBro NHol WLin WPat
¶ - var. *umbellatum*  LBee
*ursinum*  Last listed 1998
*wrightii*  Last listed 1996

## ERIOPHORUM (Cyperaceae)
*angustifolium*  CBen COIW CWat EHoe EHon
 EMFW EPPr EPla GCHN GOrn
 LPBA MCCP MMoz MSta NDea
 SWat WCot WHer WMAq WPer
 WWeb
*latifolium*  LPBA
*vaginatum*  See Scirpus fauriei var. vaginatus

## ERIOPHYLLUM (Asteraceae)
*lanatum*  CHal EBee ECha GAbr GMaP
 MBNS MHlr MWat NArg SBla
 SChu SRms WEas WWin
\* - *achilleifolium*  Last listed 1996
- 'Bella'  NLar
\* - 'Pointe'  EWll GSki MCCP SSca

## ERIOSTEMON (Rutaceae)
*myoporoides*  ECon LCns

## ERITRICHIUM (Boraginaceae)
§ *canum*  NTow
*howardii*  Last listed 1996
*nanum*  CGra
*rupestre*  See E. canum
- var. *pectinatum*  NWCA
\* *sibiricum*  Last listed 1997
*strictum*  See E. canum

## ERODIUM ✿ (Geraniaceae)
*absinthoides*  GCHN LRHS MDHE NChi
- var. *amanum*  EMan GCHN MBri
- blue  GCHN
§ *acaule*  GCHN NRog NRoo
*alnifolium*  GCHN
¶ 'Ardwick Redeye'  MDHE
*balearicum*  See E. x variabile 'Album'
*battandierianum*  GCHN
*boissieri*  GCHN
*botrys*  Last listed 1998
*brachycarpum*  GCHN
¶ 'Caroline'  WHoo
*carvifolium*  CElw EPPr GCHN MBri MDHE
 MHar NRoo NWCA WLin WPnn
§ *castellanum*  ESis GCHN NBro NMen NRog
 NRoo NSti SBla SCro SRms
¶ *celtibericum*  MDHE
¶ - 'Peñagolosa'  SIGM
*chamaedryoides*  See E. reichardii
§ *cheilanthifolium*  EPot GCHN GMaP MDHE NLak
 WAbe WMaN
- 'Bidderi'  MDHE NChi NRoo
*chrysanthum*  More than 30 suppliers
- pink  CGle EPPr LGre MDHE SMrm
 SUsu SWas
- *sulphureum*  WPnn WShe
*ciconium*  Last listed 1998
*cicutarium*  EWFC
§ - subsp. *cicutarium*  GCHN
*corsicum*  CGle EBur ElAn MDHE MTho
 NMen NRog
- 'Album'  CSam GCHN MDHE
- dark pink  Last listed 1996
'County Park'  See E. foetidum 'County Park'
*crinitum*  GCHN
♦ *crispum*  See E. cheilanthifolium
*danicum*  Last listed 1998
*daucoides* hort.  See E. castellanum
¶ - ex L Kreeger 4593  MRPP
'Eileen Emmett'  GCHN MDHE
\* 'Elizabeth'  GCHN WPnn
§ *foetidum*  EGle GCHN LFis MDHE MWat
 NMen NRog NSla WOld
§ - 'County Park'  CMea CPlt ECha ECou EDAr EPPr
 EWes GCHN GMaP MDHE MMil
 MOne NChi NHed NMen NRog
 NRoo SAga SBla SChu SMrm
 SRms WKif WPnn
- 'Pallidum'  CHal CSam
- 'Roseum'  GCal MWat SBla WPer

| | |
|---|---|
| * 'Frans Choice' | Last listed 1998 |
| 'Fran's Delight' | CMea MBro MDHE WHoo |
| ¶ 'Géant de Saint Cyr' | EMon |
| N *glandulosum* ♀ | CMea ELan EMon GCHN GCal |
| | LBee LHop MBro MOne NRog |
| | SAga SBla SIng SRms SRob WBea |
| | WEas WKif WPat WPer |
| ¶ - 'Espiguette' | SIgm |
| *gruinum* | ECoo GCHN LFis SRCN SSca |
| | WPnn WSan |
| *guicciardii* | EDAr |
| N *guttatum* | CGle CHea EMan LPio MDHE |
| | MPla MWat NMen NTow SAga |
| | SRms WHal WPer WSHC |
| 'Helen' | GCHN |
| ♦ *heteradenum* | See *E. foetidum* |
| *hirtum* | Last listed 1998 |
| x *hybridum* hort. | See *E.* 'Sara Francesca' |
| - Sünderm. | EGle ELan EWes NRoo WAbe |
| | WHal |
| *hymenodes* hort. | See *E. trifolium* |
| *jahandiezianum* | GCHN |
| 'Julie Ritchie' | MDHE WHoo |
| 'Katherine Joy' | CNic EWes MDHE NChi NHed |
| | NRog WAbe |
| x *kolbianum* | MBro MDHE NChi SWas WHoo |
| | WPnn WPyg |
| ¶ - 'Nadia' | MBri |
| - 'Natasha' | CMHG ECha ELan EMan EPot EPri |
| | EWes GCHN LBee MDHE NHol |
| | NMGW NMen NRog SChu SMrm |
| | SWat WFar WKif |
| 'Las Meninas' | CRDP GCHN |
| x *lindavicum* | MDHE WPnn |
| - 'Charter House' | GCHN WPnn |
| - pink form | WPnn |
| *macradenum* | See *E. glandulosum* |
| *malacoides* | GCHN |
| *manescaui* | More than 30 suppliers |
| - dwarf form | CSpe |
| 'Merstham Pink' | See *E. foetidum* 'County Park' |
| *moschatum* | Last listed 1998 |
| - Guitt 88041904 | GCHN |
| *munbyanum* | GCHN |
| *neuradifolium* Guitt | GCHN |
|   86040601 | |
| 'Nunwood Pink' | GCHN MDHE |
| *pelargoniiflorum* | More than 30 suppliers |
| ¶ *petraeum* | MWat |
| ¶ - (Gowan) Willd. | See *E. foetidum* |
| - subsp. *crispum* | See *E. cheilanthifolium* |
| - subsp. *glandulosum* | See *E. glandulosum* |
| 'Pickering Pink' | GCHN MDHE NMen NRog SWat |
| *pimpinellifolium* | GCHN |
| 'Princesse Marion' | GCHN |
| 'Rachel' | GCHN MDHE |
| *recorderi* | GCHN |
| 'Red Eve' | Last listed 1998 |
| § *reichardii* | CElw ESis IMGH LBee MPla MTho |
| | NRog SBla SIng SRms SUsu SWat |
| | WCla WPnn |
| - cultivars | See *E.* x *variabile* |
| - 'Derek' | ECho |
| - JR 961 | GCHN |
| - JR 962 | GCHN |
| - JR 963 | GCHN |
| - JR 964 | GCHN |
| * - 'Rubrum' | Last listed 1998 |
| *rodiei* | GCHN |
| *romanum* | See *E. acaule* |
| § *rupestre* | CBot CMea CNic ECho ECtt |
| | GCHN MDHE NHed WPnn |

| | |
|---|---|
| *salzmannii* | See *E. cicutarium* subsp. |
| | *cicutarium* |
| § 'Sara Francesca' | MDHE NSla |
| *saxatile* | GCHN |
| x *sebaceum* 'Polly' | GCHN |
| 'Spanish Eyes' | EHyt MBri MDHE SMrm SWas |
| 'Stephanie' | CElw EGle GCHN LBee MDHE |
| | NBir NChi NHol NRoo SAsh SIgm |
| *supracanum* | See *E. rupestre* |
| *tordylioides* | GCHN |
| *trichomanifolium* DC. | EWes LBee NRoo SAsh WPnn |
| - hort. | See *E. cheilanthifolium* , *E.* |
| | *valentinum* |
| § *trifolium* | CMCo EBee ELan MMil NChi NPla |
| | NSti SIng SSpi SUsu WCru WHal |
| | WHoo |
| - Guitt 85051701 | GCHN |
| - var. *montanum* | GCHN |
| § *valentinum* | GCHN NNrd NRog |
| - 'Alicante' | Last listed 1997 |
| § x *variabile* | EHyt |
| § - 'Album' | CHea CMHG ELan EMNN EPot |
| | GBuc GMac LBee MBar MPla |
| | MTho NHar NHol NMen NRoo |
| | NVic NWCA SBla SRms SUsu |
| | WAbe WCla WEas WOld WPat |
| | WPer WPnn WWin |
| - 'Bishop's Form' | CMHG ECtt EMNN EPot ESis |
| | GMac LPio MBar MBro MPla NBro |
| | NHar NHol NMen NNrd NRog |
| | NRoo NTow SBla SRms WHoo |
| | WPat |
| - 'Flore Pleno' (d) | ECtt EDAr EHyt ELan ESis EWes |
| | MPla NRog NRoo SHFr SIng SRms |
| | SUsu WAbe WOld WPer WPnn |
| | WSan |
| - 'Roseum' ♀ | CBot CNic ECho ELan NRog |
| | NRoo NWCA SIng SRms WAbe |
| | WCom WOld WPer WWin |
| I 'Westacre Seedling' | EWes |
| ¶ 'Whiteleaf' | MDHE |
| x *wilkommianum* | NRog |

# ERPETION See VIOLA

# ERUCA (Brassicaceae)

| | |
|---|---|
| *vesicaria* subsp. *sativa* | CArn CBod CJew ELau GPoy LHol |
| | MChe SIde WHer WJek WOak |
| | WSel WWye |

# ERYNGIUM ✿ (Apiaceae)

| | |
|---|---|
| § *agavifolium* | More than 30 suppliers |
| ¶ - HCM 98048 | WCru |
| *alpinum* ♀ | CB&S CElw CGle CSpe EBee |
| | ECha EFou ELan EPar LPio MBal |
| | MBro MCLN MLLN MTho NBir |
| | NChi NSti SPer SRms SWat WEas |
| | WHoo WOve WPGP |
| - 'Amethyst' | CRDP ELan GBuc MBri MCli |
| | MTed NLar WMer |
| - 'Blue Star' | CB&S CBot CHar EBee ECGN |
| | EHrv ELan EMar GCal GSki LGre |
| | LHop MTis MWll NCat NWes |
| | SLon SPla SSpi WHoo WPer |
| - 'Holden Blue' | Last listed 1998 |
| - 'Opal' | LRHS |
| - 'Slieve Donard' | EAst EBee IBlr LFis LRHS SPer |
| - 'Superbum' | CBot CRDP CSam ECGN EHrv |
| | GSki MNrw NLon NRoo SBla |
| | SMad SRms WLin |
| *amethystinum* | CBot EBee ECGN ECha EHrv |
| | EMan EWes GSki LGre MAvo |
| | MNrw NChi NLak NSla SChu |
| | SIgm SMad WLRN WPer |

*aquifolium* — Last listed 1996
*biebersteinianum* Nevski — See *E. caucasicum*
\* - from Kashmir — Last listed 1997
*bourgatii* — More than 30 suppliers
¶ - Graham Stuart Thomas's selection — CSpe EMar GBin GNau MAvo MBel MCLN WCot
- 'Oxford Blue' ♀ — CHan CLon CMea CMil CRDP EHrv EPar LGre LPio MMil NTow SSoC SSpi WCot WEas WOld
- 'Picos' — CGle EHrv LGre LPio SMrm WCom WCot
*bromeliifolium* hort. — See *E. agavifolium*
*caeruleum* — EMon EWTr EWes LGre MNrw NFai NLak WCot
*campestre* — CBot MAvo NLar SIgm SRCN WPer
§ *caucasicum* — EBee ECGN GBuc NLak
*creticum* — EBee EGar EHal EWes MAvo NBir NBro
*decaisneanum* — See *E. pandanifolium*
*dichotomum* — EMon LGre
- Caeruleum Group — MNrw
*ebracteatum* — CLon GCal LGre SIgm WCot
- var. *poterioides* — LGre SMad
§ *eburneum* — CBot CHan EBrP EBre ECha EHal EMon EWes GBuc LBre LGre MGrG MSCN MWgw NBro NChi NLak SBre SGre WCot WFar WPic
*foetidum* — CArn EOHP
'Forncett Ultra' — EFou
§ *giganteum* ♀ — More than 30 suppliers
- 'Silver Ghost' — CMea EBee EFou EGle EHrv LGre MAvo NLar NPri SDix SIgm SMrm SUsu SWat WCot WHal
*glaciale* — CFil NLak SIgm
- JJA 461.000 — NWCA SBla
\* *horridulum* — Last listed 1998
*horridum* — EBee EBrP EBre ELan EOas EWes LBre LGre MBro MFir MNrw NBro NBur NLak SArc SBre SIgm WHer WWhi WWin
¶ *humile* — CPin
'Jos Eijking' — EBee MCLN MRav
¶ *leavenworthii* — EBee
*maritimum* — CArn CBot CPou CRDP ECha GPoy LGre MHer NFla SIgm SRCN SSpi WAbe WSel
Miss Willmott's ghost — See *E. giganteum*
✕ *oliverianum* ♀ — CMea CRDP CSam ECGN ECGP EFou EHrv ELan EMan GAbr GBuc IHdy LGre MAvo MBro MCAu MCli NRoo SDix SIgm SMad SPer WByw WMer WWeb
§ *pandanifolium* — CGre CLon CMHG ETen EWes GBin GCal IBlr MSCN NLak NSti SAPC SArc SCob SDix SMad SPer WBrE WCot
¶ - purple — SDix
*paniculatum* — See *E. eburneum*
*planum* — More than 30 suppliers
- 'Bethlehem' — CLon EBee GCal WMer WPyg WWeb
§ - 'Blauer Zwerg' — CLon EFou GLil MCAu SCoo SMad SWat WMer WPyg
- 'Blaukappe' — CBot CFir CHar CKel ECGP GBri LGre MBro MOne NCut NLar SMad WElm WHoo WOve WPGP WPyg WWhi
- Blue Dwarf — See *E. planum* 'Blauer Zwerg'
- 'Blue Ribbon' — CRDP EBee EFou EMan SWat
- 'Flüela' — CGle CLon CM&M CPar EBee EMan EWes GCal GMaP LPio MRav NCat NLak SLon SPla SWat WWal

- 'Seven Seas' — CFir CMil EBee GMaP LHop LRHS MBel MHlr MRav NLak SChu SPla SRPl SWat WCot WLRN WPer
- 'Silverstone' — EBee GCal GSki NPla NPri
- 'Tetra Petra' — MCCP WHil WPer
- violet blue — GCal
*proteiflorum* — CHan CRDP GBin GCal LHop NLak SCob SWat WCot WGle
*serra* — EWes GBin
sp. CD&R — EWes
sp. RB 94054 — NSti
*spinalba* — CBot GSki LPio NLak SIgm WPer
*tricuspidatum* — CBlo EBee LRHS NLak WPer
✕ *tripartitum* ♀ — More than 30 suppliers
- 'Variegatum' — Last listed 1997
\* *umbelliferum* — Last listed 1997
\* *umbellulatum* — EMon
*variifolium* — More than 30 suppliers
¶ *venustum* — EBee LGre NChi SIgm
*yuccifolium* — CArn CB&S EBot ECoo EOld EWes GCal LHil LPio MSCN NBur NLak SCob SIgm SMad WCot WWeb
✕ *zabelii* — CRDP CSpe ELan GCal LGre MFir MHlr MLan NBir NTow WPGP
- 'Donard Variety' — CLon EWll GCal LRHS MAvo MBri SWat WMer
- 'Jewel' — CLon SUsu SWat
- 'Violetta' — CGle CLon CPlt ELan GBuc MTed SWat WHoo

---

## ERYSIMUM ✿ (Brassicaceae)

§ *alpestre* — MChR NBro
- J. Jurasek 222/96 — Last listed 1998
*alpinum* hort. — See *E. hieraciifolium*
*amoenum* — Last listed 1997
'Anne Marie' — ELan MRav SOkh SUsu
*arenicola* var. *torulosum* — See *E. torulosum*
*arkansanum* — See *E. helveticum*
§ *asperum* — NTow
'Aunt May' — SMrm
'Bowles' Mauve' ♀ — More than 30 suppliers
'Bowles' Purple' — ISea
'Bowles Yellow' — CStr EHic GBuc NChi NSti SMer
'Bredon' ♀ — ECoo ELan EOld GAbr GCHN MAsh MMil NBro NPer NSti NTow SAga SCob SRPl WFar WHil WKif WRus
'Butterscotch' — CElw CFee CFri CGle CLTr CMil CSam NHaw WEas WMaN WMer WWhi
*capitatum* — MDHE NMen
'Cheerfulness' — EGar MBri SPla
*cheiri* — CJew EWFC IBlr LHol MMal WCot WEas WHer
N - 'Baden-Powell' (d) — EGar
- 'Bloody Warrior' (d) — CBot CElw CHan ECtt ELan GBuc MPla NPer NSla SUsu WEas WMaN
- 'Chevithorne' — Last listed 1996
- 'Deben' — CBot
- 'Harpur Crewe' (d) ♀ — CB&S CBot CFee CGle CSam ELan EPot LHop MBal MBri MMil MTho NBro NChi NPer SChu SRms SUsu WCom WCot WEas WFar WHoo WPat WPyg WWin
- 'Helen Louise' — Last listed 1997
- 'Jane's Derision' — CNat
'Chelsea Jacket' ♀ — CLTr CM&M ECGP EHic GAbr GBri MCAu MMil MRav NChi NLak NSti SAga WEas WHil WMaN WMow WOve WPen WWat

| | |
|---|---|
| 'Chequers' | WPer WRus |
| * 'Clent Calcutt' | Last listed 1997 |
| *concinnum* | See *E. suffrutescens* |
| 'Constant Cheer' ♀ | CElw CSam CSpe EGoo GAbr |
| | GBuc GMac NCut NFai NPer SAga |
| | SUsu WCom WEas WHil WKif |
| | WMow WPat WPer WRha WRus |
| | WWat |
| *cuspidatum* | Last listed 1998 |
| 'Devon Cream' | WWoo |
| 'Devon Gold' | See *E.* 'Plant World Gold' |
| 'Devon Sunset' | CElw CGle CHan CLyd CM&M |
| | CSam CSpe MAvo MSCN MSte |
| | NChi NHaw SAga SChu SLod |
| | SUsu WEas WMaN WPen WRus |
| | WSan |
| 'Dorothy Elmhirst' | See *E.* 'Mrs L.K. Elmhirst' |
| dwarf lemon | WHoo |
| 'Ellen Willmott' | SIgm |
| 'Emm's Variety' | NCat |
| *gelidum* J. Jurasek 220/96 | MDHE |
| * 'Gingernut' | NPer |
| 'Glowing Embers' | MAsh MBri SOkh SUsu WHil |
| 'Gold Flame' | MWat |
| 'Golden Gem' | MDHE WLRN WPer |
| 'Golden Jubilee' | CHal ECho NTow |
| § *helveticum* | CNic ECoo GTou NPri NTow SIng |
| | SRms |
| § *hieraciifolium* | MBal NBro WLRN |
| *humile* | WCot |
| 'Jacob's Jacket' | CGle CLTr CMil EGoo GCHN LFis |
| | MBNS MSCN NChi NPer NRoo |
| | SAga SChu WEas WHil WMaN |
| | WWin |
| 'John Codrington' | CBel CFri CGle CHan CMHG CMil |
| | CPlt CSam GBuc GCHN MRav |
| | NChi NFai NFla NGdn NPer SAga |
| | SChu SIgm SUsu WEas WElm |
| | WHoo WKif WLin WPen WWat |
| 'Joseph's Coat' | WViv |
| 'Jubilee Gold' | ELan GCrs SIng |
| 'Julian Orchard' | GMac NPla SChu SUsu WRus |
| *kotschyanum* | CLyd LBee MDHE NMen NPro |
| | NRoo NSla NTow NWCA WAbe |
| 'Lady Roborough' | CMil EGar GBuc |
| * 'Lewis Hart' | Last listed 1998 |
| *linifolium* | CPea EBur ECoo MDHE SRms |
| | WGor |
| § - 'Variegatum' | CArn CBrm CGle CSam EAst ELan |
| | EOrc EPot LFis LHil LHop MAsh |
| | MSCN NPer SAga SCob SCro SPer |
| | WAbe WCot WEas WHoo |
| 'Mayflower' | Last listed 1997 |
| ¶ 'Mill Cottage Dawn' | CMil |
| ¶ 'Mill Cottage Dusk' | CMil |
| 'Miss Hopton' | NPer NTow WEas WHil |
| 'Moonlight' | CBrm CSam GBuc GCHN LBee |
| | LNor MSCN MTho NBrk NBro |
| | NChi NFor SChu SRms WCot |
| | WEas WMaN WPer WWat |
| § 'Mrs L.K. Elmhirst' | CElw CHan LFis MBri NChi NPer |
| | SHel WCot WMaN |
| *mutabile* | CB&S CElw CHar CInt CLTr CSam |
| | CTri EGoo EOrc GCHN MFir |
| | MRav NBir NBro NSti WEas |
| | WMaN WMow |
| - 'Variegatum' | CBot WEas WHoo |
| ¶ *nivale* | MChR |
| 'Onslow Seedling' | GCHN |
| 'Orange Flame' | CMHG CNic ECha ELan EPot |
| | LBee LHop MBar MPla NBro NPer |
| | NPri NRoo NTow SChu WPer |

| | |
|---|---|
| *perofskianum* | SLon WEas |
| Perry's hybrid | NPer |
| 'Perry's Peculiar' | NBur NPer |
| 'Perry's Pumpkin' | NPer |
| § 'Plant World Gold' | LRHS |
| 'Plant World Lemon' | EPri |
| 'Primrose' | GCHN LHop WCot WPer |
| § *pulchellum* | ESis MWat NHol WEas WPat WPyg |
| - *aurantiacum* | Last listed 1997 |
| - 'Variegatum' | NCut NFla WCot |
| aff. *pulchellum* JJH 9309143 | NWCA |
| *pumilum* DC. | See *E. helveticum* |
| 'Rosemoor' | EGar MRav NCat |
| 'Rufus' | CMil CSam ELan GCHN NBur |
| | NHaw SAga WEas |
| *rupestre* | See *E. pulchellum* |
| § *scoparium* | ECGP EHic MCCP NBro NLak |
| | NTow SChr |
| 'Scorpio' | NCut |
| *semperflorens* | Last listed 1997 |
| *sintenisianum* | See *E. alpestre* |
| 'Sissinghurst Variegated' | See *E. linifolium* 'Variegatum' |
| ¶ sp. from Madeira | CPLG |
| 'Sprite' | CLyd CMHG CMea CTri EPot |
| | MPla NPer |
| ¶ 'Stonyford Gem' | MSCN |
| § *suffrutescens* | CElw CPle ESis NBro NPer SUsu |
| 'Sunbright' | NCat NRoo |
| 'Sunshine' | Last listed 1998 |
| § *torulosum* | NPer |
| * 'Tricolor' | WHil |
| ¶ 'Turkish Bazaar' | GMaP |
| 'Valerie Finnis' | MBNS WMaN |
| N 'Variegatum' | CB&S WRus WWin |
| 'Wembdon Bravery' | Last listed 1998 |
| 'Wenlock Beauty' ♀ | CBel CSam ELan GCHN MTho |
| | NChi NDov NFai NGdn SAga |
| | SChu SRms WByw WEas WMaN |
| | WPer WRus WWhi |
| 'Wenlock Beauty Variegated' | CMil CSam NChi |
| *wheeleri* | EBee ECoo NPer |
| *witmannii* | Last listed 1997 |
| ¶ 'Yellow Bird' | WMow |

## ERYTHRAEA See CENTAURIUM

## ERYTHRINA (Papilionaceae)

| | |
|---|---|
| *caffra* | Last listed 1998 |
| *corallodendron* | Last listed 1996 |
| *crista-galli* ♀ | CAbb CB&S CBot CGre ELan EMil |
| | EOas ERea GQui LLew MLan SBid |
| | SOWG SPan SRCN SSoC |
| - 'Compacta' | SMad |
| *fusca* | Last listed 1998 |
| § *humeana* | CGre |
| *indica* | See *E. variegata* |
| *latissima* | Last listed 1998 |
| *livingstoneana* | Last listed 1996 |
| *lysistemon* | SOWG |
| *princeps* | See *E. humeana* |
| § *variegata* | Last listed 1997 |
| *vespertilio* | SOWG |

## ERYTHRONIUM ✿ (Liliaceae)

| | |
|---|---|
| *albidum* | CLAP CWoo EBee EPot GBuc |
| | LAma MCli NRog WCru |
| *americanum* | CArn CBro CLAP CRDP CWoo |
| | EBee ECha EPot GCrs LAma |
| | MLLN MS&S MSal NRog SSpi |
| | WAbe WCru |
| 'Blush' | IBlr |
| *californicum* ♀ | CAvo CLAP CWoo MS&S NRog |
| | SWas WAbe |

| | |
|---|---|
| - J&JA 13216 | CLAP |
| § - 'White Beauty' ♀ | CAvo CBro CCuc CLAP EBee ECha EHyt ELan EPot ETub GCrs LAma LBow LPio MBal MDun MTho NHar SIng SSpi SUsu WAbe WCru WKif WShi |
| *caucasicum* | CLAP LBow NRog |
| *citrinum* | CWoo WLin |
| - J&JA 13462 | CLAP CWoo |
| 'Citronella' | CBro CLAP ERos GBuc LAma LBow MS&S NEgg NHar NHed NRog WAbe WCru |
| *cliftonii* hort. | See *E. multiscapoideum* Cliftonii Group |
| *dens-canis* ♀ | CAvo CMea CRDP EBee ECha ELan EPot ERos ETub GCrs LAma LBow LSyl MBal MBri MLLN MNrw MS&S MTho NFai NHol NRog NRoo NRya SCob SSpi WAbe WFar WPat WShi |
| - 'Charmer' | EPot WWst |
| - 'Frans Hals' | CLAP EBee EPar EPot ERos GBuc GCrs IMGH LAma MTho NRog WCru |
| ¶ - from Serbia, white | MPhe |
| - from Slavenia | CLAP |
| - JCA 470.001 | CLAP |
| - 'Lilac Wonder' | EBee EHyt EPar EPot IMGH LAma MTho NRog WWst |
| - var. *niveum* | EHyt EPot ERos LAma |
| * - - 'Plenum' | WWst |
| - 'Old Aberdeen' | CLAP CRDP NPar |
| - 'Pink Perfection' | EPar EPot ERos GCrs LAma MCli NHar NRog WCru |
| - 'Purple King' | EBee EPot ERos IMGH LAma NHar NRog WCru |
| - 'Rose Queen' | CAvo CBos CBro EBee EPar EPot ERos ETub GBuc IMGH LAma MAvo MLLN MTho NHar NHol NRog SUsu WAbe |
| - 'Snowflake' | CAvo CLAP CMea CRDP EBee ECha EHyt EPar EPot ERos IMGH LAma MCli MLLN NHar NRog SSpi WAbe WCru |
| - 'White Splendour' | CBro NEgg |
| - WM 9615 from E Slovenia | MPhe |
| *elegans* | CFil WPGP |
| § *grandiflorum* | GCrs MS&S MWll NHar WAbe WLin |
| - subsp. *chrysandrum* | See *E. grandiflorum* |
| - J&JA 11394 | CLAP |
| - MP&S 007 | CLAP SSpi |
| *helenae* | CFil CLAP CWoo IBlr WPGP |
| *hendersonii* | CLAP CWoo LAma MPhe MS&S WLin |
| - J&JA 12945 | CLAP CWoo SSpi |
| - JCA 11116 | CLAP |
| *howellii* | CFil CLAP GCrs WLin WPGP |
| ¶ - J&JA 13428 | CWoo |
| - J&JA 13441 | CLAP |
| *japonicum* | CBro CCuc EBee EFEx EHyt LAma LBow NFai NRog WCru |
| 'Jeannine' | WCru |
| 'Joanna' | CBro CLAP CRDP LAma |
| 'Kondo' | CCuc EBee EHyt EPot ERos GMaP LAma MBro MS&S MTho NHar NRog NRoo SLod WAbe WCru |
| 'Minnehaha' ♀ | Last listed 1997 |
| * *moerheimii* | Last listed 1997 |
| * - 'Semiplena' | Last listed 1998 |
| § *multiscapoideum* | CLAP CWoo MPhe WLin |
| § - Cliftonii Group | CLAP MPhe WLin |

| | |
|---|---|
| - - J&JA 13525 | CLAP CWoo SSpi |
| ¶ - JCA 12700 | SSpi |
| *oregonum* | CLAP CWoo MS&S |
| - subsp. *leucandrum* | CLAP MPhe MS&S WLin |
| - - J&JA 13494 | CWoo SSpi |
| 'Pagoda' ♀ | More than 30 suppliers |
| *purdyi* | See *E. multiscapoideum* |
| *revolutum* ♀ | CBro CFil CLAP CWoo EPot GGar IBlr LBow MS&S NWoo SSpi WCru |
| - Johnsonii Group | CFil CWoo MBal NHar SSpi WCru WPGP |
| - 'Knightshayes Pink' | CLAP |
| - 'Pink Beauty' | WNor |
| - 'Rose Beauty' | Last listed 1996 |
| - 'White Beauty' | See *E. californicum* 'White Beauty' |
| *sibiricum* | GCrs |
| - 'Altai Snow' | EHyt |
| - 'White Fang' | Last listed 1998 |
| 'Sundisc' | ECha EHyt EPot MS&S MTho NRog |
| *tuolumnense* ♀ | CAvo CBro CLAP EBrP EBre EHyt EMon EPar EPla EPot ERos GCrs LAma LBow LBre MBal MDun MS&S NHar NRog SBre WAbe |
| *umbilicatum* | Last listed 1996 |

## ESCALLONIA (Escalloniaceae)

| | |
|---|---|
| 'Alice' | CRsw SLPl SPer |
| § *alpina* | CPle CRsw |
| 'Apple Blossom' ♀ | More than 30 suppliers |
| ¶ 'Bantry Bay' | CB&S |
| § *bifida* | CDoC CGre CHan CPle CWit LRHS WSHC WWat |
| 'C.F. Ball' | CDoC CTri EBee ELan GCHN GChr GEil GRei IOrc LBuc MGos NFla NWea SEND SRms WAbe WDin WFar WHer WMoo WPic WStI |
| 'Cardinalis' | CRsw NCut |
| ¶ 'Compacta Coccinea' | CRsw |
| 'Dart's Rosy Red' | CBlo NHol SLPl |
| 'Donard Beauty' | CBlo CChe CRsw SRms |
| 'Donard Brilliance' | CRsw MGos WPic |
| ¶ 'Donard Gem' | CRsw |
| 'Donard Radiance' ♀ | CB&S CChe CDoC CSam EBee ELan ENot ISea LHop MGos MWat NHol SBod SPer SRPl SRms WBod WDin WFar WGer |
| 'Donard Rose' | CRsw WWeb |
| ¶ 'Donard Scarlet' | CRsw |
| 'Donard Seedling' | More than 30 suppliers |
| 'Donard Star' | CDoC EBee ENot EPfP IOrc MGos NWea SBid SLPl WGwG WWeb |
| 'Donard Surprise' | NFor NLon |
| ¶ 'Donard White' | CPri CRsw |
| 'Edinensis' ♀ | CMHG ECtt EMil ENot EPfP GChr MBar NFla SBid SEND SRms WDin WGer WMoo WWat |
| 'Erecta' | CBlo EPfP SBid |
| x *exoniensis* | SRms |
| *fonkii* | See *E. alpina* |
| ¶ 'Glasnevin Hybrid' | CRsw |
| 'Glory of Donard' | CRsw ENot |
| * *gracilis alba* | CRsw |
| 'Gwendolyn Anley' | CLTr CMHG MGos NTow SBod SLPl SPer WPic WWat |
| 'Hopleys Gold' | See *E. laevis* 'Gold Brian' |
| *illinita* | CPle CRsw WPGP |
| 'Iveyi' ♀ | More than 30 suppliers |
| § *laevis* | CRsw CTrw SDry SPan |

| | |
|---|---|
| § – 'Gold Brian' | CMHG CSam EBee EBrP EBre EHic EHoe ELan ENot EPla IOrc LBre MGos MWat SAga SBid SBre SPer SRms WHar WStI WWeb |
| – 'Gold Ellen' (v) | CBlo CCbe CWSG EBee EBrP EBre EMil LBre LHop MBri MCCP MGos MRav NHol SAga SBre SCoo SEND SPla |
| ¶ Lanarth no.1 | CRsw |
| 'Langleyensis' ♀ | CB&S CTri GOrc MWat MWhi NFor NLon NWea SBod WDin WFar WHar WPic WSHC |
| *leucantha* | CGre CPle CRsw |
| *littoralis* | CPle |
| *mexicana* | CBot CFil CHan WPGP WWat |
| ¶ x *mollis* | CB&S CPle CRsw SPer |
| *montevidensis* | See *E. bifida* |
| 'Newry' | SPer |
| *organensis* | See *E. laevis* |
| 'Peach Blossom' ♀ | CCbe CDoC CPle CSam EBee ELan EMil ENot EWTr GRei MBNS MBri MGos SAga SBid SLPl SPer SRms WFar WGwG WWal WWeb |
| 'Pink Elf' | CBlo ECtt IOrc MBri NCut NLon WLRN |
| 'Pink Pearl' | CRsw |
| 'Pride of Donard' ♀ | CB&S CBlo CLan EPfP IOrc LHop SPla SRms WGwG WWeb |
| ¶ *pulverulenta* | CRsw WPic |
| *punctata* | See *E. rubra* |
| 'Rebecca' | CRsw GOrc |
| 'Red Dream' | CBlo CCbe CFai EBee EBrP EBre IOrc LBre MAsh MBri MGos NFla NPSI NPro SBre SCoo SRms SSto WFar WGer WLRN WStI |
| 'Red Dwarf' | Last listed 1998 |
| 'Red Elf' | CMHG EBee EBrP EBre ECtt ELan EMil ENot GOrc IOrc LBre LHop MBar MBri MGos MPla MRav MWat NHol NLon SBre SLPl SPer SPlb SRms WFar WHen |
| 'Red Hedger' | CBlo CCHP CDoC CDul EHic MGos MTis SBid SCoo WGwG |
| *resinosa* | CB&S CPle CRsw SAPC SArc SMrm |
| *revoluta* | CPle CRsw SDry |
| *rosea* | CPle CRsw |
| § *rubra* | CRsw SRPl |
| – 'Crimson Spire' ♀ | CB&S CCbe CDul CTri EBee EBrP EBre ENot EWTr GRei LBre MBNS MBri MGos MRav MWat SAga SBod SBre SPer SRms WBod WHen WStI |
| – 'Ingramii' | CCbe CMHG CRsw SBod |
| § – var. *macrantha* | CB&S CCbe CDoC CDul CSam EBee EGra EMil GChr GRei ISea MBri NLon SPer SPla SRms WBod WDin WGer WGwG WPic WStI WWal |
| – 'Pygmaea' | See *E. rubra* 'Woodside' |
| – var. *uniflora* | SDry |
| § – 'Woodside' | CPle EHic EHol EPfP MGos NHol NPro SBid SIng SRms WHCG |
| ¶ 'Saint Keverne' | CRsw |
| 'Silver Anniversary' | CB&S CBlo EPla MGos MPla MRav SBid WBcn WLRN WWeb |
| 'Slieve Donard' | CBlo EBee ENot MGos MRav SLPl SRms WFar WWeb |
| ¶ x *stricta* 'Harold Comber' | CRsw |
| *tucumanensis* | CGre CPle CRsw |
| *virgata* | CPle CRsw |
| *viscosa* | CPle CRsw WCwm |

## ESCHSCHOLZIA (Papaveraceae)
| | |
|---|---|
| ¶ *californica* ♀ | EWTr |

## EUCALYPTUS ✿ (Myrtaceae)
| | |
|---|---|
| ¶ *acaciiformis* | CMFo |
| *aggregata* | CMFo SAPC SArc SPer WCel WTro |
| ¶ *albens* | SPlb |
| *alpina* | Last listed 1998 |
| *amygdalina* | Last listed 1998 |
| *approximans* | WCel |
| subsp. *approximans* | |
| *archeri* | CMFo CTho EPfP GAri GQui MBal MCCP NOla WBod WCel WOVN |
| ¶ *botryoides* | SPlb |
| § *bridgesiana* | CMFo ELau |
| *brookeriana* | Last listed 1998 |
| *caesia* | GCHN |
| *cameronii* | Last listed 1998 |
| *camphora* | CMFo WCel |
| *cinerea* | CMFo CTrC GQui IOrc SPlb WCel |
| *citriodora* | ELau EOHP GQui MHer NCut NWCA SIde WCel WLRN WNor |
| *coccifera* ♀ | CDoC CMFo ELan GAri GLch IOrc LPan MBal MCCP SEND SPla SSpi WBod WCel WNor |
| – silver leaved | WCel |
| *consideniana* | Last listed 1998 |
| *cordata* | CGre CMFo CMHG LHop MBal WCel |
| *crenulata* | GQui WCel |
| *dalrympleana* ♀ | CB&S CDoC CMFo CMHG CSam CTho EBee EBrP EBre ELan ENot EWes IOrc LBre MAsh MBal MBel MGos SBid SBre SPer SPla SRCN SRPl SRms WBod WCel WTro WWeb |
| *deanei* | WCel |
| *debeuzevillei* | See *E. pauciflora* subsp. *debeuzevillei* |
| *delegatensis* | CMFo CMHG CTrC GAri IOrc WCel WTro |
| *divaricata* | See *E. gunnii divaricata* |
| ¶ *dives* | CMFo |
| * *eximia nana* | EOHP WTro |
| *ficifolia* | CB&S |
| *fraxinoides* | WCel |
| *glaucescens* | CGre CMFo CMHG EWes GQui LPan LRHS SAPC SArc SBid SPer WCel WGer |
| *globulus* ♀ | CMFo CTrC ELau GAri MBal MSal NWCA SBid SSoC WCel |
| *goniocalyx* | WCel |
| § *gregsoniana* | ISea WCel |
| *gunnii* ♀ | More than 30 suppliers |
| § – *divaricata* | EPfP GQui LPan WCel WGer |
| * – 'Silver Drop' | Last listed 1998 |
| ¶ – white | CMFo |
| *haemastoma* | Last listed 1997 |
| *johnstonii* | CMFo GAri NCut SPer |
| *kitsoniana* | CBrm MBal WCel |
| *kruseana* | Last listed 1997 |
| *kybeanensis* | CMFo GQui WBod WCel |
| *lehmannii* | SOWG |
| *leucoxylon* | WCel |
| – subsp. *megalocarpa* | Last listed 1997 |
| *macarthurii* | WCel |
| *macrandra* | Last listed 1998 |
| ¶ *macrocarpa* | SPlb |
| ¶ *macroryncha* | SPlb |
| *mannifera* subsp. *elliptica* | WCel |
| – subsp. *maculosa* | Last listed 1997 |

| | |
|---|---|
| ¶ *melliodora* | ELau |
| *mitchelliana* | WCel |
| ¶ *moorei* | WSHC |
| * – *nana* | CBlo GAri WNor WShe |
| *neglecta* | WCel |
| *nicholii* | CB&S CMFo EPfP EWes GQui |
| | WBod WCel WGer WOVN |
| *niphophila* | See *E. pauciflora* subsp. |
| | *niphophila* |
| *nitens* | CMFo CMHG GAri LLew MBal |
| | WBod WCel |
| § *nitida* | CGre CMFo CMHG WCel WNor |
| *nova-anglica* | CMFo CMHG GAri |
| ¶ *obliqua* | CMFo |
| ¶ *olsenii* | CMFo |
| *ovata* | Last listed 1998 |
| *parvifolia* ♀ | CB&S CDoC CDul CLnd CMFo |
| | CTrC GAri ISea LPan SAPC SDry |
| | SEND SRPl WBod WCel |
| *pauciflora* | CBlo CDoC CMFo CTri EBee EBrP |
| | EBre ELan EPfP GAri LBre MBal |
| | SBid SBre SEND SPar SPer WBod |
| | WCel WNor |
| – subsp. *acerina* | WCel |
| § – subsp. *debeuzevillei* | CDoC CMFo EPfP EWes GQui |
| | LRHS MCCP SAPC SArc WCel |
| – subsp. *bedraia* | WCel |
| – var. *nana* | See *E. gregsoniana* |
| § – subsp. *niphophila* ♀ | More than 30 suppliers |
| – – 'Pendula' | CMHG GAri LRHS WCel |
| *perriniana* | CB&S CMFo EBee ELan ENot IBlr |
| | MBal SAPC SDry SPer SPla WBod |
| | WCel WNor WPat |
| *phoenicea* | SOWG |
| *polyanthemos* | Last listed 1997 |
| *preissiana* | Last listed 1998 |
| *pulchella* | Last listed 1997 |
| *pulverulenta* | CBlo CBrm CGre CMFo GAri |
| | WCel WGer |
| ¶ *radiata* | CMFo ELau |
| *regnans* | GAri ISea MBal WCel |
| *remota* | Last listed 1997 |
| *risdonii* | GAri WNor WShe |
| *rodwayi* | Last listed 1998 |
| *rubida* | CGre CMFo CMHG IOrc WCel |
| § *sideroxylon* | SPlb |
| ¶ – 'Rosea' | SPlb |
| *sieberi* | Last listed 1997 |
| *simmondsii* | See *E. nitida* |
| *stellulata* | CMFo GAri MCCP WCel |
| *stricta* | Last listed 1998 |
| *stuartiana* | See *E. bridgesiana* |
| *sturgissiana* | GCHN |
| *subcrenulata* | CMFo CMHG EPfP GAri GQui |
| | ISea WBod WCel |
| *tenuiramis* | CGre |
| *urnigera* | CGre CMFo GAri GChr LRHS |
| | WCel |
| *vernicosa* | WCel |
| – subsp. *johnstonii* | CMHG GAri WCel |
| *viminalis* | CArn CMFo GAri ISea LLew WCel |
| ¶ *youngiana* | ISea |

## EUCHARIDIUM See CLARKIA

## EUCHARIS (Amaryllidaceae)

| | |
|---|---|
| § *amazonica* | LAma NRog SDeJ |
| x *grandiflora* Plan. & Lind. | LBow |
| – hort. | See *E. amazonica* |

## EUCODONIA (Gesneriaceae)

| | |
|---|---|
| 'Adele' | NMos WDib |

| | |
|---|---|
| *andrieuxii* | NMos |
| – 'Naomi' | CHal NMos WDib |
| 'Cornell Gem' | See x *Achicodonia* 'Cornell Gem' |
| 'Tintacoma' | NMos |
| *verticillata* 'Frances' | NMos |

## EUCOMIS (Hyacinthaceae)

| | |
|---|---|
| § *autumnalis* | CAbb CAvo CBro CPou CSWP |
| | CTrC EBee GBin GSki LAma LLew |
| | LPio MCCP WCot |
| ¶ – subsp. *amaryllidifolia* | CMil |
| ¶ – subsp. *clavata* | WCot |
| *bicolor* | CAvo CBro CFir CTrC EBak EBee |
| | EGoo ETub LAma LBow LHil LPio |
| | MBel NRog SAPC SAga SArc SCob |
| | SDix SHFr SMad SSoC WCot |
| | WCru WEas WFar WHil WMul |
| | WRos |
| – 'Alba' | CAvo GSki LPio |
| – hybrids | SUsu |
| § *comosa* | CAvo CB&S CBro EBee EBot |
| | EMan EMon ENot GSki LAma |
| | LBow NRog SArc WCot WCru |
| | WEas WLRN WMul |
| – purple-leaved | EBot SIgm |
| *montana* | CMil LLew WHil |
| *pallidiflora* | LEdu |
| *pole-evansii* | CFir CTrC GBin GCal LLew WCot |
| | WCru WLRN |
| *punctata* | See *E. comosa* |
| *regia* | EBee LLew |
| *undulata* | See *E. autumnalis* |
| *zambesiaca* | GBin GCal LBow |
| 'Zeal Bronze' | CDoC CFil CMHG GCal LGre NSti |
| | WCot WCru WPGP |

## EUCOMMIA (Eucommiaceae)

| | |
|---|---|
| *ulmoides* | CB&S CFil CPle SMad WPGP |

## EUCRYPHIA ✿ (Eucryphiaceae)

| | |
|---|---|
| 'Castlewellan' | ISea |
| *cordifolia* | CB&S CFil CGre CTrw ISea MBal |
| | WBod |
| – Crarae hardy form | GGGa |
| – x *lucida* | CB&S CGre IOrc ISea MBal WAbe |
| | WDin |
| *glutinosa* ♀ | CDul CGre EBee ELan ICrw ISea |
| | LHyd MAsh MBal MBri NBir SBrw |
| | SPer SSpi SSta WAbe WDin WNor |
| | WPat WWat |
| – Plena Group (d) | ISea |
| x *hillieri* 'Winton' | CGre CMHG ISea MBal SSpi |
| x *intermedia* | CDul CGre CSam CTrC CTrG |
| | ELan GCHN GGGa GOrc NHol |
| | NPal SBrw SPer SRms SSpi WDin |
| | WPat WWat WWeb |
| – 'Rostrevor' ♀ | CB&S CLan CMHG CPMA EBee |
| | ELan ICrw ISea MBal MBel SAga |
| | SLon SPer SReu SSta WCwm WPic |
| | WSHC |
| *lucida* | CFil CGre ELan EPfP GGGa GSki |
| | ISea MBal SBrw WNor WPGP |
| | WWat |
| – 'Ballerina' | CPMA ISea |
| – 'Gilt Edge' (v) | CFil ISea |
| – 'Leatherwood Cream' (v) | ISea SBrw SSta |
| – 'Pink Cloud' | CDoC CFai CFil CMHG CPMA |
| | ELan ISea LRHS SBrw SPer SSpi |
| | SSta WWat |
| ¶ – 'Spring Glow' | ISea |
| *milliganii* | CB&S CDoC CFil CGre EBee |
| | GQui ISea LHop MBal MBlu MUlv |
| | NPal SBrw SPer SRms SSpi SSta |
| | WAbe WPGP WSHC WWat |

*moorei* CB&S CFil CGre ELan ISea MBal
x *nymansensis* CB&S CDul CFil CTrG EBrP EBre
     EMil ENot EPfP LBre LHop MBal
     SAPC SAga SArc SBre SReu SRms
     SSpi WBay WBrE WHCG WStI
 - 'George Graham' GGGa ISea MBal
 - 'Mount Usher' IOrc ISea SSta
 - 'Nymansay' ♀ CB&S CBar CDoC CLan CPMA
     EAst ELan GGGa ISea LHyd LPan
     MAsh MBal MBar MBri MGos
     MRav NHol NPal SBrw SDix SPer
     SSta WAbe WDin WGer WPat
     WPyg WSpi WWat
N 'Penwith' CPMA IMGH ISea LPan MBal
     NCut SBrw SSpi WGer WWat
* *wilkiei* ISea

## EUGENIA (Myrtaceae)

*australis* LHil
*myrtifolia* CPle CSev STre
- 'Variegata' Last listed 1997

## EUMORPHIA (Asteraceae)

* *canescens* NTow
*prostrata* CSpe
*sericea* CHan GOrc NFor WSHC

## EUNOMIA See AETHIONEMA

## EUODIA (Rutaceae)

*daniellii* See *Tetradium daniellii*
*hupehensis* See *Tetradium daniellii*
     Hupehense Group

## EUONYMUS (Celastraceae)

*alatus* ♀ More than 30 suppliers
- var. *apterus* WWat
- 'Ciliodentatus' See *E. alatus* 'Compactus'
§ - 'Compactus' ♀ CDoC CEnd CPMA EHic EPla ESis
     IOrc LNet LPan MAsh MBlu MBri
     MGos MPla MRav MUlv SBid SPan
     SPer SPla SReu SSpi WDin WWat
* *atropurpureus cheatumii* CPMA
*bungeanus* CMCN EPfP EPla WWat
- 'Dart's Pride' EPfP
*cornutus* CFil CPMA EPfP EPla MAsh WPat
   var. *quinquecornutus*
*europaeus* CArn CDoC CDul CHan CKin
     CLnd CSam EBrP EBre ELan EPla
     EWFC GChr LBre LBuc LPan
     NWea SBre SRPl SRms WDin
     WHar WHer WMou
- f. *albus* CBot CPMA EMil EPla
- 'Atropurpureus' Last listed 1998
- 'Atrorubens' CBrd CPMA
- 'Aucubifolius' (v) CFil EPfP EPla WBcn WPGP
* - 'Aureus' CNat
¶ - 'Chrysophyllus' CPMA
- var. *intermedius* ENot EPla
- 'Red Cascade' ♀ More than 30 suppliers
¶ - 'Thornhayes' CTho
*farreri* See *E. nanus*
*fimbriatus* Last listed 1997
¶ *fortunei* CDul
- Blondy = 'Interbolwi' CAbP CDoC CDul COtt CPMA
     EBee EBrP EBre ECle ELan EMil
     ENot EPla LBre MAsh MBar MBri
     MGos MPla SBid SBre SCoo SPer
     SSta WBod WPyg WWeb WWes
- 'Canadale Gold' (v) CDoC EBee ENot EPla ESis GEil
     MGos MWhi NBee NFai NHol
     SPer WWeb

- 'Coloratus' CBlo CLan EBee EHol ENot MBar
     MBlu NCut SBid SLon SPer WDin
     WGwG WTro WWal
- 'Country Gold' CBlo
- 'Croftway' SCro
- 'Dart's Blanket' CBlo EGoo ELan ENot EPla MRav
     MWhi CBid SLPl SSta SSto WDin
* - 'Emerald Carpet' Last listed 1997
- 'Emerald Cushion' ENot ESis NCut SPer WShe
- 'Emerald Gaiety' (v) ♀ More than 30 suppliers
- 'Emerald 'n' Gold' (v) ♀ More than 30 suppliers
- 'Emerald Surprise' MBri NHol NPro
- 'Gold Spot' See *E. fortunei* 'Sunspot'
- 'Gold Tip' See *E. fortunei* Golden Prince
- 'Golden Pillar' (v) EHic EHoe EHol ERav MDHE
     WCot
§ - Golden Prince (v) CB&S CWSG EBee ENot EPla IOrc
     MBar MRav NFai NHol SPer WGor
     WGwG WStI
- 'Harlequin' (v) CB&S COtt CPMA CWSG EBee
     EHoe ELan GOrc LBuc LHop
     MAsh MBar MBlu MGos MPla
     MRav NHol NPro SAga SIng SMad
     SPer SRPl SSta SSto WCot WFar
     WWal WWeb
- 'Highdown' EMon WWat
- 'Hort's Blaze' Last listed 1997
- 'Kewensis' CMHG CNic CPle EBee ENot
     MBar MPla MRav MWat SAPC
     SArc SBod WCot WCru WWat
- 'Minimus' CBlo CTri EHal EHic EPla ESis
     MGos NFai NHol NPro SIng SPla
     WFar WPer
* - 'Minimus Variegatus' ECho
§ - var. *radicans* CPlN WAbe
- 'Sheridan Gold' EBee ECtt EHic EHoe EPla MPla
     MRav NHol SEas
- 'Silver Gem' See *E. fortunei* 'Variegatus'
- 'Silver Pillar' (v) EHic EHoe ENot ERav ESis LRHS
     WFar
- 'Silver Queen' (v) ♀ More than 30 suppliers
- 'Sunshine' (v) CAbP CBlo EHic ELan EPla MAsh
     NCut NPro SBid
§ - 'Sunspot' (v) More than 30 suppliers
- 'Tustin' EPla SLPl
§ - 'Variegatus' CMHG ELan ENot MBar NFor
     SPer SRms STre WCot WDin WPat
     WPyg
¶ - 'Variegatus' EM '85 NSti
- var. *vegetus* EPla SPer
*grandiflorus* CPMA EPfP
*hamiltonianus* CMCN
- 'Fiesta' Last listed 1997
- subsp. *hians* See *E. hamiltonianus* subsp.
     *sieboldianus*
¶ - 'Indian Summer' EPfP MBlu
¶ - 'Red Elf' CPMA
§ - subsp. *sieboldianus* CDul CMCN CPMA CTho EPfP
     LHop MBal MRav SLPl SMrm SPan
     SRms WCoo
- - 'Coral Charm' CPMA SMrm SMur
- 'Winter Glory' CBlo CPMA LRHS WWes
- var. *yedoensis* See *E. hamiltonianus* subsp.
     *sieboldianus*
* *hibarimisake* EPla SBla
*japonicus* ENot EPfP LRHS SAPC SArc SBid
     SPer WDin
- 'Albomarginatus' CB&S CBlo CTri MBar MPla NBrk
     SBid SEND SRms WSHC WWeb
* - 'Argenteus Compactus' LPan
* - 'Aureopictus' See *E. japonicus* 'Aureus'
- 'Aureovariegatus' See *E. japonicus* 'Ovatus Aureus'

§ – 'Aureus' (v) — CB&S CBrm CDoC CMHG ENot EPla ERav GOrc LPan MBal MBri SBid SDix SEas SHFr SLon SMac SPer SPla WDin WHar WWeb
– 'Bravo' — CDoC EBee EGra EHic EHoe EMil MBri NHol SPer
– 'Chedju' — WBcn
– 'Chollipo' — CBlo ELan LRHS MAsh
* – 'Compactus' — LPan
– 'Duc d'Anjou' Carrière (v) — CB&S EBrP EBre EHoe ELan EPla ESis EWes LBre LPan MAsh SBre SDry SMad SPla
– 'Duc d'Anjou' hort. — See *E. japonicus* 'Viridivariegatus'
– 'Golden Maiden' — CBlo ELan EPfP LRHS MAsh
– 'Golden Pillar' (v) — EPla ESis
– 'Harvest Moon' — WWeb
§ – 'Latifolius Albomarginatus' ♀ — EHic EHoe EHol EPfP EPla MNrw MRav SBid SPer
– 'Luna' — See *E. japonicus* 'Aureus'
– 'Macrophyllus Albus' — See *E. japonicus* 'Latifolius Albomarginatus'
– 'Maiden's Gold' — COtt SBid WRHF
– 'Marieke' — See *E. japonicus* 'Ovatus Aureus'
– 'Mediopictus' — MBri
– 'Microphyllus' — CDoC EMil MBal MUlv STre WGwG WShe
§ – 'Microphyllus Albovariegatus' — CLTr CMHG ELan EMil EPla EPot MBal MBar MBrN MGos MRav NHol SAga SLon SPla SRms SSca WCot WHCG WPat WPyg WSHC WStI WWat
– 'Microphyllus Aureovariegatus' — CBlo CDoC EMil MWhi NHol SEas SSto WPat WPyg WWin
– 'Microphyllus Aureus' — See *E. japonicus* 'Microphyllus Pulchellus'
§ – 'Microphyllus Pulchellus' (v) — CB&S CDoC CMHG ENot EPla EPot LHop MBar MNrw MRav NHed NHol SAga SBid SEas WHCG WPyg WWeb
– 'Microphyllus Variegatus' — See *E. japonicus* 'Microphyllus Albovariegatus'
§ – 'Ovatus Albus' (v) — SBid
§ – 'Ovatus Aureus' (v) ♀ — CChe CDoC CMHG CTri ENot ESis LPan MBal MBar MGos MPla SBid SEas SPer SPla SRPl SRms WDin WPat WRHF WStI
– 'Président Gauthier' (v) — CDoC EBee LPan MGos NCut WBay WGer
– 'Robustus' — CDoC EPla
– 'Silver King' — CBlo WRHF
* – 'Silver Princess' — Last listed 1998
– 'Susan' — EBee EGra EHic EPla
– 'Viridivariegatus' — EBee LRHS
kiautschovicus — CBrd EPla
latifolius — CMCN CPMA EPfP
– x hamiltonianus — Last listed 1997
macropterus — EPla
myrianthus — CBrd EPfP MBlu SBid WCot WWat
§ nanus — CNic CPMA CPle EHol EMon EPla ESis MBal MBlu MBro NHol WPyg
– var. turkestanicus — EHic EPla ESis NPal SPan SRms WWat
obovatus — CHan
¶ oresbius — CPMA WPGP
oxyphyllus — CBrd CMCN CPMA EPfP SLon WMou WWat
§ pendulus — CGre WPGP
phellomanus — CDul EBee EHic EPfP GDra LHop LNet MAsh MBNS MBar MBlu MBri MUlv SPan WWat
§ planipes ♀ — CDul CGre CMHG CPle CTho CWit EBee ELan ENot EPla GChr IMGH MBNS MBel MBlu MBri NHol SPer SSpi WNor WWat

* pulchellus — LPan
'AureusVariegatus'
radicans — See *E. fortunei* var. *radicans*
'Rokojô' — CLyd MBro NHol WPat
rosmarinifolius — See *E. nanus*
sachalinensis hort. — See *E. planipes*
sanguineus — CPMA EPfP
sp. B&L 12543 — EHic EPla ESis EWes
tingens — CFil CPle SBid SLon WAbe WWat
velutinus — Last listed 1997
verrucosus — CPMA EPfP EPla WWes
yedoensis — See *E. hamiltonianus* subsp. *sieboldianus*

**EUPATORIUM** (Asteraceae)
§ album — CHad CVer EPPr GBar WPer
– 'Braunlaub' — EBee LBlm LPio MCli NSti SSpi WCot
altissimum — CBot CGle EPar MSal SRms WCHb WEas
– JLS 88029 — Last listed 1998
aromaticum — CArn CSev EBee ELan LFis MBel MCLN MLLN MRav MWgw NBro NSti SCro SWat WCHb WPer WWye
cannabinum — CArn CKin CSev ECoo EHon ELan EMFW EOld EWFC GPoy LHol MBNS MHew MMal MRav MSal MSta NMir NSti SRob SWat SWyc WCer WGwG WOak WPer WWye
– 'Album' — EMon
– 'Flore Pleno' (d) — CSev EBee ECGP ECha EFou EGar EMon GCal LFis MBel MFir MHlr MLLN MRav MSte NBrk NDov NHol NSti SLon SWat WAlt WCot WWat
– 'Not Quite White' — WAlt
– 'Spraypaint' — CNat
capillifolium — CWit MLLN NSti SAPC SArc SMrm WCot
– 'Elegant Feather' — CElw EWes SMad SUsu
chinense — Last listed 1997
coelestinum — Last listed 1998
* cyclophyllum — EBee
fistulosum — Last listed 1997
* – 'Atropurpureum' — WPer
* fortunei — Last listed 1996
* – 'Variegatum' — WCot
hyssopifolium — EBee
* – 'Bubba' — Last listed 1997
§ ligustrinum ♀ — CB&S CDoC CElw CHan CLan CPle CTbh CTri CWit EBee ECha ELan EMan EPla IOrc ISea LGre SAga SDix SMad SMrm SPer SUsu WCHb WFar WRus WSHC
maculatum — See *E. purpureum* subsp. *maculatum*
madrense — CLTr
micranthum — See *E. ligustrinum*
occidentale — WCot
perfoliatum — CAgr CArn GBar GPoy LHol MNrw MSal NCut WPer WWye
purpureum — More than 30 suppliers
¶ – 'Album' — LGre
§ – subsp. maculatum — CSam EBrP EBre EMon GCal LBre LFis MHlr NLar SBre WPer
– – 'Album' — EMon NSti SUsu
– – 'Atropurpureum' ♀ — More than 30 suppliers
– – 'Berggarten' — GCal
– – 'Gateway' — CRow
– – 'Glutbal' — CHid SMad
– – 'Riesinschirm' — EBee LGre MTed SMad SWat WCot WElm

- 'Purple Bush' — CHad CPlt ECha LGre NBrk SUsu
*rotundifolium* — Last listed 1997
*rugosum* — CGle CSam ELan EOrc EPfP GBar LEdu LGre MFir NLar SDys WCHb
- *album* — See *E. album*
¶ - 'Brunette' — CMil
- 'Chocolate' — More than 30 suppliers
* 'Snowball' — SMrm
§ *sordidum* — ERav ERea GCal LHil SMrm SYvo
*triplinerve* — EGar MSte
* *variabile* 'Variegatum' — WCot
*weinmannianum* — See *E. ligustrinum*

## EUPHORBIA ✿ (Euphorbiaceae)

*acanthothamnos* — LGre
*altissima* — MSte
¶ 'Amber Glow' — SWas
*amygdaloides* — CKin CRow EWFC EWTr SPlb SSpi WCer WWye
- 'Brithembottom' — CSam
- 'Craigieburn' — EBee EWes GBri GCal SUsu
§ - 'Purpurea' — More than 30 suppliers
§ - var. *robbiae* ♀ — More than 30 suppliers
¶ - × *characias* — WCot
¶ - 'Pom Pom' — WCot
- 'Rubra' — See *E. amygdaloides* 'Purpurea'
- 'Variegata' — CRow GBuc MHar
*balsamifera* — Last listed 1998
*biglandulosa* — See *E. rigida*
*brittingeri* — EGar
*broteroi* — WCot
*canariensis* — SGre
*capitata* — WPat
*capitulata* — ELan EWes LHop MBro MTho NMen WAbe WWin
*ceratocarpa* — CB&S CEnd EGar EWes GBuc SIgm SMad SPan WCHb WOve WWeb
*characias* — CB&S CBot CGle CRow EBee ECha ECtt EOld ERav MBri MBro NFor NHlc NOak NPer NPri SPan SPer SRms SSpi WByw WCot WFar WHen WHoo WPer WWal WWat
- 'Amber Eye' — IBlr
- Ballyrogan hybrids — IBlr
- 'Black Pearl' — EFou NHol SSvw WOVN
- 'Blue Wonder' — EFou
- subsp. *characias* ♀ — GAbr WCru
- - 'Blue Hills' — CLon EFou EGar GBuc GCal IBlr LBlm NLak SMrm WRus
- - 'Burrow Silver' (v) — CBot CRDP EWes MLLN NLak SCob SPar SWat
- - 'Green Mantle' — IBlr
- - 'H.E. Bates' — NBir
- - 'Humpty Dumpty' — CMdw COtt EBrP EBre EFou GMaP LBre LHop LRHS NPer NWes SBre SChu SMrm SPan SPer SSvw WCot WGer WOVN
- - 'Percy Picton' — CHan SPan
¶ - - 'Perry's Winter Blusher' — ECtt NPer
- dwarf — SMrm
- 'Forescate' — EBee EMil GNau LRHS MRav NGdn NHol SCro SPan SRPl WFar WGer WMer WRus WSpi
- 'Goldbrook' — CDoC CM&M CSev EBee EMan LFis NCat SChu SPla SRPl SWat
¶ - 'Golden Wonder' — IBlr
- JCA 475.500 — Last listed 1998
- 'Jenetta' — WHal
- 'Portuguese Velvet' — CHan CMil ECha EGle EMan EMar GBri LGre LHop MBro MCLN MGrG MHar NHaw NHol NPer SDix SIgm SMrm SPan SWas WCot WElm WHil WKif WPen WRus WSpi WWat WWoo

- 'Sombre Melody' — IBlr
- 'Spring Splendour' — EBee NLar SPan
¶ - 'Starbright' — EFou
- 'Variegata' — CRow SMad
- 'Whistleberry Gold' — Last listed 1996
- 'Whistleberry Jade' — Last listed 1996
- subsp. *wulfenii* ♀ — More than 30 suppliers
- - 'Bosahan' (v) — CB&S EGar SPan
- - 'Emmer Green' (v) — ECha EWes GBri MGrG SBla SWat WCom WCot WRus
- - JCA 475.603 — SAga
¶ - - 'Jimmy Platt' — MWll
§ - - 'John Tomlinson' ♀ — CBlo CMil ECha EPla EWes MBro MHlr MSte MWll SChu SUsu WCot WEas WOve
- - Kew form — See *E. characias* subsp. *wulfenii* 'John Tomlinson'
- - 'Lambrook Gold' ♀ — CMHG CRow CSam ECtt EGar EPar LHop MBri MBro MRav MWat NPer WHoo WPyg WRus WWat
- - 'Lambrook Yellow' — EMon GBuc LPio MWat SMur WSPU
- - Margery Fish Group — CDoC EBee EFou EHic EMan EPla LRHS MCLN MFir MLLN NCat NWes SChu SMrm SPer SWat WMer
- - 'Minuet' — Last listed 1997
- - 'Perry's Tangerine' — EWes NPer
§ - - 'Purple and Gold' — CMil CPou EWes MGrG SBla SPan WCot WPen WRus
- - 'Purpurea' — See *E. characias* subsp. *wulfenii* 'Purple and Gold'
- - 'Red House' — Last listed 1996
- - var. *sibthorpii* — WCot WOld
*clava* — GBin
¶ *clavarioides* var. *truncata* — WCot
*cognata* — ECGN
- CC&McK 607 — EWes GCHN
- CC&McK 724 — EBee GBin
*confinalis* — GBin
*conifera* — Last listed 1998
*corallioides* — CArn EBee EBrP EBre ECha EGar ELan EMan EPPr IBlr LBre NFai NFla NLak NPer NPri NSti SBre SHFr SIgm SRCN SSca WBrE WCot WHer WLin
§ *cornigera* — More than 30 suppliers
- CC 720 — CPou
*corollata* — Last listed 1998
*cylindrica* — Last listed 1998
*cyparissias* — More than 30 suppliers
- 'Ashfield' — Last listed 1996
¶ - 'Baby' — SPan WFar
- 'Betten' — See *E. × gayeri* 'Betten'
- 'Bushman Boy' — EGar GBri IBlr NLak WCot
§ - 'Clarice Howard' — More than 30 suppliers
- Clone 2 — NCat
- 'Fens Ruby' — More than 30 suppliers
- 'Orange Man' — EBee ECoo EFou EGar EMar EMon EWes GBin GBri IBlr MBro MCLN NBrk NHol NLak NSti SChu SMad SPan SPla SWat WElm
- 'Purpurea' — See *E. cyparissias* 'Clarice Howard'
- red — SPan
- 'Red Devil' — CBre EPla IBlr NCat SChu SUsu WOve
- 'Tall Boy' — EGar EMar EMon EPla EWes GBri IBlr NLak SPan
*dendroides* — GBin
§ *donii* — ELan EWes IBlr LHop SDix

| | |
|---|---|
| **dulcis** | CGle CRow ECha ECtt EFou ELan EPar NBrk NBro NHex NOak NSti SEas SMac WByw WEas WHen WOld WRus WWat |
| - 'Chameleon' | More than 30 suppliers |
| I - 'Nana' | CBlo EHic EWll GBin NHol |
| **epithymoides** | See E. polychroma |
| ¶ **erubescens** | SIgm |
| **esula** | CGle |
| § **Excalibur = 'Froeup'** | CMil EBee EHal GBin GNau LHop LRHS LRot MBri MCCP MTis NEgg NHol NSti SPan SPla SSpi SVil |
| **fasciculata** | Last listed 1998 |
| **fimbriata** | Last listed 1998 |
| ♦ **'Froeup'** | See E. Excalibur = 'Froeup' |
| **fulgens** | CHal WCot |
| 'Garblesham Enchanter' | EPPr |
| § x **gayeri** 'Betten' | GCal |
| ¶ **'Giant Green Turtle'** | CMil |
| **glauca** | CFee IBlr WCot |
| 'Golden Foam' | See E. stricta |
| **griffithii** | CRow NBrk NBro NCat SSpi SWat WAbb WGer |
| - 'Dixter' ♀ | More than 30 suppliers |
| - 'Fern Cottage' | CRDP EWes GAbr SMrm SPan SUsu SWas WHal |
| - 'Fireglow' | More than 30 suppliers |
| - 'King's Caple' | EGar |
| - 'Robert Poland' | CSWP |
| - 'Wickstead' | EBee EGar LHop LRHS SMrm WViv |
| * **hiemale** | Last listed 1997 |
| **horrida** | Last listed 1998 |
| **hyberna** | GBri IBlr MLLN NMen SWat WLin |
| **ingens** | GBin SGre |
| **jacquemontii** | EBee LPio SIgm WWat |
| x **keysii** | MBri |
| **lathyris** | CJew CRow ELan EMar ERav EWFC LHol MHew NCat NHex NPer SIde SIng SRms WEas WWye |
| **leucocephala** | GBin |
| **longifolia** D Don | See E. donii |
| - hort. | See E. cornigera |
| - Lamarck | See E. mellifera |
| **mammillaris** | Last listed 1998 |
| x **martinii** ♀ | More than 30 suppliers |
| - 'Red Dwarf' | EOrc SPan |
| **melanocarpa** | CEnd |
| § **mellifera** | More than 30 suppliers |
| **meloformis** | Last listed 1998 |
| **milii** ♀ | CHal EBak SRms |
| - 'Koenigers Aalbäumle' | MBri |
| **monteiroi** | Last listed 1998 |
| **myrsinites** ♀ | More than 30 suppliers |
| **nicaeensis** | CFil EBee EMan EOrc GCal LGre LHop MLLN SBla SBod SCro SMad SMrm SPer SSpi SUsu WCot WPGP WWat |
| **oblongata** | CB&S CFil EBee ELan EMan EMon EWes GBuc IBlr MUlv NLak NWes SBod WCHb WWat WWeb |
| **obtusifolia** | Last listed 1998 |
| **palustris** ♀ | More than 30 suppliers |
| - 'Walenburg's Glorie' | EGar GBin MBri MRav NBrk NLak NRoo SMad SPan SUsu WCot |
| ¶ - 'Zauberflöte' | SRms |
| **pekinensis** | MSal |
| **pilosa** | CNat |
| - 'Major' | See E. polychroma 'Major' |
| **pithyusa** | CBot CGle CHan EBee ECha EGar EMan EMon LHop MArl MLLN MSCN NFla NLak SUsu WCot WHil WRus WWat WWhi |
| § **polychroma** ♀ | More than 30 suppliers |
| § - 'Candy' | More than 30 suppliers |
| - 'Emerald Jade' | EBee GBri IBlr NLak |
| § - 'Lacy' (v) | CDoC CMil CStr EBee ELan ERav EWes LWoo MCCP MGrG MMil NBir NDov NLak SMad SPan SPla SUsu WCot WSan |
| § - 'Major' ♀ | CMHG ECha ELan EPPr GCal LGre LPio NCat SPan WCot WEas |
| - 'Midas' | CFee EGle NLak SMrm |
| - 'Orange Flush' | WHoo |
| I - 'Purpurea' | See E. polychroma 'Candy' |
| * - 'Senior' | SCro |
| - 'Sonnengold' | EGar EWes GCal LBlm MBro NRoo WHoo WPyg WSHC |
| I - 'Variegata' | See E. polychroma 'Lacy' |
| - 'Vic's Purple' | Last listed 1996 |
| **portlandica** | CB&S CSev EHic EMar GBin MBri NSti WCHb WHer |
| § x **pseudovirgata** | IBlr LHop SPan |
| **pugniformis** | MBri |
| **pulcherrima** | MBri |
| 'Purple Preference' | EPPr NPri |
| ¶ **Redwing = 'Charam'** | ELan LPan MRav NSti SPer |
| **reflexa** | See E. seguieriana subsp. niciciana |
| **resinifera** | Last listed 1998 |
| § **rigida** | CBot CBro CFil CMil EBee GCal MLLN SBid SBla SIgm SMrm WCot WPGP |
| **robbiae** | See E. amygdaloides var. robbiae |
| **sarawschanica** | LGre SMrm WCot |
| **schillingii** ♀ | CAbb CB&S CFee CMHG CPle CSam EBee EBrP EBre EMar EMon EOrc GCal GMaP LBre LFis LGre LHop MBri MCLN NSti SBod SBre SCob SDix SRPl WGle WHoo WPGP WWat |
| **schoenlandii** | Last listed 1998 |
| **seguieriana** | EBee ECha EMan ERav GBin SUsu WLin |
| § - subsp. **niciciana** | CBot CGle CHan CMHG CMea CSam ECha ELan ERav IBlr MArl MBro MLLN NBir SBla SDix SMrm SUsu WEas WHoo WRus WWat |
| **serrulata** | See E. stricta |
| **sikkimensis** | CBot CElw CFee CGre CHan CMHG CRow CSam CStr EBrP EBre ECha ELan EMon LBre MBel MWgw NBrk SBre SIgm SLon SMrm SRms WCHb WCot WCru WEas WOld WWat WWin |
| **soongarica** | Last listed 1998 |
| **spinosa** | SIgm SMad |
| § **stricta** | CFri CRow ECha ELan EMan EWes GAbr GBri IBlr MCCP MCLN MFir NArg NBro NCat NSti WElm WWat |
| **stygiana** | CFil CTrF |
| * **submammillaris** 'Variegata' | MBri |
| **susanna** | Last listed 1998 |
| ¶ **terracina** | WCot |
| **transvaalensis** | Last listed 1998 |
| **uralensis** | See E. x pseudovirgata |
| **villosa** | GBin MBro |
| § **virgata** | EMFP EWes NSti SPan WCHb WCot |
| 'Virgile' | Last listed 1998 |
| x **waldsteinii** | See E. virgata |
| **wallichii** Kohli | See E. cornigera |
| - Hook.f. | CSam EBee ECha EMan IBlr MBri MUlv NFla NOrc NRoo NSti SMrm SSoC WAbb WRus WWat |

| | |
|---|---|
| - misapplied | See *E. donii* |
| * 'Welsh Dragon' | Last listed 1997 |
| *zoutpansbergensis* | Last listed 1998 |

## EUPTELEA (Eupteleaceae)
| | |
|---|---|
| *franchetii* | See *E. pleiosperma* |
| § *pleiosperma* | SSpi SVen |
| *polyandra* | CBrd CFil CGre WPGP |

## EURYA (Theaceae)
| | |
|---|---|
| *japonica* | CCHP CFil |
| - 'Variegata' | See *Cleyera japonica* 'Fortunei' |

## EURYOPS (Asteraceae)
| | |
|---|---|
| *abrotanifolius* | EBee LHil SVen WSPU |
| § *acraeus* ♀ | CBot CHea CPle ELan EPot GCHN GTou LHop MBro MPla MWat NFor NLon NMen NRoo NTow NWCA SIng SRms WAbe WLin WWin |
| *candollei* | CTrC WAbe WCot |
| § *chrysanthemoides* | CB&S CCan CMHG CSam EBee ERav ERea IBlr LHil MBEx MBNS MMil MSte WPer |
| *decumbens* | NSla |
| aff. *decumbens* JJ&JH 9401309 | NWCA |
| *evansii* | See *E. acraeus* |
| *grandiflorus* | Last listed 1997 |
| *pectinatus* ♀ | CB&S CCan CDoC CInt CMHG CSam CSev CTrG ERea IBlr LHil MBEx MBlu MFir MLLN MNrw MRav SDry SMrm SOWG SPar SYvo WEas WPer WWye |
| *sericeus* | See *Ursinia sericea* |
| ¶ 'Sonnesheim' | CHal |
| *speciosissimus* | Last listed 1997 |
| *tysonii* | CPle GGar WCot |
| *virgineus* | CB&S CCan CTrC IBlr MBEx SVen |

## EUSTEPHIA (Amaryllidaceae)
| | |
|---|---|
| *jujuyensis* | Last listed 1997 |

## EUSTOMA (Gentianaceae)
| | |
|---|---|
| § *grandiflorum* | MBri |
| *russellianum* | See *E. grandiflorum* |

## EUSTREPHUS (Philesiaceae)
| | |
|---|---|
| *latifolius* | CPlN ECou |

## EUTERPE (Arecaceae)
| | |
|---|---|
| *edulis* | LPal |

## EVOLVULUS (Convolvulaceae)
| | |
|---|---|
| *convolvuloides* | ERea |
| *glomeratus* 'Blue Daze' | See *E. pilosus* 'Blue Daze' |
| § *pilosus* 'Blue Daze' | ERea SSad |

## EWARTIA (Asteraceae)
| | |
|---|---|
| *nubigena* | NWCA |
| *planchonii* | WAbe |

## EXACUM (Gentianaceae)
| | |
|---|---|
| *affine* | MBri |
| - 'Rococo' | MBri |

## EXOCHORDA (Rosaceae)
| | |
|---|---|
| *alberti* | See *E. korolkowii* |
| *giraldii* | CBlo CBrm CPle |
| - var. *wilsonii* | CBlo CPMA CSam EBee EBrP EBre EHic EPfP GEil GOrc LBre MAsh MBNS MBlu MBri MPla MUlv SBid SBre SEas SSpi SSta WWat |

| | |
|---|---|
| § *korolkowii* | CGre WWat |
| x *macrantha* | GOrc SRCN WAbe |
| - 'The Bride' ♀ | More than 30 suppliers |
| *racemosa* | CGre CPMA EHal ISea LHop MBal MGos MWhi SPer SRPl WHCG WWat |
| *serratifolia* 'Snow White' | CPMA MBlu |

# F

## FABIANA (Solanaceae)
| | |
|---|---|
| *imbricata* | CLan EHic EMil GQui MAsh MBar MBel MBlu SAga SBra SBrw SLon SPan SPer SSta WAbe |
| - *alba* | Last listed 1996 |
| - 'Prostrata' | EBee EHic EPfP GCal SBid SBrw SDry SPer SSpi WWat WWin |
| - f. *violacea* ♀ | CB&S CFee CGre CTri EBee EMil EPla ESis GQui MBar SAga SBid SPan SPer WKif WSHC |

## FAGOPYRUM (Polygonaceae)
| | |
|---|---|
| *cymosum* | See *F. dibotrys* |
| § *dibotrys* | ELan NSti |

## FAGUS ✿ (Fagaceae)
| | |
|---|---|
| § *crenata* | CMCN WNor |
| - 'Mount Fuji' | MBlu |
| *engleriana* | CBlo CMCN |
| *grandifolia* | CMCN |
| - var. *caroliniana* | CLyn |
| *japonica* | CMCN |
| *lucida* | CMCN |
| *orientalis* | CMCN WCoo |
| ◆ *sieboldii* | See *F. crenata* |
| *sylvatica* ♀ | CB&S CDoC CDul CKin CLnd ECrN ELan ENot GChr GRei IOrc ISea LBuc LHyr LPan MAsh MBar MBri MGos NBee NWea SPer WDin WHar WMou WNor WOrn WStI |
| § - 'Albomarginata' | CDul CMCN IOrc MBlu |
| - 'Albovariegata' | See *F. sylvatica* 'Albomarginata' |
| - 'Ansorgei' | CDul CEnd CMCN LRHS MBlu MBri |
| N - Atropurpurea Group | More than 30 suppliers |
| - - 'Swat Magret' | SMad |
| - 'Aurea Pendula' | CEnd CMCN MBlu SMad |
| - 'Birr Zebra' | CEnd |
| - 'Black Swan' | CBlo CDul CEnd CMCN GChr MAsh MBlu MBri SMad WGer WGor |
| - 'Bornyensis' | CMCN |
| - 'Cochleata' | CMCN LRHS |
| - 'Cockleshell' | CDul CMCN CTho MBri |
| - 'Cristata' | CDul CMCN GAri MBlu |
| - Cuprea Group | Last listed 1996 |
| § - 'Dawyck' ♀ | CB&S CBlo CDoC CDul CLnd CMCN COtt CTho EBee EBrP EBre ECrN ELan ENot GChr IOrc ISea LBre LHyr MAsh MBal MBar MGos NWea SBre SPer WDin WOrn |
| - 'Dawyck Gold' ♀ | CAbP CBlo CDoC CDul CEnd CMCN COtt CTho EBee GChr IOrc LPan MAsh MBar MBlu MBri NBea SMad SPer SSpi WOrn |
| - 'Dawyck Purple' ♀ | CAbP CBlo CDoC CDul CEnd CMCN COtt CTho IOrc LPan MAsh MBar MBlu MBri MGos NBea SMad SPer SSpi WOrn |

| | | |
|---|---|---|
| | – 'Fastigiata' misapplied | See *F. sylvatica* 'Dawyck' |
| | – 'Felderbach' | CLyn LRHS MBlu |
| * | – 'Franken' | MBlu SMad |
| | – 'Frisio' | CEnd CMCN |
| | – 'Grandidentata' | CMCN |
| | – 'Greenwood' | CDul LRHS MBlu |
| * | – 'Haaren' | CMCN LRHS |
| * | – 'Haven' | Last listed 1998 |
| | – var. *heterophylla* | CBlo CLnd CTho GAri NWea WOrn |
| | – – 'Aspleniifolia' ♀ | CB&S CDoC CDul CEnd CMCN COtt EBee ELan EMil ENot EPfP EPla IOrc LPan LRHS MAsh MBal MBar MBri SPer WDin WMou WNor |
| | – – f. *laciniata* | CMCN MBlu |
| | – 'Horizontalis' | CLyn CMCN |
| | – 'Interrupta' | SMad |
| | – 'Luteovariegata' | CEnd CMCN |
| * | – 'Marmorata' | CDul |
| | – 'Mercedes' | CDul CLyn CMCN LRHS MBlu MBri |
| | – 'Miltonensis' | CDul CMCN |
| N | – 'Pendula' ♀ | CB&S CBlo CDoC CDul CEnd CLnd CMCN CTho ELan ENot EWTr GChr GRei IOrc MAsh MBal MBar NWea SMad SPer WDin WHar WMou WOrn WPyg WStl WWal |
| | – 'Prince George of Crete' | CDul CEnd CMCN CTho |
| | – 'Purple Fountain' ♀ | CBlo CDoC CEnd CMCN COtt EBee ELan EMil IOrc LPan MAsh MBar MBlu MBri MGos NBee SPer WPyg WWeb |
| | – Purple-leaved Group | See *F. sylvatica* Atropurpurea Group |
| | – 'Purpurea Nana' | CMCN |
| | – 'Purpurea Pendula' | CDul CEnd CMCN CTho EBee ELan ENot GChr GRei IOrc LPan MAsh MBal MBar MBlu MGos MWat NBee NWea SPer WDin WHar WPyg WStl |
| § | – 'Purpurea Tricolor' (v) | CBlo CDoC CEnd CMCN GChr IOrc LPan MBar MGos NBea NBee SMer SPer WDin WPyg |
| | – 'Quercifolia' | CMCN |
| * | – 'Quercina' | CMCN |
| | – 'Red Obelisk' | CDul CMCN MBlu |
| | – 'Remillyensis' | CMCN |
| | – 'Riversii' ♀ | CB&S CBlo CDoC CDul CEnd CLnd CMCN CTho EBee ELan EMil ENot IOrc LPan MAsh MBal MBri MGos NWea SMer SPer SSta WDin WHar WOrn WStl |
| | – 'Rohan Gold' | CDul CEnd CMCN EBee MBlu MBri |
| | – 'Rohan Obelisk' | CEnd EBee MBlu |
| I | – 'Rohan Pyramidalis' | CDul CEnd CMCN |
| | – 'Rohan Trompenburg' | CMCN MBlu |
| | – 'Rohanii' | CAbP CB&S CBlo CDoC CDul CEnd CLnd CMCN COtt CTho EBee ECrN ELan EMil EWTr IMGH IOrc LPan MBal MBlu MWat NBee SPer WDin |
| | – 'Roseomarginata' | See *F. sylvatica* 'Purpurea Tricolor' |
| | – 'Rotundifolia' | CDoC CTho NWea |
| | – 'Silver Wood' | CMCN MBlu |
| | – 'Spaethiana' | CMCN |
| | – 'Striata' | CMCN |
| | – 'Tortuosa Purpurea' | CMCN CTho MBlu |
| | – 'Tricolor' (v) | CB&S CDul CLnd EBee ELan MAsh MBal WDin |

| | | |
|---|---|---|
| | – 'Tricolor' misapplied | See *F. sylvatica* 'Purpurea Tricolor' |
| | – 'Viridivariegata' | CMCN |
| | – 'Zlatia' | CB&S CBlo CDoC CDul CLnd CMCN COtt CTho EBee ELan ENot IOrc MBal MBar MBri MGos NBee SPer WBay WDin WOrn WStl |

## FALLOPIA (Polygonaceae)

| | | |
|---|---|---|
| | *aubertii* | See *F. baldschuanica* |
| § | *baldschuanica* ♀ | CChe CMac CRHN EBee EBrP EBre ELan ENot GChr GRei LBre LBuc MBar MGos MPla MRav MWat NBee NEgg NFla SBra SBre SLon SPer SPlb WFar WHar WWeb |
| ¶ | x *bohemica* 'Spectabilis' (v) | CRow ELan WCot |
| § | *japonica* | CRow ELan |
| § | – var. *compacta* | CRow EPfP EPla NLar NPri SMrm WBea WFar WMoo |
| * | – – 'Midas' | IBlr |
| I | – – 'Variegata' | CRow EPla EWes IBlr SMad |
| | – 'Crimson Beauty' | CRow |
| § | *multiflora* | CArn EOHP MSal |
| | – var. *hypoleuca* B&SWJ 120 | WCot WCru |
| | *sachalinensis* | CRow EWes |

## FARFUGIUM (Asteraceae)

| | | |
|---|---|---|
| § | *japonicum* | MTho |
| | – 'Argenteum' (v) | CFir SMad WCot WFar WHal WSan |
| | – 'Aureomaculatum' (v) ♀ | CAbb CFir CHan CSev EGar EHoe LHil MTho SLod SMad SWat WCot WFar WHal WHer WHil WMul WSan |
| | – 'Crispatum' | CFir CHid EHic MTPN MTis SApp SMad SWat WCot WFar WHil WSpi |
| ¶ | – 'Kinkan' (v) | WCot |
| | *tussilagineum* | See *F. japonicum* |

## FARGESIA (Poaceae - Bambusoideae)

| | | |
|---|---|---|
| ¶ | *denudata* | EPla |
| | *dracocephala* | CDoC CFil EPla ISta LJus SDry WBay WJun WPGP |
| | *fungosa* | CFil ISta WBay WJun WPGP |
| § | *murieliae* ♀ | More than 30 suppliers |
| * | – *dana* | Last listed 1998 |
| | – 'Harewood' | MCCP MMoz |
| | – 'Jumbo' | CDoC EMil EPla MCCP WBay |
| § | – 'Leda' (v) | SDry |
| | – 'Simba' | CDoC CEnd CFil EBee EBrP EBre EPla ISta LBre LEdu LJus MAsh MBNS MBrN MCCP MGos MMoz MTed MWht NBee NDov SBre SCob WBay WCru WJun WLRN |
| § | *nitida* ♀ | More than 30 suppliers |
| * | – 'Anceps' | EPla |
| | – 'Eisenach' | CFil EPla ISta LRHS MMoz WBay WCru WPGP |
| | – 'Nymphenburg' | CPMA EPla ISta LPan LRHS MMoz MWhi |
| | *robusta* | EFul EPla ISta LJus MMoz SDry SLPl WBay WJun |
| ¶ | – 'Red Sheath' | EPla |
| ¶ | *rufa* | EPla |
| | *spathacea* hort. | See *F. murieliae* |
| | *utilis* | EPla ERod ISta LJus MMoz SDry WBay WJun |
| | *yulongshanensis* | CFil EPla WPGP |

## FARSETIA (Commelinaceae)

| | | |
|---|---|---|
| | *clypeata* | See *Fibigia clypeata* |

**FASCICULARIA** (Bromeliaceae)
*andina* — See *F. bicolor*
*bicolor* — CFil CFir CGre EBak ECre EOas EWes GCal GGar IBlr ICrw IGri LHil LHop MFir MTed MTho SAPC SArc SSpi SSta WAbe WBor WCot WEas WGer WPGP WPic
§ - subsp. *canaliculata* — CFil WPGP
*kirchhoffiana* — See *F. bicolor* subsp. *canaliculata*
♦ *pitcairniifolia* hort. — See *F. bicolor*

x **FATSHEDERA** (Araliaceae)
*lizei* ♀ — CB&S CBot CDoC EBee EPla GQui IBlr MBal MBri MGrG NPal NRog SArc SBid SBra SDix SDry SLon SMac SPer SPla SPlb SSoC WDin WWal WWat
§ - 'Annemieke' (v) ♀ — CBot CSWP EPfP EPla IBlr MBri SMac SMad SPer
§ - 'Aurea' (v) — EPfP LRHS SBra SDry SEND
- 'Aureopicta' — See x *F. lizei* 'Aurea'
- 'Lemon and Lime' — See x *F. lizei* 'Annemieke'
- 'Maculata' — See x *F. lizei* 'Annemieke'
- 'Pia' — CSWP MBri
* - 'Silver Prusca' — EPla
- 'Variegata' ♀ — CB&S CMHG ELan IBlr MBal MBri MGrG SBid SBra SDry SEND SMer SPer SPla WFar WWat

**FATSIA** (Araliaceae)
§ *japonica* ♀ — More than 30 suppliers
- 'Variegata' ♀ — CB&S CBot EPla LRHS MBri MGos NMoo NPal SArc SEND WCot
*papyrifera* — See *Tetrapanax papyrifer*

**FAUCARIA** (Aizoaceae)
*tigrina* — MBri

**FAURIA** See NEPHROPHYLLIDIUM

**FEIJOA** See ACCA

**FELICIA** (Asteraceae)
§ *amelloides* — CHal CLTr ERea ESis SChu SRms
- 'Astrid Thomas' — CInt CSpe LHil MBEx
- 'Read's Blue' — CCan CSev CSpe LHil LHop LIck
- 'Read's White' — CCan ERea ESis GMac LHil LIck MBEx MSte WEas
§ - 'Santa Anita' ♀ — CCan CHal CSev CTri ECtt EOrc ERea LHil LHop LIck MBEx NPer SCro WEas
- 'Santa Anita' large flowered — LHil
- 'Santa Anita Variegated' ♀ — Last listed 1996
§ - variegated — CBar CCan CSev ECtt ELan ERea ESis IBlr LHil LHop LIck MBEx MBNS MSte NPer SHFr SPar SRms SUsu WEas WRus
- variegated, white flower — LIck
*amethystina* — See *F.* 'Snowmass'
§ *amoena* — CCHP CHad CHal CInt CTri ELan GBri LHil MBEx MHar NPla SChu SRms
- 'Variegata' — CTri EOrc NPla SChu
*bergeriana* — Last listed 1998
*capensis* — See *F. amelloides*
- 'Variegata' — See *F. amelloides* variegated
*coelestis* — See *F. amelloides*
*drakensbergensis* — IDac NTow
*filifolia* — CTrC
*natalensis* — See *F. rosulata*
*pappei* — See *F. amoena*

§ *petiolata* — CHan ECha EMan ERea IBlr LHil LIck MBEx NSti SSpi WCot WWin
*plena ensbergensis* (d) — Last listed 1997
§ *rosulata* — EBee EHyt ELan EMan EMon ESis GAri MRPP MTho NBro NMen NNrd NRoo NTow SOkh SRms SSmi WWin
§ 'Snowmass' — Last listed 1997
*uliginosa* — CFee CHan CMHG EDAr EWes GCrs GGar GTou LBee MDHE MTho NTow

**FERRARIA** (Iridaceae)
§ *crispa* — LBow
*uncinata* — Last listed 1998
*undulata* — See *F. crispa*

**FERREYRANTHUS** (Asteraceae)
*excelsus* — Last listed 1998

**FERULA** (Apiaceae)
*assa-foetida* — CArn EBee MSal
*chiliantha* — See *F. communis* subsp. *glauca*
§ *communis* — CArn CHad CRDP CSpe ECha EOas EPla IHdy LEdu LGre LHol NBid NChi NLar NSti SMad SMrm WCot WHal
- 'Gigantea' — See *F. communis*
§ - subsp. *glauca* — CMil EBee NSti SDix SIgm WCot
'Giant Bronze' — See *Foeniculum vulgare* 'Giant Bronze'
*tingitana* — SIgm
* - 'Cedric Morris' — EBee ECha SIgm

**FESTUCA** (Poaceae)
*alpina* — Last listed 1997
*amethystina* — CBrm CCuc EBee EHoe EMon EPPr EPla EPot ESis GBin GBri MBri MBro MCLN MNrw MWhi NHol NOak NPla NVic SBea WPer
- 'Aprilgrün' — EHoe
- 'Bronzeglanz' — Last listed 1997
*ampla* — Last listed 1997
*arundinacea* — CKin
*californica* — Last listed 1997
*curvula* subsp. *crassifolia* — EBee EPPr EPla NHol
*dalmatica* — Last listed 1997
*dumetorum* — Last listed 1997
*elatior* 'Demeter' — Last listed 1997
*elegans* — EPPr
*erecta* — EHoe EPPr EPla
*eskia* — CCuc EBee EHoe EPPr EPla GAri GBin GOrn MWhi NEgg NHol SPer WCot WPer
*extremiorientalis* — Last listed 1997
*filiformis* — EHoe EMon EPPr LRHS
§ *gautieri* — ELan EMon EPPr GBin LHil MBar MBrN MMoz NOrc SCob SPer WFoF
- 'Pic Carlit' — EMon
*gigantea* — CKin GBin LRot
*glacialis* — EHoe MBal MDHE NHol
- 'Czakor' — Last listed 1997
*glauca* — More than 30 suppliers
I - 'Auslese' — MAvo SGre
- 'Azurit' — EHoe EMon EPPr EPla EWes LRHS NHol SCob
§ - 'Blaufuchs' ♀ — CLTr CM&M CSam CWSG EBee EBrP EBre ECot EHoe EPPr EPla EPot ESis EWes GBin GOrn IOrc LBre LHop MAvo MMoz MSte NHol SBre SCob WWat

| | |
|---|---|
| § - 'Blauglut' | EBee EBrP EBre EGar EHoe EOrc EPla GAri LBre MWgw NFla NHar NHol NMir NRoo SBre SCob WGer WLRN |
| - Blue Fox | See *F. glauca* 'Blaufuchs' |
| - Blue Glow | See *F. glauca* 'Blauglut' |
| - 'Elijah Blue' | More than 30 suppliers |
| - 'Golden Toupee' | More than 30 suppliers |
| - 'Harz' | CCuc EBee EBrP EBre EGar EHoe EMil EMon EPla IBlr LBre MBar SBre SCob |
| § - 'Meerblau' | CCuc |
| * - *minima* | CVer ESis |
| - 'Pallens' | See *F. longifolia* |
| - Sea Blue | See *F. glauca* 'Meerblau' |
| - Sea Urchin | See *F. glauca* 'Seeigel' |
| § - 'Seeigel' | CBrm CCuc EBee EBrP EBre EGar EGle EHoe EPPr EPla LBre LHil MAvo MBel MBri NPro SBre SCob |
| - 'Seven Seas' | See *F. valesiaca* 'Silbersee' |
| - 'Silberreiher' | EBee EPPr |
| *heterophylla* | Last listed 1997 |
| * *bogar* | EHoe |
| ¶ *idaboebsis* | EPPr |
| *juncifolia* | Last listed 1997 |
| § *longifolia* | CKin |
| *mairei* | CCuc CLTr EHoe EMon EPPr IBlr |
| *novae-zelandiae* | GBin |
| *ovina* | CBrm EBee EHoe NOrc SPla WPer |
| - subsp. *coxii* | EHoe |
| I - 'Kulturform' | EBee SGre |
| - 'Söhrewald' | EPPr EPla |
| * - 'Tetra Gold' | Last listed 1998 |
| *paniculata* | EHoe EMon EPla GOrn LRHS |
| *pulchella* | EBee |
| *punctoria* | CCuc CMea EBee ECha EHoe EPPr EWes MRav NHar SDys SIng SSmi |
| *rubra* 'Jughandles' | Last listed 1998 |
| - var. *nankotaizanensis* B&SWJ 3190 | WCru |
| - 'Variegata' | Last listed 1998 |
| - var. *viridis* | NHol |
| *sclerophylla* | Last listed 1997 |
| *scoparia* | See *F. gautieri* |
| sp. B&SWJ 1555 | Last listed 1998 |
| *tenuifolia* | CKin |
| *valesiaca* | GOrn |
| - var. *glaucantha* | EPPr LRHS MBri |
| § - 'Silbersee' | CCuc CInt CSam ECha EFou EHoe EPPr EPla IBlr MBar MBri MNrw MSte NBee NCat NHol NOak SCob SIng SRms WFar |
| - Silver Sea | See *F. valesiaca* 'Silbersee' |
| *vivipara* | CCuc CInt EGoo EHoe EMon EPPr LEdu NHol SUsu |
| * 'Willow Green' | CBlo CMGP MSte SCob |

## FIBIGIA (Brassicaceae)

| | |
|---|---|
| § *clypeata* | WEas |

## FICUS ✿ (Moraceae)

| | |
|---|---|
| *australis* hort. | See *F. rubiginosa* 'Australis' |
| *benghalensis* | MBri |
| *benjamina* ♀ | CHal EBrP EBre LBre MBri SBre SRms |
| - 'Exotica' | MBri |
| - 'Flandriana' | Last listed 1996 |
| - 'Golden King' | MBri |
| - 'Golden Princess' | Last listed 1996 |
| - 'Green Gem' | Last listed 1996 |
| - var. *nuda* | MBri |
| - 'Starlight' (v) | MBri |
| I *binnendijkii* 'Alii' | CHal |
| *carica* (F) | GAri LPan MBri SArc |
| - 'Adam' (F) | ERea |
| - 'Alma' (F) | ERea |
| - 'Angélique' (F) | ERea |
| - 'Beall' (F) | ERea |
| - 'Bellone' (F) | ERea |
| - 'Bifère' (F) | ERea |
| - 'Black Ischia' (F) | ERea |
| - 'Black Mission' (F) | ERea |
| - 'Boule d'Or' (F) | ERea |
| - 'Bourjassotte Grise' (F) | ERea SDea |
| ¶ - 'Breva' | CGOG |
| - 'Brown Turkey' (F) ♀ | More than 30 suppliers |
| - 'Brunswick' (F) | CGre EBee ERea GBon GTwe WCot |
| - 'Castle Kennedy' (F) | ERea GTwe |
| - 'Col de Dame' (F) | ERea |
| - 'Conandria' (F) | ERea |
| - 'Figue d'Or' (F) | ERea |
| - 'Goutte d'Or' (F) | ERea |
| - 'Grise de Saint Jean' (F) | ERea |
| - 'Grise Ronde' (F) | ERea |
| - 'Grosse Grise' (F) | ERea |
| - 'Kaape Bruin' (F) | ERea |
| - 'Kadota' (F) | ERea |
| - 'Lisa' (F) | ERea |
| - 'Longue d'Août' (F) | ERea |
| - 'Malcolm's Giant' (F) | ERea |
| - 'Malta' (F) | ERea |
| - 'Marseillaise' (F) | ERea GTwe SDea |
| - 'Negro Largo' (F) | ERea |
| - 'Noir de Provence' | See *F. carica* 'Reculver' |
| - 'Osborn's Prolific' (F) | ERea |
| - 'Palmata' | SMad |
| - 'Panachée' (F) | ERea |
| - 'Pastilière' (F) | ERea |
| - 'Petite Grise' (F) | ERea |
| - 'Pied de Boeuf' (F) | ERea |
| - 'Pittaluse' (F) | ERea |
| - 'Précoce Ronde de Bordeaux' (F) | ERea |
| § - 'Reculver' (F) | ERea |
| - 'Rouge de Bordeaux' (F) | ERea SDea |
| - 'Saint Johns' (F) | ERea |
| - 'San Pedro Miro' (F) | ERea |
| - 'Sollies Pont' (F) | ERea |
| - 'Sugar 12' (F) | ERea |
| - 'Sultane' (F) | ERea |
| - 'Tena' (F) | ERea |
| - 'Verte d'Argenteuil' (F) | ERea |
| - 'Violette Dauphine' (F) | ERea |
| - 'Violette de Sollies' (F) | ERea |
| - 'Violette Sepor' (F) | ERea |
| - 'White Genoa' | See *F. carica* 'White Marseilles' |
| - 'White Ischia' (F) | ERea |
| § - 'White Marseilles' (F) | CCHP ERea SDea |
| *cyathistipula* | MBri |
| *deltoidea* var. *diversifolia* | MBri |
| ¶ *elastica* | SEND |
| - 'Robusta' | MBri |
| - 'Schrijveriana' (v) ♀ | Last listed 1991 |
| - 'Zulu Shield' | Last listed 1996 |
| *foveolata* Wallich | See *F. sarmentosa* |
| *lyrata* ♀ | MBri |
| *microcarpa* | STre |
| - 'Hawaii' (v) | CHal MBri |
| *natalensis* subsp. *leprieurii* 'Westland' | MBri |
| *palmata* | Last listed 1996 |
| *pumila* ♀ | CB&S CHal EBak MBri SAPC SArc |

| | |
|---|---|
| - 'Minima' | CFee |
| - 'Sonny' (v) | CHal MBri |
| - 'Variegata' | CHal MBri WCot |
| ♦ *radicans* 'Variegata' | See *F. sagittata* 'Variegata' |
| *rubiginosa* ♀ | Last listed 1994 |
| § - 'Australis' | MBri |
| § *sagittata* 'Variegata' | MBri |
| § *sarmentosa* | MBri |
| *triangularis* | See *F. natalensis* subsp. *leprieurii* |

## FILIPENDULA ✿ (Rosaceae)

| | |
|---|---|
| *alnifolia* 'Variegata' | See *F. ulmaria* 'Variegata' |
| *camtschatica* | CRow ECoo ELan NDea NLar NMir SMac WCot |
| - *rosea* | IBlr LHop NBrk SMad |
| ♦ *digitata* 'Nana' | See *F. multijuga* |
| *hexapetala* | See *F. vulgaris* |
| - 'Flore Pleno' | See *F. vulgaris* 'Multiplex' |
| 'Kahome' | CHan CMCo CPlt CRow GBuc GCHN GMaP MBro NHol NLar NMir NOrc NRoo NSti NTow SMrm SPer WCot WFar WHil |
| *kiraishiensis* B&SWJ 1571 | WCru |
| § *multijuga* | CRow ECha GCal MBal MBro MCli SAsh WFar WHoo WPyg |
| *palmata* | ECha EFou MCli WFar |
| - 'Alba' | GCal |
| ♦ - 'Digitata Nana' | See *F. multijuga* |
| ¶ - dwarf form | CLAP |
| ♦ - 'Elegantissima' | See *F. purpurea* 'Elegans' |
| ♦ - 'Nana' | See *F. multijuga* |
| - *purpurea* | See *F. purpurea* |
| - 'Rosea' | CGle IBlr NBir NCat WCHb |
| - 'Rubra' | CBlo MRav NGdn |
| - *rufinervis* B&SWJ 941 | WCru |
| § *purpurea* ♀ | CMea CRow ECha EFou EGar GGar MBel MTis NFla SSoC WCru WEas WFar |
| - f. *albiflora* | CBre GAbr LGre MUlv NDov |
| § - 'Elegans' | CHea CRow EBee ECha EMil GCal GGar NArg NCat NFai NFla SAsh SCob WHil |
| ¶ - 'Plena' | NLar |
| 'Queen of the Prairies' | See *F. rubra* |
| § *rubra* | CBlo CHan CRow EAst LSyl NWoo WWat |
| § - 'Venusta' ♀ | More than 30 suppliers |
| - 'Venusta Magnifica' | See *F. rubra* 'Venusta' |
| § *ulmaria* | CArn CKin EBee ECoo EHon ELau EWFC EWTr GMaP GPoy LHol MChe MHew MMal MTho NHol NLan NMir SIde SWat WCla WOak WPer WShi WWye |
| - 'Aurea' | More than 30 suppliers |
| - 'Flore Pleno' (d) | CBre CMil CRDP CRow EAst EHon MBel MCli NFai NHol NSti SPer SWat WCot WLRN |
| - 'Rosea' | CRDP IBlr SPer |
| § - 'Variegata' | More than 30 suppliers |
| § *vulgaris* | CArn CFee CKin EAst EBee ECtt EWFC LHol LPBA MChe MHew MSal MWgw NArg NBro NLan NMir NOrc SIde SUsu WBea WByw WCla WPer WWye |
| - 'Grandiflora' | MUlv NCat WCot |
| § - 'Multiplex' (d) | CGle CRow CSpe EBee ECha ELan EOrc GAbr LHop MBal MCLN MRav MTho NDea NFla NHol NSti SEas SLon SPer SRms WCot WEas WFar WLin WRus WWat WWye |
| - 'Plena' | See *F. vulgaris* 'Multiplex' |

## FINGERHUTHIA (Poaceae)

| | |
|---|---|
| *sesleriiformis* S&SH 1 | CHan CInt |

## FIRMIANA (Sterculiaceae)

| | |
|---|---|
| *simplex* | CFil IDee LPan |

## FITTONIA (Acanthaceae)

| | |
|---|---|
| *albivenis* Argyroneura Group ♀ | Last listed 1996 |
| - Verschaffeltii Group | Last listed 1996 |

## FITZROYA (Cupressaceae)

| | |
|---|---|
| *cupressoides* | CMac GAri IOrc LCon MBal MBar SLim SLon WCwm |

## FOENICULUM (Apiaceae)

| | |
|---|---|
| *vulgare* | CArn CHad EBot ECha EEls ELan ELau GBar GMaP GPoy LHol MChe MHew MMal MSal NRoo SIde SPlb SRCN WByw WCer WOak WPer WSel WWye |
| - 'Bronze' | See *F. vulgare* 'Purpureum' |
| - var. *dulce* | CSev SIde WGwG |
| § - 'Giant Bronze' | CGle ELan SPer WHen |
| § - 'Purpureum' | More than 30 suppliers |
| - 'Smokey' | EFou IIve MRav WOve |

## FOKIENIA (Cupressaceae)

| | |
|---|---|
| *hodginsii* | Last listed 1997 |

## FONTANESIA (Oleaceae)

| | |
|---|---|
| *phillyreoides* | Last listed 1998 |

## FONTINALIS (Sphagnaceae)

| | |
|---|---|
| *antipyretica* | EMFW SAWi |

## FORESTIERA (Oleaceae)

| | |
|---|---|
| ♦ *neomexicana* | See *F. pubescens* |
| § *pubescens* | CB&S CFil |

## FORSYTHIA (Oleaceae)

| | |
|---|---|
| 'Arnold Dwarf' | CBlo SEas SRms |
| N 'Beatrix Farrand' | CTri EBee ECtt MGos MPla MWat NFor SEas SPer SRms WLRN WMoo |
| § Boucle d'Or = 'Courtacour' | COtt ENot |
| ♦ 'Courtasol' | See *F. Marée d'Or* = 'Courtasol' |
| 'Fiesta' (v) | CPMA CPle EAst EBee EBrP EBre ELan ENot IOrc LBre MAsh MBar MBel MBri MGos MPla MRav MTis NHol NLon NPro SBre SLod SPer SSta WCot WHer |
| *giraldiana* | CPle SRms WBcn WBod WSPU |
| 'Gold Cluster' | See *F. Melée d'Or* |
| 'Gold Splash' | Last listed 1998 |
| 'Gold Tide' | See *F. Marée d'Or* = 'Courtasol' |
| ¶ 'Golden Bells' | MBri |
| 'Golden Curls' | See *F. Boucle d'Or* = 'Courtacour' |
| 'Golden Nugget' | CBlo EBrP EBre EHic ELan EPfP ESis GRei IOrc LBre MAsh SBre SLon SPer WCFE WWeb |
| 'Golden Times' (v) | CBlo EHic EHoe EPla EWes IOrc MAsh MBri MGos NPro SApp SCoo SEas SMad SPla SSto WBcn WCot |
| ¶ x *intermedia* | SRPl |
| - 'Arnold Giant' | CBlo MBlu SPan WBod |
| - 'Densiflora' | NWea |
| ¶ - Goldzauber | MBri |
| * - 'Karl Sax' | CChe NOla NWea SBid WLRN |
| * - 'Liliane' | EMil |

| | |
|---|---|
| - 'Lynwood' ♀ | CB&S CBlo CChe CDoC EBee ELan ENot GRei ISea MBal MBar MBri MGos NBee NFla NFor NRoo NWea SLon SPer SRPl SReu SSta WBod WDin WFar WWeb |
| - 'Lynwood' LA '79 | EHic MLan SPla |
| - 'Minigold' | ECtt GEil MAsh MGos MWat SEas SRms WPyg WRHF WStl WWeb |
| - 'Spectabilis' | CBlo ELan EWTr IOrc LBuc MBar NBee NFla NWea SPer WDin WRHF WTro WWal |
| - 'Spectabilis Variegated' | CPle EHic EPla MBNS MPla NPro SPan SRPl WCot WPyg WWeb |
| - 'Spring Glory' | EBee ECtt ENot MBri |
| - 'Variegata' | CBlo NSti NWea SPer SSta |
| - Week-End ♀ | CBar CBlo ENot GAri MBri MGos |
| § Marée d'Or = 'Courtasol' | COtt ENot MBri MGos MRav SPer WLRN |
| § Melée d'Or | ENot SPer |
| * 'Melissa' | NWea |
| 'Northern Gold' | CB&S EPfP |
| *ovata* | EPla |
| - forms | Last listed 1997 |
| - 'Tetragold' | CB&S CBlo MBal MBar NFla NWea |
| 'Paulina' | CBlo ESis GAri |
| * *pumila* | EWes |
| * 'Spring Beauty' | MAsh |
| *suspensa* ♀ | CB&S CTri ENot EOHP EPfP IIve IOrc MBar MSal MWat NWea SEas SLon SPer WStl |
| - f. *atrocaulis* | CPle GAri NWea |
| - 'Cynthia Barber' (v) | Last listed 1997 |
| - 'Decipiens' | WBod |
| - var. *fortunei* | WWal |
| ¶ - 'Hewitt's Gold' | EMon |
| - 'Nymans' | EPfP MBri MRav NSti SBid SLPl SMad |
| § - 'Taff's Arnold' (v) | CBlo CMil CPMA MBri WBcn WSPU |
| - 'Variegata' | See *F. suspensa* 'Taff's Arnold' |
| 'Tremonia' | EBee EHal EWTr MBal |
| *viridissima* | NFor |
| - 'Bronxensis' | EHyt ELan EPar EPot ESis MPla NBir NNrd SMad WPyg |
| - var. *koreana* | EPla |
| * - - 'Variegata' | CPMA SBid |
| - 'Weber's Bronx' | MBar |

## FORTUNELLA (Rutaceae)

| | |
|---|---|
| x *crassifolia* (F) | SCit |
| x - 'Meiwa' (F) | CAgr ERea |
| 'Fukushu' (F) | ECon ERea SCit |
| *hindsii* (F) | SCit |
| § *japonica* (F) | LHol SArc SCit |
| § *margarita* (F) | CGOG LPan MBri SCit |
| - 'Nagami' (F) | CAgr ECon ERea |

## FOTHERGILLA (Hamamelidaceae)

| | |
|---|---|
| *gardenii* | CB&S CPMA EBrP EBre ELan EPfP IOrc LBre MAsh MBlu MBri SBre SPer SSpi SSta WDin WWat |
| - 'Blue Mist' | CAbP CDoC CPMA CSam ELan GChr IOrc MAsh MBri MGos NHed SBrw SPer SReu SSpi SSta WWat |
| 'Huntsman' | CAbP SSta WWat |
| *major* ♀ | CB&S CPMA EBee EBrP EBre ECtt ELan EWTr GChr LBre MAsh MBal MBri MGos NBee NFla NHol SBre SBrw SPer SReu SSpi WDin WHar WNor WPat WStl WWat |

| | |
|---|---|
| - Monticola Group | CDoC CPMA ELan ENot IMGH MBal MBar MBri MPla NHed NPal SBrw SChu SPer SSpi SSta WBod WBrE WHar WSHC |
| ¶ 'Mount Airy' | CDoC SBrw |

## FRAGARIA ✿ (Rosaceae)

| | |
|---|---|
| *alpina* | See *F. vesca* 'Semperflorens' |
| - 'Alba' | See *F. vesca* 'Semperflorens Alba' |
| ¶ x *ananassa* (F) | NRog |
| - 'Aromel' (F) ♀ | CWSG GTwe MBri SDea WWeb |
| - 'Auchincruive Climax' (F) | EMui |
| - 'Bogota' (F) | GTwe LRHS NBee |
| * - 'Bolero' | EMui GTwe |
| - 'Bounty' (F) | Last listed 1997 |
| - 'Calypso' (F) | CSut EMui GTwe |
| - 'Cambridge Favourite' (F) ♀ | CMac CWSG EMui GRei GTwe MBri NRog SDea WWeb |
| - 'Cambridge Late Pine' (F) | CWSG EMui GTwe |
| - 'Cambridge Sentry' (F) | EMui |
| - 'Cambridge Vigour' (F) | GTwe NBee NRog SDea |
| - 'Domanil' (F) | Last listed 1996 |
| - 'Elsanta' (F) | CTri CWSG EMui GRei GTwe NRog SDea |
| - 'Elvira' (F) | EMui |
| * - 'Emily' | CSut EMui GTwe |
| - 'Eros' (F) | EMui GTwe NRog |
| - 'Evita' (F) | EMui |
| ¶ - 'Florence' | GTwe |
| - 'Fraise des Bois' | See *F. vesca* |
| - 'Gorella' (F) | WWeb |
| - 'Hapil' (F) ♀ | EMui GTwe LRHS NRog WLRN |
| - 'Honeoye' (F) ♀ | EMui GTwe LRHS |
| - 'Korona' (F) | CSut |
| - 'Kouril' (F) | LRHS |
| * - 'Laura' | EMui GTwe |
| - 'Maraline' (F) | EMui |
| - Marastil (F) | EMui |
| - 'Maxim' (F) | EMui |
| - 'Melody' (F) | Last listed 1998 |
| - 'Ostara' (F) | Last listed 1998 |
| - 'Pandora' (F) | WWeb |
| - 'Pantagruella' (F) | Last listed 1996 |
| - 'Pegasus' (F) ♀ | EMui GTwe LRHS NRog |
| - pink-flowered | CFee |
| - 'Rapella' (F) | GTwe |
| - 'Redgauntlet' (F) | GTwe NRog |
| - 'Rhapsody' (F) ♀ | EMui GTwe |
| - 'Royal Sovereign' (F) | CMac EMui GTwe |
| - 'Serenata' (F) | MHlr NBur NOla |
| - 'Sophie' | CSut GTwe |
| - 'Symphony' (F) ♀ | EMui GRei |
| - 'Talisman' (F) | Last listed 1996 |
| - 'Tamella' (F) | EMui GTwe NRog |
| - 'Tango' (F) | EMui |
| - 'Tenira' (F) | Last listed 1996 |
| - 'Totem' (F) | GTwe |
| § - 'Variegata' (F) | CGle CLTr CMea CSev EBee ELan EPla MCCP MHar MRav NEgg NHol NRoo NSti NTay SCob SIng SPer WBea WOak WRha WRus |
| - 'Viva Rosa' (F) | EMui |
| 'Baron Solemacher' (F) | WHer |
| 'Bowles' Double' | See *F. vesca* 'Multiplex' |
| *chiloensis* (F) | EMon LEdu NDov |
| - 'Chaval' | CHid ECGP ECha EGoo EMon EPPr MRav MWgw NWoo SIng |
| N - 'Variegata' | GCal LBuc MAvo WByw WEas |
| - x *virginiana* | CArn |
| *daltoniana* | NHol SIng |
| - CC&McK 390 | Last listed 1997 |
| - CC&McK 559 | GCHN |

| | |
|---|---|
| *indica* | See *Duchesnea indica* |
| ¶ 'Lipstick' | EBee NDov |
| ¶ *nubicola* | GPoy |
| Pink Panda = 'Frel' (F) | CM&M CTri EBee EBrP EBre ECtt EGra LBre LEdu MAsh MBri MOne NHol NLar NRoo SBre SHFr SIng SPer WByw WEas WElm WLRN WMaN |
| 'Red Ruby' | EBee EBrP EBre ECGP EMar LBre MCAu NLar NRoo SBre SPer |
| * 'Ruby Surprise' | LRHS |
| sp. from Taiwan | WHer |
| 'Variegata' | See *F.* x *ananassa* 'Variegata' |
| § *vesca* (F) | CAgr CArn CKin ECoo EWFC GPoy LHol LSyl MHew NLon NMir SIde SPlb WCla WGwG WJek WOak WPer WShi WWye |
| – 'Alexandra' (F) | CArn CBod ELau GAbr MChe MMal SIde WCHb |
| – 'Flore Pleno' | See *F. vesca* 'Multiplex' |
| – 'Fructu Albo' (F) | CRow WAlt WPer |
| – Mara des Bois (F) | EMui GTwe |
| – 'Monophylla' (F) | CRow EMon NHol SIde WHer |
| § – 'Multiplex' (d) | CGle CJew CRow CSev EMon EMou GAbr MInt MRav NHex NHol NSti SSvw WAlt WCHb WHer WOak WWye |
| § – 'Muricata' | CFee CLTr CPou CRow EMon GAbr LEdu NBrk WAlt WCer WHer WWye |
| * – 'Pineapple Crush' | WHer |
| – 'Plymouth Strawberry' | See *F. vesca* 'Muricata' |
| – 'Rügen' (F) | CHal WGwy WHoo WPyg |
| § – 'Semperflorens' (F) | CLTr ILis MBNS NBrk WAlt WOak |
| § – 'Semperflorens Alba' (F) | WOak |
| N – 'Variegata' | EAst EHoe EPar MCLN MSCN MWgw NMir SMac WPer WSel |

## FRANCOA (Saxifragaceae)

| | |
|---|---|
| *appendiculata* | CGre EMFP EMar ETen GMac LPio MGrG SSca WHer WPic |
| Ballyrogan strain | IBlr |
| 'Confetti' | LFis MTed SOkh WCot |
| * dwarf purple | EBee |
| 'Purple Spike' | See *F. sonchifolia* Rogerson's form |
| § *ramosa* | CGle CHan CSpe CTri EBee GAbr GBri GBuc IBlr LFis MAvo MGed MHlr MNrw NBro NRog NRoo WFar WWeb |
| – *alba* | See *F. ramosa* |
| § *sonchifolia* | More than 30 suppliers |
| – 'Alba' | CRDP CSpe SUsu |
| § – Rogerson's form | CGle CNic CRDP CSpe EMar GBuc IBlr LFis LPio MAvo SDix SOkh WSan |

## FRANKENIA (Frankeniaceae)

| | |
|---|---|
| *laevis* | CHal CTri SRms WWye |
| *thymifolia* | CHal CInt CMHG ELan EPar EPot ESis GCHN MBar MPla MWat NMen NRoo SAga SBod SChu SIng SSmi WFar WPer WPyg WWin |

## FRANKLINIA (Theaceae)

| | |
|---|---|
| ¶ *alatamaha* | EPfP LHyd SLPl WNor |

## FRAXINUS ✿ (Oleaceae)

| | |
|---|---|
| *americana* | CDul CMCN WLRN WPGP |
| – 'Autumn Purple' | CBlo CDul CEnd CTho MAsh MBlu |
| – 'Rose Hill' | CTho |
| § *angustifolia* | CLnd CMCN CTho |

| | |
|---|---|
| – 'Elegantissima' | CTho |
| – 'Flame' | See *F. angustifolia* 'Raywood' |
| – var. *lentiscifolia* | CTho |
| § – 'Monophylla' | CLnd CTho |
| § – 'Raywood' ♀ | CB&S CBlo CDoC CDul CEnd CLnd CTho EBee ECrN ELan ENot GChr IOrc MAsh MBlu MGos NWea SMad SPer WDin WJas WOrn |
| * – 'Variegata' | CBot CPMA |
| ¶ *bungeana* | CMCN |
| *chinensis* | CDul CLnd CMCN CTho |
| – subsp. *rhyncophylla* | Last listed 1998 |
| *elonza* | CTho |
| *excelsior* ♀ | CB&S CBlo CDoC CDul CKin CLnd EBee ECrN ENot GRei LBuc LHyr LPan MBar MGos NBee NWea SPer WDin WMou WOrn WStI |
| – 'Allgold' | CEnd SMad |
| – 'Altena' | Last listed 1996 |
| – 'Atlas' | Last listed 1996 |
| ¶ – 'Aurea Pendula' | CEnd SMad |
| – 'Crispa' | WCom |
| – f. *diversifolia* | CDul CLnd CTho WMou |
| – 'Diversifolia Pendula' | See *F. excelsior* 'Heterophylla Pendula' |
| – 'Geesink' | ENot SLPl |
| § – 'Heterophylla Pendula' | GAri |
| – 'Jaspidea' ♀ | CB&S CBlo CDoC CDul CEnd CLnd COtt CTho EBee ECrN ENot EWTr GChr IOrc MBar MBlu MBri MGos MRav NBea NBee SPer SSpi SSta WDin WJas WOrn WStI |
| – 'Nana' | EMon WPat |
| – 'Pendula' ♀ | CBlo CDoC CDul CEnd CLnd CTho EBee EBrP EBre ELan ENot GChr IMGH IOrc LBre LPan MAsh MBlu MBri NBee NWea SBre SPer WDin WJas WMou WOrn WStI |
| – 'Pendula Wentworthii' | Last listed 1998 |
| – 'R.E. Davey' | CDul CTho |
| – 'Stanway Gold' | Last listed 1997 |
| – 'Stripey' | Last listed 1997 |
| – 'Westhof's Glorie' ♀ | CDoC CDul CLnd EBee ENot EWTr WDin WJas WOrn |
| *holotricha* | CTho |
| *mariesii* | See *F. sieboldiana* |
| *nigra* | CFil CMCN |
| – 'Fallgold' | CBlo CEnd MAsh |
| *oregona* | See *F. latifolia* |
| *ornus* ♀ | CBlo CLnd CTho CTri ECrN ELan ENot EPfP GChr IOrc MBri NBee NWea SPer SSta WDin WFar WTro WWat |
| – 'Arie Peters' | CDul WStI |
| – 'Fastigiata Pyramidalis' | Last listed 1996 |
| ¶ – 'Obelisk' | MBri |
| – Sch 3177 | WHCr |
| *oxycarpa* | See *F. angustifolia* |
| *pennsylvanica* | CDul CLnd CMCN WWes |
| – 'Aucubifolia' | CTho |
| – var. *lanceolata* | See *F. pennsylvanica* var. *subintegerrima* |
| – 'Patmore' | CBlo |
| – 'Summit' | CTho |
| – 'Variegata' | CBlo CLnd CTho EBee EPfP MAsh MBri SSta |
| *quadrangulata* | WDin WWoo |
| § *sieboldiana* | CFil CLnd CPMA MBlu SSpi WCoo |
| *spaethiana* | Last listed 1998 |
| 'Veltheimii' | See *F. angustifolia* 'Monophylla' |

*velutina*  CDul CLnd CMCN CTho SLPl

# FREESIA (Iridaceae)
*alba* Foster  See *F. lactea*
'Ballerina'  Last listed 1996
'Diana'  LAma
double mixed (d)  ETub
*elimensis*  Last listed 1998
'Fantasy' (d)  LAma
hybrids  CSut NRog
§ *lactea*  LAma
'Melanie' (d)  Last listed 1996
'Oberon'  Last listed 1996
'Romany' (d)  LAma
'Royal Blue'  Last listed 1996
'Royal Gold'  Last listed 1996
'White Swan'  LAma
*xanthospila*  LBow

# FREMONTODENDRON (Sterculiaceae)
'California Glory' ♀  More than 30 suppliers
*californicum*  CAbb EBee ELan EMil EWTr IOrc
MBlu MBri MDun MGos MWhi
SOWG SRPl WAbe WBod WDin
WNor WStI WWat WWin
§ - subsp. *decumbens*  SSpi
♦ *decumbens*  See *F. californicum* subsp.
*decumbens*
¶ 'Ken Taylor'  SMad
*mexicanum*  CGre SAga
'Pacific Sunset'  CPMA EBee ENot LHop LRHS
MBri SBid SMur SPer WWeb

# FREYLINIA (Scrophulariaceae)
*cestroides*  See *F. lanceolata*
§ *lanceolata*  CB&S CPle CTre

# FRITILLARIA ✿ (Liliaceae)
*acmopetala* ♀  CAvo CBro ELan EPar EPot ERos
EWal GCrs ITim LAma MBal MS&S
MTho NMen NRog NWCA SUsu
SWas WAbe WLin
- subsp. *wendelboi*  LAma WCot
§ *affinis*  EHyt EWal GCrs LAma MS&S
NHar SBid WLin
§ - var. *gracilis*  CAvo EHyt LAma SBid SPer WLin
- 'Limelight'  EBee EPot GCrs
- 'Sunray'  GCrs NHar
§ - var. *tristulis*  EHyt NMen
- 'Vancouver Island'  EBee EPot
- 'Wayne Roderick'  EPot GCrs
*alburyana*  EPot
*arabica*  See *F. persica*
*armena*  EHyt EPot LAma
*assyriaca*  See *F. uva-vulpis*
*atropurpurea*  Last listed 1998
*aurea*  CLAP EPot GCrs MS&S
¶ - 'Golden Flag'  CMea ETub WWst
*biflora*  CLAP EHyt
- 'Martha Roderick'  CAvo CBro CMea EBrP EBre EPot
ETub EWal LAma LBre MCli NTow
SBid SBla SBre WWst
§ *bithynica*  CBro CLAP EHyt EPot GCrs LAma
MS&S NMen
*brandegeei*  EWal LAma
*bucharica*  CAvo CGra CLAP EHyt EPot
¶ - 'Aman Kutan'  EHyt
*camschatcensis*  CAvo CBro CRDP ECha EFEx
EHyt EPar EPot ETub GCrs LAma
MS&S MTho NDov NHar NMen
NRog SSpi WAbe WLin
* - *alpina aurea*  GCrs

¶ - 'Aurea'  EHyt
- black  Last listed 1998
- f. *flavescens*  EFEx LAma
- from Alaska  GCrs
- *multiflora*  WLin
*carducborum*  See *F. minuta*
*carica*  CAvo EHyt EPot GCrs MS&S
NMen
- subsp. *serpenticola*  EHyt EPot
*caucasica*  CLAP EHyt LAma
'Chatto'  Last listed 1998
*citrina*  See *F. bithynica*
§ *collina*  WWst
*conica*  EHyt EPot GCrs NHar
*crassifolia*  EPot LAma MS&S
- subsp. *crassifolia*  CGra EHyt
§ - subsp. *kurdica*  EHyt EPot GCrs SSpi
*davisii*  CMea EHyt EPot ETub LAma
NHar
*delphinensis*  See *F. tubiformis*
*drenovskyi*  CLAP EPot
*eastwoodiae*  EPot GCrs LAma WLin
*ehrhartii*  EHyt EPot SBla
*elwesii*  CAvo EHyt
*epirotica*  Last listed 1996
¶ *fleischeriana*  WWst
*forbesii*  GCrs
¶ *gentneri*  EHyt
*glauca*  LAma
- 'Goldilocks'  CAvo CMea EPot ETub
*graeca*  EPot MTho
- subsp. *graeca*  Last listed 1998
- subsp. *ionica*  See *F. graeca* subsp. *thessala*
§ - subsp. *thessala*  EHyt MS&S MTho WLin
§ *grayana*  EHyt EPot MS&S
- tall form  CLAP
*gussichiae*  CLAP MS&S
*hermonis* subsp. *amana*  CAvo EBee EHyt EPot LAma
NMen SBid
*hispanica*  See *F. lusitanica*
*hupehensis*  EPot GCrs LAma
*imperialis*  CAvo CB&S EBot ECGP EWTr
MBal MBri NRog
- 'Aureomarginata'  EBee EPar LAma LBow LEdu MBri
NRog WCot WHil
- 'Aurora'  CAvo EBee EBrP EBre EMon EPar
ETub EWTr LAma LBow LBre LFis
MBNS MCli MWat NCut NRog
SBre
- 'Crown upon Crown'  See *F. imperialis* 'Prolifera'
- 'Lutea'  CHar CMGP CMea EBot EMon
EWTr MAvo SUsu
- 'Lutea Maxima'  See *F. imperialis* 'Maxima Lutea'
- 'Maxima'  See *F. imperialis* 'Rubra Maxima'
§ - 'Maxima Lutea' ♀  CBro EBrP EBre ELan EPar EPfP
ETub LAma LBow LBre LFis MCli
MLLN NRog SBre
§ - 'Prolifera'  EBot EPar LAma LBow MLLN
- 'Rubra'  CMGP ELan EPar ETub LAma
LBow MAvo MCli NBir NCut
NRog
§ - 'Rubra Maxima'  CBro CHar EBot EMon EPfP EPot
EWTr LAma MLLN SUsu
- 'Sulpherino'  EMon LRHS
- 'The Premier'  EMon EPar LAma
*involucrata*  CAvo CBro EHyt GCrs LAma
MS&S
*ionica*  See *F. graeca* subsp. *thessala*
*japonica* var. *koidzumiana*  EFEx
*karadaghensis*  See *F. crassifolia* subsp. *kurdica*
I *karelinii*  WWst
¶ *kotschyana*  WWst

| | |
|---|---|
| ◆ *lanceolata* | See *F. affinis* var. *tristulis* |
| *latakiensis* | Last listed 1997 |
| § *latifolia* | EPot GCrs LAma |
| - var. *nobilis* | See *F. latifolia* |
| *liliacea* | LAma |
| § *lusitanica* | CLAP GCrs LAma MS&S WLin |
| - MS 440 | Last listed 1998 |
| *lutea* | See *F. collina* |
| *macrocarpa* SB&L 258 | Last listed 1998 |
| *meleagris* ♀ | More than 30 suppliers |
| - 'Aphrodite' | CAvo EPot WCot |
| - 'Jupiter' | LRHS |
| - 'Mars' | LRHS |
| - var. *unicolor* | CBro EBee ELan EPot ETub LAma |
| subvar. *alba* ♀ | LBow MBri MBro MS&S NHar |
| | NRya SUsu WCru WShi |
| § *messanensis* | EHyt GCrs LAma MBal MS&S |
| ¶ - from Ólimbos, Greece | WLin |
| - subsp. *gracilis* | EHyt GCrs MBal MS&S |
| - subsp. *messanensis* | CBro |
| *michailovskyi* ♀ | CAvo CBro EBee ELan EPar EPot |
| | ETub EWal GBuc GCrs LAma MBri |
| | MNrw MTho NMen NRog SSoC |
| | WAbe WCla WHil WHoo WPyg |
| | WSel |
| *micrantha* | LAma |
| *minima* | Last listed 1998 |
| - JCA 500.100 | Last listed 1998 |
| § *minuta* | EHyt EPot GCrs MS&S |
| *montana* | EHyt GCrs LRHS MS&S NMen |
| *nigra* hort. | See *F. pyrenaica* |
| *obliqua* | EHyt EPot GCrs |
| *olivieri* | CLAP EHyt GCrs |
| § *orientalis* | WWst |
| *pallidiflora* ♀ | CAvo CBro CLAP EHyt EMon EPar |
| | EPot ERos ETub EWal GMaP LAma |
| | MBal MLLN MS&S MTho NHar |
| | NMen NSla SPer SSpi WAbe WBea |
| | WCru WLin |
| § *persica* | CB&S CHar CMdw EBee EBot |
| | EPar EPot EWTr LAma MBNS MBri |
| | MCli SBid WSel |
| - 'Adiyaman' ♀ | CAvo CBro EBee EBrP EBre EHyt |
| | ELan EMon ETub EWTr LBow |
| | LBre LFis NRog SBre |
| - S&L 118 | Last listed 1998 |
| *phaeanthera* | See *F. affinis* var. *gracilis* |
| *pinardii* | EPot |
| *pluriflora* | EPot |
| ¶ - JA 94109 | EHyt |
| *pontica* | CAvo CBro CLAP CMea EBee |
| | EHyt EPar EPot ERos EWal GMaP |
| | ITim LAma MBal MCli MLLN |
| | MS&S MTho NChi NMen NSla |
| | SBid SBla SIng SSpi WCru WLin |
| *pudica* | CMea EBee EHyt ETub GCrs |
| | LAma MS&S MTho NHar WLin |
| * - 'Fragrant' | EPot GCrs NOla |
| - 'Richard Britten' | EHyt GCrs |
| *puqiensis* | LAma |
| *purdyi* | CAvo CLAP EHyt EPot GCrs MS&S |
| | NMen SPer |
| § *pyrenaica* ♀ | CBro CLAP EHyt GCrs LAma MBal |
| | MS&S NHar NMen NSla SChu |
| | SIng SSpi |
| *raddeana* | CLAP LAma MS&S |
| *recurva* | Last listed 1998 |
| - 'Sensational' | LAma |
| *rhodocanakis* | EHyt EPot |
| ¶ - subsp. *argolica* | WWst |
| - JCA 502.600 | Last listed 1998 |
| *roderickii* | See *F. grayana* |

| | |
|---|---|
| *roylei* | MS&S |
| *rubra major* | See *F. imperialis* 'Rubra Maxima' |
| *ruthenica* | EHyt ERos MS&S NMen |
| *sewerzowii* | EHyt EPot LAma WLin |
| *sibthorpiana* | CBro EPot GCrs LAma |
| *spetsiotica* | EHyt |
| *sphaciotica* | See *F. messanensis* |
| *stenanthera* | EPot GCrs LAma |
| *striata* | Last listed 1998 |
| ¶ *stribrnyi* | WWst |
| *tenella* | See *F. orientalis* |
| *thunbergii* | EBee EHyt EPar EPot NMen SBid |
| § *tubiformis* | GCrs WLin |
| *tuntasia* | GCrs |
| *usuriensis* | LAma |
| § *uva-vulpis* | CAvo CBro CMea EBee EHyt ELan |
| | EPar EPot ETub EWal GMaP ITim |
| | LAma LEdu MNrw MTho NWCA |
| | SSpi WAbe WCru WLin |
| *verticillata* | CAvo CBro ECha EPar EPot GCrs |
| | LAma MTho NHar SSpi WCru |
| *whittallii* | EHyt EPot MS&S |
| *zagrica* | Last listed 1998 |

## FUCHSIA ✿ (Onagraceae)

| | |
|---|---|
| 'A.M. Larwick' | CSil EBak |
| 'A.W. Taylor' | EBak |
| 'Aalt Groothuis' | EGou |
| 'Abbé Farges' | CLoc CSil EBak ECtt EKMF EPts |
| | LCla LFli MAsk MWhe NArc SKen |
| | SLBF |
| ¶ 'Abbey Hill' | MWar |
| 'Abbey Kilner' | Last listed 1996 |
| 'Abbigayle Reine' | NArc |
| 'Abigail' | EGou EKMF |
| 'Achievement' ♀ | CLoc CSil LCla MAsk MJac NArc |
| | SKen |
| 'Achilles' | Last listed 1996 |
| 'Ada Perry' | ECtt NArc |
| 'Adagio' | CLoc |
| 'Ada's Love' | EKMF MAld |
| 'Adinda' | EGou |
| 'Admiration' | CPor CSil |
| 'Adrian Young' | MAsk |
| 'Ailsa Garnett' | EBak |
| 'Aintree' | CSil NArc |
| 'Airedale' | CPor MAsk MJac NArc |
| 'Ajax' | Last listed 1998 |
| 'Alabama Improved' | MAsk SKen |
| 'Aladna' | Last listed 1998 |
| 'Aladna's Rosy' | Last listed 1996 |
| 'Aladna's Sanders' | NArc |
| 'Alan Ayckbourn' | CSil MWar NArc |
| 'Alan Stilwell' | Last listed 1998 |
| ¶ 'Alan Titchmarsh' | SLBF |
| 'Alaska' | CLoc EBak EKMF NArc WGwG |
| 'Albert H' | Last listed 1996 |
| 'Albertus Schwab' | LCla |
| 'Alde' | CSil EGou NArc |
| 'Alf Thornley' | CSil EKMF LFli MAsk MWhe NArc |
| 'Alfie' | CSil |
| 'Alfred Rambaud' | CSil NArc |
| 'Algerine' | SLBF |
| 'Alice Ashton' | EBak EKMF NArc |
| 'Alice Doran' | LCla SLBF |
| 'Alice Hoffman' | CDoC CLoc CPor CSil EBak EBee |
| | EGou EKMF EPts LCla LFli LVER |
| | MAld MAsk MBar MBri MGos |
| | MJac MWat MWhe NArc SKen |
| | SPer SSea WGwG |
| 'Alice Mary' | EBak EKMF EMan |
| 'Alice Rowell' | EKMF |

| | |
|---|---|
| 'Alice Stringer' | ECtt |
| 'Alice Sweetapple' | Last listed 1996 |
| 'Alice Travis' | EBak |
| 'Alipatti' | EKMF |
| 'Alison Ewart' | CLoc CSil EBak EKMF MAsk MJac MWhe NArc |
| 'Alison June' | MBri |
| 'Alison Patricia' | CSil EBak EKMF EMan LCla MAld MWar MWhe SLBF |
| 'Alison Reynolds' | LCla MBri NArc |
| 'Alison Ryle' | CSil EBak |
| 'Alison Sweetman' | CSil EKMF MJac MWhe SKen |
| 'Allure' | Last listed 1998 |
| 'Alma Hulscher' | Last listed 1998 |
| 'Alma Muir' | Last listed 1997 |
| § *alpestris* | CDoC EBak EGou EKMF LCla |
| 'Altmark' | Last listed 1996 |
| 'Alton Water' | EGou EKMF |
| 'Alwin' | CSil MWhe NArc |
| 'Alyce Larson' | CSil EBak LFli MAsk MJac NArc WGwG |
| 'Amanda Bridgland' | EKMF |
| 'Amanda Jones' | EKMF MAsk MWhe NArc |
| 'Ambassador' | EBak MAsk SKen |
| 'Amelie Aubin' | CLoc EBak EKMF NArc |
| 'America' | EBak NArc |
| 'American Dream' | NArc |
| 'American Flaming Glory' | CSil NArc |
| 'American Spirit' | Last listed 1996 |
| 'Amethyst Fire' | CSil |
| 'Amigo' | EBak NArc |
| § *ampliata* | EGou EKMF LCla |
| 'Amy Lye' | CLoc CSil EBak EKMF MAsk NArc SKen |
| § 'Andenken an Heinrich Henkel' | CDoC CLoc EBak EKMF LCla LFli MAsk MWhe |
| 'André Le Nostre' | EBak NArc |
| *andrei* | EGou EKMF LCla |
| 'Andrew' | EBak EKMF MAsk NArc |
| 'Andrew Carnegie' | CLoc |
| 'Andrew George' | MJac |
| 'Andrew Hadfield' | CSil EKMF MAsk MWar NArc SLBF |
| 'Andrew Ryle' | NArc |
| 'Angela Leslie' | CLoc EBak EKMF NArc |
| 'Angela Rippon' | MJac MWhe NArc |
| 'Angelina' | EKMF |
| 'Angel's Dream' | CSil MAsk |
| 'Angel's Flight' | EBak |
| 'Anita' | CSil EKMF EPts LCla MAld MAsk MWhe NArc SLBF SYvo |
| 'Anj' | Last listed 1997 |
| 'Anjo' (v) | EGou EKMF MAsk NArc SLBF SSea |
| 'Ann Adams' | CSil MJac |
| 'Ann Howard Tripp' | CLoc CSil LFli MAsk MBri MJac MWhe NArc |
| 'Ann Lee' | EBak |
| 'Ann Roots' | EGou |
| 'Anna Douling' | Last listed 1997 |
| 'Anna of Longleat' | CLoc EBak EMan LFli NArc SKen SLBF |
| 'Annabel' ♀ | CDoC CGre CLoc CPor CSil EBak EKMF EMan EPts LCla LFli LVER MAld MAsk MBri MJac MWar MWhe NArc NFai SKen SLBF SSea WGwG WWol |
| ¶ 'Annabelle Stubbs' | MAsk |
| ¶ 'Anne Strudwick' | EGou |
| 'Annie Earle' | EKMF |
| 'Annie Johnson' | Last listed 1996 |
| 'Anthea Day' | CLoc |

| | |
|---|---|
| 'Anthonetta' | Last listed 1997 |
| 'Antigone' | SLBF |
| ¶ 'Antonella Merrills' | EKMF |
| 'Aphrodite' | CLoc EBak NArc |
| 'Applause' | CLoc CSil EBak EKMF EMan EPts LVER MAld MAsk MJac NArc |
| 'Apple Blossom' | EKMF |
| *aprica* hort. | See *F.* x *bacillaris* |
| – Lundell | See *F. microphylla* subsp. *aprica* |
| 'Aquarius' | MWhe |
| ¶ 'Arabella' | CSil MWhe |
| 'Arabella Improved' | EKMF |
| *arborea* | See *F. arborescens* |
| § *arborescens* | CDoC CLoc CSil EBak ECre EGou EKMF ERea LCla MAsk NArc SLBF SMrm SYvo WGwG |
| 'Arcadia' | MWar |
| 'Arcadia Aubergine' | NArc |
| 'Arcadia Gold' | ECtt LFli MWhe NArc WGwG |
| 'Arcadia Lady' | MAsk MJac NArc |
| 'Arcady' | CLoc |
| 'Archie Owen' | Last listed 1998 |
| 'Arel's Avondzon' | NArc |
| 'Ariel' | CSil NArc |
| 'Army Nurse' ♀ | CDoC CLoc CPor CSil EKMF GCHN LFli LVER MAsk MWhe NArc SLBF |
| 'Art Deco' | NArc |
| 'Ashley Jane' | MAld |
| 'Ashmore' | NArc |
| 'Ashwell' | Last listed 1996 |
| 'Athela' | EBak |
| 'Atlantic Crossing' | Last listed 1997 |
| 'Atlantic Star' | EKMF MBri MJac NArc WGwG |
| 'Atlantis' | MAsk MJac NArc |
| 'Atomic Glow' | EBak NArc |
| 'Aubergine' | CLoc SLBF SSea |
| 'Audray' | LFli MAsk NArc |
| 'Audrey Booth' | EGou |
| 'Audrey Hepburn' | EKMF NArc |
| ¶ 'Augustin Thierry' | MWhe |
| 'Aunt Juliana' | EBak |
| ¶ 'Auntie Bertha' | EPts |
| 'Auntie Jinks' | CPor CSil EBak EKMF LCla LFli MAsk MJac MWar MWhe NArc SLBF WGwG |
| * *aureifolia* | Last listed 1998 |
| 'Aurora Superba' | CLoc CSil EBak EKMF LFli SLBF |
| 'Australia Fair' | CLoc CSil EBak MAsk NArc WGwG |
| § *austromontana* | EBak |
| 'Autumnale' | CDoC CLoc CSil EBak EKMF EMan LCla LFli LVER MAsk MBri MWhe NArc SKen SLBF SMrm SSea |
| 'Avalanche' | CLoc CSil EBak LFli MAsk NArc |
| 'Avocet' | CLoc EBak NArc |
| 'Avon Celebration' | CLoc |
| 'Avon Gem' | CLoc CSil |
| 'Avon Gold' | CLoc |
| 'Axel of Denmark' | Last listed 1998 |
| *ayavacensis* | EGou EKMF LCla |
| 'Azure Sky' | EKMF LCla MJac |
| 'Babette' | EKMF |
| 'Babs' | MAsk |
| 'Baby Blue Eyes' | CSil SLBF |
| 'Baby Bright' | CSil LCla MAsk SLBF |
| 'Baby Chang' | CSil EGou MWhe |
| 'Baby Face' | NArc |
| 'Baby Girl' | EKMF |
| 'Baby Pink' | CSil NArc |
| 'Baby Thumb' | CPor CSil |

§ x *bacillaris* — CWit EBak EHic EWes MBlu MTed SIng SLBF SRms SSoC
§ - 'Cottinghamii' — CDoC CSil WPen WSHC
§ - 'Oosje' — CSil EKMF LCla
§ - 'Reflexa' — CTrC GQui SVen
'Bagworthy Water' — CLoc
'Baker's Tri' — EBak
'Balcony Queen' — LFli
'Bali Hi' — Last listed 1996
'Balkonkönigin' — CLoc CSil EBak MAsk SKen
'Ballet Girl' — CLoc CPor CSil EBak ECtt EKMF LCla SLBF
'Bambini' — CSil EPts
'Banks Peninsula' — GQui
'Banzai' — Last listed 1998
'Barbara' — CLoc CPor CSil EBak EKMF LFli MAsk MJac MWar MWhe NArc SKen
'Barbara Hallett' — Last listed 1996
'Barbara Pountain' — LVER
'Barbara Windsor' — MAld MJac MWhe
'Barnsdale' — Last listed 1996
'Baron de Ketteler' — CSil EKMF NArc
'Baroness van Dedem' — CSil
'Baroque Pearl' — EKMF NArc
'Barry M. Cox' — CSil EGou
'Barry Sheppard' — Last listed 1996
'Barry's Queen' — CSil EBak
'Bart Simpson' — Last listed 1998
'Bashful' — CSil EPts LCla LFli MAsk MBri NArc
'Basketfull' — CSil NArc
'Beacon' — CDoC CLoc CPor CSil EBak EKMF EMan LCla LFli LHil MAsk MBri MJac MWhe NArc SRob SSea WStI
'Beacon Rosa' — CLoc CPor CSil EGou EKMF EMan LCla LFli MAld MAsk MBri MJac MWar MWhe NArc SKen SLBF
'Bealings' — CLoc CSil ECtt EGou EMan LFli MAsk MBri MJac MWhe NArc
'Beatrice Burtoft' — EKMF
'Beau Nash' — CLoc
'Beautiful Bobbie' — SLBF
'Beauty of Bath' — CLoc EBak NArc
'Beauty of Clyffe Hall' — CSil EBak
'Beauty of Exeter' — COtt CSil EBak EKMF MAsk NArc
'Beauty of Prussia' — CDoC CLoc CSil ECtt
'Beauty of Swanley' — EBak
'Beauty of Trowbridge' — CDoC LCla NArc SKen
'Becky' — EGou
'Becky Jane' — CSil
'Bella Forbes' — CLoc CPor CSil EBak NArc
¶ 'Bella Rosella' — EPts
'Bella Rozella' — CSil EGou EKMF LFli MAsk SCoo SLBF
'Belsay Beauty' — MJac NArc
'Belvoir Beauty' — CLoc MJac
'Ben de Jong' — SLBF
¶ 'Ben Gunn' — SLBF
'Ben Jammin' — CLoc EGou LCla SLBF
'Ben's Ruby' — Last listed 1996
N 'Beranger' — CSil EBak EKMF
'Berba's Coronation' — EKMF NArc
'Berba's Happiness' — CSil
'Berba's Ingrid' — MAld
'Bergnimf' — EKMF LCla NArc WGwG
'Berliner Kind' — CSil EBak
'Bermuda' — CSil EKMF
'Bernadette' — CLTr
'Bertha Gadsby' — EKMF MAsk
'Beryl Shaffery' — EGou
'Beryl's Choice' — Last listed 1998

'Beth Robley' — CSil MAsk
'Betsy Ross' — EBak NArc
'Bette Sibley' — CSil
'Betty Jean' — EGou
'Beverley' — CSil EBak EPts LFli
'Bewitched' — EBak NArc
'Bianca' — SMur
'Bicentennial' — CLoc CSil EBak EGou EKMF EPts LFli LVER MAsk MJac MWar MWhe SKen SSea
'Big Charles' — EGou
'Big Slim' — EGou
'Bill Gilbert' — LCla
'Bill Stevens' — EKMF
'Billy Green' ♀ — CDoC CLTr CLoc CPor CSil EBak ECtt EKMF EPts LCla LFli MAld MAsk MJac MWar MWhe NArc SKen SLBF SSoC WHen
'Bishop's Bells' — CSil MAsk MJac NArc
'Bits' — NArc
'Bittersweet' — CSil LFli MAsk NArc
'Black Beauty' — CSil
'Black Prince' — CSil LFli MAsk MBri MWar NArc
'Blackberry Ripple' — Last listed 1996
I 'Blanche Regina' — MJac MWhe
'Bland's New Striped' — EBak EKMF EPts NArc SLBF
'Blazeaway' — MBri MWar
'Blood Donor' — EKMF MAld MJac
'Blowick' — EMan LFli MAsk MBri NArc
'Blue Beauty' — CSil EBak EKMF NArc
'Blue Bush' — CPor CSil EKMF MAsk MJac NArc
'Blue Butterfly' — EBak NArc
'Blue Eyes' — LFli
'Blue Gown' — CDoC CLoc CSil EBak EKMF LCla LVER MAsk MWar MWhe NArc SBid SKen
'Blue Halo' — Last listed 1997
'Blue Ice' — CSil MWhe
'Blue Lace' — CSil
N 'Blue Lagoon' — MAsk
'Blue Lake' — CSil LVER MAsk
'Blue Mink' — EBak
'Blue Mirage' — CSil LCla MAsk MWar WGwG
'Blue Mist' — EBak
'Blue Pearl' — EBak LFli MAsk NArc
'Blue Petticoat' — CLoc
'Blue Pinwheel' — CSil EBak
'Blue Sails' — NArc
'Blue Satin' — COtt LVER MAld MWhe NArc
'Blue Tit' — CSil SKen
'Blue Veil' — CLoc CSil EKMF LFli LVER MAsk MJac MWar SKen SLBF
'Blue Waves' — CLoc CPor CSil EBak EGou EKMF EMan LFli MAsk MJac MWar MWhe NArc WGwG
'Blush of Dawn' — CLoc CSil EBak EGou EKMF EPts LFli LVER MAld MAsk MWar NArc WGwG
'Blythe' — EPts SLBF
'Bob Pacey' — Last listed 1998
'Bob Paisley' — MBri
'Bobby Boy' — EBak
'Bobby Dazzler' — CSil ECtt EKMF NArc
'Bobby Shaftoe' — EBak EKMF MWhe NArc
'Bobby Wingrove' — EBak NArc
¶ 'Bobby's Girl' — EPts
'Bobolink' — EBak NArc
'Bob's Best' — CSil EPts LVER MJac
'Bob's Choice' — MAsk WLow
'Boerhaave' — EBak MAsk
'Bohémienne' — Last listed 1996
*boliviana* Britton — See *F. sanctae-rosae*

§ *boliviana* Carrière — CAbb CDoC CLoc CSil EBak EKMF LCla LHil MBEx NArc SBid SMrm SYvo

§ - var. *alba* ♀ — CDoC CLoc CPin CSil EBak EGou EKMF LCla LFli LHil MAsk MBEx MWhe NArc SBid SMrm

- 'Alba' — See *F. boliviana* Carrière var. *alba*
- var. *boliviana* — EGou
- var. *luxurians* — See *F. boliviana* Carrière var. *alba*
- f. *puberulenta* — See *F. boliviana* Carrière
'Bon Accorde' — CLoc CPor CSil EBak EKMF EPts LCla MAsk MJac SSea
'Bon Bon' — CSil EBak LFli NArc
'Bonita' — CSil MAsk MJac NArc
'Bonnie Doan' — NArc
'Bonnie Lass' — CSil EBak NArc
'Bonny' — CLoc
¶ 'Bookham Beauty' — SLBF
'Bora Bora' — CSil EBak EKMF
¶ 'Borde Hill' — SLBF
'Border Princess' — EBak LCla
'Border Queen' ♀ — CDoC CLoc CSil EBak EKMF EMan LCla LFli MAld MAsk MJac MWar NArc
'Border Reiver' — EBak NArc
'Börnemanns Beste' — CDoC CLoc CSil EBak EKMF LCla MAsk SKen
'Bouffant' — CLoc CSil MAsk MJac
'Bountiful' — CGre CLoc CSil EKMF MAsk MWhe NArc SKen
'Bouquet' — CSil EKMF LCla SKen
'Bouvigne' — NArc
'Bow Bells' — CLoc CSil MAld MAsk MJac MWhe NArc
'Boy Marc' — EGou LCla
'Brandt's Five Hundred Club' — CLoc EBak LFli
'Breckland' — EBak MJac NArc
'Breeders' Delight' — MBri
'Breeder's Dream' — EBak NArc
'Brenda' — CLoc CSil EBak NArc
'Brenda Pritchard' — CSil ECtt LVER
'Brenda White' — CLoc CSil EKMF MAsk NArc
'Brentwood' — EBak
*brevilobis* — CSil EGou EKMF
'Brian A McDonald' — EGou
'Brian Breary' — EGou LCla
'Brian C. Morrison' — EGou EKMF LCla MAsk
'Brian Ellis' — NArc
¶ 'Brian Kimberley' — EGou
'Brian Soames' — EBak
'Brian Stannard' — EGou LCla
'Bridal Pink' — LFli
'Bridal Veil' — EBak NArc
'Bridesmaid' — CSil EBak EKMF MAsk NArc
'Brigadoon' — CLoc EBak
'Brightling' — CSil
'Brighton Belle' — CDoC CSil EGou LCla NArc SSoC WGwG
N 'Brilliant' — CLoc CSil EBak LCla LFli LHil MAsk MGos MPla MWat MWhe
'Briony Caunt' — CSil EKMF LFli
'British Jubilee' — CSil EKMF MAsk NArc
'British Sterling' — NArc
'Brodsworth' — CPor CSil MAsk
'Bronze Banks Peninsula' — EKMF
'Brookwood Belle' ♀ — EPts LCla MAld MJac SLBF SYvo
'Brookwood Dale' — MWhe
'Brookwood Joy' — CSil EGou MAsk MJac NArc SLBF
'Brookwood Lady' — MWhe
'Brutus' ♀ — CLoc CSil EBak EKMF EMan EPts LCla LFli MAsk MWat MWhe NArc SKen WGwG WStI

'Bryan Breary' — EKMF
'Bubble Hanger' — CSil LFli NArc
'Buddha' — EBak
'Buena Maria' — Last listed 1996
'Buenos Aires' — Last listed 1996
'Bugle Boy' — EGou
'Bunny' — CSil EBak LFli NArc
'Burma Star' — MAsk
'Burton Brew' — MJac
'Buttercup' — CLoc CSil EBak LFli MAsk NArc
'Butterfly' — MAsk
'Buttons and Bows' — Last listed 1996
'Byron Rees' — EGou
'C.J. Howlett' — CSil EBak
'Caballero' — EBak
'Cable Car' — Last listed 1997
'Caesar' — EBak MAsk NArc
'Caledonia' — CSil EBak EKMF
'Calumet' — Last listed 1998
'Cambridge Louie' — CPor CSil EBak LCla LFli MAld MAsk MBri MWar MWhe NArc
'Camel Estuary' — NArc
'Camelot' — NArc
*campii* — EKMF
* - var. *rubra* — EGou
*campos-portoi* — CDoC CSil EGou EKMF
'Cancun' — MJac
'Candlelight' — CGre CLoc CSil EBak NArc
'Candy Kisses' — Last listed 1998
'Candy Stripe' — CLoc
*canescens* Bentham — Last listed 1998
- Munz — See *F. ampliata*
'Cannenburch Floriant' — Last listed 1996
'Canny Bob' — MJac NArc
'Capri' — CSil EBak NArc
¶ 'Captain Al Sutton' — EGou
'Cara Mia' — CLoc CSil SKen
'Caradela' — MAld SLBF
'Cardinal' — CLoc EKMF NArc
'Cardinal Farges' — CLoc CPor CSil EKMF LCla LFli NArc SKen SLBF SSea
'Carillon van Amsterdam' — MWhe
'Carioca' — EBak
'Carisbrooke Castle' — EKMF
'Carl Drude' — LCla
'Carl Wallace' — EKMF MJac
'Carla Johnston' — CLTr CLoc CSil EKMF EPts LCla LFli LVER MAld MAsk MBri MJac MWar MWhe NArc SSea
'Carlisle Bells' — NArc
'Carmel Blue' — CDoC CLTr CLoc CSil EKMF LCla LFli MAsk MWar MWhe NArc WGwG
'Carmen' — CDoC CSil
'Carmen Maria' — LCla NArc
'Carmine Bell' — CSil EKMF
'Carnea' — CSil
'Carnival' — LCla NArc
'Carnoustie' — EBak EGou NArc
'Carol Grace' — CLoc NArc
'Carol Nash' — CLoc
'Carol Roe' — EKMF
'Carole Hardwick' — Last listed 1996
'Carole Scott' — Last listed 1996
'Caroline' — CGre CLoc CSil EBak EKMF EPts LFli MAsk MBlu MWhe NArc SLBF
'Cascade' — CLoc CSil ECtt EKMF EMan LCla LFli MAsk MBri MJac MWar MWhe NArc SKen SRms SSea
'Casper Hauser' — CSil EGou EKMF MAsk NArc
'Catherina' — Last listed 1998
'Catherine Bartlett' — EKMF NArc

| | |
|---|---|
| 'Catherine Claire' | Last listed 1998 |
| 'Cathie MacDougall' | EBak NArc |
| ¶ 'Cecil Glass' | EKMF |
| 'Cecile' | CSil ECtt EGou EKMF EPts LFli LVER MAsk MJac MWar MWhe NArc SLBF |
| 'Celadore' | CSil LVER MAsk MJac NArc SKen |
| 'Celebration' | CLoc CSil EGou |
| 'Celia Smedley' ♀ | CGre CLoc CPor CSil EBak EGou EKMF EPts LCla LHil LVER MAld MAsk MBri MJac MWar MWhe NArc SKen SLBF |
| 'Centerpiece' | EBak |
| 'Central Scotland' | LCla |
| 'Ceri' | CLoc NArc |
| 'Cerrig' | NArc |
| 'Chameleon' | CSil NArc WGwG |
| 'Champagne Celebration' | CLoc |
| 'Chancellor' | Last listed 1996 |
| 'Chandleri' | EKMF NArc SLBF |
| 'Chang' | CLoc CSil EBak EKMF LBlm LCla LFli MAsk MWar MWhe NArc SLBF |
| 'Chantry Park' | EGou LCla SLBF |
| 'Charisma' | LFli NArc |
| 'Charles Edward' | CSil EKMF |
| 'Charlie Gardiner' | EBak MWhe NArc |
| 'Charlie Girl' | EBak |
| 'Charlotte Clyne' | MJac |
| 'Charming' | CDoC CLoc CPor CSil EBak GCHN LFli MAsk MJac MWar MWhe NArc |
| 'Chase Delight' | EKMF |
| 'Checkerboard' ♀ | CLoc CPor EBak EGou EKMF LCla LFli LVER MAld MAsk MJac MWar MWhe NArc SKen SLBF SSea SYvo WEas WGwG |
| ¶ 'Cheeky Chantalle' | SLBF |
| 'Cheers' | CSil EKMF MAsk MWar MWhe |
| 'Cherry Pie' | Last listed 1998 |
| 'Cheryl' | MJac |
| 'Chessboard' | CLoc CSil |
| 'Chillerton Beauty' ♀ | CDoC CLTr CLoc CSil CTri ECtt EKMF LCla LFli MAsk MJac MWhe NArc SLBF SPer |
| 'China Doll' | EBak LFli MWhe NArc SKen |
| 'China Lantern' | CLoc CSil EBak LFli MAsk |
| 'Chiquita Maria' | NArc |
| 'Chris' | Last listed 1998 |
| 'Christ Driessen' | Last listed 1998 |
| 'Christina Becker' | NArc |
| 'Christine Bamford' | EGou |
| 'Christine Shaffery' | EGou |
| Christmas Candy | Last listed 1996 |
| 'Christmas Ribbons' | Last listed 1998 |
| *cinerea* | EGou EKMF LCla |
| 'Cinnabarrina' | SLBF |
| 'Circe' | EBak EKMF MAsk NArc |
| 'Circus' | EBak |
| 'Circus Spangles' | COtt CSil LFli MAsk MWar SCoo SMur |
| 'Citation' | CLoc CSil EBak EKMF LFli MJac SSea |
| 'City of Adelaide' | CLoc CSil MWhe |
| 'City of Leicester' | CSil LCla MAsk MBri |
| 'Claire Belle' | SLBF |
| 'Claire de Lune' | EBak MAsk NArc SLBF |
| 'Claire Evans' | CLoc |
| 'Claire Oram' | CLoc SSea |
| 'Claudine Sanford' | Last listed 1996 |
| 'Cliantha' | MAsk MJac MWhe NArc |
| 'Clifford Gadsby' | EBak NArc |

| | |
|---|---|
| 'Cliff's Hardy' | CPor CSil EKMF LCla MAsk NArc |
| 'Cliff's Own' | CSil NArc |
| 'Cliff's Unique' | CSil EPts MAsk MWar |
| 'Clifton Beauty' | MAsk MJac |
| 'Clifton Belle' | Last listed 1996 |
| 'Clifton Charm' | CSil EPts MJac |
| 'Clipper' | CSil |
| 'Cloth of Gold' | CLoc EBak MAsk MJac MWhe SKen SSea |
| 'Cloverdale Jewel' | CSil EBak ECtt LCla MWhe NArc |
| 'Cloverdale Joy' | EBak MAsk |
| 'Cloverdale Pearl' ♀ | CSil EBak EKMF EMan ENot LCla LFli MAsk MJac MWhe NArc WPyg |
| 'Coachman' | CLoc CSil EBak EKMF EMan EPts LCla LFli MAld MAsk MWar MWhe NArc SLBF WGwG |
| *coccinea* | CGre CSil EGou EKMF LCla |
| 'Coconut Ice' | NArc |
| 'Col' | Last listed 1996 |
| x *colensoi* | ECou EKMF LCla MAsk SHFr |
| 'Colin Chambers' | EGou |
| 'Collingwood' | CLoc CSil EBak MAsk NArc |
| 'Colne Fantasy' | EKMF EPts LFli |
| 'Colne Greybeard' | CSil NArc |
| 'Come Dancing' | CSil ECtt LCla LFli MAsk NArc SKen |
| N 'Comet' | CLoc CSil EBak NArc |
| 'Conchilla' | EBak |
| 'Confection' | NArc |
| 'Congreve Road' | MAsk |
| 'Connie' | CSil EBak |
| 'Conspicua' | CSil EBak EGou EKMF NArc SKen |
| 'Constable Country' | NArc |
| 'Constance' | CDoC CLoc CSil EGou EKMF LCla LFli LVER MAsk MJac MWar MWhe NArc SKen SLBF |
| 'Constance Comer' | MJac |
| N 'Constellation' | CLoc EBak MAsk MWhe NArc |
| 'Continental' | EGou NArc |
| ¶ 'Coombe Park' | MJac |
| 'Copycat' | CSil |
| 'Coquet Bell' | EBak MAsk NArc |
| 'Coquet Dale' | EBak EGou EKMF MAsk MJac MWhe NArc |
| 'Coquet Gold' | CSil ECtt NArc |
| 'Coral Baby' | EGou |
| 'Coral Seas' | EBak |
| § 'Coralle' ♀ | CLoc CPor CSil EBak EGou EKMF EMan EPts LCla LFli MAsk MJac MWar MWhe NArc SKen SLBF WLow |
| 'Corallina' ♀ | CDoC CLoc CSil EBak EKMF LFli MAsk MWhe NArc SRms SSea WFar WLow WPic WWat |
| *cordifolia* hort. | See *F. splendens* |
| - Bentham | CTre EBak MAsk MBEx |
| 'Core'ngrato' | CLoc EBak |
| 'Cornelia Smith' | EGou |
| 'Cornwall Calls' | Last listed 1998 |
| 'Corsage' | NArc |
| 'Corsair' | CSil EBak EKMF LFli NArc |
| § *corymbiflora* | CDoC EBak EGou EKMF LCla |
| - alba | See *F. boliviana* Carrière var. *alba* |
| 'Cosmopolitan' | CSil EBak NArc |
| 'Costa Brava' | CLoc EBak NArc |
| 'Cotta Bella' | EKMF NArc |
| 'Cotta Bright Star' | EKMF LCla MAsk NArc |
| 'Cotta Fairy' | EKMF |
| 'Cotta Princess' | EKMF |
| 'Cotta Vino' | EKMF MAsk NArc SLBF |
| 'Cottinghamii' | See *F. x bacillaris* 'Cottinghamii' |

| | |
|---|---|
| 'Cotton Candy' | CLoc CSil EGou EPts LCla LFli MAsk MWhe SLBF |
| 'Countdown Carol' | EPts |
| 'Countess of Aberdeen' | CLoc CSil EBak EGou EKMF MAsk NArc SLBF |
| 'Countess of Maritza' | CLoc |
| 'County Park' | ECou EWes |
| 'Court Jester' | CLoc EBak NArc |
| 'Cover Girl' | EBak LFli MWhe NArc |
| 'Coverdale Jewel' | Last listed 1997 |
| 'Coxeen' | EBak |
| 'Crackerjack' | CLoc EBak |
| *crassistipula* | EGou EKMF LCla |
| 'Creampuff' | NArc |
| 'Crescendo' | CLoc |
| 'Crinkley Bottom' | EKMF EPts LCla LVER MJac SLBF |
| 'Crinoline' | EBak NArc |
| 'Croix d'Honneur' | Last listed 1996 |
| 'Crosby Serendipidy' | CLoc |
| 'Crosby Soroptimist' | CSil LCla MAsk MWar MWhe |
| 'Cross Check' | EMan MAsk MBri MJac NArc |
| 'Crusader' | CSil |
| 'Crystal Blue' | EBak MAsk NArc |
| 'Crystal Stars' | CSil NArc |
| 'Cupcake' | NArc |
| 'Cupid' | CSil EBak NArc |
| 'Curly Q' | CSil EBak EKMF LFli MAsk NArc |
| 'Curtain Call' | CLoc EBak NArc SKen |
| ¶ 'Cutie Karen' | SLBF |
| *cylindracea* | CSil EKMF LCla |
| - (f) | EGou |
| - (m) | EGou |
| 'Cymon' | CSil MAsk MWhe |
| 'Cymru' | NArc |
| 'Cyril Holmes' | NArc |
| *cyrtandroides* | EGou EKMF |
| 'Daffodil Dolly' | NArc |
| 'Dainty' | EBak |
| 'Dainty Lady' | EBak |
| 'Daisy Bell' | CLoc CSil EBak ECtt EKMF LCla LFli MAsk MJac MWhe NArc SSea WGwG |
| 'Dalton' | EBak NArc |
| 'Dancing Bloom' | EPts |
| 'Dancing Flame' | CLoc CSil EKMF EMan EPts LCla LFli LHil LVER MAld MAsk MBri MJac MWar MWhe NArc SKen SLBF SYvo WGwG |
| ¶ 'Daniel Austin' | MJac |
| 'Danielle' | Last listed 1996 |
| 'Danish Pastry' | LFli NArc |
| 'Danny Boy' | CLoc EBak EKMF EMan MAsk MWhe NArc |
| 'Daphne Arlene' | CSil |
| 'Dark Eyes' ♀ | CLoc CPor CSil EBak EGou EKMF EMan LCla LFli LVER MAld MAsk MBri MJac MWar MWhe NArc NFai NHaw SLBF SSea WGwG |
| 'Dark Lady' | MWhe |
| 'Dark Secret' | EBak NArc |
| 'Dark Treasure' | CDoC CSil LFli |
| 'Darreen Dawn' | Last listed 1997 |
| 'David' | CSil EGou EKMF EOHP LCla MAsk MPla MWhe SKen SLBF |
| 'David Alston' | CLoc EBak |
| 'David Lockyer' | CLoc |
| 'David Ward' | EKMF |
| 'Dawn' | EBak SKen |
| 'Dawn Carless' | EGou |
| 'Dawn Sky' | EBak |
| 'Dawn Star' | CSil LVER MJac MWhe NArc |
| 'Dawn Thunder' | LFli NArc SMur |

| | |
|---|---|
| 'Dawning' | Last listed 1998 |
| 'Day by Day' | CPor MAsk |
| 'Day Star' | EBak |
| 'Daytime Live' | EKMF |
| ¶ 'De Groot's Moonlight' | EGou |
| 'De Groot's Pipes' | Last listed 1998 |
| 'Debby' | EBak NArc |
| 'Deben' | Last listed 1996 |
| 'Deben Petite' | CSil LCla |
| 'Deben Rose' | CSil LFli MAsk NArc WGwG |
| 'Deborah' | Last listed 1996 |
| 'Deborah Mitchell' | WGwG |
| 'Deborah Street' | CLoc |
| N *decussata* | EBak EGou EKMF LCla |
| 'Dedham Vale' | Last listed 1996 |
| 'Dee Copley' | EBak NArc |
| 'Dee Star' | NArc |
| 'Deep Purple' | CLoc CSil EKMF MAsk MJac SCoo SLBF |
| 'Delaval Lady' | CSil |
| 'Delicia' | CSil |
| 'Delilah' | EKMF MJac |
| 'Delta's Bride' | EGou SLBF |
| 'Delta's Delight' | Last listed 1998 |
| 'Delta's Dream' | NArc WGwG |
| ¶ 'Delta's Drop' | EGou |
| 'Delta's Groom' | EGou |
| 'Delta's K.O.' | NArc |
| 'Delta's Night' | EGou |
| 'Delta's Paljas' | Last listed 1997 |
| 'Delta's Parade' | NArc |
| 'Delta's Song' | NArc SLBF |
| 'Delta's Sprinkler' | NArc |
| 'Delta's Symphonie' | Last listed 1998 |
| 'Delta's Trick' | Last listed 1998 |
| 'Delta's Wonder' | CSil |
| § *denticulata* | CLoc CSil EBak EGou EKMF ERea LCla MAsk MBEx NArc SKen SLBF WGwG |
| *dependens* | See *F. corymbiflora* |
| 'Derby Imp' | MAsk NArc |
| 'Derby Star' | CSil |
| 'Desperate Daniel' | EKMF LCla |
| 'Destiny' | Last listed 1997 |
| 'Deutsche Perle' | Last listed 1998 |
| 'Devonshire Dumpling' | CGre CLTr CLoc CSil EBak ECtt EGou EKMF EMan EPts LCla LFli LVER MAld MAsk MBri MJac MWar MWhe NArc NHaw SKen SLBF |
| 'Diablo' | CSil EBak |
| 'Diamond Celebration' | EKMF LCla MWar |
| 'Diamond Wedding' | Last listed 1997 |
| 'Diana' | EBak LFli |
| 'Diana Wills' | MWhe SKen |
| 'Diana Wright' | CSil LHil MHlr WSPU |
| 'Diane Brown' | EKMF LFli MAsk MWhe SSea |
| 'Diann Goodwin' | Last listed 1996 |
| 'Dick Swinbank' | EKMF |
| 'Die Fledermaus' | NArc |
| 'Dilly-Dilly' | MAsk |
| 'Dimples' | CPor CSil MAsk MBri |
| 'Diny Hetterscheid' | Last listed 1998 |
| 'Dipton Dainty' | CLoc CSil EBak LCla NArc |
| 'Dirk van Delen' | MWhe |
| 'Display' ♀ | CDoC CLoc CPor CSil EBak EBee ECtt EKMF EMan LCla LFli LVER MAld MAsk MBri MJac MWar MWhe NArc SLBF SSea WGwG WStI |
| 'Doc' | CSil LCla LFli MAsk |
| 'Docteur Topinard' | CLoc EBak EKMF |

'Doctor'                    See *F.* 'The Doctor'
'Doctor Brendan Freeman'    MJac NArc
'Doctor Foster'             CDoC CLoc CSil CTri EBak ENot NArc SBid WEas
'Doctor Olson'              CLoc EBak
'Doctor Robert'             EKMF EPts MBri MJac MWhe NArc
§ 'Dollar Princess' ♀       CDoC CLoc CPor CSil EBak EBee ECtt EGou EKMF EMan EPts LCla LFli MAld MAsk MBri MJac MWar MWhe NArc NFai SChu SKen SLBF SPlb WFar WGwG WStI
'Dolly Daydream'            EKMF NArc
'Domacin'                   Last listed 1998
'Dominique'                 EKMF
'Dominyana'                 EBak EKMF LCla
'Don Peralta'               EBak
'Dopey'                     CSil LCla LFli MAsk
'Doreen Gladwyn'            SLBF
'Doreen Redfern'            CLoc CSil EKMF LFli MAsk MJac MWhe NArc
'Doris Birchell'            Last listed 1996
'Doris Coleman'             EMan LFli
'Doris Deaves'              Last listed 1996
'Doris Hobbs'               EKMF
¶ 'Doris Joan'              CSil
'Dorking Delight'           LCla
'Dorothea Flower'           CLoc CSil EBak
'Dorothy'                   CSil LCla SLBF
'Dorothy Day'               CLoc
'Dorothy Hanley'            EGou
'Dorothy M. Goldsmith'      EGou
'Dorothy Shields'           LCla MAld MJac
'Dorrian Brogdale'          EGou LCla
'Dove House'                EKMF
'Drake 400'                 CLoc
'Drame'                     CDoC CPor CSil EBak EKMF LCla LFli LHil MAsk NArc SKen SSea WLow
'Dreamy Days'               Last listed 1996
'Drum Major'                EBak NArc
'Du Barry'                  EBak NArc
'Duchess of Albany'         CLoc CSil EBak MAsk NArc
'Duchess of Cornwall'       CSil
'Duet'                      CSil SMur
N 'Duke of Wellington'      CLoc
'Dulcie Elizabeth'          CSil EBak LCla LFli MJac MWar NArc
'Dunrobin Bedder'           Last listed 1996
'Dusky Beauty'              CSil MJac NArc
'Dusky Rose'                CLoc CSil EBak LFli MAsk MJac MWhe NArc WGwG
'Dutch King Size'           EGou
'Dutch Mill'                CLoc EBak
'Duyfken'                   CSil NArc
'Earl of Beaconsfield'      See *F.* 'Laing's Hybrid'
'Earre Barré'               EGou
'East Anglian'              CLoc CSil EBak NArc
'Easter Bonnet'             CLoc
'Easterling'                NArc
'Ebbtide'                   CLoc EBak NArc
'Echo'                      CLoc
'Ed Largarde'               EBak EKMF MAsk
'Edale'                     CSil
'Eden Beauty'               NArc
'Eden Lady'                 CLoc CSil MBri MWar NArc
'Eden Princess'             MJac MWhe
'Edith'                     CSil EKMF LCla SLBF
'Edith Emery'               LFli
'Edith Hall'                EKMF
'Edith Jack'                CPor
'Edith of Kimbolton'        Last listed 1996

'Edna W. Smith'             CSil ECtt
'Edwin J. Goulding'         EGou EKMF LCla
'Eileen Raffill'            EBak
'Eileen Saunders'           CSil EBak
'Eira Goulding'             EGou
'El Camino'                 CPor CSil LFli MAsk MWhe NArc NFai
'El Cid'                    CLoc CSil EBak EKMF MAsk NArc
'Elaine Ann'                CInt EPts LHil MJac
'Eleanor Clark'             EKMF LCla NArc
'Eleanor Leytham'           EBak EKMF LCla MAsk NArc
'Eleanor Rawlins'           CSil EBak EKMF NArc SKen
'Elfin Glade'               CLoc CPor CSil EBak
'Elfrida'                   CSil EKMF
'Elfriede Ott'              CLoc EBak EKMF MWhe SLBF
'Elisabeth Honorine'        NArc
N 'Elizabeth'               EBak EKMF LFli NArc
'Elizabeth Anne'            Last listed 1996
'Elizabeth Broughton'       EKMF
'Elizabeth Tompkins'        EKMF LFli MJac
'Elizabeth Travis'          EBak
'Ellen Morgan'              EBak
'Elma'                      Last listed 1998
'Elsa'                      ECtt
'Elsie Downey'              NArc
'Elsie Mitchell'            CSil LCla MAsk MWar MWhe NArc
'Elsstar'                   Last listed 1996
§ 'Emile de Wildeman'       EBak EKMF LVER MWar
'Emily Austen'              EKMF NArc
'Emma Louise'               NArc
'Emma Massey'               Last listed 1997
'Emma Rowell'               EKMF
'Empress of Prussia' ♀      CDoC CLoc CSil EBak EKMF EMan LFli MAsk NArc SKen SLBF SSea
'Enchanted'                 EBak MWar
*encliandra*                EKMF LCla
  subsp. *encliandra*
§ - subsp. *tetradactyla*   EKMF LCla SLBF
§ 'Enfant Prodigue'         CDoC CLoc CSil EKMF
'Englander'                 Last listed 1998
'English Rose'              CSil MAsk
'Enstone'                   See *F. magellanica* var. *molinae* 'Enstone'
'Eppsii'                    CSil
'Eric Cooper Taylor'        Last listed 1996
'Erica Julie'               MWhe NArc SLBF
'Eric's Hardy'              CSil
'Eric's Majestic'           EKMF MJac
'Erika Frohmann'            SLBF
'Erika Köth'                CSil
'Ernest Rankin'             CSil EKMF NArc
'Ernestine'                 MWhe
'Ernie Bromley'             EGou NArc SLBF
'Eroica'                    NArc
'Errol'                     CLoc
'Estelle Marie'             CLoc CSil EBak EGou EKMF MAsk MBri MJac MWar MWhe SLBF SSea
'Esther Divine'             CSil MAsk
'Eternal Flame'             CSil EBak LFli MBri MWhe NArc SKen
'Eureka Red'                MAsk
'Eurydice'                  CLoc
'Eusebia'                   EKMF LFli MAsk MJac NArc
'Eva Boerg'                 CLoc CPor CSil EBak ECtt EKMF EMan LCla LFli MAsk MBri MWar MWhe NArc NFai SKen WGwG WKif
¶ 'Eva Dayes'               EKMF
'Eva Twaites'               EGou LCla

| Cultivar | Sources |
|---|---|
| 'Evanson's Choice' | SKen |
| 'Eve Hollands' | Last listed 1998 |
| 'Evelyn Stanley' | Last listed 1998 |
| 'Evelyn Steele Little' | EBak |
| 'Evening Sky' | EBak NArc |
| 'Evensong' | CLoc CSil EBak LFli MWhe NArc |
| 'Excalibur' | EGou NArc |
| *excorticata* | CB&S CDoC CSil CTre CTrw ECou EGou EKMF GVic LCla WPGP WSHC |
| 'Exton Beauty' | NArc |
| 'Fabian Franck' | LCla |
| 'Fairy Floss' | Last listed 1998 |
| 'Fairytales' | NArc |
| 'Falklands' | CPor CSil LFli MAsk |
| 'Falling Stars' | CLoc CSil EBak MWhe |
| 'Fan Dancer' | EBak |
| 'Fancy Flute' | CSil NArc |
| 'Fancy Free' | LFli MBri WLRN |
| 'Fancy Pants' | CLoc EBak EGou MAsk MBri |
| 'Fanfare' | CDoC EBak EKMF LCla NArc SLBF |
| 'Fascination' | See *F.* 'Emile de Wildeman' |
| 'Fashion' | EBak |
| 'Fasna 1100' | NArc |
| 'Favourite' | EBak |
| 'Feather Duster' | Last listed 1996 |
| 'Fenman' | EPts MJac NArc |
| 'Fergie' | LCla |
| 'Festival' | MAsk MWhe |
| 'Festival Lights' | Last listed 1998 |
| 'Festoon' | EBak |
| 'Fey' | EKMF MAsk |
| 'Fiery Spider' | EBak EKMF NArc |
| 'Figaro' | Last listed 1998 |
| § 'Filigraan' | CSil NArc |
| Filigree | See *F.* 'Filigraan' |
| 'Fine Lady' | Last listed 1998 |
| 'Finn' | EGou EPts |
| 'Fiona' | CLoc CSil EBak EGou LFli MAsk NArc |
| 'Fiona Jane' | EKMF |
| 'Fiona Lynn' | Last listed 1998 |
| 'Fiona Pitt' | Last listed 1998 |
| 'Fire Mountain' | CLoc CSil MWhe NArc SKen SSea |
| ¶ 'Firecracker' | LFli MJac MWar WWeb |
| 'Firefly' | NArc |
| 'Firefox' | NArc |
| 'Firelite' | EBak NArc |
| 'Firenza' | MWar |
| 'First Lady' | CSil MAsk NArc |
| 'First Lord' | Last listed 1996 |
| ¶ 'First Love' | LFli |
| 'First Success' | EGou EKMF LCla MAsk SLBF |
| 'Flair' | CLoc |
| 'Flame' | EBak |
| 'Flamenco Dancer' | CLoc LFli SLBF |
| 'Flash' ♀ | CDoC CLoc CSil CTri EBak EKMF LCla LFli MAld MAsk MJac MWhe NArc SLBF WFar WStI |
| 'Flashlight' | EGou MAsk |
| 'Flat Jack o' Lancashire' | CSil ECtt EKMF |
| 'Flavia' | EBak |
| 'Flirtation Waltz' | CGre CLoc CSil EBak EKMF EMan LCla LFli LVER MAld MAsk MBri MJac MWhe NArc SSea |
| 'Flocon de Neige' | EBak EKMF NArc |
| 'Floral City' | CLoc EBak NArc |
| 'Florence Mary Abbott' | CSil EGou EMan MWar |
| 'Florence Turner' | CSil EBak EKMF MAsk MWhe SKen |
| 'Florentina' | CLoc CSil EBak EKMF NArc |
| 'Floretta' | Last listed 1998 |
| 'Flowerdream' | Last listed 1996 |
| 'Fluffy Frills' | CSil |
| 'Flyaway' | EBak NArc |
| 'Fly-by-night' | NArc |
| 'Flying Cloud' ♀ | CLoc CSil EBak EKMF LFli MAsk MBri NArc |
| 'Flying Scotsman' | CLoc CSil EBak EGou EKMF EPts LFli LVER MAsk MJac NArc SLBF |
| 'Folies Bergères' | EBak |
| 'Foline' | NArc |
| 'Fondant Cream' | Last listed 1996 |
| 'Foolke' | EBak EPts LHil |
| 'Forest King' | NArc |
| N 'Forget Me Not' | CLoc CSil EBak EKMF MAsk NArc |
| 'Formosissima' | Last listed 1998 |
| 'Fort Bragg' | EBak NArc SKen |
| 'Forward Look' | MWhe |
| 'Fountains Abbey' | EMan NArc |
| 'Foxgrove Wood' | CSil EBak EPts LCla MAld SLBF |
| ¶ 'Frances Haskins' | MWhe |
| 'Frank Sanford' | NArc |
| 'Frank Saunders' | CSil LCla |
| 'Frank Unsworth' | ECtt EKMF MAsk MJac MWar NArc |
| ¶ 'Frankie's Magnificent Seven' | EPts |
| 'Frau Hilde Rademacher' | CPor CSil EBak EKMF EMan LFli LVER MAld MPla NArc SLBF |
| 'Frauke' | NArc |
| 'Fred Swales' | CSil EKMF |
| 'Fred's First' | CSil |
| 'Freefall' | EBak |
| 'Freeland Ballerina' | Last listed 1997 |
| 'Friendly Fire' | CLoc EKMF LFli NArc |
| 'Friendship' | Last listed 1998 |
| 'Frosted Amethyst' | Last listed 1996 |
| 'Frosted Flame' | CLoc CSil EKMF LCla LFli MAsk MJac MWar MWhe NArc SSea |
| 'Frühling' | CSil EBak |
| * *fuchsia* | EGou |
| I 'Fuchsia Fan' | Last listed 1998 |
| 'Fuchsiade '88' | CLoc EBak EKMF LCla MAsk MWhe |
| 'Fuchsiarama' | EKMF |
| 'Fuchsiarama '91' | MAsk NArc |
| 'Fuji San' | EGou EPts LCla |
| 'Fuksie Foetsie' | CSil EGou EKMF LCla MAsk SLBF |
| *fulgens* ♀ | CDoC EKMF LCla LHil MAsk MBEx MBal MWhe NArc SYvo |
| - 'Gesneriana' | See *F.* 'Gesneriana' |
| * - var. *michocan* | EGou |
| - 'Rubra Grandiflora' | See *F.* 'Rubra Grandiflora' |
| * - 'Variegata' | CLoc CSil EGou LCla |
| 'Fulpila' | EGou |
| 'Für Elise' | EBak |
| *furfuracea* | EKMF |
| 'Gala' | EBak NArc |
| 'Galadriel' | EGou SLBF |
| 'Galahad' | EBak NArc |
| 'Garden News' ♀ | CDoC CLoc CSil ECtt EGou EKMF EPts LCla LFli LVER MAld MAsk MGos MJac MPla MWar MWhe NArc SKen SLBF WFar WLow |
| 'Garden Week' | LVER MAsk MWhe |
| 'Gartenmeister Bonstedt' ♀ | CDoC CLoc CSil EBak EKMF EPts LBlm LCla MAsk MLan NArc SKen SSea WEas WGwG WLow |
| 'Gay Anne' | EKMF LFli NArc |
| 'Gay Fandango' | CLoc CSil EBak LCla NArc SKen |
| 'Gay Future' | EKMF |
| 'Gay Parasol' | CLoc EGou LFli LVER MAsk |

| | |
|---|---|
| 'Gay Paree' | EBak |
| 'Gay Senorita' | EBak |
| 'Gay Spinner' | CLoc |
| 'Gazebo' | Last listed 1996 |
| 'Geertien' | See *F.* 'Dutch Geertien' |
| *gehrigeri* | EBak EGou EKMF LCla |
| 'Geisha Girl' | CSil |
| 'Gelre' | Last listed 1997 |
| ¶ 'Gemma Fisher' | EPts |
| 'Général Charles de Gaulle' | EGou LCla |
| 'Général Monk' | CDoC CPor CSil EBak ECtt EKMF EMan LVER MBri MPla NArc WCot |
| 'Général Voyron' | CSil MPla |
| 'General Wavell' | LFli NArc WGwG |
| 'Genii' ♀ | More than 30 suppliers |
| 'Geoff Amos' | Last listed 1996 |
| 'Geoffrey Smith' | CSil ECtt EKMF |
| 'Georg Börnemann' | NArc |
| 'Georgana' | MWhe |
| 'George Barr' | EKMF NArc SKen |
| 'George Johnson' | CDoC CSil NArc WGwG |
| 'George Travis' | EBak |
| 'Gerald Drewitt' | CSil |
| ¶ 'Geraldine' | CSil |
| 'Gerda Manthey' | EKMF |
| 'Gerharda's Aubergine' | EKMF |
| 'Gerharda's Kiekeboe' | EKMF |
| 'Gerharda's Sophie' | Last listed 1997 |
| § 'Gesneriana' | CLoc CSil EBak EGou |
| 'Ghislaine' | Last listed 1998 |
| 'Giant Pink Enchanted' | CLoc EBak LFli NArc |
| 'Gilda' | CSil MAsk NArc |
| 'Gillian Althea' | NArc |
| 'Gilt Edge' | CLoc CSil |
| 'Gina's Gold' | MAsk |
| 'Gingham Girl' | MJac |
| ¶ 'Giovanna and Wesley' | EGou |
| 'Gipping' | Last listed 1998 |
| 'Girls Brigade' | EKMF |
| 'Gladiator' | CSil EBak EKMF LCla LFli NArc |
| 'Gladys Haddaway' | LCla |
| 'Gladys Lorimer' | Last listed 1996 |
| 'Gladys Miller' | CLoc |
| *glaziouana* | CSil EGou EKMF LCla SLBF SYvo |
| 'Glenby' | NArc |
| 'Gleneagles' | EGou |
| 'Glitters' | EBak EKMF LFli NArc |
| § 'Globosa' | CAgr EBak EKMF SKen SRms |
| 'Gloria Johnson' | EKMF MAsk NArc |
| 'Glow' | CSil EBak |
| 'Glowing Embers' | EBak MAsk NArc |
| Glowing Lilac | CSil EKMF EMan NArc |
| 'Glyn Jones' | EKMF |
| ¶ 'Goena-Goena' | CSil |
| 'Gold Brocade' | CSil NArc |
| 'Gold Crest' | EBak |
| 'Gold Leaf' | Last listed 1997 |
| 'Golden Anniversary' | CLoc EBak EGou EKMF EMan LFli MAld MAsk MJac MWar SSea |
| 'Golden Arrow' | EGou LCla LHil NArc |
| 'Golden Border Queen' | CLoc |
| 'Golden Dawn' | CLoc EBak ECtt NArc |
| 'Golden Drame' | Last listed 1997 |
| 'Golden Eden Lady' | MWhe |
| 'Golden Herald' | SLBF SSea |
| 'Golden Jessimae' | NArc |
| 'Golden La Campanella' | CLoc CSil ECtt MBri SSea |
| 'Golden Lena' | CSil EKMF EMan |
| 'Golden Marinka' ♀ | CLoc EBak ECtt EKMF LFli MAsk MBri MWhe |
| 'Golden Melody' | CSil |
| 'Golden Penny Askew' | MAsk |
| 'Golden Runner' | MAsk |
| 'Golden Spring Classic' | Last listed 1996 |
| 'Golden Swingtime' | CSil EGou LFli MAsk MBri MJac MWhe NArc NHaw SSea WGwG WLow |
| 'Golden Tolling Bell' | Last listed 1997 |
| 'Golden Treasure' (v) | CLoc CSil ECtt EKMF LFli MBEx MBri MWar |
| 'Golden Vergeer' | EGou SLBF |
| 'Golden Wedding' | EKMF |
| 'Goldsworth Beauty' | CSil LCla |
| 'Golondrina' | CSil EBak MWhe |
| 'Goody Goody' | EBak |
| 'Gordon Thorley' | EKMF MWhe |
| 'Gordon's China Rose' | LCla SKen |
| ¶ 'Gorgeous Gemma' | SLBF |
| 'Gottingen' | CSil EBak |
| 'Göttinger Ruhm' | NArc |
| 'Governor 'Pat' Brown' | EBak MAsk |
| 'Graaf Christian' | EGou |
| 'Grace Darling' | EBak MWhe |
| 'Grace Durham' | Last listed 1998 |
| *gracilis* | See *F. magellanica* var. *gracilis* |
| 'Graf Spee' | Last listed 1998 |
| 'Graf Witte' | CDoC CLTr CSil LFli NArc SKen WGwG |
| 'Grand Duchess' | EGou |
| 'Grand Duke' | EGou |
| 'Grand Prix' | CSil LFli MAsk NArc SKen |
| 'Grand Slam' | LFli SKen |
| ¶ 'Grandad Fred' | SLBF |
| 'Grandma Sinton' | CLoc CSil EMan LCla MAld MAsk MBri MJac MWar MWhe NArc SKen |
| 'Grandpa George' | CSil LCla |
| 'Grandpa Jack' | SLBF |
| 'Grasmere' | MAsk |
| 'Grayrigg' | CPor CSil EKMF EPPr |
| 'Great Ouse' | EPts |
| 'Great Scott' | CLoc CSil SKen |
| 'Green 'n' Gold' | CSil EBak |
| 'Greenpeace' | EKMF LCla MAsk |
| 'Greg Walker' | CSil |
| 'Greta' | CSil EGou |
| 'Gretna Chase' | MBri MWhe |
| 'Grey Lady' | CSil |
| 'Grietje' | EGou |
| 'Groene Kan's Glorie' | CGre EKMF MAsk NArc |
| 'Grumpy' | CSil EHol EPts LCla LFli MAsk MBri MWhe NArc NLak SKen |
| 'Gruss aus dem Bodethal' | CLoc EBak EGou EKMF EPts |
| 'Guinevere' | EBak |
| 'Gustave Doré' | CPor CSil EBak EKMF NArc |
| 'Guy Dauphine' | EBak |
| 'Gwen Dodge' | EGou LCla WGwG |
| 'Gwen Wakelin' | NArc |
| 'Gwen Wallis' | EGou |
| 'Gwendoline' | EGou |
| 'Gypsy Girl' | CPor MAsk NArc SKen |
| 'Gypsy Prince' | CLoc |
| 'H.G. Brown' | CSil EBak MWhe |
| 'Halsall Beauty' | MBri |
| 'Halsall Belle' | LFli MBri |
| 'Halsall Pride' | LFli MBri |
| 'Hampshire Beauty' | MJac |
| 'Hampshire Blue' | CDoC CSil NArc SSea |
| 'Hampshire Pride' | WGwG |
| 'Hampshire Prince' | CSil LVER |
| 'Hampshire Treasure' | CSil |
| 'Hanna' | CSil |
| 'Hannah Gwen' | EKMF |
| 'Hannah Louise' | CInt EPts |

| | |
|---|---|
| 'Hannah Williams' | CLTr MAsk |
| 'Hans van Beek' | NArc |
| 'Happiness' | CSil |
| 'Happy' | CSil EPts LCla LFli MAsk MWhe NArc |
| 'Happy Anniversary' | CLoc EKMF LFli MAsk NArc |
| 'Happy Fellow' | CLoc CSil EBak |
| 'Happy Wedding Day' | CLoc CSil EKMF LCla LFli MAsk MWar MWhe SLBF SSea WLow |
| 'Hapsburgh' | EBak |
| 'Harlow Car' | EKMF LCla LFli MAsk NArc WGwG |
| 'Harlyn' | NArc |
| N 'Harmony' | EBak |
| 'Harnser's Flight' | CSil EGou LCla |
| 'Harriett' | MAsk |
| 'Harrow Pride' | CSil |
| 'Harry Dunnett' | EBak |
| 'Harry Gray' | CLoc CPor CSil EBak ECtt EMan EPts LCla LFli MAsk MBri MJac MWar MWhe NArc SKen SLBF SSea WGwG WLow |
| 'Harry Lye' | Last listed 1996 |
| *hartwegii* | CDoC CSil EGou EKMF LCla MAsk |
| 'Hathersage' | EBak |
| 'Hathor' | EGou |
| *hatsbachii* | CDoC CSil |
| *hatschbachii* | EGou EKMF LCla |
| 'Haute Cuisine' | CLoc CSil EGou EKMF EMan LVER MAsk MWhe NArc |
| 'Hawaiian Night' | NArc |
| 'Hawaiian Princess' | ECtt |
| 'Hawaiian Sunset' | SLBF |
| 'Hawkshead' | CDoC CGle CInt CLoc CSil ECha EGou EKMF ELan EPts GCal GOrc GQui LCla LHil MAsk MBri MGos MJac MWhe NArc NRoo SBid SChu SLBF SMrm WCot WCru |
| 'Hayley Marie' | SLBF |
| * 'Hazel' | EKMF LFli MAsk MWhe |
| 'Heart Throb' | EBak |
| 'Heathfield' | CDoC CPor |
| ¶ 'Heavenly Hayley' | SLBF |
| 'Hebe' | EBak MWhe |
| 'Heidi Ann' ♀ | CDoC CLoc CSil EBak EKMF EMan EPts LCla LFli MAsk MBri MJac MWar MWhe NArc SLBF SSea WGwG |
| 'Heidi Weiss' | NArc |
| 'Heinrich Henkel' | See *F.* 'Andenken an Heinrich Henkel' |
| 'Heirloom' | ECtt EKMF |
| 'Helen Clare' | CLoc EBak NArc |
| 'Helen Elizabeth' | EKMF MBri |
| 'Helen Spence' | EKMF NArc |
| 'Hellan Devine' | MJac |
| 'Hello Dolly' | CLoc |
| 'Hemsleyana' | See *F. microphylla* subsp. *hemsleyana* |
| 'Hendrik Schwab' | Last listed 1996 |
| 'Henri Poincaré' | CDoC EBak EKMF |
| 'Henriette Prins' | Last listed 1998 |
| 'Herald' ♀ | CDoC CSil EBak EKMF LFli MWhe NArc SLBF WGwG WLow |
| 'Herbe de Jacques' | EKMF SKen |
| 'Heritage' | CLoc CSil EBak EKMF NArc |
| 'Herman de Graaff' | EGou |
| 'Hermiena' | CLoc CPor CSil EGou EKMF LCla LFli MAld MWar MWhe NArc SLBF WGwG |
| 'Heron' | CSil EBak EKMF SKen |

| | |
|---|---|
| 'Hessett Festival' | CSil EBak EGou LFli MAsk MWhe NArc |
| 'Heston Blue' | EKMF NArc |
| 'Hi Jinks' | EBak MAsk |
| 'Hiawatha' | NArc |
| *hidalgensis* | See *F. microphylla* subsp. *hidalgensis* |
| 'Hidcote Beauty' | CDoC CLoc CSil EBak EKMF LFli MAsk MWhe NArc SKen SLBF SSea SYvo WGwG |
| 'Hidden Beauty' | NArc |
| ¶ 'Hidden Treasure' | EGou |
| 'Highland Pipes' | CSil EKMF LCla NArc |
| 'Hilda May Salmon' | NArc |
| 'Hindu Belle' | EBak |
| 'Hinnerike' | CSil EKMF LCla MAsk NArc |
| 'Hiroshige' | LCla |
| 'His Excellency' | CSil EBak |
| 'Hobo' | EGou |
| 'Hobson's Choice' | LCla MWar SLBF |
| 'Hokusai' | EKMF |
| 'Holly's Beauty' | LFli MAsk MWar SMur WGwG |
| 'Hollywood Park' | EBak |
| 'Horatio' | CSil ECtt MJac |
| 'Hot Coals' | CSil ECtt EGou EPts |
| 'Howlett's Hardy' | CDoC CLoc CSil EBak ECtt EKMF GCHN LFli MAsk MBal MBri NArc |
| 'Hula Girl' | CSil EBak EKMF LFli MAsk MJac MWar MWhe SLBF |
| 'Humboldt Holiday' | EKMF LFli MAsk NArc |
| 'Hummeltje' | SLBF |
| 'Hungarton' | Last listed 1996 |
| 'Huntsman' | CDoC EKMF LFli MAsk MWhe WGwG WLRN |
| 'Ian Brazewell' | CLoc |
| 'Ian Leedham' | CSil EBak EKMF |
| 'Ice Cream Soda' | EBak NArc |
| 'Iceberg' | CSil EBak NArc |
| 'Icecap' | CSil EKMF LFli MBri NArc |
| 'Iced Champagne' | CLoc EBak LFli MAsk MJac MWar NArc |
| 'Ichiban' | CLoc |
| 'Ida' | EBak |
| 'Igloo Maid' | CLoc CSil EBak EKMF LFli MAsk MJac MWhe NArc SSea |
| 'Imagination' | Last listed 1996 |
| 'Impala' | EGou |
| 'Imperial Crown' | CSil |
| 'Imperial Fantasy' | NArc |
| 'Impudence' | CLoc CSil EBak LFli MAsk SSea |
| 'Impulse' | CLoc EKMF NArc SKen SLBF |
| 'Ina' | MAsk |
| 'Ina Jo Marker' | Last listed 1996 |
| 'Independence' | CSil |
| 'Indian Maid' | EBak EKMF LVER MAsk MBri NArc SKen WGwG |
| 'Inferno' | CSil EKMF |
| 'Ingleore' | Last listed 1998 |
| 'Ingram Maid' | MAsk |
| 'Insa' | NArc |
| 'Insulinde' | CDoC CSil EGou EKMF LCla MAld MWar NArc SLBF |
| 'Intercity' | NArc |
| 'Interlude' | EBak |
| 'Iolanthe' | Last listed 1998 |
| 'Irene L. Peartree' | EGou LCla |
| 'Irene van Zoeren' | MAld NArc |
| 'Iris Amer' | CLoc CSil EBak |
| 'Irma' | Last listed 1998 |
| ¶ 'Isabel Ryan' | CSil |
| 'Isis' | CSil EKMF |
| 'Isle of Mull' | NArc |

| | |
|---|---|
| 'Isle of Purbeck' | LFli MJac |
| 'Italiano' | MJac |
| 'Ivy Grace' | CSil |
| 'Ixion' | NArc |
| 'Jaap Brummel' | Last listed 1998 |
| 'Jack Acland' | ECtt SKen |
| 'Jack Rowlands' | EGou |
| 'Jack Shahan' ♀ | CDoC CLoc CPor CSil EBak EKMF |
| | EMan LCla LFli MAsk MBri MJac |
| | MWar MWhe NFai SKen SLBF |
| | SSea WGwG |
| 'Jack Stanway' | CSil EGou MAsk WEas |
| 'Jackie Bull' | EBak |
| 'Jackpot' | EBak |
| 'Jackqueline' | CSil EKMF LCla MAsk NArc |
| 'Jam Roll' | LVER MAsk |
| 'Jamboree' | EBak MAsk NArc |
| 'James Lye' | EBak EKMF MAsk SKen |
| ¶ 'James Shurvell' | CSil |
| 'James Travis' | CDoC CSil EBak LCla |
| 'Jan Bremer' | NArc |
| ¶ 'Jan S. Kamphuis' | EGou |
| 'Jane Humber' | EKMF LCla MJac NArc |
| 'Jane Lye' | EBak |
| 'Janet Goodwin' | NArc |
| 'Janet Williams' | CSil |
| 'Janice Ann' | EKMF LCla |
| ¶ 'Janice Perry' | CLoc |
| 'Janice Revell' | Last listed 1996 |
| 'Janie' | CLyn |
| 'Janneke Brinkman-Salentijn' | EGou SLBF |
| 'Jap Van't Veer' | LCla SLBF |
| 'Jasper's Likkepot' | NArc |
| 'Javelin' | Last listed 1996 |
| 'Jayess Wendy' | Last listed 1998 |
| 'Jayne Louise Mills' | NArc |
| 'Jean Baker' | CSil |
| 'Jean Campbell' | EBak |
| 'Jean Clark' | SLBF |
| 'Jean Dawes' | Last listed 1998 |
| 'Jean Muir' | Last listed 1996 |
| 'Jean Pidcock' | NArc |
| 'Jeane' | EKMF |
| 'Jennie Rachael' | NArc |
| 'Jennifer Hampson' | CSil |
| 'Jennifer Haslam' | LCla |
| 'Jennifer Lister' | CSil EKMF |
| ¶ 'Jenny May' | SLBF |
| 'Jenny Sorensen' | CSil EKMF LCla MAld MAsk MJac |
| | MWar NArc SLBF |
| 'Jess' | LCla NArc SLBF |
| ¶ 'Jessica's Dream' | SLBF |
| 'Jessie Pearson' | Last listed 1996 |
| 'Jessimae' | LFli MAsk NArc |
| N 'Jester' | CLoc CSil |
| 'Jet Fire' | CSil EBak NArc |
| 'Jiddles' | SLBF |
| 'Jill Storey' | EKMF |
| 'Jill Whitworth' | Last listed 1996 |
| 'Jim Coleman' | MWhe NArc SLBF |
| ¶ 'Jim Dodge' | EPts LCla |
| 'Jim Missin' | MAld MAsk |
| 'Jim Muncaster' | EKMF MAsk NArc |
| *jimenezii* | EGou EKMF LCla |
| ¶ – hybrid | EKMF |
| 'Jimmy Carr' | EKMF |
| 'Jimmy Cricket' | EKMF |
| 'Joan Barnes' | CSil |
| 'Joan Cooper' | CLoc CSil EBak EKMF MAsk |
| 'Joan Gilbert' | CSil |
| 'Joan Goy' | EKMF EPts MAsk MJac MWar |
| | MWhe |

| | |
|---|---|
| 'Joan Knight' | CLoc |
| ¶ 'Joan Leach' | CSil |
| 'Joan Margaret' | MJac |
| 'Joan Morris' | SLBF |
| 'Joan Pacey' | CSil EBak LFli MAsk NArc |
| 'Joan Paxton' | LCla |
| 'Joan Smith' | CSil EBak SYvo |
| 'Joan Young' | EGou LCla |
| 'Jo-Anne Fisher' | EPts |
| 'Joe Kusber' | CSil EBak EKMF MAsk MJac NArc |
| | SKen |
| 'Joe Nicholls' | EKMF |
| 'Joel' | SLBF |
| 'John Boy' | EGou |
| 'John E. Caunt' | CSil EKMF |
| 'John Grooms' | CLoc EKMF LFli MJac MWar |
| 'John Lockyer' | CLoc EBak NArc |
| 'John Maynard Scales' | CDoC EGou LCla MAsk MJac |
| | MWhe NArc |
| 'John Oram' | Last listed 1998 |
| 'John Pitt' | Last listed 1998 |
| 'John Suckley' | EBak |
| 'John Yardell' | Last listed 1996 |
| 'Johnny' | CLoc SSea |
| 'Jomam' | CLoc LCla MAld MAsk MWar |
| | NArc SLBF |
| 'Jon Oram' | CLoc |
| 'Jose's Joan' | MAsk MWhe NArc |
| 'Joy Bielby' | EKMF NArc |
| 'Joy Patmore' ♀ | CLoc CSil EBak EKMF EPts LCla |
| | LFli MAsk MBri MWar MWhe |
| | NArc SKen SLBF |
| 'Joyce Maynard' | MJac |
| 'Joyce Sinton' | EKMF EMan MBri MWar NArc |
| ¶ 'Joyce Storey' | EKMF |
| ¶ 'Joyce Wilson' | LCla |
| 'Jubie-Lin' | Last listed 1998 |
| ¶ 'Jubilee Quest' | SLBF |
| 'Judith Alison Castle' | GCHN |
| 'Judith Mitchell' | Last listed 1996 |
| 'Julchen' | Last listed 1998 |
| 'Jules Daloges' | EBak EKMF |
| 'Julia' | CSil EKMF |
| 'Julie' | MAsk |
| 'Julie Horton' | Last listed 1998 |
| 'Julie Marie' | CSil LCla MAld MJac NArc |
| 'June Gardner' | EKMF |
| 'June Spencer' | EGou |
| N 'Juno' | EBak |
| *juntasensis* | EGou EKMF |
| 'Jupiter Seventy' | EBak |
| 'Justin's Pride' | CSil EKMF MAsk |
| 'Kabibi' | Last listed 1996 |
| 'Kaboutertje' | EKMF |
| 'Kaleidoscope' | CSil EBak LFli NArc |
| 'Karen Bielby' | EKMF |
| 'Karen Bradley' | MJac NArc |
| 'Karen Isles' | EKMF SLBF |
| 'Karen Louise' | CLoc |
| 'Karin de Groot' | EKMF LCla NArc |
| 'Karin Siegers' | CSil |
| 'Kate Harriet' | LCla WGwG |
| 'Kath van Hanegem' | EGou |
| 'Kathleen Muncaster' | EKMF |
| 'Kathleen Smith' | ECtt EKMF NArc |
| 'Kathryn Maidment' | EKMF NArc |
| 'Kathy Louise' | EMan LFli SLBF |
| 'Kathy Scott' | Last listed 1996 |
| 'Kathy's Prince' | ECtt EKMF NArc |
| 'Kathy's Sparkler' | CSil EGou EKMF |
| ¶ 'Katie Elizabeth Ann' | MWar |
| 'Katinka' | EGou EKMF LCla |

| | | |
|---|---|---|
| 'Katrina' | CLoc EBak NArc | |
| 'Katrina Thompsen' | CLoc EKMF LCla MAld MWar SLBF SSea | |
| ¶ 'Katy James' | EKMF | |
| 'Kay Riley' | Last listed 1998 | |
| 'Keele '92' | EKMF | |
| 'Keepsake' | CLoc CSil EBak | |
| 'Kegworth Beauty' | MAsk | |
| 'Kegworth Carnival' | LCla MAsk NArc | |
| 'Kegworth Delight' | Last listed 1997 | |
| 'Kegworth Supreme' | MAsk MJac | |
| 'Kelly Jo' | LCla | |
| 'Kelly Rushton' | Last listed 1997 | |
| 'Ken Goldsmith' | EPts LCla | |
| 'Ken Jennings' | MJac | |
| 'Ken Sharp' | NArc | |
| 'Kenny Dalglish' | CSil EKMF | |
| 'Kernan Robson' | CLoc EBak NArc | |
| 'Kerry Anne' | Last listed 1998 | |
| ¶ 'Kevin Stals' | LCla | |
| 'Keystone' | EBak | |
| 'Khada' | MWhe | |
| 'Kim Wright' | MWhe | |
| 'Kimberly' | EBak | |
| 'King George V' | MBlu | |
| 'King of Bath' | EBak | |
| 'King of Hearts' | EBak | |
| 'King's Ransom' | CLoc CSil EBak MAsk MWhe NArc | |
| 'Kiss 'n' Tell' | MJac MWhe NArc | |
| 'Kit Oxtoby' | ECtt EGou EKMF EMan LCla LFli LVER MAsk MJac NArc SKen SYvo | |
| 'Kiwi' | EBak MAsk SKen | |
| 'Klassic' | Last listed 1998 | |
| 'Kleine Gärtnerin' | Last listed 1997 | |
| 'Kleine Sandra' | EGou | |
| 'Knight Errant' | CSil SLBF SSea | |
| 'Knockout' | CSil EKMF LFli MAsk | |
| 'Kolding Perle' | CSil | |
| ¶ 'Komeet' | LFli | |
| 'Königin der Frühe' | NArc | |
| 'Kon-Tiki' | CLoc CSil EKMF NArc | |
| 'Koralle' | See *F.* 'Coralle' | |
| 'Kwintet' | EBak LCla MJac SKen | |
| 'Kyoto' | CSil EKMF | |
| 'La Apache' | Last listed 1998 | |
| 'La Bianca' | EBak | |
| 'La Campanella' ♀ | CDoC CLoc CSil EBak ECtt EKMF EMan EPts LCla LFli MAld MAsk MBri MJac MWar MWhe NArc NFai SLBF WGwG | |
| 'La Fiesta' | EBak LFli NArc | |
| 'La France' | EBak EKMF | |
| N 'La Neige' | CSil EBak EKMF LCla LFli MAsk | |
| 'La Porte' | CLoc | |
| 'La Rosita' | CSil EBak EGou MAsk SLBF | |
| N 'La Traviata' | EBak | |
| 'Lace Petticoats' | EBak EKMF NArc | |
| 'Lady Beth' | NArc | |
| 'Lady Boothby' | CSil EBak EKMF LCla LFli MAsk NArc SBid SKen SLBF SMrm SRms | |
| ¶ 'Lady Framlingham' | EPts | |
| ¶ 'Lady Heytesbury' | EKMF | |
| 'Lady in Grey' | EKMF | |
| 'Lady in Pink' | LFli SLBF | |
| 'Lady Isobel Barnett' | CLoc CSil EBak EKMF LCla LFli MAsk MBri MJac MWar MWhe NArc | |
| 'Lady Kathleen Spence' | CSil EBak EKMF MAsk MWhe NArc | |
| 'Lady Love' | MBri | |
| 'Lady Patricia Mountbatten' | CSil EKMF EMan LCla MAsk MBri MWhe NArc WGwG | |
| 'Lady Ramsey' | EBak MJac NArc | |
| 'Lady Rebecca' | CLoc | |
| 'Lady Thumb' ♀ | More than 30 suppliers | |
| 'Lady's Smock' | EKMF | |
| § 'Laing's Hybrid' | Last listed 1996 | |
| 'Lakeland Princess' | EBak NArc | |
| 'Lakeside' | CLoc EBak | |
| 'Laleham' | Last listed 1996 | |
| 'Lambada' | EKMF LFli SLBF | |
| 'Lamme Goedzak' | Last listed 1997 | |
| 'Lancashire Lad' | CDoC LCla MWar | |
| 'Lancashire Lass' | EMan MBri NArc WLRN | |
| 'Lancelot' | EBak LCla | |
| 'Land van Beveren' | MWar NArc SLBF SYvo | |
| 'Lark' | EPts | |
| 'L'Arlésienne' | CLoc | |
| 'Lassie' | CDoC CLoc CPor EBak LFli NArc | |
| N 'Laura' | CLoc CSil EKMF EPts MAsk MWhe SLBF | |
| 'Laura Amanda' | EPts | |
| ¶ 'Lavender Ann' | EGou | |
| ¶ 'Lavender Blue' | LCla | |
| 'Lavender Cascade' | Last listed 1996 | |
| 'Lavender Kate' | CLoc EBak MJac | |
| 'Lavender Lace' | MWhe | |
| 'Lavender Lady' | CSil MAld | |
| 'Lazy Lady' | EBak | |
| 'Le Berger' | EKMF | |
| 'Lechlade Apache' | EGou LCla | |
| 'Lechlade Chinaman' | CDoC CSil LCla MAsk | |
| 'Lechlade Debutante' | EGou EKMF LCla | |
| 'Lechlade Fire-eater' | LCla | |
| 'Lechlade Gorgon' | CDoC CSil EKMF LCla MAsk NArc | |
| 'Lechlade Magician' | CDoC CSil EKMF LCla MAsk NArc | |
| 'Lechlade Maiden' | CSil | |
| 'Lechlade Martianess' | EGou EKMF | |
| 'Lechlade Potentate' | EGou LCla MAsk | |
| 'Lechlade Rocket' | EGou EKMF | |
| 'Lechlade Tinkerbell' | LCla | |
| 'Lechlade Violet' | CDoC CSil EKMF SSoC | |
| 'Lee Anthony' | CSil | |
| 'Leica' | EKMF MJac | |
| 'Leicestershire Silver' | MJac NArc | |
| 'Len Bielby' | CDoC EKMF LCla | |
| 'Lena' ♀ | CDoC CLoc CPor CSil EBak EKMF EPts LFli LVER MAsk MBal MBri MJac MPla MWhe NArc NFai SKen SPer SRms SSea WEas WGwG | |
| 'Lena Dalton' | CLoc EBak EKMF LFli MAsk MBri MJac MWhe NArc | |
| 'Leonhart von Fuchs' | EGou | |
| 'Leonora' ♀ | CLoc CPor CSil EBak EKMF LCla MAsk MBri MWar MWhe NArc SLBF WGwG | |
| 'Lesley' | LCla | |
| 'Lett's Delight' | EGou EPts | |
| 'Letty Lye' | EBak LCla | |
| 'Leverhulme' | See *F.* 'Leverkusen' | |
| § 'Leverkusen' | CDoC CLoc CSil EBak EGou EKMF LCla LHil MJac MWhe SSoC WGwG | |
| 'Li Kai Lin' | CSil | |
| 'Libra' | Last listed 1996 | |
| N 'Liebesträume' | EBak | |
| 'Liebriez' | CDoC CSil EBak EKMF EPts NArc | |
| * 'Lilac' | CSil EBak | |
| ¶ 'Lilac Dainty' | CSil | |
| 'Lilac Lady' | MJac | |
| 'Lilac Lustre' | CGre CLoc CSil EBak EKMF MBri NArc | |
| 'Lilac Princess' | MJac | |

| | |
|---|---|
| 'Lilac Queen' | EBak |
| 'Lillian Annetts' | LCla LFli SLBF |
| 'Lillibet' | CLoc CSil EBak LFli NArc SKen WGwG |
| 'Lillydale' | CSil |
| 'Lilo Vogt' | LCla MAsk NArc WGwG |
| 'Linda Goulding' | CSil EBak EGou MAld MAsk MWhe NArc SSea |
| 'Linda Grace' | EKMF MJac |
| 'Lindisfarne' | CLoc EBak EKMF LCla LFli MAsk MJac MWar NArc |
| 'Linet' | Last listed 1997 |
| 'Lisa' | CDoC CSil EPts |
| 'Lisa Ashton' | NArc |
| 'Lisa Jane' | MWhe |
| ¶ 'Lisa Rowe' | CSil |
| 'Lisi' | EKMF NArc |
| 'Little Beauty' | EKMF MWhe NArc |
| 'Little Gene' | EBak |
| 'Little Jewel' | SKen |
| 'Little Ouse' | EGou LCla MWhe |
| 'Little Ronnie' | MWhe |
| 'Little Witch' | EGou EKMF LCla SLBF |
| 'Lively Lady' | Last listed 1998 |
| 'Liver Bird' | NArc |
| 'Liz' | CSil EBak NArc |
| 'Lochinver' | CSil |
| 'Loeky' | CLoc EBak SLBF SSea |
| 'Logan Garden' | See *F. magellanica* 'Logan Woods' |
| 'Lolita' | EBak MAsk |
| 'Lonely Ballerina' | CLoc |
| 'Long Distance' | Last listed 1997 |
| 'Long Preston' | Last listed 1998 |
| 'Long Wings' | CSil EKMF LCla MAld MAsk NArc |
| 'Look East' | EGou |
| 'Lora Fairclough' | MJac NArc |
| 'Lord Byron' | CLoc EBak EKMF LCla NArc |
| 'Lord Derby' | NArc |
| 'Lord Lonsdale' | CSil EBak EPts LCla LHil MAsk MWhe NArc WEas |
| 'Lord Roberts' | CLoc CSil NArc SKen |
| 'Lorelei' | Last listed 1998 |
| 'Lorna Hercherson' | Last listed 1996 |
| 'Lorna Swinbank' | CLoc NArc |
| 'Lorraine's Delight' | Last listed 1998 |
| 'Lottie Hobby' | CDoC CInt CLoc CMGP CSil ECtt EKMF EPts GEil LBlm LCla LFli MAld MAsk MHar NArc WFoF WPyg |
| 'Lou Rinzema' | Last listed 1998 |
| 'Louise Emershaw' | CSil EBak MAsk MJac |
| 'Louise Foster' | MWar |
| ¶ 'Louise Nicholls' | EKMF |
| 'Lovable' | EBak MAsk |
| 'Love in Bloom' | EGou |
| 'Love Knot' | Last listed 1996 |
| 'Loveliness' | CLoc CSil EBak EKMF MWhe |
| 'Lovely Linda' | SLBF |
| 'Love's Reward' | CLoc CSil EKMF EPts LCla MAld MJac MWar MWhe SLBF |
| I 'Loxensis' ♀ | EBak EGou EKMF LCla MAsk |
| 'Loxhore Angelus' | CSil |
| 'Loxhore Calypso' | EKMF |
| 'Loxhore Cancan' | CSil EKMF |
| 'Loxhore Cavalcade' | Last listed 1998 |
| 'Loxhore Chorale' | CSil |
| 'Loxhore Clarion' | Last listed 1997 |
| 'Loxhore Cotillon' | CSil |
| ¶ 'Loxhore Herald' | CSil |
| ¶ 'Loxhore Lullaby' | CSil |
| 'Loxhore Mazurka' | CSil |
| 'Loxhore Minuet' | CSil |

| | |
|---|---|
| 'Loxhore Operetta' | CSil |
| 'Loxhore Posthorn' | CSil |
| 'Loxhore Tarantella' | CSil |
| 'Lubbertje Hop' | Last listed 1998 |
| 'Lucille' | NArc |
| 'Lucky Strike' | CLoc CSil EBak LFli NArc |
| 'Lucy Harris' | CSil |
| 'Lucy Locket' | MJac |
| 'Lula Bell' | LCla |
| 'Lunter's Trots' | NArc |
| 'Luscious' | LFli |
| 'Lustre' | EBak NArc SLBF |
| *lycioides* hort. | See *F.* 'Lycioides' |
| § 'Lycioides' | CSil LCla |
| § *lycioides* Andrews | CSil EBak EGou EKMFf |
| 'Lye's Elegance' | CSil LCla MAsk |
| 'Lye's Excelsior' | EBak LCla |
| 'Lye's Favourite' | Last listed 1996 |
| 'Lye's Own' | EBak MAsk SYvo |
| 'Lye's Unique' | CDoC CLTr CLoc CSil EBak EGou EKMF EPts LCla LFli MAld MAsk MJac MWar MWhe NArc SKen SLBF SYvo |
| 'Lylac Sunsa' | EKMF |
| 'Lynette' | CLoc |
| 'Lynn Ellen' | EBak NArc |
| 'Lynne Marshall' | CSil |
| 'Mabel Greaves' | CSil MAsk |
| 'Machu Picchu' | CLoc CSil EKMF EPts LCla MWar NArc |
| *macrophylla* | EKMF |
| ¶ *macrostigma* | EGou |
| ¶ 'Madame Aubin' | EKMF |
| 'Madame Butterfly' | CLoc |
| 'Madame Cornélissen' ♀ | CDoC CLoc CPor CSil EBak EBee EKMF ENot GChr LFli LVER MAsk MBar MBri MGos MJac MWhe NArc NLak SPer SRms WFar WGwG |
| 'Madame Eva Boye' | EBak EKMF |
| 'Maddy' | Last listed 1996 |
| 'Madelaine Sweeney' | MBri |
| 'Maes-y-Groes' | EKMF |
| *magdalenae* | EGou EKMF |
| *magellanica* | EKMF EMil GOrc LHil MHlr MWhi NFor NPer SPer WFar WOak WRha WWat |
| - 'Alba' | See *F. magellanica* var. *molinae* |
| I - 'Alba Aureovariegata' | CDoC EPfP LHop LRHS MBri SPer SSea |
| - 'Alba Variegata' | CSil EKMF NHaw WEas |
| ¶ - 'Americana Elegans' | CSil |
| ¶ - 'Comber' | CSil |
| - var. *conica* | CSil EKMF |
| ¶ - 'Fire Gold' | LRHS |
| - 'Globosa' | See *F.* 'Globosa' |
| § - var. *gracilis* ♀ | CDoC CLoc CSil EKMF LBlm MAsk NArc SRms WPic |
| - - 'Aurea' | CBot CDoC CMHG CSil CTre EAst EBee EGou EHoe EKMF ELan ENot GCHN GQui LCla LFli MAsk MWat MWhe SDix SKen SLBF SPer SPla SSea WFar WGwG WHen WRus |
| § - - 'Tricolor' (v) | CDoC CSil EHol EKMF EPts EWes GOrc LCla LFli MAld MAsk SKen SLBF SRms SSea |
| - - 'Variegata' ♀ | CGle CMHG CSil CTre EBak EBee EGou ENot LCla LHil MAsk MBal MGos MRav NArc SChu SDix SKen SPer WAbe WEas |
| § - 'Logan Woods' | CLTr CSil EKMF GCal LFli SMrm WAbe |

| | |
|---|---|
| – 'Longipedunculata' | CSil EKMF |
| – var. **macrostema** | EKMF |
| – – 'Variegata' | EGou |
| § – var. **molinae** | CDoC CGle CHad CSil EBak EGou EKMF ELan GOrc ISea LCla LFli MBlu MNrw MWgw MWhe NChi NFai NFor NPer NRoo SKen SPer WAbe WBod WEas WOak |
| § – – 'Enstone' | EGou |
| – – 'Enstone Gold' | Last listed 1996 |
| – – 'Golden Sharpitor' | WAbe WCot |
| ¶ – – 'Mr Knight's Blush' | EOld |
| § – – 'Sharpitor' (v) | CB&S CDoC CSil CTre EBak ECha EGou EKMF ELan LHop MAsk MBar MBri MPla MRav MWat NPer SMrm SPer SSea WCru WFar WKif WRus WSHC |
| ¶ – var. **myrtifolia** | CDoC |
| – var. **prostrata** | CSil |
| – var. **pumila** | CDoC CSil EWes GCal SIng SPer SRot |
| – 'Riccartonii' ♀ | See *F.* 'Riccartonii' |
| § – 'Thompsonii' ♀ | CDoC ECGP EKMF GCal MBel SKen SRms |
| § – 'Versicolor' (v) ♀ | More than 30 suppliers |
| 'Magenta Flush' | Last listed 1996 |
| 'Magic Flute' | CLoc CSil MJac |
| 'Maharaja' | EBak NArc |
| 'Maike' | NArc |
| 'Majebo' | NArc |
| 'Major Heaphy' | EBak EKMF MAsk MWar MWhe NArc |
| 'Malibu Mist' | CSil EGou EKMF LCla LVER MAsk NArc |
| 'Mama Bleuss' | EBak NArc |
| 'Mancunian' | CSil EGou LCla LFli MAsk NArc |
| N 'Mandarin' | EBak LFli NArc |
| 'Mandi' | EGou EKMF LCla SLBF |
| 'Mandy' | Last listed 1998 |
| 'Mantilla' | CDoC CLoc CSil EBak EKMF LCla LFli MAsk MJac MWhe NArc |
| 'Maori Pipes' | CSil EGou |
| 'Marbled Sky' | NArc |
| 'Marco Jan' | Last listed 1998 |
| 'Marcus Graham' | CLoc EGou EKMF LCla LFli MAsk MWar MWhe NArc SLBF |
| 'Marcus Hanton' | CSil EKMF LCla MAsk NArc |
| 'Mardale' | Last listed 1996 |
| 'Mardi Gras' | EBak WGwG |
| 'Margaret' ♀ | CDoC CLoc CPor CSil CTri EBak EGou EKMF ENot GCHN LCla LFli LVER MAsk MBal MWar MWhe NArc SKen SLBF SRms SSea WGwG WStI |
| 'Margaret Brown' ♀ | CDoC CLTr CLoc CSil CTri EBak EKMF LCla LFli MAsk MPla MWhe NArc SKen SLBF WLow WStI |
| 'Margaret Davidson' | CLoc |
| 'Margaret Dawson' | MAsk |
| 'Margaret Hazelwood' | EKMF |
| 'Margaret Kendrick' | MBri |
| 'Margaret Pilkington' | CGre EKMF LCla LFli MAsk MBri MJac MWar NArc SSea |
| 'Margaret Roe' | CDoC CSil EBak EKMF MJac NArc SKen |
| 'Margaret Rose' | MJac |
| 'Margaret Susan' | EBak |
| 'Margaret Tebbit' | Last listed 1996 |
| 'Margarita' | Last listed 1996 |
| 'Margarite Dawson' | CSil NArc |
| 'Margery Blake' | CSil EBak |
| 'Maria Landy' | EKMF EMan LCla MAsk MWar NArc SLBF |

| | |
|---|---|
| 'Maria Merrills' | EKMF EMan NArc |
| 'Marietta' | Last listed 1998 |
| 'Marilyn Olsen' | CSil EKMF EPts LCla LFli MAld MWar NArc |
| 'Marin Belle' | EBak LCla NArc |
| 'Marin Glow' ♀ | CLoc CSil EBak EKMF LCla LFli MAsk MWhe NArc SLBF SYvo |
| 'Marinka' ♀ | CLoc CSil EBak ECtt EKMF EMan LCla LFli LVER MAld MAsk MBri MJac MWar MWhe NArc NFai SKen SLBF SSea WGwG |
| 'Marjory Almond' | Last listed 1998 |
| 'Mark Kirby' | EKMF |
| 'Marlea's Vuurbol' | EGou |
| 'Marlene Gilbee' | MAsk |
| 'Martha Brown' | Last listed 1996 |
| 'Martha Franck' | Last listed 1998 |
| 'Martin Hayward' | SKen |
| ¶ 'Martin's Catherina' | EGou |
| ¶ 'Martin's Choice' | EGou |
| 'Martin's Cinderella' | EGou |
| ¶ 'Martin's Double Delicate' | EGou |
| 'Martin's Midnight' | Last listed 1998 |
| 'Martin's Yellow Suprise' | CLoc EGou EKMF SLBF |
| 'Marton Smith' | MWhe |
| 'Marty' | EBak |
| 'Mary' ♀ | CDoC CLoc CSil EGou EKMF EPts LCla LFli MAld MAsk MLan MWar MWhe NArc SKen SLBF SSea WGwG |
| 'Mary Caunt' | EKMF |
| 'Mary Ellen' | Last listed 1996 |
| 'Mary Ellen Guffey' | Last listed 1998 |
| 'Mary Fairclo' | EGou |
| 'Mary Joan' | EKMF MAsk |
| 'Mary Lockyer' | CLoc EBak NArc |
| 'Mary Neujean' | MBri |
| 'Mary Poppins' | LCla NArc |
| 'Mary Reynolds' | Last listed 1998 |
| 'Mary Thorne' | CSil EBak |
| 'Mary Wright' | MWhe |
| 'Masquerade' | EBak EKMF EMan MWhe NArc |
| 'Matador' | CSil |
| **mathewsii** | EGou EKMF |
| ¶ 'Matthew Morrison' | EGou |
| 'Maureen' | NArc |
| 'Maureen Ward' | EKMF |
| 'Mauve Beauty' | CSil EGou EKMF |
| 'Mauve Lace' | CSil |
| 'Mauve Wisp' | NArc |
| 'Max Jaffa' | CSil MAsk NArc |
| 'May Rogers' | Last listed 1998 |
| 'Mayblossom' | ECtt SLBF |
| 'Mayfayre' | CLoc |
| 'Mayfield' | MWhe NArc |
| 'Maytime' | Last listed 1998 |
| 'Meadowlark' | EBak ECtt EKMF NArc |
| 'Medalist' | Last listed 1996 |
| 'Meditation' | CLoc CPor CSil |
| 'Meike Meursing' | Last listed 1997 |
| 'Melanie' | CDoC NArc SLBF |
| 'Melody' | CSil EBak LFli MAsk MWhe NArc |
| 'Melody Ann' | EBak |
| 'Melting Moments' | EKMF NArc |
| 'Memo' | Last listed 1998 |
| 'Mendocino Mini' | EKMF |
| 'Menna' | NArc |
| 'Merlin' | CSil LCla |
| 'Merry England' | MAsk |
| 'Merry Mary' | CSil EBak EKMF NArc |
| 'Mexicali Rose' | CLoc |
| 'Michael' | CSil EPts MAsk |

| | |
|---|---|
| 'Michael Kurtz' | NArc |
| 'Michele Wallace' | Last listed 1998 |
| *michoacanensis* | Last listed 1998 |
| 'Micky Goult' | CLoc CSil EKMF EPts LCla LFli |
| | MAld MAsk MJac MWhe NArc |
| | SSea |
| 'Microchip' | SLBF |
| *microphylla* | CB&S CDoC CGle CLoc CSam |
| | CSil CTre EBak ERav ERea GRei |
| | MHlr SLon SSea STre WCot WCru |
| | WEas |
| § - subsp. *aprica* | EKMF LCla MAsk |
| § - subsp. *hemsleyana* | CDoC CSil EGou EKMF LCla |
| | MWhe SKen |
| § - subsp. *hidalgensis* | CSil EGou EKMF LBlm LCla SLBF |
| | SRms |
| ¶ - Kew form | CDoC |
| - subsp. *microphylla* | CSil WWat |
| - subsp. *quercetorum* | EGou EKMF LCla LFli |
| 'Midas' | LFli MAsk MBri NArc |
| 'Midnight Sun' | CSil EBak EPts LFli NArc SKen |
| 'Midwinter' | NArc |
| 'Mieke Alferink' | Last listed 1998 |
| 'Mieke Meursing' | CLoc CSil EBak ECtt EKMF LFli |
| | MBri MJac MWar MWhe NArc |
| | SLBF |
| 'Miep Aalhuizen' | EGou EKMF LCla |
| N 'Mikado' | EGou |
| 'Mike Oxtoby' | EKMF MAsk |
| 'Millrace' | LCla |
| 'Mimi Kubischta' | NArc |
| 'Mina Knudde' | NArc |
| 'Ming' | CLoc CPor CSil |
| 'Miniature Jewels' | SLBF |
| N *minimiflora* | See *F. microphylla* subsp. |
| | *hidalgensis* |
| 'Minirose' | CSil EKMF LCla LFli MAsk MWar |
| | MWhe SKen |
| 'Minnesota' | EBak |
| 'Minutifolia' | CLyn |
| * *minutissima* | Last listed 1996 |
| 'Mipam' | SLBF |
| 'Mirjana' | NArc |
| 'Mischief' | CSil NArc |
| 'Miss Aubrey' | Last listed 1998 |
| 'Miss California' | CLoc EBak ECtt EKMF LFli MAsk |
| | MBri MWhe NArc SKen |
| 'Miss Debbie' | LFli MJac |
| 'Miss Great Britain' | CSil |
| 'Miss Marilyn' | Last listed 1998 |
| 'Miss Muffett' | Last listed 1998 |
| 'Miss Vallejo' | EBak NArc |
| 'Mission Bells' | CDoC CLoc CSil EBak EKMF LCla |
| | LFli MAsk MWhe NArc SKen |
| | WGwG |
| 'Mistoque' | CDoC CSil NArc |
| 'Misty Blue' | CSil NArc |
| 'Misty Haze' | CSil LVER MWar |
| 'Misty Morn' | Last listed 1996 |
| 'Misty Pink' | EKMF NArc |
| 'Moira Ann' | ECtt |
| 'Molesworth' | CSil EBak EKMF LFli MJac MWhe |
| | NArc SKen |
| 'Mollie Beaulah' | CSil ECtt EKMF NArc |
| 'Molly Chatfield' | NArc |
| 'Money Spinner' | CLoc EBak |
| ¶ 'Monica Dare' | EGou |
| 'Monsieur Thibaut' | ENot LCla MAld SKen |
| 'Monte Rosa' | CLoc |
| 'Monterey' | MWhe |
| 'Montevideo' | EGou |
| 'Montrose Village' | CPor CSil MWhe |

| | |
|---|---|
| 'Monty Python' | Last listed 1998 |
| 'Monument' | CSil |
| 'Mood Indigo' | CSil LVER MAsk MWar NArc SLBF |
| | WGwG |
| 'Moon Glow' | Last listed 1996 |
| 'Moonbeam' | CLoc CSil MAsk MWhe |
| 'Moonlight Sonata' | CLoc CSil EBak MAsk MJac NArc |
| | SKen |
| 'Moonraker' | CSil LFli NArc |
| 'Moonshot' | SKen |
| 'Morcott' | NArc |
| 'More Applause' | CLoc EKMF LVER MWhe NArc |
| 'Morning Cloud' | LFli NArc |
| 'Morning Glow' | LFli NArc |
| 'Morning Light' | CLoc CSil EBak NArc |
| 'Morning Mist' | EBak NArc |
| 'Morning Star' | MBri |
| 'Morrells' | EBak |
| 'Moth Blue' | CSil EBak LFli NArc |
| 'Mother's Day' | Last listed 1996 |
| 'Mountain Mist' | EKMF LFli MJac |
| 'Moyra' | EKMF |
| 'Mr A. Huggett' | CLoc CSil EKMF EPts LCla MAsk |
| | MWhe NArc |
| 'Mr P.D. Lee' | MWhe |
| 'Mr W. Rundle' | EBak NArc |
| 'Mrs Churchill' | CLoc |
| 'Mrs Janice Morrison' | EGou |
| 'Mrs John D. Fredericks' | CSil |
| 'Mrs Lawrence Lyon' | EBak |
| 'Mrs Lovell Swisher' | CDoC CSil EBak EKMF LCla MBri |
| | MJac MWhe NArc |
| 'Mrs Marshall' | CSil EBak MAsk NArc SLBF |
| 'Mrs Popple' ♀ | More than 30 suppliers |
| 'Mrs Susan Brookfield' | LCla NArc |
| 'Mrs Victor Reiter' | CSil |
| 'Mrs W. Castle' | CSil NArc WGwG |
| 'Mrs W.P. Wood' ♀ | CDoC CLoc EKMF NArc |
| 'Mrs W. Rundle' | CLoc CSil EBak EKMF LFli MAld |
| | MWhe NArc SLBF |
| 'Muirfield' | Last listed 1996 |
| 'Multa' | Last listed 1997 |
| 'Muriel' | CLoc EBak ECtt EKMF MWhe |
| | NArc SKen |
| 'Musi' | Last listed 1998 |
| 'My Beauty' | Last listed 1996 |
| 'My Dear' | Last listed 1998 |
| 'My Fair Lady' | CLoc CSil EBak NArc |
| 'My Honey' | CSil LFli MAsk NArc |
| 'Mystique' | MAsk |
| 'Nancy Darnley' | EKMF |
| 'Nancy Lou' | CDoC CGre CLoc EKMF EPts LCla |
| | LFli LVER MAld MAsk MJac MWar |
| | MWhe NArc SKen SLBF |
| 'Nancy Scrivener' | NArc SLBF |
| 'Nanny Ed' | LFli MBri |
| 'Natalie Jones' | Last listed 1998 |
| 'Natasha Sinton' | CLoc CSil ECtt EKMF EMan LCla |
| | LFli LVER MAld MAsk MBri MJac |
| | MWar MWhe NArc SLBF WGwG |
| | WLRN |
| 'Native Dancer' | EBak |
| 'Naughty Nicole' | SLBF |
| 'Nautilus' | EBak |
| 'Navato' | LFli |
| 'Navy Blue' | CSil NArc |
| 'Neapolitan' | EPts MAsk MWhe SKen SLBF |
| 'Neil Clyne' | MWhe |
| 'Nell Gwyn' | CLoc CSil EBak NArc |
| 'Nellie Nuttall' ♀ | CLoc CSil EBak EGou EKMF EPts |
| | LCla LFli MAld MAsk MWar |
| | MWhe NArc SLBF SSea |

| | |
|---|---|
| 'Neopolitan' | CLoc CSil EGou EKMF LCla NArc |
| 'Nettala' | EGou |
| 'Neue Welt' | CSil EBak |
| 'Neville Young' | MAsk |
| 'New Fascination' | EBak NArc SKen |
| 'Nice 'n' Easy' | LVER MBri MJac MWar MWhe NArc |
| 'Nicholas Hughes' | NArc |
| 'Nicis Findling' | CSil EKMF EPts LCla MAsk NArc SLBF |
| 'Nicky Veerman' | Last listed 1998 |
| 'Nicola' | CLoc EBak |
| N 'Nicola Claire' | NArc |
| 'Nicola Jane' | CDoC CPor CSil EBak EKMF EPts LCla LFli MAld MAsk MBri MJac MWhe NArc SLBF |
| 'Nicolette' | MJac |
| 'Night and Day' | Last listed 1997 |
| 'Nightingale' | CLoc CSil EBak NArc |
| § nigricans | EGou EKMF LCla |
| – x gehrigeri | EKMF |
| 'Nimue' | EGou MAsk NArc |
| 'Nina Wills' | EBak |
| 'Niobe' | EBak |
| 'Niula' | EKMF LCla |
| 'No Name' | EBak |
| 'Norah Henderson' | NArc |
| 'Norfolk Belle' | Last listed 1998 |
| 'Norfolk Ivor' | EGou |
| 'Norma Nield' | Last listed 1998 |
| 'Norman Greenhill' | Last listed 1997 |
| 'Norman Mitchinson' | EGou |
| 'Normandy Bell' | CSil EBak |
| 'North Cascades' | MAsk |
| 'Northern Pride' | MAsk |
| 'Northilda' | NArc |
| 'Northumbrian Belle' | EBak MJac NArc WGwG |
| 'Northway' | CLoc CSil LCla LFli MAsk MJac MWhe NArc |
| 'Norvell Gillespie' | EBak |
| 'Novato' | EBak NArc |
| 'Novella' | EBak NArc |
| 'Noyo Star' | CSil LFli |
| 'Nunthorpe Gem' | CSil NArc |
| 'Nuwenspete' | Last listed 1998 |
| 'Oakham' | Last listed 1996 |
| obconica | EGou EKMF LCla |
| ¶ 'Obcylin' | EGou |
| 'Obergärtner Koch' | EKMF LCla NArc |
| 'Ocean Beach' | EPts MAsk NArc |
| 'Oddfellow' | CSil NArc |
| 'Oetnang' | SCoo |
| 'Old Somerset' | LCla LFli MAsk MWhe |
| 'Ole 7 Up' | MAld |
| 'Olive Moon' | SLBF |
| 'Olive Smith' | CSil EPts LCla MAld MAsk MJac MWhe NArc |
| 'Olympia' | CSil EKMF MWhe |
| 'Olympic Lass' | EBak NArc |
| 'Olympic Sunset' | Last listed 1997 |
| 'Oosje' | See F. x bacillaris 'Oosje' |
| 'Opalescent' | CLoc |
| 'Orange Bell' | Last listed 1996 |
| ¶ 'Orange Cocktail' | EKMF |
| 'Orange Crush' | CLoc CSil EBak LFli MAsk MWar MWhe NArc |
| 'Orange Crystal' | CSil EBak EKMF LFli MAsk MBri MJac MWhe NArc NFai SKen |
| 'Orange Drops' | CLoc CSil EBak EKMF EPts LHil MAsk MWhe NArc SKen SYvo |
| 'Orange Flare' | CLoc CSil EBak EKMF LCla MJac MWhe NArc SLBF SSea |
| 'Orange King' | CLoc CSil EGou EMan SSea |
| 'Orange Mirage' | CLoc CSil EBak LCla LFli LVER MAld MAsk MBri MWar MWhe NArc |
| 'Orangeblossom' | CSil LCla NArc SLBF |
| 'Oranje van Os' | MJac MWhe |
| 'Orchid Princess' | Last listed 1996 |
| 'Orient Express' | CDoC CSil EGou LCla MAsk MWar MWhe NArc |
| Oriental Flame | EKMF NArc |
| 'Oriental Sunrise' | MAsk MWhe |
| 'Ornamental Pearl' | CLoc EBak NArc SLBF |
| 'Ortenburger Festival' | NArc |
| 'Orwell' | EGou |
| 'Oso Sweet' | Last listed 1996 |
| 'Other Fellow' | CSil EBak EKMF EPts LCla MAsk MJac MWhe NArc SLBF SYvo |
| 'Our Darling' | CSil MWhe NArc |
| 'Our Ted' | EGou |
| 'Ovation' | Last listed 1996 |
| 'Overbecks' | See F. magellanica var. molinae 'Sharpitor' |
| 'Overbecks Ruby' | GBuc WCot |
| 'P.J.B.' | LCla LFli NArc |
| 'Pabbe's Teudebel' | Last listed 1998 |
| 'Pabbe's Tudebekje' | CSil EGou |
| pachyrrhiza | EKMF |
| 'Pacific Grove' | EBak |
| 'Pacific Queen' | CLoc EBak EKMF NArc |
| 'Pacquesa' ♀ | CDoC CSil EBak EKMF EPts LFli MAsk MJac MWar MWhe NArc |
| 'Padre Pio' | MJac |
| 'Pale Flame' | MWhe NArc |
| pallescens | EGou EKMF LCla |
| 'Pam Plack' | LCla |
| 'Pamela Hutchinson' | MAld NArc |
| 'Pamela Knights' | EBak |
| 'Pan' | EGou LCla NArc |
| 'Pan America' | EBak |
| 'Pangea' | Last listed 1998 |
| paniculata | CBot CDoC CEnd CLTr CSam CTbh EBak EGou EKMF LCla LHop MAsk NArc SHFr SLBF SLod SMrm WFoF WRos |
| * – var. mixensis | Last listed 1997 |
| 'Pantaloons' | EBak NArc |
| 'Panylla Prince' | LCla SLBF |
| 'Papa Bleuss' | CLoc EBak |
| 'Papoose' | CDoC CSil EBak EKMF LCla MAsk MPla NArc |
| 'Paramour' | LFli NArc |
| 'Party Frock' | CLoc CSil EBak LCla LFli LVER NArc |
| parviflora hort. | See F. x bacillaris |
| – Lindley | EBak |
| 'Pa's Princess' | Last listed 1996 |
| 'Pastel' | EBak |
| 'Pat Crofts' | NArc |
| 'Pat Meara' | CLoc EBak |
| 'Pathetique' | CLoc |
| 'Patience' | CSil EBak EGou EKMF MJac NArc |
| 'Patio Party' | MBri |
| 'Patio Princess' | CDoC CPor CSil LCla LFli MBri MJac MWar MWhe NArc SSea |
| N 'Patricia' | CSil EBak |
| 'Patricia Ann' | EKMF MWar |
| 'Patricia Joan Yates' | EGou |
| 'Patty Evans' | EBak MBri NArc |
| 'Patty Sue' | LCla LFli MBri MWar WLRN |
| 'Paul Berry' | CSil EKMF SLBF |
| 'Paul Cambon' | EBak EKMF NArc |
| 'Paul Roe' | EKMF MBri MJac |

'Paula Jane' ♀ — CLoc LCla LFli MAsk MBri MJac MWar MWhe SLBF
'Paula Johnson' — Last listed 1997
'Pauline Rawlins' — CLoc EBak
¶ 'Paulus' — SLBF
'Paxos Trail' — MAld
PC&H 247 — CFee
'Peace' — EBak
'Peaches 'n' Cream' — Last listed 1998
'Peachy' — EGou MAsk MJac
'Peachy Keen' — EBak
'Peacock' — CLoc
'Pearly Gates' — Last listed 1996
'Pebble Mill' — Last listed 1996
'Pee Wee Rose' — CSil EBak EKMF NArc
'Peggy King' — CDoC CSil EBak LCla MWhe NArc SRms
'Peloria' — CLoc EBak MAsk NArc
'Pennine' — MBri MWar
'People's Princess' — MJac
'Peper Harow' — EBak
'Pepi' — CLoc EBak
'Peppermint Candy' — EKMF LFli SCoo WGwG
'Peppermint Stick' — CDoC CLoc CSil EBak EKMF EMan LCla LFli LVER MAsk MBri MJac MWhe NArc SKen SSea
'Perestroika' — Last listed 1998
'Perky Pink' — EBak EPts LCla MAsk MWhe NArc SKen
'Perry Park' — EBak MAsk MBri MJac NArc
'Perry's Jumbo' — NPer
*perscandens* — CSil EGou EKMF LCla SLBF SVen
'Personality' — EBak NArc
'Peter Bielby' — EGou EKMF MWar SLBF
'Peter Crooks' — CSil EKMF LCla MAsk NArc
'Peter James' — CSil EKMF
'Peter Pan' — CSil EHol SPer
'Peter Sanderson' — EKMF MJac NArc
*petiolaris* — EGou EKMF LCla
'Petit Fleur' — CSil
'Petit Four' — CSil
'Petit Point' — LFli
'Petite' — EBak NArc
'Petronella' — MAsk MWar
'Pharaoh' — CLoc
'Phénoménal' — CPor CSil EBak EKMF EPts LFli MAsk SKen
'Phyllis' ♀ — CDoC CLoc CPor CSil EBak EKMF EPts LCla LFli LHil MAsk MBal MJac MWhe NArc NFai SKen SLBF SSoC WGwG
'Phyrne' — CSil EBak EKMF NArc
'Piet G. Vergeer' — NArc
'Piet Heemskerke' — LCla
*pilaloensis* — EKMF
'Pinch Me' — CSil EBak EKMF LFli LVER MAsk SKen
'Pink Aurora' — CLoc CSil
'Pink Ballet Girl' — CLoc CPor EBak ECtt NArc
'Pink Bon Accorde' — CLoc NArc
'Pink Bouquet' — Last listed 1998
'Pink Campanella' — Last listed 1996
'Pink Chiffon' — NArc
'Pink Cloud' — CLoc EBak NArc
¶ 'Pink Cornet' — LCla
'Pink Crystal' — Last listed 1998
'Pink Darling' — CLoc EBak LFli MWhe SKen
'Pink Dessert' — EBak NArc SKen
'Pink Domino' — EKMF
'Pink Fairy' — CSil EBak NArc
'Pink Fandango' — CLoc

'Pink Fantasia' — CLoc CSil EBak EGou EKMF EPts LCla LFli MAld MAsk MJac MWar MWhe SSea
'Pink Flamingo' — CLoc CSil EBak NArc
'Pink Galaxy' — Last listed 1996
'Pink Galore' — CLoc CSil EBak EKMF EMan LCla LFli LVER MAld MAsk MBri MJac MWhe NFai NHaw SKen SSea WGwG
'Pink Goon' — CDoC CSil EKMF LCla LFli MAsk SLBF
'Pink Jade' — EBak
'Pink la Campanella' — CSil EMan LFli MAld MBri MWhe NArc SKen WGwG WLRN
'Pink Lace' — CSil
N 'Pink Lady' — MWhe
'Pink Marshmallow' — CLoc CSil EBak EKMF EMan LCla LFli LVER MAld MAsk MJac MWar MWhe NHaw SLBF WGwG
'Pink Panther' — EKMF MAsk MJac
N 'Pink Pearl' — CSil EBak EKMF LVER
'Pink Picotee' — LCla MJac
¶ 'Pink Pineapple' — MAsk
'Pink Profusion' — EBak
'Pink Quartet' — CLoc CSil EBak LCla NArc
'Pink Rain' — CSil EKMF MAsk MJac NArc
'Pink Slipper' — CLoc
'Pink Snow' — Last listed 1996
'Pink Spangles' — EMan LFli MAsk MBri NHaw SSea WGwG WWol
'Pink Surprise' — MJac NArc
'Pink Temptation' — CLoc EBak
'Pinkmost' — ECtt EKMF
'Pinto' — CDoC LFli NArc
'Pinto de Blue' — EGou
'Pinwheel' — CLoc CSil EBak
'Piper' — CDoC CSil MWar
'Piper's Vale' — EGou EKMF LCla SLBF
'Pirbright' — EKMF
'Pixie' — CDoC CLoc CSil EBak EKMF MAsk MJac MWhe NArc SLBF
'Pixie Bells' — CInt
* *platyphylla* — WWye
'Playford' — EBak NArc
'Plenty' — CSil EBak
'Ploughman' — Last listed 1998
'Plumb-bob' — EGou EKMF
'Poacher' — Last listed 1998
'Pop Whitlock' (v) — EKMF NArc SSea
'Popely Pride' — EGou
'Popsie Girl' — EGou LCla SLBF
'Port Arthur' — EBak NArc
'Postiljon' — CSil EBak EKMF MAsk NArc
N 'Powder Puff' — CLoc CSil ECtt EKMF LFli LVER MAsk MBri NArc SKen
N 'Prelude' — CLoc CSil EBak NArc
'President' — CDoC CSil EBak LCla SKen
'President B.W. Rawlins' — EBak
§ 'President Elliot' — CSil MWhe
'President George Bartlett' — EKMF MJac SLBF
'President Leo Boullemier' — CSil EBak ECtt EKMF LCla LFli MAsk MJac NArc SKen WGwG
'President Margaret Slater' — CDoC CLoc CPor CSil EBak EMan LFli MAsk MJac MWhe NArc SLBF
'President Moir' — CPor CSil LFli
'President Norman Hobbs' — EKMF MWar NArc
'President Roosevelt' — CDoC CSil ECtt
'President Stanley Wilson' — EBak ECtt EPts MAsk
'President Wilf Sharp' — NArc
'Preston Belle' — Last listed 1998
'Preston Field' — CSil SLBF SSea
'Preston Guild' — CDoC CLoc CSil EBak EKMF LFli MAsk MWhe NArc NPer SLBF

'Pride and Joy' — Last listed 1996
'Pride of the West' — CSil EBak EKMF
'Prince of Orange' — CLoc CSil EBak EKMF NArc
'Prince of Peace' — CSil
'Princess Dollar' — See *F.* 'Dollar Princess'
'Princess of Bath' — CLoc
'Princess Pamela' — SLBF
'Princess Pat' — EKMF
'Princessita' — CSil EBak ECtt EKMF EMan LFli MAld MAsk MBri MJac MWar MWhe NArc SKen
¶ *pringsheimii* — EGou
'Priscilla Spek' — Last listed 1998
*procumbens* — CDoC CGre CLoc CSil EBak ECou EGou EKMF ELan ERea ESis GCHN LCla MAsk MHar MWhe NArc NWCA SHFr SLBF SSea SSoC SYvo WAbe
I - 'Argentea' — CLoc CSil EKMF GCal
'Prodigy' — See *F.* 'Enfant Prodigue'
¶ 'Profusion' — MWhe
'Prosperity' ♀ — CDoC CLoc CSil EBak EBee EGou EKMF ENot EPts LCla LVER MAld MAsk MJac MWar MWhe NArc
'Prove Thyself' — EGou
N 'Pumila' — CTri EKMF ELan MAsk MBal NArc
'Purbeck Mist' — EKMF
'Purperklokje' — CLTr CSil EBak EGou EKMF LCla MAld MAsk NArc
'Purple Ann' — Last listed 1996
'Purple Emperor' — CLoc
'Purple Graseing' — MAsk
'Purple Heart' — CLoc CSil EBak LFli SKen
'Purple Patch' — LFli MBri SLBF WLRN
'Purple Pride' — MBri
'Purple Rain' — CLoc CSil EKMF
'Purple Showers' — CSil NArc
'Purple Splendour' — CDoC CSil LFli
'Pussy Cat' — CLoc CSil EBak EKMF LCla MAsk SKen SSoC
'Putney Pride' — EPts
'Put's Folly' — EBak LFli MJac SKen
*putumayensis* — CSil EBak
'Quasar' — CDoC CLoc CSil EKMF EPts LFli LVER MAsk MJac MWhe NHaw SLBF WGwG
'Queen Mabs' — EBak
'Queen Mary' — CLoc CSil EBak EKMF
'Queen of Bath' — EBak
'Queen of Derby' — CSil LCla MAld MAsk
'Queen of Hearts' — CSil
N 'Queen Victoria' — EKMF
'Queen's Park' — EBak
'Query' — CPor CSil EBak EKMF NArc
¶ 'Quintet' — SKen
'R.A.F.' — CLoc CSil EBak ECtt EKMF EPts LCla LFli LVER MAsk MWar NArc SKen SLBF SSea
'Rachel Craig' — MWar
'Rachel Sinton' — EMan LFli MBri WLRN
'Radcliffe Beauty' — MWhe
'Radcliffe Bedder' — CDoC CSil EKMF MAsk SKen
'Radings Gerda' — EGou
'Radings Inge' — EKMF
'Rading's Juma' — Last listed 1998
'Radings Karin' — CDoC EKMF
'Radings Magma' — Last listed 1998
'Radings Mapri' — EKMF
'Rading's Marjorie' — Last listed 1998
'Radings Mia' — Last listed 1998
'Radings Michelle' — CSil
'Rahnee' — Last listed 1996

'Rainbow' — Last listed 1996
'Raintree Legend' — NArc
'Ralph Oliver' — EGou
'Ralph's Delight' — EGou
'Rambling Rose' — CLoc CSil EBak ECtt LFli MAsk MJac NArc
'Rambo' — NArc
'Rams Royal' — LCla LVER MAsk MJac NArc
¶ 'Rascal' — MWar
* 'Raspberry' — CLoc CSil EBak LCla LFli MAsk MWar MWhe NArc
'Ratatouille' — CSil EKMF LFli MAsk NArc
*ravenii* — EGou EKMF
'Ravensbarrow' — NArc
'Ravenslaw' — EKMF
'Ray Redfern' — MJac
'Raymond Scopes' — Last listed 1998
'Razzle Dazzle' — EBak
'Reading Show' — CSil EPts LCla SLBF
'Rebecca Williams' — Last listed 1996
'Rebecca Williamson' — LCla MJac MWhe NArc
'Rebekah Sinton' — EBak LFli MAsk MBri MWar
'Red Ace' — CSil
'Red Imp' — CDoC CSil
'Red Jacket' — EBak NArc
'Red Ribbons' — EBak
'Red Rover' — EGou
'Red Rum' — CSil
'Red Shadows' — CLoc CSil EBak LFli MJac MWhe NArc WGwG
'Red Spider' — CLoc CSil EBak EKMF EMan LFli MAsk MWar MWhe NArc NHaw SKen SSea SYvo WGwG
'Red Sunlight' — LCla
'Red Wing' — CLoc
'Reflexa' — See *F.* x *bacillaris* 'Reflexa'
'Reg Dickenson' — MJac MWhe
'Reg Gubler' — SLBF
'Regal' — CLoc
'Regal Robe' — CSil
*regia* — CSil
- var. *alpestris* — See *F. alpestris*
- subsp. *regia* — CDoC CSil EKMF LCla
- subsp. *reitzii* — CDoC CSil EKMF LCla
- subsp. *serrae* — CSil EKMF
¶ 'Reinholt Leuthardt' — EGou
'Remembrance' — CSil EKMF EPts LCla SSea
'Remus' — CSil EKMF MAsk MBri NArc
'Requiem' — CLoc
'Reverend Doctor Brown' — EBak NArc
'Reverend Elliott' — See *F.* 'President Elliot'
N 'Rhapsody' — CLoc
¶ 'Rhombifolia' — CSil
'Riant' — NArc
§ 'Riccartonii' ♀ — CB&S CChe CDoC CHad CLoc CPor EBak EBee EKMF ELan ENot ISea LCla MBar MBri MGos MRav NBee NFla NPer NWea SKen SMrm SPer WFar WPic WStI WWal WEas
'Riccartonii Variegated' — WEas
'Richard John' — EGou NArc
'Richard John Carrington' — CSil
'Ridestar' — CLoc CSil EBak EMan LCla MAsk MJac MWhe
'Rina Felix' — EGou
'Ringwood Market' — ECtt EKMF EPts LCla LFli MJac MWhe NArc
'Robbie' — EGou EKMF NArc
'Robert Lutters' — NArc
'Robin' — Last listed 1997
'Robin Hood' — CSil
'Rocket Fire' — LFli

| | |
|---|---|
| 'Rodeo' | EGou LCla |
| 'Rolla' | EBak EGou EKMF NArc |
| 'Rolt's Ruby' | EKMF EPts NArc |
| 'Roman City' | CLoc |
| 'Romance' | EKMF LFli |
| 'Romany Rose' | CLoc |
| 'Ron Chambers Love' | EGou |
| 'Ron Ewart' | EKMF MWhe |
| 'Ron Venables' | Last listed 1997 |
| 'Ronald L. Lockerbie' | CLoc EKMF LFli SMur |
| 'Ron's Ruby' | MWhe |
| 'Roos Breytenbach' | CDoC CSil EGou EKMF LCla |
| 'Rosamunda' | CLoc |
| 'Rose Aylett' | EBak |
| 'Rose Bower' | Last listed 1996 |
| 'Rose Bradwardine' | EBak NArc |
| 'Rose Churchill' | LCla LFli MBri MJac |
| 'Rose Fantasia' | CLoc CSil EGou EKMF EPts LCla |
| | MAld MJac MWar MWhe SLBF |
| | SSea |
| 'Rose Lace' | Last listed 1998 |
| 'Rose Marie' | CLoc NArc |
| 'Rose of Castile' ♀ | CDoC CLoc CSil EBak EKMF LCla |
| | LFli MAsk MJac MWhe NArc |
| | SRms |
| 'Rose of Castile Improved' | CSil EBak EKMF LCla MAsk MJac |
| | MWar |
| 'Rose of Denmark' | CLoc CSil EBak EKMF LFli MAsk |
| | MBri MJac MWar MWhe NHaw |
| | WGwG WLRN |
| 'Rose Reverie' | EBak NArc |
| 'Rose Winston' | EKMF MWhe |
| *rosea* Ruiz & Pav. | See *F. lycioides* Andrews |
| – hort. | See *F.* 'Globosa' |
| 'Rosebud' | EBak NArc |
| 'Rosecroft Beauty' | CSil EBak MAsk MWhe NArc |
| | SKen SSea |
| 'Rosemary Day' | CLoc |
| 'Roslyn Lowe' | CDoC CSil EKMF NArc |
| 'Ross Lea' | CSil |
| 'Rosy Bows' | Last listed 1996 |
| 'Rosy Frills' | CSil EKMF LCla LFli MJac MWhe |
| | NArc |
| 'Rosy Morn' | CLoc EBak |
| Rosy Ruffles | EKMF |
| 'Rough Silk' | CLoc CSil EBak LCla LFli |
| 'Roy Walker' | CLoc CSil EKMF MAld MAsk MJac |
| | MWar NArc |
| 'Royal and Ancient' | Last listed 1998 |
| ¶ 'Royal Mosaic' | MAsk |
| 'Royal Orchid' | EBak |
| 'Royal Purple' | CPor CSil EBak EKMF MAsk MBri |
| | NArc |
| 'Royal Touch' | EBak |
| 'Royal Velvet' ♀ | CLTr CLoc CPor CSil EBak EKMF |
| | EMan EPts LCla LFli LVER MAld |
| | MAsk MJac MWar MWhe NArc |
| | NHaw SKen SLBF WGwG |
| 'Royal Wedding' | CSil LCla LFli NArc |
| 'Rozientje' | NArc |
| 'Rubicon' | NArc |
| § 'Rubra Grandiflora' | EBak EGou EKMF LCla SLBF |
| 'Ruby' | Last listed 1998 |
| 'Ruby Wedding' | CSil EGou LCla LFli SLBF SSea |
| 'Ruddigore' | MAsk NArc |
| 'Ruffles' | CSil EBak NArc |
| § 'Rufus' | CDoC CLoc CSil CTri EBak EKMF |
| | EPts LCla LFli MAsk MJac MWar |
| | MWhe NArc SKen SLBF WGwG |
| 'Rufus the Red' | See *F.* 'Rufus' |
| 'Ruth' | CSil |
| 'Ruth Brazewell' | CLoc |

| | |
|---|---|
| 'Ruth King' | EBak ECtt LFli WGwG |
| 'Rutland Water' | LFli MAsk NArc |
| 'Rutti Tutti' | Last listed 1996 |
| 'Sahara' | Last listed 1996 |
| 'Sailor' | MAld MJac SLBF |
| 'Sally Ann' | Last listed 1998 |
| 'Sally Gunnell' | Last listed 1996 |
| 'Salmon Cascade' | CSil EBak ECtt EKMF EMan EPts |
| | LCla LFli MAld MAsk MJac MWar |
| | MWhe NArc SLBF SSea |
| 'Salmon Glow' | MAsk MJac MWhe NArc |
| 'Sampson's Delight' | MAsk |
| 'Sam's Song' | MJac |
| 'Samson' | EBak |
| 'San Diego' | CSil NArc |
| 'San Francisco' | EBak |
| 'San Leandro' | EBak NArc |
| 'San Mateo' | EBak |
| § *sanctae-rosae* | EBak EGou EKMF LBlm LCla |
| 'Sandboy' | CSil EBak |
| 'Sanrina' | EKMF |
| 'Santa Barbara' | Last listed 1996 |
| 'Santa Cruz' | CSil EBak EGou EKMF LCla MAsk |
| | MWhe NArc SSea |
| 'Santa Lucia' | CLoc EBak NArc |
| 'Santa Monica' | CPor EBak |
| 'Sapphire' | CSil EBak NArc |
| 'Sara Helen' | CLoc EBak |
| 'Sarah Eliza' | LFli MJac |
| 'Sarah Greensmith' | EKMF NArc |
| 'Sarah Jayne' | CSil EBak LCla NArc |
| 'Sarong' | CSil EBak NArc |
| 'Saskia' | EKMF NArc |
| 'Satchmo' | EGou |
| 'Satellite' | CLoc EBak EKMF MAsk NArc |
| 'Saturnus' | CSil EBak |
| *scabriuscula* | EGou EKMF LCla |
| *scandens* | See *F. decussata* |
| 'Scarborough Rock' | NArc |
| 'Scarborough Rosette' | EGou |
| 'Scarcity' | CDoC CSil EBak MWhe NArc |
| | SKen |
| 'Scarlett O'Hara' | EGou |
| 'Schiller' | EKMF |
| 'Schneeball' | CSil EBak EKMF NArc |
| 'Schneewittchen' Hoech | CSil EKMF |
| 'Schneewittchen' Klein | CSil EBak EPts |
| 'Schönbrunner Schuljubiläum' | EBak LCla SLBF |
| 'Schöne Wilhelmine' | Last listed 1998 |
| 'Scotch Heather' | NArc |
| 'Sea Shell' | EBak MAsk NArc |
| 'Seaforth' | EBak |
| 'Sealand Prince' | CSil ECtt EKMF LCla MAsk NArc |
| 'Sebastopol' | CLoc EKMF |
| *serratifolia* Hooker | See *F. austromontana* |
| – Ruiz & Pavón | See *F. denticulata* |
| *sessilifolia* | EGou EKMF LCla |
| 'Seventh Heaven' | CLoc EGou LFli MAsk MWar |
| 'Severn Queen' | CSil |
| 'Shady Lady' | NArc |
| 'Shangri-La' | EBak |
| 'Shanley' | NArc |
| 'Sharon Allsop' | CSil MWhe WGwG |
| 'Sharon Caunt' | CPor CSil EKMF |
| 'Sharpitor' | See *F. magellanica* var. *molinae* |
| | 'Sharpitor' |
| 'Shawn Rushton' | EKMF MWar |
| 'Shawna Ree' | EKMF |
| 'Sheila Crooks' | EBak EMan LCla LFli MAld MAsk |
| | MJac MWhe |
| 'Sheila Kirby' | MJac |
| 'Sheila Mary' | EKMF MJac |

| | |
|---|---|
| 'Shell Pink' | CSil |
| 'Shelley Lyn' | NArc SKen |
| 'Shellford' ♀ | CLoc CSil EBak EKMF EMan EPts LCla LFli MAld MAsk MJac MWar MWhe NArc SLBF SSea |
| 'Shepard's Delight' | Last listed 1996 |
| 'Sherborne Las' | Last listed 1996 |
| 'Shining Knight' | CSil |
| 'Shirley Halladay' | EKMF |
| 'Shooting Star' | EBak |
| 'Showtime' | CSil |
| 'Shugborough' | EKMF MJac MWar |
| 'Shy Lady' | MWhe |
| 'Sierra Blue' | CLoc EBak EKMF NArc |
| 'Silver Anniversary' | EKMF NArc |
| 'Silver Dawn' | CSil EKMF EPts MWhe SLBF |
| 'Silver Dollar' | LFli MWhe NArc SKen WGwG |
| ¶ 'Silver Pink' | CSil |
| 'Silverdale' | CDoC CSil EKMF MAsk MWhe NLak |
| 'Simon J. Rowell' | EKMF LCla |
| *simplicicaulis* | EBak EGou EKMF LCla MAsk |
| 'Sincerity' | CLoc CSil |
| 'Sinton's Standard' | MBri MWar |
| 'Siobhan' | Last listed 1996 |
| 'Sir Alfred Ramsey' | EBak MJac MWhe |
| 'Sir Matt Busby' | MWar |
| N 'Siren' | EBak NArc |
| 'Sister Ann Haley' | CSil EKMF EPts |
| 'Skylight' | Last listed 1996 |
| 'Sleepy' | CSil LCla LFli MAsk MBri NArc SKen |
| 'Sleigh Bells' | CLoc CSil EBak EKMF MAsk MWhe NArc |
| 'Small Pipes' | EKMF LCla NArc |
| 'Smokey Mountain' | EKMF LFli MAsk MWar NArc |
| 'Smoky' | CSil |
| 'Sneezy' | CSil EHol LFli MAsk MWhe NArc |
| 'Snow Burner' | MJac |
| 'Snow Country' | Last listed 1997 |
| 'Snow Goose' | EGou |
| 'Snow White' | CSil LFli MAsk NArc SMur WGwG |
| § 'Snowcap' ♀ | CDoC CLoc CPor CSil EBak EKMF EMan EPts LCla LFli LVER MAld MAsk MBNS MBri MGos MJac MWar MWhe NArc NFai NPer SIng SKen SLBF SSea SYvo WGwG WStl |
| 'Snowdon' | MWar |
| N 'Snowdrift' | CLoc EBak |
| 'Snowfire' | CLoc CSil ECtt EGou EKMF LFli MAld MAsk MJac MWhe NArc WGwG |
| 'Snowflake' | EKMF |
| 'Snowstorm' | CSil ECtt |
| 'Snowy Summit' | CSil SMur WGwG |
| 'So Big' | EKMF NArc |
| Software | MAsk NArc |
| 'Son of Thumb' ♀ | CChe CDoC CLoc CSil EAst EKMF ELan EMan EPts GCHN LCla LFli MAld MAsk MBri MGos MJac MWhe NArc SLBF SSea |
| 'Sonia Ann Bary' | Last listed 1998 |
| 'Sonota' | CLoc CSil EBak EKMF NArc |
| 'Sophie Claire' | LCla |
| 'Sophie Cochrane' | NArc |
| ¶ 'Sophie Louise' | EKMF |
| 'Sophie's Surprise' | EGou EKMF |
| 'Sophisticated Lady' | CLoc CSil EBak ECtt EKMF EPts LFli LVER MAsk MJac MWar NArc |
| ¶ 'Soroptimist International' | MWar |

| | |
|---|---|
| 'South Gate' | CLoc CPor CSil EBak EKMF EMan LFli MAsk MBri MJac MWar MWhe NArc NHaw WGwG |
| 'South Lakeland' | Last listed 1998 |
| 'South Seas' | EBak NArc |
| 'Southlanders' | EBak |
| 'Southwell Minster' | EKMF NArc |
| 'Space Shuttle' | CLoc CSil EKMF LCla LFli MAsk MWhe NArc |
| 'Sparky' | EPts LCla MAsk |
| 'Speciosa' | EBak EKMF LCla MWhe |
| 'Spellbinder' | EGou |
| 'Spion Kop' | CSil EBak EKMF LFli MAsk MJac MWar MWhe NArc NFai |
| § *splendens* ♀ | CFee CLoc CSil EBak EGou EKMF LCla NPer SMrm |
| – 'Karl Hartweg' | CDoC LBlm |
| ¶ 'Sporty' | MJac |
| 'Spring Classic' | Last listed 1996 |
| 'Springtime' | Last listed 1996 |
| 'Squadron Leader' | EBak EPts LCla LVER |
| 'Square Peg' | LFli NArc |
| 'Stad Elburg' | Last listed 1996 |
| 'Stanley Cash' | CLoc CSil EKMF LFli LVER MAsk MWar MWhe NArc SCoo |
| 'Stan's Choice' | CSil |
| 'Star of Pink' | MWhe |
| 'Star Rose' | EKMF |
| 'Stardust' | CSil EBak LCla LFli MJac MWhe NArc |
| 'Starlight' | Last listed 1998 |
| 'Steeley' | MWhe |
| 'Steirerblut' | LCla |
| 'Stella Ann' | CSil EBak EGou EPts LCla MAld NArc |
| 'Stella Marina' | CLoc EBak |
| 'Stephanie Morris' | Last listed 1996 |
| 'Sterretje' | LCla |
| 'Stoney Creek' | LFli MWar |
| 'Stormy Sunset' | NArc |
| 'Straat Napier' | EGou |
| 'Strawberry Delight' | CLoc CSil EBak ECtt EKMF LCla LFli LVER MAsk MJac MWhe NArc SKen |
| 'Strawberry Fizz' | Last listed 1996 |
| 'Strawberry Mousse' | LVER |
| 'Strawberry Sundae' | CLoc CSil EBak NArc |
| 'Strawberry Supreme' | CSil EKMF |
| 'String of Pearls' | CLoc CSil EKMF LCla MAsk MBri MJac NArc SKen SLBF SSea |
| 'Stuart Joe' | EKMF |
| 'Student Prince' | Last listed 1996 |
| 'Sugar Almond' | MJac |
| 'Sugar Blues' | EBak NArc |
| Sugarbush | See F. 'Suikerbossie' |
| § 'Suikerbossie' | MJac NArc |
| 'Summerwood' | Last listed 1998 |
| 'Sunkissed' | COtt EBak |
| 'Sunlight Path' | LCla |
| 'Sunningdale' | LCla |
| 'Sunny' | COtt LFli SKen |
| 'Sunny Skies' | Last listed 1996 |
| 'Sunny Smiles' | CSil EKMF NArc |
| 'Sunray' (v) | CLTr CLoc EBak EGou EKMF LFli MAld MAsh MAsk MBel MWhe NArc SKen SPla SSto WWeb |
| 'Sunset' | CLoc CSil EBak MAsk MWhe NArc SKen SPer |
| 'Sunsrise First' | Last listed 1996 |
| 'Supernova' | NArc |
| ¶ 'Supersport' | EGou |
| 'Superstar' | CSil EPts MAsk MBri SSea |

| | |
|---|---|
| 'Surrey Symphony' | Last listed 1998 |
| 'Susan' | COtt LCla |
| 'Susan Arnold' | MAsk |
| 'Susan Diana' | Last listed 1998 |
| 'Susan Ford' | CSil LFli MAsk NArc WGwG |
| 'Susan Green' | CSil EBak EKMF EMan LCla LFli MAld MAsk MJac MWar MWhe NArc WGwG |
| 'Susan Joy' | Last listed 1996 |
| 'Susan McMaster' | CLoc |
| 'Susan Olcese' | EBak NArc |
| ¶ 'Susan Skeen' | MJac |
| 'Susan Travis' | CLoc CSil EBak EKMF MAsk MWhe NArc SBid SKen |
| 'Susan Young' | MAsk |
| 'Suzy' | Last listed 1996 |
| 'Swanland Candy' | Last listed 1996 |
| 'Swanley Gem' ♀ | CLoc EBak EKMF LFli MAsk MWhe SLBF SSea |
| 'Swanley Pendula' | CLoc |
| 'Swanley Yellow' | EBak NArc SKen |
| 'Sweet Leilani' | CLoc CSil EBak NArc |
| 'Sweet Sixteen' | CLoc |
| N 'Sweetheart' | EBak NArc |
| 'Swingtime' ♀ | CGre CLoc CSil EBak EKMF EMan EPts LCla LFli LVER MAld MAsk MGos MJac MWar MWhe NArc NFai NHaw SKen SLBF SYvo WGwG |
| 'S'Wonderful' | CLoc EBak |
| *sylvatica* Munz | See *F. nigricans* |
| – Benth. | EKMF LCla |
| 'Sylvia Barker' | EGou LCla MAld MAsk MWar |
| 'Sylvia Foster' | NArc |
| 'Sylvy' | CSil MWhe NArc |
| 'Symphony' | CLoc EBak MAsk |
| 'T' Vorske' | Last listed 1998 |
| 'Tabatha' | Last listed 1996 |
| 'Taco' | EGou |
| 'Taddle' | EMan MJac NArc SLBF WGwG |
| 'Taffeta Bow' | CLoc CSil EKMF LFli LVER MAsk |
| 'Taffy' | EBak |
| 'Tam O'Shanter' | CSil LFli |
| 'Tamino' | Last listed 1998 |
| 'Tammy' | Last listed 1996 |
| 'Tamworth' | CLoc EBak LCla LFli MAsk MJac NArc SSea |
| 'Tangerine' | CLoc CSil EBak EKMF MWhe NArc SSea |
| 'Tania Leanne' | NArc |
| ¶ 'Tantalising Tracy' | SLBF |
| 'Tanya' | CLoc EKMF |
| 'Tanya Bridger' | EBak NArc |
| 'Tarra Valley' | EGou LCla MWhe NArc |
| 'Tartan' | Last listed 1996 |
| 'Task Force' | CSil LCla MAsk NArc |
| 'Tausendschön' | CLoc ECtt EKMF NArc |
| 'Tear Fund' | Last listed 1998 |
| 'Ted Heath' | MAsk NArc |
| 'Ted Perry' | CSil |
| 'Television' | LFli MAsk NArc |
| 'Tempo Doelo' | Last listed 1998 |
| N 'Temptation' | CGre CLoc CSil EBak ECtt MBri |
| 'Tennessee Waltz' ♀ | CGre CLoc CSil EBak EKMF EMan EPts LCla LFli LVER MAld MAsk MJac MWar MWhe NArc SChu SKen SLBF SPla WGwG |
| 'Terrysue' | EKMF |
| *tetradactyla* | See *F. encliandra* subsp. *tetradactyla* |
| 'Teupels Erfolg' | NArc |
| 'Texas Longhorn' | CLoc CSil EBak EKMF NArc |

| | |
|---|---|
| 'Texas Star' | Last listed 1996 |
| 'Thalia' ♀ | CDoC CGre CLoc CSam CSil EBak ECtt EGou EKMF EMan EPts ERea LCla LFli LHil LVER MAld MAsk MBri MJac MWar MWhe NArc SKen SLBF SPla SUsu WEas WGwG |
| 'Thamar' | CLoc CSil EGou EKMF LCla MWar MWhe SYvo |
| 'That's It' | EBak NArc |
| 'The Aristocrat' | CLoc EBak WGwG |
| § 'The Doctor' | CLoc CSil EBak EKMF MAsk MWhe NArc |
| 'The Jester' | EBak |
| 'The Madame' | EBak MAsk NArc |
| 'The Patriot' | EKMF NArc |
| 'The Red Arrows' | Last listed 1996 |
| 'The Rival' | EKMF |
| 'The Spoiler' | Last listed 1996 |
| 'The Tarns' | CSil EBak EKMF MAsk NArc NPla WCru |
| 'Therese Dupois' | CSil |
| 'Théroigne de Méricourt' | EBak EKMF NArc |
| 'Thilco' | EKMF |
| 'Think Pink' | WGwG |
| 'This England' | CSil NArc |
| 'Thistle Hill' | EKMF |
| 'Thompsonii' | See *F. magellanica* 'Thompsonii' |
| 'Thornley's Hardy' | CSil EKMF EMan LCla LFli MAsk MBri NArc |
| 'Three Cheers' | CLoc EBak |
| 'Three Counties' | EBak |
| 'Thumbelina' | Last listed 1998 |
| 'Thunderbird' | CLoc EBak |
| *thymifolia* | ELan ESis GMac GQui LHop MBal MPla SBid SHFr SMrm WKif |
| – subsp. *minimiflora* | EGou EKMF LCla |
| – subsp. *thymifolia* | EGou EKMF LCla |
| 'Tiara' | EBak |
| N 'Tiffany' | EBak |
| *tillettiana* | EGou EKMF |
| 'Tillingbourne' | LCla |
| 'Tillmouth Lass' | EKMF MAsk |
| 'Timlin Brened' | CSil EBak LCla MAsk MWhe NArc |
| 'Timothy Titus' | EGou |
| ¶ 'Tina's Teardrops' | SLBF |
| 'Ting-a-ling' | CLoc CSil EBak EKMF LFli LHil LVER MAld MAsk MWhe NArc SLBF SSea |
| N 'Tinker Bell' | CPor CSil EBak EKMF LFli NArc WLRN |
| 'Tintern Abbey' | NArc |
| 'Toby Bridger' | CLoc EBak NArc |
| 'Tolling Bell' | CSil EBak EKMF LCla LFli MAsk MJac MWhe NArc WGwG |
| ¶ 'Tom Coulson' | EGou |
| 'Tom H. Oliver' | EBak |
| 'Tom Knights' | EBak EKMF MAsk MWhe NArc WGwG |
| 'Tom Redfern' | MJac |
| 'Tom Thorne' | EBak |
| 'Tom Thumb' ♀ | More than 30 suppliers |
| 'Tom West' (v) | CBrm CDoC CGre CInt CLoc CMHG CSil EBak EGou EKMF LBlm LCla LFli LHil LHop LVER MAld MAsk MBEx MJac MWhe NArc SKen SLBF SMrm SSea WEas |
| 'Tom Woods' | LCla MWhe |
| 'Tony Galea' | LCla |
| 'Tony Porter' | MJac |
| 'Tony's Treat' | EPts |
| ¶ 'Toos' | Last listed 1998 |

| | |
|---|---|
| 'Top Score' | Last listed 1996 |
| 'Topaz' | CLoc EBak NArc |
| 'Topper' | EMan NArc |
| 'Torch' | CLoc CSil EBak EKMF MJac NArc |
| 'Torchlight' | CSil EPts LCla MAsk |
| 'Torvill and Dean' | CDoC CLoc CSil EGou EKMF EPts |
| | LFli LVER MAsk MJac MWar |
| | MWhe NArc SKen |
| 'Tosca' | Last listed 1996 |
| 'Tour Eiffel' | Last listed 1996 |
| 'Towi' | NArc |
| 'Trabant' | Last listed 1996 |
| 'Tracid' | CLoc CSil |
| 'Tracie Ann' | EKMF |
| 'Tradewinds' | Last listed 1996 |
| 'Trail Blazer' | CLoc CSil EBak LCla MJac NArc |
| 'Trailing Queen' | CSil EBak EKMF MAsk MJac NArc |
| 'Tranquility' | Last listed 1996 |
| 'Trase' | CDoC CPor CSil EBak EKMF EPts |
| | LVER MAsk NArc |
| 'Traudchen Bonstedt' | CDoC CLoc CSil EBak EPts LCla |
| | LFli MAsk MWhe NArc SLBF |
| 'Traviata' | LFli NArc |
| 'Treasure' | EBak |
| 'Trés Long' | EGou |
| 'Trewince Twilight' | NArc |
| 'Tricolor' | See *F. magellanica* var. *gracilis* |
| | 'Tricolor' |
| 'Tricolorii' | See *F. magellanica* var. *gracilis* |
| | 'Tricolor' |
| 'Trientje' | Last listed 1998 |
| 'Trio' | CLoc SSea |
| ***triphylla*** | EBak EGou EKMF LCla SVen |
| 'Trish Dewey' | Last listed 1996 |
| 'Tristesse' | CLoc CSil EBak MAsk MJac NArc |
| 'Troika' | EBak EKMF |
| 'Troon' | MAsk NArc |
| 'Tropic Sunset' | CSil LFli MAsk MBri MWhe NArc |
| 'Tropicana' | CLoc EBak LFli NArc |
| 'Troubadour' | CLoc |
| 'Trudy' | CSil EBak EKMF LCla MAsk NArc |
| ¶ 'Truly Treena' | SLBF |
| 'Trumpet Voluntary' | Last listed 1998 |
| N 'Trumpeter' | CDoC CLoc CSil EBak EKMF EPts |
| | LCla LFli MAsk MJac MWhe NArc |
| 'TSJ' | Last listed 1998 |
| 'Tsjiep' | MAsk |
| 'Tuonela' | CLoc CSil EBak EKMF MAsk |
| | MWhe NArc |
| 'Tutone' | MAsk MJac NArc |
| 'Tutti-frutti' | CLoc MWhe |
| 'Tutu' | EKMF NArc |
| 'T'Vosk' | NArc |
| 'Twink' | EGou |
| 'Twinkling Stars' | CSil EKMF LCla MAsk MJac NArc |
| ¶ 'Twinny' | SLBF |
| 'Twirling Square Dancer' | Last listed 1998 |
| 'Twist of Fate' | EKMF |
| 'Two Tiers' | EKMF NArc WGwG |
| 'UFO' | CSil LFli EBak NArc |
| 'Uillean Pipes' | Last listed 1998 |
| 'Ullswater' | EBak LVER MAsk NArc |
| 'Ultramar' | EBak NArc |
| 'Uncle Charley' | CDoC CLoc EBak EKMF LFli WEas |
| 'Uncle Steve' | EBak LFli NArc |
| 'University of Liverpool' | MJac NArc |
| 'Uppingham Lass' | Last listed 1996 |
| 'Upward Look' | EBak EKMF MAsk SSea |
| 'Vale of Belvoir' | Last listed 1998 |
| 'Valentine' | EBak |
| 'Valerie Ann' | EBak LCla LFli |
| 'Valiant' | EBak |

| | |
|---|---|
| 'Vanessa' | CLoc |
| 'Vanessa Jackson' | CLoc CSil LCla LFli MAsk MJac |
| | MWar MWhe NArc SKen WGwG |
| 'Vanity Fair' | CLoc CSil EBak NArc |
| ***vargarsiana*** | EGou EKMF LCla |
| 'Variegated Brenda White' | EKMF MAsk MWar NArc |
| 'Variegated La Campanella' | MWhe |
| 'Variegated Lottie Hobby' | CSil LCla MAld |
| I 'Variegated Procumbens' | See *F. procumbens* 'Argentea' |
| 'Variegated Snowcap' | MWhe |
| 'Variegated Superstar' | MBri |
| 'Variegated Swingtime' | EBak LFli |
| 'Variegated Vivienne | MBri |
| Thompson' | |
| 'Variegated Waveney Sunrise' | MBri |
| 'Variegated White Joy' | EKMF |
| 'Veenlust' | EGou WWol |
| 'Velma' | NArc |
| 'Venus Victrix' | CSil EBak EGou EKMF MWhe |
| | SLBF |
| ***venusta*** | CSil EBak EGou EKMF LCla |
| 'Vera Wilding' | NArc |
| 'Versicolor' | See *F. magellanica* 'Versicolor' |
| 'Vi Whitehouse' | CSil |
| 'Victorian' | CSil |
| 'Victory' | EBak |
| 'Vielliebchen' | CDoC CSil |
| ¶ 'Vienna Waltz' | LFli MJac |
| 'Vincent van Gogh' | EGou |
| I 'Violacea' | Last listed 1996 |
| 'Violet Bassett-Burr' | CLoc CSil EBak NArc |
| 'Violet Gem' | CLoc |
| 'Violet Lace' | CSil |
| 'Violet Rosette' | EBak NArc |
| 'Viva Ireland' | EBak ECtt MAsk NArc |
| 'Vivien Colville' | CLoc SSea |
| 'Vivienne Davis' | LCla |
| 'Vivienne Thompson' | NArc |
| 'Vobeglo' | EKMF |
| 'Vogue' | EBak |
| 'Voltaire' | CSil EBak EKMF |
| 'Voodoo' | CGre CLoc CSil EBak EKMF EMan |
| | LFli MAsk MWar SCoo SLBF SSea |
| 'Vulcan' | CSil |
| ***vulcanica*** André | See *F. ampliata* |
| – Berry | EGou EKMF LCla |
| – subsp. ***hitchcockii*** | EKMF |
| 'Vuurwerk' | Last listed 1998 |
| 'Vyvian Miller' | MJac |
| 'W.F.C. Kampionen' | NArc |
| 'W.P. Wood' | CSil MAsk |
| 'Wagtails White Pixie' | Last listed 1998 |
| 'Waldfee' | CDoC CSil EKMF LCla MAsk |
| | MWhe |
| 'Wally Yendell' | EGou |
| 'Walsingham' | CSil EBak EGou MAld MAsk MJac |
| | SKen |
| 'Waltraud' | NArc |
| 'Waltzing Matilda' | Last listed 1998 |
| 'Walz Bella' | LCla SLBF |
| 'Walz Blauwkous' | Last listed 1998 |
| 'Walz Citer' | NArc |
| 'Walz Doedelzak' | LCla |
| 'Walz Freule' | EKMF MJac |
| 'Walz Gamelan' | NArc |
| 'Walz Gitaar' | NArc |
| 'Walz Harp' | EGou LCla NArc SLBF |
| 'Walz Jubelteen' | CLoc CSil EGou EKMF EMan LCla |
| | LFli MAsk MJac MWar MWhe |
| | SLBF SSea |
| 'Walz Lucifer' | EKMF LCla SLBF |
| 'Walz Luit' | CDoC NArc |

'Walz Mandoline' — EGou NArc
'Walz Parasol' — NArc
'Walz Tamtam' — Last listed 1998
'Walz Triangel' — CSil EKMF NArc
'Walz Trommel' — NArc
'Walz Waterval' — CSil
'Walz Wipneus' — NArc
'Wapenfeld's 150' — Last listed 1998
'Wapenfeld's Bloei' — CSil EGou EKMF LCla MAsk NArc SLBF
'War Dance' — MWhe
'War Paint' — CLoc CSil EBak NArc
'Warton Crag' — CSil NArc
'Washington Centennial' — Last listed 1996
'Wassernymph' — CSil SYvo
'Water Baby' — Last listed 1996
'Water Nymph' — CLoc SLBF
'Waterways' — Last listed 1998
'Wave of Life' — CSil EKMF MAld MAsk MWhe SKen
'Waveney Gem' — CDoC CSil EBak EKMF EMan LCla MAld MAsk MJac MWar NArc SLBF
'Waveney Queen' — MJac NArc
'Waveney Sunrise' — CSil EKMF MAsk MJac MWar MWhe NArc
'Waveney Valley' — EBak MJac NArc
'Waveney Waltz' — EBak LCla MAsk MJac MWar MWhe NArc
'Wedding Bells' — Last listed 1997
'Wee Lass' — CSil
'Welsh Dragon' — CLoc EBak MAsk NArc
'Wendy' — See F. 'Snowcap'
'Wendy Atkinson' — EKMF
'Wendy Brooks' — Last listed 1996
'Wendy Harris' — MJac
'Wendy Leedham' — ECtt EKMF
'Wendy van Wanten' — Last listed 1998
'Wendy's Beauty' — CLoc EPts LFli MJac
'Wessex Belle' — LCla
'Westgate' — EKMF
'Westham' — LCla
'Westminster Chimes' ♀ — CLoc CSil EKMF MAsk MWhe NArc
'Wharfedale' — CSil MAld MJac NArc
'Whickham Beauty' — CSil
'Whickham Blue' — MWar
'Whirlaway' — CLoc CSil EBak EKMF MAsk NArc
'Whirlybird' — NArc
'White Ann' — CDoC CLoc LCla MBri
'White Clove' — CSil LCla
'White Falls' — MAsk NArc
'White Galore' — EBak EKMF EMan LVER MAsk NArc
'White Gold' — EBak
'White Heidi Ann' — CPor LFli MWhe SSea WGwG
'White Joy' — CSil EBak EKMF MAsk NArc
'White King' — CLoc CSil EBak EKMF EMan LFli LVER MAld MAsk MWar MWhe SLBF
'White Lady Patricia Mountbatten' — EMan
'White Marshmallow' — Last listed 1997
'White Pixie' — CDoC CSil EKMF EPts LCla LFli LVER MJac MPla NArc SPer
'White Pixie Wagtail' — CSil EBak
N 'White Queen' — CSil EBak MWhe
'White Spider' — CLoc CSil EBak EKMF LBlm LFli MAsk MWhe NArc SKen SSea
'Whitehaven' — NArc
'Whiteknights Amethyst' — CDoC CSil SLod
'Whiteknights Blush' — CSil GCal GQui LFli SBid SKen SLod SMrm

'Whiteknights Cheeky' — CSil EBak LCla NArc
'Whiteknights Glister' — Last listed 1997
'Whiteknights Goblin' — See F. denticulata 'Whiteknights Goblin'
'Whiteknights Green Glister' — CDoC CSil
'Whiteknights Pearl' — CSil ECtt EKMF LCla LFli MAsk NArc SLBF SYvo WGwG
'Whiteknights Ruby' — CSil EKMF LCla
'Whitton Pride' — MJac
'Wicked Queen' — CSil LCla LFli NArc
'Wickham Blue' — MJac
'Wiebke Becker' — EKMF NArc
¶ 'Wigan Peer' — MWar
'Wild and Beautiful' — EKMF MAsk NArc
'Wildfire' — NArc
'Wilfred C. Dodson' — Last listed 1998
'William C. Dodson' — Last listed 1996
'William Caunt' — EKMF
¶ 'William Grant' — EGou
'William Jay' — Last listed 1998
'Wilson's Colours' — EPts
¶ 'Wilson's Joy' — LFli
'Wilson's Pearls' — CSil NArc SLBF WGwG
'Wilson's Sugar Pink' — EPts LCla MJac
'Win Oxtoby' — EKMF NArc
'Wine and Roses' — EBak NArc
'Wingrove's Mammoth' — CSil LFli MAsk NArc
'Wings of Song' — CSil EBak NArc
'Winifred' — NArc
'Winston Churchill' ♀ — CLoc CSil EBak EKMF EMan EPts LCla LFli LVER MAsk MBri MJac MWar MWhe NArc NFai SPlb SRms
'Wm's Las' — Last listed 1996
'Woodnook' — CSil MAsk
'Woodside' — CSil
* 'Woodside Gem' — NArc
wurdackii — CSil EKMF ERea
'Xmas Tree' — MAsk
'Y Me' — Last listed 1998
'Ymkje' — LCla
'Yolanda Franck' — CSil
'Yorkshire Rally' — Last listed 1998
'Yuletide' — CSil
'Zara' — CSil MWhe
'Zets Bravo' — WGwG
'Ziegfield Girl' — EBak NArc
'Zulu King' — EGou NArc
'Zulu Queen' — EGou
'Zwarte Dit' — Last listed 1998
'Zwarte Snor' — NArc

## FUMANA (Cistaceae)
procumbens — Last listed 1997
thymifolia — NWCA

## FUMARIA (Papaveraceae)
lutea — See Corydalis lutea
officinalis — MSal

## FURCRAEA (Agavaceae)
bedinghausii — CFil CGre EOas WMul WPGP
§ foetida — WCot
§ - var. mediopicta — Last listed 1998
- 'Variegata' — See F. foetida var. mediopicta
gigantea — See F. foetida
longaeva — CAbb CB&S CTor CTrC CTrF EOas LEdu LHil MBEx SAPC SArc
selloa — LHil
- var. marginata — LHil

# G

**GAGEA** (Liliaceae)
| | |
|---|---|
| *fibrosa* | Last listed 1997 |
| *lutea* | EPot WShi |
| *pratensis* | EPot |

**GAILLARDIA** (Asteraceae)
| | |
|---|---|
| *aristata* hort. | See *G.* x *grandiflora* |
| 'Bremen' | CPou EPfP GMaP NPri NTow |
| 'Burgunder' | CBot CDoC CHar EAst EBrP EBre ECtt EFou ELan EOld EWTr GChr LBre MBri MNrw MRav MWat MWhi NFai NFla NLon NMir NOak NVic SBre SPer SRms WGor WPer |
| 'Dazzler' ♀ | CHar CTri EBee ECtt ELan EMan ENot EOld EPfP EWTr MBri MCAu NFor NLar SPer WGor WMow WPer WStI |
| § 'Fackelschein' | CBrm CMdw NFai SRCN WHer |
| Goblin | See *G.* 'Kobold' |
| § 'Goldkobold' | ELan EPar MOne |
| § x *grandiflora* | EMan NOak |
| - 'Aurea' | WLRN |
| - 'Aurea Plena' (d) | EBee MWhi |
| ¶ - giant hybrids | WFar |
| Kelway's hybrids | Last listed 1996 |
| § 'Kobold' | CB&S COlW EBee EBrP EBre ECtt EMan ERic GAbr LBre MBri MRav NBus NRoo SBre SOkh SPer SPla SPlb SRms WFar WMow WWin |
| 'Mandarin' | EBrP EBre LBre MRav SBre SRms |
| Monarch Group | CMGP NCut |
| 'Nana Nieske' | NTow |
| * New Giant hybrids | Last listed 1998 |
| *suavis* | EBee |
| * 'Summer Fire' | WRHF |
| 'Summer Sun' | Last listed 1996 |
| 'Tokajer' | CBrm EBee EPfP NCut NLar |
| Torchlight | See *G.* 'Fackelschein' |
| 'Wirral Flame' | EPar |
| Yellow Goblin | See *G.* 'Goldkobold' |

**GALACTITES** (Asteraceae)
| | |
|---|---|
| *tomentosa* | CInt CPle CRDP ECha EHrv ELan EMan EMar MAvo MHlr SUsu WBea WEas WWye |

**GALANTHUS** ✿ (Amaryllidaceae)
| | |
|---|---|
| *allenii* | CAvo CBro EMor |
| *alpinus* | CLAP LAma |
| 'Anglesey Abbey' | EMor |
| 'Anne of Geierstein' | EMor |
| 'April Fool' | Last listed 1996 |
| 'Armine' | CAvo EMor LFox |
| 'Atkinsii' ♀ | CAvo CBro CLAP EMon EMor EOrc EPar EPot ERav LAma LFox MBri MRav NBir WRus WWat WWye |
| 'Augustus' | CAvo CBel EMor ERos LFox WIvy |
| 'Barbara's Double' (d) | EMor |
| 'Benhall Beauty' | EMor LFox |
| 'Benton Magnet' | EMor |
| 'Bertram Anderson' | EMor LFox |
| 'Bitton' | CBro CLAP LFox WRus |
| *bortkewitschianus* | CBro LFox |
| 'Brenda Troyle' | CBel CBro CLAP EPar EPot LFox WIvy WRus |
| *byzantinus* | See *G. plicatus* subsp. *byzantinus* |
| *cabardensis* | See *G. transcaucasicus* |
| 'Cassaba' | EPot WCot |
| *caucasicus* ♀ | CAvo CBro ECha EMor EPot ERav LAma LFox MTho |
| - 'Comet' | EMor |
| - var. *biemalis* | CBro ECha EMor LAma WCot |
| - 'John Tomlinson' | EMor |
| - 'Mrs McNamara' | EMor |
| 'Charmer Flore Pleno' (d) | EMor |
| 'Clare Blakeway-Phillips' | EMor |
| 'Colesbourne' | EMor |
| *corcyrensis* Spring flowering | See *G. reginae-olgae* subsp. *vernalis* |
| - Winter flowering | See *G. reginae-olgae* subsp. *reginae-olgae* Winter-flowering Group |
| 'Cordelia' (d) | EMon EMor LFox |
| 'Curly' | EMor |
| 'David Shackleton' | EMor |
| 'Desdemona' | CLAP EPot LFox WIvy |
| 'Dionysus' (d) | CBro CLAP EHyt EMor EPot LFox MBri NBir WRus |
| 'Double Scharlokii' (d) | Last listed 1998 |
| 'Edinburgh Ketton' | EMor |
| § *elwesii* ♀ | CAvo CBro EMon EMor EOrc EPot ERav ERos LAma LFox MBri NBir NRog SRms WCot WIvy WShi |
| - 'Flore Pleno' (d) | LFox |
| - 'Grumpy' | Last listed 1998 |
| * - 'Magnus' | CLAP |
| ¶ - var. *monostictus* | EMon |
| ¶ - - 'Hyemalis' | EMon |
| - var. *wbitallii* | CLAP |
| - 'Zwanenburg' | EMon |
| 'Ermine Street' | Last listed 1996 |
| 'Falkland House' | EMor |
| 'Fieldgate Superb' | EMor |
| *fosteri* | CAvo CBro EHyt EPot LAma LRHS |
| - PD 256830 | EMor |
| 'Foxton' | EMor |
| 'Galatea' | CLAP EMon EMor LFox WIvy |
| § *gracilis* | CBro CLAP EMor EPar EPot ERav LFox MTho WIvy WOld |
| - 'Corkscrew' | EMor |
| - Highdown form | EHyt |
| *graecus* hort. | See *G. gracilis* |
| - Boissier | See *G. elwesii* |
| 'Grayling' | EMor |
| Greatorex double (d) | CLAP EMon SSvw |
| 'Heffalump' | EMor |
| 'Hill Poë' (d) | CBro EMor EPar LFox |
| 'Hippolyta' (d) | CBro CLAP ECha EMor EPar EPot LFox WIvy |
| 'Icicle' | EMor |
| *ikariae* ♀ | EHyt EOrc EPar EPot ERav LAma |
| - subsp. *ikariae* Butt's form | EMor |
| § - Latifolius Group | CAvo CBro EHyt EMor EOrc EPot LAma LFox WAbe WOld |
| - Woronowii Group | CAvo CLAP EMon EPot LAma |
| 'Imbok' | EMor |
| 'Jacquenetta' (d) | CBro CLAP EMor EPot |
| 'John Gray' | CBel CBro EMon EMor LFox |
| *kemulariae* | See *G. transcaucasicus* |
| *ketskovelii* | See *G. transcaucasicus* |
| 'Ketton' | CBro EMon EMor ERav LFox WIvy |
| 'Kingston Double' (d) | CLAP |
| 'Kite' | CBro EMor |
| 'Lady Beatrix Stanley' (d) | CAvo CBro CLAP EMon EMor EPar EPot ERav LAma LFox MTho NHar |

| | |
|---|---|
| *lagodechianus* | See *G. transcaucasicus* |
| *latifolius* | See *G. ikariae* Latifolius Group |
| 'Lavinia' (d) | CAvo ERav WRus |
| 'Lime Tree' | CBel CLAP EPot LFox |
| ¶ 'Little Dorrit' | EMor |
| *lutescens* | See *G. nivalis* 'Sandersii' |
| 'Magnet' ♀ | CAvo CBel CBro CFee CLAP EMor EPot ERav LAma LFox NHar WRus |
| 'Maidwell C' | EMor |
| 'Maidwell L' | CAvo EMor LFox |
| 'Melvillei' | NHar |
| 'Merlin' | CAvo EMor EOrc LFox NHar WRus |
| 'Mighty Atom' | EMor ERav LFox |
| 'Moccas' | WOld |
| 'Modern Art' | EMor |
| 'Mrs Backhouse's Spectacles' | EPot |
| 'Mrs Thompson' | ECha EMor |
| 'Mrs Wrightson's Double' (d) | EMor |
| 'Neill Fraser' | LFox |
| 'Nerissa' (d) | EPot |
| *nivalis* ♀ | CBro CKin ELan EMor EOld EPar EPot ERav ETub EWFC LAma LFox MBri MMal MRPP NRog SRms WCot WShi |
| - var. *angustifolius* | CBro |
| - 'Appleby' | EPot |
| - 'Appleby One' | Last listed 1996 |
| - 'April Fool' | LFox |
| - 'Blewbury Tart' | Last listed 1998 |
| ¶ - 'Blonde Inge' | EMor |
| ¶ - subsp. *cilicicus* | EPot |
| - dwarf form | LFox |
| - 'Flore Pleno' (d) ♀ | CBro EBrP EBre EPar EPla EPot ERav ETub LAma LBre LFox NMGW NRog NRya SBre SRms WCot WHen WShi WWye |
| - 'Greenish' | EMor |
| - 'Humberts Orchard' | EMor LFox |
| - subsp. *imperati* | Last listed 1996 |
| - - 'Ginns' | CLAP EMor LFox WRus |
| - JRM 3139 | EMor |
| - 'Lady Elphinstone' (d) | CAvo CBro CRow ECha EMor EPar EPot ERav GCrs LAma LFox MRav MTho NHar WAbe |
| - 'Lutescens' | See *G. nivalis* 'Sandersii' |
| - 'Maximus' | Last listed 1996 |
| - 'Pewsey Vale' (d) | EMor |
| - (Poculiformis Group) | EMor |
| 'Sandhill Gate' (d) | |
| - 'Pusey Green Tip' (d) | CAvo CBro CLAP EMor EPar EPot ERav ITim LFox MRav |
| ¶ - 'Rushmere Green' | EMor |
| § - 'Sandersii' | CBro CRDP EMor EPot GCrs SSpi |
| ¶ - 'Savill Gold' | EMor |
| § - Scharlockii Group | CAvo CBel EHyt EMon EMor EOrc LAma LFox NHar |
| - 'Sibbertoft White' | EMor |
| - 'Tiny' | CAvo |
| - 'Tiny Tim' | EPot NRya |
| § - 'Virescens' | CLAP EMor |
| - 'Viridapicis' | CAvo CBro ECha EHyt EMor EPar EPot ERav LAma LFox WIvy WRus WShi |
| - 'Walrus' (d) | EMor |
| - 'Warei' | EMor LFox |
| - WM 9615 from E. Slovenia | Last listed 1998 |
| - WM 9630 from C. Hungary | Last listed 1997 |
| 'Ophelia' (d) | CAvo CBro EMor EOrc EPar EPot ERav LAma LFox WRus |
| * 'Paradise Double' | EPar |
| * 'Paradise Giant' | EPar |
| 'Peg Sharples' | EMor EPot ERav |
| *peshmenii* | Last listed 1998 |
| *platyphyllus* | See *G. ikariae* Latifolius Group |
| *plicatus* ♀ | CAvo CFee EMon EPot LFox |
| - 'Baxendale's Late' | EMor |
| § - subsp. *byzantinus* | CAvo CBro EMor EOrc EPar LFox LRHS |
| ¶ - - early form | WIvy |
| - - LB 17 | EMor |
| ¶ - - 'Sophie North' | GCrs |
| - - 'Three Ships' | EMor |
| - - 'Trym' | EMor |
| ¶ - 'Finale' | ECha |
| - 'Gerard Parker' | EMor |
| - large form | EOrc |
| - 'Ron Ginns' | LFox |
| - 'Upcher' | Last listed 1996 |
| - 'Warham' | CBro EMor EOrc EPot WOld |
| - 'Washfield Warham' | EMon |
| - 'Wendy's Gold' | EMor |
| ¶ 'Primrose Warburg' | EMor |
| 'Ransom's Dwarf' | EMor |
| *reginae-olgae* | CAvo CBro CWoo EHyt EMor EPot ERos LAma SSpi WCot |
| - from Sicily | ERav |
| - subsp. *reginae-olgae* | EMor |
| 'Cambridge' ♀ | |
| § - - Winter-flowering Group | CBro CWoo EMor ERav LAma LFox |
| § - subsp. *vernalis* | EMor EPot GCrs |
| - - AJM 75 | EMor |
| - - CE&H 541 | EMor |
| *rizehensis* | CBro EPot WIvy |
| 'Robin Hood' | EMor LFox LRHS |
| 'S. Arnott' ♀ | CAvo CBel CBro CElw CLAP EMor EPar EPot ERav LAma LFox NBir NHar WCot WOld |
| 'Sally Ann' | LFox |
| 'Scharlockii' | See *G. nivalis* Scharlockii Group |
| ¶ sp. WM 9803 from Slovenia | MPhe |
| ¶ sp. WM 9808 from Hungary | MPhe |
| ¶ sp. WM 9809 from Croatia | MPhe |
| ¶ sp. WM 9817 from Bosnia | MPhe |
| 'Straffan' | CAvo CBel CBro EHyt EMor EOrc EPar EPot ERav LAma LFox NHar WOld WRus |
| ¶ 'The Pearl' | EMor |
| 'Three Leaves' | EMor |
| 'Titania' (d) | CBro EMor |
| § *transcaucasicus* | CBro EMon ERav LRHS |
| 'Trotter's Merlin' | EMor |
| 'Tubby Merlin' | EMor LFox |
| 'Washfield Colesbourne' | EMor |
| 'William Thomson' | LFox |
| 'Winifrede Mathias' | EMor LFox |
| 'Wonston Double' (d) | EMor |

## GALAX (Diapensiaceae)

| | |
|---|---|
| *aphylla* | See *G. urceolata* |
| § *urceolata* | CFil IBlr MBal SSpi WCru WThi |

## GALEGA (Papilionaceae)

| | |
|---|---|
| *bicolor* | CMdw CWit EGar EMFP EWTr EWes IBlr MSte NBir NBrk NChi NLar SRms SWat WFar WWhi |
| ¶ 'Duchess of Bedford' | CFir NCat |
| x *hartlandii* | IBlr MRav |
| - 'Alba' ♀ | CPlt EFou EMon EWes GBar GBri GCal IBlr LGre MArl MAvo MBel MHlr MRav NBrk NBro SAga SOkh SWat WCot WMaN WPer |
| - 'Candida' | CGle CWit NTow SPer |

| - 'Lady Wilson' | CGle CPlt CWit EMan EWes MArl |
| | MAvo MHlr MRav NBrk NCat |
| | NDov NLar WCot WFoF WRus |
| 'Her Majesty' | See *G.* 'His Majesty' |
| § 'His Majesty' | EMan LFis MArl MAvo MRav NBrk |
| | NLar SAga SWat WBea WCot |
| *officinalis* | More than 30 suppliers |
| - 'Alba' | CBot CHad CHan CKel CMdw |
| | CStr ECGN ELan ELau EMan EMar |
| | IBlr LFis LHol MBrN NChi NLar |
| | WBea WByw WCHb WHer WHoo |
| | WPyg WRus |
| *orientalis* | CGle CHan EBee ECGP ECha |
| | EMon GCal MArl MBel MHlr |
| | MRav SWat WAbb WCot |

## GALEOBDOLON See LAMIUM

## GALEOPSIS (Lamiaceae)

| *segetum* | Last listed 1997 |
| *speciosa* | Last listed 1997 |
| *tetrahit* 'Contrast' (v) | WAlt |
| - 'Dirbach Variegated' | MInt |

## GALIUM (Rubiaceae)

| ¶ *aquaticum* var. *crispum* | IIve |
| 'Krause Münze' | |
| *arenarium* | Last listed 1996 |
| *aristatum* | MLLN WCot |
| *aureum* | See *G. firmum* |
| *cruciata* | See *Cruciata laevipes* |
| *mollugo* | CArn CKin MSal NLan WCHb |
| § *odoratum* | More than 30 suppliers |
| *palustre* | CKin |
| *perpusillum* | See *Asperula perpusilla* |
| ¶ *saxatile* | IIve |
| ¶ *tinctorium* | WOak |
| *verum* | CArn CKin EWFC IIve MChe |
| | MHew MSal NLan NMir SIde |
| | WCHb WGwy WHbs WHer WOak |

## GALPINIA (Lythraceae)

| *transvaalica* | Last listed 1998 |

## GALTONIA (Hyacinthaceae)

| § *candicans* | More than 30 suppliers |
| *princeps* | CAvo CBro CHea EBee EBrP EBre |
| | ECha EPla ERos GBuc LBre LPio |
| | NRoo SBre WCot |
| *regalis* | CHan EBee GCal MWll WCot |
| *viridiflora* ♀ | CB&S CBot CBrm CBro CEnd |
| | CHar CHea CSam EAst EBee EBrP |
| | EBre ECha ELan GCHN GCal LBre |
| | NBid NChi NHol SAga SBre SDix |
| | SIgm WHer WPnP WWat |
| - S&SH 3 | CHan |

## GAMOLEPIS See STEIRODISCUS

## GARDENIA (Rubiaceae)

| § *augusta* | EBak ELau EPfP MBri |
| - 'Prostrata Variegata' | See *G. augusta* 'Radicans |
| | Variegata' |
| § - 'Radicans Variegata' | Last listed 1996 |
| - 'Veitchiana' | Last listed 1997 |
| *florida* | See *G. augusta* |
| *globosa* | See *Rothmannia globosa* |
| *grandiflora* | See *G. augusta* |
| * 'Grandiflora Star' | LChe |
| *jasminoides* | See *G. augusta* |
| *thunbergia* | Last listed 1997 |

## GARRYA ✿ (Garryaceae)

| *elliptica* | CB&S CDul CPle EBee EBrP EBre |
| | EMui ENot EWTr GOrc GRei ISea |
| | LBre LPan MBri MGos NFla NFor |
| | NHol SBre SPer SRPl SReu SSoC |
| | WBod WHar WPat WWat WWin |
| - (m) | CDoC EHol WFar WGwG |
| - (f) | WPat |
| - 'James Roof' (m) ♀ | More than 30 suppliers |
| *fremontii* | EPfP ISea NEgg WLRN |
| x *issaquahensis* | CAbP CDoC CEnd CFai CPMA |
| 'Glasnevin Wine' | EBee ELan GOrc IOrc MAsh MBlu |
| | MBri NHol WBcn WWat |
| - 'Pat Ballard' (m) | CPMA ELan EPfP LRHS MAsh |
| | NHol NOla SPer SReu SSta |
| ¶ x *thuretii* | MGos WWat |

## GARULEUM (Asteraceae)

| ¶ *woodii* JCA 324000 | CPBP |

## GASTERIA ✿ (Liliaceae)

| ¶ *armstrongii* | CCpl |
| ¶ *excelsa* | CCpl |
| ¶ *verrucosa* | CCpl |

## x GAULNETTYA See GAULTHERIA

## GAULTHERIA ✿ (Ericaceae)

| *adenothrix* | EPot MBal WAbe |
| *antipoda* | MBal SSta |
| - x *macrostigma* | Last listed 1998 |
| *crassa* | NHol |
| - x *depressa* | MBal |
| *cuneata* ♀ | ELan EPot GChr GCrs GDra MAsh |
| | MBal MBar MGos NHed SSta |
| | WAbe |
| - 'Pinkie' | ELan EPfP MAsh |
| *depressa* | MBal |
| § *fragrantissima* | NHol |
| *furiens* | See *G. insana* |
| 'Glenroy Maureen' | EHic MBal MCCP |
| *glomerata* var. *petraea* | SSta |
| *griffithiana* BM&W 69 | MBal |
| *hispidula* | MBal MDun MGos |
| *hookeri* | IBlr NHol |
| - B 547 | MBal |
| *humifusa* | MBal |
| § *insana* | MBal |
| *itoana* | GChr MBal MBar MGos WAbe |
| - B&SWJ 1576 | WCru |
| *littoralis* | MBal |
| *macrostigma* | MBal |
| *miqueliana* | MBal MGos MMHG NHar WFro |
| | WWat |
| *mucronata* | CMHG EBee ELan ENot EPfP |
| | MAsh MBal MBar WWal |
| - (m) | CDoC CTri ELan EWTr GRei MBar |
| | MBri MGos MRav NHol SEas SPer |
| | SReu SRms WPat |
| - 'Alba' (f) | GRei MAsh MBar MGos MRav |
| - 'Atrococcinea' (f) | WPat WPyg |
| - 'Barry Lock' (f) | WPat WPyg |
| - 'Bell's Seedling' (f) ♀ | CChe CDoC CTri EPfP GRei |
| | MAsh MGos SPer SReu SSta WPat |
| | WPyg |
| - C 9510 | GGGa |
| - 'Cherry Ripe' (f) | IOrc SEas |
| - 'Crimsonia' (f) ♀ | CB&S CChe CTri ELan EPfP GRei |
| | MAsh MBar MGos SEas SLon SPer |
| | SReu SRms WPat WPyg |
| - 'Indian Lake' | NHol SEas |

| | |
|---|---|
| - 'Lilacina' (f) | CBlo MAsh MBal MGos NCut WGwG |
| - 'Lilian' (f) | CBlo CTri EBee ENot EPfP GSki MAsh NHol SEas SPer |
| - Mother of Pearl | See *G. mucronata* 'Parelmoer' |
| - 'Mulberry Wine' (f) ♀ | CBlo EPfP IOrc NHol |
| - 'October Red' (f) | NHol SEas |
| § - 'Parelmoer' (f) | CB&S CBlo CBrm ELan ENot EPfP SEas SPer WPat WPyg |
| - 'Pink Pearl' (f) ♀ | MAsh NHol SRms WLRN |
| - RB 94095 | GTou |
| - 'Rosalind' (f) | SEas WWeb |
| - 'Rosea' (f) | MBar MGos |
| - 'Rosie' (f) | SBod |
| - 'Sea Shell' (f) ♀ | IOrc |
| § - 'Signaal' (f) | CBlo CBrm CDoC EBee ELan ENot GRei MAsh MGos MPla SPer SReu WLRN WPat |
| - Signal | See *G. mucronata* 'Signaal' |
| § - 'Sneeuwwitje' (f) | CBlo CChe CDoC ENot GSki MAsh NHol SPer SReu WPat |
| - Snow White | See *G. mucronata* 'Sneeuwwitje' |
| - 'Stag River' (f) | GDra MGos NCut |
| - 'Thymifolia' (m) | CChe EPfP GAri SPer SPla |
| - 'White Pearl' (f) | IOrc WLRN |
| - 'Wintertime' (f) ♀ | CBrm ELan MGos SRms WWeb |
| § *myrsinoides* | GAri MBal SRms |
| *nana* Colenso | See *G. parvula* |
| *nummarioides* | GAri NMen |
| - B 673 | MBal |
| § - var. *elliptica* | SSta |
| - *minor* | MBal |
| - 'Minuta' | See *G. nummularioides* var. *elliptica* |
| *ovalifolia* | See *G. fragrantissima* |
| I *paraguayensis* | MBal |
| § *parvula* | Last listed 1998 |
| ¶ 'Pearls' | GCrs WAbe |
| *phillyreifolia* | CMHG SSta |
| 'Pink Champagne' | SSta |
| *poeppigii* | WPyg |
| - *racemosa* | SSta |
| *procumbens* ♀ | More than 30 suppliers |
| *prostrata* | See *G. myrsinoides* |
| - *purpurea* | See *G. myrsinoides* |
| *pumila* | GAri GCrs IMGH MBal MBar MGos NHar NHol NMen |
| § - C&W 5226 | MBal NHol |
| - 'E.K. Balls' | EPot NHar NHol |
| *pyroloides* | GCrs MBal |
| - BM&W 5 | MBal |
| *rupestris* | MBal |
| *schultesii* | Last listed 1998 |
| *shallon* | CB&S CDoC ENot GOrc GRei MBar MGos SPer SRms WBay WDin WFar WFro WTro |
| - dwarf form | MBal |
| *sinensis* | MBal MDun |
| *tasmanica* | ECou GCrs GDra IMGH MBal MBar NHol |
| - x *pumila* | MBal |
| - white-berried | Last listed 1998 |
| - yellow-berried | MBal |
| *thymifolia* | MBal |
| *trichophylla* | GCrs MBal MDun NMen |
| *willisiana* | See *G. eriophylla* |
| x *wisleyensis* | MAsh MBal SRms SSta WAbe WBod WPat WPyg |
| - 'Pink Pixie' | CMHG EHic ELan EPfP MAsh MBar MCCP MGos SBrw SIng SPer SSta WAbe |

| | |
|---|---|
| - 'Wisley Pearl' | CB&S EHic GDra IBlr IMGH MBar MGos NHar SBid SBrw SIng SReu WPat |
| *yunnanensis* | Last listed 1997 |

**GAURA** (Onagraceae)

| | |
|---|---|
| *lindheimeri* ♀ | More than 30 suppliers |
| - 'Corrie's Gold' (v) | CFri CKel CMea CSpe EBee ECha ECtt EHoe ELan EMan EOrc LGre LHil LHop LPio MLLN SAga SChu SPer SUsu WRus WWeb |
| - 'Jo Adela' (v) | ELan LHop MTed SUsu SWat |
| - 'Siskiyou Pink' | More than 30 suppliers |
| - 'The Bride' | CTri EBee EFou EWTr MArl MLan MNrw MWgw NFai STes WMow WOve |
| - 'Whirling Butterflies' | CSam CSpe EBee EGoo EHic EMan EMil EMon EPfP EWTr LFis LPio LWoo MCli MLLN MMil SAsh SBod SEas SMrm SWat WMer WWoo |

**GAUSSIA** (Arecaceae)

| | |
|---|---|
| *maya* | LPal |

**GAYLUSSACIA** (Ericaceae)

| | |
|---|---|
| *brachycera* | GGGa |
| *ursinum* | Last listed 1997 |

**GAZANIA** (Asteraceae)

| | |
|---|---|
| 'Aztec' ♀ | CHal LHil MBEx NHaw NPri |
| 'Bicton Orange' | NPri |
| 'Blackberry Ripple' | EAst EBee NPla |
| 'Blackberry Split' | Last listed 1996 |
| 'Brodick' | Last listed 1997 |
| 'Christopher' | CHal LHil MBEx MSte NPla NPri WPer |
| 'Circus' | LHil |
| 'Cookei' ♀ | MBEx MSte WCot WEas |
| 'Cornish Pixie' | CHal |
| cream | CHal NPla |
| cream and purple | LLWP NPla SUsu WPer |
| 'Cream Beauty' | MSte NTow SAga SUsu |
| 'Cream Dream' | EAst MBEx |
| crimson and green | MSte |
| 'Daybreak Bronze' (Daybreak Series) | LIck MLan |
| 'Daybreak Red Stripe' (Daybreak Series) | LIck |
| Daybreak Series | LPVe |
| 'Dorothy' ♀ | MBEx WPen |
| double yellow | See *G.* 'Yellow Buttons' |
| 'Dwarf Orange' | LLWP |
| 'Evening Sun' | LHil |
| 'Flash' | WEas |
| * 'Flore Pleno' | Last listed 1996 |
| 'Freddie' | SMrm |
| 'Garden Sun' | MLan |
| * 'Hazel' | MSte |
| hybrids | ELan WPer |
| *krebsiana* | Last listed 1997 |
| 'Lemon Beauty' | NPri |
| ¶ *linearis* RMRP 95-0283 | IDac |
| 'Magenta' | Last listed 1998 |
| 'Magic' | Last listed 1998 |
| 'Michael' ♀ | Last listed 1995 |
| ¶ Mini Star Series | CBrm |
| ¶ 'Mini Star White' | SRms |
| 'Mini Star Yellow' | Last listed 1998 |
| 'Northbourne' ♀ | LHil |
| 'Orange Beauty' | ELan |
| 'Orange Magic' | WLRN |

'Patricia Morrow'          Last listed 1997
'Red Velvet'               MSte
§ *rigens*                 CB&S MBri
  - 'Aureovariegata'       Last listed 1996
  - var. *uniflora* ♀      MBEx MSte WEas
  - - 'Variegata'          CBot
  - 'Variegata' ♀          CHal ELan MBEx NPri WLRN
                           WPer
  'Silver Beauty'          CBot NTow
  'Silverbrite'            CHal LLWP
  *splendens*              See *G. rigens*
  'Sundance'               Last listed 1997
  'Talent' ♀               CHal
§ 'The Serpent'            Last listed 1998
  'Tiger'                  NPla
§ 'Yellow Buttons' (d)     CHal EHic MBEx WLRN

## GEISSORHIZA (Iridaceae)

*aspera*                   Last listed 1998
*inflexa*                  Last listed 1998
*monantha*                 Last listed 1998
*radians*                  Last listed 1998
*splendidissima*           Last listed 1997
*tulbaghensis*             Last listed 1997

## GELASINE (Iridaceae)

*azurea*                   See *G. coerulea*
§ *coerulea*               WCot
*uruguaiensis*             Last listed 1998

## GELIDOCALAMUS (Poaceae - Bambusoideae)

♦ *fangianus*              See *Drepanostachyum*
                           *microphyllum*

## GELSEMIUM (Loganiaceae)

*rankinii*                 CMCN CPlN CPle WCru
*sempervirens* ♀           CArn CLTr CMCN CPlN CTrC
                           ERea LCns SOWG
  - 'Flore Pleno' (d)      CPlN ERea
  - 'Pride of Augusta'     CMCN

## GENISTA (Papilionaceae)

*aetnensis* ♀              CB&S CMCN CMHG CPle CSam
                           EBee ELan ENot IOrc LHop MBri
                           MCCP MNrw MWat SAPC SArc
                           SDix SMad SPer SRCN SRms SSpi
                           SSta WBod WDin WWat
*anglica*                  Last listed 1996
  - 'Cloth of Gold'        Last listed 1997
§ *canariensis*            CGre ERea LCns WAbe
*cinerea*                  CBlo WCFE
*decumbens*                See *Cytisus decumbens*
*delphinensis*             See *G. sagittalis* subsp.
                           *delphinensis*
'Emerald Spreader'         See *G. pilosa* 'Yellow Spreader'
*fragrans*                 See *G. canariensis*
*hispanica*                CB&S EBee EBrP EBre ELan ENot
                           IOrc LBre MBal MBar MGos MWat
                           NFla SBre SHel SMer SRms WAbe
                           WDin WGwG WHar WPyg WRHF
                           WStI WWal
  - 'Compacta'             EHol EPla ESis SIng
*humifusa*                 See *G. pulchella*
*lydia* ♀                  More than 30 suppliers
*monosperma*               See *Retama monosperma*
§ *monspessulana*          Last listed 1998
*pilosa*                   CTri ENot EPot ISea LNet MBar
                           MBro MGos MPla NHar NMen
                           NRoo SPer SRms WAbe WWin
  - 'Goldilocks'           CBlo ECtt EHic MBar MLan NHar
                           SLon WBod WWeb
  - 'Lemon Spreader'       See *G. pilosa* 'Yellow Spreader'

* - *major*                Last listed 1998
  - var. *minor*           GTou IMGH NLon SRms WAbe
  - 'Procumbens'           CMea GDra MBal NHol WHoo
                           WPat WPyg
  - 'Vancouver Gold'       CB&S EAst EHal ELan ENot GOrc
                           IOrc LBuc MAsh MGos MNrw
                           NHar SRPl WGor WHar WStI
                           WWat WWeb
§ - 'Yellow Spreader'      CB&S CLTr CMHG ECtt GOrc
                           MBal WBod WWeb
  'Porlock'                Last listed 1997
§ *pulchella*              CTri MBro NHol WLin
*sagittalis*               CHan EPfP LHop MBal MWhi
                           NFor NLon NWoo SLon SPer
                           SRCN
§ - subsp. *delphinensis* ♀  NOla
  - *minor*                See *G. sagittalis* subsp.
                           *delphinensis*
§ x *spachiana* ♀          CTri GEil
*striata*                  See *Cytisus striatus*
*subcapitata*              Last listed 1997
  - dwarf form             NWCA
¶ *tenera*                 SDix
  - 'Golden Shower' ♀      SLPl
*tinctoria*                CArn CJew CKin EWFC GBar
                           GPoy ILis MBar MChe MHew
                           MSal NFor NLon SIde WDin WHer
                           WOak WWye
  - 'Flore Pleno' (d) ♀    CLyd CMHG ELan GChr MBal
                           MGos MPla NHar NMen SPer
                           WCot WHar WWeb
  - 'Humifusa'             EPot NHar NNrd NWCA
  - var. *humilior*        Last listed 1998
  - 'Moesiaca'             Last listed 1996
  - var. *prostrata*       WOak
  - 'Royal Gold' ♀         ECtt ENot GChr MGos MRav SPer
                           SRms WBod WWeb
  - var. *virgata*         Last listed 1996
*tournefortii*             MBal
*umbellata*                Last listed 1998
*villarsii*                See *G. pulchella*

## GENNARIA (Orchidaceae)

*diphylla*                 Last listed 1996

## GENTIANA ✿ (Gentianaceae)

§ *acaulis* ♀              More than 30 suppliers
  - f. *alba*              WLin
  - Andorra form           Last listed 1997
  - 'Belvedere'            WAbe
  - 'Coelestina'           EHyt GCrs
  - 'Dinarica'             See *G. dinarica*
  - Excisa Group           Last listed 1998
  - 'Harlin'               Last listed 1996
  - 'Holzmannii'           NNrd
  - 'Krumrey'              EHyt EPot WAbe
  - *occidentalis*         See *G. occidentalis*
  - 'Rannoch'              EPot MBro NMen NNrd
  - 'Trotter's Variety'    Last listed 1996
  - 'Undulatifolia'        NHar
  - 'Velkokvensis'         EHyt
*affinis*                  Last listed 1996
*algida*                   Last listed 1998
  - white                  Last listed 1998
  'Alpha'                  See *G. x hexafarreri* 'Alpha'
  'Amethyst'               GCrs NHar NHed WAbe WOld
*andrewsii*                Last listed 1998
*angustifolia*             EHyt GCrs NTow WAbe
  - 'Montagne d'Aurouze'   WAbe
  'Ann's Special'          ELan GCrs GMaP MDHE NHar
                           NHol NRoo

| | |
|---|---|
| *asclepiadea* ♀ | CFil CGle CHea EBee EHyt ELan |
| | EPar GCHN GMac LSyl MBri MBro |
| | MTho NChi NRoo NSla SBla SDix |
| | SMad SPer SRms SSpi WAbe WCot |
| | WHoo WPGP WPyg WWat |
| - var. *alba* | CBot CFil CHea CLyd GMac LHop |
| | MBri MBro MTho NRoo SBla SPer |
| | SRms SUsu WAbe WCot WHoo |
| | WWat |
| - 'Knightshayes' | CLyd EGle LHop MBro WHoo |
| - 'Nymans' | ELan |
| - pale blue | CFil NRoo WPGP |
| - 'Phyllis' | CLyd GBuc MBro SIgm WHoo |
| - 'Pink Cascade' | Last listed 1998 |
| - 'Rosea' | GBuc MNrw WHoo |
| - 'Whitethroat' | Last listed 1996 |
| 'Barbara Lyle' | WAbe |
| *bavarica* var. *subacaulis* | Last listed 1997 |
| *bellidifolia* | GTou |
| x *bernardii* | See *G.* x *stevenagensis* 'Bernardii' |
| ¶ *bisetaea* | SRms |
| 'Black Boy' | Last listed 1998 |
| 'Blauer Diamant' | GCrs MDHE NHar |
| 'Blauer Zwerg' | NHar |
| 'Blue Flame' | GCrs GDra NHar WAbe |
| 'Blue Heaven' | GCHN GDra NHar WAbe |
| 'Blue Sea' | NHar |
| 'Blue Shell' | NHar |
| 'Blue Silk' | EWes GCrs NHar WAbe WLin |
| 'Blue Spot' | NHar |
| *brachyphylla* | Last listed 1996 |
| § *burseri* var. *villarsii* | EBee SUsu |
| N *cachemirica* | GTou MTho |
| *caelestis* CLD 1087 | EPot |
| 'Cairngorm' | EWes GAbr GCrs GMaP MDHE |
| | NHar NHed NRoo SUsu |
| ¶ *calycosa* | NWCA |
| Cambrian hybrids | Last listed 1998 |
| x *caroli* | NHar SBla WAbe WPat |
| 'Christine Jean' | GTou MDHE NHar NHed NMen |
| | SIng |
| *clusii* | EPot GCrs WAbe |
| - *alba* | GCrs |
| ¶ - *clusii* | WLin |
| - subsp. *costei* | WAbe |
| *coelestis* CLD 1087 | GCrs |
| 'Compact Gem' | EPot GCrs NHar WAbe WOld |
| 'Coronation' | Last listed 1996 |
| *corymbifera* | GCrs |
| *crassicaulis* | EBee |
| - SBEL 220 | MSte |
| *crinita* | See *Gentianopsis crinita* |
| § *cruciata* | GTou LHop MTho WLRN |
| § *daburica* | CPea GCal LBee NHar NRoo |
| 'Dark Hedgehog' | GCrs |
| *decumbens* | GCal LHop MHar WFar |
| *depressa* | MTho WAbe |
| 'Devonhall' | GCrs |
| § *dinarica* | CLyd EHyt MTho WAbe |
| Drake's strain | GDra LRHS WAbe |
| 'Dumpy' | EPot GCrs NHar WAbe WOld |
| | WPat |
| 'Dusk' | GDra NHar |
| 'Eleanor' | NHar |
| 'Elizabeth' | EWes GCrs MDHE MOne NHar |
| | NHed NRoo |
| x *farorna* | Last listed 1998 |
| *farreri* | EWes WAbe |
| - 'Duguid' | WAbe |
| 'Fasta Highlands' | NBir |
| ¶ *fetisowii* | EBee |
| *freyniana* | LHop |

| | |
|---|---|
| *froelichii* | WLin |
| *gelida* | EBee GAbr MBro WLin |
| Glamis Strain | GCrs GMaP NHar NHed NRoo |
| 'Glen Isla' | EWes MDHE MOne NHar NHed |
| | NRoo |
| 'Glen Moy' | EWes GMaP MDHE MOne NRoo |
| 'Glendevon' | WAbe |
| § *gracilipes* | ECho LBee MSte MWat NRoo |
| | NWCA SPlb SRms |
| - 'Yuatensis' | See *G. wutaiensis* |
| *grossheimii* | GAbr WHoo WWin |
| x *hascombensis* | See *G. septemfida* var. |
| | *lagodechiana* 'Hascombensis' |
| 'Henry' | WAbe |
| x *hexafarreri* | NHar |
| § - 'Alpha' | GCHN IMGH NHar WAbe |
| *hexaphylla* | NHar |
| 'Indigo' | Last listed 1998 |
| Inshriach hybrids | GDra GMaP MOne NHar NHol |
| 'Inverleith' ♀ | ELan EWes IMGH MBri MBro |
| | MOne NHar NHol SPlb WGor |
| | WOld WPat |
| *ishizuchii* | EDAr |
| ◆ *japonica* Maxim. | See *G. thunbergii* |
| 'John Aitken' | GCrs |
| 'Juwel' | NHar |
| *kauffmanniana* | Last listed 1997 |
| *kesselringii* | See *G. walujewii* |
| 'Kirriemuir' | EWes GCrs NHed NRoo |
| 'Kobold' | Last listed 1998 |
| *kochiana* | See *G. acaulis* |
| ¶ *kolalowskyi* | GCrs |
| *kurroo* | EOld MHar NHol WPat |
| - var. *brevidens* | See *G. daburica* |
| *lagodechiana* | See *G. septemfida* var. |
| | *lagodechiana* |
| 'Leslie Delaney' | NHar |
| ¶ *linearis* | EBee |
| *loderi* | GCrs |
| *lucerna* | GCrs MDHE NHar SUsu |
| *lutea* | EBee ECha GPoy LFis LHop MHar |
| | NHar NSla SDix SMad SRms WCot |
| | WGle WLin WWye |
| x *macaulayi* ♀ | CLyd CPla GCrs MBri NHol NRoo |
| | NRya SIng WHoo WOld |
| - 'Blue Bonnets' | MDHE NHar |
| - 'Edinburgh' ♀ | GCrs |
| - 'Elata' | GCrs MBri MDHE NHar NHed |
| | NHol NRoo |
| - 'Kidbrooke Seedling' | ELan EWes GCrs GTou IMGH |
| | MOne NHar NRoo NRya WAbe |
| - 'Kingfisher' | CPla ELan GDra MOne NBir NFor |
| | NHar NMen SBla SBod SIng SUsu |
| | WAbe WHil WOld |
| § - 'Praecox' | ELan GCHN GCrs GTou MBri |
| | MDHE NHar NHed |
| § - 'Wells's Variety' | EPot MBri WAbe |
| *macrophylla* | See *G. burseri* var. *villarsii* |
| - 'Alba' | Last listed 1996 |
| *makinoi* | NWCA |
| - *alba* | Last listed 1997 |
| 'Margaret' | WAbe |
| *melandriifolia* | WAbe |
| - ACE 2515 | EPot NHar |
| 'Merlin' | GCrs |
| *microdonta* ACE 1161 | NHar |
| 'Multiflora' | EWes GCrs MDHE NRoo |
| ¶ *nipponica* | EBee |
| aff. *obconica* ACE 2140 | Last listed 1998 |
| - RH 61 | Last listed 1996 |
| § *occidentalis* | EPot WLin |
| *ochroleuca* | See *G. villosa* |

| | |
|---|---|
| x *oliviana* | CSam |
| *olivieri* | GAbr GCrs WAbe |
| *oreodoxa* | CHid GCrs GTou NRoo WAbe |
| *ornata* | Last listed 1996 |
| 'Orva' | Last listed 1996 |
| *pannonica* | Last listed 1998 |
| – hybrids | Last listed 1998 |
| *paradoxa* | EPot GCHN GCrs LBee NHar |
| | NHed NSla SBla SIgm SUsu WAbe |
| *parryi* | GCrs |
| *phlogifolia* | See *G. cruciata* |
| *platypetala* | Last listed 1996 |
| *pneumonanthe* | SSpi |
| *prolata* | NHar WAbe |
| – K 214 | Last listed 1996 |
| *przewalskii* | WWin |
| *pumila* | GCrs SIgm WLin |
| ¶ – subsp. *delphinensis* | GCrs |
| ¶ *punctata* | EBee |
| *purdomii* | See *G. gracilipes* |
| *purpurea* | WFar |
| *robusta* | CRDP ELan EMon GAbr NWCA |
| ¶ 'Robyn Lyle' | WAbe |
| 'Royal Highlander' | ELan GCrs MDHE NHar |
| *rubicunda* | Last listed 1997 |
| *saxosa* | CRDP ECou GCrs GTou ITim |
| | LHop MSte MTho NBir NHar |
| | NMen NWCA SIgm SIng WAbe |
| | WCom WLin |
| *scabra* | MHar WWye |
| § – var. *buergeri* | Last listed 1998 |
| – var. *saxatilis* | See *G. scabra* var. *buergeri* |
| – 'Toki-rindo' | EDAr |
| ¶ *sceptrum* | NWCA |
| 'Sensation' | NHar |
| *septemfida* ♀ | EHyt ELan EMNN EMan EPot |
| | GDra LBee LHop MBri MBro |
| | MTho MWat SBla SPlb SRms |
| | WAbe WCla WFar WHoo WPat |
| § – var. *lagodechiana* ♀ | CSam EHyt GAbr LPVe NRoo |
| | NWCA SIng SRms |
| – – 'Doeringiana' | ECho GCHN NMen NRoo |
| § – – 'Hascombensis' | ECho GCHN |
| – – 'Latifolia' | Last listed 1996 |
| – – 'Select' | NLar |
| 'Serenity' | NHar NMen WAbe WOld |
| *setigera* | Last listed 1996 |
| 'Shot Silk' | EWes NHar NMen SUsu WAbe |
| | WOld WWin |
| *sikkimensis* | Last listed 1998 |
| *sikokiana* | Last listed 1996 |
| *sino-ornata* ♀ | CPla EHyt ELan GCHN GCrs GDra |
| | IMGH LFis MBri NHar NHol |
| | NMen NRoo SBla SCob SIng SRms |
| | WAbe WOld |
| – ACE 2190C | EPot |
| – 'Alba' | CPla GDra NHar WWin |
| – 'Angel's Wings' | ELan GCrs GTou MBri MDHE |
| | NHar NHol NRoo |
| – 'Brin Form' | NRoo SBod SIng SRms WAbe |
| – 'Downfield' | GCrs MOne NHar NHed NHol |
| – 'Edith Sarah' | ELan GCrs IMGH MBri MOne |
| | NHar NHol NRoo SBla SRms |
| | WOld WPat WWin |
| – 'Lapis' | NHar NHol |
| – 'Mary Lyle' | MBri MOne MTho NHar WAbe |
| – 'Praecox' | See *G.* x *macaulayi* 'Praecox' |
| – 'Trogg's Form' | EWes GCrs MOne NHar NHed |
| | NHol NRoo |
| – 'White Wings' | ELan EWes GCrs NHar NHed |
| | NHol NRoo |
| – 'Woolgreaves' | WAbe |

| | |
|---|---|
| sp. Olga's pale | GCrs |
| x *stevenagensis* ♀ | CLyd CPla GAbr MBri MBro NHar |
| | NRoo SIng WPyg |
| § – 'Bernardii' | MBri MDHE NOla SIng WAbe |
| – dark form | EPot GCrs MBro WAbe WPat |
| – 'Frank Barker' | MBri MDHE WAbe |
| *stragulata* | GCrs |
| *straminea* | GAbr MHar WCot |
| 'Strathmore' ♀ | CNic EHyt ELan EWes GAbr GCrs |
| | MBri MDHE MOne NHar NHol |
| | NRoo SIng SPlb WAbe WLin WOld |
| | WWin |
| 'Susan Jane' | GTou WOld |
| *ternifolia* | ELan GAbr GCrs GDra MSte |
| – 'Cangshan' ex SBEC 1053 | NHar NHol WAbe |
| – 'Dali' ex SBEC 1053 | EWes MBri MOne NHar NHol |
| | WAbe |
| – SBEC 1053 | Last listed 1997 |
| § *thunbergii* | WFar |
| *tibetica* | CPea CPla EBee EGar ELau GAbr |
| | GCal GCrs GPoy IIve MCli MNrw |
| | NRoo SDys SSca WCom WEas |
| | WWye |
| *trichotoma* | GAbr WAbe |
| – ACE 1768 | Last listed 1998 |
| – ACE 1812 | Last listed 1997 |
| – ACE 2241 | Last listed 1998 |
| *triflora* | GAbr GBuc GCrs |
| – 'Alba' | EBee GBuc |
| – var. *japonica* | GBuc |
| – var. *montana* | Last listed 1998 |
| – 'Royal Blue' | GCal WCot WShe |
| *trinervis* | Last listed 1996 |
| Tweeddale Strain | GCrs NRoo |
| *veitchiorum* | MBri NRoo |
| 'Veora' | Last listed 1996 |
| *verna* | CGle CPBP EWes IIve LHop MBro |
| | MOne MTho NNrd NRoo NSla |
| | SBla WAbe WLin WPat |
| – 'Alba' | CP.BP MBro NHar NHol SBla |
| | WAbe WPat WPyg |
| – subsp. *angulosa* | See *G. verna* subsp. *balcanica* |
| § – subsp. *balcanica* ♀ | CPla ELan GAbr GCrs GTou MBro |
| | MTho NHar NHol SBla SIng SRms |
| | WAbe WHoo WPat WPyg |
| – subsp. *pontica* 'Alba' | Last listed 1996 |
| – x *pumila* | WAbe |
| – slate blue form | NHol WPat |
| 'Violette' | GCrs MDHE |
| 'Vip' | NHar |
| *waltonii* | ECho EWes |
| § *walujewii* | SIng |
| *wellsii* | See *G.* x *macaulayi* 'Wells's |
| | Variety' |
| § *wutaiensis* | CNic ECho GAbr SSca WCom |
| *yakushimensis* | GCrs |

## GENTIANELLA (Gentianaceae)

| | |
|---|---|
| *cerastioides* JCA 14003 | WAbe |
| *hirculus* JCA 13880/93 | Last listed 1997 |
| sp. K&LG 94/63 | Last listed 1998 |

## GENTIANOPSIS (Gentianaceae)

| | |
|---|---|
| sp. ACE 2331 | Last listed 1998 |

## GEOGENANTHUS (Commelinaceae)

| | |
|---|---|
| *undatus* | See *G. poepigii* |

## GERANIUM ✿ (Geraniaceae)

| | |
|---|---|
| *aconitifolium* L'Héritier | See *G. rivulare* |
| *albanum* | CElw CMCo CSev EGra EMar |
| | EMou EOrc EPPr GCHN MNrw |
| | NSti SCou SDad SDix SRGP WBea |
| | WByw WCru WMoo WPnP |

*albiflorum*  EBee EPPr GCHN IMGH MWhe NCat NRoo SCou SDys WMoo WPnP

*anemonifolium*  See *G. palmatum*

'Ann Folkard' ♀  More than 30 suppliers

'Anne Thomson'  More than 30 suppliers

¶ *antrorsum*  SDys

¶ *argenteum*  CElw

- 'Purpureum'  See *G.* x *lindavicum* 'Alanah'

'Aria'  WCru

*aristatum*  CBel CPou EBee EMar EOrc EWes GCHN MNrw NCot NRoo SCou SDad SRGP STes WCru WMoo WPGP WPer WPnP

- NS 649  NWCA

*armenum*  See *G. psilostemon*

*asphodeloides*  More than 30 suppliers

§ - subsp. *asphodeloides*  CElw ECGP EMan EOrc EPPr

white  SCou SRGP WFar WHen WRus

¶ - 'Catforth Sam'  NCat

- subsp. *crenophilum*  CElw SCou

- forms  CBre LBlm NCat SCou WCru WHen WPnP

- 'Prince Regent'  CHid EPPr GCHN LPio NCat NRoo SCou WPnP

- subsp. *sintenisii*  Last listed 1997

- 'Starlight'  CElw GCHN GMac LBlm MBro NRoo SCou SHel WCru WPnP

- white  CVer WMoo

*atlanticum* Hooker f.  See *G. malviflorum*

'Baby Blue'  CBel CBos CElw EBee EBla GBuc GCHN GCal MBri MBro MNrw NBrk NBus NCat NRoo NSti SCou SCro SHel SSoC SWas WBea WCru WHen WMoo WPnP

'Bertie Crûg'  CElw CHid CSpe EPPr NRoo SIng SRms SRot SWat WCru WHoo

'Bethany'  Last listed 1998

*biflorum*  EBee

*biuncinatum*  EMar SCou WWin

'Black Ice'  GBuc WCru WMoo

'Blue Cloud'  CElw CHil EBee LGre NBrk SCou SHel SMrm SUsu SWas WPnP

'Blue Pearl'  Last listed 1998

§ 'Blue Sunrise'  LPio LRHS MCLN MWhe NCat SCou

*bohemicum*  EBee GAbr GCHN NCot NDov NSti SCou SHel SRGP WBea WByw WCru WHen WHer WPnP

- DS&T 89077T  Last listed 1998

'Brookside'  More than 30 suppliers

*brutium*  GCHN WHen

*brycei*  EBee GVic MNrw

'Buxton's Blue'  See *G. wallichianum* 'Buxton's Variety'

*caffrum*  CHan CPla GBuc GCHN MNrw NBus NBus SCou SRGP WBea WCru WMoo

*californicum*  WCru

*canariense*  CBod CFri CGre CPla CSev CSpe CTbh EBee EWes SCou SDad SRGP WCru WElm WPnP

*candicans* hort.  See *G. lambertii*

§ x *cantabrigiense*  More than 30 suppliers

- 'Berggarten'  EPPr

- 'Biokovo'  More than 30 suppliers

- 'Cambridge'  More than 30 suppliers

- 'Karmina'  CElw CHil CMCo EBee EMil EPPr EPla LBlm MBro MCli MNrw NBus NRoo NTay SCou SHel WHoo WMoo WPnP

- 'Show Time'  CMCo SCro WHal

- 'St Ola'  More than 30 suppliers

*carolinianum*  SCou

*cataractarum*  GCHN MNrw SCou WCru

- subsp. *pitardii*  SRGP

'Chantilly'  CElw CHar CMCo CMil CSam EBee EGra EPPr GAbr GCHN GCal MBro MNrw NBir NCat NChi NFai NPro NRoo SCou SCro SUsu WBea WCru WMoo WPnP

¶ 'Chocolate Candy'  WWeb

* 'Chocolate Pot'  CHil

*cinereum*  CGle CSev ENot SIng

- 'Apple Blossom'  See *G.* x *lindavicum* 'Apple Blossom'

- 'Ballerina' ♀  More than 30 suppliers

- var. *cinereum*  GCHN NRoo SWat WCru WViv

- - 'Album'  GCHN MBal NRoo

- hybrids  MLLN WCru

- 'Laurence Flatman'  More than 30 suppliers

- subsp. *nanum*  NCat

- var. *ponticum*  Last listed 1998

¶ - 'Souvenir de René Macé'  LPio

- var. *subcaulescens* ♀  More than 30 suppliers

- - 'Giuseppii'  CTri EBee EBrP EBre EFou EMan GCHN GMaP LBre LGro MCLN MGed MNrw MRav MWhe NBro NCat NPar NRoo NSti SBre SCou SHel SRGP WBea WCru WFar WHoo WPnP WPyg

¶ - - 'Glühwein'  NPar

¶ - - 'Signal'  NPar

- - 'Splendens' ♀  CSpe EBee EBrP EBre EFou ELan GCHN LBre LFis MBNS MBal MCLN MTis MWhe NLon NRoo NSla NSti SBre SRGP SRms SWat WCru WFar WHoo WIvy WPnP WRus

¶ - - 'Violaceum'  NPar

'Claridge Druce'  See *G.* x *oxonianum* 'Claridge Druce'

¶ *clarkei* x *collinum*  EBee

- 'Kashmir Blue'  See *G.* 'Kashmir Blue'

- 'Kashmir Pink'  More than 30 suppliers

§ - 'Kashmir Purple'  More than 30 suppliers

§ - 'Kashmir White' ♀  More than 30 suppliers

- Raina 82.83  SCou

'Coffee Time'  SCro

*collinum*  CFri CHil CMCo GBuc GCHN LLWP MNrw NBus NCat NCot NDov NSti SCou SCro SRGP SUsu WCru WHen WIvy

*columbinum*  SCou

'Coombland White'  CElw CHil CMCo MAvo MNrw MWhe NCot NPro WBea WCru WHoo WMoo WPnP

¶ 'Crûg Pewter'  CSpe MBri

Crûg strain  CMil CSev CSpe EMan MCCP MTis NPSI NSti SRPl SVil WCru WWat

'Crûg's Darkest'  WCru

¶ *daburicum*  WCru

*dalmaticum* ♀  More than 30 suppliers

- 'Album'  CHil CVer ELan EPot MBal MBro MPla MTho MWhe NHol NRoo SCou SIng SRGP SRms WAbe WBea WCla WEas WFar WHCG WOld WWat WWin

- 'Bressingham Pink'  EPPr

- x *macrorrhizum*  See *G.* x *cantabrigiense*

*delavayi* Franchet  CBot WCru

- hort.  See *G. sinense*

'Delight'  CHil

'Dilys'                         More than 30 suppliers
*dissectum*                     EWFC MSal SCou SIde
'Distant Hills'                 CHil GBuc GCHN NRoo
'Diva'                          CElw CMCo CMil EPPr NCat
                                NDov SCou SCro SUsu WCot
                                WCru WPnP
*donianum* CC 1074              Last listed 1997
- HWJCM 311                     WCru
'Dusky Crûg'                    MHlr WCru
'Dusky Rose'                    EPfP LRHS SCou
'Elizabeth Ross'                CElw EPPr MAvo MNrw NBus
                                WCru WMoo WWeb WWhi
'Elizabeth Wood'                EBee
*endressii* ♀                   More than 30 suppliers
- *album*                       CElw CMCo MCLN SApp SCro
                                SHel WCot
¶ - 'Betty Catchpole'           NCat
- 'Castle Drogo'                CElw CHil EPPr NCat NFai WBea
- dark form                     NBus WCru
♦ - 'Prestbury White'           See *G.* x *oxonianum* 'Prestbury
                                Blush'
- 'Priestling's Red'            CElw CMCo EGra EMar SMrm
- 'Rose'                        CHil LBlm SCob WPer WShe
*erianthum*                     GBuc GCHN GMac MSte MUlv
                                MWhe NBus NCat NFai NLar
                                SCou SRGP STes WBea WCru
                                WElm
- 'Calm Sea'                    CElw GBuc GCHN SHel WCru
                                WMoo
- 'Neptune'                     CElw SUsu WCru WPnP
*eriostemon* Fischer            See *G. platyanthum*
'Eva'                           Last listed 1996
§ *farreri* ♀                   CBot CLyd EBee GBri GBuc
                                GCHN GCal MNrw NBir NRoo
                                NWCA SBla SCou SWat WCru
                                WEas WPnP
*flanaganii*                    CElw GCHN WCru
*fremontii*                     EBee GBuc GCHN SCou
'Gillian Perrin'                WWeb
¶ *goldmannii*                  SSpi
*gracile*                       CElw CFri CHil EBee EMou EOrc
                                EPla GBuc GCHN GMaP MBro
                                MCLN MNrw NBir NBur NChi
                                SCou SCro WCru WHal WMoo
                                WPGP WPnP WPrP
- 'Blanche'                     Last listed 1997
- 'Blush'                       CHil CMCo EMan EPPr NCat SHel
                                WBea
- pale form                     CElw LBlm NCot SCou
*grandiflorum*                  See *G. himalayense*
- var. *alpinum*                See *G. himalayense* 'Gravetye'
*gymnocaulon*                   CHil CMCo GCHN LRHS NCat
                                NRoo WBea WCru
'Harmony'                       NCat
*harveyi*                       CElw CHan CHar CHil CMea
                                CPBP CSpe CVer EBee EWes GBin
                                LHop MBro MNrw WCru WKif
                                WPat WPnn
¶ *hayatanum*                   CAbP CHil
- B&SWJ 164                     CBod EBee NSti SCou STes WCru
                                WMoo
§ *himalayense*                 More than 30 suppliers
- *alpinum*                     See *G. himalayense* 'Gravetye'
- 'Birch Double'                See *G. himalayense* 'Plenum'
- 'Frances Perry'               SMur
§ - 'Gravetye' ♀                More than 30 suppliers
- 'Irish Blue'                  CElw CHad CHil CMCo EBee
                                EFou EGar EPPr EPla GBuc GCHN
                                GCal MBel MBri MCLN MSte NCat
                                NRoo NSti SCou SCro SHel SOkh
                                WAbb WBea WCru WHal WHen
                                WPnP

- *meeboldii*                   See *G. himalayense*
- 'Pale Irish Blue'             GCal
§ - 'Plenum' (d)                More than 30 suppliers
*bispidissimum*                 Last listed 1998
¶ *ibericum*                    SRGP
- subsp. *jubatum*              CElw EBee EGle EPPr GCHN
                                GCal MMal MNrw MUlv NRoo
                                SCou SRms WBea WMoo WPnP
- - x *libani*                  Last listed 1998
- - x *renardii*                GCal
- misapplied                    See *G.* x *magnificum*
- Boissier var. *platypetalum*  See *G. platypetalum* Fisch. & C.A.
                                Mey
- hort. var. *platypetalum*     See *G.* x *magnificum*
*incanum*                       CMHG CSev CSpe ECoo EWes
                                GCHN LHop MNrw NBir NTow
                                SCou SDad SMrm SRGP WCot
                                WHal WHoo
- var. *incanum*                GCHN WCru
- var. *multifidum*             GCHN LLWP SUsu SWat WAbe
                                WCru WFar
- white form                    SRGP
'Ivan'                          CElw CHil CMil EBla GBuc LGre
                                NCat SCou SCro SWas WCot
                                WPGP WPnP
'Janette'                       COtt EBrP EBre LBre LRHS MAsh
                                MBri MWhe NCat SBre WWeb
'Johnson's Blue' ♀              More than 30 suppliers
'Joy'                           CBos CElw CHad CHil CMCo CStr
                                CVer EGle EPPr GCHN MNrw
                                MWrn NBir NChi NHaw NPro
                                SHel SMrm SUsu SWat WCru
                                WMoo WPnP
§ 'Kashmir Blue'                GCHN GMac NCat SCro WMoo
                                WPnP WPrP
§ 'Kate'                        CElw GCHN NBus NChi NRoo
                                SWat WCru WPnn
'Kate Folkard'                  See *G.* 'Kate'
'Khan'                          EPPr NCat SWas
*kishtvariense*                 CMCo EBee ECoo EOrc GAbr
                                GCHN GCal LPio MNrw MRav
                                NDov NHol NRoo NSti SBla SCou
                                SSpi WCru WMoo WOVN WPnP
- 'Blackthorn Garnet'          Last listed 1997
¶ *koraiense*                   CAbP CBod
- B&SWJ                         WCru WMoo WWat
¶ - B&SWJ 797                   WCru
- B&SWJ 878                     EBee SCou WCru
*koreanum*                      CFil CMil CSpe EBee GCHN NPSI
                                SPar SSpi STes SUsu WBea WCru
                                WFar WMoo WPGP WPnP
- B&SWJ 602                     EBee SCou WCru
§ *kotschyi* var. *charlesii*   EBee SCou WCru
¶ *krameri*                     NSti
- B&SWJ 1142                    EBee NCat WCru
§ *lambertii*                   CVer EWes GBuc LPio MCLN
                                NBir WEas
- CC 1077                       CPou
- hybrid                        Last listed 1998
- 'Swansdown'                   GCHN WCru
*lanuginosum*                   EMar SCou SRGP WUnu
*libani*                        CElw CHan EBee EBrP EBre
                                EMou GBuc GCHN GCal LBre
                                LLWP MAvo MBel MTho MWhe
                                NBus NRoo NSti SBre SCou SCro
                                WByw WCot WCru WEas WPGP
                                WPnP
¶ - x *peloponnesiacum*         CRDP
'Libretto'                      NCat WCru
x *lindavicum*                  Last listed 1998
§ - 'Alanah'                    Last listed 1998

§ - 'Apple Blossom'   EBla EPot GBuc LPio MBel NBus
NChi NRoo SAga SAsh WAbe
WCru WHCG WWin
- 'Lissadell Purple'   NWCA SBla WIvy
*linearilobum*   WCru
  subsp. *transversale*
§ 'Little David'   Last listed 1997
'Little Devil'   See *G.* 'Little David'
'Little Gem'   CHil EFou GCHN MRav NChi
NDov SCou SHel SUsu WCru
*lucidum*   EPPr EWFC GCHN MSal NCat
NDov NSti SCou SDad
x *luganense*   SCou
'Lydia'   SRGP
§ *macrorrhizum*   More than 30 suppliers
- AL & JS 90179YU   EPPr
- 'Album' ♀   CBre CElw CHil EFou ELan EMou
EPot GCHN LHop MBri MBro
MCAu MMal MWhe NBro NFai
NRoo NSti SCou SHel SPer SUsu
WCot WCru WEas WGwG WHCG
WRus WWat
- 'Bevan's Variety'   More than 30 suppliers
- 'Bulgaria'   EBla EPPr NBus
- 'Czakor'   More than 30 suppliers
- 'Ingwersen's Variety' ♀   More than 30 suppliers
- 'Lohfelden'   CElw CHil EPPr GCHN MBro
SDys SHel SRGP SUsu WCru
WMoo WPnP WRHF
- *macrorrhizum*   CElw SRms
- 'Mount Olympus'   MAvo
- 'Mount Olympus White'   CElw CLAP CLTr WHal WPGP
WSan
- 'Pindus'   CElw CHil EPPr GCHN MBro
NCat NRoo NSti SCou SDys SHel
SRGP SUsu WCru WMoo WPnP
- 'Ridsko'   CElw CFee CHil CMCo EBee EOrc
EPPr GCHN GCal NBro NCat
NDov NTow SCou SCro SDys
SHel WCru WHen WPnP
- *roseum*   See *G. macrorrhizum*
- 'Spessart'   CRos EBee EPPr EPla ETub MBel
MGed MOne MUlv NBee NBur
NRoo NTay NTow SCob SCou
SRPl WCru WFar WOVN WPyg
WRHF
- 'Variegatum'   CElw CHan CHil CRDP EBee
ECha EFou ELan EPla GCal MBri
MCLN MTho MWhe NBir NRoo
NTay SCob SPer WBea WFar
WHCG WHen WHil WPnP WWin
- 'Velebit'   CBel CElw CHil EPPr GCHN MSte
NBus NCat WCru WMoo
- 'White-Ness'   EBee GCHN NCat WCru WFar
WMoo
*macrostylum*   CElw CMCo CMil CPou GCHN
MBro SCou WCot WCru WPGP
WPer
- JCA 6000   Last listed 1996
*maculatum*   CElw CHad CMCo CRDP CSev
CVer EBee ECha EFou EMou
GCHN GCal GPoy MBro MHew
MRav MSal NRoo NSti SCou SCro
SHel SUsu WCru WHal WHen
WHoo WPGP WPnP WWye
- f. *albiflorum*   CElw CGle CHil CRDP CVer
EMon EMou GCHN GCal MBel
MBro MNrw NRoo NSti SCou
SHel SSpi SUsu WCru WMaN
WMoo WPnP WPrP
- 'Chatto'   CMCo CMil CSpe EBee EFou EMar
EMil EMon EPPr MBro MCAu MCli
MNrw MRav NHol NWes SCob
SWat WFar WPnP WRus WWat

- 'Shameface'   EBee NBrk SHel WPnP
*maderense* ♀   CAbb CFri CInt CPla CSam CTbh
CTrC EOas EWes GCHN IBlr
MNrw NBrk NPer SAPC SArc
SCou SDad SDix SRGP WCot
WCru WPer WPnP WRos WWin
WWye
§ x *magnificum* ♀   More than 30 suppliers
- Clone C   CMHG NCat NSti
- 'Wisley Variety'   Last listed 1996
*magniflorum*   CHil GCHN WAbe WBea WCru
- S&SH 32   Last listed 1996
§ *malviflorum*   More than 30 suppliers
- pink   CMil SBla SCro WCru WMoo
'Mary Mottram'   MMil NBir NCat WEas
¶ 'Maxwelton'   CHil
♦ *microphyllum*   See *G. potentilloides*
*molle*   EBee EWFC MSal SCou SDad
- *album*   Last listed 1997
§ x *monacense*   CBre CElw CHil CMCo CSam
EBee EFou ELan EMar EPla GGar
MBel MWat MWhe NFai NRoo
NSti SCou SCro SDad SWat WBea
WByw WCru WHer WPnP
- var. *anglicum*   CHil CMCo EBrP EBre ECtt EGle
EOld EOrc GAbr GCHN LBre
MBel MBro MWhe NBus NSti SBre
SCou SCro SHel WMoo
- dark form   WMoo
- var. *monacense*   CElw WFar WHen
§ - 'Muldoon'   CInt CMHG CSev EBrP EBre ECha
ECoo EOld EPla GAbr GMac LBre
MAvo MCLN MRav NBrk NOak
NTay SBre WCru WFar WHCG
WHen WOak WPer WPnP WPrP
§ - 'Variegatum'   CSev EBee EFou EMar EOld EPla
ERic LFis MBro MCLN MSCN
MWhe NLar NPro SCou SLon SPer
SRGP WAbb WBea WCru WEas
WGwG WHil WMoo WRha WRus
WWal
¶ 'Money Peniche'   LPio
'Mourning Widow'   See *G. phaeum*
*multisectum*   WCru
*nakaoanum* HWJCM 504   WCru
*napuligerum* hort.   See *G. farreri*
- Franchet   NSla
'Natalie'   NCat
*nepalense*   CMCo NBus SCou SRGP SRms
WHer WMoo WPnP
*nervosum*   CElw CHar CSev EBee EMou
MCCP NBus NLar NPro NSti SCou
SMad STes WElm WPnP WWhi
'Nicola'   CElw CHil NCat SHel
'Nimbus'   More than 30 suppliers
*nodosum*   More than 30 suppliers
- dark form   See *G. nodosum* 'Swish Purple'
¶ - 'Julie's Velvet'   WHoo
- pale form   See *G. nodosum* 'Svelte Lilac'
§ - 'Svelte Lilac'   CElw ECGP EMon EPPr LRHS
MBro NBrk NCat NLon NWes
SCou SHel SMrm SUsu SWat WBea
WCot WCru WMoo WPnP
§ - 'Swish Purple'   CBos CElw EBee EBla EPPr MSte
NPla SHel SLod SWat WCru WFar
WHen WMoo
- 'Whiteleaf'   CBos CElw CLTr EBee EBla ECoo
EPPr MBro NBrk NBus SAga SBla
SWas SWat WBea WCru WMoo
¶ - 'Whiteleaf' seedling   SHel
¶ 'Nora Bremner'   WPnP
*ocellatum*   EBee EMar NDov NSti SCou

| | |
|---|---|
| 'Orchid Blue' | LRHS |
| *oreganum* | CElw GCHN NBrk SCou SCro WCru |
| § *orientalitibeticum* | More than 30 suppliers |
| ¶ 'Orion' | LPio |
| 'Orkney Pink' | CHil CPBP EGra EMan EMou EPPr GBuc GCal LGro LLWP MAvo MBro MHlr MSte NChi NPro NRoo WBea WCot WCru WHoo WMoo WWhi WWin |
| ¶ *ornithopodon* | EBee |
| x *oxonianum* | SAga SCou SHel WCru WMoo |
| – 'A.T. Johnson' ♀ | More than 30 suppliers |
| – 'Armitage' | EPPr MBro NCat SHel SRGP |
| – 'Breckland Sunset' | EPPr |
| – 'Bregover Pearl' | CBre CElw CHil CMCo EBee MBro NCat SCou SHel SRGP WMoo |
| – 'Bressingham Delight' | CElw CMCo EBee EBrP EBre EWTr LBre MCLN MUlv MWhe NBus NRoo SBre SCou SHel SRGP |
| – 'Buttercup' | CElw EMan EPPr |
| I – 'Cally Seedling' | EWes GCal |
| § – 'Claridge Druce' | More than 30 suppliers |
| – 'Coronet' | EPPr NBrk NCat SHel WBea WMoo |
| – 'Crûg Star' | CElw CHil |
| – 'David McClintock' | CElw CHil EMan EPPr MTed SCou SHel WFar WMoo |
| – 'Dawn Time' | SCro |
| ¶ – 'Elworthy Misty' | CElw |
| – 'Frank Lawley' | CElw CHil CMCo EBee EPPr GBuc GMac MBro NCat NChi NHex NRoo NSti SCou SCro SHel SUsu WBea WMoo WPnP |
| ¶ – 'Fran's Star' | WCru |
| – 'Hexham Pink' | NCat NRoo |
| – 'Hollywood' | CElw CFri CHil CMCo EBee ELan EOrc EPPr GAbr GCHN LBlm LFis LRot MBro MSte MTho NBus NPer NRoo SCou SCro SHel SMrm SSpe WBea WBor WFar WMoo WPnP |
| – 'Julie Brennan' | CElw NCat NGdn SRGP WBea WMoo WPnP |
| – 'Kate Moss' | CHil EPPr GCHN GCal NCat NChi NDov NHex NRoo NSti |
| – 'Kingston' | EBee |
| – 'Lace Time' | CBre CElw CHil CMCo CSev EBee EPPr GMac LFis MBro MNrw MWhe MWrn NCot NOak NRoo SCro SDys SHel SUsu WBea WMoo |
| – 'Lady Moore' | CElw CHil CMCo EBee EMar EPPr EPla GAbr GBuc GCHN MBro MNrw MWhe NBro NBur NBus NCot NRoo SCou SCro SHFr SHel SRGP WBea WBor WHen WPnP |
| – 'Lambrook Gillian' | CElw CHil EPPr MBro SCou SHel SMer WBea WPnP |
| – 'Lasting Impression' | EPPr |
| – 'Miriam Rundle' | CElw CHil CMdw EOrc EPPr MNrw NBus NRoo SCou SDys SHel SRGP WBea WCru WMoo WPnP |
| – 'Mrs Charles Perrin' | Last listed 1997 |
| – 'Old Rose' | CElw CHil CMCo EPPr GCHN MBri NBus NCat NPla SCou SHel SRGP SUsu WBea WCru WMoo WPnP |
| – pale form | Last listed 1998 |
| – 'Pat Smallacombe' | CElw CHil LRot NCat NDov SHel WBea WCru WMoo |
| – 'Phoebe Noble' | CBel CBre CElw CHil CMCo CMil EBla EPPr MBro MNrw NBus NCat NSti SCou SCro SHel SRGP SSpe SUsu SWas WBea WPnP |
| – 'Phoebe's Blush' | CElw NCat NChi NRoo SHel WBea |
| – 'Pink Lace' | Last listed 1998 |
| § – 'Prestbury Blush' | CBre CElw EOrc EPPr GCHN NPar SCou SHel WBea WCot WCru WMoo WWin |
| ♦ – 'Prestbury White' | See *G.* x *oxonianum* 'Prestbury Blush' |
| – 'Rebecca Moss' | More than 30 suppliers |
| – 'Red Sputnik' | EPPr GVic |
| – 'Rohina Moss' | Last listed 1997 |
| – 'Rose Clair' | CElw CHid CHil CMil EBee EMou EOrc GCHN MCLN MWhe NFai NRoo NSti SChu SCou SHel SRPl WBea WCru WEas WElm WHen WMoo WPer WWeb |
| I – 'Rosemary' | SCou |
| ¶ – 'Rosemary Verey' | SHel |
| – 'Rosenlicht' | More than 30 suppliers |
| – x *sessiliflorum* subsp. *novae-zelandiae* 'Nigricans' | CHil |
| – 'Sherwood' | More than 30 suppliers |
| – 'Southcombe Double' (d) | CElw CHil CM&M CPla CSev CStr EGle EMar EMou GMac MCLN MFir MUlv MWhe NCat NFai NGdn NRoo NSchu SRGP SUsu WBea WByw WCru WHal WHen WWhi WWin |
| § – 'Southcombe Star' | EAst EGar EHal EOrc EPPr GAbr GCal MBel MBro NBrk NBro NBus NGdn NLon NRoo NSti SHel SLod WBea WCru WHal WHen WMoo WPer WPnP |
| – 'Stillingfleet' | GCHN |
| – 'Summer Surprise' | NCat SCro |
| ¶ – 'Susie White' | EPPr |
| § – f. *thurstonianum* | More than 30 suppliers |
| I – 'Thurstonianum Isherwood' | Last listed 1997 |
| ¶ – 'Trevor's White' | NCat |
| – 'Wageningen' | CBre CElw CHil CMCo EBee EGar GCal GMac LBlm LGre LVER MAvo MMil NBus NCat NGdn NLak NPro NRoo SAga SCou SHel SRGP WBea WCru WHal WHen WMoo |
| – 'Walter's Gift' | More than 30 suppliers |
| – 'Wargrave Pink' ♀ | More than 30 suppliers |
| – 'Waystradi' | CElw EBla EPPr |
| ¶ – 'Waystrode' | SHel |
| – 'Winscombe' | CElw CHil EBee EFou EMou GCHN GCal LBlm LHop LLWP MBri MRav MTho MWhe NCat NHol NRoo NSti NTay SCou SCro WBea WCru WGwG WHen WPnP WRus WWal |
| 'Pagoda' | EOrc MNrw WPnP |
| § *palmatum* ♀ | More than 30 suppliers |
| *palustre* | CElw CHil EBee EMou GCHN LLWP MBel MNrw NBro NChi NHol NSti SCou SRGP WCru WHen WMoo WPnP |
| – 'Plus' | Last listed 1996 |
| ¶ 'Pamir' | CHil |
| *papuanum* | GCHN NLar WCru |
| 'Patricia' | More than 30 suppliers |
| ¶ 'Patricia Josephine' | MCAu |
| *peloponnesiacum* | CStr GGar WPGP |

| | |
|---|---|
| – NS 660 | CElw CPou |
| § *phaeum* | More than 30 suppliers |
| – 'Album' | More than 30 suppliers |
| – 'All Saints' | CElw EMon |
| * – *aureum* | Last listed 1996 |
| – black | See *G. phaeum* 'Mourning Widow' |
| ¶ – 'Blue Shadow' | EPPr |
| – 'Calligrapher' | CElw EPPr NBrk SHel WBea |
| | WMoo WPnP |
| – 'Charles Perrin' | CElw CHid |
| ¶ – dark form | SCou |
| – forms | EMou EPPr SSvw |
| – 'Golden Spring' | NCat NChi NPro NRoo |
| – 'Hannah Perry' | CBel CElw CHil CVer EPPr LLWP |
| | WBea WBro |
| – var. *bungaricum* | CHil EGar MFir NCat SCou SHel |
| | WBea WCru |
| – 'Joan Baker' | More than 30 suppliers |
| – 'Joan Grey' | Last listed 1996 |
| – 'Langthorn's Blue' | CElw CHil CMea CSev ELan |
| | MNrw NBus NCat NRoo SCro |
| | WBea WHal WHen WPnP |
| § – 'Lily Lovell' | More than 30 suppliers |
| – 'Little Boy' | CElw EMon NCat |
| – var. *lividum* | More than 30 suppliers |
| – – 'Majus' | CElw CHil EGle EMil EMon EPPr |
| | GCal LBlm LGre NRoo NTay SCou |
| | SCro SWat WBea WFar WPnP |
| | WPrP |
| – 'Mierhausen' | CCuc CElw CGle |
| § – 'Mourning Widow' | CMil EPPr GBin GCal LBlm MWhe |
| | NCat NRoo NTay SCro SHel SRms |
| | WBea WCru WHen WMoo |
| – 'Night Time' | LLWP MBro SCro SHel WBea |
| ¶ – purple | EBee |
| – red form | MRav |
| – 'Rose Air' | EBee EPPr NBrk WMoo WPnP |
| – 'Rose Madder' | CBos CElw CHad CHil CM&M |
| | CMCo CVer GBuc GCal LGre |
| | LLWP MBro MCLN MNrw SCou |
| | SHel WBea WMoo WPnP |
| – 'Samobor' | More than 30 suppliers |
| – 'Saturn' | Last listed 1998 |
| – 'Small Grey' | CHil |
| – 'Stillingfleet Ghost' | NCat NChi NHex NSti |
| – 'Taff's Jester' (v) | CElw CHad CMCo NBus NSti |
| | SCro SHel WBea WCot WCru |
| | WHer |
| – 'Variegatum' | CElw CHan CMCo EBrP EBee |
| | ELan EMou LBre MBro MFir |
| | MNrw MRav NBir NBro NCat |
| | NDov NSti SBre SChu SCro WBea |
| | WCru WFar WHer WPnP |
| 'Phillippe Vapelle' | More than 30 suppliers |
| 'Pink Spice' | CHil MRav MWhe MWrn NHar |
| § *platyanthum* | CElw CGle CHil CVer EMou |
| | GCHN GCal LBlm MNrw MUlv |
| | NChi NRoo NSti SCou SRGP |
| | WBea WCot WCru WHCG WHen |
| | WMoo WPer |
| ¶ – giant form | SCou |
| – var. *reinii* | NCat |
| – – f. *onoei* | WCru |
| *platypetalum* misapplied | See *G. x magnificum* |
| *platypetalum* Franchet | See *G. sinense* |
| § *platypetalum* Fisch. & | CElw EBrP EBre ELan EMou ENot |
| C.A. Mey. | GAri GCHN LBre MBri NBir NCat |
| | NFla NSti SBre SCou SRms SWat |
| | WBea WCru WMoo |
| – 'Georgia Blue' | CFil CLTr NCat SSpi WCru WMoo |
| | WPGP |
| § *pogonanthum* | GBuc GCHN GCal GMac MNrw |
| | NBir NRoo SCou WCru WMoo |
| | WPrP |
| *polyanthes* | CElw CMCo CRDP EMan GAbr |
| | GAri GBuc GDra GTou WCru |
| § *potentilloides* | CHil GCHN MNrw NBir NBus |
| | NHex WBea WPrP |
| *pratense* | More than 30 suppliers |
| – f. *albiflorum* | CBot CElw CGle CHil CSpe EBee |
| | GCHN GCal LHop MBri MCLN |
| | MHew MMal MNrw NFai NOrc |
| | NRoo NSti SCou SDad SPer WBea |
| | WHCG WHal WHen WRus WWin |
| – – 'Galactic' | CHan CHil CMCo EMar GMac |
| | MBro MCli MWll NRoo SRGP |
| | WBro WCru WHen WMoo |
| – – 'Plenum Album' (d) | CElw CStr GVic |
| – – 'Silver Queen' | CBre CFri CGle CHil ELan EOrc |
| | EPPr GCHN MBel MBro MCLN |
| | MMal MNrw MWhe MWll NBrk |
| | NRoo SCou SOkh SRGP WBea |
| | WCru WElm WFar WHen WHoo |
| | WMoo WPnP WPyg WUnu |
| – – 'Whimble White' | WWhi |
| – 'Bittersweet' | CHil EBee EMon NBrk |
| – 'Blue Chip' | NBur SHel |
| – 'Bodenfalle' | Last listed 1998 |
| – 'Catforth Cadense' | Last listed 1996 |
| – 'Catforth Carnival' | Last listed 1998 |
| – CC 806 | Last listed 1996 |
| – CC&McK 442 | CMCo GTou |
| – 'Cluden Ruby' | GCHN |
| – 'Cluden Sapphire' | CAbP CBod CHil EBee GAbr |
| | GCHN LRHS MBri MWhi NCut |
| | NHol NPSI NPro NSti WCru |
| – 'Fiona' | Last listed 1996 |
| – 'Flore Pleno' | See *G. pratense* 'Plenum |
| | Violaceum' |
| – forms | CHil GCHN SCou WCru WPnP |
| – from Nepal | Last listed 1998 |
| – 'Gay Hellyer' | SCro |
| * – 'Himalayanum' | LGro |
| ¶ – Midnight Reiter strain | CSpe WCot |
| – 'Mrs Kendall Clark' ♀ | More than 30 suppliers |
| – 'Nunwood Purple' | CHil |
| § – 'Plenum Caeruleum' (d) | More than 30 suppliers |
| – 'Plenum Purpureum' | See *G. pratense* 'Plenum |
| | Violaceum' |
| § – 'Plenum Violaceum' (d) ♀ | More than 30 suppliers |
| – 'Rectum Album' | See *G. clarkei* 'Kashmir White' |
| – 'Rosalyn' (d) | EWes |
| – 'Rose Queen' | CBel EBee MRav NCat NLar NSti |
| | SHel WBea WCru WHen WUnu |
| – *roseum* | CGle CHil CMea ELan EOrc MBro |
| | MNrw NBir NHex SSpi WHoo |
| – 'Splish-splash' | CBod CBrm CFri EMan EWTr |
| | MLLN NRoo SCoo WHil WMow |
| – subsp. *stewartianum* | CElw MRav WCru |
| – – 'Elizabeth Yeo' | EBee SCou SCro |
| – – ex CC 31 | Last listed 1997 |
| – 'Striatum' | More than 30 suppliers |
| – 'Striatum Akaton' | Last listed 1996 |
| – 'Striatum' pale form | CBre |
| – Summer Skies = | CStr CTri EBee EBrP EBre EGra |
| 'Gernic' (d) | LBre LRHS MCLN MWhe NRoo |
| | SBre SCou SPer |
| – Tibetan Border form | EBee |
| – Victor Reiter Strain | CElw CHad CSpe SMrm WCot |
| | WCru |
| – 'Wisley Blue' | CMCo SCou SCro SHel SRGP |
| – 'Yorkshire Queen' | NCat NGdn NHex NSti SHel |
| 'Prelude' | CElw NCat WBea |

| | |
|---|---|
| ¶ 'Priestley's Pink' | EBee |
| 'Prima Donna' | NCat |
| *procurrens* | More than 30 suppliers |
| *pseudosibiricum* | SCou |
| § *psilostemon* ♀ | More than 30 suppliers |
| - 'Bressingham Flair' | CMCo EBee EBrP EBre ECha GCal |
| | LBre LHop MCLN MRav MWhe |
| | NGdn NHol NLar NOrc NRoo |
| | SBre SChu SCob SCou SHel SMrm |
| | SRms WCot WCru WMoo WPnP |
| | WWat |
| - 'Gold Leaf' | WCot |
| - hybrid | WCru |
| *pulchrum* | CBel CElw CHan CMea CSev |
| | CSpe EBee ECre EOrc GCHN LPio |
| | MMal MNrw NLar NPro SCou |
| | SIgm SRGP STes SWas SWat WCot |
| | WCru |
| *punctatum* hort. | See *G.* x *monacense* 'Muldoon' |
| - *variegatum* | See *G.* x *monacense* 'Variegatum' |
| *purpureum* | SCou |
| *pusillum* | CKin MSal SCou |
| *pylzowianum* | CElw CHid CNic GCHN MBro |
| | MMal NBid NNrd NRoo NRya |
| | NTay SChu SDys SHel SRms SSmi |
| | WBea WByw WCru WFar WHal |
| | WHen WMoo WPnP |
| *pyrenaicum* | CElw CHil CKin CM&M CRDP |
| | CSev EBee EOrc EWFC GAbr |
| | GCHN MHew NFla NSti SCou |
| | WBea WHen WPrP |
| - f. *albiflorum* | CElw EBee EMou EOrc ESis GAbr |
| | GCHN LLWP MNrw MTho NBir |
| | NDov NSti SCou SCro SHel SUsu |
| | WBea WCla WHen WMoo WPer |
| | WPrP WWin |
| - 'Bill Wallis' | More than 30 suppliers |
| ¶ - 'Isparta' | NCat |
| 'Rambling Robin' | EPPr NCat WCot WCru |
| *rectum* | CMCo NBus NCat SCou WCru |
| | WMoo |
| - 'Album' | See *G. clarkei* 'Kashmir White' |
| ¶ 'Red Admiral' | NCat |
| 'Red Dwarf' | CHil GCHN WMoo |
| * 'Red Madder' | EBee |
| *reflexum* | CBre CElw CHid CHil CMCo CSev |
| | EPPr GCHN LFis MCLN NCat |
| | NHol NRoo NVic SCou SCro |
| | WCru WHCG WHal WMoo WOve |
| | WPnP |
| - dark form | Last listed 1998 |
| *regelii* | CElw CMCo CSam CVer EBee |
| | EBla EMar EOrc EPPr GCHN MBel |
| | NSla SHel SUsu WCru WMoo |
| | WPnP |
| - CC 806 | CPou |
| *renardii* ♀ | More than 30 suppliers |
| - blue | See *G. renardii* 'Whiteknights' |
| - 'Tcschelda' | CElw CFai CHil CMCo EBee EBla |
| | EFou EMil LBuc LPio MAvo MBri |
| | NBus SBod SCob SPla SWat |
| § - 'Whiteknights' | CElw CHil EGra EMou GCHN |
| | MBro MRav NBir NBus NLar NPro |
| | SMac WBea WBro WCru WEas |
| | WIvy WMoo WPnP |
| - 'Zetterland' | CElw CMCo CMdw CMil |
| | CSpe EBee EBrP EBre EHrv EPPr |
| | LBre LFis LLWP MAvo MCLN |
| | MLLN NBus NRoo SBre SCob |
| | SCou SHel SWat WBea WCru |
| | WMoo |

| | |
|---|---|
| *richardsonii* | CElw CHil EBee GCHN GCal |
| | MNrw NBir NBus NCat NLar |
| | NRoo NSti SChu SCou SCro SRms |
| | WBea WCru WMoo WPnP WPrP |
| x *riversleaianum* | SCou WCru WMoo |
| - 'Jean Armour' | CHil EPPr GCHN WCru WMoo |
| - 'Mavis Simpson' | More than 30 suppliers |
| - 'Persian Carpet' | NLar |
| - 'Russell Prichard' ♀ | More than 30 suppliers |
| § *rivulare* | CElw CMCo GCHN MBro NSti |
| | STes WBea WHCG |
| - 'Album' | CHil MBro |
| *robertianum* | CKin EEls ELau EPPr EWFC MChe |
| | SCou SIde SRCN SRms WHbs |
| | WHen WJek |
| § - 'Album' | MHar NSti SCou SIde SRms |
| - f. *bernettii* | See *G. robertianum* 'Album' |
| - 'Celtic White' | CBre CHil ECoo EMon GCal NBus |
| | NCat NDov NHex NRoo NSti |
| | SRGP WElm WHen WPnP |
| *robustum* | CElw CGle CHan EBee EMar EOrc |
| | EPri GCHN LBlm MNrw NBro |
| | NCat NChi NSti SCou SDad SIgm |
| | SRGP WBea WByw WCot WCru |
| | WElm WHal WWin |
| - Hannays' form | CSpe |
| - x *incanum* | CElw CMea EWes WCru |
| - 'Norman Warrington' | WHer |
| - S&SH 14 | CElw CHan CMea SUsu WBea |
| | WCru |
| ¶ 'Rosanne' | SCou |
| ¶ 'Rosie Crûg' | CElw EBee EHic EMan NDov |
| | WCot WCru WWhi |
| *rotundifolium* | SCou |
| *rubescens* | CSpe EMar EMou GGar MNrw |
| | NBir NBro NCat NSti SCou SRGP |
| | SUsu WCru WHal WWye |
| *rubifolium* | CAbP CBod CHid EBee MBri |
| | MCCP NBrk NBus NPri NSti SCou |
| | SSpi WCru WGwy WMoo WPnP |
| *ruprechtii* | CElw CHar CHil CMCo CRDP |
| | EBee EMar GCHN MNrw NBus |
| | NCat NSti SCou SRGP WBea |
| | WElm WPnP WWin |
| 'Salome' | More than 30 suppliers |
| *sanguineum* | More than 30 suppliers |
| - 'Alan Bloom' | CMCo EBrP EBre LBre LRHS |
| | MCLN MWhe NRoo NWes SBre |
| | SIng |
| - 'Album' ♀ | More than 30 suppliers |
| - 'Alpenglow' | CHil WCru |
| - 'Ankum's Pride' | CBlo CFri CGle CHil CRDP EBee |
| | EPPr GNau MCLN WCot WHil |
| | WPen WWat |
| ¶ - 'Aviemore' | NCat |
| - 'Barnsley' | SCou SHel |
| - 'Belle of Herterton' | CHil CMCo EPPr GCHN NCat |
| | NPro SHel WCru |
| - 'Bloody Graham' | MWhe NBur NHaw SHel WMoo |
| - 'Catforth Carnival' | NCat |
| - 'Cedric Morris' | CElw CFil CHil ECha EFou EGra |
| | EPPr ERav LPio MRav MTho SCou |
| | SHel SUsu WCot WCru WHen |
| | WPnP |
| - 'Elliott's Variety' | Last listed 1997 |
| - 'Elsbeth' | CElw CHil CMil CRDP EBee EPPr |
| | EWes GBuc GCHN MCLN NBus |
| | NCat NHol NRoo SCob SCou |
| | SHel SRGP WCru WFar WHal |
| | WMoo WSan |
| - 'Farrer's Form' | EPPr GBuc WCru WMoo |
| - 'Glenluce' | More than 30 suppliers |

| | |
|---|---|
| - 'Hampshire Purple' | CHil WCru |
| - 'Holden' | CElw CMea EPPr NRoo SCou SHel WCru |
| - 'John Elsley' | CBos CElw CHil CMCo CSam EBrP EBre EMou EPPr LBre LLWP MMil MSCN MWhe NBus NGdn NLar NRoo SBre SHel SWat WPer |
| - 'Jubilee Pink' | CHil EGar EPPr NRoo SBla SCou SHel SWas WCru |
| - var. *lancastrense* | See *G. sanguineum* var. *striatum* |
| * - 'Leeds Variety' | LPio WHal |
| I  - 'Lloyds Form' | SHel |
| - 'Max Frei' | More than 30 suppliers |
| - 'Minutum' | SCou WCou WPnP |
| - 'Nanum' | CMea EPar NHol NMen NNrd WCru |
| - 'Nyewood' | CMCo ECGP EMon EPPr GCHN IMGH MLLN SCou SEND SRGP WCru WPnP |
| * - 'Plenum' | WPnP |
| * - hort. var. *prostratum* | Last listed 1997 |
| * - (Cav.) Pers. - | See *G. sanguineum* var. *striatum* |
| - 'Purple Flame' | WCru |
| - 'Sara' | SDad WHen WPnP |
| - 'Shepherd's Warning' ♀ | CHil CMea CSev EBrP EBre ECtt GAbr GCHN LBre LHop MCLN MLLN MRav MWhe NLar NRoo SBre SCou SRGP SWat WBea WByw WCru WHCG WHoo WIvy WMow WPnP WRus |
| § - var. *striatum* ♀ | More than 30 suppliers |
| - - deep pink | SCro |
| - - 'Splendens' | CElw CSev ECha ELan ENot EPPr LHop MRav MWat NChi NRoo NWes SAga SCou SSmi WCru WEas WOld WWhi |
| ¶ - x *swatense* | WMoo |
| - 'Vision' | NWes |
| ¶ - 'Westacre Poppet' | EWes |
| 'Scheherezade' | Last listed 1996 |
| *schlechteri* | Last listed 1996 |
| 'Sea Fire' | CElw CMCo GCHN MNrw MTho NCat SCro SHel WCru WMoo |
| 'Sea Pink' | CElw GCHN MNrw MTho NCat NHar WCru WHal WMoo |
| 'Sea Spray' | CPlt EBee EPPr EWes GBuc GCHN MNrw MSte MTho MWrn NRoo SWat WCru WMoo WPrP |
| *seemannii* | Last listed 1998 |
| *sessiliflorum* | ECou EPar NHar SAga SCou |
| ¶ - 'Maria' | WByw |
| - subsp. *novae-zelandiae* green-leaved | GCHN SWat |
| - - 'Nigricans' | CFri CGle CHan CMea CSev EBee ECha ELan EOrc EPot GBin GCHN IMGH LLWP MBal MRav NRoo SCou SHFr SIng SRGP WBro WCru WEas WFar WHCG WWin |
| - - 'Nigricans' x *traversii* var. *elegans* | CBos CHan CRDP EBee ESis GCHN NCat NSti SWat WCru WFar |
| § - - 'Porter's Pass' | CHil CMea EHoe EWes GBri GBuc GCHN MBro MHar MNrw NBir NChi NHex NRoo SCou SDad SUsu SWat WCru WPGP WPnP |
| - - 'Porter's Pass' hybrid | Last listed 1998 |
| - - red-leaved | See *G. sessiliflorum* subsp. *novae-zelandiae* 'Porter's Pass' |
| * - 'Rubrum' | SCou |
| *shikokianum* | CHil EBee NChi SPer SRGP WBea WPnP |
| ¶ - var. *kaimontanum* | WCru |

| | |
|---|---|
| ¶ - var. *quelpaertense* B&SWJ 1234 | WCru |
| - var. *quelpartense* | EBee |
| - var. *yoshiianum* | CElw GBuc GCHN WCru WMoo |
| *sibiricum* | EBla GCHN SCou |
| 'Silver Pink' | CStr LRHS |
| § *sinense* | CBel CElw CHil CLTr CPou EBee GCHN GCal NChi NLar NRoo NWCA SCou SRGP SSoC STes WBea WCru WHCG WHal WHer WMaN WPnP WWhi |
| 'Sirak' | CElw CHil CLAP EBla GCal MAvo NCat NRoo SHel SUsu SWas WBea WPnP |
| *soboliferum* | CAbP CBod CHil EBee GCHN GCal NBir NCut NHed NSti SCou SCro SPla WCru WGwy WWat NRoo |
| 'Sonata' | |
| 'Southcombe Star' | See *G.* x *oxonianum* 'Southcombe Star' |
| sp. from Chile | Last listed 1996 |
| sp. from Pamirs, Tadzhikistan | EBee EPPr NCat WPnP |
| 'Spinners' | More than 30 suppliers |
| 'Stanhoe' | CHil EMan EMar EPPr MAvo SCou SCro SUsu WBea |
| *stapfianum* var. *roseum* | See *G. orientalitibeticum* |
| 'Stephanie' | NCat |
| 'Strawberry Frost' | CElw CMil EBee EHic EMan EMil MMil MTis NDov SMad WCot |
| 'Sue Crûg' | CBos CElw CHil GCHN MAvo NBus NChi SCro SUsu WBea WByw WCot WCru WHen WMoo WPnP WWin |
| ¶ 'Summer Cloud' | SRGP |
| *suzukii* B&SWJ 016 | WCru |
| *swatense* | CHil EMou MNrw SCou SWat WCru |
| - SEP 131 | Last listed 1996 |
| 'Sydney Wharf' | CHan |
| *sylvaticum* | CM&M CSev EMou EWFC GMac MBal MSCN MSal NHex SCou SRGP SSpi WHal WHen WMoo WPer WShi |
| - f. *albiflorum* | CBel CBot CBre CElw CMil ELan EMar EMou GCHN MBro MWhe NRoo NSti SCou SSpi WCru WOld WWin |
| - 'Album' ♀ | More than 30 suppliers |
| - 'Amy Doncaster' | More than 30 suppliers |
| - 'Angulatum' | CHil CPlt EBee EPPr LGre SCou WMoo |
| - 'Baker's Pink' | CElw CFil CHil CMCo CMea CMil CVer EBee EMou GCHN MBro MCLN MRav MWhe NCat NChi SCou SHel SMrm SSpi SUsu WBea WCom WCru WHCG WLin WMoo WPGP WPnP WTin |
| - 'Birch Lilac' | CElw CHil CMCo EBee EGar EMou EPPr GBuc GCal NBus NCat NHol NRoo NSti SCou SHel WBea WFar WMoo WPnP |
| - 'Cyril's Fancy' | NCat |
| - 'Mayflower' ♀ | More than 30 suppliers |
| - 'Meran' | EBrP EBre LBre SBre |
| ¶ - 'Ray's Pink' | CHil |
| - f. *roseum* | CHil CMCo EBee ECGP EGle EMou GCHN NCat NRoo SCro SPer WPnP |
| - 'Silva' | CElw CGle EBee EMan GCHN MRav NBrk NCut SCou SWat WCru |
| - subsp. *sylvaticum* | CGle CHil CMea EMou EPPr |

| | |
|---|---|
| var. *wanneri* | GCHN MBro MRav NCat SCou SCro WCru |
| § *thunbergii* | CLTr CSam CVer EAst EBee EMar EMou GCHN LGro MMal MNrw MRav NBro NFai NHol NOak NSti SCou SDad WBea WHen WPer WPnP |
| ¶ – dark form | CSev NCut |
| ¶ – pink | SCou SRGP WCru |
| – purple | LBlm |
| – white | LBlm NCot SRGP |
| ♦ *thurstonianum* | See *G.* x *oxonianum* f. *thurstonianum* |
| *transbaicalicum* | EBee EPPr GCHN MBri MMal MNrw SCro SRGP WBea WCru WPGP WPnP |
| *traversii* | CBot CLyd CPBP EWes WSan |
| ¶ – 'Big White' | GCal |
| – var. *elegans* | CFee CFri CSpe EBee ELan GCHN LGre MNrw MTho NRoo SCou SRGP SWas WCru WEas WHCG WKif WPnP |
| – 'Seaspray' | EBee EBrP EBre LBre NGdn SBre SCou |
| – 'Sugar Pink' | Last listed 1996 |
| *tripartitum* | Last listed 1998 |
| *tuberosum* | CAvo CBro CElw CFri CHan CHid EBee ECha ELan ETub GCHN IMGH LLWP MBro MTho MWhe NBro NFla NGdn NSti SCou SIng SPer SRGP WBea WFar WHoo WPnP WRus |
| – var. *charlesii* | See *G. kotschyi* var. *charlesii* |
| – 'Leonidas' | ETub LRHS |
| – subsp. *linearifolium* | WCru |
| – M&T 4032 | Last listed 1998 |
| – pink form | WCru |
| – S&L 99 | Last listed 1998 |
| ♦ 'Verguld Saffier' | See *G.* 'Blue Sunrise' |
| *versicolor* | More than 30 suppliers |
| – *album* | CBel CElw CHan NBus NRoo WBea WHer WPnP |
| – 'Bill Baker' | Last listed 1996 |
| ¶ – 'Knighton' | EBee |
| § – 'Snow White' | CHil EBee EOrc EPPr GMac MNrw NBrk NMGW SCou SHel WCru WMoo |
| – 'The Bride' | EBee EGra |
| – 'White Lady' | See *G. versicolor* 'Snow White' |
| *violareum* | See *Pelargonium* 'Splendide' |
| *viscosissimum* | GCal GMac LLWP MMal NRoo NTay SCou SDad SRGP WCot WPnP |
| ¶ – rose pink | NBir |
| *wallichianum* | CBod CLTr CMCo CPou ECGP EWTr NBir NChi NSti SBla WBea WFar WHen WMoo WPyg WWat |
| § – 'Buxton's Variety' ♀ | More than 30 suppliers |
| ¶ – 'Chadwell's Pink' | EBee |
| – magenta form | GCHN |
| – pink | CAbP GBuc SUsu WCru WWat |
| – purple | WCru |
| – 'Syabru' | CBos CElw CHar CMea EBee EBla EHic EMar EMil GBuc LFis MMil MNrw NLar NSti SCou SSpi SWas WCot WCru WFar WMoo WPnP WSpi |
| ¶ 'Welsh Guiness' | NCat WCru |
| *wilfordii* hort. | See *G. thunbergii* |
| – Maximowicz | WThi |
| 'Wisley Blue' | WHal |
| 'Wisley Hybrid' | CBos CHil GCHN NBus NDov NRoo WCru WMoo |

| | |
|---|---|
| *wlassovianum* | More than 30 suppliers |
| *yesoense* | EBee EPPr GBin GCHN LFis NBir NBus NRoo NSti SCou SWat WCru WFar WHal WOut WPnP WPrP |
| ¶ – var. *nipponicum* | WCru |
| ¶ – white | EBee |
| *yoshinoi* | EBee EBla EMar EMou EPPr EWes GBuc SHel SRGP SUsu SWat WMoo WPnP |
| ¶ *yunnanense* | CElw |
| ¶ – misapplied | See *G. pogonanthum* |
| ¶ – Franchet | EBee EBla GGar MNrw SCou |

## GERANIUM hort. See PELARGONIUM

## GERBERA (Asteraceae)

| | |
|---|---|
| *jamesonii* | Last listed 1998 |

## GESNERIA (Gesneriaceae)

| | |
|---|---|
| *cardinalis* | See *Sinningia cardinalis* |
| x *cardosa* | See *Sinningia* x *cardosa* |

## GEUM ✿ (Rosaceae)

| | |
|---|---|
| ¶ 'Abendsonne' | CElw |
| *aleppicum* | CFee CLyd WMoo |
| – CLD 610 | Last listed 1997 |
| – subsp. *strictum* | Last listed 1996 |
| *alpinum* | See *G. montanum* |
| ¶ *andicola* | EBee |
| 'Beech House Apricot' | CBre CElw CGle CHan CHea CLon CMdw CPlt CRDP CSev EBee EMan GBri LGre MAvo MBel MNrw MRav NChi NCot SMac SUsu WLin WPnP WPrP WRus |
| 'Birkhead's Creamy Lemon' | Last listed 1996 |
| N 'Borisii' | More than 30 suppliers |
| 'Borisii' x *montanum* | LHop |
| *bulgaricum* | CMea LRHS MNrw NBir NPro NRya NTow WByw WMer WPrP |
| *calthifolium* | CSam EBee MCCP MOne NBro NCut NLak SBea WElm |
| *canadense* | Last listed 1998 |
| ¶ *capense* from Lesotho | CSpe |
| – JJ&JH 9401271 | EBee |
| ¶ – S&SH 33 | WCot |
| 'Carlskaer' | CElw CLon CRDP EBee GCal MAvo MNrw NTow SDys SMrm |
| § *chiloense* | Clyd EBee |
| ¶ – 'Farncombe' | CElw |
| – P&W 6513 | CHan MSte NWCA |
| *coccineum* | CPlt WRha |
| – hort. | See *G. chiloense* |
| – Sibth. & Sm. NS 653 | MRPP |
| 'Coppertone' | CElw CGle CHad CLon CPla CRDP EBee ECha ECtt EHal ELan GCal GMac IBlr LFis MCLN MNrw MRav NBir NBro NCat NLon SAga SPer SUsu WHoo WMoo WPGP WSan WWhi |
| 'Dingle Apricot' | MRav NBir |
| 'Dolly North' | CHea EBee EGar EPPr GAbr GBri GGar MAvo MBNS MBri MCAu MRav NBro NCat NFai WMer |
| *elatum* CC&McK 390 | Last listed 1996 |
| I 'Farmer John Cross' | CBre EBee MAvo MTPN |
| 'Feuermeer' | LHop MBel MSte NLak NPro |
| 'Fire Opal' ♀ | CPlt CSam MNrw NBir WMow |
| ¶ 'Georgeham' | CPla |
| 'Georgenburg' | CRDP EBee EBrP EBre ECtt EOrc LBre LFis LPio MCLN MNrw MWgw NBir NDov NFai NHol NLon NOak SBre SChu SPer SRms WBea WByw WMer WMoo WMow WOve WSan |

¶ 'Glencoe'                CElw
* 'Gordon Cooper'          Last listed 1996
x *heldreichii*           Last listed 1996
* *hybridum luteum*        MBel NSti
x *intermedium*            CHor CRow EBee EMan EMon
                           MCLN MNrw NLak NLar SChu
                           SCro SUsu WLRN WMow
- 'Muriel' (v)             MInt
'Karlskaer'                EGle LPio
'Lady Stratheden' ♀        More than 30 suppliers
*leiospermum*             Last listed 1996
'Lemon Drops'              CBre CElw CGle ECha EGol ELan
                           EMan EPPr GBri GMac MNrw
                           MRav MSte NBur NCat NChi
                           NCot SChu SUsu WFar WMoo
                           WPGP WPrP
'Lionel Cox'               More than 30 suppliers
*macrophyllum*            GBar MNrw NBus WMoo
- var. *sachalinense*      Last listed 1996
* 'Mandarin'               GCal
'Marika'                   CBre CHid CRow MAvo MNrw
                           NBrk SChu
¶ 'Marmalade'              MAvo
§ *montanum* ♀             CFri CHan CSam ECha ELan GTou
                           MBro NBir NBro NHed NLak
                           NRoo NRya SBea SIng SRms SSca
                           WBea WCla WMoo WPer WWin
- 'Maximum'                Last listed 1998
'Mrs J. Bradshaw' ♀        More than 30 suppliers
'Mrs W. Moore'             GBri NCat NChi NPro
'Nordek'                   GMac MBri MNrw WMow
* 'Orangeman'              Last listed 1996
§ *parviflorum*            CPou EBee EGar EOld MBro
                           MLLN MNrw NBro NBus NCut
                           NLar WCot
*pentapetalum*            CGle CLyd NRya WAbe
¶ - 'Flore Pleno'          WAbe
¶ 'Present'                EBee
'Prince of Orange'         CElw EGar GAbr NLak
'Prinses Juliana'          CHan EFou EGar GCal GMac MBri
                           MCLN MRav MUlv NCat NDov
                           NLak WCot WMer
¶ *pseudococcineum*        CElw
*pyrenaicum*              NBus NLak
*quellyon*                See *G. chiloense*
'Red Wings'                CM&M EFou EGar GCal MAvo
                           WMer WRus
*reptans*                 See *Sieversia reptans*
x *rhaeticum*             NMen
*rhodopeum*               MNrw
'Rijnstroom'               MBel MTed NFai
*rivale*                  CArn CBen CKin CRow EHon
                           EMar EWFC EWTr GAbr GDra
                           MFir MHew MMal MSta MSte
                           MWat NBro NFor NLan NMir
                           SRms SWat WCla WHal WMer
                           WMow WOve WPer WRus WWin
- 'Album'                  More than 30 suppliers
- apricot                  LGro WPrP WWin
¶ - 'Cream Drop'           NWoo
¶ - cream form from Tien   CFee
   Shan, China
- lemon seedling           CRDP
* - 'Leonard's Double'     ECtt WElm
- 'Leonard's Variety'      More than 30 suppliers
¶ - 'Marmalade'            NChi
¶ *roylei*                 EBee
'Rubin'                    EBee EFou EGar LHop MBNS
                           MBel MCAu MCLN MTis NDov
                           NGdn NLak SCro SLod SPla SSpe
                           WCot WElm WMow
'Sigiswang'                EFou GAbr MBel MFir MNrw
                           MSte

'Tangerine'                GGar MNrw MRav NRoo
x *tirolense*             EBee
*triflorum*               CPBP EBee EHyt EMan EOld
                           EWTr GTou LGre LPio MBri
                           MNrw MRav NLar WFar WHil
                           WLin WMoo WRus
- var. *campanulatum*      EDAr EHyt NChi NTow
*urbanum*                 CArn CKin ELau EWFC GPoy
                           MChe MCli MHew NLan NPri
                           SIde SWat WCla WHbs WHer
                           WMoo
- 'Checkmate' (v)          EMon
'Werner Arends'            EBee GCal LRHS MAvo MBri
                           MRav WFar

## GEVUINA (Proteaceae)
*avellana*                CB&S CGre CTrG CTrw GSki
                           LEdu

## GILIA (Polemoniaceae)
*aggregata*               See *Ipomopsis aggregata*
*caespitosa*              Last listed 1996
*californica*             See *Leptodactylon californicum*
*stenothyrsa*             See *Ipomopsis stenothyrsa*

## GILLENIA (Rosaceae)
*stipulata*               CHea CRDP EMon LGre LHol
                           MTPN
*trifoliata* ♀            More than 30 suppliers

## GINKGO (Ginkgoaceae)
*biloba* ♀                More than 30 suppliers
- 'Autumn Gold' (m)        CDoC CDul CEnd ETen LNet
                           LRHS MBlu MBri SMad
- 'Fairmount' (m)          MBlu
- 'Fastigiata' (m)         CCHP CMCN MGos WMou
- 'Hekt Leiden'            CMCN
- 'Horizontalis'           CMCN MBlu NMoo
- 'Icho'                   MBlu
- 'King of Dongting' (f)   LEdu MBlu MBri WMou
- 'Lakeview'               Last listed 1996
- 'Mayfield' (m)           Last listed 1996
¶ - Pendula Group          CDul CMCN EPfP LPan WMou
- 'Princeton Sentry' (m)   LRHS MBlu MBri SMad
I - 'Prostrata'            CPMA WWes
- 'Saratoga' (m)           CEnd CMCN CPMA LCon LNet
                           MBlu MGos
- 'Tit'                    CMCN EPfP LNet
- 'Tremonia'               CDoC LCon LNet LRHS MBlu
                           MBri
- 'Tubifolia'              MBlu
- 'Umbrella'               CDul CMCN
¶ - Variegata Group (v)    CMCN CPMA EPfP LNet MBlu
                           SMad

## GLADIOLUS ✿ (Iridaceae)
¶ 'Acapulco' (L)           CGrW
¶ *acuminatus*             CGrW
¶ 'Advantage' (L)          CGrW
*alatus*                  CGrW
¶ 'Alba' (N)               CGrW
'Alice' (Min)              LAma
'Aloha' (L)                CSut
'Amanda Mahy' (N)          CBro CGrW LAma NRog
¶ 'Ambiance' (L)           CGrW
¶ 'Amsterdam' (G)          CGrW
¶ 'Anchorage' (L)          CGrW
¶ 'Andre Viette'           WCot
¶ 'Angel of Mine' (S)      CGrW
¶ *angustus*               GCal
¶ 'Anitra' (P)             CGrW
¶ 'Anna Leorah' (L)        CGrW

| | |
|---|---|
| ¶ *antakiensis* | CPou |
| ¶ 'Antica' (L) | CGrW |
| 'Applause' (L) | LAma NRog |
| ¶ 'Apricot Perfection' (S/P) | CGrW |
| * 'Arabian Night' | CSut |
| ¶ 'Ashram' (M) | CGrW |
| ¶ 'Athelney Aztec' (P) | CGrW |
| ¶ 'Athelney Sunburst' (L) | CGrW |
| 'Atom' (S/P) | CBro CGrW ETub LAma |
| *atroviolaceus* | WPGP |
| ¶ 'Aubrey Lane' (M) | CGrW |
| ¶ *aurantiacus* | GCal WCot |
| ¶ 'Aureus' (S) | CGrW |
| 'Avalanche' (B) | LAma |
| ¶ 'Baltica' (L) | CGrW |
| ¶ 'Barn Owl' (L) | CGrW |
| ¶ 'Beauty of Holland' (L) | CGrW |
| ¶ 'Belair' (S) | CGrW |
| 'Bell Boy' (B) | LAma |
| ¶ 'Beryl Jones' (L) | CGrW |
| ¶ 'Bettine' (S) | CGrW |
| ¶ 'Bewitched' (L) | CGrW |
| ¶ 'Black Lash' (S) | CGrW |
| 'Blackpool' (M) | LAma NRog |
| *blandus* var. *carneus* | See G. carneus |
| ¶ 'Blue Beauty' (L) | CGrW |
| ¶ 'Blue Dart' (M) | CGrW |
| ¶ 'Blue Frost' (L) | CGrW |
| ¶ 'Blue Tina' (Min) | CGrW |
| ¶ 'Blue Tit' (P) | CGrW |
| ¶ 'Bombay' (G) | CGrW |
| *bonaespei* | WCot |
| * 'Bread and Butter' | CSut |
| ¶ 'Brenda Jo' (S) | CGrW |
| ¶ 'Bronzed Beauty' (S) | CGrW |
| ¶ 'Burrowbridge Beauty' (P) | CGrW |
| *byzantinus* | See G. communis subsp. byzantinus |
| ¶ 'Cairngorm' (S/P) | CGrW |
| *callianthus* ♀ | CSWP MSCN WCot WWhi |
| § - 'Murieliae' ♀ | CAvo CBro CGrW EBee LAma LBow NRog SDeJ |
| 'Cambourne' (Min) | LAma NRog |
| *cardinalis* | CFil CGrW CHan CRDP GCal IBlr SIgm SSpi WCot WPGP |
| *carinatus* | CGrW NRog |
| ¶ 'Carine' (N) | CGrW |
| ¶ 'Carla Gabor' (L) | CGrW |
| *carmineus* | CGrW LBow |
| § *carneus* | CBro CGrW NRog WCot WHal |
| ¶ 'Carquirenne' (G) | CGrW |
| ¶ 'Cartago' (L) | CGrW |
| ¶ 'Centrepiece' (M) | CGrW |
| ¶ 'Cerise Spire' (M) | CGrW |
| 'Charm' (N) | CAvo CBro CGrW LAma |
| ¶ 'Charmer' (L) | CGrW |
| 'Charming Beauty' (Tub) | NRog SCoo |
| * 'Charming Lady' | CGrW SCoo |
| 'Chartres' (B) | CGrW LAma |
| ¶ 'Chiltern Beauty' (L) | CGrW |
| 'Chiquita' (M) | CSut |
| ¶ 'Chloe' (M) | CGrW |
| ¶ 'Chloe's Dream' (S) | CGrW |
| 'Christabel' (L) | CGrW ERos |
| ¶ 'Christofel' (N) | CGrW |
| ¶ 'Cimarosa' (L) | CGrW |
| *citrinus* | CGrW LBow |
| 'City Lights' | Last listed 1998 |
| 'Columbine' (P/L) | CGrW LAma NRog |
| x *colvillei* | ECha IBlr |
| 'Comet' (N) | CGrW ETub NRog |
| *communis* | LAma |
| § - subsp. *byzantinus* ♀ | CB&S CBro CFee CGle CGrW CHad CHid EBee ECha ELan EPar ETub GCrs LAma LBow MBri MLLN NChi NRog NSti SRms SUsu WBea WCot WEas WShi |
| ¶ 'Coral Dream' (L) | CGrW |
| ¶ 'Cordoba' (L) | CGrW |
| ¶ 'Corrinna' (P) | CGrW |
| 'Côte d'Azur' (G) | Last listed 1997 |
| ¶ *crassifolius* | WCot |
| ¶ 'Cream of the Crop' (M) | CGrW |
| ¶ 'Creme de Mint' (S) | CGrW |
| ¶ 'Crimson Fire' (G) | CGrW |
| *cunonius* | Last listed 1998 |
| ¶ 'Curload Champion' (P) | CGrW |
| ¶ *dalenii* | SSpi |
| ¶ - *bookeri rubra* | CGrW |
| ¶ 'Dame Edna II' (L) | CGrW |
| 'Dancing Doll' | Last listed 1996 |
| ¶ 'Dawn Jane' (S) | CGrW |
| ¶ 'Desirée' (B) | CGrW |
| ¶ 'Devotion' (S) | CGrW |
| 'Don Juan' | CGrW CSut |
| ¶ 'Drama' (L) | CGrW |
| 'Dyanito' (B/S) | LAma |
| ¶ 'Eastbourne' (S/B) | CGrW |
| *ecklonii* | Last listed 1997 |
| 'Edna' (S) | CGrW |
| ¶ 'Elin' (M) | CGrW |
| 'Elvira' (N) | CGrW LAma NRog SCoo |
| ¶ 'Emerald Spring' (S) | CGrW |
| ¶ *equitans* | CGrW |
| ¶ 'Esperanto' (M) | CGrW |
| ¶ 'Essex' (P/S) | CGrW |
| ¶ 'Esta Bonita' (G) | CGrW |
| ¶ 'Estonia' (G) | CGrW |
| ¶ 'Eugenie' (M) | CGrW |
| 'Eurovision' (L) | Last listed 1998 |
| 'Fair Lady' (Tub) | NRog |
| ¶ 'Fidelio' (L) | LAma |
| ¶ 'Final Touch' (G) | CGrW |
| ¶ 'Finesse' (L) | CGrW |
| ¶ 'Fingerprints' (L) | CGrW |
| ¶ 'Flevo Fire' (M) | CGrW |
| ¶ 'Flevo Maitre' (L) | CGrW |
| ¶ 'Florence C' (M) | CGrW |
| *floribundus* | CGrW LBow |
| ¶ 'Flowersong' (L) | LAma |
| ¶ 'Frank's Perfection' (S/P) | CGrW |
| 'Friendship' (L) | Last listed 1996 |
| 'Frosty Pink' | Last listed 1997 |
| *garnieri* | CGrW SSpi |
| 'Georgette' (B) | LAma |
| ¶ 'Giallo Antico' (L) | Last listed 1998 |
| 'Gillian' (L) | LBow |
| ¶ 'Golden Melody' (M) | CGrW |
| 'Good Luck' (N) | CAvo CBro |
| ¶ *gracilis* | CGrW |
| ¶ 'Grand Finale' (L) | CGrW |
| ¶ 'Grand Prix' (L) | CGrW |
| *grandis* | See G. liliaceus |
| ¶ 'Granny White' (S/P) | CGrW |
| 'Green Woodpecker' (M) ♀ | CGrW LAma NRog |
| ¶ 'Greyfriars' (P) | CGrW |
| 'Guernsey Glory' (N) | CGrW NRog |
| 'Halley' | CBro CGrW SCoo |
| ¶ 'Hastings' (S/P) | CGrW |
| ¶ 'Heidi' (S) | CGrW |
| ¶ 'Hi-era' (L) | CGrW |
| ¶ 'High Brow' (G) | CGrW |
| ¶ 'High Style' (L) | CGrW |
| 'Holland Pearl' (B/M) | CGrW LAma NRog |

| | |
|---|---|
| ¶ 'Hradec Kralove' (L) | CGrW |
| 'Hunting Song' (L) | LAma NRog |
| ¶ *buttonii* | CGrW |
| ¶ 'Ice Cap' (L) | CGrW |
| *illyricus* | CFil CGrW CSam WPGP |
| ¶ - 'Mallorca' | CGrW |
| *imbricatus* | CGrW ERos |
| 'Impressive' (N) | NRog |
| 'Inca Queen' (L) | CGrW |
| § *italicus* | CGrW WPGP |
| 'Ivanhoe' (L/P) | CGrW |
| 'Ivory Beauty' (L) | CGrW |
| 'Ivory Tower' (G) | CGrW |
| 'Jacksonville Gold' (L) | LAma |
| ¶ 'Jeannie Rose' (S) | CGrW |
| ¶ 'Jennifer Kay' (S) | CGrW |
| ¶ 'Joyce' (P) | CGrW |
| ¶ 'Judy Jean' (S) | CGrW |
| 'Jupiter' | Last listed 1996 |
| § *kotschyanus* | Last listed 1998 |
| ¶ 'Kristin' (L) | CGrW |
| ¶ 'La Petite' (Min) | CGrW |
| ¶ 'Lady Eleanor' (S/P) | CGrW |
| 'Lady Godiva' (P/S) | LAma NRog |
| ¶ 'Lady Lucille' (M) | CGrW |
| ¶ 'Lavender Flare' (S) | CGrW |
| ¶ 'Lavender Ruffles' (L) | CGrW |
| 'Leonore' (S) | LAma |
| 'Liebelei' | Last listed 1996 |
| § *liliaceus* | LBow |
| ¶ 'Little Wiggy' (P) | CGrW |
| ¶ 'Lorena' (B) | CGrW |
| 'Lowland Queen' (L) | CGrW CSut |
| ¶ 'Lowri' (M) | CGrW |
| 'Madonna' (L) | CSut |
| 'Magistral' (L) | CGrW |
| ¶ 'Margaret Lyall' (L) | .CGrW |
| *marlothii* | CGrW |
| 'Mary Housley' (L) | CSut LAma |
| ¶ 'Meersen' (L) | CGrW |
| ¶ 'Mileesh' (L) | CGrW |
| 'Mirella' (N) | CGrW MRav NRog |
| ¶ 'Miss America' (M) | CGrW |
| ¶ 'Mondiale' (G) | CGrW |
| ¶ 'Moon Mirage' (G) | CGrW |
| ¶ 'Moonshine' (G) | CGrW |
| ¶ 'Mother's Day' (G) | CGrW |
| 'Murieliae' | See *G. callianthus* 'Murieliae' |
| 'My Love' (L) | CSut LAma |
| § *natalensis* | CGrW ERos GCal IBlr WCot |
| ¶ 'Nathaly' (N) | CGrW |
| *nerineoides* | Last listed 1998 |
| ¶ 'Nicholas' (S) | CGrW |
| 'Nova Lux' (L) | LAma NRog |
| 'Nymph' (N) | CAvo CGrW ETub LAma NRog |
| 'Obelisk' (P) | NRog |
| ¶ *odoratus* | CGrW |
| ¶ *oppositiflorus* | CPou |
|    subsp. *salmoneus* | |
| ¶ 'Orange Rascal' (Min) | CGrW |
| *orchidiflorus* | CGrW CSWP LBow |
| 'Oscar' (G) | LAma NRog |
| ¶ *palustris* | ERos |
| *papilio* | More than 30 suppliers |
| § - Purpureoauratus Group | CBro CGle CSam EMan ERos IBlr |
| | MFir SOkh SRms |
| ¶ - 'Red Papilio' | CGrW |
| ¶ *pappei* | CGrW |
| ¶ 'Parade' (G) | CGrW |
| ¶ 'Pauline Johnson' (S) | CGrW |
| 'Perky' (Min) | LAma |
| 'Perseus' (P/Min) | LAma |

| | |
|---|---|
| 'Peter Pears' (L) | LAma NRog |
| 'Picturesque' (P) | NRog |
| ¶ 'Pink Elf' (S) | CGrW |
| ¶ 'Pink Ice' (L) | CGrW |
| ¶ 'Pink Lady' (L) | CGrW |
| ¶ 'Plum Splash' (S) | CGrW |
| 'Plum Tart' (L) | Last listed 1998 |
| ¶ 'Pole Position' (L) | CGrW |
| 'Praha' (L) | LAma NRog |
| ¶ 'Pretty Woman' (L) | CGrW |
| *primulinus* | See *G. natalensis* |
| Primulinus hybrids | SDeJ |
| 'Princess Margaret Rose' | CSut LAma |
|    (Min) | |
| 'Prins Claus' (N) | CBro CGrW LAma NRog |
| *priorii* | CGrW LBow |
| 'Priscilla' (L) | LAma SLod |
| ¶ 'Pulchritude' (M) | CGrW |
| *punctulatus* | LBow |
| ¶ - var. *punctulatus* | ERos |
| ¶ 'Purple Princess' (M) | CGrW |
| *purpureoauratus* | See *G. papilio* Purpureoauratus |
| | Group |
| *quadrangularis* | Last listed 1998 |
| ¶ 'Queen's Blush' (L) | CGrW |
| ¶ 'Queen's Lace' (M) | CGrW |
| ¶ 'Rachelle' (G) | CGrW |
| 'Ramona' | Last listed 1997 |
| ¶ 'Red Jewel' (P/S) | CGrW |
| ¶ 'Richards' Renown' (M) | CGrW |
| 'Richmond' (B) | NRog |
| ¶ 'Rob Roy' (S/P) | CGrW |
| 'Robin' (P) | Last listed 1996 |
| 'Robinetta' (*recurvus* | CGrW LAma NRog SCoo |
|    hybrid) ♀ | |
| ¶ 'Roncalli' (L) | CGrW |
| ¶ 'Rooster' (P) | CGrW |
| ¶ 'Rose Elf' (S) | CGrW |
| 'Rougex' | Last listed 1998 |
| 'Royal Dutch' (L) | Last listed 1996 |
| ¶ 'Sabrina' (M/N) | CGrW |
| 'Sabu' | Last listed 1996 |
| ¶ *saccatus* | CGrW |
| ¶ 'Safari' (Min/B) | CGrW |
| ¶ 'Sailor's Delight' (L) | CGrW |
| ¶ 'Sally's Orange' (P) | CGrW |
| ¶ 'Samantha' (N) | CGrW |
| ¶ 'San Remo' (L) | CGrW |
| *saundersii* | CFil CGrW WPGP |
| 'Saxony' (P) | Last listed 1996 |
| ¶ 'Scarlet Lady' (P) | CGrW |
| ¶ 'Scarlet Opening' (L) | CGrW |
| ¶ 'Scarlet Perfection' (S/P) | CGrW |
| ¶ 'Sceptre' (L) | CGrW |
| ¶ 'Scrimshaw' (S) | CGrW |
| *scullyi* | CGrW LBow |
| *segetum* | See *G. italicus* |
| ¶ *sericeovillosus* | CGrW |
| ¶ 'Sharkey' (G) | CGrW |
| ¶ 'Shawna' (Min) | CGrW |
| ¶ 'Silent Snow' (M) | CGrW |
| ¶ 'Silver Jubilee' (G) | CGrW |
| ¶ 'Silver Shadow' (S) | CGrW |
| ¶ 'Sirael' (L) | CGrW |
| ¶ 'Snow Castle' (S) | CGrW |
| ¶ 'Song' (L) | CGrW |
| 'Spic and Span' (L) | Last listed 1996 |
| ¶ *splendens* | CGrW |
| ¶ 'Stephanie' (L) | CGrW |
| ¶ 'Stromboli' (L) | CGrW |
| 'Sweet Shadow' | WCot |
| ¶ 'Tan Royale' (S/P) | CGrW |

¶ *tenellus*  CGrW
¶ 'Tesoro' (M)  CGrW
'The Bride' (x *colvillei*) ♀  CAvo CBro CGle CGrW CHad
  CMil CSpe EBee EBrP EBre GBri
  LAma LBre NCat NRog SBre SLod
  WPen
'Theresa'  Last listed 1996
¶ 'Titania' (L)  CGrW
¶ 'Tommy O' (S)  CGrW
¶ 'Topaz' (L)  CGrW
'Tout à Toi'  CSut
'Trader Horn' (G)  CGrW LAma NRog
*tristis*  CBro CFee CGrW CPou CRow
  ECha ELan LBow NRog SAga SSpi
  SWas WAbe WBor WCot WHal
- var. *concolor*  CGrW ERos WHer
¶ 'Uganda'  CSut
*undulatus*  CGrW CSWP ERos LBow
¶ 'Velvet Eyes' (M)  CGrW
'Velvet Joy' (P)  LAma
'Vera Lynn'  Last listed 1998
¶ 'Verve' (L)  CGrW
¶ 'Vicki Cream' (L)  CGrW
'Victor Borge' (L)  NRog
¶ 'Victoria' (M)  CGrW
¶ 'Vienna' (L)  CGrW
*violaceolineatus*  Last listed 1998
¶ 'Violetta' (M)  CGrW
*virescens*  LBow WCot
¶ 'Visionary' (L)  CGrW
¶ 'Walter P' (G)  CGrW
¶ 'Warmunda' (N)  CGrW
*watsonioides*  CPou ERos
¶ 'Welcome' (L)  CGrW
'White City' (P/B/S)  LAma
'White Friendship' (L)  LAma NRog
¶ 'White Knight' (L)  CGrW
¶ 'White Willie' (S)  CGrW
'Wind Song' (L)  LAma
'Wine and Roses' (L)  Last listed 1996
'Wise Cracks'  Last listed 1996
¶ 'You'll Be Lucky' (L)  CGrW

## GLANDULARIA (Verbenaceae)
*bipinnatifida*  See *Verbena bipinnatifida*
*pulchella*  See *Verbena tenera*

## GLAUCIDIUM (Glaucidiaceae)
*palmatum* ♀  CFir EFEx EMan GCrs GDra MBal
  NHar NSla WAbe WCru WHil
  WThi
- 'Album'  See *G. palmatum* var.
  *leucanthum*
§ - var. *leucanthum*  EFEx GCrs

## GLAUCIUM (Papaveraceae)
* *caucasicum*  Last listed 1997
§ *corniculatum*  CBot CGle CHar CLon EBee MHlr
  SEND SSca SSoC WCot WEas
  WPGP WPyg
*flavum*  CArn CGle CLon CSpe ECha
  EGoo EMFP EWFC SMrm SSca
  WHer WWin
- *aurantiacum*  See *G. flavum* f. *fulvum*
§ - f. *fulvum*  ECha EMan EPPr LHop LPio
  MGed NFai SDix
- orange  See *G. flavum* f. *fulvum*
- red  See *G. corniculatum*
*grandiflorum*  EBee WWin
*phoenicium*  See *G. corniculatum*
*squamigerum*  Last listed 1996

## GLAUX (Primulaceae)
*maritima*  ELan WPer
- dwarf form  NWCA

## GLECHOMA (Lamiaceae)
*hederacea*  CAgr CArn CKin EWFC GBar
  GPoy Ilve MHew NBro NMir SIde
  SRms WCer WHbs WHer WWye
- 'Barry Yinger Variegated' (v)  CRow
- 'Little Crown' (v)  WAlt
- 'Rosea'  LRHS
- 'Spot Check'  Last listed 1998
§ - 'Variegata'  CHal CRow ELan EPfP GBar ILis
  MBri MRav
*hirsuta* AL&JS 90069YU  Last listed 1998

## GLEDITSIA (Caesalpiniaceae)
*caspica*  CB&S
*japonica*  EPfP SMad
*koraiensis*  CMCN
¶ *sinensis*  SMad
*triacanthos*  CAgr CDul CPle ENot IOrc LEdu
  LPan MWhi WNor
¶ - 'Elegantissima' (v)  SPer
- 'Emerald Cascade'  CBlo CEnd CLnd CPMA LRHS
- f. *inermis*  CAgr WNor
- 'Rubylace'  CB&S CBlo CDul CEnd CLnd
  COtt EBee ELan EPfP EWTr LBuc
  LPan MAsh MBar MBlu MBri
  MGos MRav SMad SMer SSpi
  WDin WOrn
- 'Shademaster'  ENot
- 'Skyline'  LPan
- 'Sunburst' ♀  More than 30 suppliers

## GLIRICIDIA (Leguminosae)
¶ *sepium*  MPEx

## GLOBBA (Zingiberaceae)
*marantina*  Last listed 1997
*winitii*  LChe

## GLOBULARIA (Globulariaceae)
*albiflora*  Last listed 1996
*bellidifolia*  See *G. meridionalis*
*bisnagarica*  WLin
- NS 695  NWCA
*cordifolia* ♀  CHea CTri EDAr EHyt IMGH LBee
  MBro MTho NHar NHol NMen
  NTow SAga SBla SIng SUsu WAbe
  WHoo WMoo
- NS 696  NWCA
- *purpurescens*  Last listed 1998
*incanescens*  CLyd LBee WCla WWin
§ *meridionalis*  CFee CHea CPBP EWes ITim
  MBro MWat NHar NMen NWCA
  SBla SSmi WCom WLin
- 'Hort's Variety'  CTri GMaP NNrd NTow WAbe
*nana*  See *G. repens*
*nudicaulis*  EBot MBro NHar SBla
- 'Alba'  CLyd WIvy
§ *punctata*  CNic EHyt LFis MBro NTow
  NWCA SRms WHil WHoo
*pygmaea*  See *G. meridionalis*
§ *repens*  CLyd CNic CPBP MBro MTho
  NMen
*spinosa*  Last listed 1998
*stygia*  NSla
*trichosantha*  CFee EDAr GAbr MRPP NRya
  SMrm SRms WCom

| | |
|---|---|
| *vulgaris* | CInt ELan |

## GLORIOSA (Colchicaceae)

| | |
|---|---|
| *carsonii* | See *G. superba* 'Carsonii' |
| *lutea* | See *G. superba* 'Lutea' |
| *rothschildiana* | See *G. superba* 'Rothschildiana' |
| § *superba* ♀ | LAma MBri NRog SDeJ |
| § - 'Carsonii' | Last listed 1996 |
| § - 'Lutea' | LAma LBow NRog |
| § - 'Rothschildiana' | CB&S CHal CPlN CRHN ETub |
| | LAma LBow SOWG SRms SSoC |

## GLOXINIA (Gesneriaceae)

| | |
|---|---|
| 'Chic' | NMos |
| * *latifolia* | EBak |
| 'Medusa' | WDib |
| *perennis* | NMos |
| *sylvatica* | CHal WDib |
| - 'Bolivian Sunset' | WDib |

## GLUMICALYX (Scrophulariaceae)

| | |
|---|---|
| ¶ *flanaganii* | EBee GCrs WCot |
| - HWEL 0325 | NWCA |
| *goseloides* | CFee SSpi WPat |
| aff. *goseloides* JJ&JH | Last listed 1996 |
| 9401347 | |
| *lesuticus* | EBee |
| *montanus* | EBee WCot |
| ¶ *nutans* | EBee |

## GLYCERIA (Poaceae)

| | |
|---|---|
| *aquatica variegata* | See *G. maxima* var. *variegata* |
| *grandis* | Last listed 1997 |
| *maxima* | Last listed 1998 |
| § - var. *variegata* | More than 30 suppliers |
| *plicata* | See *G. notata* |
| *spectabilis* 'Variegata' | See *G. maxima* var. *variegata* |

## GLYCYRRHIZA (Papilionaceae)

| | |
|---|---|
| *acanthocarpa* | EOHP |
| *echinata* | CAgr CArn EWTr MSal |
| § *glabra* | CAgr CArn ELau EOHP LHol |
| | MHer MHew MSal WHer WJek |
| | WWye |
| - 'Poznan' | GPoy |
| *glandulifera* | See *G. glabra* |
| *lepidota* | Last listed 1996 |
| *uralensis* | CArn ELau EOHP GPoy MSal |
| ¶ *yunnanensis* | LGre |

## GLYPTOSTROBUS (Taxodiaceae)

| | |
|---|---|
| § *pensilis* | IDee |

## GNAPHALIUM (Asteraceae)

| | |
|---|---|
| 'Fairy Gold' | See *Helichrysum* |
| | *thianschanicum* 'Goldkind' |
| *keriense* | See *Anaphalis keriensis* |
| *norvegicum* | Last listed 1997 |
| *subrigidum* | See *Anaphalis subrigida* |
| *trinerve* | See *Anaphalis trinervis* |

## GODETIA See CLARKIA

## GOMPHOCARPUS (Asclepiadaceae)

| | |
|---|---|
| § *fruticosus* | Last listed 1998 |
| § *physocarpus* | CArn MSte |

## GOMPHOLOBIUM (Papilionaceae)

| | |
|---|---|
| *polymorphum* | Last listed 1998 |

## GOMPHOSTIGMA (Buddlejaceae)

| | |
|---|---|
| *virgatum* | EBee WCot |

## GONIOLIMON (Plumbaginaceae)

| | |
|---|---|
| § *incanum* 'Blue Diamond' | CM&M |
| § *tataricum* | EMan NBur |
| § - var. *angustifolium* | EBee LFis NBur NMir SRms WByw |
| | WPer |
| - 'Woodcreek' | Last listed 1996 |

## GOODIA (Papilionaceae)

| | |
|---|---|
| *lotifolia* | CHan |

## GOODYERA (Orchidaceae)

| | |
|---|---|
| *biflora* | EFEx |
| *hachijoensis* | EFEx |
| var. *yakushimensis* | |
| *oblongifolia* | Last listed 1997 |
| *pubescens* | EFEx LRHS WCru WThi |
| *schlechtendaliana* | EFEx |

## GORDONIA (Theaceae)

| | |
|---|---|
| *axillaris* | CB&S |

## GOSSYPIUM (Malvaceae)

| | |
|---|---|
| *herbaceum* | MSal |

## GRAPTOPETALUM (Crassulaceae)

| | |
|---|---|
| *bellum* | MBri SChr |
| - 'Super Star' | Last listed 1998 |
| § *paraguayense* | CHal EOas |

## GRATIOLA (Scrophulariaceae)

| | |
|---|---|
| *officinalis* | CArn EHon EMan LHol MHer |
| | MHew MSal SIde WHer WMoo |
| | WSel WWye |

## GREENOVIA (Crassulaceae)

| | |
|---|---|
| *aizoon* | NTow |
| § *aurea* | SIng |

## GREVILLEA ✿ (Proteaceae)

| | |
|---|---|
| *alpina* | CFee CPle EBee GQui SBid SMur |
| | SOWG WAbe |
| - Olympic Flame | CB&S CCHP CDoC CPLG CTrw |
| | LHil MSag SOWG |
| * 'Apricot Queen' | CB&S |
| ¶ *asplenifolia* | SOWG |
| 'Robyn Gordon' | |
| ¶ *australis* var. *brevifolia* | CPLG |
| *banksii* | Last listed 1998 |
| * - 'Canberra Hybrid' | SSto |
| ¶ - var. *forsteri* | SOWG |
| 'Bonnie Prince Charlie' | SOWG |
| 'Canberra Gem' ♀ | CGre CHan CPLG CPle CTrG |
| | CWSG ECou GLch LCns LEdu |
| | LHil LHop MBal MBel MBri MBro |
| | MSag SAga SDry SIgm SMrm |
| | SOWG SSpi WAbe WCru WGer |
| | WPat |
| ¶ 'Clearview David' | SOWG |
| 'Cranbrook Yellow' | CDoC CPLG LHil SBid |
| *crithmifolia* | CPLG SOWG |
| ¶ *curviloba* | CPLG |
| ¶ 'Desert Flame' | CPLG |
| ¶ 'Honey Gem' | SOWG |
| ¶ *intricata* | SOWG |
| *juniperina* | Last listed 1998 |
| - 'Aurea' | Last listed 1998 |
| ¶ - 'Molonglo' | CPLG |
| - f. *sulphurea* ♀ | CB&S CChe CDoC CFil COtt |
| | CPLG CTrG CTrw EHic EPfP |
| | GQui SBid SIgm SOWG WAbe |
| | WBod WPat |

| | |
|---|---|
| *lanigera* | CPLG |
| ¶ – *prostata* | SOWG |
| ¶ 'Mason's Hybrid' | SOWG |
| *monticola* | Last listed 1998 |
| ¶ 'Moonlight' | SOWG |
| ¶ 'Orange Marmalade' | SOWG |
| ¶ 'Poorinda Peter' | CPLG |
| *prostrata* 'Aurea' | CPLG |
| *robusta* ♀ | CHal MBri SOWG |
| *rosmarinifolia* ♀ | CChe CDoC CFil COtt CTrG |
| | CTrw EAst EBee EPfP GQui MBal |
| | SAga SArc SBid SIgm SLon SOWG |
| | SSta SSto WAbe WCru WPic WSHC |
| – 'Jenkinsii' | CB&S CPLG |
| ¶ 'Sandra Gordon' | SOWG |
| x *semperflorens* | CB&S CCHP CDoC CGre SOWG |
| ¶ 'Sid Reynolds' | CPLG |
| *thelemanniana* | CPLG |
| *thyrsoides* | CB&S SDry |
| ¶ *tridentifera* | CPLG |
| *victoriae* | SSpi |
| – 'Mount Annan' | MSag |
| *williamsonii* | SOWG |

### GREWIA (Tiliaceae)

| | |
|---|---|
| § *biloba* | Last listed 1996 |
| *parviflora* | See *G. biloba* |

### GREYIA (Greyiaceae)

| | |
|---|---|
| *radlkoferi* | Last listed 1998 |
| *sutherlandii* | CTrC CTrF |

### GRINDELIA (Asteraceae)

| | |
|---|---|
| § *camporum* | EBee EMan SIgm WCot WPer |
| | WWye |
| *chiloensis* | CAbb CPle EBee IBlr LLWP SDix |
| | SDry SMad |
| ♦ *robusta* | See *G. camporum* |
| sp. G&K 4423 | Last listed 1997 |
| *squarrosa* | SUsu |
| *stricta* | CArn |

### GRISELINIA (Griseliniaceae)

| | |
|---|---|
| * 'Crinkles' | SDry SMad |
| *littoralis* ♀ | More than 30 suppliers |
| – 'Bantry Bay' (v) | CAbP CDoC CLan CWSG EBee |
| | EHoe ELan EPla IOrc ISea MBal |
| | MSag SAga SEND SPer SSto |
| – 'Dixon's Cream' (v) | CB&S CDoC EPfP GQui SBid SDry |
| | SLon |
| – 'Green Jewel' (v) | CB&S EHic SDry SPla |
| ¶ – 'Luscombe's Gold' | CPin |
| – 'Variegata' | More than 30 suppliers |
| *lucida* | Last listed 1998 |
| *ruscifolia* | CPle |
| *scandens* | CPle WSHC |
| * *serrata* | Last listed 1998 |

### GUELDENSTAEDTIA (Papilionaceae)

| | |
|---|---|
| *himalaica* B&SWJ 2631 | WCru |

### GUICHENOTIA (Sterculiaceae)

| | |
|---|---|
| *ledifolia* | Last listed 1998 |

### GUNDELIA (Asteraceae)

| | |
|---|---|
| *tournefortii* | EMan |

### GUNNERA (Gunneraceae)

| | |
|---|---|
| *arenaria* | GAri IBlr |
| *chilensis* | See *G. tinctoria* |
| *dentata* | CFee CPla IBlr SCob |
| *flavida* | CFee CPla CRow GAri GGar IBlr |
| | SCob |

| | |
|---|---|
| *fulvida* | IBlr |
| *hamiltonii* | CCuc CPla CRow ECha ECou |
| | EMan GGar IBlr MUlv SCob |
| *magellanica* | CB&S CFee CHid CRow EBrP |
| | EBre ECha ECoo EPot GAbr IBlr |
| | LBre MBal NBee NFor NHol |
| | NMen NWCA SBid SBre SMad |
| | SPer SWat WCru WFar WLin WWat |
| | WWye |
| – (f) | Last listed 1996 |
| *manicata* ♀ | More than 30 suppliers |
| *monoica* | CRow IBlr |
| *prorepens* | CFee CPla CTre ECha EMan IBlr |
| | LWoo SCob SSpi WWat WWye |
| *scabra* | See *G. tinctoria* |
| § *tinctoria* | CBen CCuc CFil CRow CWSG |
| | EBee ECha EHon EPla NOrc SAWi |
| | SBid SDix SSoC SSpi WCot WCru |
| | WLRN WPat WWat WWeb |
| – 'Nana' | IBlr |

### GUTIERREZIA (Asteraceae)

| | |
|---|---|
| *spathulata* F&W 8005 | CPBP |

### GUZMANIA (Bromeliaceae)

| | |
|---|---|
| 'Amaranth' | MBri |
| 'Cherry' | MBri |
| 'Claret' | See *Neoregelia* Claret Group |
| *dissitiflora* | MBri |
| 'Exodus' | MBri |
| Festival Group | MBri |
| 'Gran Prix' | MBri |
| *lindenii* | MBri |
| *lingulata* ♀ | MBri |
| – 'Empire' | MBri |
| – var. *minor* ♀ | MBri |
| Marlebeca Group | MBri |
| *monostachya* ♀ | MBri |
| *musaica* ♀ | Last listed 1992 |
| 'Orangeade' | MBri |
| *sanguinea* ♀ | MBri |
| * 'Surprise' | MBri |
| 'Vulkan' | MBri |
| * 'Witten Lila' | MBri |

### GYMNADENIA (Orchidaceae)

| | |
|---|---|
| *conopsea* | CHdy EFEx |

### GYMNOCARPIUM (Woodsiaceae)

| | |
|---|---|
| *dryopteris* ♀ | CCuc EFer EMar EMon EPar EPot |
| | LSyl MBri MWgw NBus NMar |
| | NWCA SDix SRms WAbe WFib |
| | WNor WRic WWat |
| – 'Plumosum' ♀ | CBos CCuc CFil EBee EMon GQui |
| | LHil NHar NHed NHol NLak |
| | NMar SChu SLod SLon WAbe |
| | WFib WHal WPGP |
| *fedtschenkoanum* | WRic |
| *oyamense* | NMar WRic |
| *robertianum* | EFer NHed SRms WRic |

### GYMNOCLADUS (Caesalpiniaceae)

| | |
|---|---|
| ¶ *chinensis* | WNor |
| *dioica* | CB&S CDul CFil CSam EBee ELan |
| | EPfP GBin MBlu MBri SMad SPer |
| | SSpi WDin WGer WNor WPGP |

### GYMNOGRAMMA See GYMNOPTERIS

### GYMNOPTERIS (Adiantaceae)

| | |
|---|---|
| *vestita* | EMon |

## GYMNOSPERMIUM (Berberidaceae)
§ *albertii* — EHyt WCot
¶ *altaicum* — EHyt GCrs

## GYNANDRIRIS (Iridaceae)
*setifolia* — Last listed 1998
*sisyrinchium* — EBee SSpi
- MS 416 — Last listed 1998
\* - *purpurea* AB&S 4447 — Last listed 1998

## GYNERIUM (Poaceae)
*argenteum* — See *Cortaderia selloana*

## GYNURA (Asteraceae)
§ *aurantiaca*
  'Purple Passion' ♀ — MBri
*sarmentosa* hort. — See *G. aurantiaca* 'Purple Passion'

## GYPSOPHILA (Caryophyllaceae)
*acutifolia* — ELan LPio
*altissima* — CPou MNrw
*aretioides* — NMen NNrd NWCA
§ - 'Caucasica' — CPBP EBur EHyt EPot NHar NHed SIng WLin
- 'Compacta' — See *G. aretioides* 'Caucasica'
*briquetiana* — WPat
- Mac&W 5920 — EPot
*bungeana* — Last listed 1998
*cerastioides* — CTri ELan EMNN EMan ESis EWTr GCHN GTou LBee LHop MMal MRPP MRav NMen NTow NWCA WAbe WElm WMoo WPer WWin WEas
\* - *farreri* — WEas
*dubia* — See *G. repens* 'Dubia'
*fastigiata* — EBee EGar EMan MLLN WPer
'Festival' — CB&S CHan EBrP EBre LBre SBre
'Festival Happy' — LRHS
'Festival Pink' — GMac LRHS WFar
*glomerata* HH&K 221 — Last listed 1998
- HH&K 275 — CHan
*gracilescens* — See *G. tenuifolia*
*muralis* 'Garden Bride' — LIck
¶ - 'Gypsy Pink' (d) — LIck
¶ *nana* — SIng
- 'Compacta' — CLyd CPBP
*oldhamiana* — CBlo EBee MLLN MTed NLak
*pacifica* — EBee ECtt GBuc IIve MWll NBro NCut NOak WHer
§ *paniculata* — CBlo CTri EHic EWTr NFor NMir SRms SWat WEas
- 'Bristol Fairy' (d) ♀ — CB&S CSam EBee EBrP EBre ECha EFou ELan EMan ENot LBre MBel MBri MCAu NFai NFla NOrc NRoo SBre SMad SPer SPla SRms WHoo
- 'Compacta Plena' (d) — EBee EFou ELan EPfP GCal LHop MMil NHol NRoo SMrm SPer SPla SRms SSpe WLRN WPer
- double pink (d) — Last listed 1998
- double white (d) — Last listed 1998
- 'Flamingo' (d) — CB&S ECha ECot ECtt EFou EWTr MBri NFai SPer SRms WMaN WWal
¶ - 'Magic Gilbou' — COtt
¶ - 'Magic Golan' — COtt
- 'Perfekta' — Last listed 1998
- 'Pink Star' (d) — Last listed 1996
§ - 'Schneeflocke' (d) — CBlo CMGP CTri ECtt LFis MWat NPri NVic SEas SRms WViv
- 'Snow White' — NOrc
- Snowflake — See *G. paniculata* 'Schneeflocke'
§ *petraea* — EPot SIng
*repens* ♀ — CSpe GTou LBee MOne MPla MWat SPlb WFar WPer
- 'Dorothy Teacher' ♀ — CLyd CMea EMNN LHop SIng WEas WGor WPat WPyg
§ - 'Dubia' — CLyd ECha ELan EMNN EPot ESis MPla SBod SChu SIgm SRms WLin WPer WWin
- 'Fratensis' — ELan EMNN ESis ITim MPla NMen WLin
- 'Letchworth Rose' — EWes
- Pink Beauty — See *G. repens* 'Rosa Schönheit'
§ - 'Rosa Schönheit' — EBrP EBre ECha EGar EPot EWes LBre NRoo SBre SIgm SMrm SPer
- 'Rose Fountain' — NHol WPat WPyg
- 'Rosea' — CSpe EFou EMNN ESis LBuc LFis LPVe MWat MWll NArg NFor NMen NNrd NOak NRoo NWCA SBla SLon SRPl SRms WFar WHal WHoo
- white — CHor CM&M CTri EFou ELan ESis MPla MWll NFor WHoo WPer
§ 'Rosenschleier' (d) ♀ — EBee EBrP EBre ECha EFou EGoo ELan LBre LFis MCAu MRav NFla NHol NRoo SBre SIgm SMer SMrm SOkh SRms SWat WEas WHoo WMaN WOld WWal
'Rosy Veil' — See *G.* 'Rosenschleier'
*stevenii* — EBee
§ *tenuifolia* — CLyd EHyt EPot ITim LBee MBro MPla MWat NHed NHol NMen SIng
*transylvanica* — See *G. petraea*
Veil of Roses — See *G.* 'Rosenschleier'
¶ 'White Festival' — WFar

# H

## HAASTIA (Asteraceae)
¶ *pulvinaris* — WLin

## HABENARIA (Orchidaceae)
*radiata* — See *Pecteilis radiata*

## HABERLEA (Gesneriaceae)
*ferdinandi-coburgii* — CGle CLAP GNor NWCA SIgm SIng WAbe
*rhodopensis* ♀ — EHyt EPar GCrs GNor IMGH MBal MBro MSte MWat NHar NRya NWCA SBla SIng SRms WAbe WOld
\* - *austinii* — Last listed 1996
- 'Virginalis' — CElw CLAP GDra NHar NMen SBla SIng

## HABLITZIA (Chenopodiaceae)
*tamnoides* — CPIN

## HABRANTHUS (Amaryllidaceae)
*andersonii* — See *H. tubispathus*
*brachyandrus* — CBro SRms
*gracilifolius* — CBro SIng
*howardii* — Last listed 1997
*martinezii* — CBro
§ *robustus* — CBro EBee LAma LLew MBri NRog NWCA
*texanus* — CBro ERos LBee SIng
§ *tubispathus* — CBro CPea LBow NWCA WCot WWin

## HACQUETIA (Apiaceae)

§ **epipactis** ♀ — CElw CHan CRDP CSam ELan EMar EPot LHop LSpr MBal MTho MWgw NBro NMen SBla SIgm SIng SOkh SSpi SWas WAbe WCot WCru WFar WHil WOld WRus WWat WWin
- 'Thor' (v) — Last listed 1997
I - 'Variegata' — Last listed 1996

## HAEMANTHUS (Amaryllidaceae)

**albiflos** — CAvo CHal LAma LHil SRms
**coccineus** — Last listed 1998
**crispus** — Last listed 1997
**deformis** — Last listed 1997
**humilis** — CHan
  subsp. **hirsutus** S&SH 72
**kalbreyeri** — See Scadoxus multiflorus subsp. multiflorus
**katherinae** — See Scadoxus multiflorus subsp. katherinae
**natalensis** — See Scadoxus puniceus
**sanguineus** — NRog

## HAKEA (Proteaceae)

¶ **baxteri** — CCpl
**bucculenta** — Last listed 1997
¶ **clavata** — CCpl
**dactyloides** — Last listed 1998
**epiglottis** — CTrC
**gibbosa** — Last listed 1998
**laurina** — CTrC
¶ **lissocarpha** — CCpl
§ **lissosperma** — CDoC CFil CTrC ECou
**microcarpa** — CPle
§ **salicifolia** — CB&S SMad
¶ - 'Gold Medal' — CTrC
**saligna** — See H. salicifolia
**sericea** hort. — See H. lissosperma
- pink — CTrC
¶ **suaveolens** — CCpl CTrC
**teretifolia** — CTrC

## HAKONECHLOA (Poaceae)

**macra** — CFil CPla EBrP EBre EHoe EMon EPar EPla LBre LGre LRHS MRav NFai SApp SBre SCob
§ - 'Alboaurea' — CB&S CFee CFil CHad CHea EBee EBrP EBre ECha EFul EGol ELan ENot IOrc LBre LHil MRav MUlv NHed NOak NPSI SApp SBre SCob SMrm SPer SPla WPic WRus WWye
* - 'Albolineata' — EMon LRHS
* - 'Aureola' ♀ — More than 30 suppliers
* - 'Mediovariegata' — CFil EPPr EPla SCob SSpi WPGP
- 'Variegata' — See H. macra 'Alboaurea'

## HALENIA (Gentianaceae)

**elliptica** — Last listed 1998

## HALESIA (Styracaceae)

§ **carolina** — CAgr CBlo CBrm CDoC CDul CEnd CLnd CMCN CPMA CTho ELan ENot GChr GGGa IMGH IOrc LPan MBel MBri MGos SMer SPer SSta WDin WHar WWat CMCN MBlu
**diptera** — CMCN MBlu
**monticola** — CB&S CDul CMCN COtt EBrP EBre ELan EPfP GGGa LBre MAsh MBal MBri NSti SBre SPer SReu SSpi WFro WNor

## - var. **vestita** ♀ — CAbP CDoC CPMA CSam CTho CWSG CWit GChr GOrc IMGH IOrc MBlu SBrw SPer SSpi SSta WPat WWat
- - f. **rosea** — CB&S CPMA EPfP MBlu SSta
**tetraptera** — See H. carolina

## x HALIMIOCISTUS (Cistaceae)

**algarvensis** — See Halimium ocymoides
§ 'Ingwersenii' — CB&S CDoC CLTr CMHG CVer EGoo EWes MWhi NHol NTow SIng SPan SPer SRms WBod WPer
**revolii** hort. — See x H. sabucii
§ **sabucii** ♀ — CDoC EBee EBrP EBre ECha EGoo ELan GCHN LBre LFis LHop MAsh MBNS MBal MBel MGrG MPla MRav MWat NTow SBre SDys SEas SPan SPer WCru WFar WHoo WKif WWin
- 'Ice Dancer' (v) — CDoC MAsh SPer
'Susan' — See Halimium 'Susan'
§ **wintonensis** ♀ — More than 30 suppliers
§ - 'Merrist Wood Cream' ♀ — CB&S CDoC CFee EAst EBee EBrP EBre ELan ENot EPla GOrc LBre LHop MAsh MBel MBri MGrG MPla NBir NChi SBre SChu SPer SSpi SSta WAbe WOve WPat WSHC WWat

## HALIMIONE (Chenopodiaceae)

§ **portulacoides** — EEls

## HALIMIUM ✿ (Cistaceae)

N **alyssoides** — CSam GCHN
§ **atriplicifolium** — Last listed 1998
§ **calycinum** — CHan EBee ELan GCHN MAsh MBel SAga SCoo SPan SSpi WAbe WCFE WPyg
**commutatum** — See H. calycinum
**formosum** — See H. lasianthum
N **halimifolium** — WSHC
§ **lasianthum** ♀ — CB&S CTri CWit EBee ELan ENot GCHN LGre MAsh MBal MBel MRav MTis SChu SEas SPer WEas WPyg WWat WWin
- f. **concolor** — EHic LHop NTow SDry SPan WAbe WDin WWin
- subsp. **formosum** — CHar CMil GEil MBri NOla SDix WSHC
- 'Sandling' — EGoo ELan MAsh SPan
**libanotis** — See H. calycinum
§ **ocymoides** ♀ — CB&S CCche CDoC EBee EGoo ELan LGre MAsh MBal MBel MPla MWat SLon SPan SPer WBod WHar WSHC WWat
x **pauanum** — LGre LRHS MAsh
¶ x **santae** — LGre
§ 'Susan' ♀ — CDoC EBee ELan LHop MAsh MBro MPla NFai NLon NMen SPer WAbe WPat WPyg WSHC WWat
§ **umbellatum** — LGre MBri SAga WKif WTro
**wintonense** — See x Halimiocistus wintonensis

## HALIMODENDRON (Papilionaceae)

**halodendron** — CB&S CPle ELan EMil EPfP MBlu SBid SPer SRPl

## HALLERIA (Scrophulariaceae)

**lucida** — CGre CPLG

## HALOCARPUS (Podocarpaceae)

§ **bidwillii** — CDoC ECou

## HALORAGIS (Haloragaceae)

| | |
|---|---|
| colensoi | ECou |
| erecta | CPle ECou SRCN SVen |
| - 'Rubra' | CElw EBee WCot WPer |
| - 'Wellington Bronze' | CPea CVer ECoo GSki MCCP |
| | NChi NCut NSti SDys SMad |
| | WMoo |

## HAMAMELIS ✿ (Hamamelidaceae)

| | |
|---|---|
| § 'Brevipetala' | CB&S IOrc MAsh MBri NHol SBid |
| | SSta |
| ¶ x *intermedia* 'Allgold' | LRHS |
| - 'Angelly' | SSta |
| - 'Arnold Promise' ♀ | CDoC CEnd COtt CPMA EBee |
| | ELan IOrc LNet LPan MAsh MBal |
| | MBri MGos MLan MWat NBee |
| | NHol SBid SBrw SPer SPla SRPl |
| | SReu SSpi SSta WCFE WOrn |
| - 'Aurora' | Last listed 1998 |
| - 'Barmstedt Gold' ♀ | EPfP MAsh MBri MGos NHol SReu |
| | SSta |
| - 'Carmine Red' | SMur WNor |
| - 'Copper Beauty' | See *H.* x *intermedia* 'Jelena' |
| - 'Diane' ♀ | CB&S CDoC CDul CEnd EBrP |
| | EBre ELan IOrc LBre LNet LPan |
| | MAsh MBri MGos MUlv NHol |
| | SAga SBid SBre SBrw SPer SReu |
| | SSoC SSpi SSta WBod WDin WPGP |
| | WWat |
| § - 'Feuerzauber' | GChr IOrc LBuc NFla SPer SSta |
| | WOrn WPyg |
| * - 'Fire Cracker' | Last listed 1997 |
| - 'Gimborn's Beauty' | Last listed 1998 |
| - 'Hiltingbury' | LRHS SMur SSpi |
| § - 'Jelena' ♀ | CB&S CDoC CEnd ELan ENot |
| | GOrc IMGH IOrc LNet LPan |
| | MAsh MBal MBri MGos NFla NHol |
| | SAga SBid SBrw SPer SReu SSoC |
| | SSpi SSta WBod WDin WWat |
| - 'Luna' | SSta |
| - Magic Fire | See *H.* x *intermedia* 'Feuerzauber' |
| - 'Moonlight' | CPMA |
| - 'Orange Beauty' | CB&S CBlo CPMA EPfP MBal |
| | MGos SReu SSta |
| - 'Pallida' ♀ | More than 30 suppliers |
| - 'Primavera' | CBlo CDoC EPfP IOrc MAsh MBal |
| | MUlv NHol SSta |
| - 'Ruby Glow' | CB&S CBlo ECho MBal MGos SPer |
| | SSta |
| ¶ - 'Strawberries and Cream' | EPfP |
| - 'Sunburst' | CBlo CDoC EPfP SSta WWeb |
| - 'Vesna' | CBlo EPfP MBlu SSta |
| § - 'Westerstede' | CBlo COtt EBee IOrc LPan MAsh |
| | MGos NHol SBid SSta WDin WHar |
| *japonica* | MBal WWat |
| - 'Arborea' | WNor |
| - var. *flavopurpurascens* | SSta |
| - 'Sulphurea' | EWTr SSta |
| - 'Zuccariniana' | CB&S CBlo MUlv |
| *mollis* ♀ | CB&S CEnd ELan ENot EWTr |
| | GRei ISea LNet MAsh MBal MBar |
| | MBri MGos NFla NHol NWea |
| | SBrw SPer SRPl SReu SSpi SSta |
| | WDin WFar WPGP WPat WWat |
| - 'Boskoop' | SSta |
| - 'Brevipetala' | See *H.* 'Brevipetala' |
| - 'Coombe Wood' | Last listed 1997 |
| - 'Goldcrest' | CAbP CBlo CPMA |
| - 'Nymans' | Last listed 1998 |
| - 'Select' | See *H.* x *intermedia* 'Westerstede' |
| - 'Superba' | Last listed 1998 |

| | |
|---|---|
| - Wilson clone | Last listed 1998 |
| *vernalis* | WDin |
| - 'Carnea' | Last listed 1998 |
| - 'Christmas Cheer' | Last listed 1997 |
| - Compact form | Last listed 1997 |
| - 'Orange Glow' | Last listed 1998 |
| - 'Pendula' | Last listed 1998 |
| - 'Red Imp' | Last listed 1998 |
| - 'Sandra' ♀ | CB&S EPfP MBri MGos MUlv SBid |
| | SPer SReu SSpi SSta |
| - f. *tomentella* | Last listed 1998 |
| *virginiana* | CB&S CBlo GPoy LHol MWhi |
| | WDin WWal WWat |

## HANABUSAYA (Campanulaceae)

| | |
|---|---|
| ¶ *asiatica* | EBee |

## HANNONIA (Amaryllidaceae)

| | |
|---|---|
| *hesperidum* SF 21 | Last listed 1998 |

## HAPLOCARPHA (Asteraceae)

| | |
|---|---|
| *rueppellii* | MBro NBro SIng SRms SRot WHil |
| | WPer |

## HAPLOPAPPUS (Asteraceae)

| | |
|---|---|
| *acaulis* | See *Stenotus acaulis* |
| *brandegeei* | See *Erigeron aureus* |
| *coronopifolius* | See *H. glutinosus* |
| *foliosus* | Last listed 1996 |
| § *glutinosus* | CMHG CSev ECha ECtt EMan |
| | EPot LBee LHop MMil MTho |
| | NTow NWCA SAga SRms SSmi |
| | WAbe |
| § *lanceolatus* | EBee |
| *lyallii* | See *Tonestus lyallii* |
| *microcephalus* | WPer |
| - AJW 93/559 | Last listed 1997 |
| *prunelloides* | LBee NNrd NTow |
| *rehderi* | Last listed 1998 |
| sp. RB 94063 | Last listed 1996 |

## HARDENBERGIA (Papilionaceae)

| | |
|---|---|
| *comptoniana* ♀ | CPIN CSpe SRCN |
| * - *rosea* | ERea |
| *violacea* ♀ | CAbb CPIN CSpe CTrC ECon |
| | ELan EMil ERea EWTr GQui LBlm |
| | LChe LCns MSag SBid SBra SEND |
| - 'Alba' | See *H. violacea* 'White Crystal' |
| - 'Happy Wanderer' | EBee EMil ERea SLon SOWG |
| - 'Rosea' | CB&S |
| § - 'White Crystal' | ECon ERea |

## HARPEPHYLLUM (Anacardiaceae)

| | |
|---|---|
| *caffrum* (F) | LBlo |

## HARRIMANELLA See CASSIOPE

## HASTINGSIA (Hyacinthaceae)

| | |
|---|---|
| ¶ *alba* | EBee |

## HAWORTHIA ✿ (Aloaceae)

| | |
|---|---|
| x *cuspidata* | Last listed 1998 |
| *reinwardtii* | CHal |

## HAYNALDIA See DASYPYRUM

## HEBE ✿ (Scrophulariaceae)

| | |
|---|---|
| *albicans* ♀ | CChe CHan CLan CLyn ECou |
| | ELan ENot ESis EWTr MBal MBar |
| | MBel MBri MGos NLon NMen |
| | NSti SPer SSmi SUsu WBod WEas |
| | WFar WHCG WWat WWin |

| | Name | Codes |
|---|---|---|
| | – 'Cobb' | ECou |
| | – 'Cranleigh Gem' | ECou NFai NHed |
| | – 'Pewter Dome' | See *H.* 'Pewter Dome' |
| * | – 'Pink Elephant' | CAbP CDoC CFai EAst EPfP LRHS MAsh SPer WWeb |
| | – prostrate form | See *H. albicans* 'Snow Cover' |
| | – 'Red Edge' | See *H.* 'Red Edge' |
| § | – 'Snow Carpet' | CLyn |
| § | – 'Snow Cover' | ECou EWes NHed SPar |
| ◆ | – 'Snow Drift' | See *H. albicans* 'Snow Cover' |
| | – 'Snow Mound' | ECou |
| § | – 'Sussex Carpet' | ECou ESis |
| § | 'Alicia Amherst' ♀ | CBlo CLyn CSam ECou EHol GCHN SRms WLRN |
| | *allanii* | See *H. amplexicaulis* var. *hirta* |
| | 'Amanda Cook' (v) | ECou EHoe ESis MPla NPer SDry |
| | 'Amethyst' | Last listed 1996 |
| | *amplexicaulis* | CNic NHed |
| ¶ | – clone 4 | STre |
| § | – var. *hirta* | ECou ESis GDra GEil MBro NHed NHol NTow |
| § | 'Amy' | CLyn ECou ELan ESis IOrc MBel NFai NPer NSti SPer WAbe WCom WRus WSHC |
| ¶ | x *andersonii* | CLyn CPri |
| | – 'Argenteovariegata' | See *H.* x *andersonii* 'Variegata' |
| § | – 'Aurea' | ECou SDry |
| * | – 'Aureovariegata' | See *H.* x *andersonii* 'Aurea' |
| | – 'Compacta' | Last listed 1998 |
| § | – 'Variegata' | CLyn ECou IOrc NSti NTow SDry SRCN SRms WCot WEas WLRN |
| ¶ | 'Andressa Paula' | CLyn |
| | 'Anne Pimm' (v) | WSHC |
| | *anomala* (Armstr.) Cockayne | See *H. odora* |
| | – hort. | See *H.* 'Imposter' |
| | 'Aoira' | See *H. recurva* 'Aoira' |
| § | *armstrongii* | CBot CMHG ECou EHic EHoe ELan EOrn EPla MBar NFor NHed NLon SPan SPer WBay WDin WPer |
| | – yellow | Last listed 1997 |
| | 'Arthur' | ECou |
| | *astonii* | Last listed 1998 |
| ¶ | 'Autumn Beauty' | CPri |
| | 'Autumn Blush' | MPla |
| | 'Autumn Glory' | CLyn CMHG CPri EBee EBrP EBre ECou ELan ERav ESis GCHN LBre LGro MBar MGos MWgw NBee NFor NSti SBod SBre SHFr SPer WAbe WBod WDin WMow WWat |
| | 'Autumn Joy' | MPla |
| | 'Autumn Queen' | Last listed 1998 |
| | 'Azurea' | See *H. venustula* |
| | 'Azurens' | See *H.* 'Maori Gem' |
| | 'Baby Marie' | CAbP CDoC CLyd CLyn COtt EBee ECot ECou ELan ESis EWTr MAsh MBel MGos MWhi NBee NHed NLon NPer STre WPer WStI |
| | 'Balfouriana' | WHCG |
| | *barkeri* | ECou |
| | 'Barnettii' | EBee |
| | 'Beatrice' | ECou NHed |
| § | x *bishopiana* | CFai ECou ESis LRHS MAsh |
| | – 'Champagne' | See *H.* x *bishopiana* |
| | 'Blonde' | Last listed 1998 |
| | 'Blue Clouds' ♀ | ECou ELan ESis MLan NHed SAga SIgm SPer SSmi SVil WRus |
| | 'Blue Diamond' | Last listed 1998 |
| | 'Blue Wand' | MBal |
| | 'Bluebell' | Last listed 1998 |
| | 'Blush Wand' | NCut |
| | *bollonsii* | ECou MSte |
| | 'Boscawenii' | CTrG MGos |
| | 'Bowles' Variety' | See *H.* 'Bowles's Hybrid' |
| § | 'Bowles's Hybrid' | CLyn CNic CPri EBee ECou LHil MGos MPla MRav NBee NFai NFor NLon SRms WAbe WEas |
| | *brachysiphon* | EBee ECou ENot EPfP GOrc MGos MWhi SPer WDin WHCG |
| | – 'White Gem' | See *H.* 'White Gem' (*brachysiphon* hybrid) |
| | 'Bracken Hills' | Last listed 1997 |
| | *breviracemosa* | ECou |
| * | 'Brill Blue' | CLyd NMen WWin |
| | 'Brockiei' | Last listed 1998 |
| | *buchananii* | ECou ESis GDra GTou MDHE MGos MTho NFai NFor NHed NLon NPer WPer |
| | – 'Christchurch' | ECou |
| | – 'Minima' | Last listed 1997 |
| § | – 'Minor' | CLyd ECou EPot ESis GCHN GCrs GNor LBee MBar NBir NHar NHed NMen NNrd NWCA |
| | – 'Nana' | See *H. buchananii* 'Minor' |
| | – 'Ohau' | ECou |
| | – 'Otago' | ECou |
| § | – 'Sir George Fenwick' | ECou MBro WHoo |
| | – 'Wanaka' | ECou |
| | *buxifolia* (Benth.) Ckn. & Allan | EBrP EBre ELan ENot GCHN LBre MBal NFai NSti NWea SBre SPer WDin WStI |
| | – hort. | See *H. odora* |
| | – 'Champagne' | See *H.* x *bishopiana* |
| | – (Benth.) Ckn.& Allan 'Nana' | CLyd EPot ESis MAsh NCut NPer SRms WWin |
| | – 'Nana' | CLyn EHoe NFla |
| | – (Benth.)Ckn. & Allan *patens* | Last listed 1997 |
| N | 'C.P. Raffill' | ECou |
| § | 'Caledonia' | CLyn CNic ECou ESis GAbr MAsh MBri MGos MSte NFai NHed NHol NLon NPer NTow SPer SSmi WEas WFar WHoo WPat WPer WPyg WSHC |
| | 'Candy' | ECou |
| § | *canterburiensis* | ECou EHal |
| N | 'Carl Teschner' | See *H.* 'Youngii' |
| | 'Carnea' | Last listed 1997 |
| | 'Carnea Variegata' | CLyn ECou ESis SBod SPer |
| | *carnosula* | EBee ECou EHoe ESis MBrN MGos NFor NLon SPer WCom WPer |
| | 'Cassinioides' | CLyn |
| | *catarractae* | See *Parahebe catarractae* |
| I | 'Chalk's Buchananii' | CNic WCom |
| * | 'Charming White' | EBee LRHS MAsh |
| | *chathamica* | CLyn ECou ESis GGar MBal MMHG MPla NMen SDry WSHC |
| | *cheesemanii* | ESis |
| | 'Christabel' | CLyn ECou ESis |
| § | 'Christensenii' | ECou NFai NHed NMen |
| | *ciliolata* | Last listed 1998 |
| | *coarctata* | ECou |
| | *cockayneana* | ECou |
| | *colensoi* | ECou ESis |
| | – 'Glauca' | See *H.* 'Leonard Cockayne' |
| | 'Colwall' | CBlo CLyd ECho ESis SSto WAbe WHen |
| * | 'Colwall Blue' | Last listed 1997 |
| ◆ | 'Cookiana' | See *H. stricta* var. *macroura* 'Cookiana' |
| * | 'Coral Blue' | Last listed 1998 |
| * | 'Coral Pink' | WWeb |
| | *corriganii* | ECou |

| | |
|---|---|
| *corstorphinensis* | Last listed 1997 |
| 'County Park' | CLyd ECou ECtt ESis EWes MBal MGos MMil NHed NHol NLon NMen SBod SSmi WMow |
| 'Craig Park' | Last listed 1998 |
| 'Cranleighensis' | ECou SBod SSto |
| 'Crawii' | ECou |
| 'Cressit' | Last listed 1997 |
| ◆ 'Cupins' | See *H. propinqua* 'Cupins' |
| *cupressoides* | CLyn CMHG ECou GOrc MBal MBar MGos NFor NHed NLon SEND SUsu WDin WGwG WWal |
| - 'Boughton Dome' ♀ | CSam ECha ECou EHoe EMNN ESis GCHN GTou LHil MAsh MBro MGos MPla MTho NCat NMen SAga SUsu WAbe WCot WEas WHoo WOld WPer WSHC |
| - 'Golden Dome' | CB&S EAst ESis WAbe |
| - 'Nana' | ECou |
| *darwiniana* | See *H. glaucophylla* |
| 'David Hughes' | NFai |
| ¶ 'Dazzler' (v) | CAbP EBee LRHS SPer WWeb |
| * 'Deans Fya' | ESis |
| 'Debbie' | ECou |
| *decumbens* | CLyd CNic ECou ESis EWes GDra NHol |
| * 'Denise' | ELan ENot NFai WWeb |
| ¶ 'Diamond' | CLyn |
| ¶ 'Diana' | ECou |
| * 'Dianne' | CLyn |
| *dieffenbachii* | ECou |
| *diosmifolia* | CBot CDoC CLan EBee ECou ESis WSHC |
| - 'Marie' | ECou ESis |
| *divaricata* | ECou |
| - 'Marlborough' | ECou |
| - 'Nelson' | ECou |
| x *divergens* | CLan NHed |
| 'Dorothy Peach' | See *H.* 'Watson's Pink' |
| 'Douglasii' | NHed |
| 'E.A. Bowles' | CBlo ECou |
| 'E.B. Anderson' | See *H.* 'Caledonia' |
| 'Early Blue' | NBir WMow |
| 'Edinensis' | CNic ECou GEil NFor NMen WPer WSHC |
| 'Edington' | CHal CLyn ECou SCoo WCFE |
| *elliptica* | ECou IBlr SPer |
| - 'Anatoki' | CLTr ECou |
| - 'Bleaker' | ECou |
| - 'Charleston' | ECou |
| - 'Dwarf Blue' | Last listed 1997 |
| - 'Kapiti' | ECou |
| - 'Variegata' | See *H.* x *franciscana* 'Variegata' |
| 'Emerald Dome' | NMen WPer |
| 'Emerald Gem' | See *H.* 'Emerald Green' |
| § 'Emerald Green' ♀ | CChe CLyn CSam EBee ECou ERav ESis MBar MBri MBro MGos MPla MTis MWat NHed NHol NMen NWCA SEas WAbe WPat WPer WPyg |
| *epacridea* | ESis EWes GTou NHed NHol NMen WAbe |
| ◆ 'Eveline' | See *H.* 'Gauntlettii' |
| 'Evelyn' | Last listed 1997 |
| *evenosa* | ECou |
| 'Eversley Seedling' | See *H.* 'Bowles's Hybrid' |
| 'Fairfieldii' | EHol ESis IBlr NMen WAbe |
| 'Fairlane' | ECou |
| 'Fragrant Jewel' | CLyn SEND SEas SMrm |
| x *franciscana* | ECou |
| § - 'Blue Gem' ♀ | CLan CLyn CPri EHal ENot ESis LPVe MGos NBir NFai NPer NWea SPer SRms WBod WHar |
| - 'Jura' | Last listed 1998 |
| ¶ - 'Lavender Queen' | CLyn |
| - 'Purple Tips' misapplied | See *H. speciosa* 'Variegata' |
| - 'Red Gem' | Last listed 1997 |
| - 'Tresco Magenta' | ECou |
| § - 'Variegata' ♀ | CLyn EBee EBrP EBre ECou ELan EMil ENot ESis LBre MBal MBar MGos NFai NPer NSti SBre SPer SSoC WBod WHar WStI |
| - 'White Gem' | SRms |
| 'Franjo' | ECou SSmi |
| *fruticeti* | Last listed 1997 |
| * 'Garths Glory' | SSto |
| § 'Gauntlettii' | CChe CLyn CPri MBal NBir NLon SPer |
| *gibbsii* | ECou |
| 'Gibby' | ECou |
| N *glaucophylla* | ECou SBod |
| - 'Clarence' | ECou NHed |
| 'Glaucophylla Variegata' | CChe CLyn CNic ECou ESis MBel NFai NHed NSti SPer WHer WKif WRus WSHC |
| 'Glengarriff' | NHol |
| § 'Gloriosa' | CSam IOrc NPla |
| 'Gnome' | CBlo CLyn |
| 'Godefroyana' | See *H. pinguifolia* 'Godefroyana' |
| *gracillima* | CBlo ECou SRPl |
| 'Gran's Favourite' | CLyn ECou |
| 'Great Orme' ♀ | More than 30 suppliers |
| 'Green Globe' | See *H.* 'Emerald Green' |
| 'Greensleeves' | CBlo CSam EBee ECou EPfP ESis MGos NHed |
| 'Gruninard's Seedling' | Last listed 1997 |
| *haastii* | CBlo ECou ESis NFor NHed |
| 'Hadspen Pink' | CLyn |
| 'Hagley Park' | EGoo ESis LHil LRHS MAsh MMil MPla SAga SUsu WCot WEas WHCG |
| § 'Hartii' | MRav SPer |
| 'Havering Green' | ECou |
| 'Headfortii' | CLyn |
| *hectorii* | CBlo ESis GTou MBal NFla NHed |
| - var. *demissa* | ECou NHed |
| 'Heidi' | ESis |
| 'Hidcote' | Last listed 1998 |
| 'Hielan Lassie' | CLyn |
| 'Highdownensis' | ECou SEas SSto |
| 'Hinderwell' | NPer |
| 'Hinerua' | ECou |
| *hookeriana* | See *Parahebe hookeriana* |
| *hulkeana* ♀ | CBot CHan ECou ELan LHil MBel MPla NBir NFai NLon SAga SIgm WAbe WEas WHCG WHoo WKif WPat WWat |
| - 'Averil' | Last listed 1998 |
| - 'Lilac Hint' | ECou |
| - 'Sally Blunt' | Last listed 1998 |
| § 'Imposter' | CLyn ECou NFai NOla SRms |
| 'Inspiration' | CDoC ECou |
| *insularis* | CBlo ECou |
| 'Jack's Surprise' | ECou |
| 'James Platt' | ECou ESis |
| 'James Stirling' | See *H. ochracea* 'James Stirling' |
| 'Jane Holden' | CLyn NLak SBla WSHC |
| ¶ 'Janet' | CPri |
| 'Jasper' | CNic ECou ESis |
| 'Jewel' | SDix |
| 'Joan Lewis' | ECou ESis NHed |
| 'Joanna' | ECou |
| § 'Johny Day' | CLyn ECou |
| 'Joyce Parker' | ECou NHed |
| 'Judy' | CLyn ECou |

| | |
|---|---|
| 'June Small' | CNic |
| 'Karo Golden Esk' | ECou |
| 'Kewensis' | Last listed 1996 |
| 'Killiney Variety' | ECou MBal |
| 'Kirkii' | CBlo ECou EMil LNor MWhi SPer |
| 'Knightshayes' | See *H.* 'Caledonia' |
| 'La Séduisante' | See *H. speciosa* 'La Seduisante' |
| 'Lady Ardilaun' | See *H.* 'Amy' |
| *laevis* | See *H. venustula* |
| *laingii* | CNic ECou |
| *lapidosa* | See *H. rupicola* |
| *latifolia* | See *H.* x *franciscana* 'Blue Gem' |
| *lavaudiana* | ESis MRPP WAbe WWat |
| * 'Lavender Lady' | Last listed 1997 |
| 'Lavender Queen' | Last listed 1997 |
| 'Lavender Spray' | See *H.* 'Hartii' |
| *leiophylla* | Last listed 1997 |
| § 'Leonard Cockayne' | CBlo MOne NFai WSHC |
| 'Lewisii' | Last listed 1996 |
| *ligustrifolia* | ECou |
| 'Lilac Haze' | Last listed 1998 |
| 'Lindleyana' | CLyd |
| 'Lindsayi' | CLyn CNic ECou NHed |
| § 'Loganioides' | CFai CTri ECou ESis GAbr MBal |
| | NFor NLon NMen SSmi WPer |
| 'Longacre Variety' | ECou |
| 'Lopen' (v) | CLyn ECou EWes |
| ¶ 'Louise' | CPri |
| *lyallii* | See *Parahebe lyallii* |
| *lycopodioides* | ESis EWes NHed |
| – 'Aurea' | See *H. armstrongii* |
| – var. *patula* | Last listed 1998 |
| – 'Peter Pan' | MBro SRms |
| ¶ 'Lynash' | CLyn |
| § 'Macewanii' | CMHG ECou ESis NFai NHed |
| | WHCG |
| *mackenii* | See *H.* 'Emerald Green' |
| *macrantha* ♀ | ECou EPla ESis GAbr GCHN GCrs |
| | ITim LGre MAsh MPla MTis |
| | NFor NHed NLon NMen SIng SPer |
| | SRms WAbe WPat WSHC WWin |
| – var. *brachyphylla* | ECou |
| *macrocarpa* | ECou |
| – var. *brevifolia* | ECou EWes |
| – var. *latisepala* | ECou |
| § 'Maori Gem' | CTrC EWes SCoo SEND SMrm |
| | WLRN |
| 'Margery Fish' | See *H.* 'Primley Gem' |
| 'Margret' | COtt EBee EBrP EBre EMil GRei |
| | LBre MAsh MBNS MBel MGos |
| | NMen NRoo SBre SCoo SMrm |
| | SPer SRPl WStI WWhi |
| ¶ 'Marjery Joan' | LFis |
| 'Marjorie' | CChe CLyn EBee ECou ENot |
| | GOrc MBal MGos MRav NFai |
| | NFor NHed NPer NRoo NWea |
| | SBod SPer SRPl WDin |
| *matthewsii* | ECou |
| 'Mauve Queen' | CLyn EHol |
| ¶ 'Mauvena' | SPer |
| 'McEwanii' | See *H.* 'Macewanii' |
| 'McKean' | ECou |
| 'Megan' | ECou |
| 'Melanie' | Last listed 1998 |
| 'Menzies Bay' | Last listed 1998 |
| 'Mercury' | See *H. pimeleoides* 'Mercury' |
| 'Midsummer Beauty' ♀ | More than 30 suppliers |
| 'Milmont Emerald' | See *H.* 'Emerald Green' |
| 'Mini' | Last listed 1998 |
| * *minima* 'Calvin' | Last listed 1998 |
| 'Miss E. Fittall' | ECou |
| 'Miss Lowe' | Last listed 1996 |

| | |
|---|---|
| 'Mist Maiden' | ESis |
| 'Monica' | ECou GCHN NHed NHol |
| 'Mont Blanc' | Last listed 1996 |
| 'Monticola' | Last listed 1997 |
| * 'Moppets Hardy' | SPer |
| 'Morning Clouds' | Last listed 1998 |
| § 'Mrs Winder' ♀ | More than 30 suppliers |
| x *myrtifolia* | Last listed 1998 |
| 'Mystery' | ECou |
| 'Nantyderry' | CHal MBel MSCN MWgw NMen |
| | WEas WLRN WWat |
| § 'Neil's Choice' | CLyn ECou EWes MBri MSte |
| 'Netta Dick' | ECou |
| 'Nicola's Blush' | More than 30 suppliers |
| 'Northumbria Beauty' | NFor |
| 'Northumbria Gem' | NFor NLon |
| *obtusata* | ECou |
| *ochracea* | ECou MGos MMal NFla STre |
| § – 'James Stirling' ♀ | More than 30 suppliers |
| 'Oddity' | ECou |
| § *odora* | CBlo CChe EBee ECou EPfP |
| | MWhi SPer WIvy WWal |
| – 'New Zealand Gold' | CNic CSam ECou ESis MAsh NFai |
| | NHed NLon SAga SLon WPyg |
| | WStI |
| * – *patens* | MGos WHCG |
| – prostrate form | ECou |
| – 'Stewart' | ECou |
| – 'Wintergreen' | EBee |
| ¶ 'Oratio Beauty' | CLyn MAsh NCut NFai |
| 'Orientale' | Last listed 1998 |
| 'Otari Delight' | CMHG |
| 'Pageboy' | ECou NHed |
| *parviflora* hort. | See *H.* 'Bowles's Hybrid' |
| § – var. *angustifolia* ♀ | ECou EPla EWes LBlm MTed |
| | SAPC SArc SDix SHFr |
| – 'Holdsworth' | CLyn SDys |
| – 'Palmerston' | ECou |
| 'Patti Dossett' | See *H. speciosa* 'Patti Dossett' |
| ◆ *pauciflora* hort. | See *H.* 'Christensenii' |
| – Simpson & Thomson | Last listed 1998 |
| *pauciramosa* | ECou ESis NTow SRms SSto |
| 'Paula' | Last listed 1996 |
| 'Penny Day' | Last listed 1998 |
| *perfoliata* | See *Parahebe perfoliata* |
| 'Perryhill Lilac' | SPer |
| 'Perry's Bluey' | Last listed 1996 |
| * 'Perry's Cerise' | NFai |
| 'Perry's Rubyleaf' | NPer |
| * 'Peter Chapple' | EPot |
| 'Petra's Pink' | ECou ESis SIgm WEas |
| *petriei* | WLin |
| § 'Pewter Dome' ♀ | More than 30 suppliers |
| 'Pimeba' | NHol WCom |
| *pimeleoides* | ECou MWhi NMen |
| – 'Glauca' | NLon NPer |
| – 'Glaucocaerulea' | ECou ESis NHed SPer WKif WRHF |
| § – 'Mercury' | ECou |
| – var. *minor* | ECou ESis WPat |
| – – 'Elf' | ECou |
| – – 'Imp' | ECou |
| – 'Quicksilver' ♀ | CLyn EBee EBrP EBre ECou EHoe |
| | ELan ENot ESis EWTr GOrc LBre |
| | LHop MAsh MBar MBri MGos |
| | NFai NPer SBre SPer SSmi WEas |
| | WGwG WHCG WLin WSHC WWal |
| – var. *rupestris* | ECou ESis |
| *pinguifolia* | CLyn ECou NHed SPer SPlb WFar |
| ¶ – 'Dobson' | CLyn |
| – 'Forma' | Last listed 1998 |
| § – 'Godefroyana' | ECou |
| – 'Hutt' | ECou |

| | |
|---|---|
| - 'Mount Dobson' | ECou NHol |
| - 'Pagei' ♀ | More than 30 suppliers |
| - 'Sutherlandii' | CDoC CLyn CNic EBee ECou ESis |
| | GCHN GDra LEdu MBar MWhi |
| | NBee NFai NHed NLon NSti |
| § - 'Wardiensis' | CMHG ECou |
| ¶ 'Pink Elephant' | EBee LHop |
| 'Pink Fantasy' | MAsh WWeb |
| ¶ 'Pink Paradise' | ELan MAsh |
| ◆ 'Pink Payne' | See *H.* 'Gauntlettii' |
| 'Pink Pearl' | See *H.* 'Gloriosa' |
| 'Pink Wand' | CLTr LHop WGer |
| 'Polly Moore' | MBal |
| *poppelwellii* | ITim NHed WAbe |
| 'Porlock Purple' | See *Parahebe catarractae* |
| | 'Delight' |
| 'Port e Vullen' | Last listed 1998 |
| § 'Primley Gem' | CLyn CNic ESis WSHC |
| 'Princess' | Last listed 1998 |
| *propinqua* | ECou ESis NMen |
| § - 'Aurea' | MBal |
| § - 'Cupins' | ESis SIng |
| - 'Minor' | NHed |
| 'Prostrata' | ECou NHed |
| * 'Pulchella' | Last listed 1997 |
| * 'Purple Elf' | EHic SPer |
| ◆ 'Purple Emperor' | See *H.* 'Neil's Choice' |
| 'Purple Picture' | ECou ECtt NCut NFai SDry |
| Purple Pixie = 'Mohawk' | COtt MAsh MGos WLRN |
| 'Purple Princess' | CLyn |
| § 'Purple Queen' | MAsh |
| ◆ 'Purple Tips' misapplied | See *H. speciosa* 'Variegata' |
| *rakaiensis* ♀ | CChe CLyn ECou EHoe ELan |
| | ENot EWTr GAbr ISea LHop MAsh |
| | MBar MBri MGos MWat NBir |
| | NLon SPer SRPl STre WAbe WBod |
| | WDin WFar WHCG WPer WWin |
| *ramosissima* | ESis GTou NHed |
| *raoulii* | GBri WAbe WHoo WSHC |
| - var. *maccaskillii* | ESis |
| - 'Mount Hutt' | GTou |
| - var. *pentasepala* | ESis |
| § *recurva* | CLyn CNic CSam EBee ECou EPla |
| | ESis LHop MAsh MBri NBee NFai |
| | NFor NHol SHFr SRms WBod |
| | WCom WDin WPer WRus |
| § - 'Aoira' | ECou NHed SPer |
| - 'Boughton Silver' ♀ | MBNS SDry |
| - green-leaved | Last listed 1998 |
| - 'White Torrent' | ECou |
| § 'Red Edge' ♀ | More than 30 suppliers |
| ◆ 'Red Ruth' | See *H.* 'Gauntlettii' |
| *rigidula* | ECou ESis NMen |
| 'Ritt' | ESis |
| 'Ronda' | ECou |
| 'Rosie' | MAsh NBee SCoo WEas WLRN |
| * 'Royal Blue' | CLyn |
| 'Royal Purple' | See *H.* 'Alicia Amherst' |
| *salicifolia* | CChe CLTr CLyn CPri EBee ECou |
| | ELan ENot GCHN LGro MLan |
| | NFai NFor SPer SPlb SRms WFar |
| | WHCG WTro |
| - 'Snow Wreath' | See *H.* 'Snow Wreath' |
| - 'Variegata' | Last listed 1996 |
| *salicornioides* | ECou |
| - 'Aurea' | See *H. propinqua* 'Aurea' |
| 'Sapphire' | CDoC CLyn ECou ESis EWTr |
| | MAsh MBar MGos NPla WGer |
| 'Sarana' | ECou |
| *selaginoides* hort. | See *H.* 'Loganioides' |
| ¶ 'Silver Dollar' | CAbP CFai ELan LPan LRHS MAsh |
| | SPer SPla WWeb |
| 'Silver Gilt' | CBot |
| 'Silver Wings' (v) | ECou NFai |
| 'Simon Delaux' ♀ | CLyn CSam EBee ECou MBal NPla |
| | SPer WEas WRus |
| § 'Snow Wreath' (v) | ECou IBlr |
| I 'Southlandii' | Last listed 1996 |
| *speciosa* | MLan |
| - 'Dial Rocks' | ECou |
| - 'Johny Day' | See *H.* 'Johny Day' |
| - 'Kapiti' | Last listed 1996 |
| § - 'La Seduisante' ♀ | CLTr CLyn EBee ECou ENot IOrc |
| | MGed MLan MRav SEND SPer |
| | WSHC |
| § - 'Patti Dossett' | CLTr |
| ◆ - 'Purple Queen' | See *H.* 'Purple Queen' |
| - 'Rangatira' | ECou EWes |
| ◆ - 'Ruddigore' | See *H. speciosa* 'La Seduisante' |
| § - 'Variegata' (v) | CHal CLyn ECou IBlr NPer SDry |
| | WEas |
| 'Spender's Seedling' | CLan CLyn ECou GOrc MWgw |
| | NBee SEND SPan SPer SRms STre |
| 'Spender's Seedling' hort. | See *H. parviflora* var. *angustifolia* |
| 'Spring Glory' | EBrP EBre LBre LRHS SBre |
| *stricta* | CLyn ECou |
| - var. *egmontiana* | ECou |
| - var. *macroura* | ECou EPla SDry |
| § - - 'Cookiana' | Last listed 1996 |
| *subalpina* | CHar CLan EBee EBrP EBre ECou |
| | ESis LBre MOne MTis NCut NHed |
| | SBre |
| *subsimilis* | Last listed 1996 |
| - var. *astonii* | ESis |
| ¶ 'Summer Blue' | CLyn |
| 'Susan' | ECou |
| 'Sussex Carpet' | See *H. albicans* 'Sussex Carpet' |
| *tetrasticha* | ESis WAbe |
| * - AGS 74 | MRPP |
| 'Tiny Tot' | CLyd EHyt ESis MTho |
| 'Tom Marshall' | See *H. canterburiensis* |
| *topiaria* | More than 30 suppliers |
| * - 'Doctor Favier' | CLyn |
| 'Torlesse' | ECou |
| *townsonii* | CLyn ECou |
| *traversii* | CBlo ECou MSte SRms SSto |
| - 'Mason' | ECou |
| - 'Woodside' | ECou |
| 'Trenchant Rose' | CBlo |
| ◆ 'Tricolor' | See *H. speciosa* 'Variegata' |
| 'Trixie' | CLyn CNic ECou |
| *tumida* | Last listed 1998 |
| 'Underway' | Last listed 1998 |
| *urvilleana* | ECou |
| 'Veitchii' | See *H.* 'Alicia Amherst' |
| § *venustula* | ECou ELan MAsh MBri NHed |
| | NMen SMrm WPer |
| - 'Blue Skies' | ECou NFai |
| - 'Patricia Davies' | CLTr ECou NHed |
| *vernicosa* | CLyn CNic EBee ECou EPla ESis |
| | GDra GRei LHop MBar MBri |
| | MGos NBee NFor NHed NHol |
| | NLon NPer NTow SIgm SPer SPlb |
| | SSmi WAbe WHCG |
| 'Violet Queen' | Last listed 1996 |
| 'Violet Wand' | Last listed 1996 |
| 'Waikiki' | See *H.* 'Mrs Winder' |
| 'Walter Buccleugh' | ECou WCom |
| 'Wardiensis' | See *H. pinguifolia* 'Wardiensis' |
| 'Warley Pink' | CLyn |
| 'Warleyensis' | See *H.* 'Mrs Winder' |
| § 'Watson's Pink' | CLTr CNic EBee ECou GOrc SPer |
| | SUsu WAbe WKif |
| ¶ 'White Diamond' | SPer |

§ 'White Gem'                    ECou ECtt ESis EWTr GRei MBal
  (*brachysiphon* hybrid)        MGos NBee NFor NHed NPer
                                 WEas WStI
* 'White Grape'                  CM&M
  'White Heather'                ESis MTPN
  'White Summer'                 Last listed 1997
  'White Wand'                   NFai
* 'White Wings'                  Last listed 1998
  'Willcoxii'                    See *H. buchananii* 'Sir George
                                 Fenwick'
  'Wingletye'                    CAbP CLyd CLyn CNic ECou
                                 EGoo ESis MBal MBri MGos MWhi
                                 NHed WAbe WGwG WPer WPyg
  'Winter Glow'                  CLyd COtt ECou EHic NFai
  'Wiri Blush'                   CLyn
  'Wiri Charm'                   CAbP CDoC COtt EBee ECle ELan
                                 EMil ENot ESis IOrc MLan MTis
                                 SSto SVil WGer WWeb
  'Wiri Cloud'                   CAbP ECle ELan ESis IOrc MGed
                                 MTis SSto SVil WWeb
  'Wiri Dawn'                    CAbP CB&S CLyn COtt ECle ELan
                                 ESis EWes IOrc NFai SSto SVil
                                 WLRN WWeb
  'Wiri Gem'                     CLyn EMil LRHS
¶ 'Wiri Icing Sugar'            CLyn
  'Wiri Image'                   CB&S CDoC CLyn COtt EMil IOrc
                                 LRHS SVil
  'Wiri Joy'                     CLyn LRHS SVil
  'Wiri Mist'                    CLyn COtt EBee EMil ESis IOrc
                                 LRHS NFai
  'Wiri Splash'                  CDoC COtt CTrC ECle ELan EMil
                                 MAsh MWat SPan SSto WWeb
  'Wiri Vision'                  COtt ESis LRHS SSto
  'Wootten'                      Last listed 1996
§ 'Youngii'                      CPri EBee ECha ECou ELan
                                 EMNN ENot ESis MBal MBar
                                 MGos MPla NBee NMen NWCA
                                 SPer SRCN SRms SSmi WEas
                                 WMow WSHC WWin

# HECHTIA (Bromeliaceae)
§ *argentea*                     Last listed 1996
  *montana*                      Last listed 1996
  *tillandsioides*               LHil

# HEDEOMA (Lamiaceae)
  *pulegioides*                  Last listed 1998

# HEDERA ✿ (Araliaceae)
  *algeriensis*                  See *H. canariensis* hort.
§ *azorica*                      CWhi WFib WWat
  - 'Aurea'                      Last listed 1998
  - 'Pico'                       CWhi WFib
  - *typica*                     See *H. azorica* 'São Miguel'
  - 'Variegata'                  WCot
§ *canariensis* hort.            CDoC SAPC SArc WFib
§ - Willd.                       Last listed 1997
  - 'Algeriensis'                See *H. canariensis* hort.
  - 'Argyle Street'              WFib
  - var. *azorica*               See *H. azorica*
  - 'Cantabrian'                 See *H. maroccana* 'Spanish
                                 Canary'
* - 'Casablanca'                 CWhi
* - 'Etna'                       CWhi
§ - hort. 'Gloire de Marengo'    More than 30 suppliers
    (v) ♀
  - 'Marginomaculata' ♀          EPfP LRHS NEgg WFib WLeb
                                 WWeb
* - 'Mirandela'                  CWhi
  - 'Montgomery'                 LRHS WFib
* - 'Nevada'                     CWhi
  - 'Ravensholst' ♀              CMac EHic NLon NSti WFib WWat

  - 'Stauss'                     WFib
  - hort. 'Variegata'            See *H. canariensis* hort. 'Gloire
                                 de Marengo'
  *caucasigena*                  See *H. helix* f. *caucasigena*
  *chinensis*                    See *H. nepalensis* var. *sinensis*
  - *typica*                     See *H. nepalensis* var. *sinensis*
§ *colchica* ♀                   CBlo EBee ENot EPfP LRHS SPer
                                 WDin WFib
* - 'Arborescens Variegata'      SPer
  - 'Dentata' ♀                  CBlo CWhi EPla LBuc LPri MBal
                                 SEas WFib
  - 'Dentata Aurea'              See *H. colchica* 'Dentata Variegata'
§ - 'Dentata Variegata' ♀        More than 30 suppliers
  - 'My Heart'                   See *H. colchica*
  - 'Paddy's Pride'              See *H. colchica* 'Sulphur Heart'
§ - 'Sulphur Heart' (v) ♀        More than 30 suppliers
  - 'Variegata'                  See *H. colchica* 'Dentata Variegata'
  *cristata*                     See *H. helix* 'Parsley Crested'
§ *cypria*                       EPla WCot WFib
  *helix*                        CKin CTri CWhi EWFC GChr
                                 MBar MGos NWea WFib WHer
  - 'Abundance'                  See *H. helix* 'California'
  - 'Adam' (v)                   CBlo CWhi EAst MAsh MBri
                                 MTho NPla SEND STre WByw
                                 WFib WLeb WWat WWeb
I - 'Ahorn'                      CWhi WFib
  - 'Albany'                     See *H. hibernica* 'Albany'
  - 'Alpha'                      CWhi
  - 'Alte Brücke'                CWhi WFib
  - 'Alte Heidelberg'            CWhi WFib
  - 'Amberwaves'                 WFib
I - 'Ambrosia' (v)               CWhi WFib
  - 'Anchor'                     CWhi
§ - 'Angularis'                  CWhi ECot
  - 'Angularis Aurea' ♀          CWhi EBee EHoe EPfP EPla MPla
                                 NBir NPla SMad WFib
  - 'Anne Borch'                 See *H. hibernica* 'Anna Marie'
  - 'Anne Marie'                 See *H. hibernica* 'Anna Marie'
  - 'Annette'                    See *H. helix* 'California'
  - 'Appaloosa'                  WCot WFib
  - 'Aran'                       See *H. hibernica* 'Aran'
  - misapplied 'Aran'            See *H. helix* 'Rutherford's Arran'
  - 'Arapahoe'                   WFib
  - 'Arborescens'                CNat EPla
  - 'Arborescens Variegata'      Last listed 1996
  - 'Ardingly' (v)               CWhi MWhi NBea NOla SPer
                                 WFib
  - 'Arran'                      See *H. helix* 'Rutherford's Arran'
  - 'Asterisk'                   CWhi EPla NBrk NCat WBro WFib
                                 WLeb
  - 'Astin'                      CWhi WFib
  - 'Atropurpurea' ♀             CBlo CNat CWhi EPPr EPla ETen
                                 MBar NHol NPla WBay WFib
  - 'Aurea Densa'                See *H. helix* 'Aureovariegata'
§ - 'Aureovariegata'             CMac CNic CWhi WFib
  - 'Avon' (v)                   WFib
  - 'Baby Face'                  CWhi
  - 'Baccifera'                  CWhi WFib
  - 'Baden-Baden'                CWhi WFib
  - var. *baltica*               CWhi WFib
  - 'Barabits' Silver'           EPla
  - 'Big Deal'                   CWhi
  - 'Bill Archer'                CWhi EPla WFib
  - 'Bird's Foot'                See *H. helix* 'Pedata'
  - 'Blodwen' (v)                WFib
  - 'Bodil' (v)                  CWhi NOla SHFr WFib
  - 'Boskoop'                    CWhi WFib
  - 'Bowles Ox Heart'            WFib
  - 'Bredon'                     WFib WSPU
  - 'Brigette'                   See *H. helix* 'California'
  - 'Brightstone'                WFib
§ - 'Brokamp'                    CWhi NFai NOla SLPl WFib

- 'Bruder Ingobert' (v) — CWhi NCat WFib
- 'Buttercup' ♀ — More than 30 suppliers
- 'Butterflies' — WFib
§ - 'Caecilia' (v) — CB&S CBlo CMac ELan EPla LHop MBrN NFai NSti SPer WCot WCru WDin WFib WLRN WLeb
N - 'Caenwoodiana' — See H. helix 'Pedata'
- 'Caenwoodiana Aurea' — CWhi WFib
- 'Calico' — See H. helix 'Schäfer Three'
§ - 'California' — CWhi MBri NSti WFib
- 'California Fan' — CWhi
- 'California Gold' (v) — CCuc CWhi NPro WFib
- 'Caristian' — WFib
- 'Carolina Crinkle' — CNat CWhi EPla MWhi NBrk WBro WFib
- 'Cascade' — WFib
- 'Cathedral Wall' — WFib
§ - 'Cavendishii' (v) ♀ — CWhi MPla NBrk SRms WCru WFib WLRN
§ - 'Ceridwen' (v) — CRHN CWhi MBri SPlb WFib
- 'Chedglow' fasciated — CNat
¶ - 'Cheltenham Blizzard' (v) — CNat
- 'Chester' (v) — CWhi MAsh MBri WFib WWat
- 'Chicago' — CBlo WFib
- 'Chicago Variegated' — See H. helix 'Harald'
- 'Christian' — See H. helix 'Direktor Badke'
- 'Chrysanna' — WFib
- 'Chrysophylla' — CWhi EPla
- 'Cleeve' — WFib
- 'Clotted Cream' — See H. helix 'Caecilia'
- 'Clouded Gold' — Last listed 1996
- 'Cockle Shell' — CWhi WFib
- 'Congesta' ♀ — CWhi EPla EPot GDra MBal MTho SRms SSmi STre WEas WFib WLeb
- 'Conglomerata' — CWhi ELan EPla MBal MBar MBri MBro NBir NFor NRya SMad SPer SRms SSmi WAbe WEas WFib WPyg
- 'Conglomerata Erecta' — CSWP MAsh NLon SLon SRms WFib
- 'Corrugata' — WFib
- 'Crenata' — CWhi WFib
- 'Crispa' — MRav NFor
- 'Cristata' — See H. helix 'Parsley Crested'
- 'Cristata Melanie' — See H. helix 'Melanie'
- 'Curleylocks' — See H. helix 'Manda's Crested'
- 'Curley-Q' — See H. helix 'Dragon Claw'
- 'Curvaceous' (v) — WCot WFib
- 'Cuspidata Major' — See H. hibernica 'Cuspidata Major'
- 'Cuspidata Minor' — See H. hibernica 'Cuspidata Minor'
- 'Cyprus' — See H. cypria
* - 'Dead Again' — WCot
- 'Dean' (v) — WFib
- 'Deltoidea' — See H. hibernica 'Deltoidea'
- 'Denmark' (v) — WFib
- 'Denticulata' — CWhi WFib
- 'Diana' — CWhi
- 'Dicke von Stauss' — CWhi
§ - 'Direktor Badke' — CWhi WFib
- 'Discolor' — See H. helix 'Minor Marmorata'
- 'Domino' (v) — CWhi EPla EWes WFib WLeb
§ - 'Donerailensis' — CWhi GAri NFai WFib WPer
- 'Dovers' — CCuc WFib
§ - 'Dragon Claw' — CNat CWhi EHic EPla ETen NBrk NPla SMad WCot WCru WFib WLeb
- 'Duckfoot' — CCuc CHal CInt CLTr CSWP CWhi MTho MWhi NFai NPla NSti WBro WFib WLeb WWat
- 'Dunloe Gap' — EPla

- 'Edison' — CWhi
- 'Elegance' — CWhi WFib
- 'Elfenbein' (v) — CWhi WFib
- 'Emerald Gem' — See H. helix 'Angularis'
- 'Emerald Globe' — CWhi WFib
- 'Emerald Jewel' — See H. helix 'Pittsburgh'
- 'Erecta' ♀ — CMac CNat CTri CWhi EHic EMFP EPla GAri MBar MGos MTho MWhi NRya SSto WCot WFib WPat
- 'Erin' — See H. helix 'Pin Oak'
- 'Ester' — See H. helix 'Harald'
- 'Eugen Hahn' (v) — CWhi EPla WCot WFib
§ - 'Eva' (v) ♀ — CMac CWhi MBal MBri MGos NBir WFib
- 'Evesham' — WFib
- 'Fallen Angel' — CWhi WFib
- 'Fan' — CWhi
- 'Fantasia' (v) — CMac CWhi WFib
¶ - 'Faye' (v) — WCot
- 'Ferney' — WFib
- 'Filigran' — CNat CWhi SMad WFib WHer WLeb
- 'Flamenco' — CWhi EPla WFib
- 'Flava' (v) — CWhi
- 'Fleur de Lis' — CNat CWhi WFib
- 'Florida' — WFib
- 'Fluffy Ruffles' — CWhi EPla WLeb
* - 'Francis' — MBri
- 'Fringette' — See H. helix 'Manda Fringette'
- 'Frosty' (v) — Last listed 1997
- 'Gavotte' — CWhi MTho WFib
- 'Gertrud Stauss' (v) — CWhi MBri WFib
- 'Glache' (v) — SHFr WFib
- 'Glacier' (v) ♀ — More than 30 suppliers
- 'Glacier Improved' (v) — NBea
- 'Glymii' — CWhi EPla SLPl WFib
- 'Gold Harald' — See H. helix 'Goldchild'
- 'Gold Knight' — Last listed 1996
- 'Gold Nugget' — CWhi
§ - 'Goldchild' (v) ♀ — CB&S CDoC CPri CSam CWhi EAst EBee EBrP EBre ELan EPla GOrc LBre MAsh MBar MBri MGos MTho MWhi NBir NFla NHol SBre SEas SHFr SPer WBay WByw WFib WLeb
- 'Goldcraft' (v) — CWhi WFib
- 'Golden Ann' — See H. helix 'Ceridwen'
* - 'Golden Arrow' — LRHS MAsh
- 'Golden Curl' (v) — EPla
- 'Golden Ester' — See H. helix 'Ceridwen'
- 'Golden Gate' (v) — MBri
¶ - 'Golden Gem' — NPro
- 'Golden Ingot' (v) — CPri CWhi ELan EPla MAsh MBar MGos MWhi NFai WFib WLeb
- 'Golden Kolibri' — See H. helix 'Midas Touch'
- 'Golden Mathilde' (v) — CHal
- 'Golden Medal' — WCot WFib
- 'Golden Shamrock' — See H. helix 'Golden Envoy'
- 'Golden Snow' (v) — MBri
- 'Goldfinger' — See H. helix 'Goldstern'
- 'Goldheart' — See H. helix 'Oro di Bogliasco'
§ - 'Goldstern' (v) — CNat CWhi EPla MWhi WFib WLeb WWat
- 'Goldwolke' (v) — SLPl
- 'Gracilis' — See H. hibernica 'Gracilis'
§ - 'Green Feather' — CWhi EGoo ESis WFib WOak
- 'Green Finger' — See H. helix 'Très Coupé'
§ - 'Green Ripple' — CB&S CChe CMac CNat CSam CTri CWhi EBee ENot IOrc MAsh MBar MWht NBro NCat NLon NPla NPro SEND SEas SPer SPlb WFib WHen WLeb

| | | |
|---|---|---|
| | - 'Green Spear' | See *H. helix* 'Spear Point' |
| | - 'Hahn's Green Ripple' | See *H. helix* 'Green Ripple' |
| | - 'Hamilton' | See *H. hibernica* 'Hamilton' |
| § | - 'Harald' (v) | CBlo CDoC CWhi EBee MAsh MBNS MBal MBri NSti WFib WLeb |
| | - 'Harlequin' (v) | WFib |
| | - 'Harrison' | CWhi |
| | - 'Harry Wood' | See *H. helix* 'Modern Times' |
| * | - 'Hazel' (v) | WFib |
| | - 'Heise' (v) | CWhi WFib |
| | - 'Heise Denmark' (v) | WFib |
| | - 'Helvetica' | CWhi |
| | - 'Helvig' | See *H. helix* 'White Knight' |
| | - 'Heron' | Last listed 1998 |
| | - subsp. **hibernica** | See *H. hibernica* |
| | - 'Hispanica' | See *H. maderensis* subsp. *iberica* |
| | - 'Hite's Miniature' | See *H. helix* 'Merion Beauty' |
| | - 'Holly' | See *H. helix* 'Parsley Crested' |
| ¶ | - 'Hullavington' | CNat |
| | - 'Humpty Dumpty' | CDoC MBar |
| | - 'Ideal' | See *H. helix* 'California' |
| | - 'Imp' | See *H. helix* 'Brokamp' |
| | - 'Ingelise' | See *H. helix* 'Sagittifolia Variegata' |
| | - 'Ingrid' | See *H. helix* 'Harald' |
| | - 'Innuendo' | WFib |
| | - 'Itsy Bitsy' | See *H. helix* 'Pin Oak' |
| | - 'Ivalace' ♀ | CB&S CNat CWhi EBee ECha EPla ESis GOrc MAsh MBal MBri MGos MNrw MRav MWhi MWht NBid NChi NFai NSti NWoo SEas SRms WFib WLeb |
| | - 'Jack Frost' (v) | ETen |
| | - 'Jane's Findling' (v) | CNat |
| | - 'Jasper' | WFib |
| | - 'Jerusalem' | See *H. helix* 'Schäfer Three' |
| | - 'Jester's Gold' | MAsh MBri MGos NEgg WWeb |
| | - 'Jubilee' (v) | CWhi ELan WCFE WFar WFib WLeb |
| | - 'Knülch' | EHic EPla WFib |
| | - 'Kolibri' (v) ♀ | CBlo CChe CDoC CMac CPri CWhi EAst EBee EBrP EBre EMil EPfP LBre MAsh MBar MBri NPla NPro SBre WFib WWeb |
| | - 'Königers Auslese' | CRHN CWhi EPla MBrN NBea SLPl WFib |
| | - 'Kurios' | CNat CWhi |
| | - 'La Plata' | CWhi |
| § | - 'Lady Kay' | WFib |
| | - 'Lalla Rookh' | CWhi NBrk WFib WLeb |
| | - 'Lemon Swirl' (v) | CWhi WFib |
| | - 'Leo Swicegood' | CSWP CWhi EPla MWhi WFib |
| | - 'Light Fingers' | CCuc CNat MAsh SPer WFib |
| * | - 'Lime Regis' | CWhi |
| * | - 'Limelight' | Last listed 1996 |
| | - 'Limey' | CWhi |
| | - 'Little Diamond' (v) ♀ | CDoC CLTr CSam CTri CWhi EBee EHoe ELan EMil EPla GChr MAsh MBar MBri MGos MHar MWht NPla SLon SRPl WAbe WBay WHib WWat |
| | - 'Little Gem' | CWhi WFib |
| | - 'Little Luzii' (v) | WFib |
| | - 'Little Picture' | WFib |
| | - 'Little Witch' | EPla |
| | - 'Liz' | See *H. helix* 'Eva' |
| | - 'Liziz' (v) | WFib |
| | - 'Lopsided' | Last listed 1998 |
| | - 'Lucy Kay' | See *H. helix* 'Lady Kay' |
| § | - 'Luzii' (v) | CBlo EBee EHic EHoe EPla MBar MGos NFai NLon NSti SPer SRms WByw WFib |
| | - 'Maculata' | See *H. helix* 'Minor Marmorata' |
| | - 'Malvern' | WFib |
| § | - 'Manda Fringette' | CWhi MTho NFai WFib WLeb |
| § | - 'Manda's Crested' ♀ | CBlo CSWP CWhi ELan MBal NPla WFib WLeb |
| | - 'Manda's Fan' | WFib |
| | - 'Maple Leaf' | CNat CWhi EPla WCot WFib |
| | - 'Maple Queen' | MBri |
| | - 'Marginata' (v) | CBlo SRms |
| | - 'Marginata Elegantissima' | See *H. helix* 'Tricolor' |
| | - 'Marginata Major' (v) | CWhi WFib WLeb |
| | - 'Marginata Minor' | See *H. helix* 'Cavendishii' |
| | - 'Marie-Luise' | WFib |
| | - 'Marmorata' | See *H. helix* 'Luzii' |
| | - 'Masquerade' (v) | CBlo WGor WLeb |
| | - 'Mathilde' (v) | CWhi EBee WFib WWeb |
| | - 'Meagheri' | See *H. helix* 'Green Feather' |
| § | - 'Melanie' | ECha ELan EPla NBrk NPla SOkh WCot WCru WFib WLeb WRHF |
| | - 'Meon' | WFib |
| § | - 'Merion Beauty' | CWhi EHic GAri NPro WFib |
| § | - 'Midas Touch' (v) ♀ | CBlo CChe COtt CWhi EBee EPfP EPla LHop MBri SPer WFib |
| | - 'Midget' | CRow WEas WFib |
| | - 'Mini Ester' (v) | CWhi MBri |
| | - 'Mini Heron' | CInt MBri |
| | - 'Miniature Knight' | CNat |
| | - 'Minima' | See *H. helix* 'Donerailensis' |
| § | - 'Minor Marmorata' (v) | CHal CWhi EPla MBal MTho WEas WFib WSHC |
| | - 'Mint Kolibri' | EHoe MBri WBcn |
| | - 'Minty' (v) | MWht NCat WLeb |
| * | - 'Minutissima' | EPla |
| | - 'Miss Maroc' | See *H. helix* 'Manda Fringette' |
| | - 'Misty' (v) | CWhi WFib |
| § | - 'Modern Times' | CWhi |
| | - 'Mrs Pollock' (v) | CWhi WFib |
| | - 'Mrs Ulin' | CWhi |
| | - 'Needlepoint' | CBlo IOrc |
| | - 'Neilson' | CLTr CWhi SPer WFib |
| | - 'Neptune' | CWhi |
| | - 'New Ripples' | CCuc CWhi EHal NBrk NMoo WFib |
| | - 'Nigra' | CWhi |
| | - 'Nigra Aurea' (v) | CWhi WFib |
| | - 'Norfolk Lace' | EWes |
| | - 'Northington Gold' | WBcn WFib |
| | - 'Obovata' | CWhi |
| | - 'Olive Rose' | CWhi EPla MTho WFib |
| N | - 'Oro di Bogliasco' (v) | CChe CMac CSam CWhi EBee ELan ENot GOrc MBal MBar MBri NBea NBee NFai NFla NLon NSti NWea SBra SPer SRCN SRPl SRms WEas WPat WWat |
| | - 'Pallida' | See *H. hibernica* 'Hibernica Variegata' |
| | - 'Paper Doll' (v) | CWhi |
| | - 'Parasol' (v) | Last listed 1998 |
| § | - 'Parsley Crested' AM | CBlo CMac CNat EBee ELan EPla GOrc MAsh MBal MBar NChi NSti SPer SRms WCru WFib WLeb WMoo WOak WRHF WWat |
| N | - 'Pedata' ♀ | CSWP CWhi EPfP NOla WFib WLeb WWat |
| ¶ | - 'Pedata Heron' | CCuc |
| | - 'Pencil Point' | CWhi |
| | - 'Pennsylvanian' | CWhi |
| | - 'Perkeo' | CWhi EGoo EPla ESis NPla SPan WFib |
| | - 'Perle' (v) | CWhi NBir WFib |
| | - 'Persian Carpet' | CWhi WFib |
| | - 'Peter' (v) | EPla NBrk WFib |
| * | - 'Pin Oak' | CBlo NPla WCru |

I - 'Pink 'n' Very Curly'    EPla WCot
- 'Pirouette'    WFib
§ - 'Pittsburgh'    WFib WWal
- 'Pixie'    CWhi WFib
- 'Plume d'Or'    CHal CSam MTho WFib
§ - f. *poetarum*    EPla IOrc WBcn WFib WWat
- - 'Poetica Arborea'    ECha SDix
♦ - 'Poetica'    See *H. helix* f. *poetarum* McAllister
- 'Preston Tiny'    NBir
- 'Professor Friedrich Tobler'    CNat CWhi EPla NPro WFib WLeb
- 'Quatermas'    WFib
- 'Raleigh Delight'    WCot
- 'Ralf'    CWhi EPla WFib
- 'Rambler'    NBir
- 'Ramsgate'    Last listed 1998
- 'Rauschgold' (v)    CWhi
- 'Ray's Supreme'    See *H. helix* 'Pittsburgh'
- 'Reef Shell' (v)    WFib
- 'Regency' (v)    CWhi
- subsp. *rhizomatifera*    EPla WFib
- 'Ritterkreuz'    CWhi WFib
- 'Romanze' (v)    CWhi WFib
- 'Rottingdean'    See *H. hibernica* 'Rottingdean'
- 'Rüsche'    CNat CWhi WFib
- 'Russell's Gold'    WFib
§ - 'Rutherford's Arran'    CWhi WFib
- 'Sagittifolia'    CLTr CMac CNic CTri CWhi ELan ENot GOrc MAsh MBal NChi NFor NLon SHFr SRms WCot WEas WFib WWat
§ - 'Sagittifolia Variegata'    CBlo CChe CMac CWhi EBee EHal EMil EPla GOrc MAsh MBri NBea SPer SRms WFib WLeb WRHF
- 'Sally' (v)    CWhi EPla WFib
- 'Salt and Pepper'    See *H. helix* 'Minor Marmorata'
§ - 'Schäfer Three' (v)    WFib
- 'Serenade' (v)    WFib
- 'Shamrock' ♀    CCuc CWhi EPfP EPla MBri SPer WCot WFib
- 'Shannon'    CWhi
- 'Silver Emblem' (v)    WFib
- 'Silver King' (v)    EBee EPla NBir WFib
- 'Silver Queen'    See *H. helix* 'Tricolor'
- 'Sinclair Silverleaf'    WFib
- 'Small Deal'    CWhi WFib
§ - 'Spear Point'    CWhi WFib
- 'Spectabilis Aurea'    WLeb
- 'Spectre' (v)    CNat CWhi MTho WFib WHer WLeb
- 'Spetchley' ♀    CHal CNic CSWP CWhi EPla ESis EWes MBar MRav MTho NPer SHel SMad WAlt WBay WBcn WCFE WCot WFib WLeb WPat
- 'Spinosa'    CWhi EPla
- 'Spiriusa'    WFib
- 'Staghorn'    CWhi
- 'Stevenage' (v)    WFib
- 'Stift Neuberg' (v)    WFib
- 'Stuttgart'    CWhi WFib
- 'Succinata'    WFib
- 'Sunrise'    WFib
- 'Suzanne'    See *H. nepalensis* var. *nepalensis* 'Suzanne'
- 'Sylvanian'    WFib
- 'Symmetry'    CWhi
- 'Tango'    WFib
- 'Teardrop'    NCat WBro
- 'Telecurl'    CWhi EPla WFib
- 'Tenerife'    ELan EPla WFib WLeb
- 'Thorndale'    CWhi WFib

- 'Tiger Eyes'    CWhi
¶ - 'Tony'    CPri
* - 'Touch of Class'    CWhi
§ - 'Très Coupé'    CB&S CDoC CSWP EBee EGoo MBal MTho NPla SAPC SArc SPer WFib WLeb
§ - 'Tricolor' (v)    CB&S CBlo CMac CTri CWhi ELan EPfP EPla MAsh MGos MWht SBra SPer
- 'Trinity' (v)    CRHN WByw WFib
- 'Tristram' (v)    CWhi MAsh WFib
- 'Triton'    CWhi MBal MBar MTho WFib
- 'Troll'    CWhi WLeb
- 'Trustee'    CWhi
- 'Tussie Mussie' (v)    CWhi WFib
- 'Ursula' (v)    CSWP NChi WFib
- 'Ustler'    CWhi
* - 'Variegata'    Last listed 1998
* - 'Verity'    CWhi
I - 'Victoria'    MAsh WWeb
- 'Walthamensis'    CWhi WFib
§ - 'White Knight' (v)    CWhi EPla MBri WFib
- 'White Kolibri'    MBri
- 'Whitehall'    WFib
- 'Wichtel'    CWhi
- 'William Kennedy' (v)    CWhi WFib WLeb
- 'Williamsiana' (v)    CWhi
- 'Woeneri'    CWhi SLPl WFib
- 'Woodsii'    See *H. helix* 'Modern Times'
¶ - 'Yellow Ripple'    CPri
- 'Zebra' (v)    CWhi NCat WFib
§ *hibernica* ♀    CB&S CBlo CNat CWhi GCHN GChr LBuc MBar MRav NBea NFor SBra SPer SRms WFib WLeb WStI WWat
§ - 'Albany'    WFib
§ - 'Anna Marie' (v)    CMac CPri CWhi GOrc LRHS MBri WEas WFib WLeb
- 'Aracena'    EPla
§ - 'Cuspidata Major'    CWhi WFib
§ - 'Cuspidata Minor'    CWhi WFib
- 'Dealbata' (v)    CMac CWhi GOrc WFib
§ - 'Deltoidea'    CCuc CWhi EPla MBal MBri MWht WCot WFib
- 'Digitata'    EPla WFib
I - 'Digitata Crûg Gold'    WCru
§ - 'Gracilis'    CWhi WFib
§ - 'Hamilton'    WFib
- 'Helena' (v)    WFib
* - 'Lactimaculata'    CWhi
- 'Lobata Major'    SRms
- 'Maculata' (v)    EPla
- 'Palmata'    WFib
- 'Rona'    CWhi WFib
- 'Sulphurea' (v)    CWhi WFib
- 'Tess'    CNat EPla WFib
- 'Variegata'    CPri CWhi MBar WWat
*maderensis*    WFib
§ - subsp. *iberica*    WFib
*maroccana* 'Morocco'    WFib
- 'Spanish Canary'    WFib WSHC
*nepalensis*    MBal WBcn WFib
- - CC&MR 460    Last listed 1997
§ - var. *nepalensis* 'Suzanne'    MBar WFib
§ - var. *sinensis*    CWhi WFib
¶ - - L 555    EPla
*pastuchovii*    CWhi WFib
- from Troödos, Cyprus    See *H. cypria*
* - 'Volga'    CWhi
§ *rhombea*    CWhi WCot WFib
- var. *formosana*    WFib
- 'Japonica'    See *H. rhombea*

- var. *rhombea* 'Variegata'  WFib

# HEDYCHIUM ✿ (Zingiberaceae)
| | |
|---|---|
| *aurantiacum* | WMul |
| *chrysoleucum* | CGle LAma LBow LPio WCru |
| *coccineum* ♀ | CB&S LAma LBlm LBow LChe |
| - var. *angustifolium* | WMul |
| - var. *aurantiacum* | LAma LBow |
| - 'Tara' ♀ | CFil CGle EOas LEdu LPio MSte |
| | SAPC SArc WCru WMul |
| *coronarium* | CAvo CGle LBlm LBow LChe |
| | MBEx MSte NFai SLon SYvo WMul |
| - var. *flavescens* | See *H. flavescens* |
| ¶ - var. *maximum* | CFir |
| *densiflorum* | CBrd CFil CTre EOas MBEx SDix |
| | SSpi WPGP |
| - 'Assam Orange' | CFil CGle CInt EOas GCal LChe |
| | LEdu LPio MBEx MSte SAPC |
| | WCru WMul WPGP |
| - 'Stephen' | CBrd CFil |
| *ellipticum* | LAma LBlm LBow WCru |
| § *flavescens* | CFil LAma LHil WCru WPGP |
| *forrestii* | CFil CGle CTre EOas LLew LPio |
| | MSte SArc WMul WPGP |
| ¶ - B&SWJ 2303 | WCru |
| *gardnerianum* ♀ | CFil CFir CGre CHan CLTr EBee |
| | EOas ERea LAma LBlm LBow |
| | LChe LEdu LPio MSte SArc SSoC |
| | SYvo WCru WMul WPGP |
| 'Goldflame' | CFir |
| *greenei* | CFil CFir CGle CGre LBow LEdu |
| | LPio MSte SArc SDix SYvo WCot |
| | WCru WMul |
| *longicornutum* | MSte |
| ¶ 'Luna Moth' | WMul |
| *muluense* | WMul |
| *pradhanii* | CFir WMul |
| x *rafflilii* | WCot |
| * 'Shamshiri' | LBlm |
| *spicatum* | CBrd CFil CFir CHan CMdw EOas |
| | GPoy MSte WMul |
| *thyrsiforme* | WMul |
| *villosum* | LAma WMul |
| *yunnanense* | CFil EOas WCot WCru WMul |
| | WPGP |

# HEDYSARUM (Papilionaceae)
| | |
|---|---|
| *coronarium* | CArn CGle CHan CPle CSev CSpe |
| | EBee ECGN EHrv ELan EMan |
| | MBrN MHlr MNrw MSte MTis |
| | SAga SHFr SRCN SUsu WCot |
| | WHal WOve WWin |
| - 'Album' | Last listed 1996 |
| *hedysaroides* | EMan |
| *multijugum* | CB&S CDoC LBuc MBlu SPer |
| | WSHC |
| - var. *apiculatum* | ELan |
| *nitidum* | Last listed 1996 |
| *occidentale* | Last listed 1998 |

# HEIMERLIODENDRON See PISONIA

# HEIMIA (Lythraceae)
| | |
|---|---|
| *salicifolia* | CArn CPle ELan MBlu MSal MWhi |
| | SOWG WWye |

# HELENIUM (Asteraceae)
| | |
|---|---|
| *autumnale* | CBlo CMea CTri EHal EWTr MBNS |
| | MBel MSal NBus NChi SEas SSvw |
| | WBea |
| - 'All Gold' | WPer |
| - JLS 88007WI | EMon |

| | |
|---|---|
| - 'Praecox' | Last listed 1998 |
| ¶ - 'Sunset Shades' | WElm |
| 'Baudirektor Linne' | CSam CWit SCro |
| * 'Biedermeier' | CRDP EFou |
| *bigelovii* | WByw |
| 'Blütentisch' | SUsu |
| 'Bressingham Gold' | Last listed 1996 |
| 'Bruno' | CHar CRDP EBrP EBre ECGN |
| | ELan LBre MArl MMil MRav NGdn |
| | SBre SMrm SOkh SPer |
| 'Butterpat' | CB&S EFou EHic EMan EPPr |
| | GMaP MAvo MBel MCLN MMil |
| | MRav NFai NFla NPri NVic SChu |
| | SPer WOld |
| 'Chipperfield Orange' | CBlo CHad EFou EMan EPfP LRHS |
| | MArl MCAu MHlr MMil NGdn |
| | NLak NVic SRPl SSvw SUsu WCot |
| | WLRN |
| 'Coppelia' | CKel CSam EBrP EBre LBre MBro |
| | NFla NGdn SBre WHoo WOld |
| Copper Spray | See *H.* 'Kupfersprudel' |
| 'Crimson Beauty' | CMea EBee EBrP EBre ELan LBre |
| | MBel MBri MLLN NRoo SBre |
| | WMer |
| 'Croftway Variety' | SCro |
| Dark Beauty | See *H.* 'Dunkelpracht' |
| 'Die Blonde' | LGre |
| § 'Dunkelpracht' | EPPr LGre WCot WOld |
| 'Feuersiegel' | EGar LGre WOld |
| 'Flammendes Käthchen' | LGre SAga |
| ¶ *flexuosum* | EBee |
| 'Gold Fox' | CKel CSam CWit WMer |
| Golden Youth | See *H.* 'Goldene Jugend' |
| § 'Goldene Jugend' | EGar ELan MRav NRoo SSpe |
| | WCot WEas |
| 'Goldrausch' | EFou SCro WMoo |
| *hoopesii* | CKel CPea EBee EBrP EBre EOld |
| | EWTr GChr GMaP LBre MBNS |
| | MBel MNrw MRav NBro NFai |
| | NOak NPri NSti SBre SCro SMrm |
| | SRms WFar WOve WPer WWal |
| 'Indianersommer' | Last listed 1997 |
| 'July Sun' | SSpe |
| 'Kanaria' | EFou EPPr NCat WOld |
| ¶ 'Karneol' | EFou SOkh |
| § 'Kupfersprudel' | MRav |
| 'Kupferzwerg' | LGre SOkh |
| 'Mahogany' | See *H.* 'Goldlackzwerg' |
| 'Moerheim Beauty' | More than 30 suppliers |
| ¶ 'Pipsqueak' | LRHS |
| 'Pumilum Magnificum' | CSam EFou EPar EPfP MBri MWat |
| | NRoo SCro SPer SUsu WByw |
| | WMer |
| Red and Gold | See *H.* 'Rotgold' |
| 'Riverton Beauty' | EBee |
| 'Riverton Gem' | ECtt |
| § 'Rotgold' | CBlo CM&M CMGP EBrP EBre |
| | ECGN ECtt LBre MSCN NArg |
| | NOak SBre SRms WHil WLRN |
| | WPer |
| 'Rubinkuppel' | LGre SUsu |
| 'Rubinzwerg' | SOkh SUsu |
| 'Sahin's Early Flowerer' | EFou WCot |
| 'Septemberfuchs' | EFou EPPr SCro |
| 'Sonnenwunder' | CWit ECha EGar SUsu |
| 'Sunshine' | WSan |
| 'The Bishop' | CBlo CSam EBee EFou EGar EMan |
| | EWTr LFis MBri MCAu MLLN |
| | MRav MTis NBro NCut NFai NLak |
| | NRoo SChu SLon WMer WOld |
| 'Waldtraut' | CBlo CKel CM&M CMGP CMil |
| | CSam EBee ECot EFou EGar ELan |
| | LEdu MRav NOak SAga SCro SPer |
| | WHoo WMer |

| | |
|---|---|
| 'Wonadonga' | EFou EGar |
| 'Wyndley' | CB&S CSam EBrP EBre ECGN |
| | EFou EGar LBre MBel MCAu |
| | MRav NRoo SBre SChu SEas WCot |
| | WMer |
| 'Zimbelstern' | CMil EGar LGre MRav SAga SOkh |
| | WFar |

## HELIAMPHORA (Sarraceniaceae)

| | |
|---|---|
| **heterodoxa** | WMEx |
| - × **ionasii** | WMEx |
| - × **minor** | WMEx |
| - × **nutans** | WMEx |
| **minor** | WMEx |
| **nutans** | WMEx |
| **tatei** | WMEx |

## HELIANTHELLA (Asteraceae)

| | |
|---|---|
| § **quinquenervis** | EBee EBrP EBre EMan GCal GNau |
| | LBre MBel MSte NTow SBre |

## HELIANTHEMUM ✿ (Cistaceae)

| | |
|---|---|
| 'Alice Howarth' | EWes MBro MDHE SRms WHCG |
| | WHoo WPnn WPyg |
| **alpestre serpyllifolium** | See *H. nummularium* subsp. |
| | *glabrum* |
| 'Amabile Plenum' (d) | EPfP GAbr GCal GDra MBNS |
| | NCut SIgm |
| * 'Amber' | GAbr |
| 'Amy Baring' ♀ | EBrP EBre EGle EGoo GAbr GDra |
| | LBee LBre LHop NMen SBod SBre |
| | SMer WPer WSHC |
| 'Annabel' | CPri EPfP EWTr GAbr GCHN |
| | MPla NMGW NSla SChu SIde |
| | SMer WHCG WLin WPer |
| **apenninum** | MDHE NTow WCla WPer |
| - var. **roseum** | WCla |
| 'Apricot' | SBod SUsu |
| 'Apricot Blush' | WAbe |
| 'Baby Buttercup' | CLyd CMea GAbr MBro MPla |
| | NHol NPro WPat |
| 'Barbara' | Last listed 1998 |
| 'Beech Park Red' | CLTr CMea CPBP ECtt ESis GAbr |
| | LBee LBuc MBro MDHE MMil |
| | MWat MWgw SChu SIgm WCer |
| | WHoo WKif WPyg |
| 'Ben Afflick' | LBee MBNS SAga SBod SIgm |
| | SRms WCer WPnn |
| 'Ben Alder' | GAbr LFis MDHE NMen SSca |
| 'Ben Dearg' | CMea ECtt EGle EMNN ESis GAbr |
| | SBod SRms |
| 'Ben Fhada' | CB&S CMea CPBP CPri EGle |
| | EGoo ELan EMNN ESis GAbr |
| | GDra LBee MBal NLon SAga SBod |
| | SRms WAbe WEas WPer WPnn |
| | WWin |
| 'Ben Heckla' | CPri CSam ECtt GAbr GCHN MSte |
| | NMen NRoo WEas WPer |
| 'Ben Hope' | CPri EMNN EPfP GAbr GDra LIck |
| | MBal NLon NMen NRoo SAga |
| | SRms WPer WWin |
| 'Ben Lawers' | Last listed 1998 |
| 'Ben Ledi' | CB&S CInt CMea CPri ELan |
| | EMNN ESis GAbr GCHN GDra |
| | LHop MBal MTis NLon NSla NVic |
| | SBod WAbe WCer WHoo WLin |
| | WPer WPnn WWin |
| 'Ben Lomond' | MBal |
| 'Ben Macdui' | GAbr |
| 'Ben More' | CB&S CPri ECtt EGle ELan EMNN |
| | GAbr GDra GTou LBuc MBal |
| | MWat NLak NLon NMen SBod |
| | SIng SRob SSmi WPat WWin |

| | |
|---|---|
| 'Ben Nevis' | CLon CTri ECha EGoo ELan GAbr |
| | GDra MDHE SRms WHoo WPyg |
| | WWin |
| 'Ben Vane' | EGle GAbr MDHE SIng |
| 'Birch White' | GAbr MDHE SIng |
| 'Bishopsthorpe' | Last listed 1997 |
| 'Boughton Double | CGle ELan EWes GAbr GCal GMac |
| Primrose' (d) | GOrc LHop MGed SChu SIgm |
| | SMer SUsu WEas WHoo WLin |
| | WPen WSHC |
| 'Broughty Beacon' | GAbr GDra MDHE WGor |
| 'Broughty Sunset' | CLTr CSam EWTr GAbr MBro |
| | MDHE NBir SIgm WHoo WPyg |
| 'Brown Gold' (d) | Last listed 1997 |
| 'Bunbury' | CMea MDHE MWhi NPri NRoo |
| * 'Butter and Eggs' | CInt SRms |
| 'Butterball' (d) | MDHE |
| **canum** | WPer |
| - subsp. **balcanicum** | NTow |
| 'Captivation' | EGoo GAbr NHol |
| 'Cerise Queen' (d) | EBrP EBre ECha GAbr GMac LBre |
| | LHop MBro MPla NCut SBre SDix |
| | SIgm SRms SSoC WCla WCom |
| | WHoo WPer WPnn WPyg |
| **chamaecistus** | See *H. nummularium* |
| 'Cheviot' | CMea MBro MDHE WEas WHoo |
| | WPer WPyg WSHC WWat |
| 'Chocolate Blotch' | CLTr ECtt EOrc GAbr LBuc LFis |
| | MHar NLon NPri SChu SEND SIng |
| | WBea WPer |
| 'Coppernob' | SRms |
| 'Cornish Cream' | CLTr EWes GAbr |
| **croceum** | Last listed 1998 |
| **cupreum** | CInt EFou GAbr NHol |
| 'David' | EGoo |
| 'Doctor Phillips' | WHCG |
| double apricot (d) | EGle GAbr |
| double cream (d) | CMea ECha ECtt EGar MDHE |
| | WFar |
| 'Double Orange' (d) | LHop MBNS MWat NCut |
| ¶ double pale pink (d) | SIgm |
| double pale yellow (d) | NWoo |
| double pink (d) | CLTr CMGP ECha GAbr MWat |
| | NWoo WFar |
| 'Double Primrose' (d) | CLTr SIng |
| double red (d) | ECha NChi |
| double yellow (d) | ECha MPla |
| 'Elaine' | ELan |
| 'Elisabeth' | EGoo |
| 'Fairy' | EDAr EGle MDHE |
| * 'Fire' | NCat |
| § 'Fire Dragon' ♀ | CPea CPri CSam CTri EGle ELan |
| | GAbr GCHN LBee LBuc MWgw |
| | NRoo NWCA SChu SIgm SRms |
| | SUsu WAbe WPyg |
| 'Fireball' | See *H.* 'Mrs C.W. Earle' |
| 'Firefly' | SGre |
| 'Firegold' | WAbe |
| ¶ 'Flame' | CPri |
| 'Gaiety' | Last listed 1996 |
| 'Georgeham' | CLTr CSam ELan GAbr LBee LHop |
| | MDHE NCat SMer SRms WEas |
| | WGor WHCG WHoo WLin WPer |
| **georgicum** | NSla |
| **globulariifolium** | See *Tuberaria globulariifolia* |
| § 'Golden Queen' | CPri ECtt ENot EPfP EWTr GAbr |
| | LIck MBNS SChu WCla WPer |
| | WPyg |
| 'Henfield Brilliant' ♀ | CInt CPBP CPri EBrP EBre EGle |
| | EOrc GAbr GDra GOrc LBee LBre |
| | LHop MBro MHar NHol NRoo |
| | NVic SBre SMer SRms SSmi SSoC |
| | WEas WHoo WLin WPer WSHC |
| | WWat |

'Hidcote Apricot' — GAbr MMHG MTis
'Highdown' — CLTr GAbr SRms WAbe
¶ 'Highdown Apricot' — MDHE
'Honeymoon' — MDHE SIde WLRN
'John Lanyon' — LRHS MDHE
'Jubilee' (d) ♀ — CPri ECtt EGle ELan EMNN GAbr GOrc LBuc LFis LHop MMal NChi NFor NLon NRoo SChu SDix SRms WAbe WCla WEas WHCG WHoo WWin
I 'Jubilee Variegatum' — GAbr NLon
¶ 'Karen's Silver' — WAbe
'Kathleen Druce' (d) — EWes GAbr LHop MWat WHoo
_ledifolium_ — WPer
'Lucy Elizabeth' — GAbr
_lunulatum_ — CInt CLyd EGoo ESis LBee MBro MPla NHol NMen NTow SIgm WAbe WPat WWin
'Magnificum' — MDHE MWat
'Moonbeam' — WWin
§ 'Mrs C.W. Earle' (d) ♀ — CHar CInt CLTr CPri CSam CTri EAst ECtt ELan ESis GAbr LFis LHop NRoo SBod SDix SRms WAbe WPer WWin
'Mrs C.W. Earle Variegated' (d) — ELan
'Mrs Clay' — See H. 'Fire Dragon'
'Mrs Croft' — WPer
'Mrs Hays' — GMac
'Mrs Jenkinson' — Last listed 1998
'Mrs Lake' — Last listed 1998
'Mrs Moules' — SRms
'Mrs Mountstewart Jenkinson' — LHop MBro
_mutabile_ — SPlb WPer
§ _nummularium_ — CKin EHic EWFC GOrc GPoy IIve MDHE MHew MMal NMir NWCA SIde WCla WPat
§ - subsp. _glabrum_ — GAbr MBro NHol NMGW NMen WHoo WPat WPer WPyg
- subsp. _grandiflorum_ 'Variegatum' — MWat
* - 'Lemon Queen' — NCat WBcn
§ - subsp. _tomentosum_ — MWat
_oelandicum_ — NWCA
- subsp. _alpestre_ — CLyd MBro NNrd NTow SRms SSmi WPer
- subsp. _piloselloides_ — CLyd WWin
'Old Gold' — CLTr EBrP EBre GAbr LBee LBre MHar NRoo SBre SIgm SRms WAbe WPer WPnn
_ovatum_ — See H. _nummularium_ subsp. _obscurum_
_pilosum_ — LRHS SIgm
'Pink Beauty' — WBcn
'Pink Glow' — WPer
'Pink Perfection' — CSam
'Praecox' — CMea CTri EHic GAbr LBee MBal MPla SIgm SMer SRms WCom WHoo WPer WPyg
'Prostrate Orange' — SRms
'Raspberry Ripple' — CInt CPBP EAst EBrP EBre EGle ELan ENot GAbr GCHN GMac LBre LBuc LFis LHop MPla NChi NEgg SBre SChu SRms WHoo WPat WRus WWin
'Red Dragon' — WAbe
'Red Orient' — See H. 'Supreme'
'Regenbogen' — SChu SWas
§ 'Rhodanthe Carneum' ♀ — CMea CSam EFou ELan ENot GAbr GCHN GTou LBee LGro LHop MBal MRav MWat NHol NMir NRoo SSmi WAbe WEas WHoo WLin WSHC WWin

§ 'Rosa Königin' — EMNN GAbr LBee MDHE SEND WAbe
'Rose of Leeswood' (d) — CInt CMea ELan GAbr GMaP GMac LHop MBro MHar NChi NEgg NLon SAga SIgm SIng SMrm SRms WEas WHCG WHoo WKif WPyg WSHC WWin
Rose Queen — See H. 'Rosa Königin'
'Roxburgh Gold' — SRms
'Rushfield's White' — WHCG WRus WShe
'Saint John's College Yellow' — CLTr CSam GAbr MBNS SSmi WFar WHCG WPer
'Salmon Bee' — Last listed 1997
'Salmon Queen' — CHar CPri ECtt EMNN GAbr LBee MHar MSCN NPri NRoo SAga SIng SRms WPer WRHF WWin
_serpyllifolium_ — See H. _nummularium_ subsp. _glabrum_
'Shot Silk' — EWes MDHE NRoo
'Silvery Salmon' (v) — WAbe
'Snow Queen' — See H. 'The Bride'
'Snowball' — Last listed 1997
'Southmead' — GAbr
'Sterntaler' — GAbr GDra SIng SRms WLin
'Sudbury Gem' — CPri CTri EBrP EBre ECha GAbr LBre LHop NRoo NSla SBre SMer WPer WPnn
x _sulphureum_ — SDys
'Sulphureum Plenum' (d) — EPfP
'Sunbeam' — CSam EMNN GAbr MDHE SRms
'Sunburst' — GAbr
§ 'Supreme' — CLTr ELan EPfP EWes GAbr LBee LHop MWat SDix SIgm SRms WHCG WPer
'Tangerine' — GAbr
§ 'The Bride' ♀ — CMea CTri EBrP EBre ECha EFou EGle ELan ENot EOrc GCHN GOrc LBre LBuc LHop MBro MSte MWat SBre SChu SDix SRms SSoC SUsu WAbe WHoo WPnn WSHC
'Tigrinum Plenum' (d) — CPBP ESis EWes LBee MDHE NPro NRoo WWin
'Tomato Red' — ECha NSla SMrm
_tomentosum_ — See H. _nummularium_
_umbellatum_ — See Halimium umbellatum
'Venustum Plenum' (d) — CInt MBro WEas
'Voltaire' — EMNN GAbr MDHE MOne NPri WWin
'Watergate Rose' — MWat NBir NCat
'Welsh Flame' — WAbe
'White Queen' — Last listed 1997
'Windermere' — SIgm
'Wisley Pink' — See H. 'Rhodanthe Carneum'
'Wisley Primrose' ♀ — More than 30 suppliers
'Wisley White' — CLon CPri CSam CTri ECha EGoo EWTr GAbr LHop MBal MBro NRoo WHCG WHoo WPyg
'Yellow Queen' — See H. 'Golden Queen'

# HELIANTHUS ✿ (Asteraceae)
_angustifolius_ — Last listed 1998
_atrorubens_ — LFis MBel MBri MRav
'Capenoch Star' ♀ — EBee EFou EMan GBuc LFis MArl MBel MCAu MFir MLLN MRav NDov SDix SMad WByw WCot WLRN
¶ _cusickii_ — EBee
_decapetalus_ — CStr LFis NFla WCot WWye
* - 'Kastle Kobena' — Last listed 1997
- 'Maximus' — SRms
- 'Morning Sun' — CBlo CTri MLLN WCot
- 'Soleil d'Or' — CTri ECtt EHic WCot

| | |
|---|---|
| - 'Triomphe de Gand' | CBos GBri LGre MRav MTed MWat SAga SSvw WOld |
| *doronicoides* | CFee SRms |
| 'First Light' | Last listed 1997 |
| *giganteus* 'Sheila's Sunshine' | CElw CStr WCot WOld |
| 'Golden Pyramid' | Last listed 1997 |
| *grosseserratus* | Last listed 1998 |
| 'Gullick's Variety' | CBre CStr EBee EFou EPfP IBlr LFis LLWP NBro NSti WCot WOld |
| x *kellermanii* | CStr EMon LGre MTed SMad |
| § x *laetiflorus* | EBee ELan EMan EMon MTis NChi NOrc WCot |
| * - var. *rigidus* | EMon |
| * - 'Superbus' | IBlr |
| § 'Lemon Queen' | More than 30 suppliers |
| ♦ 'Limelight' | See *H.* 'Lemon Queen' |
| § 'Loddon Gold' ♀ | CBlo EBee EBrP EBre ECtt EFou ELan EMan EPfP IBlr LBre LFis MHlr MRav MTis NVic SBre SLon WCot WMow WWye |
| § *maximilianii* | ECGN MSte MTed |
| *mollis* | WCot |
| 'Monarch' ♀ | LFis MFir WCot WOld WOve |
| *nuttallii* | EMon LEdu MTed WCot |
| *occidentalis* | EMon IBlr WPer |
| *orgyalis* | See *H. salicifolius* |
| *quinquenervis* | See *Helianthella quinquenervis* |
| *rigidus* | See *H.* x *laetiflorus* |
| § *salicifolius* | CRDP CStr ECGN ECha EMon LFis LGre MBri MLLN MSte MWat NSti SDix SMad SSoC SSpe WCot WOld |
| *scaberrimus* | See *H.* x *laetiflorus* |
| ¶ - C&D 137 | WCot |
| *strumosus* | Ilve WCot |
| 'Summer Gold' | Last listed 1997 |
| *tuberosus* | GPoy NRog |
| ¶ - 'Dwarf Sunray' | Ilve |
| ¶ - 'Fuseau' | Ilve LEdu |

## HELICHRYSUM ✿ (Asteraceae)

| | |
|---|---|
| *acuminatum* | See *Bracteantha subundulata* |
| § *aggregatum* | Last listed 1996 |
| *alveolatum* | See *H. splendidum* |
| *ambiguum* | CHan EFou LHop MPla MRav NOak SIgm |
| *angustifolium* | See *H. italicum* |
| - Cretan form | See *H. italicum* subsp. *microphyllum* |
| *arenarium* | MWll SSmi |
| § *argyrophyllum* | Last listed 1997 |
| § *arwae* | EHyt EPot SBla WAbe |
| *asperum* | See *Ozothamnus purpurascens* |
| *basalticum* | NWCA WLin |
| *bellidioides* | ECha ECou GGar IMGH MBal NMen SMer SRms WCru WPer |
| *bellum* | NHol |
| *bracteatum* | See *Bracteantha bracteata* |
| *chionophilum* | NWCA |
| 'Coco' | See *Bracteantha* 'Coco' |
| *confertum* | Last listed 1998 |
| ¶ *cooperi* | CTrC |
| *coralloides* | See *Ozothamnus coralloides* |
| 'County Park Silver' | See *Ozothamnus* 'County Park Silver' |
| ¶ *dasyanthum* | CTrC |
| *depressum* | Last listed 1996 |
| *diosmifolium* | See *Ozothamnus diosmifolius* |
| ¶ *doerfleri* | NMen |
| 'Elmstead' | See *H. stoechas* 'White Barn' |
| *ericifolium* | See *Ozothamnus purpurascens* |
| *ericoides* | See *Dolichothrix ericoides* |

| | |
|---|---|
| *foetidum* | Last listed 1996 |
| *fontanesii* | LHil SPer WHer |
| *frigidum* | CPBP EPot GNor NNrd NWCA SBla WAbe |
| *glomeratum* | See *H. aggregatum* |
| *gmelinii* | CHan |
| *gunnii* | Last listed 1996 |
| *heldreichii* | EPot NHol SMrm |
| - NS 127 | NWCA |
| *hookeri* | See *Ozothamnus hookeri* |
| ¶ *hypoleucum* | WCot |
| § *italicum* ♀ | CArn CHan ECha ELau GCHN GPoy LGro LHol MBar MBri MMal MPla NChi NRoo NSti SPar SRCN SRms WCer WDin WEas WHCG WOak WOve WWat WWye |
| - 'Dartington' | CBod WJek WSel |
| § - subsp. *microphyllum* | CSam ELau ESis GBar MHer NPri NWoo SIde SIgm SSvw WEas WOak WSel WTro |
| - 'Nanum' | See *H. italicum* subsp. *microphyllum* |
| § - subsp. *serotinum* | CBrm CChe CTri EBee EGoo EPfP GChr GPoy MAsh MRav NFla SPer SPla SRms SSoC STre WAbe WPer WSel WWeb |
| *lanatum* | See *H. thianschanicum* |
| *ledifolium* | See *Ozothamnus ledifolius* |
| *lingulatum* JJ&JH 9401733 | NWCA |
| *lobbii* | Last listed 1998 |
| *marginatum* | See *H. milfordiae* |
| *microphyllum* hort. | See *Plecostachys serpyllifolia* |
| - Benth. & Hooker | See *Ozothamnus microphyllus* |
| - Cambess. | See *H. italicum* |
| § *milfordiae* ♀ | EPot MBal NHar NHol NMen NNrd NSla NWCA SBla SIng SRms WAbe WPat |
| 'Mo's Gold' | See *H. argyrophyllum* |
| *orientale* | CHan EPot NHol SGre SIng SMer |
| *pagophilum* | CLyd CPBP GCrs ITim |
| - JJ&JH 9401304 | NWCA |
| - JJH from Lesotho | Last listed 1998 |
| 'Pale Skynet' | GCal |
| § *petiolare* ♀ | EBak ECtt EWTr LPVe MRav SRms WEas |
| - 'Aureum' | See *H. petiolare* 'Limelight' |
| - 'Goring Silver' | CHal LHil MBEx NPri |
| § - 'Limelight' ♀ | CHal ECtt MBEx MRav SLod |
| - 'Roundabout' (v) | GPin LHil MBEx NPri |
| - 'Variegatum' ♀ | CHal ECtt MRav |
| *petiolatum* | See *H. petiolare* |
| *plicatum* | MBEx MBNS MWhi |
| *plumeum* | EHyt GNor ITim |
| *populifolium* | MBEx WHer |
| *praecurrens* | EHyt ITim NWCA |
| aff. *praecurrens* | Last listed 1997 |
| *purpurascens* | See *Ozothamnus purpurascens* |
| *rosmarinifolium* | See *Ozothamnus rosmarinifolius* |
| § 'Schwefellicht' | CSam EBee ECha EFou MBri MCLN MRav MWgw NFla NLon NRoo NSti SChu SMer SPer SRPl SWat WBea WEas WSHC WWal WWat |
| *scorpioides* | Last listed 1998 |
| *selaginoides* | See *Ozothamnus selaginoides* |
| *selago* | See *Ozothamnus selago* |
| *serotinum* | See *H. italicum* subsp. *serotinum* |
| *serpyllifolium* | See *Plecostachys serpyllifolia* |
| *sessile* | See *H. sessilioides* |
| § *sessilioides* | CLyd EPot ITim NHar NNrd NSla NTow NWCA SBla |
| § *sibthorpii* | CPBP CSev LBee LHil MDHE NMen NTow SIng SSmi WAbe |

| | |
|---|---|
| *siculum* | See *H. stoechas* subsp. *barrelieri* |
| 'Silver Bush' | Last listed 1998 |
| * 'Skynet' | GCal |
| sp. from Drakensburg Mountains, South Africa | GAbr NHol NWCA |
| sp. H&W 336 | Last listed 1998 |
| sp. JJ&JH 9401733 | NWCA |
| § *splendidum* ♀ | CFee CHan ECha EHoe GAbr GCHN LHil NBro NFor SDix SLon SPer SRms WBrE WCot WDin WHer WPer WWat |
| *stoechas* | CArn |
| § - subsp. *barrelieri* | CNic |
| § - 'White Barn' | CBel ECha LPio WEas |
| Sulphur Light | See *H.* 'Schwefellicht' |
| 'Sussex Silver' | NPro |
| § *thianschanicum* | EBee EMan ENot NWCA SRms |
| - Golden Baby | See *H. thianschanicum* 'Goldkind' |
| § - 'Goldkind' | EPfP GAbr LFis NBir NPri WMoo |
| *thyrsoideum* | See *Ozothamnus thyrsoideus* |
| *trilineatum* | See *H. splendidum* |
| aff. *trilineatum* JJ&JH 9401783 | NWCA |
| *tumidum* | See *Ozothamnus selago* var. *tumidus* |
| *virgineum* | See *H. sibthorpii* |
| *woodii* | See *H. arwae* |

## HELICHRYSUM x RAOULIA (Asteraceae)

| | |
|---|---|
| *H.* x *R.* 'Rivulet' | Last listed 1997 |
| *H.* x *R.* 'Silver Streams' | Last listed 1997 |

## HELICODICEROS (Araceae)

| | |
|---|---|
| *muscivorus* | CAvo |

## HELICONIA (Heliconiaceae)

| | |
|---|---|
| *bihai* | LChe WMul |
| § 'Bucky' | Last listed 1998 |
| 'Guyana Red' | See *H.* 'Bucky' |
| *mariae* | Last listed 1996 |
| *psittacorum* | LChe WMul |
| *rostrata* | LChe |
| - dwarf | WMul |
| *stricta* 'Dwarf Jamaican' | LChe WMul |

## HELICTOTRICHON (Poaceae)

| | |
|---|---|
| *filifolium* | Last listed 1997 |
| *pratense* | EHoe EMon EPPr |
| § *sempervirens* ♀ | More than 30 suppliers |
| - 'Berlin Oxblood' | Last listed 1998 |
| - var. *pendulum* | EMon MUlv SPer SPla WWat |
| * *splendens* | SSoC |

## HELIOPHILA (Brassicaceae)

| | |
|---|---|
| *carnosa* | Last listed 1998 |
| *longifolia* | Last listed 1997 |

## HELIOPSIS ✿ (Asteraceae)

| | |
|---|---|
| Golden Plume | See *H. helianthoides* var. *scabra* 'Goldgefieder' |
| *helianthoides* | CStr EMon EWTr |
| - 'Benzinggold' | EFou MRav SMrm |
| - 'Bressingham Doubloon' (d) | Last listed 1996 |
| - 'Hohlspiegel' | ECha EMan MBri WLRN |
| - 'Limelight' | See *Helianthus* 'Lemon Queen' |
| - var. *scabra* | CBlo EPfP EWTr |
| - - Golden Plume | See *H. helianthoides* var. *scabra* 'Goldgefieder' |
| § - - 'Goldgefieder' ♀ | EPfP MBel WBea WRus |
| - - 'Goldgrünherz' | LRHS MBri WCot |
| ¶ - - 'Goldspitze' | EBee |

| | |
|---|---|
| - - 'Incomparabilis' | Last listed 1998 |
| - - 'Light of Loddon' | MWat |
| - - New hybrids | NLar SSvw |
| § - - 'Sommersonne' | CHar CM&M EBee EBrP EBre ECGN ECtt EFou GMaP LBre LHop MRav NArg NFai NMir NPer NTow SBre SPer SRCN SRms WOld WPer WWin |
| - - Summer Sun | See *H. helianthoides* var. *scabra* 'Sommersonne' |
| - - 'Sunburst' | WPyg |
| - 'Sonnenglut' | LRHS MBri |
| - 'Spitzentänzerin' | LRHS MBri |
| ¶ 'Lorraine Sunshine' | LRHS NCat |
| *orientalis* | Last listed 1996 |

## HELIOTROPIUM (✿) (Boraginaceae)

| | |
|---|---|
| § *amplexicaule* | EBee SIgm SMrm SSad |
| *anchusifolium* | See *H. amplexicaule* |
| § *arborescens* | CArn EPfP SYvo |
| * - 'Album' | Last listed 1996 |
| 'Chatsworth' ♀ | CHad CPle CSev EHol EMan EREa LHil MBEx MSte SIde SMer SSad SSoC SUsu WEas WPen |
| 'Dame Alicia de Hales' | EREa LLew MBEx |
| 'Gatton Park' | EREa LHil MBEx MRav SMrm SSad |
| 'Lord Roberts' | EREa MBEx SYvo |
| 'Marine' | CSpe LIck SRCN |
| * 'Midnight' | Last listed 1997 |
| 'Mrs J.W. Lowther' | Last listed 1997 |
| 'Netherhall White' | EREa |
| 'P.K. Lowther' | EREa MBEx WEas |
| *peruvianum* | See *H. arborescens* |
| 'President Garfield' | LHil MBEx |
| 'Princess Marina' ♀ | CSev EREa LHil MBEx MHlr MSte NPri SSad WEas WWol |
| 'The Speaker' | MBEx |
| 'W.H. Lowther' | LChe SYvo |
| 'White Lady' | CHal CSev CSpe EHol EREa LHil MBEx SSad WSan WSpi |
| 'White Queen' | LHil LLew |

## HELIPTERUM (Asteraceae)

| | |
|---|---|
| *albicans* | See *Leucochrysum albicans* |
| *anthemoides* | See *Rhodanthe anthemoides* |

## HELLEBORUS ✿ (Ranunculaceae)

| | |
|---|---|
| § *argutifolius* ♀ | More than 30 suppliers |
| ¶ - from Italy | EHrv |
| ◆ - mottled-leaved | See *H. argutifolius* 'Pacific Frost' |
| § - 'Pacific Frost' (v) | CAvo CHar ECha EMon MAsh NRar WHal |
| - silver-leaved form | CRDP |
| - x *sternii* | Last listed 1996 |
| *atrorubens* hort. | See *H. orientalis* Lamarck subsp. *abchasicus* Early Purple Group |
| *atrorubens* Waldst. & Kit. | CLCN ECha WStI |
| - WM 9028 from Slovenia | Last listed 1997 |
| - WM 9101 from Slovenia | Last listed 1997 |
| - WM 9216 from Slovenia | MPhe WCru |
| - WM 9317 | MPhe |
| - WM 9319 from Slovenia | MPhe |
| - WM 9407 | WLin |
| - WM 9617 from Slovenia | MPhe |
| ¶ - WM 9805 from Croatia | MPhe |
| x *ballardiae* | EOrc LRHS MAsh NRar WAbe WFar |
| ¶ - Anne Watson's strain | NRar |
| *bocconei* subsp. *bocconei* | See *H. multifidus* subsp. *bocconei* |
| *colchicus* | See *H. orientalis* Lamarck subsp. *abchasicus* |
| *corsicus* | See *H. argutifolius* |

*croaticus*                          CBel CLCN MAsh
  - WM 9313                          MPhe
  - WM 9416                          MPhe
¶ - WM 9810 from Croatia            MPhe
*cyclophyllus*                       CFil EBee EPfP GBuc MAsh MPhe
                                     NHol SPer SSpi WFar WPGP
  - JCA 560.625                      CLCN SSpi
* - WM 9412                          Last listed 1998
*dumetorum*                          CBel CFil CLCN MAsh NHol WFar
                                     WPGP
  - WM 9209 from Hungary             MPhe
  - WM 9307 from Hungary             Last listed 1997
  - WM 9301 from Slovenia            MPhe
  - WM 13.1                          WLin
  - WM 13.3                          WLin
  - WM 9025 from Croatia             MPhe
  - WM 9413                          WCru
  - WM 9627 from Croatia             MPhe
§ x *ericsmithii*                    CRDP EHrv LRHS MAsh MBri
                                     NDov SBla WAbe WBay WFar
*foetidus* ♀                         More than 30 suppliers
  - Bowles' form                     CBro EWes
  - 'Chedglow'                       CNat LHop
* - 'Curio' (v)                      CNat
  - 'Geddington Mist'                MGed
  - 'Green Giant'                    CBel CSam MTho WCru
  - Italian form                     GBin MAsh NHol NTow WCot
                                     WRus
  - Kurt's Strain                    Last listed 1998
  - 'Melle'                          Last listed 1996
  - 'Miss Jekyll's Scented'          WLin
  - 'Ruth'                           CBel MAsh MPhe
  - 'Sopron'                         GBin MAsh MPhe WCru WFar
                                     WViv
  - Wester Flisk Group               More than 30 suppliers
  - 'Yorkley'                        Last listed 1996
*lividus* ♀                          CAvo CBot CBro CGle CHan
                                     CLCN CLon EBee EBrP EBre EHyt
                                     ELan EWes LBre MAsh MPhe
                                     NHar NHol NLar NPSI SBla SBre
                                     SIgm SWas SWat WAbe WCot
                                     WCru WFar
  - subsp. *corsicus*                See *H. argutifolius*
*multifidus*                         CLCN EBee EMar EPfP NBir NHol
                                     SPer WFar
§ - subsp. *bocconei*                NDov WFar WPGP
  - - WM 9713 from Italy             MPhe
  - - WM 9719 from Italy             MPhe
  - - WM 9720 from Italy             MPhe
  - subsp. *hercegovinus*            CBel SIgm WFar
  - - WM 9011/9105                   Last listed 1996
  - - WM 9105                        MPhe
  - subsp. *istriacus*               CBro MAsh WFar
  - - WM 9222                        Last listed 1997
  - - WM 9321/22/24                  Last listed 1996
  - - WM 9322                        MPhe
  - - WM 9324                        MPhe
  - - WM 9421                        WLin
  - subsp. *multifidus*              MAsh
  - - WM 9104                        MPhe
  - - WM 9529                        MPhe
  - - WM 9748 from Croatia           MPhe
¶ - - WM 9833 from Croatia           MPhe
  - WM 9225                          WCru
*niger* ♀                            More than 30 suppliers
  - Ashwood strain                   MAsh
  - Blackthorn Group                 EHrv NCut SBla
I - 'Crûg Hybrid'                    WCru
  - Farmyard strain                  WFar
  - from Austria                     WByw
  - Harvington hybrids               COtt EHrv LRHS MAsh
  - 'Louis Cobbett'                  EHyt

§ - subsp. *macranthus*              Last listed 1997
  - - WM 9030                        WCru
  - 'Madame Fourcade'                MBri
  - *major*                          See *H. niger* subsp. *macranthus*
  - pink strain                      NRar
  - 'Potter's Wheel'                 CPMA CRDP EBee EBrP EBre
                                     ECot GBuc LBre NPSI SBla SBre
                                     SRms SSpi SVil WCru WPyg
  - 'Saint Bridgid'                  NRar
  - Sunrise Group WM 9519            CLCN MPhe
  - Sunset Group WM 9113             GBuc MPhe SPla
  - 'White Magic'                    CB&S CBlo CPMA LRHS NDov
                                     SSON WCru WWeb
x *nigercors* ♀                      CHan CRDP EBrP EBre LHop
                                     LPio MBri SBre WAbe WBay WCru
  - 'Alabaster'                      NBir
x *nigristern*                       See *H.* x *ericsmithii*
*odorus*                             CBel CFil CLCN EBee EHrv NRoo
                                     SBla WCot WFar
¶ - WM 9088 from Hungary            MPhe
  - WM 9103                          Last listed 1998
  - WM 9202                          MPhe WCru
  - WM 9310                          GBuc
  - WM 9415                          MPhe
  - WM 9728 from Hungary             MPhe
N *orientalis* hort.                 More than 30 suppliers
  - 'Agnes Brook'                    WFib
  - 'Albin Otto'                     Last listed 1997
  - Anderson's Red hybrids           CLCN NHol
  - 'Angela Tandy'                   WFib
  - 'Apricot'                        LCTD WFar
  - Aquarius                         CLCN
  - 'Ariel'                          LCTD
  - Ashwood Garden hybrids           EHrv GNau MAsh MRav MUlv
                                     WBod WSpi
  - Ashwood Garden hybrids,          MAsh
    anemone-centred
  - Ashwood Garden hybrids,          MAsh
    double
  - 'Baby Black'                     ECot
  - Ballard's Group                  EBee EBrP EBre ECha LBlm LBre
                                     MBri NRar SBre SMad WCot WCru
                                     WFar
  - black                            CBel CGle CLCN CRDP GDra
                                     NRar WCru
¶ - blue-grey                        NPar
¶ - 'Blue Wisp'                      LCTD
  - 'Button'                         LCTD
  - 'Carlton Hall'                   WFib
  - 'Chartreuse'                     Last listed 1997
  - 'Cheerful'                       LCTD NBir WCru
  - 'Citron'                         LCTD
¶ - 'Compact Cream'                  NRar
  - cream                            EBee MCCP NHol NPSI WFar
  - 'Cygnus'                         ECha
  - 'Dawn'                           LCTD
  - deep red                         ERav WFar
  - 'Dick Crandon'                   Last listed 1998
  - Draco strain                     CLCN
  - 'Dusk'                           LCTD WCru
  - 'Elizabeth Coburn'               WFib
  - 'Eric's Best'                    ECha
  - 'Fred Whitsey'                   WFib
¶ - Galaxy Group                     NPar
¶ - 'Garnet'                         LCTD WFar
  - 'Gertrude Raithby'               WFib
  - 'Gladys Burrow'                  WFib
¶ - green                            WCru
  - green, spotted                   CBel CRDP EBee EBrP EBre LBre
                                     SBre WFar
  - 'Greencups'                      LCTD

| | |
|---|---|
| - subsp.***guttatus*** hort. | CAvo CLCN EBee EBrP EBre LBlm LBre MCCP NHol SApp SBla SBre SMad WCot WCru |
| - - cream | ECha |
| - - light purple | Last listed 1997 |
| - - pink | NHol WCru |
| - 'Hades' seedling | NHol WCru |
| - Hadspen hybrids | CHad |
| - 'Harvington Pink' | LRHS |
| - 'Harvington Red' | LRHS MHlr |
| - 'Harvington Speckled' | LRHS MHlr |
| - 'Harvington White' | LRHS |
| - 'Harvington Yellow' | LRHS MHlr |
| - 'Helen Ballard' | LCTD |
| - 'Ian Raithby' | WFib |
| - 'Ingot' | LCTD |
| - ivory | CLCN CRDP WFar |
| - ivory, spotted | Last listed 1996 |
| - 'Joan Bridges' | LCTD |
| - 'John Raithby' | WFib |
| ¶ - Kaye's garden hybrids | EMar |
| - Kochii Group | CAvo ECha NBrk NRar WCru |
| - 'Lady Charlotte Bonham-Carter' | WFib |
| ¶ - large-flowered pink | NPar |
| - 'Leo' | MTed |
| - 'Limelight' | ECha |
| - 'Little Black' | ECho EWes |
| ¶ - 'Lynne' | LCTD |
| - maroon | CRDP EBrP EBre ERav LBre NRar SBre WCru WFar |
| - 'Mary Petit' | WFib |
| - 'Maureen Key' | WFib |
| - Midnight Sky Group | WPyg WWat |
| ¶ - mixed | MPEx |
| ¶ - 'Mystery' | WCru |
| - nearly black | ERav |
| - 'Orion' | LCTD |
| ¶ - 'Parrot' | CPMA |
| ¶ - 'Patchwork' | LCTD |
| - 'Pebworth White' | WFib |
| ¶ - 'Petsamo' | NRar |
| - 'Philip Ballard' | EBee LCTD |
| - 'Philip Wilson' | LCTD |
| - 'Picotee' | CRDP MHlr WCru WFar WHoo |
| - pink | CBel CLCN CPMA CRDP EBee ERav LFis MBro MCCP NRar WAbe WCru WFar |
| - pink, spotted | CBel CRDP EBee EBrP EBre LBre NCut NDov NRar SBre WCru WFar |
| - plum | WFar |
| - 'Plum Stippled' | ECha |
| ¶ - 'Pluto' | LCTD |
| - primrose | CBel CRDP EBee EBrP EBre LBre NCut NHed NHol NRar SBre WAbe WCot WCru WFar |
| - primrose, spotted | WFar |
| - purple | CBel CLCN CPMA CRDP ECha MBro NCut NHol NPSl NRar SApp SIng SMad WAbe WCru WFar |
| * - 'Purpurescens' | MCCP |
| - 'Queen of the Night' | CRDP |
| - 'Red Mountain' | Last listed 1997 |
| - 'Rosa' | LCTD |
| - 'Rubens' | LCTD |
| - 'Shades of Night' | LRHS MHlr |
| ¶ - slaty blue | CRDP EBrP EBre LBre NDov NRar SBre WFar |
| ¶ - slaty purple | NRar |
| - smokey purple | EBee SMad WFar |

| | |
|---|---|
| - 'Sunny' | LCTD |
| - 'Sylvia' | LCTD |
| - 'Tommie' | LCTD |
| - 'Trotter's Spotted' | Last listed 1998 |
| - 'Ushba' | EBee LCTD MFir |
| - 'Ushba' seedlings | GCal WCot |
| - 'Victoria Raithby' | WFib |
| - white | CGle CRDP EBrP EBre ECha ERav LBre MBal MBro NRar SBre SIng WCru WFar |
| - white, spotted | CBel CRDP EBrP EBre LBre NCut NDov NRar SBre WAbe WCot WCru WFar |
| - white veined | WFar |
| - yellow | ERav WCru WFar |
| - Zodiac Group | CLCN EOrc GBuc |
| ***orientalis*** Lamarck | MBro MPhe |
| § - subsp. ***abcbasicus*** | SRms WCru WWat |
| § - - Early Purple Group | CBel CLCN CTri LPio MAsh NBee NFla NRoo WCru WFar |
| - subsp. ***guttatus*** | EWTr SSpi |
| - IBT 9401-7 | WLin |
| - JCA 562.402 | CLCN |
| - ***olympicus*** | See *H. orientalis* Lamarck subsp. *orientalis* |
| § - subsp. ***orientalis*** | NHol WPyg |
| ***purpurascens*** | CAvo CBel CLCN EBee EOld GMaP MAsh MBNS MCAu MRav NBir NHol NRoo SBla SCob SIgm SPer SWas WAbe WFar WPyg |
| - WM 9208 from Hungary | Last listed 1997 |
| - WM 9211 from Hungary | MPhe |
| - WM 18/1 | WLin |
| - WM 18/3 | WLin |
| - WM 9303 | MPhe |
| - WM 9412 | MPhe WCru |
| - WM 9644 | GBuc |
| x ***sternii*** | More than 30 suppliers |
| - Ashfield strain | Last listed 1996 |
| - Ashwood strain | MAsh |
| - Blackthorn Group ♀ | CBel CFil CPMA CRos EBrP EBre EHrv GBuc LBre MBri MBro MRav NHol NSti SBla SBre SMad SPla SSpi WAbe WByw WCot WCru WHoo WPGP WWat |
| - Blackthorn dwarf strain | CLCN |
| - Boughton Group | MAsh |
| - 'Boughton Beauty' | CAvo CMGP CMea EBee ECha EHrv ELan GBuc MTho NHol WByw WCot |
| - Bulmer's blush strain | EBee EMan MAsh |
| - Cally strain | GCal MTed |
| - dwarf strain | WAbe WFar |
| - pewter strain | WHal |
| ***thibetanus*** | CLCN EFEx GBuc LAma MAsh MPhe SSpi WCru WViv |
| ***torquatus*** | CAvo CBel CBro CFil CLCN EHrv MPhe MTho NHol WFar WMer WTin |
| - 'Dido' (d) | WFar |
| - double-flowered hybrids (d) | CBos WFar |
| - hybrids | ECGP SBla WCom WCru WFar |
| - Montenegran Doubles (d) | WFar |
| - Party Dress Group (d) | CCHP CRDP EHrv NRar SBla WFar |
| - semi-double (d) | CRDP WFar |
| - WM 9003 from Bosnia | Last listed 1997 |
| - WM 9106 from Montenegro | GBuc MPhe WCru |
| - WM 9111 from Bosnia | Last listed 1997 |
| - WM 9743 from Bosnia | MPhe |
| - WM 9745 from Bosnia | MPhe |
| ¶ - WM 9820 from Bosnia | MPhe |

| | |
|---|---|
| - Wolverton hybrids | SBla WFar |
| *vesicarius* | MPhe |
| *viridis* | EBee EBrP EBre ECha EPfP LBre |
| | MSal NSti SBre SRms WCot WCru |
| | WFar WTin |
| - from Germany | Last listed 1997 |
| - from Spain | Last listed 1996 |
| - subsp. *occidentalis* | CAvo CBel CBro GCal |
| - - WM 9401 | MPhe |
| - - WM 9502 from Germany | MPhe |
| - subsp. *viridis* | MAsh |
| - - WM 9723 from Italy | MPhe |

## HELONIOPSIS (Melanthiaceae)

| | |
|---|---|
| *acutifolia* B&SWJ 218 | WCru |
| *japonica* | See *H. orientalis* |
| § *orientalis* | CBro CPou EHyt EPot SIng WCru |
| * - var. *albiflora* | WCru |
| - B&SWJ 956 from Korea | WCru |
| § - var. *breviscapa* | CFil WCru WPGP WThi |
| § - var. *kawanoi* | WCru |
| - var. *yakusimensis* | See *H. orientalis* var. *kawanoi* |
| *umbellata* B&SWJ 1839 | WCru |

## HELWINGIA (Helwingiaceae)

| | |
|---|---|
| *chinensis* | CPle |
| *japonica* | CBot CPle EFEx WWat |

## HELXINE See SOLEIROLIA

## HEMEROCALLIS ✿ (Hemerocallidaceae)

| | |
|---|---|
| 'Absolute Zero' | SApp SDay |
| 'Adah' | SDay |
| 'Addie Branch Smith' | EGol SDay |
| 'Admiral' | Last listed 1996 |
| 'Adoration' | SPer |
| 'Aglow' | MTed NCut |
| 'Alan' | EBrP EBre ENot LBre SBre SCro |
| | WFar |
| 'Albany' | SApp |
| 'Alec Allen' | SDay SRos |
| 'Alpine Mist' | SDay |
| *altissima* | EMon |
| ¶ 'Always Afternoon' | SApp |
| 'Amadeus' | Last listed 1997 |
| 'Amazon' | LRHS |
| 'Amazon Amethyst' | Last listed 1998 |
| 'Ambassador' | Last listed 1998 |
| 'Amber Star' | LPBA |
| 'Amen' | WGle |
| 'American Revolution' | CPar EWll SApp SRos WCot WRus |
| 'Amersham' | EBee EBla GSki SMrm WLRN |
| 'Angel Curls' | EGol |
| 'Angel Flight' | Last listed 1996 |
| 'Angel's Delight' | WGle |
| ¶ 'Ann Kelley' | SDay |
| ¶ 'Anna Warner' | SPer |
| 'Anne Welch' | ECle EPla MMil |
| 'Annie Go Lightly' | Last listed 1998 |
| 'Anzac' | EBrP EBre ECha ECtt EPla ERou |
| | GAri LBre MBri NHol NMGW |
| | NWes SBre WFar WMow |
| ¶ 'Apple Court Champagne' | SApp |
| 'Apple Court Damson' | Last listed 1996 |
| ¶ 'Apple Tart' | SDay |
| ¶ 'Apricot Angel' | SApp |
| 'Apricot Beauty' | CBlo EBee LBuc NPri |
| 'Apricot Surprise' | WGle |
| 'Apricotta' | WBro WCot WPnP |
| 'Arctic Snow' | SDay SRos |
| 'Arriba' | NBro WLRN |
| 'Arthur Moore' | SDay |

| | |
|---|---|
| 'Artistic Gold' | EGol |
| 'Artist's Brush' | LBuc |
| 'Atlanta Bouquet' | SRos |
| 'Aten' | CBlo |
| ¶ 'Atlanta Full House' | SDay |
| 'Attention Please' | WGle |
| 'Aurora Raspberry' | WGle |
| 'Autumn Red' | CBlo ERou NBir NCat NFai NHaw |
| | NOak NWes WPnP |
| 'Ava Michelle' | SDay |
| 'Aztec Furnace' | Last listed 1997 |
| 'Baby Betsy' | SDay |
| 'Baby Darling' | SDay |
| 'Baby Julia' | MTed WGle |
| ¶ 'Baby Talk' | CFir NWes |
| * 'Bailey Hay' | COlW EFou LRHS MBNS |
| 'Bald Eagle' | EFou MSCN NWes WCot WMer |
| 'Ballerina Girl' | SRos |
| 'Ballet Dancer' | ERou |
| ¶ 'Bangkok Belle' | SDay |
| 'Barbara Corsair' | Last listed 1996 |
| ¶ 'Barbara Mitchell' | SApp |
| 'Baroni' | ECha |
| 'Battle Hymn' | Last listed 1996 |
| 'Beauty Bright' | MCAu |
| 'Beauty to Behold' | SApp SDay SRos |
| 'Bed of Roses' | Last listed 1998 |
| 'Bedarra Island' | Last listed 1997 |
| 'Beijing' | SDay |
| 'Bejewelled' | CBlo EBee EFou EGol NMoo |
| 'Beloved Country' | EHal |
| ¶ 'Beloved Returns' ♀ | MCAu |
| 'Benchmark' | SRos |
| 'Berlin Lemon' ♀ | Last listed 1995 |
| 'Berlin Red' ♀ | ECGN EMar EPla LBuc LRHS MMil |
| | MTed SChu |
| 'Berlin Red Velvet' ♀ | Last listed 1995 |
| 'Berliner Premiere' | Last listed 1998 |
| 'Bernard Thompson' | SApp |
| 'Bertie Ferris' | LBuc |
| 'Bess Ross' | CMHG MCAu |
| 'Bess Vestale' | ENot ERou MWat NHol |
| 'Bette Davis Eyes' | SRos |
| 'Betty Woods' (d) | CRDP SRos |
| 'Bibury' | SCro |
| ¶ 'Big Bird' | SApp |
| 'Big World' | LRHS |
| 'Bitsy' | EGol MSte WRHF |
| ¶ 'Black Falcon' | CMdw |
| 'Black Knight' | SRms |
| 'Black Magic' | CBlo CBro CHad CMGP CSev |
| | EGol ELan EMan EPla ERou GMaP |
| | MBro MRav NGdn NHol NWes |
| | SChu SPer WElm WHer WMoo |
| 'Black Prince' | EWll SPer WViv |
| 'Blonde Is Beautiful' | SRos |
| 'Blue Sheen' | CFir EAst EBee EFou MSCN NWes |
| | WMoo WWeb |
| 'Blushing Angel' | Last listed 1997 |
| 'Blushing Belle' | CMil EBee EMar LRHS WWin |
| 'Bold Courtier' | Last listed 1998 |
| 'Bold One' | SRos |
| 'Bonanza' | More than 30 suppliers |
| 'Booger' | SRos |
| 'Border Honey' | WGle |
| 'Bourbon Kings' | EBee EGar EGol ERou MBel SDay |
| 'Bowl of Roses' | WGle |
| ¶ 'Brand New Lover' | SApp |
| § 'Brass Buckles' | Last listed 1996 |
| 'Bright Spangles' | SApp SRos |
| 'Brilliant Circle' | EFou SApp |
| 'Brocaded Gown' | SRos |

'Brunette'    SApp
'Bruno Müller'    Last listed 1997
'Bubbly'    Last listed 1998
'Buffy's Doll'    SDay SRos
'Bugs Ears'    Last listed 1998
'Bumble Bee'    WTin
'Buried Treasure'    LRHS
'Burlesque'    Last listed 1997
'Burning Daylight' ♀    CMGP CMil EBee EBrP EBre EGar
    EMar EPla ERou GSki LBre LHop
    MBel MNrw NHol NVic SBre
    SCob SMrm SPer SRms WOld
    WViv
'Buttercurls'    Last listed 1998
'Butterfly Ballet'    SDay
'Butterfly Charm'    Last listed 1997
¶ 'Butterscotch Ruffles'    SDay
'Button Box'    Last listed 1996
'Buttons'    Last listed 1997
'Buzz Bomb'    CRDP EBrP EBre GSki LBre NRoo
    NWes SBre SPer SRos WLRN
    WWal
'California Sunshine'    SRos
'Camden Ballerina'    Last listed 1996
'Camden Gold Dollar'    SDay
¶ 'Canadian Goose'    EFou NWes
'Canary Glow'    CTri EBrP EBre ERav LBre NWes
    SAsh SBre SRos SSpe WWat
¶ 'Candide'    SApp
¶ 'Cantique'    SApp
'Captured Heart'    Last listed 1996
'Caramea'    EAst NFai WFar WWal
'Carolpiecrust'    SApp
'Cartwheels' ♀    EBee EBrP EBre ECha EGra EPfP
    EPla LBre MBel MCAu MCli MMil
    NFai SBre SPer
'Casino Gold'    SRos
'Catherine Wheel'    Last listed 1996
'Catherine Woodbery'    CHea COtt CSev EAst EBee EBrP
    EBre ECtt EFou EGol ELan EMar
    EOrc EPla ERav LBre MCAu MRav
    NFla NHol NRoo NSti SAga SApp
    SBre SPer SSpe WCot WFar WPyg
'Cedar Waxwing'    CBlo EBee EGol NWes SCro WMer
'Chantilly Lace'    CMHG
'Charles Johnston'    SDay SRos
'Charlie Brown'    SDay
'Charlie Pierce Memorial'    MBel SRos
'Chartreuse Magic'    EGol SChu SPer
'Cherry Cheeks'    EBrP EBre EGol ELan EPfP EPla
    ERav ERou LBre MBNS MBri
    MCAu MRav SBre SRos SVil WCot
    WFar WMow
'Cherry Kiss'    SRos
¶ 'Cherry Smoke'    SApp
¶ 'Chestnut Lane'    SApp
'Chic Bonnet'    SPer
'Chicago Apache'    COtt LRHS MBNS MBel MUlv
    SDay SRos SVil
'Chicago Arnie's Choice'    WGle
¶ 'Chicago Blackout'    CFir COtt EBee EFou EGol NCut
'Chicago Cattleya'    CFir EGol MRav NWes
¶ 'Chicago Cherry'    NCut
'Chicago Coral'    WGle
'Chicago Fire'    EGol
'Chicago Heirloom'    COtt EGol
'Chicago Jewel'    CFir EBee NWes SCro
'Chicago Knobby'    WGle
¶ 'Chicago Knockout'    COtt EGol NCut
¶ 'Chicago Peach'    NCut
'Chicago Petite Lace'    WGle
'Chicago Petticoats'    EGol NCut SDay WGle

¶ 'Chicago Picotee Lace'    SApp
'Chicago Picotee Memories'    WGle
'Chicago Picotee Pride'    SDay WGle
'Chicago Picotee Queen'    EBrP EBre LBre LRHS MUlv SBre
    WGle
'Chicago Plum Pudding'    WGle
'Chicago Princess'    EGol NCut WGle
¶ 'Chicago Queen'    SDay
¶ 'Chicago Rosy'    NCut
'Chicago Royal'    SDay
'Chicago Royal Crown'    MBri
'Chicago Royal Robe'    EBrP EBre EFou EGol LBre LLWP
    MBNS MBel MRav MSte MUlv
    SBre SCro WCot WWhi WWin
'Chicago Silver'    CFir COtt MCAu
¶ 'Chicago Sugar Plum'    SDay
'Chicago Sunrise'    CHad EGol ENot EPla GMaP IBlr
    MBNS MBri MSta NHaw NHol
    NOrc NWes SApp SRos SVil WMer
    WPer
'Chicago Violet'    MCAu
'Chief Sarcoxie' ♀    Last listed 1998
'Children's Festival'    CHad CMGP CSev EBee EBrP
    EBre ECtt EFou EGol EMar EMil
    GMaP GSki LBre MBNS MBel
    MGed MRav NHol NRoo SBre
    SCro SLon SRos SSpe WFar WMoo
    WPer WRus WWat
'Childscraft'    CLTr
'Chinese Autumn'    SRos
'Chinese Coral'    CKel WBcn
'Chinese Imp'    Last listed 1997
'Chloe's Child'    SCro
¶ 'Chocolate Dude'    SApp
'Choral Angel'    WGle
'Chorus Line'    MBel SDay SRos
'Chosen Love'    SApp
'Christmas Candles'    Last listed 1997
'Christmas Is'    EFou MBNS
¶ 'Ciao'    SApp
'Cinnamon Glow'    WGle
*citrina*    CAvo ELan EMon NPla SEas
'Civil Rights'    SRos
'Classic Simplicity'    LRHS MCAu
'Classy Lassie'    MTed WGle
'Colonial Dame'    CKel
'Colour Me Mellow'    Last listed 1998
¶ 'Comanche Eyes'    SDay
'Coming up Roses'    SRos
'Conspicua'    Last listed 1997
'Contessa'    CBro EHon SCro
'Cookie Monster'    Last listed 1998
'Cool Jazz'    SRos
'Coral Mist'    EFou
'Coreana Yellow'    Last listed 1997
'Corky' ♀    CHad EBee EBrP EBre ECGP ECha
    EMar EPla GCal GMaP LBre MBel
    MCAu MNrw SApp SBre SChu
    SDix SPer SRos SSpi WMow WWat
¶ 'Corryton Pink'    SApp
¶ 'Corsican Bandit'    CM&M
'Cosmic Hummingbird'    SDay
'Countess Zora'    CMHG
'Country Club'    CBlo EAst EBee EFou NWes
    WWeb
'Court Magician'    SRos
'Cranberry Baby'    SRos
'Cream Cloud'    WGle
'Cream Drop'    CMGP EBee EBrP EBre ECtt EGol
    EMar GMaP LBlm LBre MBel
    MRPP MRav MWat NHol NOrc
    NPla NRoo NSti NWes SBre SChu
    SPer SSpe WCot WMer WMoo
    WRus

| | |
|---|---|
| 'Crimson Icon' | MSte SDay |
| 'Crimson Pirate' | EMil ERou LRot NHol SPlb SRob WPnP WRHF |
| 'Croesus' | NHol SCro SRms |
| 'Croftway' | SCro |
| 'Cupid's Bow' | EGol |
| 'Cupid's Gold' | SDay SRos |
| ¶ 'Custard Candy' | SRos |
| 'Cynthia Mary' | Last listed 1997 |
| 'Dad's Best White' | EGol SCro |
| 'Daily Bread' | Last listed 1998 |
| 'Daily Dollar' | LRHS MBri |
| 'Dainty Dreamer' | Last listed 1996 |
| 'Dainty Pink' | EGol |
| ¶ 'Dallas Star' | SApp |
| 'Dance Ballerina Dance' | SDay SRos |
| 'Dancing Dwarf' | Last listed 1998 |
| 'Dark Elf' | Last listed 1996 |
| 'Dawn Play' | CKel |
| 'Decatur Imp' | EGol |
| 'Decatur Piecrust' | MBel |
| 'Delightsome' | Last listed 1996 |
| 'Demetrius' | Last listed 1998 |
| 'Designer Gown' | Last listed 1998 |
| 'Devon Cream' | SChu |
| 'Devonshire' | SRos |
| 'Diamond Dust' | EBee EPla LRHS MTed NCat SChu SPer WLRN |
| 'Dido' | CTri ERou GBuc MSte |
| 'Display' | CKel |
| ¶ 'Divertissment' | SApp |
| 'Dominic' | SRos |
| 'Dorethe Louise' | CRDP SDay SRos |
| 'Dorothy McDade' | COlW EGol |
| 'Double Coffee' (d) | Last listed 1998 |
| 'Double Cutie' (d) | EFou |
| ¶ 'Double Daffodil' (d) | MCAu |
| ¶ 'Double Delicious' (d) | WCot |
| 'Double Firecracker' (d) | CB&S MBNS NLar |
| 'Double Gardenia' (d) | WGle |
| 'Double Honey' (d) | WGle |
| 'Double Oh' (d) | MTed WGle |
| 'Double Oh Seven' (d) | SDay |
| 'Double Pleasure' (d) | MBel |
| 'Double Pompom' (d) | MCAu WGle |
| 'Double River Wye' (d) | CBlo CFir EBee EGol LBuc MTed NPla WCot WWat |
| ¶ 'Dragon's Eye' | SDay |
| 'Dresden Doll' | SPer |
| § 'Dubloon' | CKel CMGP ERou GAbr GBuc NHol |
| dumortieri | CAvo CBot CBro CHea CMHG EBee EBrP EBre ECGN ECha EFou EGol ELan EMar EOrc LBre MNrw MRav MWat NBir NHaw NHol NSti NVic SBre SPer SSpe WPnP WWin |
| 'Dutch Beauty' | Last listed 1998 |
| 'Dutch Gold' | MNrw NBro |
| 'Ed Murray' | MCAu SRos |
| 'Edelweiss' | SDay |
| 'Edna Spalding' | SDay SRos |
| 'Eenie Allegro' | CBro NWes SPer SPla |
| 'Eenie Fanfare' | COtt CSpe EFou LRHS NWes |
| 'Eenie Gold' | LRHS |
| 'Eenie Weenie' | CBro CFee CKel EBla ECtt EGol EMil ERos MBel MBri NBur NHol SApp SChu SRms WMer WPer |
| 'Eenie Weenie Non-stop' | ECha SLod |
| 'Elaine Strutt' | SApp WCot |
| 'Elegant Greeting' | EBee LBuc NOak |
| 'Elizabeth Ann Hudson' | Last listed 1997 |

| | |
|---|---|
| ¶ 'Elizabeth Salter' | SRos |
| 'Emerald Dew' | SDay |
| 'Enchanting Blessing' | Last listed 1996 |
| ¶ 'English Toffee' | SApp |
| ¶ 'Entransette' | SDay |
| 'Erica Nichole Gonzales' | Last listed 1997 |
| ¶ 'Erin Prairie' | SApp |
| 'Esther Walker' | WBcn |
| 'Evelyn Claar' | SCro |
| 'Evening Gown' | WGle |
| 'Fairy Charm' | WGle |
| 'Fairy Delight' | Last listed 1996 |
| 'Fairy Frosting' | Last listed 1997 |
| 'Fairy Jester' | Last listed 1996 |
| 'Fairy Tale Pink' | MBel SRos |
| 'Faith Nabor' | SRos |
| 'Fan Dancer' | EGol |
| 'Fandango' | SPer |
| 'Fashion Model' | SApp WPer |
| 'Feather Down' | Last listed 1997 |
| 'Feelings' | Last listed 1996 |
| 'Felicity' | CKel |
| 'Femme Osage' | SRos |
| 'Fire Dance' | SCro |
| 'Fire Music' | Last listed 1996 |
| 'First Formal' | SPer |
| ¶ 'Flamboyant Show' | LBuc |
| 'Flames of Fantasy' | MTed NCut SRos |
| 'Flaming Sword' | CMGP GBuc NHol |
| *flava* | See *H. lilioasphodelus* |
| 'Florissant Charm' | WGle |
| 'Floyd Cove' | SDay |
| *forrestii* | Last listed 1996 |
| - 'Perry's Variety' | EMon |
| 'Fragrant Pastel Cheer' | WGle |
| 'Frances Fay' | SRos |
| 'Francis Russell' | CKel |
| 'Frans Hals' | EBrP EBre ECGN EFou EMar EPla ERou LBre LLWP LSpr MBri MBro MNrw MRav NFai SBre SEND SPer SPla SRos WHoo WMow WPer WPyg |
| 'French Porcelain' | Last listed 1996 |
| 'Frosted Encore' | Last listed 1998 |
| 'Full Reward' | Last listed 1996 |
| *fulva* | CRow IBlr MHar NLon SRms WWin |
| N - 'Flore Pleno' (d) | CAvo CFee CHan CKel CMHG CRow ECGN EFou EGol EHon ELan EPla IBlr LFis LHop MCAu MFir MRav NBro NFai SPer SRms SWat WEas WMoo WWin |
| N - 'Green Kwanso' (d) | CHar CRow CSWP IBlr MAvo MMHG NTow SMad SPla WCot WFar WRha |
| § - 'Kwanzo Variegata' | CBot CGle CRow CStr EBee ELan IBlr LHop MRav MTed MTho SCob WBcn WCot WFar |
| ¶ - var. *littorea* | SSpi |
| 'Gala Gown' | Last listed 1998 |
| 'Garnet Garland' | CKel |
| 'Gay Nineties' | Last listed 1998 |
| 'Gay Rapture' | SPer |
| 'Gay Troubadour' | Last listed 1998 |
| 'Gemini' | SRos |
| 'Gentle Country Breeze' | SRos |
| 'Gentle Shepherd' | CBro CKel CSpe EAst EBrP EBre EGol EMar EMil LBre LFis LGre MBNS MBri MBro MCAu MRav MUlv NCut NHaw NSti NWes SApp SBre SRos WMoo WRus WWat |

| | | |
|---|---|---|
| 'George Cunningham' | CMGP CSev ECtt EGol ELan EPla ERou MBri MCli MRav NBir SChu SRos SUsu | |
| 'Georgette Belden' | WGle | |
| 'Giant Moon' | CBre CMHG EBrP EBre EGol ELan EPla EPri ERou LBre MBri MUlv SBre SChu SDay WRus | |
| 'Giddy Go Round' | Last listed 1997 | |
| 'Gingerbread Man' | CRDP | |
| 'Gold Crest' | LRHS | |
| 'Gold Imperial' | EWll NFla | |
| 'Golden Bell' | EGar LNor NGdn NHol | |
| 'Golden Chimes' ♀ | More than 30 suppliers | |
| 'Golden Gate' | Last listed 1997 | |
| 'Golden Ginko' | LRHS MBri | |
| 'Golden Orchid' | See H. 'Dubloon' | |
| 'Golden Peace' | SRos | |
| 'Golden Prize' | EBrP EBre EFou EPla LBre NGdn SBre SDay SRos | |
| 'Golden Scroll' | SRos | |
| ¶ 'Graceful Eye' | SApp | |
| 'Grand Palais' | Last listed 1998 | |
| 'Grape Magic' | EGol | |
| 'Grape Velvet' | CBlo CSpe MCAu MSCN NWes SAga WMer | |
| 'Green Chartreuse' | ECha | |
| 'Green Drop' | WFar WMow | |
| 'Green Eyed Giant' | Last listed 1998 | |
| 'Green Flutter' ♀ | CSev EBee EBla EMar LGre MCLN NBir NGdn NRoo SAsh SRos SVil WCot | |
| 'Green Glitter' | LRHS | |
| 'Green Gold' | CMHG LRHS | |
| 'Green Magic' | Last listed 1996 | |
| 'Grumbly' | EBee ELan | |
| 'Guardian Angel' | WGle WTin | |
| 'Halo Light' | Last listed 1998 | |
| 'Happy Returns' | CB&S CMGP COtt ECha EGol MBNS MBri SRos | |
| ¶ 'Harbor Blue' | SApp | |
| 'Harvest Hue' | Last listed 1998 | |
| 'Hawaian Punch' | EGol | |
| 'Hazel Monette' | EGol WGle | |
| 'Heartthrob' | Last listed 1996 | |
| 'Heather Green' | Last listed 1997 | |
| 'Heavenly Treasure' | SApp SRos WGle | |
| 'Heaven's Trophy' | WGle | |
| 'Heirloom Lace' | MUlv WFar | |
| 'Helios' | Last listed 1997 | |
| 'Helle Berlinerin' ♀ | Last listed 1995 | |
| 'Hemlock' | Last listed 1998 | |
| 'Her Majesty' | Last listed 1998 | |
| 'Hercules' | NFla | |
| 'Hermitage Newton' | Last listed 1998 | |
| 'Heron' | WGle | |
| 'Hey There' | SRos | |
| ¶ 'High Energy' | SApp | |
| 'High Tor' | GCal GQui | |
| 'Holiday Mood' | ELan ERou NOla NWes | |
| 'Honey Redhead' | CKel | |
| 'Hope Diamond' | CRDP | |
| 'Hornby Castle' | CBro NHol NVic WPer | |
| 'Hortensia' | CBlo | |
| 'Hot Ticket' | SRos | |
| 'Humdinger' | SRos | |
| 'Hyperion' | CSev EBrP EBre ECGP ECha ECtt EGol EMan GAri LBre MCAu MRav NGdn NHol NRoo SApp SBre SChu SPer SUsu WOld | |
| 'Ice Cap' | MCli WPnP | |
| 'Ice Carnival' | EPfP LRHS MBNS | |
| 'Ice Castles' | Last listed 1998 | |

| | | |
|---|---|---|
| 'Ice Cool' | Last listed 1996 | |
| 'Icy Lemon' | SRos | |
| 'Imperator' | EPla LPBA NHol WViv | |
| 'Imperial Blush' | Last listed 1998 | |
| ¶ 'Indian Paintbrush' | MBri | |
| ¶ 'Inner View' | EFou | |
| 'Inspired Word' | SRos | |
| 'Invictus' | SRos | |
| 'Iridescent Jewel' | SDay | |
| 'Irish Elf' | LRot SApp | |
| 'Iron Gate Gnome' | Last listed 1997 | |
| 'Iron Gate Iceberg' | Last listed 1998 | |
| 'Jade Bowl' | WGle | |
| 'Jake Russell' | Last listed 1998 | |
| 'James Marsh' | SRos | |
| 'Janice Brown' | SRos | |
| 'Jedi Dot Pearce' | SApp SRos | |
| 'Jenny Wren' | EMar GSki LRHS | |
| 'Jo Jo' | WWin | |
| 'Joan Senior' | EGol LBlm MBel MCAu MNrw NBur NWes SApp SDay SRos WCot WRus | |
| 'John Bierman' | SRos | |
| ¶ 'John Robert Biggs' | SApp | |
| 'Journey's End' | Last listed 1996 | |
| 'Jovial' | Last listed 1996 | |
| 'Joylene Nichole' | SRos | |
| 'Judah' | SRos | |
| 'Kate Carpenter' | SRos | |
| 'Katie' | NPri | |
| 'Katie Elizabeth Miller' | SRos | |
| 'Kazuq' | Last listed 1998 | |
| 'Kecia' | Last listed 1998 | |
| 'Kelly's Girl' | Last listed 1997 | |
| 'Killer Purple' | Last listed 1996 | |
| 'Kindly Light' | SRos | |
| 'King Haiglar' | Last listed 1998 | |
| N 'Kwanso Flore Pleno' | See H. fulva 'Green Kwanso' | |
| N 'Kwanzo Flore Pleno Variegata' | See H. fulva 'Kwanzo Variegata' | |
| 'La Mer' | EFou | |
| 'La Peche' | Last listed 1998 | |
| ¶ 'Lacy Marionette' | SApp | |
| 'Lady Cynthia' | Last listed 1998 | |
| 'Lady Inora Cubiles' | Last listed 1996 | |
| ¶ 'Lady Louise' | SApp | |
| 'Lady Mischief' | SDay | |
| 'Lady Neva' | SApp | |
| 'Lady of Leisure' | MBel | |
| 'Ladykin' | MBel | |
| 'Lark Song' | CKel EBrP EBre EGol EOrc LBre SBre WBcn | |
| 'Late Cream' | WGle | |
| 'Lavender Aristocrat' | WGle | |
| 'Lavender Bonanza' | NWes | |
| ¶ 'Lavender Memories' | SApp | |
| 'Lemon Bells' ♀ | EFou EMan EMar EPfP EPla EWll GSki LNor MCAu SChu SDay | |
| 'Lemon Mint' | EGol MTed | |
| 'Lenox' | SRos | |
| ¶ 'Leonard Bernstein' | SApp | |
| 'Lilac Wine' | ECha EPla WMer | |
| § lilioasphodelus ♀ | More than 30 suppliers | |
| 'Lillian Frye' | EGol | |
| 'Lilting Lady' | Last listed 1996 | |
| 'Linda' | CMGP ERou EWll MRav NHol | |
| 'Lion Cub' | WGle | |
| 'Little Audrey' | NWes | |
| 'Little Bee' | EFou | |
| 'Little Beige Magic' | EGol | |
| ¶ 'Little Big Man' | SDay | |
| ¶ 'Little Bugger' | MBNS | |

| | |
|---|---|
| 'Little Bumble Bee' | CFir EGol MBNS NWes |
| 'Little Business' | SApp SDay |
| 'Little Cameo' | EGol |
| 'Little Carnation' | SCro |
| 'Little Cranberry Cove' | EGol |
| 'Little Dandy' | EGol |
| 'Little Dart' | ECha |
| 'Little Deeke' | SDay SRos |
| 'Little Dream Red' | Last listed 1998 |
| 'Little Fantastic' | EGol |
| 'Little Fat Dazzler' | SDay |
| 'Little Grapette' | CHad EGol MCAu SApp SCro |
| | SDay SRos |
| 'Little Gypsy Vagabond' | SRos |
| ¶ 'Little Heavenly Angel' | SApp |
| 'Little Lavender Princess' | EGol |
| 'Little Maggie' | MSte SDay |
| 'Little Men' | CBlo WMer |
| 'Little Missy' | EMil |
| 'Little Prince' | SDay |
| 'Little Pumpkin Face' | EGol |
| 'Little Rainbow' | EGol |
| 'Little Red Hen' | LRHS SDay |
| 'Little Showoff' | Last listed 1996 |
| 'Little Tawny' | MCAu |
| 'Little Violet Lace' | GSki SDay |
| 'Little Wart' | EGol SDay |
| 'Little Wine Cup' | More than 30 suppliers |
| 'Little Woman' | SDay |
| 'Little Zinger' | SDay |
| 'Littlest Angel' | SDay |
| 'Lochinvar' | EBee ENot |
| *longituba* B&SWJ 625 | Last listed 1998 |
| 'Look' | Last listed 1997 |
| 'Lotus Land' | Last listed 1998 |
| 'Louis McHargue' | Last listed 1996 |
| 'Lowenstine' | Last listed 1996 |
| 'Lukey Boy' | Last listed 1996 |
| 'Lullaby Baby' | EGol SDay SRos |
| *luna* | LNor NOak |
| 'Luna Danca' | Last listed 1996 |
| 'Lupine' | MTed WGle |
| 'Lusty Leland' | CBlo CPar NWes SCro |
| x *luteola* | SDay |
| 'Luxury Lace' | CMGP EAst EBrP EBre EFou EGol |
| | ELan EMar EOrc LBre MBel MCAu |
| | MOne MUlv NBir NGdn NHaw |
| | NMGW NWes SBre SPer SRos |
| | WElm WFar WWhi |
| 'Lynn Hall' | EGol WViv |
| 'Mabel Fuller' | SCro |
| 'Malaysian Monarch' | MBel |
| 'Mallard' | EBrP EBre ECtt EGol LBre MBri |
| | MRav SBre SRos WBcn WCot |
| | WGle WMer WPer |
| 'Manchurian Apricot' | SRos |
| 'Marion Moss' | Last listed 1998 |
| 'Marion Vaughn' ♀ | CM&M CMil CSev EBee EBrP EBre |
| | ECot EFou EGol ELan EMan EPla |
| | GSki LBre MCAu MMil MWat |
| | NRoo NSti NWes SBre SDix SSpi |
| | WCot WWat |
| 'Mariska' | SRos |
| 'Mary Todd' | EGol |
| 'Mary's Gold' | SRos |
| 'Matador Orange' | Last listed 1997 |
| 'Matt' | SRos |
| ¶ 'Mauna Loa' | EFou |
| 'Mavoureen Nesmith' | SCro |
| 'May Colven' | EBrP EBre EGol LBre SBre |
| 'Meadow Gold' | Last listed 1998 |
| 'Meadow Mist' | EGol |

| | |
|---|---|
| 'Meadow Sprite' | SDay SRos |
| 'Mega Stella' | Last listed 1998 |
| 'Melody Lane' | EGol |
| 'Meno' | EGol |
| 'Metaphor' | Last listed 1997 |
| 'Mexican Way' | NWes |
| 'Michele Coe' | EMan LBuc LRHS MCAu NGdn |
| | SChu WLRN WMoo |
| *middendorffii* | CAvo EMon EPPr GCal GMaP |
| | MCli NSti |
| - var. *esculenta* | EMon |
| - 'Major' | CFee |
| 'Midnight Magic' | Last listed 1996 |
| 'Mikado' | MWgw |
| 'Millie Schlumpf' | SApp SRos |
| 'Ming Lo' | SDay |
| 'Ming Porcelain' | SRos |
| 'Ming Snow' | WGle |
| 'Mini Pearl' | EGol MBel MBri SDay SRos WPer |
| 'Mini Stella' | CBro EMil EPla LRHS SDay |
| Miniature hybrids | SRms WPer |
| *minor* | CBro EGol GCal SPla SRms |
| 'Missenden' ♀ | MNrw NHaw |
| 'Mission Moonlight' | COtt MCAu |
| 'Missouri Beauty' | CPar CRos EBee MBNS WMow |
| 'Misty' | Last listed 1996 |
| 'Mokan Cindy' | Last listed 1996 |
| 'Monica Marie' | SRos |
| ¶ 'Moon Witch' | SRos |
| 'Moonlight Mist' | SRos |
| ¶ 'Moonlit Crystal' | SApp |
| 'Mormon Spider' | Last listed 1996 |
| 'Morning Dawn' | CBlo EFou WMer |
| 'Morocco Red' | CBro CTri ELan GSki MMil NGdn |
| | WWat |
| 'Mosel' | Last listed 1997 |
| 'Mountain Laurel' | LRHS MBri MUlv |
| 'Mrs David Hall' | CMdw SCro SMrm |
| 'Mrs Hugh Johnson' | CHad CMGP CSev EBee ECGN |
| | ECot EHon EOld LNor NHol |
| 'Mrs John J. Tigert' | ERou |
| 'Mrs Lester' | CKel SDay |
| *multiflora* | NHol WCot |
| 'My Belle' | Last listed 1998 |
| 'My Hope' | WCot WGle |
| ¶ 'Nanuq' | SApp |
| 'Naomi Ruth' | EAst EGol |
| 'Nashville' | CBro EBrP EBre ELan ERou IBlr |
| | LBre MMil SBre |
| 'Neal Berrey' | SRos |
| ¶ 'Netsuke' | SApp |
| 'Neyron Rose' ♀ | CHea CMGP EGar EGol EMar |
| | ERou GSki MCAu NGdn SChu |
| | WMoo |
| 'Night Beacon' | EBee EFou EGol MBNS SApp |
| 'Night Raider' | SDay SRos |
| 'Nigrette' | LPBA MTed MWat NHol |
| 'Nile Plum' | Last listed 1996 |
| 'Nina Winegar' | Last listed 1996 |
| 'Nob Hill' | CLTr CMdw EGol SApp SRos |
| 'North Star' | GCal MTed |
| 'Norton Beauté' | MBel |
| 'Nova' ♀ | Last listed 1996 |
| 'Numinous Moments' | WGle |
| 'Nutmeg Elf' | Last listed 1996 |
| 'Ocean Rain' | SApp |
| 'Ochroleuca' | SSpi |
| 'Olive Bailey Langdon' | EGol SRos |
| 'Oom-pa-pa' | ECha |
| 'Optic Elegance' | SAsh |
| 'Orangeman' hort. | GSki |
| 'Orchid Beauty' | ECha WPrP |

| | |
|---|---|
| ¶ 'Orchid Corsage' | SApp |
| 'Orford' | WWin |
| 'Oriental Ruby' | EGol |
| ¶ 'Outrageous' | SApp |
| 'Paige Parker' | EGol |
| 'Painted Lady' | Last listed 1998 |
| 'Painted Trillium' | WGle |
| 'Pandora's Box' | EFou EGol ELan SRos |
| 'Paper Butterfly' | SRos |
| 'Paradise Pink' | EFou |
| 'Paradise Prince' | EGol |
| 'Pardon Me' | CMHG EGol LRHS MCAu SRos |
| | WRus |
| 'Parian China' | WGle |
| 'Pastel Ballerina' | SRos |
| 'Pastel Classic' | SRos |
| 'Patchwork Puzzle' | SRos |
| 'Patricia Fay' | SApp |
| ¶ 'Patsy Bickers' | SApp |
| 'Penelope Vestey' | EBee EBla EMar LRHS SDay SPla |
| | SRos |
| 'Penny's Worth' | EGol EMil MBri |
| ¶ 'Permaquid Light' | CMHG |
| 'Persian Princess' | WBcn |
| 'Persian Shrine' | EGol |
| 'Petite Ballerina' | SDay |
| 'Phoebe' | WGle |
| 'Piccadilly Princess' | MBel SDay SRos |
| ¶ 'Pink Attraction' | SApp |
| ¶ 'Pink Ballerina' | EBee EGol |
| 'Pink Charm' | CHan CM&M CMGP EBee EMan |
| | ENot LPBA MBal MCAu MWat |
| | NGdn NHol NOrc SChu SEas |
| | SLod WMow WViv |
| ¶ 'Pink Cotton Candy' | SRos |
| 'Pink Damask' ♀ | More than 30 suppliers |
| 'Pink Dream' | EGar GChr LRHS NHol |
| 'Pink Heaven' | EGol |
| 'Pink Interlude' | Last listed 1998 |
| 'Pink Lady' | ERou MBrN MNrw MRav SRms |
| 'Pink Lavender Appeal' | EGol |
| 'Pink Opal' | Last listed 1998 |
| 'Pink Prelude' | CBlo EBee ENot EWll LRHS NRoo |
| | SChu WWat |
| 'Pink Salute' | SRos |
| 'Pink Snowflake' | Last listed 1996 |
| 'Pink Sundae' | ECha |
| 'Pink Super Spider' | SRos |
| 'Piquante' | EBee |
| 'Pixie Pipestone' | Last listed 1998 |
| ¶ plicata | SWas WCot |
| 'Pojo' | Last listed 1998 |
| 'Pompeian Purple' | EGol WGle |
| 'Poneytail Pink' | EGol |
| 'Pony' | EGol WGle |
| 'Pookie Bear' | SApp |
| 'Potter's Clay' | WGle |
| 'Prairie Bells' | CSWP EHal MBro MCAu NFai |
| | NPla WHoo WLRN WWhi |
| 'Prairie Blue Eyes' | EBee EGol NWes SApp SCro |
| | WBcn WHoo |
| ¶ 'Prairie Charmer' | SLod |
| ¶ 'Prairie Moonlight' | SApp |
| 'Prairie Sunset' | MCAu |
| 'Pretty Mist' | WGle |
| 'Pretty Peggy' | Last listed 1998 |
| 'Prima Donna' | SCro |
| 'Primrose Mascotte' | NBir WWin |
| ¶ 'Prince Redbird' | SDay |
| ¶ 'Princeton Grape' | SApp |
| 'Prize Picotee Deluxe' | WGle |
| 'Prize Picotee Elite' | WGle |

| | |
|---|---|
| 'Protocol' | Last listed 1998 |
| 'Puddin' | See H. 'Brass Buckles' |
| 'Pumpkin Kid' | SRos |
| 'Puppet Show' | SDay |
| 'Purple Rain' | EFou MBNS SApp |
| 'Purple Waters' | EMar EPfP EWll MBNS |
| 'Pursuit of Excellence' | SRos |
| 'Pyewacket' | Last listed 1998 |
| ¶ 'Queen Beatrice' | EBee |
| 'Queen of May' | WCot |
| ¶ 'Queen's Gift' | SApp |
| 'Quick Results' | SDay SRos |
| 'Quietness' | SRos |
| 'Quinn Buck' | Last listed 1998 |
| 'Radiant' | Last listed 1997 |
| 'Raindrop' | EGol |
| 'Rajah' | EGra LNor MBel MGed NBro |
| | NBus NPla |
| 'Rare China' | Last listed 1996 |
| ¶ 'Raspberry Pixie' | SDay |
| 'Raspberry Sundae' | Last listed 1996 |
| 'Raspberry Wine' | ECha |
| 'Real Wind' | Last listed 1998 |
| 'Red Cup' | Last listed 1997 |
| 'Red Damask' | Last listed 1997 |
| 'Red Joy' | Last listed 1997 |
| 'Red Precious' ♀ | EGol LRHS MBel MNrw SAsh |
| 'Red Rum' | EFou EWll LBuc MBNS MCli |
| 'Red Torch' | Last listed 1998 |
| ¶ 'Ricky Rose' | SDay |
| 'Roger Grounds' | SApp |
| 'Romany' | LPBA |
| ¶ 'Ron Rousseau' | SApp |
| 'Root Beer' | MCAu WGle |
| 'Rose Emily' | SRos |
| 'Rose Festival' | WGle |
| ¶ 'Rosella Sheridan' | SRos |
| 'Royal Charm' | SRos |
| 'Royal Corduroy' | MBel |
| 'Royal Crown' | MBri |
| 'Royal Heritage' | Last listed 1997 |
| 'Royal Palace Prince' | WGle |
| 'Royal Prestige' | Last listed 1998 |
| 'Royal Robe' | EFou EGar |
| 'Royal Ruby' | Last listed 1996 |
| ¶ 'Royal Saracen' | SDay |
| 'Royalty' | CKel |
| 'Ruffled Apricot' | LRHS SDay SRos |
| 'Russell Prichard' | ERou |
| 'Russian Rhapsody' | Last listed 1997 |
| 'Rutilans' | CFee |
| 'Sabie' | Last listed 1998 |
| 'Sabra Salina' | SRos |
| 'Salmon Sheen' | Last listed 1998 |
| 'Sammy Russell' | CHan CMGP EAst ECGN EFou |
| | EGol EMar EOrc EPla ERic GBuc |
| | GMac LHop MBNS MBal MBro |
| | MCli MWat MWgw NBro NFai |
| | NGdn NHol NSti SBod SEas SRms |
| | WMoo WPer WWhi |
| 'Sandra Walker' | EGol |
| 'Sari' | Last listed 1996 |
| 'Sariah' | Last listed 1996 |
| 'Satin Clouds' | EGol WGle |
| 'Satin Glow' | ECha |
| 'Satin Silk' | EBrP EBre LBre SBre |
| 'Scarlet Flame' | ECha |
| * 'Scarlet Oak' | MBri SApp |
| 'Scarlet Orbit' | SApp SDay SRos |
| 'Scarlet Romance' | WGle |
| 'Scarlet Royalty' | WGle |
| 'Scarlet Tanager' | LRHS |

| | |
|---|---|
| 'Schoolgirl' | EBrP EBre LBre SBre |
| 'Screech Owl' | LRHS |
| 'Searcy Marsh' | EGol |
| 'Sebastian' | SRos |
| 'Serena Sunburst' | MBel SRos |
| 'Shaman' | SApp SRos |
| 'Shooting Star' | EGol SPla |
| 'Show Amber' | Last listed 1998 |
| 'Silent Stars' | WGle |
| 'Silent World' | Last listed 1996 |
| 'Silken Fairy' | EGol SDay |
| 'Siloam Angel Blush' | SDay |
| 'Siloam Baby Doll' | Last listed 1997 |
| 'Siloam Baby Talk' | CRDP EFou EGol NBir SRos WGle |
| 'Siloam Bertie Ferris' | EFou |
| 'Siloam Bo Peep' | CRDP EGol |
| 'Siloam Brian Henke' | SRos |
| 'Siloam Button Box' | EGol |
| 'Siloam Byelo' | EGol SDay |
| 'Siloam Cinderella' | EGol SDay SRos |
| 'Siloam David Kirchhoff' | SRos |
| 'Siloam Doodlebug' | EGol WGle |
| 'Siloam Double Classic' (d) | MBel SRos |
| 'Siloam Edith Scholar' | EGol WGle |
| 'Siloam Ethel Smith' | EGol SDay |
| 'Siloam Fairy Tale' | CRDP EGol |
| ¶ 'Siloam Frosted Mint' | SApp |
| 'Siloam Gold Coin' | SDay |
| 'Siloam Grace Stamile' | SRos |
| 'Siloam Gumdrop' | WGle |
| 'Siloam Joan Senior' | EGol |
| 'Siloam June Bug' | EGol NWes WPnP |
| 'Siloam Kewpie Doll' | EGol WGle |
| 'Siloam Little Girl' | EGol SDay SRos WGle |
| 'Siloam Merle Kent' | SRos |
| ¶ 'Siloam Nugget' | SApp |
| 'Siloam Orchid Jewel' | EGol SDay |
| 'Siloam Pee Wee' | EGol |
| 'Siloam Pink Glow' | EGol WGle |
| 'Siloam Pink Petite' | EGol |
| 'Siloam Plum Tree' | EGol |
| 'Siloam Pocket Size' | EGol |
| 'Siloam Prissy' | EGol |
| 'Siloam Purple Plum' | EGol |
| 'Siloam Red Ruby' | EGol |
| 'Siloam Red Toy' | EGol |
| 'Siloam Red Velvet' | EGol |
| 'Siloam Ribbon Candy' | EGol SDay |
| 'Siloam Rose Dawn' | SDay SRos |
| ¶ 'Siloam Rose Queen' | SDay |
| 'Siloam Royal Prince' | SCro |
| 'Siloam Shocker' | EGol |
| 'Siloam Show Girl' | EGol SDay |
| 'Siloam Sugar Time' | EGol |
| 'Siloam Tee Tiny' | EGol |
| 'Siloam Tinker Toy' | EGol WGle |
| 'Siloam Tiny Mite' | EGol SDay |
| 'Siloam Toddler' | EGol WGle |
| 'Siloam Tom Thumb' | EGol |
| 'Siloam Ury Winniford' | CBro CRDP EBee EGol SDay |
| 'Siloam Virginia Henson' | EGol MCAu SRos WRus |
| 'Silver Ice' | MBel SDay SRos |
| 'Silver Trumpet' | EFou MSCN NWes SCro |
| 'Silver Veil' | Last listed 1997 |
| 'Sirius' | NHol |
| 'Sirocco' | CBlo EBee EFou NWes |
| ¶ 'Smoky Mountain Autumn' | SApp |
| 'Snowfall' | EGol |
| 'Snowy Apparition' | EWTr EWll MBri |
| ¶ 'Snowy Eyes' | MBNS |
| 'Solano Bulls Eye' | Last listed 1996 |
| 'Solid Scarlet' | Last listed 1996 |

| | |
|---|---|
| 'Sombrero Way' | NWes |
| 'Someone Special' | SRos |
| 'Song Sparrow' | MBri WPer |
| 'Spanish Gold' | Last listed 1996 |
| 'Sparkling Dawn' | MBel |
| 'Sparkling Stars' | WGle |
| 'Spiderman' | SRos |
| ¶ 'Spring Ballerina' | SApp |
| 'Stafford' | More than 30 suppliers |
| ¶ 'Staghorn Sumach' | MBri |
| 'Starling' | CFir CPar EFou EGol |
| 'Stars and Stripes' | Last listed 1998 |
| 'Stella de Oro' ♀ | More than 30 suppliers |
| 'Stineette' | WCot |
| 'Stoke Poges' ♀ | CSev EAst EBee ECGP EMar EPfP |
| | EPla ERic LRHS MMil NRoo SChu |
| | SRos |
| 'Strawberry Candy' | SDay SRos |
| 'Streaker' hort. (v) | WCot |
| ¶ 'Strutter's Ball' | SDay SRos |
| 'Sugar Cookie' | CRDP SDay |
| 'Summer Air' | LRHS MBri MUlv |
| 'Summer Interlude' | WMoo |
| 'Summer Jubilee' | SDay |
| 'Summer Wine' | CHad CMGP CPar CRos EFou |
| | EGol EMar EPla LBlm LRHS MBNS |
| | MBro MMil MUlv NFai NPri NSti |
| | NWes SChu SDay SMrm WCot |
| | WHoo WMer WPyg WWat |
| ¶ 'Sun Pixie' | SCro |
| 'Sunday Gloves' | EGol |
| 'Sunset Pea' | Last listed 1997 |
| 'Superlative' | SRos |
| 'Suzie Wong' | MArl |
| 'Sweet Pea' | EGol |
| 'Sweet Refrain' | Last listed 1997 |
| 'Swirling Water' | SDay |
| 'Taffy Tot' | Last listed 1996 |
| 'Tang' | Last listed 1998 |
| 'Tasmania' | SPer |
| 'Techny Peach Lace' | WGle |
| 'Techny Spider' | SRos |
| 'Teenager' | EGol |
| 'Tejas' | EMil MBNS |
| 'Telstar' | Last listed 1996 |
| 'Tender Sheperd' | EGol WGle |
| ¶ 'Tetraploid Bubbles' | MBri |
| 'Tetraploid Stella de Oro' | SDay |
| ¶ 'Tetrina's Daughter' ♀ | CMGP |
| 'Thousand Voices' | WGle |
| 'Thumbelina' | ECha |
| § *thunbergii* | ECha MNrw SMac SSpi |
| 'Thy True Love' | Last listed 1996 |
| 'Time Lord' | Last listed 1997 |
| 'Timeless Fire' | SApp SRos |
| 'Tinker Bell' | SRos |
| 'Tiny Temptress' | Last listed 1997 |
| 'Todd Munroe' | WGle |
| 'Tom Wise' | SRos |
| 'Tonia Gay' | CRDP SRos |
| 'Tootsie' | Last listed 1996 |
| 'Tootsie Rose' | SRos |
| 'Torpoint' | LRHS |
| 'Towhead' | EGol ENot LRHS MRav MTed |
| | WCot |
| 'Toyland' | CMGP CSev EBee EGar EGol GSki |
| | LRHS NGdn NRoo SSpe WLRN |
| 'Triple Threat' | SDay |
| 'Tropical Toy' | SDay |
| ¶ 'True Glory' | SApp |
| 'Twenty Third Psalm' | Last listed 1996 |
| ¶ 'Tylwyth Teg' | SApp |

'Upper Class Peach' WGle
'Varsity' EBee EBrP EBre EGol LBre MCAu
NBir SBre SRos
'Veiled Beauty' Last listed 1996
'Vera Biaglow' Last listed 1998
*vespertina* See *H. thunbergii*
'Vicountess Byng' Last listed 1998
'Victoria Aden' CBro
¶ 'Video' SDay
¶ 'Vintage Bordeaux' SDay
¶ 'Virginia Henson' COtt EBee
'Virgin's Blush' Last listed 1997
* 'Vohann' Last listed 1998
'Walk Humbly' WGle
'Wally Nance' LRHS
'War Paint' Last listed 1996
'Water Witch' EGol
'Waxwing' WPer
'Wayside Green Imp' EBee EFou EGol NWes SCro WGle
¶ 'Wayside Green Lamp' EFou
'Wayside Princess' WGle
'Wee Chalice' EGol
'Whichford' ♀ CBro CLTr CMea EBrP EBre ECtt
EGol ELan LBre LGre NRoo SBre
SChu SUsu WWal WWat WWin
'White Coral' LRHS
'White Dish' EGol
'White Temptation' EGol MBel
'Whooperie' MBel
'Wild Welcome' Last listed 1997
'Wind Song' Last listed 1998
¶ 'Windfrills' SApp
'Window Dressing' EGol
'Windsor Tan' Last listed 1997
'Wine Bubbles' EGol LRHS SApp
'Wine Delight' Last listed 1998
'Winnetka' MCAu
'Winnie the Pooh' SDay
'Winsome Lady' ECha WPrP
'Wishing Well' SChu
* 'Witch Hazel' COtt WGle
¶ 'Witches Coven' SDay
¶ 'Wood Duck' COtt EFou
'Woodbury' Last listed 1998
'World of Peace' Last listed 1996
'Wren' COtt WGle
'Wynn' MBel
'Yellow Lollipop' SDay SRos
'Yellow Mantle' Last listed 1998
'Yellow Petticoats' MTed MUlv
'Yellow Rain' SAsh WCot
'Yesterday Memories' SRos
'Zampa' SDay
'Zara' SPer

## HEMIGRAPHIS (Acanthaceae)
§ *alternata* Last listed 1998
*colorata* See *H. alternata*

## HEMIONITIS (Adiantaceae)
*arifolia* Last listed 1997

## HEMIPHRAGMA (Scrophulariaceae)
¶ *heterophyllum* CC 2428 MChR

## HEMIZYGIA (Lamiaceae)
*obermeyerae* Last listed 1996
*transvaalensis* Last listed 1997

## HEPATICA ✿ (Ranunculaceae)
*acutiloba* CBro CLAP EBee GCrs GMaP
LAma MAsh MAvo SIng WCru

*americana* CArn GBuc GCrs MAsh WCru
*angulosa* See *H. transsilvanica*
*henryi* EPot WCru
¶ *maxima* B&SWJ 4344 WCru
¶ x *media* WCom
– 'Ballardii' ♀ IBlr
¶ – 'Harvington Beauty' CLAP
§ *nobilis* ♀ More than 30 suppliers
– blue CRDP GAbr LPio MAsh MS&S
NHar NSla SBla SWas WCru
– 'Cobalt' Last listed 1998
– double pink See *H. nobilis* 'Rubra Plena'
¶ – dwarf white WHil
– grey/lilac semi-double (d) CRDP
– var. *japonica* CBro CRDP LAma MAsh SBla
WCru
– lilac MTho SWas
– mottled leaf MAsh MTho
– pink CRDP ELan EPot GCrs MAsh
MS&S NWCA SBla SIng SRms
SWas WIvy
* – 'Pyrenean Marbles' CLAP
– red MAsh NNrd WAbe
– var. *rubra* CLAP CRDP NMen NSla
§ – 'Rubra Plena' (d) Last listed 1997
– white CRDP ELan GAbr GCrs LPio
MAsh MS&S NSla SBla SIng WCru
WHil WIvy
§ *transsilvanica* ♀ CBro CLAP ECha EHyt ELan EPla
EPot GCrs LAma LHop MBro
MS&S MWat NHar NHol NMen
NRya SBla SPer WAbe WCru
WGwy
– *alba* Last listed 1997
– 'De Buis' CAvo CLAP LPio MDun MLLN
¶ – 'Eisvogel' NPar
– 'Elison Spence' (d) IBlr
¶ – January/February flowered form NPar
– 'Lilacina' NPar
¶ – 'Loddon Blue' NPar
¶ – pink SBla
*triloba* See *H. nobilis*

## x HEPPIMENES (Gesneriaceae)
I 'Purple Queen' NMos

## HEPTACODIUM (Caprifoliaceae)
*miconioides* CB&S CBar CBot CDoC CFil
CPMA CPle CWSG ELan EPfP
GBin GQui IDee LBuc MBlu
MCCP MTis SAga SMac SMad
SPan WCot WCwm WPGP WSHC
WWat

## HEPTAPLEURUM See SCHEFFLERA

## HERACLEUM (Apiaceae)
*antasiaticum* See *H. stevenii*
¶ *candicans* B&SWJ 2988 WCru
¶ *lanatum* 'Washington
Limes' (v) WCot
*lehmannianum* WCot
*mantegazzianum* CRow EOas EPfP MFir WOak
*minimum* 'Roseum' CInt ELan WFar WPat
*nepalense* B&SWJ 2105 Last listed 1996
*sphondylium* Last listed 1997
– *roseum* CNat

## HERBERTIA (Iridaceae)
§ *lahue* LRHS
*pulchella* Last listed 1996

**HERMANNIA** (Sterculiaceae)
| | |
|---|---|
| *candicans* | See *H. incana* |
| *erodioides* | See *H. depressa* |
| ¶ *flammea* | WCot |
| § *incana* | CHal MBEx |
| § *pinnata* | Last listed 1996 |
| ¶ sp. JCA 15523 | CPBP |
| * *stricta* | Last listed 1998 |
| *verticillata* | See *H. pinnata* |

**HERMODACTYLUS** (Iridaceae)
| | |
|---|---|
| § *tuberosus* | CAvo CBos CBro CMea CMil CTri |
| | EBee EBrP EBre ECha EGoo EHal |
| | EMan EPar LAma LBre LPio MNrw |
| | MRav NFai NRog SBre WCot |
| - MS 976/762 | Last listed 1998 |

**HERNIARIA** (Caryophyllaceae)
| | |
|---|---|
| *glabra* | EOHP EWFC GBar GPoy LHol |
| | MSal SIde WHer WOak WWye |

**HERTIA** See OTHONNA

**HESPERALOE** (Agavaceae)
| | |
|---|---|
| *funifera* | CTbh |
| *parviflora* | CTbh EOas SIgm |
| - 'Rubra' | Last listed 1997 |

**HESPERANTHA** (Iridaceae)
| | |
|---|---|
| § *baurii* | CLAP GBuc IMGH NMen SSpi |
| | WAbe WCot |
| *buhrii* | See *H. cucullata* 'Rubra' |
| § *cucullata* 'Rubra' | NWCA |
| * *geminata* | Last listed 1998 |
| *huttonii* | GBuc MFir WCot |
| *mossii* | See *H. baurii* |
| *pauciflora* | WCot |
| *vaginata* | WCot |
| ¶ *woodii* | CFir |

**HESPERIS** ✿ (Brassicaceae)
| | |
|---|---|
| *lutea* | See *Sisymbrium luteum* |
| *matronalis* | More than 30 suppliers |
| - *alba* | See *H. matronalis* var. *albiflora* |
| § - var. *albiflora* | EFou EMar EWTr MCAu MCLN |
| | NPri SMrm SPer SSvw WCot WFar |
| | WOve WPer WWat |
| - - 'Alba Plena' (d) | CGle CMea CRDP ELan LHol |
| | MNrw MTis SIde SWat WCot WFar |
| - double form (d) | CHad CSev MBri WCru |
| - double pink (d) | SWat |
| - 'Lilacina' | MBel |
| - 'Lilacina Flore Pleno' (d) | CBos CGle CHan CMil GMaP |
| | GMac MBNS MCLN NBrk NHaw |
| | NHol NPri NSti SUsu SWat WFar |
| - violet | LRHS |
| * *silviniana* | Last listed 1998 |
| *steveniana* | CGen ECoo MBNS SWat WElm |
| * *sylviniana* | NCat |

**HETEROCENTRON** (Melastomataceae)
| | |
|---|---|
| § *elegans* | CLTr CTre |

**HETEROMELES** See PHOTINIA

**HETEROMORPHA** (Apiaceae)
| | |
|---|---|
| *arborescens* | SIgm |

**HETEROPAPPUS** (Asteraceae)
| | |
|---|---|
| *altaicus* | GBin SHut WPer |

**HETEROTHECA** (Asteraceae)
| | |
|---|---|
| *horrida* | Last listed 1998 |
| *mucronata* | EBee |
| § *villosa* | CFri CRDP LBuc WCot |

**HEUCHERA** ✿ (Saxifragaceae)
| | |
|---|---|
| § *americana* | CHid CRDP CRow ECha EOrc |
| | GBar MHar NBir NFai NSti SCro |
| | SLod WTin WWat |
| ¶ - 'Biddulph Brown' | WCot |
| - Dale's Strain | EBee EMan EPPr GMaP MNrw |
| | MTed MWrn NCat NDov NLar |
| | WPrP WWoo |
| ¶ - 'Harry Hay' | CHan |
| - 'Picta' | EPPr WCot |
| 'Amethyst Mist' | WCot |
| ¶ 'Angel's Pink' | WCot |
| 'Apple Blossom' | Last listed 1996 |
| 'Autumn Leaves' | NLar |
| ¶ 'Beauty Colour' | CFee EPfP MBri |
| ¶ 'Black Velvet' | EFou |
| ¶ 'Blackbird' | MBri |
| ¶ *bracteata* | CHid |
| Bressingham hybrids | CSpe EAst EBrP EBre EWTr LBre |
| | MBri MMal NArg NBir NFla NMir |
| | NOak NRoo SBre SPer SRms SSca |
| | WMoo WPer WWin WWoo |
| x *brizoides* 'Gracillima' | CGle EPPr |
| 'Can-can' | CHid CMHG COtt EBee EHic |
| | MBri MCLN MLLN NDov NHol |
| | NPri SCob WCot |
| 'Canyon Delight' | WCot |
| ¶ 'Canyon Pink' | WCot |
| ¶ 'Cappucchino' | WCot |
| 'Cascade Dawn' | CHid CMHG EMan EMar EPPr LFis |
| | LHop LPio LRot MBel MBri MCLN |
| | MSCN NCut NHol NLak NLar |
| | NPro SBid SCob SWat WCot |
| 'Cathedral Windows' | WCot |
| ◆ 'Chablo' | See *H.* Charles Bloom = 'Chablo' |
| ¶ 'Champagne Bubbles' | WCot |
| § Charles Bloom = 'Chablo' | EBrP EBre LBre SBre |
| ¶ 'Cherries Jubilee' | WCot |
| 'Cherry Red' | Last listed 1997 |
| 'Chiqui' | SUsu SWas |
| *chlorantha* | GBin |
| 'Chocolate Ruffles' | More than 30 suppliers |
| coral bells | See *H. sanguinea* |
| ¶ 'Coral Bouquet' | WCot |
| 'Coral Cloud' | CB&S ENot GCHN MRav |
| *cylindrica* | GCHN MBNS MBel MRav MSte |
| | SSca WPer WWin |
| - var. *alpina* | Last listed 1998 |
| - - NNS 96-116 | MRPP |
| - 'Chartreuse' | CGle LPio |
| - 'Greenfinch' | CB&S CFee CFri CGle CKel |
| | CMHG CRow EBrP EBre ECha |
| | ECtt ELan EWTr GCal GTou LBre |
| | MCLN NBro NOrc SBre SCob |
| | SHel SMer SSoC WBea WCot WEas |
| | WPer WWat WWhi |
| - 'Hyperion' | EPPr MBal |
| ¶ 'Dainty Bells' | WCot |
| 'David' | Last listed 1997 |
| 'Dennis Davidson' | See *H.* 'Huntsman' |
| ¶ 'Diana Clare' | WCot |
| 'Dingle Amber' | Last listed 1996 |
| 'Dingle Mint Chocolate' | Last listed 1996 |
| ¶ 'Ebony and Ivory' | WCot |
| I 'Eco Magnififolia' | CLAP NWes WCot WGle |
| ¶ 'Eden's Joy' | EBee |

¶ 'Eden's Mystery' — EBee
¶ 'Eden's Shine' — MCLN
'Edge Hill' — SRms
¶ *elegans* NNS 95-289 — MRPP
'Emperor's Cloak' — EWTr MWll NLar NPri NPro STes WBea WElm WSan WUnu
'Firebird' — CBlo ELan EPPr MBal NVic
Firefly — See *H.* 'Leuchtkäfer'
*glabra* — EBee
*glauca* — See *H. americana*
'Green Ivory' — CGle CHar EBee EBrP EBre EHal EMan EOrc EPPr GCHN GMaP LBre LNor MBal MBel MBri MRav MUlv NBus NCat NGdn NSti SBre SPer SRCN
'Greenfinch' — WGwG
*grossulariifolia* — EBee MTho WCot WPer
¶ 'Hailstorm' (v) — EMon
*hallii* — NTow WCot
'Helen Dillon' (v) — More than 30 suppliers
◆ 'Heuros' — See *H.* Rosemary Bloom = 'Heuros'
¶ 'High Society' — WCot
*hispida* — EBee EMan MSte MWrn SAga
§ 'Huntsman' — CGle EBee ECha EGar ELan EMan GBri GBuc MRav NRoo SUsu WBcn WRus
'Jack Frost' — NWes WGle
'Lady Romney' — GCal
§ 'Leuchtkäfer' — CB&S CFee EBee EGoo ESis EWTr GChr MBro MCli MFir MRav MTis NBrk NFai NMir NOrc NRoo SCob SCro SLon SMac SPer SRms SWat WGor WHoo WMoo WPer
¶ 'Magic Wand' — WCot
¶ 'Martha's Compact' — WCot
'Mary Rose' — Last listed 1996
¶ *maxima* — IHdy
*mexicana* — WCot
* *micans* — EHyt NHar NMen SIng
*micrantha* — EBee ELan MWgw SRms WCot
- var. *diversifolia* — EBee ECle LRHS MBri NHol SPer
  Bressingham Bronze = SPla
  'Absi'
N - - 'Palace Purple' ♀ — More than 30 suppliers
- JLS 86275CLOR — Last listed 1998
- 'Martha Roderick' — WCot
'Mint Frost' — CLAP CMHG COtt EBee EFou EHic EMan EPPr GBin GBri GNau MBri MCLN MLLN NDov NHol NPro SWat WCot WFar WOVN WSpi
¶ 'Monet' (V) — MBri
* 'Moondrops' — Last listed 1996
¶ 'Morden Pink' — CLAP
'Mother of Pearl' — Last listed 1997
'Northern Fire' — CLAP EBee
'Oakington Jewel' — CHid EBee EMan SMad WCot
¶ 'Opal' — WCot
'Orphei' — NChi
'Painted Lady' — EBee GBuc LFis LPio SCob
¶ 'Palace Passion' — WCot
*parishii* — NWCA
*parvifolia* — EBee
- var. *nivalis* — Last listed 1998
'Pearl Drops' — EBee EPPr
'Persian Carpet' — More than 30 suppliers
¶ 'Petite Marble Burg' — COtt NDov WCot
¶ 'Petite Marble Burgundy' — EBee MBri
¶ 'Petite Pearl Fairy' — COtt EBee GNau MBri NDov WCot

'Pewter Moon' — CBro EFou EHoe ELan EMil EPla LFis LHop LPio LRHS MBel MRav NBir NCat NHol NLak NSti SChu SCob SPer SPla WAbe WCot WGle WWat
'Pewter Veil' — EBee EFou EMan EMar EPfP SCob WCot WEas WGle
*pilosissima* — GBin GBuc
'Pink Spray' — EPPr
◆ 'Pluie de Feu' — See *H.* Rain of Fire = 'Pluie de Feu'
'Plum Puddin' — CBlo CFee CHea CHid CMHG EBee EHic EWes LRHS MBri MBro MCLN MGrG MMil MTed NChi NDov NHol NLar NPri NPro SApp SCob WCot WHoo WOve WWeb WWhi
'Pretty Polly' — WPnP
◆ *pringlei* — See *H. rubescens*
¶ x *pruboniciana* — WCot
'Brown-coral'
*pubescens* — GBri GCHN
- 'Alba' — CMGP NChi WCot WHoo
¶ - 'Hob' — WCot
*pulchella* — CPBP EBee ESis NFla NTow SSca WMoo
- JCA 9508 — NMen NWoo
'Purple Petticoats' — EFou WCot
¶ 'Purple Sails' — WCot
'Rachel' — More than 30 suppliers
§ Rain of Fire = 'Pluie de Feu' — CFir EBee EPfP GBri GCal MBNS MCli MRav WGle
'Raspberry Regal' — CMHG EAst EBee LWoo MCLN MHlr MLLN MRav NCut NDov NHol NSti NWes WCot
'Red Spangles' ♀ — CGle CKel EBrP EBre GCHN LBre MCAu NBir SBre SCob
'Regal Robe' — WCot
¶ 'Regina' — EFou
*richardsonii* — GBin MNrw WUnu
'Ring of Fire' — CLAP COtt EBee EFou EHic EPfP GBri MBri NHol NPri SApp WCot WFar
§ Rosemary Bloom = 'Heuros' — EBrP EBre LBre SBre SPer SWat
§ *rubescens* — EDAr ELan MTho NBro NMen WCot WPer WWin
*rubra* 'Redstart' — SUsu
'Ruby Ruffles' — WCot WGle
'Ruby Veil' — EFou EHic NHol NWes SCob WCot WGle WGor
'Ruffles' — CRow
§ *sanguinea* — CAgr CGle GCHN MBal NBro NCat NFor SHFr SHel WByw WLin WPer
- 'Alba' — EMon
- 'Sioux Falls' — Last listed 1998
- 'Splendens' — MWhi WOve
- 'Taff's Joy' (v) — CRow EWes MNrw NPro SMac WCot
- 'White Cloud' (v) — EBee MWll NCut SRms WMoo
'Santa Anna Cardinal' — Last listed 1998
'Schneewittchen' (v) — EMan EPPr EPfP EWTr MRav NCat WCot WMer
'Scintillation' ♀ — CB&S CKel EBrP EBre ECtt GCHN LBre NCat SBre SRms
¶ 'Shady Barbara' — EPPr WCot
'Shere Variety' — EBee
¶ 'Silver Streak' — EFou LHop
'Silver Veil' — CRow
'Sioux Falls' — EWes GBri
¶ 'Smokey Rose' — WCot
'Snow Storm' (v) — EBee ELan EMon GCHN LHop MBar MBel MBri SPer SPlb WAbe WCot WFar WGle WWhi

'Souvenir de Wolley-Dod'        MAvo WCot
'Splish Splash'                 WCot WGle
'Stormy Seas'                   More than 30 suppliers
¶ 'Strawberries and Cream'      WCot
'Strawberry Swirl'              CB&S CFai CMHG EAst EBee EHal
                                EHic GMac LFis LHop LRot MBel
                                MBri MLLN MMil MRav NHol
                                NLar NSti NWes SPer SSpi SWat
                                WCot WOVN
Super hybrids                   WFar WHil
¶ 'Velvet Cloak'                WCot
¶ 'Velvet Night'                WCot
*versicolor*                    Last listed 1997
*villosa*                       ECGN ECha EGar GCHN MRav
- 'Royal Red'                   ECha EGar MRav
'Wendy Hardy'                   CLAP WCot
¶ 'Whirlwind'                   WCot
¶ 'White Spires'                WCot
'Widar'                         EPPr WCot
'Winter Red'                    EFou
'Yeti'                          EFou
'Zabelliana'                    GBri GCal NPro NRoo

## x HEUCHERELLA (Saxifragaceae)

*alba* 'Bridget Bloom'          CB&S CDoC CGle CSam EBee
                                ECha ELan EMar EOld EPar GCHN
                                GMaP LGro LHop MBro MRav
                                MUlv NFai NHol NOrc NRoo
                                SCob SPer SRms SUsu WBea WFar
                                WHil WHoo WRus
- 'Rosalie'                     CElw CFee CGle CMHG CMea
                                EBrP EBre ECha EPri LBre LPio
                                MBel MBri MMal MRav MSte
                                MUlv NHol NLak SBre SLod SLon
                                SSpe SUsu WAbe WFar WHoo
                                WRus WWhi
♦ 'Ninja'                       See *Tiarella* 'Ninja'
'Pink Frost'                    WThi
'Quicksilver'                   CB&S EBee EHic EMan EMar EPPr
                                GMaP LWoo MBri NCut NDov
                                NPri SAsh SCob SMad SSpi WCot
                                WFar WMaN
'Silver Streak'                 CHid CMHG CMil CSpe EBee
                                EHic EMar EPPr GMaP GNau
                                LWoo MBri MGrG MSte NDov
                                NHol NPri SCob SSpi WCot
*tiarelloides* ♀                CSev EBee EMan EPfP MWgw
                                NCat NFai NFor NLon SCob SPer
                                WRus
* 'White Blus'                  WThi

## HEXASTYLIS See ASARUM

## x HIBANOBAMBUSA (Poaceae - Bambusoideae)
I *tranquillans*               EFul EPla LJus LPan NDov SDry
                                WJun
I - f.*kimmei*                  MCCP
I - 'Shiroshima' (v)            CFil CPMA EBee EOas EPla ERod
                                ISta MBrN MCCP MWhi NDov
                                SDry WBay WCru WJun WPGP

## HIBBERTIA (Dilleniaceae)
*aspera*                       CGre CPle CRHN LHil SAga WWat
§ *cuneiformis*                CPle EREa LHil
*dentata*                      Last listed 1998
*procumbens*                   EHyt ESis ITim WAbe
§ *scandens* ♀                 CGre CPlN CPle CRHN ECou
                                ELan EREa GQui LBlm LChe LCns
                                LHil SAga SOWG WMul
*tetrandra*                    See *H. cuneiformis*
*volubilis*                    See *H. scandens*

## HIBISCUS ✿ (Malvaceae)
*acetosella*                   Last listed 1998
*biseptus*                     Last listed 1998
*cannabinus*                   SIde
*cardiophyllus*                Last listed 1998
*coccineus*                    MSte SOWG
*geranioides*                  Last listed 1996
*hamabo*                       SMad SSta
*huegelii*                     See *Alyogyne huegelii*
*leopoldii*                    IOrc SPer SRms
*manihot*                      See *Abelmoschus manihot*
* *moesiana*                   MBri
'Morning Glory'                Last listed 1996
*moscheutos*                   CArn CFir CHan MSte SMad
- Southern Belle Group         Last listed 1996
*mutabilis*                    SOWG
¶ - pink                       CPLG
¶ - var. *versicolor*          CPLG
*paramutabilis*                SMad
*pedunculatus*                 WMul
*rosa-sinensis*                EBak MBri SOWG
- 'Casablanca'                 MBri
- 'Cooperi' (v)                CHal LChe SOWG
- 'Dainty Pink'                See *H. rosa-sinensis* 'Fantasia'
§ - 'Dainty White'             LChe
- 'El Capitolio'               SOWG
- 'El Capitolio' sport         LChe
§ - 'Fantasia'                 LChe
- 'Full Moon'                  LChe
- 'Helene'                     ELan EMil MBri
- 'Herm Geller'                LChe
- 'Holiday'                    MBri
- 'Kardinal'                   MBri
- 'Koeniger'                   MBri
- 'La France'                  See *H. rosa-sinensis* 'Fantasia'
- 'Lemon Chiffon' (d)          LChe
- 'Meteor'                     LChe
- 'Pink la France'             See *H. rosa-sinensis* 'Fantasia'
- 'Rose of China'              MBri
- 'Swan Lake'                  See *H. rosa-sinensis* 'Dainty
                               White'
- 'Thelma Bennell'             SOWG
- 'Tivoli'                     MBri
- 'Weekend'                    LChe MBri
- 'White la France'            See *H. rosa-sinensis* 'Dainty
                               White'
*rubis*                        ELan
*sabdariffa*                   ECon
*schizopetalus* ♀              LChe SOWG
¶ *sinosyriacus*               EPfP
- 'Lilac Queen'                MBri WBcn
* - 'Red Centre'               Last listed 1996
- 'Ruby Glow'                  MGos
*syriacus*                     WNor
- 'Admiral Dewey'              IOrc MGos SPla
- 'Ardens' (d)                 CBlo CEnd ELan IOrc MGos MRav
                               SPer
- Blue Bird                    See *H. syriacus* 'Oiseau Bleu'
- 'Coelestis'                  EMil IOrc MGos SPer
- 'Diana' ♀                    CDoC EMil EPfP EPla SBid SLon
                               WBcn
- 'Dorothy Crane'              CBlo CEnd EBee ENot MGos
                               WWes
- 'Duc de Brabant' (d)         CDoC EMil IOrc SCoo SEas SPer
                               SRms
- 'Elegantissimus'             See *H. syriacus* 'Lady Stanley'
- 'Hamabo' ♀                   CB&S CDoC EBee ECle ELan EMil
                               ENot IOrc MBri MGos MRav
                               MWat SBid SPar SPer SPla SPlb
                               WStI
¶ - 'Helene'                   CDoC MBri

|  |  |
|---|---|
| - 'Jeanne d'Arc' (d) | EMil IOrc SLon |
| § - 'Lady Stanley' (d) | CMil IOrc SEas SPer SPla |
| ¶ - 'Lavender Chiffon' | ENot LRHS MGos SMad |
| - 'Lenny' | EBee ENot MGos |
| § - 'Meehanii' (v) | CBot CEnd EBee ELan ENot EPfP |
|  | MAsh MBri MGos SBid SCoo SPla |
|  | SSta |
| - 'Monstrosus' | CBlo IOrc SMad |
| § - 'Oiseau Bleu' ♀ | CB&S CDoC CTri EBee ELan EMil |
|  | ENot EPla GOrc IOrc MBri MGos |
|  | MWat NBee NFla SBod SEas SPer |
|  | SPla SPlb SReu SRms SSpi SSta |
|  | WDin WGwG WSHC WStI |
| - Pink Giant™ ♀ | CB&S CDoC CEnd EBrP EBre |
|  | ELan EPfP IOrc LBre MBri MGos |
|  | SBid SBre SLon SPer WDin |
| - 'Red Heart' ♀ | CDoC CEnd EBee ECle ELan EPfP |
|  | GChr IOrc MBri MWat SBid SPer |
|  | SRms WDin WStI WWeb |
| ¶ - 'Rosalbane' | MBri |
| ¶ - 'Roseus Plenus' (d) | WBcn |
| - Russian Violet | CDoC CEnd COtt EBee ELan EMil |
|  | IOrc MBri MGos MRav SMad |
| - 'Speciosus' | IOrc SLon SPer |
| - 'Totus Albus' | EMil IOrc WSHC |
| - 'Variegatus' | See H. syriacus 'Meehanii' |
| ¶ - 'White Chiffon' | ENot LRHS MGos |
| - 'William R. Smith' | CBlo EBee ECle ELan ENot IOrc |
|  | MGos SPer SRPl SSta WWeb WWes |
| - 'Woodbridge' ♀ | CB&S CDoC CEnd CTri EBee |
|  | ELan EMil ENot EPfP GChr GOrc |
|  | IOrc MBri MGos MRav MWgw |
|  | NFla SEas SPer SPla SPlb SReu |
|  | SSpi SSta WDin WStI |
| *tiliaceus* | Last listed 1998 |
| *trionum* | CArn CHad CInt SOWG WKif |
| - 'Spirits Bay' | Last listed 1997 |
| - 'Sunny Day' | ELan |

## HIERACIUM (Asteraceae)

|  |  |
|---|---|
| *alpinum* | Last listed 1996 |
| *argenteum* | WGwy |
| *auriantiacum* | See *Pilosella aurantiaca* |
| *bombycinum* | See *H. mixtum* |
| *brunneocroceum* | See *Pilosella aurantiaca* subsp. |
|  | *carpathicola* |
| *glabrum* | Last listed 1996 |
| § *glaucum* | LNor NHol WByw WEas WWin |
| § *lanatum* | CGle GBin NBir NBro NNrd WEas |
|  | WPer WRos WWin |
| *maculatum* | CInt CRow ECoo EHoe EMar EPar |
|  | EPla GGar MFir MPEx NCat NGdn |
|  | NPer NSti WOak WPer WRos |
| ¶ - 'Blue Leaf' | WCot |
| § *mixtum* | Last listed 1996 |
| *murorum* | CPea |
| *pilosella* | See *Pilosella officinarum* |
| *praecox* | See *H. glaucum* |
| *scotostictum* | Last listed 1998 |
| ◆ x *stoloniflorum* | See *Pilosella* x *stoloniflora* |
| *variegatum* | See *Hypochaeris variegata* |
| *villosum* | CInt EBee EHoe MDun NBro |
|  | NFor WHer WLin WPer WRos |
|  | WWin |
| *waldsteinii* | MBro NFor WCru |
| *welwitschii* | See *H. lanatum* |

## HIEROCHLOE (Poaceae)

|  |  |
|---|---|
| *odorata* | ELau GPoy IIve |
| *redolens* | GAbr GAri GOrn |

## HIMALAYACALAMUS (Poaceae - Bambusoideae)

|  |  |
|---|---|
| § *falconeri* | CFil EFul EPla SDix SDys WPGP |
| § - 'Damarapa' | EPla ISta LJus SCob SDix WJun |
| § *hookerianus* | CFil ISta LJus WBay WJun |

## HIMANTOGLOSSUM (Orchidaceae)

|  |  |
|---|---|
| ¶ *hircinum* | EFEx |

## x HIPPEASPREKELIA (Amaryllidaceae)

|  |  |
|---|---|
| 'Mystique' | Last listed 1996 |

## HIPPEASTRUM ✿ (Amaryllidaceae)

|  |  |
|---|---|
| x *acramannii* | GCal |
| ◆ *advenum* | See *Rhodophiala advena* |
| - BCW 4764 | Last listed 1998 |
| 'Ambiance' | ETub |
| 'Apple Blossom' | ETub LAma NRog |
| 'Baby Star' | ETub |
| 'Beautiful Lady' | LAma |
| 'Bestseller' ♀ | LAma |
| *bifidum* | See *Rhodophiala bifida* |
| 'Byjou' | NRog |
| 'Christmas Gift' | ETub |
| 'Double Record' (d) | Last listed 1998 |
| 'Dutch Belle' | LAma |
| *elwesii* | SBla |
| - BCW 4999 | Last listed 1998 |
| 'Fantastica' | LAma |
| 'Germa' | ETub |
| 'Green Goddess' | ETub |
| ¶ 'Inca' | LAma |
| 'Jewel' | ETub |
| 'King of the Stripes' | Last listed 1996 |
| 'Lady Jane' | ETub |
| ¶ 'Lemon Lime' | LAma |
| ¶ 'Lima' | LAma |
| 'Lucky Strike' | Last listed 1996 |
| 'Ludwig's Goliath' | LAma |
| ¶ 'Mary Lou' | LAma |
| ¶ 'Melusine' | ETub |
| 'Orange Souvereign' ♀ | Last listed 1991 |
| 'Oskar' | NRog |
| *papilio* | LAma LHil NRog |
| * - 'Butterfly' | ETub |
| 'Papillon' | LAma |
| 'Pasadena' | ETub |
| 'Picotee' | ETub LAma |
| 'President Johnson' | Last listed 1998 |
| 'Red Lion' | Last listed 1998 |
| *roseum* | See *Rhodophiala rosea* |
| 'Rosy Queen' | Last listed 1996 |
| sp. BCW 5038 | Last listed 1998 |
| sp. BCW 5154 | Last listed 1998 |
| 'Spotty' | Last listed 1996 |
| 'Star of Holland' ♀ | Last listed 1998 |
| *stylosum* | Last listed 1998 |
| 'United Nations' | LAma |
| 'Vera' | Last listed 1996 |
| 'White Dazzler' | LAma |
| 'White Snow' | Last listed 1996 |
| 'Wonderland' | Last listed 1996 |
| 'Yellow Pioneer' | LAma |

## HIPPOBROMA See LAURENTIA

## HIPPOCREPIS (Papilionaceae)

|  |  |
|---|---|
| § *comosa* | CKin EWFC SSpi |
| - 'E.R. Janes' | MPla |
| § *emerus* | CB&S CHan CMHG CPle CTri |
|  | EHic ELan ERea GOrc LHop MBal |
|  | NFla STre SUsu WCot WHCG |
|  | WPat WSHC WTro |

**HIPPOLYTIA** (Asteraceae)
§ *berderi*  CHan LHop LLWP WCot

**HIPPOPHAE** (Elaeagnaceae)
*rhamnoides* ♀  CB&S CHan CKin CLnd EBee
EBrP EBre ELan ENot GChr GPoy
GRei IOrc LBre LBuc MBar MBlu
MCoo MWat NWea SBre SPlb
WDin WFar WHCG WMou WStI
WWal WWat
¶ - 'Askola' (f)  MGos
- 'Leikora' (f)  CAgr MBlu MGos SPer WMou
WPat
- 'Pollmix' (m)  CAgr LEdu MBlu MGos SPer
*salicifolia*  CLnd SLon WPGP

**HIPPURIS** (Hippuridaceae)
*vulgaris*  CBen CRDP EHon EMFW WMAq
WWye

**HIRPICIUM** (Asteraceae)
*armerioides*  NWCA

**HISTIOPTERIS** (Dennstaedtiaceae)
*incisa*  CFil

**HOHERIA** ✿ (Malvaceae)
§ *angustifolia*  CFil CHan CPMA ECou SMac
WPGP WPic
'Borde Hill'  EPfP SBid SPer SSpi SSta WHCG
*glabrata* ♀  CB&S CFil ECou MBal WPGP
WSpi
¶ - 'Silver Stars'  EPfP
'Glory of Amlwch' ♀  CFil CGre CMHG CSam CWit
GCal MBel SBid SSpi SSta WCru
WPGP WSHC
§ *lyallii* ♀  CB&S CDoC CPle CSam ECou
ELan EPfP IOrc SSta WDin
*microphylla*  See *H. angustifolia*
*populnea*  CB&S CBot
*sexstylosa* ♀  CAbb CBot CDoC CFee CHid
ELan EPfP IOrc ISea MBel MBlu
SLon SPer SSta
- 'Pendula'  CB&S
- 'Stardust' ♀  CAbP CFil CMCN CPMA LRHS
MBri NOla SMad SPer SReu SSpi
WPGP WWat

**HOLBOELLIA** (Lardizabalaceae)
*coriacea*  CB&S CBot CGre CPlN CSam
EPfP SAPC SArc SBra SOWG
WCru
*fargesii* DJHC 506  WCru
*latifolia*  COtt CPlN CSam CTrG EBee EHic
SAPC SArc SOWG SPer WCot
WCru WWat
- SF 95134  ISea

**HOLCUS** (Poaceae)
*lanatus*  CKin
*mollis* 'Albovariegatus'  CCuc EBee ECha EHoe ELan
EMon EPGN EPla EWsh GCHN
GMaP MBar MFir MMoz MWgw
NBro NHol NPer NRya NSti NVic
SCob SPer SSoC WCot WEas WLin
WPer WWat
¶ - 'White Fog'  CCuc EBee

**HOLODISCUS** (Rosaceae)
*discolor*  CFil CPle EBee ECtt ELan EPla
EWes GOrc MBlu MTis MWhi NSti
SBid SDys SLon SMad SSpi SSta
WHCG WPat WSHC

- var. *ariifolius*  EPfP
¶ - var. *discolor*  CB&S
- NJM 94044  WPGP
*dumosus*  Last listed 1998

**HOMALOCLADIUM** (Polygonaceae)
§ *platycladum*  CHal

**HOMERIA** (Iridaceae)
*breyniana*  See *H. collina*
- var. *aurantiaca*  See *H. flaccida*
§ *collina*  SMrm
§ *flaccida*  LAma LBow NRog
*marlothii*  Last listed 1998
*ochroleuca*  LAma LBow NRog

**HOMOGLOSSUM** See GLADIOLUS

**HOMOGYNE** (Asteraceae)
*alpina*  Last listed 1997

**HOOKERIA** (Hookeriaceae)
*lucens*  Last listed 1996

**HORDEUM** (Poaceae)
*jubatum*  CCuc CInt CKel EHoe EPGN EPPr
EPla EWes GAri LHil LIck NChi
NSti SIng SLod SUsu WElm WPrP
WRos WWhi WWye
*murinum*  Last listed 1996

**HORKELIA** (Rosaceae)
¶ *fusca capitata*  EBee
*rydbergii*  NHol

**HORMINUM** (Lamiaceae)
*pyrenaicum*  CMHG CNic ELan GCrs GDra
LLWP MBro NMen SBla SHFr
SRms SSmi WCla WLin WPer
WPyg WWin WWye
- pale blue  MSte

**HOSTA** ✿ (Hostaceae)
'Abba Dabba Do' (v)  CBdn EGol SApp
'Abby'  CBdn EGol EPGN LHos
'Abiqua Ariel'  NWes SApp
'Abiqua Blue Krinkles'  CWin NWes SApp
'Abiqua Drinking Gourd'  CBdn EFou EGol EPGN GSki
'Abiqua Moonbeam' (v)  CBdn EPGN
'Abiqua Recluse'  EGol LHos
'Abiqua Trumpet'
(*tokudama*)  EGol EMic
*aequinoctiiantha*  EGol LHos
'Aksarben'  EMic
'Alba' (*sieboldiana*)  See *H.* 'Elegans Alba'
(*sieboldiana*)
*albomarginata*  See *H.* 'Paxton's Original'
(*sieboldii*)
§ 'Albomarginata' (*fortunei*)  CB&S CBdn CHar EBee EGol EMic
EPGN LFis MBar MNrw MOne
NBir NFai SPer WHoo WViv
'Allan P. McConnell' (v)  CBdn EGol EMic EPGN LHos
NHar SApp
'Alpine Aire'  EMic
¶ 'Alvatine Taylor'  CBdn
'Amanuma'  EGol EMic NWes
'Amber Maiden' (v)  EGol LHos
'Antioch' (*fortunei*) (v)  CBdn CWin EGol EMic MBel
MMiN MMoz MRav MSte NCut
'Aoki' (*fortunei*)  EBee EMic EPGN LHos NHol
NWes SCob
'Aphrodite' (*plantaginea*) (d)  CBlo CFir EGol EPGN LHos LRHS
NCut NWes WRus

'Apple Green' — EMic
'Aqua Velva' — EGol LHos
'Argentea Variegata' — See *H. undulata* var. *undulata*
(*undulata*)
'Aspen Gold' (*tokudama* — EMic
hybrid)
'August Beauty' — CBdn
'August Moon' — More than 30 suppliers
I 'Aurea' (*nakaiana*) — Last listed 1998
'Aurea' (*sieboldii*) — See *H. sieboldii* f. *subcrocea*
**aureafolia** — See *H.* 'Starker Yellow Leaf'
♦ 'Aureoalba' (*fortunei*) — See *H.* 'Spinners' (*fortunei*)
'Aureomaculata' (*fortunei*) — See *H. fortunei* var. *albopicta*
\* 'Aureomarginata' — CBlo
§ 'Aureomarginata' (*montana*) — CBdn EBrP EBre EGol EHoe EMic
EPGN GCal LBre LSyl MMiN NHol
NLar NWes SApp SBre SCro SPla
SSpi WRus WWoo
§ 'Aureomarginata' — CBdn CBro CHad EBrP EBre ECha
(*ventricosa*) ♀ — EGol EMic EPGN LBre MBro
MMiN SBre SPer SRms WHil WRus
'Aureostriata' (*tardiva*) — See *H.* 'Inaho'
'Aurora Borealis' — EGol EPGN LHos
(*sieboldiana*) (v)
'Azure Snow' — EGol LHos
¶ 'Babbling Brook' — EGol
'Banyai's Dancing Girl' — EMic
'Barbara White' — EGol
'Beauty Substance' — CBdn EGol
¶ 'Bee's Colossus' — SApp
**bella** — See *H. fortunei* var. *obscura*
'Bennie McRae' — EGol
'Betcher's Blue' — EGol EMic
'Betsy King' — EBee EHic EMic EPGN LHos
MRav NCut NHol WMer WWoo
'Bette Davis Eyes' — EGol
'Betty' — EGol
'Big Boy' (*montana*) — EGol
'Big Daddy' (*sieboldiana* — More than 30 suppliers
hybrid)
'Big Mama' (*sieboldiana* — EGol EMic LHos LRHS
hybrid)
'Bill Brincka' (v) — EGol
¶ 'Birchwood Elegance' — CBdn
§ 'Birchwood Parky's Gold' — CBdn CHan CMHG EBee EGol
EMic EPGN LHos MBNS MMiN
MTed NHar NHol SApp SCob SRPl
SRms SSpi SWas
'Birchwood Ruffled Queen' — EGol EMic
'Black Beauty' — Last listed 1998
'Black Hills' — CBdn EGol LHos LRHS
§ 'Blonde Elf' — EGol EMic EPGN LHos SApp
♦ 'Blue Angel' misapplied — See *H. sieboldiana* var. *elegans*
'Blue Angel' (*sieboldiana*) ♀ — CB&S CBdn EGol EHoe ELan
EMic EOrc EPGN GMaP LFis LHos
MBal MBel MBro MMiN MWat
NOrc NTay SMrm
'Blue Arrow' — CBdn EGol EMic EPGN LHos
SApp
'Blue Blazes' — LHos
'Blue Boy' — CBdn CHad EGol EMic EPGN
LHos MMiN NHol
'Blue Cadet' — CB&S CBdn CHad EAst EBee EGol
EMic GSki LHos MBar MBel MMiN
MUlv NCat NCut NFai NHol NLar
NOak WRus WWoo
'Blue Edger' — CBdn EGol
'Blue Heart' (*sieboldiana* — ECha EMic LPio
var. *elegans*)
'Blue Jay' — EGol
'Blue Lake' — Last listed 1997
'Blue Mammoth' — CBdn EGol EMic EPGN
(*sieboldiana*)

'Blue Seer' (*sieboldiana*) — CBdn EGol
'Blue Shadows' — CBdn CBlo CWin EBee LHos
(*tokudama*) (v) — NCut SApp WRus WSan
'Blue Umbrellas' — CBdn EFou EGol ELan EMic EOrc
(*sieboldiana* hybrid) — EPGN GSki LHos MMiN NGdn
NHol NWes WTin
'Blue Velvet' — CBdn
'Blue Vision' — EMic EPGN LHos
'Bold Edger' (v) — CBdn LHos
'Bold Ribbons' (v) — CBdn EGol EMic LHos MMiN
NWes
'Bold Ruffles' (*sieboldiana*) — EGol LRHS
'Bonanza' (*fortunei*) — EMic
'Border Bandit' (v) — EGol LHos
'Borsch 1' — CBdn
'Borwick Beauty' — CBdn
(*sieboldiana*) (v)
'Bountiful' — EGol EMic
'Bouquet' — EGol
'Bressingham Blue' — CBdn EBrP EBre ECtt EGol EMic
LBre LHos MRav NDea SBre SPer
WFar
'Bright Gold' — LHos
'Bright Lights' (*tokudama*) — CBdn EGol EMic EPGN LHos
(v)
'Brim Cup' (v) — CBdn CWin EGol EMic EPGN
LHos NWes WRus
'Brooke' — EGol EMic
'Bruce's Blue' — EGol GSki
'Buckshaw Blue' — CBdn CBos EGol EMic EPGN
GBin MBal MMiN MMoz NBir
NGdn NTay NTow SSpi
'Butter Rim' (*sieboldii*) (v) — EGol
\* 'Caerula' (*ventricosa*) — CWin
I 'Calypso' — EPGN
'Camouflage' — ECha
¶ 'Canada Blue' — EFou
'Candy Hearts' — CBdn CHan CMHG EGol EMic
EPGN MMiN WMer
**capitata** MSF 850 — CFil WPGP
**caput-avis** — See *H. kikutii* var. *caput-avis*
'Carnival' (v) — CBdn EGol
'Carol' (*fortunei*) (v) — CBdn CLAP CWin EGol EMic
LHos MMiN WHal
♦ 'Carrie Ann' — See *H.* 'Carrie' (*sieboldii*)
§ 'Carrie' (*sieboldii*) (v) — EGol EMic SApp
'Celebration' (v) — EGol ELan EMic EPGN LHos
MMiN MRPP WRus
'Challenger' — EMic
'Change of Tradition' (v) — CBdn EMic
'Chantilly Lace' (v) — EGol
'Chartreuse Wiggles' — CBdn EGol LHos
(*sieboldii*)
'Cheatin Heart' (v) — EGol
'Chelsea Babe' (v) — EGol LHos
'Chelsea Ore' — Last listed 1996
(*plantaginea*) (v)
'Cherry Berry' — CBdn EGol
'Chinese Sunrise' — CBdn EGol EMic EOrc EPGN
(*cathayana*) (v) — MBel MMiN NHol SCro WHil
WMer
'Chiquita' — EGol LHos
§ 'Chôkô Nishiki' — CBdn EBee EGol EPGN MMiN
(*montana*) (v) — NWes
'Christmas Tree' (v) — CBdn EGol EMic EPGN GBri LHos
LRHS MMiN NWes SApp WRus
'Citation' (v) — EGol
'Clarence' — CBdn
'Claudia' — MMiN
**clausa** — EMic
- var. **normalis** — CBdn EBrP EBre EGol EMic GCal
GQui LBre LHos MCli MGed
NGdn NLar SBre

| | |
|---|---|
| 'Collectors Choice' | EGol |
| 'Color Glory' (*sieboldiana*) (v) | CBlo CWin EBee EGol EPGN GNau LHos NCut NWes SApp |
| 'Colossal' | EGol EMic LRHS |
| ¶ 'Coquette' (v) | CBdn |
| 'County Park' | EGol |
| 'Cream Delight' (*undulata*) | See *H. undulata* var. *undulata* |
| 'Cream Edge' | See *H.* 'Fisher Cream Edge' (*fortunei*) |
| 'Crepe Suzette' (v) | CBdn EGol EMic LHos LRHS |
| 'Crested Reef' | CBdn EBee EGol EMic NHol |
| § *crispula* ♀ | CB&S CBdn CBos CHad CRow EGol EHon EMic EPGN EPar EWTr GGar LGro LHos MBal MBar NChi NFai NLon SChu SRms SSpi |
| 'Crown Jewel' (v) | EMic EPGN LHos |
| 'Crown Prince' | CBdn EGol EMic EPGN |
| § 'Crowned Imperial' (*fortunei*) (v) | CBdn EMic EPGN NHol |
| 'Crumples' (*sieboldiana*) | CWin SApp |
| 'Crusader' (v) | CBdn EGol EPGN LHos |
| 'Cupid's Dart' (v) | EGol |
| ¶ 'Dark Star' (v) | EGol EPGN SApp |
| ¶ 'Dartmoor Forest' | CBdn |
| ¶ 'Darwin's Standard' | CBdn |
| 'Dawn' | CBdn EGol EPar LHos |
| 'Daybreak' | CBdn EGol EMic EPGN LHos LRHS |
| *decorata* | CBdn EGol EMic LHos MBar MCli MMiN |
| 'Delia' | EPGN |
| ¶ 'Devon Desire' | CBdn |
| ¶ 'Devon Discovery' | CBdn |
| 'Devon Giant' | Last listed 1996 |
| 'Devon Gold' | CBdn |
| 'Devon Green' | CBdn EPGN GBri LHos NBro SApp WIvy WRus |
| 'Devon Mist' | CBdn NWes |
| 'Devon Tor' | CBdn EPGN LHos NWes |
| 'Dew Drop' (v) | CBdn EGol |
| 'Diamond Tiara' (v) | CBdn EGol EMic LHos LRHS |
| 'Dimple' | ECha |
| 'Domaine de Courson' | CWin GBin GNau WFar |
| 'Don Stevens' (v) | CBdn EGol |
| 'Dorothy' | EMic |
| 'Dorset Blue' | EGol EMic EPGN GSki |
| 'Doubloons' | EGol LHos LRHS |
| 'Drummer Boy' | CBdn EGol EMic MGan |
| 'Duchess' | LHos |
| 'DuPage Delight' (*sieboldiana*) (v) | CBdn EGol EMic LHos NWes |
| 'El Capitan' (v) | CBdn EGol EMic EPGN LRHS NWes |
| § *elata* | EGol EMic MCli MMiN NWes WWat |
| 'Elatior' (*nigrescens*) | CBdn EMic LHos |
| 'Eldorado' | See *H.* 'Frances Williams' (*sieboldiana*) |
| 'Elegans' | See *H. sieboldiana* var. *elegans* |
| § 'Elegans Alba' (*sieboldiana*) | Last listed 1997 |
| 'Elfin Power' (*sieboldii*) (v) | EGol |
| 'Elisabeth' | CBdn CWin EAst EBee LBuc |
| 'Elizabeth Campbell' (*fortunei*) (v) | CBdn CLAP EMic EPGN LHos MMiN MSte SSpi |
| 'Ellen' | EMic |
| 'Ellerbroek' (*fortunei*) (v) | EGol EMic GSki MMiN |
| 'Elsley Runner' | EGol |
| 'Elvis Lives' | CBdn EGol |
| 'Emerald Carpet' | EMic |
| 'Emerald Skies' | EGol |
| 'Emerald Tiara' (v) | CBdn EGol EMic EPGN LHos LRHS MMiN |

| | |
|---|---|
| 'Emily Dickinson' (v) | CBdn EGol LHos LRHS SApp |
| 'Eric Smith Gold' | ECha |
| 'Evelyn McCafferty' (*tokudama* hybrid) | EGol |
| 'Evening Magic' (v) | EGol EMic EPGN LHos |
| 'Excitation' | EGol EMic LPio |
| 'Fair Maiden' (v) | CBdn EGol EPGN |
| 'Fall Bouquet' (*longipes hypoglauca*) | EGol |
| 'Fall Emerald' | CBdn EMic |
| 'Fantastic' (*sieboldiana* hybrid) | EGol |
| 'Feather Boa' | EMic EPGN NHar |
| * 'Fenman's Fascination' | EMic |
| ¶ 'Fire and Ice' (v) | CBdn EGol EPGN |
| § 'Fisher Cream Edge' (*fortunei*) | CBdn MMiN WMer |
| 'Floradora' | CBdn EGol EMic EPGN NDov |
| 'Flower Power' | CBdn EGol LHos LRHS |
| *fluctuans* | EMic |
| 'Fond Hope' (*sieboldiana*) | MMiN |
| 'Fool's Gold' (*fortunei*) | CBdn CWin EMic WMer |
| 'Formal Attire' (*sieboldiana* hybrid) (v) | CBdn EGol LHos |
| 'Forncett Frances' (v) | EGol LHos |
| 'Fortis' | See *H. undulata* var. *erromena* |
| *fortunei* | CBdn CHad CRow EGol EMic MBal NDea NHol NLon SChu SPer WEas WWal |
| § - var. *albopicta* ♀ | More than 30 suppliers |
| § - - f. *aurea* ♀ | CBdn CHad CMGP CMHG CRow ECha EGol EHoe ELan EPGN EPla GMaP LHyd MBal MBar MLov MMal MMiN NLar SChu SCro SPer SPla SRms WFar WRus |
| - - - dwarf form | Last listed 1997 |
| - f. *aurea* | See *H. fortunei* var. *albopicta* f. *aurea* |
| § - var. *aureomarginata* ♀ | More than 30 suppliers |
| - var. *gigantea* | See *H. montana* |
| § - var. *hyacinthina* ♀ | CBdn CGle CHad EGol EMic EOld EOrc EPGN GCal LHos MBal MBar MMiN NBus NCut NDea NOrc SSpi WFar WWin |
| ◆ - - variegated | See *H.* 'Crowned Imperial' (*fortunei*) |
| § - var. *obscura* | CBdn ECho EGol EMic LHos NWes |
| - var. *rugosa* | EMic |
| 'Fountain' | NHol |
| 'Fragrant Blue' | CBdn EGol |
| 'Fragrant Bouquet' (v) | CBdn CBlo EFou EGol EMic EPGN LHos MMiN NWes SChu |
| 'Fragrant Gold' | EGol EMic EPGN LHos MMiN |
| 'Francee' (*fortunei*) (v) ♀ | More than 30 suppliers |
| 'Frances Williams Improved' (*sieboldiana*) (v) | EGol EWTr MMiN |
| 'Frances Williams' seedlings | NSti |
| § 'Frances Williams' (*sieboldiana*) (v) ♀ | More than 30 suppliers |
| ¶ 'Freising' (*fortunei*) | EBee |
| 'Fresh' (v) | EGol EPGN LHos |
| ¶ 'Fried Green Tomatoes' | CBdn |
| 'Fringe Benefit' (v) | CBdn EBrP EBre EGol EMic EPGN LBre LHos MMiN NWes SApp SBre WLin WMer |
| 'Frosted Jade' (v) | CBdn EGol EMic EPGN LHos LRHS NDov NWes |
| 'Gaiety' (v) | EGol EMic EPGN |
| ¶ 'Gaijin' | CBdn |
| 'Gala' (v) | EMic EPGN |
| 'Gay Blade' (v) | EGol |

| | |
|---|---|
| 'Geisha' (v) | CBdn EGol EMic EPGN LHos MCCP SApp |
| 'Gene's Joy' | EPGN LHos |
| 'Gigantea' (*sieboldiana*) | See *H. elata* |
| 'Gilt Edge' (*sieboldiana*) (v) | EMic |
| 'Ginko Craig' (v) | More than 30 suppliers |
| *glauca* | See *H. sieboldiana* var. *elegans* |
| * 'Glauca' (*fortunei*) | MMiN |
| I 'Gloriosa' (*fortunei*) (v) | EGol EMic EPGN LHos MMiN |
| ¶ 'Glory' | CBdn |
| 'Gold Drop' | CBdn ECho EGol EMic EOrc LGre LHos MMiN NHol WMer |
| 'Gold Edger' | More than 30 suppliers |
| ◆ 'Gold' (*fluctuans*) | See *H.* 'Ogon Sagae' |
| § 'Gold Haze' (*fortunei*) | CBdn CHad EGol EMic EOrc EPGN MBel NHol NTay |
| 'Gold Leaf' (*fortunei*) | EGol |
| 'Gold Regal' | CBdn EGol EMic EPGN MMiN |
| 'Gold Splash' | MBro WHoo |
| 'Gold Standard' (*fortunei*) (v) | More than 30 suppliers |
| 'Goldbrook' (*fortunei*) (v) | EGol WBcn |
| 'Goldbrook Genie' | EGol |
| 'Goldbrook Glamour' (v) | EGol |
| 'Goldbrook Gold' | EGol |
| 'Goldbrook Grace' | EGol |
| 'Goldbrook Gratis' (v) | EGol |
| 'Goldbrook Grayling' | EGol |
| 'Goldbrook Grebe' | EGol |
| 'Golden Age' | See *H.* 'Gold Haze' (*fortunei*) |
| 'Golden Anniversary' | CBdn EBee EMic LHos NHol WRHF |
| 'Golden Bullion' (*tokudama*) | CBdn EGol EMic EPGN GBri |
| 'Golden Circles' | See *H.* 'Frances Williams' (*sieboldiana*) |
| 'Golden Decade' | EGol |
| 'Golden Isle' | EGol EMic |
| ¶ 'Golden Mammoth' (*sieboldiana*) | LHos |
| 'Golden Medallion' (*tokudama*) | CBdn CBro CMHG CTri EGol ELan EMic EOrc EPGN LHos MBNS MBel MMiN NFai NGdn NHol SApp WFar WWat |
| 'Golden Nakaiana' | See *H.* 'Birchwood Parky's Gold' |
| 'Golden' (*nakaiana*) | See *H.* 'Birchwood Parky's Gold' |
| 'Golden Oriole' | CBdn LHos |
| 'Golden Prayers' (*tokudama*) | CBdn CBro CHad CPlt EGol ELan EMic ENot EOrc EPGN ERos GSki LGre LHos MBel MMiN MRPP MRav NBro NFai NGdn NHol NOrc NTay SChu WAbe WRus |
| 'Golden Scepter' (*nakaiana*) | CBdn CMHG EGol EMic EPGN LHos MMiN NHol |
| 'Golden Sculpture' (*sieboldiana*) | CBdn EGol LHos |
| 'Golden Spider' | EGol EMic LHos |
| 'Golden Sunburst' (*sieboldiana*) | CBdn CHad EBee EGol ELan EMic EPGN GSki LHos MBal MMiN MOne NHol SMrm WFar |
| 'Golden Tiara' (v) ♀ | More than 30 suppliers |
| 'Goldsmith' | EGol EMic |
| 'Good as Gold' | EMic EPGN LHos |
| *gracillima* | CRow EPGN EPar |
| 'Granary Gold' (*fortunei*) | CBdn EGol EPGN LHos LRHS |
| 'Grand Master' | CBdn CBlo EGol EMic LHos |
| 'Grand Tiara' (v) | CBdn EGol EMic EPGN |
| 'Great Expectations' (*sieboldiana*) (v) | CBdn CLAP CWin EGol EMic EPGN GBri LHos LRHS MBNS NBro NWes SApp WRus WWoo |
| 'Green Acres' (*montana*) | EMic LGre MMiN WFar |
| 'Green Angel' | EGol |
| ¶ 'Green Formal' | MMiN |
| 'Green Fountain' (*kikutii*) | CBdn EFou EGol EMic EPGN LHos MLov MMiN MSte NWes WMer |
| 'Green Gold' (*fortunei*) (v) | CBdn EMic MMiN WMer |
| 'Green Piecrust' | CBdn CWin EGol EMic EPGN LHos |
| ¶ 'Green Ripples' | CHid |
| 'Green Sheen' | CWin EGol EMic EPGN LHos |
| 'Green Summer Fragrance' | CBdn |
| 'Green Velveteen' | CBdn EGol |
| 'Green with Envy' (v) | EGol |
| 'Greenwood' | EMic |
| 'Grey Beauty' | EHic |
| ¶ 'Grey Piecrust' | EGol |
| 'Ground Master' (v) | More than 30 suppliers |
| 'Ground Sulphur' | EGol EMic |
| 'Guacamole' (v) | CBdn EGol EPGN |
| 'Gum Drop' | EMic EPGN |
| 'Hadspen Samphire' | CBos CHad CHan EGol EMic EPGN |
| 'Hadspen Seersucker' | CHad SLod |
| 'Hadspen White' (*fortunei*) | EMic LHos |
| 'Haku-chu-han' (*sieboldii*) (v) | CBdn |
| 'Hakujima' (*sieboldii*) | EGol LGre |
| 'Happy Hearts' | EGol EMic MMiN |
| 'Harrison' | EMic |
| 'Harvest Glow' | EGol EMic SSpi |
| * 'Hazel' | EMic |
| 'Heart Ache' | EGol |
| 'Heartleaf' | EMic MMiN |
| 'Heartsong' (v) | EGol LHos |
| 'Heide Eurm' | LHos |
| 'Helen Doriot' (*sieboldiana*) | EGol EMic |
| 'Helen Field Fischer' (*fortunei*) | CBdn EMic |
| *belonioides* hort. f. *albopicta* | See *H. rohdeifolia* |
| 'Herifu' (v) | EGol EMic MMiN |
| ¶ 'Hilda Wassman' (v) | EGol |
| 'Hirao Majesty' | CBdn EGol |
| 'Hirao Splendor' | LHos |
| 'Hirao Supreme' | EGol |
| 'Hirao Tetra' | CBdn |
| 'Hoarfrost' | EMic |
| 'Holstein' | See *H.* (Tardiana Group) 'Halcyon' |
| ¶ 'Honey Moon' | CBdn |
| § 'Honeybells' ♀ | More than 30 suppliers |
| 'Honeysong' (v) | CBdn EPGN |
| 'Hoosier Harmony' (v) | CBdn EGol |
| ¶ 'Hoosier Homecoming' | SApp |
| § 'Hyacintha Variegata' (*fortunei*) | CMHG GBri MMiN |
| 'Hydon Gleam' | EMic EPGN LHos MMiN |
| 'Hydon Sunset' (*nakaiana*) | CBdn CHan CM&M CMHG EBee EBrP EBre EGol EMic EOrc EPGN LBre LHos LHyd MBal MBel MBro MMiN NFai NHol NOak NSti NTay SBre SMad SUsu WAbe WHoo WWat |
| *hypoleuca* | EGol WLin |
| § 'Inaho' | CBdn EGol EMic EPGN LHos MMiN NWes |
| 'Inniswood' (*montana*) (v) | CBlo CLAP CWin EGol EMic EPGN LHos MMiN NSti NWes SApp |
| 'Invincible' | CBdn CLAP EFou EGol EMic EPGN LGre LHos MLov MMiN NWes WMer WTin |
| 'Iona' (*fortunei*) | CBdn EGol EMic EPGN LHos MMiN SSpi |
| 'Irish Breeze' | EPGN |
| ¶ 'Iron Gate Delight' (v) | CBdn |

'Iron Gate Glamor'               EGol EPGN LHos
'Iron Gate Supreme' (v)          EMic
'Iwa Soules'                     EGol
'Jade Beauty'                    CBdn
'Jade Cascade'                   CB&S CLAP CMil EBee EFou EGol
                                 EHic MSte NHol NLar NWes SApp
                                 SMrm SPla WCot WOVN
'Jade Scepter' (*nakaiana*)      EGol EMic LRHS
'Jadette' (v)                    EGol
'Janet' (*fortunei*) (v)         CBdn EGol EMic EOrc MMiN
                                 WMer WSan WWoo
'Japan Boy'                      See *H*. 'Montreal'
'Japan Girl'                     See *H*. 'Mount Royal' (*sieboldii*)
'Joker' (*fortunei*) (v)         CBdn EBee NHol
'Jolly Green Giant'              EMic
  (*sieboldiana* hybrid)
'Journeyman'                     EGol LHos
'Julie Morss'                    CBdn CBlo EGol EMic EPGN LHos
                                 MMiN MMoz NWes
'Jumbo' (*sieboldiana*)          EMic LHos
'June Beauty' (*sieboldiana*)    MMiN
'Just So' (v)                    CBdn EGol LHos
'Kabitan'                        See *H. sieboldii* f. *kabitan*
'Kath's Gold'                    SIng
'Kelly'                          Last listed 1997
'Kelsey'                         EMic
'Kifukurin' (*kikutii*) (v)      CBdn
I 'Kifukurin' (*pulchella*) (v)  CBdn EGol
'Kifukurin Ubatake'              EPGN
  (*pulchella*)
*kikutii*                        EGol EMic EOrc MMiN
§ - var. *caput-avis*            EBrP EBre EGol EMic LBre SBre
  - var. *polyneuron*            CLAP EGol
  - var. *pruinosa*              Last listed 1996
  - var. *tosana*                EGol
§ - var. *yakusimensis*          CRDP EGol EMic GCrs GDra
                                 NTow SMad
§ 'Kirishima'                    CBdn EMic EPGN MBel NHar SIng
*kiyosumiensis*                  CRow CWin NHol
'Klopping Variegated'            EGol EMic
  (*fortunei*)
'Knave's Green'                  EPGN
'Knockout' (v)                   CBdn EGol EPGN LHos
'Krinkled Joy'                   EMic NWes
'Krossa Cream Edge'              EBee LHos NHol
  (*sieboldii*) (v)
'Krossa Regal' ♀                 More than 30 suppliers
'Lacy Belle' (v)                 EGol
'Lady Helen'                     EMic MMiN
¶ 'Lady Isobel Barnett' (v)      SApp
¶ 'Lakeside Black Satin'         EPGN
'Lakeside Symphony' (v)          EGol LHos
§ *lancifolia* ♀                 More than 30 suppliers
'Leather Sheen'                  EGol EMic EPGN
'Lee Armiger' (*tokudama*        EGol
  hybrid)
'Lemon Delight'                  CBdn EGol EPGN LHos
'Lemon Lime'                     CBdn EGol EMic LHos MMiN
                                 MNrw SIng WHil WMer
¶ 'Lemon Twist'                  LHos
'Leola Fraim' (v)                CBdn EGol EPGN LHos MMiN
'Leviathan'                      EMic
* *lilacina*                     SCro WFar WMoo
'Lime Krinkles'                  Last listed 1996
'Little Aurora' (*tokudama*      EGol EMic EPGN MBal
  hybrid)
'Little Blue' (*ventricosa*)     EGol EMic SLod
'Little Fatty'                   MMiN
'Little Razor'                   CBdn EGol
'Little White Lines' (v)         CBdn EGol EMic EPGN LHos
                                 LRHS
'Little Wonder' (v)              EGol LHos

*longipes*                       EGol LGre
*longissima*                     CMHG EGol NHed SRPl WCru
  - var. *longissima*            Last listed 1998
'Louisa' (*sieboldii*) (v)       ECha EGol LHos MSte NNrd
'Love Pat' (*tokudama*) ♀        CBdn CFir EGol EMic EPGN GSki
                                 LHos MLov MMiN MRav NWes
                                 WMer WWoo
'Lucky Charm'                    EMic
¶ 'Lucy Vitals' (v)              CBdn
'Lunar Eclipse' (v)              EGol EMic LGre MMiN NWes
                                 SApp
'Maculata'                       Last listed 1996
'Maculata Aurea'                 Last listed 1998
'Maekawa'                        EGol
'Maple Leaf' (*sieboldiana*) (v) EMic
N 'Marginata Alba' (*fortunei*)  CBot CHad EBee ECha LPBA
                                 MMiN NDea WWin
'Marilyn'                        EGol EMic EPGN LHos LRHS
'Marquis' (*nakaiana* hybrid)    EGol
'Maruba Iwa' (*longipes*         CBdn
  var. *latifolia*)
'Maruba' (*longipes*             EGol
  var. *latifolia*)
'Mary Jo'                        EMic
'Mary Marie Ann'                 EMic EPGN LHos
  (*fortunei*) (v)
§ 'Masquerade' (v)               CBdn EGol EPGN LHos NHar
                                 WFar
'Mediovariegata' (*undulata*)    See *H. undulata* var. *undulata*
'Mentor Gold'                    EGol EMic LHos
'Mesa Fringe' (*montana*)        CBdn MMiN
* 'Metallic Sheen'               CBdn LHos
* 'Metallica'                    CBdn
'Midas Touch' (*tokudama*        CBdn EGol EMic EOrc LHos NBus
  hybrid)                        NDov NHol NLar WRus
'Middle Ridge'                   EBee EMic NHol
§ 'Midwest Gold'                 Last listed 1996
'Midwest Magic' (v)              CBdn EGol LHos MMiN
'Mildred Seaver'                 CBdn CWin EGol EMic LHos
                                 LRHS MMiN NWes
¶ 'Millie's Memoirs' (v)         EGol
'Minnie Klopping'                EMic EPGN NDov
§ *minor*                        CBdn CBro EBrP EBre EGol ELan
                                 EMic ERos GDra GSki LBre LHos
                                 MTho NHol SBre SSpi WFar
  - hort. f. *alba*              See *H. sieboldii* var. *alba*
  - Goldbrook form               EGol
'Minor' (*ventricosa*)           See *H. minor*
* 'Minuta' (*undulata*)          CBdn WMer
¶ 'Minuteman' (*fortunei*)       CBdn CWin EAst EBee EPGN
                                 GBin NCut SApp
'Misty Waters' (*sieboldiana*)   EMic
'Moerheim' (*fortunei*) (v)      CBdn EGol EMic EPGN EPar GBin
                                 LHos MBar MBri MLov MMiN
                                 NHol SChu WHal WMer
N *montana*                      CBdn CBlo CHad ECha EGol EMic
                                 MMiN NHol
§ 'Montreal'                     EMic
'Moon Glow' (v)                  EGol EMic EPGN LHos LRHS
'Moon River' (v)                 CBdn EGol EPGN LHos
* 'Moon Shadow' (v)              EGol
'Moonbeam'                       CBdn
'Moonlight' (*fortunei*) (v)     CBdn EGol EMic EPGN GMaP
                                 LRHS MMiN NWes SApp WMer
                                 WRus
'Moscow Blue'                    EGol
'Mount Fuji' (*montana*)         MMiN
* 'Mount Hope' (v)               EGol
'Mount Kirishima' (*sieboldii*)  See *H*. 'Kirishima'
§ 'Mount Royal' (*sieboldii*)    EMic NHol
'Mountain Snow'                  CBdn EGol EMic EPGN LHos
  (*montana*) (v)

'Mountain Sunrise'    EGol
  (*montana*)
'Munchkin'    CBdn
*nakaiana*    SRms WWat
'Nakaimo'    CBdn EMic NHol
'Nameoki'    NHol SRPl
'Nana' (*ventricosa*)    See *H. minor*
§ 'Nancy Lindsay' (*fortunei*) (v) CBdn EBee EGol EMic EPGN
    LHos NGdn SChu SMrm
'Neat Splash' (v)    CBdn CWin EBee NBir NHol
'Neat Splash Rim' (v)    EMic EPGN WWoo
'New Wave'    EGol LHos
'Night before Christmas' (v)    CBdn CFir CMGP COtt CWin
    EBee EGol EPGN GBin GNau
    MBel MSCN NCut NWes SApp
    WRus WWoo
*nigrescens*    CBdn EBee EGol EMic EPGN GCal
    LHos LRHS MTed
'Nokogiryama'    EGol EMic
'North Hills' (*fortunei*) (v)    CBdn EBee EGol EMic LHos LPio
    MMiN NBir NGdn NWes SChu
    SLon SMrm WWat
'Northern Halo'    EGol ELan EMic LHos LRHS MMiN
  (*sieboldiana*) (v)
'Northern Lights'    EGol LHos LRHS
  (*sieboldiana*)
'Northern Sunray'    EMic
  (*sieboldiana*) (v)
'Obscura Marginata'    See *H. fortunei* var.
  (*fortunei*)    *aureomarginata*
§ 'Ogon Sagae'    WFar
'Okazuki Special'    CBdn EGol
¶ 'Old Faithful'    EGol
'Olga's Shiny Leaf'    EGol EMic
♦ 'On Stage' (*montana*)    See *H.* 'Chôkô Nishiki' (*montana*)
*opipara*    Last listed 1996
'Oriana' (*fortunei*)    CBdn CWin EGol EMic
'Oxheart'    EMic
*pachyscapa*    EMic
'Pacific Blue Edger'    CBdn CBlo CFir EFou EGol EPGN
    LHos NWes
¶ 'Pandora's Box' (v)    CBdn EGol EPGN
¶ 'Paradigm' (v)    EGol
'Paradise Joyce'    CBdn EGol
'Paradise Power'    CBdn EGol
'Paradise Puppet'    CBdn
¶ 'Paradise Red Delight'    CBdn
'Paradise Standard'    CBdn
'Pastures Green'    EGol
'Pastures New'    EFou EGol EMic EPGN LGre LHos
    NHol SApp
¶ 'Patrician' (v)    CBdn
'Patriot' (v)    CBdn CBlo CLAP EAst EBee EGol
    EMic EPGN GBin GBri LHos LRHS
    MBNS MBri MLov NEgg NWes
    SApp SMrm WFar WMer WRus
    WWeb WWoo
'Paul's Glory' (v)    CBdn EGol EMic EPGN LHos
    NWes
§ 'Paxton's Original'    CMGP ECha EGol EPGN LHyd
  (*sieboldii*) (v) ♀    MBal MBar MRav NLar SApp
    SRms WPer
'Peace' (v)    CBdn EGol EPGN LHos
'Pearl Lake'    CBdn EBee EGol EMic EPGN LGre
    LHos MBel MMiN NHol NTay
    NWes
'Peedee Gold Flash'    CBdn EPGN LHos NHar
'Pelham Blue Tump'    EGol EMic
'Perry's True Blue'    EMic
'Peter Pan'    CBdn EGol EMic
'Phoenix'    EGol GBin SApp
'Phyllis Campbell' (*fortunei*) See *H.* 'Sharmon' (*fortunei*)

'Picta' (*fortunei*)    See *H. fortunei* var. *albopicta*
'Piecrust Power'    EGol
'Piedmont Gold'    EGol EMic EOrc EPGN LGre
    MMiN MSte NTay
'Pineapple Poll'    CBdn EMic EPGN LHos LRHS
    MMiN MMoz NWes
'Pizzazz' (v)    CBdn EGol EMic EPGN LHos
    MMiN NWes SApp
*plantaginea*    CBdn EGol EMic EPar LGre LSyl
    SSpi
- var. *grandiflora*    See *H. plantaginea* var. *japonica*
§ - var. *japonica* ♀    CBot CGle CHad CHan CLAP
    ECha EPGN EPar GSki MCAu
    NBus NWes SChu WWat
'Platinum Tiara'    CBdn EPGN LHos MMiN
  (*nakaiana*) (v)
'Pooh Bear' (v)    CBdn EGol
'Popo'    EGol
'Potomac Pride'    CBdn EPGN LHos
'Puck'    EGol
'Purple Dwarf'    CBdn CBlo CWin EBee EGol LBuc
    LHos NHol NLar WWoo
'Purple Lady Finger'    SApp
'Purple Profusion'    EGol EMic
*pycnophylla*    EGol SWas
'Queen Josephine' (v)    CBdn EGol EPGN
'Radiant Edger' (v)    CBdn CWin EBee EGol EPGN
    LHos LRHS
'Raleigh Remembrance'    EGol LHos LRHS
'Rascal' (v)    CBdn EGol LHos
'Raspberry Sorbet'    CBdn EGol
*rectifolia*    EMic LHos NHol WWat
'Regal Splendor' (v)    CBdn EBee EGol EMic EPGN GSki
    LHos MMiN NWes SCob WRus
'Resonance' (v)    EMic EPGN LHos LRHS MBri
    MMiN NTay
'Reversed' (v)    CBdn CBlo EGol ELan EMic EPGN
    EPfP LHos NBro NCut NGdn
    NWes WRus
'Rhapsody' (*fortunei*) (v)    EGol
'Richland Gold' (*fortunei*)    EGol EMic EPGN LRHS
* 'Rippling Waters'    EGol
'Rippling Waves'    EMic
'Robert Frost' (v)    EGol
'Robusta' (*fortunei*)    See *H. sieboldiana* var. *elegans*
§ *rohdeifolia* (v)    CLAP EGol EMic LBuc WHal
- f. *albopicta*    CBdn EGol ELan EPGN EPar
    NDov NHol SChu WTin
'Rosemoor'    EGol
'Rough Waters'    Last listed 1997
'Royal Sovereign'    Last listed 1998
§ 'Royal Standard' ♀    More than 30 suppliers
'Royalty'    EGol LHos
¶ 'Ruffles'    MMiN
*rupifraga*    EGol EMic
'Russell's Form' (*ventricosa*)    EMic
'Ryan's Big One'    EMic
§ 'Sagae' ♀    CBdn CLAP EBrP EBre EGol EMic
    EPGN GNau LBre MBri NWes
    SApp SBre SCob SMrm WFar
¶ 'Saint Elmo's Fire'    EGol
§ 'Saishu Jima' (*sieboldii*    EGol EMic NHol WCru
    *spatbulata*)
¶ 'Salute'    EGol
'Samual Blue'    Last listed 1998
'Samurai' (*sieboldiana*) (v)    CBdn CWin EBee EGol EMic LHos
    MRav NWes
'Savannah'    EGol LHos
'Sazanami' (*crispula*)    See *H. crispula*
'Scooter'    CBdn EPGN
'Sea Bunny'    EGol
'Sea Dream' (v)    CWin EGol EMic EPGN LHos
    MMiN

'Sea Drift' — EGol EPGN
'Sea Fire' — EGol
'Sea Gold Star' — CBdn EGol EPGN LRHS
'Sea Lotus Leaf' — CBdn EGol EMic EPGN LRHS SApp
¶ 'Sea Mist' (v) — CBdn
'Sea Monster' — EGol LRHS
'Sea Octopus' — EGol EMic NWes
'Sea Sapphire' — EGol LHos LRHS
'Sea Sprite' (v) — LBuc LHos MMiN MRPP
'Sea Thunder' (v) — CBdn EGol EPGN
'Sea Yellow Sunrise' — CBdn EGol EMic
'Second Wind' (fortunei) (v) — CBdn EPGN LHos
'See Saw' (undulata) — CBdn EGol EMic MMiN
'Semperaurea' (sieboldiana) — GSki
'Sentinels' — Last listed 1998
'September Sun' (v) — CBdn EGol EMic EPGN LHos LRHS MMiN
'Serendipity' — CBdn EGol EMic EPGN LHos
'Shade Fanfare' (v) ♀ — CBdn CBro EBrP EBre EGol ELan EMic EOrc EPGN EPar LBre LHos MBNS MBal MBri MMiN MRav MWat NBir NFai NGdn NLar NSti NTay SBre SCro WHil WHoo
'Shade Master' — CB&S CBdn CBlo EAst EBrP EBre EGol EMic GBin LBre MOne NHol SBre WHil
§ 'Sharmon' (fortunei) (v) — CBdn EGol EMic EPGN LWoo MBel MMiN NHol NTay NWes SChu
'Sheila West' — CBdn
'Shelleys' (v) — EGol
'Sherborne Swift' — CBdn EGol EMic MMiN
'Shining Tot' — EGol EMic EPGN LHos
'Shogun' (v) — EGol LHos
* 'Showboat' — CBdn EGol EPGN
sieboldiana — CHad CHan CMHG CRow EFou EGol ELan EMic EPar LFis LHos LHyd MBNS MBal MRav NChi NFor NHol SPer SPlb SRms WAbe WFar WWat
§ – var. elegans ♀ — More than 30 suppliers
– var. mira — Last listed 1997
§ sieboldii var. alba — CHad CHan CMGP EGol ELan SSpi
§ – f. kabitan (v) — CBdn CLAP CWin EGol EPGN LHos NHar
– f. shiro-kabitan (v) — EGol EPGN
– var. thunbergiana — See H. sieboldii f. spathulata
'Silver and Gold' — MMiN
* 'Silver Chimes' — Last listed 1998
'Silver Crown' — See H. 'Albomarginata' (fortunei)
'Silver Lance' — EGol EMic EPGN
'Sitting Pretty' (v) — EGol EPGN
'Snow Cap' (v) — CBdn CBlo CWin EGol EPGN LHos NWes SApp WWoo
'Snow Crust' (elata) (v) — CBdn EGol EMic LRHS MMiN
'Snow Flakes' (sieboldii) — CBdn EBee EGol EMic EMil EPGN GCal LHos LPio MBar MBri MCli NBro NFla NHol NPro SCob SLod SPer WFar WMer
¶ 'Snow White' (undulata) (v) — EGol
'Snowden' — More than 30 suppliers
'Snowstorm' (sieboldii) — CBdn NHol
'So Sweet' — CBdn CBlo CLAP EGol EMic EPGN GSki LHos MBro MLov SMrm WRus WWat WWoo
'Something Blue' — CBdn LHos
sp. from Japan — Last listed 1998
'Sparkling Burgundy' — CBdn EGol
'Special Gift' — EBee EGol EMic LBuc LHos
¶ 'Spinners' — LHos

§ 'Spinners' (fortunei) (v) — CBdn CHad ECha EGol EMic MMiN SChu SSpi
'Sprengeri' — Last listed 1998
'Spritzer' (v) — CBdn EGol EMic EPGN LHos
'Squash Edge' (sieboldiana) (v) — EPGN
'Squiggles' (v) — EGol LHos
§ 'Starker Yellow Leaf' — EMic
'Stenantha' (fortunei) — EMic
'Stenantha Variegated' (fortunei) (v) — NHol
'Stiletto' (v) — CBdn EGol EMic EPGN LHos NHar
'Striptease' (fortunei) (v) — CBdn CWin EGol EPGN GBin GNau
'Sugar and Cream' (v) — CBdn CM&M EAst EGol EMic EOrc EPGN LHos LPio MCLN MMiN NGdn NRoo NWes SChu
'Sugar Plum Fairy' (gracillima) — EGol
'Sultana' (v) — CBdn
'Sum and Substance' ♀ — More than 30 suppliers
'Summer Fragrance' — CBdn CWin EGol EMic EPGN LHos LRHS MMiN SApp
'Summer Music' (v) — CBdn CWin EGol EPGN LHos NCut NWes SApp WRus
'Summer Snow' (sieboldiana) (v) — EPGN
'Sun Glow' — EMic
'Sun Power' — CBdn CBro EBrP EBre EGol EMic EOrc EPGN EPar LBre LHos MMiN MWat NTay SBre WRus
'Sundance' (fortunei) (v) — EGol EMic
* 'Sunflower' — NOak
'Super Bowl' — EGol LRHS
'Super Nova' (v) — EGol
¶ 'Susy' — MMiN
'Suzuki Thumbnail' — EMic
'Sweet Standard' — Last listed 1997
'Sweet Susan' — CBlo EGol EMic EOrc MMiN SPer WMer
'Sweet Tater Pie' — CBdn EPGN
'Sweetheart' — EMic
¶ 'Sweetie' (v) — EGol LHos
'Swirling Hearts' — EGol LHos
'Tall Boy' — CBdn CSev EBee ECha EGol EMic EPla GCal LHos MWgw SPer SSpi WWat
'Tall Twister' — EMic
'Tamborine' (v) — CBdn EGol EPGN LHos SApp
Tardiana Group — CBdn CBro CMGP EGol ELan MBal NGdn NHol SPer WKif
– 'Blue Belle' — CBdn ECha EGol EMic LHos MBro MMiN MSte NGdn WHoo
– 'Blue Blush' — CBdn CWin EGol LHos
– 'Blue Danube' — EGol EMic MMiN
– 'Blue Diamond' — CBdn CHad CMHG EGol EMic EPGN MMiN WShe
– 'Blue Dimples' — CBdn CWin EGol EMic LRHS MMiN
– 'Blue Moon' — CBro EBrP EBre EFou EGol ELan EMic EOrc EPGN ERos LBre LGre LHop LHos MBNS MLov MRPP NHol SBre WEas
– 'Blue Skies' — CBlo EGol EMic EPGN LHos
– 'Blue Wedgwood' — CBdn CBro CRow EAst EGol ELan EMic EOrc EPGN LHos MBel MWat NDov NHol NTay SChu SPla WRus WWat
– 'Bright Glow' — CBdn EGol EMic
– 'Brother Ronald' — CBdn EGol LRHS
– 'Camelot' — CBdn EGol EMic LHos LRHS

| | |
|---|---|
| - 'Curlew' | CBdn EGol EMic |
| - 'Devon Blue' | CBdn EGol EMic MMiN NWes |
| - 'Dorset Charm' | CBdn EGol EMic MBal MMiN |
| - 'Dorset Flair' | EGol EMic |
| - 'Eric Smith' | CBdn CWin EGol EMic EPGN LGre SChu WFar |
| - 'Goldbrook Glimmer' (v) | EGol |
| - 'Hadspen Blue' | CBdn CMHG EAst EBrP EBre EGol EMic EPGN LBre MBNS MBel MBrN MBro MRav NBir NBro NHol NRoo NSti SBre SChu SCob SMrm SRPl SUsu WMow WRus WWat |
| - 'Hadspen Blue Jay' | CBro CHad |
| - 'Hadspen Dolphin' | EMic |
| - 'Hadspen Hawk' | CBdn EGol LGre LRHS |
| - 'Hadspen Heron' | CBdn CHad EGol EMic EPGN LHos MBal NPar SChu |
| § - 'Halcyon' ♀ | More than 30 suppliers |
| - 'Happiness' | CBdn CWin EGol EHoe EMic LHos MRav |
| - 'Harmony' | CBdn EGol EMic LRHS |
| - 'Irische See' | Last listed 1997 |
| - 'June' (v) | CBdn EBrP EBre EGol EMic ENot EPGN GBin GSki LBre LHos MCLN MLov MRav NHar SApp SBre SCob SMrm SPer WSan WWeb |
| - 'Nicola' | EGol EMic EPGN MMoz WRus |
| - 'Osprey' | EGol LRHS |
| - pink-flowered | MMiN |
| - 'Serena' | Last listed 1997 |
| - 'Sherborne Profusion' | EMic |
| - 'Sherborne Songbird' | EMic |
| - 'Sherborne Swan' | EMic |
| - 'Silvery Slugproof' | CBdn NWes SApp |
| - 'Wagtail' | EMic |
| *tardiflora* | CBdn CFil EGol EMic ERos MBal SApp WCot WPGP |
| *tardiva* | LHos |
| ¶ 'Tea and Crumpets' | EPGN |
| 'Temple Bells' | EGol LHos |
| 'Tenryu' | EGol LHos |
| 'The Twister' | EGol EMic MMiN |
| 'Thomas Hogg' | See *H. undulata* var. *albomarginata* |
| 'Thumb Nail' | CBdn ECha EGol GAri GSki |
| *tibae* | EMic |
| 'Tiny Tears' (*venusta*) | EGol |
| *tokudama* | CBdn CHad CHan EFou EGol EPGN LNor MBro MMiN NBir NFai NGdn NHol NSti SChu SCob WKif |
| § - f.*aureonebulosa* | EGol EPGN LGre LHos |
| - f.*flavocircinalis* (v) | CBdn EBee ECha EGol EMic EPGN LHos MMiN SApp WFar WWoo |
| ¶ 'Torchlight' (v) | EGol EMic |
| 'Tot Tot' | EMic GAri |
| 'Trail's End' | EMic |
| 'True Blue' | CBdn EBee EGol EMic LHos MMiN NWes SApp WWoo |
| 'Tutu' | EGol |
| ¶ 'Twilight' | CBdn EPGN MBNS |
| 'Twinkle Toes' | EGol EMic |
| ¶ 'Twist of Lime' (v) | EGol SApp |
| *undulata* | EMic LFis NDea NLon SRms WFar |
| § - var. *albomarginata* | More than 30 suppliers |
| § - var. *erromena* ♀ | CBdn CHan CMGP EHon EMic LFis LHos LPBA MBro NFla NHol SChu SPer SSpi |
| § - var. *undulata* (v) ♀ | CBdn CBot CBro CRow EAst EBee EHoe EHon ELan ENot EPGN EWTr GChr LGro LPBA MMiN SChu SPer WEas WKif WRus WWin |
| - var. *univittata* (v) ♀ | CBro CRow ECha EGol EMic EPGN EPfP LHos MBel MMiN MMoz NDov NFai NPro NTay SCob SPla WFar WKif |
| 'Urajiro Hachijo' | EGol |
| 'Urajiro' (*hypoleuca*) | EGol |
| 'Valentine Lace' | CBdn EGol EMic EPGN NWes WMer |
| 'Vanilla Cream' (*cathayana*) | CBdn EGol EMic EPGN LHos |
| 'Variegata' (*gracillima*) | See *H.* 'Vera Verde' |
| 'Variegata' (*tokudama*) | See *H. tokudama* f. *aureonebulosa* |
| 'Variegata' (*undulata*) | See *H. undulata* var. *undulata* |
| 'Variegata' (*ventricosa*) | See *H.* 'Aureomarginata' (*ventricosa*) |
| 'Variegated' (*fluctuans*) | See *H.* 'Sagae' |
| *ventricosa* ♀ | CB&S CBdn CBro CHad CHid CKel EAst EBot EBrP EBre EGol EGoo EMic GDra GMaP LBre LPBA MBel MNrw MRav NHar NHol NVic SBre SLon SMrm SSpi WFar WWat |
| ¶ - *aureo* 'Maculata' | NBir |
| - var. *aureomaculata* | CHad EBee EGol EMic ENot EPGN LHos MMiN NCut NSti NTay SPer    - |
| I 'Venucosa' | EGol EMic WFar |
| 'Venus Star' | EPGN GSki LHos |
| *venusta* ♀ | CBdn CBro CRow CSWP EBrP EBee EGol ELan EMic EOrc EPGN EPar ERos LBre LGre LHil MBal MBel MMiN NBir NHar NMen NNrd NSti SBre SHFr WEas WHil WWat |
| - dwarf form | CSWP LGre |
| - x *sieboldiana* | CHan |
| - *yakusimensis* | See *H. kikutii* var. *yakusimensis* |
| § 'Vera Verde' (v) | CBdn CWin EBee EPGN ERos GQui NBir |
| 'Verna Jean' (v) | EGol |
| 'Veronica Lake' (v) | CBdn EGol |
| 'Verte' (*sieboldii*) | See *H. sieboldii* f. *spathulata* |
| 'Viette's Yellow Edge' (*fortunei*) (v) | MMiN |
| 'Vilmoriniana' | EGol EMic MMiN |
| 'Viridis Marginata' | See *H. sieboldii* f. *kabitan* |
| 'Wahoo' (*tokudama*) (v) | EGol |
| ¶ 'Warwick Essence' | EGol |
| ¶ 'Waving Winds' (v) | EGol LHos |
| 'Wayside Blue' | EMic |
| 'Wayside Perfection' | See *H.* 'Royal Standard' |
| 'Weihenstephan' (*sieboldii*) | EGol |
| 'Wheaten Gold' | Last listed 1996 |
| 'Wheaton Blue' | CBdn LHos |
| ¶ 'Whirlwind' (*fortunei*) (v) | CBdn EGol EPGN |
| ¶ 'White Christmas' (*undulata*) (v) | EPGN LHos |
| 'White Fairy' (*plantaginea*) | CBdn EPGN WShe |
| ¶ 'White Feather' (*undulata*) | EBee |
| 'White Gold' | CBdn EGol EPGN LHos |
| 'White Tacchi' | EMon |
| ¶ 'White Triumphator' | CBdn |
| 'Wide Brim' (v) ♀ | More than 30 suppliers |
| 'Wind River Gold' | EGol NWes |
| 'Windsor Gold' | See *H.* 'Nancy Lindsay' (*fortunei*) |
| ¶ 'Winfield Blue' | EGol |
| * 'Winfield Gold' | CBdn EGol |

| | |
|---|---|
| 'Winning Edge' (*tokudama*) | EGol |
| 'Wogon Giboshi' | See *H.* 'Wogon' (*sieboldii*) |
| § 'Wogon' (*sieboldii*) | CBdn CM&M CRDP CRow EFou EGol EMic EPGN EPla GMaP MAvo NHar NHol NSti |
| 'Wogon's Boy' | CBdn EGol EPGN |
| 'Wrinkles and Crinkles' | EMic LRHS |
| 'Yakushima-mizu' (*gracillima*) | CBdn EGol EMic |
| * *yakushimana* | NHar |
| 'Yellow Boa' | EMic |
| 'Yellow Edge' (*fortunei*) | See *H. fortunei* var. *aureomarginata* |
| 'Yellow Edge' (*sieboldiana*) | See *H.* 'Frances Williams' (*sieboldiana*) |
| 'Yellow River' (*montana*) (v) | CBdn ECha EGol EMic EPGN LHos LRHS |
| 'Yellow Splash' (v) | CBdn CWin ECha EPGN LHos MBel NTay |
| 'Yellow Splash Rim' (v) | EGol LHos MBel MMiN WBcn |
| *yingeri* | EGol WCot |
| - B&SWJ 546 | WCru |
| 'Zager Blue' | EMic |
| 'Zager Green' | EMic |
| 'Zager White Edge' (*fortunei*) (v) | CLAP EMic EPGN LHos |
| 'Zounds' | More than 30 suppliers |

## HOTTONIA (Primulaceae)

| | |
|---|---|
| *palustris* | CBen ECoo EHon ELan EMFW LPBA MSta NDea NVic SWat SWyc |

## HOUSTONIA (Rubiaceae)

| | |
|---|---|
| *caerulea* L. | ECho ELan WWin |
| - hort. | See *H. michauxii* |
| - L. var. *alba* | CInt ELan EWes WPer |
| § *michauxii* | GAri SGre |
| - 'Fred Mullard' | EPot EWes NPri |

## HOUTTUYNIA (Saururaceae)

| | |
|---|---|
| *cordata* | CAgr EMar GBar IBlr MWgw NLak NSti SWat WFar |
| ¶ - 'Boo-Boo' (v) | EPla |
| § - 'Chameleon' (v) | More than 30 suppliers |
| - 'Flame' | LRHS |
| - 'Flore Pleno' (d) | CBen CGle CRow ECha EHon ELan EPla EWTr LPBA MBal MRav MSta NBir NBro NWes SIde SIng SLon SPer SRms SWat SWyc WFar WMAq WRus WWin |
| ¶ - 'Joker's Gold' | EBee |
| ¶ - 'Terry Clarke' | EMan MCLN |
| - 'Tricolor' | See *H. cordata* 'Chameleon' |
| - Variegata Group | EPot GBar IBlr LPBA MAsh NBro NDea |
| * 'Pied Piper' | CDoC SAga WCot |

## HOVEA (Papilionaceae)

| | |
|---|---|
| *celsii* | See *H. elliptica* |
| § *elliptica* | Last listed 1997 |

## HOVENIA (Rhamnaceae)

| | |
|---|---|
| *acerba* | CFil WPGP |
| *dulcis* | CB&S CGre CMCN CPle ELan EPfP SCob |

## HOWEA (Arecaceae)

| | |
|---|---|
| § *belmoreana* | LPal |
| *forsteriana* ♀ | LPal MBri |

## HOYA (Asclepiadaceae)

| | |
|---|---|
| *acuta* | Last listed 1998 |

| | |
|---|---|
| *angustifolia* | LChe |
| *archboldiana* | LChe |
| *arnottiana* | Last listed 1998 |
| § *australis* | LCns SOWG |
| *bandaensis* | Last listed 1998 |
| *bilobata* | LChe |
| *carnosa* ♀ | CB&S EBak ELan GQui LCns NRog SRms |
| - 'Compacta' | CHal |
| * - *compacta* 'Hindu Rope' | NPer |
| * - 'Exotica' ♀ | Last listed 1998 |
| * - 'Jungle Garden' | Last listed 1998 |
| * - 'Krinkle' | NPer |
| - 'Krinkle Eight' | Last listed 1998 |
| - 'Latifolia' | ECon |
| - 'Prolifica' | Last listed 1996 |
| - 'Red Princess' | MBri |
| - 'Rubra' | Last listed 1998 |
| - 'Tricolor' | NPer |
| - 'Variegata' | LCns MBri SRms |
| *cinnamomifolia* | LChe SOWG |
| * *compacta* 'Tricolor' | NPer |
| *crassicaulis* | Last listed 1996 |
| *cumingiana* | LChe |
| *curtisii* | Last listed 1996 |
| *darwinii* hort. | See *H. australis* |
| *densifolia* | LChe |
| *eitapensis* | LChe |
| *engleriana* | Last listed 1998 |
| *fusca* 'Silver Knight' | Last listed 1997 |
| *fuscomarginata* | See *H. pottsii* |
| *globulosa* | LChe |
| *imperialis* | LChe |
| *inconspicua* | LChe |
| *ischnopus* | Last listed 1996 |
| *kenejiana* | Last listed 1996 |
| *kerrii* | LChe |
| *lacunosa* | LChe |
| *lanceolata* subsp. *bella* ♀ | CB&S CHal GQui LCns MBri NRog SRms |
| *linearis* | LChe |
| *longifolia* | LChe |
| *macgillivrayi* | LChe |
| *magnifica* | LChe |
| *meredithii* | Last listed 1996 |
| *motoskei* | LChe |
| *multiflora* | LChe LCns MBri SOWG |
| - 'Variegata' (v) | LChe |
| *neocaledonica* | Last listed 1998 |
| *nicholsoniae* | LChe |
| *nummularioides* | LChe |
| *obovata* | Last listed 1996 |
| *odorata* | LChe |
| *parasitica* var. *citrina* | Last listed 1996 |
| *parviflora* | LChe |
| *pauciflora* | LChe |
| *polyneura* | Last listed 1998 |
| § *pottsii* | Last listed 1996 |
| *pubicalyx* 'Red Buttons' | LChe |
| * - 'Silver Pink' | LChe |
| *purpureofusca* | Last listed 1998 |
| *serpens* | Last listed 1996 |
| *shepherdii* | LChe |
| 'Shibata' | LChe |
| *uncinata* | Last listed 1996 |

## HUGUENINIA (Brassicaceae)

| | |
|---|---|
| *alpina* | See *H. tanacetifolia* |
| § *tanacetifolia* | SSvw |
| ¶ - subsp. *suffruticosa* | GVic |

**HUMATA** (Davalliaceae)
*pyxidata*          See *Davallia solida* var. *pyxidata*
¶ *tyermannii*      NMar

**HUMEA** (Asteraceae)
*elegans*           See *Calomeria amaranthoides*

**HUMULUS** (Cannabaceae)
*japonicus*         ECoo MSal
*lupulus*           CAgr CArn CB&S CPln ECoo
                    ELau GAri GBar GPoy ILis LHol
                    MSal SIde WHer WSel WStI WWye
- (f)               Last listed 1996
- (m)               Last listed 1996
- 'Aureus' ♀        More than 30 suppliers
- 'Aureus' (f)      MCCP SMad WCot WWat
- 'Aureus' (m)      MCCP WWat
- 'Cobbs'           GPoy SDea
¶ - 'First Gold'    SDea
- 'Fuggle'          GPoy SDea
¶ - 'Hallertauer'   SDea
- 'Hip-hop'         EMon
¶ - 'Mathon'        SDea
¶ - 'Northdown'     SDea
- 'Taff's Variegated'  EMon EWes GVic
- 'Wye Challenger'  GPoy

**HUNNEMANNIA** (Papaveraceae)
*fumariifolia* 'Sunlite'   CPle

**HUTCHINSIA** See PRITZELAGO

**HYACINTHELLA** (Hyacinthaceae)
*acutiloba*         Last listed 1996
*lineata* M&T 5048  Last listed 1998
*millingenii*       EHyt

**HYACINTHOIDES** (Hyacinthaceae)
§ *hispanica*       CAvo CBro CHid EWFC IBlr MBri
                    NBir NHol WWye
- 'Alba'            Last listed 1998
- *algeriensis* AB&S 4337   Last listed 1998
- Donau             See *H. hispanica* 'Danube'
- 'Excelsior'       ETub
- 'La Grandesse'    CBro
- 'Rosabella'       CBro
¶ - 'Rose'          NCat
§ *italica*         Last listed 1998
§ - *vicentina*     Last listed 1998
- - *alba*          Last listed 1997
§ *non-scripta*     CArn CAvo CBro CKin EOld EPar
                    EPot ETub EWFC IBlr LAma LFox
                    MMal NMir NRog SPlb WCla WShi
- pink bell         Last listed 1998

**HYACINTHUS** ✿ (Hyacinthaceae)
*amethystinus*      See *Brimeura amethystina*
*azureus*           See *Muscari azureum*
*comosus* 'Plumosus'   See *Muscari comosum*
                    'Plumosum'
*fastigiatus*       See *Brimeura fastigiata*
*orientalis* 'Amethyst'   EWal LAma NRog
- 'Amsterdam'       EWal LAma NRog
- 'Anna Liza'       NRog
- 'Anna Marie' ♀    CAvo CBro ETub EWal LAma MBri
                    NRog
- 'Ben Nevis' (d)   LAma MBri NRog
- 'Bismarck'        LAma NRog
- 'Blue Giant'      LAma NRog
- 'Blue Jacket' ♀   CBro ETub LAma NRog
- 'Blue Magic'      EWal LAma NRog

- 'Blue Orchid' (d)   LAma
- 'Blue Star'       LAma
- 'Borah' ♀         EWal LAma NRog
- 'Carnegie'        CBro ETub EWal LAma NRog
- 'City of Haarlem' ♀   CBro ETub EWal LAma NRog
- 'Colosseum'       LAma
- 'Concorde'        Last listed 1998
- 'Delft Blue' ♀    CAvo CBro EWal LAma MBri
                    NRog
- 'Distinction'     LAma
- 'Edelweiss'       Last listed 1998
- 'Fondant'         LAma
- 'Gipsy Queen' ♀   CBro ETub EWal LAma MBri
                    NRog
- 'Hollyhock' (d)   EWal LAma MBri NRog
- 'Jan Bos'         CAvo EWal LAma NRog
- 'King Codro' (d)  LAma MBri NRog
- 'King of the Blues'   LAma NRog
- 'La Victoire'     LAma NRog
- 'Lady Derby'      EWal LAma
- 'L'Innocence' ♀   CBro LAma NRog
- 'Lord Balfour'    LAma
- 'Madame Krüger'   Last listed 1998
- 'Marconi' (d)     LAma NRog
- 'Marie'           LAma NRog
- 'Mont Blanc'      EWal
- 'Mulberry Rose'   EWal LAma NRog
- 'Myosotis'        LAma
§ - 'Oranje Boven'  LAma
- 'Ostara' ♀        CBro EWal LAma MBri NRog
¶ - 'Paul Hermann'  ETub
- 'Peter Stuyvesant'   ETub EWal LAma NRog
- 'Pink Pearl' ♀    CBro LAma NRog
- 'Pink Royal' (d)  LAma NRog
- 'Pink Surprise'   Last listed 1996
- 'Princess Margaret'   LAma
- 'Prins Hendrik'   Last listed 1998
- 'Queen of the Pinks'   LAma NRog
- 'Queen of the Violets'   NRog
- 'Rosalie'         EWal
- 'Rosette' (d)     LAma
- 'Salmonetta'      See *H. orientalis* 'Oranje Boven'
§ - 'Sneeuwwitje'   LAma NRog
- Snow White        See *H. orientalis* 'Sneeuwwitje'
- 'Violet Pearl'    CBro LAma NRog
- 'Vuurbaak'        LAma
- 'White Pearl'     CAvo LAma NRog
* 'Woodstock'       ETub LAma

**HYBANTHUS** (Violaceae)
*floribundus*       Last listed 1998

**HYDRANGEA** ✿ (Hydrangeaceae)
*angustipetala*     CFil
- B&SWJ 3454        WCru
¶ - B&SWJ 3814      WCru
*anomala*           Last listed 1997
- subsp. *anomala*  SSpi
- - B&SWJ 2411      WCru
- from Taiwan B&SWJ 3117   WCru
§ - subsp. *petiolaris* ♀   More than 30 suppliers
§ - - var. *cordifolia*   CFil CHan EPla MBNS SBra WPGP
                    WWeb
♦ - - dwarf form    See *H. anomala* subsp. *petiolaris*
                    var. *cordifolia*
- - *tiliifolia*    EPfP GCal MBlu SNut WWat
- - 'Yakushima'     CFil WPGP
§ *arborescens*     CArn CFil MRav NFor WPGP
                    WWeb
- 'Annabelle' ♀     More than 30 suppliers
§ - subsp. *discolor*   WCru
- - 'Sterilis'      CFil EHic SPla SSpi WCru WPGP

| | |
|---|---|
| - 'Grandiflora' ♀ | CB&S CBot CFil GOrc MRav SBod SPer WDin WHCG WPGP WSHC WWin |
| - subsp. *radiata* | CFil CHan ELan NHlc SNut SSpi WCru WPGP WWat |
| *aspera* | CBlo CFil CGre GOrc IOrc SAga SSpi SSta WCru |
| - Kawakamii Group | CFil CMil EPla SSta WPGP |
| § - 'Macrophylla' ♀ | CBlo CFil CMil EPfP MBri NPal SSpi WCru WGer WPGP WWat |
| - 'Mauvette' | CFil MBlu NPal SSpi SSta WCru WPGP |
| - 'Peter Chappell' | SSpi |
| § - subsp. *robusta* | CFil GAri SNut WCru WPGP |
| - 'Rocklon' | CFil WCru WPGP |
| - 'Rosthornii' | See *H. aspera* subsp. *robusta* |
| - 'Sam Macdonald' | CFil SSpi WPGP |
| § - subsp. *sargentiana* ♀ | CB&S CBot CFil COtt EBee ELan LNet MBal MBlu MBri MRav NPal SMad SPer SSpi SSta WAbe WCru WDin WPGP WWat |
| ¶ - - large-leaved | WPGP |
| ¶ - 'Spinners' | SSpi |
| - subsp. *strigosa* | CFil CMil EPfP GOrc SBid SVen WCru WPGP WWat |
| - 'Taiwan' | SSpi |
| § - Villosa Group ♀ | More than 30 suppliers |
| § 'Blue Deckle' (L) | CFil CMHG MBNS MRav NHlc SBid SNut SSpi WBcn WPGP |
| 'Blue Tit' | See *H. macrophylla* 'Blaumeise' |
| ¶ 'Brilliant' | NHlc |
| *cinerea* | See *H. arborescens* subsp. *discolor* |
| *cordifolia* | Last listed 1996 |
| 'Diabolo' | Last listed 1998 |
| ♦ 'Frau Katsuko' | See *H. macrophylla* Lady Katsuko |
| § 'Grant's Choice' (L) | EHic NHlc |
| *heteromalla* | CFai CFil CMHG CMil SSpi WCru WPGP |
| - B&SWJ 2142 | WCru |
| - Bretschneideri Group ♀ | CMCN GAri GQui NHlc WBod WCru WWat |
| - DJHC 493 | WCru |
| - HWJCM 148 | WCru |
| ¶ - HWJCM 180 | WCru |
| - 'Morrey's Form' | WCru |
| - SF 338 | ISea |
| - 'Snowcap' | GQui NHlc WBcn WCru |
| - f. *xanthoneura* | CFil GAri SSpi WPGP |
| - - 'Wilsonii' | WCru |
| ¶ - 'Yalung Ridge' | NHlc WCru |
| ¶ *hirta* | CFil |
| ¶ - B&SWJ 5000 | WCru |
| *integerrima* | See *H. serratifolia* |
| *integrifolia* | CFil CPIN |
| - B&SWJ 022 | WCru |
| *involucrata* | CFil EPfP MBal MPla NHlc SBid SMrm SSpi SSta WCru |
| - dwarf form | CFil WCru |
| - 'Hortensis' (d) ♀ | CFil CPle EPfP IOrc SSpi WAbe WCot WCru WKif WPGP WSHC |
| 'Korale Red' | WBcn |
| ¶ 'Lavender Blue' | SRPl |
| ¶ *lobbii* B&SWJ 3214 | WCru |
| *longipes* | CFil CHan ERav WCru WPGP WWat |
| *luteovenosa* | CFil WCru |
| ¶ *macrophylla* | SPlb |
| - Alpen Glow | See *H. macrophylla* 'Alpenglühen' |
| § - 'Alpenglühen' (H) | CB&S CFil ELan ESis IOrc NHlc NPro SBid SBod SPla SRms WPGP |
| - 'Altona' (H) ♀ | CB&S CFil GAri IOrc ISea MBal MGos MRav NHlc SBid SBod SPer WPGP WStI |
| - 'Amethyst' (H/d) | CFil WPGP |
| - 'Ami Pasquier' (H) ♀ | CB&S CBlo CDoC CFil EBee EPfP IOrc MRav NHlc SBid SSpi WGer WPGP |
| * - 'Aureomarginata' | EPfP |
| - 'Aureovariegata' | CEnd CFil ELan SNut WBcn WPGP |
| - 'Ayesha' (H) ♀ | More than 30 suppliers |
| - 'Ayesha Blue' | MAsh |
| - 'Beauté Vendômoise' (L) | CFil SBid SSpi WPGP |
| ¶ - 'Belzonii' (L) | NHlc |
| - 'Benelux' (H) | CB&S CWSG EHic SBid WAbe WGwG WLRN WTro |
| * - 'Bicolour' | MAsh |
| § - 'Blauer Prinz' (H) | CB&S CFil GCHN IOrc NHlc WLRN |
| § - 'Blauling' (L) | CDoC CWSG NHlc |
| § - 'Blaumeise' (L) | CFil MAsh NHlc SBid SSpi WGer WPGP |
| - 'Blue Bonnet' (H) | CFil COtt EPfP MAsh SPer WHen WLRN WPGP |
| - Blue Prince | See *H. macrophylla* 'Blauer Prinz' |
| - 'Blue Sky' | See *H. macrophylla* 'Blaumeise' |
| - 'Blue Wave' | See *H. macrophylla* 'Mariesii Perfecta' |
| ♦ - Bluebird | See *H. macrophylla* 'Blauling' |
| ♦ - 'Bluebird' | See *H. serrata* 'Bluebird' |
| - 'Bodensee' (H) | CB&S COtt NFla SBod WStI |
| - 'Bouquet Rose' (H) | CBlo COtt ECtt EHal EHic EWTr MGos MRav NFla WBod WGwG |
| - 'Brunette' (H) | CFil CMil |
| - 'Buchfink' (L) | CFil WPGP |
| - 'Cordata' | See *H. arborescens* |
| - 'Covent Garden' | Last listed 1998 |
| - 'Deutschland' (H) | CTri IOrc |
| - 'Domotoi' (H/d) | CFai CFil SPan WPGP |
| * - 'Dwaag Pink' | MRav |
| - 'Eldorado' (H) | EHol |
| § - 'Enziandom' (H) | CB&S CFil SSpi WAbe WPGP |
| - 'Europa' (H) ♀ | CB&S CTrw IOrc MAsh MGos NCut NHlc SBod SEND WGwG WStI WWal |
| § - Fasan™ (L) | CFil NHlc WPGP WSPU |
| - 'Firelight' | See *H. macrophylla* 'Leuchtfeuer' |
| - 'Fischers Silberblau' (H) | CFil |
| - 'Forever Pink' | EBrP EBre LBre SBre WGer |
| - 'Frillibet' (H) | CDoC CFil LRHS NHlc SBid WPGP WRHF |
| - 'Gartenbaudirektor Kuhnert' (H) | SMe |
| § - 'Générale Vicomtesse de Vibraye' (H) ♀ | CB&S CDoC CEnd CFil CMHG CTri EBee EPfP GCHN MBal MBar MBri NFla NHlc SBid SNut SPer SSpi WBod WLRN WPGP WWin |
| - Gentian Dome | See *H. macrophylla* 'Enziandom' |
| - 'Geoffrey Chadbund' | See *H. macrophylla* 'Möwe' |
| - 'Gerda Steiniger' | CB&S CBlo |
| - 'Gertrud Glahn' (H) | CB&S CBlo NCut |
| - 'Glowing Embers' | CFil MBri SEND WPGP |
| - 'Gold Dust' | CFil WPGP |
| - 'Goliath' (H) | CBlo CFil EPfP SBid WPGP |
| - 'Hamburg' (H) | CB&S CEnd CFil CTri EBee ECtt ENot EPfP IOrc LPVe MGos MRav NCut NHlc SBid SDix WPGP WStI WWeb |
| - 'Harlequin' | CFil WPGP |
| - 'Harry's Pink Topper' (H) | MAsh |
| - 'Hatfield Rose' (H) | CB&S |
| - 'Heinrich Seidel' (H) | CB&S CFil NHlc WPGP |
| - 'Holstein' (H) | CFil MAsh SBid WPGP |

| Name | Suppliers |
|---|---|
| § - 'Hörnli' | CFil WPGP |
| - 'Intermezzo' | NHlc WLRN |
| · - 'Izu-no-hana' (L/d) | CFil SWas |
| - 'James Grant' | See *H.* 'Grant's Choice' |
| § - 'Joseph Banks' (H) | CB&S EHic |
| - 'Kardinal' (L) | CFil WPGP |
| - 'King George' (H) | CB&S CDoC CFil CWSG EBee EBrP EBre EHic EOld IOrc LBre MBar MGos MRav NHlc SBid SBre SPer SRPl WPGP WStI WWal |
| - 'Kluis Superba' (H) | CB&S CBlo CFil CTri GOrc IOrc MRav NHlc WPGP |
| § - 'Koningin Wilhelmina' (H) | CFil WBcn WPGP |
| - 'La France' (H) | CB&S CBlo COtt CTri CWSG EHic GChr MBar MRav SBid SRPl WAbe |
| - 'Lady Fujiyo' | CB&S |
| § - Lady Katsuko | CB&S SPer |
| - 'Lady Mariko' | SPer |
| - 'Lady Nobuko' | CB&S SPer |
| - 'Lady Taiko Blue' | CB&S SPer |
| - 'Lady Taiko Pink' | CB&S |
| - 'Lanarth White' (L) ♀ | CB&S CDoC CFil CTri EBee EHic ELan MPla MRav NHlc SBid SPer SReu SRms SSpi WBod WPGP WWat WWeb |
| § - 'Le Cygne' (H) | Last listed 1996 |
| § - 'Leuchtfeuer' (H) | MBel MBri WGer |
| § - 'Libelle' (L) | CB&S CBlo CDoC CFil CWSG EHic MAsh MBri NHlc NMoo SNut SPer WKif WPGP WWat WWeb |
| - 'Lilacina' (L) | CFil EHic EPfP MWhi NHlc SBid SLPl SPer SSpi WKif WPGP |
| § - 'Maculata' (L) | EHol ELan GQui IOrc SEas WWat |
| - 'Madame A. Riverain' (H) | CFil COtt CWSG EHic SBod WLRN WTro |
| § - 'Madame Emile Mouillère' (H) ♀ | CB&S CBot CDoC CEnd CFil EBee ENot IOrc MBel MBri MRav NFla NHlc SAga SBod SDix SMad SMer SNut SPan SPer SPla SRms SSoC SSpi SSta WBod WGwG WPGP WTro |
| * - 'Magic Light' | Last listed 1996 |
| - 'Maréchal Foch' (H) | CFil CTri IOrc WPGP |
| § - 'Mariesii' (L) | CFil CMHG CTri EBee ELan ENot EPla ISea MBal NHlc SBid SDix SPer WAbe WKif WLRN WStI WWat |
| § - 'Mariesii Perfecta' (L) ♀ | CChe CDoC CPri CTri ELan ENot EWTr ISea MBar MGos MRav NFla NSti SDix SNut SPer SPlb SSta WAbe WBod WFar WGwG WHen WStI WWal WWat |
| - 'Mariesii Variegata' (L) | WAbe |
| - 'Masja' (H) | CB&S COtt CWSG EBee EHic IOrc MBri MGos MRav NFla SVil WAbe |
| - 'Mathilda Gutges' (H) | CFil CWSG EHic SSpi WPGP WStI |
| - 'Mini Hörnli' | See *H. macrophylla* 'Hörnli' |
| - 'Miss Belgium' (H) | CFil CTri IOrc MBal MBri NHlc SBod SEas |
| - 'Miss Hepburn' | COtt NHlc SPer |
| - Morning Red | See *H. macrophylla* 'Morgenrot' |
| - 'Mousmée' | CFil WPGP |
| § - 'Möwe' (L) ♀ | CB&S CDoC CEnd CFil CMil EBee ECtt ENot EPla MBri MRav NHlc SBod SChu SDix SMad SNut SPer SRms SSpi SSta WPGP WWeb |
| ¶ - 'Münster' (H) | NHlc |
| - 'Niedersachsen' (H) | CFil MRav NHlc SBid SMer WPGP |
| - 'Nigra' (H) ♀ | CB&S CChe CFil CGre CHan CTre ELan EPla IOrc MBal MBel MGos SBid SDix SNut SPer WAbe WCru WFar WGwG WPGP WStI WWal |
| - 'Nikko Blue' | CB&S CBlo CDoC CFil EPfP MBri SBid SEND WBod WPGP |
| ¶ - var. *normalis* | NHlc |
| § - 'Nymphe' (H) | Last listed 1998 |
| ¶ - 'Oamacha' | NHlc |
| - 'Otaksa' (H) | CFil NHlc |
| - 'Parzifal' (H) ♀ | CB&S CFil CTrw EHic EPfP NHlc WPGP WWal |
| - 'Pax' | See *H. macrophylla* 'Nymphe' |
| ◆ - Pheasant | See *H. macrophylla* Fasan |
| - 'Pia' (H) | CB&S CFil CPla EBee EHyt ELan IOrc MAsh MBal MPla MTho NHol SBod SIng SMad SPer SPla SRms WFar WGwG WPat WWat |
| - 'Pink Wave' (L) | Last listed 1998 |
| - 'Prinses Beatrix' | CB&S CChe CFil WBcn WPGP |
| - 'Quadricolor' (L/v) | CAbb CFil CHan CMil EBee EHoe EPla MBel MBri MRav NRoo NSti SDix SNut SPer SPla SRPl SRms WCot WCru WHCG WPGP WSHC |
| - Queen Wilhelmina | See *H. macrophylla* 'Koningin Wilhelmina' |
| - 'R.F. Felton' | CB&S |
| - 'Red Emperor' (H) | Last listed 1997 |
| - 'Red Lacecap' | Last listed 1996 |
| - Redbreast | See *H. macrophylla* 'Rotkehlchen' |
| - 'Regula' (H) | CTrw |
| ¶ - 'Renate Sleiniger' (H) | CFai |
| ¶ - 'Rex' | NHlc |
| - 'Rosita' (H) | LPan MAsh |
| § - 'Rotkehlchen' (L) | CFai CFil SBid WPGP |
| - 'Rotschwanz' (L) | CFil NHlc SSpi WPGP |
| - 'Saint Claire' | CB&S |
| - 'Sea Foam' (L) | EPla IOrc NHlc WSPU |
| ¶ - 'Seascape' | NHlc |
| * - 'Shower' | Last listed 1997 |
| - 'Sibylla' (H) | CB&S CFil NHlc WPGP WWeb |
| - Sister Therese | See *H. macrophylla* 'Soeur Thérèse' |
| § - 'Soeur Thérèse' (H) | CBlo CFil GAri IOrc MAsh MBri MGos WPGP WStI WWeb |
| - 'Souvenir du Président Paul Doumer' (H) | CBlo |
| - 'Taube' | CB&S CFil GQui WPGP |
| N - Teller Blau (L) | CBlo CDoC COtt EBee MBri NHlc NMoo SCoo SSta WDin WWeb |
| N - Teller Rosa (L) | CDoC MAsh NMoo SCoo SSta |
| N - Teller Rot (L) | CBlo CDoC EHic MAsh MBri NMoo SCoo WDin |
| N - 'Teller Variegated' | See *H. macrophylla* 'Tricolor' |
| N - Teller Weiss | See *H. macrophylla* 'Libelle' |
| - 'Thomas Hogg' (H) | Last listed 1997 |
| - 'Tödi' (H) | Last listed 1996 |
| - 'Tokyo Delight' | CBlo CBrd CChe CDoC CEnd CFil EHic IOrc NHlc SBid SSpi WPGP |
| - 'Tovelit' | GAri WWeb |
| N - 'Tricolor' (L/v) ♀ | CB&S CBot CDoC CFil CGre EAst ERav GOrc MAsh MBel MGos SAga SBod SLon SPer SReu WCru WKif WPGP WPyg WWal |
| ¶ - 'Universal' (H) | NHlc |
| - 'Ursula' | Last listed 1997 |
| - 'Val de Loire' | CBlo CWSG |
| - 'Variegata' | See *H. macrophylla* 'Maculata' |
| - 'Veitchii' (L) ♀ | CB&S CBot CFil CMHG EBee ENot EPfP MBri MRav NHlc SBid SBod SDix SPer SSpi WPGP WWat |
| - 'Vicomte de Vibraye' | See *H. macrophylla* 'Générale Vicomtesse de Vibraye' |
| - Vulcan | See *H. macrophylla* 'Vulcain' |
| - 'Westfalen' (H) ♀ | NCat NHlc SMrm SPla WWal |
| - 'White Lace' (L) | ELan |

| | |
|---|---|
| - 'White Swan' | See *H. macrophylla* 'Le Cygne' |
| - 'White Wave' (L) ♀ | CBlo CFil CHad EBee ENot EWTr MBar NFla SBid SBod SEND SNut SPer SRms SSpi WDin WLRN WPGP WStI |
| *paniculata* | CFil CMCN CTrw |
| - 'Brussels Lace' | CAbP CFil CPMA LRHS MAsh SNut SSpi WPGP |
| - 'Burgundy Lace' | CB&S CMil CPMA MBlu |
| - 'Everest' | LRHS SNut |
| - 'Floribunda' ♀ | CFil CHad LRHS SNut SPer SSpi WPGP WRHF |
| ¶ - from Taiwan B&SWJ 3556 | WCru |
| - from Taiwan B&SWJ 3804 | WCru |
| - 'Grandiflora' ♀ | More than 30 suppliers |
| - 'Greenspire' | CPMA LRHS MBlu WBcn |
| - 'Kyushu' ♀ | More than 30 suppliers |
| - Pink Diamond = 'Interhydia' | CAbP CBlo CDoC CLAP CMCN CPMA EBee EBrP EBre ENot LBre LHop MAsh MBlu MBri NRoo SBre SMad SSpi SSta WCru |
| - 'Praecox' ♀ | SPer WCru WPat WWin |
| - 'Tardiva' | CB&S CBot CDoC EPla LPan MAsh MGos MRav SDix SPer SPla SRms WFar WHCG WLRN WPat WPyg |
| - 'Touchard' | Last listed 1996 |
| - 'Unique' ♀ | CDoC CFil CPMA EHic EPla GOrc LFis LHop MAsh MBri SNut SPer SPla SSpi WAbe WBod WCru WPGP WWat |
| ¶ - 'White Lace' | CB&S MBlu |
| - 'White Moth' | CB&S CFil CPMA SNut WPGP |
| ¶ 'Pink Showers' | NHlc |
| § 'Preziosa' ♀ | More than 30 suppliers |
| *quelpartensis* | CB&S CHan CPlN CRHN CTre GQui SBid SSpi WCru |
| *quercifolia* ♀ | More than 30 suppliers |
| - 'Flore Pleno' | See *H. quercifolia* Snow Flake |
| - 'Harmony' | CEnd CFil CHad SSta WPGP |
| ¶ - 'Pee Wee' | EPfP LRHS NOla |
| - 'Sike's Dwarf' | CEnd CFil LRHS SSpi WPGP WWat |
| * - 'Snow' | CWSG |
| § - Snow Flake™ (d) | CAbP CB&S CDoC CDul CEnd CFil CMil CPMA CSPN ELan EMil ERav IOrc MBri SLon SPer SSpi SSta WHCG WPGP WWat |
| - Snow Queen = 'Flemygea' | CB&S CDoC CMil CPMA GOrc IOrc MAsh MBal MBri MGos MRav MSte SCob SPer SPla SSta WHCG |
| - 'Stardust' | CRos |
| - 'Tennessee Clone' | CFil WPGP |
| ¶ *robusta* | SLPl |
| *sargentiana* | See *H. aspera* subsp. *sargentiana* |
| *scandens* | CFil CPle |
| - subsp. *chinensis* B&SWJ 3420 | WCru |
| - subsp. *liukiuensis* | WCru |
| *seemannii* | More than 30 suppliers |
| *serrata* | CTrw NHlc WCru |
| - 'Acuminata' | See *H. serrata* 'Bluebird' |
| - 'Aigaku' | WPGP |
| - 'Amacha' | CFil WPGP |
| ¶ - 'Amagyana' | CMil CPLG |
| - 'Belle Deckle' | See *H.* 'Blue Deckle' |
| - 'Beni-gaku' | CB&S CFil CMil NFla SBid WLRN WPGP |
| - 'Blue Deckle' (L) | WPGP |
| § - 'Bluebird' ♀ | More than 30 suppliers |
| * - *chinensis* | NHlc |
| - 'Diadem' | CBlo CBrd CFai CFil CHan CMil NHlc NPro SBid SBod SDix SNut SSpi WCru WLRN WPGP |
| - 'Grayswood' ♀ | CB&S CEnd CFil CHig ENot GEil GQui LHop MBal MRav NHlc SBid SDix SPer WKif WLRN WPGP WWat |
| - 'Intermedia' | CFil WPGP |
| ¶ - 'Jogasaki' | CFil |
| ¶ - 'Kiyosumi' | CFil |
| - *koreana* | WLRN |
| - 'Macrosepala' | EHic |
| - 'Miranda' (L) | CBrd CEnd CFil COtt EHic NHlc SBid SSpi WLRN WPGP WWat |
| ¶ - 'Miyama-yae-murasaki' (d) | CFil |
| ¶ - 'Preziosa' | See *H.* 'Preziosa' |
| * - 'Pulchella' | SPla |
| * - 'Pulchra' | CEnd SSpi |
| - 'Rosalba' ♀ | CBrd CFil EPfP MRav SPer SPla WPGP WSHC |
| ¶ - 'Shichidanka-nishiki' (d/v) | CFil CMil |
| ¶ - 'Shirofugi' | CFil |
| ¶ - 'Shirotae' (d) | CFil |
| - var. *thunbergii* | CB&S CFil GQui WPGP |
| - 'Tiara' | CFil SSpi WPGP |
| ¶ - 'Uzu Azisai' | CFil |
| - subsp. *yezoensis* 'Wryneck' (H) | CFil NHlc WPGP |
| § *serratifolia* | CBot CFil CGre CPlN EPfP EPla SAPC SArc SBra SLon SSpi SSta WCru WPGP WSHC |
| ¶ *sikokiana* B&SWJ 5035 | WCru |
| 'Silver Slipper' | WWeb |
| *sinensis* | See *H. scandens* subsp. *chinensis* |
| *tiliifolia* | See *H. anomala* subsp. *petiolaris* |
| *umbellata* | See *H. scandens* subsp. *chinensis* |
| *villosa* | See *H. aspera* Villosa Group |

## HYDRASTIS (Ranunculaceae)

| | |
|---|---|
| *canadensis* | CArn GBuc GPoy MSal WCru WThi |

## HYDROCHARIS (Hydrocharitaceae)

| | |
|---|---|
| *morsus-ranae* | CBen CRDP CRow CWat EHon EMFW LPBA MSta NDea NVic SWat |

## HYDROCOTYLE (Apiaceae)

| | |
|---|---|
| § *americana* | NHol |
| *asiatica* | See *Centella asiatica* |
| *moschata* | GAri WPer WWin |
| * *palustris* | Last listed 1998 |
| *ranunculoides* | See *H. americana* |
| * *sibthorpioides* 'Variegata' | EMon EPPr |
| *vulgaris* | CRDP EMFW EWFC MSta WWeb |

## HYDROPHYLLUM (Hydrophyllaceae)

| | |
|---|---|
| *appendiculatum* | Last listed 1996 |
| *canadense* | EMar WCru |
| *virginianum* | CRDP MSal |
| - purple form | EBee |

## HYLOMECON (Papaveraceae)

| | |
|---|---|
| § *japonica* | CRDP EBee EPar ERos GCrs IMGH MSte NBir NHol NMGW NRya NTow WAbe WCru WElm WFar WPer |

HYLOTELEPHIUM See SEDUM

HYMENANTHERA See MELICYTUS

## HYMENOCALLIS (Amaryllidaceae)
| | |
|---|---|
| 'Advance' | LAma LBow |
| § *caroliniana* | LAma WCot |
| x *festalis* | ERea LAma LBow MBri NRog SDeJ |
| - 'Zwanenburg' | Last listed 1998 |
| *barrisiana* | LBow |
| *littoralis* | NRog |
| § *longipetala* | LBow |
| *narcissiflora* | Last listed 1997 |
| *occidentalis* | See *H. caroliniana* |
| 'Sulphur Queen' | LBow NRog SDeJ |

## HYMENOSPORUM (Pittosporaceae)
| | |
|---|---|
| ¶ *flavum* | CPLG SOWG |

## HYMENOXYS (Asteraceae)
| | |
|---|---|
| *grandiflora* | See *Tetraneuris grandiflora* |
| *lapidicola* | Last listed 1996 |
| *subintegra* | Last listed 1998 |
| *torreyana* | Last listed 1996 |

## HYOPHORBE (Arecaceae)
| | |
|---|---|
| § *lagenicaulis* | LPal |
| *verschaffeltii* | LPal |

## HYOSCYAMUS (Solanaceae)
| | |
|---|---|
| *albus* | GBar MChe MSal |
| *aureus* | Last listed 1996 |
| *niger* | CArn CJew EMFP EWFC GPoy MChe MSal WHer |
| * - 'Capel Ulo' | Last listed 1997 |

## HYPERICUM ✿ (Clusiaceae)
| | |
|---|---|
| *acmosepalum* | CFil WPGP |
| - SBEC 93 | Last listed 1997 |
| § *addingtonii* | EPla SPan |
| *adenotrichum* | CNic GCHN |
| *aegypticum* | CInt CLyd CPBP EDAr EHyt GCHN LBee NHol NMen NWCA NWoo SIgm WAbe WFar WPat WPer WPyg |
| *amblycalyx* | SIgm |
| *androsaemum* | CAgr CArn ECha EGoo ENot GOrc ISea MHew MSal NMir NPer NRoo WDin WOak |
| § - 'Albury Purple' | CB&S CFai CHad CHan CPle GBuc GCHN MCCP MRav MTed NLak WPat |
| - 'Autumn Blaze' | MBal MGos NBee SSto |
| § - 'Dart's Golden Penny' | SLPl SPer WBcn |
| ¶ - 'Excellent Flair' | NPro |
| - 'Orange Flair' | CBlo |
| § - f.*variegatum* 'Mrs Gladis Brabazon' (v) | CBlo MHar NSti WCom WCot WWeb |
| § *annulatum* | EMon |
| 'Archibald' | Last listed 1996 |
| *ascyron* | EBee EWes |
| *athoum* | CLyd EHyt GCHN LHop MBro MPla NBir NTow SIng WPat WPer |
| *atomarium* | WPGP |
| *augustinii* | CPle |
| *balearicum* | CFil CHan CLyd CPle EPot MPla MTho SDry SIgm SIng SPan WAbe |
| § *beanii* | LRHS MBlu WAbe |
| *bellum* | CPle EPfP GCal SBid |
| ¶ cf. - ACE 2467 | EPot |

| | |
|---|---|
| - subsp. *latisepalum* | Last listed 1997 |
| - pale form | Last listed 1996 |
| *buckleyi* | GCHN SIng WPat |
| *calycinum* | CB&S CChe CLan EBee ELan ENot GChr GOrc IIve LBuc LGro MBal MBar MGos MRav MWat NLon NWea SPer SRms WDin WGwG |
| § *cerastioides* | CCHP ECGP ESis GCHN LBee MHar MPla SIgm SIng SRms WAbe WPer WWin |
| *choisyanum* B&L 12469 | Last listed 1997 |
| *coris* | CLyd ECha EWes MBro MHar MTho MWat NFla NMen NTow SRms WCla WHoo |
| *crux-andreae* | EBee |
| *cuneatum* | See *H. pallens* |
| x *cyathiflorum* 'Gold Cup' | CDoC MBal SBid SPan SVil |
| x *dummeri* 'Peter Dummer' | CBlo EMil MBri NHol |
| ¶ 'Eastleigh Gold' | SLon |
| *elatum* | See *H.* x *inodorum* |
| *elodeoides* | CLyd EBee MSta SRms |
| *elongatum* | EMon |
| *empetrifolium* | CPle EWes |
| § - subsp. *oliganthum* | GCHN |
| - 'Prostatum' | See *H. empetrifolium* subsp. *tortuosum* |
| § - subsp. *tortuosum* | CLyd EWes |
| § *forrestii* ♀ | CFil CLan CPle EBee EPfP MBal MGos SBid WPGP WWat |
| N *fragile* hort. | See *H. olympicum* f. *minus* |
| *frondosum* | SPer |
| - 'Buttercup' | CBlo |
| - Sunburst™ | CBlo EPfP MBri MGos SBid SPan |
| N 'Gemo' | EGoo |
| 'Gold Penny' | See *H. androsaemum* 'Dart's Golden Penny' |
| *grandiflorum* | See *H. kouytchense* |
| *henryi* L 753 | SRms |
| 'Hidcote' ♀ | More than 30 suppliers |
| 'Hidcote Variegated' | EBee ELan GCHN GOrc LHop MBal MCCP SEas SHFr SPer SRms WFar WWeb |
| *bircinum* | Last listed 1998 |
| - subsp. *albimontanum* | SPan |
| - subsp. *cambessedesii* | LRHS |
| - subsp. *majus* | EMon |
| *birsutum* | CKin |
| *bookerianum* | CPle |
| *bumifusum* | EHyt GAri WCla |
| *byssopifolium* | CPle SHFr |
| x *inodorum* 'Albury Purple' | See *H. androsaemum* 'Albury Purple' |
| - 'Elstead' | ECtt ELan MBal MBar MGos MRav MWat NFla NRoo SRms WDin WHCG WWin |
| - 'Summergold' (v) | CBlo MCCP |
| - 'Ysella' | ECha ECtt ELan EWes MRav NPro SDry |
| *japonicum* | ECou EWes |
| *kalmianum* | CChe EWes SBid |
| *kamtschaticum* | EDAr MHar |
| *kelleri* | EHyt GCHN ITim |
| § *kiusianum* | CInt CLyd GCHN MBar MTho |
| var. *yakusimense* | NWCA SIng |
| § *kouytchense* ♀ | CB&S CPle CSam EPfP EWes GOrc GQui MBri SDry SPan WKif WPat WPyg |
| *lagarocladum* | ELan MBlu |
| *lancasteri* | CBlo EBee ELan EPfP LRHS SPan WBcn WWat |
| - L 750 | Last listed 1997 |

◆ *leschenaultii* hort.  See *H. addingtonii, H.* 'Rowallane'
*linarioides*  EHyt GTou
¶ 'Locke'  EAst
*maclarenii* L 863  Last listed 1998
¶ 'Milkmaid'  GEil
*montanum*  MSal
x *moserianum* ♀  CB&S CLan EBee EBrP EBre ENot
  LBre MBal MBar MBri MRav NPer
  SBre SPer SRms SUsu WStI
§ - 'Tricolor' (v)  More than 30 suppliers
- 'Variegatum'  See *H.* x *moserianum* 'Tricolor'
◆ 'Mrs Brabazon'  See *H. androsaemum* f.
  *variegatum* 'Mrs Gladis Brabazon'
*nummularium*  NBir
*oblongifolium*  CPle WLRN
- CC 1706  MRPP WAbe
*olympicum* ♀  CAgr CArn CInt CNic ECha EFer
  ELan EPot GCHN GDra GLil LGro
  MBrN MFir MPla MWat NFor
  NLon NMen SEas SHel SIng SPer
  SPla SRms SSmi WHen
I - 'Calypso'  CBlo NPro
- 'Eden Star'  NPro
- 'Edith'  SAsh WPyg
- 'Grandiflorum'  See *H. olympicum* f. *uniflorum*
§ - f.*minus*  ECtt EGoo ELan EMNN GCHN
  GCal GDra MOne NRoo SMer
  SRms WPer WStI WWin
§ - - 'Sulphureum'  CBot EHyt ESis EWes MHar MLLN
  MRav MWhi SPer SRms WSHC
  WWin
§ - - 'Variegatum'  EHyt EWes LBee LHop NRoo SIng
  WPat WPyg
- f.*uniflorum*  CM&M GAri LIck MBal MBar
  MBro NBro NPri NRoo NVic
  SEND WAbe WCla
- - 'Citrinum' ♀  CLyd CMea CNic ECha ECtt EHyt
  EPot GCHN LBee LHop MBal
  MBro MWat NBro NHol NRoo
  SBid SBla SIgm WAbe WCla WEas
  WHoo WKif WLin WPat WWat
*orientale*  EWes GCHN MBro MPla NMen
  NRoo WCla WPer
- JCA 3302  NHol
§ *pallens*  ECho SRms
*patulum* var.*forrestii*  See *H. forrestii*
- var. *henryi* Rehder et hort.  See *H. pseudohenryi*
- - Veitch ex Bean  See *H. beanii*
*perforatum*  CArn CJew CKin ELau EWFC
  GPoy LHol MChe MHew MPEx
  NHex NMir SIde WCla WHer WJek
  WOak WSel WWye
¶ - 'Crusader' (v)  WAlt
*polyphyllum*  See *H. olympicum* f. *minus*
- 'Citrinum'  See *H. olympicum* f. *minus*
  'Sulphureum'
- 'Grandiflorum'  See *H. olympicum* f. *uniflorum*
- 'Sulphureum'  See *H. olympicum* f. *minus*
  'Sulphureum'
- 'Variegatum'  See *H. olympicum* f. *minus*
  'Variegatum'
*prolificum*  CFai CPle ECtt ELan ENot EPla
  GCHN MAsh MMHG SChu SPan
§ *pseudohenryi*  SPan
- B&L 12009  Last listed 1997
- L 1029  GBuc
*pseudopetiolatum*  GTou
I - *orientale*  Last listed 1998
- var. *yakusimense*  See *H. kiusianum* var.
  *yakusimense*
*pulchrum*  IIve NCut
*quadrangulum* L.  See *H. tetrapterum*

*reptans* hort.  See *H. olympicum* f. *minus*
- Dyer  CPBP ECha ESis EWes
*rhodoppeum*  See *H. cerastioides* subsp.
  *meuselianum*
*roeperianum*  SBid
§ 'Rowallane' ♀  CB&S CBot CLTr CLan CPle CTrw
  EPfP EPla ISea SDix
*scouleri* subsp. *nortoniae*  Last listed 1997
sp. ACE 2321  Last listed 1997
sp. ACE 2524  Last listed 1997
¶ sp. S&SH 381  CHan
*stellatum*  CGre EMon EPla SLon WWat
*subsessile*  Last listed 1996
- B&L 12486  EMon
'Sungold'  See *H. kouytchense*
*tenuicaule* KR 743  ISea
§ *tetrapterum*  CArn CKin EWFC MHew MSal
*tomentosum*  GCHN
*trichocaulon*  CLyd ELan EWes GCHN MBro
  NHol NRoo WPat WPyg WWin
*uralum*  Last listed 1997
- CC 1225  Last listed 1997
*wilsonii*  Last listed 1997
¶ *xylosteifolium*  SLon
*yakusimense*  See *H. kiusianum* var.
  *yakusimense*
*yezoense*  Last listed 1998

# HYPOCALYMMA (Myrtaceae)
*robustum*  Last listed 1998

# HYPOCHAERIS (Asteraceae)
*radicata*  CKin IIve NMir
*uniflora*  Last listed 1998
§ *variegata*  CLTr

# HYPOCYRTA See NEMATANTHUS

# HYPOESTES (Acanthaceae)
*aristata*  ERea
§ *phyllostachya* (v) ♀  MBri
- 'Bettina' (v)  MBri
- 'Carmina' (v)  MBri
- 'Purpuriana' (v)  MBri
- 'Wit' (v)  MBri
*sanguinolenta* misapplied  See *H. phyllostachya*

# HYPOLEPIS (Dennstaedtiaceae)
*millefolium*  GAri
*punctata*  Last listed 1996

# HYPOXIS (Hypoxidaceae)
*argentea*  Last listed 1997
*hirsuta*  EWes WThi WWye
*hygrometrica*  CRDP ECou EPot WAbe
*krebsii*  Last listed 1996
*parvula*  SBla
- var. *albiflora*  EPot
§ - - 'Hebron Farm Biscuit'  EHyt EWes SBla WAbe
- pink-flowered  EPot
*setosa*  Last listed 1997
*villosa*  Last listed 1997

# HYPOXIS x RHODOHYPOXIS (Hypoxidaceae)
◆ *H. parvula* x *R. baurii*  See x *Rhodoxis hybrida*

# HYPSELA (Campanulaceae)
*longiflora*  See *H. reniformis*
§ *reniformis*  ELan EMNN ESis LBee MRav NHar
  NMen NNrd NOak NVic NWCA
  SSmi WFar WWin
- 'Greencourt White'  CLyd ESis GBuc GGar

| | |
|---|---|
| sp. RB 94066 | ELan MNrw |

## HYPSEOCHARIS (Oxalidaceae)
*bilobata*    CGen

## HYSSOPUS (Lamiaceae)

| | |
|---|---|
| *aristatus* | See *H. officinalis* subsp. *aristatus* |
| *officinalis* | CArn CFri CHan CSev ECha EGoo ELan ELau GPoy LBuc LHol MBNS MBar MBri MChe NFai NLon SChu SIde SRob WCHb WGwG WHbs WHer WOak WOve WPer WWye |
| - f. *albus* | ECha EGoo ELau GPoy MChe SChu SIde SPil WCHb WCer WHer WJek WPer WSel WWye |
| § - subsp. *aristatus* | EBee EBrP EBre ELau ESis GPoy LBre LHol LLWP MChe NChi NRoo SBre SIde WCHb WEas WJek WSel WWin WWye |
| * - *decussatus* | Last listed 1996 |
| - *roseus* | CM&M EBee ECha EGoo ELau GPoy MBNS MChe MLLN NChi NFai NFor SChu SIde SPil SSca WCHb WCer WHer WJek WKif WPer WWye |
| § - f. *ruber* | LLWP |
| * *schugnanicus* | EBee |
| * - *albus* | EBee |
| *tianschanicus* | Last listed 1998 |

## HYSTRIX (Poaceae)

| | |
|---|---|
| *patula* | CBrm CCuc CInt CKel EBee EHoe EMan EMon EPGN EPPr EPla GBin GBri GCal MCCP MMoz MNrw MWhi NBro NChi NFai NSti SHFr SUsu WCot WHal WLRN WPer |

# I

## IBERIS (Brassicaceae)

| | |
|---|---|
| *amara* | EWFC MSal |
| *candolleana* | See *I. pruitii* Candolleana Group |
| *commutata* | See *I. sempervirens* |
| 'Correvoniana' | Last listed 1998 |
| 'Dick Self' | EBrP EBre LBre NRoo SBre |
| *gibraltarica* | EMan NFor NPri SRms WGor |
| *jordanii* | See *I. pruitii* |
| § *pruitii* | CPBP EBur MBal SBla |
| § - Candolleana Group | Last listed 1998 |
| *saxatilis* | WPer |
| - *candolleana* | See *I. pruitii* Candolleana Group |
| *semperflorens* | MAvo MHlr WCot WSPU |
| § *sempervirens* ♀ | CB&S CTri ELan EMan ERic LGro MBal MWat NArg NBro NFai NFla NFor NLon NOrc NRoo NVic SEND SRms STre WPer WWal |
| - 'Little Gem' | See *I. sempervirens* 'Weisser Zwerg' |
| - 'Pinky Perpetual' | Last listed 1998 |
| - 'Pygmaea' | CLyd EWes MWat NHar NMen |
| § - 'Schneeflocke' ♀ | ENot GAri MBro SIng SPer SRCN WHoo WPyg |
| I  - Snowdrift | See *I. sempervirens* 'Zwergschneeflocke' |
| - Snowflake | See *I. sempervirens* 'Schneeflocke' |
| - 'Starkers' | Last listed 1997 |

| | |
|---|---|
| § - 'Weisser Zwerg' | CMea CNic EBrP EBre ECha ECtt ELan EMNN LBee LBre MBro MPla NHar NMen NTow SBla SBre SIng SRms WAbe WHoo WWin |
| *spathulata* | CLyd NMen |

## IDESIA (Flacourtiaceae)

| | |
|---|---|
| *polycarpa* | CB&S CFil CMCN CPle LRHS MAsh MBel SMad SSpi SSta WPat WWat WWoo |
| - Sich 848 | WPGP |

## ILEX ♀ (Aquifoliaceae)

| | |
|---|---|
| N x *altaclerensis* | SHHo |
| - 'Atkinsonii' (m) | CRos |
| - 'Balearica' | SRPl WWat |
| - 'Barterberry' (f) | CBar |
| - 'Belgica' (f) | SHHo |
| § - 'Belgica Aurea' (f/v) ♀ | CB&S CMHG CRos ELan EPfP LNet LPan MBal MBar MBri MWat SEND SHHo WBcn WWat |
| - 'Camelliifolia' (f) ♀ | CCHP CMCN CMHG CRos EBee LPan MBlu MBri MRav MWat NWea SBid SBod SHHo SPer WBcn WWat |
| - 'Golden King' (f/v) ♀ | More than 30 suppliers |
| - 'Hendersonii' (f) | CBlo SBod WBcn |
| - 'Hodginsii' (m) ♀ | CBlo CMCN CRos ECot IOrc MBar SBid SEND SHHo |
| - 'Howick' (f/v) | SHHo WBcn |
| - 'Lady Valerie' (f/v) | SHHo |
| - 'Lawsoniana' (f/v) ♀ | More than 30 suppliers |
| - 'Maderensis Variegata' | See *I. aquifolium* 'Maderensis Variegata' |
| - 'Marnockii' (f) | SHHo |
| ¶ - 'Mundyi' (m) | CCHP |
| - 'Nigrescens' (m) | Last listed 1997 |
| - 'Purple Shaft' (f) | CMCN MRav SHHo |
| - 'Ripley Gold' (f/v) | CBlo CMHG LPan MAsh NHol SAga SBid SHHo |
| - 'Silver Sentinel' | See *I.* x *altaclerensis* 'Belgica Aurea' |
| - 'W.J. Bean' (f) | SHHo |
| - 'Wilsonii' (f) ♀ | IOrc LPan MWat SBid SBod SHHo |
| *aquifolium* ♀ | CB&S CChe CKin CSam CTri EBee ELau ENot EWTr GChr GRei IOrc LHyr LNet MBar MBri MGos MWat NLon SHFr SHHo WDin WMou WOrn WStI |
| - 'Alaska' (f) | CBlo CDoC CEnd CMCN EBee EBrP EBre EMil ENot LBre LBuc MAsh MBal NHol NSti SBre SHHo WRHF |
| - 'Alcicornis' (m) | CMCN |
| - 'Amber' (f) ♀ | CTri EBee MWat SHHo WLRN |
| - 'Angustifolia' (m or f) | CRos EBee EPla GAri IOrc MBar MHlr MWat SHHo WBcn WPat |
| - 'Angustimarginata Aurea' (m) | WPyg |
| § - 'Argentea Marginata' (f/v) ♀ | More than 30 suppliers |
| § - 'Argentea Marginata Pendula' (f/v) | CBlo CDoC CTri ENot EPfP LPan MAsh MBal MBri NHol NWea SBod SHHo SPer SRms WPat WPyg WWat |
| - 'Argentea Pendula' | See *I. aquifolium* 'Argentea Marginata Pendula' |
| - 'Argentea Variegata' | See *I. aquifolium* 'Argentea Marginata' |
| - 'Atlas' (m) | CB&S CDoC LBuc SHHo |
| - 'Aurea Marginata' (f) | CBlo CMHG EBee ECtt EHic EHoe ELan LPan MAsh MGos SBod SHHo WCFE WPat |

| | | |
|---|---|---|
| | - 'Aurea Marginata Pendula' (f) | CBlo CDoC CRos MAsh NHol WPat WPyg |
| | - 'Aurea Marginata Stricta' (f) | WCru |
| | - 'Aurea Ovata' | See *I. aquifolium* 'Ovata Aurea' |
| | - 'Aurea Regina' | See *I. aquifolium* 'Golden Queen' |
| | - 'Aureovariegata Pendula' | See *I. aquifolium* 'Weeping Golden Milkmaid' |
| | - 'Aurifodina' (f) | EHic IMGH SHHo WBcn WLRN |
| § | - 'Bacciflava' (f) | CB&S CDoC CDul CEnd CPle CSam CTri EBee ECtt ELan GCHN IOrc MBal MBlu MBri MGos MMea MRav MWat NBee NHol SHHo SPer SRms WDin WWal WWeb |
| | - 'Bowland' (f/v) | MAsh NHol |
| | - 'Crassifolia' (f) | SHHo SMad |
| | - 'Crispa' (m) | CPle EHic MBal MBlu NHol SHHo |
| | - 'Crispa Aureomaculata' | See *I. aquifolium* 'Crispa Aureopicta' |
| § | - 'Crispa Aureopicta' (m/v) | WBcn WPat |
| ¶ | - 'Elegantissima' (m/v) | SHHo |
| | - 'Ferox' (m) | CBlo CDul CLan EHal ELan EPfP MBal NSti SHHo WBcn WGwG |
| | - 'Ferox Argentea' (m/v) ♀ | More than 30 suppliers |
| * | - 'Ferox Argentea Picta' (m) | LRHS MAsh SPla |
| | - 'Ferox Aurea' (m/v) | CBlo CDoC CMHG CPle EAst EBee ELan GRei MCCP NHol SHHo SLon SPer WPat WPyg |
| § | - 'Flavescens' (f) | CBot EBee EPfP EPla NHed NHol SHHo WLRN |
| * | - 'Forest Weeping' | LRHS |
| | - 'Foxii' (m) | SHHo |
| | - 'Fructo Aurantiaco' (f) | EBee |
| | - 'Fructu Luteo' | See *I. aquifolium* 'Bacciflava' |
| | - 'Gold Flash' (f/v) | CRos ECtt ELan EMil MAsh MBri MGos NBee NHol SHHo WBcn |
| | - 'Golden Milkboy' (m/v) ♀ | CB&S CLan CRos EBee ECtt ELan EMil ENot LNet MBal MBlu NSti SBid SHHo SPla WCot WPat WPyg |
| | - 'Golden Milkmaid' (f/v) | EHol IOrc SBid |
| § | - 'Golden Queen' (m/v) ♀ | CB&S CDoC CRos EBee ELan ENot LHyr LNet MBal MBri MGos MWat NHol SPer SRPl SReu SRms WPat |
| | - 'Golden Showers' | SPer |
| | - 'Golden Tears' | SHHo WBcn |
| | - 'Golden van Tol' (f/v) | CB&S CDoC CRos CTri EAst EBee EBrP EBre ECtt ELan ENot IOrc LBre LNet LPan MAsh MBal MBar MBlu MBri MGos NBee NSti SBre SHHo SRms WGwG WStI WWal |
| | - 'Green Pillar' (f) ♀ | CMCN LBuc SHHo |
| | - 'Handsworth New Silver' (f/v) ♀ | More than 30 suppliers |
| | - 'Harpune' (f) | CPle SHHo |
| § | - 'Hascombensis' | CDoC CRos EHol EPla EPot GDra LGre LHop MBal MGos MPla NHar NHol SPan WFar WPyg WWat |
| | - 'Hastata' (m) | CMHG EPla SHHo |
| | - 'Ingramii' (m/v) | EHic EPla SHHo WBcn |
| | - 'J.C. van Tol' (f) ♀ | More than 30 suppliers |
| | - 'Latispina' (f) | SHHo |
| | - 'Laurifolia Aurea' (m) | SHHo WGwG WWal |
| | - 'Lichtenthalii' (f) | SHHo |
| | - 'Madame Briot' (f/v) ♀ | CDoC CMHG CTri EBee ELan ENot IMGH IOrc LHyr MAsh MBal MBar MBri NHol NWea SBod SHHo SPer SPla SReu SRms WDin WFar WWal WWeb |
| § | - 'Maderensis Variegata' (m/v) | SHHo |
| | - 'Monstrosa' (m) | SHHo |
| | - Moonlight holly | See *I. aquifolium* 'Flavescens' |
| | - 'Myrtifolia' (m) | CDoC ELan EPfP LRHS MBar MBlu MGos MRav MTed WFar |
| | - 'Myrtifolia Aurea' (m/v) | SHHo |
| § | - 'Myrtifolia Aurea Maculata' (m/v) ♀ | CBlo CBrm CDoC CMHG CPl CRos EAst EBee EHoe ELan IMGH LNet MAsh MBal MBri NHol NWea SLon SMad SPer SRPl WPat |
| | - 'Myrtifolia Aureovariegata' | See *I. aquifolium* 'Myrtifolia Aurea Maculata' |
| § | - 'Ovata Aurea' (m/v) | CRos SHHo |
| | - 'Pendula' (f) | CBlo CRos EPfP MWat SBod SHHo |
| | - 'Pendula Mediopicta' | See *I. aquifolium* 'Weeping Golden Milkmaid' |
| § | - 'Pyramidalis' (f) ♀ | CBlo CDoC CEnd CTri EBee ELan ENot GCHN GChr GRei LHyr MAsh MBar MBri MGos MLan NBee NHol NWea SHHo SPer SPla SRms WDin WOrn |
| | - 'Pyramidalis Aureomarginata' (f) | CDoC MGos MLan SHHo WBcn WGwG WWal |
| | - 'Pyramidalis Fructu Luteo' (f) ♀ | CBlo MBar SHHo WBcn |
| | - 'Recurva' (m) | Last listed 1997 |
| | - 'Rubricaulis Aurea' (f/v) | MBal NHol NOla SHHo WBcn |
| * | - 'Samuel Foster' | Last listed 1996 |
| ¶ | - Siberia® = 'Limsi' (f) | SHHo |
| | - 'Silver King' | See *I. aquifolium* 'Silver Queen' |
| ¶ | - 'Silver Lightning' | SHHo |
| | - 'Silver Milkboy' (f/v) | EHoe ELan EMil MBal MBlu MGos NOla SEas WFar |
| | - 'Silver Milkmaid' (f/v) ♀ | CDoC EAst EPfP MAsh MBar MRav MWat NHol SHHo SPer SPla SSta WWal |
| § | - 'Silver Queen' (m/v) ♀ | More than 30 suppliers |
| | - 'Silver Sentinel' | See *I.* x *altaclerensis* 'Belgica Aurea' |
| | - 'Silver van Tol' (f/v) | EAst EBee ELan ENot IOrc MBri NHol SHHo WBcn WLRN WStI WWeb |
| | - 'Silver Wedding' (f/v) | Last listed 1996 |
| § | - 'Watereriana' (m/v) | EHol MAsh MBal SBod SMur WBcn |
| | - 'Waterer's Gold' | See *I. aquifolium* 'Watereriana' |
| § | - 'Weeping Golden Milkmaid' (f/v) | NHol SHHo WPat |
| | x *aquipernyi* | SHHo |
| § | - Dragon Lady® = 'Meschick' (f) | COtt LPan SHH |
| ♦ | - 'Meschick' | See *I.* x *aquipernyi* Dragon Lady = 'Meschick' |
| | - 'San Jose' (f) | CMCN SHHo |
| | x *attenuata* | WWat |
| | - 'Sunny Foster' (f/v) ♀ | CDul CMCN EBee ENot EPla LRHS MBlu MGos NSti SHHo WBcn |
| § | *bioritsensis* | CMCN CTri NWea WBcn |
| | *buergeri* | CMCN |
| | *cassine* | CMCN |
| * | - yellow-berried | Last listed 1996 |
| | *chinensis* misapplied | See *I. purpurea* |
| | *ciliospinosa* | CMCN |
| | *colchica* | CMCN |
| | *corallina* | CMCN |
| | *cornuta* | CLan CMCN CRos ERom LPan SHHo WBcn |
| * | - 'Aurea' | EAst SHHo |
| ¶ | - 'Burfordii' (f) | CMCN |
| § | - 'Dazzler' (f) | SHHo |
| ¶ | - 'Ira S. Nelson' (f/v) | SHHo |
| | - 'O. Spring' (f/v) | CMHG EPla SBid SHHo |
| | - 'Rotunda' (f) | Last listed 1996 |

| | | |
|---|---|---|
| *crenata* | CBlo CMCN EHic ERom ESis GAri MBar SRms WFar WHCr WNor WWat | |
| - 'Aureovariegata' | See *I. crenata* 'Variegata' | |
| § - 'Bennett's Compact' (m) | Last listed 1996 | |
| ¶ - 'Braddock Heights' (f) | SHHo | |
| ¶ - 'Cape Fear' (m) | SHHo | |
| ¶ - 'Carolina Upright' (m) | SHHo | |
| ¶ - 'Cole's Hardy' (f) | SHHo | |
| - 'Compacta' | See *I. crenata* 'Bennett's Compact' | |
| - 'Convexa' (f) ♀ | CB&S EBee EHic ENot GDra IMGH MBal MBar MBri MWhi NHol NWea SHHo WPat WPyg WWat | |
| - 'Fastigiata' | CBlo CDoC CEnd CRos EAst EBee EBrP EBre EPla LBre LHol LHop LPan MAsh MBNS MBri MGos MLan NSti SBre SCoo SHHo SPer WGwG WTro WWal WWes | |
| ◆ - 'Fructo Luteo' | See *I. crenata* f. *watanabeana* | |
| - 'Fukarin' | See *I. crenata* 'Shiro-fukurin' | |
| * - 'Glory Gem' (f) | SHHo | |
| - 'Golden Gem' (f) ♀ | More than 30 suppliers | |
| - 'Green Dragon' | Last listed 1996 | |
| - 'Green Hedge' | LBuc | |
| - 'Green Island' (m) | CRos LRHS SHHo | |
| ¶ - 'Green Lustre' (f) | SHHo | |
| - 'Helleri' (f) | CMCN EPla MBar MBro NHol SBla SHHo WPat WPyg | |
| ¶ - 'Hetzii' (f) | SHHo | |
| ¶ - 'Ivory Hall' (f) | EPla SHHo | |
| ¶ - 'Ivory Tower' (f) | SHHo | |
| * - 'Kobold' | SHHo | |
| * - 'Korean Gem' | EPla | |
| ¶ - var. *latifolia* (m) | SHHo | |
| - 'Luteovariegata' | See *I. crenata* 'Variegata' | |
| - 'Mariesii' (f) | CMCN IMGH MBlu MBro MPla NHol SBla SHHo SIng WPat WPyg | |
| - 'Mount Halla' (f) | CMCN | |
| ¶ - 'Nakada' (m) | SHHo | |
| ¶ - 'Pride's Tiny' | SHHo | |
| I - 'Pyramidalis' (f) | CHar CLTr CMil MPla NHar NHol SPan WPat | |
| I - 'Rotundifolia' | Last listed 1996 | |
| - 'Sentinel' (f) | Last listed 1996 | |
| § - 'Shiro-fukurin' (f/v) | CBlo CMCN CMHG EAst ELan EPfP NHar NHol SBid SHHo WCru WPat WPyg | |
| - 'Sky Pencil' (f) | CMCN | |
| - 'Snowflake' | See *I. crenata* 'Shiro-fukurin' | |
| - 'Stokes' (m) | GAri LRHS MBri SHHo WPat WPyg | |
| - upright form | CMCN | |
| § - 'Variegata' | CChe CMCN CMHG ELan EPla MBar MBlu NHol SHHo SRms WPat | |
| § - f. *watanabeana* (f) | ESis SHHo | |
| 'Dazzler' | See *I. cornuta* 'Dazzler' | |
| *decidua* | CMCN | |
| - 'Warren's Red' (f) | CMCN | |
| *dimorphophylla* | CB&S CDoC CMCN EPla SHHo | |
| - 'Somerset Pixie' | SHHo | |
| 'Doctor Kassab' (f) | CMCN SHHo | |
| 'Drace' (f) | SHHo | |
| 'Elegance' (f) | Last listed 1997 | |
| *fargesii* | CMCN | |
| *ficoidea* | CMCN | |
| *glabra* 'Snow White' (f) | MBal | |
| *hascombensis* | See *I. aquifolium* 'Hascombensis' | |
| *hookeri* | Last listed 1996 | |
| 'Indian Chief' (f) | MBlu WWat | |

| | | |
|---|---|---|
| *insignis* | See *I. kingiana* | |
| *integra* | Last listed 1998 | |
| 'John T. Morris' (m) | MBal | |
| § *kingiana* | CMCN WWat | |
| x *koehneana* | CBot | |
| - 'Chestnut Leaf' (f) ♀ | CDoC CMCN CMHG EBee MBri MRav MWat SHHo SMad WBcn WCru WGer WLeb WWat | |
| § *kusanoi* | CMCN | |
| *latifolia* | CMCN SHHo SMad | |
| * 'Little Diamond' | SRPl | |
| *longipes* | CMCN | |
| 'Lydia Morris' (f) | CMHG CSam SBid SHHo WWat | |
| *macrocarpa* | Last listed 1996 | |
| *macropoda* | CMCN | |
| x *makinoi* | Last listed 1997 | |
| 'Mary Nell' (f) | SHHo | |
| ◆ x *meservae* 'Mesgolg' (f) | See *I.* x *meserveae* Golden Girl = 'Mesgolg' | |
| x *meserveae* | SHHo | |
| - Blue Angel® (f) ♀ | More than 30 suppliers | |
| § - Blue Maid® = 'Mesid' (f) | EMil | |
| - Blue Prince® (m) | CB&S CBrm CMHG COtt CRos EHoe EWTr IOrc LBuc LHol MBal MBar MBlu MBri MMea NHol SHHo SPer WDin WStl WWeb | |
| - Blue Princess® (f) ♀ | CB&S CBrm CMHG COtt EAst ENot EWTr LBuc LPan MBal MBar MBlu MBri MMal MMea MRav NHol SHHo SPer WStl | |
| * - 'Glenroy Purple' | MBal | |
| § - Golden Girl® = 'Mesgolg' (f) | EMil | |
| ◆ - 'Mesid' (f) | See *I.* x *meserveae* Blue Maid = 'Mesid' | |
| * - 'Red Darling' (f) | Last listed 1996 | |
| *muchagara* | CB&S CMCN | |
| *myrtifolia* | CBlo CMCN ECot NHar SBid SPar WCFE WLRN | |
| - yellow-berried | Last listed 1996 | |
| 'Nellie R. Stevens' (f) | CBlo CDoC EBee ENot LPan WBcn | |
| *nothofagifolia* C&H 424 | Last listed 1997 | |
| *opaca* | CGre CMCN | |
| *pedunculosa* | CMCN SHHo | |
| *perado latifolia* | See *I. perado* subsp. *platyphylla* | |
| § - subsp. *platyphylla* | CB&S CMCN CSam EPla MBlu SAPC SArc SHHo | |
| *pernyi* | CMCN CTrG EPla IOrc MBal SHHo SLon SSta WBcn WFar WWat | |
| - var. *veitchii* | See *I. bioritsensis* | |
| *poneantha* | See *I. kusanoi* | |
| *pringlei* | CMCN | |
| § *purpurea* | CMCN | |
| 'Pyramidalis' | See *I. aquifolium* 'Pyramidalis' | |
| *rotunda* | CMCN | |
| *rugosa* | CMCN | |
| 'September Gem' (f) | CMCN | |
| *serrata* | CMCN | |
| 'Sparkleberry' (f) | LPan | |
| *suaveolens* | CMCN | |
| *verticillata* | CAgr CGre CMCN EPla IMGH LEdu LPan NWea | |
| - (f) | CPle EPfP GAri SBid SMur | |
| - (m) | CDoC EPfP GAri NPoe SBid SMur WWat | |
| - 'Afterglow' (f) | MBlu | |
| - f. *aurantiaca* (f) | CBlo MBlu SMur | |
| - f. *chrysocarpa* | CMCN | |
| * - 'Compacta' | See *I. verticillata* 'Nana' | |
| * - 'Fructu Albo' (f) | CMCN | |

| | |
|---|---|
| * – 'Golden Male' (m) | Last listed 1998 |
| – 'Golden Rain' | Last listed 1998 |
| – 'Jim Dandy' (m) | MBlu |
| § – 'Nana' (f) | CMCN MBlu |
| – 'Red Sprite' | See *I. verticillata* 'Nana' |
| – 'Southern Gentleman' (m) | MBlu |
| – 'Stop Light' (f) | MBlu |
| – 'Sunset' (f) | MBlu |
| – 'Winter Red' (f) | CDoC CMCN CWSG MBlu MMHG |
| | NPoe WRHF WWat |
| *vomitoria* | CMCN |
| x *wandoensis* | CMCN SHHo |
| 'Washington' (f) | CPle |
| *yunnanensis* | CMCN GAri |

## ILIAMNA See SPHAERALCEA

## ILICIUM (Illiciaceae)

| | |
|---|---|
| *anisatum* | CArn CB&S CFil CPle SRPl SSpi |
| | WPat WPyg WSHC WWat |
| *floridanum* | CB&S CFil CPle EPfP MBal SBid |
| | SSpi WBod WPGP WWat |
| *henryi* | CFil CMCN CPle WPGP WSHC |

## IMPATIENS (Balsaminaceae)

| | |
|---|---|
| *auricoma* | EBak SHFr |
| *balfourii* | WCot |
| 'Ballerina' | CInt |
| 'Blackberry Ice' | CHal |
| *capensis* | Last listed 1998 |
| 'Cardinal Red' | CHal CInt |
| ¶ *congolensis* | EPfP |
| ¶ *cristata* | SHFr |
| 'Dapper Dan' (v) | Last listed 1997 |
| 'Diamond Orange' | CInt |
| 'Diamond Rose' | CHal |
| 'Diamond Scarlet' | CHal |
| double flowered (d) | EBak |
| 'Evening Blush' | CInt |
| ¶ 'Fiesta Lavender Orchid' | WWol |
| (Fiesta Series) (d) | |
| ¶ 'Fiesta Sparkler Salmon' | WWol |
| (Fiesta Series) (d) | |
| *glandulifera* | MCCP WHer |
| – 'Candida' | CBre EMon |
| 'Golden Surprise' | Last listed 1997 |
| *hawkeri* | EBak |
| ¶ *hians* | SHFr |
| ♦ 'Kigula' (Paradise Series) | See *I.* Tagula = 'Kigula' (Paradise |
| | Series) |
| 'Madame Pompadour' | CHal |
| New Guinea Group | CHal EBak MBri WLRN |
| *niamniamensis* | EBak ERea LCns LHil |
| – 'Congo Cockatoo' | CHal CInt ECon EOHP LIck SHFr |
| | SRms |
| ¶ – 'Golden Cockatoo' | EBak WSpi |
| I – 'Variegata' | ECon |
| *omeiana* | EBee WCot |
| 'Orange Surprise' | CHal |
| 'Peach Ice' | CHal |
| *pseudoviola* | LHil SHFr |
| * – 'Alba' | Last listed 1997 |
| – 'Woodcote' | CSpe LHil |
| 'Purple Chico' | CInt |
| 'Raspberry Ripple' | CHal |
| 'Salmon Princess' | CHal CInt |
| *sodenii* | GCal LHil SDys SHFr |
| sp. from Uganda | GCal |
| *sulcata* | SHFr |
| *sultani* | See *I. walleriana* |
| ¶ *sylvicola* | CFir |
| § Tagula = 'Kigula' (Paradise | WWol |
| Series) | |

| | |
|---|---|
| *tinctoria* | CDoC CFil CFir CGre CTre CWit |
| | GCal LHil SIgm SVen WCru WPGP |
| – subsp. *elegantissima* | CFee |
| – subsp. *tinctoria* | Last listed 1998 |
| *ugandensis* | GCal |
| § *walleriana* | EBak MBri |
| * – 'Variegata' | CHal |
| ¶ *zombensis* | SHFr |

## IMPERATA (Poaceae)

| | |
|---|---|
| ¶ *brevifolia* | CBrm |
| *cylindrica* | CPla EPar MHlr MSal WCot |
| – 'Red Baron' | See *I. cylindrica* 'Rubra' |
| § – 'Rubra' | More than 30 suppliers |

## INCARVILLEA (Bignoniaceae)

| | |
|---|---|
| § *arguta* | CBot CHan GCal LGre LPio MHar |
| | WAbe WWin |
| *brevipes* | See *I. mairei* |
| *compacta* | NHar SIng |
| – ACE 1455 | WCot |
| – CLD 0233 | Last listed 1996 |
| *delavayi* | CBot EAst EBee ECha EFou EHyt |
| | ELan ENot LBow LHop MBri |
| | MDun MRav NFla NLar NRoo |
| | NVic SDeJ SPer SRms WBea WBro |
| | WCla WCot WFar WHil WHoo |
| | WMow WWin |
| – 'Bees' Pink' | EBee GBuc |
| – 'Snowtop' | More than 30 suppliers |
| *diffusa* | EHyt |
| ¶ *forrestii* | LPio |
| – KGB 43 | Last listed 1998 |
| *grandiflora* | CLAP CRDP ELan MTho NWoo |
| | SBla |
| ¶ *himalayensis* | GBuc GCrs NHar NSla SBla SIgm |
| 'Frank Ludlow' | |
| ¶ – 'Nyoto Sama' | GBuc GDra SBla |
| ¶ *longiracemosa* | GCrs |
| *lutea* L 1986 | SBla |
| § *mairei* | EAst EBee EHyt GDra LHop MHar |
| | MLLN MTho NLar SIgm SLod |
| | SMrm WPer WWin |
| – B&L 12602 | SWas |
| – var. *mairei* ACE 2233 | NHar WCot |
| – – ACE 2420 | NHar |
| – – CLD 101 | GCrs |
| – – f. *multifoliata* | See *I. zhongdianensis* |
| – – – ACE 64 | See *I. zhongdianensis* ACE 2201 |
| – pink | Last listed 1996 |
| § *olgae* | CSam ELan EMan NPSI WCot |
| *przewalskii* | Last listed 1998 |
| ¶ *sinensis* | SRms |
| – 'Alba' | EBee WCot |
| – 'Cheron' | WCot |
| * 'Snowcap' | Last listed 1997 |
| *younghusbandii* | Last listed 1998 |
| § *zhongdianensis* | EBee GBuc GCrs NSla SBla |
| – ACE 1600 | Last listed 1998 |
| § – ACE 2201 | NHar |
| – ACE 2278 | NHar NWCA WCot |
| – CLD 233 | EHyt |

## INDIGOFERA (Papilionaceae)

| | |
|---|---|
| *amblyantha* ♀ | CArn CB&S EHic EMil EPfP GCal |
| | MBlu SBid SDry SSpi WKif WSHC |
| | WSpi |
| ¶ *articulata* | CFil |
| *australis* | CTrC SOWG |
| *decora* f. *alba* | EPfP |
| *dielsiana* | CB&S |
| * *frigida* HWJCM 107 | WCru |

| | |
|---|---|
| *gerardiana* | See *I. heterantha* |
| *hebepetala* | WAbe WCru WDin WSHC |
| § *heterantha* ♀ | CArn CB&S CBar CBot CMCN |
| | CPle EBee ELan EMil ENot IMGH |
| | IOrc LHop MAsh MBlu MPla NPro |
| | SCob SLon SPer SReu SSpi SSta |
| | WAbe WCot WFar WOve WSHC |
| | WWat |
| – CC 1708 | MRPP |
| *kirilowii* | CFil CGre EPfP SOWG WSHC |
| *pendula* | WPGP |
| *potaninii* | WCru WHer |
| *pseudotinctoria* | CFil EPfP SRms |
| *tinctoria* | CArn MSal |

## INDOCALAMUS (Poaceae - Bambusoideae)

| | |
|---|---|
| *hamadae* | EPla ERod SDry |
| *latifolius* | EOas EPla ISta LJus SDry WJun |
| ¶ – 'Hopei' | EPla |
| *longiauritus* | EPla SDry |
| *solidus* | EPla ISta LJus MMoz MWht NPal |
| | SDry WJun WMul |
| § *tessellatus* | CDoC CFil CMCo EBee EFul EPfP |
| | EPla ERod ISta LEdu LJus MCCP |
| | WBay WJun |

## INULA ✿ (Asteraceae)

| | |
|---|---|
| *acaulis* | MBro SSca WCot |
| ¶ *candida* | CSam |
| *conyzae* | MHew MSal |
| *crithmoides* | WHer |
| *dysenterica* | See *Pulicaria dysenterica* |
| *ensifolia* | CHan IBlr LFis MLLN MRav MSte |
| | MTho NBro NDea NFai NVic SBea |
| | WBea WEas WHoo WMer WPyg |
| ¶ – 'Compacta' | SUsu |
| – 'Gold Star' | CBlo CMGP ECtt MWgw NBir |
| | NFor NLon NOak WFar WLRN |
| | WMow WPer |
| *glandulosa* | See *I. orientalis* |
| 'Golden Beauty' | See *Buphthalmum salicifolium* |
| | 'Golden Wonder' |
| *helenium* | CArn CSev ECGN ELau EWFC |
| | GPoy ILis LHol MChe MFir MHew |
| | MLLN MSal NArg NMir SRCN |
| | SRms WBea WByw WCer WGwy |
| | WHbs WHer WOak WPer WWye |
| *helianthus-aquaticus* | Last listed 1997 |
| CLD 658 | |
| *hookeri* | More than 30 suppliers |
| *magnifica* | CHan CSam ECGN ECha ELan |
| | EMon GGar LFis MBro MCAu MFir |
| | MNrw MRav NBro NDea NHol |
| | SDix SMad WBea WCot WHer |
| | WHoo WMer WMow WOld WPer |
| | WPic WWin WWye |
| * 'Mediterranean Sun' | Last listed 1998 |
| *oculus-christi* | EWes |
| * 'Oriental Star' | Last listed 1997 |
| § *orientalis* | CKel CPea EBee EFou EWTr MBri |
| | MBro MCAu NFai NFla NLak |
| | NLon NMir NSti SMac SPer WBea |
| | WByw WFar WHoo WOld WPer |
| | WPyg |
| *racemosa* | EBee ECha EHal EMon EPPr EPla |
| | GBin GCal IBlr MNrw MSte NChi |
| | NSti SMrm SRms WFar |
| – CC&McK 620 | GCHN |
| – 'Sonnenspeer' | NLar SGre WPer |
| *rhizocephala* | CSam EHyt |
| *royleana* | CHan GCal MNrw MRav MSte |
| | SSca |

| | |
|---|---|
| *verbascifolia* | EMan GVic |

## IOCHROMA (Solanaceae)

| | |
|---|---|
| § *australe* | CB&S CGre CHan CPlN CPle |
| | EWTr LLew MBEx SOWG SVen |
| | WCot |
| § – 'Andean Snow' | CBot SVen |
| § – 'Bill Evans' | EWll WHer |
| – large-flowered form | Last listed 1998 |
| § *calycinum* | CGen |
| *coelestis* | Last listed 1996 |
| *cyaneum* | CGre CPle ERea LLew SOWG |
| | SVen SYvo WMul |
| – dark form | Last listed 1998 |
| – large form | LHil |
| § – 'Trebah' | CB&S ERea LBlm LHil LLew SYvo |
| § – 'Woodcote White' | LHil |
| ¶ *gesnerioides* 'Coccineum' | WMul |
| § *grandiflorum* | CSev LHil SOWG SVen WMul |
| ♦ *macrocalyx* | See *I. calycinum* |
| ♦ *violaceum* misapplied | See *I. cyaneum* 'Trebah' |
| ♦ *warscewiczii* | See *I. grandiflorum* |

## IPHEION (Alliaceae)

| | |
|---|---|
| 'Alberto Castillo' | CAvo CBro CLAP CMea EHyt |
| | ELan EPot EWes MTho WCot |
| | WIvy |
| *dialystemon* | Last listed 1998 |
| § 'Rolf Fiedler' ♀ | CAvo CBro CMea CSpe EBee EBur |
| | ECho EHyt ELan EPar EPot ETub |
| | EWes LAma MRav MTho NChi |
| | NMen SBla SIng WAbe WCot WFar |
| *sellowianum* | LBow |
| § *uniflorum* | CBro CHal EBee ECha ETub LAma |
| | MBri MBro MNrw MRav NMen |
| | NRog NWCA NWoo SIng SRms |
| | WAbb WBea WCla WCot WFar |
| | WHoo WPer |
| – 'Album' | CBro CMea ECha EHyt ELan EPar |
| | EPot ERos EWes LPio MRav MTho |
| | NMGW SBla SIng |
| – 'Charlotte Bishop' | SBla SDys SWas |
| – 'Froyle Mill' ♀ | CAvo CBro CHal CMea CPin EBee |
| | EBur EHyt ELan EPar EPot ERos |
| | EWes LPio MBro MRav MTho |
| | NMGW NMen SAga SBla SIng |
| | SUsu WCom WHoo WWat |
| – 'Wisley Blue' ♀ | CAvo CBro CMea CPlt EBee ECha |
| | ELan EPar EPot ERos ETub LAma |
| | MBro MRav MS&S MTho NMen |
| | NNrd SBla SIng SRms WBea WCot |
| | WFar WHoo WPyg |

## IPOMOEA (Convolvulaceae)

| | |
|---|---|
| *aculeata* | Last listed 1996 |
| *acuminata* | See *I. indica* |
| *alba* | CPlN |
| * *andersonii* | CPlN |
| *batatas* 'Blackie' | CPlN |
| *bonariensis* | SVen |
| ♦ *brasiliensis* | See *I. pes-caprae* subsp. |
| | *brasiliensis* |
| *carnea* | LChe SOWG |
| – subsp. *fistulosa* | Last listed 1998 |
| *coccinea* | Last listed 1998 |
| – (L.) A.Gray | See *I. hederifolia* |
| var. *hederifolia* | |
| *costata* | Last listed 1996 |
| § *hederifolia* | Last listed 1998 |
| *borsfalliae* ♀ | CPlN |
| § *indica* ♀ | CHal CLTr CPlN ERea LCns MGrG |
| | SOWG SYvo WMul |

| | |
|---|---|
| *learii* | See *I. indica* |
| *leptophylla* | EBee |
| *leptotoma* | Last listed 1996 |
| § *lobata* | LIck SHFr SUsu SYvo |
| *palmata* | See *I. cairica* |
| *pennata* 'Relli Valley' | Last listed 1998 |
| § *pes-caprae* subsp. | Last listed 1998 |
| *brasiliensis* | |
| *purpurea* | SRCN WHer |
| - 'Kniola's Purple-black' | Last listed 1998 |
| *quamoclit* | CPlN |
| 'Quebra Plata' | Last listed 1998 |
| 'Scarlett O'Hara' | Last listed 1997 |
| *tuberosa* | See *Merremia tuberosa* |
| *versicolor* | See *I. lobata* |
| *violacea* L. | Last listed 1998 |
| - hort. | See *I. tricolor* |

## IPOMOPSIS (Polemoniaceae)

| | |
|---|---|
| § *aggregata* | WCot |
| - subsp. *aggregata* | Last listed 1997 |
| ¶ - subsp. *bridgesii* | WCot |
| *spicata* var. *orchidacea* | Last listed 1996 |

## IRESINE (Amaranthaceae)

| | |
|---|---|
| *herbstii* | CHal EBak ERea IBlr LHil |
| - 'Aureoreticulata' | CHal LHil |
| - 'Brilliantissima' | CHal LHil MBEx |
| *lindenii* ♀ | LHil MBEx |

## IRIS ✿ (Iridaceae)

| | |
|---|---|
| 'A.W.Tait' (Spuria) | GCal |
| 'Abracadabra' (SDB) | LBro LGre |
| 'Abridged Version' (MTB) | NZep |
| 'Acapulco Gold' (TB) | SCro |
| 'Ace of Clubs' (SDB) | NZep |
| 'Action Front' (TB) | CHad CMil COtt EHic ERou NCat |
| | NGdn WLRN |
| 'Actress' (TB) | EFou |
| 'Adobe Sunset' (Spuria) | LBro |
| 'Adrienne Taylor' (MDB) ♀ | LBro MCAu |
| *afghanica* | Last listed 1998 |
| ¶ 'Afternoon Delight' (TB) | MCAu |
| 'Agnes James' (CH) ♀ | CBro LBro |
| 'Ain't She Sweet' (IB) | SCro |
| *aitchisonii* var. *chrysantha* | Last listed 1996 |
| 'Alastor' (TB) | Last listed 1998 |
| 'Albatross' (TB) | CKel |
| *albicans* ♀ | MCAu SCro WHal |
| 'Alcazar' (TB) | EPfP EWTr NMoo |
| 'Alenette' (TB) | MCAu |
| 'Alice Goodman' (TB) | Last listed 1997 |
| 'Alien' (IB) | LBro |
| 'Alizes' (TB) | Last listed 1996 |
| 'All Right' (IB) | NZep SCro |
| 'Allegiance' (TB) | WEas |
| 'Alpine Lake' (MDB) | NZep |
| 'Already' (MDB) | EHyt |
| ¶ 'Alsterquelle' (SDB) | WTin |
| 'Altruist' (TB) | SCro |
| 'Amadora' (TB) | CKel LBro |
| 'Amaranth Gem' (SDB) | LBro |
| 'Ambassadeur' (TB) | ERou EWTr |
| 'Amber Blaze' (SDB) | NZep |
| 'Amber Queen' (DB) | CGle COtt ECtt ELan EMan ERos |
| | MCCP NMen SCro SLon WGwG |
| | WLRN WWal WWeb |
| 'Amber Tambour' (TB) | Last listed 1998 |
| 'American Sweetheart' (TB) | LIri |
| ¶ 'America's Cup' (TB) | LIri |
| 'Amethyst Crystal' (CH) | LBro |
| 'Amethyst Flame' (TB) | CKel EBrP EBre ERou LBre |
| | NMGW SBre SRPl SRms |

| | |
|---|---|
| 'Amethyst Sunset' (MTB) | LBro |
| 'Amigo' (TB) ♀ | SCro |
| 'Amphora' (SDB) | CBro ERos |
| N 'Amsterdam' (TB) | Last listed 1996 |
| 'Anastasia' (TB) | CKel |
| 'Ancilla' (Aril) | CLAP |
| 'Angel Unawares' (TB) | MCAu |
| 'Angelic' (SDB) | LBro MCAu |
| 'Angel's Kiss' (SDB) | Last listed 1996 |
| 'Angel's Tears' | See *I. histrioides* 'Angel's Eye' |
| *anglica* | See *I. latifolia* |
| 'Anna Belle Babson' (TB) | MCAu SCro |
| 'Annabel Jane' (TB) | CKel LBro MCAu SCro |
| 'Anne Elizabeth' (SDB) | CBro ERos |
| 'Annikins' (IB) ♀ | Last listed 1998 |
| 'Antarctic' (TB) | Last listed 1996 |
| 'Antique Ivory' (TB) | Last listed 1996 |
| *aphylla* | NOla NOrc |
| 'Aplomb' (TB) | LIri |
| 'Apollodorus' (TB) | Last listed 1998 |
| 'Apollo's Touch' (IB) | NZep |
| * 'Apple Court' | SApp |
| 'Appledore' (SDB) | CBro EHyt ERos MBro NNrd |
| 'Apricot Skies' (BB) | NZep |
| 'April Accent' (MDB) | Last listed 1996 |
| 'April Ballet' (MDB) | Last listed 1998 |
| 'Apropos' (TB) | Last listed 1996 |
| 'Aquilifer' (AB) | Last listed 1996 |
| 'Arab Chief' (TB) | CKel |
| 'Arabi Pasha' (TB) | MCAu SCro WLRN |
| 'Arabi Treasure' (IB) | LBro |
| * 'Arabic Night' (IB) | MCAu |
| 'Archie Owen' (Spuria) | LBro |
| 'Arctic Fancy' (IB) ♀ | LBro MMil |
| 'Arctic Snow' | MCAu |
| 'Arctic Star' (TB) | CKel MFir |
| 'Arctic Tern' (TB) | LBro |
| 'Arden' (BB) ♀ | LBro |
| *arenaria* | See *I. humilis* |
| 'Argus Pheasant' (SDB) | Last listed 1998 |
| 'Arnold Sunrise' (CH) ♀ | LBro WWst |
| 'Arnold Velvet' (SDB) | LBro |
| 'Around Midnight' (TB) | LIri SCro |
| 'Arpège' (TB) | EBee |
| 'Art Gallery' (IB) | Last listed 1996 |
| 'Ask Alma' (IB) | CKel NZep SCro |
| * 'Atlantique' (TB) | CKel |
| § *atrofusca* | CHar |
| - MS&CL 56 | Last listed 1998 |
| - S&L 38 | Last listed 1998 |
| 'Attention Please' (TB) | CKel |
| § *attica* | CBro CHan CMea CPBP ERos |
| | GCrs LBee MBro MNrw NNrd |
| | WAbe WLin |
| ¶ - lemon | NNrd |
| - S&L 486 | Last listed 1998 |
| § *aucheri* ♀ | CBro EPot LAma |
| 'Audacious' (BB) | NZep |
| 'Aunt Martha' (BB) | MBri NMGW |
| 'Austrian Sky' (SDB) | CMea CSam EBrP EBre EHyt ELan |
| | ENot LBre MBro MMil SBre WCot |
| 'Autumn Leaves' (TB) | MCAu MMil |
| 'Avanelle' (IB) | EFou ERou LBro WBcn |
| 'Az Ap' (IB) | NZep SCro |
| 'Aztec Star' (SDB) | LBro |
| 'Azure Exchoˈ (IB) | MMil |
| 'Azurea' (MDB) | NFla |
| 'Baboon Bottom' (BB) | LIri |
| 'Babushka' (SDB) | LBro |
| 'Baby Bengal' (BB) | Last listed 1998 |
| 'Baby Bibs' (MTB) | NZep |

| | |
|---|---|
| 'Baby Blessed' (SDB) | CBro NZep |
| 'Baby Face' (TB) | MMil |
| 'Baccarat' (TB) | Last listed 1998 |
| ¶ 'Back in Black' (TB) | CKel |
| 'Baked Alaska' (TB) | MMil |
| *bakeriana* | EBee LAma LRHS |
| 'Ballerina Blue' (TB) | ERou |
| 'Ballyhoo' (TB) | LRHS |
| 'Banbury Beauty' (CH) ♀ | CLAP CPlt NSti |
| 'Banbury Fair' (CH) | GMac LBro WWst |
| 'Banbury Gem' (CH) ♀ | LBro |
| 'Banbury Melody' (CH) ♀ | CFee WBcn |
| 'Banbury Ruffles' (SDB) | MCAu MMil NMGW NMen NSti |
| | SCro |
| 'Banbury Velvet' (CH) ♀ | Last listed 1995 |
| 'Banbury Welcome' (CH) | IBlr |
| 'Bang' (TB) | CKel |
| 'Barbara's Kiss' (Spuria) | Last listed 1996 |
| 'Baria' (SDB) | LBro |
| 'Barletta' (TB) | Last listed 1998 |
| 'Barnett Anley' | MBri |
| *barnumae* | EHyt |
| - *polakii* | See *I. polakii* |
| 'Baroque Prelude' (TB) | CKel MMil |
| 'Barrymore Charmer' (TB) | Last listed 1998 |
| 'Basso' (IB) | SCro |
| 'Batik' (BB) | LIri SCro WCot |
| 'Batsford' (SDB) | CBro EHyt NNrd |
| 'Battle Shout' (IB) | LBro |
| 'Bayberry Candle' (TB) | LIri |
| 'Be Dazzled' (SDB) | EFou |
| 'Be Happy' (SDB) | NZep |
| 'Beauty Mark' (SDB) | NZep |
| 'Beckon' (TB) | CKel |
| 'Bedford Lilac' (SDB) | NZep |
| 'Bedtime Story' (IB) | Last listed 1996 |
| 'Bee Wings' (MDB) | NZep WEas |
| 'Before the Storm' (TB) | LIri SCro |
| 'Bel Azur' (IB) | Last listed 1996 |
| 'Belise' (Spuria) ♀ | LBro |
| 'Belissinado' (Spuria) | LBro |
| 'Bellboy' (MTB) | NZep |
| 'Belle Meade' (TB) | Last listed 1996 |
| 'Belvi Queen' (TB) | MNrw |
| * 'Ben Hasel' | ECha |
| 'Bengal Tiger' (TB) | Last listed 1996 |
| N 'Benton Arundel' (TB) | SCro |
| 'Benton Cordelia' (TB) | Last listed 1997 |
| 'Benton Dierdre' (TB) | SCro SRms |
| 'Benton Evora' (TB) | ENot EOld |
| N 'Benton Lorna' (TB) | SCro |
| 'Benton Nigel' (TB) | Last listed 1998 |
| 'Benton Sheila' (TB) | SCro |
| 'Berkeley Gold' (TB) | CBlo COtt EBrP EBre ECtt EPfP |
| | ERav EWes LBre LBro LNor NGdn |
| | NMGW NOrc SBre SCob SPer |
| | SWat WLRN WLin |
| 'Best Bet' | Last listed 1997 |
| 'Betsey Boo' (SDB) | CKel |
| 'Betty Chatten' (TB) | NMen WLRN |
| 'Betty Cooper' (Spuria) | LBro |
| 'Betty my Love' (Spuria) | Last listed 1997 |
| 'Betty Simon' (TB) | CKel |
| 'Betty Wood' (SDB) | LBro |
| 'Beverly Sills' (TB) | CKel LBro LIri MCAu SCro |
| 'Bewdley' (IB) | LBro |
| 'Bewick Swan' (TB) | Last listed 1996 |
| 'Bewilderbeast' (TB) | LIri |
| 'Beyond' (TB) | SCro |
| 'Bibury' (SDB) ♀ | EGle LBro MCAu MMil SCro |
| N 'Big Day' (TB) | CKel WBcn |
| 'Big Money' (TB) ♀ | Last listed 1996 |
| 'Big Wheel' (CH) | Last listed 1996 |
| *biglumis* | See *I. lactea* |
| *biliottii* | CBro |
| 'Black as Night' (TB) | Last listed 1998 |
| 'Black Dragon' (TB) | SCro |
| 'Black Flag' (TB) | Last listed 1997 |
| 'Black Gamecock' (La) | SAWi |
| 'Black Hills' (TB) | MCAu |
| ¶ 'Black Hills Gold' (TB) | LIri |
| ¶ 'Black Ink' (TB) | COIW |
| 'Black Knight' (TB) | MHlr MRav NGdn SLod |
| 'Black Lady' (MTB) | Last listed 1997 |
| 'Black Swan' (TB) | CHad COtt EBrP EBre ECha ECtt |
| | ELan EMan ERav LBre MCAu |
| | NGdn NLon SBre WCot WWal |
| 'Black Watch' (IB) | CKel |
| 'Blackbeard' (BB) | CKel |
| 'Blackberry Brandy' (BB) | Last listed 1996 |
| * 'Blackfoot' | Last listed 1996 |
| 'Blazing Saddles' (TB) | NZep |
| 'Blenheim Royal' (TB) | MCAu SCro |
| 'Blitz' (SDB) | NZep |
| 'Blockley' (SDB) | Last listed 1996 |
| 'Blood Covenant' (SDB) | NZep |
| *bloudowii* | CLAP CPBP |
| 'Blue Admiral' (TB) | CKel |
| 'Blue Ballerina' (CH) ♀ | LBro |
| 'Blue Denim' (SDB) | CBro CM&M ECtt EGle EHyt ENot |
| | GMaP LBro MBNS MRav NBir |
| | WElm WHoo WMer WPen WWeb |
| 'Blue Doll' (MDB) | NZep |
| 'Blue Duchess' (TB) | CKel |
| ¶ 'Blue Emperor' | SRPl |
| 'Blue Eyed Blond' (IB) | SCro |
| 'Blue Eyed Brunette' (TB) ♀ | MCAu |
| 'Blue Hendred' (SDB) | LBro MCAu NBir |
| 'Blue Horizon' | ERos NMen |
| 'Blue Icing' (IB) | Last listed 1996 |
| 'Blue Lassie' (Spuria) | LBro |
| 'Blue Line' (SDB) | NZep |
| 'Blue Luster' (TB) ♀ | CHar CKel LBro SCro |
| 'Blue Magic' (Dutch) | NRog |
| 'Blue Moss' (SDB) | LBro |
| 'Blue Neon' (SDB) | Last listed 1996 |
| 'Blue Pigmy' (SDB) | CBlo CGle CMil EBee MCCP NCat |
| | NMen SCob SCro SPer WElm |
| | WGwG WLRN WWal |
| 'Blue Pools' (SDB) | EFou EGle EHyt LBro MBri NBir |
| | NZep SCro WPnP WTin |
| 'Blue Reflection' (TB) | MMil |
| 'Blue Rhythm' (TB) | CBlo CKel CM&M EMan ERou |
| | LBro MCAu MCli MWgw NFai |
| | SCro SMrm SPer WLRN |
| 'Blue Shimmer' (TB) | CBlo COtt EBee ECGN ELan |
| | EMan ENot MCAu MRav NFai |
| | NGdn SCro SPer SWat WGwG |
| | WWal |
| 'Blue Smoke' (TB) | CKel |
| 'Blue Sparks' (SDB) | Last listed 1996 |
| 'Blue Staccato' (TB) | CKel SCro |
| 'Blue Zephyr' (Spuria) | LBro |
| 'Bluebeard' (TB) | EHyt |
| 'Bluebird in Flight' (IB) | Last listed 1996 |
| 'Bluebird Wine' (TB) | MCAu |
| 'Blues Singer' (TB) | Last listed 1996 |
| 'Blushes' (IB) | SCro |
| 'Blushing Pink' (TB) | SCro |
| 'Bodderlecker' (SDB) | EFou |
| 'Bold Lassie' (SDB) | WHer |
| 'Bold Print' (IB) | MCAu SCro WWin |
| 'Bonny' (MDB) | CBro |
| 'Boo' (SDB) | CKel MCAu NZep |

'Border Town' (Spuria) — Last listed 1996

'Bourne Graceful' — CMGP EBee GCal NSti SCob SSpi WElm WGwG WLRN WWal

*bracteata* — CFil CNic EWoo WPGP WPer
- JCA 13427 — CLAP

'Braithwaite' (TB) — CBlo CKel CMGP COtt EBee EBrP EBre EHic ELan ENot ERou LBre LBro MCAu NLak SBre SCob SCro SMrm SRms SSpe SWat WElm WLRN

*brandzae* — See *I. sintenisii* subsp. *brandzae*

'Brannigan' (SDB) — CBro EHyt LBro MBri MCli MMil NBir NSti

'Brass Tacks' (SDB) — LBro NZep

'Brassie' (SDB) — CBro CKel ERos LBro MBNS MCli NNrd

¶ 'Breakers' (TB) ♀ — CKel LIri

¶ *brevicaulis* — GBin

'Bridal Crown' (TB) — SCro

§ 'Bride' (DB) — CCuc CM&M MBro

'Bride's Halo' (TB) — SCro

'Bright Button' (DB) — CKel

'Bright Moment' (SDB) — LBro

'Bright Vision' (SDB) — NZep

'Bright White' (MDB) — CBlo CBro CKel EHyt EPot ERos LBro MBNS NMen NNrd

'Bright Yellow' (DB) — MRav

'Brighteyes' (IB) — ESis LBro MBro NNrd SChu SCro SRms WLin WPer

'Brilliant Excuse' (TB) — NZep

'Brindisi' (TB) — CKel SCro

'Bristo Magic' (TB) — SCro

'Bristol Gem' (TB) — SCro

'Broad Grin' (SDB) — LBro

'Broadleigh Ann' (CH) — CBro WWst

'Broadleigh Carolyn' (CH) ♀ — CBro WWst

'Broadleigh Charlotte' — CBro WWst

'Broadleigh Clare' (CH) — CBro

'Broadleigh Dorothy' (CH) — CBro GMac WWst

'Broadleigh Elizabeth' (CH) — CBro

N 'Broadleigh Emily' (CH) — CBro

N 'Broadleigh Florence' (CH) — CBro

'Broadleigh Jean' — CBro WWst

'Broadleigh Joan' (CH) — CBro

'Broadleigh Joyce' (CH) — CBro WWst

¶ 'Broadleigh Karen' (CH) — WWst

'Broadleigh Lavinia' (CH) — CBro MRav WWst

'Broadleigh Mitre' (CH) — CBro

'Broadleigh Nancy' (CH) — CBro GMac

'Broadleigh Peacock' (CH) — CBro CHad CNic IBlr MMil MRav SUsu

N 'Broadleigh Rose' (CH) — CBro CElw CHad CMdw GBuc IBlr MRav NSti SMrm SWas WLin

'Broadleigh Sybil' (CH) — CBro

'Broadleigh Victoria' (CH) — CBro GBuc

'Broadway' (TB) — NZep SCro

'Broadway Baby' (IB) — CKel

'Bromyard' (SDB) ♀ — CBro MMil

'Bronzaire' (IB) ♀ — MCAu

'Bronze Beauty' (*boogiana* hybrid) — EPot

'Bronze Bird' (TB) — Last listed 1998

N 'Bronze Charm' (TB) — Last listed 1998

'Bronze Cloud' (TB) — CKel

'Bronze Queen' (Dutch) — Last listed 1998

'Broseley' (TB) — LBro

'Brown Doll' (IB) — Last listed 1996

'Brown Lasso' (BB) ♀ — LBro LIri SCro

¶ 'Brown Trout' (TB) — NBir

'Brownstone' (Spuria) — Last listed 1997

'Brummit's Mauve' — MCAu

'Bryngwyn' (TB) — LBro

'Bubbling Over' (TB) — SCro

'Bubbly Blue' (IB) — Last listed 1996

*bucharica* Foster ♀ — CBro EBee EPar EPot LAma NRog
- hort. — See *I. orchioides*

¶ - 'Yellow Dushanbe' — WWst

'Buckden Pike' (TB) ♀ — Last listed 1995

*bulleyana* — EWoo GCrs MBro NWoo SIgm SIng SRms SSpi SWas
- ACE 1665 — EBee
- ACE 1819 — Last listed 1996
- ACE 1890 — Last listed 1996
- ACE 2296 — EBee EHyt GBuc WCot

'Bumblebee Deelite' (MTB) — NZep

'Burford' (BB) — LBro

'Burgundy Brown' (TB) — NZep

'Burmese Dawn' (TB) — Last listed 1997

'Butter Pecan' (IB) — SCro

'Buttercup Bower' (TB) — MBri MCAu NMGW

'Buttercup Charm' (MDB) — NZep

'Buttered Chocolate' (Spuria) — Last listed 1996

'Buttermere' (TB) — SRms

'Buttermilk' — Last listed 1996

'Butterpat' (TB) — NZep

'Butterscotch Kiss' (TB) — CHad EBrP EBre ELan EMan ERou LBre MMil MRav NGdn NPla SBre SCro SMrm

'Button Box' (SDB) — NZep

'Bygone Era' (TB) — Last listed 1998

'Byword' (SDB) — LBro

'Cabaret Royale' (TB) — Last listed 1996

'Cable Car' (TB) — CKel

*caerulea* — See *I. albomarginata*

'Caliente' (TB) — EPfP MCAu

'California Style' (IB) — NZep

§ Californian hybrids — CElw CGle CLTr ELan MAvo MBal MRav SSpi WCot WWhi

'Calypso Mood' (TB) — SCro

'Cambridge Blue' — See *I.* 'Monspur Cambridge Blue'

'Camelot Rose' (TB) — MCAu

¶ 'Camera Shy' (TB) — LIri

'Campbellii' — See *I. lutescens* 'Campbellii'

'Can Can Red' (TB) — Last listed 1997

*canadensis* — See *I. hookeri*

'Canary Bird' (TB) — CKel

'Cannington Bluebird' (TB) — LBro

¶ 'Cannington Ochre' (SDB) — CBro

'Cannington Skies' (IB) ♀ — LBro MMil

'Cannington Sweet Puff' (TB) — LBro

'Cannonball' (TB) — Last listed 1998

'Can't Stop' (SDB) — Last listed 1996

'Cantab' (Reticulata) — CAvo CBro EBrP EBre EHyt ELan EPar EPot ETub LAma LBre NRog SBre

'Capricious' (TB) — SCro

'Captain Gallant' (TB) — Last listed 1997

'Caramba' (TB) — SCro

'Caramel' (TB) — EWoo

'Cardew' (TB) ♀ — LBro

'Caress' (SDB) — Last listed 1996

N 'Carey' (TB) — CKel

¶ 'Caribbean Dream' (TB) — LIri

'Carilla' (SDB) — ERos LBro LGre

'Carnaby' (TB) — LBro MBri MCAu WBcn

'Carnival Glass' (BB) — Last listed 1996

'Carnival Time' (TB) — EFou

'Carnton' (TB) — WEas

'Carolina Gold' (TB) — SCro

'Carolyn Rose' (MTB) — LBro NZep

'Carved Pink' (TB) — SCro

'Casbah' (TB) — SCro

'Cascade Sprite' (SDB) — SRms

'Cascadian Skies' (TB) — ERou

'Catalyst' (TB) — SCro

*caucasica* — MHar
'Cayenne Capers' (TB) — MMil MWat
\* 'Cedric Morris' — EWes
¶ 'Celebration Song' (TB) — LIri
'Celestial Glory' (TB) — Last listed 1997
'Centering Point' (Spuria) — LBro
'Centerpiece' (SDB) — LBro
'Centre Court' (TB) — SCro
'Chain White' — See *I.* 'Chian Wine'
*chamaeiris* — See *I. lutescens*
'Champagne Elegance' (TB) — LBro LIri MCAu MMil NBir
'Champagne Music' (TB) — Last listed 1996
'Champagne Waltz' (TB) — LIri
'Change of Pace' (TB) — SCro
'Chanted' (SDB) — NZep
'Chanteuse' (TB) — SCro
'Chantilly' (TB) — CBlo CM&M COtt EBee EBrP EBre ELan EMan ERav LBre MRav NGdn NOrc SBre SCob SCro
'Chapeau' (TB) — MCAu
'Chapel Hill' (SDB) — LBro
'Charger' (TB) — MMil
'Charm Song' (IB) — LBro
'Charmaine' (TB) — CKel
I 'Charming' (TB) — CKel
'Chartreuse Ruffles' (TB) — SCro
'Cheers' (IB) — LBro NZep
'Cherry Falls' (TB) — LBro
'Cherry Garden' (SDB) — CBlo CBro CKel CPlt EBee ECtt EGoo ELan EWes LGre MBNS MBri MBro MMil MRav MTis NBir SCro SIng WCot WEas WWeb
'Cherry Orchard' (TB) — NFor NLon
'Cherry Ripe' (TB) — Last listed 1997
'Cherry Smoke' (TB) — SCro
'Cherub Tears' (SDB) — NZep
'Cherub's Smile' (TB) — SCro
§ 'Chian Wine' (MTB) — LBro
'Chickee' (MTB) — NZep
'Chicken Little' (MDB) — CBro NMoo
'Chico Maid' (TB) — Last listed 1996
'Chief Chickasaw' (TB) — LBro
'Chief Moses' (TB) — MBri MCAu
'Chief Quinaby' (TB) — SCro
'Chief Waukesha' (TB) — SCro
I 'Chieftain' (SDB) — MRav NSti WWin
'Chiltern Gold' (IB) ♀ — CKel
'China Dragon' (TB) — SCro
'Chivalry' (TB) — LBro
'Chocolate Vanilla' (TB) — LIri
'Chorus Girl' (TB) — CKel
'Christening Party' (TB) — CKel
'Christmas Angel' (TB) — EBrP EBee ERou LBre MCAu SBre WWeb
'Christmas Time' (TB) — NMGW
Chrysofor Group — WPGP WRHF
*chrysographes* ♀ — CGle CHid CKel CVer EBrP EBre GMac LBre LBro MBal MRav MSCN NLar NRya SBre SHel SLon SMac SRms SUsu SWas WRHF WWin
– *alba* — NBir
– B&L 12617 — Last listed 1998
– black — CHad CHan CHar CMil CRow CSam ECGN GAbr GCal GDra IBlr MBal MBro MFir MTis NBrk NBur NGdn NHar NMen NWoo SChu SMad SSpi SWyc WCru WFar WHoo WLin WPyg
I 'Black Beauty' — CFir
I 'Black Knight' — CBot CHid EBee EPfP GBuc GCHN GCal MBel NChi NFor NLar NOrc NSti SWat WOve WPen WWin

I 'Black Velvet' — Last listed 1998
– crimson — IBlr NCat NWoo
– x *forrestii* — GDra NBir WViv
N 'Inshriach' — CFai CHan EHyt GBuc GDra IBlr WLin
¶ 'Kew Black' — MUlv WHil
– 'Mandarin Purple' — EBee GBuc GCal GMac NSti SPer SWyc WCot
– purple — MBro
– red — MBal
– 'Rob' — GMac
§ – var. *rubella* — CPlt CRow GMac MMil MSte SCro SWyc WPGP
\* – – 'Wine' — CHad
– 'Rubra' — See *I. chrysographes* var. *rubella*
*chrysophylla* — Last listed 1998
– JCA 13233 — CLAP SSpi
'Church Stoke' (SDB) — SCro
N 'Cider Haze' (TB) — CKel
'Cimarron Rose' (SDB) — NZep
'Circus Stripes' (TB) — Last listed 1996
'City Lights' (TB) — Last listed 1998
'City of David' (TB) — SCro
'Clairette' (Reticulata) — CBro EPar LAma
'Clap Hands' (SDB) — LBro
'Clara Garland' (IB) ♀ — CKel
'Clarke Cosgrove' (Spuria) — LBro
*clarkei* — CHan ELan NNrd
¶ 'Classic Look' (TB) — LIri
'Clay's Caper' (SDB) — EFou LBro
'Cleeton Buff' (Sino-Sib) — CMil
N 'Cleo' (TB) — CKel NBir NSti
'Clever Devil' (CH) — Last listed 1996
'Cliffs of Dover' (TB) ♀ — CKel SRms WBcn
N 'Climbing Gold' — Last listed 1998
N 'Clotted Cream' (CH) — ECha
'Cloudcap' (TB) — SRms
'Cloudless Sunrise' (TB) — ERou
'Clyde Redmond' (La) — SAWi
'Codicil' (TB) — LIri
'Cold Cold Heart' (TB) — Last listed 1997
¶ 'Colonial Gold' (TB) — MCAu
'Color Brite' (BB) — SCro
'Color Focus' (Spuria) — LBro
'Color Splash' (TB) — SCro
'Columbia Blue' (TB) — SCro
'Colwall' (TB) — LBro WBcn
'Combo' (SDB) — CKel
'Competitive Edge' (TB) — LIri
'Concord Touch' (SDB) — Last listed 1996
'Condottiere' (TB) — SCro
'Confederate Soldier' (IB) — Last listed 1996
'Confetti' (TB) — LRHS MBri
*confusa* ♀ — CGle CHad CHan CKel CPla CSev ECha ECre EOas EPla MTho SAPC SArc SEND SSpi SUsu WFar WMul WPic
§ – 'Martyn Rix' — CHad CHid CLAP CPou CSev EPPr LHil MHlr NPla WCot WPer
'Conjuration' (TB) — LIri MMil
'Connoisseur' (Spuria) — LBro WTin
'Constant Wattez' (IB) — CKel LBuc
'Consummation' (MTB) — NZep
'Copper Classic' (TB) — NZep SCro
N 'Copper Pot' (TB) — Last listed 1996
'Cops' (SDB) — NZep
'Coral Chalice' (TB) — ERou LIri
'Coral Joy' (TB) — LBro
'Coral Strand' (TB) — Last listed 1998
'Coral Wings' (SDB) — NZep
'Corn Harvest' (TB) — MMil NZep
'Corrida' (TB) — LBuc

'Cotati' (BB) — Last listed 1996
'Côte d'Or' (TB) — SCro
'Cotton Blossom' (SDB) — LBro
'Cotton Plantation' (La) — LBro
'Cozy Calico' (TB) — SCro
'Cracklin Burgundy' (TB) — SCro
'Cranberry Crush' (TB) — Last listed 1996
'Cranberry Ice' (TB) — CKel SCro
'Cream Cake' (SDB) — NZep
¶ 'Cream Soda' (TB) ♀ — CKel
'Creative Stitchery' (TB) — SCro
'Cregrina' (TB) — LBro
*cretensis* — See *I. unguicularis* subsp. *cretensis*
'Cricket Lane' (SDB) — NZep
'Crimson Fire' (TB) — SCro
'Crinoline' (TB) — Last listed 1998
N 'Crispen Rouge' (TB) — Last listed 1998
'Crispette' (TB) — MCAu
*cristata* ♀ — CAvo CHea CPBP EPot GBuc LAma MDHE MOne SRms WCru
- 'Abbey's Violet' — SWas
- 'Alba' — EBee EPot ERos GCrs LBee MBal MDHE NHar SChu SIng SWas WAbe
- x *gracilipes* — EPot
- x *lacustris* — CHan EPot NMen NTow
*crocea* ♀ — Last listed 1998
'Croftway Lemon' (TB) — SCro
'Cross Stitch' (TB) — MMil NZep
'Crown Sterling' (TB) — SCro
'Crushed Velvet' (TB) — MCAu
'Cruzin' (TB) — CKel LIri
'Cum Laude' (IB) — SCro
*cuniculiformis* ACE 2224 — EHyt
'Cup Race' (TB) — Last listed 1998
'Curio' (MDB) — Last listed 1996
'Curlew' (IB) — MCAu
'Cutie' (IB) — NZep
'Cyanea' (DB) — SIng
'Cycles' (TB) — Last listed 1996
*cycloglossa* — EBee SWas WWst
- HW&E 7727 — CLAP
'Daisy Fresh' (MDB) — LBro
'Dale Dennis' (DB) — LBro
'Dame Judy' (TB) — Last listed 1997
'Dancer's Veil' (TB) ♀ — CKel EBrP EBre ECtt EFou EHic ELan ERou LBre LBro MRav NVic SBre SCoo SCro SMer
'Dancin'' (IB) — NZep
'Dancing Eyes' (SDB) — LBro
'Dancing Gold' (MDB) — NZep
*danfordiae* — CAvo CB&S CBro EBrP EBre ELan EPar EPot ETub GCrs LAma LBre MBNS MBri NRog SBre WCot
'Dante' (TB) — CKel
'Dappled Pony' (MTB) — Last listed 1997
'Dardanus' (Aril) — Last listed 1996
'Dark Blizzard' (IB) — NZep
'Dark Bury' (TB) — LBro
'Dark Rosaleen' (TB) ♀ — LBro
'Dark Spark' (SDB) — MCAu
'Dark Vader' (SDB) — NZep
'Darkover' (SDB) — LBro
'Darkside' (TB) — SCro
'David Chapman' (TB) — CKel LBro
'Dawn Candle' (Spuria) — LBro
'Dawn Favour' (SDB) — LBro
'Dawn Glory' (TB) — SCro
'Dawning' (TB) — LIri
'Dazzling Gold' (TB) — SCro
§ *decora* — CBro MNrw WLin

- B&SWJ 2122 — WCru
'Deep Black' (TB) — CBlo CMGP COtt EBee EMan EOld EPfP ERav MCAu MWgw NOrc SCob SCro SPer SWat
'Deep Fire' (TB) — SCro
'Deep Pacific' (TB) — LRHS MBri MCAu
'Deep Space' (TB) — Last listed 1996
'Deft Touch' (TB) — MCAu
*delavayi* ♀ — CKel GMaP GMac IBlr LSyl MRPP WCot WOut WViv
'Delicate Air' (SDB) — LBro
'Delphi' (TB) — SCro
¶ 'Delta Blues' (TB) — LIri
¶ 'Delta Butterfly' (La) — WMAq
'Deltaplane' (TB) — Last listed 1996
'Demelza' (TB) — LBro
'Demon' (SDB) — CKel CPlt EFou EHyt LBro LRHS MBri
'Denys Humphries' (TB) — CKel LBro
'Depth of Field' (TB) — LRHS
'Deputé Nomblot' (TB) — Last listed 1997
'Derring Do' (SDB) — LBro
'Derry Down' (SDB) — Last listed 1996
'Derwentwater' (TB) — CBlo CKel MCAu MMil SRms
'Desert Dream' (AB) — SWyc
'Desert Dream' (Sino-sib) — GDra
'Desert Echo' (TB) — EFou LIri
'Desert Quail' (MTB) — LBro
'Desert Song' (TB) — CKel EBee MCAu
'Designer Gown' (TB) — ERou
'Designer's Choice' (TB) ♀ — LBro
¶ 'Devilry' (SDB) — CNic EHyt
'Dew Point' (IB) — SCro
'Die Braut' — See *I.* 'Bride'
'Diligence' (SDB) ♀ — Last listed 1996
'Disco Jewel' (MTB) — Last listed 1996
'Discretion' (TB) — SCro
'Dixie Pixie' (SDB) — EGle WTin
'Doctor Behenna' (TB) — LBro
'Doll Dear' (SDB) — LBro
'Doll House' (MDB) — CBlo CMea
'Doll Ribbons' (MTB) — NZep
'Doll Type' (IB) — LBro
* 'Don Brownsay' — MMil
'Dorothy Marquart' (TB) — LIri
¶ 'Dorothy Robbins' (CH) — WWst
'DoSiDo' (SDB) — SCro
'Dot and Dash' (TB) — MBri WWeb
'Dotted Doll' (MTB) — NZep
'Double Lament' (SDB) ♀ — CBro ERos LBro MMil NNrd SCro
*douglasiana* ♀ — CBre CHad CMil EPar EPla IBlr SMac SSpi WFar
* - 'Bandon Strain' — SSpi
'Dovedale' (TB) ♀ — LBro MCAu
'Doxa' (IB) — SCro
'Dragonsdawn' (AB) — Last listed 1996
'Dream Builder' (TB) — NMGW
¶ 'Dream Indigo' (IB) — CKel
'Dreamcastle' (TB) — CKel
'Dreamsicle' (TB) — SCro
'Dresden Candleglow' (IB) — CKel
'Driftwood' (Spuria) — LBro
'Drive You Wild' (CH) — LBro
'Dualtone' (TB) — CKel
'Dundee' (TB) — SCro
'Dunlin' (MDB) — CBro ERos MBri NBir NMen NNrd NRar
'Dusky Challenger' (TB) — LBro LIri MCAu SCro
'Dusky Dancer' (TB) ♀ — Last listed 1993
'Dutch Chocolate' (TB) — MMil
*dykesii* — CRow
'Eagle's Flight' (TB) — LBro NMGW

| | |
|---|---|
| 'Eardisland' (IB) ♀ | LBro MMil |
| 'Earl' (TB) | MMil |
| 'Earl of Essex' (TB) | MCAu MMil SCro |
| 'Early Edition' (IB) | LBro |
| 'Early Frost' (IB) | SCro |
| 'Early Light' (TB) ♀ | LBro |
| 'East Indies' (TB) | MCAu |
| 'Eastertime' (TB) | LIri |
| 'Easy Strolling' (SDB) | LBro |
| ¶ 'Echo de France' (TB) | CKel |
| 'Edale' (TB) ♀ | Last listed 1996 |
| 'Edge of Winter' (TB) | CKel |
| 'Edith Wolford' (TB) | LBro LIri MCAu SCro |
| 'Edward' (Reticulata) | EPot LAma |
| 'Edward of Windsor' (TB) | CHad CMil EBee ELan ERou EWTr |
| | NOrc NPla WLRN |
| 'Eirian' (TB) | LBro |
| 'Eleanor's Pride' (TB) | CKel LBro MCAu MMil |
| **elegantissima** | See *I. iberica* subsp. |
| | *elegantissima* |
| 'Elisa Renee' (TB) | Last listed 1996 |
| 'Elixir' (Spuria) | LBro |
| 'Elizabeth Arden' (TB) | CKel |
| 'Elizabeth of England' (TB) | Last listed 1996 |
| 'Elizabeth Poldark' (TB) | LBro LIri |
| 'Ellen Manor' (TB) | MCAu |
| 'Elvinhall' | CBro |
| 'Ember Days' (TB) | MMil |
| ¶ 'Empress of India' (TB) | EBee |
| 'Encanto' (SDB) | Last listed 1996 |
| 'Enchanted Blue' (SDB) | Last listed 1996 |
| 'Enchanted Gold' (SDB) | NZep |
| 'Encircle' (CH) | Last listed 1996 |
| 'English Cottage' (TB) | EGar GCal MMil MWat SCro WIvy |
| 'Ennerdale' (TB) | MCAu SRms |
| § **ensata** ♀ | CBen CBlo CMHG EBee ECGP |
| | ELan ERic EWTr LBro LPBA LSyl |
| | MCAu MNrw MSta NBro NGdn |
| | NLar NRoo SAWi SPlb SRms SWat |
| | WFar WHil WPen WPer WPyg |
| | WWin |
| - 'Activity' | CBlo CRow LRHS |
| - 'Agrippine' | Last listed 1997 |
| - 'Alba' | CGle ECha |
| - 'Aoigata' | Last listed 1996 |
| - 'Apollo' | CBen CRow |
| ¶ - 'Barnhawk Sybil' | SSpi |
| - 'Bellender Blue' | LBro |
| - 'Beni Renge' | Last listed 1996 |
| - 'Blue Embers' | Last listed 1997 |
| I - 'Blue Peter' | CBen CRow |
| - 'Blue Skies' | SIng |
| - 'Butterflies in Flight' | LBro |
| - 'Calamari' | Last listed 1997 |
| - 'Caprician Butterfly' | EWTr SWyc |
| * - 'Carnival Prince' | CFir NPri |
| - 'Center of Attention' | LBro |
| - 'Chico Geisho' | SWyc |
| - 'Chitose-no-tomo' | CRow |
| - 'Chiyo-no-haru' | Last listed 1997 |
| - 'Continuing Pleasure' ♀ | Last listed 1995 |
| * - 'Cry of Rejoice' | EBee LBuc |
| - 'Crystal Halo' | LBro NBrk |
| - 'Dancing Waves' | CRow NBrk |
| - 'Darling' | CRow EBee IBlr LRHS NBrk |
| - 'Dresden China' | CRow NBrk |
| ¶ - 'Edens Charm' | MSCN |
| - 'Emotion' | Last listed 1997 |
| - 'Enchanting Melody' | CRow |
| - 'Fairy Carillon' | LBro |
| - 'Flashing Koi' | NBrk |
| - 'Flying Tiger' ♀ | Last listed 1995 |

| | |
|---|---|
| - 'Freckled Geisha' | CRow |
| - 'Frilled Enchantment' | Last listed 1997 |
| - 'Fringed Cloud' ♀ | SWyc |
| - 'Frosted Pyramid' | NBrk |
| I - 'Galatea' | CRow |
| * - 'Galathea' | GCal |
| - 'Geisha Gown' | Last listed 1996 |
| - 'Geisha Obi' | Last listed 1996 |
| - 'Geisha Parasol' | SWyc |
| - 'Gei-sho-mi' | Last listed 1997 |
| N - 'Ghost' (v) | CGle |
| - 'Gipsy' | CSpe LRHS |
| - 'Glitter and Gayety' | NBrk |
| ¶ - 'Gracieuse' | EBee |
| - 'Hakug-yokuro' | Last listed 1998 |
| - 'Hana-aoi' | IBlr |
| - 'Happy Awakening' | SWyc |
| - 'Hatsu-shimo' | CRow IBlr |
| - 'Hercule' | CDoC CRow EBee NBrk NGdn |
| - Higo hybrids | CRow IBlr LPBA MSta SPer |
| N - 'Hokkaido' | See *I. ensata* 'Perry's Hokkaido' |
| - 'Hoyden' | Last listed 1996 |
| - 'Imperial Magic' ♀ | SWyc |
| - 'Imperial Velvet' | Last listed 1996 |
| * - 'Innocence' | CBlo MBri |
| ¶ - 'Iso-no-nami' | MBri |
| N - 'Iso-no-ob' | WMer |
| ¶ - 'Kalamazo' | WFar |
| - 'Katy Mendez' ♀ | Last listed 1995 |
| - 'Komo-no-ibo' | SWat |
| - 'Kuma-funjin' | CRow IBlr |
| - 'Labby White' | SWyc |
| - 'Laced' | SPer |
| - 'Landscape at Dawn' | CMHG CRow |
| * - 'Laughing Lion' | CDoC COtt LRHS MBri |
| - 'Light at Dawn' | LBro |
| - 'Lilac Blotch' | SPer |
| - 'Magic Opal' ♀ | CRow |
| - 'Manadzuru' | IBlr |
| I - 'Mandarin' | CGle CRow NBrk |
| - 'Midnight Stars' | LBro |
| - 'Midsummer Reverie' | CRow |
| - 'Miss Coquette' | Last listed 1997 |
| § - 'Moonlight Waves' | CMGP CRDP EBee ELan EOld |
| | LHop MFir MSte NBrk NGdn |
| | NRoo SChu SSpi SWat WElm |
| | WRus WWal WWat |
| - 'Narihira' | IBlr |
| - 'Oku-banri' | CRow IBlr |
| - 'Oriental Eyes' | LBro |
| - pale mauve | SPer |
| - 'Peacock' | SMrm |
| * - 'Perry's Hokkaido' | CGle CRow IBlr NBrk NCat |
| - 'Pin Stripe' | CBlo EBee |
| - 'Pink Frost' | CHad CRDP CRow EBrP EBee |
| | EGle GAri LBre LRHS SBre |
| - 'Pleasant Journey' | Last listed 1998 |
| - 'Prairie Glory' | Last listed 1996 |
| - 'Prairie Noble' | Last listed 1996 |
| - 'Prairie Twilight' | LBro NBrk |
| - purple | SPer |
| I - 'Purple East' | CRow NBrk |
| - 'Ranpo' | CRow |
| I - 'Red Dawn' | Last listed 1998 |
| § - 'Rose Queen' ♀ | CBos CRDP CRow EBrP EBee |
| | ECGN ECha EGle ELan EMFW |
| | EPar ERou EWTr GCal LBre LPBA |
| | MCCP MRav MSta NBrk NBro |
| | NGdn NRoo SBre SChu SLon SPer |
| | SSpi WRus |
| - 'Rowden' | CRow |
| * - 'Royal Banner' | Last listed 1996 |

| | | |
|---|---|---|
| | - 'Royal Crown' | CRow NBrk SWyc |
| | - 'Royal Game' | Last listed 1996 |
| | - 'Royal Purple' | CGle CMHG |
| I | - 'Ruby King' | CBlo LRHS MBri |
| * | - 'Sensation' | EOld |
| N | - 'Shihainami' | IBlr |
| | - 'Silverband' | NBrk |
| | - 'Sorceror's Triumph' | Last listed 1996 |
| | - 'Southern Son' ♀ | Last listed 1995 |
| | - 'Summer Storm' ♀ | SPer SWyc |
| | - 'Taga-sode' | NBrk SWyc |
| | - 'The Great Mogul' ♀ | SWyc |
| | - 'Time and Tide' | SWyc |
| | - 'Umi-botaro' | CRow |
| | - 'Valiant Prince' | Last listed 1998 |
| | - 'Variegata' ♀ | CBen CMil CRDP CRow EBee ECha EHoe EHon EMFW IBlr LEdu LPBA MBri MSta MUlv SCro SMad SWat WCot WFar |
| | - 'Vintage Festival' ♀ | SWyc |
| | - 'Waka-murasaki' | MBri WMer |
| | - 'White Chiffon' | Last listed 1996 |
| I | - 'White Pearl' | CRow NBrk |
| | - 'World's Delight' ♀ | Last listed 1996 |
| | - 'Worley Pink' | Last listed 1998 |
| | - 'Yako-no-tama' | CRow |
| | - 'Yezo-nishiki' | LBro LRHS |
| | - 'Yusho' | CRow |
| | 'Erleen Richeson' (TB) | SCro |
| | 'Escalona' (CH) | LBro |
| | 'Essay' (Spuria) | LBro |
| ¶ | 'Etched Apricot' (TB) | MCAu |
| | 'Evening Gown' (TB) | LBro |
| | 'Evening Magic' (TB) | SCro |
| | 'Ever After' (TB) | Last listed 1996 |
| | 'Everything Plus' (TB) | ERou |
| | ewbankiana | See I. acutiloba subsp. lineolata |
| I | 'Excelsior' (DB) | Last listed 1997 |
| | 'Exotic Gem' (TB) | MCAu |
| | 'Exotic Isle' (TB) | NZep |
| | 'Exotic Shadow' (SDB) | LBro |
| | 'Exotic Star' (TB) | Last listed 1997 |
| | 'Extravagant' (TB) | SCro |
| ¶ | 'Eye Magic' ♀ | CKel |
| | 'Eyebright' (SDB) ♀ | CBro LBro MCAu WWeb WWin |
| | 'Fairy Footsteps' (SDB) | LBro |
| | 'Fairy Time' (IB) | LBro |
| | 'Fakir's Fire' (MTB) | NZep |
| | 'Fall Fiesta' (TB) | Last listed 1998 |
| | 'Fall Primrose' (TB) | Last listed 1996 |
| | 'Fancy Tales' (TB) | Last listed 1997 |
| | 'Fancy Woman' (TB) | Last listed 1998 |
| | 'Fanfaron' (TB) | SCro |
| | 'Fantaisie' (TB) | CKel |
| | 'Fantasy World' (IB) | Last listed 1996 |
| | 'Farolito' (Spuria) | LBro WBcn |
| | 'Fashion Jewel' (TB) | Last listed 1997 |
| | 'Fashion Lady' (MDB) | CBro |
| | 'Favorite Angel' (SDB) | NMGW NZep |
| | 'Feature Attraction' (TB) | LIri |
| | 'Feminine Charm' (TB) | Last listed 1998 |
| | 'Feminist' (TB) | SCro |
| | 'Femme Fatale' (TB) | Last listed 1997 |
| | fernaldii | WLin |
| | - J&JA 12807 | SSpi |
| | 'Festival Crown' (TB) | LBro |
| | 'Festive Skirt' (TB) | CKel MCAu |
| | 'Fierce Fire' (IB) ♀ | CKel MCAu |
| | 'Fiery Song' (TB) | CKel |
| | filifolia | CBro |
| | - var. latifolia SF 332 | Last listed 1998 |
| | - MS 437 | Last listed 1998 |

| | | |
|---|---|---|
| | 'Fine Line' (CH) ♀ | Last listed 1995 |
| N | 'Fire and Flame' (TB) | NBir |
| | 'Fire One' (SDB) | LBro |
| | 'Fire Siren' (TB) | MMil |
| | 'Firecracker' (TB) | ERou MBri MCAu MRav |
| ¶ | 'First Chapter' (AB) | WWst |
| | 'First Interstate' (TB) | SCro |
| | 'First Lilac' (TB) | Last listed 1996 |
| | 'First Step' (SDB) | NZep |
| | 'First Violet' (TB) | LBro |
| | 'Five Star Admiral' (TB) | SCro |
| | 'Flaming Dragon' | CKel SRPl |
| I | 'Flamingo' (TB) | CKel |
| | 'Flammenschwert' (TB) | Last listed 1996 |
| | 'Flapjack' (SDB) | NZep |
| | 'Flareup' (TB) | MBri WWeb |
| | 'Flash' | WHil |
| | 'Flashing Beacon' (MTB) | NZep |
| | flavescens | MCAu NSti |
| | 'Flea Circus' (MDB) | NZep |
| | 'Flirty Mary' (SDB) | EGle |
| | 'Florentina' (IB) ♀ | CArn CBro CKel ECha EFou ELau EMFP ERav GPoy IBlr LBro LHol MCAu MChe MHer MHew MRav NFai SCro SIde WPic WWye |
| | florentina alba | ELau |
| | - blue | WOak |
| ¶ | 'Flumadiddle' (IB) | CBro |
| | 'Focal Point' | LBuc |
| | 'Focus' (TB) | SCro |
| § | foetidissima ♀ | More than 30 suppliers |
| | - 'Aurea' | WCot |
| | - aurea MS 902 | Last listed 1998 |
| | - chinensis | See I. foetidissima var. citrina |
| § | - var. citrina | CFil CKel CRow CSam EGle ELan EPla GAbr GCal IBlr LBro LPio MBal MBro MMal MRav SLon SSpi SUsu WCot WEas WHoo WPGP WPyg WRus WWin WWye |
| | - 'Fructu Albo' | CRow MTed SUsu WCot |
| | - var. lutescens | CHid MTed |
| | - 'Moonshy Seedling' | CSWP EGol |
| | - 'Variegata' ♀ | CBro CFil CGle CHan CRow CSam EBee EGle ELan EOrc EPla LHil MBrN MBri MRav NDea NHol NLar NPar NPer NRoo SCob SSpi WCot WEas WRus WWat WWhi |
| | - yellow seeded | MTed |
| | 'Foggy Dew' (TB) | MBri |
| | 'Fondation Van Gogh' (TB) | LIri |
| | 'Forest Hills' (TB) | CKel |
| | 'Forest Light' (SDB) | CBro LBro MBro |
| | formosana | Last listed 1998 |
| | forrestii ♀ | CHad CHan CHid CKel CLon CRow EBee EPar GBin GCal GDra GMac IBlr LPBA LSyl MBri MHar MNrw NBro NChi NGdn NNrd NRya SRot SSpi WAbe WCla WHer WWat |
| | - hybrids | IBlr |
| I | - 'Sibirica' | MPEx |
| | 'Fort Apache' (TB) | SCro |
| | 'Fort Regent' (TB) | LBro |
| | 'Foxcote' (IB) | Last listed 1996 |
| N | 'Foxtor' (TB) | Last listed 1997 |
| | 'Frank Elder' (Reticulata) | CBro EHyt EPot LAma LPio MRav MTho WIvy |
| | 'French Gown' (TB) | EFou |
| ¶ | 'Fresno Calypso' (TB) | MCAu |
| | 'Fresno Flash' (TB) | SCro |
| | 'Fringe of Gold' (TB) | SCro |

| | |
|---|---|
| 'Frontier Marshall' (TB) | NMoo |
| 'Frost and Flame' (TB) | CM&M EBrP EBre ECtt ELan ENot ERav ERou EWll LBre MBri MRav NOrc SBre SCro SPer |
| 'Frosted Angel' (SDB) | Last listed 1996 |
| 'Frosty Crown' (SDB) | Last listed 1996 |
| 'Full Tide' (TB) | SCro |
| *fulva* | EBee GCal IBlr LBro NBir NBro NSti SMrm SWyc WCot WEas |
| x *fulvala* ♀ | EBee EMon IBlr LBlm NBir NSti SCob SWyc WRus WWat |
| 'Funtime' (SDB) | WViv |
| 'Furnaceman' (SDB) | CBro ERos MBro MMil |
| 'Fuzzy' (MDB) | ERos LBro |
| 'Fuzzy Face' (SDB) | NZep |
| 'Gala Gown' (TB) | Last listed 1998 |
| 'Galathea' | See *I. ensata* 'Galathea' |
| § *galatica* | EPot |
| 'Gallant Moment' (TB) | Last listed 1996 |
| 'Galleon Gold' (SDB) | NZep |
| *gatesii* | EPot LAma |
| 'Gay Parasol' (TB) ♀ | LBro |
| N 'Gay Prince' (TB) | Last listed 1998 |
| N 'Gay Trip' (TB) | WBcn |
| § 'Gelbe Mantel' (Sino-sib) | CBot EBee EHic NBir NSti WCot |
| 'George' (Reticulata) | CAvo CBro EBrP EBre EPar EPot ERos ETub LBre SBre WBea |
| 'Gerald Darby' | See *I.* x *robusta* 'Gerald Darby' |
| *germanica* ♀ | LBro MCAu NFor WPyg |
| ¶ – 'Amas' | MCAu |
| – 'Kharput' | LBro |
| * – 'Mel Jope' | Last listed 1997 |
| – 'Nepalensis' | EGoo |
| * – 'The King' | MCAu |
| 'Gibson Girl' (TB) | MMil |
| 'Gift of Dreams' (TB) | LIri |
| 'Gigglepot' (SDB) | LGre MMil |
| 'Ginger Swirl' (TB) | SCro |
| 'Gingerbread Castle' (TB) | Last listed 1998 |
| 'Gingerbread Man' (SDB) | CBro CHad CLon CMea EFou EGle ERos LBro LGre MBro MCAu MMil NMen WHoo |
| 'Giraffe Kneehiz' (TB) | LIri |
| 'Glacier' (TB) | CKel |
| 'Glacier Gold' (TB) | CKel |
| 'Glad Rags' (TB) | NZep |
| 'Gleaming Gold' (SDB) | Last listed 1996 |
| N 'Glen' (TB) | Last listed 1997 |
| 'Glenwillow' (MDB) | NZep |
| 'Gnu Again' (TB) | LIri |
| 'Godfrey Owen' (TB) | MCAu WBcn |
| 'Godsend' (TB) | LIri |
| 'Going My Way' (TB) | LRHS MBri MCAu SCro |
| 'Gold Burst' (TB) | SCro |
| 'Gold Canary' (MDB) | Last listed 1998 |
| I 'Gold Flake' (TB) | CKel |
| 'Gold Galore' (TB) | SCro |
| 'Gold Intensity' (BB) | Last listed 1996 |
| 'Gold of Autumn' (TB) | CKel |
| 'Goldberry' (IB) | Last listed 1998 |
| 'Golden Alps' (TB) | ENot LBro |
| I 'Golden Bow' (TB) | Last listed 1998 |
| 'Golden Dewdrops' (SDB) | LBro |
| 'Golden Encore' (TB) | CKel MCAu MWat |
| 'Golden Fair' (SDB) | NBir SIng |
| 'Golden Forest' (TB) | MBri MCAu |
| 'Golden Harvest' (Dutch) | CB&S LAma SHel |
| 'Golden Lady' (Spuria) | LBro |
| 'Golden Muffin' (IB) | LBro NZep |
| 'Golden Oldie' (La) | LBro |
| 'Golden Planet' (TB) | CKel WBcn |
| 'Golden Ruby' (SDB) | LBro |
| 'Golden Spice' (TB) | LBro |
| 'Golden Starlet' (SDB) | LBro |
| N 'Golden Surprise' (TB) | CKel |
| 'Golden Veil' (TB) | CKel |
| 'Golden Waves' (Cal-Sib) ♀ | CBro LBro |
| N 'Goldfinder' (TB) | CKel |
| I 'Goldilocks' (TB) | CKel |
| 'Good and True' (IB) | SCro |
| ¶ 'Good Looking' (TB) | LIri |
| 'Good Nature' (Spuria) | LBro |
| 'Good Show' (TB) | SCro |
| 'Gordon' (Reticulata) | EPot LAma |
| ¶ 'Goring Ace' (CH) ♀ | WWst |
| *gormanii* | See *I. tenax* |
| ¶ 'Gosh' (SDB) | CKel |
| *gracilipes* | MBal |
| – 'Alba' | Last listed 1998 |
| *graeberiana* | CLAP EPot |
| – white fall | EHyt LRHS WWst |
| – yellow fall | LRHS WWst |
| *graminea* ♀ | More than 30 suppliers |
| – 'Hort's Variety' | EGar GCal NCat |
| – var. *pseudocyperus* | CRow LHop NSti SDys |
| *graminifolia* | See *I. kerneriana* |
| 'Granada Gold' (TB) | ENot SRms |
| 'Grand Baroque' (TB) | MMil |
| 'Grand Waltz' (TB) | SCro |
| 'Grandpa's Girl' (MTB) | LBro |
| 'Grapelet' (MDB) | ERos NZep |
| 'Grapesicle' (SDB) | NZep |
| 'Graphic Arts' (TB) | NZep |
| 'Grecian Skies' (TB) | SCro |
| 'Green Halo' (DB) | EGle LBro LGre |
| 'Green Ice' (TB) | CKel |
| 'Green Jungle' (TB) | LBro |
| N 'Green Little' (DB) | Last listed 1997 |
| 'Green Spot' (IB) ♀ | CBot CBro CHad CHan ECtt ELan EPla ESis LGre MMil MRav MWat NBir NHol NMGW NMen NNrd SChu SPer WEas WElm WFar WHoo |
| 'Greenstuff' (SDB) | LBro LGre MMil |
| ¶ 'Gringo' (TB) | MCAu |
| 'Gudrun' (TB) | LBlm |
| 'Gypsy Boy' (SDB) | MMil NMGW NZep |
| 'Gypsy Caravan' (TB) | CKel SCro |
| 'Gypsy Jewels' (TB) | CKel |
| 'Gypsy Romance' (TB) | LIri |
| 'Gyro' (TB) | LIri |
| 'H.C. van Vliet' (Dutch) | LAma NRog SHel |
| 'Hagar's Helmet' (IB) | LBro |
| 'Hallowed Thought' (TB) | MMil MWat |
| 'Halo in Pink' (TB) | Last listed 1996 |
| 'Halo in Yellow' (TB) | Last listed 1996 |
| *halophila* | See *I. spuria* subsp. *halophila* |
| 'Handshake' (TB) | LIri |
| 'Happening' (SDB) | NZep |
| * 'Happy Border' | Last listed 1998 |
| 'Happy Choice' (Spuria) | LBro |
| 'Happy Mood' (IB) ♀ | Last listed 1996 |
| 'Happy Song' (BB) | LBro |
| 'Happy Thought' (IB) | Last listed 1997 |
| 'Harbor Blue' (TB) | CKel EWes MCAu MWat SCro |
| 'Harleqinade' (BB) | LBro |
| 'Harlow Gold' (IB) | NZep |
| 'Harmony' (Reticulata) | CAvo CBro EBrP EBre EPot LAma LBre MBri MHlr NRog SBre |
| 'Harriette Halloway' (TB) | CBlo CMGP SMrm WElm |
| *hartwegii* | Last listed 1996 |
| – subsp. *columbiana* | Last listed 1996 |
| – subsp. *pinetorum* | Last listed 1998 |
| 'Hazy Skies' (MTB) | LBro |

| | |
|---|---|
| 'Headlines' (TB) | CKel MCAu |
| 'Heather Hawk' (TB) | MCAu |
| ¶ 'Heavenly Days' (TB) | MCAu |
| 'Hedge' | Last listed 1996 |
| 'Helen Boehm' (TB) | SCro |
| 'Helen McGregor' (TB) | CKel |
| 'Helen Proctor' (IB) | NZep SCro |
| 'Helen Traubel' (TB) | Last listed 1998 |
| 'Helge' (IB) | COIW EPfP NFai SCob |
| 'Hellcat' (IB) | NZep |
| 'Hello Darkness' (TB) | LIri |
| 'Hell's Fire' (TB) | SCro |
| 'Hercules' (Reticulata) | GCal LAma |
| 'Hers' (IB) | SCro |
| 'High Barbaree' (TB) | MBri |
| 'High Command' (TB) | CKel SCro |
| 'High Life' (TB) | SCro |
| 'Highline Halo' (Spuria) | Last listed 1998 |
| 'Hills of Lafayette' (IB) | Last listed 1998 |
| 'Hindenburg' (TB) | Last listed 1997 |
| 'Hindu Magic' (TB) | LBro |
| 'His' (IB) | SCro |
| *histrio* | LAma |
| - subsp. *aintabensis* | EHyt EPot LAma |
| - subsp. *histrio* | Last listed 1998 |
| *histrioides* | Last listed 1996 |
| § - 'Angel's Eye' | CLAP ERos |
| - 'Angel's Tears' | See *I. histrioides* 'Angel's Eye' |
| - 'Lady Beatrix Stanley' | CLAP |
| N - 'Major' ♀ | CBro CLAP LAma MBal MBri |
| - 'Reine Immaculée' | ERos |
| - var. *sophenensis* | CLAP |
| 'Hocus Pocus' (SDB) | EFou EPPr LBro |
| 'Holden Clough' ♀ | CBot CBre CGle CHad CHar CKel |
| | EBee EFou ELan EMFW EPla EPri |
| | GMaP LBro MCAu MFir MMil |
| | MRav MUlv NChi NGdn NSti |
| | SSvw SUsu SWyc WEas WMaN |
| | WPnP WSan WWin |
| 'Hollywood Blonde' (TB) | Last listed 1997 |
| 'Holy Night' (TB) | Last listed 1997 |
| 'Honey Behold' (SDB) | CKel |
| ¶ 'Honey Crunch' (TB) | LIri |
| 'Honey Dip' (SDB) | Last listed 1996 |
| 'Honey Glazed' (IB) | LBro MCAu NZep WBcn |
| 'Honey Mocha' (TB) | SCro |
| 'Honey Pot' (MDB) | Last listed 1998 |
| 'Honington' (SDB) ♀ | LBro MCAu MMil |
| 'Honky Tonk Blues' (TB) | LIri |
| 'Honorabile' (MTB) | CKel |
| 'Hoodwink' (SDB) | Last listed 1996 |
| *boogiana* ♀ | EBee EPot LAma MTho |
| - 'Alba' | EPot |
| - 'Purpurea' | EPot |
| § *bookeri* | CMea EDAr EHal EHyt ELan |
| | GCHN GMac MBal MHar NTow |
| | NWoo SPer WAbe |
| *bookeriana* | WRHF |
| 'Hopscotch' (BB) | SCro |
| ¶ 'Horatio' (TB) | LIri |
| 'Hot Chocolate' (TB) | LIri |
| 'Hot Fudge' (IB) | NZep |
| 'Hot Spice' (IB) | NZep |
| 'Howard Weed' (TB) | Last listed 1997 |
| 'Hubbub' (IB) | SCro |
| ¶ 'Hugh Miller' (TB) | MCAu |
| 'Hula Doll' (MDB) | CBlo CMea EGle MBri NMen |
| | NOla |
| § *bumilis* | NNrd |
| *byrcana* | CBro LAma |
| 'I Do' (TB) | MMil NZep |
| § *iberica* | EPot |
| § - subsp. *elegantissima* | EHyt EPot |
| - subsp. *iberica* | Last listed 1997 |
| 'Ice Chip' (SDB) | LBro |
| 'Ice Dancer' (TB) ♀ | Last listed 1995 |
| * 'Ice White' | Last listed 1996 |
| 'Ida' (Reticulata) | EPot LAma |
| 'Ideal' (Dutch) | LAma |
| 'Ila Remembered' (Spuria) | LBro |
| *illyrica* | See *I. pallida* |
| *imbricata* | Last listed 1998 |
| 'Immortality' (TB) | MCAu SCro |
| 'Imperator' (Dutch) | CB&S EBee EWTr SHel |
| 'Imperial Bronze' (Spuria) | EFou LBro |
| 'Imperial Sun' (Spuria) | Last listed 1996 |
| 'Impetuous' (BB) | LBro |
| 'Inaugural Ball' (TB) | Last listed 1997 |
| 'Indeed' (IB) | LBro |
| 'Indian Chief' (TB) | LBro LRHS LWoo MBri MCAu |
| 'Indian Jewel' (SDB) | EGle EHyt |
| 'Indian Pow Wow' (SDB) | CRDP LBro |
| N 'Indian Sunset' (TB) | CKel |
| 'Indigo Flight' (IB) | EFou LBro |
| ¶ 'Indigo Princess' (TB) | LIri |
| 'Indiscreet' (TB) | Last listed 1996 |
| 'Inferno' (TB) | Last listed 1996 |
| 'Infinite Grace' (TB) | SCro |
| 'Ingenuity' (SDB) | LBro |
| 'Innocent Heart' (IB) ♀ | LBro SCro |
| *innominata* | CFil CGle CLon CRow ECha EPot |
| | IBlr LBee MNrw MRPP MTho |
| | NBro NHar NMen NSti SIng SRms |
| | WCla WEas WGwG WPGP WWal |
| | WWat |
| - 'Alba' | SIng |
| - apricot | IBlr NWoo |
| - Ballyrogan hybrids | IBlr WShe |
| - copper | IBlr |
| N - 'Doctor Riddle's Form' | CGle MBal |
| ¶ - hybrids | SIng |
| - J&JA 12897 | SSpi |
| - JCA 13225 | CLAP SSpi |
| - JCA 13227 | SSpi |
| - JCA 1460800 | CPBP |
| - rose | CNic ERos |
| N - 'Spinners' | SSpi |
| - yellow | NNrd |
| 'Inscription' (SDB) | EGle LBro |
| 'Interpol' (TB) | Last listed 1998 |
| ¶ 'Into the Night' (TB) | LIri |
| 'Irish Doll' (MDB) | CMea EGle LBro |
| 'Irish Spring' (TB) | Last listed 1996 |
| * 'Irish Temper' (SDB) | MMil |
| 'Irish Tune' (TB) | SCro |
| 'Ishmael' (SDB) | EGle LBro |
| 'Ivor Knowles' (CH) | Last listed 1996 |
| J 437 | NSti |
| 'J.S. Dijt' (Reticulata) | CAvo CBro EBrP EBre EPar EPot |
| | LAma LBre MBNS MBri MMal |
| | NRog SBre |
| 'Jack o' Hearts' (SDB) | CMea ERos LBro |
| 'Jade Mist' (SDB) | EGle LBro LRHS MBri |
| 'Jaime Lynn' (TB) | Last listed 1998 |
| 'Jan Reagan' (SDB) | NZep |
| 'Jana White' (MTB) | Last listed 1996 |
| 'Jane Phillips' (TB) ♀ | CKel EBrP EBre ECha ECtt EGle |
| | ELan ENot ERav ERou LBre LBro |
| | MCAu MCLN MMil MRav NGdn |
| | NOrc SBre SChu SCro SMrm SPer |
| | SWat WPnP |
| 'Jane Taylor' (SDB) | CBro EGle |
| 'Janice Chesnik' (Spuria) | LBro |
| *japonica* ♀ | NPer WFar |

| | |
|---|---|
| – 'Aphrodite' (v) | Last listed 1998 |
| – L 638 | SCro |
| N – 'Ledger's Variety' | CAvo CBro CGre CHan CKel CRow ECha ELan EPar EPla EPri LHil MRav MUlv WEas WRus WWat |
| – 'Variegata' ♀ | CAvo CBot CHad CHan CKel CLon CRow ECha EPar EPla MBal NBro NFai NFla NOrc NPer SArc SCob SSpi WBea WEas WFar WHer WPic WRus WViv WWeb |
| 'Jasper Gem' (MDB) | EGle EHyt ERos MMil NBir |
| 'Java Charm' (TB) | MMil |
| 'Jay Kenneth' (IB) | LBro |
| 'Jazzamatazz' (SDB) | LBro |
| 'Jazzebel' (TB) | SCro |
| 'Jean Guymer' (TB) | MMil NBir WBcn |
| ¶ 'Jeanne Price' (TB) | MCAu |
| 'Jeannine' (Reticulata) | LAma |
| 'Jeremy Brian' (SDB) ♀ | LBro MMil SUsu |
| 'Jersey Lilli' (SDB) | NSti WViv |
| 'Jesse's Song' (TB) | LBro NZep SCro |
| 'Jewel Baby' (SDB) | CBro NMGW NZep |
| 'Jewel Bright' (SDB) | EFou |
| ¶ 'Jiansada' (SDB) | CBro |
| ¶ 'Jitterbug' (TB) | LIri |
| 'Jo Jo' (TB) | Last listed 1997 |
| 'Joan Lay' (TB) | Last listed 1996 |
| 'Joanna Taylor' (MDB) | CBro ERos NMen NZep |
| N 'Joe Elliott' (CH) | EBee EGle |
| 'Joette' (MTB) | LBro |
| 'John' (IB) | SCro |
| 'John Taylor' (SDB) | CKel |
| 'Jolly Fellow' (SDB) | LBro SUsu |
| 'Jolt' (TB) | Last listed 1998 |
| *jordana* | See *I. atrofusca* |
| 'Joyce' (Reticulata) | CAvo CBro ELan EPar EPot LAma MBri MMal NRog |
| 'Joyce McBride' (SDB) | Last listed 1996 |
| 'Joyce Terry' (TB) | LRHS MBri |
| 'Joyful' (SDB) | LBro SCro |
| 'Joyous Isle' (SDB) | Last listed 1997 |
| 'Jubilee Gem' (TB) | CKel |
| 'Juliet' (TB) | Last listed 1997 |
| *juncea* | CArn |
| 'June Prom' (IB) | SCro |
| 'Juneau' (TB) | CKel |
| 'Jungle Fires' (TB) | Last listed 1997 |
| 'Jungle Shadows' (BB) | LGre MCAu MRav |
| 'Just Jennifer' (BB) | LBro MCAu |
| 'Just Magic' (TB) | LBro |
| *kaempferi* | See *I. ensata* |
| 'Karen Christine' (TB) | SCro |
| 'Karen Maddock' (TB) | LBro |
| 'Kashmir White' (TB) | Last listed 1996 |
| ¶ *kashmiriana* | CB&S |
| 'Katharine Hodgkin' (Reticulata) ♀ | CAvo CBro CLAP EBee EBrP EBre EHyt EPot ERos ETub GAbr GCrs LAma LBre MRPP MRav MTho NHar NRog NSla SBre SMrm WAbe WCot WIvy |
| 'Katie-Koo' (IB) ♀ | CKel |
| 'Katinka' (CH) | LBro WWst |
| 'Katy Petts' (SDB) | EFou MRPP NZep |
| ¶ 'Kayleigh Jayne Louise' (TB) | CKel |
| 'Kayo' (SDB) | EFou EGle EHyt LBro MMil NZep |
| 'Kelway Renaissance' (TB) | CKel |
| *kemaonensis* | GDra NHar |
| 'Kent Pride' (TB) | CMGP CMil EBee EBrP EBre EFou EHic EPPr ERou LBre LBro MMil MRav MWat NLak SBre SChu SCro SMrm SPer SWat WElm |

| | |
|---|---|
| 'Kentucky Bluegrass' (SDB) | EFou LBro LGre MMil SUsu WWin |
| 'Kentucky Derby' (TB) | SCro |
| 'Kermit' (IB) | SCro |
| § *kerneriana* ♀ | CBro ELan EMon ERos GBuc MNrw MRPP SIgm SUsu SWas WPen |
| 'Keyhaven' (SDB) | LBro |
| ¶ 'Kildonan' (TB) | MCAu |
| 'Kilt Lilt' (TB) | MCAu SCro |
| 'Kinetic' (SDB) | CKel |
| 'Kirkstone' (TB) | Last listed 1997 |
| *kirkwoodii* MS&CL 555 | Last listed 1998 |
| 'Kissing Circle' (TB) | LBro |
| 'Kista' (SDB) | Last listed 1998 |
| 'Kiwi Capers' (SDB) | NZep |
| 'Kiwi Slices' (SDB) | NMGW |
| *klattii* | See *I. spuria* subsp. *musulmanica* |
| 'Knick Knack' (MDB) | CBro CGle CM&M EGle EHyt ELan EMan ERic ERos GMaP LGre LPio MRav NMGW NMen SChu SCro SIng SLon WGwG WWal WWin |
| *kochii* | LBro |
| *kopetdagensis* | Last listed 1997 |
| *korolkowii* 'Violacea' | Last listed 1998 |
| *kuschakewiczii* | Last listed 1998 |
| * 'Kuvatuib' (SDB) | Last listed 1998 |
| 'La Nina Rosa' (BB) | Last listed 1998 |
| ¶ 'La Senda' (Spuria) | WCot |
| 'Lace Artistry' (TB) | SCro |
| 'Lace Jabot' (TB) | Last listed 1996 |
| 'Laced Cotton' (TB) | SCro |
| 'Laced Lemonade' (SDB) | EFou LBro LRHS MBri |
| § *lactea* ♀ | GBin NSla SCro |
| – CC 220 | MRPP |
| – SULE 1 | Last listed 1997 |
| *lacustris* ♀ | CBro ELan EPot ERos GCrs MBro NBro NCat NHar NMen NTow NWCA WAbe |
| – x *gracilipes* | CRDP EPot SWas WAbe |
| 'Lady Belle' (MTB) | LBro |
| 'Lady Friend' (TB) | ERou SCro |
| 'Lady Ilse' (TB) | Last listed 1996 |
| 'Lady Madonna' (TB) | SCro |
| 'Lady Mohr' (AB) | CKel MCAu |
| 'Lady of Nepal' (IB) | LBro |
| 'Lady River' (TB) | Last listed 1996 |
| § *laevigata* ♀ | CKel CRow CWat ECha EGle EGol EHon ELan LPBA MRav MSta NBrk NBro NDea NGdn SPer SWat SWyc WAbe WMAq WShi |
| – 'Alba' | CBen CRDP CRow ECha EGol EHon LEdu LPBA SAWi SSpi SWat SWyc |
| – 'Albopurpurea' | EMFW |
| – 'Atropurpurea' | CRow EGol IBlr LPBA |
| – 'Colchesterensis' | CBen CRDP CRow CWat EGol EHon EMFW LPBA MSta SWat SWyc |
| I – 'Dorothy' | LPBA MSta NGdn SAWi |
| * – 'Dorothy Robinson' | SWat |
| – 'Elegant' | See *I. laevigata* 'Weymouth Elegant' |
| I – 'Elegante' | CRow SWat SWyc |
| – 'Goshobeni' | CRow |
| I – 'Midnight' | See *I. laevigata* 'Weymouth Midnight' |
| N – 'Monstrosa' | SWyc |
| – 'Mottled Beauty' | CBen CRow CWat MSta SWyc |
| – 'Murasama' | CRow |
| – 'Odiham' | SWyc |

| | | |
|---|---|---|
| | - 'Plena' (d) | SWyc |
| N | - 'Plum Purple' | EGle |
| | - 'Purity' | See *I. laevigata* 'Weymouth Purity' |
| | - 'Regal' | CBen SWyc |
| I | - 'Reveille' | EGle |
| | - 'Richard Greany' | CRow |
| | - 'Rose Queen' | See *I. ensata* 'Rose Queen' |
| | - 'Shirasagi' | CRow |
| I | - 'Snowdrift' | CBen CRow CWat EGol EHon EMFW LPBA MCAu MSta NDea NGdn SAWi SCro SWat SWyc WMAq |
| | - 'Surprise' | See *I. laevigata* 'Weymouth Surprise' |
| | - 'Tamagawa' | CRow |
| | - 'Variegata' ♀ | CBen CRDP CRow CWat ECha EGol EHoe EHon EMFW EPla EWTr LEdu LPBA MSta NDea NGdn NOrc NRoo SCob SPer SSpi SWat SWyc WMAq WRus WWat |
| | - 'Violet Garth' | CRow |
| I | - 'Weymouth' | See *I. laevigata* 'Weymouth Blue' |
| § | - 'Weymouth Blue' | CRDP CRow EGol SAWi SWyc |
| § | - 'Weymouth Elegant' | CBen |
| § | - 'Weymouth Midnight' | CBen CRow CWat EGol EHon SAWi SWat SWyc |
| § | - 'Weymouth Surprise' | CWat |
| | 'Lake Placid' (TB) | SCro |
| | 'Lamorna' (TB) | Last listed 1996 |
| | 'Land o' Lakes' (TB) | SCro |
| N | 'Langport Chapter' (IB) | CKel |
| N | 'Langport Chief' (IB) | CKel |
| N | 'Langport Chimes' (IB) | CKel |
| N | 'Langport Claret' (IB) | CKel |
| N | 'Langport Curlew' (IB) | CKel |
| N | 'Langport Dolly' (IB) | Last listed 1996 |
| N | 'Langport Duchess' (IB) | CKel |
| N | 'Langport Duke' (IB) | Last listed 1997 |
| N | 'Langport Fairy' (IB) | CKel |
| N | 'Langport Fashion' (IB) | Last listed 1997 |
| N | 'Langport Finch' (IB) | Last listed 1996 |
| N | 'Langport Flame' (IB) | CKel EWTr MMil |
| N | 'Langport Flash' (IB) | Last listed 1996 |
| N | 'Langport Flush' (IB) | SCro |
| N | 'Langport Haze' (IB) | CKel |
| N | 'Langport Hero' (IB) | Last listed 1997 |
| N | 'Langport Honey' (IB) | CKel |
| N | 'Langport Hope' (IB) | CKel |
| N | 'Langport Jane' (IB) | CKel |
| N | 'Langport Judy' (IB) | Last listed 1996 |
| N | 'Langport Kestrel' (IB) | Last listed 1996 |
| N | 'Langport Lady' (IB) | Last listed 1996 |
| N | 'Langport Lord' (IB) | CKel |
| N | 'Langport Magic' (IB) | MMil |
| N | 'Langport Minstrel' (IB) | CKel |
| N | 'Langport Myth' (IB) | CKel |
| N | 'Langport Pagan' (IB) | WTin |
| N | 'Langport Pearl' (IB) | Last listed 1998 |
| N | 'Langport Phoebe' (IB) | CKel |
| | 'Langport Phoenix' (IB) | CKel |
| N | 'Langport Pinnacle' (IB) | CKel |
| N | 'Langport Pleasure' (IB) | CKel |
| N | 'Langport Prince' (IB) | MMil |
| N | 'Langport Robe' (IB) | CKel |
| N | 'Langport Robin' (IB) | CKel |
| N | 'Langport Romance' (IB) | CKel |
| N | 'Langport Secret' (IB) | Last listed 1996 |
| N | 'Langport Smoke' (IB) | CKel |
| N | 'Langport Snow' (IB) | Last listed 1996 |
| N | 'Langport Song' (IB) | CKel MMil |
| N | 'Langport Star' (IB) | CKel |

| | | |
|---|---|---|
| N | 'Langport Storm' (IB) | CKel EFou MMil WBcn |
| N | 'Langport Sultan' (IB) | CKel |
| N | 'Langport Sun' (IB) | CKel |
| N | 'Langport Sunbeam' (IB) | CKel |
| N | 'Langport Swift' (IB) | CKel |
| | 'Langport Sylvia' (IB) | CKel |
| N | 'Langport Tartan' (IB) | Last listed 1996 |
| N | 'Langport Tempest' (IB) | CKel |
| N | 'Langport Vale' (IB) | CKel |
| N | 'Langport Violet' (IB) | CKel EWTr |
| N | 'Langport Vista' (IB) | CKel |
| N | 'Langport Warrior' (IB) | CKel |
| N | 'Langport Wren' (IB) | CBro CKel CMil LBro LGre MBel MBri MMil NBir |
| ¶ | 'Lark Rise' (TB) | CKel |
| ¶ | 'Larry Gaulter' (TB) | LIri |
| | 'Late Lilac' (TB) | Last listed 1997 |
| § | *latifolia* ♀ | WCot WLin WMaN |
| | - *alba* | ELan |
| ¶ | - 'Queen of the Blues' | EBee |
| | 'Latin Rock' (TB) | SCro |
| | 'Lavanesque' (TB) | CKel MCAu |
| | 'Lavender Royal' (CH) ♀ | Last listed 1996 |
| § | *lazica* ♀ | CAvo CBro CMea ECre EHyt EPot GMac IBlr MBel MBri NChi NSti SChu SCro SIng SSpi SUsu WCot WEas WWat |
| | 'Leda's Lover' (TB) | SCro |
| ¶ | 'Lemon Brocade' (TB) | MBri |
| I | 'Lemon Drop' (TB) | CKel |
| | 'Lemon Flare' (SDB) | EBrP EBre ECtt LBre LBro MCAu MRav SBre SRms |
| | 'Lemon Flurry' (IB) | LBro |
| | 'Lemon Glitter' (TB) | EFou EPri |
| | 'Lemon Ice' (TB) | MMil |
| | 'Lemon Mist' (TB) | MCAu MMil |
| | 'Lemon Puff' (MDB) | CBro LBro |
| | 'Lemon Reflection' (TB) | MMil |
| | 'Lemon Tree' (TB) | Last listed 1998 |
| | 'Lemon Wine' (IB) | CKel |
| N | 'Lena' (SDB) | CBro LBuc MBel WGwG |
| | 'Lenna M' (SDB) | CKel |
| | 'Lent A Williamson' (TB) | CBlo SCro |
| | 'Libation' (MDB) | LBro MBri NOla |
| ¶ | 'Licorice Stick' (TB) | MCAu |
| | 'Light Cavalry' (TB) | NZep |
| | 'Light Laughter' (IB) | MCAu |
| | 'Lighted Signal' (Spuria) | LBro |
| | 'Lighted Within' (TB) | SCro |
| | 'Lighten Up' (SDB) | NZep |
| | 'Likiang' (Chrysographes) | Last listed 1996 |
| | 'Lilac and Lavender' (SDB) | MMil NZep |
| | 'Lilli-white' (SDB) | CKel EBrP EBre EGle ENot LBre LBro MCAu MMil MRav SBre |
| | 'Lime Grove' (SDB) ♀ | Last listed 1998 |
| | 'Limelight' (TB) | SRms |
| | 'Limpid Pools' (SDB) | SCro |
| | 'Lincoln Imp' (CH) ♀ | Last listed 1995 |
| | 'Lindis' (AB) | Last listed 1996 |
| | 'Linesman' (SDB) | NZep |
| | 'Lions Share' (TB) | LIri |
| | 'Liquid Smoke' (TB) | MMil |
| | 'Listowel' (IB) | LBro |
| | 'Little Amigo' (SDB) | NZep |
| N | 'Little Amoena' | ERos NMen |
| | 'Little Annie' (SDB) | NZep |
| | 'Little Bill' (SDB) | EFou EGle |
| | 'Little Black Belt' (SDB) | EFou LBro NZep |
| | 'Little Blackfoot' (SDB) | CHad MMil WHoo WWin |
| | 'Little Chestnut' (SDB) | LBro WWin |
| | 'Little Cottage' (SDB) | SCro |
| | 'Little Dandy' (SDB) | EGle |

'Little Dogie' (SDB)            EGle LBro
'Little Dream' (SDB)            EGle MCAu NZep
'Little Episode' (SDB)          NZep
'Little Jewel' (DB)             Last listed 1996
'Little Paul' (MTB)             LBro
'Little Pearl' (MDB)            NZep
'Little Rosy Wings' (SDB)       CBro ERos LBro LGre MMil
'Little Sapphire' (SDB)         Last listed 1997
'Little Shadow' (IB)            ECtt ENot GMaP LBro MRav SRms
'Little Sheba' (AB)             LBlm
'Little Sir Echo' (BB)          Last listed 1996
'Little Snow Lemon' (IB)        NZep
¶ 'Little Tilgates' ♀           WWst
'Little Vanessa' (TB)           Last listed 1996
'Live Jazz' (SDB)               MMil NZep
'Lively Rose' (MTB)             LBro
'Llanthony' (SDB)               Last listed 1998
*loczyi*                        Last listed 1998
'Lodestar' (TB)                 LBro
'Lodore' (TB)                   MBri SRms
'Lofty Dreams' (TB)             LIri
*longipetala*                   NBir
'Look Again' (Spuria)           LBro
'Lookin' Good' (IB)             NZep
'Loop the Loop' (TB)            CKel EBee EBrP EBre EGle EPfP
                                LBre NBro SBre SMer
'Lord Baltimore' (TB)           SCro
'Lord Warden' (TB)              EFou
'Lord Wolseley' (Spuria)        LBro
'Lorilee' (TB)                  SCro
'Los Angeles'                   LRHS MBri
'Lothario' (TB)                 CKel
'Loud Music' (TB)               MBri WWeb
'Loudmouth' (AB)                LBro
Louisiana hybrids               Last listed 1998
'Louisiana Lace' (TB)           SCro
'Louvois' (TB)                  Last listed 1998
'Loveday' (TB)                  LBro
'Lovely Again' (TB)             MCAu MWat
'Lovely Kay' (TB)               SCro
'Lovely Letty' (TB)             MBri
'Lovely Light' (TB)             MBri
'Love's Tune' (IB)              SCro
'Loveshine' (SDB)               MMil MRav NZep
'Low Snow' (SDB)                NZep
N 'Lucinda' (TB)                Last listed 1996
'Lucky Charm' (MTB)             LBro
'Lucky Devil' (Spuria)          Last listed 1997
'Lucky Duck' (SDB)              Last listed 1998
'Lugano' (TB)                   COIW MMil
'Lullaby of Spring' (TB)        LIri
'Luscious One' (SDB)            LBro
§ *lutescens* ♀                 CPBP EPot ERos MCAu
§ - 'Campbellii'                CBro ECGP EHyt ERos LGre MBri
                                MBro NMen WPen
- *cyanea*                      Last listed 1998
* - 'Goldcrest'                 MBro
- L 22                          WPGP
- subsp. *lutescens*            WLin
§ - 'Nancy Lindsay'             MCAu
'Lydia Jane' (Spuria) ♀         LBro WBcn
*macrosiphon*                   Last listed 1996
'Madeira Belle' (TB)            Last listed 1998
I 'Maestro' (TB)                CKel
N 'Magenta and Peach' (TB)      MCAu
'Magharee' (TB)                 Last listed 1996
'Magic Carpet' (TB)             CKel
'Magic Flute' (MDB)             EGle LBro MBri
'Magic Hills' (TB)              CKel
¶ 'Magic Kingdom' (TB)          LIri
'Magic Man' (TB)                LBro
*magnifica* ♀                   CBro CLAP EHyt EPot GCrs
                                NWCA

¶ - 'Agalik'                    WWst
  - f. *alba*                   EHyt
* - 'Samarkhand Gem'            GCrs
'Mahogany Snow' (SDB)           MMil NZep
¶ 'Main Sequence' (AB)          WWst
'Malaguena' (TB)                LIri
I 'Mandarin' (TB)               GDra
'Mandarin Purple' (Sino-sib)    GGar IBlr NGdn NHol
'Maori King' (TB)               Last listed 1996
*maracandica*                   Last listed 1998
'Margarita' (TB)                Last listed 1998
'Margot Holmes' (Cal-Sib)       EBee GCal GDra GMac IBlr SChu
                                WCot
'Margrave' (TB)                 Last listed 1998
'Marhaba' (MDB)                 CBro ERos
'Maria Tormena' (TB)            SCro
'Mariachi' (TB)                 Last listed 1997
'Marilyn Holloway' (Spuria)     ECha
'Marmalade Skies' (BB)          LBro NZep
'Marmot' (MDB)                  Last listed 1996
¶ 'Maroon Caper' (IB)           NSti
'Marshlander' (TB)              EFou SCro
'Marty' (IB)                    Last listed 1998
'Martyn Rix'                    See *I. confusa* 'Martyn Rix'
'Mary Frances' (TB) ♀           LBro LIri SCro
'Mary McIlroy' (SDB) ♀          CBro LBro MMil WTin
'Mary Randall' (TB)             Last listed 1997
'Master Touch' (TB)             SCro
'Matchpoint' (TB)               LBro
'Matinata' (TB)                 CKel EBrP EBre LBre SBre
'Maui Moonlight' (IB) ♀         MMil NZep
'May Melody' (TB)               CKel MBri
'Meadow Court' (SDB)            CBro CKel EBee ERos MCAu
                                NBro NZep WMer WSan
'Meadow Moss' (SDB)             Last listed 1996
'Media Luz' (Spuria)            LBro
'Meg's Mantle' (TB) ♀           CKel LBro
'Melbreak' (TB)                 Last listed 1997
'Melissa Sue' (TB)              SCro
*mellita*                       See *I. suaveolens*
- var. *rubromarginata*         See *I. suaveolens*
'Melon Honey' (SDB) ♀           CKel EGle LBro MCAu MMil
                                NZep WWin
'Menton' (SDB)                  Last listed 1997
I 'Merry Day' (IB)              Last listed 1997
'Merry Madrigal' (TB)           Last listed 1996
'Merseyside' (SDB)              CNic EGle LBro
'Mesmerizer' (TB)               LIri
'Metaphor' (TB)                 MCAu MMil
'Michael Paul' (SDB)            Last listed 1997
'Michele Taylor' (TB)           SCro
'Midas Kiss' (IB)               Last listed 1996
'Midday Blues' (IB)             NZep
'Midnight Fire' (TB)            ERou
'Midnight Madness' (SDB)        Last listed 1996
*milesii* ♀                     CPou MHar NBir SCro WPer WPic
- CC&McK  357                   Last listed 1996
- CC&McK  741                   GCHN
- CR 346                        CHan WPer
'Mini Agnes' (DB)               CBro
'Mini Dynamo' (SDB)             Last listed 1996
'Minnesota Glitters' (TB)       SCro
'Minnie Colquitt' (TB)          CKel SCro
'Miss Carla' (IB) ♀             LBro MMil SCro
'Mission Ridge' (TB)            CKel
'Mission Sunset' (TB)           EBrP EBre LBre MCAu SBre
'Missouri Gal' (Spuria)         LBro
*missouriensis* ♀               CRow EWoo IBlr LBro NMen SSpi
- var. *arizonica*              EBee
'Mister Roberts' (SDB)          LBro NZep
'Modern Classic' (TB)           Last listed 1996
'Moment' (SDB)                  NZep

'Monaco' (TB)                     EFou
'Money' (TB)                      SCro
**monnieri**                      EFou IBlr NLar SDix
Monspur Group                     ECGP GCal SSpi WCot WPic
§ 'Monspur Cambridge              MCAu WPic
  Blue' (Spuria)
'Moon Shadows' (SDB)              MCAu WViv
'Moon Sparkle' (IB)               CKel CMGP WSan
'Moonlight' (TB)                  LBro NFor
'Moonlight Waves'                 See *I. ensata* 'Moonlight Waves'
'Moon's Delight' (TB)             Last listed 1997
'Morning Hymn' (TB)               SCro
'Morning Show' (IB)               SCro
'Morocco' (TB)                    SCro
'Morwenna' (TB) ♀                 LBro MCAu
* 'Mount Stewart Black'           EGar GCal
'Mrs Horace Darwin' (TB)          CFir
'Mrs Kate Rudolph' (SDB)          EFou EGle LBro LGre MBri
* 'Mrs Richmond'                  SAWi
'Mulberry Rose' (TB)              CKel
**munzii**                        EWoo
'Muriel Neville' (TB)             MCAu
'Murmuring Morn' (TB)             Last listed 1997
'Music Box' (SDB)                 NZep
'Music Caper' (SDB)               Last listed 1996
'Mute Swan' (TB)                  Last listed 1996
'My Honeycomb' (TB)               MCAu
'My Mary' (TB)                     CKel
N 'My Seedling' (MDB)             CBro ERos NMen WIvy
'My Smoky' (TB)                   CKel
'Myra's Child' (SDB)              Last listed 1996
'Mystique' (TB)                   SCro
'Naivasha' (TB)                   CKel
'Nambe' (MTB)                     LBro
'Nampara' (TB)                    LBro
'Nancy Hardy' (MDB)              CBro ERos NNrd
'Nancy Lindsay'                   See *I. lutescens* 'Nancy Lindsay'
'Nashborough' (TB)                CKel
'Natascha' (Reticulata)          EHyt ELan EPot LAma
'Navajo Blanket' (TB)            SCro
¶ 'Navajo Jewel' (TB)            LIri
¶ 'Navy Blues' (TB)              LIri
'Navy Doll' (MDB)                Last listed 1996
'Nectar' (TB)                     CKel
**nectarifera**                   EHyt
'Needlecraft' (TB)                CKel MMil
'Needlepoint' (TB)                SCro
¶ 'Neil Diamond' (TB)            LIri
* 'Nel Jupe' (TB)                EOld
'Neon Pixie' (SDB)                NZep
'Neophyte' (Spuria)               LBro
**nepalensis**                    See *I. decora*
**nertschinskia**                 See *I. sanguinea*
'New Idea' (MTB)                  LBro
'New Snow' (TB)                   CKel LBlm MCAu WCot
'New Wave' (MTB)                  Last listed 1996
'Nibelungen' (TB)                 CKel EPfP NFai
'Nice 'n' Nifty' (IB)            NZep WTin
¶ **nicolai**                    WWst
'Niebelungen' (TB)                EOld
¶ 'Nigerian Raspberry' (TB)      LIri
'Night Affair' (TB)               Last listed 1996
'Night Edition' (TB)              Last listed 1996
'Night Owl' (TB)                  CKel MMil SCro
'Night Ruler' (TB)                Last listed 1997
**nigricans** S&L 148            Last listed 1998
'Nimble Toes' (SDB)              LBro
'Nineveh' (AB)                   Last listed 1998
'No-Name' (CH) ♀                 Last listed 1997
* 'Nova' seedling                WWst
'Nylon Ruffles' (SDB)           LBro SUsu
'Ochraurea' (Spuria)            GCal

**ochroleuca**                    See *I. orientalis*
'Offenham' (TB)                   LBro
'Oklahoma Bandit' (IB)           LBro
'Oktoberfest' (TB)                Last listed 1996
'Ola Kala' (TB)                   CMGP EBrP EBre ECle EHic ERou
                                  EWTr LBre LBro MCAu SBre SCob
                                  SCro SPer WLRN
'Old Flame' (TB)                  Last listed 1997
'Oliver' (SDB)                    LBro
'Olympiad' (TB)                   LIri
'Olympic Challenger' (TB)        Last listed 1998
'Olympic Torch' (TB) ♀           CKel MCAu
'On Fire' (SDB)                   Last listed 1996
'One Accord' (SDB)               SCro
'One Desire' (TB)                 NZep
'Open Sky' (SDB)                 MMil NZep
'Orange Blaze' (SDB)            CBro
'Orange Caper' (SDB)            EBrP EBre LBre MRav NZep SBre
§ 'Orange Chariot' (TB)          Last listed 1998
'Orange Dawn' (TB) ♀            LBro
'Orange Grove' (TB)              MBri
'Orange Jewelius' (TB)           LIri
'Orange Maid' (Spuria)          WBcn
N 'Orange Plaza'                 NMen
'Orange Tiger' (SDB)            NZep
'Orchardist' (TB)                CKel
'Orchidarium' (TB)               CKel
§ **orchioides**                 CMea EBee ELan EPot ERos MMal
 – yellow                        Last listed 1998
'Oregold' (SDB)                  NZep
'Oregon Skies' (TB)             SCro
'Oriental Baby' (IB)            CKel
'Oriental Blush' (SDB)          LBro WBcn
'Oriental Glory' (TB)            MCAu
'Oriental Touch'                 CRow
§ **orientalis** ♀               CAvo CBot CHan CMil CRow
                                 ECGP ELan LBlm LBro LPBA MBal
                                 MCAu MNrw MWgw SChu SSpi
                                 WPic WWin WWst
 – 'Alba'                        See *I. sanguinea* 'Alba'
'Orinoco Flow' (BB) ♀           CKel LIri
'Oritam' (TB)                    SCro
'Ornament' (SDB)                LBro
'Oroville' (Spuria)             Last listed 1996
'Ouija' (BB) ♀                  Last listed 1995
'Out Yonder' (TB)                MCAu
'Outline' (AB)                   Last listed 1996
'Outstep' (SDB)                 Last listed 1996
'Ovation' (SDB)                 SCro
'Overnight Sensation' (TB)      SCro
'Pacer' (IB)                     NZep
'Pacific Coast Hyb'             See *I.* Californian hybrids
'Pacific Gambler' (TB)          EFou
'Pacific Mist' (TB)              SCro
'Pagan Pink' (TB)                LIri
'Pagan Princess' (TB)           MCAu
'Paint It Black' (TB)           LIri
'Painted Rose' (MTB)            Last listed 1996
'Pajaro Dunes' (CH) ♀           LBro
'Palace Gossip' (TB)            Last listed 1997
'Pale Primrose' (TB)            WEas
'Pale Shades' (IB) ♀           CBro CKel LBro
'Pale Suede' (SDB)             LBro
pale yellow (Sino-sib)          NWoo
§ **pallida**                    ECGN EFou ELau GMaP LHol
                                 MCAu MCCP MRav
 – 'Argentea Variegata'          More than 30 suppliers
 – 'Aurea'                       See *I. pallida* 'Variegata'
 – 'Aurea Variegata'             See *I. pallida* 'Variegata'
 – subsp. **cengialtii** ♀      Last listed 1998
 – var. **dalmatica**            See *I. pallida* subsp. *pallida*
 – JCA 589.800                   Last listed 1996

| | |
|---|---|
| § - subsp. *pallida* ♀ | CBot CKel CPlt EBrP EBre ECha ELan LBre LBro LHil MBri MCAu MUlv SBre SCob SCro SDix SMrm SPer WCot WWal |
| N - 'Variegata' ♀ | More than 30 suppliers |
| 'Paltec' | CHad CPlt CPou EBee LGre SWas |
| 'Pandora's Purple' (TB) | SCro |
| ¶ 'Panocha' (TB) | LIri |
| 'Paradise' (TB) ♀ | EPfP LBro LIri SCro |
| 'Paradise Bird' (TB) ♀ | LBro |
| 'Paradise Pink' (TB) | Last listed 1996 |
| *paradoxa* f. *choschab* | EHyt EPot |
| 'Paricutin' (SDB) | CBro EGle |
| 'Paris Lights' (TB) | SCro |
| 'Party Dress' (TB) | CMGP EBee ECtt EHic ELan ENot EPla ERav ERou EWTr LBro MRav NGdn NOrc SCoo SMrm SPer WWal |
| 'Pascoe' (TB) ♀ | LBro |
| 'Pastel Charm' (SDB) | CKel CMGP EBee MCli MSCN WSan |
| 'Pastel Delight' (SDB) | NZep |
| 'Path of Gold' (DB) | CBro LBro MBri WWeb |
| 'Patina' (TB) | Last listed 1996 |
| 'Patterdale' (TB) | NBir NMGW NVic |
| 'Pauline' (Reticulata) | CAvo CBro EPot LAma NRog |
| 'Peace and Harmony' (TB) | LIri |
| 'Peach Band' (TB) | ERou |
| 'Peach Bisque' (TB) | Last listed 1997 |
| 'Peach Eyes' (SDB) | LBro NZep |
| ¶ 'Peach Float' (TB) | MCAu |
| 'Peach Melba' (TB) | Last listed 1996 |
| 'Peach Petals' (BB) | LBro NZep |
| 'Peach Picotee' (TB) | SCro |
| 'Peach Spot' (TB) | MCAu MMil |
| 'Peaches ala Mode' (BB) | MCAu |
| 'Peaches 'n' Topping' (BB) | LBro |
| 'Peachy Face' (IB) | LBro |
| 'Pearly Dawn' (TB) | EBee ECtt MWat NGdn SCro SPer WLRN |
| 'Pegasus' (TB) | SCro |
| 'Peggy Chambers' (IB) ♀ | EFou LBro MMil |
| 'Peking Summer' (TB) | SCro |
| 'Pennies' (MDB) | NZep |
| 'Penny Bunker' (Spuria) | Last listed 1996 |
| 'Penny Candy' (MDB) | Last listed 1996 |
| 'Pennyworth' (IB) | SCro |
| 'Penrhyn' (TB) | LBro |
| 'People Pleaser' (SDB) | NZep SCro |
| 'Peppermint Twist' (SDB) | NZep |
| 'Perfect Interlude' (TB) | Last listed 1997 |
| 'Persian Berry' (TB) | SCro |
| 'Persian Doll' (MDB) | NZep |
| 'Persian Romance' (TB) | Last listed 1998 |
| *persica* | Last listed 1998 |
| 'Pet' (SDB) | NSti NZep |
| 'Phil Keen' (TB) ♀ | CKel |
| 'Phillida' (CH) ♀ | Last listed 1995 |
| 'Pied Pretty' (SDB) | SCro |
| 'Pigeon' (SDB) | NZep |
| 'Pigmy Gold' (IB) | EBee ENot ERos LBro |
| 'Pinewood Amethyst' (CH) | CPlt LBro WWst |
| 'Pinewood Charmer' (CH) | LBro |
| 'Pinewood Poppet' (CH) | LBro |
| 'Pinewood Sunshine' (CH) | CPlt LBro |
| 'Pink Angel' (TB) | SCro |
| 'Pink Bubbles' (BB) | NZep |
| 'Pink Clover' (TB) | LBro |
| 'Pink Confetti' (TB) | SCro |
| 'Pink Divinity' (TB) | MMil |
| 'Pink Horizon' (TB) | SCro |
| 'Pink Kitten' (IB) | NZep |

| | |
|---|---|
| 'Pink Lamb' (BB) | LBro |
| N 'Pink Lavender' (TB) | SCro |
| 'Pink 'n' Mint' (TB) | SCro |
| 'Pink Pussycat' | MBri |
| N 'Pink Randall' (TB) | SCro |
| 'Pink Ruffles' (IB) | CHar CKel WBcn |
| 'Pink Taffeta' (TB) | CKel SCro |
| 'Pinnacle' (TB) | CKel |
| 'Pipes of Pan' (TB) | MCAu MRav |
| 'Pippi Longstockings' (SDB) | Last listed 1996 |
| 'Piquant Lass' (MTB) | NZep |
| ¶ 'Pirate's Quest' (TB) | LIri |
| * - 'Pixie' (Reticulata) | EPot |
| I - 'Pixie' (DB) | Last listed 1996 |
| 'Pixie Flirt' (MDB) | ERos LBro |
| 'Pixie Plum' (SDB) | Last listed 1996 |
| *planifolia* AB&S 4609 | Last listed 1998 |
| * - 'Alba' | Last listed 1998 |
| - S&L 301 | Last listed 1998 |
| 'Planned Treasure' (TB) | Last listed 1998 |
| 'Playgirl' (TB) | SCro |
| 'Pledge Allegiance' (TB) | MMil SCro |
| *plicata* | Last listed 1996 |
| 'Plickadee' (SDB) | EPot |
| 'Plum Perfect' (SDB) | SCro |
| * 'Plums 'n' Cream' | Last listed 1998 |
| 'Pogo' (SDB) | CMil EBee ECtt EGle EHyt ELan ENot EPot GMaP MMil MRav NNrd SCro SRms |
| 'Pogo Doll' (AB) | LBro |
| § *polakii* (Oncocyclus) | Last listed 1997 |
| 'Pony' (IB) | LBro |
| 'Popinjay' (CH) | Last listed 1996 |
| 'Port of Call' (Spuria) | LBro |
| 'Post Time' (TB) | SCro |
| 'Pot Luck' (IB) | Last listed 1997 |
| 'Powder Pink' (TB) | CKel |
| ¶ 'Prairie Sunset' (TB) | COIW |
| 'Praise the Lord' (TB) | LBro |
| 'Prancing Pony' (TB) | CKel SCro |
| 'Pretender' (TB) | LRHS MBri MCAu |
| 'Prettie Print' (TB) | SCro |
| 'Priceless Pearl' (TB) | SCro |
| 'Pride of Ireland' (TB) | SCro |
| 'Prince' (SDB) | EFou EGle LBro |
| 'Prince Indigo' (TB) | ENot |
| 'Princess' (TB) | Last listed 1997 |
| 'Princess Beatrice' | See *I. pallida* subsp. *pallida* |
| *prismatica* | EPla NNrd WTin |
| - *alba* | GAbr |
| 'Professor Blaauw' (Dut) ♀ | ETub LAma SHel |
| 'Prophetic Message' (AB) | Last listed 1996 |
| 'Prosper Laugier' (IB) | SCro |
| 'Protégé' (Spuria) | LBro |
| 'Proud Land' (TB) | Last listed 1996 |
| 'Proud Tradition' (TB) | LIri SCro |
| 'Provencal' (TB) | CKel MCAu |
| *pseudacorus* ♀ | More than 30 suppliers |
| - 'Alba' | CRow SSpi SWyc |
| - var. *bastardii* | CBre CKel CRDP CRow CWat ECGP ECha EGol EMFP EMFW LPBA SLon SWyc WFar |
| - 'Beuron' | CRow |
| - cream | EGol MUlv NBir NBrk |
| - dwarf form | SWyc |
| N - 'Ecru' | CRow SWyc |
| N - 'Esk' | GCal |
| N - 'Flore Pleno' (d) | CAvo CBot CKel CRow EBee EMFW MCAu MInt SWyc WCot |
| - 'Golden Daggers' | CRow |
| I - 'Golden Fleece' | SPer |
| - 'Golden Queen' | CRow MSta SWyc |

| | |
|---|---|
| - 'Ilgengold' | CRow |
| N - 'Ivory' | CRow |
| - 'Kimboshi' x *ensata* | Last listed 1996 |
| - 'Lime Sorbet' | WCot |
| * - *nana* | LPBA |
| - 'Roy Davidson' | CKel |
| - 'Sun Cascade' | CRow |
| - Tangarewa Cream Group | SWyc |
| - 'Tiger Brother' | Last listed 1996 |
| - 'Tiggah' | CRow NSti |
| - 'Turnipseed' | CRow |
| - 'Variegata' ♀ | More than 30 suppliers |
| - x *versicolor* | SCro |
| - 'Wychwood Multifloral' | SWyc |
| *pseudocaucasica* | EPot |
| *pseudopumila* | Last listed 1997 |
| - MS 986/975 | Last listed 1998 |
| *pumila* | EHyt EPla EPot MBro NFor |
| | NMGW NMen NWCA SRPl WCla |
| | WWin |
| - *atroviolacea* | CKel MBro |
| - subsp. *attica* | See *I. attica* |
| - 'Aurea' | MBro NTow WWeb |
| * - 'Gelber Mantel' | MSCN |
| - 'Goldcrest' (I) | Last listed 1998 |
| - 'Lavendel Plicata' | CNic EBee MSCN NBro NNrd |
| | WSan |
| - 'Purpurea' | EHyt |
| - 'Violacea' | MBro SCro SRms |
| - yellow | LWoo NFla |
| 'Pumpkin Center' (SDB) | NZep |
| 'Puppet' (SDB) | EGle EPot LBro |
| 'Puppet Baby' (MDB) | NZep |
| 'Puppy Love' (MTB) | NMGW NZep |
| ¶ *purdyi* | NSti |
| - x *tenuissima* | Last listed 1996 |
| 'Pure Allure' (SDB) | NZep |
| 'Pure-as-the' (TB) | LIri |
| 'Purgatory' (TB) | LIri |
| 'Purple Dream' (CH) | Last listed 1996 |
| 'Purple Gem' (Reticulata) | CBro EPot LAma WRHF |
| 'Purple Landscape' (SDB) ♀ | LBro |
| 'Purple Sensation' (Dut) | CB&S LAma SHel |
| 'Purple Song' (TB) | Last listed 1998 |
| 'Purple Streaker' (TB) | SCro |
| *purpurea* | See *I. galatica* |
| *purpureobractea* | EPot |
| 'Pushy' (SDB) | LBro |
| 'Quark' (SDB) | CBro CKel LBro NZep |
| 'Quechee' (TB) | CBlo CHad CMGP EHic EPfP |
| | ERou EWTr EWll GMaP LNor |
| | MRav NBur NGdn NLak SCro |
| | WLRN |
| 'Queen in Calico' (TB) | MCAu SCro |
| 'Queen of Hearts' (TB) | SCro |
| 'Queen's Ivory' (SDB) | Last listed 1998 |
| 'Queen's Pawn' (SDB) | NMGW NZep |
| 'Quiet Lagoon' (SDB) | NZep |
| 'Quiet Thought' (TB) | LBro |
| 'Quintana' (CH) | LBro WWst |
| 'Rabelais' (TB) | CKel EBee |
| 'Radiant Summer' (TB) | SCro |
| 'Rain Dance' (SDB) ♀ | LBro NMGW NZep |
| 'Rainbow Goddess' (TB) | LIri |
| 'Rainbow Trout' (TB) | LBro |
| 'Rajah' (TB) | EBee EHic EPfP ERav ERou LBro |
| | MRav NGdn NLak NOrc SLod |
| | WWal |
| 'Rancho Grande' (TB) | Last listed 1997 |
| 'Rancho Rose' (TB) | SCro |
| 'Ranger' (TB) | Last listed 1997 |
| ¶ 'Rapture in Blue' (TB) | LIri |

| | |
|---|---|
| 'Rare Edition' (IB) | CKel EBrP EBre EFou LBre LBro |
| | MBri NZep SBre SCro |
| 'Rare Treat' (TB) | NZep |
| 'Raspberry Acres' (IB) | LRHS MBri MCAu |
| 'Raspberry Blush' (IB) ♀ | CKel NZep SCro |
| 'Raspberry Frills' (TB) | Last listed 1997 |
| 'Raspberry Fudge' (TB) | LIri |
| 'Raspberry Jam' (SDB) | EGle EHyt LBro MMil NZep SUsu |
| 'Raspberry Sundae' (BB) | NZep |
| 'Rathe Primrose' (IB) | SCro |
| 'Raven Hill' (TB) | Last listed 1998 |
| ¶ 'Razoo' (SDB) | CKel |
| 'Real Jazzy' (MTB) | CKel |
| I 'Red Flash' (TB) | CKel COIW |
| 'Red Hawk' (TB) | SCro |
| 'Red Heart' (SDB) | CBlo GMaP MRav WPer |
| 'Red Kite' (TB) | Last listed 1996 |
| 'Red Lion' (TB) | NZep |
| ¶ 'Red Orchid' (IB) | MCli |
| 'Red Revival' (TB) | MCAu MWat SCro |
| 'Red Rufus' (TB) | EFou |
| N 'Red Rum' (TB) | CKel |
| 'Red Tornado' (TB) | Last listed 1997 |
| 'Red Zinger' (IB) | NZep SCro |
| 'Redwing' (TB) | MWat WPer |
| 'Redwood Supreme' (Spuria) | LBro |
| 'Reflection' | Last listed 1996 |
| 'Regal Surprise' (SpecHybrid) | CRow WCot |
| 'Regards' (SDB) | CBro EGle LBro |
| 'Reginae' | See *I. variegata* var. *reginae* |
| § *reichenbachii* | CPBP ERos LBee NLar SWas |
| - Balkana Group | SIng |
| - NS 700 | CPou |
| 'Repartee' (TB) | SCro |
| § *reticulata* ♀ | CB&S CBro EPar EPot ETub MBNS |
| | NRog |
| 'Riches' (SDB) | NZep |
| 'Rickshaw' (SDB) | Last listed 1996 |
| 'Ride Joy' (TB) | Last listed 1996 |
| 'Ride the Wind' (TB) | LIri SCro |
| 'Right Royal' (TB) | ENot MCAu |
| 'Rime Frost' (TB) | MCAu MMil |
| 'Ring o' Roses' (CH) ♀ | Last listed 1995 |
| 'Ringo' (TB) | CKel LIri MCAu SCro |
| 'Rio del Mar' (CH) ♀ | Last listed 1995 |
| 'Ripple Chip' (SDB) | NZep WTin |
| 'Rippling Waters' (TB) | WBcn |
| 'Rising Moon' (TB) | SCro |
| 'Ritz' (SDB) | CKel WGwG |
| 'River Hawk' (TB) | SCro |
| 'River Patrol' (TB) | EFou |
| 'Roaring Camp' (CH) ♀ | Last listed 1995 |
| 'Robert J. Graves' (TB) | Last listed 1997 |
| § x *robusta* 'Dark Aura' | CRDP |
| § - 'Gerald Darby' ♀ | CBro CElw CFee CHad CKel |
| | CMGP CRDP CRow EBee ECha |
| | EGol EMFW EMon EPar GMac IBlr |
| | LBlm MBri MBro MUlv NSti SCro |
| | SUsu SWat SWyc WCot WEas |
| | WPen WRus WWhi |
| - 'Mountain Brook' | CRow |
| - 'Nutfield Blue' | NSti |
| § 'Rocket' (TB) | CMGP EBee ECGP ERav EWTr |
| | GMaP MBel MRav NBir NGdn |
| | SCro SMrm WLRN |
| * 'Rogue Orange' (TB) | CKel |
| 'Role Model' (TB) | Last listed 1997 |
| 'Roman Emperor' (TB) ♀ | EFou |
| 'Romance' (TB) | ERou |
| 'Romantic Mood' (TB) | LIri |
| 'Romp' (IB) | LBro |
| 'Ron' (TB) | SCro |

| | |
|---|---|
| 'Rose Caress' (TB) | Last listed 1996 |
| 'Rose Queen' | See *I. ensata* 'Rose Queen' |
| 'Rose Violet' (TB) ♀ | NMGW |
| 'Roselene' (TB) | SCro |
| 'Rosemary's Dream' (MTB) | CKel |
| *rosenbachiana* | Last listed 1997 |
| 'Roseplic' (TB) | CKel |
| 'Rosy Air' (SDB) | NZep |
| 'Rosy Wings' (TB) | EHyt |
| ¶ 'Roulette' (TB) | MBri |
| 'Roustabout' (SDB) | EFou EGle LBro |
| N 'Roy Elliott' | CHad MBro NMen WPer |
| 'Royal Ascot' (TB) | LBro |
| 'Royal Contrast' (SDB) ♀ | LBro MMil NZep |
| 'Royal Eyelash' (SDB) | Last listed 1996 |
| 'Royal Fairy' (SDB) | LBro |
| 'Royal Intrigue' (TB) | SCro |
| 'Royal Magician' (SDB) | WHoo WTin |
| 'Royal Midget' (SDB) | LBro |
| 'Royal Regency' (TB) | SCro |
| 'Royal Ruffles' (TB) | Last listed 1996 |
| N 'Royal Toss' (TB) | Last listed 1998 |
| 'Royal Touch' (TB) | EFou |
| 'Royal Viking' (TB) | Last listed 1997 |
| 'Royal Yellow' (Dut) | NRog |
| 'Royalist' (TB) | Last listed 1997 |
| 'Ruby Chimes' (IB) | LGre MCAu SCro |
| 'Ruby Contrast' (TB) | MCAu |
| 'Ruby Gem' (TB) | CKel |
| 'Ruby Locket' (SDB) | LBro |
| 'Ruby Mine' (TB) | MCAu |
| *rudskyi* | See *I. variegata* |
| 'Ruffled Ballet' (TB) | SCro |
| 'Ruffled Revel' (SDB) | CKel |
| 'Ruffled Surprise' (TB) | SCro |
| 'Ruffles and Lace' (TB) | SCro |
| ¶ 'Rushing Stream' (TB) | MCAu |
| 'Russian White' (Spuria) | LBro |
| 'Rustam' (TB) | CKel |
| 'Rustic Cedar' (TB) | EPfP |
| N 'Rustic Jewel' (TB) | CKel EWTr |
| 'Rustler' (TB) | SCro |
| 'Rusty Dusty' (SDB) | NZep |
| 'Ruth Couffer' (BB) | LBro |
| 'Ruth Knowles' (SDB) | LBro |
| 'Ruth Margaret' (TB) | CKel |
| 'Ruth Nies Cabeen' (Spuria) | Last listed 1996 |
| *ruthenica* | ERos GVic NMen WPer |
| - var. *nana* L 1280 | SBla |
| 'Sable' (TB) | EBee EHic MCAu MRav MWat NGdn NOrc SCro SMrm SPer WLRN |
| 'Sable Night' (TB) | CKel ERou |
| 'Safari Boy' (IB) | Last listed 1996 |
| 'Sager Cedric' (TB) | MCAu |
| 'Sahara Sands' (Spuria) | ECha |
| 'Sailor's Dance' (TB) | Last listed 1996 |
| 'Saint Crispin' (TB) | CM&M ERou EWTr LBro MRav MWat NLak SCob SCro SMrm SPer WGwG WLRN WWal |
| 'Sally Jane' (TB) | MCAu |
| 'Salonique' (TB) | MCAu NFai |
| * 'Saltbox' (SDB) | WIvy |
| 'Saltwood' (SDB) ♀ | CBro LBro |
| 'Sam' (SDB) | NZep |
| 'Sam Carne' | MCAu |
| 'Samurai Warrior' (TB) | SCro |
| 'San Jose' (TB) | Last listed 1996 |
| 'San Leandro' (TB) | NOla |
| 'Sand and Sea' (TB) | LBro |
| 'Sand Princess' (MTB) | EFou |
| 'Sandy Caper' (IB) | MCAu |

| | |
|---|---|
| 'Sangreal' (IB) | LBuc |
| § *sanguinea* ♀ | CAvo WCot |
| - AGSJ 625 | Last listed 1998 |
| § - 'Alba' | CRow GCHN IBlr |
| - x *laevigata* | SCro |
| - 'Nana Alba' | SWas |
| § - 'Snow Queen' | CHad CKel EBee EGle EHon ELan EMan ERou LPBA MBNS MBro MRav NGdn NHol NSti SCob SCro SOkh SPer SSpe SSpi WCot WPer WWat |
| 'Santa Clarita' (CH) | Last listed 1996 |
| 'Santana' (TB) | SCro |
| 'Sapphire Beauty' (Dutch) | NRog |
| 'Sapphire Gem' (SDB) | CKel MCAu |
| 'Sapphire Hills' (TB) | MCAu SCro |
| 'Sapphire Jewel' (SDB) | NZep |
| 'Sarah Taylor' (SDB) ♀ | CBro EFou LBro MCAu SCro |
| *sari* | EHyt |
| 'Sass with Class' (SDB) | WTin |
| 'Satin Gown' (TB) | EPri MBri MCAu |
| 'Saturnalia' (TB) | SCro |
| 'Saucy Peach' (BB) | LBro |
| 'Saxon Princess' (TB) | LBro |
| 'Scarlet Ribbon' (TB) | Last listed 1997 |
| *schachtii* MS&CL 510 | Last listed 1998 |
| 'Schortman's Garnet Ruffles' (TB) | SCro |
| 'Scintilla' (IB) ♀ | MMil SCro |
| 'Scintillation' (TB) | SCro |
| 'Scribe' (MDB) | CBro EBee EGle LRHS MBri NBir |
| 'Scrimmage' (SDB) | NZep |
| 'Sea Double' (TB) | MMil |
| 'Sea Fret' (SDB) | CBro |
| 'Sea of Joy' (TB) | LIri SCro |
| 'Sea Urchin' (SDB) | Last listed 1996 |
| 'Second Opinion' (MTB) | NZep |
| 'Secret Melody' (TB) | Last listed 1997 |
| 'Senlac' (TB) | Last listed 1998 |
| *serbica* | See *I. reichenbachii* |
| 'Serenity Prayer' (SDB) | MCAu NZep |
| *setosa* ♀ | CBro CRow EBee ECha EGle EMNN ERos GMaP ITim MHar MNrw MOne MSta NGdn NHed SCro |
| - *alba* | CMea CRow MBro NLar SIng |
| - var. *arctica* | CRDP CRow EMon EPot GCHN LBee MBro NHol NMen NWCA SBla SCro SIng SWas WHoo WPer WPyg |
| - subsp. *canadensis* | See *I. hookeri* |
| - dwarf form | See *I. hookeri* |
| § - 'Hondoensis' | EMon |
| - 'Hookeri' | See *I. hookeri* |
| - 'Kirigamini' | See *I. setosa* 'Hondoensis' |
| - var. *nana* | See *I. hookeri* |
| - *tricuspis* | NNrd |
| 'Shampoo' (IB) | EFou MCAu |
| 'Sheila Ann Germaney' (Reticulata) | EHyt EPot |
| 'Shelford Giant' (Spuria) ♀ | CRow LBro |
| 'Shepherd's Delight' (TB) ♀ | MBri MCAu |
| 'Sherbet Lemon' (IB) ♀ | MCAu |
| 'Short Distance' (IB) | Last listed 1996 |
| 'Short Order' (CH) ♀ | LBro |
| 'Show Me Yellow' (SDB) | NZep SCro |
| 'Showcase' (TB) | NMGW |
| 'Showman' (TB) | ERou |
| *shrevei* | See *I. virginica* var. *shrevei* |
| 'Shrinking Violet' (MTB) | LBro |
| 'Shy Violet' (SDB) | NZep |
| *sibirica* ♀ | More than 30 suppliers |

| | |
|---|---|
| - 'Alba' | See *I.* 'Sibirica Alba' |
| - 'Anglesey' | LBro |
| - 'Ann Dasch' | EFou EGar LBro WLin |
| - 'Annemarie Troeger' ♀ | EFou LBro NCat |
| - 'Anniversary' ♀ | CBos LBro LRHS MTed MUlv SCro |
| - 'Baby Sister' | EBee EFou MBri |
| - 'Baxteri' | See *I.* 'Sibirica Baxteri' |
| - 'Beaumaris' | LBro |
| ¶ - 'Berlin Bluebird' | LGre |
| - 'Berlin Ruffles' ♀ | Last listed 1995 |
| - 'Berliner Runde' | LBro |
| ¶ - 'Bickley Cape' | EBee |
| - 'Blue Brilliant' | WLin WWat |
| - 'Blue Burgee' | ECha SCro |
| * - 'Blue Emperor' | EBee |
| - 'Blue King' | CHid CKel COtt EPfP MBro MRav |
| | NFla WLin WRHF |
| - 'Blue Meadow Fly' | EFou |
| - 'Blue Mere' | LBro WLin |
| - 'Bracknell' | LGre NDov |
| - 'Brynmawr' | LBro |
| - 'Butter and Sugar' ♀ | More than 30 suppliers |
| - 'Caesar' | CKel CRow LBro NCat SDys SRms |
| | WLin WViv |
| - 'Caesar's Brother' | CMGP EMil IBlr MCau MSta SPer |
| | WLin WWat WWin |
| - 'Camberley' | WLin |
| - 'Cambridge' ♀ | EBee EFou LBro MCau MTed |
| | MUlv MWat NHol |
| - 'Canonbury Belle' | WLin |
| * - 'Catforth Corsage' | Last listed 1998 |
| - 'Chartreuse Bounty' | EBee |
| ¶ - 'Circle Round' | LGre |
| - 'Clee Hills' | Last listed 1998 |
| - 'Cleeton Double Chance' ♀ | Last listed 1995 |
| - 'Clouded Moon' | See *I. sibirica* 'Forncett Moon' |
| - 'Cool Spring' | WLin |
| - 'Coquet Waters' | WLin |
| - cream | See *I. sibirica* 'Primrose Cream' |
| - 'Crème Chantilly' ♀ | SCro |
| - 'Dance Ballerina Dance' | CRow EGar LBro NBrk |
| - 'Dark Desire' | MRav SCro |
| N - 'Dark Lavender' | Last listed 1997 |
| - 'Dear Delight' | EBee |
| ¶ - 'Dear Dianne' | CKel |
| ¶ - 'Dewful' | WLin |
| - 'Dragonfly' | WWhi |
| - 'Dreaming Green' | ECha |
| - 'Dreaming Spires' ♀ | LBro WCot WLin |
| - 'Dreaming Yellow' ♀ | CBre CFee EBee EBrP EBre ECha |
| | EFou EGar EGle EPla EPri LBre |
| | LBro MCau MRav MUlv NBro |
| | NLar NRoo SBre SCro SPer SSpe |
| | WLin WRus |
| - 'Ego' | CBlo CDoC CMil COtt ECha EWTr |
| | GMaP MCLN NHol WFar |
| - 'Elinor Hewitt' | LBro |
| - 'Ellesmere' | LBlm NGdn |
| - 'Emperor' | CB&S CKel CRow ERou LGre |
| | LPBA NHol NSti WElm WLin |
| - 'Eric the Red' | CB&S IBlr NBur |
| - 'Ewen' | CBos CBot CPou CRow EFou |
| | EGar IBlr MHlr MNrw MTed SCro |
| | WCot |
| - 'Feathered Giant' | Last listed 1996 |
| - 'Flight of Butterflies' | More than 30 suppliers |
| § - 'Forncett Moon' | EFou LBro |
| - 'Fourfold Lavender' | LBro NBrk |
| - 'Fourfold White' | LBro |
| - 'Friendly Welcome' | LBro |
| - 'Gatineau' | GBuc GDra GGar NCat NHol |
| | WLin |

| | |
|---|---|
| - 'Germantet One' | LBro |
| - 'Glaslyn' ♀ | LBro |
| - 'Halcyon Seas' | WLin |
| - 'Harpswell Hallelujah' | SCro |
| - 'Harpswell Happiness' ♀ | LBro WWal |
| - 'Harpswell Haze' | ECha |
| - 'Heavenly Blue' | EHon LPBA MWat SSpe WLin |
| | WViv |
| - 'Helen Astor' | CMea CRow GAri GGar MRav |
| | MTed NHol SWyc |
| - 'Hoar Edge' | LBro WLin |
| - 'Isla Serle' ♀ | LBro |
| - 'Japanese White' | Last listed 1998 |
| - 'Kingfisher' | LBro |
| - 'Lady of Quality' | LBro SCro |
| - 'Lady Vanessa' | CKel EGle MRav SCro |
| - 'Langthorns Pink' | CRDP ELan LWoo MRav |
| - 'Laurenbuhl' | LBro SCro WLin |
| * - 'Lavender Bonanza' | Last listed 1996 |
| - 'Lavender Bounty' | EBee SCro |
| - 'Lavender Light' | WLin |
| - 'Limeheart' | CPou EGle ELan ERou LBro NHol |
| | NRoo NSti |
| N - 'Limelight' | Last listed 1997 |
| - 'Little Blue' (TB) | SCro |
| - 'Llangors' | LBro |
| - 'Llyn Brianne' | LBro |
| ¶ - 'Maranatha' | EFou |
| N - 'Marcus Perry' | CRow MSte |
| - 'Marilyn Holme's' | GGar MHlr WCot |
| - 'Marlene Ahlburg' | Last listed 1998 |
| - 'Marshmallow Frosting' | Last listed 1996 |
| § - 'Melton Red Flare' | SDys WCot |
| - 'Mikiko' ♀ | LBro |
| * - 'Moonlight' | NWoo |
| - 'Mrs Rowe' | CFee CPou CRow EFou EGar LBro |
| | LLWP MCAu MRav MSte SWat |
| | WLin WRus |
| - 'Mrs Saunders' | CRow WLin |
| ¶ - 'My Love' | WLin |
| - 'Navy Brass' | CRow EGle LBro SApp |
| - 'Nora Distin' | EGar WLin |
| - 'Nottingham Lace' | EGle LBro NBrk SWyc WBcn |
| | WCom |
| - 'Oban' ♀ | LBro |
| - 'Orville Fay' ♀ | EFou EGar LBro SApp SCro SLod |
| | WCot |
| - 'Ottawa' | CLTr CPou CRow ELan ERou |
| | MBNS MBri NRoo SCro SDys SPer |
| - 'Outset' | SCro |
| - 'Papillon' | CLTr CMGP ECGN EGle ELan |
| | ERou MCli MUlv MWat NBro |
| | NCat NFai NGdn NHol NRoo NSti |
| | SChu SLon SPer SSpi WLin WPer |
| | WRus WWat |
| N - 'Pearl Queen' | MTPN |
| - 'Perry's Blue' | More than 30 suppliers |
| I - 'Perry's Favourite' | CFee CRow |
| - 'Perry's Pigmy' | CRow GBuc MSte |
| - 'Persimmon' | CFir CRos EBee EGar EGle EMan |
| | EMou ERou GCHN MArl MCli |
| | MWat |
| - 'Pink Haze' | CHar CKel CRow EGar SCro |
| - 'Pirate Prince' | LBro NPer |
| - 'Pirouette' | Last listed 1998 |
| - 'Pontypool' | LBro |
| * - 'Pounsley Purple' | CPou |
| § - 'Primrose Cream' | CMea WCot |
| - 'Purpeller' | LBro |
| - 'Purple Cloak' | LBro MSte WBcn |
| - 'Purple Mere' | LBro WLin |
| - 'Rebeboth Gem' | Last listed 1997 |

| | | |
|---|---|---|
| N – 'Red Flag' | NHol | |
| – 'Reddy Maid' | LBro NBrk | |
| I – 'Redflare' | See *I. sibirica* 'Melton Red Flare' | |
| ¶ – 'Rejoice Always' | WTin | |
| – 'Rimouski' | LBro | |
| N – 'Roger Perry' | CFee CRow | |
| I – 'Royal Blue' | ECha GBuc | |
| – 'Ruffled Velvet' ♀ | CBlo CHar CHea CHid CKel EBee | |
| | EFou EGle LBro MBNS MCAu | |
| | MRav MSte NBrk NBro SCro WFar | |
| | WHoo | |
| – 'Ruffles Plus' | LBro | |
| – 'Sally Kerlin' | SCro | |
| – 'Savoir Faire' | CRDP ECha EGle LBro | |
| – 'Sea Horse' | NCat WLin | |
| – 'Sea Shadows' ♀ | EFou LBro MBel NBir NSti WCot | |
| | WLin | |
| – 'Shirley Pope' ♀ | EBrP EBre EGar LBre LBro LGre | |
| | MBri NPri SBre | |
| – 'Showdown' | EBee ECtt EGar LBro MCAu MUlv | |
| | NFai NHol SCro WWat | |
| N – 'Shrawley' | EGar | |
| – 'Silver Edge' ♀ | CHid CRos EBee EFou EGar GMac | |
| | LBlm LBro MBro MCAu MLLN | |
| | MTis MUlv NFai NHol SCro SUsu | |
| | SWat WEas WFar WHoo WPen | |
| – 'Sky Wings' | CRow EBee ECha EGle EMou | |
| | MArl | |
| – 'Snow Queen' | See *I. sanguinea* 'Snow Queen' | |
| – 'Snowcrest' | CBre EBee NBrk | |
| – 'Soft Blue' ♀ | LBro SCro | |
| N – 'Southcombe White' | COlW CRow CVer EGar GBuc | |
| | GCal LPio MBel NGdn SWas | |
| – 'Sparkling Rosé' | More than 30 suppliers | |
| – 'Splash Down' ♀ | Last listed 1995 | |
| ¶ – 'Steve' | EBrP EBre LBre SBre | |
| – 'Summer Sky' | EBla MCAu WCot WLin WTin | |
| | WViv | |
| – 'Super Ego' | WCot WTin | |
| – 'Superba' | WLin | |
| – 'Swank' | LBro | |
| – 'Teal Velvet' | LBro | |
| ¶ – 'Temper Tantrum' | CKel | |
| – 'The Gower' | Last listed 1998 | |
| – 'Thelma Perry' | WCot | |
| – 'Towanda Redflare' | EGle EHon ELan LBro SOkh WHer | |
| – 'Tropic Night' | CHad CHea CVer EBee ECGP | |
| | EFou EPla ERou GMac LGre LHop | |
| | MBel MBri MCAu MRav MSta | |
| | NBrk NHol NRoo NRya NSti SPer | |
| | SSoC WFar WHal WRus WWat | |
| – 'Tycoon' | CHid EBee IBlr NCat NChi NHol | |
| | SPer WLRN WLin | |
| ¶ – 'Velvet Night' | WLin | |
| – 'Vi Luihn' | CB&S ECha EGle LBro | |
| – 'Violetmere' | LBro WLin | |
| – 'Weisse Etagen' ♀ | SCro | |
| – 'Welcome Return' | Last listed 1997 | |
| – 'Welfenprinz' ♀ | Last listed 1995 | |
| – white | EGle | |
| – 'White Magnificence' | Last listed 1998 | |
| I – 'White Queen' | LBro SSvw | |
| * – 'White Swan' | EBee | |
| – 'White Swirl' | More than 30 suppliers | |
| – 'Wisley White' ♀ | EGle LBro NFai SRms | |
| – 'Zakopane' ♀ | Last listed 1995 | |
| § 'Sibirica Alba' | CRow ECGP ECha EHic EWTr | |
| | GDra GGar LLWP LPio SRms | |
| § 'Sibirica Baxteri' | CFee CRow | |
| **siboldii** | See *I. sanguinea* | |
| 'Sierra Grande' (TB) | LIri | |
| 'Sierra Nevada' (Spuria) | EFou LBro WBcn | |

| | | |
|---|---|---|
| 'Silent Strings' (IB) | LBro MBri | |
| ¶ 'Silhouette' (TB) | LIri | |
| 'Silicon Prairie' (TB) | LIri | |
| 'Silkirim' (TB) | LBro | |
| 'Silver Down' (SDB) | MCAu | |
| 'Silver Tide' (TB) | WEas | |
| 'Silverado' (TB) | LIri MCAu MMil SCro | |
| 'Silvery Moon' (TB) | SCro | |
| **sindjarensis** | See *I. aucheri* | |
| 'Sindpers' (Juno) ♀ | Last listed 1993 | |
| 'Sing Again' (IB) | CBlo | |
| **sintenisii** ♀ | CBro CHan CHid EHyt LBlm SIng | |
| 'Sister Helen' (TB) | MMil | |
| 'Siva Siva' (TB) | EBrP EBre ENot ERou LBre MCAu | |
| | MRav SBre WHer | |
| 'Skating Party' (TB) | LIri | |
| 'Skiers' Delight' (TB) | LIri MCAu SCro | |
| 'Skip Stitch' (SDB) | LBro | |
| 'Sky and Snow' (SDB) | Last listed 1997 | |
| 'Sky Hooks' (TB) | LIri SCro | |
| 'Sky Search' (TB) | LIri | |
| ¶ 'Skyblaze' (TB) | LIri | |
| 'Skyfire' (TB) | Last listed 1997 | |
| 'Slap Bang' (SDB) | NZep | |
| 'Sleepy Time' (MDB) | NZep | |
| 'Slim Jim' (MTB) | LBro | |
| 'Small Sky' (SDB) | CBro LBro | |
| 'Small Wonder' (SDB) | LBro | |
| N 'Smart Girl' (TB) | CKel | |
| 'Smarty Pants' (MTB) | LBro | |
| 'Smell the Roses' (SDB) | NZep | |
| 'Smiling Gold' (TB) | Last listed 1996 | |
| 'Smoke Rings' (TB) | SCro | |
| 'Smokey Dream' (TB) | CKel | |
| 'Smooth Orange' | See *I.* 'Orange Chariot' | |
| 'Sneak Preview' (TB) | Last listed 1998 | |
| 'Sno Jo' (SDB) | SCro | |
| 'Snow Elf' (SDB) | LBro | |
| 'Snow Festival' (IB) | MMil NZep | |
| 'Snow Fiddler' (MTB) | NZep | |
| 'Snow Tracery' (TB) | ENot MBri | |
| 'Snow Tree' (SDB) | NZep | |
| 'Snow Troll' (SDB) | MCAu MMil WWin | |
| 'Snowbrook' (TB) | LIri SCro | |
| 'Snowcone' (IB) | SCro | |
| 'Snowdrift' | See *I. laevigata* 'Snowdrift' | |
| 'Snowmound' (TB) | MCAu SCro | |
| 'Snowshill' (TB) | LBro | |
| 'Snowy Owl' (TB) ♀ | LBro MCAu | |
| 'Snowy River' (MDB) | NZep | |
| 'Snowy Wonderland' (TB) | Last listed 1998 | |
| 'Soaring Kite' (TB) ♀ | LBro | |
| 'Social Event' (TB) | LIri | |
| 'Social Register' (TB) | Last listed 1998 | |
| 'Soft Breeze' (SDB) | NZep | |
| ¶ 'Soft Caress' (TB) | LIri | |
| ¶ 'Solar Wind' (AB) | WWst | |
| 'Solid Gold' (TB) | Last listed 1997 | |
| 'Solid Mahogany' (TB) | MCAu MMil MRav | |
| 'Somerset Blue' (TB) | CKel | |
| 'Somerset Girl' (TB) | CKel | |
| N 'Somerset Vale' (TB) | CKel | |
| * 'Somerton Brocade' (SDB) | CKel | |
| * 'Somerton Gold' (SDB) | CKel | |
| 'Song of Norway' (TB) ♀ | MCAu MMil NZep SCro WBcn | |
| 'Song of Spring' (TB) | Last listed 1996 | |
| 'Sonja's Selah' (TB) | LIri | |
| 'Sonoran Senorita' (Spuria) | LBro | |
| ¶ 'Sooner Serenade' (TB) | LIri | |
| ¶ 'Sostenique' (TB) | MCAu | |
| ¶ 'Soul Power' (TB) | ERou | |
| 'Sounder' (BB) | Last listed 1996 | |

'Southern Clipper' (SDB)    LRHS MBri
'Souvenir de Madame
   Gaudichau' (TB)    CKel
sp.AGSJ 431    EWoo
sp. CLD 1399    Last listed 1996
'Space Mist' (TB)    Last listed 1998
'Spanish Coins' (MTB)    LBro NZep
'Spanish Lime' (Spuria)    LBro
'Sparkling Cloud' (SDB)    EGle WWin
'Spartan'    CKel
N 'Specify' (TB)    Last listed 1998
'Spiced Custard' (TB)    SCro
'Spin-off' (TB)    SCro
'Spirit of Memphis' (TB)    MMil
'Splash of Red' (SDB)    LBro MMil NZep
'Split Decision' (SDB)    NZep
'Spring Bells' (SDB)    EFou
'Spring Dancer' (TB)    SCro
'Spring Festival' (TB)    CKel
'Spring Signal' (TB)    LBro
'Spring Wine' (IB)    Last listed 1996
'Springtime' (Reticulata)    LAma NRog WSan
*spuria*    CPou ECGP ELan MUlv SWyc
   - subsp. *carthaliniae*    NSti WPer
   - subsp. *demetrii*    Last listed 1996
§    - subsp. *halophila*    LBro MCAu
   - subsp. *maritima*    SIng
§    - subsp. *musulmanica*    LBro NTow
   - subsp. *notha* CC 1550    MRPP SGre
   - subsp. *ochroleuca*    See *I. orientalis*
   - subsp. *sogdiana*    Last listed 1997
N 'Spuria Alba'    SWyc
'Spyglass Hill' (TB)    Last listed 1997
x *squalens*    LBro
'Squeaky Clean' (SDB)    Last listed 1997
'Stability' (Spuria)    Last listed 1996
'Stapleford' (SDB)    CBro EGle
'Star Sailor' (TB)    SCro
'Star Shine' (TB)    MCAu
'Starcrest' (TB)    LIri SCro
'Starlit River' (TB)    Last listed 1996
'Starry Eyed' (SDB)    EGle LBro
'Startler' (TB)    SCro
'Staten Island' (TB)    CKel ELan ENot MBri MCAu MMil
   SRms
¶ 'Status Seeker' (TB)    LIri
'Stella Polaris' (TB)    SCro
'Stellar Lights' (TB)    Last listed 1997
'Step by Step' (BB)    Last listed 1997
'Stepping Little' (BB)    Last listed 1996
'Stepping Out' (TB) ♀    EBrP EBre EFou LBre LIri MBri
   SBre SCro
'Sterling Prince' (TB)    Last listed 1997
'Stitch in Time' (TB)    MCAu SCro
'Stockholm' (SDB)    CKel NZep
*stolonifera*    Last listed 1998
   - 'George Barr'    Last listed 1996
'Stop the Music' (TB)    SCro
N 'Storrington' (TB)    SCro
'Storybook' (TB)    SCro
'Strange Child' (SDB)    NZep
'Stratagem' (TB)    LIri
'Strawberry Love' (IB)    MMil
'Strawberry Sensation' (TB)    NZep
¶ 'Stylish' (DB)    ETub
*stylosa*    See *I. unguicularis*
'Suave' (TB)    SCro
§ *suaveolens*    CBro EPot LPio MBro NLar NMen
   NNrd WIvy
*    - var. *flavescens*    WWst
   - 'Rubromarginata'    ERos
*    - var. *violacea*    WWst

*subbiflora*    Last listed 1998
'Sudeley' (SDB)    SCro
'Sugar' (IB)    MCAu NSti
'Sugar Candy' (CH)    LBro WWst
'Sullom Voe' (TB)    Last listed 1996
'Sultan's Palace' (TB)    CKel SCro
'Sultry Mood' (TB)    LIri
'Sultry Sister' (TB)    Last listed 1996
'Summer Luxury' (TB)    NMGW NZep
'Sumptuous' (TB)    SCro
'Sun Dappled' (TB)    ERou MMil
'Sun Doll' (SDB)    NZep
'Sun King' (TB)    MCAu WWeb
'Sun Miracle' (TB) ♀    Last listed 1993
'Sun Symbol' (SDB)    Last listed 1996
'Sunday Chimes' (TB)    SCro
'Sundown Red' (IB)    NBir
'Sunlit Sea' (Spuria)    LBro
'Sunny Dawn' (IB) ♀    LBro
'Sunny Day' (Spuria) ♀    LBro
'Sunny Heart' (SDB)    Last listed 1997
'Sunny Honey' (IB)    NZep SCro
'Sunny Side' (Spuria)    Last listed 1996
'Sunny Smile' (IB) ♀    Last listed 1995
'Sunset Fires' (TB)    Last listed 1996
'Sunset Sky' (TB)    Last listed 1997
'Sunset Trail' (AB)    Last listed 1996
'Sunshine Isle' (SDB)    MMil NZep
'Superlation' (TB)    SCro
'Superstition' (TB) ♀    EFou LIri MCAu MMil SCro
'Supreme Sultan' (TB)    SCro
'Surprise Orange' (MDB)    NZep
'Susan Bliss' (TB)    CKel EBee ELan EPfP GMaP
   MCAu NFai SMer
*susiana*    EBot LAma
'Suspense' (Spuria)    Last listed 1996
'Svelte' (IB)    Last listed 1996
'Swahili' (TB)    Last listed 1996
¶ 'Swaledale' (TB)    MCAu
'Swazi Princess' (TB)    CKel SCro
'Sweertii'    Last listed 1997
'Sweet Kate' (SDB) ♀    MCAu
'Sweet Musette' (TB)    MCAu SCro
'Sweet 'n' Neat' (SDB)    SCro
'Sweeter than Wine' (TB)    SCro
¶ 'Swing and Sway' (TB)    LIri
'Swizzle' (IB)    LBro
'Sybil'    Last listed 1998
'Syllable' (SDB)    Last listed 1998
'Sylvia Murray' (TB)    MCAu
'Symphony' (Dutch)    Last listed 1996
'Syncopation' (TB)    LBro
'Tall Chief' (TB)    EBrP EBre LBre MCAu NBrk SBre
   SCro
'Tall Ships' (TB)    LIri
'Tan Tingo' (IB)    EFou
'Tangerine Sky' (TB)    MCAu SCro
'Tangerine Sunrise' (TB) ♀    LBro
'Tantara' (SDB)    SCro
*taochia*    Last listed 1998
*    - *flava*    WWst
¶ 'Tarheel Elf' (SDB)    WTin
'Tarn Hows' (TB)    MCAu SRms
'Taupkin' (SDB)    LBro
*tauri*    See *I. stenophylla*
'Tease' (SDB)    Last listed 1997
*tectorum*    CSWP ERos GSki MHar MNrw
   WHil
   - 'Alba'    CKel CPou EHic
   - Burma form    Last listed 1997
   - 'Variegata'    EHic EPla MBrn MCCP MRav SVil
'Tell Fibs' (SDB)    CBro EGle

| | |
|---|---|
| 'Temple Gold' (TB) | CKel |
| 'Temple Meads' (IB) | CKel |
| 'Templecloud' (IB) ♀ | CKel |
| 'Ten' (SDB) | NZep SCro |
| § *tenax* | CBlo CLAP CNic ECho GSki MBal |
| – 'Alba' | SIng |
| 'Tennessee Vol' (TB) | LIri |
| 'Tennessee Woman' (TB) | LIri |
| *tenuis* | Last listed 1998 |
| *tenuissima* | MRPP |
| I 'Tequila Sunrise' (TB) | Last listed 1996 |
| 'The Bride' | See *I.* 'Bride' |
| 'The Citadel' (TB) | CKel SCro |
| N 'The Monarch' (TB) | Last listed 1998 |
| 'The Rocket' | See *I.* 'Rocket' |
| 'Theatre' (TB) | MMil SCro |
| 'Theda Clark' (IB) | SCro |
| 'Theseus' (Aril) | Last listed 1998 |
| 'Third Charm' (SDB) | CBro |
| 'Third World' (SDB) | CBro |
| ¶ *thompsonii* | EPot |
| 'Thornbird' (TB) | LIri |
| 'Thousand Lakes' (SDB) | NZep |
| 'Three Cherries' (MDB) | CBro EGle |
| 'Thrice Blessed' (SDB) | Last listed 1996 |
| 'Thriller' (TB) | LIri MMil NZep |
| 'Throb' (TB) | LIri |
| *thunbergii* | See *I. sanguinea* |
| 'Thunder Mountain' (TB) | Last listed 1998 |
| 'Thundercloud' (TB) | MCAu |
| 'Tide's In' (TB) | ERou SCro |
| 'Tidle de Winks' (BB) | Last listed 1996 |
| 'Tiger Butter' (TB) | Last listed 1997 |
| 'Tiger Honey' (TB) | LIri |
| 'Tillamook' (TB) | MCAu |
| 'Time for Love' (TB) | NZep |
| 'Timeless Moment' (TB) | SCro |
| 'Timmie Too' (BB) | LBro |
| *tingitana* var. *fontanesii* | Last listed 1998 |
| AB&S 4452 | |
| – SB&L 218 | Last listed 1998 |
| 'Tinkerbell' (SDB) | CKel COtt CPBP EGle EMan LGre NLak SChu SCro WGwG WLRN WWal WWin |
| 'Tinted Crystal' (TB) | Last listed 1997 |
| 'Tintinara' (TB) ♀ | CKel |
| 'Tiny Freckles' (MDB) | NZep |
| 'Tirra Lirra' (SDB) ♀ | LBro MMil |
| 'Titan's Glory' (TB) ♀ | CKel LBro LIri MCAu MHlr MRav SCro WCot |
| ¶ Tol-Long | IHdy |
| 'Tom Tit' (TB) | Last listed 1998 |
| 'Tomingo' (SDB) | Last listed 1998 |
| 'Tomorrow's Child' (TB) | SCro |
| 'Toni Lynn' (MDB) | Last listed 1998 |
| 'Toots' (SDB) | EGle LBro |
| 'Top Flight' (TB) | EHic ENot ERou SRms WElm WLRN |
| N 'Topolino' (TB) | CKel WBcn |
| 'Topsy Turvy' (MTB) | LBro |
| 'Torchlight' (TB) | Last listed 1998 |
| 'Tornado' (AB) | Last listed 1996 |
| ¶ 'Tornado Watcher' (AB) | WWst |
| 'Total Eclipse' | SRms |
| 'Touch of Spring' (TB) | MMil |
| 'Toy Boat' (SDB) | NMGW |
| 'Transcribe' (SDB) | Last listed 1996 |
| ¶ 'Treasure' (TB) | MCAu |
| 'Trevaunance Cove' (TB) | LBro |
| ¶ 'Triffid' (TB) | LIri |
| 'Triplicate' (SDB) | LGre MBri |
| *trojana* | EWes LBro SIng |

| | |
|---|---|
| 'Truly' (SDB) | SCro |
| ¶ 'Trust' (TB) | LIri |
| 'Tu Tu Turquoise' (SDB) | NZep |
| *tuberosa* | See *Hermodactylus tuberosus* |
| 'Tumbleweeds' (SDB) | NZep |
| 'Turkish Warrior' (AB) | Last listed 1996 |
| N 'Tuscan' (TB) | CKel WBcn |
| 'Tut's Gold' (TB) | SCro |
| 'Twice Thrilling' (TB) | LIri |
| 'Twist of Fate' (TB) | SCro |
| 'Two Rubies' (SDB) | NZep |
| 'Tyke' (MTB) | NZep |
| *typhifolia* | Last listed 1997 |
| 'Ultimatum' (TB) | LIri |
| 'Ultra Pretty' (TB) | SCoo |
| 'Unfurled Flag' | Last listed 1997 |
| § *unguicularis* ♀ | More than 30 suppliers |
| – 'Abington Purple' | CAvo CBro EBee |
| – 'Alba' | CAvo CBro ECha |
| N – 'Bob Thompson' | CAvo ECha |
| – broken form | CMea MHlr WCot |
| – subsp. *carica* | |
| var. *angustifolia* | IBlr SWas |
| § – subsp. *cretensis* | EHyt EPot |
| – – MS 720 | Last listed 1998 |
| – – S&L 478 | Last listed 1998 |
| – – S&L 550 | Last listed 1998 |
| N – 'Francis Wormsley' | ECha MRav |
| – JCA 600.412 | Last listed 1998 |
| – L&R 65 | Last listed 1998 |
| – var. *lazica* | See *I. lazica* |
| – 'Mary Barnard' | CAvo CBro CFee CGle CHar CPou CSam CSev ECha GCHN LBro MBro MRav NLar NMen SCob SIng SWas WByw WGwG WLin WRus |
| N – 'Oxford Dwarf' | CBro ECho |
| – 'Palette' | ELan |
| – 'Unguicularis Marginata' | LBro |
| § – 'Walter Butt' | CAvo CGle ECha IHdy MRav NBir SBla SWas WCot WFar WRus |
| *uniflora* var. *caricina* | MNrw WCot |
| *urmiensis* | See *I. barnumae* f. *urmiensis* |
| *uromovii* | MArl MBro WHoo WPyg |
| 'Vague a l'Ame' (TB) | Last listed 1996 |
| 'Vamp' (IB) | CKel |
| 'Vanity' (TB) ♀ | LBro NZep SCro |
| 'Vanity's Child' (TB) | ERou |
| § *variegata* ♀ | CMea CRDP EPar GCal MCAu NLar SIng SUsu WWst |
| – var. *pontica* | SCro |
| 'Vegas Showgirl' (SDB) | NZep |
| 'Velvet Bouquet' (MTB) | LBro |
| 'Vera' (AB) | EPot ETub |
| *verna* | CGle EPot NHol |
| *versicolor* ♀ | CArn CBen CRow EGol EHon EMFW EPar IBlr LBro LPBA MHew MNrw MSal MSta NDea NGdn SDix SPlb SRms SWyc WOak WShi |
| – 'Between the Lines' | CRow |
| N – 'Blue Light' | CBlo WViv |
| – 'Dottie's Double' | CRow |
| N – 'Goldbrook' | EGol |
| – 'Kermesina' | CRDP CRow ECha EGol EHon ELan EMFW EPar GCal GGar IBlr MSta NDea NGdn NRoo NSti SRms SWat WEas WRus |
| – 'Mysterious Monique' | CRDP CRow |
| – 'Party Line' | CRow |
| – purple | CRow |
| – var. *rosea* | CRow |

| | | |
|---|---|---|
| * | - 'Signagoniga Ridska' | NCat |
| | - 'Silvington' | CRow |
| | - 'Version' | CRow LBlm |
| | *vicaria* | Last listed 1998 |
| | 'Victor Herbert' (TB) | SCro |
| | 'Victoria Falls' (TB) | MCAu SCro |
| | 'Vigilante' (TB) | LIri |
| | 'Viking Princess' (TB) | Last listed 1997 |
| | 'Vim' (SDB) | Last listed 1996 |
| | 'Vinho Verde' (IB) ♀ | Last listed 1995 |
| | 'Vintage Year' (Spuria) | LBro |
| | *violacea* | See *I. spuria* subsp. *musulmanica* |
| | 'Violet Beauty' (Reticulata) | EPot LAma MMal |
| | 'Violet Classic' (TB) | EFou MMil |
| | 'Violet Icing' (TB) ♀ | CKel LBro |
| | 'Violet Lass' (SDB) | NZep |
| | 'Violet Lulu' (SDB) | Last listed 1997 |
| | 'Violet Miracle' (TB) | MMil |
| N | 'Violet Zephyr' (Spuria) | Last listed 1996 |
| I | 'Violetta' (DB) | Last listed 1996 |
| I | *virginica* 'Crown Point' | CRow |
| | - 'De Luxe' | See *I.* x *robusta* 'Dark Aura' |
| I | - 'Lilac Dream' | CRow |
| N | - 'Purple Fan' | CRow |
| § | - var. *shrevei* | CRow |
| | 'Visual Arts' (TB) | SCro |
| | 'Vitality' (IB) | SCro |
| | 'Vivien' (TB) | SCro |
| | 'Voila' (IB) | EFou LBro NZep |
| | 'Voltage' (TB) | LIri |
| | 'Volts' (SDB) | LBro |
| | 'Wabash' (TB) | CBlo EBrP EBre ERou LBre LBro MCAu MMil SBre |
| | 'Walter Butt' | See *I. unguicularis* 'Walter Butt' |
| | 'War Sails' (TB) | Last listed 1997 |
| | 'Warleggan' (TB) ♀ | LBro |
| ¶ | *warleyensis* | WWst |
| | 'Warrior King' (TB) | Last listed 1997 |
| | 'Watchman' (AB) | Last listed 1996 |
| | 'Waterboy' (SDB) | NZep |
| | 'Watercolor' (SDB) | NZep |
| | *wattii* | GCal |
| ¶ | - 'Trengwainton' | WWst |
| | 'Webelos' (SDB) | CLon EGle LBro LGre MBri MBro |
| | 'Wedding Candles' (TB) | SCro |
| | 'Wedgwood' (Dut) | Last listed 1998 |
| * | 'Wedgwood Blue' (Sino-sib) | NWoo |
| | 'Well Endowed' (TB) | Last listed 1997 |
| | 'Wenlock' (IB) | MCAu |
| | 'Wensleydale' (TB) ♀ | Last listed 1995 |
| | 'West Vale' (IB) | LBro |
| | 'Westar' (SDB) | NZep |
| | 'Westwell' (SDB) | MCAu |
| | 'Wharfedale' (TB) ♀ | Last listed 1995 |
| | 'What Again' (SDB) | SCro |
| | 'White Bridge' (Dut) | NRog |
| | 'White Canary' (MTB) | LBro |
| | 'White City' (TB) | CHad CMGP EGle EMan EOrc EPfP ERav EWTr LBro MMil MWat NGdn NPer SChu SCob SRms SWat |
| | 'White Excelsior' (Dut) | CB&S LAma |
| | 'White Gem' (SDB) | WWin |
| | 'White Heron' (Spuria) | LBro |
| | 'White Knight' (TB) | ELan EPfP SMer WCot |
| | 'White Superior' (Dut) | Last listed 1996 |
| | 'White van Vliet' (Dut) | NRog |
| | 'White Wedgwood' (Dut) | SHel |
| | 'Whiteladies' (IB) ♀ | LBro |
| | 'Whoop 'em Up' (BB) | LBro NZep |
| | 'Why Not' (IB) | NMGW NZep WBcn |

| | | |
|---|---|---|
| | 'Widecombe Fair' (SDB) | WWin |
| | 'Widget' (MTB) | LBro |
| | 'Wild Dancer' (TB) | SCoo |
| N | 'Wild Echo' (TB) | CKel |
| | 'Wild Ginger' (TB) | NOla WWeb |
| | 'Wild Thing' (TB) | SCro |
| | 'Wild West' (TB) | Last listed 1997 |
| | *willmottiana* | Last listed 1997 |
| | - 'Alba' | EPot |
| | 'Willow Ware' (IB) | SCro |
| | 'Willowmist' (SDB) | NZep |
| | *wilsonii* ♀ | CVer GBuc MMil SSpi |
| | - 'Gelbe Mantel' | See *I.* 'Gelbe Mantel' |
| ¶ | 'Windrider' (AB) | WWst |
| | 'Windrose' (SDB) | NZep |
| | 'Windsor Rose' (TB) | CHar SCro |
| ¶ | 'Wine and Lilac' (AB) | WWst |
| | 'Winged Melody' (TB) | MBri |
| | *winogradowii* ♀ | CBro EHyt ERos GCrs LAma MTho NHar SDix WAbe |
| | 'Winter Olympics' (TB) | EFou |
| | 'Wirral Gold' ♀ | Last listed 1995 |
| | 'Wisteria Sachet' (IB) | Last listed 1998 |
| | 'Witch of Endor' (TB) | MMil |
| | 'Witch's Wand' (TB) | LIri |
| | 'Wizard of Id' (SDB) | EGle NZep WTin |
| | 'Woodling' (SDB) | Last listed 1996 |
| | 'World News' (TB) | SCro |
| | 'Wow' (SDB) | EGle EHyt LBro |
| N | 'Wright's Pink' (SDB) | Last listed 1998 |
| | 'Wyckhill' (SDB) | LBro |
| | 'Wyevale' (TB) | LBro |
| | *xanthospuria* LT 10 | Last listed 1998 |
| | *xiphioides* | See *I. latifolia* |
| | *xiphium* | EBee SSpi |
| ¶ | - 'Lusitanica' | EBee EHyt |
| | 'Yellow Girl' (SDB) | NMGW NZep |
| | 'Yellow Queen' (Dut) | SHel |
| | 'Yo-yo' (SDB) | NZep |
| | 'Yvonne Pelletier' (TB) | MCAu |
| | 'Zantha' (TB) | CKel |
| | 'Zeeland' (BB) | LBro |
| | 'Zink Pink' (BB) | SCro |
| | 'Zipper' (MDB) | Last listed 1996 |
| | 'Zowie' (SDB) | NZep |
| | 'Zua' (IB) | LGre MTed SCro |
| | 'Zulu Chief' (Spuria) | Last listed 1997 |
| | 'Zwanenburg Beauty' | Last listed 1997 |

## ISATIS (Brassicaceae)

| | |
|---|---|
| *tinctoria* | CArn CSev EOHP EWFC GPoy ILis LHol MChe MHew MSal SIde WCHb WHbs WHer WJek WOak WPer WSel WWye |

## ISCHYROLEPIS (Restionaceae)

| | | |
|---|---|---|
| ¶ | *ocreata* | LHil WNor |
| § | *subverticillata* | Last listed 1998 |

## ISMENE See HYMENOCALLIS

## ISOLEPIS (Cyperaceae)

| | | |
|---|---|---|
| § | *cernua* | CHal EMFW MBri MCCP |

## ISOLOMA See KOHLERIA

## ISOMERIS See CLEOME

## ISOPLEXIS (Scrophulariaceae)

| | | |
|---|---|---|
| | *canariensis* | CAbb CBot CFil CSpe LEur SHFr SSoC SUsu WEas |
| * | *isabelliana* | CFil WCot |

| | |
|---|---|
| *sceptrum* | CBot CFil CFir CHan CSpe GSki SAPC SArc SIgm SSoC WCot |

## ISOPOGON (Proteaceae)
| | |
|---|---|
| *anethifolius* | Last listed 1998 |
| *dubius* | Last listed 1997 |

## ISOPYRUM (Ranunculaceae)
| | |
|---|---|
| § *nipponicum* | |
| var. *sarmentosum* | Last listed 1997 |
| *ohwianum* | See *I. nipponicum* var. *sarmentosum* |
| *thalictroides* | CGle EPot |

## ISOTOMA (Campanulaceae)
| | |
|---|---|
| *axillaris* | See *Laurentia axillaris* |
| * 'Fairy Carpet' | CLTr |

## ISOTOMA See SOLENOPSIS

## ITEA (Escalloniaceae)
| | |
|---|---|
| *ilicifolia* ♀ | More than 30 suppliers |
| *japonica* 'Beppu' | MGos SLPl |
| *virginica* | CB&S CDoC CLTr CMCN CMHG CPle CWit ELan EWTr MBal MBlu MGos MRav NArg SBid SLon SPer WBod WDin WHCG WPGP WSHC WTro WWat |
| § - 'Henry's Garnet' | CDoC CFai CMCN CPMA CWSG EBee MBlu SBrw SRPl WCwm WWes |
| - 'Sarah Eve' | CMCN |
| - Swarthmore form | See *I. virginica* 'Henry's Garnet' |
| *yunnanensis* | IOrc |

## ITOA (Flacourtiaceae)
| | |
|---|---|
| *orientalis* SF 92300 | ISea |

## IVESIA (Rosaceae)
| | |
|---|---|
| *gordonii* | NWCA |
| *pygmaea* | Last listed 1998 |

## IXIA (Iridaceae)
| | |
|---|---|
| Bird of Paradise | See *I.* 'Paradijsvogel' |
| 'Blue Bird' | LAma |
| 'Castor' | Last listed 1998 |
| *flexuosa* | NRog |
| 'Hogarth' | LAma |
| hybrids | SDeJ |
| 'Mabel' | NRog |
| *maculata* | NRog |
| 'Marquette' | NRog |
| *monadelpha* | LBow |
| *paniculata* | LBow NRog |
| § 'Paradijsvogel' | LAma |
| *polystachya* | LBow NRog |
| 'Rose Emperor' | LAma NRog |
| ¶ *thomasiae* | WCot |
| 'Venus' | LAma |
| *viridiflora* | CAvo WCot |

## IXIOLIRION (Amaryllidaceae)
| | |
|---|---|
| *pallasii* | See *I. tataricum* |
| § *tataricum* | EBee LAma MBri NRog WShe WViv |
| - Ledebourii Group | CAvo LAma |

## IXORA (Rubiaceae)
| | |
|---|---|
| *chinensis* 'Apricot Queen' | SOWG |
| *coccinea* | ECon |
| 'Golden Ball' | SOWG |
| 'Pink Malay' | SOWG |

# J

## JABOROSA (Solanaceae)
| | |
|---|---|
| *integrifolia* | CFir EBee ELan GCal MNrw MTed WCot WCru WPGP |
| *magellanica* | Last listed 1996 |
| *squarrosa* F&W 7836 | EWes |

## JACARANDA (Bignoniaceae)
| | |
|---|---|
| *acutifolia* Kunth | MBri |
| - hort. | See *J. mimosifolia* |
| § *mimosifolia* | CB&S ECon ERea GQui LCns SOWG |

## JACOBINIA See JUSTICIA

## JAMESBRITTENIA (Scrophulariaceae)
| | |
|---|---|
| ¶ *breviflora* JCA 3-810-200 | EHyt |
| § *grandiflora* | CSpe |
| § *jurassica* | EHyt NMen |

## JAMESIA (Hydrangeaceae)
| | |
|---|---|
| *americana* | CPle WAbe WWin |

## JASIONE (Campanulaceae)
| | |
|---|---|
| *amethystina* | Last listed 1997 |
| § *crispa* | Last listed 1998 |
| § *heldreichii* | GAbr MBro NNrd NRoo SBla SRms WElm WPyg WWin |
| *humilis* | See *J. crispa* subsp. *amethystina* |
| *jankae* | See *J. heldreichii* |
| § *laevis* | ECot ELan LRot NBro SAga SRms SSca |
| § - 'Blaulicht' | CMCo EBee ECha EMan EMar EPfP ESis MBNS MBri MWgw NBrk NLar SLod WMoo WMow WOve WPer WRos WWal |
| - Blue Light | See *J. laevis* 'Blaulicht' |
| *montana* | CMea EWFC MChe SSca WCla WHer |
| *perennis* | See *J. laevis* |
| sp. from Spain | Last listed 1996 |

## JASMINUM ✿ (Oleaceae)
| | |
|---|---|
| *angulare* | CGre CPIN CRHN EHol EMil ERea SOWG |
| *azoricum* ♀ | CB&S CGre CPIN CRHN ECon ELan EPfP ERea GQui LCns LRHS NPal WMul |
| *beesianum* | More than 30 suppliers |
| *bignoniaceum* | CPIN |
| *floridum* | CPIN EWes |
| *fruticans* | CMac CPle ELan EPla WCru |
| - HH&K 126 | CHan |
| *grandiflorum* 'De Grasse' | CPIN ERea LCns SOWG |
| *humile* | CBlo CPle GOrc GSki IBlr IMGH SHFr WBod WFar WKif WPic |
| - B&L 12086 | Last listed 1996 |
| - f. *farreri* | WCru |
| § - 'Revolutum' ♀ | More than 30 suppliers |
| - f. *wallichianum* | CPle |
| - - B&SWJ 2987 | WCru |
| § *laurifolium* f. *nitidum* | CPIN ERea LChe |
| § *mesnyi* ♀ | CGre CMac CPIN CPle EBak ECtt ELan ERea IOrc LBlm NBea SBra SOWG SSta SYvo WCot WSHC |
| *multipartitum* | CSpe |
| *nitidum* | See *J. laurifolium* f. *nitidum* |

§ **nobile** subsp. *rex* — CPIN LChe
**nudiflorum** ♀ — More than 30 suppliers
- 'Argenteum' — See *J. nudiflorum* 'Mystique'
- 'Aureum' — EBee ELan EPla GQui MAsh MCCP MRav NHol NSti SPer SPla WCot WHCG WPat
\* - 'Compactum' — MAsh
§ - 'Mystique' (v) — CPMA EBee ELan EPfP LRHS MAsh SMur SPer WCot WPat
- 'Nanum' — ELan MBro NHol WPat
**odoratissimum** — ERea LCns SOWG
**officinale** ♀ — More than 30 suppliers
§ - f. *affine* — CB&S CRHN CSam CTri EBrP EBre ELan ENot EOrc EPla ERea IOrc LBre LPri MAsh MRav NHol SBre SDix SEas SMad SRms WCru WWeb
§ - 'Argenteovariegatum' ♀ — CArn CB&S CBot CHar EAst EBee ECha EHoe ELan EPla GQui LHop MAsh MBri MGos NHol SBra SHFr SMad SPar SPer SPla SSta WCot WPat WSHC WWat WWeb
- 'Aureovariegatum' — See *J. officinale* 'Aureum'
§ - 'Aureum' — More than 30 suppliers
¶ - CC 1709 — WCot
- 'Devon Cream' — SPar
- Fiona Sunrise = 'Frojas' — More than 30 suppliers
- 'Grandiflorum' — See *J. officinale* f. *affine*
- 'Inverleith' — CDoC EAst EBee EHic ELan GCal GOrc LHop MBNS MBri MCCP MRav NFai SBra SCoo SMad SPan SPla SSoC SVil WGwG WWal
- 'Variegatum' — See *J. officinale* 'Argenteovariegatum'
**parkeri** — CB&S CBot CFee EHyt EMil EPla ESis GOrc IMGH LHop MAsh MBNS MBlu MBro MPla MUlv NHol NNrd SIde SIgm SIng SSta WAbe WCru WFar WPat WPyg WWat
**polyanthum** ♀ — CArn CB&S CPIN CRHN CTri CTrw EBak EBee ELan ERea ERom GQui ISea LBlm LHop MBri NBea NRog SRms
**primulinum** — See *J. mesnyi*
**reevesii** — See *J. humile* 'Revolutum'
**rex** — See *J. nobile* subsp. *rex*
**sambac** — CB&S CPIN ECon ELan EPfP LChe LCns LPri LRHS NPal SOWG SYvo WMul
- 'Grand Duke of Tuscany' — ERea LChe SOWG
- 'Maid of Orleans' — ERea LChe SOWG
§ **simplicifolium** — CPIN
subsp. *australiense*
§ - subsp. *suavissimum* — SVen
x **stephanense** ♀ — More than 30 suppliers
**suavissimum** — See *J. simplicifolium* subsp. *suavissimum*
**tortuosum** — CPIN
**volubile** — See *J. simplicifolium* subsp. *australiense*

## JATROPHA (Euphorbiaceae)
¶ **integerrima** — ECon
**multifida** — Last listed 1997
**podagrica** — ECon LChe

## JEFFERSONIA (Berberidaceae)
**diphylla** — CArn CBro CElw CGle CHid EBee EPar IBlr LAma MDun MSal MTho NBir NHar NHol NRog NRya SBla SWas WAbe WCru WFar WWat

**dubia** — EHyt EPot EWes GCrs IBlr NBir NMen NRog NTow SBla SIgm SWas WCru
- 'Alba' — SBla

## JOHANNESTEIJSMANNIA (Arecaceae)
**lanceolata** — LPal
**magnifica** — LPal

## JOVELLANA (Scrophulariaceae)
**punctata** — CGre CPle LHil MBlu
**repens** — CFir ECou IBlr IDac WCot
**sinclairii** — CGle CPin ECou EHyt IBlr SSpi SUsu WCot WCru
**violacea** ♀ — CAbP CAbb CB&S CGle CPle CSpe CWit EMil ERea GCal IBlr ISea ITim LHil LHop MBal SAPC SArc SBid SDry SYvo WBod WPic WSHC

## JOVIBARBA ✿ (Crassulaceae)
§ **allionii** — CMea CTri CWil EPot LBee MBro MOne SIng SSmi WAbe WPer WWin
- x *hirta* — CWil GAbr MBro MOne NHol NNrd SDys SSmi
- x - 'Oki' — CWil MOne
- x *sobolifera* — SSmi
§ **arenaria** — CWil ESis GAbr GCHN MBro MDHE MOne MRPP NMen SIng SSmi
- from Murtal — MDHE SSmi
¶ - from Passo Monte Crocecar Nico — CWil
'Emerald Spring' — CWil
§ **heuffelii** — CWil NHol NMen NPri WPer
- 'Aga' — Last listed 1998
¶ - 'Aiolos' — NHol
- 'Alemene' — Last listed 1998
- 'Almkroon' — Last listed 1998
- 'Angel Wings' — CWil
- 'Apache' — Last listed 1998
- 'Aquarius' — CWil
- 'Artemis' — Last listed 1998
- 'Beacon Hill' — CWil MBro
- 'Belcore' — CWil
¶ - 'Benjamin' — NHol
- 'Bermuda' — CWil
- 'Bermuda Sunset' — NHol
- 'Brandaris' — NHol
¶ - 'Brocade' — NHol
- 'Bronze Ingot' — CWil
- 'Bronze King' — Last listed 1996
- 'Bros' — Last listed 1998
- 'Chocoleto' — CWil WTin
- 'Cleopatra' — Last listed 1998
- 'Copper King' — Last listed 1998
- 'Cythera' — Last listed 1998
¶ - 'Dunbar Road' — NHol
- 'Fandango' — CWil
- 'Gento' — CWil NHol
¶ - 'Geronimo' — NHol
- 'Giuseppi Spiny' — CWil NHol
- var. *glabra* — Last listed 1998
- - from Anabakanak — CWil NHol WTin
- - from Anthoborio — CWil NMen WTin
- - from Backovo — Last listed 1998
- - from Bansko Vihren — CWil NMen
- - from Galicica — Last listed 1998
- - from Haila — CWil NMen
- - from Jakupica, Macedonia — CWil NMen
- - from Kapaenianum — WTin

| | |
|---|---|
| – – from Koprovnik | CWil |
| – – from Kosovo, Yugoslavia | Last listed 1998 |
| – – from Ljuboten | CWil NMen WTin |
| – – from Osljak | Last listed 1998 |
| – – from Pasina Glava | CWil |
| – – from Pelister | Last listed 1998 |
| – – from Rhodope | CWil NHol |
| – – from Stogovo | Last listed 1998 |
| – – from Treska Gorge, Macedonia | CWil MBro WTin |
| – – from Vitse | CWil |
| ¶ – 'Gold Rand' | NHol |
| – 'Goya' | Last listed 1998 |
| – 'Grand Slam' | Last listed 1998 |
| * – 'Green Land' | CWil |
| – 'Greenstone' | CWil MBro NHol NMen WTin |
| – 'Harmony' | Last listed 1998 |
| – 'Helena' | Last listed 1998 |
| – 'Henry Correvon' | CWil |
| – 'Iason' | Last listed 1998 |
| – 'Ikaros' | Last listed 1998 |
| – 'Inferno' | CWil NHol |
| – 'Iole' | Last listed 1998 |
| – 'Iuno' | CWil |
| – 'Jade' | CWil NMen |
| – 'Kapo' | Last listed 1998 |
| – var. *kopaonikensis* | CWil NMen |
| – 'Mary Ann' | Last listed 1998 |
| – 'Miller's Violet' | CWil |
| – 'Minuta' | CWil NHol NMen WTin |
| – 'Mont Rose' | Last listed 1998 |
| – 'Mystique' | CWil MBro |
| – 'Nannette' | Last listed 1998 |
| – 'Nobel' | Last listed 1998 |
| ¶ – 'Opele' | NHol |
| – 'Orion' | CWil NMen |
| – 'Pampero' | Last listed 1998 |
| – 'Passat' | Last listed 1998 |
| – var. *patens* | MOne |
| – 'Pink Skies' | MBro |
| – 'Prisma' | CWil WTin |
| – 'Purple Haze' | MBro |
| – 'Pyrope' | Last listed 1998 |
| – 'Red Rose' | Last listed 1998 |
| – 'Rhodope' | Last listed 1998 |
| – 'Springael's Choice' | Last listed 1998 |
| – 'Sundancer' | Last listed 1996 |
| – 'Suntan' | CWil |
| – 'Sylvan Memory' | CWil |
| – 'Tan' | CWil MBro |
| – 'Tancredi' | Last listed 1998 |
| – 'Torrid Zone' | CWil WTin |
| – 'Tuxedo' | CWil |
| – 'Vesta' | Last listed 1998 |
| – 'Violet' | CWil |
| – 'Vulcan' | Last listed 1998 |
| § *hirta* | CHal CWil GAbr GCrs MDHE MOne NHol NMen SBla STre WPer |
| – subsp. *borealis* | CWil MBro MOne NHed NHol |
| * – 'Dunbar Red' | NHol |
| ¶ – from Wintergraben | SDys |
| – subsp. *glabrescens* | ESis |
| – – from Belansky Tatra | CWil GCHN MDHE MOne NHed SSmi |
| – – from High Tatra | CCuc MDHE |
| – – from Smeryouka | CCuc CWil MBro SIng SSmi |
| – – var. *neilreichii* | SIng |
| – 'Lowe's 66' | MOne |
| – 'Preissiana' | CWil MBro MOne NHed NHol NMen NNrd |
| x *mitchellii* 'Sandy' | Last listed 1998 |

| | |
|---|---|
| – 'Suzan' | Last listed 1998 |
| x *nixonii* 'Jowan' | Last listed 1998 |
| § *sobolifera* | CWil ELau ESis GCHN MBro MOne NHol NMen SIng SSmi WPer |
| ¶ – 'August Cream' | CWil |
| – 'Green Globe' | CWil ELau MDHE NNrd SDys |
| * – 'Miss Lorainne' | CWil |

## JUANULLOA (Solanaceae)

| | |
|---|---|
| *aurantiaca* | See *J. mexicana* |

## JUBAEA (Arecaceae)

| | |
|---|---|
| § *chilensis* | CBrP CRoM LPJP LPal SAPC WMul |
| *spectabilis* | See *J. chilensis* |

## JUGLANS ✿ (Juglandaceae)

| | |
|---|---|
| § *ailanthifolia* | CMCN |
| – var. *cordiformis* | CAgr |
| – – 'Fodermaier' seedling | CAgr |
| § x *bixbyi* | WGWT |
| *californica* (F) | WGWT |
| *cathayensis* (F) | WGWT |
| *cinerea* (F) | CDul CMCN WGWT |
| – x *ailanthifolia* | See *J.* x *bixbyi* |
| – 'Craxezy' (F) | CAgr |
| – 'Kenworthy' seedling | CAgr |
| § *elaeopyren* | CTho |
| x *intermedia* (F) | WGWT |
| *mandschaurica* | CMCN WGWT |
| *microcarpa* | WGWT |
| – subsp. *major* | See *J. elaeopyren* |
| *nigra* (F) ♀ | CB&S CLnd CMCN GChr GTwe IOrc LHol LHyr LNet MAsh MGos NBea NRog NWea SDea SEND SKee SPer WBay WDin WMou WStI WWal |
| – 'Emma Kay' (F) | CAgr |
| – 'Laciniata' | CMCN CTho MBlu WGWT |
| – 'Purpurea' | MBlu |
| *regia* (F) ♀ | CB&S CKin CLnd CMac ELan ENot ERea EWTr GTwe IOrc LBuc LHyr LPan MBar MBri MRav NRog NWea SDea SKee SLPl SPer WDin WFar WMou WOrn |
| – 'Axel' (F) | WGWT |
| – 'Broadview' (F) | CBlo CDoC CDul CEnd CTho EMui ERea GTwe MBlu MBri MCoo MGos SCoo SDea SKee WGWT WMou |
| – 'Buccaneer' (F) | CDul CTho ERea GTwe SDea SKee WGWT WMou |
| – 'China B' (F) | WGWT |
| – 'Coenen' (F) | WGWT WMou |
| – 'Corne du Périgord' (F) | Last listed 1996 |
| – 'Franquette' | CDoC CTho ENot GTwe LRHS MCoo SKee |
| – 'Hansen' (F) | WGWT |
| – 'Hartley' (F) | SKee |
| – 'Laciniata' | IDee MBlu WGWT WMou |
| – 'Lara' | GTwe |
| – 'Mayette' (F) | SKee |
| ¶ – 'Meylannaise' (F) | SKee |
| – 'Northdown Clawnut' | Last listed 1998 |
| – Number 139 | Last listed 1998 |
| – Number 16 (F) | WGWT |
| – Number 26 | Last listed 1998 |
| – 'Parisienne' (F) | SKee |
| – 'Plovdivski' (F) | WGWT WMou |
| – 'Proslavsk' (F) | WGWT WMou |
| – 'Purpurea' | CDul CMCN WGWT |
| – 'Rita' | WGWT WMou |
| ¶ – 'Ronde de Montignac' (F) | SKee |

- 'Soleze' (F)    SKee WGWT
*sieboldiana*    See *J. ailanthifolia*

## JUNCUS (Juncaceae)

*acutus*    WWye
*articulatus*    CKin
\* *balticus* 'Spiralis'    WCot
*bulbosus*    CKin
'Carmen's Grey'    CCuc CHar EPla GCal LRHS SApp WCot
*compressus*    CKin
*concinnus*    Last listed 1997
*conglomeratus*    CKin EHoe
¶ - 'Spiralis'    WCot
§ *decipiens* 'Curly-wurly'    CCuc CFee CMea CMil CSpe EBrP EBre EHoe EMan EMon EPla EWes GCal LBre MFir NWCA SBre SUsu SWat WHal
- 'Spiralis'    See *J. decipiens* 'Curly-wurly'
*effusus*    CKin EMFW LPBA NSti SWat SWyc WMAq
- 'Cuckoo' (v)    CNat WAlt
¶ - 'Gold Strike' (v)    WCot
§ - f. *spiralis*    CBrm CCuc CFee CFil CRow CWat EBee EHoe ELan EMFW EMon EPla GCal IBlr LEdu LPBA MBal MSta NCat NDea SCob SLon SUsu WCot WHal WPGP
\* - 'Spiralis' dwarf    LPBA
*ensifolius*    CAgr CCuc CRow CWat EHoe LHil MSta WCot
¶ *filiformis* 'Spiralis'    WCot
*inflexus*    CAgr CKin EHon SWat SWyc
- 'Afro'    CMea EMon EPGN LRHS MBrN NBro WAlt
¶ *membranaceus*
HLMS 94.0541    NRya
*pallidus*    EBee GCal WCot
*squarrosus*    CKin
*tenuis*    Last listed 1998
*xiphioides*    CCuc EHoe EPla
- JLS 86161LACA    EPPr

## JUNELLIA (Verbenaceae)

*wilczekii*    WFar
¶ - F & W 7770    NWCA

## JUNIPERUS ✿ (Cupressaceae)

*chinensis*    SEND
- 'Aurea' ♀    CB&S CKen CMac EHul EOrn EPla LCon LNet MAsh MBal MBar MGos
§ - 'Blaauw' ♀    CDoC CMac EHul ENot EOrn GAri GPin LCon LLin MAsh MBar MGos SLim STre WStI
- 'Blue Alps'    CDoC CMHG CSli EBrP EBre EHul EOrn EPla IMGH LBre LCon LLin LNet LPan MAsh MBal MBar MBri MGos SBre SEND SLim WFar WGwG
- 'Blue Point'    MBar MGos
- 'Densa Spartan'    See *J. chinensis* 'Spartan'
- 'Echiniformis'    CKen CMac EOrn
- 'Expansa Aureospicata' (v)    CBlo CDoC CKen CMac EBrP EBre EHul EOrn EPfP LBre LCon LLin MBar MGos SBod SBre SLim SRms SSmi
§ - 'Expansa Variegata' (v)    CDoC CMac EBrP EBre EGra EHul EOrn GAri IMGH LBre LCon LLin MAsh MBal MBar MGos MPla NHol SBod SBre SLim SRms SSmi WDin WGwG WMoo WStI WWal

- 'Globosa Cinerea'    MBar
- 'Japonica'    EOrn MBar SMer
- 'Japonica Variegata' (v)    EBrP EBre LBre SBre SLim
- 'Kaizuka' ♀    CBlo CDoC EBrP EBre EHul EOrn GAri LBee LBre LCon MAsh MBal MBar SBre SLim SMer WLRN
- 'Kaizuka Variegata'    See *J. chinensis* 'Variegated Kaizuka'
¶ - 'Keteleeri'    LCon MBar WCwm
- 'Obelisk' ♀    CBlo CDoC EHul LBee LCon MBar MGos SBod WGer WLRN WShe
- 'Oblonga'    EHul EPla LCon LLin MAsh MBar SMer STre
§ - 'Parsonsii'    CMac MBar STre WCFE
- 'Plumosa'    MBar
- 'Plumosa Albovariegata'    EOrn LCon MBar
- 'Plumosa Aurea' ♀    CBlo CDoC EHul ENot EOrn LCon MBar WDin WFar
- 'Plumosa Aureovariegata'    CKen EOrn LCon MBar SLim
- 'Pyramidalis' ♀    CDoC EBrP EBre EHul ENot GAri IMGH LBre LCon LLin MAsh MGos MWat NRoo SBod SBre SRms WAbe WFar WWeb
- 'Pyramidalis Variegata'    See *J. chinensis* 'Variegata'
¶ - 'Robust Green'    EOrn LCon MBar SLim
- 'San José'    CDoC EHul EOrn LCon LLin MAsh MBar MPla SLim WLRN
¶ - var. *sargentii*    CBlo GAri MBal STre
¶ - - 'Glauca'    GAri
¶ - - 'Viridis'    GAri
- 'Shimpaku'    CKen EGra EOrn EPla LCon LLin MBar
§ - 'Spartan'    EHul LBee
- 'Stricta'    CKen EHul LBee MAsh MBal MBar MGos MPla NBee NEgg SLim SPla WDin WStI
- 'Stricta Variegata'    See *J. chinensis* 'Variegata'
♦ - 'Sulphur Spray'    See *J.* x *pfitzeriana* 'Sulphur Spray'
§ - 'Variegata' (v)    MBar MPla
§ - 'Variegated Kaizuka' (v)    EHul EOrn EPla LCon MAsh MBar NHol WWeb
¶ - 'Wilson's Weeping'    WBcn
*communis*    CArn CKin CTrG EHul GAri GChr GPoy GRei ITim LHol MSal NHex NWea SIde
- (f)    SIde
- 'Arnold'    LCon LLin MBar MGos
- 'Arnold Sentinel'    CKen
- 'Atholl'    CKen GAbr
I - 'Aureopicta'    MBar
- 'Barton'    CBlo LLin MBar NHol
- 'Berkshire'    CKen EPot MAsh
- 'Brien'    CDoC CKen
¶ - var. *communis*    ECho MBar NHed SRms
- 'Compressa' ♀    More than 30 suppliers
§ - 'Constance Franklin' (v)    ECho EHul MBar WBcn
¶ - 'Corielagen'    CKen LCon MBar MGos MPla MWat
- 'Cracovia'    CKen EHul
- var. *depressa*    GPoy MBal MBar
- 'Depressa Aurea'    CDoC CKen CMac CSli EHul ENot LBee LLin LPan MAsh MBal MBar MGos MPla NHed NRoo SBod WStI
- 'Depressed Star'    EHul GPin MBar
- 'Derrynane'    EHul
- 'Effusa'    CKen
- 'Gelb'    See *J. communis* 'Schneverdingen Goldmachangel'
§ - 'Gold Cone'    CDoC CKen CSli EBrP EBre EHul ESis LBee LBre LCon LLin MAsh MBar MBri MGos MPla NHed NHol SBre SLim WAbe

| | |
|---|---|
| - 'Golden Showers' | See *J. communis* 'Schneverdingen Goldmachangel' |
| - 'Green Carpet' ♀ | CDoC CKen EBrP EBre EHul EOrn EPla IMGH LBee LBre LCon LLin MAsh MBar MBri SBre SLim SMer SSmi WCFE WFar WWeb |
| - 'Greenmantle' | SPla |
| - 'Haverbeck' | CKen |
| - 'Hibernica' ♀ | CBrm CDoC CKen CMac CSam EHul EOrn GRei IMGH LBee LCon LLin MBal MBar MGos MPla MWat NWea SBod SLim SPer SPla WDin WStI |
| - 'Hibernica Variegata' | See *J. communis* 'Constance Franklin' |
| - 'Hornibrookii' ♀ | CDoC CMac EHul ENot EOrn LLin MBal MGos MWat NWea SBod SPla STre WDin WWin |
| - 'Horstmann' | EPla GAri MBar SLim |
| I - 'Horstmann's Pendula' | LCon WBcn |
| - 'Kemerton Priory' | Last listed 1998 |
| - 'Mayer' | Last listed 1996 |
| § - 'Minima' | SBod |
| § - var. *montana* | EHul |
| - 'Prostrata' | ISea |
| - 'Pyramidalis' | WGor |
| - 'Repanda' ♀ | CB&S CBrm CDoC CMac CSli EHul ENot EPfP GChr GRei LCon LLin MAsh MBar MGos NBid NHed NRoo NWea SBod SLim SPer SSta WCFE WFar WGwG |
| § - 'Schneverdingen Goldmachangel' | CBlo EOrn LCon MAsh SLim SMer WWeb |
| - 'Sentinel' | CDoC CSli EBrP EBre EHul EPfP IOrc LBre LCon LPan MAsh MBar MBri MPla NBee SBre SLim |
| - 'Sieben Steinhauser' | CKen |
| - 'Silver Mist' | CKen |
| - 'Spotty Spreader' (v) | SCoo SLim |
| ¶ - 'Suecica Group' | EHul ENot MBar NWea SBod SRms |
| - 'Suecica Aurea' | CBlo EHul EOrn |
| - 'Zeal' | CKen |
| * *conferta* 'Blue Ice' | CKen EOrn GPin LCon LLin WGwG |
| - 'Blue Pacific' | CBlo CMac COtt EHul GAri LCon MAsh MBar MBri SLim |
| - 'Emerald Sea' | EHul |
| ♦ - var. *maritima* | See *J. taxifolia* |
| *davurica* | EHul |
| - 'Expansa' | See *J. chinensis* 'Parsonsii' |
| - 'Expansa Albopicta' | See *J. chinensis* 'Expansa Variegata' |
| ♦ - 'Expansa Variegata' | See *J. chinensis* 'Expansa Variegata' |
| *deppeana* var. *pachyphlaea* | GAri WCwm |
| - 'Silver Spire' | EGra MBar MGos |
| x *gracilis* 'Blaauw' | See *J. chinensis* 'Blaauw' |
| *horizontalis* | NWea |
| - 'Alpina' | CKen |
| § - 'Andorra Compact' | CKen MBar WMoo |
| § - 'Bar Harbor' | CB&S CKen CMac EHul LLin MBar MGos NWea SBod WGor |
| - 'Blue Chip' | CKen CMac EBrP EBre EHul ENot EOrn EPfP LBee LBre LCon LLin MAsh MBar MBri MGos NRoo SBod SBre SLim SPer SPla SSmi |
| - 'Blue Moon' | See *J. horizontalis* 'Blue Chip' |
| - 'Blue Pygmy' | CKen EPot |
| - 'Blue Rug' | See *J. horizontalis* 'Wiltonii' |
| - 'Douglasii' | CKen CMac EHol EHul MBal MBar WGor |
| - 'Emerald Spreader' | CKen EHul ENot MBar MGos SLim |
| - 'Glacier' | CKen |
| - Glauca Group | CMac EHul ENot GOrc LLin MBal MBar MGos MOne WWin |
| - 'Glomerata' | CKen MBar |
| - 'Golden Carpet' | EOrn IMGH LCon MBri NPro SLim |
| - 'Golden Spreader' | CDoC NPoe WBcn |
| - 'Grey Pearl' | CKen CSli EBrP EBre EHul LBre LCon MAsh MBri NHed NHol SBod SBre SLim SMer |
| - 'Hughes' | CKen CMac CSli EBrP EBre EGra EHul ENot LBee LBre LCon LLin MAsh MBar MBri MGos MPla NHed SBod SBre SLim |
| - 'Jade River' | CKen EHul LBee LRHS MGos NEgg SLim WLRN |
| - 'Montana' | See *J. communis* var. *montana* |
| - 'Mother Lode' | CKen |
| - 'Neumänn' | CKen |
| - 'Petraea' | Last listed 1998 |
| - 'Plumosa' ♀ | NHed |
| - 'Plumosa Compacta' | See *J. horizontalis* 'Andorra Compact' |
| - 'Prince of Wales' | CDoC CKen CSli EBrP EBre EHul GRei LBee LBre LCon LLin MAsh MGos NHol SBre SLim WGor WLRN |
| - 'Turquoise Spreader' | CBlo CKen EHul MBar MPla WWeb |
| - 'Variegata' | MBar |
| - 'Villa Marie' | CKen |
| ¶ - 'Webber' | MAsh MBar SLim |
| - 'Wilms' | Last listed 1998 |
| § - 'Wiltonii' ♀ | CKen CSli EHul ENot EOrn LLin MAsh MBal MGos |
| - 'Winter Blue' | LBee LRHS SLim SPla |
| - 'Youngstown' | CBlo CMac CSWP EBrP EBre LBre LCon MBar MGos NHol SBod SBre SPla WFar WGor |
| - 'Yukon Belle' | CKen |
| N x *media* | See *J.* x *pfitzeriana* |
| *oxycedrus* | GAri |
| x *pfitzeriana* 'Armstrongii' | EHul |
| - 'Blaauw' | See *J. chinensis* 'Blaauw' |
| ♦ - 'Blound' | See *J.* x *pfitzeriana* Gold Sovereign = 'Blound' |
| - 'Blue and Gold' (v) | CKen EHul EOrn MBar SLim SPer |
| - 'Blue Cloud' | See *J. virginiana* 'Blue Cloud' |
| § - 'Carbery Gold' | CDoC CMac CSam CSli EHul EOrn LBee LCon MAsh MBar MBri MGos NHol SAga SLim SSmi WLRN WWeb |
| - 'Gold Coast' | CDoC CKen CMac EBrP EBre EHul ENot GPin LBee LBre LCon MBar MBri MGos MWat SBre SLim |
| § - 'Gold Sovereign = 'Blound' | EBrP EBre EOrn LBee LBre LCon MAsh MGos NHol SBre SMer |
| - 'Gold Star' | EOrn NEgg WBcn |
| - 'Golden Saucer' | CSli MAsh MBar MBri SBod SCoo |
| - 'Goldkissen' | MBri |
| - 'Kuriwao Gold' | CBlo CMac EBrP EBre EHul LBee LBre LLin LNet MBar MGos NHol SBod SBre SLim STre WStI |
| ¶ - 'Kuriwao Sunbeam' | NHol |
| - 'Mint Julep' | CDoC CMac EBrP EBre EHul ENot GChr IMGH LBee LBre LCon LLin LPan MBar MGos MPla SBre SLim SPer WFar |
| - 'Mordigan Gold' | EGra LPan |

| | |
|---|---|
| – 'Old Gold' ♀ | More than 30 suppliers |
| – 'Old Gold Carbery' | See *J.* x *pfitzeriana* 'Carbery Gold' |
| – 'Pfitzeriana Aurea' | CB&S CDoC CDul CMac EHul ENot EPfP GChr LCon LLin MBal MBar MBri MGos MPla MWat NFla NWea SBod SLim SRms WDin WFar WGwG WWal |
| – 'Pfitzeriana Compacta' ♀ | CMac ECho EHul MBar SLim |
| – 'Pfitzeriana Glauca' | CSli EHul GChr IMGH LCon LPan MBar MWat SLim WGor |
| – 'Richeson' | MBar |
| ¶ – 'Saybrook Gold' | LPan MBri |
| – 'Silver Cascade' | EHul |
| § – 'Sulphur Spray' ♀ | CBlo CBrm CDoC CKen CMac EAst EBrP EBre EHul EOrn EPla GRei LBee LBre LCon MBar MBri MGos MPla NHol SBre SLim SPer SPla SSmi WFar WMoo |
| § – 'William Pfitzer' ♀ | CMac EHul ENot LLin MBal MBar MGos NWea SBod SLim SRms WFar WStI |
| – 'Winter Surprise' (v) | CBlo LCon MGos |
| § *pingii* 'Glassell' | ECho LCon MBar MGos |
| § – 'Pygmaea' | CBlo CDoC EOrn ESis LCon MBar MPla |
| § – var. *wilsonii* | CBlo CKen ECho EHul EOrn LCon MBar |
| *procera* | Last listed 1996 |
| *procumbens* | Last listed 1998 |
| – 'Bonin Isles' | LLin MBal MGos SLim SPla SRms |
| – 'Nana' ♀ | CDoC CKen CMac EBrP EBre EHul EOrn IMGH LBee LBre LCon LLin MAsh MBal MBar MBri MGos MPla MWat NHol SBre SLim SPla SSmi WPyg WWal |
| *recurva* 'Castlewellan' | EOrn EPla LCon LLin MGos SMad WCwm |
| – var. *coxii* | CMac EHul EOrn EPla GGGa ISea LCon LLin MBar MBri MGos SLim SRms WCFE WCwm WPic |
| § – 'Densa' | CKen EHul EOrn GAri LLin MBar NHol SPla |
| – 'Embley Park' | EHul MAsh MBar SLim |
| – 'Nana' | See *J. recurva* 'Densa' |
| *rigida* | CDoC EHul GCal LBee LCon LLin MBar MWat SAga SBod SIng SLim SPer SRms STre WFar WWal |
| *sabina* | GPoy NWea |
| – 'Arcadia' | SRms |
| § – 'Blaue Donau' | CBlo EHul MBar MGos SRms WGor |
| – Blue Danube | See *J. sabina* 'Blaue Donau' |
| – 'Broadmoor' | EHul |
| – 'Buffalo' | EHul |
| ¶ – Cupressifolia Group | MBar |
| – 'Hicksii' | CMac MBar NWea |
| ◆ – 'Knap Hill' | See *J.* x *pfitzeriana* 'William Pfitzer' |
| – 'Rockery Gem' | CBlo EHul EOrn MGos MOne SLim SPla WGor |
| – 'Skandia' | CKen |
| – 'Tamariscifolia' | More than 30 suppliers |
| – 'Variegata' (v) | CMac EHul MAsh MBar SLim WPyg |
| ¶ *scopulorum* | CKen MBar |
| – 'Blue Arrow' | CKen COtt EOrn EPla GChr IMGH LBee LCon LLin LPan MAsh MBar MBri MGos MWat NBee NEgg SCoo SLim |
| – 'Blue Banff' | CKen |
| – 'Blue Heaven' ♀ | EHul GAri LCon MBal MBar SLim SPla |
| – 'Blue Pyramid' | EHul |
| – 'Boothman' | EHul |
| – 'Gray Gleam' | Last listed 1998 |
| – 'Moonglow' | CSli EBrP EBre EHul LBre MBar SBre |
| ¶ – 'Mountaineer' | EHul |
| – 'Mrs Marriage' | CKen |
| – 'Repens' | MBar MGos |
| – 'Silver Globe' | Last listed 1996 |
| – 'Silver Star' (v) | CBlo CKen EHul MBar MGos |
| – 'Skyrocket' | More than 30 suppliers |
| – 'Springbank' | CSli EHul LBee LCon MAsh MBar |
| ¶ – 'Tabletop' | MBar WBcn |
| ¶ – 'Tolleson's Blue Weeping' | LCon |
| – 'Wichita Blue' | CBlo EHul EPfP LCon LPan SEND WGor |
| *squamata* | Last listed 1998 |
| – 'Blue Carpet' ♀ | More than 30 suppliers |
| – 'Blue Spider' | CKen LLin LRHS MBar SLim WGor WLRN |
| – 'Blue Star' ♀ | More than 30 suppliers |
| – 'Blue Star Variegated' | See *J. squamata* 'Golden Flame' |
| – 'Blue Swede' | See *J. squamata* 'Hunnetorp' |
| – 'Chinese Silver' | EHul LCon MBar SLim WBcn WLRN |
| – 'Filborna' | CBlo CDoC CKen LBee MBar MWat NHol SLim SMer |
| – 'Forrestii' | See *J. pingii* 'Forrestii' |
| – 'Glassell' | See *J. pingii* 'Glassell' |
| § – 'Golden Flame' | CKen |
| – 'Holger' ♀ | CBrm CDoC CKen CMac EBrP EBre EHul EOrn EPla GAri LBee LBre LCon LLin MAsh MBar MBri MGos MPla MWat SBod SBre SLim WStI WWeb |
| § – 'Hunnetorp' | CBlo EOrn LCon MAsh MBar MBri MGos |
| ◆ – 'Loderi' | See *J. pingii* var. *wilsonii* |
| – 'Meyeri' | EHul ENot EOrn GOrc IMGH MAsh MBal MBar MWat NWea SBod SLim SRms STre WFar WStI WWin |
| – 'Pygmaea' | See *J. pingii* 'Pygmaea' |
| ◆ – 'Wilsonii' | See *J. pingii* var. *wilsonii* |
| § *taxifolia* | EOrn GPin IMGH LBee LCon MBal MPla MWat WWeb |
| *virginiana* | CAgr |
| § – 'Blue Cloud' | CDoC EHul LCon MBar SLim WGor WLRN |
| – 'Burkii' | EHul LCon MBal |
| – 'Frosty Morn' | CKen ECho EHul LCon MBar |
| – 'Glauca' | CSWP EHul LCon NWea |
| – 'Golden Spring' | CKen |
| – 'Grey Owl' ♀ | CMac CSli EHul ENot GRei LCon LLin MBal MBar MGos MPla SLim SLon SPla SRms STre WDin WGor WGwG WPyg WWal |
| – 'Helle' | See *J. chinensis* 'Spartan' |
| – 'Hetzii' | CB&S CBlo CKen CMac ECho EHul LCon MBal MBar NWea SBod WLRN |
| – 'Hillii' | MBar |
| – 'Hillspire' | EHul |
| – 'Nana Compacta' | MBar |
| – 'Pendula' | Last listed 1997 |
| – 'Silver Spreader' | CBlo EHul LCon MGos WBcn WGwG |
| ¶ – 'Staver' | EHul |
| ¶ – 'Tripartita' | MBar |
| ¶ – 'Venusta' | CKen |

**JURINEA** (Asteraceae)
¶ *alata* — GVic
  *ceratocarpa* — See *Saussurea ceratocarpa*
  *mollis* — GBuc
  *moschus* subsp. *moschus* — Last listed 1996

**JURINELLA** See JURINEA

**JUSSIAEA** See LUDWIGIA

**JUSTICIA** (Acanthaceae)
  *aurea* — ERea
§ *brandegeeana* ♀ — CHal MBri
  - 'Lutea' — See *J. brandegeeana* 'Yellow Queen'
§ - 'Yellow Queen' — CHal
§ *carnea* — CHal CSev EBak EHol ERea GCal LCns LHil MBri SLdr SMad SOWG WMul
  *floribunda* — See *J. rizzinii*
  *guttata* — See *J. brandegeeana*
\* 'Norgard's Favourite' — MBri
  *pauciflora* — See *J. rizzinii*
  *pectoralis* — Last listed 1998
  - Puerto Rican cultivar — Last listed 1998
\* - var. *stenophylla* — Last listed 1998
  *peruviana* — Last listed 1998
  *pohliana* — See *J. carnea*
§ *rizzinii* ♀ — CHal CInt CSev ERea IBlr LBlm LCns LHil SOWG SVen
  *spicigera* — ERea
  *suberecta* — See *Dicliptera suberecta*

**KADSURA** (Schisandraceae)
  *japonica* — CB&S CGre CPlN EMil EPfP SBid
  - B&SWJ 1027 — WCru
  - 'Shiromi' — CPlN EMil SMur
  - 'Variegata' — EPfP GOrc MCCP SAga SBid SBra WSHC
  sp. — CMac

**KAEMPFERIA** (Zingiberaceae)
  *ovalifolia* — See *K. parishii*
  *rotunda* — GPoy LAma LChe

**KALANCHOE** (Crassulaceae)
  *beharensis* — CHal MBri
  *blossfeldiana* — EOHP
¶ - 'Variegata' — CHal
  *daigremontiana* — CHal SRms
§ *delagoensis* — CHal STre
  *fedtschenkoi* — CHal
§ *lateritia* — LHil
  *manginii* — CHal EOHP
  *pumila* ♀ — CHal EWoo IBlr STre WEas
  'Tessa' ♀ — MBri MLan STre
  *tomentosa* ♀ — CHal WEas
  *tubiflora* — See *K. delagoensis*
  'Wendy' ♀ — MBri
  *zimbabwensis* — See *K. lateritia*

**KALIMERIS** (Asteraceae)
§ *incisa* — EMon EWll WCot
  - 'Alba' — EFou EMon SHel SSvw
  - 'Blue Star' — EFou
\* - 'Variegata' — SCob

---

  *integrifolia* — CPlt ECha WPrP WTin
§ *mongolica* — EBee WPer
§ *pinnatifida* — EBee
§ *yomena* 'Shogun' (v) — CHal CRDP EBee ECha EFou EHal EHoe ELan EMan EMon GBri GBuc LFis LHop MAvo MLLN NBir NRoo NSti SCob SUsu WAbe WCot WFar WHer WOve WWeb
  - 'Variegata' — See *K. yomena* 'Shogun'

**KALMIA** ✿ (Ericaceae)
  *angustifolia* ♀ — MBar SPar SRms WDin
  - var. *angustifolia*
    f. *candida* — Last listed 1998
  - var. *pumila* — WAbe
  - f. *rubra* — CB&S CDoC CMHG EBrP EBre ELan GChr ISea LBre MBal MGos NHed NHol NRoo SBre SBrw SPer SReu SSta WBay WHar WPat WPyg WWat
  *cuneata* — Last listed 1997
  *latifolia* ♀ — CB&S CTrG EBee ELan EMil ENot GGGa GRei LNet MBal MBar MGos NBee NWea SBrw SPer SReu SSpi SSta WBrE WDin WGer WHar WNor WPyg WStl WWat WWeb
  - 'Alpine Pink' — Last listed 1998
  - 'Brilliant' — NHol
  - 'Bullseye' — GGGa
  - 'Carol' — SBid
  - 'Carousel' — CAbP CB&S ELan EPfP GGGa LRHS MGos SVil
  - 'Clementine Churchill' — CBlo
  - 'Elf' — LRHS MGos
  - 'Freckles' — CB&S ELan EPfP GGGa GOrc ISea LRHS MGos MLan NHed SBrw SPer
  - 'Fresca' — LRHS SVil
  - 'Goodrich' — Last listed 1998
  - 'Heart of Fire' — CAbP CDoC GGGa ISea LRHS NHed NOla
  - 'Heart's Desire' — SBid
  - 'Little Linda' — CBlo GGGa GOrc IMGH LRHS MAsh MBri NHed SBid WBod
  - 'Minuet' — CAbP CBlo CDoC EPfP GGGa MAsh MBri MMHG NHed SBrw SSpi WBod
¶ - 'Nipmuck' — MGos
  - 'Olympic Fire' — ELan EPfP GGGa MAsh MBal MGos NHed SBrw SPer SSpi
  - 'Ostbo Red' ♀ — CB&S CBlo CDoC EBee EMil GGGa GOrc IMGH IOrc ISea LNet MBal MBri MGos MLan NHed SBrw SPer SReu SSpi SSta WBod WLRN
¶ - 'Peppermint' — MBri
  - 'Pink Charm' — ELan GGGa ISea MAsh MBal MGos NHed WLRN
  - 'Pink Frost' — CB&S GGGa LPan MGos NHol SBid SBrw WBod WWat
  - 'Pink Star' — Last listed 1997
  - 'Pinwheel' — Last listed 1996
¶ - 'Quinnipiac' — LPan
¶ - 'Raspberry Glow' — MBri
  - 'Richard Jaynes' — LRHS SVil
  - 'Sarah' — MBri SBid SSpi
  - 'Shooting Star' — Last listed 1996
  - 'Silver Dollar' — GGGa LPan NHol
  - 'Snowdrift' — LRHS SPer
§ *microphylla* — GGGa MBal WAbe WPat
\* - 'Mount Shasta' — Last listed 1998

| | |
|---|---|
| - var. *occidentalis* | Last listed 1998 |
| **polifolia** | CB&S MBar MBro MRav NHol WPat WPyg WSHC |
| - *compacta* | WSHC |
| - 'Glauca' | See *K. microphylla* |
| - f. *leucantha* | GGGa SSta WAbe |
| ¶ - 'Nana' | SSta |
| * **pygmaea** | Last listed 1996 |

**KALMIOPSIS** (Ericaceae)

| | |
|---|---|
| **leachiana** ♀ | EPot GCrs MBal NHar SSta WAbe |
| - Cedar Park form | Last listed 1997 |
| - 'Curry County' | WAbe |
| - 'Glendoick' | GGGa MAsh MBro MDun NHar NHol WPat WPyg |
| - 'Marcel le Piniec' | GGGa |
| * - 'Shooting Star' | NHol WAbe WPat |
| - Umpqua Valley form | Last listed 1997 |

**x KALMIOTHAMNUS** (Ericaceae)

| | |
|---|---|
| **ornithomma** | GGGa |
| - 'Cosdon' | WAbe |
| - 'Haytor' | WAbe |

**KALOPANAX** (Araliaceae)

| | |
|---|---|
| **pictus** | See *K. septemlobus* |
| § **septemlobus** | CB&S CFil ELan NPal SCob SMad |
| - var. *maximowiczii* | CDoC EPfP MBlu NBee SMad |

**KECKIELLA** (Scrophulariaceae)

| | |
|---|---|
| § **antirrhinoides** | NWCA |
| - **antirrhinoides** | Last listed 1996 |
| § **cordifolia** | EBee EMan LHop |
| **corymbosa** | CGra |
| - JCA 11618 | NWCA |
| **rothrockii** | Last listed 1998 |

**KELSEYA** (Rosaceae)

| | |
|---|---|
| **uniflora** | CGra |

**KENNEDIA** (Papilionaceae)

| | |
|---|---|
| **beckxiana** | LChe SOWG |
| **coccinea** | CPlN GQui LPan |
| **macrophylla** | CPlN SHFr |
| **nigricans** | CPlN LChe MSag SOWG |
| **prostrata** | EMan SVen |
| **rubicunda** | CPlN CRHN |

**KENTIA** (Arecaceae)

| | |
|---|---|
| **belmoreana** | See *Howea belmoreana* |
| **canterburyana** | See *Hedyscepe canterburyana* |

**KENTRANTHUS** See CENTRANTHUS

**KERRIA** (Rosaceae)

| | |
|---|---|
| ♦ **japonica** (d) | See *K. japonica* 'Pleniflora' |
| - (single) | See *K. japonica* 'Simplex' |
| - 'Albescens' | CBot CPMA NPro WWat |
| - 'Golden Guinea' ♀ | CChe EBee ECtt ELan EPfP MAsh MGos MNrw NPro SCoo SPer WTro WWat WWeb |
| § - 'Picta' (v) | CB&S CDul CHan EAst EBee EBrP EBre EHoe ELan GOrc IOrc LBre LFis MBar MBri MGos MHar NBee SBre SHel SLon SPer SRms WDin WSHC WWal WWat |
| § - 'Pleniflora' (d) ♀ | More than 30 suppliers |
| § - 'Simplex' | CB&S CPle EBee ELan IOrc NFla NWea WDin WFar |
| - 'Variegata' | See *K. japonica* 'Picta' |

**KHADIA** (Aizoaceae)

| | |
|---|---|
| sp. | CTrC EOas |

**KICKXIA** (Scrophulariaceae)

| | |
|---|---|
| **elatine** | EWFC |
| **spuria** | EWFC |

**KIRENGESHOMA** (Hydrangeaceae)

| | |
|---|---|
| **palmata** ♀ | More than 30 suppliers |
| ¶ - dwarf | WCot |
| § - Koreana Group | CHid CLAP CRDP EBee ECha ELan EPar LHop MBel MBri MCli MRav NDov SCro SLod WAbe WFar WMer WOVN |

**KITAIBELA** (Malvaceae)

| | |
|---|---|
| **vitifolia** | CFee CGen CGle CHan CPea CSpe EBee ECoo ELan EMar EMon EWTr GCal MNrw NBro NSti SRCN WBea WCer WCot WFar WHer WPer WPic WRos WWin WWye |

**KITCHINGIA** See KALANCHOE

**KLEINIA** (Asteraceae)

| | |
|---|---|
| **articulata** | See *Senecio articulatus* |
| ♦ **repens** | See *Senecio serpens* |
| **senecioides** | WEas |

**KNAUTIA** (Dipsacaceae)

| | |
|---|---|
| § **arvensis** | CArn CKin ECoo EWFC MChe MHer MHew MLLN NLan NMir WCla WGwy WHer WJek |
| **dipsacifolia** | LFis LGre WCot |
| * **jankiae** | WHer |
| § **macedonica** | More than 30 suppliers |
| - Melton Pastels | EPfP SCob SWat WElm |
| - pink | CMil CSam SSpi SWas |
| - 'Red Dress' | Last listed 1998 |
| § **tatarica** | EBee |

**KNIGHTIA** (Proteaceae)

| | |
|---|---|
| **excelsa** | Last listed 1998 |

**KNIPHOFIA** ✿ (Asphodelaceae)

| | |
|---|---|
| 'Ada' | EBee ECGP ERou EWes GCHN MLLN MRav MUlv |
| 'Alcazar' | CKel ECot EPar EPfP MCAu MRav NPri WCot WFar WMer WViv |
| * 'Amber' | IBlr |
| ¶ 'Amsterdam' | CKel |
| 'Apple Court' | NBir |
| 'Apricot' | CHad CMdw EPla |
| ¶ 'Apricot Sensation' | ECha |
| 'Apricot Souffle' | ECha GBri MLLN WCot |
| 'Atlanta' | CFil EBee GCal IBlr LBlm MUlv SHel SMrm WCot |
| **baurii** | EBee LLew WCot |
| 'Bees' Flame' | EWTr SLod SMad |
| 'Bees' Lemon' | CCuc IBlr IHdy LPio WCot |
| 'Bees' Sunset' ♀ | EBee EWTr GBri IBlr IHdy MCAu MRav MWgw SMrm WCot WLRN |
| * **bicolor** | MHlr WCot |
| 'Border Ballet' | ECtt EMan MFir MOne MRav NBir NBro NFai NLar NMir SCob SMrm WFar |
| **brachystachya** | CTrC WCot |
| 'Bressingham Comet' | CGle CLon CPea EBee EBrP EBre ECtt EGle LBre MRav SBre SCob SDys WRus |

| | |
|---|---|
| 'Bressingham Gleam' | WCot |
| Bressingham hybrids | EBrP EBre IBlr LBre NBir SBre |
| 'Bressingham Sunbeam' | EGar |
| *breviflora* | EBee |
| Bridgemere hybrids | LRHS |
| 'Brimstone' ♀ | CPlt EAst ECGP EHic EPla GBri IBlr MBri MMil NDov SCob SIgm SPla SUsu WAbb WCot |
| *buchananii* | EBee WCot |
| 'Buttercup' ♀ | CCuc CGle CMHG CMdw |
| 'C.M. Prichard' hort. | See *K. rooperi* |
| 'C.M. Prichard' Prichard | WCot |
| 'Candlelight' | CPlt WCot |
| * 'Candlemass' | LPio |
| 'Catherine's Orange' | WCot |
| *caulescens* ♀ | CAbb CBot CFil CHan CMil CPou CSam EBee EBrP EBre EMan LBlm LBre LEdu MUlv MWat MWgw NFla NLar SAPC SArc SBla SBre SCob SCro WCot WPGP |
| - BH 5020 | Last listed 1996 |
| *citrina* | CB&S CBot CFir EBee EMan EPfP LLew MBal NBus NChi NLar WPer WWat |
| 'Cobra' | CPou CRDP CStr EFou ERou GCHN MTed WCot |
| 'Corallina' | EHal EWll MAvo NHaw NPri WPnP WViv |
| 'Cream Flame' | Last listed 1996 |
| 'David' ♀ | Last listed 1987 |
| 'Dawn Sunkiss' | WCot |
| 'Dorset Sentry' | GBuc WCot |
| 'Dr E.M. Mills' | Last listed 1996 |
| * 'Drummore Apricot' | WCot |
| 'Earliest of All' | COtt EBee MBNS NHol |
| 'Early Buttercup' | ECot GBri MMil NCat NHaw WFar |
| * 'Early Yellow' | Last listed 1997 |
| *elegans* | See *K. schimperi* |
| § *ensifolia* | CMdw CPou EBee EGar EOas MBal WBcn |
| 'Erecta' | IBlr WCot |
| 'Ernest Mitchell' | MRav WCot |
| Express hybrids | EBee NLar WCot |
| 'Fairyland' | MNrw NBus NCut WCot |
| * 'Fat Yellow' | MWgw |
| *fibrosa* | CTrC EBee WCot |
| 'Fiery Fred' | EGar EGle ELan EOld NHaw WCot WPnP |
| ¶ 'Flamenco' | EWll |
| *foliosa* | EBee SChr |
| ¶ 'Frances Victoria' | WCot |
| *galpinii* hort. | See *K. triangularis* subsp. *triangularis* |
| - Baker ♀ | CBot CGle CHan CMGP CMdw EBee ECGN ENot GBri LGre MBal NBir NFla SAga SPer SRms WAbe WWat |
| ¶ 'Gladness' | WCot |
| 'Goldelse' | CLon ECha EGle IBlr NBir SDys |
| 'Goldfinch' | CMdw SMrm |
| *gracilis* | EBee SApp WCot |
| ¶ 'Green and Cream' | MNrw |
| 'Green Jade' | CMdw COtt CRow EBee ECha EGar EPar GBri IBlr LGre MRav MTed NBir NCat SChu SEND SIgm WCot WIvy |
| 'H.E. Beale' | GCal MRav NHaw WCot |
| *hirsuta* | EBee EBrP EBre LBre LPio MUlv SBre WCot |
| - H&B 16444 | EMon |
| - JCA 346 900 | SSpi |
| 'Hollard's Gold' | MRav WCot |
| 'Ice Queen' | EFou EGle EOrc GBri LEdu LGre LPio MCAu MRav SMad WCot |
| *ichopensis* | CFil CHan EBee GBuc IBlr WCot WPGP |
| 'Innocence' | WCot |
| *isoetifolia* | IBlr |
| 'Jenny Bloom' | More than 30 suppliers |
| 'John Benary' | COtt EHic IBlr WCot |
| ¶ 'Johnathan' | WCot |
| 'Kingston Flame' | Last listed 1998 |
| late orange | Last listed 1998 |
| *laxiflora* | CFil CPou EBee IHdy WPGP |
| 'Lemon Ice' | WCot |
| 'Light of the World' | CBos CElw CFai CMil COtt CSpe EAst EBee GNau MCLN MMil NDov NLar SMad WCot |
| 'Limelight' | Last listed 1997 |
| *linearifolia* | CFil EBee IBlr MNrw SDix SMrm WCot |
| 'Little Elf' | CLon LGre LPio SBla SDys SWas WCot |
| 'Little Maid' ♀ | More than 30 suppliers |
| *littoralis* | EBee |
| 'Lord Roberts' | WCot |
| ¶ 'Luna' | WCot |
| 'Lye End' | Last listed 1998 |
| *macowanii* | See *K. triangularis* subsp. *triangularis* |
| 'Maid of Orleans' | CRow GBri IBlr NHaw WCot |
| 'Mellow Yellow' | IBlr |
| 'Mermaiden' | CMHG EGar MTed WCot |
| 'Minister Verschuur' | EBee GBin GNau WCot WViv |
| 'Modesta' | GBri IBlr SUsu WCot |
| 'Mount Etna' | CGle WCot |
| *multiflora* | Last listed 1998 |
| 'Nancy's Red' | CMil COtt EHic GBri LGre LHop LPio MSte NLar WCot WPGP |
| *natalensis* | EBee EOas GBuc LPio WCot |
| *nelsonii* | See *K. triangularis* subsp. *triangularis* |
| 'Nobilis' | See *K. uvaria* 'Nobilis' |
| *northiae* | CBot CFil CFir CPou EBee EOas GCal IBlr SAPC SArc SCob SIgm SSpi WAbe WCot WPGP |
| 'Notung' | IBlr |
| * 'Old Court Seedling' | WCot |
| 'Painted Lady' | CTri GCal MBro MRav WCot WHoo |
| *parviflora* | Last listed 1998 |
| *pauciflora* | EBee GCal SIgm WCot |
| 'Pencil' | Last listed 1996 |
| 'Percy's Pride' | More than 30 suppliers |
| 'Pfitzeri' | SRms |
| *porphyrantha* | EBee WCot |
| *praecox* | CFil CTrC EBee LLew WCot WPGP |
| 'Primrose Beauty' | WCot WMer |
| ¶ 'Primulina' hort. | EBee |
| 'Prince Igor' | ECha EFou LBlm MBal MTed SChu SIgm |
| *pumila* | EBee EGar MNrw MTis |
| ¶ 'Ranelagh Gardens' | SArc |
| *ritualis* | CFil GCal WCot WPGP |
| § *rooperi* | CBot CFil GBri GCal IBlr LGre LHil LLew LPio MBal MNrw WCot WViv |
| ¶ - 'Torchlight' | CPin |
| 'Royal Caste' | EBee MMil MRav NCut NOrc WWeb |
| 'Royal Standard' ♀ | CB&S COtt EBee EBrP EBre ELan EMan ENot EPfP GBri IBlr LBre LHil MCAu MNrw MRav SAga SBre SLon SMad SRms WCot WFar |

*rufa* — CPou EBee WCot
'Safranvogel' — EGar IBlr MMHG
'Samuel's Sensation' ♀ — EBrP EBre EGar GBri IBlr LBre
  MHlr SBre WCot
*sarmentosa* — CFil EBee LLew WCot WPGP
  WWoo
'September Sunshine' — MRav
'Shining Sceptre' — CSam EBee EBrP EBre ECha ECtt
  EFou EGar LBre LIck LPio MLLN
  MRav MUlv NCut SBre SIgm SMad
  WCot WMer
'Sir C.K. Butler' — EGar IBlr
*splendida* — GCal
'Springtime' — WCot
'Star of Baden-Baden' — NBir SMad WCot
'Strawberries and Cream' — EBee LGre LPio MGrG MSte SAga
  SUsu WCot WPnP
*stricta* — LLew WCot
'Sunbeam' — NBir
'Sunningdale Yellow' ♀ — CMdw COlW CPou EBee ECha
  EGar EHrv MFir SChu SLod SRms
  WCot WEas
'Tawny King' — WCot
¶ *thomsonii* var.*snowdenii* — LEdu WCru
- var.*thomsonii* — CBot CFir ECha EOrc GBri IBlr
  LHil MNrw MSte NTow WCot
  WHal WIvy
- - triploid variety — Last listed 1998
'Timothy' — EGle LGre NHaw SAga SChu SUsu
  WCot
'Toasted Corn' — Last listed 1997
'Toffee Nosed' ♀ — ECGP EFou EGar ERou GBri GCal
  IBlr LBlm LPio MRav NBir NTow
  SChu SWas
'Torchbearer' — EGar IBlr WCot WTre
*triangularis* ♀ — CBot CHad CInt CMHG CTrC
  EAst EBee ECGN EPfP SMrm
§ - subsp.*triangularis* — CBot CGle GBuc IBlr MRav NBro
  NPri SIgm SRms
¶ 'Tubergeniana' — WCot
I 'Tuckii' — CHan EBee EWll MBal MNrw
*tuckii* Baker — See *K. ensifolia*
*typhoides* — EBee LLew WCot WHal
¶ *tysonii* — GVic
'Underway' — Last listed 1997
*uvaria* — CTrC EBee EOas LEdu LPio LRHS
  MCAu NBir NVic SCob SPer SRms
  SSpi WByw WCot WHoo WPnP
  WPyg
* - Fairyland hybrids — LIck
§ - 'Nobilis' ♀ — IBlr LBlm MLLN SAPC SArc SDix
  WCot
'Vanilla' — LPio MRav
'Vesta' — EGar
'Wrexham Buttercup' — EBee EGar EMan GBri IBlr MLLN
'Yellow Hammer' — CBot ECha IBlr NCat WFar
'Zululandiae' — WCot

## KNOWLTONIA (Ranunculaceae)
*bracteata* — Last listed 1997
*transvaalensis* — Last listed 1997

## KOCHIA See BASSIA

## KOELERIA (Poaceae)
♦ *cristata* — See *K. macrantha, K. pyramidata*
*glauca* — More than 30 suppliers
§ *macrantha* — EMan EPPr SBea
§ *pyramidata* — Last listed 1997
*vallesiana* — CCuc EHoe EMon EPPr EPla ESis
  LRHS

## KOELLIKERIA (Gesneriaceae)
'Red Satin' — NMos

## KOELREUTERIA (Sapindaceae)
*bipinnata* — CGre
- var.*integrifoliola* — CFil WPGP
*paniculata* ♀ — More than 30 suppliers
- var.*apiculata* — CMHG
- 'Fastigiata' — EPfP MBlu SSpi

## KOHLERIA (Gesneriaceae)
'Clytie' — MBri
'Dark Velvet' — CHal WDib
*digitaliflora* — See *K. warscewiczii*
*eriantha* ♀ — CHal CPle MBri WDib
'Hanna Roberts' — WDib
*hirsuta* — CPle
* x *hybrida* — NMos
'Jester' — CHal WDib
* 'Linda' — CHal
'Strawberry Fields' ♀ — MBri NMos
§ *warscewiczii* ♀ — CHal WDib

## KOLKWITZIA (Caprifoliaceae)
*amabilis* — CB&S CGre CTrw ELan EMil
  GOrc GRei ISea LPan MGos MHar
  MPla MWat NBee NFor NWea
  SEas SRms WDin WFar WFro
  WGwG WHCG WHar WNor WStI
  WWin
¶ - 'Maradco' — EPfP LRHS NPro
- 'Pink Cloud' ♀ — More than 30 suppliers

## KOSTELETZKYA (Malvaceae)
*virginica* — EMan

## KUNZEA (Myrtaceae)
*ambigua* — CGre ECou SOWG
*baxteri* — CTrC SOWG
*capitata* — SOWG
§ *ericoides* — ECou GAbr SOWG
¶ - 'Blue Leaf' — CCpl
¶ 'Mauve Mist' — MSag
*muelleri* — Last listed 1998
*parvifolia* — CTrC MSag SOWG
*pomifera* — Last listed 1998
*recurva* — Last listed 1998

# L

## LABLAB (Caesalpiniaceae)
§ *purpureus* — Last listed 1996

## + LABURNOCYTISUS (Papilionaceae)
'Adamii' — CBlo CDoC CDul COtt CPMA
  ELan EPfP GAri IOrc LBuc MBlu
  MBri SMad SPer SSpi

## LABURNUM ✿ (Papilionaceae)
¶ *alpinum* — EPfP
- 'Pendulum' — CB&S CBlo CDoC EBrP EBre ELan
  EPfP IOrc LBre LNet MAsh MBar
  MBri MGos MRav MWat NBee
  SBre SPer WDin WOrn WStI
§ *anagyroides* — CBlo ENot GAri GRei ISea NWea
  SEND SRms WDin
- 'Aureum' — SPer
- 'Pendulum' — CLnd

| | |
|---|---|
| *vulgare* | See *L. anagyroides* |
| x *watereri* 'Alford's Weeping' | Last listed 1996 |
| - 'Vossii' ♀ | More than 30 suppliers |
| * - 'Vossii Pendulum' | CBlo |

## LACHENALIA (Hyacinthaceae)

| | |
|---|---|
| § *aloides* | LBow LHil MBri SRob |
| - var. *aurea* ♀ | LBow MSte |
| - var. *luteola* | LBow |
| - 'Nelsonii' | Last listed 1996 |
| - var. *quadricolor* ♀ | LBow WCot |
| - var. *vanzyliae* | LBow |
| § *bulbifera* | LBow MBri |
| - 'George' | LBow |
| *contaminata* | LBow |
| hybrid Lac. 213 | Last listed 1997 |
| *liliiflora* | Last listed 1998 |
| *pallida* | Last listed 1998 |
| *pendula* | See *L. bulbifera* |
| *purpureocoerulea* | Last listed 1998 |
| *pustulata* | Last listed 1998 |
| *reflexa* | Last listed 1996 |
| *rubida* | Last listed 1998 |
| *tricolor* | See *L. aloides* |

## LACHNANTHES (Haemodoraceae)

| | |
|---|---|
| § *caroliana* | MSal |
| *tinctoria* | See *L. caroliana* |

## LACTUCA (Asteraceae)

| | |
|---|---|
| *alpina* | See *Cicerbita alpina* |
| *perennis* | CHan MAvo MTho NChi WCot |
| *virosa* | CArn MSal |

## LAGAROSIPHON (Hydrocharitaceae)

| | |
|---|---|
| § *major* (m) | CBen CRow EHon ELan EMFW NDea SRms SWyc |

## LAGAROSTROBOS (Podocarpaceae)

| | |
|---|---|
| § *franklinii* | CB&S CTrG IOrc LLin WPic |

## LAGENOPHORA (Asteraceae)

| | |
|---|---|
| *pinnatifida* | Last listed 1996 |

## LAGERSTROEMIA (Lythraceae)

| | |
|---|---|
| *indica* ♀ | CPle LPan SEND |
| - 'Rosea' | CB&S LPan SEND |
| *subcostata* | CB&S |

## LAGUNARIA (Malvaceae)

| | |
|---|---|
| *patersonii* | CFil WPGP |
| - 'Royal Purple' | ERea |

## LALLEMANTIA (Lamiaceae)

| | |
|---|---|
| ¶ *iberica* | EBee |
| ¶ *peltata* | EBee |

## LAMBERTIA (Proteaceae)

| | |
|---|---|
| *formosa* | Last listed 1998 |

## LAMIASTRUM See LAMIUM

## LAMIUM ✿ (Lamiaceae)

| | |
|---|---|
| *album* | CKin EWFC SMrm |
| - 'Aureovariegatum' | See *L. album* 'Goldflake' |
| - 'Brightstone Gem' | EMon NBrk |
| - 'Friday' (v) | EGar EHoe EMan EMar EMon EPPr LHop MCLN MSCN MTho NPla WCHb WHer WHil WRos |
| - 'Golden Halo' | Last listed 1998 |
| § - 'Goldflake' (v) | WCHb |
| - 'Pale Peril' | NBrk |

| | |
|---|---|
| *armenum* | EHyt |
| *eriocephalum* | Last listed 1998 |
| subsp. *eriocephalum* | |
| *flexuosum* | EPPr |
| § *galeobdolon* | CArn CTri EWFC EWTr LGro MHar MSal MWat NFai SRms WOak |
| - subsp. *galeobdolon* | EMon |
| - 'Hermann's Pride' | More than 30 suppliers |
| - 'Kirkcudbright Dwarf' | EBee EWes |
| - subsp. *montanum* | EMon |
| 'Canford Wood' | |
| § - - 'Florentinum' | CHal CRow ECha EHoe ELan ENot EPPr EPar MCAu MRav NLon NVic SEas SHel WFar WPer |
| - 'Purple Heart' | EMon |
| § - 'Silberteppich' | CRow ECha EFou ELan EMar EOrc MRav MTho NFor NVic SBla WCot WPer WWat |
| - 'Silver Angel' | EMon MBel NSti |
| - Silver Carpet | See *L. galeobdolon* 'Silberteppich' |
| - 'Silver Spangled' | EGar |
| ♦ - 'Variegatum' | See *L. galeobdolon* subsp. *montanum* 'Florentinum' |
| *garganicum* | CGle CHan EGar EPPr EWes NChi |
| subsp. *garganicum* | WCot WPer WWye |
| - subsp. *garganicum* | Last listed 1998 |
| LM&S 94023B | |
| - 'Golden Carpet' (v) | Last listed 1996 |
| - 'Laevigatum' | Last listed 1998 |
| - subsp. *laevigatum* | CHan |
| HH&K 315 | |
| - - HH&K 332 | CHan |
| - subsp. *pictum* | See *L. garganicum* subsp. *striatum* |
| - subsp. *reniforme* | See *L. garganicum* subsp. *striatum* |
| § - subsp. *striatum* | ELan SBla SMrm |
| - - DS&T 89011T | EPPr |
| *luteum* | See *L. galeobdolon* |
| *maculatum* | CArn CRow EGoo EMon MMal NArg SEND SHFr SMac SRms WByw WGwG WRos WWye |
| - AL&JS 90226JU | EMon |
| - 'Album' | CGle CRow EFou ELan EMon ENot LGro MWat NChi NLon SHel SPer SRms WByw WRos WWat |
| - 'Anne Greenaway' | EPPr GBri MCLN MGrG MHlr NCat SMrm WCot |
| - 'Annecy' | MInt |
| § - 'Aureum' | CArn CGle CInt EBee EBrP EBre EHoe ELan EMon LBre LGro LHop MBro MCLN MTho NFai NVic SBre SUsu WCot WEas WHil WPer |
| - 'Beacon Silver' | More than 30 suppliers |
| - 'Beedham's White' | NBir NSti SCro |
| - 'Brightstone Pearl' | EGoo EMon WCer |
| - 'Cannon's Gold' | EBee ECtt EGar EHoe ELan EWes GBuc NSti SCob WCru |
| N - 'Chequers' | CDoC CJew EBee SCob SPer SPla |
| ¶ - 'Chequers Board' | EPla |
| - 'Dingle Candy' | CElw CMdw EMon |
| - 'Edinburgh Broadstripes' | EPla |
| - 'Elaine Franks' | CHid CSam NCat |
| - 'Elisabeth de Haas' (v) | CHal EBee EGar EGoo EMan EMon EWes GPin LHop MMal SCob WCHb WCer WHer WPer |
| - 'Gold Leaf' | See *L. maculatum* 'Aureum' |
| - Golden Anniversary = 'Dellam' (v) | EBee LEdu LWoo MCCP NArg NHol NPri SCob WWeb |
| - 'Golden Nuggets' | CMGP EAst LFis MLLN NCut NPla NPro NTay SMrm WEas |

¶ – 'Golden Wedding'    COtt
– 'Hatfield'    EMon GAbr GBuc
– 'Ickwell Beauty' (v)    EMon EWes GBri LFis MBrN
     MLLN NLak WElm WRHF
– 'Immaculate'    EPla
– 'James Boyd Parselle'    CLTr EBee EGoo MCAu MHlr
     MLLN SCro WCHb WCot WRHF
     WWat
– 'Margery Fish'    SRms WEas
– 'Pink Nancy'    CBot CMea EGoo GAbr MTho
     WCer WFar
– 'Pink Pearls'    EGar EMan EPPr MMal NHaw
     NPla SCob
– 'Pink Pewter'    CElw CGle CLTr EBee EBrP EBre
     ECGP ECha ECtt EFou EPla EWTr
     LBre LGro MBel NBrk NSti SBre
     SCro SPer SPlb SRPl SUsu WByw
     WCHb WCru WPer WRus WWat
– 'Purple Winter'    EPla
– 'Red Nancy'    CBlo EBee EGar EMar EMon EPPr
     EPla GCal NChi WCer
§ – 'Roseum'    CGle CHan CHar CRow EBee
     EFer EFou ELan EMar EPar EPla
     LGro LHop MMal MRav MWat
     NArg NChi NFai NFor NLon SPer
     WMow WPer WWat
– 'Shell Pink'    See *L. maculatum* 'Roseum'
– 'Silver Dollar'    Last listed 1996
– 'Sterling Silver'    EWes WPer
– 'White Nancy' ♀    More than 30 suppliers
– 'Wild White'    EPla
– 'Wootton Pink'    CBos CLTr EBee EGar GBuc GCal
     GMac LFis MBri MBro NBir NChi
     NLak SSvw WBro WEas WElm
     WHoo WPer
*microphyllum*    EHyt
*orvala*    CBot CGle CHan CLyd CPle ECha
     EGar EPla LFis MBel MCAu MFir
     MRav NChi SIgm SSpi SUsu WCot
     WCru WHer WPer WWat WWye
– 'Album'    CBot CBre CHan CPle EGar ELan
     EOrc EPPr MFir SAga SEas SMrm
     WCot WHer
¶ – 'Silva'    WCot
*sandrasicum*    EHyt

## LAMPRANTHUS (Aizoaceae)

*aberdeenensis*    See *Delosperma aberdeenense*
¶ *amoenus*    EOas
*aurantiacus*    CB&S NBrk
*aureus*    CTrC EOas SChr
'Bagdad'    Last listed 1998
*blandus*    CB&S
§ *brownii*    CB&S CHal EHcho ELan EOas NBir
     SEND WPat
'Carn Brea'    CHal
*coccineus*    Last listed 1998
*coralliflorus*    CTrC EOas
§ *deltoides*    CTrC MRav
*edulis*    See *Carpobrotus edulis*
¶ *falcatus*    EOas
*falciformis*    Last listed 1996
*glaucus*    SEND
*haworthii*    CHal SVen
*lehmannii*    See *Delosperma lehmannii*
*multiradiatus*    CTrC EOas SEND
*oscularis*    See *L. deltoides*
*pallidus*    See *Delosperma pallidum*
*primavernus*    Last listed 1996
*roseus*    EOas SSoC WEas
*scaber*    CTrC
*spectabilis*    CB&S EOas SAPC SArc WBrE

– 'Tresco Apricot'    CB&S
– 'Tresco Brilliant'    CB&S
– 'Tresco Fire'    CHal
– 'Tresco Peach'    Last listed 1998
– 'Tresco Red'    CB&S
*stayneri*    Last listed 1996
¶ *tegens*    EOas
'Tresco Pearl'    Last listed 1998
*zeyheri*    Last listed 1996

## LANTANA (Verbenaceae)

'Aloha' (v)    LHil
*camara*    ELan EPfP ERea MBri SRms WMul
– 'Brasier'    ERea
– Cloth of Gold    See *L. camara* 'Drap d'Or'
– 'Cocktail'    NPri
– 'Feston Rose'    ERea
– 'Firebrand'    SYvo
– forms    ERea
– 'Mine d'Or'    ERea
– 'Mr Bessieres'    ERea
– 'Snow White'    ERea
* 'Cocktail'    CLTr
'Gold Dust'    Last listed 1998
'Gold Mound'    MBEx
§ *montevidensis*    CHal ERea LHil MBEx SYvo WIvy
* – *alba*    ERea LHil
§ – 'Boston Gold'    CHal MBEx
– 'Malans Gold'    ERea
– 'White Lightning'    Last listed 1998
– 'Whiteknights'    MBEx
– 'Radiation'    ERea
*sellowiana*    See *L. montevidensis*
'Spreading Sunset'    SOWG WCot

## LAPAGERIA (Philesiaceae)

*rosea* ♀    CB&S CGre CMac CPIN CRHN
     CSam CWSG EPla ERea GQui
     IMGH MBal MDun SOWG SPer
     SReu SSpi SYvo WNor WWat
– var. *albiflora*    CPIN
– – 'White Cloud'    CGre
– 'Flesh Pink' ♀    CGre CPIN CRHN
– 'Nash Court' ♀    CPIN CSam ECot EMil ERea ISea
     SYvo WStI

## LAPEIROUSIA (Iridaceae)

*cruenta*    See *Anomatheca laxa*
*laxa*    See *Anomatheca laxa*

## LAPIEDRA (Amaryllidaceae)

*martinezii* MS 423    Last listed 1998

## LAPORTEA (Urticaceae)

* *bulbifera* 'Variegata' (v)    WCot

## LAPSANA (Asteraceae)

¶ *communis*    WJek
– 'Inky'    CNat
– 'Patchy' (v)    Last listed 1998

## LARDIZABALA (Lardizabalaceae)

*biternata*    CGre CPIN CTrG

## LARIX (Pinaceae)

*decidua* ♀    CB&S CDoC CDul ENot EWTr
     GChr GRei LCon LPan MBal MBar
     NWea SMad SPar SPer WDin WFar
     WHar WMou WStI WWal
– 'Corley'    CKen LCon LLin MBlu
– 'Croxby Broom'    CKen
¶ – 'Globus'    NHol SLim

| ¶ - 'Horstmann Recurved' | SLim |
| - 'Little Bogle' | CKen NHol |
| - 'Oberförster Karsten' | CKen |
| - 'Pendula' | CB&S |
| - 'Poulii' | CEnd COtt MBlu NHol SLim SPer |
| x *eurolepis* | See *L.* x *marschlinsii* |
| I *europaeus* | Last listed 1997 |
| *gmelinii* | ETen GAri ISea |
| - var. *olgensis* | GAri |
| - 'Tharandt' | CKen |
| § *kaempferi* ♀ | CDoC CDul CLnd CTri ENot |
| | GChr GRei LBuc LCon LNet MBar |
| | MGos NWea SLim SPer STre WFro |
| | WMou WNor WStI |
| - 'Bambino' | CKen |
| - 'Blue Ball' | CKen LLin |
| - 'Blue Dwarf' | CEnd CKen COtt IMGH LCon |
| | LNet MAsh MGos SLim |
| ¶ - 'Blue Haze' | CKen |
| ¶ - 'Blue Rabbit' | CKen |
| - 'Blue Rabbit Weeping' | COtt LCon LLin LPan MGos NHol |
| | SLim WDin |
| - 'Cruwys Morchard' | CKen |
| ¶ - 'Cupido' | NHol |
| - 'Diane' | CBlo CEnd CKen GAri LCon LLin |
| | MAsh MBlu MBri NHol SLim |
| - 'Elizabeth Rehder' | CKen |
| - 'Grant Haddow' | CKen LLin |
| - 'Green Pearl' | CKen LLin |
| ¶ - 'Grey Green Dwarf' | NHol |
| - 'Grey Pearl' | CKen |
| - 'Hobbit' | CKen |
| * - 'Jacobsen's Pyramid' | LLin NHol |
| - 'Little Blue Star' | Last listed 1997 |
| - 'Nana' | CKen GAri IMGH LLin WWes |
| I - 'Nana Prostrata' | CKen |
| - 'Pendula' | CBlo CDoC CEnd IOrc MBar |
| | MBlu MGos NHol SLim SPer |
| ¶ - 'Stiff Weeping' | SLim |
| ¶ - 'Swallow Falls' | CKen |
| - 'Varley' | CKen NHol |
| - 'Wehlen' | CKen |
| - 'Wolterdingen' | CKen LLin MBlu |
| - 'Yanus Olieslagers' | CKen |
| *laricina* | GAri |
| - 'Arethusa Bog' | CKen |
| * - 'Bear Swamp' | CKen |
| - 'Newport Beauty' | CKen |
| *leptolepis* | See *L. kaempferi* |
| § x *marschlinsii* | ENot GChr GRei NWea WMou |
| - 'Domino' | CKen LLin |
| - 'Gail' | CKen |
| - 'Julie' | CKen |
| *occidentalis* | GAri |
| x *pendula* 'Pendulina' | GAri |
| *russica* | See *L. sibirica* |
| § *sibirica* | GAri ISea MBar |
| *sukaczevii* | See *L. sibirica* |

**LARREA** (Zygophyllaceae)
| *tridentata* | MSal |

**LASER** (Apiaceae)
| *trilobum* | Last listed 1996 |

**LASERPITIUM** (Apiaceae)
| *siler* | NLar SIgm |

**LASIAGROSTIS** See STIPA

**LASTREOPSIS** (Dryopteridaceae)
| ¶ *microsora* | WRic |

**LATANIA** (Arecaceae)
| *loddigesii* | LPal |
| *verschaffeltii* | LPal |

**LATHYRUS** ✿ (Papilionaceae)
| *albus* | CEnd |
| *amphicarpos* | Last listed 1998 |
| *angulatus* | Last listed 1998 |
| *angustifolius* | WCot |
| *annuus* | Last listed 1998 |
| - red | Last listed 1998 |
| *aphaca* | Last listed 1998 |
| § *articulatus* | WBor |
| *aurantius* | NHol WLRN |
| § *aureus* | CBos CHan CLTr EBee ECha |
| | EMon GCal MAvo MHar MTho |
| | NChi NSti SUsu WCru WEas WHal |
| | WHil WPat WViv |
| *azureus* hort. | See *L. sativus* |
| *belinensis* | Last listed 1998 |
| *chilensis* | Last listed 1998 |
| *chloranthus* | EWll |
| *cicera* | Last listed 1998 |
| *cirrhosus* | EMon WCot |
| *clymenum* | Last listed 1998 |
| - *articulatus* | See *L. articulatus* |
| *cyaneus* (Steven) K.Koch | Last listed 1998 |
| - hort. | See *L. vernus* |
| * - 'Alboroseus' | CGle MTho |
| *davidii* | EMon WCot |
| *filiformis* | NChi SBla |
| *fremontii* hort. | See *L. laxiflorus* |
| *gloeospermus* | Last listed 1998 |
| § *gmelinii* | Last listed 1998 |
| - 'Aureus' | See *L. aureus* |
| *gorgonii* | Last listed 1998 |
| *grandiflorus* | CGle CSev EBee ECha EMon LGre |
| | NLar SMad SMrm SSad SUsu SWat |
| | WCot |
| *heterophyllus* | EBee EMon MNrw WHal WViv |
| *hierosolymitanus* | Last listed 1998 |
| *hirsutus* | MLLN |
| *hirticarpus* | Last listed 1998 |
| ¶ aff. *hookeri* | EBee |
| *inconspicuus* | Last listed 1998 |
| *inermis* | See *L. laxiflorus* |
| *japonicus* | SMad WViv |
| - subsp. *maritimus* | EBee LFis WMoo |
| *laetiflorus* var. *vestitus* | See *L. vestitus* |
| ¶ *laevigatus* | NLar |
| *lanszwertii* | Last listed 1998 |
| *latifolius* ♀ | CAgr CArn CGle CRHN EBrP EBre |
| | ECGP ELan EOld EWTr GCHN |
| | LBre LHop MFir MMal NFla NPer |
| | SBre SIng SRCN SRms SUsu WEas |
| | WFar WHer WOak WPer WStI |
| | WWin WWye |
| - 'Albus' ♀ | CBot ELan EMan EMon GChr |
| | GDra LGre MNrw SHFr SRms SSpi |
| | SUsu SWas WEas WHoo |
| - 'Blushing Bride' | WCot |
| - deep pink | NSti |
| - pale pink | CSam NSti |
| - Pink Pearl | See *L. latifolius* 'Rosa Perle' |
| - 'Red Pearl' | CBlo CPlN ECtt EFou ELan MBri |
| | NCut NPri SMrm SPer SSvw WPer |
| | WRus |
| § - 'Rosa Perle' ♀ | CBlo CDoC CHid CTri ECtt EFou |
| | EMan EWTr GAbr MAvo MBri |
| | MCAu MSte NCut NFai NLar NPer |
| | SMrm SPer SRPl SSvw WRus WViv |

| | |
|---|---|
| - 'Rose Queen' | CB&S |
| I - 'Rubra' | EPfP |
| - 'Splendens' | CB&S MAvo NFai WOak |
| - Weisse Perle | See *L. latifolius* 'White Pearl' |
| § - 'White Pearl' ♀ | CB&S CGle CHea CMea ECha |
| | EFou EOrc EWTr GAbr LPVe |
| | MBNS MBri MCAu MSte NChi |
| | NFai NLar NPer NSti SBra SMad |
| | SPer SSoC SSvw WOve WPer |
| | WRus WWat |
| § *laxiflorus* | CSpe EBee EMon GMac MNrw |
| | MTho NLar NTow SOkh SSca |
| | WCom WWin |
| *linifolius* | EMon SOkh |
| - var. *montanus* | CKin EBee WGwy |
| ♦ *luteus* (L.) Peterm. | See *L. gmelinii* |
| ♦ - Munby | WLin |
| - 'Aureus' | See *L. aureus* |
| * *macrocarpus* F&W 7737 | Last listed 1996 |
| *marmoratus* | Last listed 1998 |
| *montanus* | WViv |
| § *nervosus* | CPlN CPou CSpe MAvo MFir |
| | MTho SBla SMad SRCN SRms |
| *neurolobus* | CNic EHyt EWll MOne |
| *niger* | CHan CHid EBee EMar EMon |
| | NLar SHFr SOkh WGwy |
| *nissolia* | ELan |
| *ochrus* | EWll |
| *odoratus* ♀ | CGle CHan CHar EWll SAga SUsu |
| | WEas |
| - 'America' ♀ | Last listed 1996 |
| - 'Bicolor' | ELan |
| - 'Captain of the Blues' | Last listed 1996 |
| - 'Countess Cadogan' | Last listed 1996 |
| - 'Cupani' | Last listed 1996 |
| - 'Matucana' | Last listed 1998 |
| - 'Painted Lady' | CGle |
| - 'Quito' | Last listed 1996 |
| - 'The Busby Pea' | Last listed 1998 |
| - 'Violet Queen' | Last listed 1996 |
| *palustris* | MNrw NLar |
| *pannonicus* | MFir |
| *paranensis* | Last listed 1998 |
| *polyphyllus* | WCot |
| *pratensis* | CKin EWFC SSca WViv |
| *pubescens* | CRHN EBee EMon GBuc |
| ¶ *roseus* | EMon |
| *rotundifolius* | CPlN EBee ECoo EMon GCal |
| | GDra LGre MNrw MTho NSti |
| | SUsu SWas WCom WCot WEas |
| | WHoo WPyg |
| - hybrids | LGre |
| - 'Tillyperone' | EMon |
| § *sativus* | CHad CSpe LHop SSad WBor |
| | WEas |
| - var. *albus* | Last listed 1996 |
| - var. *azureus* | See *L. sativus* |
| *setifolius* | Last listed 1998 |
| *sphaericus* | Last listed 1998 |
| *sylvestris* | CKin EBee ELan EMon EWll |
| | MLLN MNrw MSCN MSte SHel |
| | WGwy |
| - 'Wagneri' | CSpe |
| *tingitanus* | CRHN CSpe |
| - 'Flame' | Last listed 1998 |
| - *roseus* | Last listed 1998 |
| - 'Roseus' | SUsu |
| - salmon pink | Last listed 1998 |
| ¶ *transsilvanicus* | EMon |
| *tuberosus* | EBee EMon MNrw WCot |
| 'Tubro' | EMon |
| *undulatus* | Last listed 1997 |

| | |
|---|---|
| * *uniflorus* | MSCN |
| *venetus* | EMon MNrw WViv |
| § *vernus* ♀ | More than 30 suppliers |
| - 'Alboroseus' ♀ | More than 30 suppliers |
| - var. *albus* | EWes GAri |
| - *aurantiacus* | See *L. aureus* |
| - 'Caeruleus' | CRDP LGre SMrm WPGP |
| * - *cyaneus* | NTow SOkh SWas SWat WRus |
| | WSan |
| - 'Flaccidus' | WKif WSan |
| - 'Rosenelfe' | CBot EMan MAvo WHil WSan |
| | WViv |
| - f. *roseus* | ECha MRav WCot |
| - 'Spring Melody' | EBee LFis LPio SMrm SOkh WCot |
| | WPat WRHF WShe |
| § *vestitus* | Last listed 1998 |
| - var. *alefeldii* | Last listed 1998 |
| ¶ - var. *vestitus* | EMon |
| *vinealis* | Last listed 1998 |

## LAURELIA (Monimiaceae)

| | |
|---|---|
| § *sempervirens* | CB&S CGre CTrw SAPC SArc |
| *serrata* | See *L. sempervirens* |

## LAURENTIA (Campanulaceae)

| | |
|---|---|
| § *axillaris* | CBar CLTr EBrP EBre LBre LHil |
| | LHop LLck SBre SCoo SHFr WWin |
| *minuta* | Last listed 1997 |

## LAURUS (Lauraceae)

| | |
|---|---|
| § *azorica* | CB&S CGre WSPU WWat |
| *canariensis* | See *L. azorica* |
| *nobilis* ♀ | More than 30 suppliers |
| - f. *angustifolia* | CSWP EPla GQui LHol MBlu |
| | MRav SAPC SArc SDry WCHb |
| | WOak WSel |
| - 'Aurea' ♀ | CB&S CGre CMHG EBee ELan |
| | ELau EMil ERav ERea GQui IOrc |
| | LHol LNet MAsh MBlu MChe |
| | SBrw SLon SPer WCHb WPat |
| | WPyg WSel WWat |
| - 'Crispa' | MRav |

## LAVANDULA ✿ (Lamiaceae)

| | |
|---|---|
| N 'Alba' | CArn CB&S CBot CSev EFou ELan |
| | GCHN LHol NYoL SIde SPer SPil |
| | SWat WEas WOak WPer |
| x *allardii* | CArn CSev EMil ENor EOHP GBar |
| | MChe NHHG SPan SRCN WJek |
| | WPen WSel |
| - 'African Pride' | SDow |
| - Clone B | SDow |
| - forms | WTus |
| § *angustifolia* | CArn CLan EBee ELau ENot GOrc |
| | GPoy LBuc MBar MBri MChe |
| | MGos MMal MPla MWat NChi |
| | NFla NFor NPer NYoL SEas SMac |
| | SRPl WAbe WPyg WTus WWye |
| - 'Alba' | CChe EHic EHoe ELau EWTr |
| | GChr GPoy LBuc LHop MBNS |
| | MChe NFai NLon NMen SLon |
| | WSel WWat |
| - 'Alba Nana' | See *L. angustifolia* 'Nana Alba' |
| ¶ - 'Arabian Knight' | LRHS |
| - 'Ashdown Forest' | CSev EBee MChe SDow SRPl |
| | WJek WLRN WTus |
| - 'Beechwood Blue' | NYoL SDow WTus |
| ¶ - 'Blue Mountain' | LRHS |
| § - 'Bowles' Early' | CSam ENor GBar MChe SDow |
| | WJek WTus |
| - 'Bowles' Grey' | See *L. angustifolia* 'Bowles' Early' |
| - 'Bowles' Variety' | See *L. angustifolia* 'Bowles' Early' |

- 'Cedar Blue'                CSev EGoo ELau NYoL SDow
                              SHDw SIde SPla WTus
- 'Compacta'                  WTus
- 'Dwarf Blue'                EMil MWhi WTus
I - 'Eastgrove Nana'          WEas WTus
- 'Folgate'                   CArn CB&S EAst EFou ELau LHol
                              MChe MHlr MPla NHHG NLon
                              NYoL SDow SIde SPil WGwG
                              WSel WTus
- 'Fring Favourite'           SDow WTus
- 'Heacham Blue'              Last listed 1996
§ - 'Hidcote' ♀              More than 30 suppliers
- 'Hidcote Pink'              CArn CGle EFou EOld ESis LHol
                              MWat NFai NFla NFor NMen
                              NRoo NSti SDow SPer SRPl SSoC
                              WGwG WHen WPer WSel WStI
                              WTus WWat
- 'Imperial Gem'              CRos EBee EHic ENor ESis GBar
                              MAsh MBri MChe NHHG NPer
                              SDow SEas SIde WHoo WSel WTus
                              WWeb
§ - 'Jean Davis'             EBee GBar LHop NHHG SDow
                              SIde WSel WTus WWat
- 'Lady'                      CM&M EOHP GBar MChe MWat
                              NOrc NRoo SDow SEND SHDw
                              WElm WLRN WTus
N - 'Lavender Lady'          EAst NYoL WPer WWeb
¶ - Little Lady = 'Batlad'   ENor WGwG WTus
¶ - Little Lottie = 'Clarmo' ENor LRHS NDov SVil WTus
- 'Loddon Blue'               CB&S CWSG EBee ELau GBar
                              LHol NFla NHHG NLon NYoL
                              SDow SIde WJek WTus
§ - 'Loddon Pink'            CDoC CWSG ECle ELan ENor
                              ENot EOHP ERea GBar GCHN
                              MAsh MChe MPla MUlv NYoL
                              SDow SRPl WAbe WEas WGwG
                              WHoo WJek WStI WTus WWal
                              WWat WWeb
- 'Maillette'                 Last listed 1997
¶ - 'Miss Donnington'        ENor
- 'Miss Katherine'            ENor SDow WTus
- 'Munstead'                  More than 30 suppliers
§ - 'Nana Alba'              CB&S CSev ECha EFou ELan ELau
                              ENor ENot GPoy LHol LHop MBar
                              MBri MMal MPla MUlv NHHG
                              SDow SPer WEas WGwG WHoo
                              WKif WPat WSel WTus WWat
- 'Nana Atropurpurea'         SDow WSel WTus
- No. 9                       Last listed 1996
- 'Princess Blue'             ELan ENor ESis GBar LFis MAsh
                              MBNS NYoL SDow SIde SRPl SSca
                              WPer WSel WTus WWeb WWoo
§ - 'Rosea'                  CArn CB&S CChe CDul CMea
                              CPri ECha EGoo EHoe GChr
                              GPoy LHop MBar MBri NHHG
                              SDow SIde SPer WGwG WHer
                              WOak WTus WWeb
- 'Royal Purple'              CArn ENor EOld EWes GBar LFis
                              LHol MBNS MUlv NHHG NYoL
                              SDow SIde WSel WTus WWye
N - 'Twickel Purple' ♀       EBee LHop MBNS MChe MPla
                              NChi NDov NHHG NYoL SAga
                              SCoo SDow SIde SSoC WGwG
                              WSel WTus
'Blue Cushion'                EBee EBrP EBre LBre MAsh MBNS
                              SBre
* 'Blue Star'                EFou
'Bowers Beauty'               WTus
buchii var. buchii            Last listed 1997
- var. gracilis               SDow WTus
N 'Cambridge Lady'            WHer
canariensis                   CSev ENor EOHP ERea MHer
                              NHHG SDow SHDw SSad WCHb
                              WJek WTus

x christiana                  ELau SDow SHDw WTus
'Cornard Blue'                See L. 'Sawyers'
dentata                       CArn CInt CSev ELan ELau ENor
                              EPri ERea LFis MChe NBrk NHHG
                              SDow SDry SPil WAbe WHer
                              WOak WTus WWye
§ - var. candicans           CGle CSev ENor EOHP LHil LHop
                              MChe MSCN NHHG SAga SDow
                              SMrm SPil SSad WCHb WEas WPer
                              WTus WWye
- 'Linda Ligon'               SDow WTus
- 'Ploughman's Blue'          SDow WTus
- 'Royal Crown'               CStr ENor SDow WTus
- silver                      See L. dentata var. candicans
- 'Silver Queen'              SHDw WTus
'Devantville Cuche'           NSti WJek WTus
'Dilly Dilly'                 WTus
* 'Fontwell'                 SRPl
'Fragrant Memories'           ELau ERea MAsh SDow SSoC
                              WTus
'Goodwin Creek Grey'          MChe SDow WTus
'Hidcote Blue'                See L. angustifolia 'Hidcote'
§ x intermedia               SRPl
- 'Abrialii'                  SDow WTus
- 'Alba'                      ECle ENor NHHG SDow SRPl
                              WLRN WTus
N - 'Arabian Night'          COtt LRHS SDow WTus
¶ - 'Bogong'                 WTus
§ - Dutch Group ♀            CArn CDoC EFou ELan ENot EOld
                              EPfP EWTr MBar MBri NYoL SChu
                              SCoo SDow SPer SWat WHen
                              WJek WPer WSel WTus
§ - - Walberton's Silver
      Edge = 'Walvera' (v)   ENor LRHS WWeb
- 'Grappenhall'               CArn CEnd CSam EBee ELau EMil
                              ENor LHol LHop MAsh MBNS
                              MChe MPla MRav NFai NFla NLon
                              NVic NYoL SChu SDow SPer
                              WGwG WOak WPer WSel WTus
                              WWat WWye
- 'Grey Hedge'                LHol SDow WTus
- 'Grosso'                    CChe COtt CPri CSev ELau ENor
                              LHol NDov NSti NYoL SDow
                              WJek WLRN WTus
- 'Hidcote Giant'             EHal LRHS MAsh NPer SAga
                              SDow WSel WTus WWat
* - 'Hidcote White'          CDul WTus
- 'Lullingstone Castle'       CBod ELau NYoL SDow SIde
                              WJek WTus
- 'Mitcham Blue'              Last listed 1996
- Old English Group           CArn CBod ELan ELau MMal NBrk
                              NYoL SDow SIde WHoo WJek
                              WOak WSel WTus WWat
- 'Seal'                      CArn EBee ECle EFou ELau GBar
                              LHol MChe NHHG NSti NWoo
                              NYoL SDow SIde WGwG WHCG
                              WPer WSel WTus WWal WWat
- 'Super'                     SDow
N - 'Twickel Purple'         CArn CMHG CSev ECGP ELau
                              ENot EWes LFis LHol NHHG SChu
                              SWat WGwG WJek WOak WWat
'Jean Davis'                  See L. angustifolia 'Jean Davis'
lanata ♀                     CArn CBot CFri CGle CHan CLon
                              ECha ELan ENor GPoy MBro
                              MChe MPla MWat NHHG NLon
                              NSti SDow SDry WEas WGwG
                              WSHC WTus WWye
- x angustifolia              NHHG WTus
§ latifolia                  CArn GBar SDow WTus
* - 'Alba'                   Last listed 1997
¶ 'Little Lottie'            ERic LHop LRHS MTis
'Loddon Pink'                 See L. angustifolia 'Loddon Pink'

| | |
|---|---|
| *mairei* × *intermedia* | WTus |
| *minutolii* | ENor SDow WTus |
| *multifida* | CArn CSev EEls ENor ERea MChe MHer SDow SSad WCHb WGwG WTus WWal |
| *officinalis* | See *L. angustifolia* |
| § *pinnata* | CArn CSev ENor ERea GBar MChe NHHG SDow SDry SSad WCHb WEas WHal WTus |
| *pterostoechas pinnata* | See *L. pinnata* |
| ¶ *pubescens* | SDow |
| 'Richard Gray' | EBee EMon GBar LHop LRHS NBrk WAbe WBcn WHen WTus |
| 'Rosea' | See *L. angustifolia* 'Rosea' |
| *rotundifolia* | SDow WTus |
| 'Saint Brelade' | SDow WTus |
| § 'Sawyers' | More than 30 suppliers |
| * 'Silber Dwarf' | EFou |
| ♦ 'Silver Edge' | See *L.* × *intermedia* (Dutch Group) Walberton's Silver Edge = 'Walvera' |
| N *spica* nom. rejic. | See *L. angustifolia, L. latifolia, L.* × *intermedia* |
| - 'Hidcote Purple' | See *L. angustifolia* 'Hidcote' |
| *stoechas* ♀ | More than 30 suppliers |
| - var. *albiflora* | See *L. stoechas* f. *leucantha* |
| - subsp. *atlantica* | SDow WTus |
| - subsp. *cariensis* | SDow |
| - dark form | WTus |
| - 'Fathead' | CChe COtt ENor EPfP LRHS MAsh SDow WTus |
| - 'Helmsdale' | CDoC CJew CRos CStr EBrP EBre ELan ENor IOrc LBre LHop MAsh MBri MLan MRav MUlv MWgw NYoL SAga SBre SCoo SDow SPer SPla SUsu SVil WTus WWat WWeb |
| - 'Kew Red' | CMea MAsh SDow SHDw WTus |
| § - f. *leucantha* | CArn CBot CMHG CSev CTre EAst EBee ECha ELan ELau LHol MAsh MBNS MBri MChe MPla NSti NWoo SChu SDow SPer WCHb WPer WTus WWat |
| - subsp. *luisieri* | SDow WHer |
| - subsp. *lusitanica* | SDow WTus |
| - 'Marshwood' | CRos EBee EBrP EBre ELan ENor EPfP ERic LBre LBuc MAsh MBel MMal MUlv NYoL SAga SBre SCoo SDow SMad SPer SPla WElm WTus WWat WWeb |
| * - 'Nana' | CArn |
| - 'Papillon' | See *L. stoechas* subsp. *pedunculata* |
| § - subsp. *pedunculata* ♀ | More than 30 suppliers |
| - - 'Avonview' | CB&S SDow |
| - - 'James Compton' | EBee EHic EMon ERea LHop LRHS MAsh NDov NPSI SDow SSoC SUsu WLin WTus |
| - 'Pippa' | WTus |
| - 'Pukehou' | WTus |
| - subsp. *sampaioana* | SDow WTus |
| - 'Snowman' | ELan ENor IOrc LRHS MAsh MWat NDov NYoL SDow SPla SRPl WFar WTus WWal |
| - 'Sugar Plum' | WTus |
| - 'Summerset Mist' | WTus |
| - 'Willow Vale' | CMHG COtt ENor LGre LRHS SDow SPan SRCN WEas WSPU WTus WWeb |
| * - 'Wine Red' | WTus WWoo |
| *subnuda* | WTus |
| *vera* DC. | See *L. angustifolia* |
| - hort. | See *L.* × *intermedia* Dutch Group |

| | |
|---|---|
| *viridis* | CArn CPla CSev ELan ENor ERav GOrc LGre MAsh MChe NHHG NPer SDow SPer SSad WCHb WHer WPer WTus WWat WWye |

## LAVATERA (Malvaceae)

| | |
|---|---|
| * 'Alba' | LFis |
| *arborea* | CArn GBar SChr WHer |
| - 'Ile d'Hyères' | Last listed 1996 |
| - 'Rosea' | See *L.* 'Rosea' |
| - 'Variegata' | CHan CInt ELan GBar LHop MHlr NPer NSti SBod SDix SEND WCot WCru WEas WHer WWal |
| *assurgentiflora* | GBri |
| 'Barnsley' ♀ | CB&S CChe CDoC CMHG EAst EBee EBrP EBre ECha ENot EWTr GCHN GRei IOrc ISea LBre LHop MAsh MBar MBri MGos NFai SBre SPer SRms WAbe WBod WDin WFar WWat |
| 'Barnsley Perry's Dwarf' | Last listed 1997 |
| *bicolor* | See *L. maritima* |
| 'Blushing Bride' | CBlo EBee EBrP EBre EHic ELan EPfP GMac LBre LFis MAsh MBri MLLN MSCN NPri SBod SBre SDix SMrm WHar |
| 'Bredon Springs' ♀ | CB&S CChe CDoC EBee EBrP EBre ECha ECtt EMil EWTr GBri LBre LFis LHop MAsh MBri MNrw NBrk SBid SBod SBre SMrm SPar SRPl SSoC WFar WPyg WStl WWal WWeb |
| * 'Bressingham Pink' | SMad |
| 'Burgundy Wine' ♀ | CB&S CChe EBee EBrP EBre ECtt ELan GRei LBre MAsh MBar MBri MGos MRav NBee NChi NPer SBod SBre SLon SPer WCFE WDin WFar WHar WHen WStl WWeb |
| *cachemiriana* | EBee ELan GBuc GCal MFir NLak NPer WWat |
| 'Candy Floss' ♀ | CB&S EBee ELan ENot ERic GChr MAsh MBNS MBar MGos NPer SMrm SPer WDin WStl WWal WWeb |
| 'Chedglow' (v) | Last listed 1998 |
| 'Eye Catcher' | LFis LRHS MAsh MAvo SPer SUsu WElm WRHF |
| 'Kew Rose' | CB&S CBlo EBee EMil EPfP LHop MAsh NPer SBid SPla SSoC WGwG |
| 'Lara Rose' | MGos |
| 'Lavender Lady' | SMrm |
| 'Lilac Lady' | CB&S LFis LRHS MAsh MAvo MCCP SLod SMad SPer SUsu |
| 'Linda' | WBcn |
| 'Lisanne' | EBee EHic EOrc MCCP MNrw NChi NHol NPri NPro SUsu |
| § *maritima* ♀ | CBot CDoC CGle CGre CHan CMHG ELan EOld GMac LHil LHop MAsh SDry SMrm SPer SUsu WCot WEas WFar WHCG WKif |
| - *bicolor* | See *L. maritima* |
| 'Mary Hope' | CHan LHop NPro WWeb |
| 'Memories' | ELan LRHS |
| 'Moonstone' | SMrm |
| *oblongifolia* | CBot |
| N *olbia* | CGle MPla MSCN MWat NFai SDix |
| 'Pavlova' | CDoC EBee LRHS MAsh MCCP MTis NHol SSto |
| 'Peppermint Ice' | See *L. thuringiaca* 'Ice Cool' |

'Pink Frills' — CBot EBrP EBre EMil LBre LHop MAvo MBar MNrw NBrk SBid SBre SDry SSoC WCot WHar WPyg WRus WStl WWeb

*plebeia* — Last listed 1998

'Poynton Lady' — MGos NEgg

§ 'Rosea' ♀ — CB&S CChe EBee EBrP EBre ECha ELan ENot EWTr GRei LBre LHop MBar MBri MGos NFor SBod SBre SLon SPer WAbe WBod WDin WFar WWin

¶ 'Shadyvale Star' — NPro

'Shorty' — ELan NBrk WFar

'Snowcap' — CBlo

¶ 'Sweet Dreams' — MBri

*tauricensis* — Last listed 1996

N *thuringiaca* — EBot MWhi NBro NPri WFar WShe

– AL&JS 90100YU — Last listed 1998

§ – 'Ice Cool' — CBot CElw ECha ECtt ELan EOrc ERav GCal LHop MAsh MBar MGos NBee NBrk NPer SBid SMrm SPer SSoC WFar WHen

'Variegata' — See *L.* 'Wembdon Variegated'

§ 'Wembdon Variegated' — ELan MCCP MLLN NPer

¶ 'White Angel' — MBNS MBri

## LAWSONIA (Lythraceae)

*inermis* — MSal WGwG

## LEDEBOURIA (Hyacinthaceae)

*adlamii* — See *L. cooperi*

§ *cooperi* — CHal CRDP EBla EHyt ELan ERos ESis GCal GCrs IBlr LHil SCob WAbe

\* *pauciflora* — Last listed 1997

§ *socialis* — CHal CSWP CSev CSpe EOHP ERav ERos IBlr LHil MBro NChi NRog

*violacea* — See *L. socialis*

## x LEDODENDRON (Ericaceae)

§ 'Arctic Tern' ♀ — CDoC GChr GGGa ITim LHyd LMil MAsh MBal MBar MBri MDun MGos MLea NHar NHol SPer SReu WAbe WPic

## LEDUM (Ericaceae)

*glandulosum* — Last listed 1996

– var. *columbianum* — MBal

*groenlandicum* — EWTr GEil MBar MGos WAbe WGer WSHC

– 'Compactum' — LRHS MAsh MBal

*hypoleucum* — See *L. palustre* f. *dilatatum*

*macrophyllum* — CFir

*palustre* — EPot GGGa GPoy MBal MGos SRPl WAbe

– subsp. *decumbens* — GCrs GGGa

'Teshio' — SSta

## LEEA (Leeaceae)

*coccinea* — See *L. guineensis*

§ *guineensis* — MBri

## LEGOUSIA (Campanulaceae)

*hybrida* — EWFC

## LEIBNITZIA (Asteraceae)

*anandria* — NWCA

## LEIOPHYLLUM (Ericaceae)

*buxifolium* ♀ — CB&S EPfP EPot GCrs LRHS MAsh MBal MBro NHol SBrw SSpi SSta WPat WPyg

\* – 'Compactum' — Last listed 1996

– var. *bugeri* — NHar WAbe

## LEMBOTROPIS See CYTISUS

## LEMNA (Lemnaceae)

*gibba* — CWat LPBA SAWi

*minor* — CWat EHon EMFW LPBA MSta SAWi SWat

*minuscula* — Last listed 1997

*polyrhiza* — See *Spirodela polyrhiza*

*trisulca* — CWat EHon EMFW LPBA MSta SAWi SWat

## LEONOTIS (Lamiaceae)

*dysophylla* — WCot

– 'Pussytoes' — Last listed 1998

– 'Toastytoes' — WCot

*leonitis* — See *L. ocymifolia*

¶ *leonurus* — ERav LHil

\* *menthifolia* — SSpi

*nepetifolia* — EMan WCot

§ *ocymifolia* — CFee CTrC EPPr LBlm SHFr WHer WWye

– var. *ocymifolia* — WCot

'Staircase' — WRos WSan

## LEONTICE (Berberidaceae)

*albertii* — See *Gymnospermium albertii*

## LEONTODON (Asteraceae)

*autumnalis* — CKin

*hispidus* — CKin NMir

§ *rigens* — EMan GAri GBri GBuc LFis MUlv NBid NSti NTow SMrm WCot

¶ – 'Girandole' — CInt EBee LIck MNrw NHol SUsu WPer WWal

## LEONTOPODIUM (Asteraceae)

*alpinum* — EBot EBrP EBre ESis GAbr GCHN GLil GTou LBre MBal MBro MMal NFla NFor NMen NNrd SBre SIng SPlb SRms WPer WWin

– 'Mignon' — CMea ELan EMNN EWes GCrs GDra GTou MBro NMen NNrd NRoo NVic SSmi WHoo

– subsp. *nivale* — WLin

*bayachinense miyabeanum* — Last listed 1998

*bimalayanum* — Last listed 1998

*kamtschaticum* — EWes

¶ *linearifolium* KS 2111 — WCot

§ *ochroleucum* — WPer

var. *campestre*

*palibinianum* — See *L. ochroleucum* var. *campestre*

*sibiricum* — See *L. leontopodioides*

*souliei* — Last listed 1996

*tataricum* — See *L. discolor*

*wilsonii* — ECha

## LEONURUS (Lamiaceae)

*artemisia* — MSal

*cardiaca* — CArn EBee EMan EMon EWFC GBar GPoy MChe MHew MSal NHex SIde WHbs WHer WOak WSel WWye

– 'Crispus' — EMon

*macranthus* — EFEx

– var. *alba* — EFEx

*sibiricus* — EBee GBar IIve MSal WElm

## LEOPOLDIA (Hyacinthaceae)
*brevipedicellata*  Last listed 1996
*comosa*  See *Muscari comosum*
*spreitzenhoferi*  See *Muscari spreitzenhoferi*
*tenuiflora*  See *Muscari tenuiflorum*

## LEPECHINIA (Lamiaceae)
*calycina*  Last listed 1998
§ *chamaedryoides*  CGre
*floribunda*  CPle

## LEPIDIUM (Brassicaceae)
*barnebyanum*  Last listed 1997
- NNS 93-420  Last listed 1998
*nanum*  MRPP

## LEPIDOTHAMNUS (Podocarpaceae)
§ *laxifolius*  CMHG SIng

## LEPIDOZAMIA (Zamiaceae)
*hopei*  LPal
*peroffskyana*  CBrP LPal

## LEPTARRHENA (Saxifragaceae)
*pyrolifolia*  Last listed 1996

## LEPTINELLA (Asteraceae)
§ *albida*  GCrs LGro WLin
§ *atrata*  MDHE NMen
- subsp. *luteola*  EWes GGar MDHE NMen NWCA
SChu SDys SSmi WAbe
§ *dendyi*  EHyt EWes NMen
- forms  Last listed 1996
- 'Southley'  Last listed 1997
*filicula*  ECou
* *hispida*  Last listed 1998
*maniototo*  ECou
§ *minor*  ECou MOne SSmi WCru
§ *pectinata*  ECou
- var. *sericea*  See *L. albida*
§ *potentillina*  CTri ECha EHoe ELan ESis MBNS
MWgw NHol SChu SIng SRms
WCru WPer WRHF WWin
§ *pusilla*  SDys SSmi
§ *pyrethrifolia*  CInt CSam NMen
- var. *linearifolia*  ELan SIng
- var. *pyrethrifolia*  NTow
*reptans*  See *L. scariosa*
§ *rotundata*  ECou WPer
§ *scariosa*  Last listed 1998
§ *serrulata*  GCHN MBar NHol WCru
* aff. *socialis* JJ&JH 9401641  Last listed 1998
§ *squalida*  CNic ECha IBlr MBar NBro NRya
NSti NVic SIng SSmi WPer
§ - 'Platt's Black'  EDAr GCrs LRHS NSti SDys SSmi

## LEPTODACTYLON (Polemoniaceae)
§ *californicum*  CPBP LGre
- subsp. *glandulosum*  Last listed 1998
*pungens pulchriflorum*  Last listed 1998

## LEPTOPTERIS (Osmundaceae)
*hymenophylloides*  Last listed 1997
* *laxa*  Last listed 1997
* *media*  Last listed 1997
*moorei*  Last listed 1997
*superba*  Last listed 1997
*wilkesiana*  Last listed 1997

## LEPTOSPERMUM ✿ (Myrtaceae)
*arachnoides*  Last listed 1998

*argenteum*  CB&S
*brachyandrum*  Last listed 1998
  weeping, silver-leaved form
*citratum*  See *L. petersonii*
* *compactum*  CPLG
*cunninghamii*  See *L. myrtifolium*
*epacridoideum*  Last listed 1998
*ericoides*  See *Kunzea ericoides*
*flavescens* misapplied  See *L. glaucescens*
- Sm.  See *L. polygalifolium*
§ *glaucescens*  Last listed 1998
§ *grandiflorum*  CFil CHan CTrG ELan ISea SOWG
WSHC WWeb
*grandifolium*  ECou SSpi
'Green Eyes' (*minutifolium*  ECou MSag
x *scoparium*)
*humifusum*  See *L. rupestre*
*juniperinum*  CB&S CPle SPlb
*laevigatum*  Last listed 1997
- 'Yarrum'  ECou
§ *lanigerum* ♀  CB&S CMHG CPle CTri ECou
GCHN GLch IOrc SOWG WWin
* - 'Citratum'  ECou
- 'Cunninghamii'  See *L. myrtifolium*
- 'King William'  ECou
- 'Silver Sheen'  See *L. myrtifolium* 'Silver Sheen'
- 'Wellington'  ECou
*liversidgei*  CPle ECou
*macrocarpum*  Last listed 1997
*minutifolium*  ECou
§ *myrtifolium*  CDoC CPMA CTri ECou ELan
EPfP EPla EWes SDry SOWG SPer
SSta WPat WPic WPyg
- 'Newnes Forest'  ECou
- x *scoparium*  ECou
§ - 'Silver Sheen'  MSag SLon
*nitidum*  ECou
* - 'Cradle'  ECou
*obovatum*  CMHG
§ *petersonii*  CArn ECou EOHP
*phylicoides*  See *Kunzea ericoides*
'Pink Surprise'  ECou MSag SOWG
(*minutifolium*
x *scoparium*)
*polyanthum*  Last listed 1998
§ *polygalifolium*  CTrC SRms
*prostratum*  See *L. rupestre*
*pubescens*  See *L. lanigerum*
*riparium*  Last listed 1998
*rodwayanum*  See *L. grandiflorum*
*rotundifolium*  CTrC ECou EOHP
- from Jervis Bay  Last listed 1998
* 'Ruby Wedding'  LRHS
§ *rupestre* ♀  CTri ECou EPot GTou LHop MBal
MBar MGos NHar SDry SIng SRms
WLin WSHC WWat
- x *scoparium*  ECou
*scoparium*  CArn CMFo ECou ELau ERom
GAri IOrc WDin
- 'Autumn Glory'  EHoe GOrc MSag SMrm WStI
- 'Avocet'  ECou EWes
- 'Black Robin'  SOWG
- 'Blossom'  CB&S ECou SOWG
¶ - 'Boscawenii'  CB&S LHil
- 'Bunting'  Last listed 1997
- 'Burgundy Queen'  CB&S ECou
- 'Chapmanii'  CB&S CMHG CTrG CTri
- 'Charmer'  Last listed 1998
- 'Cherry Brandy'  Last listed 1998
- 'Chiff Chaff'  Last listed 1997
- 'Coral Candy'  CB&S SOWG
- 'Elizabeth Jane'  EWes GCHN GQui

| | |
|---|---|
| - 'Fascination' | CGre |
| - 'Firecrest' | Last listed 1997 |
| - 'Fred's Red' | EWes |
| - 'Grandiflorum' | CTrw GCHN WGer |
| - var. *incanum* 'Keatleyi' ♀ | CMHG ECou EPfP MSag SOWG WPyg |
| - - 'Wairere' | ECou |
| - 'Jubilee' (d) | CB&S ISea |
| - 'Leonard Wilson' (d) | CTri ECou EWes LBlm MSag |
| - 'Lyndon' | ECou |
| - 'Martini' | CDoC CTrC CTrG IOrc LHil SOWG WCot WWeb |
| - 'McLean' | ECou |
| - (Nanum Group) 'Huia' | CB&S ENot IOrc |
| - - 'Kea' | ESis GQui MRav WPyg |
| - - 'Kiwi' ♀ | CB&S CBrm CDoC ELan ENot EWes GOrc GQui IOrc ISea ITim MAsh MDun NHol WLRN WPat WPyg |
| ¶ - - 'Kompakt' | EPot |
| - - 'Nanum' | CDoC EPot NMen SBod SIng |
| - - 'Pipit' | EPot EWes |
| - - 'Tui' | CTrC MSag |
| - 'Nichollsii' ♀ | CB&S CGre CHan CMHG CTri ENot GQui ITim SOWG WHar WSHC |
| - 'Nichollsii Nanum' ♀ | CDoC CMea EPot ITim NHol SIng SRms WAbe WPat WPyg |
| - 'Pink Cascade' | CB&S CBlo CTri IOrc MBal MSag SAga |
| - 'Pink Champagne' | Last listed 1997 |
| - hort. var. *prostratum* | See *L. rupestre* |
| - 'Red Damask' (d) ♀ | CB&S CChe CDoC CGre CLan CTrC CTre EBee ELan GQui IMGH IOrc LHil LHop MAsh MRav SBod SIng SOWG SRms WSHC WWeb |
| - 'Red Ensign' | SBod |
| - 'Red Falls' | CDoC ECou MSag SOWG |
| - 'Redpoll' | ECou |
| - 'Redstart' | Last listed 1997 |
| - 'Robin' | Last listed 1998 |
| - 'Rosy Morn' | ISea |
| - 'Ruby Glow' (d) | LRHS WBod |
| - 'Ruby Wedding' | Last listed 1997 |
| * - 'Silver Spire' | SOWG |
| - 'Snow Flurry' | CB&S CTrC ENot GOrc IMGH ISea SRPl WWeb |
| - 'Sunraysia' | CDoC CTrw |
| - 'Winter Cheer' | Last listed 1998 |
| - 'Wiri Amy' | Last listed 1996 |
| ¶ - 'Wiri Joan' | CDoC |
| ¶ - 'Wiri Linda' | CDoC |
| *sphaerocarpum* | Last listed 1998 |
| *squarrosum* | CTrC |
| *trinervium* | Last listed 1998 |

## LESCHENAULTIA (Goodeniaceae)

| | |
|---|---|
| *formosa* | Last listed 1996 |
| - orange | Last listed 1996 |

## LESPEDEZA (Papilionaceae)

| | |
|---|---|
| *bicolor* | CAgr CB&S CWit EHal GOrc SEND WFar |
| *buergeri* | CB&S LRHS SMur WSHC |
| *floribunda* | CPle |
| *hedysaroides* | See *L. juncea* |
| sp. from Yakushima | MPla |
| *thunbergii* ♀ | CB&S CDul EBee ELan EMil EWTr LHop MAsh MBel MBlu MGos MWhi NFla SBid SLon SMad SOWG SPer SSpi SSta WDin WFar WSHC |

| | |
|---|---|
| - 'Albiflora' | WThi |
| ¶ - 'Summer Beauty' | EPfP MGos |
| * - 'Variegata' | LRHS |
| *tiliifolia* | See *Desmodium elegans* |

## LESQUERELLA (Brassicaceae)

| | |
|---|---|
| *alpina* | NWCA |
| *arctica* var. *purshii* | WPat |
| *kingii sherwoodii* | Last listed 1996 |

## LEUCADENDRON (Proteaceae)

| | |
|---|---|
| *argenteum* | CBrP CTrC CTrF SIgm |
| *comosum* | Last listed 1998 |
| *discolor* | Last listed 1997 |
| ¶ *eucalyptifolium* | CTrC |
| *galpinii* | CTrC |
| *laureolum* | CTrC |
| ¶ *nobile* | CTrC |
| ¶ 'Safari Sunset' | CTrC |
| *salicifolium* | CTrC |
| *salignum* | CTrC |
| ¶ - 'Early Yellow' | CTrC |
| ¶ - 'Fireglow' | CTrC |
| ¶ *strobilinum* | CTrC |
| *tinctum* | CTrC |
| ¶ *uliginosum* | CTrC |

## LEUCAENA (Mimosaceae)

| | |
|---|---|
| *leucocephala* | See *L. latisiliqua* |

## LEUCANTHEMELLA (Asteraceae)

| | |
|---|---|
| § *serotina* ♀ | More than 30 suppliers |

## LEUCANTHEMOPSIS (Asteraceae)

| | |
|---|---|
| § *alpina* | EPot GCrs LBee MDHE |
| *hosmariensis* | See *Rhodanthemum hosmariense* |
| § *pectinata* | LBee NSla |
| - JCA 627.801 | CPBP |
| *radicans* | See *L. pectinata* |

## LEUCANTHEMUM ✿ (Asteraceae)

| | |
|---|---|
| ◆ *atlanticum* | See *Rhodanthemum atlanticum* |
| ◆ *catananche* | See *Rhodanthemum catananche* |
| 'Fringe Benefit' | EMon NPer |
| *hosmariense* | See *Rhodanthemum hosmariense* |
| *mawii* | See *Rhodanthemum gayanum* |
| § *maximum* hort. | See *Leucanthemum* x *superbum* |
| § - (Ramond) DC. | CBlo EWTr GAbr GCHN MWgw NBro NPer NSti NVic WBea WCer WOak |
| - *uliginosum* | See *Leucanthemella serotina* |
| *nipponicum* | See *Nipponanthemum nipponicum* |
| § x *superbum* | MNrw WFar |
| - 'Aglaia' (d) ♀ | More than 30 suppliers |
| - 'Alaska' | EMan NFai NOak SPer SRCN WPer WViv WWal |
| - 'Amelia' | NCut |
| - 'Anita Allen' | CElw CMil MAvo WCot |
| - 'Annie House' | Last listed 1997 |
| - 'Antwerp Star' | MFir NCat |
| - 'Beauté Nivelloise' | CHea CMil ECha EMan LFis MAvo MBel NRoo SUsu WPer WRHF WRha |
| - 'Bishopstone' | CBre CMGP CMil EBee ELan EMan MRav NLon SCou WEas |
| - 'Christine Hagemann' | EBee EFou LRHS MBri NHaw WHoo WWoo |
| - 'Cobham Gold' (d) | CBre CElw CMil EBee ECha ERea GBuc NFla NOrc SHel |

| | |
|---|---|
| - 'Coconut Ice' | EBee EWTr GAbr WPer |
| ¶ - 'Colwall' | LHil |
| ¶ - double cream | EBee |
| - 'Droitwich Beauty' | WSPU |
| - 'Esther Read' (d) | CBlo CGle CM&M CMCo CMdw EAst ELan EMan ERea EWes LFis MFir NFla NRoo SHel SRms SWat WByw WCot WFar |
| - 'Everest' | EMan NOak SRms |
| - 'Fiona Coghill' | CElw EBee EFou GBri IBlr LFis MAvo MFir MLLN NBrk WCot WLin |
| - 'H. Seibert' | CMil CSam MArl |
| ¶ - 'Highland White Dream' | LRHS |
| - 'Horace Read' (d) | CHea CMGP CMdw CMil CSev ECha ELan EMan ERea LFis NPer SAga WEas WPer |
| - 'Jennifer Read' | ERea |
| - 'John Murray' | WAbb |
| - 'Little Miss Muffet' | LRHS MBri NCat |
| - 'Little Princess' | See L. x superbum 'Silberprinzesschen' |
| - 'Manhattan' | EBee EBrP EBre GBuc GNau LBre NCat SBre |
| - 'Mayfield Giant' | WPer |
| - 'Mount Everest' | CBlo EGar SRms WCot |
| - 'Phyllis Smith' | CGle CHea CMdw CVer ECha EGar EMan GAbr LFis MAvo MBel MBri MTis NFai NGdn NPla SHel SSvw WAbb WBea WFar WLin WMoo |
| - 'Polaris' | NFai NOak WHer WMoo |
| - 'Rheinblick' | NCut WLRN |
| - 'Rijnsburg Glory' | SGre |
| * - 'Schneehurken' | MAvo SAsh |
| - 'Schwabengruss' | CStr |
| - 'Shaggy' | CBos CVer GMaP LFis MLLN NFla NRoo SWat |
| § - 'Silberprinzesschen' | CMea ECGP GAbr MFir NHol NMir NOak NPri NRoo SRms SSea WBea WCot WFar WHen WMoo WPer |
| - 'Snow Lady' | CM&M GCHN NMir NPer NRoo WFar WHen |
| - 'Snowcap' | CBlo EBrP EBre ECha EGar EHic EMan ENot GAri LBre MBri MOne MRav NFla NLon SBre SLon SMrm SPer SSpe SUsu WLRN WMow |
| § - 'Sonnenschein' | More than 30 suppliers |
| - 'Starburst' (d) | EFou EMan MBri NRoo SHel SRms WHen |
| - 'Summer Snowball' | CPar EMan EWes MAvo MBri SHel WCot WFar |
| - Sunshine | See L. x superbum 'Sonnenschein' |
| - 'Supra' | SGre |
| - 'T.E. Killin' (d) ♀ | CElw CGle EBee ECha MAvo |
| - 'White Iceberg' | WPer |
| ¶ - 'White Knight' | EBee |
| § - 'Wirral Supreme' (d) ♀ | CBlo CHea EAst EFou ELan EMan ENot EOrc GAbr GMaP LFis MBro MCAu MCLN MFir MRav MWat NFai NFla SPer SRms SSvw WBea WByw WEas WFar WHil |
| 'Tizi-n-Test' | See Rhodanthemum gayanum 'Tizi-n-Test' |
| § vulgare | CArn CKin ECoo EPar EWFC LEdu MWeh MMal NLan NMir WCla WHen WHer WJek WOak WWye |
| - 'Avondale' | MAvo MCCP |
| - 'Hullavington' (v) | CNat |
| § - 'Maikönigin' | GCal NCut NSti WRHF |
| - 'Maistern' | MBro |
| - May Queen | See L. vulgare 'Maikönigin' |
| - 'Sunny' | CBre WAlt |
| - 'Woodpecker's' | Last listed 1998 |

## LEUCOCHRYSUM (Asteraceae)

| | |
|---|---|
| § albicans | EBee |
| § - subsp. albicans var. incanum | Last listed 1997 |

## LEUCOCORYNE (Alliaceae)

| | |
|---|---|
| 'Andes' | Last listed 1997 |
| 'Caravelle' | Last listed 1997 |
| coquimbensis | Last listed 1998 |
| ixioides | ETub LBow WCot |
| - alba | Last listed 1998 |
| ¶ odorata | WCot |
| ¶ purpurea | LBow WCot |

## LEUCOGENES (Asteraceae)

| | |
|---|---|
| acklandii | NHar NSla |
| grandiceps | EPot GCrs ENor GTou ITim NHar NSla WAbe |
| leontopodium | EPot GNor GTou ITim NHar NMen NRoo NSla WAbe |
| tarahaoa | EPot |

## LEUCOGENES x HELICHRYSUM (Asteraceae)

| | |
|---|---|
| L. grandiceps x H. bellidioides | Last listed 1996 |

## LEUCOJUM ✿ (Amaryllidaceae)

| | |
|---|---|
| aestivum | CB&S CBlo CFee LAma MAvo MBri NChi NEgg NMGW NMen NRog SRms WAbe WCla WCot WEas WFar WGwy WHil WHoo WShi |
| - 'Gravetye Giant' ♀ | CAvo CBro CHad EBee ECha ELan EMar EPar EPot ERav ETub LAma LFox LGre LHop MBro MCAu MNrw MRav NFla NRog SIng WAbb WCot WHil WPGP WShi |
| autumnale ♀ | CAvo CBro CFee CLyd CRDP EBrP EBre EHyt ELan ERos ESis ETub EWes ITim LAma LBee LBow LBre MTho NMen SBre SIng SRms SSpi WAbe WCot WHoo |
| - 'Cobb's Variety' | GCal LHop WCot |
| - var. oporanthum | EPot NRog |
| - var. pulchellum | CBro EPot |
| nicaeense ♀ | CBro CGra CLyd CRDP EBur EHyt EPot GCrs LHop MTho NMen SSpi |
| roseum | CLyd EBur EHyt EPot LAma NSla SIgm SWas WAbe |
| tingitanum | Last listed 1998 |
| trichophyllum | CBro ERos |
| - f. purpurascens | EPot |
| valentinum | CAvo CBro |
| vernum ♀ | CBro ELan EMon EPar ETub GCrs GDra LAma LPio MBri MNrw MRav NMGW NMen SIng SRms WAbe WBod WCot WFar WHil WPGP WShi |
| - var. carpathicum | CLAP ECha EHyt EPot LAma MRav |
| - 'Podpolozje' | Last listed 1997 |
| - var. vagneri | CLAP ECha EHyt LFox |

## LEUCOPHYTA (Asteraceae)

| | |
|---|---|
| § brownii | CInt ECou LHil MBEx MRav SVen |

## LEUCOPOGON (Epacridaceae)

| | |
|---|---|
| *ericoides* | MBar WPat |
| § *fasciculatus* | ECou |
| § *fraseri* | ECou IMGH WAbe |
| *parviflorus* | See *Cyathodes parviflora* |

## x LEUCORAOULIA (Asteraceae)

| | |
|---|---|
| § *loganii* | CPBP EHyt EPot GCrs ITim NWCA WAbe |
| § hybrid (*Raoulia bectorii* x *Leucogenes grandiceps*) | EPot GTou NSla SIng |

## LEUCOSCEPTRUM (Lamiaceae)

| | |
|---|---|
| *canum* | Last listed 1996 |
| *stellipilum formosanum* B&SWJ 1804 | WCru |

## LEUCOSIDEA (Rosaceae)

| | |
|---|---|
| *sericea* | CTrC |

## LEUCOSPERMUM (Proteaceae)

| | |
|---|---|
| ¶ *conocarpodendron* | CTrF |
| *cordifolium* | Last listed 1997 |

## LEUCOTHOE (Ericaceae)

| | |
|---|---|
| *axillaris* | Last listed 1996 |
| - 'Royal Red' | WLRN |
| - 'Scarletta' | See *L.* Scarletta = 'Zeblid' |
| *carinella* | CB&S LRHS MBri MGos |
| *catesbyi* | GCHN |
| *davisiae* | MBal SSta |
| *fontanesiana* | See *L. walteri* |
| *grayana* | MBal |
| *keiskei* | EPfP MAsh |
| - 'Royal Ruby' | CEnd MAsh NHol SEas WDin WWeb |
| *populifolia* | See *Agarista populifolia* |
| § Scarletta® = 'Zeblid' | More than 30 suppliers |
| § *walteri* ♀ | EHic MBal MGos STre WStI WWat |
| - Lovita™ | CEnd GCal MBri MRav NHol SBid SSta |
| - 'Nana' | MAsh |
| - 'Rainbow' | CB&S CLan EBee ELan EMil ENot GRei IOrc LHop LNet MAsh MBal MBar MGos MRav NBee SBrw SPer SRPl SReu SRms SSta WDin WFar WWal WWeb |
| * - 'Red Pimpernel' | Last listed 1997 |
| - 'Rollissonii' ♀ | MBal MBar MRav SPla SReu SRms SSta WBod |
| ◆ 'Zeblid' | See *L.* Scarletta = 'Zeblid' |

## LEUZEA (Asteraceae)

| | |
|---|---|
| § *centauroides* | CGle EBee EBrP EBre ECGP ECha EGle ELan EMon EOld GCal LBre LGre MAvo MBro NWoo SBre WByw WCot WHoo |
| *conifera* | NWCA |
| - *macrocephala* | EHyt WAbe |
| § *rhapontica* | Last listed 1998 |

## LEVISTICUM (Apiaceae)

| | |
|---|---|
| *officinale* | CAgr CArn CSev ECha ELau GMaP GPoy LHol MBar MChe MHew NBid SDix SIde SWat WGwG WHbs WHer WMow WOak WPer WWye |

## LEWISIA ✿ (Portulacaceae)

| | |
|---|---|
| 'Archangel' | NRya |
| 'Ashwood Carousel Hybrids' | MAsh |
| 'Ashwood Pearl' | MAsh |
| 'Ben Chace' | MAsh |
| Birch strain | CB&S ECho ELan SIng |
| *brachycalyx* ♀ | CGra EWes GTou ITim MAsh MBal MTho NHar NNrd NWCA WLRN |
| - pink | Last listed 1996 |
| *cantelovii* | CPBP MAsh |
| *columbiana* | EHyt GTou MAsh MDHE NHar SIng |
| - 'Alba' | EHyt GCHN MAsh |
| - 'Edithiae' | Last listed 1998 |
| - 'Rosea' | CMea GCrs MAsh SIng WCom WGor |
| - subsp. *rupicola* | EHyt GCHN MAsh NNrd NWCA WGor |
| - subsp. *wallowensis* | CGra EHyt EPot MAsh MDHE NMen WGor |
| *congdonii* | MAsh |
| *cotyledon* ♀ | ESis MAsh MNrw MOne NNrd NWCA NWBrE WPat |
| - f. *alba* | CLyd EHyt EPot ESis GDra GTou LHop MAsh MBro NWCA WCla WHoo WPyg |
| - Ashwood Ruby Group | MAsh NHar |
| - Ashwood strain | CNic EBrP EBre ESis EWes LBee LBre MAsh MBri MOne NRoo NRya NSla SBre SIng SRms WGor WHoo WPyg |
| - Crags hybrids | NCLN |
| - var. *beckneri* ♀ | GDra MAsh WGor |
| - JCA 11031 | Last listed 1998 |
| - var. *bowellii* | SRms WGor |
| - hybrids | CBrm CFee CNic EMNN EPot GDra GTou ITim LHop MBro NHar NMen SCob WAbe WGor WLin WWin |
| - J&JA 12959 | NWCA |
| - 'John's Special' | GCHN GCrs GDra |
| - magenta strain | MAsh WGor WPyg |
| - 'Rose Splendour' | EPar WGor |
| - 'Sundance' | Last listed 1998 |
| - Sunset Group ♀ | EOld GAbr GCHN GDra MBal MBri NHar WCla WCom WPer |
| - 'White Splendour' | MAsh SIng WGor |
| 'George Henley' | EBrP EBre EHyt EPot EWes LBre LHop MAsh NMen NRya SBre SIng SRms WAbe |
| * 'Holly' | MDHE |
| ¶ hybrids | WBod |
| 'Joyce Halley' | GCrs |
| *leana* | EHyt MAsh WGor |
| 'Little Plum' | GCHN SIng |
| *longifolia* | See *L. cotyledon* var. *cotyledon* |
| § *longipetala* | GCHN GCrs GDra GTou MAsh MOne NRya NTow NWCA WAbe |
| - x *cotyledon* | GTou |
| * *longiscapa* | MAsh |
| 'Margaret Williams' | Last listed 1997 |
| § *nevadensis* | CMea EHyt EPot ERos ESis GCHN GDra GTou ITim MAsh MBri MBro MNrw MTho NMen NNrd NWCA SRms SRot WAbe WCla WLin WPer WPyg |
| - *bernardina* | See *L. nevadensis* |
| - 'Rosea' | CGra GCrs WAbe |
| *oppositifolia* | EHyt MAsh NNrd WGor |
| - J&JA 13450 | NWCA |

| | |
|---|---|
| ¶ - 'Richeyi' | MAsh |
| 'Oxstalls Lane' | Last listed 1996 |
| 'Phyllellia' | MAsh |
| 'Pinkie' | CPBP EPot GCrs MAsh MBro MDHE NMen NNrd |
| *pygmaea* | CGra EHyt EPot ESis EWes GCHN GCrs GTou ITim MAsh MBri NBir NHar NNrd NWCA WPer |
| - subsp. *longipetala* | See *L. longipetala* |
| - 'Whiskey Peak' | Last listed 1998 |
| ¶ Rainbow mixture | WGor |
| *rediviva* | CGra EWes GCHN GCrs GTou ITim MAsh NHar NRya NSla NWCA SIgm WAbe WLin |
| - Jolon strain | MAsh WGor |
| - subsp. *minor* | CGra EPot NMen WAbe |
| ¶ - var. *rediviva* | EHyt |
| - white | MAsh NWCA |
| 'Regensbergen' | WPer |
| *serrata* | CGra MAsh |
| *sierrae* | MAsh MBro NMen NNrd WGor |
| 'Trevosia' | MAsh MDHE SIng |
| *triphylla* | MAsh NNrd NWCA |
| *tweedyi* ♀ | CPBP EBrP EBre EHyt GCrs GDra GTou LBre LHop MAsh MOne NHar NWCA SBre SIgm SIng SRms WAbe WGor |
| - 'Alba' | EHyt GCrs MAsh NWCA WGor |
| - 'Elliott's Variety' | MAsh WGor |
| - 'Rosea' | EHyt GDra MAsh WAbe WGor WLin |

## LEYCESTERIA (Caprifoliaceae)

| | |
|---|---|
| *crocothyrsos* | CBrm CGre CInt CPle GQui NCut SLon STes WLRN WWat |
| *formosa* | More than 30 suppliers |

## LEYMUS (Poaceae)

| | |
|---|---|
| § *arenarius* | More than 30 suppliers |
| *hispidus* | See *Elymus hispidus* |
| *mollis* | Last listed 1998 |
| § *racemosus* | MMHG |

## LHOTZKYA See CALYTRIX

## LIATRIS (Asteraceae)

| | |
|---|---|
| *aspera* | EMan NBur SIgm |
| *cylindracea* | Last listed 1996 |
| *elegans* | Last listed 1998 |
| *ligulistylis* | EMan SIgm WCot WMoo |
| *pycnostachya* | CMil CPea EMon GMac MBNS MLLN SRms WMoo WPer |
| *scariosa* 'Alba' | Last listed 1996 |
| - 'Magnifica' | CB&S |
| - 'September Glory' | WViv |
| § *spicata* | More than 30 suppliers |
| - 'Alba' | CHor EAst EBee ECha EFou ELan LAma LBow LHol LPio MBel MNrw NFai SDeJ SLon SPer SPlb WHoo WPer |
| - *callilepis* | See *L. spicata* |
| - 'Floristan Violett' | CBlo EAst EBee EOld EPfP EWTr GAbr GCHN GMac NLon NPri NRoo SCoo SMer WFar WLRN WMoo WPer |
| - 'Floristan Weiss' | CArn CBlo CBrm EAst EBee EBrP EBre ELau EWTr GAbr GBuc GCHN GMaP LBre MRav MTis NOak NRoo SBre SCro SMrm WFar WLRN WMoo WPer WWin |
| - Goblin | See *L. spicata* 'Kobold' |
| § - 'Kobold' | CB&S CBlo CHan CHar EBee ECtt ENot EPfP GMac MBri MRav NGdn NLak NLar NRoo SPla SRms SSca SSea WCot WHil WHoo WMer WMoo WPer |

## LIBERTIA (Iridaceae)

| | |
|---|---|
| 'Amazing Grace' | CPin IBlr SCob SLod SMrm |
| 'Ballyrogan Blue' | IBlr |
| Ballyrogan hybrid | IBlr |
| * *breunioides* | CPLG IBlr |
| *caerulescens* | CAbb CHan CLTr CPou GBin IBlr MHar NBir NChi NLar WCot WPic WSan WWhi |
| *chilensis* | See *L. formosa* |
| *elegans* | GBuc IBlr WCot |
| § *formosa* | More than 30 suppliers |
| - brown-stemmed form | IBlr |
| *grandiflora* | More than 30 suppliers |
| *ixioides* | CAvo CGle ECha ECou EMan GGar IBlr MFir NSti WPyg WRHF |
| - 'Tricolor' | IBlr |
| - 'Nelson Dwarf' | IBlr |
| *paniculata* | CHan IBlr |
| *peregrinans* | CAbb CElw CFee CHan EBee EBrP EBre ECha EMan EPla ESis GCal IBlr LBre LPio MFir MRav SBre SUsu WAbe WHal WPrP WThi |
| - East Cape form | IBlr |
| - 'Gold Leaf' | CB&S CElw GVic IBlr LPio MRav NOla SOkh WCot |
| * *procera* | CHan EBee IBlr |
| *pulchella* | CGle GBin IBlr |
| - Tasmanian form | Last listed 1997 |
| *sessiliflora* | CFee EBee IBlr NBir WPic |
| - RB 94073 | MNrw SMad |
| Shackleton hybrid | IBlr |
| sp. from New Zealand | Last listed 1996 |
| *tricolor* | EBee GBuc |
| * *umbellata* | IBlr |

## LIBOCEDRUS (Cupressaceae)

| | |
|---|---|
| *chilensis* | See *Austrocedrus chilensis* |
| *decurrens* | See *Calocedrus decurrens* |

## LIBONIA See JUSTICIA

## LICUALA (Arecaceae)

| | |
|---|---|
| *grandis* | MBri |
| *spinosa* | LPal |

## LIGULARIA ✿ (Asteraceae)

| | |
|---|---|
| *alatipes* | GBin |
| *alpigena* | Last listed 1996 |
| *altaica* | Last listed 1998 |
| *amplexicaulis* | IBlr |
| *calthifolia* | CRow |
| *clivorum* | See *L. dentata* |
| § *dentata* | CHan CRow EGar NBro NCut SPla SRms SWat WCru WFar WOld |
| - 'Dark Beauty' | GSki |
| - 'Desdemona' ♀ | More than 30 suppliers |
| - 'Orange Princess' | EBee NPer WPer |
| - 'Othello' | CBlo CRow EAst EBee EGar EMan IBlr MBal MBel MBri MCAu MWgw NCut NLar SCro SLod SSpe SWat WCot WHil WLin WMer WGer |
| - 'Ox-eye' | WGer |
| - 'Rubrifolia' | GDra |
| - 'Sommergold' | ECha EGar IBlr SPer |
| *fischeri* | EBee EGar MCCP MLLN WCot |

| | |
|---|---|
| ¶ - B&SWJ 1158 | WCru |
| - B&SWJ 2570 | WCru |
| - B&SWJ 606a | WCru |
| *glabrescens* | CRow |
| § 'Gregynog Gold' ♀ | CBlo CHad CRow EBee ECha |
| | EGol EOld GMaP IBlr MBri NBro |
| | NDea NOrc SChu SCro SMrm |
| | SPer WCru WElm WHoo WMer |
| | WMow WOld WPyg |
| x *bessei* | CRow EBee ECha EGar GAri |
| | GMaP SWat WFar |
| *hodgsonii* | EBrP EBre EGar IBlr LBre MBri |
| | MNrw SBre WCru WMer WOld |
| | WPer |
| ¶ *intermedia* B&SWJ 4383 | WCru |
| ¶ - B&SWJ 606a | WCru |
| *japonica* | CRow ECha EGar NLar |
| ¶ - B&SWJ 2883 | WCru |
| *macrophylla* | CHan CRow WFar |
| *oblongata* | See *Cremanthodium* |
| | *oblongatum* |
| x *palmatiloba* | CFir EBee EBrP EBre EGar EGol |
| | EPar GCal IBlr LBre MCli MRav |
| | NDea NOak NSti NWes SBre SCro |
| | SLon SWat WCot WFar |
| § *przewalskii* | More than 30 suppliers |
| ¶ - 'B-M's Lacerated' | GNau |
| *reniformis* | See *Cremanthodium reniforme* |
| *sachalinensis* | GBin GCal WCot |
| *sibirica* | WCot |
| *smithii* | See *Senecio smithii* |
| sp. B&SWJ 2977 | WCru |
| sp. HWJCM 211 from Nepal | WCru |
| * *speciosa* | ECha EGar |
| *stenocephala* | CBlo EGar EGol EMil EWTr IBlr |
| | LFis MSCN NBro NDea WCot |
| - B&SWJ 283 | WCru |
| * 'Sungold' | NDov |
| *tangutica* | See *Sinacalia tangutica* |
| 'The Rocket' ♀ | More than 30 suppliers |
| *tsangchanensis* | EBee |
| *tussilaginea* | See *Farfugium japonicum* |
| *veitchiana* | CHan CRow EBee EGar EOas |
| | GCal GDra IBlr MBri MSte NDea |
| | NSti SWat WCot WCru |
| 'Weihenstephan' | IBlr LRHS MBri WGer WMer |
| *wilsoniana* | CHan CRow EBee EBrP EBre ECtt |
| | EGar LBre MCAu MCli MLLN |
| | MRav NCut SBre WFar |
| 'Zepter' | EGar GBuc GCal MBri |

## LIGUSTICUM (Apiaceae)

| | |
|---|---|
| ¶ *jeholense* | EBee |
| *lucidum* | CDul CMCN EHol IIve MSal SIgm |
| | WCwm WGer |
| *porteri* | MSal |
| *scoticum* | EOHP GBar GPoy IIve ILis LHol |
| | MSal NLak |

## LIGUSTRUM ✿ (Oleaceae)

| | |
|---|---|
| *chenaultii* | See *L. compactum* |
| § *compactum* | CFai EPla WWat |
| *delavayanum* | CB&S ERom GAri LPan SAPC SArc |
| | WWat |
| *japonicum* | ENot LPan SMur WDin WWat |
| - 'Coriaceum' | See *L. japonicum* 'Rotundifolium' |
| § - 'Rotundifolium' | CDoC CPle CTrC EMil EPfP EPla |
| | LNet MRav MTed SBid SPer |
| * - 'Silver Star' | CPMA |
| § - 'Texanum' | LPan |
| * - 'Texanum Argenteum' | LPan |

| | |
|---|---|
| *lucidum* ♀ | CDoC CPle EBee ELan ELau ENot |
| | EWTr IOrc LPan MGos MRav |
| | SAPC SArc SMad SPer SRPl SSpi |
| | SVen WDin WFar WGer WWat |
| - 'Excelsum Superbum' (v) ♀ | CAbP CEnd CPMA ELan EPfP |
| | LPan MAsh MBar MGos MMea |
| | SLon SPer SPla SRPl SSpi WWat |
| - 'Golden Wax' | CPMA MRav WBcn |
| - 'Latifolium' | Last listed 1997 |
| - 'Tricolor' (v) | CPMA ELan EPfP EPla IOrc MAsh |
| | MBal SPer SPla SSpi SSta WWat |
| *obtusifolium* 'Dart's Elite' | Last listed 1998 |
| ¶ - 'Darts Perfecta' | SLPl |
| ¶ - var. *regelianum* | WWat |
| *ovalifolium* | CB&S CChe CDoC CLnd CTri |
| | EBrP EBre GChr GRei ISea LBre |
| | LBuc LPan MBar MBri MGos |
| | NBee NWea SBre SPer WDin |
| | WGwG WMou WWal |
| § - 'Argenteum' (v) | CB&S CDoC CDul CGle EBee |
| | EHoe ISea LBuc MBar MBri NBee |
| | NFla NHol SPer SPla WFar WWin |
| - 'Aureomarginatum' | See *L. ovalifolium* 'Aureum' |
| § - 'Aureum' (v) ♀ | More than 30 suppliers |
| * - 'Lemon and Lime' (v) | SPla |
| - 'Taff's Indecision' (v) | CPMA |
| - 'Variegatum' | See *L. ovalifolium* 'Argenteum' |
| *quihoui* ♀ | CFai CHan EHol ELan EPfP MGos |
| | SDix SMad SPer SSpi SSta WHCG |
| | WPat WWat |
| § *sempervirens* | EPfP SSta |
| - B&L 12033 | Last listed 1998 |
| *sinense* | CHan CMCN MRav WWat |
| - 'Midsummer Lady' | LRHS |
| - 'Multiflorum' | WWat |
| - 'Pendulum' | Last listed 1998 |
| - 'Variegatum' | CMHG CPMA CPle EHic EPfP |
| | EPla MBNS MRav SBid SPla WWat |
| - 'Wimbei' | CPMA CPle EPla ESis NPro SSpi |
| | WWat |
| ¶ sp. Guiz 296 | EPla |
| ¶ *strongylophyllum* | WWat |
| *texanum* | See *L. japonicum* 'Texanum' |
| *tschonoskii* | CBlo SLPl |
| 'Vicaryi' | CBlo CMHG CPMA EAst EBrP |
| | EBre ELan EPla LBre MBar MGos |
| | NHol NPro SBre SDix SPer WBay |
| | WPyg WWat |
| *vulgare* | CCVT CKin CTri EBrP EBre ENot |
| | EWFC GRei LBre LBuc NWea |
| | SBre WDin WHer WMou |
| - 'Lodense' | SLPl |
| - variegated | Last listed 1998 |

## LILIUM (Liliaceae)

| | |
|---|---|
| 'Acapulco' (VIId) | LAma |
| 'Admiration' (Ia) | Last listed 1996 |
| African Queen Group (VIa) | CHar EBrP EBre ECot LAma LBre |
| | MBNS NRog SBre SDeJ SRms |
| 'Aladdin' (Ia) | Last listed 1996 |
| *albanicum* | See *L. pyrenaicum* subsp. |
| | *carniolicum* var. *albanicum* |
| 'Alliance' (VII) | Last listed 1998 |
| 'Allright' (VIIb-d) | Last listed 1996 |
| *amabile* | CLAP |
| 'Angela North' (Ic) | Last listed 1998 |
| 'Annabelle' (Ia) | Last listed 1997 |
| 'Anton Geesink' | Last listed 1998 |
| 'Apeldoorn' (Ie) | LAma SCoo |
| 'Aphrodite' (Ia/d) | NBir |
| 'Apollo' (Ia) | CHar EPot ETub LAma MBri |
| | NOak SDeJ |

¶ 'Ariadne' | CLAP
'Aristo' | See *L.* 'Orange Aristo'
* Asiatic hybrids (VI/VII) | LAma SDeJ
'Attila' (Ib) | SDeJ
***auratum*** | EFEx LAma
　- 'Crimson Beauty' (IX) | LAma
　- 'Gold Band' | See *L. auratum* var. *platyphyllum*
§ - var. ***platyphyllum*** (IX) ♀ | Last listed 1998
　- var. ***virginale*** | ETub
　Aurelian hybrids (VIIa) | Last listed 1996
'Avignon' (Ia) | LAma
¶ ***bakerianum*** | EPot LAma
'Barcelona' (Ia) | ETub MNrw NOak
'Batist' (Ia) | LAma
'Bel Ami' | Last listed 1998
Bellingham Group (IV) ♀ | SSpi
'Bellona' (Ia) | NRog
'Berlin' (VIId) | Last listed 1998
'Black Beauty' (VIId) | CLAP LAma
'Black Dragon' (VIa) ♀ | CHar LAma
Black Magic Group (VIa) | SDeJ
'Blitz' (Ia) | Last listed 1996
***bolanderi*** (IX) | Last listed 1998
'Bonfire' (VIIb) | SDeJ
'Brandywine' (Ib) | WRHF
'Bright Star' (VIb) | EBrP EBre ETub LAma LBre SBre SDeJ
***brownii*** | Last listed 1998
　- var. ***australe*** B&SWJ 4082 | WCru
'Buff Pixie' (Ia) | ETub LAma
***bulbiferum*** | CLAP ETub GCrs SIng
　- var. ***croceum*** (IX) ♀ | Last listed 1993
'Bums' (Ia/d) | EMon
'Butter Pixie' (Ia) | LAma NMoo
§ ***canadense*** | CBro GGGa LAma LPio MBal NRog SDeJ SSpi
　- var. ***editorum*** | CLAP LAma
　- var. ***flavum*** | See *L. canadense*
***candidum*** ♀ | CArn CAvo CB&S CBro CGle CSWP CTri EBrP EBre ECha ELan ETub GAbr LAma LBre MBri NRog SBre SDeJ SIgm SRms WElm
　- 'Plenum' (d) | EMon
'Capitol' (VII) | Last listed 1998
'Carmen' (VIIc) | Last listed 1998
***carniolicum*** | See *L. pyrenaicum* subsp. *carniolicum*
'Casa Blanca' (VIIb) ♀ | CBro CHar EBrP EBre ETub LAma LBre NRog SBre SDeJ
'Casa Rosa' | CHar CSWP NBir SWat
◆ 'Ceb Golden' | See *L.* Golden® Pixie = 'Ceb Golden'
***cernuum*** | SDeJ
***chalcedonicum*** ♀ | CLAP
'Charisma' (Ia) | MBri
'Charmeur' (7c) | Last listed 1996
'Chinook' (Ia) | NRog
Citronella Group (Ic) | CAvo CHar ETub LAma NRog
¶ 'Colombo' (Ia) | CSut
***columbianum*** (IX) | Last listed 1998
***concolor*** var. ***partheneion*** (IX) | Last listed 1997
'Concorde' (Ia) | SDeJ
'Connecticut King' (Ia) | CHar EBrP EBre LAma LBre NBrk NRog SAga SBre SDeJ
'Connection' (Ia) | Last listed 1996
'Corina' (Ia) | CHar MBNS MBri NCat NOak SDeJ
'Corsage' (Ib) | NRog
'Côte d'Azur' (Ia) | CBro CHar EBrP EBre EPot ETub LAma LBre MAvo NCat SBre SDeJ
'Crimson Pixie' (Ia) | Last listed 1998

x ***dalhansonii*** | CLAP
§ - 'Marhan' (II) ♀ | LAma
'Dame Blanche' (VII) | LAma
'Dandy' (Ia) | WWeb
'Darling' (VII) | Last listed 1998
§ ***dauricum*** | CPou GCrs
***davidii*** (IX) ♀ | Last listed 1995
§ - var. ***willmottiae*** (IX) | EPot
'Delta' | See *L. leichtlinii* 'Delta'
'Denia' (Ib) | LRHS
'Destiny' (Ia) | NRog SRms
'Devon Early Gems' | CLAP
'Domination' | Last listed 1996
'Dominique' (VII) | NRog
***duchartrei*** | CBro CNic GCrs LAma SMac SSpi WAbe
§ 'Ed' (VII) | LAma
'Electric' (Ia) | LAma
'Elfin Sun' | LAma LRHS
'Elite' | See *L.* 'Gibraltar'
¶ 'Ellen Willmott' (II) | CLAP
'Elvin's Son' | Last listed 1998
'Elysee' | Last listed 1998
'Enchantment' (Ia) ♀ | CHar LAma MBri NRog SDeJ SRms WLRN
¶ 'Eros' | CLAP
'Esperanto' | Last listed 1998
***euxanthum*** ACE 1268 | Last listed 1997
　- KGB 492 | Last listed 1997
¶ Everest Group (VIId) | CHar
'Exception' (Ib/d) | LAma
¶ 'Fata Morgana' (Ia) | ETub
'Festival' (Ia) | LAma
'Fiesta Gitana' (Ia) | Last listed 1996
'Fire King' (Ib) | CBro CLAP LAma NBir NRog SDeJ SRms
'Fire Star' (VIIc-d) | Last listed 1996
'Flamenco' (Ib) | Last listed 1996
***formosanum*** | NBro SEND WCot WSan
　- B&SWJ 1589 | WCru
　- var. ***formosanum*** | Last listed 1998
　- var. ***pricei*** (IX) ♀ | More than 30 suppliers
¶ - 'Snow Queen' (IX) | CMil
　- 'White Swan' | GCrs
'Fresco' (VII) | Last listed 1998
'Friendship' (VII) | Last listed 1998
'Furore' (VIIc) | Last listed 1998
¶ 'Garden Party' (VII) | ETub
'Geisha' (VII) | Last listed 1998
§ 'Gibraltar' (Ia) | Last listed 1996
'Golden Melody' (Ia) | LSyl
§ Golden® Pixie = 'Ceb Golden' (Ia) | Last listed 1998
Golden Splendor Group (VIa) | ETub LAma NRog SWat
'Golden Sunrise' (Ia) | Last listed 1997
'Gran Cru' (Ia) | EBrP EBre LBre SBre
'Gran Paradiso' (Ia) | LAma
'Grand Cru' | CSut LAma NOak SDeJ
§ ***grayi*** | GCrs SSpi
'Green Dragon' (VIa) ♀ | Last listed 1995
Green Magic Group (VIa) | Last listed 1997
'Hannah North' (Ic) | Last listed 1997
***hansonii*** ♀ | IBlr LAma NRog
Harlequin Group (Ic) | SDeJ
***henryi*** ♀ | CAvo CHar CSWP EBee EPot LAma LBow MLLN MWll NRog SDeJ SRms SSoC WCot
'Her Grace' (Ia) | Last listed 1996
'Hit Parade' (VII) | LAma
***humboldtii*** (IX) | Last listed 1997
Imperial Gold Group (VIIc) | Last listed 1997
Imperial Silver Group (VIIc) | LAma

| | |
|---|---|
| *japonicum* | EFEx |
| ¶ - 'Albomarginatum' (IX) | WThi |
| 'Jazz' (Ia) | Last listed 1996 |
| 'Jetfire' (Ia) | SDeJ |
| 'John Dix' (Ib) | ETub |
| 'Journey's End' (VIId) | CHar EBrP EBre ETub LAma LBre |
| | MLLN NRog SBre SDeJ |
| § 'Joy' (VIIb) | CHar ETub LAma |
| 'Karen North' (Ic) ♀ | Last listed 1997 |
| § *kelleyanum* | CLAP GGGa |
| *kelloggii* | Last listed 1998 |
| 'King Pete' (Ib) | NOak SCoo SDeJ |
| 'Kiss Proof' (VIIb) | Last listed 1998 |
| ¶ 'Kiwi Fanfare' | CBrm |
| 'Kyoto' (VIId) | LAma |
| 'Lady Alice' (VI) | CLAP |
| 'Lady Ann' (VIb) | SDeJ |
| 'Ladykiller' (Ia) | NRog |
| § *lancifolium* | CLTr EMFP LAma LBow MHar |
| | MHlr SDeJ SRms WCot WRHF |
| - B&SWJ 539 | WCru |
| - 'Flore Pleno' (IX/d) | CMil CSWP CSam EBee EMFP |
| | EMar EMon EPot GCal GSki IBlr |
| | MHar NSti SWas WCot WCru WFar |
| - Forrest's form | IBlr |
| - var. *fortunei* | Last listed 1997 |
| § - var. *splendens* (IX) | CBro EBot LAma LBow MLLN |
| | SDeJ |
| *lankongense* | GCrs NPro |
| - ACE 2210 | EPot |
| 'Le Rêve' | See *L.* 'Joy' |
| § *leichtlinii* 'Delta' (IX) | Last listed 1996 |
| ¶ - 'Iwashimiza' | WCot |
| 'Lemon Pixie' (Ia) | LAma LRHS |
| *leucanthum* | LAma WCru |
| 'Levant' (Ic) | Last listed 1996 |
| 'Liberation' (I) | NBir |
| 'Limelight' (VIa) ♀ | LAma |
| 'Little Girl' (VIIb) | Last listed 1996 |
| 'Little Kiss' (Ia/d) | ETub SCoo |
| 'Little Snow White' (V) | Last listed 1998 |
| ¶ 'Lollypop' (Ia) | ETub MNrw |
| *longiflorum* (IX) ♀ | CAvo EBee LAma NRog WCot |
| - 'Casa Rosa' | Last listed 1996 |
| - 'Gelria' (IX) | SDeJ |
| - 'White American' (IX) | CBro CSWP MBri |
| ¶ *lophophorum* | EHyt LAma WCru |
| - ACE 1767 | EPot |
| 'Lovely Girl' (VIIb) | ETub |
| 'Luxor' (Ib) | CSut NBir NCat |
| *mackliniae* ♀ | ECha GBuc GCrs GGGa GTou IBlr |
| | MBal NHar SBla SIgm SSpi WAbe |
| *maculatum* var. *davuricum* | See *L. dauricum* |
| ¶ - Japanese double | EMon |
| - *monticola* | EHyt |
| 'Marco Polo' (Ia) | LAma |
| 'Marhan' | See *L.* x *dalhansonii* 'Marhan' |
| x *marhan* 'J.S. Dijt' | See *L.* 'Jacques S. Dijt' |
| 'Marie North' (Ic) | Last listed 1997 |
| *martagon* | CArn CAvo CBro CMea EBot ECha |
| | EFou ETub LAma LBow MBal NBir |
| | NPSI NRog SDeJ SIgm SRms |
| | WAbe WGwy WShi WWat |
| - var. *album* (IX) ♀ | CAvo CBro CMea CPou EBot |
| | ECGP EFou ELan ETub LAma |
| | LBow LPio MFir MRav MTho |
| | MWll SDeJ WAbe WCot WGwy |
| | WShi |
| - var. *cattaniae* (IX) ♀ | Last listed 1998 |
| ¶ - 'Inshriach' (IX) | WCot |
| - 'Netherhall Pink' (IX/d) | Last listed 1998 |
| - 'Netherhall White' (IX/d) | Last listed 1998 |

| | |
|---|---|
| - pink | Last listed 1996 |
| - 'Plenum' (IX/d) | EMon |
| 'Mecca' | Last listed 1998 |
| 'Medaillon' (Ia) | LAma NRog |
| *medeoloides* | EFEx EHyt GCrs GGGa |
| *michiganense* | GCrs |
| 'Milano' (Ia) | Last listed 1998 |
| 'Miss America' | LRHS |
| 'Miss Burma' (VII) | LRHS |
| 'Miss Rio' (VII) | SCoo |
| 'Mona Lisa' (VIIb-d) | ETub LAma LRHS MBri SCoo |
| § *monadelphum* ♀ | CBro CCuc EHyt EPot ETub LAma |
| | LBow MHar NRog SIgm SSpi |
| 'Mont Blanc' (Ia) | CBro ETub LAma MLLN NBir |
| | SDeJ |
| 'Monte Rosa' (Ic) | SDeJ |
| 'Montreux' (Ia) | LAma LSyl NCat |
| 'Moonflower' (Ia) | Last listed 1998 |
| 'Moulin Rouge' (Ib) | NRog |
| 'Mr Ed' | See *L.* 'Ed' |
| 'Mr Ruud' | See *L.* 'Ruud' |
| 'Mrs R.O. Backhouse' (II) ♀ | Last listed 1996 |
| 'Muscadet' (VII) | CSut |
| § *nanum* | GCrs GGGa GNor NRog NSla |
| - CH&M | Last listed 1997 |
| - var. *flavidum* (IX) | EHyt EPot WCru |
| - from Bhutan | WCru |
| - Kirkpatrick 242 | GCrs |
| - 'Len's Lilac' (IX) | EHyt WCru |
| ¶ - McBeath's form (IX) | WCru |
| ¶ *neilgherrense* (IX) | CFil |
| *nepalense* | CBro CLAP CMil CSWP EBee EBla |
| | EPot GCrs LAma NRog SBla SDeJ |
| | SSpi WCot WCru |
| - B&SWJ 2985 | WCru |
| 'New Yellow' | MBri |
| 'Nippon' (VIId) | Last listed 1998 |
| I 'Nivea' (I) | Last listed 1996 |
| *nobilissimum* | EFEx |
| 'Olivia' (Ia) | CHar ETub LAma MLLN SDeJ |
| Olympic Group (VIa) | LAma SDeJ |
| 'Omega' (VII) | LAma SDeJ |
| § 'Orange Aristo' (Ia) | MBri |
| 'Orange Delight' | WWeb |
| 'Orange Pixie' (Ia) | EBrP EBre LAma LBre LRHS MBri |
| | NMoo SBre |
| 'Orange Triumph' (Ia) | EPot LAma |
| 'Orchid Beauty' (Ia) | MBri |
| ¶ 'Orestes' (Ib) | CLAP |
| *oxypetalum* | GCrs GGGa |
| - var. *insigne* (IX) | CLAP EHyt GDra GGGa GNor |
| | LAma NHar NSla NTow SSpi |
| | WCru |
| Paisley Group (II) | Last listed 1996 |
| 'Pandora' (Ia) | Last listed 1998 |
| *pardalinum* | CAvo CCuc CGle CMea ELan NSla |
| | WWhi |
| - var. *giganteum* (IX) ♀ | CLAP |
| 'Parisienne' (Ia) | Last listed 1996 |
| *parryi* | SSpi |
| *parvum* | Last listed 1997 |
| 'Passage' (VIIc) | Last listed 1996 |
| 'Peach Pixie' (Ia) | LAma NBir NCat |
| 'Peachblush' (Ia) | Last listed 1998 |
| 'Peau Douce' | Last listed 1996 |
| 'Peggy North' (Ic) | Last listed 1997 |
| 'Perugia' (VIId) | LAma |
| *philadelphicum* | Last listed 1998 |
| *philippinense* | CBrm EGar NSla NTow SIgm |
| - B&SWJ 4000 | WCru |
| 'Picture' (VIId) | Last listed 1996 |
| 'Pink Beauty' (VIIc) | Last listed 1996 |

| | |
|---|---|
| Pink Perfection Group (VIa) ♀ | CAvo CBro EBrP EBre LAma LBre NRog SBre SWat |
| 'Pink Pixie' (Ia) | NCat |
| ‖ 'Pink Regale' | CSut |
| 'Pink Sunburst' (VId) | SDeJ |
| 'Pink Tiger' (Ib) | CBro CHar ETub |
| 'Pirate' (Ia) | LAma |
| *pitkinense* | EMon |
| 'Polka' | WWeb |
| *pomponium* | CLAP SIng |
| 'Prominence' | See *L.* 'Firebrand' |
| 'Providence' | Last listed 1996 |
| § *pumilum* ♀ | CAvo CBro CLAP EHyt EPot LAma MLLN MTho NBir SDeJ |
| *pyrenaicum* ♀ | CAvo CBro CLAP CMea ELan LPio MWll WByw WGwy WRha WShi |
| - var. *aureum* | See *L. pyrenaicum* var. *pyrenaicum* |
| § - subsp. *carniolicum* var. *albanicum* | Last listed 1996 |
| § - var. *pyrenaicum* (IX) | Last listed 1996 |
| - var. *rubrum* (IX) | Last listed 1998 |
| - yellow | See *L. pyrenaicum* var. *pyrenaicum* |
| 'Red Carpet' (Ia) | CBro ETub MBri NBir NCat |
| Red Jewels Group (Ic) | LAma |
| Red Knight | See *L.* 'Roter Cardinal' |
| 'Red Lion' (Ia) | SDeJ |
| 'Red Night' (I) | EGoo NRog |
| *regale* ♀ | CArn CAvo CBro CHar CSam CSut EBrP EBre ETub LAma LBow LBre LEdu MBal MCLN MLLN NEgg NRog SBre SDeJ SRms WCot WEas WFar WPyg WWat |
| - 'Album' (IX) | CAvo CHar CSWP EBrP EBre LAma LBow LBre NRog SBre SDeJ |
| § - 'Royal Gold' (IX) | CMil LAma SAga SDeJ SRms |
| ‖ 'Rodeo' (VIII) | ETub |
| 'Roma' (Ia) | LAma LPio MBNS NBir |
| ‖ 'Rosefire' (Ia) | NOak |
| 'Rosemary North' (I) ♀ | Last listed 1994 |
| 'Rosita' (Ia) | MBri NRog |
| 'Royal Gold' | See *L. regale* 'Royal Gold' |
| ‖ 'Royal Queen' (VIIb) | CSut |
| *rubellum* | EFEx |
| § 'Ruud' (VII) | CBro LAma SCoo |
| 'Sahara' (Ia) | Last listed 1996 |
| 'Sam' (VII) | LAma SCoo |
| 'Sancerre' (Ia) | Last listed 1998 |
| 'Sans Pareil' (Ia) | SDeJ |
| 'Sans Souci' (VIId) | MBri |
| *sargentiae* | CPou |
| 'Sensation' | Last listed 1998 |
| *shastense* | See *L. kelleyanum* |
| ‖ 'Shocking Pink' | CSut |
| 'Showbiz' (VIII) | LAma |
| 'Shuksan' (IV) | Last listed 1996 |
| 'Silhouette' (Ia) | Last listed 1996 |
| 'Silly Girl' (Ia) | Last listed 1998 |
| 'Simoen' (Ia) | SDeJ |
| 'Snow Princess' | LAma |
| 'Snow Trumpet' (V) | CSam WLRN |
| 'Sorisso' (Ia) | Last listed 1996 |
| *souliei* ACE 1192 | Last listed 1997 |
| ‖ sp. from China | WCru |
| *speciosum* ♀ | Last listed 1995 |
| - var. *album* (IX) | CBro EBot EPot LAma LPio NBir SDeJ WBor |
| - 'Grand Commander' (IX) | SDeJ |
| - var. *roseum* (IX) | CHar SDeJ |
| - var. *rubrum* (IX) | CAvo CBro CHar CLAP EBot EPot ETub LAma LBow MLLN NBir NRog SAga SDeJ SRms |

| | |
|---|---|
| § - 'Uchida' (IX) | LAma SDeJ |
| 'Sphinx' (Ia/d) | SCoo |
| 'Star Gazer' (VIIc) | CBro CHar CSut EBrP EBre ECot LAma LBre MAvo NRog SBre SDeJ SSoC |
| * 'Sterling Silver' | LAma NOak |
| 'Sterling Star' (Ia) | CLAP CSut ETub LAma NRog SDeJ |
| *stewartianum* (IX) | LAma |
| 'Sun Ray' (Ia) | NRog |
| *superbum* ♀ | LAma NRog |
| 'Sweet Kiss' (Ia) | SCoo |
| 'Symphony' (Ib) | Last listed 1996 |
| *szovitsianum* | See *L. monadelphum* |
| ‖ *taliense* (IX) | LAma |
| 'Tamara' (Ib) | MBri NRog |
| 'Taptoe' (Ia) | Last listed 1996 |
| *tenuifolium* | See *L. pumilum* |
| × *testaceum* (IX) ♀ | LAma NRog SDeJ |
| *tigrinum* | See *L. lancifolium* |
| 'Trance' (VIIb) | MBri |
| 'Uchida Kanoka' | See *L. speciosum* 'Uchida' |
| 'Ventoux' (Ia) | Last listed 1996 |
| *vollmeri* | WAbe |
| *wallichianum* | CPou EBee LAma LEdu NRog SDeJ WCru |
| 'Walter Bentley' (Ic) | SRms |
| *washingtonianum* (IX) | Last listed 1998 |
| - var. *purpurascens* | Last listed 1998 |
| 'White America' | CBro ETub LRHS |
| 'White Happiness' (Ia) | LAma |
| 'White Henryi' (VId) | EFEx |
| 'White Journey's End' (VIId) | Last listed 1998 |
| 'White Kiss' (Ia/d) | LAma SCoo |
| 'White Mountain' (VIIc) | SDeJ |
| 'White Star Gazer' (VII) | Last listed 1996 |
| *wigginsii* | EHyt GCrs GGGa |
| *willmottiae* | See *L. davidii* var. *willmottiae* |
| Yellow Blaze Group (Ia) | CHar LAma NRog |
| 'Yellow Giant' | See *L.* 'Joanna' |
| 'Zephyr' (Ia) | Last listed 1998 |

## LIMNANTHES (Limnanthaceae)

| | |
|---|---|
| *douglasii* ♀ | CFee CMGP CTrG CTri ELan IBlr NBus SIng WEas WElm WHer |

## LIMNOPHILA (Scrophulariaceae)

| | |
|---|---|
| *aromatica* | EOHP MSal |

## LIMONIUM (Plumbaginaceae)

| | |
|---|---|
| *bellidifolium* | ECha ELan ESis IMGH MBro MGed MHar SBla WCla WEas WHoo WPer |
| *binervosum* | Last listed 1996 |
| *cosyrense* | CInt CMea ESis NMen SIng SRms WAbe WPer WWin |
| ‖ aff. *delicatulum* | MChR |
| § *dregeanum* | Last listed 1996 |
| *dumosum* | See *Goniolimon tataricum* var. *angustifolium* |
| *globulariifolium* | See *L. ramosissimum* |
| *gmelinii* | SPlb WPer |
| - 'Perestrojka' | Last listed 1998 |
| *gougetianum* | CLyd NTow |
| *latifolium* | See *L. platyphyllum* |
| * *maritimum* | CSpe |
| *minutum* | ELan MTPN |
| *otolepis* | CLTr CM&M |
| *paradoxum* | ELan |
| *peregrinum* | CSpe EBee |
| ‖ *perezii* | CTrF WPer |

| | |
|---|---|
| § *platyphyllum* | CGle EBee EWTr LFis MCAu MNrw MWat MWgw NArg NMir SCob SLon SPer SRCN SRms SUsu WBrE WEas WGwG WHoo WPer WWal WWin |
| - 'Robert Butler' | EBee EMan GCal LBuc MRav NCat SSpe |
| - 'True Blue' | Last listed 1997 |
| - 'Violetta' | CTri EBrP EBre ECGN ECGP ECha ELan EMan LBre MBri MRav MUlv NLar SBre SPer WHoo |
| *purpuratum* | CSpe EBee |
| § *ramosissimum* | EBee |
| *rumicifolium* | Last listed 1997 |
| ♦ *speciosum* 'Blue Diamond' | See *Goniolimon incanum* 'Blue Diamond' |
| *tataricum* | See *Goniolimon tataricum* |
| *tetragonum* | See *L. dregeanum* |
| *tomentellum* | Last listed 1998 |
| *vulgare* | EEls |

## LINANTHASTRUM See LINANTHUS

## LINANTHUS (Polemoniaceae)
| | |
|---|---|
| *nuttallii* | Last listed 1997 |

## LINARIA (Scrophulariaceae)
| | |
|---|---|
| *aeruginea* | Last listed 1998 |
| - subsp. *nevadensis* | CPea WCla |
| *alpina* | CMea CSpe EBee ELan EPfP EWes GTou LFis LPVe MTho NWCA SRms WCla WPer |
| - 'Purpurea' | NMGW |
| - 'Rosea' | NMGW WCla |
| 'Anstey' | CElw EMan |
| *anticaria* | EWTr |
| - 'Antique Silver' | CSpe ECha EFou EMan EPPr GBuc MBro NLak WHoo |
| § *bipunctata* | Last listed 1996 |
| * 'Blue Pygmy' | Last listed 1996 |
| *cymbalaria* | See *Cymbalaria muralis* |
| § *dalmatica* | CFri CGle CHad CHan EBee ECha ELan MFir MHar MInt NBro NChi SChu SOkh WCot WGwy WKif WOld WOut WPer |
| x *dominii* 'Carnforth' | CGle CHan CVer EBee EMar EPPr LHop MBrN NBro NLak NSti WMaN WWhi |
| - 'Yuppie Surprise' | CHid EAst ECGP EMan EMon LPio MCLN NBir NGdn SCob SMad SPer WLRN |
| *genistifolia* | MGed |
| ♦ - subsp. *dalmatica* | See *L. dalmatica* |
| 'Globosa Alba' | See *Cymbalaria muralis* 'Globosa Alba' |
| *glutinosa* | See *L. bipunctata* |
| *hepaticifolia* | See *Cymbalaria hepaticifolia* |
| 'Natalie' | SAga |
| *nevadensis* | Last listed 1998 |
| ¶ - 'Gemstones' | EWll |
| *origanifolia* | See *Chaenorhinum origanifolium* |
| *pallida* | See *Cymbalaria pallida* |
| § *peloponnesiaca* | EBee |
| *pilosa* | See *Cymbalaria pilosa* |
| *purpurea* | CGle CKin EBee EFou ELan ERav EWFC EWTr LHol MCAu MCLN MChe MFir NBro NCat NFai NFla NFor NLon NPer SIde SRms WCla WHen WOve WPer |
| - 'Alba' | See *L. purpurea* 'Springside White' |

| | |
|---|---|
| ¶ - Anstey's form | CPou |
| - 'Canon Went' | More than 30 suppliers |
| - Harbutt's hybrids | Last listed 1996 |
| - 'Radcliffe Innocence' | See *L. purpurea* 'Springside White' |
| § - 'Springside White' | CElw CGle ECha EMan ERav EWTr GBuc LGre LHop MAvo MCAu MSte SSvw SUsu SWat WCot WHer WLRN WMaN WPer WRha |
| - 'Thurgarton Beauty' | MAvo WCot |
| ¶ - 'Vainglorious' | CNat |
| - 'Winifrid's Delight' | CBlo CHea EBee EMan GCal LHop MRav NBrk NLak NSti SCoo SSpe SUsu SWat WCot WGle WLRN |
| *repens* | CKin EHal EWFC MHlr MNrw SSvw WCot WHbs WHer |
| ♦ *sibthorpiana* | See *L. peloponnesiaca* |
| 'Sue' | EBee EMan LHop |
| *supina* | EHal WCla |
| 'Tony Aldis' | CSpe WKif |
| *triornithophora* | CFir CFri CGle CPea CSpe EBee ECha GBin GBuc MBel MFir MSCN NLak SRCN WBea WCot WFar WHoo WOld WOve WRha WWin WWye |
| - pink | CBot CGle CHan CSpe EMan WEas WPer |
| - purple | CHan ELan WBea |
| *tristis* var. *lurida* 'Toubkal' | SBla |
| *vulgaris* | CArn CKin ELau EOHP EWFC LHol MChe MMal NMir SIde WHer WJek WPer |
| - peloric form | CNat CPBP EMon WAlt |

## LINDELOFIA (Boraginaceae)
| | |
|---|---|
| *anchusoides* hort. | See *L. longiflora* |
| - Lehmann | CHan GMac NBid |
| § *longiflora* | CFir CWit EBee ECGN GBin GBuc GCal MLLN MRav MTed WPer |
| - 'Alba' | ECha |

## LINDERA (Lauraceae)
| | |
|---|---|
| *aggregata* | Last listed 1998 |
| *angustifolia* | CFil WPGP |
| *benzoin* | CFil CMCN EPfP SBid SLon WPGP WWoo |
| *erythrocarpa* | CFil CMCN WPGP |
| ¶ *megaphylla* | CB&S |
| *obtusiloba* ♀ | CFil CMCN EPfP MBlu SSpi WNor WPGP WWoo |
| *praecox* | CFil WPGP |
| *praetermissa* | CFil WPGP |
| ¶ *sericea* | CFil |
| *triloba* | CFil WPGP |
| *umbellata* | CFil |

## LINNAEA (Caprifoliaceae)
| | |
|---|---|
| *borealis* | GAri GDra ILis IMGH MBal MHar |
| - var. *americana* | NHar NMen NWCA |

## LINUM ✿ (Linaceae)
| | |
|---|---|
| *alpinum* subsp. *julicum* | Last listed 1998 |
| *altaicum* | EBee NChi |
| *arboreum* ♀ | CLon MBro MPla NHol NMen SBla SIgm SMrm WAbe WKif WPat WWat |
| *aretioides* | Last listed 1997 |
| *austriacum* | EBee |
| *bienne* | CKin |
| *bulgaricum* | See *L. tauricum* |

| | |
|---|---|
| *campanulatum* | Last listed 1998 |
| *capitatum* | CPBP EBee NSla WLin |
| * *columbianum* | Last listed 1998 |
| *dolomiticum* | Last listed 1998 |
| *flavum* | CGle CTri EPfP GTou NLak WHoo |
| - 'Compactum' | LHop MBro MHar MNrw NWCA |
| | SBla SMer SMrm SRCN SRms |
| | WCot WMer WWin |
| 'Gemmell's Hybrid' ♀ | CLyd CMea CStr EMan EPot MBro |
| | NBir NHar NHol NMen NWCA |
| | SBla SIng WAbe WLin WPat |
| *hirsutum* | Last listed 1996 |
| *kingii* var. *sedoides* | Last listed 1998 |
| *leonii* | WKif |
| *marginale* | Last listed 1998 |
| *mongolicum* | Last listed 1996 |
| *monogynum* | EBee ECou EPPr MTho NMen |
| | NTow NWCA WCom WPGP |
| § - var. *diffusum* | ECou |
| - dwarf form | CNic GTou NWCA SUsu |
| - 'Nelson' | See *L. monogynum* var. *diffusum* |
| *narbonense* | CLon CLyd EBee LGre LGro MBri |
| | MBro NFai NOak SIgm SMrm |
| | SRms WHoo WKif WMer WPyg |
| - 'Heavenly Blue' ♀ | EWTr SUsu WEas WHen |
| § *perenne* | CArn CMea ECha EFer ELan EOld |
| | EWFC EWTr GCal GMaP LHol |
| | MBri MCAu MChe MWgw NFor |
| | NMir NVic NWoo SIde SPer SRCN |
| | SRms WHer WPer WWin WWye |
| - *album* | CGle CStr ECha ELan EMan EWTr |
| | LHol MCAu NChi SPer SRms |
| | WHen WPer WRus |
| - subsp. *alpinum* | WPer |
| - - 'Alice Blue' | CPBP NHar NMen SBla WLin |
| | WWin |
| - subsp. *anglicum* | Last listed 1997 |
| § - 'Blau Saphir' | CFri CSam EGar ESis GAbr NArg |
| | NOrc NRoo SMrm SRms WHen |
| | WLRN |
| - Blue Sapphire | See *L. perenne* 'Blau Saphir' |
| - 'Diamant' | CBod LPVe NArg NPla NPri WLRN |
| - subsp. *extra-axillare* | CLyd |
| - 'Himmelszelt' | Last listed 1996 |
| - subsp. *lewisii* | CHad EBee EHyt LHop NBir |
| | NTow SMrm |
| - 'White Diamond' | WHen |
| *rubrum* | MChe |
| *sibiricum* | See *L. perenne* |
| *spathulatum* | Last listed 1996 |
| *suffruticosum* | CPBP |
| - subsp. *salsoloides* | CLyd NHar NWCA SBla SIng WPat |
| 'Nanum' | |
| - - 'Prostratum' | GBuc SIgm |
| § *tauricum* | EBee |
| *tenuifolium* | Last listed 1998 |
| * *tweedyi* | NBir |
| *viscosum* | Last listed 1998 |

## LIPARIS (Orchidaceae)

| | |
|---|---|
| ¶ *coelogynoides* | ECou |
| *cordifolia* | EFEx |
| *fujisanensis* | EFEx |
| *krameri* var. *krameri* | EFEx |
| *kumokiri* | EFEx |
| *makinoana* | EFEx |
| *nigra* | EFEx |
| *sootenzanensis* | EFEx |

## LIPPIA (Verbenaceae)

| | |
|---|---|
| *alba* | MSal |
| *canescens* | See *Phyla canescens* |
| *chamaedrifolia* | See *Verbena peruviana* |
| *citriodora* | See *Aloysia triphylla* |
| *dulcis* | CArn EOHP MSal |
| ¶ *graveolens* | EOHP |
| *nodiflora* | See *Phyla nodiflora* |
| *repens* | See *Phyla nodiflora* |
| ¶ *scaberrima* | EOHP |
| sp. RB 94075 | Last listed 1996 |

## LIQUIDAMBAR ✿ (Hamamelidaceae)

| | |
|---|---|
| *acalycina* | SSta WNor WPat |
| ¶ *chinensis* | CDul |
| *formosana* | CGre CLnd CMCN CPle CTho |
| | ELan GChr LPan MAsh MBlu SBir |
| | SFur SMad SPer SSta WNor WWat |
| - Monticola Group | EPfP SSta |
| *orientalis* | CBar CMCN CPMA EPfP LPan SBir |
| | SSta |
| *styraciflua* | More than 30 suppliers |
| - 'Andrew Hewson' | CLnd CPMA SBir SSta |
| - 'Anja' | SBir SMad SSta |
| - 'Anneke' | SBir SSta |
| - 'Aurea' | CDul CLnd COtt IOrc LNet SMad |
| | SSta WPat |
| - 'Aurea Variegata' | CDoC CPMA SBir |
| ¶ - 'Aurora' | CPMA |
| - 'Burgundy' | CDul CLnd CPMA MAsh SBir SSta |
| | WPat WWes |
| * - *festeri* | CEnd SBir SSta |
| - 'Festival' | SSta |
| ¶ - 'Globe' | CPMA |
| - 'Golden Treasure' (v) | CPMA LNet SMad WPat |
| - 'Gumball' | CLnd CPMA EPfP SMad SSta WPat |
| - 'Kia' | CEnd CPMA |
| - 'Lane Roberts' ♀ | CDoC CDul CLnd CMCN CTho |
| | EPfP IOrc LNet LPan MAsh MBri |
| | SBir SMad SReu SSta WDin WPat |
| | WPyg |
| - 'Manon' (v) | CDoC CEnd CPMA |
| - 'Moonbeam' (v) | CB&S CDul CEnd CPMA MAsh |
| | SBir SSta WPat |
| - 'Moraine' | Last listed 1996 |
| ¶ - 'Naree' | CPMA |
| - 'Palo Alto' | CPMA MAsh SSta WPat |
| - 'Parasol' | CPMA SMad SSta |
| - 'Pendula' | CPMA SBir SMad SSta WWes |
| * - 'Rotundifolia' | CPMA |
| - 'Rotundiloba' | SSta |
| - 'Silver King' (v) | CB&S CDul CPMA EBee EPfP SBir |
| | SPer SSta |
| - 'Stared' | CLnd CPMA |
| - 'Thea' | SMad SSta |
| - 'Variegata' | CB&S CBot CPMA ELan EPfP LNet |
| | LPan MAsh MGos NHol NPal SPer |
| | SSpi SSta WDin WPat |
| - 'Worplesdon' ♀ | CB&S CDoC CDul CEnd CMCN |
| | COtt CTho EBee EBrP EBre ECrN |
| | ELan ENot IOrc LBre LNet LPan |
| | MAsh MBri MGos MRav SBir SBre |
| | SRPl SReu SSpi SSta WDin WPat |
| | WWat |

## LIRIODENDRON ✿ (Magnoliaceae)

| | |
|---|---|
| *chinense* | CAbP EPfP MBlu SSpi WPGP |
| | WWat |
| *tulipifera* ♀ | More than 30 suppliers |
| - 'Ardis' | CMCN |
| - 'Arnold' | CMCN |
| - 'Aureomarginatum' ♀ | More than 30 suppliers |
| - 'Aureum' | CMCN |
| - 'Crispum' | CMCN |
| - 'Fastigiatum' ♀ | CB&S CDul CMCN COtt CTho |
| | EBee ELan ENot ERod LPan MAsh |
| | MBlu MBri SPer WOrn |

- 'Glen Gold'                MBlu SMad
¶  - 'Integrifolium'           CDul
  - 'Mediopictum'            CMCN CTho LNet MBlu

## LIRIOPE (✿) (Convallariaceae)

◆  'Big Blue'                 See *L. muscari* 'Big Blue'
§  *exiliflora*               CEnd EBee EBrP EBre EMan EPPr
                              EPar GCal LBre NArg NLar SApp
                              SBre SMad WBea WCot
§  - 'Ariaka-janshige' (v)    CRDP EMan LHop SWat WGle
I  - 'Silvery Sunproof'       Last listed 1997
◆  - Silvery Sunproof         See *L. spicata* 'Gin-ryu' , *L.*
      misapplied              *muscari* 'Variegata'
§  *gigantea*                 SWat WWal
   *graminifolia* hort.       See *L. muscari*
      non (L.) Bak.
   *hyacintbifolia*           See *Reineckea carnea*
   *koreana*                  GCal
   'Majestic'                 ENot
§  *muscari* ♀               More than 30 suppliers
   - 'Alba'                   See *L. muscari* 'Monroe White'
   - 'Aztec Gold'             WWal
   - B&SWJ 561                WCru
§  - 'Big Blue'               EBee EMan ENot EWll LRHS MRav
                              NArg NFla SApp SCob
   - 'Christmas Tree'         WGle WWal
◆  - 'Evergreen Giant'        See *L. gigantea*
   - 'Gold-banded'            CHea GCal IOrc SCob SWat WFar
                              WGle WGwG WViv WWal
   - 'Ingwersen'              Last listed 1997
   - 'John Burch' (v)         EBee SUsu WPer WWeb
   - 'Lilac Beauty'           WGle
◆  - 'Majestic' misapplied    See *L. exiliflora*
   - 'Mini Mondo'             WGwG WWal
§  - 'Monroe White'           CBro CEnd EBee EMan EMar EPar
                              EPla GCal LEdu MBri MCAu MRav
                              NArg NFai NLar NOrc SCob SMad
                              SPla SWat WCot WFar WGle WWat
                              WWye
¶  - 'Paul Aden'              CFil
   - 'Royal Purple'           EBee ENot NOrc WCot WGwG
                              WPer WWal
   - 'Silver Ribbon'          EPfP SPer
   - 'Silvery Midget' (v)     SUsu WMoo WWal
   - 'Superba'                Last listed 1997
§  - 'Variegata'              CAbb CFir CMil CRow CWSG
                              EAst ECot ELan EMan EPPr EPar
                              EPla ERav EWes IOrc MTho NArg
                              NBir NSti SBid SCob SMad SPla
                              SRms SYvo WPGP WRus
*  - 'Variegated Alba'        CFir
   - variegated white bloom   SAga
   - 'Webster Wideleaf'       WPer
   'New Wonder'               SApp
   *platyphylla*              See *L. muscari*
   'Samantha'                 LRHS SPla
§  *spicata*                  CHor LPio NFai NOrc SSpi SWat
                              WCot WHoo
   - 'Alba'                   CRow EPPr GCal MRav MTho
                              SUsu WTin WWin
§  - 'Gin-ryu' (v)            CAvo CFir EWes LEdu LHop MBel
                              MRav MSte SCob SUsu WCot
                              WWal
◆  - 'Silver Dragon'          See *L. spicata* 'Gin-ryu'

## LISTERA (Orchidaceae)

   *ovata*                    WHer

## LITHOCARPUS ✿ (Fagaceae)

   *densiflorus*              CMCN
   *edulis*                   SArc
§  *glaber*                   Last listed 1998

¶  *pachyphyllus*             CB&S

## LITHODORA (Boraginaceae)

*  *buglossoides*             WFar
§  *diffusa*                  EWTr MWat
   - 'Alba'                   ELan EMil EPot EWTr GAri IOrc
                              LBee LHop MAsh MBri MGos
                              MPla NHar NRoo WAbe WPat
   - 'Cambridge Blue'         EPfP MPla NHol SAga SLdr SMer
   - 'Compacta'               EGle ELan EPot EWes LHop
   - 'Grace Farwell'          Last listed 1997
   - 'Grace Ward' ♀          CGle EWes MBro MGos MPla
                              NHar NHol NRoo SBod SEas SIng
                              WAbe WHen WPat
   - 'Heavenly Blue' ♀       More than 30 suppliers
   - 'Inverleith'             ELan EWes LHop WFar
   - 'Picos'                  CLyd EDAr EGle EHyt EPot GCrs
                              GTou NHol NMen SIgm WAbe
                              WPat
   - 'Star'                   IGri MAsh SBod SCoo SIng WWeb
   *graminifolia*             See *Moltkia suffruticosa*
   *hispidula*                NMen SIng
   x *intermedia*             See *Moltkia* x *intermedia*
§  *oleifolia* ♀             CLyd EPot MBro MWat NBir NHol
                              NMen NSla NTow WCot WPat
   *rosmarinifolia*           CSpe
   *zahnii*                   CMHG NTow SIgm SSpi WLin
                              WPat

## LITHOPHRAGMA (Saxifragaceae)

   *bulbiferum*               See *L. glabrum*
   *parviflorum*              CMea EHyt EPot GCrs GDra
                              MNrw MSte MTho NBir NHol
                              NMen NRya NWCA SSpi WCru
                              WGle

## LITHOSPERMUM (Boraginaceae)

   *diffusum*                 See *Lithodora diffusa*
   *doerfleri*                See *Moltkia doerfleri*
   *erytbrorbizon*            MSal
   *officinale*               ELau EWFC GBar GPoy MSal
                              WCla WHer
   *oleifolium*               See *Lithodora oleifolia*
   *purpureocaeruleum*        See *Buglossoides*
                              *purpurocaerulea*

## LITSEA (Lauraceae)

◆  *glauca*                   See *Neolitsea sericea*
   *japonica*                 Last listed 1998

## LITTONIA (Colchicaceae)

   *modesta*                  CGre CHal CRHN

## LITTORELLA (Plantaginaceae)

§  *uniflora*                 WCot

## LIVISTONA (Arecaceae)

   *australis*                CAbb CRoM CTrC LPal NPal
   *chinensis* ♀             CTrC LPJP LPal
   *decipiens*                CRoM CTrC LPal NPal
   *mariae*                   LPal
   *saribus*                  Last listed 1997

## LLOYDIA (Liliaceae)

   *flavonutans*              Last listed 1996
   *serotina*                 EPot

## LOASA (Loasaceae)

   *lateritia*                See *Caiophora lateritia*
   *tripbylla* var. *volcanica*   EWes GCal

## LOBELIA (Campanulaceae)

| | |
|---|---|
| 'Alice' | WCot |
| *anatina* | CFai CFir EWTr EWll WLRN WRha |
| angulata | See *Pratia angulata* |
| 'Bees' Flame' | CFir CLAP CRos CRow SWat WLRN |
| * 'Bees Ridge' | Last listed 1997 |
| *bridgesii* | CSpe CTbh |
| 'Brightness' | CCuc CRos CRow ELan IHdy SPer |
| 'Butterfly Blue' | CB&S EBee EBrP EBre EGle GBuc LBre MAvo MBri MTis NChi NHol NPla SBre |
| 'Butterfly Rose' | EBrP EBre EGle GBuc GMac LBre LFis SAga SBre WCHb |
| *cardinalis* ♀ | CArn CRDP CRow CWat EFou EHon GCHN GCal LPBA MSal MSta NArg NDea SChu SPer SRms SUsu SWyc WFar WMAq WMer WOld WWin WWye |
| - 'Alba' | WCot WPyg |
| ¶ - subsp. *graminea* var. *multiflora* | CFir WCot |
| - 'Rose Beacon' | WCot |
| - 'Shrimp Salad' | Last listed 1997 |
| * 'Cherry Pie' | EMan |
| 'Cherry Ripe' | CElw CLAP CM&M CRos CSev ELan IHdy NHlc NHol SChu SMrm WCHb WEas WLRN |
| 'Cinnabar Deep Red' | See *L.* 'Fan Tiefrot' |
| 'Cinnabar Rose' | See *L.* 'Fan Zinnoberrosa' |
| 'Complexion' | CHad GCHN |
| Compliment Blue | See *L.* 'Kompliment Blau' |
| Compliment Deep Red | See *L.* 'Kompliment Tiefrot' |
| Compliment Purple | See *L.* 'Kompliment Purpur' |
| Compliment Scarlet | See *L.* 'Kompliment Scharlach' |
| 'Dark Crusader' | CBos CElw CMHG CRos CRow EBee EFou ELan LFis LHop MBri MLLN NDea NPro SChu SMrm WCHb WEas WOld WRus WSan |
| *deckenii* subsp.*elgonensis* | CFir |
| *dortmanna* | EMFW |
| *erinus* 'Kathleen Mallard' (d) | ELan LHop MBEx NPri |
| - 'Richardii' | See *L. richardsonii* |
| 'Eulalia Berridge' | CGle CLAP CMil CRos CSam EBee GBuc LBlm LHop MBri MMil SAga SMrm SWas |
| *excelsa* | CTbh EWes GCal WPic |
| Fan Deep Red | See *L.* 'Fan Tiefrot' |
| * Fan Orchid Rose ♀ | EMan LIck LWoo WHil WLRN |
| 'Fan Scharlach' ♀ | CMGP LIck WHil WWeb |
| § 'Fan Tiefrot' ♀ | CMGP EAst GBuc GCHN GMac SHel SMad SRms SSpi SWat WCHb WHil WLRN WPer |
| § 'Fan Zinnoberrosa' ♀ | CB&S CFir CGle CMGP EAst EBee EMan EWTr MHlr NCut NWes SAga SLon SRms WCHb WHil WPer WWin WWye |
| 'Flamingo' | See *L.* 'Pink Flamingo' |
| 'Frances' | WCot |
| *fulgens* | IBlr WByw WEas |
| - 'Elmfeuer' | CHar CSpe EHic EOrc MAvo MLLN SMrm WCot WElm WPen |
| - 'Illumination' | GBuc |
| ¶ - 'St Elmo's Fire' | WGor |
| 'Galen' | Last listed 1998 |
| ¶ *georgiana* | EBee |
| x *gerardii* | CLAP CSam EWll NLak SSca WBor |
| ¶ - 'Alba' | CRow |
| - 'Eastgrove Pink' | WEas |
| - 'Rosencavalier' | LRHS MBri SMrm WFar |
| § - 'Vedrariensis' | More than 30 suppliers |

| | |
|---|---|
| *gibberoa* | Last listed 1998 |
| 'Hadspen Royal Purple' | Last listed 1996 |
| *inflata* | CArn GPoy MSal WCHb WWye |
| 'Jack McMaster' | Last listed 1997 |
| *kalmii* | Last listed 1996 |
| 'Kimbridge Beet' ♀ | Last listed 1997 |
| § 'Kompliment Blau' | CBlo CFir CHor EMan LIck NArg NCut NHol WHil WPer |
| § 'Kompliment Purpur' | Last listed 1998 |
| § 'Kompliment Scharlach' ♀ | CBlo CHor CRos CRow CSWP EBee EBrP EBre EPfP EWTr GCHN LBre MBNS NCut NPer SBre SSpi WCHb WFar WHil WPer |
| § 'Kompliment Tiefrot' | CHor NArg WPer |
| *laxiflora* | CBot CInt EGra MTho SIgm |
| - var. *angustifolia* | CGre CHea CPle CSam CSpe CTbh ELan EMan ERea GCal IBlr LBlm LHil LHop MSte NWes SHFr SMac SMrm SRms WAbe WPer WWye |
| 'Lena' | SWat |
| *lindblomii* | CLTr |
| *linnaeoides* | EWes GCHN MTho SPlb WEas |
| § *longiflora* RB 94066 | Last listed 1996 |
| § *lutea* | CGen CInt |
| § *oligodon* | Last listed 1996 |
| *pedunculata* | See *Pratia pedunculata* |
| *perpusilla* | See *Pratia perpusilla* |
| *physaloides* | See *Pratia physaloides* |
| 'Pink Elephant' ♀ | CGle CLAP CMHG CMil CSWP CSev EPri NBrk WCot WFar |
| § 'Pink Flamingo' | CRow EAst EBee EBrP EBre EFou EMFW EPar GCHN LBre NFai NFor NLon NSti SAga SBre SChu SCro SMrm SPer SWat WBor WCHb WFar WPyg WWye |
| ¶ *polyphylla* | WPic |
| 'Pope's Velvet' | Last listed 1996 |
| *puberula* | CFir |
| 'Purple Towers' | GBuc WCot |
| *pyramidalis* B&SWJ 316 | Last listed 1997 |
| 'Queen Victoria' ♀ | More than 30 suppliers |
| ¶ 'Rachel's Pink' | IHdy |
| ¶ 'Red Hugh' | IHdy |
| ¶ *regalis* | WHal |
| *repens* | See *Pratia repens* |
| § *richardsonii* ♀ | CInt LHil LIck MBEx WLRN |
| *roughii* | Last listed 1997 |
| 'Rowden Magenta' | CRow |
| 'Royal Robe' | CRow |
| 'Ruby Slippers' | WCot |
| N 'Russian Princess' | CGle CRDP CRos CRow CSam EBee IHdy MBEx MBri MCLN NBrk SChu SMad SSvw SUsu WCHb WCot WFar WLRN WMer WWeb |
| 'Sandy's Pink' | SWat |
| *sessilifolia* | GBuc GCal GMac SMrm SRms SUsu WCot WLRN WMow WPer WSan WWye |
| - B&L 12396 | EMon |
| - B&SWJ 520 | Last listed 1998 |
| *siphilitica* | More than 30 suppliers |
| - 'Alba' | CBlo CPea CPou CRow CSam EBee EPfP EPri LBlm LHil MCLN MLLN NChi NSti SLon SRms SSca WByw WCHb WFar WHoo WPer WPyg WWye |
| - Blue selection | NLar |
| - 'Nana' | Last listed 1996 |
| - 'Rosea' | MNrw |
| 'Sonia' | CGle |

| | |
|---|---|
| 'Spark' | GBuc WCot |
| 'Sparkle Divine' | WCot |
| x *speciosa* | CBrd CRow MNrw WLRN |
| – dark form | CMHG CRos CRow SHFr SMrm |
| *surrepens* | Last listed 1996 |
| 'Tania' | CFir CGle CRDP CRow EFou |
| | EMan EMar GBri GMac IBlr LHil |
| | MBel MCLN MHlr MLLN MUlv |
| | NSti SChu SCro SMad SMrm SUsu |
| | WCot WFar WRus |
| *treadwellii* | See *Pratia angulata* 'Treadwellii' |
| *tupa* | CBot CGen CGre CHan CHar CInt |
| | CSpe EBee ECha ELan EWTr GCal |
| | GGar IBlr IHdy LHop SHFr SMad |
| | WCHb WCru WEas WHal WHer |
| | WPer WPic WRos WSan WWat |
| | WWin WWye |
| – dark orange form | SArc SMrm |
| – JCA 12527 | WCot |
| *urens* | SSpi |
| *valida* | CFir CInt GBuc GQui SCoo WLRN |
| – 'South Seas' | EWTr |
| *vedrariensis* | See *L.* x *gerardii* 'Vedrariensis' |
| 'Wildwood Splendour' | Last listed 1997 |
| 'Will Scarlet' | CCuc CLAP CRos EBrP EBre LBre |
| | SBre SHFr |
| 'Zinnoberrosa' | See *L.* 'Fan Zinnoberrosa' |

## LOBELIA x PRATIA (Campanulaceae)
| | |
|---|---|
| *L. linnaeoides* | |
| x *P. macrodon* | Last listed 1996 |
| *L.* sp. x *P.* sp. | Last listed 1998 |

## LOBOSTEMON (Boraginaceae)
| | |
|---|---|
| *montanus* | Last listed 1997 |

## LOESELIA (Polemoniaceae)
| | |
|---|---|
| *mexicana* | ERea LHop |

## LOISELEURIA (Ericaceae)
| | |
|---|---|
| *procumbens* | NHar |
| – from Japan | GCrs WAbe |
| – 'Saint Anton' | Last listed 1997 |

## LOMANDRA (Lomandraceae)
| | |
|---|---|
| *longifolia* | ECou |

## LOMARIA See BLECHNUM

## LOMATIA (Proteaceae)
| | |
|---|---|
| *dentata* | Last listed 1998 |
| *ferruginea* | CAbb CB&S CDoC CFil CLan |
| | CTrG ISea MBal SAPC SArc WCru |
| | WPGP |
| ¶ *fraseri* | SSpi |
| ¶ *hirsuta* | CFil |
| *longifolia* | See *L. myricoides* |
| § *myricoides* | CAbb CB&S CDoC CFil CTrG |
| | CTrw EPfP SArc SSpi WBod WWat |
| *silaifolia* | CDoC EPfP |
| § *tinctoria* | CB&S CDoC CTrw ELan EPfP |
| | SArc SSpi WBod |

## LOMATIUM (Apiaceae)
| | |
|---|---|
| *brandegeei* | SIgm |
| *columbianum* | SIgm |
| ¶ *dissectum* var. *multifidum* | SIgm |
| *grayi* | SIgm |
| ¶ *laevigatum* | EBee |
| ¶ *macrocarpum* | SIgm |
| ¶ *martindalei* | EBee SIgm |

| | |
|---|---|
| ¶ *nudicaule* | SIgm |
| *utriculatum* | MSal SIgm |

## LOMATOGONIUM (Gentianaceae)
| | |
|---|---|
| sp. ACE 2331* | WAbe |

## LONICERA ✿ (Caprifoliaceae)
| | |
|---|---|
| § *acuminata* | EHal EHic ETen LRHS MAsh WCru |
| | WGwG WSHC |
| – B&SWJ 2150 | WCru |
| – B&SWJ 3480 | WCru |
| *albertii* | CFai EHic MBNS MRav SPan |
| | WHCG WSHC |
| *albiflora* | CPIN WSHC |
| – var. *albiflora* | SBra |
| *alpigena* | Last listed 1998 |
| *alseuosmoides* | CPIN ETen SBra SLon WBcn WCru |
| | WSHC WWeb |
| *altmannii* | CPle |
| § x *americana* (Miller) | CBlo CHad CRHN CSPN EPfP |
| K. Koch | LHop MAsh MBri MGos NBea |
| | SBra SEas SReu SSta WCru WWeb |
| § – hort. | See *L.* x *italica* |
| 'Anna Landers' | WCFE |
| x *brownii* | CMac CRHN |
| § – 'Dropmore Scarlet' | More than 30 suppliers |
| N – 'Fuchsioides' | EPfP MBro NBrk NSti WSHC |
| | WWat |
| *caerulea* | CPle MRav WHCG |
| – var. *altaica* | Last listed 1998 |
| – var. *edulis* | CAgr LEdu |
| – f. *emphyllocalyx* | CPle |
| § *caprifolium* ♀ | CDoC CPIN CRHN EBee ECtt |
| | ELan EOrc EPla LBuc LHol LPri |
| | MAsh MBar MBri NBea NFai |
| | NMGW NSti SBra SPer WCot |
| | WCru WWat |
| – 'Anna Fletcher' | CRHN ELan MBNS MTed NHol |
| | SBra SPan WCru WWat WWeb |
| – 'Cornish Cream' | NTay |
| – f. *pauciflora* | See *L.* x *italica* |
| *chaetocarpa* | CMHG CPle WPat |
| § *chrysantha* | CMCN CPle GBin |
| *ciliosa* | CPIN NBea SBra |
| 'Clavey's Dwarf' | IOrc MGos MPla NBrk NHol |
| *cyanocarpa* KGB 438 | Last listed 1998 |
| *deflexicalyx* KGB 165 | Last listed 1998 |
| *dioica* | SBra |
| 'Early Cream' | See *L. caprifolium* |
| *etrusca* | EHal EPla LPri MRav WWeb |
| – 'Donald Waterer' ♀ | CBlo CSam EBee EHic LHop LRHS |
| | MAsh SBra WFar WGor WWat |
| – 'Michael Rosse' | EBee EBrP EBre EHic ETen LBre |
| | LRHS MBNS SBra SBre SRms |
| – 'Superba' ♀ | CBlo CPIN CRHN EBee ECtt ELan |
| | EPfP MAsh NBrk NSti SBra SEND |
| | WCru WPen WSHC WWat |
| *ferdinandii* | Last listed 1998 |
| *flexuosa* | See *L. japonica* var. *repens* |
| *fragrantissima* | More than 30 suppliers |
| ◆ *gibbiflora* Maxim. | See *L. chrysantha* |
| ^ – Dippel | NRya |
| *giraldii* Rehder | CBot CHan CPIN EBee LPri NHol |
| | SBra WCot |
| – hort. | See *L. acuminata* |
| *glabrata* | EHic SBra SLPl WCru |
| *glaucohirta* | See *L. periclymenum* var. |
| | *glaucohirta* |
| *gracilis* | MBlu |
| *grata* | See *L.* x *americana* (Miller) K. |
| | Koch |

| | |
|---|---|
| x *beckrottii* | CB&S CBlo CDoC CMac CRHN CTri EBee ECtt GOrc LPri MAsh MBar NBea NBee WCru WDin WLRN WStl WWeb |
| N - 'Gold Flame' | More than 30 suppliers |
| § *henryi* | More than 30 suppliers |
| - var. *subcoriacea* | See *L. henryi* |
| * 'Hidcote' | Last listed 1996 |
| *hildebrandiana* | CGre CPlN SBra SOWG |
| *hirsuta* | NBea SBra |
| 'Honey Baby' | MBlu MGos MRav |
| *implexa* | CHan CPlN EHol EPla GCal LGre MBNS MBlu NPro SBra SEas WCot WCru WPat WSHC |
| ^ *infundibulum* var. *rockii* | EPfP |
| *insularis* | CMCN CPle MBlu MTPN |
| *involucrata* | CHan CMCN CMHG CPle EPla GBin GOrc LHil LHop MBNS MBar MBlu MRav NChi NHol SPan SPer WDin WFar WHCG WPyg |
| - var. *ledebourii* | CHan CPle ELan EPfP EPla GChr MBel MWat NHol SBid SDys WOve WWin |
| § x *italica* ♀ | CMac CRHN EBee EBrP EBre ELan ENot LBre LHol LPri MBri MRav NSti SBra SBre SDix SLPl SPer SPla SSpi WCru WFar WPyg WSHC WWat |
| § - Harlequin = 'Sherlite' (v) | CBlo CBot EAst EMil ENot LBuc MAsh MBel MGos MRav NBea NEgg NHol NRoo NSti SBra SMad SPer SPla SPlb SVil WCru WLRN WWat WWeb |
| ♦ - 'Sherlite' | See *L.* x *italica* Harlequin = 'Sherlite' |
| § *japonica* 'Aureoreticulata' | More than 30 suppliers |
| ¶ - 'Cream Cascade' | SPan |
| - 'Dart's Acumen' | SLPl |
| - 'Dart's World' | EHic MBel NHol SBra SLPl SVil WLRN |
| - 'Halliana' ♀ | More than 30 suppliers |
| - 'Hall's Prolific' | More than 30 suppliers |
| § - 'Horwood Gem' (v) | EBee ECtt EHic NHol SBra WBcn WWeb |
| - 'Peter Adams' | See *L. japonica* 'Horwood Gem' |
| § - var. *repens* ♀ | CCHP CDoC CMac EBee EBrP EBre ECtt ELan ENot EPla LBre LPri MRav NBea NEgg NFai SBra SBre SLPl SLon SPer SRms WCru WWat WWeb |
| - 'Soja' | Last listed 1996 |
| - 'Variegata' | See *L. japonica* 'Aureoreticulata' |
| *korolkowii* | CBot CHan CPle CSam EBee EHic LFis MBNS MWat NBir SBid SPan SPla SSta SUsu WHCG WSHC WWat WWin |
| - var. *zabelii* | ELan SEas |
| *lanceolata* KGB 488 | Last listed 1998 |
| *maackii* | CMCN CPMA WHCG WWat |
| - f. *podocarpa* | CPle |
| ¶ 'Mandarin' | LRHS MAsh MBri SCoo WWeb |
| *microphylla* | Last listed 1998 |
| *morrowii* | Last listed 1998 |
| x *muscaviensis* | CPle |
| *myrtillus* KGB 298 | Last listed 1998 |
| *nigra* | EPla |
| *nitida* | CB&S CChe CKin CTri ELan GOrc LHyr MRav NWea SPer SRPl STre WDin WFar WHar WHen WStl |
| - 'Baggesen's Gold' ♀ | More than 30 suppliers |
| - 'Eden Spring' | NPro |
| - 'Elegant' | ELan IOrc LBuc |
| - 'Ernest Wilson' | MBar SRms |
| - 'Fertilis' | SPer SRms |
| - 'Hohenheimer Findling' | Last listed 1998 |
| - 'Lemon Beauty' | EBee EHoe EPla GRei MBNS MBri MGos NFai WBcn WLeb |
| - 'Lemon Queen' | EHal WLRN |
| § - 'Maigrün' | CChe EBee EMil MBri NFai NFla NPro SPer WFar WGwG WTro |
| - Maygreen | See *L. nitida* 'Maigrün' |
| - 'Red Tips' | CWSG EGra EHic EHoe EPla LBuc LRHS MBel MBri MGos MLLN NFai NHol |
| - 'Silver Beauty' (v) | More than 30 suppliers |
| * - 'Silver Cloud' | CWSG EHic SSto WCot WShe |
| - 'Silver Lining' | See *L. pileata* 'Silver Lining' |
| - 'Silver Queen' | EWTr WEas |
| - 'Twiggy' | MGos NFai NHol NPro SVil WGer WLRN |
| *nummariifolia* | Last listed 1998 |
| *periclymenum* | CArn CKin CTri EPla EWFC GChr GPoy NBea NFor NLon NMir NWea SHFr SPlb WDin WHCG WOak |
| - misapplied 'Belgica' | See *L.* x *italica* |
| § - 'Belgica' ♀ | More than 30 suppliers |
| - *clarkii* | Last listed 1996 |
| - 'Cottage Beauty' | Last listed 1996 |
| * - 'Cream Cascade' | Last listed 1996 |
| - 'Florida' | See *L. periclymenum* 'Serotina' |
| § - var. *glaucohirta* | Last listed 1996 |
| - 'Graham Thomas' ♀ | More than 30 suppliers |
| - 'Harlequin' | See *L.* x *italica* Harlequin = 'Sherlite' |
| - 'Heaven Scent' | EMil SBra |
| ¶ - 'Honeybush' | EBee |
| - 'La Gasnaérie' | EBee EPla GAri NHol SBra SPan |
| - 'Liden' | SBra |
| - 'Munster' | CB&S EBee EPla MBri NBrk SBra WBcn |
| - 'Purple Queen' | CBlo |
| - 'Red Gables' | CBlo CSam EBee EHic MBNS MBri MRav NHol SBra SPan SPla SVil WGor WPat WWat |
| N - 'Serotina' ♀ | More than 30 suppliers |
| - 'Serotina' EM '85 | MBri WWat |
| - 'Serpentine' | SBra |
| - *sulphurea* | EPla EWll NFai |
| - 'Sweet Sue' | ECtt ELan EPfP GCal LRHS MAsh SBra WBcn WFar WWeb |
| - 'Winchester' | Last listed 1997 |
| - yellow | Last listed 1997 |
| *pileata* | More than 30 suppliers |
| - 'Moss Green' | CBlo CDoC EBee MGos SBid SLon WHCG |
| ¶ - 'Pilot' | SLPl |
| § - 'Silver Lining' (v) | CBlo EPla GBuc MLLN WCot |
| - 'Stockholm' | SLPl |
| *pilosa* Maxim. | See *L. strophiophora* |
| - Willd. CD&R 1216 | CHan SBra |
| *praeflorens* | Last listed 1997 |
| *prolifera* | SBra |
| *prostrata* | Last listed 1998 |
| x *purpusii* | CDoC CPle CSam ECle EMil GChr LHol MBNS MBar MBel MGos MPla NBea SRms WBod WCru WEas WFar WHCG WHar WPyg WSHC WWeb WWin |
| - 'Winter Beauty' ♀ | More than 30 suppliers |
| *pyrenaica* | CPle SPan WPat |
| *quinquelocularis* | CPle EHal EPla |
| - f. *translucens* | MBlu |
| *ramosissima* | CMCN |

§ *rupicola* var. *syringantha*  CBrm CDul CHan CHar CMHG
CPle CSam EAst EBee ELan GEil
LHol LHop MBlu MGos MHlr
MTis MWat MWhi NBea NLon
SPan SPer SPla WFar WHCG
WSHC WWat WWin

\- var. *syringantha*  GQui WAbe WPyg
'Grandiflora'

*ruprechtiana*  CPle
*segreziensis*  CPle
*sempervirens* ♀  CBot CPlN CRHN EBee ELan EPar
EPfP GAri LBlm LPri MBNS MCCP
NBea SBra SSta WLRN WLeb
WSHC WWeb

\- 'Dropmore Scarlet'  See *L.* x *brownii* 'Dropmore
Scarlet'

N - f. *sulphurea*  CBlo CPlN EBee EHic EPfP LRHS
NBea SBra SPan SPer WSHC WWat
WWeb

*serotina* 'Honeybush'  CPle MAsh MBlu NHol SBra
*setifera*  CBot EHol
¶ - 'Daphnis'  EPfP
*similis* var. *delavayi*  CBot CDoC CHan CLTr CPlN
CSPN CSam EBee EPla MAsh MBel
NBea NFai SBra SDix SLPl SPan
SPla WCru WPGP WPen WSHC
WWat

'Simonet'  SBra WGwG
sp. ACE 1413  Last listed 1998
sp. CLD 1451  Last listed 1996
sp. CLD 315  Last listed 1997
sp. DF 89251  Last listed 1996
¶ sp. from Sikkim B&SWJ 2654  WCru
sp. KBE 062  NHol
sp. LS&H 17465  WWat
*splendida*  CBot SBra WCru WSHC
¶ 'Spring Romance'  SLon
*standishii*  CB&S EBee LHol MBel MGos
MRav NFai SPer WDin WFar
WHCG WRha WWin WWye
'Stone Green'  NLak NPro SPla
§ *strophiophora*  WWat
*syringantha*  See *L. rupicola* var. *syringantha*
*tangutica* KGB 535  Last listed 1998
*tatarica*  CFai CHan MHlr MRav MWhi
SLon WFar WHCG WWin
\- 'Alba'  CFai CHan CPMA MTed SPan
\- 'Arnold's Red'  CB&S CBot CDoC CPle EHal ELan
EPfP EPla EWTr MBal MBlu MPla
\- 'Hack's Red'  CB&S CFai EPfP EWTr MPla MRav
SCob SPan SPer WHCG WPyg
\- 'Rosea'  Last listed 1997
\- f. *sibirica*  Last listed 1997
\- 'Zabelii'  EPfP
x *tellmanniana* ♀  More than 30 suppliers
\- 'Joan Sayer'  EBrP EBre EHic EPla LBre LHop
MBNS MCCP MGos NBrk SBra
SBre SPan WBcn WLeb WWat
*thibetica*  CPle MBlu SPer WWat
*tragophylla* ♀  CB&S CDoC CPlN CSam EBee
ELan EPla GCal ICrw IOrc LHop
LPri MAsh MBNS MBri NHol NSti
SBra SPar SPer SSpi SSta WCru
WDin WSHC WWat
*trichosantha* KGB 404  Last listed 1998
¶ *webbiana*  ELan
x *xylosteoides*  MRav
\- 'Clavey's Dwarf'  MBel MBlu MGos SLPl SPan
\- 'Miniglobe'  ESis NPro
\* *yunnanensis* 'Variegata'  Last listed 1998

## LOPEZIA (Onagraceae)

*racemosa*  CPla MCCP MTPN SHFr WMoo
WRos

## LOPHOMYRTUS (Myrtaceae)

§ *bullata*  CGre CTre ECou GQui SPer
WCHb
¶ - 'Matai Bay'  CB&S CTrC
'Gloriosa'  CB&S CPle LRHS WCHb
¶ - 'Little Star'  CB&S LRHS
§ *obcordata*  CGre CPle WWat
x *ralphii*  WCHb WPic WWat
\- 'Andrea'  Last listed 1998
§ - 'Kathryn'  CB&S CDoC CHan CPle CTre
ERea WCHb WSHC WWat
\- 'Pixie'  SBid
§ - 'Traversii'  LRHS MAsh SMur
\- 'Variegata'  EBrP EBre ERea LBre SBre
¶ - 'Wild Cherry'  CDoC
'Sundae'  CB&S
'Tricolor'  CPle CTre
'Versicolor'  CB&S

## LOPHOSORIA (Dicksoniaceae)

*quadripinnata*  CFil

## LOPHOSPERMUM (Scrophulariaceae)

§ *erubescens* ♀  CBot CHal CPlN CRHN LFis LHop
MSte MTis
\- 'Garnet'  Last listed 1997
'Red Dragon'  CSpe
§ *scandens*  CB&S CPlN CRHN ELan EWes

## LOPHOSTEMON (Myrtaceae)

§ *confertus*  Last listed 1998

## LOROPETALUM (Hamamelidaceae)

*chinense*  CFil CMCN SBid SSpi
\- 'Blush'  CFil WPGP
¶ - 'Fire Dance'  WCot
\- f. *rubrum*  CFil SLon WPGP
I  - 'Zhuzhou Fuchsia'  CMCN

## LOTUS (Papilionaceae)

*berthelotii* ♀  CFee CGle CHal CSev CSpe ECon
ELan ERea LHil MBEx SChu SRms
SSoC SYvo WEas WKif
\- deep red  LIck
\- Kew form  Last listed 1997
\- x *maculatus*  CBar CLTr CSpe LHil MBEx MSCN
WIvy
*corniculatus*  CArn CKin CLTr EWFC MCoo
MHew NLak NLan SIde WGwy
WOak
\- 'Plenus' (d)  CInt EMon EPot IBlr LFis MTho
NHol WAlt WCot WPer
'Gold Flash'  LIck
§ *hirsutus*  More than 30 suppliers
\- 'Brimstone'  EHic GBin GCal LHop SPan SPer
SPla SVil
\- dwarf form  CHan
\- 'Lois'  WSPU
\- 'Silver Mist'  SCro
*jacobaeus*  CInt
*maculatus* ♀  CGle CSpe ECon MBEx SHFr
SOWG SSoC SVen WCom WIvy
*maritimus*  CMea EWll NNrd NOla SHFr
*mascaensis* hort.  See *L. sessilifolius*
*pedunculatus*  See *L. uliginosus*
*pentaphyllus*  GCal
subsp. *herbaceus*

§ - subsp. *pentaphyllus*    NBrk
§ *sessilifolius*    ERea LHil MBEx
   *suffruticosus*    See *L. pentaphyllus* subsp.
     *pentaphyllus*
§ *uliginosus*    EWFC NMir

## LOXOSTYLIS (Anacardiaceae)
   *alata*    Last listed 1997

## LUCULIA (Rubiaceae)
   *grandifolia*    SOWG
   *gratissima* ♀    CB&S LChe
¶ - 'Early Dawn'    CTrC
   - 'Rosea'    ECon SOWG
   *pinceana* 'Fragrant Cloud'    CB&S

## LUDWIGIA (Onagraceae)
   *grandiflora*    CRow SWyc
   *palustris*    Last listed 1997
   *uruguayensis*    LPBA

## LUETKEA (Rosaceae)
   *pectinata*    EBee GCHN GDra WAbe

## LUMA (Myrtaceae)
§ *apiculata* ♀    CAbb CArn CChe CDoC CEnd
     CFil CMHG CPle CTrG CTre CTri
     CTrw ISea LHil MBal MBlu SArc
     SDix SEND SPer STre WBod
     WCHb WHCr WPic WSHC WTro
     WWat WWye
§ - 'Glanleam Gold' (v)    More than 30 suppliers
   - 'Variegata'    CMHG CTri ISea NHol WWat
     WWeb WWye
§ *chequen*    CFee CGre GAri NHex WCHb
     WCwm WJek WWat

## LUNARIA (Brassicaceae)
§ *annua*    EBot GAbr MMal MWgw NCat
     SIde SWat WByw WHer WOak
     WRha
I - 'Alba Variegata'    CSpe EBla EMar EMon EPla MFir
     WBor WByw WCot
   - var. *albiflora* ♀    CSev EBot EWTr NBir NCat SIde
     SWat WCer WCot WOak
   - 'Ken Aslet'    Last listed 1997
¶ - 'Munstead Purple'    EBla
\* - 'Stella'    WHen
   - *variegata*    CHar CJew EBla EBot IBlr MTho
     NBir SWat WCot WEas WHer
     WRha WSan
   - violet    NBir WFar
   *biennis*    See *L. annua*
   *rediviva*    ECGP ECha EMon EPla GAri
     GCHN GGar GLil IBlr MHer NBro
     NSti SSpi WCot WEas WFar WHen
     WHer

## LUPINUS ✿ (Papilionaceae)
   'Alan Titchmarsh'    MWoo
   *albifrons*    CGen CSpe EBee LHil SIgm
   - var. *douglasii*    Last listed 1996
   - var. *flumineus*    Last listed 1998
   *alopecuroides*    Last listed 1998
   *angustifolius*    Last listed 1998
   'Anne Gregg' ♀    MWoo
   *arboreus* ♀    More than 30 suppliers
   - 'Barton on Sea'    CNat
   - blue    CHar CMea MCCP NCut NLar
     SPer WShe
¶ - cream    NLon
   - ex blue form    Last listed 1998

   - 'Golden Spire'    Last listed 1998
   - 'Mauve Queen'    NBee SEND SUsu
   - mixed    NFla
   - 'Snow Queen'    Last listed 1998
   *arcticus*    EBee
   *argenteus*    Last listed 1998
◆ - var. *depressus*    See *L. argenteus* var. *utahensis*
§ - var. *utahensis*    WLin
   - var. *wyethii*    Last listed 1998
   Band of Nobles Series ♀    ECtt GAbr WFar
   'Barnsdale'    MWoo
   *benthamii*    CFri
   'Beryl, Viscountess Cowdray'    GBuc
   *bicolor*    Last listed 1998
   *breweri*    Last listed 1998
   *caespitosus*    See *L. lepidus* var. *utahensis*
   *chamissonis*    CHan CPla CSpe EBrP EBre EGoo
     EMan EWes LBre LGre LHop
     MAvo MTho SBre SDry SDys
     SMad SMrm SSpi SUsu WPen
     WRus
   'Chandelier'    CHad CTri EBee EBrP EBre ECtt
     EFou ELan EMan EWTr GAbr GAri
     GCHN LBre MBri MCAu MWgw
     NBrk NFai NMir NRoo NVic SBre
     SPer SRPl WFar WHen WPer
     WRHF
   'Chelsea Pensioner'    MWoo
   'Clifford Star'    Last listed 1996
   'Daydream'    Last listed 1996
   'Deborah Woodfield' ♀    MWoo
   *densiflorus* var. *aureus*    See *L. microcarpus* var.
     *densiflorus*
   Dwarf Gallery hybrids    LIck
   'Dwarf Lulu'    See *L.* 'Lulu'
   'Esmerelder' ♀    MWoo
   Gallery Series    EBrP EBre EFou GMaP LBre NCut
     NFai NPri NRoo SBre SCoo WHil
     WLRN
   'Gallery Blue' (Gallery Series)    ECtt EPfP NCut NLar SPer WHil
     WViv
   'Gallery Pink' (Gallery Series)    EPfP NLar SPer WHil WViv
   'Gallery Red' (Gallery Series)    ECtt NLar SPer WHil WViv
   'Gallery White' (Gallery Series)    EPfP EWTr LPVe NLar SPer SPla
     WHil WViv
   'Gallery Yellow' (Gallery Series)    ECtt EWTr NCut NLar SPer SPla
     WHil WViv
   'Garden Gnome'    WPer
   'Gold Dust'    Last listed 1996
   'Helen Sharman' ♀    MWoo
   'Household Brigade'    MWoo
   'Judith Chalmers'    MWoo
   'Kayleigh Ann Savage' ♀    MWoo
   *latifolius*    WAbe
   - subsp. *parishii*    Last listed 1998
   - var. *subalpinus*    WLin
   *lepidus*    EMan
   - var. *lobbii*    SIgm WAbe
   - var. *sellulus*    SIgm
§ - var. *utahensis*    Last listed 1998
   *leucophyllus*    Last listed 1997
   'Little Eugenie'    MWoo
   *littoralis*    EMan GDra SIgm WPer
§ - 'Lulu'    COtt EBrP EBre ECtt ELan LBre
     MRav NMir SBre SPer SRPl WFar
     WMoo
   *luteus*    Last listed 1998
   *micranthus*    Last listed 1998
   *microcarpus*    Last listed 1997
§ - var. *densiflorus*    Last listed 1998
   *microphyllus*    Last listed 1998
   Minarette Group    CBlo ECtt MBri NCut SRms WGor

| | |
|---|---|
| Mirakel hybrids | CBlo |
| 'Misty' | MWoo |
| *montanus* | Last listed 1998 |
| 'Mrs Perkins' | SMrm |
| *mutabilis* | Last listed 1998 |
| | var. *cruckshanksii* |
| 'My Castle' | EBee EBrP EBre ECtt EFou ELan |
| | EOld EWTr GAbr GAri GCHN |
| | GLil LBre MBri MCAu MRav NBrk |
| | NFai NMir NOak NRoo NVic SBre |
| | SPer SPla WFar WHen WPer |
| *nanus* | Last listed 1998 |
| ¶ 'Nigel Colborn' | MWoo |
| 'Noble Maiden' | CHad EBee EBrP EBre ECtt EFou |
| | ELan EMan EWTr GAbr GAri |
| | GCHN GLil LBre LRot MBri MCAu |
| | NBrk NFai NMir NOak NRoo |
| | NVic SBre SPer WFar WHen WPer |
| | WRHF |
| *nootkatensis* | CPea WPat |
| 'Olive Tolley' ♀ | MWoo |
| *oreophilus* F&W 7353 | Last listed 1997 |
| 'Party Dress' | MWoo |
| *perennis* | CGle ECGN SCou |
| *pilosus* | See *L. varius* subsp. *orientalis* |
| ¶ 'Pink Fortune' | SRPl |
| 'Poached Salmon' | SMrm |
| 'Polar Princess' | EWes MGrG SRPl SWat WLRN |
| | WMow |
| *polyphyllus* | EBee |
| – var. *burkei* | Last listed 1998 |
| 'Pope John Paul' ♀ | MWoo |
| *propinquus* | Last listed 1998 |
| 'Rising Sun' | CFri |
| 'Rote Flamme' | ECGN EWll LPVe |
| 'Royal Parade' ♀ | Last listed 1996 |
| 'Royal Wedding' | MWoo |
| Russell hybrids | CB&S ELan EWTr GChr NFla SPlb |
| | SRms SSea |
| *sericatus* | Last listed 1997 |
| *sericeus* | EMan WPat |
| ¶ – *fikerianus* | WLin |
| *sparsiflorus* | Last listed 1998 |
| ¶ 'Stuart Ogg V.M.H.' | MWoo |
| *succulentus* | Last listed 1998 |
| 'Sundown' | Last listed 1997 |
| 'Sunset' | MWoo |
| 'Sunshine' | CGle |
| *texensis* | Last listed 1998 |
| 'The Chatelaine' | CHad EBee EBrP EBre ECtt EFou |
| | ELan EOld GAbr GAri GCHN GLil |
| | LBre LNor MBri MCAu MRav |
| | MWgw NBrk NFai NLon NMir |
| | NRoo SBre SPer SPla WFar WHen |
| | WPer |
| 'The Governor' | CTri EBee EBrP EBre ECtt EFou |
| | ELan EMan GAbr GAri GCHN GLil |
| | LBre LPVe MBri MCAu MRav NBrk |
| | NFai NMir NRoo NVic SBre SPer |
| | SPla WFar WGwG WPer |
| 'The Page' | EBee EBrP EBre EFou ELan EMan |
| | EOld GAbr GAri LBre LNor MBri |
| | MRav NBrk NFai NMir NRoo SBre |
| | SPer WFar WGwG WPer |
| 'Thundercloud' | CHad CPlt SMrm |
| ¶ 'Troop the Colour' ♀ | MWoo |
| *variicolor* | CGen CSpe MBri NChi SIgm SSpi |
| | WFar |
| – JJA 11167 | NChi |
| *versicolor* | CElw CPea EMan LGro MCCP |
| | MLLN MSCN NSti SMad WBea |
| 'Walton Lad' | Last listed 1996 |

| | |
|---|---|
| ¶ 'Windermere' | MWoo |
| 'Yellow Boy' | Last listed 1998 |

## LUZULA (Juncaceae)

| | |
|---|---|
| *alpinopilosa* | GBin |
| x *borreri* 'Botany Bay' (v) | CCuc EMon EPPr EPla MCCP |
| | WLeb |
| *campestris* | CKin |
| *canariensis* | CPle WWye |
| *forsteri* | EPPr |
| *lactea* | EMon EPGN EPPr LRHS |
| *leptophylla* | NHar |
| *luzuloides* | WPer |
| – 'Schneehäschen' | CInt EGar EMon EPPr EPla GBin |
| | GCal MWgw |
| *maxima* | See *L. sylvatica* |
| *multiflora* | EHoe |
| *nivea* | More than 30 suppliers |
| *pilosa* | EGar EPla GCal IBlr |
| *plumosa* | Last listed 1997 |
| *pumila* | ECou |
| *purpureosplendens* | Last listed 1997 |
| *rufa* | ECou |
| sp. from New Guinea | EBee EWes GCal |
| § *sylvatica* | CCuc CKin CRow CSWP EFou |
| | EPPr EPla GOrn LNor MFir MLLN |
| | MMoz MRav NBro NOrc SCob |
| | WHer WPGP WShi |
| – 'A. Rutherford' | See *L. sylvatica* 'Taggart's Cream' |
| – 'Aurea' | CHan CHar CLTr CPlt CRDP |
| | CSWP EAst EBee ECha EFou |
| | EPGN EPPr EPla GAbr GCal LEdu |
| | MBri MMoz NSti SLod SMac SMad |
| | SPla WBea WCot WLeb WPat |
| | WRus WWat |
| – 'Aureomarginata' | See *L. sylvatica* 'Marginata' |
| I – 'Auslese' | EBee EPPr GBin LRHS |
| – 'Hohe Tatra' | CB&S CCuc CElw CMil EBee |
| | EGra EHoe EMan EMon EPPr |
| | EWes GBin GChr GMaP LFis |
| | MAvo MBNS MCCP MWgw MWhi |
| | NBro NHar NHol SCob SIng SPla |
| | WWat |
| § – 'Marginata' | More than 30 suppliers |
| – f. *nova* | EPPr MMoz |
| – 'Select' | SLPl |
| § – 'Taggart's Cream' (v) | CElw CRow EBee EHoe EMon |
| | LRHS SCob WBea WCot WLeb |
| – 'Tauernpass' | EHoe EMon EPPr EPla GCal |
| – 'Wäldler' | CCuc EHoe EMon EPPr LRHS |
| *ulophylla* | CInt ECou EGoo GBin GBuc |
| | NHol NWCA WPat |

## LUZURIAGA (Philesiaceae)

| | |
|---|---|
| *radicans* | CFee IBlr WCot WCru WSHC |
| ¶ – MK 92 | SSpi |

## x LYCENE (Caryophyllaceae)

| | |
|---|---|
| § *kubotae* | EBee |

## LYCHNIS ✿ (Caryophyllaceae)

| | |
|---|---|
| *alpina* | CMHG CTri ELan EWFC GDra |
| | GTou NFla NFor NMen NPri |
| | NRoo NVic SBea SRPl WBea WCla |
| | WPer WWal WWin |
| – 'Alba' | GTou NBir |
| – compact form | GTou |
| – 'Rosea' | SRms |
| § x *arkwrightii* | CGle EBee EBrP EBre ECha ELan |
| | LBee LBre SAga SBre SRot WBea |
| | WCla WWin |

'Vesuvius' — CB&S CGle CRDP ENot EOld EPla MNrw MTis NBir NFai SCob SPer SRms WMer WOve WPer WRos
* 'Blushing Bride' — SCoo
*chalcedonica* ♀ — More than 30 suppliers
 - var. *albiflora* — CM&M CSam EAst EBee ECha EFou ELan IBlr LFis MBri NBro NChi NFai NOak NSti SPer WCer WCot WHen WMow WPer WWhi
 - - 'Snow White' — EWTr EWll
 - apricot — MBro NBid WPyg
 - Beverley seedling — CHan
 - 'Carnea' — CVer GCal MFir NCat WCot
 - 'Flore Pleno' (d) — CMil EBee ECha ECle ELan GBuc GCal MCCP MCLN MLLN MMil MOne MUlv NChi NHaw NHol NLar NPri NSti NWes SPer SUsu WCot WFar WOld WSan
 - 'Morgenrot' — MCCP NCut NLar SGre
 - 'Rauhreif' — SGre
 - 'Rosea' — CGle CHad CSam EHal EMan LIck MBel NFai NSti WByw WCer WGwG WHen WPer
 - 'Rosea Plena' (d) — CBot
* - 'Salmonea' — CM&M EAst ECle GBri LPio MBNS MBri MTis NBir NPla SCro SLon SPer SRms WCot WLRN
 - salmon-pink — SRms WWhi
 - 'Valetta' — Last listed 1997
*cognata* — CGle EBee MAvo SMrm SWas
§ *coronaria* — More than 30 suppliers
 - 'Abbotswood Rose' — See *L.* x *walkeri* 'Abbotswood Rose'
 - 'Alba' ♀ — More than 30 suppliers
 - 'Angel's Blush' — CSev EBee EMan GCHN MBNS MTis NBus SPer SRPl WMow WPer WRHF WRha WRus WWal
 - Atrosanguinea Group — CBre CInt EBee EFou GCHN IBlr LPio MCLN MTis NFai NPri SPer WPer
 - 'Cerise' — EWTr MArl NBus WElm
 - 'Dancing Ladies' — WRHF
 - 'Eastgrove Pink' — WEas
 - 'Flottbek' — MOne NCat NCut NLar
 - Gardeners' World = 'Blych' (d) — Last listed 1998
 - 'Hutchinson's Cream' (v) — EMon WCot
 - Oculata Group — CGle CHan CMHG EGoo ELan EMar GCHN IBlr LEdu MCLN MFir MTho NFai NOak NSti SPlb SSvw SUsu WCer WFar WHen WHer WHil WPer
§ *coronata* var. *sieboldii* — EBee WSan
*dioica* — See *Silene dioica*
*flos-cuculi* — CArn CKin CNic CSam EBrP EBre EHon EMFW EWFC EWTr GAbr GCHN LBre LPBA MHew MMal MSal MSta NDea NLan NMir SBre SIng WCla WGwy WHen WHer WWhi
 - var. *albiflora* — CInt CSam ECoo EPar NBro NBus NDea WCla WHer WWhi
* - 'Little Robin' — Last listed 1998
 - 'Nana' — CInt CNic ELan GAbr NHol NRya SBea WBea WCla WPat WPer WPyg WWin
*flos-jovis* — CGle CTri ECha ELan EMan EPfP MFir NOak SRCN SRms WEas WLRN WPer
¶ - 'Alba' — EBee WCot
 - 'Hort's Variety' — CLTr MAvo MHlr NFla NSti NTow SBla SCro SUsu WBea WCla WCot

 - 'Minor' — See *L. flos-jovis* 'Nana'
§ - 'Nana' — CInt GCHN MSCN NFai NPro NWCA SSca WCot WPyg
 - 'Peggy' — EBee EMan GCal MCCP SRCN
¶ *fulgens* — EBee
 x *haageana* — EBee NWCA SIng SRms SSca
 - 'Burning Desire' — WRHF
*kubotae* — See x *Lycene kubotae*
*lagascae* — See *Petrocoptis pyrenaica* subsp. *glaucifolia*
*miqueliana* — EGar GLch MBNS MTis WMoo
¶ - 'Variegated Lacy Red' (v) — WCot
 'Molten Lava' — CBlo CFir CInt GMaP MCli MLan NArg NLak NOrc NPro SCob SRms WMoo WPer
*nutans* — MSal
¶ *preslii minor* — EBee
* *sikkimensis* — EBee
 sp. Andes — Last listed 1997
 'Terry's Pink' — EBee NCut NLar
§ *viscaria* — CGle ECha EGar EGra MHew MSal NFor NPla SCro SSca SUsu WBea WCla WGwy WHer WWhi
 - *alba* — CNic EBee ECha EMan GCal MCCP NBro WWeb
 - *alpina* — See *L. viscaria*
 - subsp. *atropurpurea* — NLon SBea SGre WBea WWhi
 - 'Feuer' — NLar NPri WLRN WWhi
 - 'Firebird' — EFou
 - 'Plena' (d) — LFis MInt WHil WOld
 - 'Schnee' — NPri SGre
 - 'Snowbird' — GMac
 - 'Splendens' — CBlo EPfP MUlv NFla SGre
* - 'Splendens Alba' — EPPr SSvw
 - 'Splendens Plena' (d) ♀ — CGle EBee ECha EGar ELan GMac MArl MBal MBri MWgw NBro WBea WEas WFar WOve
 - 'Splendens Rosea' — Last listed 1996
§ x *walkeri* 'Abbotswood Rose' ♀ — EMan GBuc
*wilfordii* — CFir CHar CPou CRDP EBee EHic MTis WCom
§ *yunnanensis* — CPea CSam EGar GBin GBuc GCHN LLWP MFir MSte NHol WBea WPer
 - *alba* — See *L. yunnanensis*

## LYCIANTHES (Solanaceae)
*rantonnetii* — See *Solanum rantonnetii*

## LYCIUM (Solanaceae)
*barbarum* — ELan IIve SMad SPan WSHC WWye
*chinense* — CArn CPlN
*europaeum* — Last listed 1997

## LYCOPODIUM (Lycopodiaceae)
*clavatum* — GPoy

## LYCOPSIS See ANCHUSA

## LYCOPUS (Lamiaceae)
*americanus* — EBee MSal
*europaeus* — CArn CJew ELau EWFC GBar GPoy MChe MHew MSal WGwG WHer WJek WWye
*exaltatus* — Last listed 1998
 sp. JLS 88040 — Last listed 1997
*virginicus* — MSal

## LYCORIS (Amaryllidaceae)
*albiflora* — SDeJ

| | |
|---|---|
| *radiata* | EBot |

**LYGEUM** (Poaceae)
| | |
|---|---|
| *spartum* | EPPr |

**LYGODIUM** (Schizaeaceae)
| | |
|---|---|
| *japonicum* | WRic |
| § *microphyllum* | NMar |
| *palmatum* | Last listed 1997 |
| ◆ *scandens* | See *L. microphyllum* |

**LYONIA** (Ericaceae)
| | |
|---|---|
| *ligustrina* | EHic SMur SSta |
| *ovalifolia* var. *elliptica* | Last listed 1998 |
| *villosa* B&SWJ 2161 | WCru |

**LYONOTHAMNUS** (Rosaceae)
| | |
|---|---|
| *floribundus* | |
| subsp. *aspleniifolius* | CAbb SAPC SArc SIgm SSpi WCru WWat |

**LYSICHITON** (Araceae)
| | |
|---|---|
| *americanus* ♀ | CB&S CBen CCuc CHad CRow CTrw CWat ECha EHon ELan EMFW EPar GAbr GDra LPBA LSyl MRav MSta NChi NDea NHol SPer SPlb SRms SSoc SSpi SWat WNor WPic WWat |
| ¶ – NNS 96-155 | WCot |
| *camtschatcensis* ♀ | CBen CCuc CLAP CRow CWat ECha EHon ELan EMFW EPar LPBA MSta NDea NOrc SLon SPer SSpi SWat WCot |
| – x *americanus* | SRms SSpi |
| ¶ 'Devonshire Cream' | CCuc |

**LYSIMACHIA** ✿ (Primulaceae)
| | |
|---|---|
| *atropurpurea* | CHal CLTr CMil CPle EAst EBee ECGN EGar ELan EMar GBri MCCP MNrw MTis NFai SBea SMad WCot WFar WMaN WPer WSpi |
| ¶ – 'Beaujolais' | WViv |
| – 'Geronimo' | CBlo |
| *barystachys* | CHea CRow EPla GCHN GMaP MRav WCot WOve |
| *ciliata* | More than 30 suppliers |
| § – 'Firecracker' ♀ | More than 30 suppliers |
| – 'Purpurea' | See *L. ciliata* 'Firecracker' |
| *clethroides* ♀ | More than 30 suppliers |
| – from Guizhou, China | EWes |
| – 'Lady Jane' | CBlo |
| § *congestiflora* | CLTr LHil LPVe MBEx NCut NPer SHFr WLRN |
| – Outback Sunset® (v) | CHal EMan GPin MLLN NBir NPri WGwG WLRN WWeb |
| – 'Silver Bird' | Last listed 1997 |
| – 'Sunbeam' | Last listed 1998 |
| – 'Sunset Gold' | Last listed 1997 |
| ¶ *decurrens* | EBee |
| ¶ – JCA 4.542.500 | WCot |
| *ephemerum* | More than 30 suppliers |
| *fortunei* | SHel WCot |
| *henryi* | CHal CLTr EWes GBuc WBrE |
| *japonica* var. *minutissima* | CInt CRow GBuc GCHN MTho NLar WCru WPer |
| *lanceolata* | Last listed 1998 |
| *lichiangensis* | CFir CSam EBee EMFP GSki MCCP MLLN NArg SHFr SMac WBor WMaN WPer WPnP |
| – B&L 12317 | CGle |
| – B&L 12464 | CRow WCot WThi |
| *lyssii* | See *L. congestiflora* |
| ¶ *mauritiana* | EBee GVic WSan |
| *minoricensis* | CBot CPle CRow EEls EHrv ELan EPri EWTr GBri SCob SHFr SMad SSca STes SWat WByw WCot WHer WLRN WOve WPer WRos WWin |
| *nemorum* | EFer EWFC WPer WRHF |
| ¶ – 'Little Sun' | WAlt |
| ¶ – 'Pale Star' | WAlt |
| *nummularia* | CBen CHal CWat EBrP EBre ECtt EHon ELau EWFC GPoy LBre LHol LPBA MBar MBri MHew MMal MWgw NBro NDea NFor SBre SHFr SWat SWyc WBea WByw WMow WOak WWye |
| – 'Aurea' ♀ | More than 30 suppliers |
| * – *nana* | Last listed 1996 |
| *ovata* | Last listed 1997 |
| *pseudohenryi* | Last listed 1997 |
| ◆ *punctata* L. | More than 30 suppliers |
| ◆ – misapplied | See *L. verticillaris* |
| § – 'Alexander' (v) | More than 30 suppliers |
| – dwarf form | EHic |
| * – 'Snow Lady' | SHel |
| ¶ – 'Sunspot' | EBee |
| ◆ – 'Variegata' | See *L. punctata* 'Alexander' |
| – *verticillata* | See *L. verticillaris* |
| * 'Purpurea' | MGrG |
| * *serpyllifolia* | SHFr |
| *sertulata* | WCot |
| *thyrsiflora* | CRow EHon MSta NDea SWat WCot WHer WMAq |
| § *verticillaris* | WCot |
| *vulgaris* | CArn EHon EWFC LPBA MHew MMal SIde WCot WFar WGwy WPer WWye |
| – subsp. *davurica* | WCot |

**LYSIONOTUS** (Gesneriaceae)
| | |
|---|---|
| *pauciflora* | NTow WCru |
| – B&SWJ 1679 | WCru |
| – B&SWJ 189 | WCru |
| – B&SWJ 303 | WCru |
| – B&SWJ 335 | WCru |

**LYTHRUM** (Lythraceae)
| | |
|---|---|
| 'Croftway' | Last listed 1997 |
| 'Red Wings' | Last listed 1998 |
| *salicaria* | More than 30 suppliers |
| – 'Blush' | More than 30 suppliers |
| – 'Brightness' | NArg NCat NFla NHol WMow |
| § – 'Feuerkerze' ♀ | CRDP CRow EBee EBrP EBre EFou EHal ELan GCal LBre LFis MBel MCLN MRav NCat NFai NHol NSti SBre SChu SCob SOkh SPer SRPl WElm WFar WPer |
| – Firecandle | See *L. salicaria* 'Feuerkerze' |
| – 'Florarose' | NCat |
| – 'Happy' | SMrm |
| – 'Lady Sackville' | CBos GBuc GCal GGar GMaP LFis MBNS MCAu NCat NPla |
| – 'Morden Pink' | LGre LRHS MBri SUsu |
| – 'Robert' | More than 30 suppliers |
| – 'Rose' | ELan MWgw |
| – 'Stichflamme' | EFou |
| – 'The Beacon' | CRow EMan GCal SRms WCot |
| – Ulverscroft form | MTed |
| – 'Zigeunerblut' | CPlt CRDP GMac LGre MRav SAga |
| ¶ *virgatum* | LGre NCat SMrm WCot |
| – 'Dropmore Purple' | CLAP CLTr CRDP EFou LRHS MBri MCAu MSte NCut WCot WFar |

| | |
|---|---|
| – 'Rose Queen' | ECha MRav SUsu WPer |
| – 'Rosy Gem' | CM&M CRow EBee ECtt EGar EMar GMac LSyl MBNS MFir MOne MWat NBro NOak NTow SBea SCob SLon SRms WBea WHoo WPer |
| ¶ – 'The Bride' | EBee |
| – 'The Rocket' | CRow CTri EAst EBee MCLN NCat NHol NLak NSti SPer WWin |

## LYTOCARYUM (Arecaceae)
| | |
|---|---|
| § *weddellianum* ♀ | MBri |

# M

## MAACKIA (Papilionaceae)
| | |
|---|---|
| *amurensis* | CAgr CB&S EBee ELan EPfP SFur SRCN WFro WNor |
| – var. *buergeri* | MBlu |
| *chinensis* | CMCN MBlu WShe |
| *fauriei* | CPle |

## MACBRIDEA (Lamiaceae)
| | |
|---|---|
| ¶ *caroliniana* | EBee |

## MACFADYENA (Bignoniaceae)
| | |
|---|---|
| § *unguis-cati* | CPIN CRHN |

## MACHAERANTHERA (Asteraceae)
| | |
|---|---|
| *lagunensis* | Last listed 1997 |
| *pattersonii* | See *M. bigelovii* |
| ¶ *shastensis* | EBee |

## MACHILUS See PERSEA

## MACKAYA (Acanthaceae)
| | |
|---|---|
| § *bella* ♀ | CSpe ERea LBlm LCns WMul |

## MACLEANIA (Ericaceae)
| | |
|---|---|
| *insignis* | CPIN |

## MACLEAYA (Papaveraceae)
| | |
|---|---|
| N *cordata* ♀ | CArn ECoo ELan EMar EPar LGre MSCN MTis MWat NOrc SCob SPar SPer SRCN SRms WAbe WCot WEas WFar WHoo WPer WWhi WWin |
| – 'Flamingo' | ECha EOld GCHN GCal GMaP MCAu MCLN MUlv SMrm WWye |
| x *kewensis* | MBro WHoo WPyg |
| § *microcarpa* | EGar EHal EPPr LBlm SRCN SWat WGwy WHer WSel |
| – 'Kelway's Coral Plume' ♀ | CB&S CGle CHad ECha ELan EOrc EPar GMaP LPio MBel MBri MCLN MRav NBro NFla SCob SLon SPer SRPl SSoC WCot WEas WOld WOve WWal WWat |
| 'Spetchley Ruby' | WCot |

## MACLURA (Moraceae)
| | |
|---|---|
| *pomifera* | CB&S CCHP CFil CMCN CPle SLon WDin WPGP WPic WWat |

## MACRODIERVILLA See WEIGELA

## MACROPIPER (Piperaceae)
| | |
|---|---|
| *crocatum* | See *Piper ornatum* |
| § *excelsum* | ECou |
| – 'Aureopictum' | Last listed 1998 |

## MACROZAMIA (Zamiaceae)
| | |
|---|---|
| *communis* | CBrP CRoM LPal WNor |
| *diplomera* | CBrP |
| *dyeri* | See *M. riedlei* |
| *lucida* | CBrP |
| *miquelii* | CBrP LPal |
| *moorei* | CBrP CRoM CTrC LPal |
| *mountperiensis* | CBrP |
| § *riedlei* | CBrP LPal |
| *spiralis* | Last listed 1998 |

## MAGNOLIA ✿ (Magnoliaceae)
| | |
|---|---|
| *acuminata* | CB&S CFil CMCN MBal NPal WPGP |
| – 'Golden Glow' | Last listed 1996 |
| * – 'Kinju' | CFil WPGP |
| – 'Koban Dori' | CFil CPMA WPGP |
| – large yellow | CFil WPGP |
| § – var. *subcordata* | CB&S WPGP |
| § – – 'Miss Honeybee' | CFil SSpi |
| 'Albatross' | CB&S CPMA CTho |
| * 'Andre Harvey' | Last listed 1996 |
| 'Ann' ♀ | COtt CTrh SSpi WPGP |
| 'Anne Rosse' | CFil WPGP |
| 'Apollo' | CB&S CFil CPMA SSpi WPGP |
| ◆ *ashei* | See *M. macrophylla* subsp. *ashei* |
| 'Athene' | CPMA WPGP |
| 'Atlas' | CB&S CEnd CFil CPMA SSpi WPGP |
| 'Betty' ♀ | CB&S CBlo CDoC CLAP EMil IOrc LNet MAsh MGos SSta WLRN WPyg |
| 'Big Dude' | CFil SSpi WPGP |
| *biondii* | CFil SSpi |
| x *brooklynensis* 'Woodsman' | CB&S CPMA SSta |
| 'Butterflies' | CAbP CDoC CFil CPMA LRHS MAsh MDun NOla SSpi WPGP |
| 'Caerhays Belle' | CB&S CFil CPMA WPGP |
| ¶ 'Caerhays Surprise' | CB&S |
| *campbellii* | CB&S CDul CFil CMCN CPMA CRos CSam CTho EBee ELan EPfP ICrw IOrc ISea MAsh SSpi WPGP |
| – 'Betty Jessel' | CMHG CTho |
| ¶ – subsp. *campbellii* var. *alba* | CB&S CEnd CMHG CPMA CTho MGos WBod |
| ¶ – 'Darjeeling' | CB&S |
| – subsp. *mollicomata* | CB&S CEnd CPMA CSam CTrw EPfP ISea WPGP |
| – – 'Lanarth' | CB&S CEnd SSta |
| – (Raffillii Group) 'Charles Raffill' ♀ | CB&S CBlo CDoC CPMA ELan GGGa MDun MGos MLan SBrw SRPl WBod WCwm WPGP |
| – – 'Kew's Surprise' | CB&S |
| ¶ – x *sargentiana* var. *robusta* | WPic |
| – 'Strybing White' | CPMA |
| 'Cecil Nice' | CFil WPGP |
| 'Charles Coates' | Last listed 1997 |
| 'Columbus' | CFil WPGP |
| *cordata* | See *M. acuminata* var. *subcordata* |
| ◆ – 'Miss Honeybee' | See *M. acuminata* var. *subcordata* 'Miss Honeybee' |
| 'Cup Cake' | Last listed 1997 |
| *cylindrica* Wilson | CMCN SSpi |
| 'David Clulow' | CB&S CFil CPMA SSpi WPGP |
| *dawsoniana* | CB&S CMCN CPMA |
| ◆ *dealbata* | See *M. macrophylla* subsp. *dealbata* |
| *delavayi* | CB&S CFil CMCN EPfP GGGa SAPC SArc SSpi WPGP |
| – SF 432 | Last listed 1998 |

§ *denudata* ♀ — CB&S CMCN CTho CTrw EMil EPfP IOrc ISea LPan MBal SPer SReu SSpi SSta WBod WNor

- 'Forrest's Pink' — CFil COtt CPMA
'Elisa Odenwald' — CFil WPGP
'Elizabeth' ♀ — CDoC CFil CLAP CMCN CPMA ELan EPfP GGGa LRHS MAsh MDun NHol SSpi SSta WBod WPGP
'Frank Gladney' — Last listed 1997
'Full Eclipse' — CFil WPGP
'Galaxy' ♀ — CB&S CDoC CEnd CFil CLAP CPMA CTho EAst IOrc MBar MBlu MGos SLdr SSpi SSta SSto WPGP
'George Henry Kern' — CB&S CBlo CDoC COtt CPMA EAst EMil IOrc ISea LPan MGos MSte SSpi SSta
*globosa* — CFil GGGa WPGP WWat
'Goldstar' — CFil LRHS SSpi WPGP
*grandiflora* — CBlo CDul CMCN EAst EBrP EBre EMil LBre MRav SAPC SArc SBre SRPl WDin WNor WWat

- 'Angustifolia' — WPGP
- 'Charles Dickens' — Last listed 1996
- 'Edith Bogue' — EBee ENot SBid
- 'Exmouth' ♀ — CB&S CBlo CBot CDoC CGre CLan CMCN EBee EBrP EBre ELan ENot IMGH IOrc LBre LNet MAsh MBal MGos SBid SBre SBrw SFam SMad SPer SReu SSpi SSta WGwG WWat
- 'Ferruginea' — CB&S
- 'Galissonière' — CBlo COtt GOrc IMGH IOrc LPan MGos SBid SBrw SSpi
I  - 'Galissonière Nana' — LPan
- 'Goliath' ♀ — CB&S CBlo CEnd CFil CTrC ELan IOrc LHyd LNet MBal SBid SBrw SPer SSpi SSta WPGP
- 'Little Gem' — CBlo CDoC CPMA CTrC LRHS SSpi WBcn WPGP WStI
*  - 'Nana Flore Pleno' — CPMA
- 'Russet' — CPMA LNet
- 'Saint Mary' — CPMA
- 'Samuel Sommer' — CPMA SAPC SArc SSpi WGer
- 'Silver Tip' — WPGP
- 'Undulata' — IOrc
- 'Victoria' — CDoC CFil EAst ELan EPfP LHyd MAsh MBlu MBri SReu SSpi SSta WCwm WPGP
'Hawk' — CFil WPGP
'Heaven Scent' ♀ — CAbP CB&S CBlo CDoC CMCN COtt CSam CTho CTrh CTrw EBee ELan IOrc LPan MAsh MBal MBar MBlu MGos MWat SBrw SPer SSpi SSta WBod WDin WPGP WPyg
'Helen Fogg' — CFil WPGP
*heptapeta* — See *M. denudata*
'Hot Lips' — CFil WPGP
*hypoleuca* ♀ — CDoC CFil CMCN CTho EPfP GGGa MBlu MLan SMad SSpi WBod WCwm WWat
'Iolanthe' ♀ — CB&S CDoC CEnd CFil CMCN CMHG CPMA CTho MAsh MGos NHol SPer SSpi SSta WBod WPGP
'Jane' ♀ — CBlo CDoC COtt ELan IOrc ISea MAsh MBri MGos NHol SBrw SLdr SSta
♦ 'Joe McDaniel' — See *M.* x *soulangeana* 'Joe McDaniel'
'Jon Jon' — CFil
'Judy' ♀ — COtt

'Kerr van Ann' — Last listed 1996
§ x *kewensis* 'Kew Clone' — Last listed 1998
- 'Kewensis' — See *M.* x *kewensis* 'Kew Clone'
- 'Wada's Memory' ♀ — CB&S CDoC CFil CLAP CMCN CMHG CPMA CTho CTri EBee EPfP MAsh MBri SPer SSpi SSta
*kobus* — CB&S CBlo CDul CGre CMCN CPMA CTho ENot EWTr IOrc LHyd LPan MAsh NMoo SPer SSta WBod WDin WNor WSpi WWat
- var. *borealis* — CTho
- 'Norman Gould' — See *M. stellata* 'Norman Gould'
*  'Laura' — CFil WPGP
'Lilenny' — SSta
§ *liliiflora* — CBlo CTrw MAsh MBar
§ - 'Nigra' ♀ — More than 30 suppliers
*  'Limelight' — CFil WPGP
x *loebneri* — CB&S WNor WShe
- 'Ballerina' — CDoC COtt SBrw SSta
- 'Leonard Messel' ♀ — More than 30 suppliers
- 'Merrill' ♀ — CB&S CBlo CFil CMCN CMHG CPMA CSam CTho CTrh EBrP EBre ELan IOrc ISea LBre LPan MAsh MBal MBri MGos NHol SBre SPer SReu SSpi SSta WDin WPGP WPyg WWat
- 'Neil McEacharn' — IOrc
- 'Powder Puff' — CFil WPGP
- 'Raspberry Fun' — CFil WPGP
- 'Snowdrift' — CMCN SSta
- 'Spring Joy' — CFil WPGP
- 'Spring Snow' — CMCN
- 'Star Bright' — Last listed 1998
*macrophylla* — CBrP CFil CMCN EPfP SAPC SSpi WNor WPGP
§ - subsp. *ashei* — CFil WNor WPGP
§ - subsp. *dealbata* — SSpi
- 'Sara Gladney' — Last listed 1998
'Manchu Fan' — CB&S CPMA EMil IOrc SSta
'Mark Jury' — CB&S CPMA
'Marwood Spring' — CB&S CTho
'Maryland' ♀ — CFil CPMA SSpi WPGP
'Milky Way' — CB&S CFil CMHG COtt CPMA CTho MGos WBod WPGP
'Nimbus' — Last listed 1997
*obovata* Diels — See *M. officinalis*
§ *officinalis* — CFil WPGP
¶ - var. *biloba* ♀ — CFil
¶ 'Pegasus' ♀ — CB&S GGGa IOrc ISea SSpi SSta
'Peppermint Stick' ♀ — CPMA MGos SSta
'Peter Smithers' — CFil IOrc WPGP
'Phelan Bright' — CFil WPGP
'Pickard's Charm' — Last listed 1996
'Pickard's Coral' — MBal
'Pickard's Crystal' — Last listed 1997
'Pickard's Opal' — Last listed 1998
'Pickard's Pink Diamond' — Last listed 1997
'Pickard's Ruby' — CDoC COtt
§ 'Pickard's Schmetterling' — CDoC SSta
'Pickard's Stardust' — Last listed 1996
'Pickard's Sundew' — See *M.* 'Sundew'
'Pinkie' ♀ — COtt IOrc MAsh MBri SSta
¶ 'Pirouette' — SSpi
x *proctoriana* ♀ — CAbP CFil ELan EPfP IOrc ISea SSta
- 'Proctoriana' — LHyd
*  'Purple Glow' — CFil WPGP
'Purple Prince' — CFil
*quinquepeta* — See *M. liliiflora*
'Randy' ♀ — COtt
'Raspberry Ice' — CDoC CLAP CMHG COtt CRos CTho CTrw IOrc MBal SSta

| | |
|---|---|
| 'Ricki' ♀ | COtt CPMA EMil IOrc MBri MGos SSta WWat |
| ¶ *rostrata* | SSpi |
| 'Royal Crown' | CDoC EMil SSta |
| ¶ 'Ruby' | CPMA MGos |
| *salicifolia* ♀ | CFil CMCN EBee EPfP ISea MAsh SBid SPer SSpi SSta WPGP WPic |
| - var. *concolor* | CFil SSpi WPGP |
| * - 'Rosea' | CFil WPGP |
| - 'W.B. Clarke' | See *M.* 'W.B. Clarke' |
| *sargentiana* | CFil IOrc WPGP |
| - var. *robusta* | CB&S CBrd CEnd CMCN ELan EPfP IOrc ISea MGos SSpi SSta WBod WCwm WPGP |
| - - *alba* | Last listed 1998 |
| ¶ - - 'Multipetal' | CBrd |
| 'Sayonara' ♀ | CB&S COtt CPMA EPfP IOrc MBlu SSpi WDin |
| 'Schmetterling' | See *M.* 'Pickard's Schmetterling' |
| 'Serene' | CFil CPMA SSpi |
| * 'Seyu' | Last listed 1998 |
| *sieboldii* | CB&S CBlo CGre CMCN CPMA EBee ELan EMil IOrc LPan MBal MBar MBri MDun MGos SLon SSpi SSta WBod WCoo WCwm WNor WSpi WWat |
| - subsp. *sinensis* ♀ | CB&S CBlo CDoC CMCN CSam ELan EPfP GGGa MDun SMad SPer SSpi SSta WDin WWat |
| x *soulangeana* | CB&S CBlo CLan CTrh CTrw EBee EBrP EBre ELan EMil ENot GOrc IOrc ISea LBre MAsh MBal MBar MBri MGos MWat NBee SBre SBrw SPer WDin WFar WNor WOrn |
| § - 'Alba' | CB&S CBlo CDul CEnd ENot IOrc LPan MAsh MGos SPer SSpi WWat |
| - 'Alba Superba' | See *M.* x *soulangeana* 'Alba' |
| - 'Alexandrina' ♀ | CBlo CDoC COtt ELan IOrc MGos EWTr |
| - 'Alexandrina Alba' | |
| - 'Amabilis' | CDoC COtt IOrc |
| - 'Brozzonii' ♀ | CMHG CSam EPfP IOrc ISea LPan SSpi |
| - 'Burgundy' Clarke | CB&S CBot CDoC SSta |
| - 'Coimbra' | Last listed 1996 |
| § - 'Joe McDaniel' | CDoC SSta |
| - 'Just Jean' | Last listed 1996 |
| - 'Lennei' ♀ | CB&S CBlo CDoC CEnd CMCN CMHG EBee IOrc LPan MAsh MGos NHol SBrw SPer SRms WGer WNor WPyg WStI |
| - 'Lennei Alba' ♀ | ELan IOrc SLdr SPer |
| - 'Nigra' | See *M. liliiflora* 'Nigra' |
| - 'Pickard's Sundew' | See *M.* 'Sundew' |
| - 'Picture' | CBlo CDoC IOrc |
| - 'Rubra' misapplied | See *M.* x *soulangeana* 'Rustica Rubra' |
| § - 'Rustica Rubra' ♀ | CB&S CDoC CEnd CMCN CPMA CSam EBee EBrP EBre ELan ENot IMGH IOrc LBre LNet LPan MAsh MBri SBre SPer SReu SRob SSpi SSta WBay WPGP WWat WWeb |
| - 'San José' | CRos IOrc MAsh MBri SSpi SSta |
| - 'Verbanica' | LRHS MAsh SSpi |
| - 'White Giant' | SBrw |
| 'Spectrum' | CB&S CFil CPMA MGos SSpi WPGP |
| *sprengeri* | WNor WShe WWes |
| ¶ - var. *diva* | CB&S CFil CMCN SSpi WPGP |
| - - 'Burncoose' | CB&S |
| - - 'Claret Cup' | CFil WPGP |
| ¶ - - 'Lanhydrock' | CFil SSpi |

| | |
|---|---|
| - var. *elongata* | COtt IOrc ISea |
| - 'Eric Savill' | CFil WPGP |
| 'Star Wars' | CB&S CDoC CFil CPMA CTho EMil EPfP SBrw SSpi SSta |
| § *stellata* ♀ | More than 30 suppliers |
| - 'Centennial' | CDoC SBrw SSta |
| - 'Chrysanthemiflora' | LRHS SPer SSpi |
| - 'Jane Platt' | SSpi |
| - f. *keiskei* | CEnd COtt |
| - 'King Rose' | CB&S CBlo CDoC COtt MAsh MBlu MBri NHed SBrw SPer WWat |
| - 'Massey' | Last listed 1997 |
| § - 'Norman Gould' | CMCN COtt EPfP SSta |
| - 'Rosea' | COtt ELan IOrc MGos WPyg |
| - 'Royal Star' | CB&S CBlo CBot CBrm CDoC CEnd CLAP CLan CMCN CSam EBee ECtt EMil ENot IOrc LPan MAsh MBri MGos NHol SBrw SPer SSpi SSta WHar WOrn WStI |
| - 'Waterlily' ♀ | CB&S CBlo CBot CEnd CMCN CRos CSam ELan EMil GOrc IOrc MAsh SPer SSpi SSta WPyg |
| ¶ 'Summer Solstice' | SSpi |
| 'Sundance' | CFil MGos WBod WPGP |
| § 'Sundew' | CB&S CDoC CMCN CPMA EPfP IOrc MGos SBrw |
| 'Susan' ♀ | More than 30 suppliers |
| x *thompsoniana* | CMCN |
| 'Tiffany' | CFil WPGP |
| 'Tina Durio' | WPGP |
| 'Todd Gresham' | CPMA WPGP |
| *tripetala* | CB&S CMCN EPfP LPan MDun MLan SMad SSpi SSta WCoo WCwm WDin WWat |
| x *veitchii* | CDoC SSpi SSta WBod |
| - 'Isca' | CTho WPGP |
| - 'Peter Veitch' | CFil CGre CTho |
| *virginiana* | CGre CMCN CPMA SSpi WPGP |
| - 'Havener' | WPGP |
| 'Vulcan' | CB&S CFil CMHG COtt CPMA CTho |
| § 'W.B. Clarke' | Last listed 1997 |
| x *watsonii* | See *M.* x *wiesneri* |
| § x *wiesneri* | CFil CMCN CPMA EPfP ISea MBlu SPer SSpi SSta WPGP |
| *wilsonii* ♀ | More than 30 suppliers |
| ¶ - 'Gwen Baker' | CEnd |
| 'Winelight' | CFil WPGP |
| 'Yellow Bird' | CFil COtt CPMA EPfP LRHS MDun MGos SSpi SSta WPGP |
| 'Yellow Fever' | CB&S CFil CPMA EMil MDun WPGP |
| 'Yellow Lantern' | CFil LRHS WPGP |

## X MAHOBERBERIS (Berberidaceae)

| | |
|---|---|
| *aquisargentii* | CAbP CPle EBee ENot EPla GBin LHop MPla MRav NHol SBid SLon WGwG WPat WPyg WWat |
| 'Dart's Treasure' | EPla WFar |
| 'Magic' | MGos |
| *miethkeana* | MBar SRms |

## MAHONIA ✿ (Berberidaceae)

| | |
|---|---|
| *acanthifolia* | See *M. napaulensis* |
| § *aquifolium* | CAgr CB&S CDul EAst EBee ENot GCHN GChr GOrc GRei MBal MBar MBri MGos MRav MWat NFla NFor NWea SPer SReu SSoC WCFE WDin WFar WStI WWat |
| - 'Apollo' ♀ | ECtt ELan EMil ENot EOld EPla IOrc MAsh MBar MBri MGos NBee NHol SPer SReu SSta WPyg |

- 'Atropurpurea' — CDoC EBee ELan ENot EPla EWTr MAsh MHlr NBee SPer SPla
* - 'Cosmo Crawl' — MGos
- 'Fascicularis' — See *M.* x *wagneri* 'Pinnacle'
- 'Green Ripple' — EPfP EPla MBri MGos WBcn WFar
- 'Mirena' — MGos
- 'Orange Flame' — MBlu
- 'Smaragd' — CB&S CBlo CDoC EBee ELan ENot EPfP EPla IOrc MBlu MGos NHol WBay WHCG WPyg
- 'Versicolor' — MBlu
*bealei* — See *M. japonica* Bealei Group
*confusa* — CFil EPla WPGP WWat
*eutriphylla* — EPla
*fortunei* — EPla MBal WBcn WSHC
*fremontii* — GCal LGre WSHC
- x *haematocarpa* — Last listed 1998
¶ *gracilipes* — MDun
'Gulf Tide' — Last listed 1997
*haematocarpa* — GCal
*japonica* ♀ — CBot CChe CDul CEnd CSam CTre CTrw EBee ELan ENot MAsh MBal MBar MBri MRav MWat NHol SPer SReu SRms SSpi SSta WDin WFar WHCG WPat WSHC WWal WWat
§ - Bealei Group — CB&S CDul CLan EAst EBee EBrP EBre ELan EPfP EPla IOrc LBre MAsh MBar MGos MRav NPer SBre SEas SRPl SSoC WDin WWeb
- 'Hiemalis' — See *M. japonica* 'Hivernant'
§ - 'Hivernant' — EPla MGos WBay WPyg
* *keiskei* — Last listed 1996
*lomariifolia* ♀ — CB&S CBot EBee ENot EPfP IOrc ISea MBal SAPC SArc SDry SLon SPer SPla SSpi WSHC WSpi
x *media* 'Arthur Menzies' — EPla
- 'Buckland' ♀ — CAbP CB&S CDul CEnd CSam CTrw EBee ECtt ISea MAsh MBal MBri SBid SPer SRPl SRms WPat WPyg WRHF WWat WWeb
- 'Charity' ♀ — More than 30 suppliers
- 'Charity's Sister' — EPla MBri
- 'Faith' — EPla
- 'Lionel Fortescue' ♀ — More than 30 suppliers
- 'Underway' ♀ — CSam EPfP EPla MBri SMur SPla WWes
- 'Winter Sun' ♀ — More than 30 suppliers
*nervosa* — CB&S COtt EPfP EPla MBlu NBee NHol SBid SSta
*pallida* — CFil EPla WPGP WWat
- T&K 553 — Last listed 1998
N *pinnata* — EBee ELan ENot EPfP EPla IOrc MBal MBar
*piperiana* — Last listed 1997
*pumila* — EPla SSpi WCru
*repens* — EPla ERav MWhi
- 'Rotundifolia' — EPla
*russellii* — CGre
* x *savillii* — EPla
*siamensis* — CGre
¶ *trifoliolata* — EPfP
- var. *glauca* — CEnd
x *wagneri* 'Fireflame' — Last listed 1997
- 'Moseri' — EMil SSpi WPat WSPU
§ - 'Pinnacle' ♀ — EPfP EPla LRHS MAsh MGos SMur SPer
- 'Sunset' — EPla MBlu
- 'Undulata' ♀ — ECtt ENot EPfP NHol SDix SPer SRms WHCG

## MAIANTHEMUM (Convallariaceae)

*bifolium* — CAvo CRDP CRow CVer EBee ELan EMon EPot EWFC GBuc MBal MDun MNrw MTho NBro NMen SLod SRms WCru WGwy WLin WTin WWat WWye
- British form — Last listed 1996
§ - subsp. *kamtschaticum* — CAvo CLAP CRDP CRow EPar LSyl SDys SUsu WCot
* - - 'Variegatum' — WCru
*canadense* — GCal MSal
♦ *dilatatum* — See *M. bifolium* subsp. *kamtschaticum*
*oleraceum* — Last listed 1998

## MALACOTHAMNUS (Malvaceae)
¶ *fremontii* — WCot WLin

## MALEPHORA (Aizoaceae)
*lutea* — CNic EOas

## MALLOTUS (Euphorbiaceae)
*japonicus* — Last listed 1997

## MALPIGHIA (Malpighiaceae)
¶ *coccigera* — ECon

## MALUS ✿ (Rosaceae)
¶ 'Adirondack' — MGos
x *adstringens* 'Almey' — Last listed 1996
- 'Hopa' — CBlo CLnd
- 'Purple Wave' — Last listed 1996
- 'Simcoe' — CDoC CLnd MGos
'Aldenhamensis' — See *M.* x *purpurea* 'Aldenhamensis'
* *arborescens* — CTho
x *atrosanguinea* — NWea
§ - 'Gorgeous' — CBlo CDul COtt GChr GTwe MAsh MBri MGos WDin WJas
*baccata* — CFil CLnd CMCN CTho GTwe SEND WNor
¶ - 'Dolgo' — COtt
¶ - 'Gracilis' — CSam
- 'Lady Northcliffe' — CLnd SFam
¶ aff. *baccata* MF 96038 — SSpi
*brevipes* — CTho
'Butterball' — CLnd MBri WJas
* 'Cheal's Weeping' — NBea SPer WStI
*coronaria* var. *dasycalyx* — CBlo CDoC CEnd CLnd CSam
'Charlottae' (d) — CTho EBee ENot MAsh MBlu MBri SFam SPer
- 'Elk River' — Last listed 1996
'Crittenden' — EBee ENot
* 'Directeur Moerlands' — CBlo CDul EPfP EWTr MAsh MBri MGos WJas
*domestica* (F) — MGos
- 'Acklam Russet' (D) — Last listed 1997
- 'Acme' (D) — SDea SKee
- 'Adams's Pearmain' — CCAT CTho GTwe LBuc SDea SFam SKee WJas
- 'Admiral' (D) — Last listed 1997
- 'Advance' (D) — SKee
- 'Akane' (D) — SDea
- 'Alderman' (C) — Last listed 1996
§ - 'Alexander' (C) — SKee
- 'Alford' (Cider) — Last listed 1996
- 'Alfriston' (C) — SKee
- 'Alkmene' (D) ♀ — GTwe SDea SKee
¶ - 'All Red Gravenstein' (D) — NRog
- 'Allen's Everlasting' (D) — GTwe SDea SKee
- 'Allington Pippin' (D) — CCAT CCVT CSam CTho CTri NRog SDea SKee WJas

- 'American Mother'    See *M. domestica* 'Mother'
- 'Ananas Reinette' (D)    Last listed 1996
- 'Andrew Johnson' (F)    Last listed 1996
- 'Anna Boelens' (D)    SDea
- 'Anne-Marie' (C)    Last listed 1996
- 'Annie Elizabeth' (C)    CCAT CCVT CTho GTwe MBri SDea SFam SKee WJas
- 'Anniversary'    SDea
- 'Api Noir' (D)    SKee
- 'Api Rose' (D)    CCVT SKee WJas
- 'Ard Cairn Russet' (D)    GTwe SDea SKee
- 'Aromatic Russet' (D)    SKee
- 'Arthur Turner' (C) ♀    CCVT CDoC EMui GTwe LBuc MGos NRog SDea SFam SKee WJas
- 'Arthur W. Barnes' (C)    Last listed 1996
- 'Ashmead's Kernel' (D) ♀    CCAT CCVT CSam CTho EBrP EBre EMui ERea GTwe LBuc MWat NRog SBre SDea SFam SKee WHar WJas
- 'Ashton Bitter' (Cider)    CCAT CCVT CEnd CTho GTwe SFam
- 'Ashton Brown Jersey'    CCAT CTho (Cider)
- 'Autumn Pearmain' (D)    CTho SDea WJas
- 'Backwell Red' (Cider)    Last listed 1996
- 'Baker's Delicious' (D)    SDea SKee
- 'Ballarat Seedling' (D)    Last listed 1997
- 'Balsam'    See *M. domestica* 'Green Balsam'
- 'Banns' (D)    SKee
- 'Barnack Beauty' (D)    CTho SKee
- 'Barnack Orange' (D)    SKee
- 'Baron Ward' (C)    Last listed 1996
- 'Bascombe Mystery' (D)    SKee
- 'Baumann's Reinette' (D)    SKee
- 'Baxter's Pearmain' (C/D)    SKee
- 'Beachamwell' (D)    Last listed 1997
- 'Beauty of Bath' (D)    CCAT CCVT CDoC CTho CTri GTwe IOrc LBuc NRog SDea SFam SKee WJas
- 'Beauty of Hants' (D)    SKee
- 'Beauty of Kent' (C)    SDea SKee
- 'Beauty of Moray' (C)    SKee
- 'Beauty of Stoke' (C)    Last listed 1996
- 'Bedwyn Beauty' (C)    CTho
- 'Beeley Pippin' (D)    GTwe SDea SKee
- 'Bell Apple' (Cider/C)    CTho
- 'Belle de Boskoop' (C/D) ♀    CCAT CTho GTwe NRog SDea SKee
- 'Belle-fille Normande' (C)    Last listed 1996
- 'Belle-fleur de France' (C)    Last listed 1996
- 'Bembridge Beauty' (F)    SDea
- 'Ben's Red' (D)    CEnd CTho SKee
- 'Bess Pool' (D)    SDea SFam SKee WJas
- 'Bewley Down Pippin'    See *M. domestica* 'Crimson King'
- 'Billy Down Pippin' (F)    CTho
- 'Bismarck' (C)    CTho NRog SKee
¶ - 'Black Dabinette' (Cider)    CCAT CTho
- 'Black Tom Putt' (C/D)    CTho
- 'Blaze' (D)    GTwe
- 'Blenheim Orange' (C/D) ♀    CCAT CCVT CDoC CTho EMui GBon GTwe LBuc MBri MWat NRog SDea SFam SKee SPer WJas WWeb
- 'Blenheim Red'    See *M. domestica* 'Red Blenheim'
- 'Bloody Ploughman' (D)    SKee
- 'Blue Pearmain' (D)    SDea SKee
- 'Blue Sweet' (Cider)    CTho
- Bolero    See *M. domestica* Bolero = 'Tuscan'
§ - Bolero = 'Tuscan' (D/Ball)    MGos SDea
- 'Boston Russet'    See *M. domestica* 'Roxbury Russet'

- 'Bountiful' (C)    CCAT COtt EMui GTwe MBri MGos SDea WHar WStI
- 'Bow Hill Pippin' (D)    SKee
- 'Box Apple' (D)    SKee
- 'Braddick Nonpareil' (D)    SKee
- 'Braeburn' (D)    SDea SKee
- 'Bramley's Seedling' (C) ♀    More than 30 suppliers
- 'Bread Fruit' (C/D)    CEnd
¶ - 'Breakwell's Seedling'    CCAT CTho (Cider)
- 'Bridgwater Pippin' (C)    CCAT CTho WJas
- 'Bringewood Pippin' (D)    WJas
- 'Broad-eyed Pippin' (C)    SKee
- 'Brown Snout' (Cider)    CCAT CTho
- 'Brown Thorn' (Cider)    CCAT
- 'Brownlees Russet' (D)    CTho EMui GTwe NRog SDea SFam SKee
- 'Brown's Apple' (Cider)    CCAT GTwe
- 'Broxwood Foxwhelp'    CCAT CTho (Cider)
- 'Bulmer's Chisel Jersey'    Last listed 1996 (Cider)
- 'Bulmer's Crimson King'    Last listed 1996 (Cider)
- 'Bulmer's Fillbarrel' (Cider)    Last listed 1996
- 'Bulmer's Foxwhelp'    Last listed 1996 (Cider)
- 'Bulmer's Norman' (Cider)    CCAT
- 'Burn's Seedling' (D)    CTho
- 'Burr Knot' (C)    SKee
¶ - 'Burrowhill Early' (Cider)    CTho
- 'Bushey Grove' (C)    SDea SKee
- 'Buxted Favorite'    Last listed 1996
- 'Calagolden Elbee' (D)    Last listed 1996
- 'Calville Blanc d'Hiver' (D)    SKee
- 'Calville des Femmes' (C)    Last listed 1997
- 'Cambusnethan Pippin' (D)    SKee
- 'Camelot' (Cider/C)    CCAT CTho
- 'Cap of Liberty' (Cider)    CCAT
- 'Captain Broad' (D/Cider)    CCAT CEnd CTho
- 'Captain Kidd' (D)    Last listed 1997
- 'Captain Smith' (F)    CEnd
- 'Carlisle Codlin' (C)    GTwe
- 'Caroline' (D)    Last listed 1997
- 'Carswell's Orange' (D)    SKee
- 'Catherine' (C)    Last listed 1997
- 'Catshead' (C)    CCAT CCVT GQui SDea SKee WJas
- 'Cellini' (C/D)    SDea
- 'Charles Eyre' (C)    Last listed 1996
- 'Charles Ross' (C/D) ♀    CCAT CCVT CDoC CMac CSam CTho EBrP EBre EMui GBon GTwe LBre MBri MWat NBea NRog SBre SDea SFam SKee WHar WJas
- 'Charlotte' (C/Ball)    LBuc MGos SDea
- 'Chaxhill Red' (Cider/D)    CTho
- 'Cheddar Cross' (D)    CTri SKee
- 'Chelmsford Wonder' (C)    SKee
- 'Chisel Jersey' (Cider)    CCAT CTho
- 'Chivers Delight' (D)    CCAT CSam EMui GTwe SDea SKee WJas
- 'Chorister Boy' (D)    CTho
- 'Christmas Pearmain' (D)    CTho GTwe SDea SFam SKee
- 'Cider Lady's Finger' (Cider)    CCAT
- 'Claygate Pearmain' (D) ♀    CCAT CTho GTwe SDea SFam SKee WJas
- 'Close' (D)    Last listed 1997
- 'Coat Jersey' (Cider)    CCAT
- 'Cockle Pippin' (D)    CTho GTwe SDea SKee
- 'Cockpit' (C)    Last listed 1997
- 'Coeur de Boeuf' (C/D)    SKee

| | |
|---|---|
| - 'Coleman's Seedling' | CTho (Cider) |
| - 'Collogett Pippin' (C/Cider) | CEnd CTho |
| - 'Colonel Vaughan' (C/D) | CTho SKee |
| - 'Cornish Aromatic' (D) | CCAT CDoC CSam CTho EMui GTwe SDea SFam SKee WJas |
| - 'Cornish Crimson Queen' (F) | GTwe |
| - 'Cornish Gilliflower' (D) | CCAT SDea SFam SKee WJas |
| - 'Cornish Honeypin' (D) | CTho |
| - 'Cornish Longstem' (D) | CEnd CTho |
| - 'Cornish Mother' (D) | CEnd |
| - 'Cornish Pine' (D) | CEnd CTho SDea SKee |
| - 'Coronation' (D) | SDea SKee |
| - 'Cortland' (C) | Last listed 1996 |
| - 'Costard' (C) | GTwe SKee |
| - 'Cottenham Seedling' (C) | SKee |
| - 'Coul Blush' (D) | SKee |
| - 'Court of Wick' (D) | CCAT CTho SKee |
| - 'Court Pendu Plat' (D) | CCAT CCVT CTho LBuc MWat NRog SDea SFam SKee WJas |
| - 'Court Royal' (Cider) | CCAT CTho |
| - 'Cox's Orange Pippin' (D) | CB&S CCAT CCVT CMac EBrP EBre GTwe LBre LBuc MBri MWat NRog SBre SDea SFam SKee SPer WJas WWeb |
| - 'Cox's Pomona' (C/D) | CTho SDea SKee WJas |
| - 'Cox's Red Sport' (D) | Last listed 1996 |
| - 'Cox's Rouge de Flandres' (D) | SKee |
| - 'Cox's Selfing' (D) | CBlo CWSG EREa GTwe LBuc MBri MGos SKee WHar WJas WWeb |
| - 'Crawley Beauty' (C) | GTwe SDea SFam SKee WJas |
| ¶ - 'Crimson Bramley' (C) | CCAT |
| - 'Crimson Cox' (D) | SDea |
| § - 'Crimson King' (Cider/C) | CCAT CTho |
| - 'Crimson Peasgood' (C) | Last listed 1996 |
| - 'Crimson Queening' (D) | SKee WJas |
| - 'Crimson Victoria' (Cider) | CTho |
| - Crispin | See *M. domestica* 'Mutsu' |
| § - 'Crowngold' (D) | CEnd EMui GBon GTwe |
| - 'Cummy Norman' (Cider) | CCAT |
| - 'Curl Tail' (D) | SKee |
| ¶ - 'Cutler Grieve' (D) | SDea |
| - 'Dabinett' (Cider) | CCAT CCVT CEnd CTho CTri EMui GTwe LBuc SDea SKee |
| - 'D'Arcy Spice' (D) | CCAT SDea SFam SKee |
| - 'Dawn' (D) | SKee |
| - 'Deacon's Blushing Beauty' (C/D) | SDea |
| ¶ - 'Deacon's Millennium' | SDea |
| - 'Decio' (D) | SKee |
| - 'Delbards' | See *M. domestica* Jubilee (Delbards) |
| - 'Delkid' (F) | GTwe |
| - 'Devon Crimson Queen' (D) | CTho |
| - 'Devonshire Buckland' (C) | CEnd CTho WJas |
| - 'Devonshire Crimson Queen' (D) | SDea |
| - 'Devonshire Quarrenden' (D) | CCAT CEnd CSam CTho EMui SDea SFam SKee WJas |
| - 'Dewdney's Seedling' (C) | GTwe |
| - 'Diamond Jubilee' (D) | SKee |
| - 'Discovery' (D) ♀ | CB&S CDoC CTri EBee EBrP EBre EMui GBon GRei GTwe IOrc LBre LBuc MBri MWat NBee NRog SBre SDea SFam SKee SPer WJas WWeb |
| - 'Doctor Hare's' (C) | WJas |
| - 'Doctor Harvey' (C) | SFam |
| ♦ - 'Doctor Kidd's Orange Red' | See *M. domestica* 'Kidd's Orange Red' |
| ¶ - 'Dog's Snout' (C/D) | NRog |
| - 'Domino' (C) | SKee |
| - 'Don's Delight' (C) | CTho |
| - 'Doux Normandie' (Cider) | CCAT |
| - 'Dove' (Cider) | CTho |
| - 'Downton Pippin' (D) | SKee WJas |
| - 'Dredge's Fame' (D) | CTho |
| - 'Duchess of Oldenburg' (C/D) | SKee |
| - 'Duchess's Favourite' (D) | SKee |
| - 'Duck's Bill' (D) | Last listed 1997 |
| - 'Dufflin' (Cider) | CCAT CTho |
| - 'Duke of Devonshire' (D) | CSam CTho SDea SFam SKee WJas |
| - 'Duke of Gloucester' (C) | WJas |
| N - 'Dumeller's Seedling' (C) ♀ | CCAT CTho SDea SKee |
| - 'Dunkerton Late Sweet' (Cider) | CCAT CTho |
| - 'Dunn's Seedling' (D) | SDea |
| - 'Dutch Codlin' (C) | CTho |
| § - 'Dutch Mignonne' (D) | SKee |
| - 'Early Blenheim' (D/C) | CEnd CTho |
| - 'Early Bower' (D) | CEnd |
| - 'Early Crimson' (F) | Last listed 1996 |
| - 'Early Julyan' (C) | SKee WJas |
| - 'Early Victoria' | See *M. domestica* 'Emneth Early' |
| - 'Early Worcester' | See *M. domestica* 'Tydeman's Early Worcester' |
| - 'Easter Orange' (D) | GTwe SKee |
| - 'Ecklinville' (C) | SDea SKee WJas |
| - 'Edward VII' (C) ♀ | CDoC GTwe SDea SFam SKee WJas |
| - 'Edwin Beckett' (D) | Last listed 1996 |
| - 'Egremont Russet' (D) ♀ | CCAT CCVT CDoC CSam CTho EBee EBrP EBre EMui GBon GTwe IOrc LBre LBuc MBri MGos MWat NBee NRog SBre SDea SFam SKee SPer WJas WWeb |
| - 'Ellis' Bitter' (Cider) | CCAT CEnd CTho GTwe SFam |
| - 'Ellison's Orange' (D) ♀ | CCAT CSam CTri EBee GBon GTwe LBuc MBri NRog SDea SFam SKee WHar WJas WStI |
| - 'Elstar' (D) ♀ | CCAT EMui GTwe IOrc SDea SKee |
| - 'Elton Beauty' (D) | SDea SKee |
| § - 'Emneth Early' (C) ♀ | CTho GTwe NRog SDea SFam SKee WJas |
| - 'Emperor Alexander' | See *M. domestica* 'Alexander' |
| - 'Empire' (D) | SKee |
| - 'Encore' (C) | SDea SKee |
| - 'English Codling' (C) | CTho |
| ♦ - 'Epicure' | See *M. domestica* 'Laxton's Epicure' |
| - 'Ernie's Russet' (D) | SDea |
| - 'Evening Gold' (C) | SDea |
| - 'Eve's Delight' (D) | SDea |
| - 'Exeter Cross' (D) | CCAT SDea SFam SKee |
| - 'Eynsham Dumpling' (C) | Last listed 1997 |
| - 'Fair Maid of Devon' (Cider) | CCAT |
| - 'Fair Maid of Taunton' (D) | CCAT WJas |
| - 'Fairfield' (D) | CTho |
| - 'Fall Pippin' (D) | Last listed 1997 |
| - 'Fall Russet' (D) | GTwe |
| - 'Falstaff' (D) ♀ | CCAT CDoC EMui GTwe MBri MGos SDea SKee WJas |
| - 'Fameuse' (D) | SKee |
| - 'Fearn's Pippin' (D) | SKee |
| - 'Feltham Beauty' (D) | Last listed 1996 |
| - 'Feuillemorte' (D) | Last listed 1997 |
| - 'Fiesta' (D) ♀ | CDoC CSam EBee EBrP EBre EMui GBon GChr GTwe LBre LBuc MBri MGos SBre SDea SFam SKee WHar WJas WWeb |

| | | |
|---|---|---|
| - 'Fillbarrel' (Cider) | CCAT CTho | |
| - 'Fillingham Pippin' (C) | Last listed 1997 | |
| - 'Fireside' (D) | Last listed 1998 | |
| - 'Firmgold' (D) | SDea | |
| - 'First and Last' (D) | Last listed 1996 | |
| - 'Five Crowns' (D) | SKee | |
| - Flamenco™ (D/Ball) | MGos SDea | |
| § - 'Flower of Kent' (C) | CCAT SKee | |
| - 'Flower of the Town' (D) | SKee WJas | |
| - 'Folkestone' (D) | Last listed 1997 | |
| - 'Forfar' | See *M. domestica* 'Dutch Mignonne' | |
| - 'Forge' (D) | SDea SKee | |
| - 'Formosa Nonpareil' (C) | WJas | |
| ♦ - 'Fortune' | See *M. domestica* 'Laxton's Fortune' | |
| - 'Foster's Seedling' (D) | SKee | |
| - 'Foulden Pearmain' (C) | Last listed 1997 | |
| - 'Franklyn's Golden Pippin' (D) | Last listed 1996 | |
| - 'Frederick' (Cider) | CCAT | |
| - 'French Crab' (C) | CTho SDea | |
| - 'Freyberg' (D) | SKee | |
| - 'Frogmore Prolific' (C) | Last listed 1996 | |
| - 'Fuji' (D) | SDea SKee | |
| - 'Gala' (D) | EBee GBon GTwe MBri SDea SFam SKee | |
| § - 'Gala Mondial' (F) | SKee WJas | |
| I - 'Gala Royal' | See *M. domestica* 'Royal Gala' | |
| - 'Galloway Pippin' (C) | GTwe SKee | |
| - 'Gascoyne's Scarlet' (D) | SDea SFam SKee | |
| - 'Gavin' (D) | SDea SKee | |
| - 'Genesis II' (D/C) | SDea | |
| - 'Genet Moyle' (C/Cider) | CCAT CTho WJas | |
| - 'George Carpenter' (D) | SDea SKee | |
| - 'George Cave' (D) | CCVT GTwe NBee NRog SDea SFam SKee WJas | |
| - 'George Neal' (C) ♀ | SDea SFam | |
| - 'Gilliflower of Gloucester' (D) | CTho | |
| - 'Gin' (Cider) | Last listed 1997 | |
| - 'Gladstone' (D) | CTho SKee WJas | |
| § - 'Glass Apple' (C/D) | CEnd | |
| - 'Gloria Mundi' (C) | SDea | |
| - 'Glory of England' (C) | WJas | |
| - 'Gloster '69' (D) | GTwe SDea SKee | |
| - 'Gloucester Cross' (D) | SKee | |
| - 'Golden Bittersweet' (D) | CCAT CTho | |
| - 'Golden Delicious' (D) ♀ | CB&S CMac EBrP EBre GBon LBre MBri NRog SBre SDea SKee SPer WHar WStI WWeb | |
| ¶ - 'Golden Glow' | SDea | |
| - 'Golden Harvey' (D) | CCAT CTho | |
| - 'Golden Knob' (D) | CCAT CTho SKee | |
| - 'Golden Noble' (C) ♀ | CCAT CDoC CSam CTho EMui GTwe SDea SFam SKee | |
| - 'Golden Nonpareil' (D) | Last listed 1996 | |
| - 'Golden Nugget' (D) | Last listed 1998 | |
| - 'Golden Pearmain' (D) | Last listed 1998 | |
| - 'Golden Pippin' (C) | CTho SKee | |
| - 'Golden Reinette' (D) | GTwe SKee | |
| - 'Golden Russet' (D) | GTwe SDea SKee WJas | |
| - 'Golden Spire' (C) | CTho NRog SDea SKee | |
| - 'Golden Wonder' (C) | CEnd | |
| - 'Goldilocks' (D) | GTwe | |
| - 'Gooseberry' (C) | SKee | |
| - 'Goring' (Cider) | CCAT CTho | |
| - 'Grand Sultan' (D) | CTho | |
| - 'Grange's Pearmain' (C) | Last listed 1996 | |
| - 'Granny Smith' (D) | CLnd EBee GTwe SDea SKee SPer | |
| - 'Gravenstein' (D) | CCAT SDea SFam SKee | |
| § - 'Green Balsam' (C) | NRog | |
| - 'Greensleeves' (D) ♀ | CCAT CDoC CSam EBee EBrP EBre EMui GTwe LBre MBri MGos NBee NRog SBre SDea SKee WHar WJas WWeb | |
| ¶ - 'Greenup's Pippin' (D) | SKee | |
| - 'Grenadier' (C) ♀ | CCAT CDoC GTwe IOrc MBri MGos NBee NRog SDea SKee SPer WJas WStI | |
| - 'Gulval Seedling' (D) | Last listed 1996 | |
| - 'Halstow Natural' (Cider) | CTho | |
| - 'Hambledon Deux Ans' (C) | SDea SKee WJas | |
| - 'Hambling's Seedling' (C) | SKee | |
| - 'Hangy Down' (Cider) | CTho | |
| - 'Haralson' (D) | Last listed 1998 | |
| - 'Harry Master's Dove' (Cider) | Last listed 1996 | |
| § - 'Harry Master's Jersey' (Cider) | CCAT CTho CTri SDea | |
| - 'Harvey' (C) | SDea SKee | |
| - 'Hawthornden' (C) | CTho SKee | |
| - 'Hereford Cross' (D) | Last listed 1997 | |
| - 'Herefordshire Beefing' (C) | CEnd SKee WJas | |
| - 'Herring's Pippin' (D) | CTri GTwe SDea SKee | |
| - 'Heusgen's Golden Reinette' (D) | CCAT SKee | |
| - 'High View Pippin' (D) | SKee | |
| - 'Hill's Seedling' (C) | SKee | |
| - 'Histon Favourite' (D) | SKee | |
| - 'Hoary Morning' (C) | CCAT CTho SDea SKee | |
| - 'Hocking's Green' (C/D) | CEnd CTho | |
| - 'Holland Pippin' (C) | SKee | |
| - 'Hollow Core' (C) | CTho | |
| - 'Holstein' (D) | COtt CSam CTho GTwe SDea SKee | |
| § - 'Honeygold' (D) | CEnd | |
| - 'Hormead Pearmain' (C) | Last listed 1996 | |
| - 'Horneburger Pfannkuchen' (C) | SKee | |
| - 'Houblon' (D) | Last listed 1997 | |
| - 'Howgate Wonder' (C) | CB&S CCAT CDoC CSam EMui GBon GChr GTwe IOrc LBuc MBri MGos NBee NRog SDea SFam SKee SPer WJas | |
| - 'Hubbard's Pearmain' (D) | SKee | |
| - 'Idared' (D) ♀ | GBon GTwe MGos SDea SKee | |
| - 'Improved Cockpit' (D) | NRog | |
| - 'Improved Dove' (Cider) | CCAT | |
| - 'Improved Keswick' (C/D) | CEnd | |
| - 'Improved Lambrook Pippin' (Cider) | CCAT CTho | |
| - 'Improved Pound' (Cider) | Last listed 1996 | |
| - 'Improved Redstreak' (Cider) | CTho | |
| - 'Improved Woodbine' (Cider) | Last listed 1998 | |
| - 'Ingrid Marie' (D) | SDea SKee WJas | |
| - 'Irish Peach' (D) | GTwe LBuc SDea SFam SKee WJas | |
| - 'Isaac Newton's Tree' | See *M. domestica* 'Flower of Kent' | |
| - 'Isle of Wight Pippin' (D) | SDea | |
| - 'Isle of Wight Russet' (D) | SDea | |
| - 'Jackson's' (Cider) | Last listed 1998 | |
| - 'James Grieve' (D) ♀ | CB&S CCAT CCVT CDoC CMac EBee EMui GBon GChr GRei GTwe IOrc LBuc MBri MWat NBea NBee NRog SDea SFam SKee SPer WHar WJas WWeb | |
| - 'James Lawson' (D) | Last listed 1996 | |
| - 'Jerseymac' (D) | SDea | |
| - 'Jester' (D) | GTwe NRog SDea SKee | |
| - 'John Apple' (C) | SKee | |
| - 'John Broad' (F) | Last listed 1996 | |
| - 'John Standish' (D) | CCAT GTwe SDea | |

- 'John Toucher's'   See *M. domestica* 'Crimson King'
- 'Johnny Andrews' (Cider)   CCAT CTho
- 'Johnny Voun' (D)   CEnd CTho
- 'Jonagold' (D) ♀   GTwe LBuc MBri SDea SFam SKee SPer WJas
- 'Jonagold Crowngold'   See *M. domestica* 'Crowngold'
§ - 'Jonagored' (D)   EBee NRog SDea
- 'Jonared' (D)   GTwe
- 'Jonathan' (D)   SDea SKee
- 'Jordan's Weeping' (C)   GTwe SDea WJas
- 'Josephine' (D)   SDea
- 'Joybells' (D)   SKee
- 'Jubilee'   See *M. domestica* 'Royal Jubilee'
§ - Jubilee (Delbards) (F)   Last listed 1996
- 'Jupiter' (D) ♀   CCAT CDoC CSam CTri EBee GBon GTwe IOrc MGos MWat NBea NRog SDea SFam SKee WJas
- 'Kandil Sinap' (D)   SKee
- 'Kapai Red Jonathan' (D)   SDea
- 'Karmijn de Sonnaville' (D)   SDea SKee
§ - 'Katja' (D)   CCAT CDoC CSam EBee EMui GBon GChr GTwe IOrc LBuc MBri NBee NRog SDea SKee SPer WHar WJas
- Katy   See *M. domestica* 'Katja'
- 'Kendall' (D)   SKee
- 'Kent' (D)   GTwe SDea SKee
- 'Kentish Fillbasket' (C)   SKee
- 'Kentish Pippin' (C/Cider/D)   SKee
- 'Kentish Quarrenden' (D)   SKee
- 'Kerry Pippin' (D)   SKee
- 'Keswick Codling' (C)   GTwe MBri NRog SDea SKee WJas
§ - 'Kidd's Orange Red' (D) ♀   CCAT COtt EBrP EBre EMui GTwe LBre LBuc SBre SDea SFam SKee WJas
- 'Kilkenny Pippin' (F)   GTwe
- 'Killerton Sharp' (Cider)   CTho
- 'Killerton Sweet' (Cider)   CTho
- 'King Byerd' (C/D)   CEnd CTho
- 'King Charles' Pearmain' (D)   CTho SKee
- 'King Coffee' (D)   SKee
- 'King George V' (D)   SKee
- 'King Luscious' (D)   SDea
§ - 'King of the Pippins' (D) ♀   CCAT CSam CTho CTri GTwe SDea SFam SKee
- 'King of Tompkins County' (D)   SKee
- 'King Russet' (D) ♀   SDea
- 'King's Acre Bountiful' (C)   SKee WJas
- 'King's Acre Pippin' (D)   CTho SDea SFam SKee WJas
- 'Kingston Bitter' (Cider)   CTho
- 'Kingston Black' (Cider/C)   CCAT CSam CTho SDea SKee
- 'Knobby Russet' (D)   GTwe SKee
- 'Lady Henniker' (D)   CCAT CTho GTwe NRog SDea SKee WJas
- 'Lady Lambourne' (C/D)   Last listed 1997
- 'Lady of the Wemyss' (C)   SKee
- 'Lady Stanley' (D)   Last listed 1997
- 'Lady Sudeley' (D)   CTho SDea SKee WJas
- 'Lady Williams' (D)   Last listed 1996
- 'Lady's Delight' (C)   Last listed 1996
- 'Lady's Finger' (C/D)   CEnd
- 'Lady's Finger of Hereford' (D)   CTho WJas
¶ - 'Lady's Finger of Lancaster' (C/D)   CSam NRog SKee
- 'Lady's Finger of Offaly' (D)   SDea
- 'Lamb Abbey Pearmain' (D)   SKee
- 'Landsberger Reinette' (D)   SKee

- 'Lane's Prince Albert' (C) ♀   CCAT CCVT CSam EMui GBon GTwe MGos MWat NRog SDea SFam SKee WJas
- 'Langley Pippin' (D)   SDea SKee
§ - 'Langworthy' (Cider)   CCAT CTho
- 'Lass o' Gowrie' (C)   SKee
§ - 'Laxton's Epicure' (D) ♀   CDoC CTho GBon GTwe IOrc NRog SDea SFam SKee WJas
§ - 'Laxton's Fortune' (D) ♀   CCAT CDoC CMac CSam EMui GTwe MGos NRog SDea SFam SKee WHar WJas
- 'Laxton's Pearmain' (D)   Last listed 1996
- 'Laxton's Rearguard' (D)   SKee WJas
- 'Laxton's Reward' (D)   Last listed 1996
- 'Laxton's Royalty' (D)   SDea SKee
§ - 'Laxton's Superb' (D)   CB&S CCAT CCVT CDoC CSam CTri GBon GTwe IOrc LBuc MBri NRog SDea SKee SPer WHar WJas
- 'Leathercoat Russet' (D)   CTho SKee
- 'Leeder's Perfection' (F)   Last listed 1996
- 'Lemon Pippin' (C)   CCAT CTho SDea SKee WJas
- 'Lewis's Incomparable' (C)   SKee
- 'Liberty' (D)   SDea
- 'Limberland' (C)   CTho
- 'Linda' (D)   SKee
- 'Listener' (Cider/D)   CCAT CTho
- 'Lobo' (D)   Last listed 1997
§ - 'Loddington' (C)   SKee
- 'Lodgemore Nonpareil' (D)   Last listed 1996
- 'Lodi' (C)   SDea
- 'London Pearmain' (D)   WJas
- 'London Pippin' (C)   CTho
- 'Longkeeper' (D)   CEnd CTho
- 'Longstem' (Cider)   CTho
- 'Lord Burghley' (D)   GTwe SDea SKee
- 'Lord Derby' (C)   CCAT CMac CTho EMui GTwe MBri MWat NRog SDea SFam SKee WJas
- 'Lord Grosvenor' (C)   GTwe SKee
- 'Lord Hindlip' (D)   GTwe LBuc SDea SFam SKee WJas
- 'Lord Lambourne' (D) ♀   CCAT CCVT CDoC CSam CTri EBrP EBre EMui GChr GTwe IOrc LBre MWat NRog SBre SDea SFam SKee WHar WJas
- 'Lord of the Isles' (F)   Last listed 1996
- 'Lord Rosebery' (D)   Last listed 1996
- 'Lord Stradbroke' (C)   SKee
- 'Lord Suffield' (C)   SKee
- 'Loyal Drain' (Cider)   Last listed 1998
- 'Lucombe's Pine' (D)   CEnd CTho
- 'Lucombe's Seedling' (D)   CTho SKee
- 'Mabbott's Pearmain' (D)   SDea
- 'Madresfield Court' (D)   SDea SKee WJas
- 'Maiden's Blush' (D)   Last listed 1996
- 'Maidstone Favourite' (D)   Last listed 1996
- 'Major' (Cider)   CCAT CTho
- 'Malling Kent' (D)   CSam EMui SDea SFam
- 'Maltster' (D)   GTwe SKee WJas
- 'Manaccan Primrose' (C/D)   CEnd
- 'Manks Codlin' (C)   CTho SKee
- 'Mannington's Pearmain' (D)   Last listed 1996
- 'Margil' (D)   CCAT CTho GTwe SDea SFam SKee
- 'Marriage-maker' (D)   Last listed 1996
- 'May Queen' (D)   SDea SFam SKee WJas
- 'Maypole' (D/Ball)   MGos SDea WJas
- 'McCutcheon' (F)   Last listed 1998
¶ - 'McIntosh' (D)   SKee WJas
- 'Mead's Broading' (C)   Last listed 1996
- 'Medaille d'Or' (Cider)   CCAT
- 'Medina' (D)   GTwe

- 'Melba' (D) — CSam SKee
- 'Melcombe Russet' (D) — CTho
- 'Melon' (D) — SDea
- 'Melrose' (D) — GTwe SKee
- 'Merchant Apple' (D) — CCAT
- 'Merchant Apple of Illminster' (D) — CCAT CTho
¶ - 'Mère de Ménage' (C) — SFam
- 'Merton Beauty' (D) — Last listed 1996
- 'Merton Charm' (D) ♀ — Last listed 1996
- 'Merton Joy' (D) — Last listed 1996
- 'Merton Knave' (D) — GTwe MGos SDea SFam
- 'Merton Russet' (D) — SDea
- 'Merton Worcester' (D) — SDea SKee
- 'Michaelmas Red' (D) — GTwe NRog SKee WJas
- 'Michelin' (Cider) — CCAT CCVT CEnd CTho EMui GTwe SDea
- Miel d'Or — See *M. domestica* 'Honeygold'
- 'Miller's Seedling' (D) — GTwe SKee WJas
- 'Millicent Barnes' (D) — SDea
- 'Mollie's Delicious' (D) — GTwe SKee
- 'Monarch' (C) — CCAT CTri GTwe NRog SDea SFam SKee WJas
- 'Monarch Advanced' (C) — Last listed 1996
I - 'Mondial Gala' — See *M. domestica* 'Gala Mondial'
- 'Morgan's Sweet' (C/Cider) — CCAT CTho CTri SDea SKee
- 'Moss's Seedling' (D) — SDea
§ - 'Mother' (D) ♀ — CDoC GTwe LBuc SDea SFam SKee WJas
- 'Mrs Crittenden' (D) — Last listed 1996
- 'Mrs Phillimore' (D) — SKee
- 'Muscadet de Dieppe' (Cider) — CCAT
§ - 'Mutsu' (D) — CCAT EBee GTwe MBri NRog SDea SKee
- 'Neasdale Favorite' (F) — SKee
- 'Nehou' (Cider) — Last listed 1996
- 'Nettlestone Pippin' (D) — SDea
- 'Newton Wonder' (D/C) ♀ — CCAT CDoC CMac CSam CTri GTwe NRog SDea SFam SKee WJas
- 'Newtown Pippin' (D) — SDea
- 'Nittany Red' (D) — SDea
- 'No Pip' (C) — CTho
- 'Nonpareil' (D) — CTho SFam SKee
- 'Norfolk Beauty' (C) — SKee
- 'Norfolk Beefing' (C) — SDea SFam SKee
- 'Norfolk Royal' (D) — CDoC GTwe SDea SKee
- 'Norfolk Summer Broadend' (C) — SKee
- 'Norfolk Winter Coleman' (C) — SKee
- 'Norman's Pippin' (D) — Last listed 1996
- 'Northcott Superb' (D) — CTho
- 'Northern Greening' (C) — GTwe SKee
- 'Northwood' (Cider) — CCAT CTho
- 'Nutmeg Pippin' (D) — SDea
- 'Oaken Pin' (C) — CTho
- 'Old Pearmain' (D) — CTho SDea SKee
- 'Old Somerset Russet' (D) — CTho
- 'Opalescent' (D) — SKee
- 'Orange Goff' (D) — SKee
- 'Orin' (D) — SKee
- 'Orkney Apple' (F) — SKee
- 'Orleans Reinette' (D) — CCAT CCVT CTho EMui GTwe MWat SDea SFam SKee WJas
- 'Osier' (Cider) — CCAT
- 'Oslin' (D) — SKee
- 'Owen Thomas' (D) — CTri
- 'Paignton Marigold' (Cider) — CTho
- 'Paulared' (D) — SKee
- 'Payhembury' (C/Cider) — CTho

- 'Peacemaker' (D) — SKee
- 'Pear Apple' (D) — CEnd
- 'Pearl' (D) — CTho SDea
- 'Peasgood's Nonsuch' (C) ♀ — CCAT GTwe LBuc SDea SFam SKee WJas
- 'Peck's Pleasant' (D) — SKee
- 'Pendragon' (D) — CTho
- 'Penhallow Pippin' (D) — CTho
- 'Pennard Bitter' (Cider) — CCAT
- 'Peter Lock' (C/D) — CCAT CEnd CTho
- 'Peter's Pippin' (D) — SDea
- 'Peter's Seedling' (D) — SDea
- 'Pickering's Seedling' (D) — SKee
- 'Pig's Nose Pippin' (D) — CEnd CTho SKee
- 'Pig's Nose Pippin' Type III (D) — CTho
- 'Pig's Snout' (Cider/C/D) — CCAT CEnd CTho
- 'Pine Golden Pippin' (D) — SKee
- 'Pitmaston Pine Apple' (D) — CCAT CSam CTho NRog SDea SFam SKee WJas
¶ - 'Pitmaston Russet Nonpareil' (D) — SKee
- 'Pixie' (D) ♀ — CCVT CSam GTwe SDea SFam SKee WJas
- 'Plum Vite' (D) — CTho CTri
- 'Plympton Pippin' (C) — CEnd CTho
§ - Polka = 'Trajan' (D/Ball) — MGos SDea
- 'Polly' (C/D) — CEnd
- 'Polly Prosser' (D) — Last listed 1997
- 'Polly Whitehair' (C/D) — CTho SDea SKee
- 'Pomeroy' (D) — CCAT
- 'Pomeroy of Somerset' (D) — CTho
- 'Ponsford' (C) — CCAT CTho
- 'Port Wine' — See *M. domestica* 'Harry Master's Jersey'
- 'Porter's Pefection' (Cider) — CCAT CTho
- 'Pott's Seedling' (C) — SKee
- 'Powell's Russet' (D) — Last listed 1996
- 'Priscilla' (D) — GTwe
- 'Puckrupp Pippin' (D) — Last listed 1996
- 'Queen' (C) — CEnd CTho SKee
- 'Queen Caroline' (C) — Last listed 1996
- 'Queen Cox' (D) — EMui GBon MRav SDea SKee
- 'Queens' (D) — CTho
- 'Racky Down' (F) — SKee
¶ - 'Red Alkmene' (D) — MBri
- 'Red Astrachan' (D) — SKee
§ - 'Red Blenheim' (C/D) — SKee
- 'Red Charles Ross' (C/D) — SDea
- 'Red Devil' (D) — COtt CWSG EMui GRei GTwe LBuc MBri NBee SDea SKee WJas
- 'Red Ellison' (D) — CCAT CTho CTri GTwe NRog SDea
¶ - 'Red Falstaff' (D) — MBri
- 'Red Fuji' (D) — SDea
♦ - 'Red James Grieve' — See *M. domestica* 'Redcoat Grieve'
- 'Red Jersey' (Cider) — CCAT
- 'Red Joaneting' (D) — SKee
♦ - 'Red Jonagold' — See *M. domestica* 'Jonagored'
- 'Red Melba' (D) — Last listed 1996
- 'Red Miller's Seedling' (D) — SDea
- 'Red Newton Wonder' (C) — Last listed 1996
- 'Red Robin' (F) — CEnd
- 'Red Ruby' (F) — CTho
- 'Red Victoria' (C) — GTwe WJas
§ - 'Redcoat Grieve' (D) — CDoC SDea
- 'Redfree' (D) — GTwe
- 'Redsleeves' (D) — GTwe SDea
- 'Redstrake' (Cider) — CCAT
- 'Reine de Pommes' (Cider) — CCAT
- 'Reine des Reinettes' — See *M. domestica* 'King of the Pippins'

I – Reine des Reinettes    Last listed 1997
 – 'Reinette d'Obry' (Cider)    CCAT
 – 'Reinette Dorée de    GTwe
 Boediker' (D)
 – 'Reinette du Canada' (D)    CTho SKee
 – 'Reinette Rouge Etoilée' (D)    CCAT SDéa
 – 'Reverend Greeves' (C)    SDea
 – 'Reverend W. Wilks' (C)    CCAT CCVT CDoC COtt EMui
  LBuc MBri MWat NRog SDea
  SFam SKee WJas
 – 'Ribston Pippin' (D) ♀    CCAT CTho CTri EMui GTwe
  LBuc MWat NRog SDea SFam
  SKee WJas
 – 'Rival' (D)    SDea SKee WJas
 – 'Rivers' Nonsuch' (D)    WJas
 – 'Robin Pippin' (D)    GTwe
 – 'Rome Beauty' (D)    SDea
 – 'Rosamund' (D)    Last listed 1996
 – 'Rosemary Russet' (D) ♀    CCAT CSam CTho GTwe NRog
  SDea SFam SKee WJas
 – 'Ross Nonpareil' (D)    GTwe SDea SKee
 – 'Rough Pippin' (D)    CEnd CTho
 – 'Roundway Magnum    CCAT CTho SDea SFam SKee
 Bonum' (D)
§ – 'Roxbury Russet' (D)    SKee
§ – 'Royal Gala' (D) ♀    EMui LBuc SDea SKee
§ – 'Royal Jubilee' (C)    SKee
 – 'Royal Russet' (C)    SDea
 – 'Royal Snow' (D)    SKee
 – 'Royal Somerset' (C/Cider)    CCAT CTho
 – 'Rubens' (D)    SKee
 – 'Rubinette' (D)    CDoC COtt CTho GTwe MBri
  MGos WJas
 – 'S.T. Wright' (C)    Last listed 1997
 – 'Saint Albans Pippin' (D)    SKee
 – 'Saint Augustine's Orange'    SKee
 (D)
 – 'Saint Cecilia' (D)    SDea SKee WJas
§ – 'Saint Edmund's Pippin'    CSam CTho ERea GTwe SDea
 (D) ♀    SFam SKee
 – 'Saint Edmund's Russet'    See M. domestica 'Saint Edmund's
  Pippin'
 – 'Saint Everard' (D)    SKee
 – 'Saint Magdalen' (D)    SKee
 – 'Saltcote Pippin' (D)    SKee
 – 'Sam Young' (D)    SKee
 – 'Sandlands'    SDea
 – 'Sandringham' (C)    SKee
 – 'Sanspareil' (D)    CTho SKee
¶ – 'Saturn'    GTwe
 – 'Saw Pits' (F)    CEnd SKee
 – 'Scarlet Crofton' (D)    Last listed 1996
 – 'Scarlet Nonpareil' (D)    SKee
 – 'Scarlet Pimpernel' (D)    Last listed 1996
§ – 'Schweizer Orange' (F)    Last listed 1996
 – 'Scilly Pearl' (C)    WJas
 – 'Scotch Bridget' (C)    SKee WJas
 – 'Scotch Dumpling' (C)    GTwe
 – 'Seaton House' (C)    SKee
 – 'Sercombe's Natural' (Cider)    CCAT CTho
 – 'Shakespeare' (D)    WJas
 – 'Sheep's Nose' (C)    CCAT SDea SKee
 – 'Shenandoah' (C)    SKee
 – 'Shoesmith' (C)    Last listed 1998
 – 'Sidney Strake' (C)    CEnd
 – 'Sir Isaac Newton's'    See M. domestica 'Flower of Kent'
 – 'Sir John Thornycroft' (D)    SDea
 – 'Sisson's Worksop    SKee
 Newtown' (D)
 – 'Slack Ma Girdle' (Cider)    CCAT CTho
 – 'Smart's Prince Arthur' (C)    SDea
 – 'Snell's Glass Apple'    See M. domestica 'Glass Apple'

 – 'Somerset Lasting' (C)    CTho
¶ – 'Somerset Redstreak'    CCAT CTho
 (Cider)
 – 'Sops in Wine' (C/Cider)    CCAT CTho SKee
 – 'Sour Bay' (Cider)    CTho
 – 'Sour Natural'    See M. domestica 'Langworthy'
 – 'Spartan' (D)    CDoC EBrP EBre EMui GBon
  GTwe LBre MGos NBea NRog
  SBre SDea SFam SKee WJas WStI
 – 'Spencer' (D)    CTri SKee
 – 'Spotted Dick' (Cider)    CTho
 – 'Spur Mac' (D)    SDea
¶ – 'Stable Jersey' (Cider)    CCAT
 – 'Stamford Pippin' (D)    SDea
 – 'Star of Devon' (D)    CCAT CTho SDea
 – 'Stark' (D)    SDea
 – 'Starking' (D)    SKee
 – 'Starking Red Delicious' (D)    Last listed 1996
 – 'Starkrimson' (D)    SKee
 – 'Stark's Earliest' (D)    Last listed 1996
 – 'Starkspur Golden    SKee
 Delicious' (D)
 – 'Stembridge' (Cider)    Last listed 1996
¶ – 'Stembridge Cluster' (Cider)    CCAT
 – 'Stembridge Jersey' (Cider)    CCAT
 – 'Steyne Seedling' (D)    SDea
 – 'Stirling Castle' (C)    GTwe SKee
 – 'Stobo Castle' (C)    SKee
 – 'Stockbearer' (C)    CTho
 – 'Stoke Edith Pippin' (D)    WJas
 – 'Stoke Red' (Cider)    CCAT CTho
 – 'Stone's'    See M. domestica 'Loddington'
 – 'Stoup Leadington' (C)    SKee
 – 'Strawberry Pippin' (D)    WJas
 – 'Striped Beefing' (C)    SKee
 – 'Stub Nose' (F)    SKee
 – 'Sturmer Pippin' (D)    GTwe MWat SDea SFam SKee
  WJas
 – 'Sugar Bush' (C/D)    CTho
 – 'Summer Golden    SKee
 Pippin' (D)
 – 'Summer Granny' (D)    Last listed 1997
 – 'Summer Stubbard' (D)    CTho
 – 'Summergold' (F)    Last listed 1996
 – 'Summerred' (D)    CWSG WStI
 – 'Sunburn' (D)    Last listed 1998
¶ – 'Sunnydale' (D/C)    SDea
¶ – 'Sunrise' (D)    EMui
 – 'Sunset' (D) ♀    CCAT CDoC CMac CSam CTri
  EMui GTwe LBuc MBri NBea
  NBee NRog SDea SFam SKee SPer
  WHar WJas
 – 'Suntan' (D) ♀    CCAT CSam CTho GBon GTwe
  MWat NBee SDea SKee
 – 'Superb'    See M. domestica 'Laxton's
  Superb'
 – 'Surprise' (D)    GTwe
 – 'Sweet Alford' (Cider)    CCAT CTho
 – 'Sweet Bay' (Cider)    CTho
 – 'Sweet Blenheim' (Cider)    Last listed 1998
 – 'Sweet Cleave' (Cider)    CTho
 – 'Sweet Coppin' (Cider)    CCAT CTho
 – Swiss Orange    See M. domestica 'Schweizer
  Orange'
 – 'Tale Sweet' (Cider)    CCAT CTho
 – 'Tamar Beauty' (F)    CEnd
 – 'Tan Harvey' (Cider)    CCAT CEnd
 – 'Taunton Cream' (F)    Last listed 1996
 – 'Taunton Fair Maid' (Cider)    CCAT CTho
 – 'Taylor's' (Cider)    CCAT SDea
 – 'Taylor's Sweet' (Cider)    CCAT
 – 'Telamon'    See M. domestica Waltz =
  'Telamon'

| | |
|---|---|
| - 'Ten Commandments' (D/Cider) | CCAT SDea SKee WJas |
| - 'The Rattler' (F) | CEnd |
| - 'Thomas Rivers' (C) | CTho SDea SKee |
| - 'Thorle Pippin' (D) | SKee |
| - 'Tidicombe Seedling' | CTho |
| - 'Tillington Court' (C) | WJas |
| - 'Tom Putt' (C) | CCAT CCVT COtt CSam CTho CTri GTwe LBuc SDea SKee WJas |
| - 'Tommy Knight' (D) | CEnd |
| - 'Tower of Glamis' (C) | GTwe SKee |
| - Town Farm Number 59 (Cider) | CTho |
| - 'Trajan' | See *M. domestica* Polka = 'Trajan' |
| - 'Transparente de Croncels' (C) | CTho |
| - 'Tregoana King' (C/D) | CEnd CTho |
| - 'Tremlett's Bitter' (Cider) | CCAT CTho SDea |
| - 'Tuscan' | See *M. domestica* Bolero = 'Tuscan' |
| - 'Twenty Ounce' (C) | CCAT GTwe SKee WJas |
| - 'Twinings Pippin' (D) | SKee |
| § - 'Tydeman's Early Worcester' (D) | CLnd GTwe NBee NRog SDea SKee WJas |
| - 'Tydeman's Late Orange' (D) | GTwe NRog SDea SFam SKee |
| - 'Tyler's Kernel' (C) | Last listed 1996 |
| - 'Underleaf' (D) | CCAT |
| - 'Upton Pyne' (D) | CCAT CSam CTho SDea SKee |
| - 'Veitch's Perfection' (C/D) | CTho |
| - 'Venus Pippin' (C/D) | CEnd |
| - 'Vickey's Delight' (D) | SDea |
| - 'Vilberie' (Cider) | CCAT |
| - 'Vista-bella' (D) | GTwe NBee SDea SKee WJas |
| - 'Wagener' (D) | NRog SDea SKee |
| § - Waltz = 'Telamon' (D/Ball/C) | MGos SDea |
| - 'Wanstall Pippin' (D) | SKee |
| - 'Warner's King' (C) ♀ | CCAT NRog SDea SKee WJas |
| - 'Wealthy' (D) | SDea SKee |
| - 'Wellington' | See *M. domestica* 'Dumeller's Seedling' |
| § - 'Wellspur' (D) | GTwe |
| - 'Wellspur Delicious' (D) | Last listed 1996 |
| ♦ - 'Wellspur Red Delicious' | See *M. domestica* 'Wellspur' |
| - 'Welsh Russet' (D) | SDea |
| - 'Wheeler's Russet' (C) | Last listed 1997 |
| - 'White Alphington' (Cider) | CTho |
| - 'White Close Pippin' (Cider) | CTho |
| - 'White Jersey' (Cider) | CCAT |
| - 'White Joaneting' (D) | CTho |
| - 'White Melrose' (C) | GTwe SDea SKee |
| - 'White Paradise' (C) | SKee |
| - 'White Transparent' (C/D) | SDea SKee |
| - 'William Crump' (D) | CCAT SDea SFam SKee WJas |
| - 'Winston' (D) ♀ | CCAT CCVT CDoC CTri EBee GTwe NRog SDea SFam SKee WJas |
| - 'Winter Banana' (D) | NRog SDea SKee |
| * - 'Winter Gem' | COtt EMui MBri MGos |
| - 'Winter Majetin' (C) | Last listed 1997 |
| - 'Winter Peach' (D/C) | CEnd CTho |
| - 'Winter Pearmain' (D) | SKee |
| - 'Winter Quarrenden' (D) | SDea SKee |
| - 'Winter Queening' (D/C) | CTho SDea |
| - 'Winter Stubbard' (C) | CTho |
| - 'Woodbine' (Cider) | Last listed 1998 |
| - 'Woolbrook Pippin' (D) | CCAT CTho |
| - 'Woolbrook Russet' (C) | CCAT CTho SKee |
| - 'Worcester Pearmain' (D) ♀ | CB&S CCAT CCVT CTho EBee EMui GBon GRei GTwe LBuc MBri MWat NRog SDea SFam SKee SPer WHar WJas WStI WWeb |
| - 'Wormsley Pippin' (D) | SKee WJas |
| - 'Wyatt's Seedling' | See *M. domestica* 'Langworthy' |
| - 'Wyken Pippin' (D) | GTwe SDea SFam SKee WJas |
| - 'Yarlington Mill' (Cider) | CCAT CTho CTri SDea SKee |
| - 'Yellow Ingestrie' (D) | SFam SKee WJas |
| - 'Yellowspur' (D) | Last listed 1996 |
| - 'Yorkshire Greening' (C) | Last listed 1997 |
| - 'Young America' (D) | Last listed 1998 |
| - 'Zabergäu Renette' (D) | SKee |
| 'Donald Wyman' | CBlo |
| 'Echtermeyer' | See *M.* x *gloriosa* 'Oekonomierat Echtermeyer' |
| § 'Evereste' ♀ | CBar CBlo CDoC CEnd CLnd EBee EMui EPfP GChr GTwe LPan MAsh MBlu MBri MRav SFam WDin WHar WJas |
| *florentina* | CMCN CTho WMou |
| *floribunda* ♀ | CBlo CDoC CDul CEnd CLnd CSam CTho EBee ELan ENot GChr GTwe IOrc LBuc LHyr LPan MBri MGos MRav NBee SPer WDin WHar WJas WNor WOrn |
| 'Gardener's Gold' | CEnd |
| § x *gloriosa* 'Oekonomierat Echtermeyer' | CBlo GQui SDea SSta WDin WJas |
| 'Golden Gem' | CBlo CEnd EPfP GTwe WJas |
| 'Golden Hornet' | See *M.* x *zumi* 'Golden Hornet' |
| 'Goldsworth Purple' | CTho |
| *halliana* | Last listed 1996 |
| x *hartwigii* 'Katherine' ♀ | Last listed 1995 |
| x *heterophylla* 'Redflesh' | CTho |
| 'Hillieri' | See *M.* x *schiedeckeri* 'Hillieri' |
| *hupehensis* ♀ | CB&S CBlo CEnd CLnd CMCN CTho EBee ENot GTwe MBri SFam SLPl SPer WMou WWat |
| 'John Downie' (C) ♀ | More than 30 suppliers |
| 'Kaido' | See *M.* x *micromalus* |
| *kansuensis* | CLnd WMou |
| * 'Laura' | CBlo COtt MGos WGor |
| x *magdeburgensis* | CLnd MRav |
| * *mahonia* | Last listed 1996 |
| * 'Mamouth' | Last listed 1997 |
| § x *micromalus* | CLnd GAri |
| x *moerlandsii* | CLnd |
| - 'Liset' | CBlo CDul CEnd CLnd COtt EBee EBrP EBre ENot GChr LBre MAsh SBre SFam SPer WFar WJas WStI |
| § - 'Profusion' | CBlo CBrm CDul CLnd EBee EBrP EBre ELan ENot IOrc LBre LHyr LPan MAsh MBri MGos MRav NBee NWea SBre SPer SRPl SSta WDin WJas WStI |
| ¶ - 'Profusion Improved' | CEnd COtt |
| *orthocarpa* | CLnd |
| Perpetu | See *M.* 'Evereste' |
| 'Pink Perfection' | CLnd EBee ENot MAsh MBri SPer |
| ¶ Pom'Zai | CDoC |
| *prattii* | CTho |
| 'Profusion' | See *M.* x *moerlandsii* 'Profusion' |
| *prunifolia* 'Cheal's Crimson' | NRog |
| - 'Pendula' | GAri |
| *pumila* 'Cowichan' | CBlo LRHS MBri |
| - 'Dartmouth' | CBlo CDul CLnd CSam CTho CTri NRog SFam SPer |
| - 'Montreal Beauty' | MAsh MBri WJas |
| - 'Niedzwetzkyana' | CLnd |
| § x *purpurea* 'Aldenhamensis' | CBlo CLnd CTho SDea WDin |
| - 'Eleyi' | CBlo CDul CLnd ENot EPfP MAsh NWea |
| - 'Lemoinei' | IOrc |
| - 'Neville Copeman' ♀ | CDoC CDul CLnd EPfP MAsh MGos WJas |

| | |
|---|---|
| - 'Pendula' | See *M.* x *gloriosa* 'Oekonomierat Echtermeyer' |
| ¶ 'Red Ace' | CDul |
| 'Red Glow' | CBlo CDoC CLnd COtt EBee GQui LHyr WJas WLRN |
| 'Red Jade' | See *M.* x *schiedeckeri* 'Red Jade' |
| § x *robusta* | CBlo CDoC CLnd CTri EBee GTwe MBal NWea SLon SRPl |
| - 'Red Sentinel' ♀ | CBlo CDoC CDul CEnd CLnd COtt CSam CTho EBee EBrP EBre ELan EMui ENot LBre MAsh MBar MBri MGos MRav MWat NBee SBre SFam SPer WCFE WJas |
| - 'Red Siberian' ♀ | SDea SPer |
| - 'Yellow Siberian' ♀ | CLnd |
| 'Royal Beauty' ♀ | CBlo CLnd EBee EBrP EBre GTwe LBre LBuc MAsh MBri MGos MRav SBre WDin WHar |
| 'Royalty' | CB&S CBlo CDul CLnd CTho EBee EBrP EBre ELan ENot GChr GRei GTwe LBre LBuc LPan MAsh MBri MGos MRav NBea NBee SBre SFam SPer SSta WHar WJas WStI |
| 'Rudolph' | CDul EBee ENot LPan |
| *sargentii* | See *M. toringo* subsp. *sargentii* |
| x *schiedeckeri* 'Exzellenz Thiel' | Last listed 1998 |
| § - 'Hillieri' | CLnd CTho SFam |
| § - 'Red Jade' | CBlo CDul CLnd EBee EBrP EBre ELan ENot GChr GTwe IOrc LBre LBuc MAsh MBar MBri MGos MRav MWat NBee SBre SPer WDin WJas WOrn WStI |
| ¶ - 'Sun Rival' | WJas |
| ◆ Siberian crab | See *M.* x *robusta* |
| *sieboldii* | See *M. toringo* |
| *sikkimensis* | WHCr |
| - B&SWJ 2431 | WCru |
| 'Snowcloud' | CBlo CDul CEnd CLnd EBee ENot MBri WShe |
| sp. CLD 417 | Last listed 1997 |
| *spectabilis* | CLnd |
| 'Strathmore' | Last listed 1996 |
| 'Sun Rival' | CBlo CDul CEnd COtt EPfP GTwe MAsh MGos SCoo SFam WHar WWeb |
| *sylvestris* | CDul CKin CLnd GAri GChr LBuc LHyr NBee NRog NWea WDin WLRN |
| § *toringo* | SSpi WShe |
| ¶ - 'Professor Sprenger' | CLnd |
| - 'Rosea' | Last listed 1996 |
| § - subsp. *sargentii* | CBlo EBee ECtt ENot EWTr MBri MGos NWea SFam SPer WNor WWat |
| - - 'Tina' | MAsh |
| *toringoides* | CDul CLnd CMCN CTho MBri SRPl WHCr WNor |
| *transitoria* ♀ | CBlo CEnd CFil CLnd CTho EPfP MBri SSpi WWat |
| - 'R.J. Fulcher' | CLnd CTho |
| - 'Thornhayes Tansy' | CDul CLnd CTho |
| *trilobata* | CBlo CLnd CTho WMou |
| *tschonoskii* ♀ | More than 30 suppliers |
| ◆ - 'White Star' | See *M.* 'White Star' |
| 'Van Eseltine' | CBlo CDul CLnd EBee EBrP EBre GTwe LBre MBri SBre SFam SPer WJas |
| 'Veitch's Scarlet' | CDul CLnd CTho GQui GTwe NRog SFam |
| 'White Candle' (d) | CBlo |

| | |
|---|---|
| § 'White Star' | CBlo CBrm CDul CEnd MAsh |
| 'Winter Gold' | CBlo CDoC CDul CLnd CSam MAsh WStI |
| 'Wisley Crab' | CLnd GTwe SDea SFam SKee |
| ¶ *yunnanensis* | CMCN |
| ¶ - 'Veitchii' | CTho |
| x *zumi* var. *calocarpa* | CLnd |
| § - 'Golden Hornet' ♀ | More than 30 suppliers |
| - 'Professor Sprenger' | Last listed 1996 |

## MALVA (Malvaceae)

| | |
|---|---|
| *alcea* | CAgr EPfP |
| - 'Alba' | NPro |
| - var. *fastigiata* | CArn CGle EMan EPPr NBro NCat NRoo NVic SAga SCob SPer SRCN SRms WCot WPer |
| 'Bibor Fehlo' | CSpe MWll NGdn WElm WRha |
| *bicolor* | See *Lavatera maritima* |
| *crispa* | See *M. verticillata* |
| 'Gibbortello' | GMac MCLN NBro |
| 'Harry Hay' | Last listed 1996 |
| *hispida* | CNat |
| *moschata* | More than 30 suppliers |
| - f. *alba* ♀ | More than 30 suppliers |
| - - 'Pirouette' | CM&M WHen WOve |
| - 'Romney Marsh' | See *Althaea officinalis* 'Romney Marsh' |
| - *rosea* | ECha LFis NCut NFor NPer WByw WPnP |
| § *neglecta* | EWFC WPer |
| * *robusta* | Last listed 1996 |
| *sylvestris* | CAgr CGle CKin EOld EWFC GCHN MChe NBro SMad SSoC SWat WFar WHer WJek WPer WRos WWin WWye |
| - 'Brave Heart' | CM&M GBri MWll NBro NPer SLod SWat WHer WRha |
| - 'Highnam' | WAlt |
| - 'Inky Stripe' | Last listed 1998 |
| - 'Marina' | LRHS MAsh MAvo MBri SUsu |
| - subsp. *mauritanica* | CHan CSpe EBee ECoo ELan EMar EPfP GBri LHop MTis NBro NChi NFai NFor NHol NPer WMoo WRus |
| - 'Perry's Blue' | NPer |
| - 'Primley Blue' | CB&S CBot CElw CGle CHan ECha ELan EOld ERav GBri LFis LGre LHop LRot MAvo MCLN MTho NBrk NGdn NPer NSti SMad WBea WFar WWin |
| - 'Richard Perry' | NPer |
| - 'Zebrina' | CM&M EAst GBri MCLN MWll NBrk NFai NGdn NPer SLod SMad SSoC WElm WFar WOve WRha |
| § *verticillata* | ELan |
| - 'Crispa' | MChe WRha |
| ◆ - var. *crispa* | See *M. neglecta* |

## MALVASTRUM (Malvaceae)

| | |
|---|---|
| x *hypomadarum* | See *Anisodontea* x *hypomadara* (Sprague) Bates |
| *lateritium* | CB&S CGle CHan CMHG CMea CSev EBee ELan EMar EOrc GBri GMac LGre LHop LLew MPla MRav MTho NSti NTow SMad SMrm SUsu WEas WHal WPer WSHC WWin |
| - 'Eastgrove Silver' (v) | Last listed 1997 |
| * - 'Variegatum' | Last listed 1998 |
| *peruvianum* | See *Modiolastrum peruvianum* |

## MALVAVISCUS (Malvaceae)

¶ *arboreus*     WMul
- var. *mexicanus*     ERea SYvo WCot WMul

## MANDEVILLA (Apocynaceae)

x *amabilis*     LRHS
x *amoena* 'Alice du Pont' ♀     CB&S CPlN ECon ELan EMil EPfP
    ERea GQui LCns SOWG SYvo
    WMul
*boliviensis*     CPlN ECon ELan EPfP LChe
    SOWG
§ *laxa*     CBot CHan CPlN CPle CSPN
    ECon ELan ERea LBlm LHil LLew
    SOWG SYvo WCot WCru WPic
    WSHC
*sanderi*     MBri
- 'Rosea'     ERea
*splendens*     EBak SOWG SVen SYvo
*suaveolens*     See *M. laxa*
* 'White Delite'     Last listed 1996
yellow form     SOWG

## MANDRAGORA (Solanaceae)

*autumnalis*     EEls GCal IIve MSal WThi
§ *officinarum*     CBrd EBee EEls EMon GCal GPoy
    MHer MSal WWye

## MANETTIA (Rubiaceae)

*inflata*     See *M. luteorubra*
§ *luteorubra*     CPlN ELan EPfP LHop

## MANGLIETIA (Magnoliaceae)

¶ *insignis*     CB&S CFil SSpi

## MANILKARA (Sapotaceae)

¶ *zapota*     LBlo

## MANSOA (Bignoniaceae)

*hymenaea*     CPlN

## MARANTA (Marantaceae)

*leuconeura* var.
  *erythroneura*     MBri
- var. *kerchoveana* ♀     CHal LBlo MBri

## MARCHANTIA (Marchantiaceae)

*calcarea*     Last listed 1996
*palmatoides*     Last listed 1996
sp. from Tristan da Cunha     Last listed 1996

## MARGYRICARPUS (Rosaceae)

§ *pinnatus*     CFee ESis NWCA WPer
*setosus*     See *M. pinnatus*

## MARISCUS See CYPERUS

## MARKHAMIA (Bignoniaceae)

*platycalyx*     See *M. lutea*

## MARRUBIUM (Lamiaceae)

*candidissimum*     See *M. incanum*
*catariifolium*     ECha
*cylleneum*     ECha EGar EMFP EMar MAvo
    WPer
* - 'Velvetissimum'     EGle EOrc LHop SBla SCro WCHb
'Gold Leaf'     ECha MBNS MBel
§ *incanum*     CGle EHal IIve MBri NChi NTow
    WEas
*libanoticum*     ECha EGar EMon MSte SCob
    WPer
¶ *pestalloziae*     WCot

*supinum*     CArn EBee NWoo
*velutinum*     CGle EGar
*vulgare*     CArn EEls ELau GBar GPoy MChe
    MHew NOrc SIde WCHb WCer
    WHer WOak WPer WSel WWye
- 'Green Pompon'     ELau IIve MCCP NLar
- variegated (v)     Last listed 1996

## MARSDENIA (Asclepiadaceae)

*erecta*     See *Cionura erecta*

## MARSHALLIA (Asteraceae)

*caespitosa*     WCot
*grandiflora*     EBee
*trinerva*     WCot

## MARSILEA (Marsileaceae)

*mutica*     SWyc
*quadrifolia*     SWyc
* *schelpiana*     SWyc

## MASCAGNIA (Malpighiaceae)

*macroptera*     CPlN

## MASCARENA See HYOPHORBE

## MASSONIA (Hyacinthaceae)

*echinata*     Last listed 1997

## MATELEA (Asclepiadaceae)

*obliqua*     MNrw

## MATRICARIA (Asteraceae)

*chamomilla*     See *M. recutita*
*maritima*     See *Tripleurospermum*
    *maritimum*
*parthenium*     See *Tanacetum parthenium*
§ *recutita*     GPoy MChe MHew

## MATTEUCCIA (Woodsiaceae)

*orientalis*     CFil EBee MBri NHar NMar NOrc
    WRic
*pensylvanica*     CCuc EMon NHar SMad WRic
*struthiopteris* ♀     More than 30 suppliers

## MATTHIOLA (Brassicaceae)

* *aborescens alba*     ECoo
§ *fruticulosa*     CArn
- subsp. *perennis*     MAvo MCCP NSti NWCA
*incana*     MArl MCCP SIng WCot WGwy
    WPer WRHF WRha WRus
- *alba*     NBir WWhi
- hybrid     NCut
pink perennial     Last listed 1998
*scapifera*     CPBP NTow
*sinuata*     CNat EWFC
*thessala*     See *M. fruticulosa*
white perennial     CArn CGle CHad CHan CMil CSev
    CSpe LCot MWgw NBrk NChi
    NFai NPer NTow SEND WEas
    WHoo WPyg

## MAURANDELLA (Scrophulariaceae)

§ *antirrhiniflora*     Last listed 1996

## MAURANDYA (Scrophulariaceae)

§ *barclayana*     CBot CPlN CRHN MBri MNrw
    SYvo
- *alba*     CBot
*erubescens*     See *Lophospermum erubescens*
*lophantha*     See *Lophospermum scandens*
*lophospermum*     See *Lophospermum scandens*

| | |
|---|---|
| * 'Pink Ice' | SOWG |
| § *purpusii* | CPIN EBee |
| 'Red Dragon' | CPla SUsu |
| ◆ *scandens* | See *Lophospermum scandens* |
| § 'Victoria Falls' | LCns SLod SOWG SYvo |
| *wislizenii* | Last listed 1996 |

## MAYTENUS (Celastraceae)
| | |
|---|---|
| *boaria* | CGre CMCN CPle SAPC SArc WPic WWat |
| ¶ *magellanica* | CFil |

## MAZUS (Scrophulariaceae)
| | |
|---|---|
| *alpinus* B&SWJ 119 | WCru |
| *pumilio* | ECou |
| *radicans* | ECou WCru |
| *reptans* | ELan EPar NPri NWCA WPer WPyg |
| - 'Albus' | ELan NOla WCru WPer |

## MECONOPSIS ✿ (Papaveraceae)
| | |
|---|---|
| *aculeata* | GGGa GTou WAbe |
| *baileyi* | See *M. betonicifolia* |
| x *beamishii* | EBee GBuc WAbe |
| § *betonicifolia* ♀ | More than 30 suppliers |
| - var. *alba* | EBee GAbr GBuc GCan GChr GCrs GGGa GMac IBlr IMGH LSyl MBal MBri NChi NHar NHol NLak NLar SIng SRms WAbe WCru WLin |
| - Harlow Carr strain | Last listed 1997 |
| * - 'Hensol Lilac' | GCal GCrs |
| - var. *pratensis* | GGGa |
| - purple | IBlr |
| - violet | Last listed 1998 |
| *cambrica* | More than 30 suppliers |
| - var. *aurantiaca* | CTri EBee NLak WAbe WHen |
| - *flore-pleno* (d) | CGle EPar GBuc MTho NCat WAbe WFar |
| - - orange (d) | CCuc EBee WAbe WCot WCru |
| - - yellow (d) | EBee WCot WCru |
| § - 'Frances Perry' | CCuc EBee GBuc GCal IBlr NTow WCru WFar |
| - 'Muriel Brown' (d) | EBee WCot WPGP |
| - 'Rubra' | See *M. cambrica* 'Frances Perry' |
| *chelidoniifolia* | CFil GCal IBlr SSpi WCru WPGP |
| *delavayi* | GGGa |
| *dhwojii* | GAbr GBri GCan GGGa MNes SIgm WAbe |
| *gracilipes* | Last listed 1998 |
| *grandis* ♀ | CBrd CGle CPBP CPla CSam EBee GAbr GCan GGGa GMac MNes NBrk NHar NLak NSla SBla WAbe WEas WHen WLin WViv |
| - Balruddry form | GGGa |
| - 'Betty Sheriff's Dream Poppy' | GBuc |
| - EMAK 473 | Last listed 1996 |
| - GS 600 | CLAP GBuc GCan IBlr NBir NWCA |
| ¶ - Kessel's strain | GAbr |
| - PS&W 5423 | Last listed 1998 |
| *horridula* | EBee EPot GCan GGGa MTho WViv |
| - var. *racemosa* | Last listed 1998 |
| - Rudis Group | WCru |
| *integrifolia* | GCrs GGGa LSyl WAbe |
| - ACE 1798 | GTou |
| § - subsp. *integrifolia* | GCrs |
| 'Wolong' | |
| 'James Cobb' | See *M. integrifolia* subsp. *integrifolia* 'Wolong' |
| Kingsbarns hybrids | GGGa |

| | |
|---|---|
| *lancifolia* | GGGa |
| aff. *lancifolia* KGB 737 | Last listed 1998 |
| ¶ *latifolia* | EBee |
| * *longifolia* | GAbr |
| § *napaulensis* | CFil CSam GAbr GCan GCrs GDra GGGa IBlr IMGH LHop MBal MBri MNes NChi NLar NWCA SLon WBor WEas WHer WViv WWin |
| - ex CMC 127 | Last listed 1998 |
| - forms | EBee GAbr |
| - HWJCM 301 | WCru |
| ¶ - pink | WLin |
| - red | EBee GBuc NBir WAbe |
| - scarlet | Last listed 1998 |
| § - Wallich's form | GCan |
| *nudicaulis* | See *Papaver nudicaule* |
| *paniculata* | GGGa IBlr IMGH NBir WAbe |
| - BC 9314 | Last listed 1998 |
| - CC&McK 296 | GTou |
| - compact form | Last listed 1998 |
| - Ghopte Group | WAbe |
| - Ghunsa Group | WAbe |
| - ginger foliage | Last listed 1998 |
| *pseudointegrifolia* | GCrs GGGa |
| - subsp. *robusta* | Last listed 1998 |
| - - ACE 1732 | Last listed 1996 |
| *punicea* | GCan GCrs GGGa NHar WAbe |
| * *quintuplinerva* | GBuc IBlr |
| 'Kay's Compact' | |
| *quintuplinervia* ♀ | CLAP CPBP EBee GBri GCrs GGGa GTou IBlr NBir NHar NRoo NRya NSla SRms |
| *regia* | CPBP CSam EBee GAbr NLak NLar NRoo WOve WViv |
| ¶ - bicolour | EBee NLar |
| - x *grandis* | GBuc |
| - hybrids | CAbP |
| *robusta* | GGGa |
| x *sarsonsii* | EBee GCan GLch |
| x *sheldonii* ♀ | CB&S CBrd CSam EAst GAbr GBuc GCrs GGGa GMaP MBri MFir NBir NHar NLon NRoo SSpi WAbe WLin WViv |
| - Ballyrogan form | IBlr |
| - 'Blue Ice' | GTou |
| - 'Branklyn' | CFil EBee GBri GCrs GGar IBlr |
| - 'Correnie' | Last listed 1996 |
| - Crewdson hybrids | CLAP GBuc GDra MNes MOne NBrk |
| - 'Jimmy Bayne' | GMaP |
| - 'Lingholm' | CLAP EBee GAbr GCal GCan GCrs GGar LHop WCru |
| * - 'Miss Jebb' | Last listed 1997 |
| * - 'Mrs McMurtrie' | IBlr |
| - 'Ormswell' | GBuc IBlr NRoo |
| - 'Silver' | Last listed 1998 |
| - 'Slieve Donard' ♀ | CFil CFir CLAP GBri GBuc GDra GGar IBlr MNes NHar NPoe NRoo SBla |
| - 'Springhill' | IBlr |
| *simplicifolia* | Last listed 1998 |
| sp. ACE 1875 | Last listed 1996 |
| sp. CH&M 1013 | Last listed 1998 |
| *superba* | GBuc GCan GGGa MBal MNes WAbe |
| *villosa* | GBuc GCan GGGa GTou IBlr NBir WAbe |
| ◆ *wallichii* hort. | See *M. napaulensis* Wallich's form |
| - *alba* BC 9370 | Last listed 1998 |
| - BC 9361 | Last listed 1998 |

**MEDEMIA** (Arecaceae)
| | |
|---|---|
| *argun* | LPal |

**MEDEOLA** (Convallariaceae)
| | |
|---|---|
| *virginica* | LAma WCru WThi |

**MEDICAGO** (Papilionaceae)
| | |
|---|---|
| *arborea* | CPle ELan IBlr WHer |
| *echinus* | See *M. intertexta* |
| *sativa* | CKin EWFC IIve MPEx WHer |
| - subsp. *sativa* | IBlr |

**MEDINILLA** (Melastomataceae)
| | |
|---|---|
| *magnifica* | LCns LRHS MBri |
| ¶ *myriantha* 'Pink Pixie' | ECon |

**MEEHANIA** (Lamiaceae)
| | |
|---|---|
| *cordata* | Last listed 1997 |
| * *garganica garganica* | Last listed 1998 |
| B&SWJ 1210 | |
| *urticifolia* | EMon MHar MSte |
| ¶ - B&SWJ 1210 | WCru |
| ¶ - 'Wandering Minstrel' | EMon GVic |

**MEGACARPAEA** (Brassicaceae)
| | |
|---|---|
| *polyandra* | GDra |

**MELALEUCA** (Myrtaceae)
| | |
|---|---|
| *acerosa* | SOWG |
| *acuminata* | Last listed 1998 |
| *alternifolia* | CArn ECou ELau EOHP GPoy |
| | MSal SOWG |
| *armillaris* | SOWG SPlb |
| *bracteata* | CTrC |
| *brevifolia* | Last listed 1998 |
| *calycina* subsp. *dempta* | Last listed 1998 |
| *capitata* | Last listed 1998 |
| *coccinea* | SOWG |
| *cuticularis* | MSag |
| *decora* | SOWG |
| *decussata* | CTrC ECou SOWG SPlb |
| *densa* | Last listed 1998 |
| § *diosmatifolia* | MSag |
| *elliptica* | CTrC SOWG |
| *ericifolia* | CTri SOWG |
| - *nana* | Last listed 1998 |
| *erubescens* | See *M. diosmatifolia* |
| *filifolia* | SOWG |
| *fulgens* | CTrC SOWG |
| *gibbosa* | CAbb SBid SOWG WSHC WTro |
| *halmaturorum* | MSag |
| *huegelii* | SOWG |
| *hypericifolia* | ECou SBid SOWG SPlb |
| *incana* | CTrC SOWG |
| *lanceolata* | Last listed 1998 |
| *lateritia* | Last listed 1998 |
| *leucadendra* | MSal |
| *linariifolia* | CTrC ECou MSag |
| *nesophila* | ECou SOWG |
| *pauciflora* | See *M. biconvexa* |
| *platycalyx* | SOWG |
| ¶ *pulchella* | SOWG |
| *pustulata* | ECou MSag SOWG |
| *quinquenervia* | See *M. viridiflora* var. *rubriflora* |
| *radula* | Last listed 1998 |
| *rhaphiophylla* | Last listed 1998 |
| * *rosmarinifolia* | SOWG |
| *sieberi* | Last listed 1998 |
| ¶ *smartiorum* | SOWG |
| *spathulata* | SOWG |
| *spicigera* | Last listed 1998 |

| | |
|---|---|
| *squamea* | ECou LHil WPic |
| *squarrosa* | CAbb CGre CTrC ECou GLch |
| | SOWG |
| *striata* | Last listed 1998 |
| *styphelioides* | MSag |
| *suberosa* | Last listed 1998 |
| *tenella* | Last listed 1998 |
| *teretifolia* | Last listed 1998 |
| *thymifolia* | ECou SOWG |
| *thymoides* | Last listed 1998 |
| *uncinata* | MSag |
| *undulata* | Last listed 1998 |
| *viminea* | Last listed 1998 |
| *viridiflora* | CB&S GQui |
| § - var. *rubriflora* | Last listed 1998 |
| *wilsonii* | CTrC SOWG |

**MELANDRIUM** (Caryophyllaceae)
| | |
|---|---|
| ♦ *rubrum* | See *Silene dioica* |

**MELANDRIUM** See VACCARIA

**MELANOSELINUM** (Apiaceae)
| | |
|---|---|
| § *decipiens* | CTrF EOHP LGre SIgm WCot |
| * *melanops* | IHdy |

**MELANTHIUM** (Melanthiaceae)
| | |
|---|---|
| *virginicum* | Last listed 1996 |

**MELASPHAERULA** (Iridaceae)
| | |
|---|---|
| *graminea* | See *M. ramosa* |
| § *ramosa* | CAvo CBre CLTr CPLG WCot |
| ¶ - 'Lea' | WCot |

**MELASTOMA** (Melastomataceae)
| | |
|---|---|
| *malabathricum* | Last listed 1997 |

**MELIA** (Meliaceae)
| | |
|---|---|
| ¶ *azadirachta* | GPoy |
| § *azedarach* | CArn CB&S CPle ELau GPoy LPan |
| - var. *japonica* | See *M. azedarach* |

**MELIANTHUS** (Melianthaceae)
| | |
|---|---|
| *comosus* | CTrC LLew |
| *major* ♀ | More than 30 suppliers |
| *minor* | CFir LLew SIgm WCot |
| *pectinatus* | IHdy |
| sp. from Richtersveld, North | LLew |
| Cape, South Africa | |
| *villosus* | CFir GVic LLew |

**MELICA** (Poaceae)
| | |
|---|---|
| *altissima* | MWhi |
| - 'Alba' | Last listed 1997 |
| - 'Atropurpurea' | More than 30 suppliers |
| *ciliata* | CCuc CPea CSam ECGN EHoe |
| | EMon EPPr EPla GCHN |
| | MMoz NChi NHol WPer |
| - bronze | Last listed 1997 |
| - subsp. *magnolii* | Last listed 1997 |
| * - 'Pearl Eyelash' | CInt |
| - subsp. *taurica* | Last listed 1997 |
| *macra* | EHoe EPla |
| * *minima* | Last listed 1997 |
| *nutans* | CCuc EHal EHoe EPla GBin NHol |
| | SBea WHal WRos WWye |
| *penicillaris* | EPPr WPer |
| *picta* | Last listed 1997 |
| *subulata* | Last listed 1997 |
| *transsilvanica* | ECGN EMan GBin |
| - 'Atropurpurea' | NCut NHol NPSI |
| *uniflora* | CKin |

| | |
|---|---|
| - f.*albida* | CCuc CFil EBee EHoe EMan EMon EPPr MAvo SUsu WCot WRHF |
| - 'Variegata' | CBre CCuc CFil CVer EHoe EMan EMon EPPr EPla GCal MBri MBrN WCot WWye |

## MELICOPE (Rutaceae)
| | |
|---|---|
| *ternata* | ECou |

## MELICYTUS (Violaceae)
| | |
|---|---|
| *alpinus* | ECou |
| *angustifolius* | CPle ECou |
| *crassifolius* | CPle ECou EPfP WHCG WWat |
| *obovatus* | ECou |
| *ramiflorus* | ECou |

## MELILOTUS (Papilionaceae)
| | |
|---|---|
| *officinalis* | CArn CJew CKin GBar GPoy MChe SIde WHer WSel |
| - subsp.*albus* | SIde WHer |

## MELINIS (Poaceae)
| | |
|---|---|
| *nerviglumis* | EBee EPPr |

## MELIOSMA (Meliosmaceae)
| | |
|---|---|
| § *dilleniifolia* | |
| subsp.*flexuosa* | Last listed 1996 |
| *myriantha* | WCoo |
| *pendens* | See *M. dilleniifolia* subsp. *flexuosa* |
| *simplicifolia* | CB&S |
| subsp.*pungens* | |
| *veitchiorum* | CB&S |

## MELISSA (Lamiaceae)
| | |
|---|---|
| *officinalis* | CArn CChe CHal EFer ELau GPoy LHol MBNS MBal MBar MBri MChe MHew MMal NArg SIde SPlb SSoC WBea WEas WGwG WOak WPer WWye |
| - 'All Gold' | CArn CBre CHal CMGP CSev ECha EGoo EHoe ELan ELau LHol MBri MChe MMal NFai NPri NSti NVic SPer WWye |
| § - 'Aurea' (v) | CArn CFee CHal CSev ECha EHoe ELan ELau ENot GPoy LGro LHol MBar MBel MBri MCLN MFir MHew MRav MWgw NBro NFai NSti SIde SPer SRms WBea WMow WOak WWin |
| * - 'Compacta' | ELau GPoy |
| - 'Small-Ness' | MNes |
| N - hort.'Variegata' | See *M. officinalis* 'Aurea' |

## MELITTIS (Lamiaceae)
| | |
|---|---|
| *melissophyllum* | CFir CHan CRDP EMan LPio MCAu MHew MRav SIgm SIng SRms SSpi WAbb WCot WWye |
| - subsp.*albida* | SSpi |
| - pink | EMon GVic MInt SOkh |

## MENISPERMUM (Menispermaceae)
| | |
|---|---|
| *canadense* | CPlN GPoy MSal |
| *davuricum* | CPlN |

## MENTHA ✿ (Lamiaceae)
| | |
|---|---|
| *aquatica* | CAgr CArn CBen CKin CRow CWat ECoo EHon ELau EWFC GAbr GPoy LPBA MChe MHew MSta SIde SLon SPlb SWat SWyc WGwG WHer WMAq WOak |
| * - *mandeliensis* | SPil |

| | |
|---|---|
| *arvensis* | CArn ELau EOHP IIve MSal SIde WHer |
| ¶ - 'New Fancy' (v) | WAlt |
| - var.*piperascens* | EOHP MSal |
| § - - 'Sayakaze' | ELau EOHP |
| *asiatica* | CStr ELau EOHP IIve SIde SPil WHer |
| * *brevifolia* | EOHP SIde SPil WHer |
| § *cervina* | CBen CWat EMFW EOHP LPBA MSta SPil SWat |
| - *alba* | EOHP MCCP |
| *citrata* | See *M.* x *piperita* f. *citrata* |
| *cordifolia* | See *M.* x *villosa* |
| *corsica* | See *M. requienii* |
| *crispa* x *piperita* | EOHP SRms |
| *diemenica* | EOHP |
| * - var.*koiscikoko* | Last listed 1997 |
| 'Eau de Cologne' | See *M.* x *piperita* f. *citrata* |
| Eucalyptus mint | ELau EOHP WBea WGwG WOak |
| *gattefossei* | CArn EOHP |
| x *gentilis* | See *M.* x *gracilis* |
| § x *gracilis* | CArn ELau EOHP GBar LHol MChe MMal NDea NPri SIde WBea WJek WOak WRHF WWye |
| - 'Aurea' | See *M.* x *gracilis* 'Variegata' |
| § - 'Variegata' | CBrm CSev ECha ECoo EHoe EMar GPoy ILis MBal MBar MHar MRav NArg NRoo NSti SHel WGwG WHer WOak WOve WPer |
| *haplocalyx* | ELau EOHP MSal |
| * 'Hillary's Sweet Lemon' | ELau EOHP |
| * *lacerata* | SIde |
| I 'Lavender' | WGwG |
| Lavender mint | CBod GBar GPoy IIve MRav WJek WOak WRha |
| § *longifolia* | CAgr CRDP ECha ECoo ELau EMar GBar IIve LHop MHar MMal MRav NSti SPil WEas WGwG WHer WJek WOak WPer WSel WWye |
| - Buddleia Mint Group | CArn ELau EWes GAbr GGar MHer MRav NBus SIde WBea WGwG WRha WSel |
| - silver form | CArn ELau SPil |
| * - 'Variegata' | CBod ELau NCat NSti WJek |
| x *piperita* | CAgr CArn CSev ECha EHoe ELau GBar GPoy ILis LHop MBNS MBri MChe MHew MMal NArg NFor NRoo SPlb WBea WGwG WHbs WOak WPer WWye |
| ¶ - 'Black Mitcham' | EOHP |
| § - f.*citrata* | More than 30 suppliers |
| * - - 'Basil' | CBod ELau EOHP IIve LLWP MRav SHDw SIde WGwG WJek WOak |
| - - 'Chocolate' | CArn CBod ELau EOHP MHer NArg SDys SHDw SIde SPil WBea WGwG WJek WPer |
| - - 'Lemon' | ELau EOHP GAbr MBri SHDw SIde SPil WBea WGwG WJek WOak WPer WRha WSel |
| - - 'Lime' | EOHP MTed SHDw SIde SPil WBea WGwG |
| - - orange | Last listed 1996 |
| - 'Logee's' (v) | EBee ELau EWes NWoo WBea WCHb WHer WJek |
| * - 'Mary Mitchum' | SIde |
| - f.*officinalis* | ELau SIde |
| - 'Reverchonii' | SPil |
| *pulegium* | CArn CSev EBot ECha ELau EWFC GPoy LHol MBNS MChe MHew MPEx NArg SIde WGwG WHbs WHer WJek WOak WPer WWye |

|   |   |
|---|---|
| - 'Upright' | CArn CBod EOHP GPoy SHDw SIde WJek WOak WPer WSel |
| *pycantheum pilosum* | Last listed 1997 |
| § *requienii* | More than 30 suppliers |
| *rotundifolia* hort. | See *M. suaveolens* |
| - 'Bowles' | See *M.* x *villosa* f. *alopecuroides* Bowles' Mint |
| *rubra* var. *raripila* | See *M.* x *smithiana* |
| ◆ - 'Sayakarze' | See *M. arvensis* var. *piperascens* 'Sayakarze' |
| § x *smithiana* | CArn ELau EOHP GAbr GBar GPoy ILis MChe NPri WBea WGwG WHer WOak WPer WRha WWye |
| - 'Capel Ulo' | EOHP WHer |
| sp. Nile Valley mint | CArn ELau EOHP SHDw SIde |
| § *spicata* | CAgr CArn CSev GPoy ILis LHol MBNS MBal MBar MBri MChe MHew MMal NFai NFor NRoo SRms WBea WGwG WHer WJek WOak WPer WWye |
| ¶ - 'Argentina' | SIde |
| * - 'Brundall' | EOHP MTed |
| - 'Crispa' | CArn CBre ELau EOHP GAbr GAri GBar NArg NFai NPri NRoo NSti SIde WCer WCot WGwG WPer WRha WSel WWye |
| ¶ - Guernsey mint | SPil |
| - 'Moroccan' | CArn CInt CJew CSev ELau EOHP GAbr GPoy IIve MHar NArg SHDw SIde WBea WCer WGwG WHer WJek WOak WSel WWye |
| - 'Newbourne' | ELau |
| - 'Spanish Furry' | EOHP |
| - 'Spanish Pointed' | ELau EOHP |
| - 'Tashkent' | ELau MTed SHDw SIde WBea WGwG WJek |
| - subsp. *tomentosa* | SPil |
| * - 'Variegata' | WHer |
| § *suaveolens* | CAgr CArn ELau GBar GPoy ILis LHol MBal MBri MHew MMal NRoo SIde WBea WGwG WHer WOak WPer |
| * - 'Mobillei' | EOHP SIde SPil |
| - subsp. *timija* | ELau WJek |
| § - 'Variegata' | CArn CRow ECha EHoe ELau GAbr GPoy MBNS MBal MBar MBri MCLN MChe MMal MRav NFai NFor NHol NSti SIde SPlb SRms WBea WGwG WHer WMow WOak WOve WPer |
| *sylvestris* | See *M. longifolia* |
| § x *villosa* | CArn |
| § - f. *alopecuroides* | CBre EGoo ELau GBar GPoy IIve ILis LHol MChe MMal NFai NSti SIde SWat WGwG WHer WJek WOak WWye |
| Bowles' Mint | |
| *viridis* | See *M. spicata* |

## MENYANTHES (Menyanthaceae)

|   |   |
|---|---|
| *trifoliata* | CBen CNic CRow CWat ECoo EHon ELau EMFW EWFC GPoy LPBA MHew MSta NDea NVic SLon SRms SWyc WMAq WShi WWye |

## MENZIESIA (Ericaceae)

|   |   |
|---|---|
| *alba* | See *Daboecia cantabrica* f. *alba* |
| ¶ *ciliicalyx* | SSpi |
| - dwarf form | SSta |
| - *lasiophylla* | See *M. ciliicalyx* var. *purpurea* |
| - var. *multiflora* | GGGa MBal MDun SSta |

|   |   |
|---|---|
| § - var. *purpurea* | GGGa SRPl SSta |
| *ferruginea* | MBal SSta |
| *polifolia* | See *Daboecia cantabrica* |
| ¶ 'Spring Morning' | SSta |

## MERCURIALIS (Euphorbiaceae)

|   |   |
|---|---|
| *perennis* | GPoy WHer WShi |
| - 'Cae Rhos Lligwy' | WHer |

## MERENDERA (Colchicaceae)

|   |   |
|---|---|
| *attica* | EPot |
| *eichleri* | See *M. trigyna* |
| *filifolia* AB&S 4665 | Last listed 1998 |
| *kurdica* | LAma |
| § *montana* | EHyt ERos WIvy |
| - MS 900/913 | Last listed 1998 |
| - SF 221 | Last listed 1998 |
| *pyrenaica* | See *M. montana* |
| *raddeana* | See *M. trigyna* |
| *sobolifera* | EHyt EPot GCrs |
| § *trigyna* | LAma |

## MERREMIA (Convolvulaceae)

|   |   |
|---|---|
| § *tuberosa* | CPlN LEdu |

## MERTENSIA (Boraginaceae)

|   |   |
|---|---|
| *ciliata* | CHan CMdw EBrP EBre LBre MArl MBri MNrw NChi SBre SPer SWat WRus |
| *echioides* | NTow |
| *franciscana* | EBee GCal WCru |
| *maritima* | GPoy MSal SMer WCru WLin WRos WWin |
| - subsp. *asiatica* | See *M. simplicissima* |
| *primuloides* | CPlt GCal WCom |
| *pterocarpa* | See *M. sibirica* |
| § *pulmonarioides* ♀ | CBot CBro CGle CLAP CRDP EAst EBee EBot EBrP EBre ELan EOrc EPot LAma LBre LHop NLar NRoo SBre SMac SPer SRms WCot WCru WHoo WShi WWat |
| § *sibirica* | CHan CLAP CSpe EBee GBri GCrs LGre MHar NHed NTow WWin |
| § *simplicissima* | CBos CBot ECho EHyt ELan EMan LHop MHar MNrw MTho NBir NWCA SBla SMad WCru WHoo WWhi |
| *virginica* | See *M. pulmonarioides* |
| *viridis* | Last listed 1998 |

## MERXMUELLERA See RYTIDOSPERMA

## MERYTA (Araliaceae)

|   |   |
|---|---|
| *sinclairii* | Last listed 1998 |
| - 'Variegata' | See *M. sinclairii* 'Moonlight' |

## MESEMBRYANTHEMUM (Aizoaceae)

|   |   |
|---|---|
| 'Basutoland' | See *Delosperma nubigenum* |
| *brownii* | See *Lampranthus brownii* |
| § *hispidum* | Last listed 1996 |
| *ornatulum* | See *Delosperma ornatulum* |
| *putterillii* | See *Ruschia putterillii* |

## MESPILUS (Rosaceae)

|   |   |
|---|---|
| *germanica* (F) | CB&S CBlo CDul CLnd ELan IOrc LHol LPan MWat WBay WDin WMou |
| ¶ *germanica* 'Bredase Reus' (F) | GTwe SKee |
| - 'Dutch' (F) | SDea SFam SKee |
| - 'Large Russian' (F) | ERea GTwe SKee |
| ¶ - 'Macrocarpa' | SKee |

- 'Monstrous' (F)              SDea
- 'Nottingham' (F)             CAgr CEnd CSam CTho EBee
                               EMui ENot ERea GTwe LBuc
                               MBlu NBee SDea SFam SKee SPer
                               WJas WMou
- 'Royal' (F)                  CAgr SKee

## METAPANAX See PSEUDOPANAX

## METASEQUOIA (Taxodiaceae)
**glyptostroboides** ♀        More than 30 suppliers
- 'Fastigiata'                See *M. glyptostroboides* 'National'
¶ - 'Gold Rush'               MBlu
* - 'Green Mantle'            EHul EWTr
§ - 'National'                Last listed 1998
- 'Sheridan Spire'            CDoC CEnd LNet

## METROSIDEROS (Myrtaceae)
**carmineus**                 Last listed 1998
- 'Carousel' (v)              ERea
- 'Ferris Wheel'              Last listed 1996
**collinus**                  CPlN
**diffusus**
§ **excelsus**                CAbb CTrC CTrG ECou
- 'Aureus'                    ECou
- 'Parnell'                   CB&S CTrC
- 'Scarlet Pimpernel'         ERea SOWG
- 'Spring Fire'               CAbb CB&S GQui
¶ - 'Upper Hut'               CTrC
**fulgens**                   Last listed 1998
'Goldfinger' (v)             ERea
**kermadecensis**             ECou LHil
¶ - 'Radiant' (v)             CPLG
- 'Variegatus'                CAbb CB&S CDoC ECou ERea
                               GQui LHil SBid SLon WMul
**lucidus**                   See *M. umbellatus*
'Moon Maiden'                ERea
'Pink Lady'                   ERea
**robustus**                  GQui
'Thomasii'                    ECon EPfP LCns SOWG
**tomentosus**                See *M. excelsus*
§ **umbellatus**              CGre ECou
**villosus**                  SOWG
- 'Tahiti'                    CB&S GQui

## MEUM (Apiaceae)
**athamanticum**              CBos CGle CRDP CSev EBee EFou
                               EGol EMan EPla GBri GCal GPoy
                               LHop MHew MRav MSal MTho
                               MUlv NBrk SIgm SMrm WFar
                               WPer WPrP

## MICHAUXIA (Campanulaceae)
**campanuloides**             NChi WLin
**laevigata**                 Last listed 1997
**tchibatchewii**             CBot CGen CSpe EWll WLin

## MICHELIA (Magnoliaceae)
**compressa**                 CFil CGre EPfP WPGP
**doltsopa**                  CB&S CFil CGre GQui IDee SBid
                               SSpi
- 'Silver Cloud'              Last listed 1996
**figo**                      CAbb CFil CGre EMil ERea GQui
                               SBid SSpi
§ **sinensis**                CFil CMCN
**wilsonii**                  See *M. sinensis*
¶ **yunnanensis**             CFil

## MICRANTHUS (Iridaceae)
**alopecuroides**             Last listed 1998
**plantagineus**              LBow

## MICROBIOTA (Cupressaceae)
**decussata** ♀               CDoC CKen CMac CSam CSli
                               EBrP EBre EHul EOrn EPla GRei
                               LBee LBre LCon LLin MAsh MBar
                               MBri MGos MWat SBre SLim SLon
                               SSmi WPyg WWat
- 'Jakobsen'                  CKen
- 'Trompenburg'               CKen

## MICROCACHRYS (Podocarpaceae)
**tetragona**                 CDoC ECho ECou EOrn EPla
                               LCon MBri SIng

## MICROCOELUM See LYTOCARYUM

## MICROGLOSSA (Asteraceae)
**albescens**                 See *Aster albescens*

## MICROLEPIA (Dennstaedtiaceae)
**speluncae**                 MBri

## MICROLOMA (Asclepiadaceae)
**hereroense**                Last listed 1998
**sagittatum**                Last listed 1998

## MICROMERIA (Lamiaceae)
**chamissonis**               ELau EOHP
**corsica**                   See *Acinos corsicus*
**croatica**                  EHyt NTow
**dalmatica**                 EBee
**rupestris**                 See *M. thymifolia*
§ **thymifolia**              EMan MPla NMen
◆ **viminea**                 See *Satureja viminea*

## MICROSERIS (Asteraceae)
I **ringens**                 See *Leontodon rigens*

## MICROSORUM (Polypodiaceae)
**diversifolium**             CFil
**punctatum** 'Grandiceps'    Last listed 1998

## MICROSTROBOS (Podocarpaceae)
**fitzgeraldii**              CKen

## MIKANIA (Asteraceae)
§ **dentata**                 CPlN MBri
**scandens**                  CPlN
**ternata**                   See *M. dentata*

## MILIUM (Poaceae)
**effusum**                   CKin
- 'Aureum'                    More than 30 suppliers
- var. **esthonicum**         EBee EMon EPPr

## MILLETTIA (Papilionaceae)
§ **japonica**                LNet
¶ 'Murasaki Natsu Fuji'       LNet

## MIMOSA (Mimosaceae)
**hostilis**                  Last listed 1998
**pudica**                    EAnd LPVe MLan
**scabrella**                 Last listed 1998

## MIMULUS (Scrophulariaceae)
'A.T. Johnson'               GCHN MSCN NVic SIng
**alatus**                    EBee
* 'Andean Nymph' F & W 8384   CPBP
'Andean Nymph' forms         CGle CSpe MNrw
§ 'Andean Nymph'              CLTr CMea CPlt EBrP EBre ELan
  Mac&W 5257 ♀                EPot GCHN LBre MBal MSCN
                               NMGW NNrd SBre SRot SWat
                               WCla WRos

| | |
|---|---|
| ¶ *aridus* | EBee |
| § *aurantiacus* ♀ | CBot CElw CFee CHal CInt CPle |
| | CSpe EBak EBrP SBre ELan EOrc |
| | EPot ERea IBlr LBre LHil LHop |
| | MPla NPer SBre SDry SHFr SMrm |
| | SPlb SUsu WEas WPer |
| – orange | See *M. aurantiacus* var. *puniceus* |
| § – var. *puniceus* | CBot CHal CLTr CSpe CTri ELan |
| | LHil LHop MBEx MHar SDry |
| | SMrm SUsu SYvo |
| ¶ – red | MHar |
| x *bartonianus* | EBee EWes |
| *bifidus* | CSpe EBee LHop SMac |
| – 'Verity Buff' | CSpe LHil LIck |
| ¶ – Verity hybrids | ERea LHil MBEx |
| – 'Verity Purple' | CSpe |
| – 'Verity Rose' | CLTr LHil |
| – 'Wine' | LIck |
| 'Burgess' | Last listed 1996 |
| x *burnetii* | LPBA NVic SRms |
| *californicus* | Last listed 1998 |
| Calypso Series | SRms SWat |
| *cardinalis* ♀ | CGen EBee EHon ELan GMac |
| | LHop LPBA MFir MNrw MTho |
| | NDea NFor NMGW SHFr SPer |
| | WCot WFar WHer WOve WPer |
| | WWeb WWin |
| – 'Dark Throat' | Last listed 1997 |
| *cupreus* | MBal |
| – 'Minor' | ECho |
| – 'Whitecroft Scarlet' ♀ | ECha ELan GDra LPBA MNrw |
| | MOne NHar SBod SIng SRms |
| | WPer WWin |
| *cusickii* | Last listed 1998 |
| 'Eleanor' | SMrm SUsu |
| *glutinosus* | See *M. aurantiacus* |
| – *atrosanguineus* | See *M. aurantiacus* var. *puniceus* |
| – *luteus* | See *M. aurantiacus* |
| § *guttatus* | CBen CKin CRow EMan EWFC |
| | GAbr GAri GBar MMal NDea |
| | SRms WMoo WPer |
| § – 'Richard Bish' (v) | CMea CRDP EBee EMan EPot |
| | LHop MAvo MCCP NCat SAga |
| | SCob WByw WCot |
| – variegated | See *M. guttatus* 'Richard Bish' |
| 'Highland Orange' | GCHN MOne NHar NLon SPlb |
| | WGor WPer |
| 'Highland Pink' | ECtt EMan GMac MOne NHar |
| | NLon NRoo SBod WGor WPer |
| 'Highland Red' ♀ | ECtt EWTr GCHN GDra LPBA |
| | MMal MOne NArg NNrd SPlb |
| | SRms WHen WPer WWin |
| 'Highland Yellow' | ECtt GCHN MMal MNrw NLak |
| | NLon NRoo NVic SBod SPlb |
| | WHen WPer |
| hose-in-hose | CLTr EBee ECha WHer |
| ¶ hose-in-hose orange | LWoo |
| hose-in-hose yellow | EBee GCal |
| 'Inca Sunset' | EWes |
| 'Inshriach Crimson' | GCHN |
| ¶ 'June Gold' | WRHF |
| *langsdorffii* | See *M. guttatus* |
| *lewisii* ♀ | CGen EBee ELan EMan GDra |
| | GTou MTho NWCA SLon SRms |
| | WPer |
| *longiflorus* | CBot CLTr LHop MBEx |
| – 'Santa Barbara' | CLTr LHil LIck MBEx SMrm SUsu |
| 'Lothian Fire' | WWeb |
| *luteus* | CBen CRow CWat ECha EHon |
| | LPBA MBal MSta NDea NFai NLon |
| | SHFr WByw WMAq |
| * – 'Variegatus' | CRow EAst GBar GMac NGdn |
| | NPer |

| | |
|---|---|
| * 'Major Bees' | EPfP GCal |
| 'Malibu Ivory' | Last listed 1996 |
| 'Malibu Scarlet' | Last listed 1998 |
| (Malibu Series) | |
| Malibu Series | NFor |
| 'Mandarin' | EBrP EBre LBre SBre |
| *moschatus* | CRow NCat WCla |
| * – 'Variegatus' | Last listed 1996 |
| *nanus* | Last listed 1998 |
| 'Old Rose' | EBee |
| 'Orange Glow' | EPfP WHal |
| 'Orkney Gold' | Last listed 1998 |
| 'Plymtree' | Last listed 1996 |
| 'Popacatapetl' | CHal CSpe GMac LHil LHop LIck |
| | MBEx MHar SChu SMrm SYvo |
| *primuloides* | ELan EPot GCHN GCrs NHar |
| | NMen NNrd NWCA SBod SPlb |
| | WFar |
| 'Puck' | GMac NCat NPro |
| 'Queen's Prize' | Last listed 1997 |
| 'Quetzalcoatl' | LIck MBEx SMrm |
| Red Emperor | See *M.* 'Roter Kaiser' |
| *ringens* | CBen CRow CWat EHon EMFW |
| | EWTr GBri GMac LPBA MSCN |
| | MSta NDea SPer SRms WFar WHil |
| | WMAq WPer WWeb |
| § 'Roter Kaiser' | MNrw SRms |
| 'Royal Velvet' | Last listed 1997 |
| sp. Mac&W 5257 | See *M.* 'Andean Nymph' Mac&W |
| | 5257 |
| Threave variegated | EBee GBri GBuc GCal NBir NRoo |
| ¶ 'Tigrinus' | MWll |
| 'Tigrinus Queen's Prize' | LIck |
| *tilingii* | CHal ECho ELan GTou NLak |
| | NNrd |
| – var. *caespitosus* | Last listed 1996 |
| 'Western Hills' | Last listed 1996 |
| * 'Wine Red' | Last listed 1997 |
| 'Wisley Red' | ECha ECot ELan SRms |
| 'Yellow Velvet' | Last listed 1997 |

## MINA See IPOMOEA

## MINUARTIA (Caryophyllaceae)

| | |
|---|---|
| *capillacea* | Last listed 1998 |
| *caucasica* | See *M. circassica* |
| § *circassica* | CLyd ESis MDHE NWCA WPer |
| *dianthifolia* | Last listed 1998 |
| *inamoena* | WLin |
| *juniperina* NS 270 | NWCA |
| *laricifolia* | LBee |
| § *obtusiloba* | NWCA |
| *parnassica* | See *M. stellata* |
| § *recurva* | Last listed 1997 |
| ¶ *rossii* subsp. *rossii* | NWCA |
| § *rubella* | NTow |
| § *stellata* | EPot NHed NMen NNrd NTow |
| | SIng |
| – NS 758 | NWCA |
| § *verna* | CLyd NHar NMen |
| ♦ – subsp. *caespitosa* 'Aurea' | See *Sagina subulata* var. |
| | *glabrata* 'Aurea' |
| – subsp. *gerardii* | See *M. verna* subsp. *verna* |

## MIRABILIS (Nyctaginaceae)

| | |
|---|---|
| *jalapa* | CArn CSWP EBot ELan LAma LIck |
| | MBri MLLN MNrw MSal SEND |
| | SRms SYvo WCot |

## MISCANTHUS (Poaceae)

| | |
|---|---|
| ¶ *flavidus* B&SWJ 3697 | WCru |
| *floridulus* ♀ | CFir CSev EBee EFou EHoe EPla |
| | GCal LEdu MMoz MUlv SCob |
| | SDix SMad SSoC WCot WWoo |

| | |
|---|---|
| ***nepalensis*** | EHoe EWes LEdu SMrm |
| - CLD 1314 | Last listed 1997 |
| § ***oligonensis*** 'Juli' | Last listed 1998 |
| § - 'Wetterfahne' | EBrP EBre EPPr LBre SBre |
| - 'Zwergelefant' | MMoz |
| ***oligostachyus*** | EBee EPPr GCal |
| § - 'Afrika' | LGre |
| § - 'Nanus Variegatus' | CRow EHoe EMon EPPr EWes WCot |
| ¶ - 'Purpurascens' | SApp |
| ***sacchariflorus*** | CB&S CRow EBee EBrP EBre ECGN ECha EFul EHrv ELan EOas EPPr EPla GOrn LBre LPBA MBrN MLLN MUlv MWgw NHol NVic SBre SCob SPer SPla WWat WWye |
| ***sinensis*** ♀ | CArn CHan EPla GBin MMoz NFla NMoo NOak SLon WRos |
| - 'Adagio' | EFou LEdu WCot |
| ♦ - 'Afrika' | See *M. oligostachys* 'Afrika' |
| - 'Arabesque' | MMoz |
| - 'Augustfeder' | Last listed 1998 |
| - 'Autumn Light' | Last listed 1998 |
| - C&L 143a | EPla |
| - 'China' | CFir CHar EHoe EMan EPPr EPla EWes GBin NHol |
| - var. ***condensatus*** | Last listed 1998 |
| - - 'Cabaret' (v) | SRos WCot WHal |
| - - 'Cosmopolitan' (v) | CCuc CHid CMil EPPr GNau LEdu MAvo MLLN MMoz NSti SApp WCot |
| - 'Dixieland' (v) | LEdu MMoz SApp WHil |
| - dwarf form | Last listed 1997 |
| - 'Emerald Giant' | SApp |
| - 'Ferne Osten' | CCuc CHar CHid CWit EBee EBrP EBre ECGN ECha EFou EPGN EPPr EPla LBre LEdu LGre MBri MMoz MWgw NHol SBre SUsu WFar |
| - 'Flamingo' | EBrP EBre EHoe EPGN EPPr EPla LBre LGre LRHS MBri MMHG MMoz NHol SBre SWas WViv |
| - 'Gearmella' | EBee EBrP EBre EPPr LBre LEdu SBre |
| - 'Goldfeder' (v) | EPla WBcn |
| - 'Goliath' | Last listed 1998 |
| - 'Gracillimus' | More than 30 suppliers |
| - 'Graziella' | CHar EBee EBrP EBre EHoe EPla LBre LGre MBri MMoz MSte NHol SBre SUsu WLRN WPGP WPrP |
| - 'Grosse Fontäne' | ECha EHoe EPla LEdu MMoz SMad WCot |
| - 'Hercules' | Last listed 1998 |
| - 'Hinjo' (v) | Last listed 1996 |
| ♦ - 'Juli' | See *M. oligonensis* 'Juli' |
| - 'Kaskade' | CKno EBrP EBre EPGN EPla LBre LRHS MBri SBre WBcn |
| - 'Kleine Fontäne' | CFee CMil EBee EBrP EBre ECGN EGar EHoe EHrv EMan EPGN EPPr EPla GBri LBre LEdu LGre MBri MCAu MMoz NHol NSti SBre SChu SCob SMad WFar |
| - 'Kleine Silberspinne' | CCuc CHad CHea CLon EBee EBrP EBre ECGN EFou EGle EHoe EHrv EMan EPGN EPPr EPla GCal LBre MMoz MRav NHol SBre SCob SHFr SPer WElm WRus |
| ¶ - 'Krater' | LEdu SApp WRHF |
| § - 'Little Kitten' | EBee ECha EGle EPPr EWsh LEdu WCru WPGP |
| - 'Malepartus' | CHad CLon CMil CRow EBee EBrP EBre ECha EFul EGar EHoe EHrv EOld EPGN EPPr EPla GCal LBre LGre LPio MMoz NHol SBre SChu SWas WCot WRHF |

| | |
|---|---|
| - 'Morning Light' (v) | CBrm CCuc CHar CMil CPou CVer CWit EBrP EBre ECha EFou EMan EPGN EPPr EPla GBri LBre LEdu LGre MCCP MLLN MMoz MNrw SBre SCob SWas WCot WMoo |
| ¶ - New Hybrids | MTis |
| - 'Nippon' | EHoe EPGN EPPr EPla LEdu LHil MCAu MCCP MMoz NHol SChu SMad WRus |
| - 'November Sunset' | EWes MMoz |
| * - 'Overdam' | MAvo |
| - 'Poseidon' | Last listed 1998 |
| - 'Positano' | MMoz |
| - 'Pünktchen' (v) | ECha EFou EPPr EPla LGre SMad SWas |
| - var. ***purpurascens*** | CInt CWit ECGN ECha EGar EGol EHoe EMan EOas EPPr EPla EWsh GAri MBrN MLLN MWhi SCob SSoC WWat |
| ¶ - - 'Roter Pfeil' | EPla LGre |
| - 'Rigoletto' (v) | Last listed 1996 |
| - 'Roland' | LGre |
| - 'Rotfuchs' | CLon LGre |
| - 'Rotsilber' (v) | EBrP EBre ECha EFou EGle EHoe EOld EPPr EPla LBre LEdu SApp SBre WCot WViv |
| - 'Sarabande' | ECGN EHoe |
| - SF 92302 | ISea |
| § - 'Silberfeder' | More than 30 suppliers |
| - 'Silberpfeil' (v) | EPla |
| - 'Silberspinne' | CPou EFou EGar EPla LEdu LGre LHil |
| - 'Silberturm' | Last listed 1998 |
| ♦ - Silver Feather | See *M. sinensis* 'Silberfeder' |
| - 'Sioux' | EBee EPla MMoz WBcn |
| - 'Sirene' | EBee EBrP EBre EPGN EPPr EPla LBre NHol SApp SBre |
| - 'Slavopour' | EPla |
| - 'Spatgrun' | EPPr EPla |
| - 'Strictus' (v) | CBrm ECha EFul EGar EHoe EMan EPPr EPla LEdu MBri MMoz MUlv NBee SDix WCot WViv |
| - 'Tiger Cub' (v) | Last listed 1996 |
| - 'Undine' | CCuc CWit EBee ECha EGle EHoe EMan EPGN EPPr EPla LEdu LHil MAvo MBri MMoz NHol SChu SDix SHFr SMad SOkh SPla SUsu WLRN |
| - 'Variegatus' | More than 30 suppliers |
| - 'Vorläufer' | EBee EBrP EBre EHoe EPla LBre LGre SBre |
| ♦ - 'Wetterfahne' | See *M. oligonensis* 'Wetterfahne' |
| - 'Yakushima Dwarf' | More than 30 suppliers |
| - 'Zebrinus' (v) | More than 30 suppliers |
| sp. from Yakushima | EPla |
| ***tinctorius*** 'Nanus Variegatus' | See *M. oligostachyus* 'Nanus Variegatus' |
| - 'Variegatus' | Last listed 1998 |
| ***transmorrisonensis*** | EBee EHoe EMan EPPr EPla GBin LEdu MMoz SMad |
| ♦ ***yakushimensis*** | See *M. sinensis* 'Little Kitten' |

## MISOPATES (Scrophulariaceae)

| | |
|---|---|
| ***orontium*** | EWFC WCla |

## MITCHELLA (Rubiaceae)

| | |
|---|---|
| ***repens*** | WCru WWat |

## MITELLA (Saxifragaceae)

| | |
|---|---|
| *breweri* | CGle CHal CHan CLyd CNic EBee ECha EEls ELan GBin LSyl MLLN MRav MSte NHol NRoo NSti SHFr SRms SSpi WByw WEas WFar WPer WWat |
| *caulescens* | ECha GAbr LFis MLLN MRav NBro NHol WPer WPrP |
| *formosana* B&SWJ 125 | WCru |
| ¶ *ovalis* | EBee |
| *stauropetala* | NCat NWoo |

## MITRARIA (Gesneriaceae)

| | |
|---|---|
| *coccinea* | More than 30 suppliers |
| - Clark's form | MDun |
| - 'Lake Caburgua' | GCal |
| - Lake Puye form | CDoC CFee CGre ERea GQui LHop LRHS SAga SBra SPan SSta SVen WCru WWal WWat |

## MITRIOSTIGMA (Rubiaceae)

| | |
|---|---|
| *axillare* | Last listed 1996 |

## MNIUM See PLAGIOMNIUM

## MOEHRINGIA (Caryophyllaceae)

| | |
|---|---|
| *glaucovirens* | Last listed 1996 |

## MOLINIA (Poaceae)

| | |
|---|---|
| *altissima* | See *M. caerulea* subsp. *arundinacea* |
| *caerulea* | CInt COtt |
| § - subsp. *arundinacea* | CCuc ECGN ECha EFou EPla GBin LHil WPer |
| - - 'Bergfreund' | ECGN EHoe EMon EPPr EPla GCal SUsu |
| - - 'Fontäne' | EFou EPla LGre MSte |
| - - 'Karl Foerster' | EBee ECGN EFou EHoe EPPr EPfP EPla GBin GCal LEdu LGre MMil MMoz SApp SVil WCot WFar WLRN |
| - - 'Skyracer' | EPPr GBri MMoz WCot |
| - - 'Transparent' | CKno CLon CPlt EFou EGle EHoe EPla GBri GCal LGre MMoz SCob SMad WCot WHal WRHF |
| - - 'Windspiel' | CInt CLTr CRow EBee ECGN ECha EFou EHoe EMil EPPr EPla GCal LGre LGre NSti WCot |
| - - 'Zuneigung' | EHoe SApp |
| - subsp. *caerulea* 'Carmarthen' (v) | CElw CNat EBee EMon EPPr LRHS WCot WPrP |
| - - 'Claerwen' (v) | EMan EPPr EPla GBuc GCal SApp |
| - - 'Dauerstrahl' | NHol |
| - - 'Edith Dudszus' | CCuc CM&M EBee ECGN ECha EHoe EPPr EPla LGre MBrN MMoz SVil WHal |
| - - 'Heidebraut' | CCuc ECGN ECha EGle EHoe EMon EPPr EPla LGre SVil |
| - - 'Moorflamme' | EPPr |
| - - 'Moorhexe' | CInt CMil EBee ECGN ECha EHoe EMan EMon EPPr EPla GBri GCal LEdu MAvo MCAu NOak NSti SMad SSoC SVil WCot |
| - - 'Strahlenquelle' | CElw EMan EMon EPGN EPPr EPla GCal LRHS MMoz |
| - - 'Variegata' ♀ | More than 30 suppliers |
| *litoralis* | See *M. caerulea* subsp. *arundinacea* |

## MOLOPOSPERMUM (Apiaceae)

| | |
|---|---|
| *peloponnesiacum* | EBee LGre NChi NLar SIgm SMrm WCot WCru |

## MOLTKIA (Boraginaceae)

| | |
|---|---|
| § *doerfleri* | CPle MBro NChi WWat |
| *graminifolia* | See *M. suffruticosa* |
| § × *intermedia* ♀ | CMea ELan LHil SRms WWin |
| *petraea* | MWat SIgm |
| § *suffruticosa* | Last listed 1998 |

## MOMORDICA (Cucurbitaceae)

| | |
|---|---|
| *balsamina* | CPIN MSal |
| *charantia* | CPIN MSal |

## MONADENIUM (Euphorbiaceae)

| | |
|---|---|
| *lugardae* | MBri |
| 'Variegatum' | MBri |

## MONARDA ✿ (Lamiaceae)

| | |
|---|---|
| 'Adam' | GAbr GCal MLLN MSte WRus WViv |
| 'Aquarius' | CBlo CGle CLTr EBee EFou EGle EMan EMon LGre MSte NLak NPro NRoo NSti SChu SCro SMad SMrm SOkh WCHb WFar WMer WOve WRha WRus WWat WWeb WWhi |
| *austromontana* | CArn CBlo ECoo EHal EWes EWll SIde WHer |
| 'Baby Spice' | LRHS SCoo |
| § 'Balance' | CGle CSev EBee EGar EGle EMon ERic GCal LGre LHol MSCN MSte NRoo NSti SChu SCro SMrm WCHb WHoo WOve WPyg WRha WRus WWat |
| 'Beauty of Cobham' ♀ | CBlo CGle CHad CHan ECha EFou EHal EWTr GAbr GMaP LPio MBri MCLN MRav MSte MUlv NChi NLar NRoo NSti SChu SLod SMad SMrm SPer WMer WOve WRus WSan |
| 'Blaukranz' | SChu |
| § 'Blaustrumpf' | CElw GBri LFis MArl MSte NLar NOrc NPla SPer WMer WRus |
| Blue Stocking | See *M.* 'Blaustrumpf' |
| Bowman | See *M.* 'Sagittarius' |
| *bradburyana* | WViv |
| 'Cambridge Scarlet' ♀ | CB&S CGle CHad CSam CSev EBee ELan EMon GMaP GPoy LEdu LHop LSyl MBal MCAu MGrG MRav MSCN NBir NRoo SPer SRms WEas WFar WMer WRus |
| 'Capricorn' | CBlo CGle CLTr CSev EBee EFou EGar EGle EMar GBuc GMac LHol LRHS MSte NCat NSti SChu SCro SOkh WCHb WCot WHoo WPyg WRus WWal |
| 'Cherokee' | EGar EPPr GBri LGre MAvo MRav WCHb |
| *citriodora* | CArn GPoy MChe MSal SIde SRms SWat WCot WGwG WJek WPer WSel WWye |
| - PC&H 215 | Last listed 1998 |
| 'Comanche' | CMea CStr EFou LGre SAga SMrm WCHb WCom WViv |
| 'Croftway Pink' ♀ | CB&S CBlo CGle CSam CStr EBrP EBre ECha EFou EGar ELan ELau EWTr GCHN GChr LBre MCAu MGrG NOrc NRoo NSti NTay SBre SPer SRms WCHb WFar WMer WOve |
| 'Dark Ponticum' | EGar LRHS MGrG |

| | |
|---|---|
| *didyma* | CAgr CArn CBlo CJew EAst LHol LSyl MChe MFir MMal MSal NArg NBro NLon SWat WHbs WJek WOak |
| - 'Alba' | CBot MSCN |
| - 'Duddiscombe' | CSam |
| - 'Goldmelisse' | WBea |
| - 'Red Explode' | Last listed 1997 |
| * - 'Variegata' | Last listed 1996 |
| 'Donnerwolke' | SChu |
| 'Elsie's Lavender' | CHal CLTr CPlt CStr EFou EGar EGle EMon GBri GBuc LPio NBro WCHb |
| § 'Feuerschopf' | MSte SAga |
| Firecrown | See *M.* 'Feuerschopf' |
| § 'Fishes' | CBlo EFou EGle EHal EMon ERic EWes GCal LGre LPio MCAu MCLN MRav MSCN MSte NCat NHol NLak NLar SChu SHel SLon SMrm WCHb WFar WHoo WRus |
| *fistulosa* | CAgr CArn CMea EBee EWTr GPoy LHol LRot MChe MHew MMal MSal NLak NTay SIde WGwG WHer WJek WMoo WPer |
| 'Forncett Bishop' | EFou |
| 'Gardenview' | EWes GCal NBrk SMrm WRHF |
| 'Gardenview Scarlet' | EBee EFou EOrc GBri NCat NChi WPer |
| 'Hartswood Wine' | LBlm MRav SMad |
| 'Kardinal' | CGle EFou LIck MSte NTay |
| * 'Keureschol' | NCat |
| 'Kruisbekje' | SMrm |
| 'Lambada' | EOHP |
| 'Libra' | See *M.* 'Balance' |
| 'Loddon Crown' | CBos CLTr EFou MBri NChi NHol WFar WMaN |
| * 'Mahogany' | CHid CSam CStr EBee EFou EGle EHic EMar EMon EWTr GAbr GBri GMaP LHop MBel MHlr MRav NChi NHaw NHol NPla NRoo NSti SHel SPer WCHb WMow WSan WWye |
| 'Marshall's Delight' | EBrP EBre LBre LPio SBre SMrm WMer WRus |
| * 'Melissa' | CGle EFou EGle EHal |
| *menthifolia* | CArn CHan EBee EGar EOHP EWTr EWll LBlm LGre NLak SAga WCot WElm WHer |
| 'Mohawk' | EBee EFou EGle LFis LGre MAvo MCAu NCat NDov NPla SAga SMrm WCHb WLRN WMow WRus |
| 'Mrs Perry' | EFou EHic EWes NHol WMer |
| 'Osage' | Last listed 1998 |
| 'Ou Charm' | CBos CHad CHid CStr EBee EFou EPPr EWes GBri LFis MLLN MMil NChi NDov NPla SAga SCro SMac SMad SMrm SUsu WCHb WCot WFar WHil WSan |
| 'Pale Ponticum' | EMon |
| 'Panorama' | CBlo ECtt EOld MBal MSal WElm WMoo WPer |
| 'Pawnee' | EFou SChu SMrm WCHb |
| ¶ *pectinata* | EBee |
| ¶ 'Petite Delight' | WWeb |
| 'Pink Tourmaline' | EBee EWes LGre LRHS MBri SAga SMad SMrm WFar |
| 'Pisces' | See *M.* 'Fishes' |
| I Pisces | Last listed 1997 |
| 'Poyntzfield Pink' | GPoy |
| Prairie Glow = 'Prärieglut' | MBri |
| Prairie Night | See *M.* 'Prärienacht' |
| 'Präriebrand' | MBri |
| § 'Prärienacht' | More than 30 suppliers |
| *punctata* | CAgr CArn CBot CGle CInt EBee ELan EMan GCal LLWP LPio MLLN MSal SIde SMrm SWat WCHb WMoo WWye |
| purple | Last listed 1998 |
| ¶ 'Purple Ann' | LGre |
| 'Ruby Glow' | LGre MArl MBri MTis NCat NHol NPla SMrm SUsu WFar WLRN |
| § 'Sagittarius' | CGle CSev EGar EGle EMan EMon LBlm LRHS MBel MSCN MWgw NCat NGdn NRoo SChu SMrm WCHb WHoo WLRN WRus WWal WWat |
| ¶ 'Sahin's Mildew-free' | WCot |
| § 'Schneewittchen' | CBlo CKel CStr EAst ECha ECtt EGar ELan EWTr MLLN MMal MSCN MTis NBro NLar NOrc NRoo NSti SChu SIde SPer WHil WMer WRus |
| I Scorpio | Last listed 1997 |
| 'Scorpio' | See *M.* 'Scorpion' |
| § 'Scorpion' | CGle CM&M EFou EMon LBlm LGre MBel MBro MCAu MSte MTis NCat SAga SChu SMad SMrm SOkh WCHb WHoo WOve WPyg WRHF WRus |
| 'Sioux' | EFou EWes GBuc MAvo NCut SAga SMrm WCHb WCot |
| 'Snow Maiden' | See *M.* 'Schneewittchen' |
| 'Snow Queen' | EBee EFou EGle EPfP LPio NRoo NWoo SCoo SMrm SPla WSan WWat |
| Snow White | See *M.* 'Schneewittchen' |
| 'Squaw' | More than 30 suppliers |
| *stipitatoglandulosa* | Last listed 1997 |
| 'Talud' | EGar SMrm |
| 'Twins' | CBod CMil EBee EFou MLLN NHaw NHol NPri SWat WHil WHoo WMer WRus |
| 'Vintage Wine' | CLTr ECtt EGar EGle ELan NFla SSca WCHb WCot WHil WRus WWye |
| * *violacea* | WRha |
| 'Violet Queen' | EMar MBel NCat NPro |

## MONARDELLA (Lamiaceae)

| | |
|---|---|
| *cinerea* | CPBP NWCA |
| *linoides* subsp. *stricta* | Last listed 1998 |
| *macrantha* | CPBP |
| ¶ - var. *arida* | CPBP |
| *nana* subsp. *tenuiflora* | NWCA |
| *neglecta* | Last listed 1998 |
| *odoratissima* | CGle ECoo EMan SVen |
| *palmeri* NNS 95354 | IDac |
| § *sheltonii* | EBee |
| ◆ *villosa* 'Sheltonii' | See *M. sheltonii* |
| *viridis* | Last listed 1997 |

## MONOPSIS (Campanulaceae)

| | |
|---|---|
| *debilis* | Last listed 1998 |
| 'Goldfinch' | EMan |
| *lutea* | See *Lobelia lutea* |
| 'Midnight' | CSpe NPri |
| *unidentata* | Last listed 1997 |

## MONSONIA ✿ (Geraniaceae)

| | |
|---|---|
| *emarginata* | GCHN |
| *speciosa* | Last listed 1998 |

## MONSTERA (Araceae)

| | |
|---|---|
| *deliciosa* (F) ♀ | LBlo MBri SRms |

- 'Variegata' ♀     MBri SRms

## MONTBRETIA See CROCOSMIA and TRITONIA

## MONTIA (Portulacaceae)

| | |
|---|---|
| *australasica* | See *Neopaxia australasica* |
| *californica* | See *Claytonia nevadensis* |
| *parvifolia* | See *Naiocrene parvifolia* |
| *perfoliata* | See *Claytonia perfoliata* |
| *sibirica* | See *Claytonia sibirica* |

## MORAEA (Iridaceae)

| | |
|---|---|
| *alpina* | Last listed 1998 |
| *alticola* | SBla |
| - CDR 180 | CHan |
| § *aristata* | LBow |
| § *bellendenii* | LBow |
| § *fugax* | IBlr |
| *gawleri* | Last listed 1998 |
| *glaucopsis* | See *M. aristata* |
| *buttonii* | CFir CGre CHan EBee |
| *iridioides* | See *Dietes iridioides* |
| *longifolia* Persoon | See *Hexaglottis longifolia* |
| - Sweet | See *M. fugax* |
| *loubseri* | Last listed 1998 |
| *natalensis* | Last listed 1996 |
| *papilionacea* | Last listed 1996 |
| *pavonia* var. *lutea* | See *M. bellendenii* |
| *polystachya* | Last listed 1998 |
| *ramosissima* | Last listed 1996 |
| *schimperi* | Last listed 1996 |
| sp. S&SH 4 | CHan |
| sp. S&SH 47 | CHan |
| sp. S&SH 78 | Last listed 1998 |
| *spathacea* | See *M. spathulata* |
| § *spathulata* | CBro CHan ERos GCal MAvo MFir SBla SMad SVen WCot WSHC |
| *stricta* | Last listed 1996 |
| ¶ *thomsonii* | LBow |
| *tripetala* | Last listed 1996 |
| *vegeta* | Last listed 1996 |
| *villosa* | LBow SIgm |

## MORICANDIA (Brassicaceae)

| | |
|---|---|
| *arvensis* | EBee |

## MORINA (Morinaceae)

| | |
|---|---|
| * *afghanica* | EBee |
| *longifolia* | More than 30 suppliers |
| *nepalensis* | WPGP |
| *persica* | EBee ECGN GBuc NLak |

## MORISIA (Brassicaceae)

| | |
|---|---|
| *hypogaea* | See *M. monanthos* |
| § *monanthos* | CInt CPla MBar NTow WPat |
| - 'Fred Hemingway' | EBrP EBre EHyt EPot GCrs IMGH ITim LBre NHar NMen NOla NSla SBla SBre SIng WAbe WPat |

## MORUS (Moraceae)

| | |
|---|---|
| § *alba* | CB&S CLnd CMCN CTho ECrN ELan EREa GTwe IOrc LBuc SPer WDin WMou WSpi WUnu WWal WWat |
| - 'Black Tabor' | WShe |
| - 'Globosa' | See *M. alba* 'Nana' |
| - 'Laciniata' | Last listed 1996 |
| - var. *multicaulis* | EREa |
| - 'Pendula' | CDoC CEnd ELan EREa GTwe IMGH LNet LPan MAsh MBlu MBri MLan MWat WDin |

---

| | |
|---|---|
| ¶ - 'Platanifolia' | MBlu |
| - var. *tatarica* | CAgr LEdu |
| 'Illinois Everbearing' (F) | Last listed 1998 |
| *nigra* (F) ♀ | More than 30 suppliers |
| § - 'Chelsea' (F) | CEnd COtt EREa GTwe MBri SPer |
| - 'King James' | See *M. nigra* 'Chelsea' |
| - 'Large Black' (F) | EMui |
| - 'Wellington' (F) | CEnd WShe |

## MUCUNA (Papilionaceae)

| | |
|---|---|
| *bennettii* | CPIN |
| *macrocarpa* | CPIN |
| *pruriens* var. *utilis* | CPIN |

## MUEHLENBECKIA (Polygonaceae)

| | |
|---|---|
| *astonii* | ECou ELan |
| *australis* | Last listed 1998 |
| *axillaris* hort. | See *M. complexa* |
| § - Walp. | CTri ECou EPla ESis GAri GCal MHar NCat NTow SDry |
| § *complexa* | CB&S CDoC CHal CPIN CTrC EBee ECou EPla ESis GQui IBlr LBlm MCCP NFai SAPC SArc SBra SDry SLon WSHC WWat WWye |
| - 'Nana' | See *M. axillaris* Walpers |
| - var. *trilobata* | CPIN EGar EPla IBlr WCru |
| *ephedroides* | ECou |
| - 'Clarence Pass' | ECou |
| - var. *muriculata* | ECou |
| *gunnii* | CPIN ECou |
| *platyclados* | See *Homalocladium platycladum* |

## MUHLENBERGIA (Poaceae)

| | |
|---|---|
| *dumosa* | Last listed 1996 |
| *japonica* 'Cream Delight' (v) | CCuc EBee EHoe EMan EMon EPPr MCCP MTed WCot |
| *lindheimeri* | WCot |
| *mexicana* | Last listed 1997 |
| *rigens* | WCot |

## MUKDENIA (Saxifragaceae)

| | |
|---|---|
| § *rossii* | CLTr CRDP EMon EPla GCal NCat SSpi WCot WCru WOld |

## MURRAYA (Rutaceae)

| | |
|---|---|
| * *elliptica* | SOWG |
| *exotica* | See *M. paniculata* |
| *koenigii* | EOHP LChe |
| § *paniculata* | EREa LChe |

## MUSA (Musaceae)

| | |
|---|---|
| § *acuminata* (F) | LPal MBri |
| § - 'Dwarf Cavendish' (F) ♀ | EREa LBlo LCns LPJP WMul |
| - 'Zebrina' | WCot WMul |
| *basjoo* | CAbb CB&S CBrP CFil CTrC ECon EOas EPfP EREa LBlo LCns LPJP LPal LPan NPal SAPC SArc SLdr SPar SSoC WCot WJun WMul WPGP |
| ¶ - 'Sakhalin' | WMul |
| *cavendishii* | See *M. acuminata* 'Dwarf Cavendish' |
| *coccinea* | See *M. uranoscopus* |
| ¶ 'Dwarf Red' (F) | LBlo |
| *ensete* | See *Ensete ventricosum* |
| ¶ 'Kru' (F) | LBlo |
| § *lasiocarpa* | LBlo LPal WMul |
| *nana* | See *M. acuminata* |
| ¶ 'Orinoco' | WMul |
| *ornata* ♀ | LBlo WMul |
| x *paradisiaca* | Last listed 1997 |

'Rajapuri' WMul
¶ 'Red Iholena' (F) LBlo
§ *uranoscopus* ♀ WMul
*velutina* WMul

## MUSCARI ✿ (Hyacinthaceae)
*ambrosiacum* See *M. muscarimi*
*armeniacum* ♀ CBro EPar ETub MBri NMGW
 NRog SRms WCot WPer WShi
- 'Argaei Album' LAma NEgg
◆ - 'Babies Breath' See *M. neglectum* 'Baby's Breath'
- 'Blue Spike' (d) CBro EPar LAma MBri NEgg NRog
 WCot WPer
- 'Cantab' Last listed 1997
- 'Early Giant' LAma
- 'Fantasy Creation' ETub LRHS WCot
- 'Heavenly Blue' LAma
- 'Saffier' LAma LRHS
§ *aucheri* ♀ EHyt EPar LAma NRog
§ *azureum* ♀ CAvo CBro CNic ELan EPar EPfP
 ERos LAma NMen NRog SRms
- 'Album' CBro EPar ERos ETub LAma NRog
 WCot
- 'Amphibolis' Last listed 1996
*botryoides* LAma NRog
- 'Album' CAvo CBro ELan EPfP LAma MBri
 NRog SRms WShi
*chalusicum* See *M. pseudomuscari*
§ *comosum* CBro EPar WPer
* - 'Album' Last listed 1997
- 'Monstrosum' See *M. comosum* 'Plumosum'
§ - 'Plumosum' CAvo CBro CRDP ELan EMan
 EMon EPar LAma MBri SUsu
 WCFE
*grandifolium* JCA 689.450 CMil WCot
- var. *populeum* AB&S 5357 Last listed 1998
*inconstrictum* S&L 19/20 Last listed 1998
*latifolium* CAvo CBro EHyt EPar LAma NRog
 WCot WPer
* - 'Blue Angels' NBir
§ *macrocarpum* CAvo CBro EHyt EPot LAma
*mirum* EHyt
*moschatum* See *M. muscarimi*
§ *muscarimi* CAvo CBro EPar ETub LAma WCot
- var. *flavum* See *M. macrocarpum*
§ *neglectum* CSWP ELan LAma SEND WShi
- B&S 349 Last listed 1998
§ - 'Baby's Breath' CMil EHyt SWas
*pallens* Last listed 1998
*paradoxum* See *Bellevalia paradoxa*
§ *pseudomuscari* ♀ Last listed 1998
- BSBE 842 EHyt
*racemosum* See *M. neglectum*
'Sky Blue' Last listed 1997
§ *spreitzenhoferi* Last listed 1997
- MS 712 Last listed 1998
§ *tenuiflorum* EHyt
- S&L 91 Last listed 1998
*tubergenianum* See *M. aucheri*
'White Beauty' Last listed 1997

## MUSCARIMIA (Hyacinthaceae)
*ambrosiacum* See *Muscari muscarimi*
*macrocarpum* See *Muscari macrocarpum*

## MUSELLA (Musaceae)
◆ *lasiocarpa* See *Musa lasiocarpa*

## MUSSCHIA (Campanulaceae)
*wollastonii* Last listed 1998

## MUTISIA (Asteraceae)
*brachyantha* x *oligodon* Last listed 1998
*clematis* CRHN
*coccinea* CPIN
*decurrens* CB&S CPIN IBlr
*ilicifolia* CPIN CRHN IBlr ISea SIgm SMur
 WSHC
*latifolia* Last listed 1998
* *microphylla* WCot
*oligodon* CGre CPIN IBlr SRCN
*retrorsa* CPIN
- JCA 14345 Last listed 1998
*retusa* See *M. spinosa* var. *pulchella*
*sinuata* JCA 14351 Last listed 1998
*spinosa* CGre CPIN
§ - var. *pulchella* MHlr SSpi
*subspinosa* Last listed 1996
*subulata* CPIN

## MYOPORUM (Myoporaceae)
*acuminatum* See *M. tenuifolium*
*debile* ECou
*insulare* Last listed 1998
*laetum* CDoC ECou LHil
§ *tenuifolium* Last listed 1997

## MYOSOTIDIUM (Boraginaceae)
§ *bortensia* CB&S CBos CFil CPla ECre EWes
 GBin GBuc GCal IBlr IHdy LHop
 NPla SBid SSpi WCot WCru WSan
- white CPLG
*nobile* See *M. bortensia*

## MYOSOTIS (Boraginaceae)
§ *alpestris* NHol WLin WPat
- 'Ruth Fischer' NBir NMen
*arvensis* EWFC MMal
*australis* GCal GGar NChi NMen NWCA
'Bill Baker' CHan
*colensoi* ECou ELan MTho NMen NNrd
 NWCA
*explanata* NMen NNrd WEas WLin
*palustris* See *M. scorpioides*
* *persicifolia* 'Coronata' Last listed 1996
'Popsy' Last listed 1998
*pulvinaris* CPBP WLin
*rakiura* GTou WCla
*rebsteineri* SRot
*rupicola* See *M. alpestris*
§ *scorpioides* CBen CRow ECoo EHon ELan
 EWFC LPBA MMal MSta NDea
 SRms SWat SWyc WEas WMAq
◆ - 'Blaqua' See *M. scorpioides* Maytime =
 'Blaqua'
- 'John Beaty' Last listed 1998
§ - Maytime = 'Blaqua' (v) EMFW LPBA NRoo
- 'Mermaid' CBen CLyd CMGP CRow CWat
 ECha EHon EPPr GMac LHop
 LPBA MFir MSta NBrk NCat SDix
 SLon SRms SWat WFar WPer
 WRus
- 'Pinkie' CElw CRDP CRow CWat EMFW
 LHop SWat WElm WMAq
- 'Snowflakes' CRow
*secunda* CKin
*sylvatica* EWFC
- alba See *M. sylvatica* f. *lactea*
§ - f. *lactea* CRow
*traversii* AGS 90 Last listed 1997
¶ *uniflora* CGra

**MYOSURUS** (Ranunculaceae)

*minimus* — Last listed 1996

**MYRCEUGENIA** (Myrtaceae)
*chrysocarpa* — CGre

**MYRICA** (Myricaceae)
*californica* — CFil CPle GAri LEdu SSta WPGP
*cerifera* — CArn CPle
*gale* — GAri GPoy LHol MGos SWat WDin WGwG WGwy WSel WWye
*pensylvanica* — MBal

**MYRIOPHYLLUM** (Haloragaceae)
§ *aquaticum* — CBen CRow CWat EHon ELan EMFW LPBA MCCP MSta NDea SLon SWat SWyc WFar WMAq WWeb
*brasiliense* — See *M. aquaticum*
*proserpinacoides* — See *M. aquaticum*
* 'Red Stem' — LPBA
*spicatum* — CBen EHon EMFW SWyc
*verticillatum* — EHon

**MYRRHIS** (Apiaceae)
*odorata* — CArn CKin CSev ECha EEls EFer ELau EWFC GMaP GPoy ILis LHol MCLN MChe MHew MMal MSal NBid SIde SIgm SPer WByw WCer WEas WHbs WHer WOak WPer WSel WWye
- 'Forncett Chevron' — EFou LEdu

**MYRSINE** (Myrsinaceae)
*africana* — CB&S CPle EPfP SAPC SBid WHCr WWat
*australis* — Last listed 1998
*nummularia* — ECou

**MYRTEOLA** (Myrtaceae)
§ *nummularia* — GAbr GAri GDra MBal NMen SIng

**MYRTUS** (Myrtaceae)
*apiculata* — See *Luma apiculata*
*bullata* — See *Lophomyrtus bullata*
*chequen* — See *Luma chequen*
*communis* ♀ — More than 30 suppliers
- 'Flore Pleno' (d) — GQui LHol MPla
- 'Jenny Reitenbach' — See *M. communis* subsp. *tarentina*
- 'Microphylla' — See *M. communis* subsp. *tarentina*
- 'Nana' — See *M. communis* subsp. *tarentina*
§ - subsp. *tarentina* ♀ — More than 30 suppliers
- - 'Compacta' — WWye
§ - - 'Microphylla Variegata' — CBlo CInt CPle LHol MBal MPla SAPC SAga SArc SPer WHal WJek WOak WSHC WWat
- 'Tricolor' — See *M. communis* 'Variegata'
§ - 'Variegata' — CArn CBot CBrm CMCN EBee ECtt EMil LEdu LHop MAsh SDry SPer SPla STre WFar WSel WStI WWat WWye
'Glanleam Gold' — See *Luma apiculata* 'Glanleam Gold'
*lechleriana* — See *Amomyrtus luma*
*luma* — See *Luma apiculata*
*nummularia* — See *Myrteola nummularia*
*obcordata* — See *Lophomyrtus obcordata*
x *ralphii* — See *Lophomyrtus* x *ralphii*

'Traversii' — See *Lophomyrtus* x *ralphii* 'Traversii'
*ugni* — See *Ugni molinae*
* *variegata* 'Penlee' — CTrG

# N

**NAIOCRENE** (Portulacaceae)
§ *parvifolia* — CNic

**NANDINA** (Berberidaceae)
*domestica* ♀ — More than 30 suppliers
- 'Fire Power' — More than 30 suppliers
- 'Harbor Dwarf' — WWat
- var. *leucocarpa* — CPle
- 'Nana' — See *N. domestica* 'Pygmaea'
- 'Nana Purpurea' — EPla
§ - 'Pygmaea' — GAri WDin
- 'Richmond' — CB&S CBlo ELan EMil EPfP MAsh MBlu MGos MMea MUlv SBod SPer SPla WFar
- 'Wood's Dwarf' — Last listed 1996

**NANNORRHOPS** (Arecaceae)
*ritchieana* — CBrP LPal

**NARCISSUS** ✿ (Amaryllidaceae)
'Abalone' (2) — EWal
'Accent' (2) ♀ — CQua ICar
'Accord' (2) — ICar
'Achduart' (3) — CQua EHof ICar
'Achentoul' (4) — ICar
'Achnasheen' (3) — CQua ICar
'Acropolis' (4) — CQua ETub EWal ICar LAma
'Actaea' (9) ♀ — ETub MBri NRog
'Admiration' (8) — CQua
'Advocat' (3) — CQua
'Affable' (4) — ICar
'Aflame' (3) — LAma MBri
'Ahwahnee' (2) — IDun
'Aintree' (3) — CQua
'Aircastle' (3) — CQua EWal ICar
'Akepa' (5) — ICar
* *albidus* subsp. *occidentalis* (13) — ERos
'Albus Plenus Odoratus' — See *N. poeticus* 'Plenus'
'Algarve' (2) — Last listed 1996
'Allafrill' (2) — Last listed 1996
'Alley Inn' (4) — Last listed 1998
'Alliance' (1) — EWal
'Alpine Glow' (1) — Last listed 1998
¶ 'Alston' (2) — IDun
'Altruist' (3) — CQua EWal
'Altun Ha' (2) — CQua EHof IDun
'Amber Castle' (2) — CQua ICar
'Amber Light' (2) — EWal
'Ambergate' (2) — EWal LAma
'Amberglow' (2) — EWal
'Amboseli' (3) — Last listed 1998
¶ 'American Shores' (1) — IDun
'Amor' (3) — EWal
'Amstel' (4) — CQua
'Andalusia' (6) — CQua ERos ICar
'Androcles' (4) — ICar
'Angel' (3) — ICar
'Angel Face' (3) — EHof
♦ 'Angel Wings' — See *N.* 'Celtic Wings'
♦ Angel's Tears — See *N. triandrus* subsp. *triandrus* var. *triandrus*

| | |
|---|---|
| 'Angkor' (4) | CQua ICar |
| 'Ann Abbott' (2) | EWal |
| 'Annalong' (3) | IBal |
| 'Anniversary' (2) | EWal |
| 'Anthea' (2) | EWal |
| 'Apostle' (1) | ICar |
| 'Apotheose' (4) | EWal |
| ¶ 'Applins' (2) | IDun |
| 'Apricot' (1) | CBro |
| 'Apricot Sundae' (4) | ICar |
| 'April Charm' (2) | ICar |
| 'April Love' (1) | CQua EHof IBal ICar |
| 'April Snow' (2) | CBro CQua |
| 'April Tears' (5) ♀ | EWal LAma NRog |
| 'Apropos' (2) | CQua |
| 'Aranjuez' (2) | LAma |
| 'Arbar' (2) | EWal |
| 'Arcady' (2) | EWal |
| 'Arctic Char' (2) | ICar |
| 'Arctic Gem' (3) | Last listed 1998 |
| 'Arctic Gold' (1) ♀ | CQua ICar |
| 'Ardglass' (3) | IBal ICar |
| 'Ardour' (3) | ICar |
| 'Ardress' (2) | CQua |
| 'Argosy' (1) | CQua |
| 'Arish Mell' (5) | CQua EWal ICar |
| 'Arizona Sunset' (3) | Last listed 1998 |
| 'Arkle' (1) | CQua ICar |
| ¶ 'Arleston' (2) | IDun |
| 'Armley Wood' (2) | ICar |
| 'Arndilly' (2) | Last listed 1996 |
| 'Arpege' (2) | CQua |
| 'Arran Isle' (2) | IDun |
| 'Arthurian' (1) | IDun |
| 'Artillery' (3) | EWal |
| 'Asante' (1) | IDun |
| 'Ashmore' (2) | CQua EHof IDun |
| 'Ashton Wold' (2) | EHof |
| 'Asila' (2) | IDun |
| 'Aslan' (4) | ICar |
| 'Aspasia' (8) | CBro |
| § *assoanus* (13) | CBro CLAP EPar EPot LAma |
| - MS 511 (13) | Last listed 1998 |
| - MS 581 (13) | Last listed 1998 |
| - MS 582 (13) | Last listed 1998 |
| - var. *praelongus* | Last listed 1998 |
| MS 656 (13) | |
| § *asturiensis* (13) ♀ | CBro CNic CSam ELan EPar IBlr |
| | LAma MNrw |
| ◆ - giant form | See *N. asturiensis* 'Wavertree' |
| § - 'Wavertree' (1) | EPot |
| 'Atholl Palace' (4) | IDun |
| *atlanticus* (13) | CLAP |
| - SB&L 78 (13) | Last listed 1998 |
| 'Attrus' (2) | EWal |
| 'Audubon' (2) | CQua EWal |
| * 'Aunt Betty' (1) | IDun |
| 'Auntie Eileen' (2) | CQua |
| § *aureus* (13) | CQua |
| ¶ 'Auspicious' (2) | IDun |
| 'Avalanche' (8) ♀ | CQua EWal |
| 'Avalon' (2) | CQua |
| 'Ave' (2) | ICar |
| 'Avenger' (2) | CQua |
| 'Baby Doll' (6) | EWal ICar |
| 'Baby Moon' (7) | CQua ELan EPar EPot ETub LAma |
| | MBNS MBri NRog SRms |
| 'Baccarat' (11a) | ICar LAma MBri |
| ¶ 'Badanloch' (3) | CQua |
| 'Badbury Rings' (3) ♀ | IDun |
| 'Bailey' (2) | ICar |
| 'Balalaika' (2) | CQua |

| | |
|---|---|
| 'Baldock' (4) | CQua |
| 'Ballyarnett' (1) | ICar |
| 'Ballycastle' (3) | ICar |
| 'Ballyfrema' (1) | ICar |
| 'Ballygarvey' (1) | CQua EWal |
| 'Ballygowan' (3) | IBal |
| 'Ballykinler' (3) | IBal |
| 'Ballylig' (1) | ICar |
| 'Ballylough' (1) | ICar |
| 'Ballymorran' (1) | IBal |
| 'Ballynahinch' (3) | IBal |
| 'Ballynichol' (3) | IBal |
| 'Ballyrobert' (1) | EHof |
| ¶ 'Ballyvaddy' (2) | ICar |
| 'Ballyvoy' (1) | ICar |
| 'Baltic Shore' (3) | IBal |
| 'Balvenie' (2) | CQua |
| 'Balvraid Lass' (2) | Last listed 1996 |
| 'Bambi' (1) | CBro ERos NRog |
| 'Banbridge' (1) | IBal ICar |
| 'Bandesara' (3) | IDun |
| 'Bandleader' (2) | EWal |
| ¶ 'Banstead Village' (2) | CQua |
| 'Bantam' (2) ♀ | CBro CQua ERos EWal |
| ¶ 'Barbizon' (4) | IDun |
| 'Barley Sugar' (3) | ICar |
| 'Barleygold' (2) | IBal |
| 'Barleythorpe' (1) | EWal |
| 'Barleywine' (2) | IBal |
| 'Barlow' (6) | CQua |
| 'Barnesgold' (1) | IDun |
| 'Barnsdale Wood' (2) | Last listed 1996 |
| 'Barnum' (1) ♀ | IDun |
| 'Baronscourt' (1) | ICar |
| 'Barrett Browning' (3) | ETub MBri NRog |
| 'Bartley' (6) | EWal |
| 'Bastion' (1) | Last listed 1997 |
| 'Beach Party' (2) | Last listed 1998 |
| 'Beauvallon' (4) | Last listed 1998 |
| 'Bebop' (7) | CBro ICar |
| 'Bedgebury' (1) | ICar |
| ¶ 'Bedruthan' (2) | CQua |
| 'Beefeater' (2) | EWal |
| 'Beige Beauty' (3) | EWal ICar |
| ¶ 'Belbroughton' (2) | EHof |
| 'Belcanto' (11a) | CQua ICar |
| 'Belisana' (2) | LAma |
| 'Bell Song' (7) | CAvo CBro CQua ERos EWal WShi |
| 'Beltrim' (2) | ICar |
| 'Ben Aligin' (1) | CQua |
| 'Ben Bhraggie' (2) | Last listed 1996 |
| 'Ben Hee' (2) | CQua |
| 'Ben Loyal' (2) | Last listed 1996 |
| 'Ben Vorlich' (2) | ICar |
| ¶ 'Berceuse' (2) | IDun |
| 'Bere Ferrers' (4) | CQua |
| 'Bergerac' (11a) | CQua |
| 'Berkeley Court' (4) | Last listed 1998 |
| 'Berlin' (2) | EWal |
| 'Berry Gorse' (3) | Last listed 1996 |
| *bertolonii* (13) | Last listed 1998 |
| 'Beryl' (6) | CBro CQua ERos EWal ICar LAma |
| 'Best of Luck' (3) | IBal |
| 'Bethany' (2) | EWal |
| 'Betsy MacDonald' (6) | CQua |
| ¶ 'Biffo' (4) | CQua |
| 'Big John' (1) | Last listed 1996 |
| 'Bilbo' (6) | CQua |
| 'Binkie' (2) | CBro EWal LAma MBri |
| 'Birdsong' (3) | CQua |
| 'Birichen' (2) | Last listed 1996 |
| 'Birma' (3) | EWal LAma |

'Birthday Girl' (2)　　Last listed 1996
'Birthright' (1)　　EWal
'Biscayne' (1) ♀　　Last listed 1997
¶ 'Bishops Light' (2)　　CQua
'Bishopstone' (1)　　ICar
'Bittern' (12)　　ICar
'Blarney' (3)　　CQua EWal
'Blessing' (2)　　EWal
'Blue Bird' (2)　　EWal
¶ 'Blue Danube' (1)　　IDun
'Blushing Maiden' (4)　　CQua
'Bob Minor' (1)　　CQua
'Bobbysoxer' (7)　　CBro CQua ERos EWal ICar LAma MTho
'Bobolink' (2)　　CQua
'Bodilly' (2)　　EWal
'Bodwannick' (2)　　CQua
'Bolton' (7)　　CBro
'Bonamargy' (2)　　ICar
'Border Beauty' (2)　　IDun
'Border Chief' (2)　　ICar
'Borrobol' (2)　　EHof
'Bosbigal' (11a)　　CQua
¶ 'Boscastle' (7)　　CQua
'Boslowick' (11a)　　CQua
'Bosmeor' (2)　　CQua
'Bossa Nova' (3)　　CQua
¶ 'Bossiney' (11a)　　CQua
'Boudoir' (1)　　ICar
¶ 'Boulder Bay' (2)　　IDun
'Bouzouki' (2)　　IDun
'Bowles' Early Sulphur' (1)　　CRow
'Bracken Hill' (2)　　ICar
¶ 'Braid Song' (9)　　ICar
'Brandaris' (11a)　　CQua
'Brave Journey' (2)　　ICar
'Bravoure' (1) ♀　　CQua EWal
'Breakthrough' (2)　　EWal
'Brentswood' (8)　　CQua
'Bridal Crown' (4)　　ETub EWal LAma
'Bridesmaid' (2)　　IBal
'Brierglass' (2)　　Last listed 1996
'Bright Flame' (2)　　CQua
'Brighton' (1)　　LAma
'Brindle Pink' (2)　　IDun
'Broadland' (2)　　CQua
'Broadway Star' (11b)　　ETub EWal LAma
'Brodick' (3)　　IDun
'Brookdale' (1)　　Last listed 1998
'Broomhill' (2) ♀　　CQua
*broussonetii* (13)　　CFil WPGP
　- SF 269 (13)　　Last listed 1998
'Brunswick' (2)　　LAma
'Bryanston' (2) ♀　　Last listed 1998
'Bryher' (3)　　ICar
¶ 'Budock Bells' (5)　　CQua
'Buffawn' (7)　　EWal
'Bugle Major' (2)　　EHof
◆ *bujei*　　See *N. hispanicus* var. *bujei*
'Bulbarrow' (2)　　Last listed 1998
*bulbocodium* (13) ♀　　CBro CFil CMea ESis ETub LBee LBow NMGW NWCA SRms WCla
§ - subsp. *bulbocodium* (13)　　CBro
§ - - var. *citrinus* (13)　　EHyt EPot MS&S SSpi
- - - var. *conspicuus* (13)　　CAvo CBro CQua CSam EHyt EPar EPot ERos GCrs LAma MBal MBri MS&S NMen NRog NRya WPyg WShi
- - - *filifolius* (13)　　CBro EHyt
¶ - - var. *genuinus* x　　EHyt
　*cantabricus* subsp.
　*tananicus* ACS
　4656 (13)

¶ - - - x - var. *kesticus*　　EHyt
　S&F 72 (13)
¶ - - - x 'Jessamy'　　EHyt
　- - - S&F 177 (13)　　Last listed 1998
§ - - var. *graellsii* (13)　　EHyt
　- - - MS 408 (13)　　Last listed 1998
　- - - MS 567 (13)　　Last listed 1998
§ - - var. *tenuifolius* (13)　　CAvo EHyt EPot MNrw
　- - - S&B 189 (13)　　Last listed 1998
　- - - x *triandrus* (13)　　EHyt
¶ - 'Golden Bells' (10)　　CBro EWal
　- subsp. *mairei* S&F　　Last listed 1998
　181 (13)
　- var. *mesatlanticus*　　See *N. romieuxii* subsp. *romieuxii* var. *mesatlanticus*
* - 'Monserrat' (10)　　EHyt
　- subsp. *praecox* var.　　EHyt
　*paucinervis* (13)
* - subsp. *viriditubus*　　EHyt
　MS 453 (13)
◆ - subsp. *vulgaris*　　See *N. bulbocodium* subsp. *bulbocodium*
'Bullseye' (3)　　EWal
'Bunclody' (2)　　CQua ICar
'Buncrana' (2)　　Last listed 1996
'Bunting' (7) ♀　　CQua ICar
'Burma Star' (2)　　ICar
'Burning Bush' (3)　　IDun
'Burning Heart' (11b)　　Last listed 1996
'Burntollet' (1)　　CQua IDun
'Bushmills' (3)　　ICar
'Buster' (2)　　EWal
'Buttercup' (7)　　CBro
'Butterscotch' (2)　　CQua ICar
'By Jove' (1)　　EWal
¶ 'Cabernet' (2)　　IDun
'Cabra' (1)　　ICar
'Cadence' (3)　　ICar
'Caedmon' (9)　　CQua
'Cairndhu' (2)　　CQua ICar
'Cairngorm' (2)　　ICar
¶ 'Cairntoul' (3)　　CQua EHof
'Calabar' (2)　　EWal
*calcicola* B&S 413 (13)　　Last listed 1998
　- MS 450 (13)　　Last listed 1998
'California Rose' (4)　　IDun
'Callaway' (3)　　ICar
'Camelford' (2)　　Last listed 1998
¶ 'Camellia' (4)　　EFam
'Camelot' (2) ♀　　EWal
'Campernelli Plenus'　　See *N.* x *odorus* 'Double Campernelle'
'Campion' (9)　　CQua IDun
'Canaliculatus' (8)　　CBro CQua EHyt EPar LAma LBow MBri
*canaliculatus* Gussone　　See *N. tazetta* subsp. *lacticolor*
'Canarybird' (8)　　CBro
'Canasta' (11a)　　CQua ICar
'Candida' (4)　　EWal
'Canisp' (2)　　CQua ICar
'Cantabile' (9)　　CBro CQua IBal
*cantabricus* (13)　　CFil SSpi WPGP
　- subsp. *cantabricus* (13)　　CLAP EHyt ERos SWas
　- - var. *foliosus* (13) ♀　　CAvo EPot LRHS
　- - - S&F 284/2 (13)　　Last listed 1998
　- - var. *petunioides* (13)　　LAma
　- - - S&F 365/2 (13)　　Last listed 1998
　- - - S&F 396 (13)　　Last listed 1998
* - subsp. *monophyllus*　　EHyt
　var. *laciniatus* (13)
　- x *romieuxii* (13)　　NHar
'Cantatrice' (1)　　Last listed 1997

| | |
|---|---|
| 'Canticle' (9) | IBal |
| 'Capax Plenus' | See *N.* 'Eystettensis' |
| 'Cape Cool' (2) | ICar |
| ¶ 'Cape Cornwall' (2) | CQua |
| ¶ 'Cape Point' (2) | IDun |
| 'Capisco' (3) | CQua IBal |
| 'Caracas' (2) | CQua |
| 'Caramba' (2) | CQua |
| 'Carbineer' (2) | LAma |
| 'Carclew' (6) | CQua |
| 'Cardinham' (3) | CQua |
| 'Cargreen' (9) | CQua |
| 'Cariad' (5) | CQua |
| 'Carib Gipsy' (2) ♀ | CQua EHof IDun |
| ¶ 'Caribbean Snow' (2) | EHof |
| 'Carlingford' (2) | IBal |
| 'Carlton' (2) ♀ | EFam ETub LAma MBri NRog |
| 'Carnearny' (3) | ICar |
| ¶ 'Carnkeeran' (2) | ICar |
| 'Carnkief' (2) | CQua |
| 'Caro Nome' (2) | EWal |
| 'Carrara' (3) | EWal |
| 'Carrickbeg' (1) | CQua |
| 'Carson Pass' (2) | Last listed 1998 |
| 'Cassata' (11) | CQua EFam EWal LAma NBir NRog |
| 'Casterbridge' (2) | IDun |
| 'Castle Dobbs' (4) | ICar |
| 'Castlehill' (3) | IBal |
| 'Catistock' (2) | CQua |
| 'Cauldron' (2) | CQua IDun |
| ¶ 'Cavalryman' (3) | IDun |
| 'Cavendish' (4) | IDun |
| 'Cavoda' (1) | ICar |
| 'Caye Chapel' (3) | EHof |
| 'Cazique' (6) | CQua |
| x *cazorlanus* (13) | Last listed 1997 |
| 'Ceasefire' (2) | IDun |
| 'Cedric Morris' (1) | CBro CElw ECha IBlr SSpi SWas WCot |
| 'Celestial Fire' (2) | EHof |
| 'Celtic Gold' (2) | CQua |
| 'Celtic Song' (2) | Last listed 1996 |
| ¶ 'Centannées' (11b) | ETub |
| 'Ceylon' (2) ♀ | EWal LAma |
| 'Chablis' (11a) | Last listed 1996 |
| ¶ 'Cha-cha' (6) | CBro CQua |
| 'Changing Colors' (11a) | ETub |
| 'Chania' (2) | ICar |
| 'Chanterelle' (11a) | EWal ICar LAma NRog |
| ¶ 'Chapman's Peak' (2) | IDun |
| 'Charity May' (6) ♀ | CBro CQua EWal IBal ICar LAma MBri NRog |
| 'Charleston' (2) | Last listed 1998 |
| 'Charter' (2) ♀ | EWal |
| ¶ 'Chaste' (1) | IDun |
| 'Chat' (7) | CQua ICar |
| 'Cheer Leader' (3) | CQua |
| 'Cheerfulness' (4) ♀ | CQua EWal LAma MBri NRog |
| 'Cheetah' (1) | IDun |
| 'Chemeketa' (2) | IDun |
| 'Chenoweth' (2) | CQua |
| 'Chérie' (7) | CBro CQua |
| 'Cherrygardens' (2) | CQua EHof IDun |
| 'Chesterton' (9) | CQua |
| 'Chickadee' (6) | CBro CQua |
| 'Chickerell' (3) | CQua IDun |
| 'Chief Inspector' (1) | CQua IDun |
| 'Chig' (2) | EWal |
| 'Chilmark' (3) | IDun |
| 'Chiloquin' (1) | CQua |
| 'China Doll' (2) | EHof |
| 'Chinchilla' (2) | IDun |
| 'Chinese White' (3) | ICar |
| 'Chinita' (8) | CBro CQua EWal |
| ¶ 'Chit Chat' (7) ♀ | CBro |
| 'Chivalry' (1) | EWal |
| 'Chobe River' (1) | IDun |
| 'Churchfield' (2) | ICar |
| 'Churchman' (2) | IBal ICar |
| 'Churston Ferrers' (4) | CQua |
| ♦ *citrinus* | See *N. bulbocodium* subsp. *bulbocodium* var. *citrinus* |
| 'Citronita' (3) | CQua EHof |
| 'Clady Cottage' (2) | ICar |
| 'Clare' (7) | CBro CQua ICar |
| 'Claridges' (4) | Last listed 1998 |
| 'Clashmore' (2) | Last listed 1996 |
| ¶ 'Claverley' (2) | IDun |
| 'Clockface' (3) | EWal |
| 'Cloneytrace' (1) | ICar |
| 'Close Encounter' (2) | ICar |
| ¶ 'Close Harmony' (4) | IDun |
| 'Cloud Nine' (2) | CBro EWal |
| 'Clouded Yellow' (2) | EHof |
| 'Clouds Rest' (2) | IDun |
| ♦ 'Codlins and Cream' | See *N.* 'Sulphur Phoenix' |
| 'Colblanc' (11a) | CQua ICar |
| 'Collector's Choice' (3) | ICar |
| 'Colloggett' (2) | Last listed 1996 |
| 'Colorama' (11a) | CQua |
| 'Colour Sergeant' (2) | IBal |
| ¶ 'Colourful' (2) | IDun |
| 'Columbus' (2) | ICar |
| 'Colville' (9) | CQua |
| ¶ 'Comal' (1) | CQua IDun |
| ¶ 'Compressus' (8) | CQua |
| ♦ *concolor* (Haworth) Link | See *N. triandrus* var. *concolor* |
| 'Conestoga' (2) | IBal IDun |
| ¶ 'Confuoco' (2) | EFam |
| 'Congress' (11a) | CQua EWal |
| * 'Connie Number 1' | EHyt |
| * 'Connie Number 2' | EHyt |
| 'Connor' (2) | ICar |
| 'Conval' (2) | CQua |
| 'Cool Autumn' (2) | CQua |
| 'Cool Crystal' (3) | CQua EHof ICar IDun |
| ¶ 'Cool Evening' (11a) | IDun |
| 'Cool Shades' (2) | EHof |
| 'Coolattin' (2) | ICar |
| 'Cophetua' (1) | ICar |
| 'Copper Nob' (2) | IBal |
| 'Coppins' (4) | Last listed 1997 |
| 'Coquille' (2) | EWal |
| 'Cora Ann' (7) | CBro |
| 'Coral Light' (2) | ICar |
| 'Corbiere' (1) | CQua EHof IDun |
| 'Corbridge' (2) | EWal |
| *cordubensis* (13) | EHyt SSpi |
| – MS 434 (13) | Last listed 1998 |
| – MS 91-71 (13) | EHyt |
| 'Cornerstone' (2) | EWal |
| 'Cornet' (6) | CQua |
| 'Cornish Cream' (10) | Last listed 1996 |
| 'Corofin' (3) | CQua |
| 'Coromandel' (2) | IDun |
| 'Corozal' (3) | EHof |
| 'Cosmic Dance' (3) | IDun |
| 'Cotehele' (1) | Last listed 1998 |
| ¶ 'Cotinga' (6) | CQua |
| ¶ 'Cotton Candy' (4) | IDun |
| 'Country Morning' (3) | ICar |
| 'Coverack Perfection' (2) | Last listed 1996 |
| 'Crackington' (4) ♀ | CQua IDun |

| | |
|---|---|
| 'Cragford' (8) | EWal LAma |
| 'Craig Stiel' (2) | CQua |
| 'Craigarusky' (2) | IBal |
| 'Craigdun' (2) | Last listed 1998 |
| 'Craigywarren' (2) | EWal |
| 'Creag Dubh' (2) | CQua ICar |
| 'Crenelet' (2) | Last listed 1998 |
| 'Crenver' (3) | Last listed 1996 |
| 'Crimson Chalice' (3) | IDun |
| 'Crinoline' (2) | EWal |
| 'Cristobal' (1) | CQua |
| 'Crock of Gold' (1) | CQua EWal |
| 'Croila' (2) | CQua IDun |
| 'Crown Royalist' (2) | IBal |
| 'Cryptic' (1) | IDun |
| 'Crystal River' (3) | EWal |
| 'Cuan Gold' (4) | IBal |
| *cuatrecasasii* (13) | Last listed 1998 |
| – MS 429 (13) | Last listed 1998 |
| – var. *segimonensis* | Last listed 1998 |
| MS 559 (13) | |
| 'Cuesta' (2) | Last listed 1998 |
| 'Cul Beag' (3) | CQua |
| 'Cupid's Eye' (3) | IDun |
| 'Cushendall' (3) | Last listed 1996 |
| *cyclamineus* (13) ♀ | CBro CFil CWoo EPar LAma NRog |
| | SBla SRms SSpi SWas WAbe WCru |
| | WPGP |
| 'Cyclataz' (8) | CQua |
| *cypri* (8) | CBro CQua |
| 'Cyros' (1) | CQua |
| 'Dailmanach' (2) | CQua EHof IDun |
| ¶ 'Dainty Miss' (7) | CQua |
| 'Daiquiri' (3) | ICar |
| 'Dallas' (3) | CQua |
| 'Dalliance' (2) | ICar |
| 'Dancer' (2) | Last listed 1997 |
| 'Dancing Partner' (2) | EWal |
| 'Danes Balk' (2) | ICar |
| 'Darlow Dale' (2) | Last listed 1996 |
| 'Dateline' (3) | CQua IDun |
| ¶ 'David Alexander' (1) | CQua |
| 'Daviot' (2) | ICar |
| 'Davochfin Lass' (1) | Last listed 1996 |
| 'Dawn' (5) | CBro |
| 'Dawn Chorus' (1) | Last listed 1998 |
| 'Dawn Mist' (2) | EWal |
| 'Dawn Run' (2) | IDun |
| 'Daydream' (2) ♀ | CQua ETub EWal ICar LAma |
| 'Debutante' (2) | CQua |
| 'Decoy' (2) | ICar IDun |
| 'Del Rey' (1) | CQua |
| 'Delabole' (2) | CQua |
| 'Delia' (6) | IDun |
| 'Delibes' (2) | LAma |
| 'Dell Chapel' (3) | ICar |
| 'Delnashaugh' (4) | CQua ICar |
| 'Delos' (3) | CQua |
| 'Delphin Hill' (4) | IBal |
| 'Delta Flight' (6) | IDun |
| 'Delta Wings' (6) | Last listed 1998 |
| 'Demand' (2) | CQua ICar |
| 'Derryboy' (3) | IBal |
| 'Dervock' (4) | ICar |
| 'Desdemona' (2) | EWal NRog |
| 'Desert Bells' (7) | CQua |
| 'Desert Rose' (2) | ICar |
| 'Diane' (6) | EWal |
| 'Diatone' (4) | IDun |
| 'Dick Wilden' (4) | EWal LAma |
| 'Dickcissel' (7) | CBro CQua ICar |
| 'Dimity' (3) | CQua |

| | |
|---|---|
| 'Dimple' (9) | Last listed 1998 |
| 'Dinkie' (3) | CBro |
| 'Discovery' (4) | ICar |
| 'Dispatch Box' (1) | Last listed 1998 |
| 'Diversion' (3) | ICar |
| 'Divertimento' (7) | ICar |
| ¶ 'Doctor Alex Fleming' (2) | EWal |
| 'Doctor Hugh' (3) | CQua EHof EWal IDun |
| ¶ 'Doctor Jazz' (2) | EHof |
| 'Dolly Mollinger' (11b) | EWal ICar LAma |
| 'Don Carlos' (2) | ICar |
| 'Dorchester' (4) | IDun |
| 'Double Blush' (4) | ICar |
| ◆ 'Double Campernelle' | See *N.* x *odorus* 'Double |
| | Campernelle' |
| 'Double Diamond' (4) | CQua |
| 'Double Event' (4) ♀ | Last listed 1993 |
| 'Double Fashion' (4) | EWal |
| ◆ Double pheasant eye | See *N. poeticus* 'Plenus' |
| ◆ Double Roman | See *N.* 'Romanus' |
| 'Doubleday' (4) | IDun |
| 'Doubtful' (3) | CQua ICar |
| 'Dove of Peace' (6) | Last listed 1998 |
| 'Dove Wings' (6) ♀ | CBro CQua EWal IBal ICar LAma |
| 'Dovekie' (12) | ICar |
| 'Dover Cliffs' (2) | CQua |
| 'Downpatrick' (1) | CQua ICar |
| 'Dream Castle' (3) | EWal |
| 'Drenagh' (2) | ICar |
| 'Drop o' Gold' (5) | Last listed 1996 |
| 'Drumadarragh' (1) | ICar |
| 'Drumawillan' (2) | ICar |
| 'Drumbeg' (2) | IBal |
| 'Drumboe' (2) | CQua |
| 'Drumlin' (1) | IBal |
| 'Drumnabreeze' (2) | ICar |
| 'Drumrunie' (2) | ICar |
| *dubius* var. *dubius* | Last listed 1998 |
| MS 512 (13) | |
| 'Duet' (4) | EWal |
| ¶ 'Duke of Windsor' (2) | EFam |
| 'Dulcimer' (9) | CQua |
| 'Dunadry Inn' (4) | IDun |
| 'Dunkery' (4) | IDun |
| ¶ 'Dunley Hall' (3) | IDun |
| 'Dunmurry' (1) | CQua |
| 'Dunskey' (3) | CQua |
| 'Dutch Master' (1) ♀ | CQua ETub EWal LAma MBri |
| | NRog |
| 'Dynamite' (2) | EWal |
| 'Earendil' (2) | IDun |
| 'Early Blossom' (1) | ICar |
| 'Early Splendour' (8) | CQua LAma |
| 'Earthlight' (3) | EHof |
| 'East Wind' (1) | ICar |
| 'Easter Bonnet' (2) | LAma |
| 'Easter Moon' (2) | ICar |
| 'Eastern Dawn' (2) | EWal |
| 'Eastertide' (4) | CQua |
| 'Eaton Park' (3) | Last listed 1998 |
| 'Eaton Song' (12) | CBro CQua |
| 'Eclat' (2) | ICar |
| ¶ 'Eddy Canzony' (2) | CQua |
| 'Edgbaston' (2) | EHof |
| 'Edge Grove' (2) | ICar |
| 'Edwalton' (2) | Last listed 1996 |
| 'Edward Buxton' (3) | LAma MBri |
| 'Egard' (11a) | CQua EWal |
| * 'Egg Nog' (4) | ICar |
| 'Eland' (7) | CQua |
| 'Elburton' (2) | CQua |
| *elegans* var. *elegans* | Last listed 1998 |
| S&F 316 (13) | |

'Elf' (2)                       CBro CQua
'Elfin Gold' (6)                IDun
'Elizabeth Ann' (6)             CQua IDun
'Elka' (1)                      CQua IBal ICar
'Elmley Castle' (1)             Last listed 1998
'Elphin' (4)                    CQua ICar
'Elrond' (2)                    CQua
'Elven Lady' (2)                IDun
'Elvira' (8)                    CBro CQua
'Elwing' (2)                    Last listed 1998
'Elysian Fields' (2)            EWal
'Embo' (2)                      Last listed 1996
'Emily' (2)                     CQua IBal ICar
'Eminent' (3)                   CQua EWal
'Emperor's Waltz' (6)           CQua IDun
'Empress of Ireland' (1) ♀      CQua EHof EWal IBal
'Englander' (6)                 EPot
¶ 'English Caye' (1)            EHof
'Ensemble' (4)                  CQua
'Entrancement' (1)              EWal
'Eribol' (2)                    Last listed 1996
'Eriskay' (4)                   Last listed 1996
'Erlicheer' (4)                 CQua
'Eskylane' (2)                  ICar
'Estrella' (3)                  CQua
'Estremadura' (2)               ICar
'Ethereal Beauty' (2)           IDun
'Ethos' (1)                     IDun
¶ 'Etincelante' (11a)           ICar
'Euphony' (2)                   Last listed 1998
'Euryalus' (1)                  CQua
'Evelix' (2)                    Last listed 1996
'Evendine' (2)                  EWal
'Everglades' (4)                Last listed 1998
'Everpink' (2)                  CQua
¶ 'Evesham' (3)                 IDun
'Exalted' (2)                   ICar
'Exemplar' (1)                  EWal
'Explosion' (8)                 Last listed 1996
'Eye Level' (9)                 IBal
'Eyecatcher' (3)                ICar
§ 'Eystettensis' (4)            CBos CBro CQua EBot ECha ERos
                                IBlr
¶ 'Fair Head' (9)               CQua IBal
'Fair Prospect' (2)             CQua ICar
'Fairgreen' (3)                 CQua ICar
'Fairlight Glen' (2)            Last listed 1996
'Fairsel' (3)                   IBal
'Fairy Chimes' (5)              CBro CQua
'Fairy Footsteps' (3)           IBal ICar
'Fairy Island' (3)              CQua ICar
'Fairy Spell' (3)               IBal
'Falconet' (8) ♀                CBro CQua ERos EWal
'Falstaff' (2)                  CQua ICar
'Fanad Head' (9)                IBal
'Far Country' (2)               CQua ICar
'Faro' (1)                      IBal
'Farranfad' (2)                 IBal
'Fastidious' (2)                CQua
'Favor Royal' (3)               IBal
'Favourite' (2)                 EWal
'February Gold' (6) ♀           CAvo CBro EPar ETub EWal IBal
                                LAma LBow MBNS MBri NBir
                                NMGW NRog SRms WShi
'February Silver' (6)           CBro EPar ETub EWal LAma
                                NMGW NRog WShi
'Feeling Lucky' (2) ♀           EWal
'Felindre' (9)                  CQua EWal IBal
'Fellowship' (2)                Last listed 1996
'Feock' (3)                     CQua
*fernandesii* (13)              CBro
'Ferndown' (3)                  CQua EHof IDun

'Festivity' (2)                 CQua EWal
'ffitch's Ffolly' (2)           CQua
'Fieldfare' (3)                 ICar
'Fiji' (4)                      ICar
'Filly' (2)                     EWal
¶ 'Filoli' (1)                  IDun
'Finchcocks' (2)                Last listed 1996
'Fine Gold' (1)                 CQua
'Fine Romance' (2)              CQua EHof
¶ 'Fiona MacKillop' (2)         IDun
'Fionn' (2)                     ICar
'Fire Raiser' (2)               ICar
¶ 'Firebrand' (2)               CQua
'Firestorm' (2)                 IBal
'First Hope' (6)                CQua
'Flaming Meteor' (2)            ICar
¶ 'Flashback' (6)               IDun
'Flirt' (6)                     CQua ICar
'Flomay' (7)                    CBro
'Florida Manor' (3)             IBal
'Flower Carpet' (1)             LAma
'Flower Drift' (4)              LAma
'Flower Record' (2)             LAma
'Fly Half' (2)                  CQua
'Flycatcher' (7)                CQua
'Flying Saucer' (2)             EWal
'Focal Point' (2)               ICar
'Fool's Gold' (4)               ICar
'Foray' (2)                     EWal
'Foresight' (1)                 ICar LAma
'Forge Mill' (2)                CQua ICar
'Fort Knox' (1)                 EWal
'Fortissimo' (2)                Last listed 1998
'Fortune' (2)                   EWal LAma NRog
'Foundling' (6) ♀               CBro CQua EWal IBal ICar
'Foxfire' (2)                   ICar
'Fragrant Breeze' (2)           EWal
'Fragrant Rose' (2)             CQua EHof EWal ICar IDun
'Francolin' (1)                 IDun
'Frank's Fancy' (9)             IBal
'Fresh Lime' (1)                EHof
'Fresh Season' (10)             CQua
'Fresno' (3)                    IDun
'Frigid' (3)                    IBal ICar
'Frolic' (2)                    EWal
'Front Royal' (2)               CQua ICar
'Frostbite' (4)                 IBal
'Frostkist' (6)                 CBro CQua
'Frou-frou' (4)                 CQua ICar
'Fruit Cup' (7)                 CQua
'Fuego' (2)                     ICar
'Full House'                    EWal
'Fulwell' (4)                   Last listed 1998
'Furnace Creek' (2)             IDun
'Fynbos' (3)                    IDun
'Gabriël Kleiberg' (11a)        ICar
*gaditanus* (13)                CBro
 – MS 526 (13)                  Last listed 1998
'Galway' (2)                    EWal
'Garden News' (3)               IDun
'Garden Princess' (6)           CBro LAma
'Gay Cavalier' (4)              CQua
'Gay Challenger' (4)            Last listed 1996
'Gay Kybo' (4) ♀                CQua
'Gay Mood' (2)                  EWal
'Gay Song' (4)                  CQua ICar
'Gay Time' (4)                  EWal
*gayi* (13)                     CBro CQua
'Geevor' (4)                    CQua
¶ 'George Leak' (2)             CQua
'George's Pink' (2)             ICar
'Georgie Girl' (6)              CQua IDun

| Name | Source |
|---|---|
| 'Geranium' (8) ♀ | CBro CQua EWal LAma MBri NRog |
| 'Gettysburg' (2) | CQua |
| 'Gigantic Star' (2) | EWal LAma MBri |
| 'Gilda' (2) | IBal |
| ¶ 'Gillan' (11a) | CQua |
| 'Gimli' (6) | Last listed 1996 |
| 'Gin and Lime' (1) ♀ | CQua EHof ICar |
| 'Gipsy Queen' (1) | CQua |
| 'Gironde' (11) | CQua |
| 'Glasnevin' (2) | ICar |
| 'Glaston' (2) | ICar |
| 'Glen Cassley' (3) | Last listed 1996 |
| 'Glen Clova' (2) | CQua |
| 'Glenamoy' (1) | ICar |
| 'Glendermott' (2) | ICar |
| 'Glendun' (3) | ICar |
| 'Glenfarclas' (1) ♀ | ICar |
| 'Glenganagh' (4) | ICar |
| 'Glenmorangie' (2) | Last listed 1996 |
| 'Glenside' (2) | CQua |
| ¶ 'Glissando' (2) | CQua |
| 'Gloriosus' (8) | CQua |
| 'Glory of Lisse' (9) | Last listed 1996 |
| 'Glowing Red' (4) | CQua |
| 'Goff's Caye' (2) | EHof IDun |
| 'Gold Bond' (2) | IDun |
| 'Gold Bullion' (1) | ICar |
| 'Gold Convention' (2) ♀ | CQua IDun |
| ¶ 'Gold Ingot' (2) | IDun |
| 'Gold Medal' (1) | EWal LAma |
| 'Gold Medallion' (1) | Last listed 1996 |
| 'Gold Mine' (2) | IBal |
| 'Gold Phantom' (1) | ICar |
| 'Gold Strike' (1) | ICar |
| 'Golden Amber' (2) | CQua IBal ICar |
| 'Golden Aura' (2) ♀ | CQua EWal IBal ICar |
| 'Golden Bear' (4) | Last listed 1998 |
| ¶ 'Golden Cheer' (2) | CQua |
| 'Golden Cycle' (6) | CQua |
| 'Golden Dawn' (8) ♀ | CQua EWal |
| 'Golden Ducat' (4) | EWal ICar LAma MBri NBir NRog |
| 'Golden Girl' (1) | ICar |
| 'Golden Halo' (2) | IBal ICar |
| 'Golden Harvest' (1) | LAma MBri NRog |
| 'Golden Jewel' (2) ♀ | CQua ICar |
| 'Golden Joy' (2) | CQua ICar |
| 'Golden Orchid' (11a) | Last listed 1997 |
| 'Golden Perfection' (7) | LAma |
| ¶ 'Golden Quince' (12) | CBro |
| 'Golden Radiance' (1) | IBal |
| 'Golden Rapture' (1) ♀ | CQua |
| 'Golden Riot' (1) | EWal |
| 'Golden Sceptre' (7) | CBro |
| 'Golden Sheen' (2) | IDun |
| 'Golden Showers' (1) | Last listed 1996 |
| 'Golden Sovereign' (1) | IBal |
| 'Golden Strand' (2) | IBal |
| 'Golden Topaz' (2) | IBal |
| 'Golden Vale' (1) ♀ | CQua |
| 'Golden Wings' (6) | IBal |
| 'Goldfinger' (1) | IDun |
| 'Goldhanger' (2) | EHof |
| 'Goldsithney' (2) | CBro |
| ¶ 'Golitha Falls' (2) | CQua |
| 'Golly' (4) | EWal |
| 'Good Measure' (2) | EWal |
| 'Goose Green' (3) | IBal |
| 'Gossamer' (3) | EWal |
| 'Gouache' | EWal |
| 'Gourmet' (2) | Last listed 1997 |
| 'Grace Note' (3) | CQua ICar |
| x *gracilis* | See *N.* x *tenuior* |
| 'Gracious Lady' (2) | Last listed 1998 |
| 'Graduation' (2) | Last listed 1998 |
| *graellsii* | See *N. bulbocodium* subsp. *bulbocodium* var. *graellsii* |
| 'Grand Primo Citronière' (8) | CQua |
| 'Grand Prospect' (2) | CQua |
| 'Grand Soleil d'Or' (8) | CQua LAma NRog |
| 'Gransha' (3) | IBal |
| 'Grapillon' (11a) | Last listed 1996 |
| ¶ 'Greatwood' (1) | CQua |
| 'Green Bridge' (3) | ICar |
| ¶ 'Green Chartreuse' (2) | EHof |
| 'Green Glens' (2) | ICar |
| 'Green Gold' (2) | EWal |
| 'Green Island' (2) | EWal |
| 'Green Lodge' (9) | IBal |
| 'Greenfinch' (3) | ICar |
| 'Greenlet' (6) | CQua |
| 'Greenodd' (3) | CQua |
| 'Greenpark' (9) | IBal |
| 'Greenstar' (4) | EWal |
| 'Greeting' (2) | Last listed 1996 |
| 'Gresham' (4) | CQua IDun |
| 'Grey Lady' (3) | ICar |
| 'Gribben Head' (4) | CQua |
| 'Grosvenor' (4) | Last listed 1998 |
| ¶ 'Grullemans Senior' (2) | EFam |
| ¶ 'Guinevere' (2) | ICar |
| ¶ 'Gulliver' (3) | CQua |
| 'Gwennap' (1) | CQua |
| 'Gwinear' (2) | CQua |
| ¶ 'Halgarry' (3) | ICar |
| 'Halley's Comet' (3) | CQua EHof |
| 'Hallworthy' (2) | Last listed 1998 |
| 'Halolight' (2) | EWal |
| 'Halstock' (2) | Last listed 1998 |
| 'Halvose' (8) | CBro |
| 'Hambledon' (2) | CQua EHof IDun |
| 'Hammoon' (3) | EWal |
| 'Happy Face' (2) | ICar |
| 'Happy Fellow' (2) | EHof IDun |
| 'Harmony Bells' (5) | CQua ICar |
| 'Hartington' (2) | CQua |
| 'Hartlebury' (3) | CQua |
| * 'Hat' (10) | EHyt SWas |
| 'Hawaii' (4) | IBal |
| 'Hawangi' (3) | IDun |
| 'Hawera' (5) ♀ | CAvo CBro CMea CQua EPar EPot ETub EWal ICar LAma MBri MBro MRPP NMGW NRog SUsu WHil |
| 'Haye' (2) | CQua |
| 'Hazel Rutherford' (2) | Last listed 1996 |
| 'Hazel Winslow' (2) | Last listed 1996 |
| ¶ 'Heamoor' (4) | CQua |
| 'Heart's Desire' (4) | EWal |
| 'Heat Haze' (2) | ICar |
| *hedraeanthus* (13) | EPot |
| – MS 419 (13) | Last listed 1998 |
| 'Helen's Tower' (2) | IBal |
| ¶ 'Helford Dawn' (2) | CQua |
| ♦ *hellenicus* | See *N. poeticus* var. *hellenicus* |
| 'Hembleton' (2) | Last listed 1998 |
| *henriquesii* | See *N. jonquilla* var. *henriquesii* |
| 'Hero' (1) | CQua EWal |
| 'Hesla' (7) | CBro ICar |
| 'Heslington' (3) | EHof |
| 'Hessenford' (2) | Last listed 1998 |
| 'Hexameter' (9) | CQua |
| 'Hexworthy' (3) | Last listed 1998 |
| 'High Note' (7) | EWal |
| 'High Society' (2) | CQua EHof EWal ICar IDun |

'Highfield Beauty' (8) CQua EWal ICar
'Highland Wedding' (2) ICar
'Highlite' (2) CQua ICar
'Highway Song' (2) ICar
'Hilford' (2) IBal
'Hill Head' (9) IBal
'Hillstar' (7) CQua
'Hilltown' (2) IBal
'Holbeck' (4) Last listed 1996
'Holiday Fashion' (2) EWal
'Holland Sensation' (1) LAma
¶ 'Holly Berry' (2) CQua
'Hollypark' (3) IBal
'Holme Fen' (2) EHof
'Homage' (2) EWal
'Honey Guide' (5) CQua
'Honeybird' (1) CQua EWal ICar
¶ 'Honeyorange' (2) IDun
'Honolulu' (4) EWal
'Hoopoe' (8) CBro CQua ICar
'Hope' (4) EWal
'Horace' (9) CQua ICar
'Horn of Plenty' (5) CBro CQua
'Hors d'Oeuvre' (8) CBro
'Hot Gossip' (2) CQua EHof ICar IDun
'Hot Toddy' (4) ICar
'Hotspur' (2) CQua
* *humilis mauretanicus* Last listed 1998
    S&F 260 (13)
'Hunting Caye' (2) EHof
'Ibis' (6) Last listed 1996
'Ice Dancer' (2) IDun
'Ice Follies' (2) ♀ CQua ETub EWal LAma MBri NBir
    NRog
'Ice King' (4) EWal NBir
'Ice Wings' (5) CAvo CBro CQua EPot EWal
'Idless' (1) CQua
'Immaculate' (2) CQua ICar
'Impresario' (2) Last listed 1998
'Inara' (4) CQua
'Inca' (6) CQua
¶ 'Indian Chief' (4) EFam
'Indian Maid' (7) CQua
'Indora' (4) CQua
'Inglescombe' (4) LAma
'Ingrid Evensen' (2) CQua
'Initiation' (1) ICar
'Innis Beg' (2) ICar
'Inniswood' (1) ICar
¶ 'Innovator' (4) IDun
¶ 'Inny River' (1) IDun
¶ 'Interim' (2) CQua
'Interloper' (6) IDun
§ x *intermedius* (13) CBro
'Interval' (2) IBal
'Intrigue' (7) EWal ICar IDun
'Inverpolly' (2) EHof
'Ireland's Eye' (9) IBal
'Irene Copeland' (4) EWal
'Irish Coffee' (3) Last listed 1998
'Irish Light' (2) CQua ICar
'Irish Linen' (3) CQua ICar
'Irish Luck' (1) EWal LAma
'Irish Minstrel' (2) ♀ Last listed 1997
'Irish Mist' (2) CQua ICar
'Irish Nymph' (3) ICar
'Irish Ranger' (3) ICar
'Irish Rover' (2) Last listed 1998
'Irish Splendour' (3) ICar
¶ 'Irvington' (3) IDun
'Islander' (4) ICar
'Islandhill' (3) IBal

¶ 'Ita' (2) IDun
'It's True' (1) EWal
'Itzim' (6) ♀ CAvo CBro CQua ERos ETub
¶ 'Ivory Gull' (5) CQua
*jacetanus* MS 580 (13) Last listed 1998
'Jack Snipe' (6) ♀ CAvo CBro CNic CQua EPot ERos
    EWal LAma LBow MBNS MBri
    NRog WShi
'Jackadee' (2) IDun
'Jacobin' (1) IDun
'Jamage' (8) CQua
'Jamaica Inn' (4) CQua
'Jambo' (2) IDun
'Jamboree' (2) CQua
'Jamestown' (3) IBal
'Jana' (6) CQua ICar
'Jane MacLennan' (4) Last listed 1996
'Jane van Kralingen' (3) Last listed 1996
'Janis Babson' (2) ICar
'Jennie Tait' (2) ICar
'Jenny' (6) ♀ CAvo CBro CQua EPar EPot ERos
    ETub EWal IBal ICar LAma NBir
    NRog
¶ 'Jessamy' (10) EHyt
¶ 'Jetage' (6) CBro
'Jetfire' (6) ♀ CBro CQua EPot ERos EWal ICar
    LAma
'Jewel Song' (2) ICar
'Jezebel' (3) CBro
'Johanna' (5) CBro
'John Ballance' (1) IBal
'John Daniel' (4) CQua
'John of Salisbury' (2) EWal
¶ 'John's Delight' (3) CQua
§ 'Jolity' (2) EWal
*jonquilla* (13) ♀ CAvo CBro CQua EPar EPot ERos
    LAma LBow NRog WPGP WShi
§ - var. *henriquesii* (13) CBro CFil
- - MS 455 (13) Last listed 1998
- var. *jonquilla* B&S 420 (13) Last listed 1998
- var. *stellaris* MS 466 (13) Last listed 1998
'Joppa' (7) CQua
'Joseph Macleod' (1) EWal
'Joy' See N. 'Jolity'
♦ 'Joy Bishop' See N. *romieuxii* 'Joy Bishop' ex
    JCA 805
'Joybell' (6) CQua
'Jubilation' (2) EWal
'Jules Verne' (2) LAma
♦ 'Julia Jane' See N. *romieuxii* 'Julia Jane' ex
    JCA 805
'Jumblie' (12) ♀ CBro CMea CQua EPot ERos EWal
    LAma MBri NRog WShi
'Jumbo Gold' (1) Last listed 1998
*juncifolius* See N. *assoanus*
'June Lake' (2) IDun
'Kamau' (9) IDun
'Karachi' (2) Last listed 1998
'Karamudli' (1) CQua
'Kathleen Munro' (2) Last listed 1996
'Kaydee' (6) ♀ CQua IDun
'Kazuko' (3) EWal
'Kea' (6) CQua
'Keats' (9) CBro CQua ICar
'Kebaya' (2) Last listed 1998
'Kehelland' (4) CBro
'Kelanne' (2) Last listed 1998
'Kenbane Head' (9) IBal
'Kenellis' (10) CBro CQua
'Ken's Favourite' (2) CQua
'Kernow' (2) CQua
'Kidling' (7) CQua

| | |
|---|---|
| 'Kildrum' (3) | EWal ICar |
| 'Kilkenny' (1) | Last listed 1997 |
| 'Killara' (8) | CQua |
| 'Killearnan' (9) | CQua EHof |
| 'Killeen' (2) | IBal |
| 'Killyleagh' (3) | IBal |
| 'Kilmood' (2) | IBal |
| 'Kiltonga' (2) | IBal |
| 'Kilworth' (2) | CQua EFam EWal LAma |
| 'Kimmeridge' (3) | CQua |
| 'Kindled' (2) | ICar |
| 'King Alfred' (1) | EWal LAma |
| 'King Size' (11a) | CQua ICar |
| 'Kinglet' (7) | ICar |
| 'King's Bridge' (1) | Last listed 1998 |
| 'King's Grove' (1) | CQua IDun |
| 'Kings Pipe' (2) | CQua |
| 'King's Stag' (1) | ICar |
| 'Kingscourt' (1) ♀ | CQua ICar |
| 'Kirkcubbin' (3) | IBal |
| 'Kirkinriola' (3) | ICar |
| 'Kirklington' (2) | CQua |
| 'Kissproof' (2) | EWal |
| ¶ 'Kit Hill' (7) | CQua |
| 'Kitten' (6) | Last listed 1996 |
| 'Kitty' (6) | CBro ERos |
| 'Klamath' (2) | EWal |
| 'Knockanure' (2) | ICar |
| 'Knocklayde' (3) | ICar |
| 'Krakatoa' (2) | EWal |
| ¶ 'La Argentina' (2) | EFam |
| 'La Vella' (2) | Last listed 1998 |
| 'Ladies' Choice' (7) | IDun |
| 'Lady Ann' (2) | IDun |
| ¶ 'Lady Be Good' (2) | EHof |
| 'Lady Emily' (2) | IBal |
| 'Lady Serena' (9) | CQua |
| 'Lake Tahoe' (2) | IDun |
| 'Lamanva' (2) | CQua |
| 'Lamerton' (2) | CQua |
| 'L'Amour' | See N. 'Madelaine' |
| 'Lanarth' (7) | CBro |
| 'Lancaster' (3) | CQua IBal |
| 'Landmark' (2) | EWal |
| ¶ 'Langford Grove' (3) | ICar |
| 'Lapwing' (5) | CBro EWal |
| 'Larkelly' (6) | CBro |
| 'Larkfield' (2) | ICar |
| 'Larkhill' (2) | CQua |
| 'Larkwhistle' (6) ♀ | CBro |
| 'Last Promise' (1) | ICar |
| 'Last Word' (3) | EWal |
| 'Latchley' (2) | CQua |
| 'Late Call' (3) | IBal |
| 'Lavender Lass' (6) | CQua |
| 'Leading Light' (2) | Last listed 1996 |
| 'Lee Moor' (1) | CQua |
| 'Lemon Beauty' (11b) | CQua EWal |
| 'Lemon Candy' (2) | Last listed 1996 |
| 'Lemon Cloud' (1) | EWal |
| ¶ 'Lemon Grey' (3) | IDun |
| 'Lemon Heart' (5) | CBro |
| ¶ 'Lemon Sails' (2) | IDun |
| 'Lemon Silk' (6) | CQua |
| 'Lemon Snow' (2) | Last listed 1998 |
| 'Lemonade' (3) | CQua |
| 'Lennymore' (2) | IDun |
| 'Leonaine' (2) | EWal |
| 'Leslie Hill' (1) | ICar |
| 'Lewannick' (2) | CQua |
| 'Liberty Bells' (5) | CBro CQua EPot EWal LAma MBri NRog |

| | |
|---|---|
| 'Lichfield' (3) | EWal |
| 'Lighthouse' (3) | Last listed 1998 |
| 'Lighthouse Reef' (1) | EHof |
| 'Lilac Charm' (6) | CQua IDun |
| 'Lilac Hue' (6) | CBro |
| 'Lillande' (4) | ICar |
| 'Limbo' (2) | CQua EWal IDun |
| 'Limegrove' (3) | Last listed 1998 |
| 'Limehurst' (2) | CQua |
| 'Limelight' (1) | EWal |
| 'Limerick' (3) | EWal |
| ¶ 'Limpopo' (3) | IDun |
| 'Lingerie' (4) | NZep |
| 'Lintie' (7) | CBro CQua EWal LAma MBri NRog |
| 'Lionheart' (4) | EWal |
| 'Lisanore' (2) | Last listed 1998 |
| 'Lisbarnett' (3) | IBal |
| 'Lisnamulligan' (3) | IBal |
| 'Lisnamurrican' (2) | ICar |
| 'Lisrenny' (1) | ICar |
| 'Little Beauty' (1) | CAvo CBro CQua EPot ERos LAma |
| 'Little Dancer' (1) | CBro |
| 'Little Gem' (1) ♀ | CAvo CBro CQua EPot LAma NRog |
| 'Little Jazz' (6) | Last listed 1996 |
| 'Little Princess' (6) | ICar |
| 'Little Rusky' (7) | Last listed 1998 |
| 'Little Sentry' (7) | CBro CQua |
| 'Little Soldier' (10) | CQua |
| 'Little Spell' (1) | CBro |
| 'Little Witch' (6) | CAvo CBro CQua EPot ERos EWal LAma MBri NRog |
| ¶ 'Liverpool Festival' (2) | CQua |
| 'Lizard Light' (2) | EWal |
| lobularis | See N. pseudonarcissus 'Lobularis' |
| ¶ 'Loch Alsh' (3) | IDun |
| 'Loch Assynt' (3) | CQua ICar |
| 'Loch Brora' (2) | CQua ICar |
| 'Loch Carron' (2) | ICar |
| 'Loch Coire' (3) | Last listed 1996 |
| 'Loch Fada' (2) | CQua |
| 'Loch Hope' (2) | CQua ICar |
| ¶ 'Loch Loyal' (2) | ICar |
| 'Loch Lundie' (2) | CQua ICar |
| 'Loch Maberry' (2) | CQua ICar |
| 'Loch Naver' (2) | CQua |
| 'Loch Owskeich' (2) ♀ | Last listed 1995 |
| 'Loch Stac' (2) | CQua ICar |
| 'Loch Tarbert' (2) | Last listed 1996 |
| 'Logan Rock' (7) | CQua |
| longispathus MS 546 (13) | SSpi |
| 'Lorikeet' (1) | CQua NZep |
| 'Lostwithiel' (2) | Last listed 1998 |
| 'Lothario' (2) | LAma NRog |
| 'Lough Bawn' (2) | ICar |
| 'Lough Cuan' (1) | IBal |
| ¶ 'Lough Gowna' (1) | IDun |
| 'Lough Ryan' (1) | IBal |
| 'Loughanisland' (1) | IBal |
| 'Loughanmore' (1) | ICar |
| 'Lovable' (3) | EWal |
| 'Loveny' (2) | CQua |
| 'Ludgvan' (4) | CQua |
| 'Lunar Sea' (1) | EWal |
| ¶ 'Lundy Light' (2) | CQua |
| 'Lurgain' (1) | EWal |
| 'Lurig' (2) | ICar |
| 'Lydwells' (2) | Last listed 1996 |
| 'Lyrebird' (3) | CQua |
| 'Lyric' (9) | CQua |
| 'Lysander' (2) | CQua |

| | |
|---|---|
| § 'Madelaine' (2) | EWal |
| * 'Madison' | EWal |
| 'Madrigal' (2) | Last listed 1996 |
| 'Magic Flute' (2) | ICar |
| 'Magic Maiden' (2) | Last listed 1996 |
| 'Magician' (2) | NZep |
| 'Magna Carta' (2) | Last listed 1998 |
| 'Magnet' (1) | LAma MBri |
| 'Magnificence' (1) | LAma |
| 'Maiden Over' (2) | Last listed 1996 |
| 'Mairead' (2) | Last listed 1996 |
| ¶ 'Majarde' (2) | EFam |
| 'Majestic Gold' (1) | Last listed 1996 |
| 'Majestic Star' (1) | CQua IDun |
| 'Makasa Sun' (2) | IDun |
| 'Malin Head' (5) | IBal |
| 'Manchu' (2) | EWal |
| 'Manly' (4) | CQua EWal |
| 'Manon Lescaut' (2) | EWal |
| 'Marabou' (4) | Last listed 1998 |
| 'Maraval' (1) | EWal |
| 'March Sunshine' (6) | CBro EWal LAma |
| 'Marie-José' (11b) | LAma |
| 'Marjorie Treveal' (4) | CQua |
| 'Marlborough' (2) | CQua |
| 'Martha Washington' (8) | CBro CQua |
| 'Martinette' (7) | CQua |
| *marvieri* | See *N. rupicola* subsp. *marvieri* |
| 'Mary Bohannon' (2) | EWal |
| 'Mary Copeland' (4) | EWal LAma |
| 'Mary Kate' (6) | CQua IDun |
| 'Mary Lou' (6) | IDun |
| 'Mary Robinson' (2) | ICar |
| 'Mary Schouten' (2) | Last listed 1996 |
| 'Mary Sumner' (1) | ICar |
| 'Mary Veronica' (3) | EHof |
| 'Mary's Pink' (2) | ICar |
| 'Marzo' (7) | IDun |
| 'Masai Mara' (2) | Last listed 1998 |
| 'Matador' (8) | CQua |
| 'Max' (11a) | CQua |
| ¶ 'Maya Dynasty' (2) | CQua |
| 'Mayan Gold' (1) | IBal |
| ¶ 'Media Girl' (2) | IDun |
| x *medioluteus* (13) | CBro |
| 'Medusa' (8) | CBro |
| 'Megalith' (2) | Last listed 1998 |
| ¶ 'Melancholy' (1) | IDun |
| 'Melbury' (2) | CQua |
| 'Meldrum' (1) | Last listed 1998 |
| 'Mellon Park' (3) | Last listed 1998 |
| 'Melodious' (2) | CQua |
| 'Menabilly' (4) | CQua |
| 'Men-an-Tol' (2) | CQua |
| 'Menehay' (11a) | CQua |
| 'Mentor' (2) | Last listed 1998 |
| 'Menucha' (2) | ICar |
| 'Mercato' (2) | LAma |
| 'Meredith' (3) | ICar |
| 'Merida' (2) | IBal |
| 'Merlin' (3) ♀ | CQua EHof IBal |
| 'Merlin's Castle' (3) | ICar |
| 'Merry Bells' (5) | CQua ICar |
| 'Merrymeet' (4) | CQua |
| 'Mexico City' (2) | IBal |
| 'Michaels Gold' (2) | EHof IDun |
| 'Midas Touch' (1) | CQua IDun |
| 'Midget' | CAvo CBro EPot ETub |
| 'Milan' (9) | CQua ICar |
| ¶ 'Milestone' (2) | ICar |
| 'Millennium' (1) | CBro |
| 'Millgreen' (1) | EWal |

| | |
|---|---|
| 'Minicycla' (6) | CBro EHyt LRHS |
| *minimus* hort. | See *N. asturiensis* |
| 'Minnow' (8) ♀ | CAvo CBro CQua EPot ERos ETub EWal LAma MBri NRog WShi |
| § *minor* (13) ♀ | CBro CQua EBot LAma NRya WShi |
| – 'Douglasbank' (1) | Last listed 1996 |
| – var. *pumilus* 'Plenus' | See *N.* 'Rip van Winkle' |
| – Ulster form | IBlr |
| 'Mint Cup' (3) | ICar |
| *minutiflorus* B&S 412 (13) | Last listed 1998 |
| 'Miss Kitty' (2) | ICar |
| ¶ 'Miss Primm' (2) | IDun |
| 'Mission Bells' (5) | CQua ICar |
| 'Missouri' (2) | EWal |
| 'Mistral' (11) | ICar |
| 'Misty Dawn' (3) | IBal |
| 'Misty Glen' (2) ♀ | CQua ICar |
| 'Misty Moon' (3) | ICar |
| 'Mite' (6) | CBro |
| ¶ 'Mitylene' (2) | CQua |
| 'Mockingbird' (7) | IDun |
| 'Modern Art' (2) | EWal |
| 'Mol's Hobby' (11a) | EWal LAma |
| 'Mona Lisa' (2) | EWal |
| 'Mondragon' (11a) | CQua EWal |
| 'Mongleath' (2) | CQua |
| ¶ 'Monks Wood' (1) | EHof |
| 'Monksilver' (3) | Last listed 1996 |
| ¶ 'Montclair' (2) | CQua |
| 'Montego' (3) | CQua |
| 'Monza' (4) | IDun |
| 'Moon Goddess' (1) | Last listed 1996 |
| 'Moon Jade' (3) | Last listed 1997 |
| 'Moon Ranger' (3) | IBal |
| 'Moon Rhythm' (4) | IBal ICar |
| 'Moon Tide' (3) | IBal |
| 'Moon Valley' (2) | IDun |
| ¶ 'Moonbird' (11a) | ICar |
| ¶ 'Moonflight' (4) | ICar |
| 'Moonshine' (5) | CBro |
| 'Moonshot' (1) | EWal |
| 'Moonspell' (2) | IBal ICar |
| 'Moralee' (4) | IDun |
| ¶ *moschatus* (13) | CBro EPot |
| ¶ – 'Cernuus Plenus' (4) | ICar |
| 'Mother Catherine Grullemans' (2) | EFam LAma |
| 'Mount Angel' (3) | Last listed 1998 |
| 'Mount Fuji' (2) | CQua |
| 'Mount Hood' (1) ♀ | ETub EWal LAma MBri NBir |
| 'Mount Oriel' (2) | IBal |
| 'Mountjoy' (7) | EWal |
| 'Mourneview' (1) | IBal |
| 'Movie Star' (2) | IDun |
| 'Mowana' (2) | Last listed 1998 |
| 'Moyarget' (3) | ICar |
| 'Moyle' (9) | IBal |
| 'Moyola' (2) | ICar |
| ¶ 'Mrs Langtry' (3) | CQua WShi |
| 'Mrs R.O. Backhouse' (2) | LAma MBri WShi |
| 'Mrs William Copeland' (4) | EWal |
| 'Muirfield' (1) | Last listed 1996 |
| 'Mulatto' (1) | EWal |
| ¶ 'Mullion' (3) | CQua |
| 'Mulroy Bay' (1) | IDun |
| 'Murlough' (9) | CQua IBal |
| 'Murrayfield' (3) | Last listed 1998 |
| 'Muscadet' (2) | CQua |
| 'My Lady' (2) | EWal |
| 'My My' (2) | EWal |
| 'My Word' (2) | ICar |

| | |
|---|---|
| 'Naivasha' (2) | IDun |
| 'Nampa' (1) | CQua |
| 'Namraj' (2) | CQua |
| 'Nancegollan' (7) | CBro CQua |
| ¶ 'Nangiles' (4) | CQua |
| 'Nansidwell' (2) | CQua |
| ¶ *nanus* | ICar |
| 'Narok' (4) | Last listed 1998 |
| 'Neahkahnie' (1) | Last listed 1998 |
| 'Nether Barr' (2) | IDun |
| *nevadensis* (13) | SSpi |
| 'New Penny' (3) | ICar |
| 'New Song' (2) | EWal |
| 'New Star' (2) | EWal |
| 'New World' (2) | EWal |
| 'New-baby' (7) | CQua EWal |
| 'Newcastle' (1) | CQua EWal ICar |
| 'Newton Ferrers' (4) | Last listed 1998 |
| ¶ 'Nick's Pink' (1) | ICar |
| 'Night Music' (4) | CQua |
| 'Nightcap' (1) | CQua |
| ¶ 'Nile' (1) | ICar IDun |
| 'Nirvana' (7) | CBro |
| 'Niveth' (5) | CQua ICar |
| *nobilis* var. *nobilis* | Last listed 1998 |
|   MS 486 (13) | |
| - var. *primigenius* | Last listed 1998 |
|   MS 593 (13) | |
| ¶ 'Nonchalant' (3) | IDun |
| 'Nor-nor' (2) | CBro |
| 'North Rim' (2) | Last listed 1998 |
| 'Northern Sceptre' (2) | IBal ICar |
| ¶ 'Northwest' (1) | IDun |
| 'Noss Mayo' (6) | CBro CQua |
| 'Notable' (3) | Last listed 1997 |
| 'Notre Dame' (2) | IDun |
| 'Nouvelle' (3) | IBal |
| 'Nuage' (2) | EWal |
| 'Numen Rose' (2) | IDun |
| Nylon Group (10) | CBro CLAP EHyt EPot SSpi |
| ¶ - yellow (10) | EPot |
| 'Oadby' (1) | CQua |
| * 'Oakham' (2) | Last listed 1996 |
| 'Oakwood' (3) | EWal |
| 'Obdam' (4) | EWal |
| 'Obelisk' (11a) | CQua |
| *obesus* (13) | CLAP EHyt EPot ERos ESis |
| - MS 451 (13) | Last listed 1998 |
| 'Obsession' (2) | Last listed 1998 |
| *obvallaris* (13) ♀ | CAvo CBro EPot ERos LBow NRog WCla WShi |
| 'Ocarino' (4) | CQua |
| ¶ 'Ocean Blue' (2) | IDun |
| ¶ x *odorus* (13) | WShi |
| § - 'Double Campernelle' (4) | CQua EPar LAma |
| 'Odyssey' (4) | ICar IDun |
| 'Oecumene' (11a) | CQua |
| 'Ohio' (2) | Last listed 1998 |
| Old Pheasant's Eye | See *N. poeticus* var. *recurvus* |
| 'Olympic Gold' (1) | Last listed 1998 |
| 'Omaha' (3) | IBal |
| 'Orange Beacon' (2) | ICar |
| ¶ 'Orange Monarch' (2) | EFam |
| 'Orange Walk' (3) | EHof |
| 'Orangery' (11a) | EFam ICar LAma MBri NRog |
| 'Oratorio' (2) | EWal |
| 'Ormeau' (2) ♀ | CQua ICar |
| 'Oryx' (7) ♀ | CQua IDun |
| 'Osmington' (2) | CQua EHof |
| 'Ottoman Gold' (2) | IBal |
| 'Ouma' (1) | CQua |
| ¶ 'Our Tempie' (3) | IDun |
| 'Ouzel' (6) | CQua |
| 'Owen Roe' (1) | Last listed 1997 |
| 'Owston Wood' (1) | Last listed 1998 |
| 'Oykel' (3) | CQua ICar |
| 'Oz' (12) | CQua |
| 'Painted Desert' (3) | CQua ICar |
| 'Pale Sunlight' (2) | CQua ICar |
| ¶ 'Palette' (11a) | ICar |
| § *pallidiflorus* (13) | ECha |
| 'Palmares' (11a) | CQua EWal ICar |
| 'Palmyra' (3) | ICar |
| 'Panache' (1) | CQua EWal ICar |
| *panizzianus* (13) | Last listed 1998 |
| 'Pankot' (2) | ICar |
| 'Paolo Veronese' (2) | EWal |
| 'Paper White' | See *N. papyraceus* |
| 'Papillon Blanc' (11b) | EWal LAma |
| 'Papua' (4) ♀ | CQua |
| § *papyraceus* (8) | CMea CQua ETub EWal LAma LBow MBri NRog |
| - AB&S 4399 (13) | Last listed 1998 |
| ¶ 'Paradigm' (4) | IDun |
| 'Parcpat' (7) | CBro |
| 'Parfait' (4) | ICar |
| 'Paricutin' (2) | EWal |
| 'Parisienne' (11a) | EWal LAma NRog |
| 'Park Avenue' (4) | Last listed 1998 |
| 'Park Gate' (2) | ICar |
| 'Park Springs' (3) | CQua ICar |
| ¶ 'Parkfields Beauty' (2) | ICar |
| 'Parterre' (2) | Last listed 1998 |
| 'Parthenon' (4) | ICar |
| ¶ 'Party Time' (2) | IDun |
| 'Passionale' (2) ♀ | CQua EWal IBal LAma NBir |
| 'Pastiche' (2) | CQua |
| 'Pastorale' (2) | EWal |
| 'Patabundy' (2) | CQua |
| 'Patois' (9) | IDun |
| *patulus* (13) | Last listed 1998 |
| 'Paula Cottell' (3) | CBro |
| 'Pawley's Island' (2) | Last listed 1998 |
| 'Pay Day' (1) | ICar |
| 'Peach Prince' (4) | CQua |
| 'Peacock' (2) | ICar |
| I 'Pearlax' | See *N.* 'Perlax' |
| ¶ 'Pearlshell' (11a) | CQua |
| 'Peeping Tom' (6) ♀ | CBro EPar EPot EWal LAma MBri NRog SRms |
| 'Pelynt' (3) | Last listed 1998 |
| 'Pencrebar' (4) | CAvo CBro CQua EPot ERos LAma MBri WShi |
| 'Pengarth' (2) | CQua |
| 'Penkivel' (2) | CQua |
| ¶ 'Pennance Mill' (2) | CQua |
| 'Pennine Way' (1) | CQua |
| 'Pennyghael' (2) | Last listed 1996 |
| 'Penpol' (7) | CBro CQua |
| 'Penril' (6) | CQua |
| 'Pentille' (1) | CQua |
| 'Penvose' (2) | EWal |
| 'Pepper' (2) | CBro |
| 'Pequenita' (7) | CBro |
| 'Percuil' (6) | CQua |
| *perez-chiscanoi* | SSpi |
|   MS 560 (13) | |
| 'Perimeter' (3) | CQua EWal IBal ICar |
| 'Peripheral Pink' (2) | CQua |
| § 'Perlax' (11a) | EWal |
| 'Perseus' (1) | ICar |
| 'Pet Finch' (7) | EWal |
| 'Petit Four' (4) | ETub EWal LAma NRog |
| 'Petrel' (5) | CAvo CBro CMea CQua ETub ICar |

¶ 'Phalarope' (6)    CQua
'Phantom' (11a)    CQua ICar
¶ 'Phinda' (2)    IDun
'Picasso' (3)    ICar
'Pick Up' (11a)    ICar
* 'Pico Yellow'    CQua
'Picoblanco' (2)    CBro
'Pinafore' (2)    EWal
'Pink Angel' (7)    CQua ICar
'Pink Champagne' (4)    CQua
'Pink Charm' (2)    EWal
'Pink Gin' (4)    EWal
'Pink Monarch' (2)    EWal
'Pink Pageant' (4)    CQua EWal IDun
'Pink Panther' (2)    Last listed 1997
'Pink Paradise' (4)    CQua ICar IDun
'Pink Silk' (1)    CQua EHof IDun NZep
'Pink Wing' (2)    CQua
'Pinza' (2) ♀    CQua
'Pipe Major' (2)    CQua EWal
'Pipers Barn' (7)    CBro CQua
¶ 'Piper's Gold' (1)    IDun
'Pipit' (7)    CAvo CBro CMea CQua ERos
     EWal ICar LAma MNrw NBir WShi
'Piquant' (3)    Last listed 1996
'Piraeus' (4)    IDun
'Pismo Beach' (2)    CQua ICar
'Pitchroy' (2)    CQua
¶ 'Pixie's Sister' (7) ♀    ICar
'Playschool' (3)    ICar
**poeticus** (13)    CAvo LAma
§ - var. **bellenicus** (13)    CQua EWal
   - Old Pheasant's Eye    See *N. poeticus* var. *recurvus*
   - var. **physaloides** (13)    CQua ICar
N - 'Plenus' (4)    CAvo CBro CQua ETub GQui
     WCot
   - 'Praecox' (9)    CBro CQua
§ - var. **recurvus** (13) ♀    CBro CGle CQua EBot EPar EPot
     ETub EWal LAma LBow NBir WShi
'Poet's Way' (9)    CQua
'Pol Dornie' (2)    CQua EHof
'Pol Voulin' (2)    EHof
'Polar Circle' (2)    ICar
'Polar Imp' (3)    ICar
'Polbathic' (2)    Last listed 1998
'Polglase' (8)    CBro
'Polglass' (3)    Last listed 1996
'Polindra' (2)    EWal
'Polly's Pearl' (8)    CQua
'Polnesk' (7)    CBro
'Pomona' (3)    LAma
'Pops Legacy' (1)    CQua EHof IBal IDun
'Port Patrick' (3)    IBal
'Port William' (3)    IBal
¶ 'Portfolio' (1)    IDun
'Porthchapel' (7)    CQua
'Portnagolan' (2)    ICar
'Portrait' (2)    CQua
'Portrush' (3)    EWal
'Portstewart' (3)    IBal
'Post House' (4)    Last listed 1998
'Powder Room' (2)    ICar
¶ 'Powerstock' (2)    IDun
'Prairie Fire' (3)    CQua IDun
'Preamble' (1)    CQua IBal ICar
'Premiere' (2)    CQua
'President Carter' (1)    LAma
¶ 'Pretty Baby' (3)    EHof
'Pride of Cornwall' (8)    CBro
¶ 'Primrose Beauty' (4)    CQua
'Primrose Path' (2)    ICar
'Prince of Brunswick' (2)    IBal

¶ 'Princeps' (1)    WShi
¶ 'Princess Alexandra' (6)    CQua
'Princess Zaide' (3)    CQua
'Printal' (11a)    Last listed 1996
'Professor Einstein' (2)    LAma NRog
'Prologue' (1)    EWal
'Prophet' (1)    EWal
'Proska' (2)    Last listed 1996
'Prosperity' (1)    ICar
'Prototype' (6)    IDun
'Pryda' (2)    ICar
**pseudonarcissus** (13)    CBro CGle CQua CRow EMon
     ETub EWFC LAma LBow SSpi
     WJek WShi
§ - 'Lobularis'    CAvo CBro EPar EPot ERos NRog
♦ - subsp. **nobilis**    See *N. nobilis*
   - subsp. **pallidiflorus**    See *N. pallidiflorus*
¶ 'Ptolemy' (1)    CQua
'Pueblo' (7)    ETub ICar
'Pukawa' (7)    ICar
♦ **pulchellus**    See *N. triandrus* subsp. *triandrus*
     var. *pulchellus*
¶ **pumilus** (13)    ERos
'Puppet' (5)    CQua ICar
'Puppy' (6)    EWal
'Purbeck' (3)    CQua EHof EWal ICar IDun
'Quail' (7) ♀    CBro CQua ERos ETub EWal ICar
     LAma NRog
'Quasar' (2)    ICar NZep
Queen Anne's Double Daffodil    See *N.* 'Eystettensis'
♦ 'Queen of Spain'    See *N.* x *johnstonii* 'Queen of
     Spain'
'Queenscourt' (1)    Last listed 1998
'Quetzal' (9)    CQua
'Quick Step' (7)    CQua
¶ 'Quiet Ann' (2)    ICar
'Quiet Day' (2)    CQua ICar
'Quiet Waters' (1)    EHof
'Quince' (12)    CAvo CBro CQua EWal
'Quirinus' (2)    LAma
'Raceview' (2)    ICar
'Radiation' (2)    EWal
'Radical' (6)    Last listed 1996
'Radjel' (4)    CQua
'Rainbow' (2)    CQua EWal ICar
'Ramada' (2)    ICar
'Rame Head' (1)    CQua
'Rameses' (2)    CQua
'Rapture' (6)    CQua
'Rarkmoyle' (2)    ICar
'Rashee' (1)    ICar
'Raspberry Ring' (2)    CQua EHof
'Ravenhill' (3)    CQua EHof
'Recital' (2)    Last listed 1998
'Reckless' (3)    ICar
'Red Arrow' (1)    Last listed 1997
'Red Cameo' (2)    Last listed 1998
'Red Cottage' (2)    ICar
'Red Devil' (2)    ICar
'Red Devon' (2) ♀    Last listed 1993
'Red Ember' (3)    IDun
'Red Goblet' (2)    LAma
'Red Haze' (2)    Last listed 1998
'Red Hot' (2)    CQua
'Red Hugh' (9)    IBal
'Red Mission' (2)    Last listed 1998
¶ 'Red Rascal' (2)    ETub
'Red Spartan' (2)    Last listed 1998
'Redhill' (2)    EWal
'Redman' (2)    IBal
'Redstart' (3)    EWal
'Refrain' (2)    EHof

'Regal Bliss' (2) — CQua
'Reggae' (6) ♀ — ICar
'Rembrandt' (1) — LAma MBri
¶ 'Rendezvous Caye' (2) — EHof
'Replete' (4) — CQua ICar
'Reprieve' (3) — Last listed 1997
*requienii* — See *N. assoanus*
'Resplendent' (2) — ICar
'Revival' (4) — EWal
'Ridgecrest' (3) — IDun
'Riding Mill' (3) — EWal
'Riesling' (11a) — CQua
*rifanus* — See *N. romieuxii* subsp.
    *romieuxii* var. *rifanus*
'Rijnveld's Early — CBro CQua EWal MBri
    Sensation' (1) ♀
'Rikki' (7) — CBro CQua ERos
'Rim Ride' (3) — ICar
'Rima' (1) — CQua
'Rimmon' (3) — CQua IDun
'Rimski' (2) — Last listed 1998
¶ 'Ring Fence' (3) — IDun
'Ringhaddy' (3) — IBal
¶ 'Ringing Bells' (5) — CQua
'Ringleader' (2) — CQua EWal
'Ringmaster' (2) — CQua ICar
'Ringmer' (3) — Last listed 1996
'Ringwood' (3) — Last listed 1998
'Rio Bravo' (2) — IBal
'Rio Gusto' (2) — IBal
'Rio Lobo' (2) — IBal
'Rio Rondo' (2) — IBal
'Rio Rouge' (2) — IBal ICar
§ 'Rip van Winkle' (4) — CAvo CBro EPar EPot ERos ETub
    LAma LBow MBri NMGW NRog
    SLod WShi
'Rippling Waters' (5) ♀ — CBro CQua EPot ICar LAma
'Riptide' (1) — ICar
'Ristin' (1) — CQua
¶ 'Rival' (6) — CQua
'Rivendell' (3) — ICar IDun
'River Dance' (2) — IDun
'Rob Roy' (3) — EWal
'Rock Creek' (3) — IDun
'Rockall' (3) — CQua ICar
'Rockport' (2) — ICar
'Rococo' (2) — EWal
'Roger' (6) — CBro
'Romance' (2) ♀ — CQua EWal LAma
§ 'Romanus' (4) — CQua
'Romany Red' (3) — Last listed 1998
*romieuxii* (13) ♀ — CAvo CBro CFil CNic EHyt EPot
    ERos SSpi WAbe WPGP
- AB&S 4384 (13) — NHar
- AB&S 4656 (13) — Last listed 1996
- subsp. *albidus* (13) — Last listed 1998
- - S&F 110 (13) — Last listed 1998
- - S&F 256 (13) — EHyt
§ - - var. *zaianicus* (13) — Last listed 1998
§ - - - f. *albus* MS 168 (13) — Last listed 1998
§ - - - f. *lutescens* (13) — EHyt
§ - - - - S&F 374 (13) — NHar
- 'Atlas Gold' — EPot
- 'Atlas Gold' JCA 805Y (10) — GCrs NHar
- JCA 805 (10) — EPot NHar
§ - 'Joy Bishop' ex JCA — EHyt EPot
    805 (10)
§ - 'Julia Jane' ex JCA 805 (10) — ERos GCrs NHar
§ - subsp. *romieuxii* var. — EHyt SWas
    *mesatlanticus* (13)
§ - - var. *rifanus* SB&L — Last listed 1998
    207 (13)

- S&F 370 (13) — Last listed 1998
- 'Treble Chance' ex — EPot
    JCA 805 (10)
¶ 'Rory's Glen' (2) — ICar
'Rosado' (11a) — EWal
'Roscarrick' (6) — CQua
'Rose Gold' (1) — IDun
'Rose of May' (4) — ICar
'Rose Royale' (2) — CQua IBal
'Roseate Tern' (2) — CQua
'Rosedown' (5) — CBro
'Roseworthy' (2) — LAma
'Rossferry' (2) — IBal
'Rosy Sunrise' (2) — LAma
'Rosy Trumpet' (1) — CBro
'Rosy Wonder' (2) — EWal
'Round Robin' (2) — ICar
¶ 'Royal Ballet' (2) — CQua
'Royal Coachman' (2) — ICar
'Royal Command' — See *N.* 'Royal Decree'
§ 'Royal Decree' (2) — EWal
'Royal Dornoch' (1) — Last listed 1996
'Royal Orange' (2) — EFam EWal
'Royal Princess' (3) — CQua EHof
'Royal Regiment' (2) — CQua ICar
'Royal Wedding' (2) — ICar
'Rubh Mor' (2) — CQua EHof
'Ruby Rose' (4) — IDun
'Ruby Tail' (2) — EWal
'Rubyat' (6) — IBal
¶ 'Rugulosus' (7) ♀ — CAvo CBro EBot EPar ERos LAma
    NRog
*rupicola* (13) — CAvo CLAP ERos LAma MRPP
    MS&S NSla SSpi
§ - subsp. *marvieri* (13) ♀ — SSpi
- - AB&S 4414 (13) — NHar
- - S&F 126 (13) — Last listed 1998
- MS 567 (13) — Last listed 1998
§ - subsp. *watieri* (13) — CBro EHyt GCrs MTho WPGP
'Rushmore' (2) — IDun
¶ 'Rustom Pasha' (2) — CQua
'Ruth Haller' (5) — ICar
'Rutland Water' (2) — Last listed 1997
'Rytha' (2) — CQua
'Saberwing' (5) — CQua ICar
'Sabine Hay' (3) — CQua EWal ICar IDun
'Sacajawea' (2) — EWal
'Saint Dilpe' (2) — CQua
'Saint Duthus' (1) — Last listed 1996
'Saint Keverne' (2) ♀ — CQua EWal IBal LAma NRog
'Saint Keyne' (8) — CQua
'Saint Mawes' (2) — Last listed 1998
'Saint Patrick's Day' (2) — CQua EWal LAma
'Saint Piran' (7) — CQua
'Salmon Trout' (2) — CQua EWal LAma
'Salome' (2) — EWal LAma MBri NBir NRog
'Samantha' (4) — CQua
'Samaria' (3) — CBro
'Samba' (5) — ERos
'Samite' (1) — EWal
'Sancerre' (11a) — CQua
¶ 'Sandycove' (2) — IDun
'Sandymount' (2) — IBal
'Sarah' (2) — EWal
'Sarah Dear' (2) — CQua
¶ 'Sargeant's Caye' (1) — EHof
'Sateen' (2) — EWal
'Satellite' (6) — EWal ICar
'Satin Pink' (2) — EWal MBri
'Saturn' (3) — CQua ICar
'Savoir Faire' (2) — IDun
*scaberulus* (13) — CBro ERos

'Scamp' (3) — ICar
'Scarlet Elegance' (2) — LAma
'Scarlet Gem' (8) — EWal LAma
'Scarlett O'Hara' (2) — CQua LAma
'Sea Dream' (3) — CQua EWal
'Sea Gift' (7) — CBro CQua
'Sea Green' (9) — CQua
'Sealing Wax' (2) — CQua EWal
'Segovia' (3) ♀ — CBro CQua ERos
¶ 'Selma Lagerlöf' (2) — EFam
'Sempre Avanti' (2) — LAma MBri NRog
'Sennocke' (5) — CBro
¶ 'Seraglio' (3) — CQua
'Serena Beach' (4) — IDun
'Serena Lodge' (4) — IDun
*serotinus* (13) — Last listed 1998
– S&F 285 (13) — Last listed 1998
– S&F 298 (13) — Last listed 1998
'Sextant' (6) — CQua EWal
'Shanes Castle' (1) — ICar
¶ 'Shangani' (2) — IDun
'She' (2) — EWal
'Sheelagh Rowan' (2) — EHof
'Sheer Joy' (6) — IDun
'Sheerline' (2) — Last listed 1998
'Shepherd's Hey' (7) — Last listed 1996
'Sherborne' (4) — IDun
'Sherpa' (1) — CQua IDun
'Sheviock' (2) — CQua
'Shimna' (1) — IBal
'Shining Light' (2) — CQua ICar
'Shorecliffe' (2) — IDun
'Shot Silk' (5) — LAma
'Show Band' (2) — Last listed 1998
¶ 'Siam' (2) — EFam
'Sidley' (3) — CQua IDun
'Sidney' (9) — Last listed 1998
'Signorina' (2) — IDun
'Silent Pink' (2) — IDun
'Silent Valley' (1) — CQua EHof
'Silk Cut' (2) — CQua
'Silken Sails' (3) — ICar
¶ 'Silken Wings' (2) — IDun
'Silver Bells' (5) — CQua IDun
'Silver Blaze' (2) — Last listed 1998
'Silver Chimes' (8) — CBro CQua EPot EWal LAma NBir NRog
'Silver Crystal' (3) — IDun
'Silver Plate' (11a) — CQua
'Silver Princess' (3) — Last listed 1997
'Silver Standard' (2) — CQua EWal
'Silver Surf' (2) — CQua IDun
'Silvermere' (2) — Last listed 1996
'Silversmith' (2) — Last listed 1996
'Silverwood' (3) — IDun
'Simply Bloomfield' (2) — ICar
¶ 'Singing Pub' (3) — IDun
¶ 'Sir Watkin' (2) — CQua
'Sir Winston Churchill' (4) ♀ — CQua EWal LAma NRog
'Skerry' (2) — ICar
'Slaney' (3) — ICar
'Sligachan' (1) — Last listed 1996
'Small Fry' (1) — Last listed 1997
'Small Talk' (1) — CQua
'Smokey Bear' (4) — CQua
'Snoopie' (6) — CQua
'Snow Bunting' (7) — CBro
'Snowcrest' (3) — CQua
'Snowfire' (4) — ICar
'Snowshill' (2) — CQua
'Snug' (1) — Last listed 1996
'Society Belle' (2) — Last listed 1998

'Solar Tan' (3) — CQua IDun
'Soldier Brave' (2) — EWal
'Soledad' (2) — ICar
'Soleil d'Or' (8) — EWal MBri
'Sonata' (9) — CQua
'Songket' (2) — Last listed 1998
'Sophia' (2) — Last listed 1998
'Soprano' (2) — IDun
'Sorbet' (11b) — EWal
'Sorcerer' (3) — CQua
'South Street' (2) — CQua
'Southease' (2) — Last listed 1996
'Sovereign' (11a) — IDun
'Spaniards Inn' (4) — CQua
'Spanish Moon' (1) — EWal
'Sparkling Eye' (8) — IBal
'Spellbinder' (1) ♀ — EFam EWal LAma MBri
'Sperrin Gold' (1) — IDun
'Spirit of Rame' (3) — CQua
'Split Image' (2) — IDun
'Sportsman' (2) — CQua
'Spring Dawn' (2) — EWal
¶ 'Spring Morn' (2) — CQua IDun
'Stadium' (2) — EWal
¶ 'Stainless' (2) — ETub
'Standard Value' (1) — LAma
'Stanway' (3) — CQua
'Star Glow' (2) — Last listed 1998
'Star War' (2) — CQua
'Starfire' (7) — CQua ICar
'State Express' (2) — CQua EHof
'Statue' (1) — EWal
'Steenbok' (3) — IDun
¶ 'Step Forward' (7) — ERos
'Stilton' (9) — CQua
'Stint' (5) — CBro CQua
'Stocken' (7) — CBro
* 'Stockens Gib' — Last listed 1997
'Stoke Charity' (2) — EHof ICar
'Stoke Doyle' (2) — EHof
'Stormy Weather' (1) — CQua ICar IDun
'Stourbridge' (2) — ICar
'Stranocum' (3) — ICar
'Strathkanaird' (1) — ICar
'Stratosphere' (7) — CQua ICar
'Stray' (6) — ICar
'Strines' (2) — CQua EWal
'Stromboli' (2) — EWal
'Suave' (1) — CQua EHof
'Suda Bay' (2) — ICar
'Sugar and Spice' (3) — EHof
¶ 'Sugar Bird' (2) — IDun
'Sugar Loaf' (4) — CQua
'Sugarbush' (7) — CBro LAma MBri NRog
'Suilven' (3) — Last listed 1996
'Sumo Jewel' (6) — CQua
'Sun Disc' (7) ♀ — CAvo CBro CQua EPot ERos EWal ICar LAma MBri
'Sunapee' (3) — Last listed 1998
'Sundial' (7) — CAvo CBro CQua EPot ERos EWal ICar LAma
'Suntory' (3) — CQua
¶ 'Suntrap' (2) — IDun
¶ 'Super Bowl' (2) — IDun
'Surfside' (6) ♀ — CBro CQua
'Surrey' (2) — CQua
'Susan Pearson' (7) — ICar
'Suzie Dee' (6) — IDun
¶ 'Suzie's Sister' (6) — IDun
'Suzy' (7) ♀ — CBro EWal ICar LAma MBri NRog
'Swaledale' (2) — CQua
¶ 'Swallow Wing' (6) — IDun

| | |
|---|---|
| 'Swallowcliffe' (6) | Last listed 1996 |
| 'Swansdown' (4) | EWal ICar |
| ¶ 'Sweet Blanche' (7) | CQua |
| 'Sweet Charity' (2) | EWal |
| ¶ 'Sweet Harmony' (2) | ETub |
| 'Sweet Pepper' (7) | CBro |
| 'Sweet Sue' (3) | EHof |
| 'Sweetness' (7) ♀ | CAvo CBro CQua EWal IBal LAma NRog WShi |
| 'Swing Wing' (6) | CQua |
| 'Sydling' (5) | CQua |
| 'Sylvan Hill' (1) | IBal |
| 'Symphonette' (2) | Last listed 1996 |
| 'Taffeta' (10) | CAvo CBro EHyt LRHS |
| 'Tahiti' (4) ♀ | CQua EWal LAma MBri NRog |
| 'Tain' (1) | ICar |
| 'Takoradi' (4) | ICar |
| 'Talwyn' (1) | CQua |
| 'Tamar Fire' (4) ♀ | CQua |
| ¶ 'Tamar Lad' (2) | CQua |
| 'Tamar Snow' (2) | CQua |
| 'Tamara' (2) | CQua |
| ♦ tananicus | See N. cantabricus subsp. tananicus |
| 'Tangent' (2) | CQua EWal ICar |
| 'Tara Rose' (2) | Last listed 1997 |
| 'Tardree' (1) | ICar |
| 'Tarlatan' (10) | CBro |
| 'Taslass' (4) | CQua |
| 'Tater-Du' (5) | CQua |
| tazetta subsp. aureus | See N. aureus |
| § - subsp. lacticolor (13) | CQua |
| ¶ - - 'Grand Monarque' (8) | CQua |
| - - MS 517 (13) | Last listed 1998 |
| - - MS 519 (13) | Last listed 1998 |
| - subsp. papyraceus | See N. papyraceus |
| 'Teal' (1) | EHof |
| 'Tedstone' (1) | EWal |
| ¶ 'Tehidy' (3) | CQua |
| § 'Telamonius Plenus' (4) | CBro LAma WShi |
| ¶ 'Temple Cloud' (4) | IDun |
| tenuifolius | See N. bulbocodium subsp. bulbocodium var. tenuifolius |
| § x tenuior (13) | CAvo |
| 'Terracotta' (2) | IDun |
| ¶ 'Terrapin' (3) | IDun |
| 'Testament' (2) | EWal |
| 'Tête-à-tête' (12) ♀ | CAvo CBro CQua EPar EPot ERos ETub EWal IBal LAma LBow MBNS MBri |
| 'Texas' (4) | LAma MBri |
| 'Thalia' (5) | CAvo CBro CMea ERos ETub EWal ICar LAma LBow MBri NBir NRog WShi |
| 'The Alliance' (6) | CQua |
| 'The Knave' (6) | CQua |
| 'The Little Gentleman' (6) | CBro |
| 'Thoughtful' (5) | CBro CQua EWal |
| 'Three Trees' (1) | ICar |
| 'Thunderbolt' (1) | EWal |
| 'Tibet' (2) | EWal |
| 'Tiercel' (1) | CQua |
| 'Tiffany' (10) | Last listed 1998 |
| 'Tiger Moth' (6) | Last listed 1998 |
| 'Timolin' (3) | CQua ICar |
| 'Tinnell' (1) | Last listed 1997 |
| ¶ 'Tiritomba' (11a) | CQua EWal |
| 'Titania' (6) | CQua |
| 'Tittle-tattle' (7) | CBro CQua EWal IBal LAma |
| 'Toby' (2) | EWal |
| 'Toby the First' (6) | CQua |
| 'Tonga' (4) | ICar |

| | |
|---|---|
| 'Top Hit' (11a) | CQua |
| 'Top of the Hill' (3) | IBal ICar |
| 'Topkapi' (2) | IBal |
| 'Topolino' (1) | CAvo CBro CQua EPot LAma NRog |
| 'Torcross' (3) | Last listed 1998 |
| 'Torr Head' (9) | IBal |
| 'Torridon' (2) | CQua EHof ICar |
| ¶ 'Toscanini' (2) | EFam |
| 'Tracey' (6) | CBro CQua |
| 'Tranquil Morn' (3) | EWal |
| 'Trebah' (2) | CQua |
| ¶ 'Treble Two' (7) | CQua |
| 'Trefusis' (1) | CQua |
| 'Tregarrick' (2) | CQua |
| 'Trehane' (6) | CQua |
| 'Trena' (6) | CBro CQua EWal |
| 'Tresamble' (5) | CBro CQua EWal LAma |
| 'Trevelmond' (2) | CQua |
| 'Treverva' (6) | CQua |
| 'Treviddo' (2) | CQua |
| 'Trevithian' (7) ♀ | CBro CQua EWal IBal LAma NRog |
| 'Trewidland' (2) | CQua |
| 'Trewirgie' (6) | CBro CQua |
| triandrus (13) ♀ | NSla WPGP |
| ♦ - var. albus | See N. triandrus subsp. triandrus var. triandrus |
| § - var. concolor (13) | CBro MS&S |
| § - subsp. triandrus var. pulchellus (13) | LAma |
| § - - var. triandrus (13) | EBot |
| 'Tricollet' (11a) | CQua EWal |
| 'Triller' (7) | ICar |
| 'Tripartite' (11a) | CQua EWal ICar NZep |
| 'Triple Crown' (3) ♀ | CQua IDun |
| 'Tristram' (2) | CQua EHof |
| 'Tropic Isle' (4) | ICar |
| ¶ 'Tropical Heat' (2) | IDun |
| 'Trousseau' (1) | CQua EWal |
| 'Troutbeck' (3) | CQua |
| ¶ 'Trumpet Warrior' (1) | IDun |
| 'Tudor Grove' (2) | Last listed 1998 |
| 'Tudor Minstrel' (2) | CQua EWal |
| 'Tuesday's Child' (5) ♀ | CQua EWal ICar MBNS |
| 'Tullygirvan' (2) | ICar |
| 'Tullynog' (4) | ICar |
| 'Tullyroyal' (2) | IBal |
| 'Turncoat' (6) | CQua |
| 'Tutankhamun' (2) | CQua |
| 'Tweeny' (2) | Last listed 1998 |
| 'Twicer' (2) | Last listed 1998 |
| 'Tyee' (2) | CQua |
| 'Tykky-dew' (2) | EHof |
| 'Tynan' (2) | ICar |
| 'Tyneham' (3) | Last listed 1998 |
| 'Tyrian Rose' (2) | IDun |
| 'Tyrone Gold' (1) ♀ | IDun |
| ¶ 'Tywara' (1) | EHof |
| 'Ufo' (3) | EWal |
| 'Ulster Bank' (3) | Last listed 1998 |
| 'Ulster Bullion' (2) | IBal |
| 'Ulster Prince' (1) ♀ | Last listed 1994 |
| 'Ultimus' (2) | EWal |
| 'Una Bremner' (2) | Last listed 1996 |
| 'Uncle Ben' (1) | Last listed 1996 |
| 'Uncle Duncan' (1) | CQua EHof IDun |
| 'Uncle Remus' (1) | EWal |
| 'Unique' (4) | CQua EWal ICar LAma |
| 'Unsurpassable' (1) | LAma |
| 'Upper Broughton' (2) | Last listed 1996 |
| 'Urchin' (3) | See N. 'Pzaz' |
| 'Vahu' (2) | IDun |

'Val d'Incles' (3) — IDun
'Valdrome' (11a) — CQua ICar MBri
'Valediction' (3) — Last listed 1998
'Valinor' (2) — Last listed 1998
'Value' (2) — IDun
'Van Sion' — See *N.* 'Telamonius Plenus'
¶ 'Vandyke' (2) — IDun
'Verdin' (7) — CQua ICar
'Verger' (3) — LAma MBri
'Vernal Prince' (3) — CQua
'Verona' (3) ♀ — CQua
'Vers Libre' (9) — CQua
'Verwood' (3) — Last listed 1998
¶ 'Vice-President' (2) — ICar
¶ 'Victorious' (2) — CQua
'Victory' (2) — EWal
'Vigil' (1) ♀ — CQua EWal ICar
'Vigilante' (1) — Last listed 1998
'Viking' (1) ♀ — CQua EHof
'Vilna' (2) — EWal
'Violetta' (2) — CQua EWal ICar
'Vireo' (7) — ICar
'Virgil' (9) — Last listed 1996
¶ *viridiflorus* (13) — WCot
— MS 500 (13) — Last listed 1998
— S&F 323 (13) — Last listed 1998
'Vivarino' (11?b) — EWal
'Volare' (2) — Last listed 1998
'Voltage' (2) — Last listed 1998
'Vulcan' (2) ♀ — CQua EWal
W.P. Milner' (1) — CAvo CBro CMea EPot LAma MBri NRog
¶ 'Waif' (6) — CQua ICar
'Waldorf Astoria' (4) — CQua IDun
'Walesby' (2) — Last listed 1998
¶ 'War Dance' (3) — IDun
¶ 'Warbler' (6) — CQua
'Warleigh' (2) — Last listed 1998
'Warm Day' (2) — ICar
'Waterperry' (7) — CBro LAma NRog
♦ *watieri* — See *N. rupicola* subsp. *watieri*
— AB&S 4518 (13) — SSpi
¶ 'Wavelength' (3) — IDun
'Waxwing' (5) — CQua
'Webster' (9) — Last listed 1996
'Wee Bee' (1) — CQua
'Wendy Walsh' (2) — ICar
'Westbury' (4) — Last listed 1998
'Westholme' (2) — Last listed 1996
'Westward' (4) — CQua EWal
'Wetherby' (3) — Last listed 1998
'Whang-hi' (6) — CQua
¶ 'Wheal Jane' (2) — CQua
'Wheal Kitty' (7) — CQua
'Whetstone' (1) — CQua
'Whipcord' (7) — IDun
¶ 'Whisky Mac' (2) — EHof
'Whisper' (5) — EWal
'Whitbourne' (3) — EWal
'White Butterfly' (2) — EWal
'White Cross' (2) — Last listed 1998
'White Hill' (2) — IBal
¶ 'White Hunter' (1) — ICar
'White Lady' (3) — CQua WShi
'White Lion' (4) ♀ — CQua EFam EWal LAma NRog
'White Marvel' (4) — CQua EWal LAma NRog
'White Mist' (2) — ICar
'White Phantom' (1) — ICar
'White Plume' (2) — EWal
'White Star' (1) — CQua EHof ICar IDun
'Whiteabbey' (2) — IBal
'Widgeon' (2) — EWal

*willkommii* (13) — CBro
'Winchester' (2) — EWal
'Wind Song' (2) — EHof
'Windjammer' (1) — EWal
'Winfrith' (2) — EWal
'Winged Victory' (6) — Last listed 1998
'Witch Doctor' (3) — IBal
'Witch Hunt' (4) — IBal
¶ 'Wodan' (2) — EFam
'Woodcock' (6) — CBro CQua
'Woodgreen' (2) — EWal
'Woodland Prince' (3) — CQua
'Woodland Star' (3) — CQua
'Woodvale' (2) — Last listed 1998
'Worcester' (2) — EWal
'Xit' (3) — CBro CQua SWas
'Xunantunich' (2) — EHof IDun
'Yeats' (9) — ICar
'Yellow Cheerfulness' (4) ♀ — ETub EWal LAma MBri NRog
'Yellow Standard' (2) — LAma
'Yellow Sun' (3) — LAma
'Yellow Tresamble' (5) — Last listed 1996
'Yes Please' (2) — EWal
'York Minster' (1) — EHof IDun
'Yoshiko' (2) — Last listed 1998
'Young Blood' (2) — IDun
'Young Idea' (7) — EWal
'Your Grace' (2) — EHof
♦ *zaianicus* — See *N. romieuxii* subsp. *albidus* var. *zaianicus*
— var. *albus* MS 168 — See *N. romieuxii* subsp. *albidus* var. *zaianicus* f. *albus* MS 168
'Zelah' (1) — Last listed 1998
'Zion Canyon' (2) — Last listed 1998

## NARDOPHYLLUM (Asteraceae)
*bryoides* — GTou

## NARDOSTACHYS (Valerianaceae)
*grandiflora* — GPoy

## NARTHECIUM (Melanthiaceae)
*ossifragum* — WShi

## NASSAUVIA (Asteraceae)
*gaudichaudii* — Last listed 1998

## NASSELLA (Poaceae)
*trichotoma* — CHar EGar EHoe EMon EPPr EPla GBin LHil MCCP SApp SMrm SPla WCot WElm

## NASTURTIUM (Brassicaceae)
*officinale* — CAgr SWat WHer

## NAUTILOCALYX (Gesneriaceae)
*pemphidius* — WDib

## NECTAROSCORDUM (Alliaceae)
¶ *bivalve* — ERos
§ *siculum* — CArn CAvo CBro CGle CMea CMil EBee EBrP EBre ELan EMan EOrc EPar GMaP LBre LLWP MBal MBel NBir NEgg NSti SBre SSoC SSvw SUsu WFar WHil WPGP WRHF
§ — subsp. *bulgaricum* — CBro CHad CRDP EBee ECha EPar EPot ERos ETub IBlr LBow LEdu LFis LPio MNrw NBid NOrc SOkh SSpi WAbb WBrE WBro WCot
*tripedale* — CLAP

## NEILLIA (Rosaceae)

| | |
|---|---|
| *affinis* | CDoC CPle EBee EHal EHic MBal NBid NPro WHCG |
| *longiracemosa* | See *N. thibetica* |
| *rubiflora* CC&McK 18 | Last listed 1997 |
| *sinensis* | CMCN CPle MRav |
| - var. *ribesioides* | MBel SPan |
| § *thibetica* | More than 30 suppliers |
| *thyrsiflora* | Last listed 1996 |

## NELUMBO (Nymphaeaceae)

| | |
|---|---|
| 'Kermesina' | MSta |
| *lutea* 'Flavescens' | MSta |
| *nucifera* | MSta |
| - 'Alba Grandiflora' | MSta |
| - 'Alba Striata' | MSta |
| - 'Pekinensis Rubra' | MSta |
| - 'Rosea' | MSta |
| - 'Rosea Plena' (d) | MSta |
| 'Osiris' | MSta |
| 'Pulchra' | MSta |

## NEMASTYLIS (Iridaceae)

| | |
|---|---|
| *tenuis* subsp. *pringlei* | Last listed 1997 |

## NEMATANTHUS (Gesneriaceae)

| | |
|---|---|
| 'Black Magic' | CHal MBri WDib |
| 'Christmas Holly' | WDib |
| 'Freckles' | WDib |
| § *glaber* | MBri SLon |
| § *gregarius* | CHal EBak LCns MBri WDib |
| § - 'Golden West' (v) | CHal MBri WDib |
| - 'Variegatus' | See *N. gregarius* 'Golden West' |
| *radicans* | See *N. gregarius* |
| *strigillosus* | MBri |
| 'Tropicana' ♀ | CHal CSpe MBri WDib |

## NEMESIA (Scrophulariaceae)

| | |
|---|---|
| 'Ainstable Charm' | Last listed 1998 |
| 'Blue Cloud' | NPri WPeH |
| § Bluebird = 'Hubbird' | CSpe EHic LLck NPri WPeH |
| § *caerulea* | CBot ECtt LHil MArl MBEx MTho NFai NTow WCot WPer WWin |
| - 'Elliott's Variety' | CBar LHil |
| - 'Joan Wilder' (clonal) | ECtt EMan WEas WPeH |
| N - 'Joan Wilder' (seed raised) | See *N. caerulea* lilac/blue |
| § - lilac/blue | EOrc LHil MBEx MBNS WCot WPer WPyg WWin |
| - 'Woodcote' | GPin LHil MArl MBEx WPeH |
| § *denticulata* | CBar CHad CHal CSpe ECtt EMar EOrc GMac IMGH LHil LHop MArl MAsh MBEx MBNS NPri SCob SCoo SMrm SRob SUsu SYvo WCot WFar WFoF WPeH WRus WWeb WWhi |
| ¶ - 'Coco Pops' | WPeH |
| - 'Confetti' | See *N. denticulata* |
| 'Evening Wine' | WPeH |
| § Fleuron = 'Melanie' | NPri SCoo WPeH |
| *foetens* | See *N. caerulea* |
| 'Fragrant Cloud' | CB&S CChe CHea EOrc GCal MAsh MBEx MBel MCCP MLLN MNrw NLak NTow SPer SPla WPeH |
| *fruticans* misapplied | See *N. caerulea* |
| - Benth. | WPeH |
| 'Georgina' | MBEx |
| 'Hermione' | Last listed 1996 |
| ♦ 'Hubbird' | See *N.* Bluebird = 'Hubbird' |
| 'Innocence' | CHal CSpe EHic EMan LFis LHil LHop LLck MArl MBEx MMil NLak SMrm WCot WEas WLRN WPeH |

| | |
|---|---|
| ♦ 'Melanie' | See *N.* Fleuron = 'Melanie' |
| 'Orchard Blue' | MMil WPeH |
| 'Penhow Pride' | WPeH |
| ¶ 'Snowstorm' | LHop WPeH |
| ¶ 'Tufty' | WCot |
| *umbonata* hort. | See *N. caerulea* lilac/blue |

## NEMOPHILA (Hydrophyllaceae)

| | |
|---|---|
| *menziesii* | Last listed 1997 |

## NEODYPSIS (Arecaceae)

| | |
|---|---|
| *decaryi* | See *Dypsis decaryi* |
| *leptocheilos* | See *Dypsis leptocheilos* |

## NEOLITSEA (Lauraceae)

| | |
|---|---|
| *glauca* | See *N. sericea* |
| § *sericea* | CB&S SSpi WCoo |

## NEOMARICA (Iridaceae)

| | |
|---|---|
| *northiana* | Last listed 1998 |

## NEOPANAX See PSEUDOPANAX

## NEOPAXIA (Portulacaceae)

| | |
|---|---|
| § *australasica* | ECou ESis |
| - blue-leaved | See *N. australasica* 'Kosciusko' |
| - bronze-leaved | See *N. australasica* 'Ohau' |
| § - 'Great Lake' | Last listed 1997 |
| - green-leaved | See *N. australasica* 'Great Lake' |
| - grey | See *N. australasica* 'Kosciusko' |
| § - 'Kosciusko' | GDra GGar |
| - 'Lakeside' | Last listed 1997 |
| - 'Lyndon' | ECou |
| § - 'Ohau' | ECou GGar |

## NEOREGELIA (Bromeliaceae)

| | |
|---|---|
| *carolinae* | MBri SRms |
| § - (Meyendorffii Group) 'Flandria' (v) | MBri |
| - - 'Meyendorffii' | MBri |
| - f. *tricolor* (v) ♀ | CHal MBri |
| § Claret Group | MBri |
| *spectabilis* ♀ | Last listed 1990 |

## NEOTINEA (Orchidaceae)

| | |
|---|---|
| ¶ *maculata* | WCot |

## NEOTTIANTHE (Orchidaceae)

| | |
|---|---|
| *cucullata* | EFEx |

## NEPENTHES (Nepenthaceae)

| | |
|---|---|
| *alata* | WMEx |
| *bongso* x *hamata* | WMEx |
| x *coccinea* | MBri WMEx |
| *gracilis* | WMEx |
| *gymnamphora* | WMEx |
| hybrids | Last listed 1998 |
| *khasiana* | WMEx |
| *lowii* | WMEx |
| *macfarlanei* | Last listed 1996 |
| *madagascariensis* | WMEx |
| *maxima* | WMEx |
| - x *mixta* | WMEx |
| *mirabilis* | WMEx |
| *muluensis* | WMEx |
| *rafflesiana* | WMEx |
| - x *ampullaria* | See *N.* x *hookeriana* |
| *rajah* | WMEx |
| *reinwardtiana* | WMEx |
| *sanguinea* | WMEx |
| *tentaculata* | WMEx |
| *tobaica* | WMEx |

| | |
|---|---|
| *tomoriana* | WMEx |
| *truncata* | WMEx |
| *ventricosa* | WMEx |
| – slim x *spectabilis* | WMEx |
| *vieillardii* | WMEx |

## NEPETA ✿ (Lamiaceae)

| | |
|---|---|
| *argolica* | See *N. sibthorpii* |
| ¶ cf.*betonicifolia* DS&T 89054T | EMon |
| 'Blue Beauty' | See *N. sibirica* 'Souvenir d'André Chaudron' |
| *bucharica* | GBuc WOut |
| * *buddlejifolium* | NLar |
| *camphorata* | CSam EMFP GAbr GTou LHol MLLN MNrw MSte NSti SCro SIde SPil WOve WRha WWye |
| *cataria* | CAgr CArn CSev EBee ELau GBar GPoy LHol MChe MMal MSal NBro SIde WHer WOak WPer WSel WWye |
| – 'Citriodora' | CArn CBot CLTr CSam CStr EFou EHal ELau GBar GPoy IIve MHer MSal NFai NSti SChu SIde SSpe WBea WCHb WHer WRha WSel WWye |
| *clarkei* | CHan CLon CMHG CMea CSam EBee EFou EMan MHar MNrw MSte NCat NLak SBla SCro SSvw SWat WPer |
| *dinphya* | Last listed 1998 |
| § x *faassenii* | CGle CHar EAst EBee ECGN EMon ERic GLil MBel MCAu MRav MWat MWgw MWhi NGdn NPer NVic SAga SChu SCro SEas SPla SRPl SRms |
| – 'Alba' | CStr EPfP NLar |
| *glechoma* 'Variegata' | See *Glechoma hederacea* 'Variegata' |
| 'Gottfried Kühn' | Last listed 1996 |
| *govaniana* | More than 30 suppliers |
| *grandiflora* | CLTr EFou LFis LHol MGrG MRav NFai NSti SIde SMrm WHer WWhi |
| – 'Bramdean' | CRDP CSam CStr EGar LGre MBri NCat SUsu SWas WKif WOut WViv |
| – 'Dawn to Dusk' | More than 30 suppliers |
| – 'Pool Bank' | CRDP CStr EFou EGoo MBel NCat NFai SAga SChu SDys SMrm SUsu |
| *hederacea* 'Variegata' | See *Glechoma hederacea* 'Variegata' |
| ¶ *kubabiana* | CStr |
| ¶ *kubanica* | EMon |
| *laevigata* | EBee |
| *lanceolata* | See *N. nepetella* |
| *latifolia* | EBee MLLN |
| * *longipes* | CHan CSam EAst EMan EMon GBri MLLN MSte NSti SAga SBla SChu SCro SHel SMrm SUsu SWas WCot WFar WHal WPer WPrP WRus WViv |
| *macrantha* | See *N. sibirica* |
| ¶ *mariae* JJH 948425 | EBee |
| *melissifolia* | EBee WCHb WPer WWye |
| ♦ *mussinii* hort. | See *N.* x *faassenii* |
| § *nepetella* | CSam EBee GBar GBri LHol NBir NChi WPer WViv WWhi |
| *nervosa* | CArn CLon CSpe EBee ELan ENot EWTr LGre LHol MCLN MFir MSte NBro NFai NOak NSti SChu SCro SEas SIde WHoo WPer WPyg |
| – 'Forncett' | CSam |
| – 'Forncett Select' | EFou EMan SDys SUsu SWas |

| | |
|---|---|
| § *nuda* | CPle CSam EBee ECha EHal EMan LHol MLLN WCot WFar WMaN WPer |
| – subsp. *albiflora* | CHan CStr EBee ECha EGar |
| * – 'Anne's Choice' | CStr WCot |
| – 'Nacre' | CStr |
| – subsp. *nuda* | CHan EGar EMou |
| *pannonica* | See *N. nuda* |
| *parnassica* | CHar CMea CMil CPlt CSam EBee EMil EWTr LRHS MWll NChi NLar SAga SMad SMrm SWat WElm WHer WUnu WWhi |
| – CDB 13073 | SCro |
| § *phyllochlamys* | CBot CLTr CPBP MSte NTow SAga SBla |
| 'Pink Dawn' | Last listed 1996 |
| 'Porzellan' | CLTr CStr EBee EFou EMon MSte |
| § *prattii* | EBee EHal EPPr SUsu |
| ¶ – BQE 903 | SWas |
| 'Purple Blotch' | CStr |
| § *racemosa* | CArn CBot COlW CSam CSev EBrP EBre ECGN ELau EHal EWTr GBar LBre LHol MChe MFir MRav NFai NRoo NWes SBre SIde SPla WOak WWin WWye |
| – *alba* | SSvw |
| – 'Blue Ice' | CStr GBuc SMer WHoo |
| – 'Grog' | EFou |
| – 'Karen's Blue' | EFou |
| – 'Little Titch' | CStr EBee ECGP EFou GCal NRoo SAga SChu SCro SMrm SSpe |
| – 'Snowflake' | More than 30 suppliers |
| § – 'Superba' | CBlo CLTr EFou ELan ELau EMon EPPr GBuc MBro SEas WHoo |
| – 'Walker's Low' | More than 30 suppliers |
| *reichenbachiana* | See *N. racemosa* |
| ¶ *salviifolia* | EBee |
| § *sibirica* | More than 30 suppliers |
| § – 'Souvenir d'André Chaudron' | More than 30 suppliers |
| § *sibthorpii* | CSam MNrw NChi WPer |
| *sintenisii* | CStr EBee EGar LBlm |
| 'Six Hills Giant' | More than 30 suppliers |
| sp. DS&T 89048T | CStr EMon |
| sp. DS&T 89054T | Last listed 1998 |
| *stewartiana* | CHar CStr GBuc MBro MFir MLLN WElm WHoo WOut WSan |
| – ACE 1611 | CMil EBee GBuc SMrm WCot |
| – CLD 551 | EBee |
| *subsessilis* | More than 30 suppliers |
| – AGSJ 251 | SDys |
| – forms | MNrw WCot |
| – pink form | CPlt CSam CStr EMon GBri GBuc MHlr SOkh WPrP |
| * – *sensibilis* | SWat WCot |
| – var. *yesoensis* | CHan CPlt CStr |
| *tenuifolia* | MSal |
| *teydea* | MNrw |
| 'Thornbury' | Last listed 1997 |
| *transcaucasica* | CStr LPio SDix |
| ¶ *troodii* | EBee |
| *tuberosa* | CHan CPle CSam CStr ECha ECoo EMan EMar GBar GBri MAvo MHar MRav SChu SCob SCro SSca WOut WPen WWhi WWye |
| *ucranica* | NHex |

## NEPHROLEPIS (Oleandraceae)

| | |
|---|---|
| *cordifolia* | GQui MBri NMar |
| *exaltata* ♀ | ERea |
| – 'Bostoniensis' | LBlm MBri |
| – 'Rooseveltii' | MBri |

| | |
|---|---|
| - 'Smithii' | MBri |
| - 'Smithii Linda' | MBri |
| - 'Teddy Junior' | MBri |
| - 'Todeoides' | NMar |

## NEPHROPHYLLIDIUM (Menyanthaceae)
*cristagalli*    IBlr

## NERINE ✿ (Amaryllidaceae)

| | |
|---|---|
| 'Afterglow' | LAma MBNS SSpr |
| ¶ 'Airies' | SSpr |
| ¶ 'Amalfi' | SSpr |
| 'Angelico' | SSpr |
| *angustifolia* | Last listed 1998 |
| ¶ 'Atlanta' | SSpr |
| 'Baghdad' | SSpr |
| ¶ 'Belladonna' | SSpr |
| 'Berlioz' | SSpr |
| 'Betty Hudson' | CRDP |
| 'Blanchefleur' | SSpr |
| * 'Borde Hill White' | SSpr |
| *bowdenii* ♀ | More than 30 suppliers |
| - 'Alba' | CBro SCoo WCot |
| - Logan strain | GCal |
| - 'Manina' | WCot |
| - 'Mark Fenwick' | CB&S ECha EPot GCal LHop |
| | WCot |
| - 'Mollie Cowie' (v) | EMon GVic IBlr WCot WCru |
| - 'Pink Triumph' | CB&S CBlo CLyd GBuc IBlr LAma |
| | LNor NRog SDeJ SPer WCot |
| - 'Wellsii' | CRDP WCot |
| ¶ 'Brahms' | SSpr |
| *breachiae* | Last listed 1996 |
| 'Brocade' | Last listed 1998 |
| 'Camellia' | Last listed 1997 |
| 'Canasta' | SSpr |
| ¶ 'Cardinal' | SSpr |
| ¶ 'Carnival' | SSpr |
| 'Caroline' | SSpr |
| 'Catherine' | SSpr |
| 'Catkin' | Last listed 1997 |
| 'Christmas' | Last listed 1997 |
| 'Clarabel' | SSpr |
| 'Clarissa' | SSpr |
| 'Clent Charm' | SSpr |
| *corusca* 'Major' | See *N. sarniensis* var. *corusca* |
| *crispa* | See *N. undulata* |
| ¶ 'Cynthia Chance' | SSpr |
| 'Dame Alice Godman' | SSpr |
| 'Darius' | SSpr |
| 'Dorellia' | SSpr |
| 'Dover' | Last listed 1997 |
| ¶ 'Drucilla' | SSpr |
| 'Druid' | Last listed 1997 |
| 'Dunkirk' | SSpr |
| 'Elspeth' | SSpr |
| 'Enchantress' | Last listed 1997 |
| 'Eve' | SSpr |
| ¶ 'Evening' | SSpr |
| 'Ffiske' | SSpr |
| *filamentosa* | CBro SWas |
| *filifolia* | CAvo CRDP EHyt EPot GCal |
| | MNrw WCot |
| *flexuosa* | MRav SSpr |
| - 'Alba' | CAvo CBro EBee LAma LGre |
| | MRav SDeJ SSpr |
| - pink | Last listed 1998 |
| 'Fortune' | SSpr |
| 'Gaby Deslys' | SSpr |
| 'Gaiety' | Last listed 1997 |
| 'Glensavage Gem' | SSpr |
| 'Glensavage Spider' | SSpr |

| | |
|---|---|
| 'Gloaming' | SSpr |
| 'Goya' | SSpr |
| 'Grilse' | Last listed 1998 |
| 'Hamlet' | SSpr |
| 'Harlequin' | SSpr |
| 'Harry Dalton' | SSpr |
| 'Hawaii' | SSpr |
| 'Helen Smith' | SSpr |
| ¶ 'Helena' | SSpr |
| ¶ 'Hera' | LGre |
| * *hirsuta* | Last listed 1997 |
| *humilis* | WCot |
| - Breachiae Group | Last listed 1998 |
| - Tulbaghensis Group | Last listed 1998 |
| 'Inchmery Kate' | SSpr |
| *innominata* | SSpr |
| 'Janet' | SSpr |
| 'Jenny Wren' | SSpr |
| 'Jill' | SSpr |
| 'Joan' | CAvo SSpr |
| 'Judith' | SSpr |
| ¶ 'Juliet Berkeley' | SSpr |
| 'Kasmir' | SSpr |
| * 'Killi' | CRDP |
| 'Kilwa' | SSpr |
| ¶ 'King Leopold' | SSpr |
| 'King of the Belgians' | LAma SSpr WCot |
| 'Kingship' | SSpr |
| 'Kola' | SSpr |
| 'Konak' | SSpr |
| 'Koriba' | SSpr |
| *krigei* | Last listed 1998 |
| 'Kymina' | SSpr |
| 'Kyoto' | SSpr |
| ¶ 'Kyrie' | SSpr |
| 'Lady Cynthia Colville' | SSpr |
| 'Lady Eleanor Keane' | CAvo SSpr |
| 'Lady Llewellyn' | Last listed 1998 |
| 'Lambourne' | SSpr |
| *laticoma* | Last listed 1998 |
| ¶ 'Latu' | SSpr |
| 'Lawlord' | SSpr |
| 'Leila Hughes' | SSpr |
| 'Lindhurst' | Last listed 1997 |
| 'Locharber' | SSpr |
| 'Lord Grenfell' | IBlr |
| ¶ 'Lottery' | SSpr |
| 'Lucinda' | SSpr |
| 'Lyndhurst Salmon' | SSpr |
| ¶ 'Mandarin' | SSpr |
| 'Mansellii' | SSpr |
| 'Maria' | SSpr WCot |
| 'Marnie Rogerson' | CBro CGle LGre WCot |
| *masoniorum* | CBro CLyd EHyt LGre MTho |
| | WCot |
| 'Meadowbankii' | SSpr |
| 'Miss Edith Godman' | SSpr |
| ¶ 'Monet' | SSpr |
| ¶ 'Mrs Goldsmith' | SSpr |
| ¶ 'Natasha' | SSpr |
| 'Nena' | Last listed 1998 |
| ¶ 'Noreen' | SSpr |
| 'Oberon' | SSpr |
| ¶ 'Orange Queen' | SSpr |
| *peersii* | WCot |
| ¶ 'Penelope' | SSpr |
| 'Pink Galore' | SSpr |
| ¶ 'Plain Jane' | SSpr |
| ¶ 'Plymouth' | SSpr |
| *pudica* | WCot |
| * 'Red Pimpernel' | LAma MBNS |
| 'Rembrandt' | SSpr |

| | |
|---|---|
| 'Rose Camellia' | Last listed 1998 |
| 'Rushmere Star' | SSpr |
| ¶ 'Salmonia' | SSpr |
| *sarniensis* | CBro EBot ECha NRog SYvo |
| * – 'Alba' | WCot |
| § – var. *corusca* | LAma WCot |
| – – 'Major' | LBow SSpr |
| – var. *curvifolia* | SSpr WCot |
| f. *fothergillii* | |
| – – – 'Queen Mary' | Last listed 1998 |
| Smee No. 11 | Last listed 1998 |
| 'Smokey Special' | SSpr |
| 'Snowflake' | SSpr |
| ¶ 'Solent Swan' | SSpr |
| 'Stephanie' | LAma SSpr |
| 'Stephanie' x 'Moscow' | SSpr |
| § *undulata* | CBlo CBro EBot ECha ERos LAma LBow LGre MBri SPer WCot |
| * – 'Alba' | WCot |
| 'Vestal' | SSpr |
| 'Vicky' | CRDP |
| 'White Swan' | LAma MBNS SSpr |
| 'Wolsey' | SSpr |
| 'Zeal Giant' | CAvo |

## NERIUM ✿ (Apocynaceae)

| | |
|---|---|
| *oleander* | CBrP CMdw EBak LPan SArc SRms |
| – 'Album' | EEls |
| – 'Album Plenum' (d) | EEls LPio |
| – 'Alsace' | EEls ERea |
| – 'Altini' | EEls |
| – 'Angiolo Pucci' | EEls |
| * – 'Avalanche' | CB&S |
| – 'Belle Hélène' | EFlo |
| ¶ – 'Bousquet d'Orb' | EEls LPio |
| § – 'Carneum Plenum' (d) | EEls |
| – 'Cavalaire' (d) | EEls |
| * – 'Clare' | EEls ERea SOWG |
| – 'Cornouailles' | EEls LPio |
| – 'Docteur Golfin' | EEls |
| – 'Emile Sahut' | EEls |
| – 'Emilie' | EEls ERea |
| – 'Flavescens Plenum' (d) | CFee EEls EFlo ERea |
| – forms | EEls |
| ¶ – 'Framboise' | LPio |
| – 'Géant des Batailles' | EEls EFlo ERea SOWG |
| – 'Hardy Pink' | EFlo ERea LPio |
| – 'Hardy Red' | EEls ERea LPio |
| – 'Hawaii' | EEls |
| * – 'Isabelle' | EEls |
| – 'Isle of Capri' | EEls ERea SOWG |
| – 'Italia' | EFlo ERea |
| – 'J.R.' | EEls |
| – 'Jannoch' | EEls EFlo ERea |
| – 'Louis Pouget' (d) | EEls |
| – 'Madame Allen' (d) | EEls |
| – 'Madame Léon Blum' | EFlo |
| – 'Madame Planchon' (d) | ERea |
| – 'Magaly' | ERea |
| – 'Maresciallo Graziani' | EEls |
| – 'Margaritha' | EEls EFlo ERea |
| – 'Marie Gambetta' | EEls EFlo |
| – subsp. *mascatense* | EEls |
| – 'Mont Blanc' | EEls LPio |
| – 'Mrs Roeding' | See *N. oleander* 'Carneum Plenum' |
| – 'Nana Rosso' | EEls |
| ¶ – 'Navajo' | LPio |
| – 'Oasis' | EEls |
| – subsp. *oleander* | EEls |
| – 'Oportum' | Last listed 1996 |
| – 'Papa Gambetta' | EEls EFlo |
| * – 'Peach Blossom' | ERea |
| – 'Petite Pink' | EEls |
| – 'Petite Red' | EEls |
| – 'Petite Salmon' | EEls |
| – 'Professeur Granel' (d) | EEls ERea LPio |
| – 'Provence' (d) | EEls EFlo ERea SOWG |
| – 'Rosario' (d) | ERea |
| – 'Rose des Borrels' | EEls |
| – 'Rosée du Ventoux' (d) | EEls EFlo ERea SOWG |
| – 'Roseum' | EEls |
| – 'Roseum Plenum' (d) | CB&S CRHN EEls |
| – 'Rosita' | EEls ERea |
| – 'Sealy Pink' | CB&S EEls |
| * – 'Snowflake' | EEls ERea SOWG |
| – 'Soeur Agnès' | EEls ERea |
| – 'Soleil Levant' | EEls EFlo ERea |
| – 'Souvenir d'Emma Schneider' | EEls |
| – 'Souvenir des Iles Canaries' | EEls EFlo |
| – 'Splendens' (d) | ERea SOWG |
| – 'Splendens Giganteum' (d) | EEls |
| – 'Splendens Giganteum Variegatum' (d/v) | EEls |
| – 'Tito Poggi' | EEls ERea SHFr |
| – 'Variegatum' | CBot CGre EEls ERea |
| – 'Variegatum Plenum' (d) | WCot |
| – 'Villa Romaine' | EEls |
| – 'Ville de Carpentras' (d) | EEls EFlo ERea |
| * – 'Ville de la Londe' | EFlo |
| * – 'Yellow Queen' | CB&S |

## NERTERA (Rubiaceae)

| | |
|---|---|
| *balfouriana* | ECou |
| *depressa* | ECou |
| *granadensis* | MBri |

## NEVIUSIA (Rosaceae)

| | |
|---|---|
| *alabamensis* | CHan |

## NICANDRA (Solanaceae)

| | |
|---|---|
| *physalodes* | CArn EMan NHex SIde SSoC SYvo WRos |
| – *alba* | LCot WHer |
| * – 'Blacky' | SMrm WCot |
| – 'Violacea' | SLod SRms |

## NICOTIANA (Solanaceae)

| | |
|---|---|
| *acuminata* | Last listed 1998 |
| *alata* | Last listed 1998 |
| *colossea* | CTrG |
| *glauca* | CGle CMdw EMan EMar EOas ERea MSte WHer |
| *knightiana* | Last listed 1998 |
| *langsdorffii* ♀ | CB&S CHad ELan EMar EMon GBri LPio MBEx SMrm SUsu WEas WHer WMaN WOve WPer WRus WWye |
| – 'Cream Splash' (v) | CPla EMar WHer |
| * *mutabilis* | CSpe |
| *noctiflora* | Last listed 1998 |
| *rustica* | Last listed 1998 |
| *suaveolens* | WRus |
| *sylvestris* ♀ | CHad CHan CJew CSpe CTrC EMan EWTr LPVe MBEx MGed SEND SMrm WEas WHer WRus WWye |
| *tabacum* | CArn IIve WWye |

## NIDULARIUM (Bromeliaceae)

| | |
|---|---|
| *flandria* | See *Neoregelia carolinae* (Meyendorffii Group) 'Flandria' |

## NIEREMBERGIA (Solanaceae)
§ *caerulea* ♀ — ECha EHrv EMan IMGH WThi
*frutescens* — See *N. scoparia*
*hippomanica* — See *N. caerulea*
§ *repens* — CFee CTri ELan EPot MBro NBus NNrd SRms SSca WWat WWin
- 'Violet Queen' — Last listed 1996
*rivularis* — See *N. repens*
§ *scoparia* — CGle CHad CHan LHop WRus
- 'Mont Blanc' — Last listed 1998
- 'Purple Robe' — Last listed 1998

## NIPHAEA (Gesneriaceae)
*oblonga* — NMos

## x NIPHIMENES (Gesneriaceae)
'Lemonade' — NMos

## NIPPONANTHEMUM (Asteraceae)
§ *nipponicum* — CNic CSam EAst ECha ERic GCal LPio NFai NRoo NSti SRms WCot WPGP
- *roseum* — CSam

## NIVENIA (Iridaceae)
*stokoei* — Last listed 1996

## NOCCAEA See THLASPI

## NOLANA (Nolanaceae)
*humifusa* 'Little Bells' — Last listed 1996

## NOLINA (Agavaceae)
*beldingii* — SIgm
*bigelowii* — Last listed 1996
*brevifolia* — SIgm
*durangensis* — CTbh
*greenii* — SIgm
*humilis* — Last listed 1996
*longifolia* — Last listed 1997
*microcarpa* — Last listed 1996
*palmeri* — SIgm
*parryi* — WCot
§ *recurvata* ♀ — LCns LPal MBri
*texana* — NWCA SIgm

## NOMOCHARIS (Liliaceae)
*aperta* — EHyt EPot GBuc GCrs GDra LAma MDun NHed SSpi WAbe WCru
- ACE 2271 — Last listed 1998
- CLD 229 — Last listed 1996
*farreri* — EHyt WCru
x *finlayorum* — GCrs
*mairei* — See *N. pardanthina*
*meleagrina* — EPot LAma
*nana* — See *Lilium nanum*
§ *pardanthina* — GBuc NHar NSla WCru
- CLD 1490 — Last listed 1996
- f. *punctulata* — GBuc GGGa MDun WCru
*saluenensis* — GTou WCru

## NONEA (Boraginaceae)
*lutea* — CMea EAst MFir MLLN NOrc WAbb WByw WHal

## NOTELAEA (Oleaceae)
*ligustrina* — Last listed 1997

## NOTHOFAGUS ✿ (Fagaceae)
*alessandrii* — Last listed 1998
x *alpina* — CDoC CDul CLnd CMCN GAri IOrc MBal SMad WMou WNor

*antarctica* — CB&S CDoC CLnd CMCN CMHG ECrN ELan EMil ENot IOrc ISea LPan MBal MBar MBri MGos NBee NHol NPal SPer WDin WNor WSHC
- 'Prostrata' — See *N. antarctica* 'Benmore'
*cunninghamii* — GAri GGGa ISea STre WNor
*dombeyi* — CB&S GAri IOrc LHyd SAPC SArc WBod WNor
¶ *fusca* — CB&S CDoC
*menziesii* — CB&S
*moorei* — CFil
*obliqua* — CDoC CDul CGre CLnd CMCN CSam EPfP GAri IOrc ISea MBal NWea WDin WFro WMou WNor
*pumilio* — CMCN GAri ISea
¶ *solanderi* — CMHG
- var. *cliffortioides* — CB&S CLnd MBal STre WCwm

## NOTHOLAENA See CHEILANTHES

## NOTHOLIRION (Liliaceae)
*bulbuliferum* — WCot
- C 5074 — Last listed 1998
*campanulatum* — MWll
*macrophyllum* — EBee GCrs WCru
*thomsonianum* — GCrs

## NOTHOPANAX See POLYSCIAS

## NOTHOSCORDUM (Alliaceae)
¶ *gracile* — CPLG
*inodorum* — GBuc
- *macrostemon* CL 7/76 — Last listed 1998
*neriniflorum* — See *Caloscordum neriniflorum*

## NOTOBUXUS (Buxaceae)
*natalensis* — SLan

## NOTOSPARTIUM (Papilionaceae)
*carmichaeliae* — ECou
¶ - 'Hodder' — ECou
¶ - 'Seymour' — ECou
*glabrescens* — ECou
¶ - 'Ben More' — ECou
¶ - 'Woodside' — ECou
¶ 'Joy' — ECou
*torulosum* — ECou
¶ - 'Blue Butterfly' — ECou
- x *glabrescens* — ECou
¶ - 'Malvern Hills' — ECou

## NOTOTRICHE (Malvaceae)
*compacta* — Last listed 1998

## NUPHAR (Nymphaeaceae)
*advena* — Last listed 1998
*japonica* var. *variegata* — CRow
*lutea* — CBen CRow EHon EMFW LPBA MSta SLon SWat
- subsp. *variegata* — See *N. variegata*
*pumila* — MSta
- *variegata* — MSta
'Shirley Bryne' — Last listed 1998
§ *variegata* — Last listed 1996

## NUXIA (Buddlejaceae)
*congesta* — Last listed 1998

## NYMPHAEA ✿ (Nymphaeaceae)
'Afterglow' (T/D) — MSta
*alba* — CBen CRow EHon EMFW LPBA MSta SAWi SWat SWyc WMAq WStl WWeb

§ - subsp. *occidentalis* (H)   MSta SWyc
  - 'Plenissima' (H)   MSta SWyc
  - var. *rubra* (H)   MSta
'Albatros' (H)   EHon LPBA MSta SWat SWyc WBcn
'Albatros' misapplied   See *N.* 'Hermine'
'Albert Greenberg' (T/D)   MSta
'Amabilis' (H)   CBen CRow EMFW LPBA MSta SWat SWyc WBcn WMAq
'American Star'   CWat MSta SWat SWyc WMAq
'Andreana' (H)   CWat EMFW LPBA MSta SWat SWyc
'Anna Epple'   SWyc
'Apple Blossom Pink'   See *N.* 'Marliacea Carnea'
'Apricot Pink' (T)   MSta
'Arc-en-ciel' (H)   MSta SWat SWyc WMAq
'Arethusa' (H)   MSta SWyc
'Atropurpurea' (H)   CBen EMFW LPBA MSta SWat SWyc WMAq
'Attraction' (H)   CBen CRow EHon EMFW LPBA MSta SWat SWyc WMAq WStl
'Aurora' (H)   EMFW LPBA MSta SWat SWyc WMAq
'Ballerina'   SWyc
'Barbara Davies'   MSta
'Barbara Dobbins'   MSta SWyc
'Baroness Orczy' (H)   MSta SWyc
'Bateau' (H)   MSta SWyc
'Berit Strawn'   SWyc
'Berthold'   CBen MSta SWyc
'Betsy Sakata'   SWyc
'Black Princess'   SWyc
'Bleeding Heart'   SWyc
'Blue Beauty' (T/D)   CBen
'Bory de Saint-Vincent' (H)   MSta SWyc
'Brakeleyi Rosea' (H)   EMFW LPBA MSta SWyc
'Burgundy Princess'   SWyc
*caerulea* (T/D)   MSta
*candida*   CBen EHon EMFW LPBA MSta SWyc
  - var. *biradiata* (H)   SWyc
  - var. *neglecta* (H)   SWyc
  - var. *rubra* (H)   MSta
'Candidissima' (H)   MSta SWyc
'Candidissima Rosea' (H)   MSta SWyc
'Cardinal' (H)   SWyc
'Carolina Sunset'   SWyc
'Caroliniana' (H)   CWat MSta SWyc
'Caroliniana Nivea' (H)   CBen CWat EMFW MSta SWyc
'Caroliniana Perfecta' (H)   CBen LPBA MSta SWat SWyc
'Caroliniana Rosea' (H)   MSta
'Celebration'   MSta SWyc
§ 'Charlene Strawn'   EMFW MSta SWat SWyc WBcn WMAq
'Charles de Meurville' (H)   CBen CRow EMFW LPBA MSta SWyc WMAq
'Charles's Choice'   SWyc
'Château le Rouge'   MSta SWyc
'Cherokee'   SWyc
'Chromelia'   SWyc
'Chrysantha' (H)   EMFW MSta SWyc
'Chubby'   MSta SWyc
'Citrus Star'   SWyc
'Clyde Itkins'   SWyc
'Colonel A.J. Welch' (H)   CBen CRow EHon EMFW LPBA MSta SAWi SWat SWyc WMAq
'Colonel Lindbergh' (T/D)   MSta
'Colorado'   SWyc
*colorata*   CBen MSta
'Colossea' (H)   CBen EHon EMFW LPBA MSta SWyc WMAq
'Comanche' (H)   CBen EMFW MSta SWat SWyc WMAq

'Comte de Bouchaud'   MSta
'Conqueror' (H)   EMFW LPBA MSta SAWi SWat SWyc WMAq WWeb
*cordata* 'Pink Pons'   Last listed 1997
'Dallas'   SWyc
'Danieda'   SWat
§ 'Darwin' (H)   CBen MSta SWat SWyc WMAq
x *daubenyana* (T/D)   MSta
'David'   MSta
'Denver'   SWyc
'Deva'   MSta
'Director George T. Moore' (T/D)   MSta
'Doll House'   SWyc
'Dorothy Lamour' (H)   SWyc
'Ellisiana' (H)   CBen EMFW LPBA MSta SWat SWyc
'Elysée' (H)   MSta
'Ernst Epple Senior'   SWyc
'Escarboucle' (H) ♀   CBen CRow EHon EMFW LPBA MSta SAWi SWat SWyc WBcn WMAq
'Esmeralda' (H)   MSta SWat
'Eucharis' (H)   MSta
'Evelyn Randig' (T/D)   MSta
'Evelyn Stetson'   SWyc
'Exquisita'   See *N.* 'Odorata Exquisita'
§ 'Fabiola' (H)   CBen CRow EHon EMFW LPBA MSta SWat SWyc WBcn WMAq
'Fantastic Pink'   SWyc
'Fenna Harder'   SWyc
'Fiesta'   SWyc
'Firecrest' (H)   CBen CWat EHon EMFW LPBA MSta SLon SWat SWyc WBcn WMAq
'Fishers Pink'   SWyc
'Florida Sunset'   SWyc
'Formosa' (H)   MSta SWyc
'France'   MSta
'Fritz Junge' (H)   MSta SWyc
'Froebelii' (H)   CBen CRow CWat EHon EMFW LPBA MSta SWat SWyc WBcn WMAq
'Fulva' (H)   MSta SWyc
'Galatée' (H)   MSta SWyc
'General Pershing' (T/D)   MSta
*gigantea*   MSta
'Gladstoneana' (H) ♀   CBen CRow EHon EMFW LPBA MSta SAWi SWat SWyc WMAq
'Gloire du Temple-sur-Lot' (H)   CBen EMFW MSta SWat SWyc WMAq
'Gloriosa' (H)   CBen EMFW LPBA MSta SWat SWyc WWeb
'Gold Medal' (H)   SWyc
'Golden West' (T/D)   MSta
'Goliath' (H)   MSta SWyc
'Gonnère' (H) ♀   CBen CRow CWat EHon EMFW LPBA MSta SWat SWyc WBcn WMAq
'Gracillima Alba' (H)   SWyc
'Granat'   SWyc
'Graziella' (H)   EMFW LPBA MSta SWat SWyc WBcn WMAq
'Green Smoke' (T/D)   MSta
'Grésilias' (h)   MSta
'Gypsy'   SWyc
'H.C. Haarstick' (T/D)   MSta
'Hal Miller' (H)   EMFW MSta SWyc
'Helen Fowler' (H)   EMFW MSta SLon SWat SWyc WMAq
x *helvola*   See *N.* 'Pygmaea Helvola'
§ 'Hermine' (H)   CBen EMFW MSta SWat SWyc WMAq

| | |
|---|---|
| 'Hever White' (H) | MSta SWyc |
| 'High Life' | SWyc |
| 'Hollandia' Koster (H) | SWyc |
| 'Hollandia' misapplied | See *N.* 'Darwin' |
| 'Improved Firecrest' | SWyc |
| 'Indiana' (H) | CBen CWat EMFW LPBA MSta SWat SWyc WMAq |
| 'Irene' (H) | SWyc |
| 'Irene Heritage' | SWyc |
| 'J.C.N. Forestier' (H) | MSta |
| 'Jack Wood' (T) | MSta |
| 'James Brydon' (H) ♀ | CBen CRow CWat EHon EMFW LPBA MSta SAWi SRms SWat SWyc WBcn WMAq |
| 'James Hudson' (H) | MSta SWyc |
| 'Jean de Lamarsalle' (H) | MSta |
| 'Jean Laydeker' | MSta |
| 'Jean Marie' | SWyc |
| 'Jim Saunders' | SWyc |
| 'Joanne Pring' | MSta SWat SWyc |
| 'Joey Tomocick' | SWyc WMAq |
| 'Julian Decelle' | MSta |
| 'Juliana' (h) | CWat EMFW MSta |
| ¶ 'Karl Epple' | SWyc |
| 'Kiss of Fire' (H) | SWyc |
| 'Labeaugere' | SWyc |
| 'Lactea' (H) | MSta |
| 'Laura Strawn' | SWyc |
| ¶ 'Laydekeri Floribunda' | SWyc |
| 'Laydekeri Fulgens' (H) | CBen EMFW LPBA MSta SWat SWyc WMAq |
| 'Laydekeri Lilacea' (H) | CBen CRow EMFW LPBA MSta SWat SWyc WMAq |
| 'Laydekeri Purpurata' (H) | EMFW LPBA MSta SLon SWat SWyc WBcn WMAq |
| 'Laydekeri Rosea' Laydeker (H) | Last listed 1997 |
| 'Laydekeri Rosea' misapplied | See *N.* 'Laydekeri Rosea Prolifera' |
| § 'Laydekeri Rosea Prolifera' (H) | CBen EMFW LPBA MSta SWyc |
| 'Lemon Chiffon' | SWyc |
| 'Leviathan' (H) | MSta |
| 'Lily Pons' | SWyc |
| 'Limelight' | SWat |
| 'Liou' | SWyc |
| 'Little Sue' | SWyc |
| 'Livingstone' (H) | MSta SWyc |
| 'Loose' (H) | SWyc |
| 'Louise' (H) | SWyc |
| 'Louise Villemarette' | SWyc |
| 'Luciana' | See *N.* 'Odorata Luciana' |
| 'Lucida' (H) | CBen CWat EMFW LPBA MSta SWat SWyc WMAq |
| 'Lusitania' (H) | MSta SWyc |
| 'Lustrous' (H) | SWyc |
| 'Madame Bory Latour-Marliac' (H) | MSta |
| 'Madame de Bonseigneur' (H) | MSta |
| 'Madame Julien Chifflot' (H) | MSta |
| 'Madame Maurice Laydeker' (H) | MSta SWyc |
| 'Madame Wilfon Gonnère' (H) | CBen CWat EHon EMFW LPBA MSta SWat SWyc WBcn WMAq WWeb |
| 'Margaret Randig' (T/D) | MSta |
| 'Marguerite Laplace' (H) | MSta SWyc |
| 'Marliacea Albida' | CBen CWat EHon LPBA MSta SWat SWyc WMAq |
| § 'Marliacea Carnea' (H) | CBen CRow EHon EMFW LPBA MSta SWat SWyc WBcn WMAq |
| § 'Marliacea Chromatella' (H) ♀ | CBen CRow EHon EMFW LPBA MSta SAWi SLon SWat SWyc WBcn WMAq |
| 'Marliacea Flammea' (H) | MSta SWyc |
| 'Marliacea Ignea' (H) | MSta SWyc |
| 'Marliacea Rosea' (H) | EMFW MSta SWyc WMAq |
| 'Marliacea Rubra Punctata' (H) | MSta SWyc |
| 'Maroon Beauty' (T/N) | MSta |
| 'Martha' | SWyc |
| 'Mary' | SWyc |
| 'Mary Exquisita' (H) | MSta |
| 'Mary Patricia' (H) | MSta SWyc |
| 'Masaniello' (H) | CBen CRow EHon EMFW LPBA MSta SWat SWyc WBcn WMAq |
| 'Maurice Laydeker' (H) | EMFW MSta SWyc |
| 'Maxima' (H) | WMAq |
| 'Mayla' | SWyc |
| § 'Météor' (H) | CWat EMFW MSta SWyc WBcn WMAq |
| *mexicana* | MSta SWyc |
| 'Moorei' (H) | CBen EHon EMFW LPBA MSta SLon SWat SWyc WMAq |
| 'Mount Shasta' | SWyc |
| 'Mrs C.W.Thomas' (H) | MSta SWyc |
| 'Mrs C.W.Ward' (T/D) | MSta |
| 'Mrs Richmond' misapplied | See *N.* 'Fabiola' |
| 'Murillo' (H) | MSta SWyc |
| 'Neptune' (H) | MSta SWyc |
| 'Newton' (H) | EMFW MSta SWat SWyc WMAq |
| 'Nigel' (H) | MSta SWat SWyc |
| 'Nobilissima' (H) | MSta |
| 'Norma Gedye' (H) | CBen CWat MSta SWat SWyc WMAq |
| 'Occidentalis' | See *N. alba* subsp. *occidentalis* |
| 'Odalisque' (H) | CWat EMFW MSta SWyc |
| § *odorata* (H) | CBen CRow EHon LPBA MSta SWyc WBcn WMAq |
| 'Odorata Alba' | See *N. odorata* |
| 'Odorata Eugénia de Land' (H) | MSta |
| § 'Odorata Exquisita' (H) | MSta SWyc |
| *odorata* var. *gigantea* (H) | MSta |
| * – 'Jasmine' | SWyc |
| 'Odorata Juliana' (H) | SWyc |
| § 'Odorata Luciana' | EMFW MSta SWyc |
| *odorata* 'Maxima' (H) | SWyc |
| § – var. *minor* (H) | CBen CRow EMFW LPBA MSta SWat SWyc WMAq |
| – 'Pumila' | See *N. odorata* var. *minor* |
| – var. *rosea* (H) | EMFW MSta SWyc |
| – 'Roswitha' (H) | SWyc |
| – f. *rubra* (H) | MSta |
| 'Odorata Sulphurea' (H) | MSta SWat SWyc WBcn |
| § 'Odorata Sulphurea Grandiflora' (H) | CBen CRow EHon EMFW LPBA MSta SWat SWyc WMAq |
| 'Odorata Turicensis' (H) | EMFW LPBA MSta SWyc |
| 'Odorata William B. Shaw' | See *N.* 'W.B. Shaw' |
| 'Osceola' | SWyc |
| 'Pam Bennett' (H) | MSta |
| 'Pamela' (T/D) | CBen MSta |
| 'Patio Joe' | SWyc |
| 'Paul Hariot' | CWat EHon EMFW LPBA MSta SWat SWyc WBcn WMAq |
| 'Peach Blossom' | SWyc |
| 'Peaches and Cream' | SWyc |
| Pearl of the Pool (H) | MSta SWat SWyc |
| 'Pennsylvania' (T/D) | MSta |
| 'Perry's Almost Black' | SWyc |
| 'Perry's Baby Red' | CBen SWyc |
| 'Perry's Black Opal' | SWyc |
| 'Perry's Cactus Pink' | SWyc |

| | |
|---|---|
| 'Perry's Crinkled Pink' | SWyc |
| 'Perry's Darkest Red' | SWyc |
| 'Perry's Double White' (d) | CBen SWyc |
| 'Perry's Dwarf Red' | SWyc |
| 'Perry's Fire Opal' | SWyc |
| 'Perry's Magnificent' | SWyc |
| 'Perry's Pink' | MSta SWat SWyc WMAq |
| 'Perry's Pink Beauty' | SWyc |
| 'Perry's Pink Bicolor' | SWyc |
| 'Perry's Pink Delight' | SWyc |
| 'Perry's Pink Heaven' | SWyc |
| 'Perry's Red Beauty' | SWyc |
| 'Perry's Red Bicolor' | SWyc |
| 'Perry's Red Blaze' | SWyc |
| 'Perry's Red Glow' | SWyc |
| 'Perry's Red Sensation' | Last listed 1997 |
| 'Perry's Red Star' | SWyc |
| 'Perry's Red Wonder' | SWyc |
| 'Perry's Rich Rose' | SWyc |
| 'Perry's Stellar Red' | SWyc |
| 'Perry's Strawberry Pink' | SWyc |
| 'Perry's Super Red' | SWyc |
| 'Perry's Super Rose' | SWyc |
| 'Perry's Vivid Rose' | SWyc |
| 'Perry's Viviparous Pink' | SWyc |
| 'Perry's White Star' | SWyc |
| 'Perry's White Wonder' | SWyc |
| 'Perry's Wildfire' | SWyc |
| ¶ 'Perry's Yellow Sensation' | CBen |
| 'Peter Slocum' | MSta SWat SWyc |
| 'Philippe Laydeker' | MSta |
| 'Phoebus' (H) | MSta SWat SWyc WBcn |
| 'Phoenix' (H) | MSta |
| 'Picciola' (H) | MSta SWyc |
| 'Pink Beauty' | SWyc |
| 'Pink Cameo' | SWyc |
| 'Pink Glory' (H) | SWyc |
| 'Pink Grapefruit' | SWyc |
| 'Pink Opal' (H) | CBen CWat EMFW LPBA MSta SLon SWyc |
| 'Pink Peony' | SWyc |
| 'Pink Platter' (T/D) | CBen |
| 'Pink Pumpkin' | SWyc |
| 'Pink Sensation' (H) | CBen CWat EMFW MSta SWat SWyc WMAq |
| 'Pink Shadow' | SWyc |
| 'Pink Sparkle' | SWyc |
| 'Pink Starlet' | SWyc |
| 'Pink Sunrise' | MSta SWyc |
| 'Pöstlingberg' (H) | MSta SWyc WMAq |
| 'Président Viger' | MSta |
| 'Pride of Palm Beach' | SWyc |
| 'Princess Elizabeth' (H) | EHon EMFW LPBA MSta SWyc |
| 'Pygmaea Alba' | See N. tetragona |
| § 'Pygmaea Helvola' (H) ♀ | CBen CRow EHon EMFW LPBA MSta SWat SWyc WMAq WWeb |
| 'Pygmaea Rubis' (H) | CRow EHon LPBA MSta SWat SWyc WMAq |
| 'Pygmaea Rubra' (H) | CBen CWat EMFW MSta SWyc WMAq |
| 'Radiant Red' (T/D) | SWyc |
| 'Ray Davies' | MSta SWyc |
| 'Red Beauty' | MSta |
| 'Red Cup' (T) | MSta |
| 'Red Flare' (T/N) | MSta |
| 'Red Sensation' | SWyc |
| 'Red Spider' | SWyc |
| 'Reflected Flame' | SWyc |
| 'Regann' | SWyc |
| 'Rembrandt' Koster (H) | SWyc |
| 'Rembrandt' misapplied | See N. 'Météor' |
| 'René Gérard' (H) | CBen CWat EHon EMFW LPBA MSta SWat SWyc WBcn WMAq |
| 'Rio' | Last listed 1997 |
| 'Robinsoniana' (H) | EMFW MSta SWyc |
| 'Rosa Mundi' | SWyc |
| 'Rosanna' | SWyc |
| 'Rosanna Supreme' (H) | MSta SWat SWyc |
| 'Rose Arey' (H) | CBen CRow EHon EMFW LPBA MSta SWat SWyc WBcn WMAq |
| 'Rose Magnolia' (H) | EMFW MSta SLon SWat SWyc |
| § 'Rosea' (H) | CBen EMFW LPBA MSta SWyc WMAq |
| 'Rosea Minima' | SWyc |
| 'Rosennymphe' (H) | CBen LPBA MSta SWat SWyc WMAq |
| 'Rosette' | Last listed 1997 |
| 'Rosita' (H) | MSta |
| 'Rosy Morn' (H) | EMFW MSta SWyc |
| 'Saint Louis' (T/D) | MSta |
| 'Saint Louis Gold' (T/D) | MSta |
| 'Sanguinea' (H) | EMFW MSta SWyc |
| 'Seignouretti' (H) | EMFW MSta SWyc WBcn WMAq |
| 'Senegal' (H) | MSta SWyc |
| 'Sioux' (H) | CBen CWat EHon EMFW LPBA MSta SAWi SWat SWyc WMAq |
| 'Sir Galahad' (T/N) | MSta |
| 'Sirius' (H) | CBen CWat EMFW MSta SWat SWyc |
| 'Solfatare' (H) | EMFW MSta SWyc |
| 'Somptuosa' (H) | EMFW MSta SWyc WMAq |
| 'Souvenir de Jules Jacquier' (H) | MSta SWyc |
| 'Speciosa' (H) | MSta |
| 'Spectabilis' | MSta |
| 'Splendida' (H) | MSta SWyc WMAq |
| 'Stardust' | SWyc |
| 'Steven Strawn' | SWyc |
| 'Sturtevantii' (T/N) | MSta |
| 'Suavissima' (H) | MSta |
| 'Sultan' (H) | EMFW MSta SWyc |
| 'Sunburst' | SWyc |
| 'Sunny Pink' | SWyc |
| 'Sunrise' | See N. 'Odorata Sulphurea Grandiflora' |
| 'Superba' (H) | MSta |
| 'Sylphida' (H) | MSta |
| 'Temple Fire' (H) | MSta |
| § tetragona (H) | CBen CRow EHon EMFW LPBA MSta SWyc WMAq |
| - 'Alba' | See N. tetragona |
| - 'Johann Pring' (H) | EMFW |
| § - var. rubra (H) | MSta |
| 'Texas Dawn' | EMFW MSta SWyc WMAq |
| 'Thomas O'Brian' | SWyc |
| tuberosa (H) | CBen LPBA MSta SWyc WMAq |
| 'Tuberosa Flavescens' | See N. 'Marliacea Chromatella' |
| tuberosa 'Maxima' (H) | MSta |
| - 'Richardsonii' (H) | EHon EMFW MSta SWyc WWeb |
| - 'Rosea' | See N. 'Rosea' |
| 'Tulipiformis' (H) | MSta |
| 'Venus' | SWyc |
| 'Venusta' (H) | MSta SWyc |
| 'Vera Louise' (H) | MSta SWyc |
| 'Vésuve' (H) | CWat EMFW MSta SWat SWyc |
| 'Victoria Longwood' (T) | MSta |
| 'Virginalis' (H) | EMFW MSta SWat SWyc WMAq |
| 'Virginia' (H) | EMFW MSta SWyc |
| § 'W.B. Shaw' (H) | CBen EHon EMFW LPBA MSta SWat SWyc WMAq |
| 'Walter Pagels' | MSta SWyc WMAq |
| ¶ 'Weymouth Red' | CBen |
| 'White Cup' | SWyc |
| 'White Sultan' | SWyc |
| 'William Doogue' (H) | EMFW MSta SWyc WBcn WMAq |

| | |
|---|---|
| 'William Falconer' (H) | CBen CWat EMFW LPBA MSta SLon SWat SWyc |
| 'Wood's White Knight' (T/N) | MSta |
| 'Wow' | SWyc |
| 'Wucai' | SWyc |
| 'Yellow Dazzler' (T/D) | MSta |
| 'Yellow Princess' | SWyc |
| 'Yellow Queen' | SWyc |
| 'Yellow Sensation' | SWyc |
| 'Yogi-gi' | SWyc |
| 'Yul Ling' | EMFW SWat SWyc |
| 'Ziyu' | SWyc |

## NYMPHOIDES (Menyanthaceae)

| | |
|---|---|
| *peltata* | CRDP CWat ECoo EMFW MHew NDea SLon SWat SWyc |
| § - 'Bennettii' | CBen EHon IBlr LPBA MSta |

## NYSSA (Cornaceae)

| | |
|---|---|
| *aquatica* | CFil CMCN SSpi SSta WPGP |
| *ogeche* | Last listed 1996 |
| *sinensis* ♀ | CAbP CB&S CDoC CEnd CGre CMCN CPMA CSam CTho ELan MBri NHol SBrw SRPl SReu SSpi SSta WCwm WNor WPGP WPat WWat |
| *sylvatica* ♀ | CB&S CDoC CDul CLnd CMCN CPMA CSam CTho ELan EMil GChr LPan MBal MBar MBri MGos MMea SBrw SPer SReu SSpi SSta WBod WDin WFro WNor WWat |
| ¶ - 'Jermyns Flame' | SSpi |
| - 'Sheffield Park' | LRHS |
| - 'Windsor' | LRHS SSpi |
| - 'Wisley Bonfire' | LRHS SSpi |

# O

## OAKESIELLA See UVULARIA

## OCHAGAVIA (Bromeliaceae)

| | |
|---|---|
| *rosea* | CFil |

## OCHNA (Ochnaceae)

| | |
|---|---|
| *serrulata* | CSpe |

## OCIMUM (Lamiaceae)

| | |
|---|---|
| 'African Blue' | CArn EOHP GPoy |
| § *americanum* | WHer WPer |
| - 'Meng Luk' | See *O. americanum* |
| *basilicum* | CArn CSev EEls GPoy LHol MBri MChe MMal SIde SWat WGwG WHer WPer WSel WWye |
| - 'Anise' | See *O. basilicum* 'Horapha' |
| ♦ - *camphorata* | See *O. kilimandscharicum* |
| * - 'Cinnamon' | CSev MChe MMal MSal SHDw SWat WGwG WHer WJek WPer WSel |
| - 'Dark Opal' | CBod SHDw SWat WJek WSel |
| - 'Genovese' | ELau WGwG |
| - 'Glycyrrhiza' | See *O. basilicum* 'Horapha' |
| - 'Green Globe' | EOHP MChe |
| - 'Green Ruffles' | MChe SWat WJek WSel |
| - 'Holy' | See *O. tenuiflorum* |
| § - 'Horapha' | CArn CSev EOHP GPoy MChe MMal MSal SIde WJek WPer |
| * - 'Horapha Nanum' | WJek |
| ¶ - 'Minette' | EOHP |
| - 'Napolitano' | CBod MChe MMal SIde SWat WJek WPer |

| | |
|---|---|
| ¶ - 'New Guinea' | EOHP |
| - 'Purple Ruffles' | EOHP MChe MMal SIde SWat WJek WPer WSel |
| - var. *purpurascens* | CArn CSev GPoy LHol MBri MChe SIde WGwG WHer WPer |
| - 'Red Rubin' | MChe WJek |
| * - 'Rubin' | EOHP |
| ¶ - 'Spicy Globe' | WJek |
| - 'Thai' | See *O. basilicum* 'Horapha' |
| *canum* | See *O. americanum* |
| × *citriodorum* | CArn MChe MMal MSal SHDw SIde SWat WGwG WJek WPer WSel |
| ¶ - 'Siam Queen' | WJek |
| ¶ *gratissimum* | ELau |
| § *kilimandscharicum* | EOHP |
| - × *basilicum* var. *purpurascens* | GPoy |
| *minimum* | CArn CBod CJew CSev ELau EOHP GPoy LHol MBri MChe SIde WHer WJek WPer WSel WWye |
| *sanctum* | See *O. tenuiflorum* |
| 'Spice' | MChe WPer |
| § *tenuiflorum* | CArn CSev GPoy MChe MSal SHDw SIde SWat WHer WJek WPer |

## ODONTONEMA (Acanthaceae)

| | |
|---|---|
| *strictum* | LHil WMul |

## OEMLERIA (Rosaceae)

| | |
|---|---|
| § *cerasiformis* | CB&S CFil CHan CPle MWat SSpi WCot WEas WHCG WPGP WSHC WWat WWin |

## OENANTHE (Apiaceae)

| | |
|---|---|
| *aquatica* 'Variegata' | EMFW |
| *crocata* | Last listed 1998 |
| *fluviatilis* | Last listed 1997 |
| *japonica* | See *O. javanica* |
| * *javanica* 'Atropurpurea' | EHoe |
| - 'Flamingo' | CBen CRow EHal ELan EMar EMon EPla EPri EWTr LFis LHop MBNS MBel MNrw MSCN NBro NHol NWes SLod SLon SRms SUsu WFar WHer WOve WPer WPrP |
| *pimpinelloides* | Last listed 1997 |

## OENOTHERA ✿ (Onagraceae)

| | |
|---|---|
| § *acaulis* | CBot CHan CSpe EBee GCal IMGH LHop MNrw SChu WAbe WRos |
| - *alba* | CMea WCot |
| § - 'Aurea' | LHop NTow NWCA SIng WCla WPer |
| - BC&W 4110 | Last listed 1997 |
| - hort. 'Lutea' | See *O. acaulis* 'Aurea' |
| ¶ *affinis* | IDac |
| 'African Sun' | EMan LWoo SBod SRot |
| * *alpina* | Last listed 1998 |
| 'Apricot Delight' | ECoo MCCP NCut WMoo |
| *argillicola* | WPer |
| 'Beach' | SUsu |
| *berlandieri* | See *O. speciosa* 'Rosea' |
| § *biennis* | CArn CKin CRow CSev EBrP EBre ECha EHoe ELau EWFC GPoy LBre LHol MChe MHew MMal MRav NBro SBre SIde SIng WHer WJek WOak WPer WSel |
| *brachycarpa* | Last listed 1997 |
| *brevipes* | Last listed 1997 |

| | |
|---|---|
| *caespitosa* | CPBP EMan MGed MTho SPil WHer |
| ¶ - subsp. *caespitosa* | NWCA |
| ¶ - subsp. *marginata* | WLin |
| * *campylocalyx* | LHop WUnu |
| *cheiranthifolia* | SRCN WPer |
| *childsii* | See *O. speciosa* 'Rosea' |
| *cinaeus* | See *O. fruticosa* subsp. *glauca* |
| 'Colin Porter' | CInt EBur LFis MNrw NBro NWCA SOkh WUnu |
| *coryi* | EBee |
| *deltoides* | Last listed 1997 |
| - var. *bowellii* | EWTr WLin |
| § *elata* subsp. *bookeri* | EMan SPil WPer |
| *erythrosepala* | See *O. glaziouana* |
| *flava* | EBee |
| *fremontii* | Last listed 1997 |
| § *fruticosa* | EBrP EBre LBre NBro SBre SPlb |
| - 'Camel' (v) | CBos CPlt EBee EMan LHop SUsu WCot WWeb |
| - cream | Last listed 1996 |
| - Fireworks | See *O. fruticosa* 'Fyrverkeri' |
| - subsp. *fruticosa* | CHan |
| § - 'Fyrverkeri' ♀ | More than 30 suppliers |
| § - subsp. *glauca* ♀ | CBlo CElw CHan EBrP EBre ECGN EPfP EWTr LBre MNrw MTho NBro SBre SRms WEas WOak WPer |
| - - 'Erica Robin' (v) | CBos CMGP CMea CMil EAst EBee EFou EGra EMan EMon GBuc LHop MArl MAvo MGrG MRav NPro SCob SMrm SSpe SUsu WCot WHil WSan |
| - - 'Frühlingsgold' (v) | CStr EMon WCot |
| - - Solstice | See *O. fruticosa* subsp. *glauca* 'Sonnenwende' |
| § - - 'Sonnenwende' | EBrP EBre EMon LBre MLLN NPro SBre SOkh WCot |
| - - 'Sundrops' | CLTr |
| - - 'Sunspot' (v) | GBuc |
| - Highlight | See *O. fruticosa* 'Hoheslicht' |
| § - 'Hoheslicht' | Last listed 1998 |
| ¶ - 'Lady Brookeborough' | LHop MRav |
| - 'Michelle Ploeger' | EBee EBrP EBre EMan LBre MUlv SBre |
| - var. *riparia* | ELan SAga SOkh WRus |
| - 'Silberblatt' | Last listed 1998 |
| - 'Yellow River' | MHar WRHF WWeb |
| - 'Youngii' | CM&M CMGP EBee EPfP EWTr LFis LIck MCCP MLLN SCob SRPl WPer |
| *glabra* hort. | CLyd NSti SIng SPer SUsu WCom |
| - Miller | See *O. biennis* |
| § *glaziouana* | CSam ECoo IBlr IIve NBir SIde WPer WWye |
| *heterantha* | Last listed 1997 |
| * 'Hollow Meadows' | Last listed 1998 |
| *bookeri* | See *O. elata* subsp. *bookeri* |
| *kuntbiana* | CStr EDAr EGoo EMan NCut NLak NWCA SCob WPer |
| § *laciniata* | Last listed 1997 |
| *lamarckiana* | See *O. glaziouana* |
| *lavandulifolia* | Last listed 1998 |
| 'Lemon Sunset' | EAst EBee ECoo MCCP SWat WMoo |
| *linearis* | See *O. fruticosa* |
| 'Longest Day' | EFou EPfP MArl MBrN NFai WHil |
| § *macrocarpa* ♀ | More than 30 suppliers |
| - 'Greencourt Lemon' | Last listed 1998 |
| *macrosceles* | CFri ECGN |
| *mexicana* | See *O. laciniata* |
| *missouriensis* | See *O. macrocarpa* |
| * *mollis* | EBee |
| *muricata* | EBee |
| ¶ *nuttallii* | NCut |
| ¶ *oakesiana* | EBee |
| *odorata* Jacquin | CArn CSpe GCal IBlr LHil NOrc |
| - Hook. & Arn. | See *O. biennis* |
| - hort. | See *O. stricta*, *O. glaziouana* |
| * - cream form | WHal |
| - 'Sulphurea' | See *O. stricta* 'Sulphurea' |
| *organensis* | EBee GCrs MLLN |
| *pallida* | EWTr IBlr NCut NFai SWat WMoo |
| - 'Innocence' | CBot CM&M LRHS SPil WHer WPer |
| - subsp. *tricbocalyx* | Last listed 1997 |
| - 'Wedding Bells' | NPer |
| 'Penelope Hobhouse' | GBuc SUsu |
| § *perennis* | EBrP EBre EMFP LBre LFis MTho NFai NNrd SBre SIng SMac SOkh SRms SWat WCla WEas WPer |
| ¶ 'Pink Domino' | WByw |
| *primiveris* | Last listed 1997 |
| *pumila* | See *O. perennis* |
| *rosea* | CHan CMea CSam NPer WWye |
| *serrulata* | Last listed 1997 |
| sp. from South America | CLyd MTho |
| *speciosa* | CBlo CMea CSev EMon EWTr MBel MHlr MRav SEND SPer SWat WCot WElm WHer WMoo WOut WPer WSan |
| - 'Ballerina' | CSpe EMan LHop |
| - var. *childsii* | See *O. speciosa* 'Rosea' |
| - 'Pink Petticoats' | CFri CM&M CSpe EAst EBee ECoo MArl MCCP MWgw NFai NPer SIde SWat WBea WBro WHil WMoo WSan |
| § - 'Rosea' | CBot CFir CGle CRDP ECoo ELan LIck MCCP MCLN MCli MNrw WCot WHer WPer WUnu WWin |
| - 'Siskiyou' | CHea CLTr COtt CRDP CSpe EBee EMan GMac LHil LRHS MArl MCAu MCLN MTis NLak NPri SBod SCob SCoo SHar SIng SLon SMrm SUsu WCru WMaN WMow WRus WWeb |
| - 'Siskiyou' variegated | Last listed 1997 |
| ¶ - yellow leaved | EBee |
| § *stricta* | CHad CHan CKin ECGP EWFC MCAu WPer WWye |
| * - 'Moonlight' | SIng |
| § - 'Sulphurea' | CHad CHan CM&M CMil ECoo ELan EMan GCal IBlr LBlm MBel NPer SAga SChu SMrm SUsu WAbb WBea WCot WHal WPer |
| ¶ 'Summer Sun' | EBee SSpe |
| ¶ 'Sunburst' | EMan |
| *taraxacifolia* | See *O. acaulis* |
| *tetragona* | See *O. fruticosa* subsp. *glauca* |
| - var. *fraseri* | See *O. fruticosa* subsp. *glauca* |
| ¶ - 'Goudsberg' | SMrm |
| - 'Sonnenwende' | See *O. fruticosa* subsp. *glauca* 'Sonnenwende' |
| *tetraptera* | NWCA |
| *texensis* | SWat |
| - 'Early Rise' | ELan EMan LHop SAga |
| *triloba* | Last listed 1997 |
| *versicolor* | CHan |
| - 'Sunset Boulevard' | CBrm CHar CM&M CMil CPou CRDP EAst ECoo GBri NBus SPer WBea WElm WHer WOve WSan WWin |
| 'Woodside White' | LRHS |

## OLEA (Oleaceae)

| | |
|---|---|
| *europaea* (F) ♀ | CArn CFil CHan CSWP CTrC EEls EPfP ERea ERom GAri LBlm LCns LHol LPan SAPC SArc SEND SHFr STre WMul WNor |
| ¶ - 'Arbequina' | CGOG |
| - 'Cailletier' (F) | ERea |
| - 'Chelsea Physic Garden' | WPGP |
| § - var. *europaea* 'Cipressino' (F) | ERea LPan |
| - - 'El Greco' (F) | CB&S ERea GAri |
| - - 'Picholine' (F) | ERea |
| - - 'Pyramidalis' | See *O. europaea* var. *europaea* 'Cipressino' |
| ¶ - 'Picual' | CGOG |

## OLEARIA ✿ (Asteraceae)

| | |
|---|---|
| *albida* hort. | See *O.* 'Talbot de Malahide' |
| - Hooker f. | CB&S |
| - var. *angulata* | CPle |
| - x *paniculata* | Last listed 1998 |
| *algida* | ECou |
| *arborescens* | GEil GSki |
| * - 'Variegata' | NPro |
| *argophylla* | ECou |
| *avicenniifolia* | CB&S CPle ECou EPla SDys WGer WLRN WSHC |
| - 'White Confusion' | WPen WWat |
| *canescens* | SBid |
| *capillaris* | CChe CPle ECou GGar NLon SDry SIgm WPen WTro WWat |
| *chathamica* | CDoC ICrw |
| § *cheesemanii* | CDoC CMHG CPle SLon SPer WSHC |
| *coriacea* | ECou |
| *erubescens* | CDoC CPle |
| ¶ - x *ilicifolia* | CPin |
| *floribunda* | CPle |
| ¶ *forsteri* Tresco form | CDoC |
| *fragrantissima* | Last listed 1998 |
| *frostii* | CPle WKif |
| *furfuracea* | CDoC CPle |
| *glandulosa* | CPle ECou |
| *gunniana* | See *O. phlogopappa* |
| x *haastii* | More than 30 suppliers |
| - 'McKenzie' | ECou |
| ¶ *hectorii* | ECou |
| § 'Henry Travers' ♀ | CDoC CPle GQui IBlr ISea MBal SRPl |
| *hookeri* | EPot |
| § *ilicifolia* | CDoC CFil CPle GSki LRHS MDun SDry SPer SSpi WCru WSHC |
| *insignis* | WCru |
| - var. *minor* | WCru |
| *lacunosa* | ICrw MDun |
| *lepidophylla* | CPle ECou |
| - green | Last listed 1997 |
| - silver | ECou |
| *lirata* | CDoC CPle ECou |
| *macrodonta* ♀ | More than 30 suppliers |
| - 'Intermedia' | Last listed 1998 |
| - 'Major' | EPfP GGar SSoC |
| - 'Minor' | CDoC ELan EPfP GQui WPat WWat |
| *microphylla* | Last listed 1998 |
| x *mollis* hort. | See *O. ilicifolia* |
| - (Kirk) Ckn. | CB&S CPle GQui NFor SBid SPer SSpi WCru WSHC |
| - 'Zennorensis' ♀ | CB&S CDoC CGre CLan CMHG CPle ISea MDun SDry SOWG SSpi WCru WWat |
| *moschata* | CPle GSki SBid SSpi WStI |
| *myrsinoides* | CFai CMHG CPle |
| § *nummulariifolia* | CDoC CMHG CPle CTri ECou EPla ISea MBal NFor NLon SAPC SArc SDry SEND SSto WAbe WBod WKif WSHC WWal WWat |
| - var. *cymbifolia* | ECou |
| - hybrids | ECou |
| *obcordata* | Last listed 1998 |
| *odorata* | CPle ECou MSag WBod WHCG |
| *oleifolia* | See *O.* 'Waikariensis' |
| *paniculata* | CGre CMHG CPle CTri GSki ISea SDry SPan SVen WAbe WPic |
| § *phlogopappa* | CPle EBee ECou ISea MTis SVen WBrE WCot WPic |
| - 'Comber's Blue' | CB&S CPle EPfP GChr IBlr ISea NOla SAga SPer SSta |
| § - 'Comber's Pink' | CB&S CDoC CPle ELan EPfP GChr IBlr SAga SBrw SPan SPer |
| - pink | CTrG SReu SSta |
| - 'Rosea' | See *O. phlogopappa* 'Comber's Pink' |
| - Splendens Group | CAbb |
| - var. *subrepanda* | CGre CPle SEND WBod |
| § *ramulosa* | CDoC CInt CPle LHil SBid WCot WGwG WWal |
| - 'Blue Stars' | ECou WWat |
| - *ramulosa* | ECou |
| ¶ *rani* Druce | ISea |
| ¶ - hort. | See *O. cheesemanii* |
| x *scilloniensis* hort. | See *O. stellulata* DC. |
| - Dorrien-Smith ♀ | Last listed 1998 |
| - 'Master Michael' | CBlo CBot CDoC LFis NFai SBrw SOWG SPan SPer SPla WBea WSHC |
| *semidentata* | See *O.* 'Henry Travers' |
| *solandri* | CDoC CHan CPle CSam CTrC CWSG ECou EPla GBin GOrc NFai SDix SDry SHFr SPer SSto |
| - 'Aurea' | CB&S GQui |
| *stellulata* hort. | See *O. phlogopappa* |
| - DC. | CBot CChe CDoC CGre CTrG CWit ECou ELan ENot ISea MWat NSti SDix SOWG SPer SPla SSta WAbe WEas WHCG WHCr WPic WStI WWeb |
| *traversii* | CAbb CB&S CDoC CFai CMHG CPle CTre EHic IOrc SBrw SEND SVen WCru WLRN |
| § - 'Tweedledum' (v) | CCHP CLyn ECou EHoe GVic SLon |
| - 'Variegata' | See *O. traversii* 'Tweedledum' |
| *virgata* | CPle ECou ELan GSki |
| - 'Laxifolia' | CTrC CTre |
| - var. *lineata* | CPle ECou SEND WCru WDin WPic WSHC |
| - - 'Dartonii' | CB&S ECou SLPl |
| - var. *ramuliflora* | Last listed 1998 |
| *viscosa* | CPle |
| § 'Waikariensis' | CBlo CBot CMHG CPle CSam CTrC ECou EHic EPla LHop SChu SEND SPan WBod WCFE WGer WWat |

## OLIGOSTACHYUM (Poaceae - Bambusoideae)

| | |
|---|---|
| *lubricum* | See *Semiarundinaria lubrica* |

## OLSYNIUM (Iridaceae)

| | |
|---|---|
| § *biflorum* | Last listed 1996 |
| § *douglasii* ♀ | CBro EBee EDAr ELan EPar EPot GCrs GDra NHar NMen NRya NTow SIng WAbe WLin |

| | |
|---|---|
| - 'Album' | EPar EPot GAbr GCrs GDra NHar NRya WAbe |
| - var. *inflatum* | EWes |
| - JCA 11132 | SBla |
| § *filifolium* | EMar MHar MNrw |
| § *junceum* | EBee EWTr GAri SBla |
| - JCA 12289 | MTho |
| - JCA 14211 | CFir |
| *scirpoideum* F&W 776 | Last listed 1996 |

## OMPHALODES (Boraginaceae)
| | |
|---|---|
| *cappadocica* ♀ | More than 30 suppliers |
| - 'Alba' | LLWP SRms WEas |
| - 'Anthea Bloom' | IBlr NTow |
| - 'Cherry Ingram' ♀ | More than 30 suppliers |
| - 'Lilac Mist' | CBos CElw EBee EHic EMan LPio MAvo MMil MRav NDov WCot |
| - 'Starry Eyes' | More than 30 suppliers |
| § *linifolia* ♀ | CMea CRDP CSpe ECoo NTow NWes WEas |
| - *alba* | See O. *linifolia* |
| *lojkae* | Last listed 1998 |
| *luciliae* | NTow WHoo |
| *nitida* | EMon GGar NRya WCot |
| *verna* | CGle CLon CLyd CSpe ECha EFou ELan EMil GAbr GCal LFis LGro LHop MBri MTho NHol NSti SCob SPer SPlb WBea WEas WFar WLin WMer WOve WWat WWye |
| - 'Alba' | CBot CBre CGle EAst EBee ECha ELan GAbr LFis LHop MCLN MTho NChi NHol NLar SCob SIng SPer SRPl SRms SSvw WBea WHoo WMer WOve WPrP WRus WWat |
| - 'Elfenauge' | CElw CMil EBee EMon SWas WCot |
| ¶ - *grandiflora* | WCot |

## OMPHALOGRAMMA (Primulaceae)
| | |
|---|---|
| *delavayi* | Last listed 1997 |
| - KGB 600 | Last listed 1996 |
| - KGB 800 | Last listed 1996 |
| *vinciflorum* | Last listed 1996 |

## ONOBRYCHIS (Papilionaceae)
| | |
|---|---|
| *gracilis* HH&K 185 | CHan |
| *montana* HH&K 325 | CHan |
| *viciifolia* | ELan EWFC MSal WCot |

## ONOCLEA (Woodsiaceae)
| | |
|---|---|
| *sensibilis* ♀ | More than 30 suppliers |
| - copper | CFil CRow CVer WPGP |

## ONONIS (Papilionaceae)
| | |
|---|---|
| *cenisia* | See O. *cristata* |
| *repens* | CArn CInt CKin EWFC MSal NMir WGwy |
| *rotundifolia* | CHan CPle MSal SLon |
| *spinosa* | CKin EWFC EWll IIve LFis MHer MSal WFar WPer |
| - 'Alba' | Last listed 1997 |

## ONOPORDUM (Asteraceae)
| | |
|---|---|
| *acanthium* | CArn CKel CLTr ECha ECoo ELan EMan EMil EOld EWFC GAbr GBar LEdu LHol MCAu MHar MWat MWgw NChi SIde SRCN SSoC WCHb WCot WCru WElm WHer WHil WOak WWye |
| *arabicum* | See O. *nervosum* |
| *bracteatum* | WPer |

§ *nervosum* ♀ — CArn CPin CSpe EBee EBot ERav LFis NBro NVic SMad SRms WFar WWhi

## ONOSERIS (Asteraceae)
| | |
|---|---|
| *salicifolia* | Last listed 1998 |

## ONOSMA (Boraginaceae)
| | |
|---|---|
| *alborosea* | CSev ECha EGoo ELan EOrc GBri GCal MFir NChi SBla SChu WEas WKif WLin WPGP WPer |
| *echioides* | Last listed 1997 |
| *helvetica* | EBee MBro WPat |
| ¶ aff. *isaurica* | WLin |
| *nana* | Last listed 1998 |
| - Mac&W 5785 | Last listed 1997 |
| ¶ - white | EBee |
| *rutila* | Last listed 1997 |
| ¶ *sericea* | WLin |
| *stellulata* | CLyd SSpi |
| *taurica* ♀ | EBee MOne NBir NChi WLin WWin |
| *tornensis* | Last listed 1996 |

## ONYCHIUM (Adiantaceae)
| | |
|---|---|
| *contiguum* | CFil WAbe |
| *japonicum* | CBos CFil CRDP GQui NMar SBla SChu SWas WAbe |
| - 'Dali' L 1649 | EMon SBla |

## OPHIOPOGON ✿ (Convallariaceae)
| | |
|---|---|
| 'Black Dragon' | See O. *planiscapus* 'Nigrescens' |
| *bodinieri* | ERos EWes SApp SIng SMac |
| - B&L 12505 | CHid EBee EPPr EPla |
| *chingii* | GCal |
| ¶ - 'Chinese Whisper' | EMon |
| *formosanus* B&SWJ 3659 | WCru |
| 'Fuku-ho-ryu' | Last listed 1998 |
| ♦ 'Gin-ryu' | See *Liriope spicata* 'Gin-ryu' |
| *graminifolius* | See *Liriope muscari* |
| * 'Haku-ryu' | EMon |
| *intermedius* | CHid EPPr EPla MSte WCot WPGP |
| § - 'Argenteomarginatus' | EBee ERos EWes LHop WPGP |
| - 'Compactus' | Last listed 1996 |
| - *parviflorus* | Last listed 1998 |
| - 'Variegatus' | See O. *intermedius* 'Argenteomarginatus' |
| § *jaburan* | CHan CHid CMGP LAma LEdu MSte WPnP WWat |
| - 'Variegatus' | See O. *jaburan* 'Vittatus' |
| § - 'Vittatus' (v) | CMHG EHoe EWes LRHS NFla SCob WCot WFar WRus |
| *japonicus* | CBro CRow EPPr EPla NSti |
| - 'Albus' | CLAP NHol |
| ¶ - B&SWJ 561 | WCru |
| - 'Compactus' | CFil EBee SMac SPla SSpi WCot WPGP |
| - 'Kigimafukiduma' | CElw CMil CWSG EPla SCob WCot WGwG WRus |
| - 'Minor' | CCuc CInt EGar EPla WPGP |
| - 'Nanus Variegatus' | Last listed 1998 |
| - 'Nippon' | Last listed 1998 |
| ¶ - 'Tama-ryu' | WThi |
| * - 'Tama-ryu Number Two' | ECho EHic EHyt ESis EWes NHar SIng |
| * - 'Variegatus' | SIng |
| ¶ *malcolmsonii* B&SWJ 5264 | WCru |
| *planiscapus* | CFee CMHG CPea CSWP CSev EPar EPla GCal GOrn LHil MBel MRav MSte MTho NBro NHar NHol NLon NPSl WPrP WWal WCot |
| - *leucanthus* | CHid WCot |
| - 'Little Tabby' (v) | CLAP SBla WCot |

| | |
|---|---|
| * – *minimus* | ERos |
| § – 'Nigrescens' ♀ | More than 30 suppliers |
| – 'Silver Ribbon' | SWat |
| – 'Silvershine' | Last listed 1996 |
| 'Rhyuko' | Last listed 1998 |
| 'Spring Gold' | EMon |
| 'Tama-hime-nishiki' | EMon |
| *wallichianus* | EBee EPla SSpi WCot WPGP WWat |

## OPHRYS (Orchidaceae)

| | |
|---|---|
| *apifera* | CHdy WHer |
| ¶ – subsp. *trollii* | CHdy |

## OPLISMENUS (Poaceae)

| | |
|---|---|
| § *africanus* 'Variegatus' ♀ | CHal |
| *hirtellus* | See *O. africanus* |

## OPUNTIA ✿ (Cactaceae)

| | |
|---|---|
| ¶ *cantabrigiensis* | SChr |
| ¶ *compressa* | SChr |
| ¶ *engelmannii* | CCpl |
| ¶ *ficus-indica* | SAPC |
| ¶ *grahamii* | SChr |
| * *grandiflora* | SChr |
| * *haematocarpa* | CCpl |
| *humifusa* | ELau EOas SMad WCot |
| § *lindheimeri* | EOas SAPC SArc SChr |
| *linguiformis* | See *O. lindheimeri* |
| *phaeacantha* | SAPC SArc SChr |
| ¶ *polyacantha* | SChr |
| ¶ *robusta* | SChr |
| ¶ *santa-rita* | CCpl |
| ♦ *tardospina* | See *O. lindheimeri* |
| ¶ *tuna* | CCpl |

## ORCHIS (Orchidaceae)

| | |
|---|---|
| *elata* | See *Dactylorhiza elata* |
| *foliosa* | See *Dactylorhiza foliosa* |
| *fuchsii* | See *Dactylorhiza fuchsii* |
| *laxiflora* | SWes |
| *maculata* | See *Dactylorhiza maculata* |
| *maderensis* | See *Dactylorhiza foliosa* |
| *majalis* | See *Dactylorhiza majalis* |
| § *mascula* | CHdy SWes WHer WShi |
| ¶ *militaris* | CHdy |
| *morio* | CHdy EFEx LAma SWes |
| *spectabilis* | EFEx |

## OREOPANAX (Araliaceae)

| | |
|---|---|
| *epremesnilianus* | Last listed 1998 |

## OREOPTERIS (Thelypteridaceae)

| | |
|---|---|
| § *limbosperma* | CCuc CFil SRms |

## ORIGANUM ✿ (Lamiaceae)

| | |
|---|---|
| *acutidens* | WCHb WLin WWye |
| *amanum* ♀ | CLyd CPBP CRDP ECha EDAr |
| | ELan EWes LBee LHop MBro |
| | MTho NBir NTow SAga SBla SChu |
| | SIgm SIng WAbe WWye |
| – var. *album* | CPBP CRDP ECho LEdu SBla SIng |
| | WAbe WPat |
| 'Barbara Tingey' | CElw CLon CLyd CRDP CSpe |
| | ECha ECou EHyt ELan EPot EWes |
| | LBee LEdu LHop MBro MNrw |
| | MTho SBla SChu SUsu WAbe |
| | WCot WCru WHoo WPat WWye |
| I 'Bristol Cross' | CElw CLyd ECha NHex WPat |
| 'Buckland' | CGle CLon CLyd CRDP EHyt ESis |
| | LBee LGre MSte NWCA SBla SWat |
| | WPat WPyg WWye |
| *caespitosum* | See *O. vulgare* 'Nanum' |

| | |
|---|---|
| § *calcaratum* | CLyd ELan LBee MTho SBla SSad |
| | WAbe WPat WPyg |
| ¶ *cordifolium* | SBla |
| *creticum* | See *O. vulgare* subsp. *hirtum* |
| *dictamnus* | CArn CMea EEls EHyt ELan EPot |
| | GPoy LBee NMen SBla SHDw |
| | SIng SSad SUsu WAbe WLin WRus |
| | WWye |
| 'Dingle Fairy' | CM&M EBee EGoo EMan EWes |
| | MLLN MMHG MNrw NHex WWye |
| 'Erntedank' | Last listed 1998 |
| 'Frank Tingey' | CPBP ECho EHyt ELan SBla SUsu |
| | WAbe |
| 'Gold Splash' | GBar |
| 'Goudgeel' | CStr WLin |
| *heracleoticum* L. | See *O. vulgare* subsp. *hirtum* |
| – hort. | See *O. x applei* |
| § x *hybridinum* | CLyd LBee LHop MBro SBla SChu |
| | WLin WPat WPyg WWat WWin |
| | WWye |
| 'Ingolstadt' | EBee LGre WWye |
| 'Kent Beauty' | CLTr CLon CMea CRDP CSpe |
| | ECha ELan EPot LGre LLWP MBro |
| | MCAu MSte NLak NWCA SAga |
| | SBla SChu SCob SUsu WAbe WCot |
| | WHoo WOVN WPat WWye |
| ¶ 'Kent Beauty Variegated' | ELan |
| *kopatdaghense* | See *O. vulgare* subsp. *gracile* |
| *laevigatum* ♀ | CArn CGle CLyd CMHG CMea |
| | CStr ELan EPot MBro MHar NBro |
| | NHol NMir NPer NWCA SAga |
| | SBla SMer SUsu WAbe WByw |
| | WEas WHoo WLin WPer WWin |
| | WWye |
| – *album* | EOHP |
| * – *aureum* | WJek |
| – 'Herrenhausen' ♀ | More than 30 suppliers |
| – 'Hopleys' | More than 30 suppliers |
| – hybrids | Last listed 1997 |
| – 'Springwood' | WCot WWat WWye |
| *libanoticum* | EPot NTow |
| – hybrids | Last listed 1997 |
| *majorana* | CArn CJew CSev ELan ELau GPoy |
| | LHol MChe MMal MSal NHex SIde |
| | SWat WGwG WJek WMow WOak |
| | WPer WSel WWye |
| *microphyllum* | CArn CBot CFee CGle CLon CLyd |
| | CMHG EDAr EHyt ESis GBar ITim |
| | LBee LGre MAvo MTho SBla SChu |
| | SIng WAbe WCot WCru WHoo |
| | WPat WPyg WWye |
| *minutiflorum* | ECho ELan |
| 'Norton Gold' | CElw CJew CLTr EBee ECha EHal |
| | EPot GBar GBuc LHop MBro |
| | NHex NPer SIde WCHb WHoo |
| | WPyg |
| 'Nymphenburg' | CFee CPlt ECha EHic MSte NDov |
| | SDys SUsu SWas WCru WWhi |
| *onites* | CArn EEls ELau GBar GPoy ILis |
| | LHol MChe MSal MWat NRoo SBla |
| | SIde WGwG WHer WJek WOak |
| | WPer WSel WWye |
| 'Pink Cloud' | Last listed 1996 |
| * *prismaticum* | SIde |
| *pulchellum* | See *O. x hybridinum* |
| ¶ 'Purple Cloud' | EBee |
| 'Rosenkuppel' | More than 30 suppliers |
| * 'Rotkugel' | CElw CRDP LGre NCat SAga |
| | WCot |
| *rotundifolium* ♀ | CArn CElw CGle CLyd CRDP CSev |
| | CStr ECha ELan ESis LEdu LGre |
| | LHop NBir NHex SBla SChu SMer |
| | WAbe WMer WOve WRus WSan |

| | |
|---|---|
| *scabrum* | CArn NHex WWye |
| - subsp. *pulchrum* | CLyd EPot |
| *sipyleum* | EHyt SBla WAbe WLin |
| sp. from Santa Cruz | CArn |
| sp. from Yunnan, China | NWoo |
| sp. Mac&W 5882 | See *Nepeta phyllochlamys* |
| *tournefortii* | See *O. calcaratum* |
| *villosum* | See *Thymus villosus* |
| ¶ *virens* | CArn |
| *vulgare* | CAgr CArn CKin CSev ECoo EWFC GBar GPoy LHol MBar MChe MHew MMal NBro NFai NHex NLan NMir NRoo SIde WByw WGwG WHer WOak WPer WWye |
| - 'Acorn Bank' | CArn CBod EBee ELau SIde WJek |
| - var. *album* | CElw LGre WHer WJek |
| - 'Aureum' ♀ | More than 30 suppliers |
| - 'Aureum Album' | EMar MCLN WHer WHil WWhi |
| - 'Aureum Crispum' | EGoo ELau EOrc ESis GAbr GBar ILis NFai NHex NLak SIde SWat WCer WJek WOak WRha WSel WWye |
| - 'Compactum' | CArn CJew CLyd CRDP CSev ECha EGoo ELau EOHP GAbr GCal GPoy ILis LEdu LHol MHar NHex NLak SAga SBla SIde SWat WCHb WCom WOak WPer WSel WWye |
| - 'Compactum Album' | Last listed 1998 |
| - 'Corinne Tremaine' (v) | WHer |
| - 'Country Cream' (v) | More than 30 suppliers |
| - *formosanum* B&SWJ 3180 | WCru |
| § - 'Gold Tip' (v) | CLTr CMea CSev CStr EHoe ELau EMar EOrc GAbr ILis NArg NFai NHex NHol NRoo NSti SIde SWat WCHb WHer WOak WPat WWye |
| - 'Golden Shine' | CBod CM&M EGra EWes MWat NRoo SIde WRha |
| § - subsp. *birtum* | CArn EOHP GPoy LEdu MSal NWoo SIde SPil WJek WPer |
| - - 'Greek' | CBod ELau IIve MMal WGwG |
| - × *majorana* | ELau |
| § - 'Nanum' | ESis GBar LHop NCat WCla WCot WJek |
| - 'Polyphant' (v) | CElw CHan CHar CInt CLTr CMHG CMil CSev EMan EOHP ESis LHop LPio MLLN NHex NPro NWoo WBea WCHb WCot WHer WJek WOve WSel WWye |
| - s.s.o.p Israeli | ELau |
| - 'Thumble's Variety' | CBod EBee EBrP EBre ECGP ECha ECoo EGoo EHic EHoe GBar LBre NHex NHol SBre SLon SWat WElm WWat |
| - 'Variegatum' | See *O. vulgare* 'Gold Tip' |
| - 'Webb's White' | SIde |
| 'White Cloud' | Last listed 1996 |

## ORIXA (Rutaceae)

| | |
|---|---|
| *japonica* | CBot EPfP EPla SSpi WDin WPGP |

## ORLAYA (Apiaceae)

| | |
|---|---|
| *grandiflora* | CRDP WCot WHal |

## ORNITHOGALUM (Hyacinthaceae)

| | |
|---|---|
| *arabicum* | CBro CGle CMea EBot LAma LBow MBri MLLN WCot |
| *arcuatum* | Last listed 1998 |
| *balansae* | See *O. oligophyllum* |
| *caudatum* | See *O. longibracteatum* |

| | |
|---|---|
| *chionophilum* | Last listed 1998 |
| *comosum* | Last listed 1998 |
| *concinnum* MS 452 | Last listed 1998 |
| *dubium* | CSut ETub WCot |
| *exscapum* | Last listed 1998 |
| *fimbriatum* | EPot |
| *lanceolatum* | CAvo EHyt LRHS |
| § *longibracteatum* | CGre ELan LHil SYvo WHer |
| *magnum* | CAvo CMea ETub WCot |
| ¶ *montanum* | WCot |
| - BSBE 2360 | LSyl |
| *nanum* | See *O. sigmoideum* |
| *narbonense* | CBro GBuc WCot |
| *nutans* ♀ | CAvo CBro CMea CRDP EBee EMan EPar EPot ETub EWFC LAma LBow MLLN MNrw MTho NMen NRog WBea WCot WPer WShi |
| § *oligophyllum* | CBro EPot MNrw |
| *orthophyllum* subsp. *kochii* | EPot |
| *ponticum* | ERos |
| *pyramidale* | CLyd EBot MNrw |
| *pyrenaicum* | CArn CAvo ECha ERos WShi |
| - AB&S 4600 | Last listed 1998 |
| - Flavescens Group | Last listed 1998 |
| *reverchonii* | CAvo CMea WCot |
| *saundersiae* | LBow |
| *sessiliflorum* AB&S 4619 | Last listed 1998 |
| *sibthorpii* | See *O. sigmoideum* |
| § *sigmoideum* | EPot |
| *spicatum* MS 585 | Last listed 1998 |
| *tenuifolium* | Last listed 1998 |
| *thyrsoides* | EBot LAma LSyl MBri SRms |
| *umbellatum* | CAvo CBro CNic ELan EPar ETub EWFC GPoy LAma MBri MNrw NHol NRog SRms WBea WCot WFar WPer WShi WWye |
| *unifolium* MS 435 | Last listed 1998 |

## ORONTIUM (Araceae)

| | |
|---|---|
| *aquaticum* | CBen CWat EHon EMFW LPBA MSta NDea SWat WWeb |

## OROSTACHYS (Crassulaceae)

| | |
|---|---|
| § *aggregata* | SChr |
| *chanetii* | Last listed 1997 |
| ¶ *furusei* | WCot |
| *iwarenge* | Last listed 1998 |
| *malacophylla* | See *O. aggregata* |
| § *spinosa* | NMen NTow SIng |

## ORPHIUM (Gentianaceae)

| | |
|---|---|
| ¶ *frutescens* | CPLG |

## ORTHOSIPHON (Lamiaceae)

| | |
|---|---|
| *labiatus* | Last listed 1996 |

## ORTHROSANTHUS (Iridaceae)

| | |
|---|---|
| *chimboracensis* | CFir WAbe WPer WPic |
| - JCA 13743 | CPou |
| *laxus* | CPBP EBee ERos GBuc SMad WWin |
| *multiflorus* | CHan GLch NTow |
| *polystachyus* | CHan WElm |

## ORYZOPSIS (Poaceae)

| | |
|---|---|
| ♦ *lessoniana* | See *Calamagrostis arundinacea* |
| *miliacea* | CLTr ECha LRHS NChi |
| *paradoxa* | EBee |

## OSCULARIA (Aizoaceae)

*deltoides*      See *Lampranthus deltoides*

## OSMANTHUS (Oleaceae)

| | |
|---|---|
| *armatus* | CFil CTri EPfP LPan NHol WWat |
| § x *burkwoodii* ♀ | More than 30 suppliers |
| § *decorus* | CB&S CTri ELan ENot EPla GOrc MGos MRav NWea SPer SSta WDin WWat |
| *delavayi* ♀ | More than 30 suppliers |
| - 'Latifolius' | WBcn WWat |
| *forrestii* | See *O. yunnanensis* |
| x *fortunei* | CGre CPle EPfP LRHS SLPl WWat |
| - 'Variegatus' | See *O. heterophyllus* 'Latifolius Variegatus' |
| *fragrans* | SAPC SArc |
| § *heterophyllus* | CB&S CGre CLan EBee EMil ENot ERav GCHN GOrc LPan MBar NFla NFor SCob SPer SRPl SReu SRms SSpi SSta WBay WDin WStI WWat |
| § - all gold | CBlo EAst EGra MBlu |
| - 'Argenteomarginatus' | See *O. heterophyllus* 'Variegatus' |
| § - 'Aureomarginatus' | CB&S CDoC CFil CMHG CPMA CPle EHoe ELan EMil IOrc ISea LHop MBal MPla SAga SLon SPer WLeb |
| - misapplied 'Aureus' | See *O. heterophyllus* all gold |
| - Rehder 'Aureus' | See *O. heterophyllus* 'Aureomarginatus' |
| § - 'Goshiki' (v) | More than 30 suppliers |
| N - 'Gulftide' ♀ | CBlo ELan EMil EPfP MAsh MGos NHol SCob SPla WFar WRHF WStI WWat |
| § - 'Latifolius Variegatus' | Last listed 1996 |
| - 'Myrtifolius' | Last listed 1996 |
| - 'Purple Shaft' | CAbP ELan EPfP LRHS NOla WWat |
| - 'Purpureus' | CAbP CB&S CBot CDoC CMHG CPle EHoe MBal MBel MBri MGos MRav NHed SDry SLon SSpi SSta WAbe WLeb WRHF WStI |
| - 'Rotundifolius' | CB&S CFil MBri |
| - Tricolor | See *O. heterophyllus* 'Goshiki' |
| § - 'Variegatus' ♀ | More than 30 suppliers |
| *ilicifolius* | See *O. heterophyllus* |
| *serrulatus* | CBot EPla |
| *suavis* | LRHS WWat |
| § *yunnanensis* | CMHG EPfP MBlu SAPC SArc WPGP WWat |

## x OSMAREA (Oleaceae)

*burkwoodii*      See *Osmanthus* x *burkwoodii*

## OSMARONIA See OEMLERIA

## OSMORHIZA (Apiaceae)

| | |
|---|---|
| *aristata* B&SWJ 1607 | WCru |
| *longistylis* | Last listed 1998 |
| ¶ *occidentalis* | ELau |

## OSMUNDA ✿ (Osmundaceae)

| | |
|---|---|
| *cinnamomea* ♀ | CFil CLAP NHar NMar WFib WPGP WRic |
| *claytoniana* ♀ | CFil CLAP EBee GCal LSyl NMar WRic |
| ¶ *japonica* | WCru |
| *regalis* ♀ | More than 30 suppliers |
| - 'Crispa' | NMar |
| § - 'Cristata' ♀ | CFil CLAP CRDP ELan EMon GCal LPBA MBri NHol SLon WFib WPGP WRic |

| | |
|---|---|
| ¶ - *grandiceps* | NMar |
| - 'Purpurascens' | CCuc CFil CLAP CRDP CRow CVer EBee EBrP EBre ELan EMan GBuc GQui IOrc LBre MBri MWgw NBus NHar NHol SBid SBre SSpi SWat WCru WFar WFib WRic WWat |
| ♦ - Undulata Group | See *O. regalis* 'Cristata' |
| § - 'Undulata' | EBee ELan GBin NHol WFib WRic WWoo |
| *schroderi* 'Contorta' | WRic |

## OSTEOMELES (Rosaceae)

| | |
|---|---|
| *schweriniae* B&L 12360 | CPle SAga |
| *subrotunda* | CPle |

## OSTEOSPERMUM ✿ (Asteraceae)

| | |
|---|---|
| 'African Queen' | See *O.* 'Nairobi Purple' |
| 'Anglia Yellow' | MBEx |
| *barberae* hort. | See *O. jucundum* |
| ¶ 'Beauty of Croftway' | SCro |
| 'Blackthorn Seedling' | See *O. jucundum* 'Blackthorn Seedling' |
| 'Bloemhoff Belle' | See *O.* 'Nairobi Purple' |
| 'Blue Streak' | CCan ECtt ELan ERav LPio MBEx SLon SMrm |
| 'Bodegas Pink' (v) | CPin MBEx |
| 'Brickell's Hybrid' | See *O.* 'Chris Brickell' |
| 'Buttermilk' ♀ | CB&S CBar CCan CGle CHal CLTr CSpe CTbh CTrw ELan EWTr GMac LHop MBEx MBri MLan NFai SLod SRms SSoC SUsu WEas WPer WRos |
| 'Cannington John' | CCan MArl |
| 'Cannington Joyce' | Last listed 1998 |
| 'Cannington Katrina' | CCan MBEx SRms |
| 'Cannington Kira' | CCan |
| 'Cannington Roy' | CBar CCan CGle CLTr CMHG CSam CTrw ECtt ELan LFis LHop LLWP LPio MBNS MBri NFai NHaw NPer SMrm SRms WAbe WHer |
| 'Cannington Vernon' | CCan |
| 'Catriona' | GAbr |
| ♦ *caulescens* hort. | See *O.* 'White Pim' |
| § 'Chris Brickell' | CCan CLTr CSev GCal MBEx MBNS MSte NHaw WHen WPer |
| 'Coconut Ice' | See *O.* 'Croftway Coconut-ice' |
| § 'Croftway Coconut-ice' | Last listed 1997 |
| § 'Croftway Silverspoons' | Last listed 1997 |
| 'Dennis Weston' | Last listed 1998 |
| 'Durban' | LHil |
| *ecklonis* | CGle CTbh GMaP ISea MCLN NBro NFla NGdn SCro SMrm WFar WPer WWin |
| * - deep pink | Last listed 1997 |
| ♦ - var. *prostratum* | See *O.* 'White Pim' |
| § - 'Starshine' (v) | Last listed 1998 |
| 'Edna Bond' | WEas |
| 'Giant' | CCan CSpe |
| 'Giles Gilbey' (v) | CHal CMHG CTbh LHil LHop MBNS NBur NHaw NPla SVen WEas WLRN WWeb |
| 'Glistener' | Last listed 1998 |
| 'Gold Sparkler' (v) | CB&S LHop NHaw SAga SMrm |
| 'Gweek Variegated' (v) | CLTr MBEx NPer WWin |
| 'Hopleys' ♀ | LHop MBNS |
| 'James Elliman' | ECtt LHop LLWP MBEx MSte NHaw SAga SRms |
| 'Jewel' | COtt |

| | |
|---|---|
| § *jucundum* ♀ | CCan CFri CMHG CMea ECha ENot MBEx MCLN MMal MNrw MRav MTis MWat NBrk NBur NChi NDov NFai NGdn NHol NPer SDix SEND SIng SRms WHen WPat |
| - 'Ballyrogan Pink' | Last listed 1998 |
| § - 'Blackthorn Seedling' ♀ | CSWP ECha GMac MBri NGdn NPla SAga SBla SUsu |
| - var. *compactum* | CB&S CLyd CMea CPBP ELan LHop WAbe WHen WLin |
| - 'Elliott's Form' | WLin |
| - 'Jackarandum' ♀ | Last listed 1997 |
| § - 'Killerton Pink' | CCan CMHG WPer |
| § - 'Langtrees' ♀ | ECtt EOrc GAbr LHop SMrm |
| § - 'Merriments Joy' ♀ | SMrm |
| 'Kerdalo' | Last listed 1997 |
| 'Killerton Pink' | See O. jucundum 'Killerton Pink' |
| 'Kirsty Louise' | CCan |
| 'Kriti' | Last listed 1997 |
| 'La Mortola' | CCan CHad CLTr MBEx |
| § 'Lady Leitrim' ♀ | CHea CLTr CTbh ECha EOld EOrc GBri LHop MArl MBNS MCLN MMal NBrk NBus SChu SSvw WAbe WCom WLin WRus |
| 'Langtrees' | See O. jucundum 'Langtrees' |
| ¶ 'Mercury' | WWol |
| Merriments Dark Seedling | Last listed 1996 |
| 'Merriments Joy' | See O. jucundum 'Merriments Joy' |
| ¶ 'Mira' | CHal |
| 'Molly's Choice' | SMrm |
| 'Mrs Reside's Purple' | Last listed 1996 |
| § 'Nairobi Purple' | CCan CFee ELan GBuc GMac MBEx MLan SRms WLRN WPer |
| 'Painted Lady' | SCro |
| 'Pale Face' | See O. 'Lady Leitrim' |
| 'Peggyi' | See O. 'Nairobi Purple' |
| 'Penny Pink' | CCan ECtt LPio NFai |
| 'Pink Whirls' ♀ | CB&S CBot CCan CTrw ELan ERav LHop MBEx MBri NFai NHaw SRms SSoC SUsu WPer |
| 'Port Wine' | See O. 'Nairobi Purple' |
| 'Royal Purple' | Last listed 1998 |
| 'Seaspray' | COtt |
| 'Silver Sparkler' (v) ♀ | CBar CBrm CCan CMHG CSpe CTbh EBrP EBre ELan ERav LBre LHop MBEx MBNS MLan NBur NFai NHaw SBre SChu SRms WEas |
| 'Silver Spoons' | See O. 'Croftway Silverspoons' |
| 'Snow White' | CHal SMrm |
| 'Soler' | Last listed 1998 |
| * 'Sophie' | CSpe |
| 'Sparkler' | EBrP EBre LBre LHil MSte SBre SVen |
| 'Stardust' ♀ | COtt MAsh NPer SCoo WWeb |
| 'Starshine' | See O. ecklonis 'Starshine' |
| ¶ 'Stringston Gemma' | CHal |
| Sunny® Alex | Last listed 1998 |
| Sunny® Boy | LIck MBNS |
| Sunny® Caroline | LIck |
| Sunny® Girl | ECtt |
| Sunny® Gustav | Last listed 1998 |
| Sunny® Ingrid | LIck |
| Sunny® Lady | CTbh MLLN |
| Sunny® Martha | LIck |
| ¶ Sunny® Sonja | LIck |
| * 'Superbum' | Last listed 1998 |
| 'Tauranga' | See O. 'Whirlygig' |
| 'Tiberias' | Last listed 1998 |
| 'Tresco Peggy' | See O. 'Nairobi Purple' |
| 'Tresco Pink' | IBlr |
| 'Tresco Purple' | See O. 'Nairobi Purple' |
| 'Tresco Sally' | SMrm |
| 'Weetwood' ♀ | CMHG ECtt EOld GAbr GCal GMaP LHop MBEx MBNS MBri MHar MSte NBrk SAga SMrm SWas WAbe WHil |
| § 'Whirlygig' ♀ | CB&S CCan CTrw EAst EBrP EBre ELan ERav LBre LHop MBEx MBri MLan MSCN NHaw SBre SRms WPer |
| § 'White Pim' ♀ | CHan CLTr CMHG ELan IBlr MBEx NPer SChu SCro SDix SMad SPer SPla SUsu SWas |
| 'Wine Purple' | See O. 'Nairobi Purple' |
| Wisley hybrids | WEas WRus |
| 'Zambesi' | CSpe |
| 'Zimbar' | ELan |
| 'Zulu' | CB&S CHal CMHG MBNS MLan SSoC |

## OSTRYA (Corylaceae)

| | |
|---|---|
| *carpinifolia* | CB&S CDul CLnd CMCN GChr IOrc MAsh MBar MBlu WMou WNor WOrn |
| *japonica* | CFil CMCN |
| *virginiana* | CB&S CFil CMCN EPfP IMGH WFro WNor |

## OTACANTHUS (Scrophulariaceae)

| | |
|---|---|
| *caeruleus* | CSpe |

## OTHONNA (Asteraceae)

| | |
|---|---|
| *capensis* | CHal |
| § *cheirifolia* | CBot CHan CPle CSam CSev EBee ECha ELan NBir NFor NLon NTow SDry SIgm SLon SMac SPer SRms WCot WEas WPer |

## OTHONNOPSIS See OTHONNA

## OURISIA (Scrophulariaceae)

| | |
|---|---|
| *caespitosa* | ELan GCrs IMGH NMen NRya NWCA |
| - var. *gracilis* | GTou IBlr |
| § *coccinea* | CGle GBuc IMGH NBir NTow SMac SRms SSpi WGle WWat |
| *crosbyi* | IBlr |
| *elegans* | See O. coccinea |
| *fragrans* | Last listed 1998 |
| 'Loch Ewe' | CPla GAbr GDra IBlr MDun NHar NRoo WCru WGwy WPGP |
| *macrophylla* | GAbr GAri GBuc GDra IBlr IMGH NHar NRoo WAbe WCru |
| *microphylla* | EHyt GCrs WAbe |
| * - *alba* | CGra EHyt WAbe |
| ¶ - JCA 2698501 | CPBP |
| *modesta* | Last listed 1997 |
| *polyantha* F & W 8487 | CPBP WAbe |
| 'Snowflake' ♀ | EBee EPot GAbr GCrs GDra GGar GMaP IBlr IMGH MDun MOne NBir NHar NMen NWCA WGle WLin WWin |

## OXALIS ✿ (Oxalidaceae)

| | |
|---|---|
| *acetosella* | CKin EWFC IIve LNor MMal MSal NMir WGwy WHer WShi |
| ¶ - 'Dappled Shade' (v) | CNat |
| ¶ - var. *subpurpurascens* | WCot |

| | |
|---|---|
| ***adenophylla*** ♀ | CBro CElw CMea ELan EPot ETub GAbr GDra LAma LHop MBal MBar MMal NEgg NHar NLon NMen NNrd NRog NWCA SIng SRms SUsu WAbe WBea WEas WPer |
|   - dark form | GDra MTho |
| ¶ ***anomala*** | WCot |
| § ***articulata*** | EMan LGro MTho NPer WCot WWin |
| ¶  - 'Alba' | NTow |
|   - 'Aureoreticulata' | MTho |
| ¶  - 'Festival' | WCot |
| ¶  - 'Foundation Pink' | WCot |
|   'Beatrice Anderson' | CPBP EHyt GCrs IMGH MBro MTho NHar NHol NMen NNrd SBla WAbe |
| ***bowiei*** | CMea EPot |
|   'Bowles' White' | MTho |
| ***brasiliensis*** | EPot GCrs MTho |
| ***chrysantha*** | SIng WAbe |
| ***compacta*** F&W 8011 | CPBP |
| ***corniculata*** | MTho |
|   var. ***atropurpurea*** | |
| ¶ ***debilis*** | CSpe LHil |
| ¶  - 'Aureoreticulata' | WCot |
| ***deppei*** | See *O. tetraphylla* |
| § ***depressa*** | CNic EPot EWes MTho NBir NHol NMen NNrd NRya NSla SRms |
| § ***drummondii*** | SMrm |
| ***enneaphylla*** ♀ | EPot GCrs MTho NMen NRya SIng |
|   - x ***adenophylla*** | See *O.* 'Matthew Forrest' |
|   - 'Alba' | EHyt EPot ERos MBro NHol NNrd NTow WAbe WCom WIvy |
| I  - 'Hythe Seedling' | EHyt |
| ¶  - 'Lady Elizabeth' | SBla |
|   - 'Minutifolia' | EHyt EPot ERos GCrs MBro MTho NHol NMen NRya SSmi WAbe WIvy |
| *  - 'Minutifolia Alba' | Last listed 1998 |
| *  - 'Minutifolia Rosea' | CGra |
| *  - 'Patagonia' | EPot |
|   - 'Rosea' | CBro EPot ERos GDra MBal MTho NHar NHol NMGW NRya SBla |
|   - 'Rubra' | GDra NHar NHol WAbe |
|   - 'Ruth Tweedie' | Last listed 1998 |
|   - 'Sheffield Swan' | EHyt NHol NMen SBla WAbe |
| ***flava*** | LAma NNrd |
| ***floribunda*** | See *O. articulata* |
| ***geminata*** | NBir |
| ***glabra*** | CSpe |
|   'Gwen McBride' | GCrs |
| ***hedysaroides*** | Last listed 1998 |
|   'Hemswell Knight' | NMen SIgm |
| ***hirta*** | CBro LBow LHil MTho NNrd |
|   - 'Gothenburg' | ERos LBow MTho NMen |
| ***imbricata*** | EPot |
| ***incarnata*** | Last listed 1997 |
| ***inops*** | See *O. depressa* |
|   'Ione Hecker' ♀ | CBro CLyd EHyt EPot ERos GMaP GTou LBee LHop MRPP MTho NHar NHol NMen NNrd NRya NSla NTow NWoo SIgm SMrm SUsu WAbe WIvy |
| ***japonica*** 'Picta' | Last listed 1996 |
| § ***laciniata*** | EHyt EPot GCrs MTho NHar NHol NMen NSla SBla |
|   - dark form | EHyt |
|   - x ***enneaphylla*** | Last listed 1998 |
|   - hybrid seedlings | NHar |
| ***lactea*** double form | See *O. magellanica* 'Nelson' |
| ¶ ***lasiandra*** | EPot |
| ***lobata*** | CBro EHyt ERos EWes IMGH LBow LHop MTho NNrd NTow WCom WCot |
| ***magellanica*** | CFee CHal CMHG CSpe CTri CVer ESis GCHN GMaP LBee MTho NHol SIng WBea WCru WPer |
|   - 'Flore Pleno' | See *O. magellanica* 'Nelson' |
| §  - 'Nelson' (d) | CElw CFee CHal CHan CLyd CRDP CRow CSpe CVer EPot ESis EWes GCHN GCal LBee MTho NBir NBro NHar NHol NPer NRya NWoo SSca WCru WLin WPer |
|   - 'Old Man Range' | Last listed 1998 |
| §  'Matthew Forrest' | NNrd |
| ***melanosticta*** | LBow |
| ¶ ***nahuelbuapiensis*** | CPBP |
|   F&W 8469 | |
| ***obtusa*** | CLyd ECha EPot MTho NCat NTow SSad SWas |
| ¶  - apricot form | WCot |
| ***oregana*** | CPBP CRDP CRow ECha GBuc IMGH NChi WCru |
|   - f. ***smalliana*** | WCru |
| ***ortgiesii*** | Last listed 1996 |
| ***palmifrons*** | MTho |
| ***patagonica*** | GCrs NHar NHol |
| ¶ ***pes-caprae*** | CPLG |
| * ***pulchra*** | CSpe |
| § ***purpurea*** | LHop NHol WAbe |
|   - 'Ken Aslet' | CBro CFee CLyd CNic EDAr EHyt EPot MTho NHol NNrd NTow SUsu WAbe |
| ***regnellii*** | See *O. triangularis* subsp. *papilionacea* |
| ***rosea*** Jacquin | See *O. articulata* |
|   - hort. | See *O. rubra* |
|   'Royal Velvet' | Last listed 1996 |
| § ***rubra*** | WCot |
| ¶ ***semiloba*** | WCot |
| ***speciosa*** | See *O. purpurea* |
| ***squamata*** | CPBP WCot |
| ***squamosoradicosa*** | See *O. laciniata* |
| ***stipularis*** | CMea |
| ***succulenta*** Barnéoud | CFee LHil |
|   'Superstar' | WAbe |
| § ***tetraphylla*** | CM&M EBot EPot LAma MBri MTho NCat NOrc NPer NRog SSoC WByw |
|   - alba | Last listed 1997 |
|   - 'Iron Cross' | CAvo CMea EBee EMan LAma MAvo NBir NHol SAga SBid SLod SUsu WBro WHal WRos |
| ***triangularis*** | CMea EMan LAma NBir NHol NPer SBid SPar SUsu WFar WPyg |
|   - 'Cupido' | CB&S CRDP EBee WPer WWin |
| §  - subsp. ***papilionacea*** | EBee LAma MMHG NRog WWin |
|   - - 'Atropurpurea' | EBee WCot |
|   - - ***rosea*** | Last listed 1998 |
|   - subsp. ***triangularis*** | Last listed 1998 |
| ***tuberosa*** | GPoy WHer |
| ¶  - 'Fat White' | IIve |
| ¶  - 'Ute' | CGra |
| ***valdiviensis*** | NTow WElm WSan |
| ***versicolor*** | EHyt EPot ERos EWes MTho NMen SBla SIng SSad WAbe WCot |
| ***vespertilionis*** | See *O. drummondii* |
|   Torrey & A Gray | |
|   - Zuccarini | See *O. latifolia* |
| ***vulcanicola*** | CFee SBid SDix WLRN |
| ¶ ***zeckoevleyensis*** | WCot |

## OXERA (Verbenaceae)
*pulchella* — CPlN

## OXYCOCCUS See VACCINIUM

## OXYDENDRUM (Ericaceae)
*arboreum* — CABP CAgr CB&S CDoC CEnd CMCN EHic EPfP GOrc IMGH LEdu MBal MBri MGos SBrw SRPl SSpi SSta WCru WDin WNor WWat
- 'Chameleon' — EPfP LRHS MAsh SPer SSpi SSta

## OXYLOBIUM (Papilionaceae)
*ellipticum* — Last listed 1997
*lancelolatum* — Last listed 1996

## OXYPETALUM (Asclepiadaceae)
*caeruleum* — See *Tweedia caerulea*

## OXYRIA (Polygonaceae)
*digyna* — CAgr GCHN GGar NBro WGwy WHer

## OXYTROPIS (Papilionaceae)
*campestris* — Last listed 1998
*chankaensis* — Last listed 1996
*oreophila* JCA 13585 — CPBP
- var. *jonesii* NNS 93-517 — Last listed 1998
*podocarpa* — NWCA
*shokanbetsuensis* — Last listed 1998
*viscida* — Last listed 1996

## OZOTHAMNUS (Asteraceae)
*antennaria* — CMHG WSHC
§ *coralloides* ♀ — EPot GCrs NWCA SIng
§ 'County Park Silver' — ECou EPot ESis EWes NHar NSla NTow NWCA SBla SIng WPat
§ *hookeri* — CAbb CDoC ECou NWCA SChu SIgm SPan SPer WPat
§ *ledifolius* ♀ — CMHG CPle CSam EBee ECha ELan EMil GTou LHop MBri MPla NFor NLon SChu SIgm SPer SSpi WHCG WHar WPat WSHC WWat
*lycopodioides* — ECou
§ *microphyllus* — ITim
§ *purpurascens* — EMar
'Rose Dazzler' — Last listed 1998
§ *rosmarinifolius* — CB&S CDoC CMHG CTrG CWit ELan EPla ERea IOrc MBlu MNrw NFor NLon SChu SPer WBod WBrE WEas WHCG WPic WSHC WWat
¶ - 'Kiandra' — ECou
- 'Purpureus' — Last listed 1998
- 'Silver Jubilee' ♀ — CB&S CBlo CDoC CEnd CHan CSam CTrC EBee ELan GOrc LHil LHop MAsh NFor NSti SAga SLon SPer SRPl SSpi WCot WFar WHCG WLeb WSHC WTro
*scutellifolius* — ECou
*secundiflorus* — CPle
§ *selago* — ESis EWes ITim
- 'Major' — Last listed 1996
- 'Minor' — EWes GCrs NMen NWCA
'Sussex Silver' — CPle SBid SPan WPyg WTro
'Threave Seedling' — SMrm SPan SPer
§ *thyrsoideus* — CB&S CPle WWat

# P

## PACHYPHRAGMA (Brassicaceae)
§ *macrophyllum* — CSev EBee ECGP ECha EHrv ELan EMon IBlr MRav NChi NPla NSti SMac SSpi WCot WCru WEas WWin

## PACHYPODIUM (Apocynaceae)
*lamerei* — MBri

## PACHYSANDRA (Buxaceae)
*procumbens* — EPla WCot WCru WThi
*stylosa* — EPla MRav SMad
*terminalis* ♀ — More than 30 suppliers
- 'Green Carpet' — CB&S CBlo CDoC EBee EBrP EBre ECot EFou EGol ENot EPfP EPla GAri LBre MAsh MBar MBri MUlv NPro SBre SCoo SPla WRHF WRus WWat
- 'Variegata' ♀ — More than 30 suppliers

## PACHYSTACHYS (Acanthaceae)
§ *lutea* ♀ — CHal ERea MBri

## PACHYSTEGIA See OLEARIA

## PACHYSTIMA See PAXISTIMA

## PACKERA (Asteraceae)
§ *aurea* — MSal
*fendleri* RMRP 96515 — IDac

## PAEDERIA (Rubiaceae)
*scandens* — CPlN WCru WSHC
- var. *velutina* — Last listed 1998

## PAEDEROTA (Scrophulariaceae)
§ *bonarota* — CLyd
*lutea* — Last listed 1998

## PAEONIA ♣ (Paeoniaceae)
*albiflora* — See *P. lactiflora*
'America' — MCAu
'Angel Cobb Freeborn' — Last listed 1998
*anomala* — CFil EPot MPhe SSpi
*arietina* — See *P. mascula* subsp. *arietina*
'Avant Garde' — ECha WKif
'B.G. Fahr' — MBri
*bakeri* — Last listed 1996
'Ballerina' — CKel
*banatica* — See *P. officinalis* subsp. *banatica*
¶ 'Barbara' — MCAu
*beresovskii* — CFil MPhe
¶ 'Black Pirate' — CKel
*broteroi* — CLAP LGre NTow SBla
*brownii* — EPot
'Buckeye Belle' — EBee MBri MCAu WGle
¶ 'Burma Midnight' — MCAu
'Burma Ruby' — Last listed 1997
* 'Byzantine' — Last listed 1997
*californica* — CLAP
*cambessedesii* ♀ — CBrd CBro CFil CKel CLAP EBee EHyt EPot LGre MTho NBir SBla SIgm SSpi SUsu SWas WAbe WPGP
* 'Carl G.Klehm' — WGle
'Carol' — Last listed 1998
*caucasica* — See *P. mascula* subsp. *mascula*
*chamaeleon* — WPGP

| | |
|---|---|
| 'Chinese Dragon' | CKel |
| 'Chocolate Soldier' | Last listed 1997 |
| 'Claire de Lune' | MCAu MPhe WGle |
| 'Claudia' | Last listed 1998 |
| *clusii* | Last listed 1998 |
| 'Coral Fay' | WGle |
| *corallina* | See *P. mascula* subsp. *mascula* |
| *coriacea* var. *maroccana* | Last listed 1998 |
| ¶ 'Crusader' | MCAu |
| *cypria* | Last listed 1996 |
| 'Cytherea' | MCAu |
| *daurica* | See *P. mascula* subsp. *triternata* |
| ¶ 'Daystar' | CKel |
| *decora* | See *P. peregrina* |
| 'Defender' ♀ | Last listed 1998 |
| *delavayi* ♀ | More than 30 suppliers |
| - dark red | GGGa |
| - × *delavayi* var. *lutea* | WWat |
| ¶ - from China | MPhe |
| - hybrid | ENot |
| § - var. *ludlowii* (S) ♀ | CB&S CBlo CGle CGre CKel |
| | CSam ELan GGGa ISea MBal |
| | MPhe NBrk NPer SBla SLPl SMad |
| | SPer SRPl SSpi WEas WHoo WSHC |
| | WWat WWoo |
| § - var. *lutea* (S) | CBlo MAsh MBro MWll SLon |
| | SRms STre SUsu WEas WHar WPyg |
| | WTin WWat |
| - 'Mrs Sarson' | CBlo SLPl SWat |
| § - Potaninii Group (S) | EBee SSpi |
| ¶ - Trollioides Group (S) | EBee |
| 'Early Bird' | EBee NLar |
| 'Eastgrove Ruby Lace' | WEas |
| 'Ellen Cowley' | Last listed 1998 |
| *emodi* | CLAP LPio MAvo MPhe |
| ¶ 'Fei Yan Hong Zhuang' (S) | MCAu |
| 'Flame' | WCot |
| Gansu Mudan Group | CKel MPhe |
| 'Heritage' | WGle |
| 'High Noon' | CKel MCAu |
| ¶ 'Honor' | MCAu |
| 'Horizon' | WGle |
| ¶ 'Huang Hua Kui' (S) | MPhe |
| *humilis* | See *P. officinalis* subsp. *microcarpa* |
| 'Illini Belle' | MCAu |
| 'Illini Warrior' | MCAu |
| 'Isani Gidui' | See *P. lactiflora* 'Isami-jishi' |
| *japonica* hort. | See *P. lactiflora* |
| 'Jean E. Bockstoce' | MCAu |
| ¶ 'Jin Yu Jiao Zhang' (S) | MPhe |
| *kavachensis* | Last listed 1997 |
| ¶ *kesrouanensis* | MPhe |
| *kevachensis* | See *P. mascula* subsp. *mascula* |
| 'Kinkaku' | See *P.* × *lemoinei* 'Souvenir de Maxime Cornu' |
| 'Kinko' | See *P.* × *lemoinei* 'Alice Harding' |
| 'Kinshi' | See *P.* × *lemoinei* 'Chromatella' |
| 'Kintei' | See *P.* × *lemoinei* 'L'Espérance' |
| Kohlein's hybrid | CLAP |
| § *lactiflora* | EBee ECha SSpi |
| - 'A.F.W. Hayward' | CKel |
| - 'Adolphe Rousseau' | CB&S CKel EBee LRHS MBri |
| * - 'Afterglow' | CKel |
| - 'Agida' | GCHN MRav |
| - 'Albâtre' | CKel |
| - 'Albert Crousse' | CB&S CKel MCAu |
| - 'Alexander Fleming' | CKel ECot MCAu NBir SMrm |
| - 'Alice Graemes' | Last listed 1996 |
| - 'Alice Harding' | MCAu WCGr |
| ¶ - 'Angel Cheeks' | MCAu |
| - 'Anna Pavlova' | CKel |

| | |
|---|---|
| - 'Antwerpen' | CKel |
| - 'Arabian Prince' | CKel |
| - 'Argentine' | CKel |
| - 'Armance Dessert' | CKel |
| - 'Artist' | CKel |
| - 'Asa Gray' | CKel |
| - 'Auguste Dessert' | CBlo CKel MPhe |
| - 'Aureole' | CKel |
| - 'Avant Garde' | MCAu |
| - 'Bahram' | Last listed 1997 |
| - 'Ballerina' | CKel |
| - 'Banner of Purity' | Last listed 1998 |
| - 'Baroness Schröder' | ELan |
| - 'Barrington Belle' | MBri |
| - 'Barrymore' | CKel |
| - 'Beacon' | CKel |
| - 'Beatrice Kelway' | CKel |
| - 'Beau Geste' | CKel |
| - 'Beauty Spot' | CKel |
| - 'Beersheba' | CKel |
| - 'Belle Center' | MCAu |
| - 'Belle of Somerset' | CKel |
| - 'Bertha Gorst' | CKel |
| - 'Bethcar' | CKel |
| ¶ - 'Better Times' | MCAu |
| - 'Blaze of Beauty' | CKel |
| - 'Blaze of Glory' | CKel |
| - 'Blenheim' | CKel |
| - 'Blithe Spirit' | CKel |
| - 'Bloodshot' | CKel |
| - 'Bloodstone' | CKel |
| - 'Blush Queen' | CKel ELan MBel MCAu |
| - 'Blush White' | CKel |
| - 'Border Gem' | GCHN MRav |
| - 'Bouchela' | CKel |
| - 'Boulanger' | CKel |
| - 'Bower of Roses' | CKel |
| - 'Bowl of Beauty' ♀ | CB&S CBlo CKel EBee EBrP EBre ELan LBre MBel MBri MCAu MPhe MTis NBir NVic SBod SBre SMad SMrm SPer SSpe WEas WKif WPyg WViv WWeb |
| - 'Bowl of Cream' | EBee MBri MCAu WCGr |
| - 'Boy Kelway' | CKel |
| - 'Break o' Day' | Last listed 1998 |
| - 'Bridal Gown' | Last listed 1996 |
| - 'Bridal Veil' | CKel |
| - 'Bridesmaid' | CKel |
| ¶ - 'Bright Knight' | MCAu |
| - 'British Beauty' | CKel EBee |
| - 'British Empire' | CKel |
| - 'Bunker Hill' | CBlo CKel SLdr SMur SRPl |
| - 'Butch' | Last listed 1998 |
| - 'Butter Ball' | Last listed 1996 |
| - 'Butter Bowl' | MCAu |
| - 'Calypso' | CKel |
| ¶ - 'Canarie' | MBri |
| - 'Candeur' | CKel |
| - 'Captain Alcock' | CKel |
| - 'Captivation' | CKel |
| - 'Carmen' | CKel |
| - 'Carnival' | CKel |
| - 'Cascade' | CKel |
| - 'Catherine Fontijn' | CKel MCAu WCGr |
| - 'Charles' White' | SPer WCGr |
| - 'Charm' | MCAu |
| - 'Cheddar Cheese' | WGle |
| - 'Cheddar Gold' | Last listed 1998 |
| - 'Cherry Hill' | CKel |
| - 'Chestine Gowdy' | CKel |
| - 'Chocolate Soldier' | Last listed 1997 |
| - 'Christine Kelway' | CKel |

| | |
|---|---|
| - 'Cincinnati' | WGle |
| - 'Claire Dubois' | MCAu WCGr |
| - 'Colonel Heneage' | Last listed 1998 |
| - 'Cornelia Shaylor' | CKel ELan |
| - 'Coronation' | CKel |
| - 'Countess of Altamont' | CKel |
| - 'Country Girl' | CKel |
| - 'Couronne d'Or' | MCAu |
| - 'Crimson Banner' | CKel |
| - 'Crimson Glory' | CKel MPhe |
| - 'Crimson Velvet' | CKel |
| ¶ - 'Cringley White' | SBod |
| - 'Dandy Dan' | Last listed 1998 |
| - 'Dark Lantern' | CKel |
| - 'Dark Song' | CKel |
| - 'Dark Vintage' | CKel |
| - 'David Kelway' | CKel |
| - 'Dawn Crest' | CKel |
| - 'Dayspring' | CKel |
| - 'Daystar' | CKel |
| - 'Denise' | CKel |
| - 'Desire' | CKel |
| - Diana Drinkwater | CKel |
| - 'Dinner Plate' | MBri MCAu WCGr |
| - 'Display' | CKel |
| - 'Docteur H. Barnsby' | CKel |
| - 'Dominion' | CKel |
| - 'Doreen' | MBel MCAu MRav |
| - 'Dorothy Welsh' | CKel |
| - 'Dragon' | Last listed 1997 |
| - 'Dresden' | CKel |
| - 'Duchess of Bedford' | CKel |
| - 'Duchess of Marlborough' | Last listed 1996 |
| - 'Duchess of Somerset' | CKel |
| - 'Duchesse de Nemours' ♀ | CBlo CKel COtt EBee EBrP EBre EFou ENot EPfP GChr GMaP LBre MBNS MBri MCAu MMil MTis NBir NLar NRoo NVic SBre SCob SPer SRms SSpe WCot WWeb |
| - 'Duke of Devonshire' | CKel |
| - 'Edith Cavell' | CKel |
| - 'Edmund Spencer' | CKel |
| - 'Edouard Doriat' | CKel |
| - 'Edulis Superba' | CBlo CKel EBee EBrP EBre ELan ENot LBre LEdu MBNS MCAu NRoo SBre SPer SRPl WWeb |
| - 'Ella Christine Kelway' | CKel |
| - 'Elsa Sass' | WCGr |
| - 'Emma Klehm' | Last listed 1998 |
| - 'Emperor of India' | CKel |
| - 'Empire State' | EBee |
| - 'Enchantment' | CKel |
| - 'English Princess' | CKel |
| - 'Ethelreda' | CKel |
| - 'Eugénie Verdier' | Last listed 1997 |
| - 'Evening Glow' | CKel |
| - 'Evening World' | CKel |
| - 'Fairy's Petticoat' | Last listed 1996 |
| - 'Fantin-Latour' | CKel |
| - 'Félix Crousse' ♀ | CBlo CKel CTri EBee ELan EPfP GChr GMaP MBri MCAu NRoo SMrm SPer SRms SWat WWeb |
| - 'Festiva Maxima' ♀ | CBlo CKel CTri EBee EBrP EBre ECot ELan EPfP LBre MBri MBro MCAu NLar SBre SCob SMrm SPer SRms WHoo WPyg WWal |
| - 'Fire Flower' | Last listed 1996 |
| - 'Flag of War' | CKel |
| - 'Flamboyant' | CKel |
| - 'Flamingo' | CKel |
| - 'France' | CKel |
| - 'Gainsborough' | CKel |

| | |
|---|---|
| - 'Garden Beauty' | CKel |
| - 'Gay Ladye' | CKel |
| - 'Gay Paree' | MBri MCAu |
| - 'Gay Sister' | CKel |
| - 'Gazelle' | CKel EBee |
| - 'Général Joffre' | CKel |
| - 'Général MacMahon' | See *P. lactiflora* 'Augustin d'Hour' |
| - 'General Wolfe' | CKel |
| - 'Germaine Bigot' | CKel |
| - 'Gertrude' | CKel |
| - 'Gilbert Barthelot' | MCAu WCGr |
| - 'Gleam of Light' | CKel |
| - 'Globe of Light' | Last listed 1996 |
| - 'Gloriana' | Last listed 1998 |
| - 'Glory Hallelujah' | Last listed 1998 |
| - 'Glory of June' | CKel |
| - 'Glory of Somerset' | CKel |
| - 'Gold Mine' | CKel |
| - 'Golly' | WGle |
| - 'Grace Loomis' | CKel |
| - 'Great Lady' | CKel |
| - 'Great Sport' | CKel |
| - 'Grover Cleveland' | CKel |
| - 'Gypsy Girl' | CKel |
| - 'Heartbeat' | CKel |
| - 'Heirloom' | CKel MPhe |
| - 'Helen Hayes' | Last listed 1998 |
| - 'Henri Potin' | CKel |
| - 'Her Grace' | CKel |
| - 'Her Majesty' | CKel |
| - 'Herbert Oliver' | CKel |
| - 'Hit Parade' | MCAu |
| - 'Honey Gold' | MCAu WGle |
| - 'Huge Delight' | CKel |
| - 'Hyperion' | CKel |
| - 'Immaculée' | CKel |
| - 'Indian Pink' | CKel |
| - 'Ingenieur Doriat' | CKel |
| - 'Inspecteur Lavergne' | CKel EBee EFou MBel MBri MCAu MRav SPer WWeb |
| - 'Instituteur Doriat' | CKel MPhe |
| § - 'Isami-jishi' | Last listed 1998 |
| - 'Jacques Doriat' | CKel |
| - 'James Kelway' | Last listed 1998 |
| - 'James Pillow' | Last listed 1998 |
| - 'James R. Mann' | CKel |
| - 'Jan van Leeuwen' | CKel |
| ¶ - 'Jappensha-Ikhu' | MBri |
| - 'Jeanne d'Arc' | CKel |
| - 'Joan Kelway' | CKel |
| - 'Joseph Plagne' | CKel |
| - 'Joy of Life' | Last listed 1998 |
| - 'June Morning' | CKel |
| - 'June Rose' | MCAu |
| - 'Kansas' | CKel ELan MBri MCAu WCGr |
| - 'Karen Gray' | MBri MCAu |
| - 'Karl Rosenfield' | CBlo CKel EBee EBrP EBre ECot ENot EPfP LBre MBri MBro MTis NBee NVic SBre SCob SMrm SPer SPla SRms SSpe WHoo WViv |
| - 'Katherine Havermeyer' | CKel |
| - 'Kathleen Mavoureen' | CKel |
| - 'Kelway's Brilliant' | CKel |
| - 'Kelway's Fairy Queen' | CKel |
| - 'Kelway's Glorious' | CBlo MBNS MBri MCAu MTed WCGr |
| ¶ - 'Kelway's Gorgeous' | EBee |
| - 'Kelway's Lovely' | CKel |
| - 'Kelway's Majestic' | CKel |
| - 'Kelway's Malmaison' | Last listed 1998 |
| - 'Kelway's Queen' | CKel |

- 'Kelway's Scented Rose' CKel
- 'Kelway's Supreme' CKel SWat
- 'Kelway's Unique' CKel
- 'Kestrel' CKel
- 'King Arthur' CKel
- 'King George VI' Last listed 1998
- 'King of England' CKel
- 'Knight of the Thistle' CKel
- 'Knighthood' CKel
- 'Krinkled White' EBee MBri MCAu MRav WCGr
  WGle
- 'La France' CKel
- 'La Lorraine' Last listed 1998
- 'Lady Alexandra Duff' ♀ CB&S CBlo CKel COtt EPfP MBri
  MCAu MRav SRms WCGr
- 'Lady Ley' CKel
- 'Lady Mayoress' CKel
- 'Lady Orchid' MCAu
- 'Langport Triumph' CKel
- 'Largo' Last listed 1998
- 'Laura Dessert' ♀ CKel LRHS SPer WCGr
¶ - 'Le Cygne' SLdr
¶ - 'Le Jour' MBri
- 'L'Eclatante' CKel MMil WViv WWal
- 'Legion of Honor' CKel
- 'Lemon Ice' CKel
- 'Letitia' CKel
- 'Lillian Wild' MCAu
- 'Lois Kelsey' MBel
- 'Lora Dexheimer' Last listed 1998
- 'Lord Avebury' CKel
- 'Lord Cavan' CKel WGle
- 'Lord Kitchener' CKel MPhe
- 'Lord Rosebery' CKel
- 'Lorna Doone' CKel
- 'Lottie Dawson Rea' Last listed 1998
- 'Lotus Queen' MCAu
- 'Louis Barthelot' CKel
- 'Louis van Houtte' CKel MBri
- 'Lyric' CKel
- 'Madame Calot' CKel EBee MCAu SRms WCGr
- 'Madame Claude Tain' LRHS WCot
- 'Madame Ducel' CKel MCAu
- 'Madame Emile Debatène' CKel EWll MBNS
- 'Madame Jules Dessert' CKel
- 'Madelon' CKel CMGP
- 'Magic Melody' CKel
- 'Magic Orb' CKel
- 'Major Loder' CKel
- 'Margaret Truman' CKel
- 'Marguérite Gerard' CKel
- 'Marie Crousse' MCAu
- 'Marie Lemoine' CKel MCAu SMur
- 'Marietta Sisson' Last listed 1998
- 'Marquisite' CKel
- 'Mary Brand' CKel
- 'Matilda Lewis' Last listed 1998
- 'Meteor Flight' CKel
- 'Mikado' Last listed 1998
- 'Minnie Shaylor' MCAu
- 'Mischief' MCAu
- 'Miss America' MCAu
- 'Miss Eckhart' CKel EWll WCGr
- 'Mister Ed' MCAu
- 'Monsieur Jules Elie' ♀ CBot CKel EBee EBrP EBre EFou
  EPfP LBre MBel MBri MCAu MMil
  MPhe SBre SPer SPla WCGr
- 'Monsieur Martin Cahuzac' MCAu
- 'Mother's Choice' MCAu WGle
- 'Mr G.F. Hemerik' CKel LRHS MBri MCAu
- 'Mrs Edward Harding' WCGr
- 'Mrs F.J. Hemerik' Last listed 1998

- 'Mrs Franklin D. Roosevelt' Last listed 1998
- 'Mrs J.V. Edlund' Last listed 1998
- 'My Pal Rudy' Last listed 1998
- 'Myrtle Gentry' CKel
- 'Nancy Nicholls' Last listed 1998
- 'Nectar' CKel
- 'Newfoundland' Last listed 1998
- 'Nice Gal' Last listed 1998
- 'Nick Shaylor' MCAu WGle
- 'Nobility' CKel
- 'Noonday' CKel
- 'Octavie Demay' Last listed 1996
- 'Ornament' CKel
- 'Orpen' CKel
- 'Othello' CKel
- 'Pageant' CKel
- 'Paper White' CKel
- 'Paul M. Wild' MCAu
- 'Pauline Maunder' CKel
- 'Peche' EBee
- 'Peregrine' CKel EBee
- 'Peter Brand' LRHS NOla
- 'Peter Pan' CKel
- 'Petticoat Flounce' WGle
- 'Phedar White' MPhe
- 'Philippe Rivoire' Last listed 1998
- 'Philomèle' Last listed 1998
- 'Pillow Talk' MCAu WCGr
- 'Pink Dawn' CKel
- 'Pink Delight' CKel
- 'Pink Giant' MBri
- 'Pink Lemonade' WGle
- 'Pink Parfait' MCAu
- 'Pink Princess' MBri MCAu
- 'President Franklin CBlo EBrP EBre GCHN LBre SBre
  D. Roosevelt' SPer SWat
- 'Président Poincaré' CBlo CKel EBrP EBre LBre MRav
  SBre SMur SPer SWat
- 'President Taft' See P. lactiflora 'Reine Hortense'
- 'President Wilson' Last listed 1998
- 'Pride of Huish' CKel
- 'Pride of Somerset' CKel
- 'Primevere' EBee EWll LRHS
- 'Princess Beatrice' CKel
- 'Pure Delight' CKel
- 'Queen Elizabeth' CKel
- 'Queen of the Belgians' CKel
- 'Queen Wilhelmina' Last listed 1996
- 'Queen's Grace' CKel
- 'Raoul Dessert' Last listed 1996
- 'Raspberry Sundae' MCAu MRav WCot
- 'Red Dwarf' CKel
- 'Red King' CKel
- 'Red Warrior' CKel
§ - 'Reine Hortense' CKel MCAu MRav WGle
- 'Rembrandt' Last listed 1998
- 'Rhododendron' Last listed 1996
- 'Rose of Delight' CKel
- 'Ruby Light' CKel
- 'Ruigegno' Last listed 1996
- 'Ruth Cobb' Last listed 1998
- 'Sainfoin' CKel
- 'Sarah Bernhardt' ♀ More than 30 suppliers
- 'Shawnee Chief' MCAu
- 'Shimmering Velvet' CKel
- 'Shirley Temple' CBlo CKel EFou ELan MBNS MBel
  MBri MCAu MMil WCGr WCot
  WPyg
- 'Silver Flare' CKel
- 'Sir Edward Elgar' CKel
- 'Smiling Morn' CKel
- 'Solange' CKel MCAu SPer

| | | |
|---|---|---|
| ¶ - 'Sorbet' | COtt EBee WCGr | |
| - 'Souvenir de Louis Bigot' | CKel | |
| - 'Spearmint' | CKel | |
| - 'Strephon' | CKel | |
| - 'Surugu' | SLdr | |
| - 'Sweet Sixteen' | MCAu | |
| - 'Tamate-boko' | Last listed 1998 | |
| - 'Thérèse' | CKel | |
| - 'Top Brass' | CBot MCAu MRav | |
| - 'Toro-no-maki' | Last listed 1997 | |
| - 'Torpilleur' | CKel | |
| - 'Tourangelle' | Last listed 1998 | |
| - 'Translucient' | CKel | |
| - var. *trichocarpa* | Last listed 1998 | |
| - 'Utopia' | CKel | |
| - 'Victoire de la Marne' | CKel SMur | |
| - 'Vogue' | CBlo CKel LRHS SMur | |
| - 'Westerner' | MCAu | |
| - 'White Wings' | CB&S CBlo CKel COtt EBee ELan | |
| | MBri MCAu NRoo SPer SSpe | |
| | WCot WGle | |
| - 'Whitleyi Major' ♀ | CKel LRHS WCot | |
| - 'Wiesbaden' | CKel | |
| - 'Wilbur Wright' | CKel | |
| - 'Windsor Lad' | CKel | |
| - 'Wings of Love' | CKel | |
| - 'Winston Churchill' | CKel | |
| - 'Wladyslawa' | SPla | |
| - 'Zus Braun' | CKel | |
| - 'Zuzu' | MCAu | |
| 'Late Windflower' | ECha | |
| x *lemoinei* | WHal | |
| § - 'Alice Harding' (S) | MCAu SPer | |
| § - 'Chromatella' (S) | CKel LAma | |
| § - 'L'Espérance' | LAma | |
| § - 'Souvenir de Maxime | CKel LAma MCAu SPer | |
| Cornu' (S) | | |
| *lithophila* | See *P. tenuifolia* subsp. *lithophila* | |
| *lobata* 'Fire King' | See *P. peregrina* | |
| 'Lois Arleen' | Last listed 1998 | |
| ♦ *ludlowii* | See *P. delavayi* var. *ludlowii* | |
| *lutea* | See *P. delavayi* var. *lutea* | |
| - var. *ludlowii* | See *P. delavayi* var. *ludlowii* | |
| ¶ *macrophylla* | MPhe | |
| - from W Georgia | WPGP | |
| 'Mai Fleuri' | LRHS MCAu WTin | |
| ¶ *mairei* | MPhe | |
| § *mascula* | CAvo CBro NBir | |
| § - subsp. *arietina* | EBee SIgm WKif | |
| - - 'Northern Glory' | LSpr WCot | |
| § - subsp. *mascula* | EPot LEdu SBla WWoo | |
| - - from SE Georgia | WPGP | |
| § - subsp. *russoi* | SRms WCot | |
| § - subsp. *triternata* | CLAP MPhe SBla SSpi WCot | |
| | WHoo | |
| - - from Crimea | WPGP | |
| *mlokosewitschii* ♀ | More than 30 suppliers | |
| - from E Georgia | Last listed 1998 | |
| *mollis* | See *P. officinalis* subsp. *villosa* | |
| 'Montezuma' | MCAu | |
| 'Moonrise' | Last listed 1998 | |
| 'Nymphe' | CKel MCAu MRav NRoo WCGr | |
| *obovata* ♀ | CLAP SSpi WThi | |
| - var. *alba* ♀ | GBin NWoo WAbe WEas | |
| - 'Grandiflora' | MRav MWgw | |
| *officinalis* | CBlo CFil NBrk | |
| - 'Alba Plena' | CBlo CAu CPou MBri MCAu | |
| | MRav SPer | |
| - 'Anemoniflora Rosea' ♀ | LRHS MBri MCAu | |
| § - subsp. *banatica* | SSpi | |
| - - WM 9727 | MPhe | |
| - 'China Rose' | LRHS | |

| | | |
|---|---|---|
| - subsp. *humilis* | See *P. officinalis* subsp. | |
| | *microcarpa* | |
| - 'James Crawford Weguelin' | Last listed 1997 | |
| - 'Lize van Veen' | NRoo | |
| § - subsp. *microcarpa* | EBee SBla SSpi | |
| - 'Mutabilis Plena' | IBlr | |
| - 'Rosea Plena' ♀ | CBlo CKel EBee EPfP GAbr LRHS | |
| | MCAu MRav NMGW SPer SWat | |
| | WLRN | |
| - 'Rosea Superba Plena' | CKel EFou SLdr | |
| - 'Rubra Plena' ♀ | CBlo CKel CPou EBee EFou ENot | |
| | EPfP MBri MCAu NRoo SPer SRms | |
| | SWat WWeb | |
| § - subsp. *villosa* | EBee ELan MBri | |
| ¶ - WM 9821 from Slovenia | MPhe | |
| *ostii* | CKel MPhe | |
| 'Paladin' | Last listed 1996 | |
| ♦ *papaveracea* | See *P. suffruticosa* | |
| *paradoxa* | See *P. officinalis* subsp. | |
| | *microcarpa* | |
| 'Paula Fay' | MCAu MRav | |
| 'Peppermint Stick' | WGle | |
| § *peregrina* | CFil CLAP EBee ECho MCAu | |
| | MPhe SBla SSpi | |
| - from Macedonia | WPGP | |
| § - 'Otto Froebel' ♀ | CBlo EBrP EBre LBre MBri NLar | |
| | NRoo SBre WCot | |
| - 'Sunshine' | See *P. peregrina* 'Otto Froebel' | |
| - 'Polindra' | Last listed 1996 | |
| *potaninii* | See *P. delavayi* Potaninii Group | |
| * 'Raspberry Ice' | WGle | |
| ¶ 'Red Charm' | MCAu | |
| 'Reine Supreme' | WGle | |
| 'Requiem' | WGle | |
| *rhodia* | MPhe | |
| *rockii* | See *P. suffruticosa* subsp. *rockii* | |
| *romanica* | See *P. peregrina* | |
| 'Rose Garland' | Last listed 1998 | |
| 'Roselette' | Last listed 1998 | |
| *russoi* | See *P. mascula* subsp. *russoi* | |
| 'Scarlett O'Hara' | MCAu | |
| *sinensis* | See *P. lactiflora* | |
| 'Smouthii' | Last listed 1998 | |
| *steveniana* | CLAP MPhe | |
| - from SE Georgia | WPGP | |
| § *suffruticosa* | CBlo CPMA EBee ELan GOrc | |
| | LPan MGos MPhe SRPl SSpi WStI | |
| * - 'Alice Palmer' | CKel | |
| - 'Bai Yu' (S) | CKel MPhe | |
| - 'Bang Ning Zi' (S) | MPhe | |
| * - Best-shaped Red = | Last listed 1996 | |
| 'Zhuan-yuan-hong' (S) | | |
| - Bird of Rimpo | See *P. suffruticosa* 'Rimpo' | |
| - Black Dragon Brocade | See *P. suffruticosa* 'Kokuryû- | |
| | nishiki' | |
| - Brocade of the Naniwa | See *P. suffruticosa* 'Naniwa- | |
| | nishiki' | |
| - 'Cai Die' (S) | MPhe | |
| * - 'Cai Jing Qui' (S) | MPhe | |
| - 'Cang Zhi Hong' (S) | MPhe WViv | |
| - 'Cardinal Vaughan' (S) | CKel | |
| - Charming Age | See *P. suffruticosa* 'Howki' | |
| ¶ - 'Chen Hong' (S) | MPhe | |
| - Cherries of Imperial | See *P. suffruticosa* 'Gosho-zakura' | |
| Palace | | |
| - Chinese hybrids (S) | SSON | |
| - 'Da Zong Zi' (S) | MPhe | |
| * - Diamond Dust = | Last listed 1996 | |
| 'Zuan-fen' (S) | | |
| - 'Dou Lu' (S) | MPhe | |
| - Double Cherry | See *P. suffruticosa* 'Yae-zakura' | |
| - 'Duchess of Kent' (S) | CKel | |

¶ - 'Duchess of Marlborough' CKel
¶ - 'Er Qiao' (S)    CKel
   - Eternal Camellias    See *P. suffruticosa* 'Yachiyo-tsubaki'
   - 'Fen Lan Zhu' (S)    MPhe
   - 'Fen Qiao' (S)    MPhe
   - 'Fen-dang-bai'    WViv
¶ - 'Feng Dan Bai'    CKel MPhe
¶ - 'Feng Zhong Guan' (S)    CKel
   - Flight of Cranes    See *P. suffruticosa* 'Renkaku'
   - Floral Rivalry    See *P. suffruticosa* 'Hana-kisoi'
   - 'Ge Jin Zi'    MPhe
* - 'Glory of Huish'    CKel
   - 'Godaishu' (S)    LAma SPer
§ - 'Guan Shi Mo Yu' (S)    MPhe
§ - 'Hakuojisi' (S)    EBee LRHS MCAu
§ - 'Hana-daijin' (S)    LAma MCAu SPer
§ - 'Hana-kisoi' (S)    LAma LRHS MCAu SPer
¶ - 'He Bai' (S)    MPhe
* - 'Hei Hue Kui' (S)    MPhe
§ - 'Higurashi' (S)    EBee LAma
¶ - 'Hong Cai Qiu' (S)    MPhe
   - 'Hou Lian Jin Dan' (S)    MPhe
§ - 'Howki' (S)    LRHS MCAu
   - 'Hu Die Qun Wu' (S)    MPhe
¶ - 'Hu Hong' (S)    MPhe
§ - Jewel in the Lotus =    LAma
   'Tama-fuyo' (S)
§ - Jewelled Screen =    LRHS MCAu
   'Tama-sudare' (S)
   - 'Jia Ge Jin Zi' (S)    CKel WViv
   - 'Jiao Rong San Bian' (S)    MPhe
   - 'Jin Pao Hong' (S)    MPhe
   - Kamada Brocade    See *P. suffruticosa* 'Kamada-nishiki'
§ - 'Kamada-fuji' (S)    CKel LAma
§ - 'Kamada-nishiki' (S)    MCAu
§ - 'Kaow' (S)    LRHS MCAu
   - King of Flowers    See *P. suffruticosa* 'Kaow'
   - King of White Lions    See *P. suffruticosa* 'Hakuojisi'
* - 'Kingdom of the Moon'    LRHS
   - 'Kinkaku'    See *P.* x *lemoinei* 'Souvenir de Maxime Cornu'
   - 'Kinshi'    See *P.* x *lemoinei* 'Alice Harding'
   - Knight's Dance    See *P. suffruticosa* 'No-kagura'
§ - 'Kokuryû-nishiki' (S)    LAma
¶ - 'Koshi-no-yuki'    CKel
   - 'Lan Tian Yu' (S)    CKel MPhe
* - 'Large Globe'    Last listed 1997
   - 'Li Hua Xue' (S)    MPhe
¶ - 'Ling Hua Zhan' (S)    MPhe
   - 'Liu Li Guan Zhu' (S)    MPhe
   - 'Lord Selbourne' (S)    Last listed 1998
   - Lotus Green =    MPhe
   'He Hua Lu' (S)
   - 'Lu He Hong'    MCAu
   - 'Luo Han Hong'    MPhe WViv
¶ - 'Luo Yang Hong'    MPhe
   - Magnificent Flower    See *P. suffruticosa* 'Hana-daijin'
   - 'Montrose' (S)    CKel
   - Moon World    See *P. suffruticosa* 'Gessekai'
* - 'Mrs Shirley Fry'    CKel
   - 'Mrs William Kelway' (S)    CKel
§ - 'Naniwa-nishiki' (S)    Last listed 1998
   - Palace of Gems    See *P. suffruticosa* 'Shugyo-kuden'
   - Pride of Taisho    See *P. suffruticosa* 'Taisho-no-hokori'
   - 'Qing Long Wo Mo Chi' (S)    MCAu MPhe
   - 'Qing Shan Guan Xue' (S)    WViv
   - 'Raphael' (S)    Last listed 1998
§ - 'Renkaku' (S)    CKel MCAu
§ - 'Rimpo' (S)    EBee LAma SPer

§ - subsp. *rockii* (S)    MPhe MWll SSpi
¶ - 'Rou Fu Rong' (S)    MCAu
   - 'Ruan-zhi-lan'    MPhe WViv
   - 'San Bian Sai Yu' (S)    MPhe WViv
   - Seven Gods of Fortune    See *P. suffruticosa* 'Sitifukujin'
¶ - 'Shimane-akashigata'    CKel
¶ - 'Shimane-chojuraku'    CKel
¶ - 'Shimane-hakugan'    CKel
¶ - 'Shou An Hong' (S)    MCAu MPhe
§ - 'Shugyo-kuden' (S)    MCAu
   - 'Si He Lian' (S)    MPhe
§ - 'Sitifukujin' (S)    MCAu
¶ - 'Sumi-no-ichi'    CKel
   - 'Superb' (S)    CKel
§ - 'Taisho-no-hokori' (S)    LRHS
§ - 'Taiyo' (S)    LAma SPer
♦ - 'Tama-fuyo'    See *P. suffruticosa* Jewel in the Lotus = 'Tama-fuyo'
♦ - 'Tama-sudare'    See *P. suffruticosa* Jewelled Screen = 'Tama-sudare'
   - 'Tao Hong Xian Mei' (S)    MPhe
   - The Sun    See *P. suffruticosa* 'Taiyo'
* - Top Table Red =    Last listed 1996
   'Sho-an-hong' (S)
   - Twilight    See *P. suffruticosa* 'Higurashi'
¶ - 'Wen Gong Hong' (S)    MPhe
   - Wisteria at Kamada    See *P. suffruticosa* 'Kamada-fuji'
¶ - 'Wu Long Feng Sheng' (S)    CKel MPhe
   - 'Xue Gui' (S)    MPhe
¶ - 'Xue Ta' (S)    CKel
§ - 'Yachiyo-tsubaki' (S)    CKel LAma LRHS MCAu
§ - 'Yae-zakura' (S)    LAma
¶ - 'Yan Long Zi Zhu Pan' (S)    CKel
   - 'Yin Fen Jin Lin' (S)    MCAu
¶ - 'Yin Hong Qiao Dui' (S)    CKel MPhe
   - 'Ying Luo Bao Zhu' (S)    WViv
   - 'Yomo-zakura' (S)    LRHS
   - 'Yoshinogawa' (S)    EBee
   - 'Yu Hu Die' (S)    MPhe
   - 'Yu Lu Dian Cui' (S)    WViv
   - 'Yu Pan Zheng Yan' (S)    MPhe
¶ - 'Yu Xi Ying Xue' (S)    CKel MPhe
¶ - 'Zhao Fen' (S)    MPhe
¶ - 'Zhi Hong' (S)    CKel
¶ - 'Zhong Sheng Hong' (S)    MPhe
   - 'Zhu Sha Lei' (S)    CKel MCAu MPhe
   - 'Zi Ban Bai' (S)    MPhe
¶ - 'Zi Er Qiao' (S)    CKel MPhe
   - 'Zi Jin Pan' (S)    WViv
¶ - 'Zi Lan Kui' (S)    CKel MPhe
   'Sunshine'    See *P. peregrina* 'Otto Froebel'
¶ **szechuanica**    MPhe
   **tenuifolia**    CBot CLAP GCal NRoo SIgm WCot
   - subsp. **biebersteiniana**    MPhe
   - subsp. **carthalinica**    MPhe
   - from E Georgia    WPGP
§ - subsp. **lithophila**    MPhe
   - 'Plena'    CRDP LRHS MBri MPhe WCot
   - 'Rosea'    Last listed 1998
   **turcica**    MPhe
   **veitchii**    CKel CLAP LGre MBal MTho SDys SIgm SSpi WAbe WEas
   - dwarf form    MPhe
¶ - from China    MPhe
¶ - var. **leiocarpa**    MPhe
   - var. **woodwardii**    CAvo CLyd ERos GDra LGre MBel MTho NHar NSla NWCA SSpi WCot WHoo
   'Windchimes'    WGle
   **wittmanniana**    CBot CLAP EBee NTow WSPU
   'Yao Huang' (S)    CKel MCAu MPhe

'Yellow Crown' (S) — Last listed 1998
'Yellow Dream' (S) — Last listed 1998

## PAESIA (Dennstaedtiaceae)
*scaberula* — CBos CFil GCal SSpi WAbe WRic

## PALIURUS (Rhamnaceae)
*spina-christi* — CArn CPle EWes MWhi SLon SMad WSPU

## PALLENIS (Asteraceae)
*spinosus* — See *Asteriscus spinosus*

## PANAX (Araliaceae)
*ginseng* — GPoy
*japonicus* — GPoy WThi
*pseudoginseng* — Last listed 1998
*quinquefolius* — GPoy

## PANCRATIUM (Amaryllidaceae)
*canariense* — Last listed 1997
*foetidum* S&L 354 — Last listed 1998
*maritimum* — EBee EBot

## PANDANUS (Pandanaceae)
*tectorius* 'Veitchii' ♀ — Last listed 1990

## PANDOREA (Bignoniaceae)
*jasminoides* — CPlN CSpe EBak ECon ECot ELan SBid SLon SOWG
- 'Alba' — See *P. jasminoides* 'Lady Di'
§ - 'Charisma' (v) — CAbb CB&S CPlN CSpe EBee EHol ELan EMil EPfP LCns LPan SHFr SOWG
§ - 'Lady Di' — CPlN CSpe ELan ERea LCns SOWG SYvo
- 'Rosea' — MCCP
- 'Rosea Superba' ♀ — CB&S CRHN ECon EHic EHol ELan EMil ERea
- 'Variegata' — See *P. jasminoides* 'Charisma'
*lindleyana* — See *Clytostoma callistegioides*
*pandorana* — CB&S CPlN CSpe EHic ERea SYvo WCot
* - 'Alba' — CPlN
- 'Golden Rain' — CB&S CPlN CRHN ECon ERea SOWG
- 'Ruby Heart' — CPlN

## PANICUM (Poaceae)
*bulbosum* — CHan EHoe EPla
*clandestinum* — EHoe EPPr EPla EWes LEdu MCCP NPro WCot
*coloratum* 'Bambatsi' — Last listed 1997
*miliaceum* — EGle MSal
- 'Violaceum' — Last listed 1996
*virgatum* — CTri ECha MSte MWhi NChi WBro WPer
- 'Hänse Herms' — CInt CMil EHoe EPPr LGre MBri
- 'Heavy Metal' — EHoe NSti WCot WHil
- 'Pathfinder' — Last listed 1997
- 'Rehbraun' — EBrP EBre ECGN EHoe EPPr LBre LEdu MCAu NOak SApp SBre SMad WCot WRus
- 'Rotstrahlbusch' — EBrP EBre EFou EHoe EPPr EPla LBre SBre SPla
- 'Rubrum' — More than 30 suppliers
- 'Squaw' — EHoe EPPr LGre SApp WCot WHil
- 'Strictum' — CCuc EHoe EMil EWes
- 'Warrior' — CInt EBrP EBre EFou EHoe EPPr LBre LEdu LGre MCCP NCut NSti SApp SAsh SBre
¶ 'Wood's Variegated' — SApp

## PAPAVER ✿ (Papaveraceae)
*aculeatum* — Last listed 1998
*alboroseum* — CInt CSam EHyt GCHN GTou MSCN NHol WPat
§ *alpinum* L. — CSpe EMNN ESis GCHN GDra GTou LHol MBal MPla SIng SPla SRms WWin
- *album* — CMea
- cut petal form — CInt
- subsp. *ernesti-mayeri* — Last listed 1998
- 'Flore Pleno' (d) — NBir
*anomalum* — Last listed 1998
- *album* — CHan CMil CSpe EBee EMon EWll GMac LEur MLLN MWgw NArg NFai NLak SIng STes WElm WSan
¶ *apokrinomenon* — MWll
*argemone* — EWFC
§ *atlanticum* — CLTr CNic EBee ECoo EMar EOld GBuc GCHN MMal NBro NSti SPlb
- 'Flore Pleno' (d) — CM&M EBee LFis MCCP MWll NBro NFai WCot WOld
*bracteatum* — See *P. orientale* var. *bracteatum*
*burseri* — SRot
*commutatum* ♀ — CInt ELan EWTr LHol MAvo MRav SMrm WCot WEas
*corona-sancti-stephani* — Last listed 1998
*degenii* — GCHN NBur
*dubium* — Last listed 1997
*fauriei* — CFri WAbe
§ 'Fireball' — CBre CMHG CRow ECha ELan GCal LHop MTis MWat NCat NTow WCot WMaN WRHF
*beldreichii* — See *P. spicatum*
x *hybridum* — EBee EMon MCLN NBrk SWat
'Flore Pleno' (d) — WWal
*julicum* — Last listed 1997
*kluanense* — CSam NLak
*lapponicum* — Last listed 1998
- subsp. *occidentale* — Last listed 1998
*lateritium* — CPou MLLN MMal SRms
- 'Flore Pleno' (d) — EBee
*microcarpum* — Last listed 1998
§ *miyabeanum* — CGle CHea CMea CSpe ELan GCHN GDra GTou LHop MPla NWCA WFar WPer WWin
- *album* — ECho ELan
- 'Pacino' — ESis EWll
- *tatewakii* — See *P. miyabeanum*
*nanum* 'Flore Pleno' — See *P.* 'Fireball'
§ *nudicaule* — CBlo ELan LEdu MHlr WPer
- Champagne Bubbles Group — EBrP EBre LBre SBre SRms WFar WLRN
- Constance Finnis Group — EMon GBuc LHop
- var. *croceum* — NWCA
¶ - 'Flamenco' — WViv
- Garden Gnome Group — See *P. nudicaule* Gartenzwerg Group
§ - Gartenzwerg Group — CBlo CSpe EMil GAbr MBri MPla NArg NCut NFla NPri SPlb WViv
§ - Oregon Rainbow Group — Last listed 1998
- 'Pacino' — SRms WFar WLRN WWeb
¶ - 'Solar Fire Orange' — WViv
- 'Wonderland Mixed' — EWll LPVe
*oreophilum* — Last listed 1998
*orientale* — CB&S EPfP MBro MMal NCut SCou SRms SWat WFar WHil WPer
¶ - 'Abu Hassan' — SWat
¶ - 'Aglaja' ♀ — CMil MCAu NHaw SWat WCot
¶ - 'Aladin' — SWat
¶ - 'Ali Baba' — SWat

- 'Allegro' — CBlo CSam EAst EBee EBrP EBre ECtt EFou EWTr GAbr LBre MBNS MBri MCLN MRav NBrk NFai NRoo NVic SBre SCob SPer SPlb SSvw SWat WByw WOve WWal
¶ - 'Arwide' — EFou SWat
¶ - 'Aslahan' — SWat
¶ - 'Atrosanguineus' — WCot WSpi
- 'Avebury Crimson' — LGre MRav MWat NCat SWat
¶ - 'Ballkleid' — ECha
- 'Beauty Queen' — CBlo EBee EBrP EBre ECot LBre MBri MRav NBrk NCat NGdn NRoo SBre SCoo SDix SRPl SWat WElm WLRN
¶ - 'Big Jim' — SWat
- 'Black and White' ♀ — CElw CGle CHad CLon CRDP CSpe EAst ECha EFou ELan EMan GCHN MAvo MCAu MRav NBrk NRoo SSoC SUsu SWat WCot WMaN WWin
¶ - 'Blackberry Queen' — WCot
- 'Blue Moon' — CMil EFou NBir SWat WLRN
- 'Bonfire Red' — CStr ELan NLak WBro
§ - var. **bracteatum** ♀ — CSam EBot ECha GCHN GDra NBir NFai
- – JCA 751202 — WPGP
- 'Brilliant' — CM&M EBee NFai WRHF
- 'Carneum' — CM&M EBee
¶ - 'Carnival' — EFou SWat
¶ - 'Catherina' — EBee LRHS SWat
- 'Cedar Hill' — EBee EFou LRHS NRoo SChu SWat WMaN WMer
- 'Cedric Morris' ♀ — CBos CGle CHad CMil EBee ECha EFou EGle EMan EOld EPri GCal MCAu MRav NRoo SChu SMrm SUsu SWat WCot WEas WElm WLRN WMaN
- 'Charming' — CHad CLon CMil CPar EBee ERic GNau LGre MCAu MHlr SChu SWat
- 'China Boy' — CMil
* - 'Choir Boy' — CM&M CRDP EBee NBrk STes WPrP
- 'Curlilocks' — CLon CMGP CPar EBee EBrP EBre ELan EMan GAbr LBre MCLN MRav NBrk NRoo SBre SPer SPla SRms SWat WCot WWin WWoo
¶ - 'Derwisch' — EFou SWat
* - 'Diana' — CBos CHad SMrm
¶ - 'Doppelte Freude' — SSvw
¶ - double red shades (d) — SSvw
- 'Doubloon' — EBrP EBre LBre NBrk NGdn NHaw NRoo SBre SWat
- 'Dwarf Allegro' — EWTr GBuc MFir NFor NLon NOak
¶ - 'Effendi' ♀ — EFou SWat
- 'Elam Pink' — CLon CMil ECha LGre MTis WCot WSpi
- 'Erste Zuneigung' — Last listed 1998
- 'Fatima' — CHad CMil SMrm SWat WWeb
¶ - 'Feuerriese' — SWat
¶ - 'Flamenco' — SWat
N - 'Flore Pleno' (d) — GLil SMad SSvw
¶ - 'Forncett Summer' — EFou WCot
- 'Garden Glory' — CMil CPar CRDP EBee EFou GNau MBri MCAu NCat SRPl SWat WLRN
- 'Garden Gnome' — Last listed 1996
- 'Glowing Embers' — EBrP EBre LBre SBre SWat
¶ - 'Glowing Rose' — SWat
* - 'Goldie' — ELan

- Goliath Group — CGle CHan CMil CSev EBee MCLN NBrk NBro NOak NVic SCob SDix SPer SRPl SUsu SWat WCot WEas WHoo WPyg
- – 'Beauty of Livermere' ♀ — CHad CLon CM&M CRDP CSam CSpe EMan MBro MCAu MHlr MMal MRav MWll NBro NGdn NLar NSti SAga SChu SLod SRms SSvw SWat WCot WElm WLRN WOve WPyg WSpi WWhi
- 'Graue Witwe' — CLon EFou GBuc NBrk SApp SUsu SWat WCot WRha
¶ - 'Halima' — SWat
- 'Harvest Moon' — EBee EBrP EBre EHol LBre LPio MBri MRav NCut NHaw SBre WCot WWeb
- 'Helen Elisabeth' — CBlo CSpe ECtt EFou EHal LPio MBel MCAu MHlr MLLN NBrk NFai NRoo SWat WCot WMer WMow
- 'Hewitt's Old Rose' — WCot
¶ - 'Hula Hula' — SWat
- 'Indian Chief' — CMil CPar CRDP EBee EGle EOld GBin MCAu MSte NFai WMer
- 'Joanne' — NLar
¶ - 'John III' ♀ — EFou SWat
- 'John Metcalf' — CBos CRDP EBee EFou GNau LPio MCAu MCLN SChu SUsu SWat WBro WCot
- 'Juliane' — CLon ECha EGle EPri LGre LHop MCAu SWat WCot
- 'Karine' ♀ — CHea CLon CMil ECha EFou LGre MAvo MBri MCAu NBrk NRoo SSca SUsu SWas SWat WBro WLRN WMaN WPen WWoo
¶ - 'Khedive' ♀ — SWat
- 'King George' — GBuc MWat SWat
- 'Kleine Tänzerin' — CLon CMil CPou EFou LGre MCAu MCLN MLLN MWgw NSti SUsu SWat WCot WLRN
¶ - 'Kollebloem' — SWat
- 'Lady Frederick Moore' — MTed SWat WCot WMer
¶ - 'Lady Roscoe' — SWat
- 'Ladybird' — ELan MRav NBrk NRoo SPla WCot
¶ - 'Lambada' — SWat
¶ - 'Leuchtfeuer' ♀ — SWat
¶ - 'Lighthouse' ♀ — SWat
- 'Lilac Girl' — CLon ECha EGle LGre MCAu NSti WCot
- 'Marcus Perry' — CBlo EBee ENot EPfP GChr GGar GMaP MCAu MRav NPri SCob SPer SWat WMer WMow
¶ - 'Master Richard' — SWat
- 'May Queen' (d) — CM&M CMGP CPou EBee EWes GBuc IBlr NLak WBro WCot WPen
- 'May Sadler' — COlW ENot EOld LBuc MTed SCoo SWat WSpi
- 'Midnight' — Last listed 1997
- 'Mrs H.G. Stobart' — CRDP
- 'Mrs Marrow's Plum' — See *P. orientale* 'Patty's Plum'
- 'Mrs Perry' ♀ — More than 30 suppliers
- 'Nanum Flore Pleno' — See *P.* 'Fireball'
¶ - 'Noema' — SWat
¶ - 'Orange Glow' — EWTr WMer
- 'Orangeade Maison' — CPou CStr EBee NLak WBro
- 'Oriana' — EBee EHol MMil SWat WLRN
¶ - 'Pale Face' — SWat
- pale pink form — Last listed 1998
§ - 'Patty's Plum' — CBos CGle CHad CLon CMil CPou CRDP CSWP CSpe EBee LBlm LGre MAvo MBel MBro MLLN SAga SChu SMrm SPla SUsu WBro WCot WElm WGle WHoo WMaN WPGP WSan WWeb

| | | |
|---|---|---|
| - 'Perry's White' | More than 30 suppliers | |
| ¶ - 'Peter Pan' | SWat | |
| ¶ - 'Petticoat' | SWat | |
| - 'Picotée' | CBlo CHea CMGP EBee EBrP EBre | |
| | EFou ELan EMan LBre MCAu | |
| | MCLN MGrG MRav MWat NBro | |
| | NRoo SBre SChu SPer SWat WBro | |
| | WByw WCot WWal | |
| - 'Pink Chiffon' | Last listed 1996 | |
| - 'Pinnacle' | CSWP EBee GLil MAvo MSCN | |
| | NFai NHaw NPri SCob SWat WCot | |
| | WMow WWoo | |
| - 'Pizzicato' | CBlo CBrm CHor CKel CM&M | |
| | CPar LGre MCli MGed MMal MWll | |
| | NArg NPer NRoo SAga SSvw SWat | |
| | WGwG WLRN WOve | |
| ¶ - 'Polka' | SWat | |
| ¶ - 'Prince of Orange' | ERic | |
| - Princess Victoria Louise | See *P. orientale* 'Prinzessin | |
| | Victoria Louise' | |
| ¶ - 'Prinz Eugen' | EFou SWat | |
| § - 'Prinzessin Victoria Louise' | CBlo CSWP EBee EHal EMan | |
| | EWTr GLil GMaP LFis MBel MCAu | |
| | MLLN MMil NBro SSoC SSvw | |
| | SWat WCer WMer WPer | |
| ¶ - 'Prospero' | SWat | |
| - 'Queen Alexandra' | EBee NChi NLar | |
| - 'Raspberry Queen' | CMil CPou EAst EBee ELan GBin | |
| | MArl MAvo MBel MHlr MRav MTis | |
| | NCut NPri SWat WBro WCot WHal | |
| | WHoo WMer WSpi WWoo | |
| - 'Redizelle' | Last listed 1997 | |
| - 'Rembrandt' | CBlo CMGP ECot MMil NCut NFla | |
| | NPri SWat WMer WPer WViv | |
| - 'Rose Queen' | WCot | |
| - 'Rosenpokal' | CM&M EBee NLak SWat | |
| - 'Royal Wedding' | CMil EBee EMan ERic LPio MMil | |
| | MRav MWll NChi NLar NPri NRoo | |
| | SChu SLon SMrm SSvw SWat | |
| | WLRN WMoo WOve | |
| * - 'Saffron' | CMil | |
| - 'Salmon Glow' | CB&S EBee GLil SCob SCoo SWat | |
| | WCot WMer WPer WViv | |
| ¶ - 'Salome' | SWat | |
| - scarlet | MWgw | |
| - 'Scarlet King' | CBlo EBee EWll MMil SWat WLRN | |
| | WMow | |
| - 'Showgirl' | CRDP SWat | |
| - 'Sindbad' | EBee EFou SLod SWat WCot | |
| - 'Snow Queen' | MNrw NCut | |
| ¶ - 'Spätzünder' | EFou SWat | |
| * - *splendidissimum* | SIng | |
| - 'Springtime' | CMGP EBee EFou MCAu MSCN | |
| | NCut SWat WWoo | |
| - Stormtorch | See *P. orientale* 'Sturmfackel' | |
| § - 'Sturmfackel' | EBee MCAu SCoo SWat | |
| - 'Suleika' | EFou SWat | |
| - 'Sultana' | CPlt ECha EOld GMac LGre SSoC | |
| | SWat | |
| - 'Türkenlouis' | EAst EBee EFou GLil MCAu MSCN | |
| | SPar SUsu SWat WBro WCot | |
| | WHoo | |
| - 'Turkish Delight' ♀ | CBlo EBee ELan GCHN GMaP | |
| | GMac MCAu MCLN MMil MRav | |
| | MTis NBir NBro NCat SLod SPer | |
| | SSoC SUsu SWat WMow | |
| ¶ - 'Tutu' | SWat | |
| - 'Watermelon' | CKel COtt CRDP EAst EBee EFou | |
| | MAvo MBel MCAu SWat WBro | |
| | WMer WWoo | |
| ¶ - 'Wild Salmon' | STes | |
| - 'Wunderkind' | EBee SWat | |

| | | |
|---|---|---|
| *paucifoliatum* | CHan | |
| - JCA 752300 | WPGP | |
| *pilosum* | EMan GBuc NCat SBea SRms | |
| | SWat | |
| *radicatum* | Last listed 1998 | |
| *rhaeticum* | ELan | |
| *rhoeas* | CArn CJew EWFC GPoy MHew | |
| | MMal WElm WJek | |
| - Angels' Choir | SWat WHer | |
| - 'Mother of Pearl' | SWat | |
| - Shirley | MMal | |
| - 'Valerie Finnis' | ELan | |
| *rupifragum* | CFir CGle ECha ESis EWTr GAbr | |
| | GCHN LEur LHil LPio MFir MLLN | |
| | MRPP NHex WEas WFar WOve | |
| | WPer WRha WWin | |
| - 'Flore Pleno' (d) | CSWP CSpe EBee LPio MRPP | |
| | MWll NChi WCot WCru WHen | |
| | WHer WWhi | |
| *sendtneri* | EWTr MOne WLin | |
| ¶ *somniferum* ♀ | CArn GPoy | |
| ¶ - 'Black Beauty' | CSpe | |
| ¶ - 'Pink Chiffon' | WEas | |
| § *spicatum* | CHea CSWP CSam ECGP ECha | |
| | EMan EWTr GCal LEur LHil LHop | |
| | MFir MHar MHlr NBir NFai SIgm | |
| | SMrm SUsu WBor WCot WEas | |
| | WElm WMoo | |
| ¶ *tauricola* | MWll | |
| *triniifolium* | CSpe | |
| * 'Witchery' | WWeb | |

## PARABENZOIN See LINDERA

## PARACHAMPIONELLA See STROBILANTHES

## PARADISEA (Asphodelaceae)

| | | |
|---|---|---|
| *liliastrum* ♀ | CHid EMan ERos LPio NCat NChi | |
| | NWoo SSpi WCot WWhi | |
| - 'Major' | CAvo | |
| *lusitanica* | CAvo CGle CMHG CMil CRDP | |
| | EBee ERos LPio NBur NEgg SSpi | |
| | WCot | |

## PARAHEBE ✿ (Scrophulariaceae)

| | | |
|---|---|---|
| ¶ 'Arabella' | LRHS | |
| x *bidwillii* | ECou EMNN GAri LFis MRav | |
| | NHed NMen NWCA SRms SRot | |
| | WWat | |
| - 'Kea' | CFee ECou ECtt ELan EMNN ESis | |
| | GCHN NHar NMen SBla SHel | |
| | SRot WFar WPer | |
| *canescens* | ECou | |
| § *catarractae* ♀ | CLyd CMHG EBee ECou ELan | |
| | EMNN EMar EWTr MFir MNrw | |
| | MPla MWat NBee NBro NFor | |
| | NMen NTow SBod SMer SOkh | |
| | SUsu WBor WBrE WFar WHen | |
| | WOve WPer WWhi | |
| - blue | CHar EHic EMar EPfP NBee SPan | |
| | SPer SPla WWat | |
| § - 'Delight' ♀ | CChe CLTr ECou ELan ESis EWes | |
| | GCHN GGar LFis LHop MAsh | |
| | MBro NBrk NPer SDix SHFr SIgm | |
| | SRot WEas WFar WHen WHoo | |
| | WPyg | |
| - subsp. *diffusa* | ECou EMNN IOrc MMil NHar | |
| | NPer NVic WCom | |
| - - 'Annie' | ECou | |
| - - 'Pinkie' | CLTr ECou | |
| - garden form | ECha LLWP SBla WAbe | |
| - subsp. *martinii* | ECou NCut | |

| | |
|---|---|
| - 'Miss Willmott' | MSCN NPri NVic SPer SPlb WPer |
| - 'Porlock Purple' | See *P. cattarractae* 'Delight' |
| - 'Rosea' | CPri ESis NVic WWat |
| - 'Tinycat' | Last listed 1998 |
| - white | CBot ECha ELan EMNN ESis |
| | GCHN IBlr LHop MBro MFir NCat |
| | NFla NMen SHel SOkh SUsu WBor |
| | WEas WPer WWat WWhi |
| *decora* | CLyd ECou GAri GCHN NSla |
| *derwentiana* | ECou EMon |
| § *formosa* | CPle ECou WHCG WSPU |
| - erect form | ECou |
| - lax form | ECou |
| - white | ECou |
| 'Gillian' | ECou ECtt GAri GGar LFis MMil |
| | WFar WPer |
| 'Greencourt' | See *P. cattarractae* 'Delight' |
| ¶ *guthrieana* | SVen |
| § *hookeriana* | GGar NMen SAga SMrm WPyg |
| | WStl WWat |
| 'Joy' | ECou EWes |
| *linifolia* | CTri EMNN EPot NMen |
| - 'Blue Skies' | ECou LHop |
| § *lyallii* | CBot CPri EAst ECou ELan ESis |
| | LHop MBar MPla MWat NChi |
| | NFor NHed NHol NWCA SAga |
| | SIng SPlb SRms WAbe WTro |
| | WWin |
| - 'Clarence' | CLyd ECou |
| - 'Engel's Blue' | Last listed 1998 |
| - 'Glacier' | CLTr ECou |
| - 'Julie-Anne' | CPri ECou ELan EPfP ESis GCal |
| | LRHS MAsh SPan |
| - 'Rosea' | CTri GGar LFis MBal WPer WPyg |
| * *martinii* | LRHS |
| 'Mervyn' | CLyd ECou ECtt GCHN LFis LHop |
| | NHed NLon NMen SUsu WHen |
| | WPer |
| *olsenii* | ECou GGar NTow |
| § *perfoliata* ♀ | More than 30 suppliers |
| - dark blue | GBuc GCal MBro SMad |
| - 'Pringle' | CAbP EPfP LRHS MAsh |
| 'Snowcap' | ELan EPfP LRHS MAsh |

### PARAJUBAEA (Arecaceae)

| | |
|---|---|
| *cocoides* | CBrP LPJP LPal |

### PARAQUILEGIA (Ranunculaceae)

| | |
|---|---|
| *adoxoides* | See *Semiaquilegia adoxoides* |
| § *anemonoides* | GCrs GGGa GTou NHar WAbe |
| - ACE 1370 | Last listed 1998 |
| *grandiflora* | See *P. anemonoides* |

### PARASERIANTHES (Mimosaceae)

| | |
|---|---|
| *distachya* | See *P. lophantha* |
| § *lophantha* ♀ | CAbb CPle ERea ISea LCns LHil |
| | SAPC SArc SOWG WMul |

### PARASYRINGA See LIGUSTRUM

### x PARDANCANDA (Iridaceae)

| | |
|---|---|
| *norrisii* | CArn CFir EAst EBee EMan EWes |
| | GSki LIck NPri WFoF |
| ¶ *norrisii* 'Dazzler' | WHil |

### PARDANTHOPSIS (Iridaceae)

| | |
|---|---|
| ¶ *dichotoma* | EBee EHal |
| ¶ - RMRP 95-0501 | IDac |

### PARDOGLOSSUM (Boraginaceae)

| | |
|---|---|
| *cheirifolium* | Last listed 1998 |

### PARIETARIA (Urticaceae)

| | |
|---|---|
| § *judaica* | ELau EWFC GPoy MHew MSal |
| | WHer |
| - 'Corinne Tremaine' | Last listed 1997 |
| *officinalis* | See *P. judaica* |

### PARIS ✿ (Trilliaceae)

| | |
|---|---|
| *birmanica* | WCru |
| *bockiana* | WCru |
| *fargesii* | WCru |
| ¶ - var. *petiolata* | WCru |
| * *hepatica henryi* | LAma |
| ¶ *incompleta* | EPot |
| *japonica* | WCru WThi |
| *lancifolia* | WCru |
| § *polyphylla* | EMar WCru |
| - var. *stenophylla* | LAma |
| ¶ - *yunnanensis alba* | SSpi |
| *pubescens* | WCru |
| *quadrifolia* | CAvo CFil CFir CLAP CRDP GPoy |
| | LGre MSal SSpi WCru WHer WShi |
| - JMH 79 | MDun |
| ¶ *tetraphylla* | WCru |
| *thibetica* | WCru |
| *verticillata* | LAma WCru |
| ¶ *violacea* | WCru |

### PARKINSONIA (Caesalpiniaceae)

| | |
|---|---|
| *aculeata* | Last listed 1996 |

### PARNASSIA (Parnassiaceae)

| | |
|---|---|
| *cabulica* | Last listed 1998 |
| *nubicola* | GDra MBal NHar |
| *palustris* | WAbe WHer |
| - *palustris* | Last listed 1997 |

### PAROCHETUS (Papilionaceae)

| | |
|---|---|
| *africanus* ♀ | CHid EWes GAri GBuc WCot |
| *communis* | CB&S CFee CGle GDra GMaP |
| | GMac MRav NBro NPer SIng |
| | SRms SVen WBea WWhi |
| * - 'Blue Gem' | Last listed 1997 |
| - dark form | GCal |
| - Himalayan form | IBlr |
| - Himalayan form | WCru |
| HWJCM 526 | |
| - summer-flowering | CRDP |

### PARONYCHIA (Illecebraceae)

| | |
|---|---|
| *argentea* | MBro NHol WPat WPer |
| § *capitata* | CHal CLyd CTri ELan NMen NNrd |
| | SRms WHoo WPat WPer WRHF |
| | WWin |
| § *kapela* | EMan NTow SSmi WPer |
| - 'Binsted Gold' (v) | CInt CMGP EMon MBro SSmi |
| - subsp. *serpyllifolia* | CPea |
| *nivea* | See *P. capitata* |
| *serpyllifolia* | See *P. kapela* subsp. *serpyllifolia* |

### PARROTIA (Hamamelidaceae)

| | |
|---|---|
| *persica* ♀ | More than 30 suppliers |
| - 'Burgundy' | CPMA |
| ¶ - 'Globosa' | LPan |
| § - 'Lamplighter' (v) | CPMA |
| - 'Pendula' | CB&S CPMA ELan EPfP IOrc MBal |
| --'Vanessa' | CMCN CPMA LPan LRHS MBri |
| | NPal SMad SSpi SSta |
| ◆ - 'Variegata' | See *P. persica* 'Lamplighter' |

### PARROTIOPSIS (Hamamelidaceae)

| | |
|---|---|
| *jacquemontiana* | CB&S CEnd CPMA LBuc NPal |
| | SMur SSpi |

## PARRYA (Brassicaceae)

| | |
|---|---|
| *eriocalyx* | Last listed 1998 |
| *menziesii* | See *Phoenicaulis cheiranthoides* |

## PARSONSIA (Apocynaceae)

| | |
|---|---|
| *capsularis* | CPlN ECou |
| *heterophylla* | ECou ERea |

## PARTHENIUM (Asteraceae)

| | |
|---|---|
| *integrifolium* | CArn GPoy IIve MSal |

## PARTHENOCISSUS ✿ (Vitaceae)

| | |
|---|---|
| § *benryana* ♀ | More than 30 suppliers |
| *himalayana* | ECtt |
| - 'Purpurea' | See *P.himalayana* var. *rubrifolia* |
| § - var. *rubrifolia* | CBlo EBee EHic EPfP ETen LHol MAsh MRav WCru WWat |
| *inserta* | Last listed 1997 |
| § *quinquefolia* ♀ | More than 30 suppliers |
| - var. *engelmannii* | EBee LBuc MGos NFla SPer WAbe |
| ¶ - 'Star Showers' (v) | WCot |
| sp. KR 708 | Last listed 1996 |
| *striata* | See *Cissus striata* |
| *thomsonii* | See *Cayratia thomsonii* |
| § *tricuspidata* ♀ | EBee ECtt GOrc MAsh MBal MGos NFor NLon SBid SPer SReu SSoC WDin |
| - B&SWJ 1162 | WCru |
| - 'Beverley Brook' | CBlo CMac ETen MBri SBid SBra SPla SRms WAbe |
| - 'Green Spring' | CBlo MBlu MBri MGos NBrk |
| - 'Lowii' | CBlo CMac EBee ECot EHic EPfP EPla MBlu MGos MRav SLon SMad SMad |
| - 'Minutifolia' | |
| - 'Robusta' | CSam EBee LPan MBNS |
| § - 'Veitchii' | More than 30 suppliers |

## PASITHEA (Anthericaceae)

| | |
|---|---|
| *caerulea* | Last listed 1996 |

## PASPALUM (Poaceae)

| | |
|---|---|
| ¶ *glaucifolium* | LEdu |
| *quadrifarium* | Last listed 1997 |

## PASSIFLORA ✿ (Passifloraceae)

| | |
|---|---|
| *actinia* | CPas CPlN CRHN LChe LPri |
| *acuminata* | CPas |
| *adenopoda* | CPas |
| 'Adularia' | CPas LChe LPri WHer |
| *adulterina* | Last listed 1996 |
| *alata* (F) ♀ | CAbb CPas CPlN EBak ELan ERea LChe LCns LPri |
| - 'Shannon' (F) | CPas |
| x *alatocaerulea* | See *P.* x *belotii* |
| *allantophylla* | CPas |
| 'Allardii' | CPas |
| *ambigua* | CPas |
| 'Amethyst' ♀ | CAbb CChe CPas CPlN CSPN ELan EMil EOrc LCns LHop LPri LRHS MCCP SAga SBid SBra WPat |
| § *amethystina* Mikan | CB&S CDoC CPas CPlN CRHN ECre EHol ERea LCns NPal SYvo |
| *ampullacea* (F) | CPas LPri |
| *anfracta* | CPas |
| N *antioquiensis* Karst ♀ | CB&S CGre CPlN CSPN CTbh EHol ELan ERea GQui IBlr LChe LPri LRHS MAsh MBlu MTis SOWG SYvo WMul |
| *apetala* | CPas |
| § *aurantia* | CPas ERea LPri WHer |
| *auriculata* | CPas |
| *banksii* | See *P.aurantia* |
| § x *belotii* | CPas ECre ELan EMui ERea LChe LCns LPri LRHS MAsh |
| - 'Impératrice Eugénie' | See *P.* x *belotii* |
| *biflora* Lamarck | CPas LPri WMul |
| *boenderi* | CPas |
| *brevipes* | CPas |
| 'Byron Beauty' | LPri |
| § *caerulea* ♀ | More than 30 suppliers |
| - 'Constance Elliot' ♀ | CB&S CBot CDoC CMac CPas CPlN CRHN CSPN EBee ELan EMil EMui EOrc LChe LHop LPri MAsh NBea SBra SOWG SPer SPla SReu SSta SSto WCru |
| - *rubra* | CBlo ECtt SBid |
| I x *caeruleoracemosa* | See *P.* x *violacea* |
| x *caponii* | ERea |
| *capsularis* | CPas SVen SYvo |
| *chinensis* | See *P.caerulea* |
| *cincinnata* | CPas |
| *cinnabarina* | CPas |
| * *cissifolia* | Last listed 1996 |
| *citrina* | CPas CPlN ECon ECtt ELan ERea LChe LCns LPri SOWG WMul |
| *coccinea* (F) | CPas CPlN LPri LRHS |
| *colinvauxii* | CPas |
| x *colvillii* | CPas CPlN LPri |
| *conzattiana* | CPas |
| § *coriacea* | CPas CPlN LChe LPri LRHS |
| *costaricensis* | CPas |
| *crenata* | CPas |
| *cumbalensis* | CPas |
| - var. *cumbalensis* | Last listed 1998 |
| JCA 13988 | |
| *cuneata* | CPas LPri |
| ¶ - 'Miguel Molinari' | CPas LPri |
| *cuprea* | CPas |
| *cuspidifolia* | CPas |
| § *cyanea* | CPas |
| x *decaisneana* (F) | CPas LPri |
| § - 'Innesii' | CPas |
| *dioscoreifolia* | Last listed 1997 |
| *discophora* | CPas |
| *edulis* (F) | CAgr CPas CPlN EBak EMui LPri WHer |
| ¶ - B&SWJ 3624 | WCru |
| - 'Crackerjack' (F) | ERea |
| § - f. *edulis* (F) | Last listed 1998 |
| - f. *flavicarpa* (F) | CPas ECon ELan LChe LPri |
| * - 'Golden Nuggett' (F) | CPas |
| - 'Norfolk' (F) | CPas |
| - 'Supreme' | Last listed 1998 |
| 'Elizabeth' (F) | CPas LChe |
| 'Empress Eugenie' | See *P.* x *belotii* |
| * *escorbariana* | CPas |
| * 'Evatoria' | Last listed 1997 |
| x *exoniensis* ♀ | CBot CGre CPas CPlN CRHN ECre LPri MAsh |
| * *exura* | Last listed 1997 |
| *filipes* | CPas |
| *foetida* | CPas LPri SOWG |
| - *hibiscifolia* | Last listed 1998 |
| - var. *hirsuta* (F) | CPas |
| - var. *hirsutissima* | CPas |
| - var. *orinocensis* | CPas |
| * *garayaglia* | CPas |
| *garckei* | CPas |
| *gibertii* | CPas |
| *gigantifolia* | CPas |
| *gilbertiana* | CPas |
| *glandulosa* | CPas |
| *gracilis* | CPas |

| | | | | |
|---|---|---|---|---|
| *gracillima* | CPas | | *punctata* | CPas |
| *guatemalensis* | CPas SYvo | | 'Pura Vida' | CPas LPri |
| *babnii* | CPas | | 'Purple Haze' | CPas CRHN LPri |
| *belleri* | CPas CPlN WMul | | 'Purple Passion' | See *P. edulis* f. *edulis* |
| *berbertiana* (F) | CPas CPlN LPri | | *quadrangularis* L. (F) ♀ | CB&S CPas CPlN CTbh EBak ERea |
| *bolosericea* | CPas | | | LChe LPan LPri SVen WMul |
| *incana* | See *P. seemannii* | * | - *macrocarpa* (F) | CPas |
| *incarnata* (F) | CAgr CArn CBlo CPas CPlN EMui | | *quadrifaria* | CPas |
| | LChe LPri MSal NBrk SPlb | | *quadriflora* | CPas |
| 'Incense' (F) ♀ | CBlo CPas CPlN EBak ECre EMui | | *quadriglandulosa* | Last listed 1996 |
| | LChe LPri | | *quinquangularis* | CPas |
| × *innesii* | See *P.* × *decaisneana* 'Innesii' | | *racemosa* ♀ | CBlo CPas CPlN CSPN ELan ERea |
| * *iralda* | Last listed 1996 | | | IBlr LChe LPri MAsh NBea SOWG |
| * *jalunsachensis* | CPas | | | WGor |
| *jamesonii* | Last listed 1996 | | 'Red Inca' | CPas |
| *jilekii* | CPas | | *retipetala* | See *P. cyanea* |
| *jorullensis* | CPas | | *rovirosae* | CPas LRHS |
| *juliana* | CPas | | *rubra* | CBlo CPas ELan EWes LPri WStI |
| *kalbreyeri* | CPas | * | *rufa* | CPas |
| *karwinskii* | CPas | | 'Saint Rule' | CPas LPri |
| × *kewensis* | CPas LChe LPri | | *sanguinolenta* | CPas ELan ERea LChe LPri LRHS |
| * *kirkii* | CPlN | | | MAsh |
| *lancearia* | CPas | | 'Sapphire' | CPas LPri |
| *laurifolia* (F) | CPas LPri | § | *seemannii* | CPas LPri |
| § *ligularis* (F) | CPas LPri LRHS | | *serrata* | See *P. serratodigitata* |
| 'Lilac Lady' | See *P.* × *violacea* 'Tresederi' | | *serratifolia* | CPas LPri |
| *lindeniana* | CPas | § | *serratodigitata* | CPas |
| *lowei* | See *P. ligularis* | | *serrulata* | CPas |
| 'Lucia' | Last listed 1996 | | *sexflora* | CPas |
| * *luismanvelii* | Last listed 1996 | | 'Smythiana' | CPas |
| *lutea* | CPas | | *standleyi* | CPas |
| *maliformis* (F) | CPas CPlN | | 'Star of Bristol' ♀ | CPas LPri |
| *manicata* (F) | CPas CPlN CRHN NBrk | | 'Star of Clevedon' | CPas CPlN |
| *matthewsii* | Last listed 1997 | | 'Star of Kingston' | CPas CPlN |
| 'Mavis Mastics' | See *P.* × *violacea* 'Tresederi' | | *stipulata* | CPas |
| *mayana* | See *P. caerulea* | | *suberosa* | CPas LPri |
| *menispermifolia* | See *P. pilosa* | | *subpeltata* | CPas LPri |
| * *microstipula* | CPas | | 'Sunburst' | CPas CPlN LPri SOWG WMul |
| *miersii* | CPas | | *talamancensis* | CPas |
| *misera* | CPas | | *tatei* | CPas |
| *mixta* (F) | CPlN ERea LChe LPri | | *tenuifila* | CPas |
| - × *antioquiensis* | CDoC CPas SAga | § | *tetrandra* | CGre CPas ECou |
| *mollissima* (F) ♀ | CAbb CB&S CDoC CGre CPas | | *tica* | CPas |
| | CPlN CRHN CSPN EBak EBee | | × *tresederi* | See *P.* × *violacea* 'Tresederi' |
| | ELan ERea LChe LPri MAsh NRog | | *tricuspis* | CPas |
| | SOWG SVen SYvo WHer WMul | | *tridactylites* | CPas |
| *morifolia* | CPas CPlN LPri WHer WMul | | *trifasciata* | CPas CPlN |
| *mucronata* | CPas | | *tripartita* | CPas |
| *multiflora* | CPas LPri | | - JCA 13982 | Last listed 1998 |
| *murucuja* | CPas | * | *triphostemmatoides* | CPas |
| *naviculata* | CPas | | *trisecta* | CPas |
| *nelsonii* | CPas | | *tuberosa* | CPas |
| *nitida* (F) | CPas | | *tulae* | CPas |
| *oblongata* | CPas | | *umbilicata* | CPas CPlN LPri WCru |
| *obtusifolia* | See *P. coriacea* | | *urbaniana* | CPas |
| *oerstedii* | CPas | | *vespertilio* | CPas |
| - var. *choconbiana* | CPas | § | × *violacea* ♀ | CAbb CB&S CBlo CPas CPlN |
| *onychina* | See *P. amethystina* | | | CRHN ECon ERea LCns MBri |
| *organensis* | CPas | | - 'Dedorina' | CPas |
| *ornitheura* | Last listed 1996 | | - 'Eynsford Gem' | CPas |
| *pallens* | CPas | | - 'Lilac Lady' | See *P.* × *violacea* 'Tresederi' |
| *palmeri* | CPas | § | - 'Tresederi' | CPas MAsh |
| *penduliflora* | CPas | | - 'Victoria' | CPas LPri |
| *perfoliata* | CPas | | *viridiflora* | CPas |
| * 'Perfume' | CPas | | *vitifolia* (F) | CPas CPlN ELan ERea LChe LPri |
| *phoenicea* | CPas LPri | | | LRHS SOWG |
| - 'Ruby Glow' (F) | CPas | | - 'Scarlet Flame' (F) | CPas LPri |
| § *pilosa* | Last listed 1996 | | *xiikzodz* | CPas |
| *pinnatistipula* (F) | CPas SVen | | *yucatanensis* | CPas LPri |
| × *piresii* | CPas | | *zamorana* | CPas |
| *pittieri* | CPas | | | |
| *platyloba* | CPas CPlN LPri | | | |

## PASTINACA (Apiaceae)

*sativa* — CKin

## PATERSONIA (Iridaceae)

*occidentalis* — Last listed 1998

## PATRINIA (Valerianaceae)

*gibbosa* — CLyd CRDP EBee ECha GCHN SSca WCru WRus
*rupestris* — IIve
\* *sambucifolia* — Last listed 1998
*saniculifolia* — WCru
*scabiosifolia* — CBlo CMil ECha ECoo EMan GBuc GVic SEND SMrm SUsu WWin
- 'Nagoya' — MNrw
*triloba* — CLyd CPla CRDP MRav NMen NRya NWoo SSpi SUsu WPrP
\* - 'Minor' — ECho
- var. *palmata* — GCHN NBus WFar
- var. *triloba* — CGle GCal NTow WWin
*villosa* — WCot

## PAULOWNIA (Scrophulariaceae)

*fargesii* Osborn — See *P. tomentosa* 'Lilacina'
- Franchet — ICrw IMGH SLPl SMad
*fortunei* — CMCN CWSG GAri WLRN WNor
*tomentosa* ♀ — More than 30 suppliers
¶ - 'Coreana' — CGre
§ - 'Lilacina' — CB&S

## PAVONIA (Malvaceae)

§ x *gledhillii* — Last listed 1998
x *intermedia* — See *P.* x *gledhillii*
*multiflora* Jussieu — ERea
- hort. — See *P.* x *gledhillii*
*praemorsa* — CBot

## PAXISTIMA (Celastraceae)

*canbyi* — EHyt MBro NPro WAbe WPat WWin
*myrsinites* — See *P. myrtifolia*
§ *myrtifolia* — EPla WWat

## PECTEILIS (Orchidaceae)

\* *dentata* — EFEx
§ *radiata* — EFEx
\* - 'Albomarginata' — EFEx
\* - 'Aureomarginata' — EFEx

## PEDILANTHUS (Euphorbiaceae)

*tithymaloides* 'Variegatus' — LChe

## PEGANUM (Zygophyllaceae)

*harmala* — CArn MSal

## PELARGONIUM ✿ (Geraniaceae)

'A Happy Thought' — See *P.* 'Happy Thought'
'A.M. Mayne' (Z/d) — CWDa
'Abba' (Z/d) — CWDa
'Abel Carrière' (I/d) — SKen WFib
*abrotanifolium* (Sc) — CNat CSev WEas WFib
- broad-leaved — Last listed 1998
'Acapulco' — NPri
*acerifolium* L'Héritier — See *P. cucullatum* subsp. *strigifolium*
- hort. — See *P. vitifolium*
*acetosum* — GCal MSte SAga SHFr SMrm
\* - 'Variegatum' — CSpe MSte
*acraeum* — WFib
Action (Z/d) — WFib
'Acushla by Brian' (Sc) — MWhe NFir

'Ada Sutterby' (Dw/d) — SKen WFib
'Adagio' (Dw) — ESul
'Adam's Quilt' (Z/C) — SKen WEas
'Adele' (Min/d) — ESul WFib
'Aerosol' (Min) — ESul WFib
'African Belle' (R) — Last listed 1998
'Afterglow' (Z) — WFib
'Ailsa' (Min/d) — ESul MBri SKen
'Ainsdale Angel' (A) — ESul LDea
'Ainsdale Beauty' (Z) — Last listed 1998
'Ainsdale Claret' (Z) — Last listed 1998
'Ainsdale Eyeful' (Z) — LVER
'Akela' (Min) — ESul
'Alan West' (Z/St) — Last listed 1998
§ 'Alba' = 'Fisalb' (Z/d) — SKen
'Albert Sheppard' (Z/C/d) — Last listed 1996
'Alberta' (Z) — SKen WFib
'Albert's Choice' (R) — WFib
*album* — CWDa
*alchemilloides* — CNat WFib
'Alcyone' (Dw/d) — ESul SKen WFib
'Alde' (Min) — ESul LHil LVER MWhe SKen WEas
'Aldenham' (Z) — WFib
'Aldham' (Min) — ESul LVER WFib
'Aldwyck' (R) — EBSP LDea WFib
'Alex' (Z) — CWDa SKen
'Alex Mary' (R) — SSea WFib
'Alfred Wolfe' — Last listed 1997
'Algenon' (Min/d) — ESul WFib
'Alice Crousse' (I/d) ♀ — SKen WFib
'Alice Greenfield' (Z) — Last listed 1996
'Alison' (Dw) — ESul
'Alison Jill' (Z/d) — CWDa
'Alison Wheeler' (Min/d) — MWhe
'All My Love' (R) — LDea WFib
'Alma' (Min/C) — ESul
'Almost Heaven' (Dw/Z/v) — MWhe
'Alpine Glow' (Z/d) — MWhe
'Alpine Orange' (Z/d) — CWDa
'Alta Bell' (R) — WFib
'Altair' (Min/d) — ESul MWhe WFib
*alternans* — CSev WEas
'Always' (Z/d) — WFib
'Alys Collins' (Z/d) — WFib
'Amarantha' (Z) — WFib
'Amari' (R) — LDea
'Ambrose' (Dw/d) — ESul WFib
'Amethyst' (R) — EBSP LDea MBri SKen WFib
§ 'Amethyst' (I/d) ♀ — ECtt GHCN LDea LVER MWhe NPri WFib WLRN
'Ami' (R) — WFib
'Anabell Stephenson' (Dw/d) — WFib
'Andersonii' (Sc) — EWoo WFib
'Andrew Salvidge' (R) — LDea WFib
¶ 'Androcles' (A) — NFir
I 'Andromeda' (Min) — WFib
'Ange Davey' (Z/d) — WFib
'Angela' (Min) — Last listed 1996
'Angela Brook' — CWDa
'Angela Read' (Dw) — ESul
'Angela Woodberry' (I/d) — CWDa
'Angelique' (Dw/d) — ESul LVER WFib
'Anglia' (Dw) — ESul
'Ann Hoystead' (R) ♀ — WFib
'Ann Redington' (R) — LDea WFib
'Ann Sothern' (Z) — WFib
'Anna' (Dw) — ESul WFib
'Anna Scheen' (Dw) — ESul
'Anne Wilkie-Millar' (Z/d) — WFib
¶ 'Annsbrook Capricorn' — ESul
'Annsbrook Jupiter' (St) — ESul NFir
¶ 'Annsbrook Mars' — ESul

¶ 'Annsbrook Pluto' (St) — ESul NFir
¶ 'Annsbrook Venus' — ESul
*antidysentericum* — Last listed 1998
'Antigua' (R) — LDea WFib
'Antoine Crozy' (ZxI/d) — WFib
'Antoinette' (Min) — ESul
'Apache' (Z/d) ♀ — CHal CWDa WFib
'Aphrodite' (Z) — CWDa ECtt WFib
'Apollo' (R) — CWDa
'Apple Betty' (Sc) — LDea WFib
Apple Blossom
Rosebud' (Z/d) ♀ — ECtt ERic LVER MBri MWhe SKen
SMrm SUsu WEas WFib
'Appledram' (R) — EBSP LDea WFib
'Apri Parmer' (Min) — ESul
'Apricot' (Z/St/d) — ESul SKen
'Apricot Queen' (I/d) — LDea
'Apricot Star' — CSpe MSte MWhe
'April Hamilton' (I) — WFib
'Aquarell' (R) — Last listed 1997
'Arctic Frost' — Last listed 1998
'Arctic Queen' (R) — Last listed 1997
§ 'Arctic Star' (Z/St/d) — CSpe ESul LHil LVER SKen WEas
'Arcturus' (Min) — WFib
'Ardens' — CSpe EWoo LHil SSad SUsu WCot
WEas
'Ardwick Cinnamon' — ESul GHCN LDea
*aridum* — Last listed 1998
'Aries' (Min/C) — ESul MBri MWhe
'Arizona' (Min/d) — ESul SKen WFib
'Arnside Fringed Aztec' (R) — LDea
'Aroma' (Sc) — EWoo LIck WFib
¶ 'Arron Dixon' (A) — NFir
'Arthington Slam' (R) — LDea
'Arthur Biggin' (Z) — MWhe SKen
*articulatum* — Last listed 1998
¶ 'Ashby' (Sc) — LVER
'Ashby' (U) — Last listed 1998
'Ashfield Blaze' (Z/d) — LVER WFib
'Ashfield Jubilee' (Z/C) — SKen
'Ashfield Monarch' (Z/d) ♀ — LVER MWhe WFib
'Ashfield Serenade' (Z) ♀ — SKen WFib
'Ashley Stephenson' (R) — WFib
'Askham Fringed Aztec' (R) ♀ — EBSP LDea LVER
'Askham Slam' (R) — LDea
*asperum* Ehr. ex Willd. — See *P.* 'Graveolens'
'Astrakan' (Z/d) — Last listed 1998
'Athabasca' (Min) — ESul
'Atomic Snowflake' (Sc/v) — CArn CHal CInt ERav ESul GBar
GHCN LDea LVER MSte MWhe
SIde SSea WCHb WEas WFib WJek
WPer
'Attar of Roses' (Sc) ♀ — CArn CBrm CHal CInt CLTr CNat
EOHP ERav ESul GBar LDea LVER
MMal MWhe NHHG SIde SKen
WCHb WEas WFib WWye
'Attraction' (Z/St/d) — WFib
'Aubusson' (R) — WFib
'Audrey' (Z/d) — WFib
'Audrey Baghurst' (I) — CWDa
'Audrey Clifton' (I/d) — ECtt SKen WFib
'Augusta' — LHop SMrm
Auralia (Z/d) — Last listed 1998
*auritum* — Last listed 1998
'Aurora' (Z/d) — MWhe SKen
'Aurore' — See *P.* 'Unique Aurore'
*australe* — CFir CNat EWes SMrm SSpi SUsu
WFib
'Australian Mystery' (R/Dec) — LHil NFir
'Autumn' (Z/d) — LVER MWhe WFib
'Autumn Colours' (Min) — ESul
'Autumn Festival' (R) — WFib
'Autumn Haze' (R) — EBSP WFib

'Autumn Mist' (R) — WFib
'Avril' — ESul
'Aztec' (R) ♀ — EBSP LDea LVER MSte WEas WFib
'Aztec Fimbriant' — SMrm
'Baby Birds Egg' (Min) — CSpe ESul WFib
'Baby Brocade' (Min/d) — ESul LVER WFib
¶ 'Baby Face' (Dw) — EWoo
'Baby Helen' (Min) — ESul
'Baby James' (Min) — ESul
'Baby Snooks' (A) — LDea WEas
'Babylon' (R) — EBSP WFib
'Badley' (Dw) — ESul
Balcon Imperial — See *P.* 'Roi des Balcons Impérial'
'Balcon Lilas' — See *P.* 'Roi des Balcons Lilas'
'Balcon Rose' — See *P.* 'Hederinum'
'Balcon Rouge' — See *P.* 'Roi des Balcons Impérial'
'Balcon Royale' — See *P.* 'Roi des Balcons Impérial'
'Bali Surprise' (Z/St) — Last listed 1998
'Ballerina' (Dw/d) — ERav MWhe
'Ballerina' (R) — See *P.* 'Carisbrooke'
'Bandit' (Min) — ESul
'Bantam' (Min/d) — ESul WFib
§ 'Barbe Bleu' (I/d) — ECtt LDea LVER MWhe SKen
WFib
'Barking' (Min) — ESul
*barklyi* — Last listed 1998
'Barnston Dale' (Dw) — ESul NFir
'Barock '96' — NPri
§ Barock = 'Fisrock' (I) — Last listed 1996
'Baron de Layres' (Z/d) — WFib
'Baronne A. de
Rothschild' (Z/d) — WFib
'Bashful' (Min) — Last listed 1997
'Bath Beauty' (Dw) — SKen WEas
'Baylham' (Min) — ESul
'Beacon Hill' (Min) — ESul
'Beatrice Cottington' (I/d) — SKen WFib
'Beatrix' (Z/d) — LVER SKen WFib
'Beatrix Little' (Dw) — Last listed 1996
'Beau Geste' (R) — EBSP
'Beauty' (Z) — WFib
'Beauty of Bath' (R) — WFib
'Beauty of Calderdale' (Z/C) — WFib
N 'Beauty of Eastbourne' — See *P.* 'Lachskönigin'
'Beauty of El Segundo' (Z/d) — SKen WFib
'Beauty of Jersey' (I/d) — WFib
'Beckwith's Pink' (Z) — SKen
'Belinda Adams' (Min/d) ♀ — MWhe WFib
§ 'Belladonna' (I/d) — ECtt NPri
'Belvedere' (R) — EBSP
'Bembridge' — SSea
'Ben Franklin' (Z/v) ♀ — LVER MWhe WFib
'Ben Matt' (R) — LDea WFib
'Ben Nevis' (Dw/d) — ESul
'Bentley' (Dw) — ESul
'Bergpalais' (Z/d) — Last listed 1998
'Berliner Balkon' (I) — SKen
'Bern' — Last listed 1998
'Bernado' — WLRN
'Bernina' (I) — Last listed 1996
'Beromünster' (Dec) — ESul EWoo LDea LIck LVER MSte
WEas WFib
'Bert Pearce' (R) — EBSP LDea WFib
'Beryl Bodey' — See *P.* 'Mrs L.R. Bodey'
'Beryl Gibbons' (Z/d) — LVER MWhe
'Beryl Read' (Dw) — ERea ESul
'Beryl Reid' (R) — LDea WFib
'Berylette' (Min/d) — ESul SKen WFib
'Bess' (Z/d) — ESul LVER SKen
'Beta' (Min/C) — ESul
'Bette Shellard' (Z/d) — MWhe
¶ 'Betty' (Z/d) — LVER

'Betty Dollery' (Z/d) — Last listed 1998
'Betty Hulsman' (A) — ESul LDea
'Betty Read' (Dw) — ESul
'Betty West' (Min/d) — Last listed 1998
*betulinum* — WFib
'Betwixt' (Z/v) — SKen SSea WFib
'Bev Foster' (d) — Last listed 1998
'Bewerley Park' (Z/C/d) — WFib
'Bianca' (Min/d) — ESul
'Bicester Gem' — Last listed 1998
'Bi-coloured Startel' (Z/St/d) — MWhe
'Biedermeier' (R) — Last listed 1998
'Bildeston' (Z/C) — ESul
'Bill West' (I) — Last listed 1998
'Billie Read' (Dw/d) — ERea ESul
'Bingo' (Min) — ESul
'Bird Dancer' (Dw/St) ♀ — CBos CSpe ERav ESul LHil LVER MSte MWhe SHFr SKen WEas WFib
'Birthday Girl' (R) — WFib
'Bitter Lemon' (Sc) — ESul
'Black Butterfly' — See *P.* 'Brown's Butterfly'
'Black Country Bugle' (Z/d) — CWDa
'Black Knight' (R) — CMdw CSpe ESul EWoo LDea LVER MSte WFib
'Black Magic' (R) — WFib
'Black Night' (A) — ESul NFir
'Black Pearl' (Z/d) — WFib
'Black Prince' (R) — WEas WPen
'Black Velvet' (R) — LDea
'Black Vesuvius' — See *P.* 'Red Black Vesuvius'
'Blackcurrant Sundae' — Last listed 1998
'Blakesdorf' (Dw) — ESul MWhe
¶ 'Blanca' (Z/d) — LVER
'Blanche Roche' — NPri SCoo WLRN
§ 'Blandfordianum' (Sc) — EWoo LDea SSad
§ 'Blauer Frühling' (I/d) — LVER SKen
'Blaze Away' — SSea
'Blazonry' (Z/v) — MBEx MWhe SKen WFib
¶ 'Blendworth' (R) — LDea
'Blizzard' — Last listed 1996
'Blizzard Cascade' — Last listed 1996
'Bloomfield Abundance' — Last listed 1998
'Blooming Gem' (Min/I/d) — LDea
'Blue Beard' — See *P.* 'Barbe Bleu'
'Blue Blizzard' — NPri
'Blue Fox' (Z) — CWDa
'Blue Orchid' (R) — LDea WFib
'Blue Peter' (I/d) — SKen
'Blue Spring' — See *P.* 'Blauer Frühling'
'Bluebeard' — ERav
§ 'Blues' (Z/d) — CWDa
'Blush Kleine Liebling' (Min) — WFib
'Blush Mariquita' (R) — WEas WFib
'Blush Petit Pierre' (Min) — ESul
'Blushing Bride' (I/d) — LDea SKen
'Blushing Emma' (Z) — ESul WFib
'Bob Legge' (Z/d) — WFib
'Bode's Trina' (I) — CWDa
'Bodey's Picotee' (R) ♀ — WFib
¶ 'Bold Candy' (R) — LDea
¶ 'Bold Carmine' (Dw) — NFir
¶ 'Bold Dawn' (Z) — NFir
'Bold Flame' (Z/d) — WFib
¶ 'Bold Queen' (Z) — NFir
'Bold Sunrise' (Z/d) — LVER
'Bold Sunset' (Z/d) — LVER WFib
¶ 'Bold White' (Z) — NFir
'Bolero' (U) ♀ — EWoo LVER MSte SSea WFib
¶ 'Bonito' (I/d) — LVER

'Boogy' — Last listed 1998
'Bosham' (R) — EBSP LDea WFib
'Botham's Surprise' (Z/d) — Last listed 1998
¶ 'Both's Snowflake' (Sc/d) — EWoo
'Botley Beauty' (R) — EBSP LDea WFib
'Boudoir' (Z/C/d) — ESul
'Bouldner' — Last listed 1998
*bowkeri* — Last listed 1998
'Brackenwood' (Min/d) ♀ — ESul LVER NFir WFib
'Bramford' (Dw) — ESul
'Braque' (R) — LDea WFib
'Brasil' — WLRN
'Bravo' (Z/d) — MWhe WFib
'Break o' Day' (R) — LDea WEas
'Bredon' (R) ♀ — WFib
'Brenda' (Min/d) — ESul
'Brenda Hyatt' (Dw/d) — ESul WFib
'Brenda Kitson' (Z/d) — LVER MWhe WFib
'Brialyn Beauty' (A) — LDea
'Brialyn Moonlight' (A) — ESul LDea
¶ 'Briarlyn Moonglow' (A) — LVER NFir
'Bridal Veil' (Min/C) ♀ — Last listed 1995
'Bridesmaid' (Dw/C/d) — ESul SKen WFib
'Brightstone' — Last listed 1998
'Brightwell' (Min/d) — ESul WFib
'Brilliant' (Dec) — CNat EWoo WFib
'Bristol' (Z/v) — SKen SSea WFib
'Britannia' (R) — LDea
'Brixworth Boquet' (Min/C/d) — MWhe
'Brixworth Charmer' (Z/v) — MWhe
'Brixworth Melody' (Z/v) — MWhe
'Brixworth Pearl' (Z) — MWhe
'Brixworth Rhapsody' (Z/v) — MWhe
'Brixworth Starlight' (I/v) — MWhe
'Broadway' (Min) — WFib
'Brocade' (Z/d) — WFib
'Brockbury Scarlet' (Ca) — WFib
'Bronze Corinne' (Z/C/d) — SKen
'Bronze Nuhulumby' (R) — EBSP WFib
'Bronze Queen' (Z/C) — Llck MWhe
'Bronze Velvet' (R) — LDea WFib
'Brook' — SSea
'Brook's Purple' — See *P.* 'Royal Purple'
'Brookside Abigail' — Last listed 1998
'Brookside Arundel' — Last listed 1996
'Brookside Astra' — Last listed 1998
'Brookside Betty' (Dw/C/d) — ESul
'Brookside Bolero' (Z) — ESul
'Brookside Candy' (Dw/d) — ESul WFib
'Brookside Champagne' (Min/d) — ESul
'Brookside Cinderella' (Z/C/d) — ESul
'Brookside Flamenco' (Min/d) — ESul MWhe WFib
'Brookside Primrose' (Min/C/d) — ESul MWhe SKen WFib
'Brookside Rosita' (Min) — ESul
'Brookside Serenade' (Z) — ESul WFib
'Brookside Spitfire' (Dw/d) — ESul
§ 'Brown's Butterfly' (R) — EBSP LDea LHop SAga WEas WFib
§ 'Bruni' (Z/d) — CHal MWhe WFib
'Brunswick' (Sc) — ESul EWoo LDea LVER MSte WFib
'Brutus' (Z) — CWDa
*bubonifolium* — Last listed 1998
'Bucklesham' (Dw) — ESul
¶ 'Budbridge' (St) — NFir
'Bumblebee' (Dw) — Last listed 1998
'Burgenlandmädel' (Z/d) — LVER SKen WFib
'Burgundy' (R) — LDea WFib
'Burnaby' (Min) — WFib

| | | |
|---|---|---|
| 'Burstall' (Min/d) | Last listed 1998 |
| 'Bushfire' (R) ♀ | EBSP LDea WFib |
| 'Butley' (Min) | ESul |
| 'Buttercup Don' (Z/d) | Last listed 1997 |
| 'Butterfly' (Min/v) | ECtt NPri |
| § Butterfly (I) | WFib |
| § Cabaret (Z/d) | MBri |
| *caffrum* | Last listed 1998 |
| 'Cal' | See *P.* 'Salmon Irene' |
| 'Caledonia' (Z) | SKen |
| 'Caledonian Maiden' (Z) | WFib |
| ¶ 'California Brilliant' (U) | NFir |
| 'Caligula' (Min/d) | WFib |
| 'Calypso' (Z) | WFib |
| 'Cameo' (Dw/d) | MWhe WFib |
| 'Camilla' (Dw) | Last listed 1998 |
| 'Camphor Rose' (Sc) | CLTr ESul |
| * 'Canadian Centennial' | CBar |
| 'Can-can' (I/d) | WFib |
| *candicans* | WFib |
| 'Candy' (Min/d) | ESul |
| 'Candy Kisses' (D) | ESul |
| *canescens* | See *P.* 'Blandfordianum' |
| 'Capel' (Dw/d) | ESul |
| 'Capella' (Min) | WFib |
| Capen (Z/d) | Last listed 1998 |
| *capitatum* | CInt CNat WCHb WEas WFib |
| 'Capri' (Sc) | WFib |
| 'Caprice' (R) | EWoo WFib |
| 'Capricorn' (Min/d) | ESul |
| 'Captain Starlight' (A) | ESul EWoo LDea LHil LVER SSea WEas WFib |
| 'Cardinal' | See *P.* 'Kardinal' |
| 'Cardinal Pink' (Z/d) | CWDa |
| 'Carefree' (U) | EWoo WFib |
| 'Cariboo Gold' (Min/C) ♀ | ESul |
| § 'Carisbrooke' (R) ♀ | CLTr LDea SKen SSea WEas WFib |
| 'Carmel' (Z) | WFib |
| 'Carnival' (R) | See *P.* 'Marie Vogel' |
| 'Carnival' (Z) | WFib |
| *carnosum* | Last listed 1998 |
| 'Carol Ann' (Z) | Last listed 1997 |
| 'Carol Gibbons' (Z/d) | MWhe |
| 'Carol Plumridge' (Dw/C) | Last listed 1996 |
| 'Carol West' (Z/v) | Last listed 1996 |
| 'Carole' (R) | EBSP |
| ¶ 'Carole Munroe' (Z/d) | LVER |
| 'Caroline Plumridge' (Dw) | ESul WFib |
| 'Caroline Schmidt' (Z/d/v) ♀ | CHal ELea LVER MBEx MBri MSte MWhe NWoo SKen SSea SYvo WFib |
| 'Carousel' (Z/d) | CWDa LVER |
| 'Casanova' (Z/d) | WLRN |
| * 'Cascade Lilac' | WFib |
| * 'Cascade Pink' | WFib |
| * 'Cascade Red' | WFib |
| § Casino (Z/d) | Last listed 1998 |
| 'Cassata' (R) | WFib |
| 'Catford Belle' (A) ♀ | CSpe ESul GHCN LDea LHil MWhe SKen SSea WEas WFib |
| 'Cathay' (Z/St) | ESul MWhe |
| ¶ 'Cathy' (Z/St) | NFir |
| ¶ 'Cathy' (R) | NFir |
| *caucalifolium* | Last listed 1998 |
| subsp. *caucalifolium* | |
| - subsp. *convolvulifolium* | WFib |
| *caylae* | Last listed 1998 |
| 'Cayucas' (I/d) | SKen |
| 'Celebration' (Z/d) | ESul LVER |
| 'Celia' (Min) | WFib |
| * Century Series (Z) ♀ | Last listed 1995 |
| *ceratophyllum* | Last listed 1998 |

| | | |
|---|---|---|
| 'Cerise Carnation' | See *P.* 'Mrs H.J. Jones' |
| 'Cézanne' (R) | ERav LDea LVER SAga SMrm WFib |
| § Champagne (Z) | CWDa |
| 'Chantilly Claret' (R) | EBSP LDea |
| 'Chantilly Lace' (R) | EBSP LDea |
| 'Charity' (Sc) ♀ | CBrm ERav EWoo LDea Llck LVER MSte MWhe NFir WFib |
| § 'Charles Gounod' (Z/d) | SKen |
| § Charleston (Z) | Last listed 1998 |
| 'Charlie Boy' (R) | LDea WFib |
| 'Charlotte Bidwell' | ESul |
| ¶ 'Charlotte Brontë' (Z/C) | NFir |
| 'Charlotte Read' (Dw) | ERea |
| 'Charm' (Min) | ESul |
| 'Charmant' | CWDa |
| 'Charmer' (R) | LDea |
| 'Charmy Snowflake' | WFib WHer |
| 'Cheerio' (seed raised) (Z) ♀ | Last listed 1996 |
| 'Chelmondiston' (Min/d) | ESul MWhe |
| § 'Chelsea Gem' (Z/d/v) ♀ | LVER MBEx SKen SSea WFib |
| 'Chelsea Morning' (Z/d) | WFib |
| 'Chelsworth' (Min/d) | ESul LVER WFib |
| 'Chelvey' (R) | WFib |
| 'Cherie' (Min) | WFib |
| 'Cherie' (R) | LDea WFib |
| 'Cherie' (Z) ♀ | Last listed 1995 |
| 'Cherie Bidwell' | ESul |
| 'Cherie Maid' (Z/v) | EWoo LHil WFib |
| 'Cherry' (Z/d) | WFib |
| 'Cherry' (Min) | LVER WFib |
| ¶ 'Cherry Baby' (Dec) | NFir |
| 'Cherry Cocktail' (Z/v) | MWhe |
| 'Cherry Galilee' (I/d) | SKen |
| 'Cherry Hazel Ruffled' (R) | LDea |
| 'Cherry Orchard' (R) | LDea LVER SKen SSea WFib |
| 'Cherry Sundae' (Z/d/v) | ESul LVER WFib |
| 'Cherryade' (Dw) | Last listed 1998 |
| 'Cheryldene' (R) | LDea |
| 'Chessington' (Z/C) | Last listed 1998 |
| 'Chew Magna' (R) | WFib |
| 'Chic' | Last listed 1998 |
| 'Chi-Chi' (Min) | ESul |
| 'Chieko' (Min/d) | ESul MWhe WFib |
| ¶ 'Chiltern Surprise' (Z/St) | NFir |
| 'Chime' (Min/d) | ESul |
| 'China Doll' (Dw/d) | WFib |
| 'Chintz' (R) | Last listed 1998 |
| 'Chiquita' (R) | WFib |
| 'Chocolate Blotch' (Z/C) | CNat |
| § 'Chocolate Peppermint' (Sc) ♀ | CHal CInt CLTr CSev ERav ESul LDea LHil MWhe NHHG SKen SUsu SYvo WCHb WEas WFib WHer WJek WPer |
| 'Chocolate Tomentosum' | See *P.* 'Chocolate Peppermint' |
| 'Choice Cerise' (R) | LDea |
| 'Chorus Girl' (R) | Last listed 1998 |
| 'Chrissie' (R) | EBSP |
| 'Christie' (Z/d) | Last listed 1998 |
| 'Christopher Ley' (Z) | LVER SKen |
| 'Cindy' (Dw/d) | ESul |
| 'Circus Day' (R) | LDea WFib |
| 'Citriodorum' (Sc) ♀ | CArn CInt EOHP LDea NHHG SIde WCHb WEas WFib WPer |
| 'Citronella' (Sc) | LDea MSte WCHb WFib |
| *citronellum* (Sc) | CInt WFib WPer |
| 'Clair' (Min) | WFib |
| 'Clara Read' (Dw) | ESul |
| 'Claret Cruz' (I) | CWDa |
| 'Claret Rock Unique' (U) | CLTr EWoo MSte SKen SMrm WFib |
| 'Clarissa' (Min) | ESul |
| 'Clatterbridge' (Dw/d) | ESul LVER WFib |

'Claude Read' (Dw) — ERea ESul
'Claudette' (Min) — ESul
'Claudius' (Min) — ESul
'Claydon' (Dw/d) — ESul
'Claydon Firebird' (R) — EBSP
'Cleopatra' (Z) — WFib
'Clevedon Joy' (Z/c) — Last listed 1996
'Clorinda' (U/Sc) — CHal CSev ERea ESul EWoo GBar LVER MSte SKen WCHb WFib WHer WJek
'Clorinda Variegated' — See *P.* 'Variegated Clorinda'
'Clown' (R) — WFib
§ Coco-Rico (I) — SKen
'Coddenham' (Dw/d) — ESul LVER WFib
'Colette' (Min) — WFib
§ 'Colonel Baden-Powell' (I/d) — LDea
'Colonel Drabbe' (Z/d) — WFib
§ 'Columbia' (Z/Sc) — Last listed 1998
*columbinum* — Last listed 1998
'Comedy' — NPri WLRN
'Concolor Lace' (Sc) — CLTr ESul
'Conspicuous' (R) — EWoo WFib
'Contrast' (Z/d/C/v) — MBri MWhe SKen SSea WEas WFib
¶ 'Cook's Freckles' (I) — NFir
'Cook's Red Spider' (Ca) — WFib
'Copdock' (Min/d) — ESul
'Copthorne' (Sc) ♀ — CLTr CMdw CNat CSpe LDea LVER SKen WFib
'Coral Frills' (Dw) — ESul
'Coral Island' (Z/d) — Last listed 1996
'Coral Reef' (Z/d) — Last listed 1996
'Coral Sunset' (d) — CWDa
'Coralglow' (Z/d) — Last listed 1998
*cordifolium* — EWoo WFib
'Coriand' (Z/d) — WFib
♦ *coriandrifolium* — See *P. myrrhifolium* var. *coriandrifolium*
'Cornell' (I/d) — ECtt MBri WFib
'Coronia' (Z/Ca) — CWDa
*coronopifolium* — Last listed 1998
'Corsair' (Z/d) ♀ — MWhe WFib
*cortusifolium* — Last listed 1998
'Corvina' (R) — Last listed 1996
'Cotswold Queen' (Z/d) — WFib
'Cotta Lilac Queen' (I/d) — LVER
'Cottenham Beauty' (A) — LDea NFir
¶ 'Cottenham Charm' — ESul
¶ 'Cottenham Delight' — ESul
¶ 'Cottenham Gem' — ESul
¶ 'Cottenham Pride' (A) — NFir
'Cottenham Surprise' (A) — LDea
'Cotton Candy' (Dw/d) — ESul
'Cottontail' (Min/d) — ESul LVER
*cotyledonis* — SUsu WFib
'Countess Mariza' — See *P.* 'Gräfin Mariza'
'Countess of Birkenhead' (Z) — WFib
'Countess of Scarborough' — See *P.* 'Lady Scarborough'
'Country Girl' (R) — WFib
'Courbet' — Last listed 1997
'Cover Girl' (Z/d) — WFib
'Cramdon Red' (Dw) — SKen WFib
¶ 'Crampel's Crimson' — EWoo
'Crampel's Master' (Z) — LVER
'Cranbrook Black' — EWoo
'Cransley Blends' (R) — EBSP LDea WFib
'Cransley Star' (A) — ESul LDea WEas WFib
*crassicaule* — Last listed 1998
'Cream and Green' — CSpe
'Creamery' (Z/d) — WFib
§ 'Creamy Nutmeg' (Sc/v) — CArn CHal CLTr EOHP ESul GBar LDea LVER MWhe SRob SSea

'Creed's Seedling' (Z/C) — ERav
'Creeting St Mary' (Min) — ESul
'Creeting St Peter' (Min) — ESul
'Crescendo' (I/d) — ECtt
'Crimson Crampel' (Z) — CWDa
'Crimson Fire' (Z/d) — MBri MWhe SKen WFib
'Crimson Unique' (U) ♀ — CSpe EWoo LHil SKen SSea WFib
§ *crispum* (Sc) — CJew CNat GBar GPoy LDea MHer NHHG WCHb WEas WFib WJek WRha
– 'Major' (Sc) — ESul SKen WFib WPer
– 'Minor' — Last listed 1998
– 'Peach Cream' (Sc/v) — CHal MWhe WFib WJek
– 'Variegatum' (Sc/v) ♀ — CHal CSev GBar GHCN GPoy LDea LVER MBEx MWhe SKen SRob SSea WCHb WEas WFib
¶ 'Crock O Day' (I/d) — LVER
'Crocketta' (I/d/v) — LVER
'Crocodile' — See *P.* 'The Crocodile'
'Crowfield' (Min/d) — ESul
'Crystal Palace Gem' (Z/v) — LVER MWhe SKen SMrm SSea WFib
*cucullatum* — ERav EWoo SVen WFib
§ – subsp. *strigifolium* — Last listed 1996
§ 'Culm' (A) — LDea MSte
'Culpho' (Min/C/d) — ESul
'Cupid' (Min/Dw/d) — ESul WFib
'Cynthia' (Min) — Last listed 1997
'Cyril Read' (Dw) — ERea ESul
§ 'Czar' (Z/C) — WFib
'Dainty Lassie' (Dw/v) — ESul
'Dainty Maid' — ESul SYvo
'Dale Queen' (Z) — WFib
'Dame Anna Neagle' (Dw/d) ♀ — ESul LVER WFib
'Dancer' (Dw) — ESul
'Dandee' (Z/d) — WFib
'Danny West' — Last listed 1998
'Dark Lady' (Sc) — WFib
§ 'Dark Mabel' (R) — Last listed 1996
'Dark Presidio' — See *P.* 'Dark Mabel'
'Dark Red Irene' (Z/d) — LVER MWhe WFib
'Dark Secret' (R) — CSpe EBSP EWoo LDea SKen WFib
'Dark Venus' (R) — LDea WFib
'Darmsden' (A) ♀ — ESul LDea
§ 'Dart' (A) — LDea
*dasyphyllum* — Last listed 1998
'David John' (Dw/d) — ESul LVER
'Davina' (Min/d) — ESul MWhe WFib
'Dawn' (Z/d) — WFib
'Dawn Star' (Z/St) — ESul WFib
¶ 'Daybreak' (Z/v) — NFir
'Daydream' (Z/C/d) — Last listed 1996
'Deacon Arlon' (Dw/d) — ESul LVER MWhe SKen
'Deacon Avalon' (Dw/d) — WFib
'Deacon Barbecue' (Z/d) — ESul MWhe SKen
'Deacon Birthday' (Z/d) — ESul LVER MWhe WFib
'Deacon Bonanza' (Z/d) — ESul MWhe SKen WFib
'Deacon Clarion' (Z/d) — ESul SKen
'Deacon Constancy' (Z/d) — ESul LVER MWhe
'Deacon Coral Reef' (Z/d) — ESul MWhe SKen WFib
¶ 'Deacon Delight' — EWoo
'Deacon Finale' (Z/d) — ESul LVER
'Deacon Finito' — See *P.* 'Finito'
'Deacon Fireball' (Z/d) — ESul LVER MWhe SKen WFib
'Deacon Flamingo' (Z/d) — ESul MWhe
'Deacon Gala' (Z/d) — ESul MWhe
'Deacon Golden Bonanza' (Z/C/d) — ESul WFib
'Deacon Golden Gala' (Z/C/d) — ESul SKen

I 'Deacon Golden Lilac Mist' (Z/C/d)   ESul SKen WFib
'Deacon Golden Mist'   See *P.* 'Golden Mist'
'Deacon Jubilant' (Z/d)   ESul MWhe SKen
'Deacon Lilac Mist' (Z/d)   ESul LVER MWhe SKen WFib
'Deacon Mandarin' (Z/d)   ESul MWhe SKen
'Deacon Minuet' (Z/d)   ESul LVER MWhe SKen
'Deacon Moonlight' (Z/d)   ESul LVER MWhe
'Deacon Peacock' (Z/C/d)   ESul MWhe SKen
'Deacon Picotee' (Z/d)   ESul LVER MBri MWhe SKen
'Deacon Regalia' (Z/d)   ESul MWhe SKen WFib
'Deacon Romance' (Z/d)   ESul MWhe SKen WFib
'Deacon Summertime' (Z/d)   ESul LVER MWhe
'Deacon Sunburst' (Z/d)   ESul MWhe SKen
'Deacon Suntan' (Z/d)   ESul LVER MWhe SKen WFib
'Deacon Trousseau' (Z/d)   ESul MWhe WFib
'Debbie Parmer' (Dw/d)   ESul
'Deborah Miliken' (Z/d)   Last listed 1998
'Decora Impérial' (I)   LVER SKen
'Decora Lavender' (I)   LVER
§ 'Decora Lilas' (I)   ECtt SKen
'Decora Mauve'   See *P.* 'Decora Lilas'
§ 'Decora Rose' (I)   ECtt SKen
'Decora Rouge' (I)   ECtt
'Deerwood Lavender Lad' (Sc)   ESul LDea WFib
'Degas' (R)   WFib
'Delhi' (R)   WFib
'Delightful' (R)   WFib
'Delilah' (R)   LDea
'Delta' (Min/d)   ESul
'Denebola' (Min/d)   ESul WFib
***denticulatum***   NHHG SKen WCHb WFib WJek
§ - 'Filicifolium' (Sc)   CHal CInt ERav EWoo GBar NHHG WFib WJek WWye
***desertorum***   Last listed 1998
'Destiny' (R)   WFib
'Devon Cream'   Last listed 1998
'Dewit's' (Dw)   Last listed 1996
'Diabolo'   Last listed 1998
'Diadem' (R)   WFib
'Diana Palmer' (Z/d)   SKen WFib
'Diane' (Min/d)   ESul WFib
'Diane Louise' (d)   Last listed 1998
'Dibbinsdale' (Z)   ESul
***dichondrifolium*** (S/c)   EWoo LVER SSad WFib
¶ - x *reniforme* (Sc)   NFir
'Didden's Improved Picardy' (Z/d)   Last listed 1996
'Diddi-Di' (Min/d)   ESul
'Didi' (Min)   ESul SKen WFib
'Dinky' (Min/d)   ESul
§ Disco (Z/d)   CWDa
'Distinction' (Z)   CSpe LHil MBEx MWhe SKen WFib
'Doctor A. Chipault' (I/d)   LDea WFib
'Doctor A. Vialettes' (Z/d)   CWDa
'Doctor Margaret Sturgis' (Z/d)   WFib
'Dodd's Super Double' (Z/d)   CHal WFib
'Dolce Vita'   Last listed 1998
'Dollar Bute' (R)   LDea
'Dollar Princess' (Z/C)   SKen
'Dolly Daydream' (C)   Last listed 1997
'Dolly Moon' (C)   Last listed 1997
'Dolly Read' (Dw)   ERea ESul WFib
'Dolly Varden' (Z/v) ♀   LDea LHil LVER MBri MWhe SKen WFib
***dolomiticum***   WFib
'Dolphin' (Min)   WFib
'Don Quixote' (A)   LDea
'Don's Carosel' (Z/v)   Last listed 1998

¶ 'Don's Claire Pearson' (Z/C)   NFir
¶ 'Don's Helen Bainbridge' (Z/C)   NFir
'Don's Judith Ann' (Z/v)   LVER NFir
¶ 'Don's Little Meg' (Z/C)   NFir
'Don's Mona Noble' (Z/C/v)   SKen
¶ 'Don's Pateley Bridge' (Z/St)   NFir
¶ 'Don's Richard A. Costain' (Z/C)   NFir
'Don's Silva Perle' (Dw/v)   SKen
¶ 'Don's Snowfire' (Z/C)   NFir
¶ 'Don's Southport' (Z/C)   NFir
¶ 'Don's Stokesley Gem' (Z/C)   NFir
¶ 'Don's Whirlygig' (Z/C)   NFir
'Dopey' (Min)   Last listed 1997
'Doreen' (Z/d)   LVER
'Doreen Featherby' (R)   WFib
\* 'Doreen Maddison'   Last listed 1998
'Doris Brook' (Z/d)   WFib
'Doris Frith' (R)   LDea WFib
'Doris Hancock' (R)   WFib
'Doris Moore' (Z)   Last listed 1998
'Doris Shaw' (R)   WFib
'Double Bird's Egg' (Z/d)   CWDa
'Double Grace Wells' (Min/d)   ESul
'Double Henry Jacoby'   See *P.* 'Double Jacoby'
§ 'Double Jacoby' (Z/d)   WFib
'Double Lilac White' (I/d)   SKen
'Double New Life' (Z/d)   CHal CWDa
'Double Orange' (Z/d)   SKen
'Double Pink Bird's Egg' (Z/d)   SKen
'Double White Lilac Eye' (I/d)   Last listed 1998
'Dove' (Z)   WFib
'Dovedale' (Dw/C)   ESul
'Downlands' (Z/d)   Last listed 1998
'Dream' (Z)   CWDa EWoo WFib
'Dresden China' (R)   LDea
'Dresden Pink' (Dw)   LVER WFib
'Dresden Pippa Rosa' (Z/S)   SKen
'Dresden White' (Dw)   LVER
'Drummer Boy' (Z)   CWDa SKen
'Dryden' (Z)   SKen WFib
'Dubonnet' (R)   LDea SYvo WFib
'Duchess of Devonshire' (Z)   SKen
'Duke of Buckingham' (Z/d)   LVER
'Duke of Devonshire' (Z/d)   LVER
'Duke of Edinburgh'   See *P.* 'Hederinum Variegatum'
'Dulcie' (Min)   ESul
'Dunkery Beacon' (R)   LDea WFib
'Dusty Rose' (Min)   ESul WFib
§ 'Dwarf Miriam Baisey' (Min)   LVER WFib
'Dwarf Miriam Read'   See *P.* 'Dwarf Miriam Baisey'
'E. Dabner' (Z/d)   CWDa SKen WFib
'Earl of Chester' (Min/d) ♀   WFib
'Earliana' (Dec)   CHal ESul LDea SKen
'Earls Four' (R)   LDea MSte
'Earth Magic' (Z/v)   Last listed 1996
¶ 'Earth Summit' (Z/v)   SSea
'Eastbourne Beauty' (I/d)   WFib
'Easter Greeting'   See *P.* 'Ostergruss'
'Easter Morn' (Z/St)   WFib
***echinatum***   LVER
- 'Album'   SSad
- 'Miss Stapleton'   See *P.* 'Miss Stapleton'
'Eclipse' (I)   ESul LHil MWhe SKen WFib
'Eden Gem' (Min/d)   ESul WFib
\* 'Eden Rose' (Sc)   Last listed 1997
'Edith Steane' (Dw/d)   ESul LVER
'Edmond Lachenal' (Z/d)   WFib
'Edna' (Z/d)   WFib
'Edward Hockey' (Z)   WFib

| | |
|---|---|
| 'Edward Humphris' (Z) | EWoo SKen |
| 'Edwin Clarke' (Dw/Min) | ESul |
| 'Eileen' (I) | LVER WFib |
| 'Eileen Postle' (R) ♀ | WFib |
| 'Eileen Stanley' (R) | LDea |
| 'Elaine' (R) | LDea |
| ¶ 'Elbe Silver' | NPri |
| 'Eldorado' | WLRN |
| 'Eleanor' (Z/d) | Last listed 1998 |
| 'Electra' (Z/d) | CWDa LVER SKen WFib |
| *elegans* | Last listed 1998 |
| 'Elfin Rapture' (R) | WFib |
| 'Elgar' (R) | WFib |
| 'Elizabeth Angus' (Z) | SKen WFib |
| 'Elizabeth Cartwright' (Z) | WFib |
| 'Elizabeth Read' (Dw) | ERea ESul WFib |
| 'Elmscfi' (Dw) | Last listed 1996 |
| 'Elmsett' (Z/C/d) | ESul LVER |
| 'Elna' (Min) | ESul |
| *elongatum* | Last listed 1998 |
| 'Els' (Min/St) | ESul LVER SKen SYvo |
| 'Els Variegated' (Min/St/v) | SMrm |
| 'Elsi' (I/d/v) | LVER WFib |
| 'Elsie Hickman' (R) | LDea WFib |
| 'Elsie Portas' (Z/C/d) | ESul SKen |
| 'Embassy' (Dw) | ESul WFib |
| 'Emerald' (I) | SKen |
| 'Emma Hössle' | See *P.* 'Frau Emma Hössle' |
| 'Emma Jane Read' (Dw/d) | ERea ESul MWhe WFib |
| 'Emma Louise' (Z) | SKen |
| 'Emmy Sensation' (R) | LDea |
| 'Emperor Nicholas' (Z/d) | MWhe SKen |
| 'Empress' (Z) | SKen |
| 'Ena' (Min) | ESul |
| 'Enchantress' (I) | MBri SKen |
| 'Encore' (Z/d/v) | LVER MWhe |
| *endlicherianum* | CGen EPot NWCA Slgm |
| 'Endora' (Min) | ESul |
| 'Endsleigh' (Sc) | Last listed 1998 |
| *englerianum* | Last listed 1998 |
| 'Enid Blackaby' (R) | WFib |
| 'Enid Read' (Dw) | ERea WFib |
| 'Eric Ellis' (Dw/d) | WFib |
| 'Eric Hoskins' (Z/d) | WFib |
| * 'Eric Lee' | CWDa |
| 'Erwarton' (Min/d) | ESul LVER |
| 'Escapade' (Dw/d) | ESul WFib |
| 'Esteem' (Z/d) | WFib |
| 'Etna' (Min) | WFib |
| 'Evelyn' | ESul |
| 'Evesham Wonder' (Z/d) | WFib |
| ¶ 'Evka' (I/v) | LVER NFir NPri |
| *exhibens* | Last listed 1998 |
| 'Explosive' | WLRN |
| *exstipulatum* | EWoo WEas WFib |
| 'Fair Dinkum' (Z/v) | MWhe |
| § 'Fair Ellen' (Sc) | CLTr ERav EWoo SKen WFib WPer |
| 'Fairlee' (Dwl) | Last listed 1998 |
| 'Fairy Orchid' (A) | ESul LDea LVER |
| 'Fairy Princess' (R) | LDea |
| 'Fairy Queen' | EWoo LDea WEas |
| 'Fairy Tales' (Dw) | WFib |
| 'Falkland Brother' (Z/C/v) | WFib |
| 'Falkland Hero' (Z/v) | MWhe WFib |
| 'Fandango' (Z/St/d) | ESul LVER MWhe WFib |
| * 'Fanfare' | CWDa |
| 'Fanny Eden' (R) | WFib |
| 'Fantasia' white (Dw/d) ♀ | ESul MWhe WFib |
| 'Fantasy' (R) | Last listed 1996 |
| 'Fareham' (R) ♀ | EBSP LDea MSte WFib |
| 'Fascination' (Z/Ca) | WFib |
| 'Felix' (I) | Last listed 1996 |

| | |
|---|---|
| 'Feneela' (Dw/d) | ESul |
| 'Fenton Farm' (Z/C) | ESul |
| 'Festal' (Min/d) | ESul |
| 'Feuerriese' (Z) | LVER SKen |
| 'Fiat' (Z/d) | CWDa SKen |
| 'Fiat Queen' (Z/d) | SKen WFib |
| 'Fiat Supreme' (Z/d) | SKen WFib |
| § 'Fidelio' (Z/d) | Last listed 1998 |
| 'Fiery Sunrise' (R) | EBSP LDea LVER |
| 'Fiesta' (I/d) | LDea |
| 'Fiesta' (R) | WFib |
| 'Fifth Avenue' (R) | CSpe EWoo MSte WFib |
| ♦ 'Filicifolium' | See *P. denticulatum* 'Filicifolium' |
| § 'Finito' (Dw/d) | ERea |
| ¶ 'Fir Trees All Gold' (R) | NFir |
| ¶ 'Fir Trees Echoes of Pink' (A) | NFir |
| ¶ 'Fir Trees Fire Star' (Z/St) | NFir |
| ¶ 'Fir Trees Raggety' (Dw) | NFir |
| ¶ 'Fir Trees Roseberry Topping' (Dw) | NFir |
| ¶ 'Fir Trees Scarlet Supreme' (Z) | NFir |
| 'Fire Cascade' (I) | Last listed 1998 |
| 'Fire Dragon' (Z/St/d) | SKen |
| 'Fire Light' (Min/d) | WFib |
| 'Firebrand' (Z/d) | LVER |
| 'Firefly' (Min/d) | ESul WFib |
| 'Fireglow' (Z/d) | Last listed 1997 |
| 'Firestone' (Dw) | ESul |
| 'First Blush' (R) | WFib |
| 'First Ladies' | Last listed 1996 |
| 'First Love' (Z) | LVER |
| *fissifolium* | Last listed 1998 |
| 'Flair' (R) | WFib |
| ¶ 'Flair' (I) | NPri |
| 'Flair Greetings' (Z/C) | Last listed 1998 |
| 'Flakey' (I/d/v) ♀ | CSpe ESul LDea MWhe SKen WFib |
| 'Flame' (Z) | WFib |
| 'Flarepath' (Z/C/v) | Last listed 1996 |
| 'Flesh Pink' (Z/d) | CWDa |
| 'Fleur d'Amour' (R) | WFib |
| 'Fleurette' (Dw/d) | CHal ESul MWhe SKen WFib |
| § Flirt (Min) | ESul MBri WFib |
| 'Floral Cascade' (Fr/d) | WFib |
| 'Florence Storey' (Z/C/d) | WFib |
| ¶ 'Floria Moore' (Dec) | NFir |
| 'Flower Basket' (R) | LDea NFir |
| 'Flower of Spring' (Z/v) ♀ | CHal LVER MWhe SKen SSea SYvo WFib |
| 'Flowerfield' (Z) | WFib |
| 'Flowton' (Dw/d) | ESul |
| * 'Forever' (d) | CWDa |
| 'Fox' (Z/d) | CHal |
| 'Foxhall' (Dw) | ESul |
| Fragrans Group (Sc) | CHal CLTr CSev ESul EWoo GHCN GPoy MMal MWhe NHHG SKen WFib WHer WPer WWol WWye |
| - 'Creamy Nutmeg' | See *P.* 'Creamy Nutmeg' |
| § - 'Fragrans Variegatum' (Sc/v) | CInt CSev CSpe ERav LIck MWhe SKen WCHb WFib WJek WPer |
| - 'Snowy Nutmeg' | See *P.* (Fragrans Group) 'Fragrans Variegatum' |
| 'Fraiche Beauté' (Z/d) | CWDa WFib |
| 'Francis James' (Z) | EWoo WFib |
| ¶ 'Francis Parmenter' (MinI/v) | NPri |
| 'Francis Parrett' (Min/d) ♀ | ESul LVER MWhe WFib |
| 'Francis Read' (Dw/d) | ERea ESul |
| 'Frank Headley' (Z/v) ♀ | CHal CSpe ERav ESul LDea LHil LVER MBEx MMil MSte MWhe SKen SMrm SSea WEas WFib |

'Frank Parrett' (Min/d)          ESul
§ 'Frau Emma Hössle' (Dw/d)      MWhe WFib
'Frau Käthe Neubronner'          CWDa
  (Z/d)
'Freak of Nature' (Z/v)          MWhe SKen SSea WEas WFib
'Freckles' (Z/d)                 WFib
'Frensham' (Sc)                  ESul EWoo WFib
'Freston' (Dw)                   ESul
'Freya' (Min)                    Last listed 1997
'Friary Wood' (Z/C/d)            ESul WFib
'Friesdorf' (Dw)                 ERav ESul LVER MWhe SKen
                                 WEas WFib
'Frills' (Min/d)                 ESul MWhe WFib
'Fringed Angel' (A)              LDea
¶ 'Fringed Apple' (Sc)           LDea
§ 'Fringed Aztec' (R) ♀          EBSP LDea LVER SAga WFib
'Fringed Rouletta' (I)           LDea
'Frosty'                         See P. 'Variegated Kleine Liebling'
'Frosty Petit Pierre'            See P. 'Variegated Kleine Liebling'
'Frühlingszauber Lilac' (R)      EBSP
*frutetorum*                     Last listed 1998
*fruticosum*                     EWoo WFib
¶ 'Fuji' (R)                     NFir
*fulgidum*                       WFib
'Funny Girl' (R)                 WFib
'Fynn' (Dw)                      ESul
'Gabriel' (A)                    LDea
'Galilee' (I/d) ♀                LDea LVER SKen WFib
'Galway Star' (Sc/v) ♀           CNat CSpe LVER WFib
'Garda' (I/d)                    ECtt
'Garibaldi' (Z/d)                CWDa WFib
¶ 'Garland' (Dw/d)               LVER
'Garland' (R)                    ESul
'Garnet' (Z/d)                   ESul LVER WFib
'Garnet Rosebud' (Min/d)         ESul
'Garnet Wings' (R)               WFib
'Gartendirektor Herman'          ERav EWoo SMrm WFib
  (Dec)
'Gary Salvidge' (R)              LDea
'Gay Baby' (DwI)                 ESul LDea MWhe
'Gay Baby Supreme' (DwI)         ESul
'Gazelle' (Z)                    Last listed 1998
§ 'Gemini' (Z/St/d)              ESul MWhe WFib
'Gemma' (Min/C)                  LVER WFib
'Gemma' (R)                      LDea LVER
'Gemma Jewel' (R) ♀              EBSP
'Gemstone' (Sc) ♀                CBrm ESul EWoo LDea WFib
'Genetrix' (Z/d)                 WFib
'Genie' (Z/d)                    LVER MWhe SKen WFib
'Gentle Georgia' (R)             WFib
'Geoff May' (Dw)                 ESul WFib
'Geoffrey Harvey' (Z/d)          WFib
'Geoffrey Horsman' (R)           WFib
'Georgia' (R)                    WFib
'Georgia Peach' (R)              EBSP WFib
¶ 'George' (R)                   LDea
'Georgina Blythe' (R) ♀          WFib
'Geo's Pink' (Z/v)               MWhe
'Gerald Caws' (d)                Last listed 1998
'Gerald Portas' (Dw/C)           ESul LIck
'Gerald Wells' (Min)             ESul
'Geraldine' (Min)                ESul
'Geronimo' (R)                   WFib
'Gess Portas' (Z/v)              ESul SKen
¶ 'Ghost Story' (Z/C)            NFir
'Giant Butterfly' (R)            LDea
'Giant Oak' (Sc)                 MSte WFib
*gibbosum*                       CNat WFib
'Gilbert West' (Z)               SKen
'Gilda' (R)                      EBSP LDea
'Gill' (Min/Ca)                  ESul
'Gillian Clifford' (Z/d)         Last listed 1998

* 'Giro Fly'                     Last listed 1998
'Glacier Claret' (Z)             Last listed 1998
'Glacier Crimson' (Z)            SKen
'Glacis' (Z/d)                   WFib
'Gladys Evelyn' (Z/d)            WFib
'Gladys Stevens' (Min/d)         ESul
x *glaucifolium*                 Last listed 1998
*glaucum*                        See P. lanceolatum
'Gleam' (Z/d)                    LVER
'Glenn Barker' (Z/d)             WFib
'Glenshree' (R)                  LVER WFib
§ Gloria = 'Fisglo' (Z/d)        Last listed 1996
'Gloria Pearce' (R)              LDea WFib
'Glory' (Z/d)                    WFib
'Glowing Embers' (R)             LDea WFib
§ *glutinosum*                   Last listed 1997
'Goblin' (Min/d)                 ESul SKen WFib
* 'Godshill'                     LDea
* 'Gold Medallion'               Last listed 1998
'Gold Star' (Z/St/C)             ESul
'Golden Baby' (Dwl/C)            LDea MWhe
'Golden Brilliantissimum'        LVER MWhe SKen WFib
  (Z/v)
'Golden Butterfly' (Z/C)         ESul
'Golden Chalice' (Min/v)         ESul MWhe
'Golden Clorinda' (U/Sc/C)       EWoo LDea WEas
'Golden Crest' (Z/C)             SKen SMrm
'Golden Ears' (Dw/St/C)          ESul MBri MWhe NPer WFib
'Golden Everaarts' (Dw/C)        ESul
'Golden Fleece' (Min/C/d)        ESul
'Golden Flora'                   Last listed 1996
'Golden Gates' (Z/C)             ESul SKen
'Golden Gleam' (Z/C)             Last listed 1996
'Golden Harry Hieover' (Z/C)     ESul LVER MBEx MBri SKen WEas
'Golden Lilac Mist'              Last listed 1996
'Golden Mirage' (Z/v)            WFib
§ 'Golden Mist' (Dw/C/d)         LVER
'Golden Orange' (Dw/C)           ESul
'Golden Orfe' (Dw/C)             WFib
'Golden Petit Pierre' (Min/C)    ESul
'Golden Princess' (Min/C)        ESul WFib
'Golden Princess' (R)            Last listed 1998
'Golden Roc' (Min/C)             ESul
'Golden Ruth' (Z)                WFib
'Golden Staphs' (Z/St/C)         ESul LIck LVER WFib
'Golden Stardust' (Z/St)         LVER
'Golden Tears' (MinI/C/d)        ESul
'Golden Wedding' (Z/d/v)         LVER MWhe
¶ 'Golden Well Sweep' (Sc)       NFir WFib
'Goldie' (R)                     WFib
'Goldilocks' (A)                 ESul LDea WFib
'Gooseberry Leaf'                See P. grossularioides
'Gordano Midnight' (R)           EWoo WFib
'Gordino Pixie' (R)              Last listed 1998
'Gosbeck' (A)                    ESul LDea SSea
'Gosport Girl' (R)               EBSP LDea
'Gothenburg'                     EBSP
'Grace Read' (Min)               Last listed 1997
'Grace Thomas' (Sc) ♀            LDea WFib
'Grace Wells' (Min)              ESul WFib
'Gracious Lady' (Z/d)            WFib
§ 'Gräfin Mariza' (Z/d)          SKen WFib
'Grand Slam' (R)                 EBSP LDea LVER SKen WFib
*grandiflorum*                   WFib
'Grandma Fischer'                See P. 'Grossmutter Fischer'
'Grandma Ross' (R)               EBSP LDea
'Granny Hewitt' (Min/d)          ESul
§ 'Graveolens' (Sc)              CHal CLTr CNat CSev ERav ESul
                                 GHCN GPoy LVER MWhe SSea
                                 WFib WJek
'Great Blakenham' (Min)          ESul
'Great Bricett' (Min/d)          ESul LVER

| | | |
|---|---|---|
| 'Green Ears' (Z/St) | ESul WFib | |
| 'Green Eyes' (I/d) | SKen | |
| 'Green Goddess' (I/d) | LDea SKen | |
| 'Green Gold Petit Pierre' (MiN) | ESul | |
| 'Green Lady' (Sc) | WFib | |
| 'Green Woodpecker' (R) | LDea LVER SSea | |
| § 'Greengold Kleine Liebling' (Min/C/v) | ESul SKen | |
| 'Greengold Petit Pierre' | See P. 'Greengold Kleine Liebling' | |
| 'Greetings' (Min/v) | ESul MBri WFib | |
| Gregor (Z/d) | Last listed 1996 | |
| § 'Grenadier' (Z/St/d) ♀ | Last listed 1998 | |
| § 'Grenadier' (Z) | CWDa | |
| 'Grenche Belle' (I/d) | Last listed 1996 | |
| 'Grey Lady Plymouth' (Sc/v) | ESul EWoo GBar LDea SIde WFib | |
| 'Grey Monk' (Z) | Last listed 1997 | |
| 'Grey Sprite' (Min/v) | ESul WFib | |
| *greytonense* | Last listed 1998 | |
| *griseum* | WFib | |
| * 'Groombridge Success' (d) | CWDa | |
| § 'Grossmutter Fischer' (R) | LDea WFib | |
| § *grossularioides* | CInt CNat EOHP ESul | |
| 'Grozser Garten' (Dw) | ESul | |
| 'Grozser Garten Weiss' (Dw) | ESul | |
| ¶ 'Guardsman' | ESul | |
| 'Guitari' (I) | Last listed 1996 | |
| 'Gurnard' | Last listed 1998 | |
| 'Gustav Emich' (Z/d) | SKen WFib | |
| ¶ 'Gwen' (Min/v) | MWhe | |
| 'H. Guinier' | See P. 'Charles Gounod' | |
| 'H. Rigler' (Z) | SKen | |
| 'H. Walker' (R) | Last listed 1996 | |
| 'Hadleigh' (Dw) | ESul | |
| 'Hamble Lass' (R) | EBSP LDea | |
| 'Hanchen Anders' (Z) | WFib | |
| § 'Hannaford Star' (Z/St/d) | ESul WFib | |
| 'Hannah' (A) | ESul NFir | |
| 'Hans Rigler' (Z/d) | WFib | |
| ¶ 'Hanson Pixie' (R) | LDea | |
| ¶ 'Happy Appleblossom' (Z/v) | LVER NFir | |
| § 'Happy Thought' (Z/v) ♀ | CHal LDea LVER MBri MWhe SKen SSea | |
| 'Happy Valley' (R) | EBSP LVER WFib | |
| 'Harbour Lights' (R) | EBSP LDea WFib | |
| 'Harewood Slam' (R) | LDea MSte SMrm WEas WFib | |
| 'Harkstead' (Min) | ESul | |
| 'Harlequin' (Dw) | Last listed 1998 | |
| 'Harlequin Alpine Glow' (I/d) | LDea LVER MWhe WFib | |
| 'Harlequin Candy Floss' (I/d) | CWDa | |
| 'Harlequin Liverbird' (I) | WFib | |
| 'Harlequin Mahogany' (I/d) | LDea LVER MBri MWhe SKen WFib | |
| § 'Harlequin Miss Liver Bird' (I) | LDea SKen | |
| 'Harlequin My Love' (I) | Last listed 1997 | |
| 'Harlequin Picotee' (I/d) | LDea LVER SKen | |
| 'Harlequin Pretty Girl' (I) | MWhe WFib | |
| 'Harlequin Rosie O'Day' (I) | LDea MWhe SKen WFib | |
| 'Harlequin Ted Day' (I/d) | LDea LVER | |
| ¶ 'Harmony' (R) | LVER | |
| 'Harold Bowie' (Z/d) | WFib | |
| 'Harold Headley' (Z/v) | Last listed 1998 | |
| 'Harriet Le Hair' (Z) | SKen | |
| 'Harvard' (I/d) | LVER WFib | |
| 'Harvey' (Z) | MWhe | |
| *havlasae* | Last listed 1998 | |
| 'Hayley Charlotte' (Z/v) | MWhe | |
| 'Hay's Radiant' (Z/d) | WFib | |
| 'Hazel' (R) | LVER WFib | |
| * 'Hazel Adair' | LDea | |
| 'Hazel Anson' (R) | LDea | |
| 'Hazel Barolo' (R) | LDea | |

| | | |
|---|---|---|
| 'Hazel Beauty' (R) | Last listed 1998 | |
| 'Hazel Birkby' (R) | EBSP LDea WFib | |
| 'Hazel Blake' (R) | WFib | |
| 'Hazel Burgundy' (R) | EBSP LDea | |
| 'Hazel Burtoff' (R) | EBSP LDea WFib | |
| 'Hazel Carey' (R) | LDea | |
| 'Hazel Cherry' (R) | LDea MSte WFib | |
| 'Hazel Chick' (R) | LDea | |
| 'Hazel Choice' (R) | EBSP LDea WFib | |
| ¶ 'Hazel Dean' (R) | NFir | |
| 'Hazel Frances' (R) | Last listed 1996 | |
| 'Hazel Frills' (R) | Last listed 1996 | |
| 'Hazel Gipsy' (R) | LDea WFib | |
| 'Hazel Glory' (R) | LDea WFib | |
| 'Hazel Gowland' (R) | LDea | |
| 'Hazel Harmony' (R) | LDea | |
| 'Hazel Heather' (R) | LDea | |
| 'Hazel Henderson' (R) | LDea LHil | |
| 'Hazel Herald' (R) | EBSP LDea | |
| 'Hazel Mistique' (R) | LDea | |
| 'Hazel Peach' (R) | Last listed 1998 | |
| 'Hazel Perfection' (R) | LDea | |
| 'Hazel Rose' (R) | LDea | |
| 'Hazel Saga' (R) | EBSP WFib | |
| 'Hazel Satin' (R) | LDea | |
| 'Hazel Shiraz' (R) | LDea | |
| 'Hazel Star' (R) | EBSP | |
| 'Hazel Stardust' (R) | EBSP LDea | |
| * 'Hazel Whitaker' | Last listed 1998 | |
| 'Hazel Wright' (R) | LDea | |
| § 'Hederinum' (I) | SKen WEas WWol | |
| § 'Hederinum Variegatum' (I/v) | CHal LDea WFib | |
| 'Heidi' (Min/d) | ESul | |
| * 'Helen Bowie' | CWDa | |
| 'Helen Christine' (Z/St) | NFir WFib | |
| 'Helena' (I/d) | LDea MWhe SKen WFib | |
| 'Helena Hall' (R) | Last listed 1996 | |
| 'Helter Skelter' (Z/v) | Last listed 1998 | |
| 'Hemingstone' (A) | ESul LDea | |
| ¶ 'Hemley' (Sc) | LDea | |
| 'Henhurst Gleam' (Dw/C/d) | ESul WFib | |
| 'Henley' (Min/d) | Last listed 1996 | |
| 'Hermione' (Z/d) | CHal MWhe WFib | |
| 'High Tor' (Dw/C/d) | ESul SKen WFib | |
| 'Highfields Always' (Z/d) | LVER | |
| 'Highfields Appleblossom' (Z) | LVER SKen | |
| 'Highfields Attracta' (Z/d) | LVER SKen | |
| 'Highfields Ballerina' (Z/d) | LVER WFib | |
| 'Highfields Came' (Z/d) | Last listed 1996 | |
| 'Highfields Candy Floss' (Z/d) | Last listed 1998 | |
| 'Highfields Charisma' (Z/d) | LVER | |
| 'Highfields Choice' (Z) | LVER SKen | |
| 'Highfields Comet' (Z) | SKen | |
| 'Highfields Contessa' (Z/d) | LVER SKen WFib | |
| 'Highfields Dazzler' (Z) | LVER | |
| 'Highfields Delight' (Z) | LVER | |
| 'Highfields Fancy' (Z/d) | SKen | |
| 'Highfields Fantasy' (Z) | Last listed 1997 | |
| 'Highfields Fashion' (Z) | Last listed 1996 | |
| 'Highfields Festival' (Z/d) | LVER MWhe SKen | |
| 'Highfields Flair' (Z/d) | LVER | |
| 'Highfields Flash' (Z/d) | Last listed 1996 | |
| 'Highfields Joy' (Z/d) | Last listed 1998 | |
| 'Highfields Melody' (Z/d) | Last listed 1998 | |
| 'Highfields Orange' (Z) | LVER MWhe | |
| 'Highfields Paramount' (Z) | SKen | |
| 'Highfields Pearl' (Z) | Last listed 1998 | |
| 'Highfields Perfecta' (Z) | CWDa | |
| 'Highfields Pink' (Z) | Last listed 1998 | |
| 'Highfields Prestige' (Z) | Last listed 1997 | |
| 'Highfields Pride' (Z) | LVER SKen | |
| 'Highfields Prima Donna' (Z/d) | LVER MWhe SKen WFib | |

| | |
|---|---|
| 'Highfields Promise' (Z) | SKen |
| 'Highfields Salmon' (Z/d) | Last listed 1996 |
| 'Highfields Serenade' (Z) | LVER |
| 'Highfields Snowdrift' (Z) | LVER SKen |
| 'Highfields Sonata' (Z) | LVER |
| 'Highfields Sugar Candy' (Z/d) | ECtt SKen WFib |
| 'Highfields Supreme' (Z) | Last listed 1998 |
| 'Highfields Symphony' (Z) | LVER WFib |
| 'Highfields Vogue' (Z) | Last listed 1998 |
| 'Highscore' (Z/d) | WFib |
| 'Hi-jinks' (Z/v) | Last listed 1998 |
| 'Hildegard' (Z/d) | CHal SKen WFib |
| 'Hills of Snow' (Z/v) | CHal LVER MBri SKen WFib |
| 'Hillscheider Amethyst' | See *P.* 'Amethyst' |
| 'Hindoo' (R) | CNat EWoo SSea WFib |
| 'Hintlesham' (Min) | ESul |
| *birtum* | Last listed 1998 |
| *bispidum* | Last listed 1998 |
| 'Hitcham' (Min/d) | ESul WFib |
| 'Holbrook' (Min/C/d) | ESul |
| 'Holly West' | Last listed 1998 |
| 'Hollywood Star' (Z) ♀ | Last listed 1994 |
| 'Holmes Miller' (Z/d) | ESul |
| 'Honeywood Hannah' (R) | WFib |
| 'Honeywood Jonathan' (R) | EBSP WFib |
| 'Honeywood Lindy' (R) | EBSP |
| 'Honeywood Matthew' (Dw) | ESul |
| 'Honeywood Suzanne' (Min/Fr) | ESul LVER SKen WFib |
| 'Honne Früling' (Z) | SKen WFib |
| 'Honneas' (Min) | ESul |
| 'Honnestolz' (Min) | ESul SKen |
| 'Hope' (Z) | WFib |
| 'Hope Valley' (Dw/C/d) ♀ | ESul MWhe SKen |
| 'Horace Parsons' (R) | LDea WFib |
| 'Horace Read' (Dw) | ERea ESul |
| 'Horning Ferry' (Dw) | ESul |
| 'House and Garden' (R) | WFib |
| 'Howard Stanton' (R) | WFib |
| 'Howard's Orange' (R) | LDea |
| 'Hugo de Vries' (Dw/d) | CWDa WFib |
| 'Hula' (U) | EWoo LVER WFib |
| 'Hulda Conn' (Ca/d) | WFib |
| 'Hunter's Moon' (Z/C) | ESul |
| 'Hurdy-gurdy' (Z/d/v) | ESul MWhe WFib |
| HWD Corelli | Last listed 1998 |
| HWD Gabrieli | Last listed 1998 |
| HWD Monteverdi | Last listed 1998 |
| HWD Onyx | Last listed 1998 |
| HWD Romanze | Last listed 1998 |
| HWD Vivaldi | Last listed 1998 |
| *bypoleucum* | Last listed 1998 |
| 'Ian Read' (Min/d) | ERea ESul WFib |
| 'Icecrystal' | CWDa WLRN |
| 'Icing Sugar' (I/d) | ESul LDea SSea WFib |
| * 'Ilse Fisher' | CWDa |
| 'Immaculatum' (Z) | EWoo WFib |
| 'Imperial Butterfly' (A/Sc) | ERav ESul LDea LVER WFib |
| 'Improved Petit Pierre' (Min) | ESul |
| 'Improved Ricard' (Z/d) | WFib |
| 'Ina' (Z/d) | WFib |
| 'Inca' (R) | LDea WFib |
| *incrassatum* | Last listed 1998 |
| 'Ingres' (I/d) ♀ | ECtt |
| 'Inka' | Last listed 1996 |
| *inquinans* | WFib |
| *iocastum* | Last listed 1998 |
| *ionidiflorum* | CSpe LHil |
| 'Ipswich Town' (Dw/d) | ESul |
| 'Irene' (Z/d) ♀ | WFib |
| 'Irene Cal' (Z/d) ♀ | Last listed 1998 |
| ¶ 'Irene Collett' (R) | LDea |
| 'Irene Corsair' (Z/d) | Last listed 1997 |
| 'Irene Hardy' (Z/d) | Last listed 1996 |
| 'Irene La Jolle' (Z/d) | Last listed 1997 |
| 'Irene Lollipop' (Z/d) | Last listed 1996 |
| 'Irene Toyon' (Z) ♀ | Last listed 1996 |
| * 'Iris Monroe' | CWDa |
| 'Isaac Middleton' (Z) | Last listed 1997 |
| § 'Isabell' (Z/d) | WFib |
| 'Isidel' (I/d) ♀ | SKen WFib |
| 'Isobel Gamble' (Z/d) | Last listed 1997 |
| 'Italian Gem' (I) | SKen |
| 'Ivalo' (Z/d) | MWhe SKen WFib |
| 'Ivory Snow' (Z/d/v) | LVER MWhe SKen |
| 'Jacey' (Z/d) | LVER SKen |
| 'Jack of Hearts' (I) | Last listed 1996 |
| 'Jack Read' (Dw) | ERea |
| 'Jack Wood' (Z/d) | ESul |
| 'Jackie' (I) | WFib |
| 'Jackie's Gem' (I/d) | MWhe |
| 'Jacky Gall' (I/d) | MBri SKen |
| 'Jacqueline' (Z/d) | SKen |
| 'Jana' (Z/d) | LVER |
| 'Jane Biggin' (Dw/C/d) | ESul MWhe SKen |
| 'Jane Shoulder' (Min) | Last listed 1996 |
| 'Janet Hofman' (Z/d) | WFib |
| 'Janet James' | Last listed 1998 |
| 'Janet Kerrigan' (Min/d) | ESul MWhe WEas WFib |
| 'Janet Scott' (Z) | CWDa |
| 'Janna Whelan' (Dw/d) | Last listed 1998 |
| 'Jasmin' (R) | EBSP LDea |
| 'Jaunty' (Min/d) | ESul WFib |
| 'Jayne Eyre' (Min/d) | CHal ESul MWhe SKen WFib |
| § 'Jazz' | CWDa |
| 'Jean Bart' (I) | CWDa |
| 'Jean Beatty' (Dw/d) | LVER |
| 'Jean Oberle' (Z/d) | SKen WFib |
| § 'Jeanne d'Arc' (I) | SKen WFib |
| 'Jenifer Read' (Dw) | ERea ESul |
| 'Jennifer' (Min) | ESul |
| 'Jer'Rey' (A) | LDea |
| 'Jessel's Unique' (U) | MSte |
| 'Jessika' (Z/d) | Last listed 1998 |
| * 'Jetfire' (d) | CWDa |
| 'Jewel' (Z/d) | Last listed 1996 |
| 'Jewel' (R) | EBSP |
| 'Jeweltone' (Z/d) | WFib |
| 'Jill Portas' (Z/C) | ESul |
| 'Jim Field' (R) | WFib |
| 'Jimmy Read' (Min) | ERea |
| 'Jinny Reeves' (R) | EBSP LDea WFib |
| 'Joan Cashmore' (Z/d) | ESul WFib |
| 'Joan Fairman' (R) | WFib |
| 'Joan Fontaine' (Z) | WFib |
| 'Joan Hayward' (Min) | ESul |
| 'Joan Morf' (R) | EBSP LDea SKen SSea WFib |
| 'Joan of Arc' | See *P.* 'Jeanne d'Arc' |
| 'Joanna Pearce' (R) | EBSP LDea SKen |
| 'John Thorp' (R) | LDea |
| 'John West' | Last listed 1997 |
| 'John's Angela' | Last listed 1998 |
| 'John's Chameleon' | Last listed 1998 |
| 'John's Dilys' | Last listed 1996 |
| 'John's Pride' | MBri |
| 'John's Wishy-washy' | Last listed 1996 |
| 'Joseph Haydn' (R) | EBSP |
| 'Joseph Haydon' (R) | LDea |
| 'Joseph Paul' (R) | Last listed 1998 |
| 'Joseph Warren' (I/d) | LDea |
| 'Joseph Wheeler' (A) | MWhe |
| 'Joy' (R) ♀ | EBSP LDea LVER SSea WFib |
| 'Joy' (Z/d) | CSpe SKen |

'Joy' (I)                              Last listed 1998
'Joy Lucille' (Sc)                     CNat CSev ESul EWoo LDea
                                       WCHb WFib
'Joyce Delamere' (Z/C/d)               WFib
'Joyden'                               CWDa
'Jubel Parr' (Z/d)                     CWDa
'Judith Thorp' (R)                     EBSP
'Judy Read' (Dw)                       ESul
'Julia' (R) ♀                          EBSP LDea
'Juliana' (R)                          LDea
'Julie' (A)                            ESul
'Julie Smith' (R)                      LDea WFib
'June Patricia' (d)                    Last listed 1998
'Jungle Night' (R)                     EBSP WFib
'Juniper' (Sc)                         WFib
'Jupiter' (Min/d)                      SKen WFib
'Jupiter' (R)                          EBSP
¶ 'Just Rita' (A)                      SSea
'Just William' (Min/C/d)               ESul
'Kamahl' (R)                           WFib
'Kandy Waterman' (d)                   Last listed 1998
§ 'Kardinal' (Z/d)                     Last listed 1998
'Kardino'                              Last listed 1998
'Kari Anne'                            Last listed 1996
'Karl Hagele' (Z/d)                    LVER SKen WFib
'Karmin Ball'                          CWDa WFib
*karooicum*                            Last listed 1998
*karrooense* 'Graham Rice'             See *P.* 'Grollie's Cream'
'Kath Peat' (Z/d)                      WFib
'Kathleen Gamble' (Z)                  SKen
'Kathleen Mott' (Z/C)                  Last listed 1996
'Kathryn' (Min)                        ESul
'Kathryn Portas' (Z/v)                 ESul SKen
'Kayleigh West' (Min)                  ESul
'Keepsake' (Dw/d)                      ESul LVER WFib
'Keith Vernon' (Fr/d)                  Last listed 1998
'Kelvedon Beauty' (Min)                WEas
'Ken Salmon' (Dw/d)                    ESul
'Kennard Castle' (Z)                   CWDa
'Kenny's Double' (Z/d)                 WFib
¶ 'Kensington' (A)                     LDea
'Kerensa' (Min/d)                      ESul SKen
'Kershy' (Min)                         ESul
'Kesgrave' (Min/d)                     ESul
'Kettle Baston' (A) ♀                  ESul LDea MWhe WFib
'Kewense' (Z)                          Last listed 1996
'Kimono' (R)                           EBSP LDea LHil
'Kinder Charm' (R)                     Last listed 1997
§ 'Kinder Gaisha' (R)                  NFir
'King Edmund' (R)                      LDea WFib
'King of Balcon'                       See *P.* 'Hederinum'
'King of Denmark' (Z/d)                LVER SKen WFib
'Kingsmill' (R)                        LDea
'Kingswood' (Z)                        Last listed 1998
'Kirton' (Min/d)                       ESul
'Kiwi'                                 MBri
§ 'Kleine Liebling' (Min)              EWoo LHop MWhe WFib
'Kosset' (Min/d)                       Last listed 1998
'Krista' (Min/d)                       ESul WFib
* 'Kristy'                             Last listed 1998
¶ 'Kumuzura' (Z/C)                     NFir
¶ 'Kyoto' (R)                          NFir
'Kyra' (Min/d)                         ESul WFib
'L.E. Wharton' (Z)                     SKen
'La France' (I/d) ♀                    LDea LVER MBri MWhe WEas
                                       WFib
'La Jolla' (Z/d)                       Last listed 1998
'La Paloma' (R)                        LDea WEas WFib
'Laced Belle Notte' (I)                Last listed 1996
'Laced Mini Cascade'                   ESul
¶ 'Laced Mini Rose                     NFir
   Cascade' (I)

'Laced Red Mini Cascade' (I)           Last listed 1997
§ 'Laced Sugar Baby' (Dwl)             Last listed 1996
Lachsball (Z/d)                        SKen WFib
§ 'Lachskönigin' (I/d)                 LDea LVER SKen WEas WFib
'Lady Alice of Valencia'               See *P.* 'Grenadier' (Z)
'Lady Churchill' (Z/v)                 WFib
'Lady Cullum' (Z/C/v)                  MWhe
'Lady Ilchester' (Z/d)                 SKen WFib
'Lady Lexington' (I)                   Last listed 1996
'Lady Love Song' (R)                   EBSP
'Lady Mary' (Sc)                       ESul EWoo LVER MHer WFib
'Lady Mavis Pilkington' (Z/d)          Last listed 1996
'Lady Plymouth' (Sc/v) ♀               CHal CInt CLTr CSpe ERav ESul
                                       LDea LHil LVER MMal MSte
                                       MWhe NHHG SKen SSea SYvo
                                       WEas WFib WHer WWye
§ 'Lady Scarborough' (Sc)              LDea MHer WFib WWye
   *laevigatum*                        WEas
'Lakeland' (I)                         Last listed 1998
'Lakis' (R)                            LDea
'Lambada'                              NPri
'Lamorna' (R)                          LDea SKen WFib
'Lancastrian' (Z/d)                    WFib
§ *lanceolatum*                        Last listed 1998
'Langley' (R)                          LDea
'Lanham Lane' (I)                      LDea MWhe
'Lanham Royal' (Min/d)                 ESul
'Lara Aladin' (A)                      WFib
'Lara Ballerina'                       Last listed 1996
'Lara Candy Dancer' (Sc) ♀             EOHP ESul LDea WFib
'Lara Jester' (Sc)                     EWoo WFib
'Lara Maid' (A) ♀                      ESul WEas WFib
'Lara Nomad' (Sc)                      EWoo
'Lara Starshine' (Sc) ♀                ESul EWoo SSea WFib
'Lark' (Min/d)                         ESul
'Larkfield'                            SSea
N 'Lass o' Gowrie' (Z/v)               LVER MBEx MSte MWhe SKen
                                       WFib
'Lass o' Gowrie'                       WFib
   (American) (Z/v)
'Laura' (Z/d)                          Last listed 1998
¶ 'Laura Parmer'                       ESul
'Laura Wheeler' (A)                    MWhe
* 'Laurel Heywood' (R)                 WFib
'Lauripen' (Z/d)                       WFib
'Lavender Feathers' (R)                Last listed 1998
'Lavender Frills' (R)                  Last listed 1997
'Lavender Grand Slam' (R) ♀            EBSP LDea LVER WFib
'Lavender Harewood                     EBSP LDea
   Slam' (R)
'Lavender Mini Cascade'                See *P.* 'Lila Mini Cascade'
'Lavender Sensation' (R)               WFib
'Lavender Wings' (I)                   LDea
*laxum*                                Last listed 1998
'Layham' (Dw/d)                        ESul
'Layton's White' (Z/d)                 CWDa SKen
'Le Lutin' (Z/d)                       CWDa WFib
'Lee Gamble' (Z)                       Last listed 1996
'L'Elégante' (I/v) ♀                   CHal CSpe EAst EWoo LDea LVER
                                       MBri MWhe SKen SSea WEas
                                       WFib WLRN
'Lemon Air' (Sc)                       ESul
♦ 'Lemon Crisp'                        See *P. crispum*
'Lemon Fancy' (Sc)                     CInt LDea LVER MWhe WFib
                                       WJek
'Lemonii'                              Last listed 1997
'Len Chandler' (Min)                   ESul
'L'Enfer'                              See *P.* 'Mephistopheles'
'Lenore' (Min)                         ESul
'Leo' (Min)                            ESul
'Leonie Holbrow' (Min)                 ESul
'Leopard' (I/d)                        CWDa

| | |
|---|---|
| 'Lerchenmuller' (Z/d) | Last listed 1998 |
| 'Leslie Judd' (R) | WFib |
| 'Leslie Salmon' (Min/C) | ESul MWhe |
| 'Lethas' (R) | LDea |
| 'Letitia' (A) | ESul LHil |
| § Leucht-Cascade | WFib |
| 'Levington' (Min/d) | WFib |
| Lila Compakt-Cascade | See P. 'Decora Lilas' |
| § 'Lila Mini Cascade' (I) | ESul MWhe |
| 'Lilac Cascade' | See P. 'Roi des Balcons Lilas' |
| 'Lilac Domino' | See P. 'Telston's Prima' |
| 'Lilac Elaine' (R) | LDea |
| 'Lilac Gem' (Min/l/d) | LDea LVER MWhe SKen WFib |
| 'Lilac Jewel' (R) | EBSP |
| 'Lilac Mini Cascade' (I) | LDea LVER |
| 'Lilac Ricard' (Z/d) | Last listed 1996 |
| 'Lilett' | Last listed 1996 |
| 'Lili Marlene' (I) | LVER SKen |
| 'Lilian' (Dw) | ESul |
| 'Lilian Lilett' | Last listed 1996 |
| 'Lilian Pottinger' (Sc) | CArn CHal CInt ESul GHCN LDea MWhe SIde SKen WEas WFib WHer |
| 'Limelight' | SSea |
| 'Limoneum' (Sc) | CSev MHer SKen WEas WFib |
| 'Lin Davis' (Z/C) | WFib |
| 'Linda' (Z/d) | WFib |
| 'Linda' (R) | EBSP LDea WFib |
| 'Lindsey' (Min) | ESul |
| 'Lindy Portas' (I/d) | SKen |
| 'Lisa' (Min/C) | ESul WFib |
| 'Little Alice' (Dw/d) ♀ | ESul LVER MWhe WFib |
| 'Little Blakenham' (A) | ESul LDea |
| 'Little Fi-fine' (Dw) | ESul WFib |
| 'Little Gem' (Sc) | EWoo LDea LVER WFib |
| ¶ 'Little Jip' (Z/C) | NFir SKen |
| 'Little John' (Min/d) | WFib |
| 'Little Margaret' (Min/v) | ESul LVER |
| 'Little Primular' (Min) | ESul |
| 'Little Trot' (Z/v) | WFib |
| 'Little Vectis' (D) | Last listed 1998 |
| 'Lively Lady' (Dw/C) | ESul |
| 'Liverbird' | See P. 'Harlequin Miss Liver Bird' |
| *lobatum* | Last listed 1998 |
| 'Lolette' (Min) | ESul |
| 'Lollipop' (Z/d) | WFib |
| 'Longshot' (R) | WFib |
| * 'Loraine Howarth' | ERav |
| 'Lord Baden-Powell' | See P. 'Colonel Baden-Powell' |
| 'Lord Bute' (R) ♀ | CNat CSpe EBSP ERav EWoo LDea LHil LHop LIck LVER MSCN MSte NPer NPla SBid SIde SKen SMer SMrm SUsu WEas WFib |
| * 'Lord Constantine' | LDea |
| 'Lord de Ramsey' | See P. 'Tip Top Duet' |
| 'Lord Roberts' (Z) | EWoo WFib |
| 'Lorelei' (Z/d) | CWDa WFib |
| 'Loretta' (Dw) | ESul |
| 'Loripen' (Z/d) | WFib |
| 'Lorna' (Dw/d) | ESul |
| * 'Lotus' | WLRN |
| 'Louise' (Min) | EBSP ESul |
| 'Love Song' (R/v) | EBSP EWoo LDea LVER SSea |
| 'Love Story' (Z/v) | ESul |
| * 'Loverly' (Min/d) | ESul |
| Lovesong (Z/d) | Last listed 1998 |
| 'Lowood' (R) | WFib |
| 'Lucilla' (Min) | ESul |
| 'Lucinda' (Min) | ESul |
| 'Lucy' (Min) | ESul |
| 'Lucy Gunnett' (Z/d/v) | ERav MWhe WFib |
| 'Lucy Jane' (R) | LDea |

| | |
|---|---|
| ¶ 'Lulu' (I) | NPri |
| 'Luna' | NPri |
| *luridum* | WCot |
| 'Lustre' (R) | EBSP WFib |
| 'Luz del Dio' (R) | WFib |
| 'Lyewood Bonanza' (R) | EBSP LDea |
| 'Lyn West' | Last listed 1997 |
| 'Lynne Valerie' (A) | LDea |
| 'Lyric' (Min/d) | ESul LVER WFib |
| 'M.J. Cole' (I/d) | LDea |
| 'Mabel Grey' (Sc) ♀ | CHal CSev CSpe ERav ESul EWoo LIck LVER MSte MWhe NHHG SKen WEas WFib WHer WJek |
| *madagascariense* | Last listed 1996 |
| § 'Madame Auguste Nonin' (U/Sc) | CHal LVER NFir NWoo SAga SKen WFib |
| 'Madame Butterfly' (Z/C/d) | ESul MWhe SKen |
| 'Madame Crousse' (I/d) ♀ | SKen WEas WFib |
| 'Madame Dubarry' (Z) | WFib |
| 'Madame Fournier' (Min/C) | ESul |
| 'Madame Guinier' | See P. 'Charles Gounod' |
| 'Madame Hibbault' (Z) | SKen |
| 'Madame Kingsbury' (U) | Last listed 1998 |
| 'Madame Layal' (A) | CSpe ESul EWoo LDea LIck SKen WFib |
| 'Madame Margot' | See P. 'Hederinum Variegatum' |
| 'Madame Recamier' (Z/d) | WFib |
| 'Madame Salleron' (Min/v) ♀ | LDea LVER MBEx MSte SKen |
| 'Madame Thibaut' (R) | LDea WFib |
| 'Madge Hill' (Min) | WFib |
| ¶ 'Madge Taylor' (R) | NFir |
| 'Magaluf' (I/C/d) | SSea WFib |
| 'Magda' (Z/d) | ESul LVER WFib |
| *magenteum* | Last listed 1998 |
| 'Magic' | WLRN |
| 'Magic Lantern' (Z/C) | SKen |
| 'Magic Moments' (R) | WFib |
| 'Magnum' (R) | WFib |
| * 'Mahogany' (I/d) | ECtt |
| 'Maid of Honour' (Min) | ESul |
| 'Mairi' (A) | ESul LDea WFib |
| 'Maja' (R) | WFib |
| 'Maloja' (Z) | SKen WFib |
| 'Mamie' (Z/d) | SKen |
| 'Mandarin' (Z) | Last listed 1997 |
| 'Mangles' Variegated' (Z/v) | SKen SSea |
| ¶ 'Mantilla' (Min) | SKen |
| 'Manx Maid' (A) | ESul LDea SKen WFib |
| ¶ 'Maple Leaf' | EWoo |
| 'Marble Sunset' | See P. 'Wood's Surprise' |
| 'Marchioness of Bute' (R) | LDea MSte WFib |
| 'Maréchal MacMahon' (Z/C) | MBEx SKen WFib |
| 'Margaret Bryan' (Z/C) | Last listed 1996 |
| 'Margaret Pearce' (R) | LDea |
| 'Margaret Salvidge' (R) | LDea WFib |
| 'Margaret Soley' (R) ♀ | LDea |
| 'Margaret Stimpson' (R) | LDea |
| 'Margaret Thorp' | LVER |
| 'Margaret Waite' (R) | WFib |
| 'Margery Stimpson' (Min/d) | ESul LVER WFib |
| 'Maria Wilkes' (Z/d) | WFib |
| 'Marie Rober' (R) | SKen WFib |
| ¶ 'Marie Thomas' (Sc) | LDea |
| ¶ 'Marie Thomson' (Sc) | SSea |
| § 'Marie Vogel' (R) | MSte WFib |
| 'Marilyn' (Dw) | ESul |
| 'Marion' (Min) | ESul |
| 'Mariquita' (R) | WFib |
| * 'Marja' | LDea |
| 'Marktbeherrscher' (Z/d) | WFib |
| 'Marmalade' (Dw/d) | ESul LVER MWhe SKen WFib |
| § 'Mars' (Z/d) | ESul WLRN |

| | |
|---|---|
| 'Martin Parrett' (Min/d) | WFib |
| 'Martin's Splendour' (Min) | ESul |
| 'Martlesham' | ESul |
| 'Mary Ellen Tanner' (Min/d) | Last listed 1997 |
| 'Mary Godwin' (Z) | Last listed 1996 |
| 'Mary Read' (Min) | ERea ESul |
| 'Mary Spink' (Z/C/d) | LVER NFir |
| 'Mary Webster' (Min) | ESul |
| 'Masquerade' (R) | ESul |
| 'Masterpiece' (Z/C/d) | ESul SKen |
| 'Mataranka' (Min/d/C/v) | MWhe |
| ¶ 'Matha Parmer' | ESul |
| 'Matisse' (I) | Last listed 1997 |
| 'Matthew Salvidge' (R) | EBSP LDea WFib |
| 'Maureen' (Min) | ESul NFir |
| 'Maureen Mew' | Last listed 1998 |
| 'Mauve Beauty' (I/d) | SKen WFib |
| 'Mauve Duet' (A) | ESul |
| 'Maverick Star' | Last listed 1996 |
| 'Maxime Kovalevski' (Z) | WFib |
| ¶ 'Maxine' (Z/C) | NFir |
| 'Maxine Colley' (Z/d/v) | LVER |
| 'May Day' (R) | LDea |
| 'May Magic' (R) | WFib |
| 'May Rushbrook' (Z) | Last listed 1998 |
| * 'Maya' | NPri SCoo |
| 'Mayor of Seville' (Z/d) | WFib |
| 'Maytime' (Z/d) | WFib |
| I 'Meadowside Dark and Dainty' | LHil |
| ¶ 'Meadowside Fancy' (Z/d/C) | LVER |
| ¶ 'Meadowside Harvest' (Z/St) | NFir |
| I 'Meadowside Mahogany' (Z/C) | LVER |
| 'Meadowside Midnight' | LHil MWhe SHFr |
| 'Meadowside Orange' (Z/d) | LVER |
| 'Medallion' (Z/C) | SKen WFib |
| 'Meditation' (Dw) | ESul |
| 'Medley' (Min/d) | ESul LVER MWhe WFib |
| 'Melanie' (R) | ESul LDea WFib |
| * 'Melissa' (Min) | ESul |
| Meloblue = 'Penblue' | WLRN |
| Melody (Z/d) | Last listed 1998 |
| 'Melva Bird' (Z/d) | WFib |
| 'Memento' (Min/d) | ESul LVER SKen WFib |
| 'Memories' (Z/d) | WFib* |
| 'Mendip' (R) | WFib |
| 'Meon Maid' (R) | EBSP LDea WFib |
| § 'Mephistopheles' (Min/C) | Last listed 1997 |
| 'Mercia' (R) | Last listed 1996 |
| 'Mercia Glory' (R) | Last listed 1996 |
| Mercutio (Z/d) | Last listed 1998 |
| ¶ 'Mere Carribean' (R) | NFir |
| 'Mere Casino' (Z) | LVER |
| * 'Mere Champagne' | Last listed 1998 |
| 'Mere Cocktail' (R) | WFib |
| 'Mere Flamenco' (R) | WFib |
| 'Mere Greeting' (Z/d) | MWhe |
| 'Mere Iced Cocktail' (R) | WFib |
| 'Mere Meteor' (R) | WFib |
| 'Mere Ripon' (R) | Last listed 1996 |
| 'Mere Sunglow' (R) | LDea WFib |
| ¶ 'Mere Seville' (Z/d) | SKen |
| 'Merry-go-round' (Z/C/v) | ESul MWhe WFib |
| 'Meshed Pink Gay Baby' | See P. 'Laced Sugar Baby' |
| 'Mexically Rose' (R) | WFib |
| 'Mexican Beauty' (I) | CHal MWhe SKen WEas WFib |
| 'Mexicanerin' | See P. 'Rouletta' |
| 'Michelle' (Min/C) | LDea WFib |
| 'Michelle West' (Min) | ESul |
| 'Midas Touch' (Dw) | ESul |
| 'Milden' (Z/C) | ESul LHil |
| 'Milkmaid' (Min) | WFib |
| 'Millbern Choice' (Z) | MWhe |
| 'Millbern Clover' (Min/d) | MWhe |
| 'Millbern Engagement' (Min/d) | MWhe |
| 'Millbern Peach' (Z) | MWhe |
| 'Millbern Serenade' | MWhe |
| 'Millbern Sharna' (Min/d) | MWhe |
| 'Miller's Valentine' (Z/v) | ESul LVER WFib |
| 'Millfield Gem' (I/d) | LDea LVER SKen WFib |
| 'Millfield Rival' (Z) | WFib |
| 'Millfield Rose' (I/d) | LVER MWhe SKen WEas |
| 'Millie' (Z/d) | CWDa WFib |
| 'Mimi' (Min/C/d) | ESul SSea |
| 'Mini-Czech' (Min/St) | ESul LVER |
| *minimum* | Last listed 1998 |
| ¶ 'Minnie' (Z/d/St) | LVER |
| 'Minnie Clifton' | Last listed 1997 |
| 'Minstrel' | ESul |
| 'Minstrel Boy' (R) | EBSP LDea WFib |
| 'Minuet' (Z/d) | WFib |
| 'Minx' (Min/d) | ESul WFib |
| * 'Mirage' | CWDa |
| 'Miranda' (Dw) | ESul |
| 'Miriam Basey' | See P. 'Dwarf Miriam Baisey' |
| 'Miss Australia' (R/v) | LDea WFib |
| 'Miss Burdett Coutts' (Z/v) | ESul LVER MWhe SKen WFib |
| 'Miss Farren' (Z/v) | SSea |
| 'Miss Flora' (I) | CWDa MWhe |
| 'Miss Liverbird' (I/d) | ECtt |
| ¶ 'Miss McKinsey' (Z/St) | NFir |
| 'Miss Muffett' (Min/d) | ESul |
| § 'Miss Stapleton' | Last listed 1998 |
| 'Miss Wackles' (Min/d) | ESul SKen WFib |
| ¶ 'Mistress' (Z/C) | NFir |
| 'Misty' (Z) | ESul |
| ¶ 'Mitzou' | LVER |
| 'Modesty' (Z/d) | SKen WFib |
| 'Modigliani' (R) | Last listed 1997 |
| 'Mohawk' (R) | EBSP LVER NFir WFib |
| 'Mole' (A) | LDea LVER SKen |
| 'Molina' (I) | NPri SCoo |
| *mollicomum* | Last listed 1998 |
| 'Mollie' (R) | WFib |
| * 'Molly' | Last listed 1998 |
| 'Molly Malone' | Last listed 1996 |
| 'Momo' | Last listed 1996 |
| 'Mona Lisa' | EBSP |
| 'Monarch' (Dw/v) | ESul SKen |
| 'Monica Bennett' (Dw) | ESul SKen WEas |
| 'Monks Eleigh' | ESul |
| 'Monkwood Charm' (R) | LDea |
| 'Monkwood Delight' (R) | Last listed 1998 |
| 'Monkwood Dream' (R) | LDea |
| 'Monkwood Rhapsody' (R) | Last listed 1998 |
| ¶ 'Monkwood Rose' (A) | NFir |
| 'Monkwood Sprite' (R) | LDea |
| 'Monsal Dale' (Dw/C/d) | ESul SKen |
| 'Monsieur Ninon' (U) | CLTr EWoo MSte WFib |
| 'Monsieur Ninon' hort. | See P. 'Madame Auguste Nonin' |
| 'Mont Blanc' (Z/v) | EWoo LVER MWhe SKen WFib |
| 'Monty' (I/d) | Last listed 1996 |
| 'Moon Maiden' (A) | ESul LDea WFib |
| 'Moonflight' (R) | WFib |
| 'Moonlight' | Last listed 1998 |
| 'Moor' (Min/d) | ESul |
| 'Moppet' (Min/d) | ESul |
| 'Morello' (R) | WFib |
| ¶ 'More's Victory' (U/Sc) | SSea |
| 'Morning Cloud' (Min/d) | ESul |
| 'Morning Star' (Z/St/d) | WFib |
| 'Morning Sunrise' (Min/v) | Last listed 1997 |

'Morph Red' (R) — WFib
'Morval' (Dw/C/d) ♀ — ESul LVER MWhe SKen WFib
'Morwenna' (R) — CMdw EWoo LDea LVER MSte SKen WFib
'Mosaic Silky' (Z/d/C/v) — LVER
'Mosaic Sugar Baby' (Dwl) — Last listed 1998
'Mountie' (Dw) — ESul
'Mr Everaarts' (Dw/d) — ESul MWhe WFib
'Mr Henry Apps' (Dw/C/d) — MWhe
'Mr Henry Cox' (Z/v) ♀ — LDea LVER MBEx MWhe SKen WFib
'Mr Pickwick' (Dw) — Last listed 1998
'Mr Ritson' (Min) — ESul
'Mr Wren' (Z) — CHal LVER MWhe SKen WFib
¶ 'Mrs A.M. Mayne' (Z) — SKen
'Mrs Cannell' (Z) — SKen
'Mrs Dumbrill' (A) — ESul LDea LIck SKen
'Mrs E G Hill' (Z) — CWDa
'Mrs Farren' (Z/v) — MWhe SKen WFib
'Mrs G.H. Smith' (A) — ESul EWoo LDea MSte MWhe SSea WFib
'Mrs G. More' (R) — SSea WFib
§ 'Mrs H.J. Jones' (I) — Last listed 1996
'Mrs J.C. Mappin' (Z/v) ♀ — EWoo SKen SSea
'Mrs Kingsbury' (U) — EWoo SKen WEas WFib
'Mrs Kingsley' (Z/v) — Last listed 1997
§ 'Mrs L.R. Bodey' (R) — Last listed 1996
'Mrs Langtry' (R) — LDea
'Mrs Lawrence' (Z/d) — SKen WFib
'Mrs Margaret Thorp' (R) — WFib
'Mrs Martin' (I) — WFib
'Mrs Mary Bard' (R) — WFib
'Mrs McKenzie' (Z/St) — WFib
'Mrs Morf' (R) — EBSP LDea
'Mrs Parker' (Z/d/v) — LVER MWhe WFib
'Mrs Pat' (Min/St/C) — ESul MWhe
'Mrs Pollock' (Z/v) — LDea LVER MBEx MWhe SKen SSea WFib
'Mrs Quilter' (Z/C) — LDea LIck LVER MBri MWhe SKen SMrm SSea WFib
'Mrs Reid's Pink' — EWoo
'Mrs Salter Bevis' (Z/Ca/d) — ESul LVER WFib
'Mrs Strang' (Z/d/v) — LVER MWhe SKen SSea WEas
'Mrs Tarrant' (Z/d) — CHal WFib
'Mrs W.A.R. Clifton' (I/d) — ERav LDea SKen WFib
*multibracteatum* — Last listed 1998
*multicaule* — Last listed 1998
'Muriel' — Last listed 1997
'Music Man' (R) — WFib
*mutans* — Last listed 1998
'Müttertag' (R) — EBSP MSte
§ 'Mutzel' (I/v) — LDea LVER
'My Choice' (R) — LDea
'My Love' (I/d) — LDea
§ *myrrhifolium* — CNat
§ - var. *coriandrifolium* — CSpe
'Mystery' (U) ♀ — WFib
¶ 'N.C. Fass' (R) — LDea
'Nacton' (Min) — ESul
'Nadine' (Dw/C/d) — ESul
Nadja (Z/d) — Last listed 1998
'Nan Greeves' (Z/v) — Last listed 1997
'Nancy Grey' (Min) — ESul
'Nancy Hiden' (R) — WFib
*nanum* — Last listed 1998
'Naomi' (R) — LDea
¶ 'Narina' (I) — NPri
'Natalie' (Dw) — ESul
'Naughton' (Min) — ESul
'Naunton Velvet' (R) — WFib
'Naunton Windmill' (R) — WFib
'Navajo' (R) — WFib

'Nedging Tye' (A) — ESul
'Needham Market' (A) — ESul LDea LHil
'Neene' (Dw) — ESul
'Neil Clemenson' (Sc) — ESul WFib
'Neil Jameson' (Z/v) — SKen
'Nell Smith' (Z/d) — WFib
'Nellie' (A) — LDea
'Nellie Nuttall' (Z) — WFib
'Nels Pierson' (I) — WFib
'Neon Fiat' (Z/d) — WFib
'Nervosum' (Sc) — ESul
'Nervous Mabel' (Sc) ♀ — ESul LDea MHer WFib
¶ 'Nettlecombe' — ESul
'Nettlestead' (I) — ESul
'Nettlestead' (Dw/d) — LVER WFib
'Neville West' (Z) — SSea
'New Life' (Z) — ESul MWhe
'New Phlox' (Z) — WFib
'Nicholas Purple' (R) — Last listed 1998
* 'Nicky' — LDea
'Nicola Buck' (R) — LDea
'Nicola Gainford' — Last listed 1997
'Nicor Star' (Min) — ESul WFib
¶ 'Nikki' (A) — LDea
'Nimrod' (R) — LDea
'Nina West' (Z) — Last listed 1996
'Noche' (R) — LDea SAga SKen SMrm WFib
*nodosum* — WEas
'Noel' (Z/Ca/d) — LVER WFib
'Noele Gordon' (Z/d) — LVER WFib
'Noir' (R) — LDea
¶ 'Nomad' (R) — NFir
'Nono' (I) — LDea WFib
'North Star' (Dw) — ESul
'Northern Lights' (R) — LDea
* 'Norvic' (d) — CWDa
'Notting Hill Beauty' (Z) — SKen
'Nouvelle Aurore' (Z) — WFib
'Nuhulumby' (R) — EBSP
'Oakfield' — Last listed 1998
'Obergarten' (Z/d) — WFib
'Occold Embers' (Dw/C/d) — ESul LVER WFib
'Occold Lagoon' (Dw/d) — ESul SKen WFib
'Occold Orange Tip' (Min/d) — ESul
'Occold Profusion' (Min/d) — ESul
'Occold Ruby' (Dw/C) — CWDa
'Occold Shield' (Dw/C/d) — ESul WFib
'Occold Surprise' (Min/d) — ESul
'Occold Tangerine' (Dw) — ESul LVER
'Occold Volcano' (Dw/d) — ESul
* 'Odessy' (Min) — WFib
*odoratissimum* (Sc) — CHal ESul GPoy LDea LVER NHHG SIde SKen WCHb WEas WFib WJek WWye
- 'Variegatum' (Sc) — WEas
*oenothera* — Last listed 1998
'Offton' (Dw) — ESul
'Old Orchard' (A) — LDea
'Old Rose' (Z/d) — WFib
'Old Spice' (Sc/v) — ESul GBar MHer WFib
'Oldbury Cascade' (I/v) — Last listed 1996
'Olga' (R) — LDea
'Olive West' — Last listed 1997
'Olivia' (R) — EBSP
'Olympia' (Z/d) — CWDa WFib
'Onnalee' (Dw) — ESul
'Opera House' (R) — WFib
'Orange Fizz' (Z/d) — Last listed 1997
'Orange Imp' (Dw/d) — ESul
'Orange Parfait' (R) — WFib
'Orange Puff' (Min) — WFib
'Orange Ricard' (Z/d) — MWhe SKen WFib

| | |
|---|---|
| 'Orange River' (Dw/d) | ESul SKen WFib |
| 'Orange Sal' (R) | Last listed 1998 |
| 'Orange Splash' (Z) | SKen |
| 'Orangeade' (Dw/d) | ESul LVER SKen WFib |
| 'Orangesonne' (Z/d) | LVER WFib |
| 'Orchid Paloma' (Dw/d) | ESul SKen |
| 'Oregon Hostess' (Dw) | ESul |
| *oreophilum* | Last listed 1998 |
| 'Orion' (Min/d) | ESul MWhe SKen WFib |
| 'Orsett' (Sc) ♀ | LDea LVER |
| * 'Oscar' | CWDa |
| 'Osna' (Z) | SKen |
| ¶ 'Otto's Red' (R) | NFir |
| *ovale* subsp. *hyalinum* | Last listed 1998 |
| - subsp. *ovale* | WFib |
| - subsp. *veronicifolium* | Last listed 1998 |
| 'Oyster' (Dw) | ESul |
| PAC cultivars | See under cultivar name |
| 'Paddie' (Min) | ESul |
| 'Pagoda' (Z/St/d) | CSpe ESul MSte MWhe SKen WFib |
| 'Paisley Red' (Z/d) | WFib |
| 'Palais' (Z/d) | SKen WFib |
| ¶ 'Pam Cragie' (R) | LDea |
| 'Pamela Underwood' (R) | WFib |
| *panduriforme* | EWoo MHer WFib |
| *papilionaceum* | CTbh EWoo LHil MBEx MHer WEas |
| 'Parasol' (R) | WFib |
| 'Parisienne' (R) | EBSP LDea |
| 'Parmenter Pink' (Min) | ESul |
| 'Partisan' (R) | Last listed 1997 |
| 'Party Dress' (Z/d) | MWhe SKen WFib |
| 'Pascal' (Z) | SKen |
| 'Pat Thorpe' (R) | WFib |
| 'Patience' (Z/d) | WFib |
| 'Paton's Unique' (U/Sc) ♀ | CHal CTbh ERav EWoo LIck LVER MSte WEas WFib |
| * 'Patricia' (I) | CWDa |
| 'Patricia Andrea' (T) | LVER NPer |
| 'Patricia Read' (Min) | ERea ESul |
| 'Patsy 'Q'' (Z/C) | SKen |
| *patulum* | Last listed 1998 |
| 'Paul Crampel' (Z) | CHal LVER MBEx WFib |
| 'Paul Gotz' (Z) | SKen |
| 'Paul Gunnett' (Min) | MWhe |
| 'Paul Humphries' (Z/d) | WFib |
| 'Paul Sloan' (Z) | WFib |
| 'Paul West' (Min/d) | ESul |
| 'Paula Scott' (R) | LDea |
| 'Pauline' (Min/d) | ESul MWhe WFib |
| 'Pavilion' (Min) ♀ | Last listed 1998 |
| 'Pax' (R) | LDea WFib |
| 'Peace' (Min/C) | ESul WFib |
| 'Peace Palace' (Dw) | ESul |
| 'Peach' (Z) | LDea |
| 'Peach Princess' (R) | EBSP NFir |
| ¶ 'Peaches and Cream' (R) | EWoo |
| 'Pearl Brocade' (R) | WFib |
| 'Pearl Eclipse' (I) | SKen |
| Pearl Necklace | See *P.* 'Perlenkette' |
| 'Pearly Queen' (Min/d) | ESul |
| 'Pegasus' (Min) | Last listed 1998 |
| 'Peggy Sue' (R) | EBSP LDea LVER |
| 'Peggy West' (Min/C/d) | Last listed 1998 |
| PELFI cultivars | See under cultivar name |
| *peltatum* | WFib |
| - 'Lateripes' | SKen |
| 'Penny' (Z/d) | MWhe SKen WFib |
| 'Penny Lane' (Z) | Last listed 1998 |
| 'Penny Serenade' (Dw/C) | ESul SKen |
| 'Pensby' (Dw) | ESul NFir |
| 'Penve' (Z/d) | Last listed 1998 |
| 'Peppermint Star' (Z/St) | LVER NFir |
| ¶ 'Perchance' (R) | SSea |
| 'Percival' (Dw/d) | Last listed 1997 |
| 'Perfect' (Z) | SKen |
| * 'Perle Blanche' (I) | CWDa |
| § 'Perlenkette' (Z/d) | Last listed 1997 |
| § Perlenkette Orange (Z/d) | Last listed 1998 |
| § Perlenkette Weiss = 'Perlpenei' | Last listed 1997 |
| 'Persian King' (R) | LDea |
| 'Persian Queen' (R) | Last listed 1996 |
| 'Persimmon' (Z/St) | WFib |
| 'Petals' (Z/v) | MSte SKen |
| 'Peter Godwin' (R) | EBSP LDea WFib |
| 'Peter Grieve' (Z/v) | WFib |
| 'Peter Read' (Dw/d) | ERea ESul |
| 'Peter's Choice' (R) | EBSP LDea |
| 'Peter's Luck' (Sc) ♀ | ESul LDea |
| 'Petit Pierre' | See *P.* 'Kleine Liebling' |
| 'Petite Blanche' (Dw/d) | LVER WFib |
| 'Petronella' (Z/d) | ESul |
| 'Phil Rose' (I) | CWDa MWhe |
| 'Philomel' (I/d) | WFib |
| 'Philomel Rose' (I/d) | LDea |
| 'Phlox New Life' (Z) | Last listed 1998 |
| 'Phyllis' (U/v) | LHil LVER SSea |
| 'Phyllis Brooks' (R) | Last listed 1996 |
| 'Phyllis Mary' (R) | WFib |
| 'Phyllis Read' (Min) | ERea ESul WFib |
| 'Phyllis Richardson' (R/d) | LDea LVER WFib |
| 'Phyllis Variegated' | LHop |
| 'Picardy' (Z/d) | SKen |
| 'Pickaninny' (Min) | ESul |
| 'Pin Mill' (Min/d) | ESul |
| 'Pink Aura' | ESul |
| 'Pink Aurore' (U) | MHer MSte |
| 'Pink Black Vesuvius' (Min/C) | WFib |
| 'Pink Blizzard' | NPri WLRN |
| ¶ 'Pink Boar' | EWoo |
| 'Pink Bonanza' (R) | EBSP LDea WFib |
| 'Pink Bouquet' (Z/d) | Last listed 1998 |
| 'Pink Bouquet' (R) | EBSP WFib |
| 'Pink Capitatum' | See *P.* 'Pink Capricorn' |
| § 'Pink Capricorn' (Sc) | WFib |
| 'Pink Carnation' (I/d) | LDea |
| 'Pink Cascade' | See *P.* 'Hederinum' |
| 'Pink Champagne' (Sc) | ESul MHer WFib |
| 'Pink Charm' (I) | Last listed 1997 |
| 'Pink Cloud' (Z/d) | WFib |
| 'Pink Countess Mariza' (Z) | SKen |
| 'Pink Crampel' (Z) | CWDa |
| ¶ 'Pink Dolly Varden' (Z/v) | SSea |
| 'Pink Eggshell' (Dw) | Last listed 1997 |
| 'Pink Flamingo' (R) | LDea |
| 'Pink Fondant' (Min/d) | ESul |
| 'Pink Gay Baby' | See *P.* 'Sugar Baby' |
| 'Pink Golden Ears' (Dw/St/C) | SKen |
| 'Pink Golden Harry Hieover' (Z/C) | ESul |
| 'Pink Grace Wells' (Min) | Last listed 1998 |
| 'Pink Grozser Garten' (Dw) | Last listed 1998 |
| 'Pink Happy Thought' (Z/v) | LVER WFib |
| 'Pink Ice' (Min/d) | ESul LVER |
| 'Pink Kewense' (Min) | Last listed 1998 |
| 'Pink Lively Lady' (Dw/C) | Last listed 1997 |
| 'Pink Margaret Pearce' (R) | WFib |
| 'Pink Mini Cascade' | See *P.* 'Rosa Mini-cascade' |
| 'Pink Parfait' (Z) | Last listed 1997 |
| 'Pink Pearl' (Z/d) | WFib |
| 'Pink Rambler' (Z/d) | MWhe SKen WFib |

| | | |
|---|---|---|
| 'Pink Raspail' (Z/d) | WFib | |
| 'Pink Rosebud' (Z/d) | SKen WFib | |
| 'Pink Ruffles' (R) | EBSP | |
| 'Pink Satisfaction' (Z) | Last listed 1998 | |
| 'Pink Slam' (R) | Last listed 1996 | |
| 'Pink Snow' (Min/d) | ESul | |
| 'Pink Splash' (Min/d) | ESul | |
| 'Pink Star' (Z/St) | WFib | |
| 'Pink Tiny Tim' (Min) | ESul WFib | |
| 'Pinnochio' (R) | WFib | |
| 'Pioneer' | Last listed 1996 | |
| 'Pixie' (Dw) | ESul | |
| 'Pixie Rose' (Z/St) | WFib | |
| 'Platinum' (Z/v) | Last listed 1998 | |
| 'Playmate' (Min/St) | ESul SKen WFib | |
| 'Plenty' (Z/d) | CWDa WFib | |
| 'Plum Rambler' (Z/d) | EWoo SKen WFib | |
| 'Poetesse' (A) | LDea | |
| 'Polka' (U) | EWoo WFib | |
| 'Pom Pom' (Z/d) | WFib | |
| 'Pompeii' (R) | LDea SAga WFib | |
| 'Portsmouth' (R) | Last listed 1997 | |
| 'Posey' (Min/d) | Last listed 1996 | |
| 'Potpourri' (Min) | SKen | |
| 'Potter Heigham' (Dw) | ESul | |
| 'Powder Puff' (Dw/d) | ESul | |
| *praemorsum* | Last listed 1998 | |
| 'Prairie Dawn' (Z/d) | WFib | |
| 'Presto' (Min) | ESul MWhe | |
| 'Preston Park' (Z/C) | MBEx SKen SMrm WFib | |
| 'Pretty Girl' (I) | LDea | |
| 'Pretty Polly' (Sc) | WFib | |
| 'Pride of the West' (Z) | SKen | |
| 'Prim' (Min/d) | ESul | |
| 'Primavera' (R) | EBSP LDea | |
| 'Prince Consort' (R) | Last listed 1998 | |
| 'Prince of Orange' (Sc) | CArn CInt CLTr CNat CSev EOHP | |
| | ESul EWoo GBar GPoy LDea LIck | |
| | LVER MSte MWhe NHHG SSea | |
| | WCHb WFib WHer WPer WWye | |
| 'Prince of Wales' (Z) | WFib | |
| 'Prince Regent' (R) | CFri | |
| 'Princeanum' (Sc) ♀ | CSpe EWoo WFib | |
| 'Princess Alexandra' (R) | LVER SSea | |
| 'Princess Alexandra' (Z/d/v) | MWhe WFib | |
| 'Princess Anne' (Z) | CSpe MSte | |
| ¶ 'Princess Consort' (R) | LDea | |
| 'Princess Josephine' (R) | LDea WFib | |
| 'Princess of Balcon' | See *P.* 'Roi des Balcons Lilas' | |
| 'Princess of Wales' (R) | EBSP ERav LDea WFib | |
| 'Princess Virginia' (R/v) | EBSP LDea LIck LVER WFib | |
| 'Professor Eckman' (R) | WFib | |
| 'Promenade' (Z/d) | WFib | |
| 'Prospect' (Z/d) | MWhe | |
| *pseudofumarioides* | Last listed 1998 | |
| *pseudoglutinosum* | WFib | |
| *pulchellum* | Last listed 1998 | |
| *pulverulentum* | Last listed 1998 | |
| 'Purple Ball' | See *P.* Purpurball | |
| 'Purple Emperor' (R) | LDea WFib | |
| 'Purple Heart' (Dw/St) | ESul | |
| 'Purple Light' | See *P.* 'Purple Gem' | |
| 'Purple Orchard' (R) | LDea | |
| 'Purple Pride' (I/d) | CWDa | |
| 'Purple Rambler' (Z/d) | MWhe | |
| 'Purple Unique' (U/Sc) | EWoo MBEx MHer MSte SKen | |
| | WCHb WFib | |
| Purple Wonder (Z/d) | Last listed 1998 | |
| § Purpurball (Z/d) | SKen WFib | |
| 'Pygmalion' (Z/d/v) | SSea WFib | |
| 'Quakeress' (R) | LDea WFib | |
| 'Quakermaid' (Min) | Last listed 1998 | |

| | | |
|---|---|---|
| 'Quantock' (R) | WFib | |
| ¶ 'Quantock Beaujolais' (A) | LDea | |
| ¶ 'Quantock Beauty' (A) | LDea | |
| ¶ 'Quantock Matty' (A) | NFir | |
| ¶ 'Quantock Rita' (A) | NFir | |
| 'Quantock Rory' (A) | LDea | |
| 'Quantock Rose' (A) | LDea | |
| ¶ 'Quantock Sapphire' (A) | LDea | |
| ¶ 'Queen Esther' (Z/d/St) | LVER NFir | |
| 'Queen Ingrid' (Z) | Last listed 1998 | |
| 'Queen of Denmark' (Z/d) | LVER SKen WFib | |
| 'Queen of Hearts' (I/d) | LVER WFib | |
| I 'Queen of the Lemons' | EWoo | |
| *quercetorum* | CGen | |
| N *quercifolium* (Sc) | CHal CNat CSev EWoo GHCN | |
| | GPoy NHHG SKen SSea WCHb | |
| | WEas WFib WJek WWye | |
| – 'Fair Ellen' | See *P.* 'Fair Ellen' | |
| *quinquelobatum* | CSpe | |
| 'R.A. Turner' (Z/d) | WFib | |
| 'Rachel' (Min) | ESul | |
| 'Rachel Fisher' (Z) | WFib | |
| *radens* (Sc) | EPfP SIde WFib | |
| 'Radiance' (Z/d) | WFib | |
| 'Radiant' (Z/d) | WFib | |
| 'Radio' (Z/d) | WFib | |
| 'Radior' (Min) | WFib | |
| 'Rads Star' (Z/St) | ESul WFib | |
| 'Radula' (Sc) ♀ | CSev ERav ESul GBar LIck MWhe | |
| | SKen WCHb WFib WPer | |
| 'Radula Roseum' | SSea | |
| *radulifolium* | Last listed 1998 | |
| 'Ragamuffin' (Min/d) | ESul MWhe WFib | |
| 'Rager's Pink' (Dw/d) | ESul | |
| 'Rager's Star' (Min) | ESul | |
| 'Ragtime' (St) | Last listed 1996 | |
| 'Rakastani' (Z) | SKen | |
| *ranunculopbyllum* | Last listed 1998 | |
| *rapaceum* | Last listed 1998 | |
| 'Rapture' (R) | WFib | |
| 'Raspberry Parfait' (R) | LDea | |
| 'Raspberry Ripple' (A) | ESul LDea | |
| 'Raspberry Sundae' (R) | CLTr | |
| 'Raspberry Sweet' (Z/St) | WFib | |
| 'Ravensbeck' | Last listed 1996 | |
| 'Raviro' (I) | WFib | |
| 'Ray Bidwell' | ESul MWhe | |
| 'Ray Coughlin' (Z/C/d) | WFib | |
| 'Raydon' (Min) | ESul | |
| 'Rebecca' (Min/d) | ESul WFib | |
| 'Rebecca' (R) | Last listed 1996 | |
| 'Red Admiral' (Min/d/v) | ESul SKen | |
| § 'Red Black Vesuvius' (Min/C) | CHal CSpe ESul LVER MWhe | |
| | SKen WEas WFib | |
| 'Red Blizzard' | NPri | |
| 'Red Brooks Barnes' (Dw/C) | Last listed 1996 | |
| 'Red Cascade' (I) ♀ | MWhe | |
| 'Red Fox' (Min) | Last listed 1998 | |
| 'Red Gables' | WCFE | |
| 'Red Galilee' (I/d) | MWhe SKen | |
| 'Red Gem' (Min) | ESul | |
| 'Red Glow' (Min) | ESul | |
| 'Red Ice' (Min/d) | ESul LVER MWhe | |
| * 'Red Irene' (Z/d) | CWDa | |
| * 'Red Kewense' | ESul | |
| 'Red Light' (Z/d) | WFib | |
| 'Red Magic Lantern' (Z/C) | SKen | |
| 'Red Mini Cascade' | See *P.* 'Rote Mini-cascade' | |
| 'Red Pandora' (T) | LVER | |
| 'Red Rambler' (Z/d) | CHal LVER MWhe SKen WFib | |
| 'Red Satisfaction' (Z) | Last listed 1998 | |
| ♦ 'Red Silver Cascade' | See *P.* 'Mutzel' | |

| | |
|---|---|
| 'Red Spangles' (R) | WFib |
| 'Red Spider' (Min/Ca/d) | ESul WFib |
| 'Red Startel' (Z/St/d) | MWhe SKen WFib |
| 'Red Streak' (Min/Ca) | Last listed 1996 |
| 'Red Susan Pearce' (R) | EBSP LDea |
| 'Red Tiny Tim' (Min) | WFib |
| 'Red Velvet' (R) | WFib |
| 'Red Witch' (Dw/St/d) | ESul LVER WFib |
| 'Redondo' (Min/d) | ESul LVER MWhe WEas WFib |
| 'Reflections' (Z/d) | WFib |
| 'Regal Perchance' | Last listed 1998 |
| 'Regina' (Z/d) | LVER SKen WEas WFib |
| 'Reifi Vanderlea' | EWoo |
| 'Rembrandt' (R) | LDea LVER SKen SSea SYvo WEas WFib |
| 'Remo' (Z/d) | Last listed 1998 |
| 'Renate Parsley' | LHil WFib |
| 'Rene Roué' (Dw) | ESul |
| 'Renee Ross' (I/d) ♀ | CWDa LVER WFib |
| *reniforme* | CNat GBar WEas WFib |
| 'Retah's Crystal' (Z/v) | MWhe |
| 'Rhineland' (I) | SKen |
| 'Rhodamant' (I/d) | WFib |
| 'Rhodamine' (R) | EBSP |
| 'Rhodo' (R) | WFib |
| *ribifolium* | Last listed 1998 |
| Rica (Z/d) | Last listed 1998 |
| 'Richard Gibbs' | EWoo |
| 'Richard Key' (Z/d/v) | WFib |
| 'Richard West' (I/d) | CWDa |
| 'Rietje van der Lee' (A) | ESul WFib |
| 'Rigel' (Min/d) | ESul MWhe SKen WFib |
| 'Rigi' (I) | ECtt LDea MBri SKen WFib |
| 'Rigoletto' (I) | LDea |
| ¶ 'Rimey' (St) | NFir |
| 'Rimfire' (R) | EBSP LDea LVER WFib |
| 'Rio' (Z) | Last listed 1998 |
| 'Rio Grande' (I/d) | LDea LVER MWhe NWoo SKen WEas WFib |
| 'Rising Sun' | LDea |
| 'Rita Brook' (Z/d) | WFib |
| 'Rita Coughlin' (R) | WFib |
| 'Rita Scheen' (A) | ESul LDea MWhe SKen SSea WFib |
| 'Rita Thomas' (Z) | WFib |
| 'Ritchie' | EBSP |
| 'Robbie Hare' (R) | WFib |
| 'Robe' (Z/d) | LVER WWol |
| 'Rober's Lavender' (Dw) | ESul |
| 'Rober's Lemon Rose' (Sc) | CInt CJew CNat ERav ESul EWoo GBar SIde SKen WCHb WEas WFib WHer WJek WWye |
| 'Rober's Salmon Coral' (Dw/d) | ESul |
| 'Robert Fish' (Z/C) | ESul |
| 'Robert McElwain' | WFib |
| ¶ 'Robin' (Sc) | LVER |
| 'Robin' (R) | EWoo LDea WEas |
| 'Robinson Crusoe' (Dw/C) | Last listed 1996 |
| *rodneyanum* | Last listed 1998 |
| 'Roger's Delight' (R) | LDea |
| *rogersianum* | See *P. worcesterae* |
| 'Rogue' (R) | EBSP EWoo LDea MSte WFib |
| 'Roi des Balcons' | See *P.* 'Hederinum' |
| § 'Roi des Balcons Impérial' (I) ♀ | LDea MWhe |
| § 'Roi des Balcons Lilas' (I) ♀ | LDea MWhe SKen |
| 'Roi des Balcons Rose' | See *P.* 'Hederinum' |
| § Rokoko (Z) | CWDa |
| 'Roller's David' (I/d) | CWDa LVER |
| 'Roller's Echo' (R) | ESul LDea LIck MWhe |
| 'Roller's Pathfinder' (I/d/v) | LDea LVER |
| 'Roller's Pioneer' (I/v) | EWoo LDea SKen |

| | |
|---|---|
| 'Roller's Satinique' (U) ♀ | EWoo LIck MHer WFib |
| 'Rollisson's Unique' (U) | ERav MHer MSte WFib |
| ¶ 'Romeo' (R) | LVER |
| § 'Romy (I) | LDea |
| § 'Rosa Mini-cascade' (I) | ESul LVER MWhe WLRN |
| § Rosais (I/d) ♀ | Last listed 1995 |
| 'Rosaleen' (Min) | ESul |
| 'Rosalie' (Min) | ESul |
| 'Rosamunda' (Z/d) | WFib |
| 'Roscobie' (Z/d) | SKen |
| 'Rose Bengal' (A) | ESul LDea WEas WFib |
| 'Rose Irene' (Z/d) | MWhe WFib |
| 'Rose Jewel' | EBSP |
| 'Rose of Amsterdam' (Min/d) | ESul |
| ¶ 'Rose Rambler' (Z/d) | WEas |
| 'Rose Silver Cascade' (I) | LDea LVER |
| 'Rose Slam' (R) | WFib |
| 'Rose Startel' (Z/St) | Last listed 1997 |
| 'Rose Unique' (Z) | Last listed 1998 |
| 'Rosebud Supreme' (Z/d) | Last listed 1997 |
| 'Rosecrystal' (Z/d) | LVER |
| 'Rosee Normande' (Z/d) | WFib |
| * 'Roselo' | CWDa |
| 'Rosemarie' (Z/d) | MWhe |
| 'Rosemine' (Z/d) | WFib |
| 'Rose's Orange' | EWoo |
| 'Rosette' (Dw) | SKen WFib |
| 'Rosina Read' (Dw) | ERea ESul WFib |
| 'Rosita' (Dw/d) ♀ | Last listed 1997 |
| 'Rosmaroy' (R) | EBSP LDea LVER |
| § 'Rospen' (Z/d) | LVER SKen WFib |
| * 'Rosseau' (Min) | WFib |
| 'Rosy Dawn' (Min/d) | WFib |
| § 'Rote Mini-cascade' (I) | LDea LVER MWhe SKen WFib |
| 'Rotherfield' (I/d) | LDea |
| 'Rotlieb' (Z/d) | WFib |
| § 'Rouletta' (I/d) | ECtt GHCN LDea LVER MWhe NPri SKen WFib WLRN |
| 'Rousillon' (R) | LDea WFib |
| 'Rousseau' (Dw/C) | ESul |
| 'Royal Ascot' (R) | CHal ERav EWoo LDea LHil MBEx MSte SMrm |
| 'Royal Blaze' (Z/v) | Last listed 1997 |
| 'Royal Carpet' (Min/d) | ESul |
| ¶ 'Royal Claret' (I/d) | WEas |
| . 'Royal Fiat' (Z/d) | Last listed 1998 |
| 'Royal Norfolk' (Min/d) | ESul LVER MWhe SKen |
| 'Royal Oak' (Sc) ♀ | CBrm CInt CJew CSev EWoo GBar LDea LHil LVER MWhe WEas WFib WHer WPer WRha |
| 'Royal Parade' (R) | Last listed 1996 |
| * 'Royal Princess' (R) ♀ | Last listed 1998 |
| § 'Royal Purple' (Z/d) | CHal SKen WFib |
| * 'Royal Salmon' | CWDa |
| 'Royal Sovereign' (Z/d/C) | LDea LVER |
| 'Royal Star' (R) | LDea |
| 'Royal Surprise' (R) | LDea |
| 'Royal Wedding' (R) | LDea |
| 'Rubella' (Z/d) | WFib |
| * 'Rubican' | CWDa |
| 'Rubin Improved' (Z/d) | SKen WFib |
| 'Ruby' (Min/d) | ESul WFib |
| 'Ruby Orchid' (A) | LDea |
| 'Ruffled Velvet' (R) | EWoo SSea |
| 'Rushmere' (Dw/d) | ESul WFib |
| 'Russet Wings' (R) | WFib |
| 'Rustler' (Min) | WFib |
| 'Rusty' (Dw/C/d) | ESul |
| 'Ruth Bessley' | Last listed 1997 |
| 'Ruth Karmen' (I/d) | LDea |
| 'Ryan Dollery' (Z) | Last listed 1997 |
| 'Ryecroft Pride' (Z/d) | WFib |

| | |
|---|---|
| 'Ryecroft White' (Z/d) | WFib |
| ¶ 'Sabine' (Z/d) | LVER |
| 'Saint Catherine' | Last listed 1996 |
| ¶ 'Saint Malo' | NFir |
| 'Sally Anne' (R) | WEas |
| 'Sally Munro' (R) | LDea |
| 'Sally Read' (Dw/d) | ERea ESul |
| 'Salmon Beauty' (Min/d) | WFib |
| 'Salmon Black Vesuvius' (Min/C) | ESul |
| 'Salmon Comet' (Min) | Last listed 1997 |
| 'Salmon Grozser Garten' (Dw) | Last listed 1996 |
| § 'Salmon Irene' (Z/d) | WFib |
| 'Salmon Queen' | See P. 'Lachskönigin' |
| 'Salmon Slam' (R) | WFib |
| 'Salmon Startel' (Z/St/d) | MWhe |
| *salmoneum* | Last listed 1998 |
| 'Saltford' (R) | WFib |
| 'Samantha' (R) | EBSP LDea WFib |
| 'Samantha Stamp' (Dw) | WFib |
| 'Samba' (R) | WFib |
| 'Sancho Panza' (Dec) ♀ | CSpe ESul LDea LVER MSte NFir SKen SSea WEas WFib |
| 'Sandra Haynes' (R) | Last listed 1998 |
| 'Sanguineum' | CSpe |
| 'Santa Maria' (Z/d) | LVER SKen WFib |
| 'Santa Marie' (R) | LDea |
| 'Santa Paula' (I/d) | ECtt LDea LVER MWhe SKen |
| 'Sante Fe' (Z/C) | Last listed 1997 |
| 'Sasha' (Min) | WFib |
| Sassa (Z/d) | CWDa |
| § Satellite (Z/St) | WFib |
| 'Satsuki' (R) | EBSP LDea |
| 'Saturn' (Z) | Last listed 1996 |
| 'Saxifragoides' | SSea |
| § *scabrum* | WFib |
| 'Scandens' | Last listed 1998 |
| 'Scarlet Crousse' (I/C) | Last listed 1996 |
| 'Scarlet Gem' (St) | Last listed 1996 |
| * 'Scarlet Kewense' | Last listed 1998 |
| 'Scarlet Nosegay' | CHal |
| 'Scarlet Pet' (U) | CLTr ESul |
| 'Scarlet Pimpernel' (Z/C/d) | ESul WFib |
| 'Scarlet Queen' (Z) | Last listed 1998 |
| 'Scarlet Rambler' (Z/d) | EWoo LVER SKen SMrm WEas WFib |
| 'Scarlet Unique' (U) | EWoo LHil MSte SKen SSea WCHb WFib |
| 'Scatterbrain' (Z) | CWDa |
| *schizopetalum* | Last listed 1998 |
| § 'Schneekönigin' (I/d) | ECtt LDea LVER MSte WEas |
| § 'Schöne Helena' (Z/d) | CWDa |
| * 'Schone von Grenchen' (I)' | NPri |
| ¶ 'Seale Orchid' (A) | SSea |
| ¶ 'Seale Rose Pink' (Z/v) | SSea |
| 'Seaview Star' (Z/St) | Last listed 1997 |
| 'Secret Love' (Sc) | WFib |
| 'Seeley's Pansy' (A) | CSpe ESul LDea WFib |
| 'Sefton' (R) ♀ | EBSP LDea WFib |
| 'Selby' (Z/C/d) | WFib |
| 'Selina' | ESul |
| 'Semer' (Min) | ESul LVER SKen |
| *senecioides* | Last listed 1998 |
| 'Senorita' (R) | LDea |
| ¶ 'Sensation' (Z) | SKen |
| 'Serena' (Min) | ESul |
| *sericifolium* | Last listed 1998 |
| * 'Serre de la Madone' (Sc) | WEas |
| 'Shalimar' (St) | CSpe MSte WFib |
| 'Shanks' (Z) | Last listed 1997 |
| 'Sharon' (Min/d) | ESul WFib |

| | |
|---|---|
| 'Sharon Louise' (Min) | Last listed 1998 |
| 'Sharon West' (Dw) | CNat |
| 'Shaun Jacobs' (Min/d) | Last listed 1998 |
| 'Shaunough' (Min) | Last listed 1997 |
| 'Sheila' (Dw) | ESul |
| 'Shelley' (Dw) | ESul SKen |
| 'Shenandoah' (Min) | WFib |
| 'Sheraton' (Min/d) | ESul |
| 'Shimmer' (Z/d) | LVER MWhe SKen WFib |
| 'Shirley Anne' (Dw/d) | Last listed 1998 |
| 'Shirley Ash' (A) | ESul LDea SKen WEas WFib |
| 'Shirley Maureen' (R) | LDea WFib |
| 'Shiva' | NPri |
| 'Shocking' (Z/d) | Last listed 1997 |
| ¶ 'Shogan' (R) | NFir |
| 'Shotley' (Min) | ESul |
| 'Shottesham Pet' (Sc) | EWoo MHer SKen |
| 'Shrubland Pet' (U/Sc) | EWoo MHer SKen |
| 'Shrubland Rose' (Sc) | WFib |
| *sidoides* | CSpe CTrC WCot WEas |
| 'Sienna' (R) | LDea |
| 'Silberlachs' (Z/d) | WFib |
| 'Silky' | ESul |
| 'Silpen' (Z/d) | WFib |
| * 'Sils' | CWDa |
| 'Silver Anne' (R) | NFir WFib |
| * 'Silver Cascade' | ERav |
| 'Silver Kewense' (Dw/v) | ESul SKen WFib |
| * 'Silver Lights' | CWDa |
| 'Silver Monarch' | ESul |
| 'Silver Wings' (Z/v) | CSpe ESul LVER MWhe SSea WFib |
| 'Silvia' (R) | EBSP |
| 'Simon Portas' (I/d) | SKen |
| 'Simon Read' (Dw) | ERea ESul |
| 'Simplicity' (Z) | LVER |
| 'Single New Life' (Z) | Last listed 1997 |
| 'Sir Arthur Hort' (I) | WFib |
| 'Sister Henry' (Z/d) | WFib |
| 'Sister Teresa' (Z/d) | Last listed 1998 |
| 'Skelly's Pride' (Z) | LVER SKen WEas |
| 'Skies of Italy' (Z/C/d) | CHal MBri SKen SSea WFib |
| 'Sleuring's Robin' (Min/d) | WFib |
| 'Small Fortune' (Dw) | ESul SKen |
| 'Smuggler' (R) | LDea |
| 'Snape' | ESul |
| 'Sneezy' (Min) | Last listed 1998 |
| Snow Queen | See P. 'Schneekönigin' |
| 'Snow White' (Min) | ESul |
| 'Snowbaby' (Min/d) | ESul |
| 'Snowball' (Z/d) | Last listed 1998 |
| 'Snowberry' (R) | EBSP |
| 'Snowdon' (Min) | WFib |
| 'Snowdrift' (I/d) | LVER WFib |
| 'Snowmass' (Z/d) | CHal MWhe SKen |
| 'Snowmite' | Last listed 1996 |
| 'Snowstorm' (Z) | EWoo SKen WFib |
| 'Snowy Baby' (Min/d) | WFib |
| 'Sofie' | See P. 'Decora Rose' |
| 'Sofie Cascade' (I) | Last listed 1996 |
| 'Solano' (R) | WFib |
| 'Solent Star' | Last listed 1997 |
| 'Solent Sunrise' (Z/C) | Last listed 1996 |
| 'Solent Waves' (R) | EBSP WFib |
| 'Solferino' (A) | ESul LDea SKen |
| § Solidor (I/d) ♀ | LDea WFib |
| ¶ Solo = 'Guillio' (Z/I) | LVER |
| 'Sombrero' (R) | WFib |
| 'Somersham' (Min) | ESul |
| 'Something Special' (Z/d) | LVER MWhe SKen WFib |
| 'Sonata' (Dw/d) | ESul |
| 'Sonnesport' (Z) | WFib |
| 'Sophie Cascade' | CWDa |

'Sophie Dumaresque' (Z/v)    LVER MBri MWhe SKen WFib
'Sophie Koniger' (Z/d)    WFib
'Sorcery' (Dw/C)    ESul MWhe SKen
'South American    LDea SKen SMrm WFib
  Bronze' (R) ♀
'South American Delight' (R)  Last listed 1996
'Southern Belle' (A)    LDea
'Southern Belle' (Z/d)    WFib
'Southern Charm' (Z/v)    LVER
¶ 'Southern Cherub' (A)    LDea
'Souvenir' (R)    CHal LDea SSea
'Spanish Angel' (A) ♀    ESul LDea SSea
'Sparkler' (Z)    LVER
'Special Moment' (R)    WFib
'Speckles' (Z)    Last listed 1998
'Spellbound' (R)    WFib
'Spital Dam'    ESul
'Spitfire' (Z/Ca/v)    ESul LVER WFib
'Spithead Cherry' (R)    EBSP LDea WFib
'Splash Down'    Last listed 1998
§ 'Splendide'    CInt CMdw CRDP CSpe LHil
                  LHop SAga SIgm SMrm SSad WEas
'Splendour' (R) ♀    Last listed 1996
* 'Spotlight Winner'    LDea
'Spot-on-Bonanza' (R)    EBSP LDea WFib
'Spring Bride' (R)    LDea
'Spring Park' (A)    ESul WFib
'Springfield Ann' (R)    EBSP
'Springfield Betty' (R)    EBSP
'Springfield Black' (R)    EBSP LDea LVER
'Springfield Charm' (R)    EBSP
'Springfield Kate' (R)    EBSP
'Springfield Lilac' (R)    Last listed 1996
'Springfield Mary Parfitt' (R) EBSP
'Springfield Pearl' (R)    LDea
'Springfield Purple' (R)    EBSP
'Springfield Rose' (R)    Last listed 1996
'Springfield Stripey' (R)    EBSP
'Springfield Unique' (R)    EBSP LDea
'Springtime' (Z/d)    MWhe WFib
¶ 'Sprite' (Min/v)    MWhe
'Sproughton' (Dw)    ESul
'St Helen's Favourite' (Min)  ESul
'Stacey' (R)    LDea
'Stadt Bern' (Z/C)    LVER MBri MSte MWhe SKen
                  WEas WFib
'Stanton Drew' (Z/d)    WFib
'Staplegrove Fancy' (Z)    EWoo SKen
x *stapletoniae*    See *P.* 'Miss Stapleton'
'Star Flecks'    Last listed 1998
'Star Glitter'    Last listed 1998
'Star of Persia' (Z/Ca)    WFib
'Starbust'    Last listed 1996
'Starlet' (Ca)    WFib
'Starlight' (R)    WFib
'Starlight Magic' (A) ♀    ESul LDea WEas
'Starry Eyed' (Dw)    ESul
'Startel Salmon' (Z/St)    WFib
'Stella Ballerina'    ERav
'Stella Read' (Dw/d)    ERea ESul WFib
'Stellar Apricot' (Z/St)    ERav
'Stellar Arctic Star'    See *P.* 'Arctic Star'
'Stellar Cathay' (Z/St/d)    CSpe ERav WFib
'Stellar Dawn Star' (Z/St)    WEas WFib
'Stellar Grenadier'    See *P.* 'Grenadier'
'Stellar Hannaford Star'    See *P.* 'Hannaford Star'
'Stellar Orange' (Z/St)    Last listed 1997
* 'Stellar Orange Pixie' (d)    CWDa
'Stellar Ragtime' (Z/St/d)    Last listed 1998
'Stellar Snowflake' (Z/St)    Last listed 1996
'Stellar Telstar' (Z/St/d)    Last listed 1997
*stenopetalum*    Last listed 1998

'Stephen Read' (Min)    ERea ESul
'Stewart Read' (Dw)    ERea
*stipulaceum*    Last listed 1998
'Stirling Stent' (Z)    CWDa
* 'Strasbourg'    Last listed 1997
¶ 'Strawberries and Cream'    NFir
  (Z/St)
¶ 'Strawberry Fayre'    LVER
'Strawberry Sundae' (R)    EBSP LDea LVER WEas WFib
'Stringer's Delight'    ESul
'Stringer's Souvenir'    ESul LVER
  (Dw/d/v)
'Stuart Mark' (R)    LDea
'Stutton' (Min)    ESul
*sublignosum*    Last listed 1998
*suburbanum*    Last listed 1998
  subsp. *bipinnatifidum*
'Suffolk Gold' (Min/C)    Last listed 1998
§ 'Sugar Baby' (Dwl)    ECtt ESul GHCN LDea MBri SKen
                WEas WFib
'Summer Cloud' (Z/d)    SKen WFib
'Summertime' (R)    Last listed 1998
'Sun Kissed' (Min)    ESul
'Sun Rocket' (Dw)    ESul LIck MWhe WFib
'Sunbeam' (Dw/d)    ESul
* 'Sundance Orange Scarlet'    Last listed 1995
  (seed raised) (Z) ♀
'Sundridge Moonlight' (Z/C)  WFib
'Sunraysia' (Z/St)    NFir WFib
'Sunrise' (R)    EBSP LDea SKen WEas WFib
'Sunset' (Z)    WFib
'Sunset Snow' (R)    LDea LVER WFib
¶ 'Sunshine Mistress' (Z/C)    NFir
'Sunspot Petit Pierre' (Min/v) ESul
'Sunstar' (Min/d)    ESul LVER WFib
'Super Rose' (I)    MBri MWhe SKen
¶ 'Super Spot on Bonanza' (R) LVER
'Supernova' (Min/d)    Last listed 1997
'Supernova' (Z/St/d)    CWDa ESul MWhe SKen WFib
'Surcouf' (I)    WFib
'Susan' (Dw)    Last listed 1996
'Susan Baldwin'    See *P.* 'Salmon Kovalevski'
'Susan Payne' (Dw/d)    ESul
'Susan Pearce' (R)    LDea SKen WFib
'Susan Read' (Dw)    ERea ESul
* 'Susan Screen'    CWDa
'Susie "Q"' (Z/C)    ESul LHil LVER MWhe SKen
'Sussex Beauty' (Dw/C/d)    CWDa ESul
'Sussex Delight' (Min)    CWDa ESul SKen ·
'Sussex Gem' (Min/d)    LVER SKen
'Sussex Jewel' (Min)    SKen
'Sussex Lace'    See *P.* 'White Mesh'
'Swanland Lace' (I/d/v)    LVER WFib
'Swedish Angel' (A)    ESul LDea LVER SSea
'Sweet Charlotte' (R)    Last listed 1997
* 'Sweet Lady Mary' (Sc)    WFib
'Sweet Mimosa' (Sc) ♀    CBrm CHal CInt CLTr CSpe EWoo
                LDea LIck LVER MSte SKen SSea
                WCot WEas WFib
¶ 'Sweet Miriam' (Sc)    LDea
'Sweet Sue' (Min)    ESul LVER WFib
'Swilland' (A)    ESul LDea MWhe
'Sybil Bradshaw' (R)    LDea WFib
'Sybil Holmes' (I/d)    ECtt LVER MBri MWhe SKen
                WFib
'Sylvia' (R)    Last listed 1996
'Sylvia Gale' (R)    WFib
'Sylvia Marie' (Dw/d)    LVER MWhe SKen
'Sylvia Mariza'    Last listed 1998
* 'Tamara'    CWDa
'Tami' (Min)    Last listed 1997
'Tamie' (Dw/d)    ESul LVER MWhe

| | |
|---|---|
| 'Tamie D' (Min) | Last listed 1997 |
| 'Tammy' (Dw/d) | ESul MWhe WFib |
| 'Tangerine' (Min/Ca/d) | ESul WFib |
| § 'Tango' (Z/d) | Last listed 1998 |
| 'Tanzy' (Min) | ESul |
| 'Tapestry' (R) | LDea |
| 'Tapestry' (Min/v) | WEas |
| 'Tashmal' (R) | EBSP |
| 'Tattingstone' (Min) | ESul |
| 'Tavira' (I/d) | LDea LVER WFib |
| 'Ted Brooke' (Z/d) | WFib |
| 'Ted Dutton' (R) | WFib |
| 'Teddy Roosevelt' (Z/d) | WFib |
| 'Telstar' (Min/d) | ESul SKen WFib |
| § 'Telston's Prima' (R) | LDea |
| 'Ten of Hearts' (I) | Last listed 1996 |
| 'Tenderly' (Dw/d) | ESul |
| 'Tenerife Magic' (MinI/d) | ESul |
| *tenuicaule* | WFib |
| 'Terence Read' (Min) | ERea |
| *ternatum* | Last listed 1998 |
| *tetragonum* | CInt SSea WFib |
| 'The Barle' (A) ♀ | LDea |
| 'The Boar' (Fr) ♀ | CSpe EWoo LVER MBEx MSte SRms WEas WPer |
| ¶ 'The Bray' (A) | LDea |
| 'The Creedy' (A) | LDea |
| § 'The Crocodile' (I/C/d) | ECtt LDea LVER MWhe SKen SSea WEas WFib |
| I 'The Culm' | See *P.* 'Culm' |
| 'The Czar' | See *P.* 'Czar' |
| I 'The Dart' | See *P.* 'Dart' |
| 'The Duchess' (I/d) | WFib |
| 'The Joker' (I) | WFib |
| 'The Kenn-Lad' (A) | LDea NFir |
| 'The Lowman' (A) | LDea |
| 'The Lynn' (A) | LDea |
| ¶ 'The Okement' (A) | LDea |
| 'The Otter' (A) | LDea |
| 'The Prince' (Min) | Last listed 1997 |
| 'The Speaker' (Z/d) | SKen WFib |
| 'The Tamar' (A) | LDea |
| 'The Tone' (A) ♀ | LDea |
| 'Thomas Earle' (Z) | WFib |
| 'Thomas Gerald' (Min/C) | ESul SKen |
| 'Thorley' | Last listed 1997 |
| 'Tiberias' (I/d) | Last listed 1998 |
| 'Tiffany' (Min/d) | Last listed 1998 |
| 'Tilly' (Min) | CHal |
| 'Tim' (Min) | ESul |
| 'Timothy Clifford' (Min/d) | ESul MWhe WFib |
| ¶ 'Tinkerbell' (A) | LDea |
| § 'Tip Top Duet' (A) ♀ | ESul EWoo LDea LIck LVER MWhe NWoo SAga SLod SSea WEas WFib |
| 'Titan' (Z) | Last listed 1996 |
| 'Token' (Z) | Last listed 1998 |
| 'Tom Portas' (Dw/d) | ESul |
| 'Tomboy' (I/d) | LVER |
| 'Tomcat' (Z/d) | SKen WWol |
| *tomentosum* (Sc) ♀ | CArn CHal CSev CSpe CTbh EWoo GPoy LDea MMal MSCN MWhe NHHG SAga SKen WEas WFib WWye |
| - 'Chocolate' | See *P.* 'Chocolate Peppermint' |
| 'Tommay's Delight' (R) | EBSP LDea WFib |
| *tongaense* | CSpe WFib |
| 'Tony' (Min) | ESul |
| 'Topscore' (Z/d) | WFib |
| 'Toreador' (Z/d) | WFib |
| 'Torento' (Sc) | CNat ESul EWoo SKen WFib |
| 'Tornado' (R) | EBSP LDea WFib |
| 'Tortoise Shell' (R) | WFib |
| 'Toyon' (Z/d) | SKen WFib |
| 'Tracy' (Min/d) | ESul LVER |
| *tragacanthoides* | Last listed 1998 |
| *transvaalense* | WFib |
| 'Traute Hausler' (A) | LDea |
| 'Trautlieb' (Z/d) | CWDa WFib |
| 'Treasure' (Z/d) | Last listed 1998 |
| 'Treasure Chest' (Z) | Last listed 1998 |
| 'Treasure Trove' (Z/v) | Last listed 1996 |
| 'Trésor' (Dw/d) | CWDa |
| *tricolor* Curt. | CPla CSpe SSad |
| - hort. | See *P.* 'Splendide' |
| *trifidum* | SSad SSea WEas WFib |
| 'Trimley' (Dw/d) | ESul |
| 'Trinket' (Min/d) | SKen |
| 'Triomphe de Nancy' (Z/d) | WFib |
| *triste* | CSpe SSad WFib |
| 'Trudie' (Dw) | ESul LVER SKen WFib |
| 'Trulls Hatch' (Z/d) | MWhe SKen |
| 'Tu Tone' (Dw/d) | ESul |
| 'Tuddenham' (Min/d) | WFib |
| 'Tuesday's Child' (Dw/C) | SKen |
| 'Tunias Perfecta' (R) | WFib |
| 'Turkish Coffee' (R) | EBSP WFib |
| 'Turkish Delight' (Dw/C) | ESul LVER MWhe WFib |
| 'Turtle's Surprise' (Z/d/v) | SKen |
| 'Turtle's White' (R) | LDea SKen |
| 'Tuyo' (R) | WFib |
| 'Tweedle-Dum' (Dw) | MWhe |
| 'Twinkle' (Min/d) | ESul WFib |
| 'Twist' (Z) | Last listed 1996 |
| 'Tyabb Princess' (R) | LDea WFib |
| 'Ullswater' (Dw/C) | ESul |
| § 'Unique Aurore' (U) | EWoo LVER MSte SKen WEas WFib |
| 'Unique Mons Ninon' | EWoo |
| 'Unity' (Dw) | LVER |
| 'Urchin' (Min) | ESul MWhe SHFr WFib |
| 'Ursula Key' (Z/v) | SKen WFib |
| 'Vagabond' (R) | Last listed 1996 |
| 'Valanza' (R) | ESul |
| 'Valcandia' (Dw) | Last listed 1997 |
| 'Valencia' (R) | EBSP LDea |
| 'Valenciana' (R) | WFib |
| 'Valentin' (R) | Last listed 1998 |
| 'Valentina' (Min/d) | ESul WFib |
| 'Valentine' | EBSP |
| 'Valerie' (Z/d) | Last listed 1996 |
| 'Valley Court' (I) | Last listed 1996 |
| 'Vancouver Centennial' (Dw/St/C) ♀ | CInt CSpe ERav ESul LDea LVER MBri MWhe SKen WFib |
| ¶ 'Vandersea' | EWoo |
| § 'Variegated Clorinda' (Sc/v) | EWoo WCHb WFib WHer |
| 'Variegated Fragrans' | See *P.* (Fragrans Group) 'Fragrans Variegatum' |
| § 'Variegated Kleine Liebling' (Min/v) | ESul SKen WFib |
| 'Variegated La France' (I) | WFib |
| 'Variegated Lorelei' (Z/d/v) | Last listed 1997 |
| 'Variegated Madame Layal' (A/v) ♀ | ESul EWoo WFib |
| * 'Variegated Peppermint' | Last listed 1998 |
| 'Variegated Petit Pierre' | See *P.* 'Variegated Kleine Liebling' |
| 'Vasco da Gama' (Dw/d) | ESul WFib |
| 'Vectis Cascade' | Last listed 1998 |
| 'Vectis Glitter' (Z/St) | LVER MWhe |
| 'Vectis Gold' (Z/St/C) | Last listed 1998 |
| 'Vectis Star' | Last listed 1997 |
| 'Velvet' (Z) | CWDa LVER |
| 'Velvet Duet' (A) ♀ | CHal ESul EWoo LDea LIck LVER SKen SSea |

'Venus' (Dw/d) — ESul
'Vera Dillon' (Z) — SKen WFib
'Vera Vernon' (Z/v) — Last listed 1996
'Verdale' (A) — LDea WFib
'Verity Palace' (R) — EWoo WFib
'Verona' (Z/C) — CHal MBri SKen
'Verona Contreras' (A) — LDea WFib
* 'Veronica' (Z) — MWhe SKen
'Vesuvius' (Z) — Last listed 1996
'Vibrant' — Last listed 1997
'Vicki Town' (R) — WFib
'Vicky Claire' (R) — EBSP LDea SBid SKen SMrm WFib
'Victoria' (Z/d) — SKen
'Victoria Regina' (R) — LDea WFib
'Video Blush' (Min) — Last listed 1998
'Viking' (Min/d) — SKen
'Viking Red' (Z) — MWhe
'Village Hill Oak' (Sc) — ESul LDea LVER MHer
* 'Ville de Dresden' (I) — Last listed 1998
'Ville de Paris' — See *P.* 'Hederinum'
'Vina' (Dw/C/d) — ESul LVER MWhe SKen WFib
'Vincent Gerris' (A) — ESul LDea MWhe
Vinco = 'Guivin' (I/d) — CWDa
*violareum* hort. — See *P.* 'Splendide'
'Violet Lambton' (Z/v) — WFib
'Violetta' (R) — LDea WFib
'Violetta' (Z/d) — Last listed 1996
'Virginia' (R) — LDea WEas WFib
'Virginia Ley' (Z) — SKen
'Viscossisimum' — ERav MHer SKen
*viscosum* — See *P. glutinosum*
§ *vitifolium* — MHer
'Vivat Regina' (Z/d) — WFib
'Voodoo' (U) ♀ — CBrm CSpe EWoo MSte NPla WFib
§ Vulcan (Z/d) — WLRN
'W.H. Heytman' (R) — WFib
'Wallace Fairman' (R) — LDea
'Wallis Friesdorf' (Dw/C/d) — ESul MWhe
'Wantirna' (Z/v) — ECtt EWoo LVER
'Warrior' (Z/C) — LVER WFib
'Washbrook' (Min/d) — ESul
'Watersmeet' (R) — LDea
'Wattisham' (Dec) — LDea WEas
'Waveney' (Min) — ESul
'Wayward Angel' (A) ♀ — ESul EWoo LDea LVER SKen WFib
'Wedding Gown' (R) — Last listed 1998
¶ 'Wedding Lace' (I) — NFir
'Wedding Royale' (Dw/d) — ESul LVER
Weisse Perle (Z/d) — Last listed 1998
'Welcome' (Z/d) — WFib
'Welling' (Sc) — LDea LVER
'Wellington' (R) — LDea WFib
'Wendy' (Min) — Last listed 1997
'Wendy Anne' — Last listed 1998
'Wendy Hawley' (R) — Last listed 1998
'Wendy Read' (Dw/d) — ERea ESul LVER MWhe WFib
'Wensum' (Min/d) — ESul WFib
'West Priory' — Last listed 1997
'Westdale Appleblossom' (Z/C) — LVER
* 'Westdale Beauty' (d) — CWDa
'Western Zoyland' (R) — WFib
'Whisper' (R) — WFib
'White Birds Egg' (Z) — WFib
'White Blizzard' — NPri
'White Boar' (Fr) — EWoo MBEx MSte
'White Bonanza' (R) — EBSP WFib
¶ 'White Butterfly' (Z/C) — LVER
'White Charm' (R) — EBSP LDea
'White Chiffon' (R) — EBSP LVER
'White Eggshell' (Min) — ESul LVER

'White Feather' (Z/St) — WFib
'White Frills' (Z/d) — WFib
'White Gem' (Min) — ESul
'White Glory' (R) ♀ — EBSP LDea WFib
'White Lively Lady' (Dw/C) — ESul
§ 'White Mesh' (I/v) — ECtt LVER MBri MWhe SKen WFib
'White Nosegay' — Last listed 1996
White Pearl Necklace — See *P.* Perlenkette Weiss = 'Perlpenei'
'White Queen' (Z/d) — CWDa
'White Unique' (U) — CHal EWoo MSte WFib
'White Wooded Ivy' — Last listed 1996
*whytei* — Last listed 1998
* 'Wickham Lad' — LDea
Wico = 'Guimongol' (I/d) — NPri WLRN
* 'Wild Spice' — LDea
'Wilf Vernon' (Min/d) — ESul LVER
'Wilhelm Kolle' (Z) — WFib
'William Sutton' (R) — WFib
'Winford Festival' — Last listed 1998
'Winford Winnie' — Last listed 1998
'Winnie Read' (Dw/d) — ERea ESul
'Winston Churchill' (R) — LDea
¶ 'Wirral Big Bang' (Z/C) — NFir
¶ 'Wirral Look Alike' (Z/C) — NFir SKen
'Wirral Moonglow' — Last listed 1997
¶ 'Wirral Moonraker' (Z/C) — NFir
¶ 'Wirral New Look' (Z/C) — NFir
¶ 'Wirral Sunlight' (Z/C) — NFir
'Wirral Target' (Z/d) — ESul MWhe
'Wishing Star' — ESul
¶ 'Wispey' (St) — NFir
'Witnesham' (Min/d) — ESul
§ 'Wood's Surprise' (MinI/d/v) — ESul LDea LVER MWhe NFir SKen WFib
'Wookey' (R) — WFib
§ *worcesterae* — Last listed 1998
'Wordsworth' — Last listed 1996
'Wrington' (R) — WFib
'Wroxham' (Dw) — ESul
* 'Wychwood' — LDea
'Wyck Beacon' (I/d) — SKen
'Wycombe Maid' (Min/d) — WFib
'Wydcombe' (d) — Last listed 1998
'Xenia Field' (Z) — Last listed 1998
*xerophyton* — Last listed 1998
'Yale' (I/d) ♀ — CHal GHCN LDea LVER MBri MSte MWhe SKen WFib
'Yarrabee Jane' (R) — WFib
'Yhu' (R) — EBSP LDea WFib
'Yolanda' (Min/C) — ESul
'York Florist' (Z/d/v) — LVER
'York Minster' (Dw/v) — SKen
'Yours Truly' (Z) — Last listed 1997
'Yvonne' (Z) — WFib
¶ 'Zamma' (R) — NFir
'Zena' (Dw) — ESul
'Zinc' (Z/d) — WFib
'Zoe' (D) — LDea
*zonale* — EWoo WFib
'Zulu King' (R) — WFib
'Zulu Warrior' (R) — WFib

# PELLAEA (Adiantaceae)

*atropurpurea* — EFer
*boivinii* var. *viridis* — Last listed 1998
§ *calomelanos* — NMar
*cordifolia* — WRic
*falcata* — MBri
*hastata* — See *P. calomelanos*
*ovata* — WRic

| | |
|---|---|
| *paradoxa* | Last listed 1997 |
| *rotundifolia* ♀ | CHal MBri NMar |
| *sagittata* | NMar |

## PELLIONIA See ELATOSTEMA

## PELTANDRA (Araceae)

| | |
|---|---|
| *alba* | See *P. saggitifolia* |
| § *saggitifolia* | SWyc |
| § *undulata* | CRow EHon LPBA MSta SRms SWat SWyc |
| *virginica* Rafinesque | EMFW SLon SWyc |
| – Schott | See *P. undulata* |

## PELTARIA (Brassicaceae)

| | |
|---|---|
| ¶ *alliacea* | LEdu |

## PELTIPHYLLUM See DARMERA

## PELTOBOYKINIA (Saxifragaceae)

| | |
|---|---|
| § *tellimoides* | CLAP EMan NHol SMac WCru WFar |
| *watanabei* | CHan EBee GTou LFis SLon SMac WFar |

## PENNANTIA (Icacinaceae)

| | |
|---|---|
| *corymbosa* | ECou |

## PENNISETUM (Poaceae)

| | |
|---|---|
| § *alopecuroides* | CBrm CKel CLTr EBrP EBre ECGN EGar EHoe GBin GCal GMaP LBre MBrN MHar MHlr MLLN MMoz NOrc SApp SBre SCob SOkh SPer SSvw SUsu WMoo WPGP WPic WRos WWye |
| – black | Last listed 1996 |
| – 'Hameln' | More than 30 suppliers |
| – 'Herbstzauber' | Last listed 1998 |
| – 'Little Bunny' | CInt GCal NPro SLod |
| – 'Moudry' | EFou LEdu |
| – f. *viridescens* | CBrm CCuc CKel ECha EFou EHoe ELan EMan MAvo MLLN MMoz MTis NPSI NSti SCob SPla SSoC WBea WHal WPrP WWat |
| – 'Weserbergland' | CElw EPPr |
| – 'Woodside' | CCuc EHoe EMan EPPr EPla SApp |
| 'Cassian's Choice' | EBee EFou |
| *compressum* | See *P. alopecuroides* |
| *flaccidum* | EMon EPPr LRHS |
| *incomptum* | EHoe SLod |
| – purple | WPGP |
| *longistylum* hort. | See *P. villosum* |
| *macrourum* | CBrm CCuc CElw CFil CHan CHea CInt CKno CRDP EHoe EPPr EPla SUsu WPGP |
| *orientale* ♀ | More than 30 suppliers |
| ¶ *purpureum* | SPla |
| *rueppellii* | See *P. setaceum* |
| § *setaceum* ♀ | CBrm CCuc CInt MNrw MWat WCot WLRN WMoo WViv |
| – 'Burgundy Blaze' | Last listed 1998 |
| sp. B&SWJ 3854 | WCru |
| § *speciosum* B&SWJ 3503 | WCru |
| § *villosum* | CB&S CBrm CCuc CInt CKel CRDP EBrP EBre ECha EHoe LBre LHop MLLN MSCN NSti SApp SBre SLod SMad SPla SUsu WCot WMoo WRos |

## PENSTEMON ✿ (Scrophulariaceae)

| | |
|---|---|
| 'Abberley' | WPer |
| 'Abbotsmerry' | CAxe EBee LGre MHlr WSPU |
| ¶ 'Agnes Laing' | LRHS |
| *albidus* | EBee |
| § 'Alice Hindley' ♀ | More than 30 suppliers |
| *alpinus* | CNic EWes GAbr GTou MLLN NOak WThi |
| – subsp. *brandegeei* | See *P. brandegeei* |
| § 'Andenken an Friedrich Hahn' ♀ | More than 30 suppliers |
| § *angustifolius* | MHew MNrw MWgw SRms WPer |
| *antirrhinoides* | See *Keckiella antirrhinoides* |
| 'Apple Blossom' ♀ | More than 30 suppliers |
| 'Apple Blossom' misapplied | See *P.* 'Thorn' |
| *aridus* | EBee WLin |
| *arizonicus* | See *P. whippleanus* |
| *arkansanus* | CGen MNrw |
| ¶ 'Ashton' | WSPU |
| 'Astley' | WPer |
| *attenuatus* | WPer |
| ¶ *auriberbis* | EBee |
| *azureus* | EBee WCot WLin WPer WRha |
| 'Barbara Barker' | See *P.* 'Beech Park' |
| § *barbatus* | CBot CGle CKel CLon EBrP EBre ECha EHrv ELan EWTr GCHN LBlm LBre LGre LPen MAsh MBro MWat SBre SChu SMac SPer SRms SSea WCFE WHCG WHer WRos |
| ¶ – 'Cambridge Mixed' | EWTr |
| – subsp. *coccineus* | MCCP MTis NHed NLar WMow |
| – 'Jingle Bells' | EBee EHic MAvo |
| – K 92.319 | CMdw NHar |
| – Limoges form | GCal |
| – orange form | SHFr |
| – var. *praecox* | SCob WPer WShe |
| – – f. *nanus* | CBot EMil GCHN GSki LRHS MSte SCob SRms |
| – – – 'Rondo' | NBro NLar |
| * – 'Roseocampanulatus' | SUsu WSPU |
| *barrettiae* | EWTr GCHN |
| 'Beckford' | CAxe WSPU |
| § 'Beech Park' ♀ | CInt EBee ELan EWes IHdy LHil LHop LPen MBNS MBel MCLN MLLN NHaw NRoo SAga SUsu WCot WHCG WPen WRus WSPU |
| § *berryi* | EPot NLak |
| 'Bisham Seedling' | See *P.* 'White Bedder' |
| 'Blackbird' | More than 30 suppliers |
| I 'Blue Spring' | See *P. heterophyllus* 'Blue Springs' |
| 'Bodnant' | EBee MBel WPer |
| * *bradburyi* | EBee |
| § *brandegeei* | WOut |
| ¶ 'Bredon' | WSPU |
| 'Breitenbush Blue' | LHop LPen SAga |
| *bridgesii* | See *P. rostriflorus* |
| 'Bridget's White' | Last listed 1998 |
| 'Burford Purple' | See *P.* 'Burgundy' |
| 'Burford Seedling' | See *P.* 'Burgundy' |
| 'Burford White' | See *P.* 'White Bedder' |
| § 'Burgundy' | CAxe CElw CLTr CMHG CSam EAst EBee EOrc GCHN GMac LLWP LPen NFai NPer NSti SChu SPer WHCG WHoo WMaN WPer WRus |
| *caeruleus* | See *P. angustifolius* |
| *caespitosus* | EBrP EBre LBre NWCA SBre |
| – *albus* | Last listed 1997 |
| – 'Claude Barr' | CPBP |
| § – subsp. *suffruticosus* | CPBP |
| – white | Last listed 1998 |
| *californicus* | See *P. linarioides* subsp. *californicus* |
| *calycosus* | NLak |

§ *campanulatus* — CMHG EBee EHyt EWes GCal LHop LPen MAsh MLLN NHar NHol NMen NNrd NTow SAga SHFr SLon SRms WAbe WBea WGwG WHCG WLin WPer WRus WSPU WWal
  - CD&R 1355 — CHan
  - var. *chibuahuensis* — SAga
  - *pulchellus* — See *P. campanulatus*
◆ - *roseus* — See *P. kunthii*
◆ 'Candy Pink' — See *P.* 'Old Candy Pink'
¶ *cardinalis* — WHil
  - *regilis* — Last listed 1998
  *cardwellii* — CMea ECha EPot EWes GTou LGre NHar SAga SRms
  - x *davidsonii* — CGra WAbe
  - K 92.321 — Last listed 1997
  'Caroline Orr' — WCot
  *caryi* — Last listed 1996
  'Castle Forbes' — CAxe MLLN WEas WHCG WPer WWoo
◆ 'Catherine de la Mare' — See *P. heterophyllus* 'Catherine de la Mare'
* 'Centra' — EBee GCHN MLLN
  *centranthifolius* JJA 13106 — SIgm
  'Charles Rudd' — CAxe CBlo CBod CGle GEil LPen MLLN NFai NLak SAga SChu WHCG WMaN WOve
§ 'Cherry' ♀ — CBlo CMea EBee EOrc GMac LHil LPen LRHS MBNS MLLN NBur NLak NPla SCro SMrm SPla WHCG WPer WPyg WRHF WRus WSPU WWoo
◆ 'Cherry Ripe' misapplied — See *P.* 'Cherry'
§ 'Chester Scarlet' ♀ — CMCo EOrc GBri GCHN GMac LHop LPen MBel MCLN MNrw MRav NBrk NFai SAga SLon WEas WHCG WMaN WPer WRus WSPU WWhi WWye
¶ *clevelandii* var. *connatus* — WLin
¶ *clutei* — EWTr
  *comarrhenus cyaneus* — WLin
¶ 'Comberton' — WSPU
  *confertus* — CGra CMHG CNic CTri EBee EHyt EMNN EWTr GAbr LPen LPio MBNS NChi NLak NMen NRoo NWCA SHFr SRms WAbe WHCG WLin WPer WSPU
  'Connie's Pink' ♀ — CAxe ENot LPen MLLN MSte NBur NPla WElm WHCG WLin WSPU
* 'Coral Pink' — Last listed 1998
  *cordifolius* — See *Keckiella cordifolia*
  'Cottage Garden Red' — See *P.* 'Windsor Red'
§ 'Countess of Dalkeith' — CBlo CHea EOrc EWTr EWes GBri LHil LHop LLWP LPen MLLN MNes MNrw NHaw NLak SOkh SPer WCom WGwG WHCG WSPU WWhi
  'Craigieburn Chenille' — Last listed 1998
  'Craigieburn Taffeta' — Last listed 1998
  *crandallii* — CPBP
  - subsp. *glabrescens* — LGre SAga SUsu WHCG WLin
  - subsp. *taosensis* — NDov NWCA
  *cristatus* — See *P. eriantherus*
¶ *cyaneus* — WLin
  *davidsonii* — CLyd EWes WAbe
  - subsp. *davidsonii* — CGra
§ - var. *menziesii* ♀ — CNic EBee GTou MFir NBus NHar NLak NWCA SRms WEas WSPU
  - - 'Microphyllus' — CLyd EPot MAsh NBus NHar NMen NSla WAbe WLin

* - - 'Tolmiei Peak' — CGra
  - var. *praeteritus* — EHyt NHar WLin
  'Dazzler' — CBlo CBod CM&M EBee NRoo SEas WPer WSPU
§ *deaveri* — CPBP EBee MGed NLak WLin WSPU
  'Delaware' — Last listed 1996
  *deustus* — SRms
  'Devonshire Cream' — CAxe CElw LPen LRHS WHCG
  'Diane' — WMer
  *diffusus* — See *P. serrulatus*
  *digitalis* — CHan CLyd CNic EBee ECha EGar EMan LGre LPen MBNS WAbb WEas WHCG WMow WPer
§ - 'Husker Red' — More than 30 suppliers
  - pink — Last listed 1997
  - 'Purpureus' — See *P. digitalis* 'Husker Red'
  *discolor* — CMea LGre SAga SMrm
¶ - pale lavender — WFar
§ 'Drinkstone' — CGle EGoo EHol LGre LHop LPen MLLN NChi NPla SAga SDix SMrm WHCG WPer WSPU
  'Drinkwater Red' — See *P.* 'Drinkstone'
  *duchesnensis* — Last listed 1997
  *eatonii* — SRms WCot
  - var. *undosus* — NWCA WLin
* *edgeworthii* — EBee
  'Edithiae' — EOrc MBal MBro NLak NLon NRoo SChu SRms WEas WHCG WIvy WKif WLin
¶ 'Elmley' — WSPU
§ *eriantherus* — CGra WHCG
¶ 'Etna' — CAxe MBri
  *euglaucus* — EBee NArg
§ 'Evelyn' ♀ — More than 30 suppliers
  'Fanny's Blush' — Last listed 1997
  'Firebird' — See *P.* 'Schoenholzeri'
  'Flame' — CGle EMan LHop LPen WHCG WPer WSPU
  'Flamingo' — CBrm CMea EAst EBee EWes LPen MAsh MBNS MBro MCLN MWrn NHaw NHol NLak SAga SMrm SUsu WHoo WLRN WMaN WSPU WWoo
  from Broken Tops Mountain, USA — Last listed 1996
  *frutescens* — GTou WSPU
  *fruticosus* — LFis MLLN MNrw NHar NWCA SRms WAbe WLin
§ - var. *scouleri* ♀ — EHic MAsh MBro MHar MOne SRms WIvy WSPU
  - - f. *albus* ♀ — CMea EHyt ELan LGre LHop LPen NWCA SAga SBla SChu WAbe WEas WIvy WKif WSPU WSan
  - - 'Amethyst' — WAbe WLin
  - - 'Hopleys' — Last listed 1998
  - var. *serratus* — WLin
  - - 'Holly' — CHan CMea LGre NMen SAga SBla SMrm
¶ 'Fujiyama' — CAxe CB&S MBri
  'Gaff's Pink' — SChu
  'Gaiety' — CAxe CM&M
¶ *gairdneri* — CGra
  'Garden Red' — See *P.* 'Windsor Red'
  'Garnet' — See *P.* 'Andenken an Friedrich Hahn'
  'Garnet Variegated' — CLyd NLak
  *gentianoides* — CMdw MNrw MWhi NBro NLak WRus WSPU
  'Geoff Hamilton' — MBNS
  'George Elrick' — LPen MBNS NBur

| | |
|---|---|
| § 'George Home' ♀ | CGle CLTr ECGP ECtt EHic EWes GAbr LHil LPen MBNS MCLN MLLN MNrw NHaw SChu WByw WHCG WMaN WRus WWoo |
| *glaber* | CElw CHan CMHG EBee GMac LGre LHop LLWP LPen MBNS MBro MLLN MRav NBro NGdn SAga SHFr SHel SMrm WEas WHCG WHoo WKif WPer WRus WSPU |
| *globosus* | Last listed 1996 |
| *gormanii* | EBee MLLN |
| *gracilis* | EBee GCHN WPer WSPU |
| *grahamii* | Last listed 1996 |
| *grandiflorus* | NLak |
| - 'Prairie Snow' | Last listed 1996 |
| *hallii* | CGra CLyd CNic EPot EWes GTou LPen WSPU |
| *hartwegii* ♀ | GMac LHop LPen SAga SChu WAbe WHCG WPer WRus WSPU |
| - 'Albus' | CAxe EBee LGre LHop LPen LRHS MSte NFor SAga WHCG WRus WSPU |
| *havardii* | Last listed 1998 |
| *heterodoxus* | NWCA |
| § *heterophyllus* | More than 30 suppliers |
| - 'Blue Eye' | WMaN WSPU |
| - 'Blue Fountain' | LPen WSPU |
| - 'Blue Gem' | CBod CElw CTri CVer EBrP EBre EOrc LBre MBro NRoo SBre SIng SMrm SPla WHoo WSPU |
| § - 'Blue Springs' | CBlo CBot CGle CLon CM&M EBrP EBre LBre LFis LPen MBri MCLN MLLN MSte NBir NFla SAga SBla SBre SMrm WAbe WRus |
| § - 'Catherine de la Mare' ♀ | CGle CHad CLTr CLyd CStr EBee EBrP EBre ECtt EFou ELan ERav GCHN LBre LFis LGre LHop LPen MSCN MWat NBir NBro SAga SBre SChu SMrm SOkh WHoo WPer WSPU |
| - 'Heavenly Blue' | CBlo EBrP EBre ECtt LBre LFis LHop MBNS NHaw NLon SBre SWat WLRN WOve WRus WWal WWhi |
| * - 'John D.' | Last listed 1997 |
| - 'Perhill Purple' | Last listed 1996 |
| - var.*purdyi* | NLak SMrm WHCG |
| - 'True Blue' | See *P.heterophyllus* |
| - 'Züriblau' | MBro SMrm WWat |
| 'Hewell Pink Bedder' ♀ | CBlo CGle EBee EBrP EBre ENot GBri GCHN LBre LPen MBNS MBel MCLN NChi NRoo SBre SChu SEas SPar WHCG WPer WSPU |
| 'Hewitt's Pink' | Last listed 1997 |
| 'Heythrop Park' | Last listed 1996 |
| § 'Hidcote Pink' ♀ | More than 30 suppliers |
| - 'Hidcote Purple' | CElw LFis LHil NBrk NPla SChu |
| * - 'Hidcote White' | CBot CM&M EOrc NHol WAbe WRus |
| 'Hillview Pink' | Last listed 1998 |
| 'Hillview Red' | Last listed 1998 |
| § *hirsutus* | CGle EBee EPPr LGre MNrw NChi NHol SOkh WPer WSan WThi |
| - f.*albiflorus* | CMea EBee |
| - bronze-leaved | WThi |
| - var.*minimus* | MLLN WThi |
| - var.*pygmaeus* | CHan CLyd CNic CRDP EBee ELan GTou LFis MBro MHar MPla NHar NMen NWCA SBla SRms WHoo WLin WPer WRus WThi WWin |

| | |
|---|---|
| - - f.*albus* | CMea EHyt WPer |
| - - 'Purpureus' | WLin |
| ¶ 'Hopleys Pink' | NDov |
| 'Hopleys Variegated' | EGar EOrc LFis LHop LPen MBel MNrw NBir NHol NLak SLod WCot WHer WSPU WSan WWeb |
| 'Hower Park' | Last listed 1997 |
| *humilis* | CM&M CNic EBee MLLN SRms WShe |
| - Mckay's form | Last listed 1998 |
| - 'Pulchellus' | LGre NWCA |
| 'Hyacinth-flowered' seed mixture from Burpee, USA | Last listed 1998 |
| *isophyllus* ♀ | CLyd CStr EBee EPfP LPen MAsh MBEx MMil MNes SChu WCom WEas WFar WHCG WPer WSPU |
| *jamesii* | CHan EBee EOrc NChi WHer WLin |
| *janishiae* | Last listed 1998 |
| 'Jill Lucas' | SCro |
| 'John Booth' | WEas |
| 'John Nash' | CAxe CSWP CSam NLak SHFr SIgm SMrm |
| 'John Nash' misapplied | See *P.*'Alice Hindley' |
| 'Joy' | CBlo EBee MBro MGed MLLN MSte NPla WOve WPer WPyg WWoo |
| 'June' | See *P.*'Pennington Gem' |
| 'King George V' | More than 30 suppliers |
| 'Knight's Purple' | WHCG |
| 'Knightwick' | CAxe WPer WSPU |
| 'Kummel' | ELan |
| § *kunthii* | CAxe WEas WSPU |
| ¶ *labrosus* | LHop NBur |
| *laetus* var.*laetus* | Last listed 1998 |
| § - var.*roezlii* | CSam GChr GCrs GDra MLLN MLan MPla MTis NHar NLak NLon NMen NWCA SIng SRms WAbe WEas WWin |
| *laricifolius* | Last listed 1998 |
| § 'Le Phare' | CBod EBee LLWP LRHS MBNS WHCG WPer WSPU |
| *leiophyllus* | MBro WLin |
| *leonensis* | CGen NBur |
| ¶ 'Lilac and Burgundy' | CAxe MBNS |
| *linarioides* | CPBP EWes LPen MBro NHol WAbe WPat |
| § - subsp.*californicus* | Last listed 1998 |
| - subsp.*coloradoensis* | Last listed 1998 |
| - JCA 9694 | WLin |
| 'Little Witley' | CAxe LPen WHCG WPer |
| * 'Logan Pink' | GMac NDov |
| 'Lord Home' | See *P.*'George Home' |
| *lyallii* | CHar CKel EBee EHrv ELan EMar ESis ITim LFis LPen MCCP MLLN MNrw MSCN NLak NLon SSca WByw WSPU WSan WWeb |
| 'Lynette' | CAxe CLyd EHic LFis LPen WHCG WPer |
| 'Macpenny's Pink' | NCat SChu WWoo |
| 'Madame Golding' | CGle CSWP LFis LGre LHil MBNS MLLN MMil MNrw SAga SMrm SPlb WHCG WPer WSPU |
| 'Margery Fish' ♀ | CElw CLyd CM&M CPou EHic ESis MAvo MMil MNrw MSte NFai SMac WPer WRha WSPU WSel |
| 'Maurice Gibbs' ♀ | CAxe CBlo LPen MLLN SIgm WHCG WSPU |
| *mensarum* | EBee |
| *menziesii* | See *P.davidsonii* var.*menziesii* |
| 'Merlin' | Last listed 1998 |
| ¶ Mexicali hybrids | EBee |

'Midnight'                   CBrm CElw CGle CHan CLTr
                             CSam GBri LFis LLWP LPen MBEx
                             MBel MBro MRav NBrk SAga
                             SChu SDys SIgm SMrm SUsu
                             WCFE WCot WHCG WMer WPer
                             WRus WSPU WWat WWin
'Modesty'                    CAxe CBlo EBee LLWP LPen
                             LRHS MBNS NPla SMac WHCG
                             WSPU
'Molly Margaret'             GCHN
*montanus*                   EBee GCHN
'Mother of Pearl'            More than 30 suppliers
* 'Mountain Wine'            WThi
'Mrs Golding'                Last listed 1997
'Mrs Miller'                 LPen MBNS NBur
'Mrs Morse'                  See *P.* 'Chester Scarlet'
*multiflorus*                EBee LPen
§ 'Myddelton Gem'            CGle CLTr ECGP LPen MBNS
                             MNrw MWat NPla WFoF WHCG
                             WSPU
♦ 'Myddelton Red'            See *P.* 'Myddelton Gem'
*nemorosus*                  EBee
*neomexicanus*               EBee
¶ *neotericus*               WLin
*newberryi* ♀                CMea ELan EPot LGre MAsh NBir
                             NMen NRoo SIng WKif WSPU
                             WWin
  - subsp. *berryi*          See *P. berryi*
  - f. *humilior*            EPot GEil
§ - var. *sonomensis*        EPot NHar NMen NWCA WAbe
§ *nitidus*                  MNrw
'Oaklea Red'                 CHar ECtt LHil MBri MLLN SSoC
                             SWat
§ 'Old Candy Pink'           EBee LLWP LPen MSte WEas WPer
                             WRus WSPU WWhi
'Old Silk'                   Last listed 1996
*oliganthus*                 Last listed 1998
*ophianthus*                 Last listed 1998
'Osprey' ♀                   CGle CLyd EBee EBrP EBre EOrc
                             EWes GMac LBre LLWP LPen
                             MAsh MBNS MNrw NBrk NHol
                             SBre SMac SUsu WBrE WCot WEas
                             WHCG WMaN WPer WRha WRus
                             WSPU WSel WWin
*ovatus*                     CBrm CLyd CMCo EBee ELan
                             GCHN GCal LFis LPen LPio MBro
                             MLLN NChi NHed NLak SAga
                             SIgm SRms SSca WHCG WKif
                             WLin WSan
¶ 'Overbury'                 WSPU
*palmeri*                    CGen EBee EWll NLak
'Papal Purple'               CKel CMHG GMac LLWP LPen
                             MBNS MBro MLLN MMil MSte
                             NBrk NLak SAga SChu SMac
                             SMrm SRms WElm WFar WHCG
                             WHoo WRus WSPU WWhi WWye
'Papal Purple' x 'Evelyn'    CAxe
'Park Garden'                Last listed 1996
*parvulus*                   CGra NWCA
'Patio Coral'                MLLN
'Patio Pink'                 LLWP MBri MLLN
'Patio Shell'                MBri NOla
'Patio Swirl'                Last listed 1998
'Patio Wine'                 LLWP MBri MLLN NOla
'Peace'                      CLTr CRos LHop LPen LRHS
                             MBNS NLak NPla SSca WHCG
                             WMaN WRus WSPU WWhi
*peckii*                     Last listed 1998
§ 'Pennington Gem' ♀         More than 30 suppliers
¶ 'Pershore Carnival'        CAxe WSPU
¶ 'Pershore Fanfare'         CAxe WSPU
'Pershore Pink Necklace'     LPen MCLN MLLN SChu WEas
                             WHCG WMaN WSPU WSan

*petiolatus*                 Last listed 1996
♦ 'Phare'                    See *P.* 'Le Phare'
'Phyllis'                    See *P.* 'Evelyn'
*pinifolius* ♀               More than 30 suppliers
  - 'Mersea Yellow'          More than 30 suppliers
  - 'Wisley Flame' ♀         CMea ESis SIgm SUsu SWas
'Pink Dragon'                CLyd GCHN GDra LGre MPla
                             MSCN NDov NHar SAga SChu
                             SMrm SOkh WHCG WSPU
'Pink Endurance'             CMea CStr EBrP EBre ELan LBre
                             LPen MBro MCLN MLLN MMil
                             NHaw NRoo SAga SBre SEas SIng
                             WEas WHCG WHal WHoo WMaN
                             WPer WSPU
'Pink Ice'                   NPla
'Pink Profusion'             SIgm SMrm SUsu
'Port Wine' ♀                CAxe CBlo CGle CHar CLTr CRDP
                             CSam ERav GCHN LHil LPen
                             MAvo MBel MLLN NChi NPla
                             SMac SPer WHCG WHoo WMaN
                             WPer WSPU WSel
'Powis Castle'               EWes WPer WWye
'Prairie Dusk'               LPen
'Prairie Fire'               EBee LPen WSPU
* 'Prairie Pride'            LPen
'Primrose Thomas'            CAxe MBel NHaw
'Priory Purple'              NLak WHCG WPer
*procerus*                   CM&M EBee GBri LPen MDHE
                             MLLN SRms WPer
  - var. *brachyanthus*      Last listed 1998
¶ - subsp. *formosus*        EPot
  - subsp. *procerus*        EHyt
§ - 'Roy Davidson' ♀         CMea CNic CPBP LBee NHol SBla
                             WFar WLin
  - var. *tolmiei*           EBee EPot GCHN GCal LGre LPen
                             NChi NHol NRoo NWCA WCla
                             WLin
  - - white                  CGra
*pruinosus*                  CGra EBee WLin
*pubescens*                  See *P. hirsutus*
*pulchellus*                 Last listed 1998
  - Lindley                  See *P. campanulatus*
*pulcherrimus*               NBro
*pumilus*                    Last listed 1998
'Purple and White'           See *P.* 'Countess of Dalkeith'
'Purple Bedder'              CGle CHea EAst EHic GAbr LPen
                             MAsh MCLN MLLN MNrw MWat
                             NHaw NPla SSoC SWat WFar
                             WGor WHCG WSPU WSel WWal
'Purple Dragon'              MPla
'Purple Gem'                 GDra
'Purple Passion'             EBee EBrP EBre EPfP EWes LBre
                             MLLN NRoo SBre SCro WLRN
'Purpureus Albus'            See *P.* 'Countess of Dalkeith'
*purpusii*                   CPBP SIgm WAbe
'Rajah'                      EBee LHop WLin
'Raspberry Ripple'           Last listed 1997
*rattanii*                   Last listed 1997
'Raven' ♀                    CLon EBee EOrc GBri LBlm LLWP
                             LPen MBel MBro MCAu MCLN
                             NBrk NBro NHaw NHol SChu
                             WCot WEas WHCG WHal WHoo
                             WMaN WMer WPer WPyg WRus
                             WSPU WWin
'Razzle Dazzle'              LRHS MBNS WPer
'Red Ace'                    MLLN MNrw
'Red Emperor'                CAxe CMHG CStr ECtt MBNS
                             MBel MLLN NFai NHaw WEas
                             WHCG WMer WPer WSPU
'Red Knight'                 LPen LRHS MBNS
'Rich Purple'                LLWP MBNS NDov SPer WMaN

'Rich Ruby'  CGle CMGP EBee EBrP EBre ELan EWes LBre LGre LHil LHop LLWP LPen MBEx MNrw NHol SAga SBre SChu SMrm SOkh SPlb SUsu WEas WHCG WMaN WPer WRus WSPU WWhi

*richardsonii*  MLLN MNrw MSCN NLak SIgm SRms WGwG

'Ridgeway Red'  WSPU

*roezlii* Regel  See *P. laetus* var. *roezlii*

♦ *roseocampanulatus*  See *P. barbatus* 'Roseocampanulatus'

§ *rostriflorus*  SAga SBla WLin

- JJA 9548  Last listed 1998

¶ 'Rosy Blush'  CAxe EBee LPen NLak WHCG

'Roundhay'  CFee

♦ 'Roy Davidson'  See *P. procerus* 'Roy Davidson'

'Royal White'  See *P.* 'White Bedder'

'Rubicundus' ♀  CBot CGle CLyd EBee ECtt ELan LFis LHil LHop LPen MAsh MBNS SAga SMrm WAbe WCot WHCG WHoo WMer WRus WSPU WWal WWeb

'Ruby'  See *P.* 'Schoenholzeri'

'Ruby Field'  EBee GAbr NPla WHCG WWoo

¶ 'Ruby Gem'  EBee MBNS

* 'Ruby Wine'  SRPl

*rupicola* ♀  CMea EBee GDra GTou LHop MBro MPla NRoo NSla NWCA SBla SIgm SRms WAbe WWin

- 'Albus'  LGre WAbe

- 'Diamond Lake'  MBro NHar WLin WPat

¶ - lilac  NDov

- mauve hybrid  GDra LGre

'Russian River'  CLTr CSWP EAst EBee EHic EWes LLWP LPen MBel MBro NHaw NLak SMrm SOkh SPlb WHCG WPer WPyg WSPU WWat

¶ *rydbergii*  EPot

¶ 'Sapphire'  NCat

* Saskatoon hybrids  NChi

*scariosus* var. *garrettii*  Last listed 1998

Scarlet Queen =  CSWP
'Scharlachkönigin'

§ 'Schoenholzeri' ♀  More than 30 suppliers

*scouleri*  See *P. fruticosus* var. *scouleri*

*secundiflorus*  CPBP WCot

§ *serrulatus*  CGen EBee ECha EWes GTou LPen MBel MSte NWCA SHFr SMad SRms WOut WSPU

- 'Albus'  EBee LPen MSte SIgm WSPU WWin

'Shell Pink'  NLon WPer

* 'Sherbourne Blue'  WPer

* 'Shrawley'  WPer

'Sissinghurst Pink'  See *P.* 'Evelyn'

'Six Hills'  CPBP MPla NHar NHol NRoo SAga SDys SRms WHCG WLin WSPU

'Skyline'  EPfP EWTr WWeb

*smallii*  EBee LGre LPen NLak SIgm SOkh

'Snow Storm'  See *P.* 'White Bedder'

'Snowflake'  See *P.* 'White Bedder'

*sonomensis*  See *P. newberryi* var. *sonomensis*

'Sour Grapes' hort.  See *P.* 'Stapleford Gem'

§ 'Sour Grapes' M. Fish  CBot CElw CHan CRos CSWP EAst ECot EHic ELan GBuc GMac LHil MBel MBri MCLN MTis MWgw NOak NPla NRoo SMrm SPla SUsu WEas WFar WPer WSPU WWat

'Southcombe Pink'  MLLN WHCG

'Southgate Gem'  GChr GRei LPen MNrw MWat SCro WHCG

'Souvenir d'Adrian Regnier'  GCHN

'Souvenir d'André Torres'  LLWP

'Souvenir d'André Torres' misapplied  See *P.* 'Chester Scarlet'

sp. P&C 150  CFee

¶ sp. PCHA 148  WHoo WLin

sp. tall pink  LPen

*speciosus*  Last listed 1998

- subsp. *kennedyi*  Last listed 1998

§ 'Stapleford Gem' ♀  More than 30 suppliers

*strictus*  CBlo EBee EWTr GCHN LGre LPio MBNS MLLN MWgw NBro NChi NLak SIgm SRms WLin WPer WSPU

- 'Bandera'  NLak WCot

¶ *subglaber*  EBee

*subserratus*  Last listed 1996

'Sutton's Pink Bedder'  LRHS MBNS WSPU

'Sylvia Buss'  LPen

N 'Taoensis'  EWes SSea

*taosensis*  See *P. crandallii* subsp. *taosensis*

*ternatus*  See *Keckiella ternata*

*teucrioides*  CMea EPot NWCA WLin WThi

- JCA 1717050  CPBP

*thompsoniae*  Last listed 1996

§ 'Thorn'  More than 30 suppliers

I 'Thorn Cross'  GMac

* 'Threave White'  WPen

'Torquay Gem'  GBuc LHop LPen NLak SDys WHCG WPer

*traceyi*  NLak

'True Sour Grapes'  See *P.* 'Sour Grapes' M. Fish

¶ *tubaeflorus*  EBee

*tusharensis*  See *P. caespitosus* subsp. *suffruticosus*

*uintahensis*  Last listed 1998

♦ *unilateralis*  See *P. virgatus* subsp. *asa-grayi*

*utahensis*  CBot EBrP EBre EWes GBri LBre MHlr SBre WPer

- white  Last listed 1998

*venustus*  CFir EBee GBuc MHar MLLN MNrw SRms WHCG WWye

¶ 'Vesuvius'  CAxe CB&S MBri

*virens* AM  EBee EHyt NRoo NTow NWCA WPat

- *albus*  GCHN NPri WWin

- R/Mr 7890  WPer

♦ *virgatus* subsp. *arizonicus*  See *P. deaveri*

§ - subsp. *asa-grayi*  Last listed 1996

- subsp. *putus*  WLin

*washingtonensis*  CGra NBur

*watsonii*  EBee EHic EMan LHop MLLN SAga SRms SWat WCot WHCG WLin WPer

'Welsh Dawn'  WSPU

§ *whippleanus*  CGle CHan CLon CLyd CRDP EBee EWes LGre LPen MSte NChi NLak SAga WAbb WLin WPer

- dark form  MBro

§ 'White Bedder' ♀  More than 30 suppliers

'Whitethroat'  LPen MBNS MHlr MLLN SOkh SRCN WCot WHCG WMaN WMer WPer WSPU WWin

*wilcoxii*  Last listed 1998

§ 'Windsor Red'  CBlo CBod EBee EHic EWTr LPen MAsh MBNS MSte NPla WGor WHCG WSPU WWoo

§ *wislizenii*  CBos EBee EBrP EBre EHic EPfP LBre LGre MLLN MLan MNrw MOne NOak SBid SBre SRms WMaN WWal

*wrightii*  EBee

## PENTAGLOTTIS (Boraginaceae)

§ *sempervirens* — CArn CKin EPfP GPoy MHew MSal WBea WGwy WHen WOak WWye

## PENTALINON (Apocynaceae)
§ *luteum* — Last listed 1996

## PENTAPTERYGIUM See AGAPETES

## PENTAS (Rubiaceae)
*lanceolata* — CHal ELan MBri WMul
- 'Candy Stripe' — WMul
- 'New Look Pink' — LPVe
- 'New Look Red' — LPVe
- 'Red Star' — WMul

## PEPEROMIA (Piperaceae)
§ *argyreia* ♀ — CHal MBri
*arifolia* — CHal
*caperata* — MBri
- 'Little Fantasy' ♀ — CHal
- 'Variegata' ♀ — Last listed 1993
*clusiifolia* — CHal
- 'Variegata' — CHal
*glabella* — CHal
*griseoargentea* — CHal
*magnoliifolia* — See *P. obtusifolia* Magnoliifolia Group
*obtusifolia* 'Jamaica' — MBri
§ - Magnoliifolia Group — SRms
- - 'Golden Gate' (v) — MBri
- - 'Greengold' — CHal MBri
- - 'USA' — MBri
- 'Tricolor' (v) — MBri
*orba* 'Pixie' — MBri
I - 'Pixie Variegata' — MBri
*pulchella* — See *P. verticillata*
*resediflora* — See *P. fraseri*
*sandersii* — See *P. argyreia*
*scandens* ♀ — MBri
- 'Variegata' — CHal MBri
§ *verticillata* — CHal

## PERESKIA (Cactaceae)
*aculeata* f. *rubescens* — WCot
*corrugata* — Last listed 1997

## PERESKIOPSIS (Cactaceae)
§ *diguetii* — CHal
*spathulata* — See *P. diguetii*

## PEREZIA (Asteraceae)
*linearis* — GBuc
*recurvata* — GCrs GTou NWCA

## PERICALLIS (Asteraceae)
§ *appendiculata* — Last listed 1996
§ *lanata* (L'Hér.) B.Nord. — CHan ELan LHil LHop MBEx MBlu SRms WEas
§ - hort. — See *P.* 'Purple Picotee'
- Kew form — CSpe SMrm WCot

## PERILLA (Lamiaceae)
* 'Acuta Kudo' — EOHP
§ *frutescens* var. *crispa* ♀ — CArn MChe WJek
¶ - green — EOHP
- var. *nankinensis* — See *P. frutescens* var. *crispa*
¶ - var. *purpurascens* — CArn EOHP MChe WJek

## PERIPLOCA (Asclepiadaceae)
*graeca* — CArn CB&S CMac CPlN CPle CRHN GQui NBea NFla SBra WCot WSHC
*sepium* — CPLG CPlN CPle

## PERISTROPHE (Acanthaceae)
*speciosa* — ERea SYvo

## PERNETTYA See GAULTHERIA

## PEROVSKIA (Lamiaceae)
*atriplicifolia* — CArn CBot CDul CPle ERav GPoy LGre LHol MAsh MBri SIde SLod WHCG WOld WViv
¶ - 'Little Spire' — EFou
'Blue Haze' — GCal
'Blue Spire' ♀ — More than 30 suppliers
'Filigran' — CStr ECGP EFou GCal NLak SChu
'Hybrida' — WWeb
*scrophulariifolia* — Last listed 1998

## PERSEA (Lauraceae)
¶ *americana* 'Hass' (F) — CGOG
*thunbergii* — CGre

## PERSICARIA (Polygonaceae)
§ *affinis* — CB&S CBlo CHan CTri ECha GCrs MBar MTho NBro NVic SWat WEas WFar WMoo WOld WOve
- 'Darjeeling Red' ♀ — CB&S CBlo CRow EBee ELan ENot EPla GCal GChr LGro LHil MBal MBri MRav NBir NChi NFla NHol SLon SMrm WAbe WBea WHen WHer
- 'Dimity' — See *P. affinis* 'Superba'
- 'Donald Lowndes' ♀ — CBlo CChe COIW CRow EBee ECha ELan ENot EWTr GMac LHop LLWP LPBA MBal MNrw MRav MSta MWat NArg NDea NFla NHol NLon NRoo SPer SRPl SRms WBea WOld WPer
- Kew form — Last listed 1996
- 'Ron McBeath' — CRow ECha
§ - 'Superba' ♀ — More than 30 suppliers
*alata* — CRow NHol SMad
*alpina* — CRow
*amphibia* — CRow
§ *amplexicaulis* — CBre CRow ELan EMar GMaP LGro MBal MBro MSCN MWat NChi NDea NFor NLon NOrc SChu SEND SUsu WFar WHoo WMoo WPyg WRHF
- 'Alba' — CRow ECha EGar EPla LGre MBri MCAu SUsu WBea WCot
- 'Arun Gem' — See *P. amplexicaulis* var. *pendula*
- 'Atrosanguinea' — CBlo CNic CRow EBee ECha EMan EPla ERic LFis MFir NBir NDea NFai NFla NHol NTow NVic SPer SRms WFar WOld WWin WWoo
♦ - 'Blotau' — See *P. amplexicaulis* Taurus = 'Blotau'
- 'Cottesbrooke Gold' — CRow
- 'Firedance' — LGre SMrm
- 'Firetail' ♀ — CHan CRow EBee EBrP EBre ECha ECtt EFou EPla LBre LHop LLWP MBel MCAu MRav NHol NLar NRoo NSti SBre SUsu WBea WElm WFar WHil WOld WRus WWhi

| | |
|---|---|
| - 'Gold Leaf' | WCot |
| - 'Inverleith' | CBre CRow ECha ECtt EGar EPla NCat NLak NRoo SCob SDys SMrm WOld WPGP WWye |
| * - var. *pendula* | CRow ECha GAri MBri NBir NRoo WBea |
| - 'Rosea' | CRow EBee ECha ELan EPla LGre MBri MRav NSti SUsu WBea WMoo |
| - 'Rowden Gem' | CRow |
| - 'Rowden Jewel' | CRow |
| - 'Rowden Rose Quartz' | CRow |
| § - Taurus = 'Blotau' | CElw EGar EPla MLLN SMrm WFar |
| § *bistorta* | CArn CBlo CJew CKin CRow ELau GPoy LHol MChe MHew MSal SWat WGwG WSel WWye |
| - subsp. *carnea* | CRow EBee ECha EGar ELan NBir WFar |
| - 'Hohe Tatra' | CRow LGre SMrm |
| - 'Superba' ♀ | More than 30 suppliers |
| *bistortoides* | MSal |
| * 'Blush Clent' | WSPU |
| *campanulata* | CElw CHan CRow ECha EMar LBlm LHop MHar MSCN MWat NBro NFai NFor NGdn NLon NRoo SLon SPer WBea WFar WOve WWin WWye |
| - Alba Group | CRow EMar GCal GGar NBro NSti SChu WHer WWat |
| - pale pink | GBuc GCal WBcn WWat |
| - 'Rosenrot' | CBre CJew CRow EPla GBuc GCal IBlr LFis NHol NLar SSpi SWat WBea WOld |
| - 'Southcombe White' | CRow EMar GAri GBri LBlm MBNS WBea WRos |
| *capitata* | CHal CInt CLTr CRow ELan SCro SIng SMac SRms WBea WEas WMoo |
| - from Afghanistan | WBea |
| ¶ *conspicua* | EBee |
| *coriacea* | CRow |
| *elata* | CHor EGoo EMar EMon GAri GBuc GGar GVic SLod |
| *emodi* | CRow WWat |
| § *longiseta* | MSal |
| § *macrophylla* | CRow NFla WOld |
| *microcephala* | CRow EWes SAga SCro SMac WCot |
| *milletii* | CRDP CRow EBee EPla EWTr EWes GAri GBuc LGre MBri MTho NLak NOak NSti WCot WCru WMer WMoo WWat |
| § *mollis* | CHan CRow EHal |
| § *odorata* | CArn EOHP IIve MSal WJek |
| *orientalis* | MSal SMrm |
| *polymorpha* | CRow EBee ECha EFou EMan EMon GNau LGre SCob SMad SMrm |
| ♦ *polystachya* | See *P. wallichii* |
| § *runcinata* | CLTr CRow EBee EHal EMar GCHN NLar WCru WFar WHer WOld WPer WWin |
| * *rupestris* | Last listed 1998 |
| *scoparia* | See *Polygonum scoparium* |
| sp. B&SWJ 1765 from Taiwan | Last listed 1996 |
| *sphaerostachya* Meissner | See *P. macrophylla* |
| *tenuicaulis* | CBlo CBre CLyd CRow EBee EMon EPar EPla GGar MBal MFir MUlv MUlv NDea NHol SIng WCot WCru WFar |
| § *tinctoria* | EOHP |

| | |
|---|---|
| *vacciniifolia* ♀ | CB&S CNic CPle CRow ECha ESis GCHN GMac MBal MBar MBel MTho MWat NHar NHol NRoo NSla SBla SDix SIng SPlb SRms SSmi WAbe WBea WRus WWat WWin |
| - 'Ron McBeath' | CRow |
| § *virginiana* | CMHG EPla MFir NLar |
| - Compton's form | WCot |
| ¶ - 'Lance Corporal' | CRow |
| § - 'Painter's Palette' (v) | More than 30 suppliers |
| - Variegata Group | CBot CHan CRow EBee ECha GCal LHop NLar WCot WOld |
| *vivipara* | CRow WCot |
| § *wallichii* | CRow EBee ECha GBri IBlr NSti SDix SLon |
| § *weyrichii* | EMan GCal MTed NBir NBro NChi NLar WBea WCot WOld |

## PETALOSTEMON See DALEA

## PETAMENES See GLADIOLUS

## PETASITES (Asteraceae)

| | |
|---|---|
| *albus* | CRow EMon GGar GPoy MHer MSal NSti |
| *fragrans* | CNat ELan EMon EPar MHer MSta SWat WFar WOak |
| *hybridus* | CKin EMFW LEdu MCli WHer |
| * - 'Variegatus' | Last listed 1997 |
| *japonicus* var. *giganteus* | CArn CRow ECha EGol ELan EMon EOld EPar EPfP LEdu MSCN MUlv NVic SBid WCru |
| § - - 'Nishiki-buki' | CRow ECoo EEls EGar EMon EPla IBlr MSCN NTow SBid WCHb WCru WHil |
| ♦ - - 'Variegatus' | See *P. japonicus* var. *giganteus* 'Nishiki-buki' |
| ¶ - f. *purpureus* | WCot |
| *kablikianus* AL&JS 90170YU | Last listed 1996 |
| *palmatus* | CRow EBee GCal NSti WCru WFar |
| - JLS 86317CLOR | EMon SMad WCot |
| *paradoxus* | CRDP EGar EMon MRav MSCN WCot |

## PETREA (Verbenaceae)

| | |
|---|---|
| *volubilis* | CPIN ECon LChe SOWG WMul |
| - 'Albiflora' | Last listed 1996 |

## PETROCALLIS (Brassicaceae)

| | |
|---|---|
| *lagascae* | See *P. pyrenaica* |
| § *pyrenaica* | GCrs NWCA WAbe WPer |
| - *alba* | GCrs WAbe |

## PETROCOPTIS (Caryophyllaceae)

| | |
|---|---|
| *pyrenaica* | EBur NMen SRms SSca |
| § - subsp. *glaucifolia* | CNic ESis GTou MNrw MPla NBir WAbe WPer |
| - - 'Alba' | SSca |

## PETROCOSMEA (Gesneriaceae)

| | |
|---|---|
| *kerrii* | Last listed 1997 |

## PETROMARULA (Campanulaceae)

| | |
|---|---|
| *pinnata* | CPou EBee GBin NChi WCot |

## PETROPHYTUM (Rosaceae)

| | |
|---|---|
| *caespitosum* | CGra GTou NHar NWCA WAbe |
| *cinerascens* | NWCA SIng |
| § *hendersonii* | NHol WAbe |

## PETRORHAGIA (Caryophyllaceae)

*nanteuilii* — CNat EWFC
§ *saxifraga* ♀ — EBur MMal MNrw MPEx NPri SRms WMoo WPat WPer WWhi
§ - 'Rosette' — MTho WWin
*velutina* — Last listed 1996

## PETROSELINUM (Apiaceae)

§ *crispum* — CArn CJew CSev GPoy ILis LHol MBar MChe NPri SIde WPer WSel WWye
- 'Bravour' ♀ — ELau MMal
¶ - 'Champion Moss Curled' — MPEx
- var. *crispum* — Last listed 1997
- 'Darki' — CSev
- French — CArn CBod ELau IIve MMal WJek
- 'Greek' — ELau
- 'Italian' — See *P. crispum* var. *neapolitanum*
§ - var. *neapolitanum* — CBod ELau IIve MHer
§ - var. *tuberosum* — CBod SIde WHer
*hortense* — See *P. crispum*
*tuberosum* — See *P. crispum* var. *tuberosum*

## PETTERIA (Papilionaceae)
*ramentacea* — CB&S CFil EPfP SLPl

## PETUNIA (Solanaceae)
¶ Surfinia Pink Vein = 'Suntosol' — WWol
¶ Surfinia White = 'Kesupite' — WWol

## PEUCEDANUM (Apiaceae)
*formosanum* B&SWJ 3647 — WCru
*officinale* — Last listed 1997
*ostruthium* — GPoy LHol
- 'Daphnis' (v) — EMan EMon MTed NPro
*palustre* — Last listed 1997
*verticillare* — EMan MUlv SDix SMrm SSca

## PEUMUS (Monimiaceae)
*boldus* — CGre

## PHACELIA (Hydrophyllaceae)
*bolanderi* — CPBP EBee
*sericea* subsp. *ciliosa* — Last listed 1998
- subsp. *sericea* — Last listed 1998
*tanacetifolia* — Last listed 1997

## PHACOCAPNOS See CYSTICAPNOS

## PHAEDRANASSA (Amaryllidaceae)
*dubia* — Last listed 1998
¶ *tunguraguae* — WCot
*viridiflora* — Last listed 1998

## PHAEDRANTHUS See DISTICTIS

## PHAENOCOMA (Asteraceae)
*prolifera* — Last listed 1997

## PHAENOSPERMA (Poaceae)
*globosa* — CHar EBee EGar EHoe EPPr EPla EWes LHil NHol SCob

## PHAGNALON (Asteraceae)
¶ *helichrysoides* — SIng

## PHAIOPHLEPS (Iridaceae)
*biflora* — See *Olsynium biflorum*
*nigricans* — See *Sisyrinchium striatum*

## PHAIUS (Orchidaceae)
*minor* — EFEx

## PHALARIS (Poaceae)
§ *aquatica* — Last listed 1997
- 'Austalia' — Last listed 1998
- 'Uneta' — Last listed 1998
*arundinacea* — CKin EPla MBNS MLan SPlb SWat
- 'Elegantissima' — See *P. arundinacea* var. *picta* 'Picta'
- 'Luteovariegata' — EMon
- var. *picta* — LSyl NCut SLon
- - 'Aureovariegata' — CB&S CRow CSWP MRav NPer SAga SWat
- - 'Feesey' (v) — More than 30 suppliers
- - 'Luteopicta' (v) — EBee EHoe EPPr EPla LRHS
§ - - 'Picta' (v) ♀ — More than 30 suppliers
- - 'Tricolor' (v) — EBee EHoe EMon EPla GAri GOrn SSoC WBea
- 'Streamlined' (v) — EMon EPla LRHS SLPl WLeb
- 'Turkey Red' — Last listed 1998
- 'Yugoslavian' — Last listed 1998
*canariensis* — Last listed 1996
*tuberosa stenoptera* — See *P. aquatica*

## PHALOCALLIS (Iridaceae)
*coelestis* — EBee

## PHANEROPHLEBIA (Dryopteridaceae)
*caryotidea* — See *Cyrtomium caryotideum*
*falcata* — See *Cyrtomium falcatum*
*fortunei* — See *Cyrtomium fortunei*

## PHARBITIS See IPOMOEA

## PHASEOLUS (Papilionaceae)
*caracalla* — See *Vigna caracalla*

## PHEGOPTERIS (Thelypteridaceae)
§ *connectilis* — CCuc CFil EFer EMon LSyl MBal NHed NMar SRms
*decursive-pinnata* — CCuc EMon NHol NMar WRic

## PHELLODENDRON (Rutaceae)
*amurense* — CB&S CFil CGre CMCN ELan EPfP SSpi WDin WNor
- var. *sachalinense* — MAsh WPGP
*chinense* — EPfP
*lavalleei* — WPGP

## PHILADELPHUS ✿ (Hydrangeaceae)
ACE 1907 — WAbe WHCr
¶ 'Albâtre' — MBri
'Atlas' — WCom
'Avalanche' — CMHG EBrP EBre NFla NPro SBre SEas SPer SRms WDin WHCG WWat
'Beauclerk' ♀ — CDoC CDul CHar CMHG CTri EBee EBrP EBre ENot GChr LBre MAsh MBri MGos MRav NBee NHol SBre SEas SPer SReu SRms SSpi WHCG WWat WWin
'Belle Etoile' ♀ — More than 30 suppliers
'Boule d'Argent' (d) — CMHG
'Bouquet Blanc' — CB&S GQui SEas SPer SRms WKif WRHF
*brachybotrys* — CFil EPfP MRav NHol WHCG WPGP
'Buckley's Quill' (d) — EBee MRav WBcn
'Burfordensis' — MAsh SBid SPer WCom WWat WWeb

| | |
|---|---|
| 'Burkwoodii' | SBid |
| *coronarius* | CTri EBee GOrc LBuc MWat NFor NLon SPer SRPl |
| - 'Aureus' ♀ | More than 30 suppliers |
| - 'Bowles' Variety' | See *P. coronarius* 'Variegatus' |
| - 'Gold Mound' | MGos MRav |
| § - 'Variegatus' (v) ♀ | More than 30 suppliers |
| *coulteri* | Last listed 1998 |
| 'Coupe d'Argent' | MRav |
| 'Dame Blanche' (d) | EBee EWTr MBri NPro |
| *delavayi* | CFil CPle EPfP WCru WHCG WPGP |
| - ACE | WHCr |
| - var. *calvescens* | See *P. purpurascens* |
| ¶ - - ACE 2206 | SSpi |
| ¶ 'Enchantement' (d) | MRav SBid SDix WLRN |
| § 'Erectus' | CBlo EBee EHol ENot EPfP MBal MRav NWea SLon WCom WHCG WWat |
| ¶ 'Etoile Rose' | EWTr |
| *fragrans* | CFil WPGP |
| 'Frosty Morn' | CB&S EBee EHal EHic GOrc MGos MUlv NHol NTow SPer SPla WCom |
| 'Galahad' | Last listed 1996 |
| 'Glacier' | WPGP |
| *incanus* | Last listed 1996 |
| § 'Innocence' (v) | CBot CEnd CHar CPMA CPle ECtt EHoe ELan EPla LHop MBri MGos MPla MRav SEas SPer SReu SSta WFar WHCG |
| 'Innocence Variegatus' | See *P.* 'Innocence' |
| *inodorus* var. *grandiflorus* | CPle |
| § *insignis* | MRav |
| *intectus* | ISea |
| x *lemoinei* | CBlo CTri EBee EMil GEil MGos NFor SEas SRPl WFar WGwG WStI WWal |
| - 'Erectus' | See *P.* 'Erectus' |
| ¶ - 'Lemoinei' | EWTr |
| 'Lemon Hill' | WBcn |
| *lewisii* | CAgr WUnu |
| - L 1896 | CFil WPGP |
| *madrensis* | LHop |
| - CD&R 1226 | CHan |
| 'Manteau d'Hermine' (d) ♀ | More than 30 suppliers |
| 'Marjorie' | CHan CHar |
| *mexicanus* | CFil WPGP |
| *microphyllus* | CBlo CBot CDul CHan CMHG ESis GOrc LGre MAsh MBro MHar MPla MRav NHol SLon SReu SSpi WHCG WPat WSHC WWat |
| 'Minnesota Snowflake' (d) | EBee ECtt EHic EWes IOrc MRav NCut NPro SBid WBcn WCom |
| x *monstrosus* 'Monster' | Last listed 1998 |
| 'Mont Blanc' | CB&S |
| 'Mrs E.L. Robinson' | CBlo EAst ECtt EPla SBid WCom WWoo |
| 'Natchez' (d) | ECtt MBNS MPla SVil |
| ¶ 'Oeil de Pourpre' | MBri |
| 'Perryhill' | SPer |
| *pubescens* | Last listed 1998 |
| § *purpurascens* | LBuc MRav SMrm SSta WAbe |
| x *purpureomaculatus* | Last listed 1998 |
| *schrenkii* | CFil WPGP |
| § 'Silberregen' | CBlo CDoC CPle EBee ECtt GOrc IOrc MAsh MBal MBar MGos MRav NBee SBid SEas SPan SRms WAbe WDin WPat WWat |
| Silver Showers | See *P.* 'Silberregen' |
| 'Snowflake' | EMil MBal NMoo WAbe WLRN |
| 'Souvenir de Billiard' | See *P. insignis* |
| *subcanus* | GOrc MRav |
| 'Sybille' ♀ | CBlo CMHG ENot GOrc ISea MBri MRav NFla NHlc SBid SPer SRms SSpi WHCG WKif WPat WSHC |
| *tomentosus* | CFil WHCG WPGP |
| ¶ - B&SWJ 2707 | WCru |
| 'Velléda' | CFil WPGP |
| 'Virginal' (d) ♀ | More than 30 suppliers |
| 'Virginal' LA '82 | CDul MBal |
| 'Voie Lactée' | MRav |
| White Rock | CDoC COtt EBee LRHS MBal MBri NMoo SPer WLRN |

## PHILESIA (Philesiaceae)

| | |
|---|---|
| *buxifolia* | See *P. magellanica* |
| § *magellanica* | CB&S EMil GGGa GSki MBal SAPC SBid SPer SSpi WCru |

## PHILIBERTIA (Asclepiadaceae)

| | |
|---|---|
| ¶ *gilliesii* | EBee |

## PHILLYREA (Oleaceae)

| | |
|---|---|
| *angustifolia* | CDoC CFil CHan COtt CPin CPle EPfP ERom SEND SHFr SLPl SPer SSpi WAbe WPGP WWat |
| - f. *rosmarinifolia* | CB&S CFil WPGP |
| *decora* | See *Osmanthus decorus* |
| § *latifolia* | CDoC CFil CPle LRHS SAPC SArc SLPl SLon SSpi WPGP WWat |
| *media* | See *P. latifolia* |

## PHILODENDRON (Araceae)

| | |
|---|---|
| § *angustisectum* ♀ | MBri |
| *elegans* | See *P. angustisectum* |
| 'Emerald Queen' | MBri |
| *epipremnum* | See *Epipremnum pinnatum* |
| *erubescens* ♀ | MBri |
| - 'Burgundy' ♀ | MBri |
| - 'Imperial Red' | MBri |
| - 'Red Emerald' | CHal EBak MBri |
| - 'Valeria' | Last listed 1996 |
| *melanochrysum* | MBri |
| 'New Red' | MBri |
| *panduriforme* | See *P. bipennifolium* |
| *pedatum* | MBri |
| 'Purple Queen' | MBri |
| *radiatum* | MBri |
| *scandens* ♀ | CHal LBlo |
| *selloum* | EOas WMul |
| *sodiroi* | See *P. ornatum* |
| *tuxtlanum* 'Royal Queen' | MBri |
| - 'Tuxtla' | MBri |

## PHLEBODIUM (Polypodiaceae)

| | |
|---|---|
| ♦ *aureum* | See *Polypodium aureum* |

## PHLEUM (Poaceae)

| | |
|---|---|
| *hirsutum* | Last listed 1997 |
| *pratense* | EHoe EPla |
| - subsp. *bertolonii* | CKin |

## PHLOMIS ✿ (Lamiaceae)

| | |
|---|---|
| *alpina* | Last listed 1997 |
| * *anatolica* | CHan ELan LRHS |
| * - 'Lloyd's Variety' | CAbP EBee EHic ELan EPla GCal LHop MBri MSte MUlv SBid SPan SPer WEas WPen WWat |
| *angustifolia* | SBid |
| aff. *anisodonta* | WPhl |
| ¶ *armeniaca* | WLin |
| *atropurpurea* | GBin GNau WPhl |
| *betonicoides* | WPhl |

| | |
|---|---|
| – B&L 12600 | Last listed 1998 |
| *bourgaei* JMT 260 | WPhl |
| – 'Whirling Dervish' JMT 271 | WPhl |
| *bovei* subsp. *maroccana* | CBot CHan EPla GCal LFis LPio |
| | NLak NTow WCot WPhl |
| *breviflora* | WPhl |
| *cancellata* | CHan |
| *cashmeriana* | CArn CBot CGle CHan CPle ECha |
| | NLar WPhl WPic |
| – CC&MR 31 | Last listed 1997 |
| *chrysophylla* ♀ | CAbP CBot CHan CPle CSam EAst |
| | EBee ELan MDun NTow SBid |
| | SDix SDry SIgm SPan SPer SRms |
| | WCot WPhl WWat |
| *crinita* | WPhl |
| *cypria* | WPhl |
| § 'Edward Bowles' | SDry SIgm SLPl SLon SPan WCot |
| | WPhl |
| * 'Elliot's Variety' | CPLG |
| *fruticosa* ♀ | More than 30 suppliers |
| – SCH 3149 | WHCr |
| *grandiflora* | CBot ELan SEND |
| – JMT 256 | WPhl |
| *italica* | More than 30 suppliers |
| *lanata* | CAbP CFee CHan CMil EBee ELan |
| | EPPr LHop SBid SBla SDry SPan |
| | SPer WEas WGer WPhl WWat |
| | WWye |
| *leucophracta* | LRHS |
| – 'Golden Janissary' JMT 255 | WPhl |
| ¶ – 'Silver Janissary' | WPhl |
| *linearis* var. *plumosa* | WPhl |
| JMT 416 | |
| *longifolia* | CBot CHad CHan SIgm SPer |
| – var. *bailanica* | CPle LRHS WFar WSPU WWat |
| – var. *longifolia* | WPhl |
| *lunariifolia* JMT 258 | WPhl |
| *lychnitis* | WPhl |
| *lycia* | CAbP CHan LRHS SIgm WPhl |
| ¶ *macrophylla* HWJCM 250 | WCru |
| *monocephala* | WPhl |
| ¶ *nissolei* JMT 268 | WPhl |
| *platystegia* | WPhl |
| *purpurea* | CHan CPle CSam ELan EPfP GVic |
| | NBir SBid SPan SRCN WCot WPhl |
| | WSHC WWat |
| – *alba* | CBot CHan EPfP LHop SBid WPhl |
| – subsp. *almeriensis* | CHan NLak WPhl |
| – dark form | Last listed 1996 |
| – 'Green Leaf' JMT 499 | WPhl |
| *rigida* | EBee WCru |
| § *russeliana* ♀ | More than 30 suppliers |
| *samia* Boissier | See *P. russeliana* |
| – L. 'Green Cap' JMT 285 | WPhl |
| – 'Green Glory' | WPhl |
| sp. B&SWJ 2210 | Last listed 1997 |
| *tuberosa* | CBot CFir CHan CPou EGar EMan |
| | EPPr GCal MCAu NChi NLar NSti |
| | SIgm SMad SOkh SSvw WCru |
| | WPGP WPhl |
| – 'Amazone' | CFir CWit EAst EBee ECha EFou |
| | LFis LGre WHil |
| *viscosa* hort. | See *P. russeliana* |
| – Poiret | WPhl |

## PHLOX ✿ (Polemoniaceae)

| | |
|---|---|
| *adsurgens* ♀ | ITim WAbe |
| – 'Alba' | SBla WAbe |
| – 'Red Buttes' | CGle CLyd ELan EPot LHop LPio |
| | SAga SBla SCro |

| | |
|---|---|
| – 'Wagon Wheel' | CHea CLyd EBee EBrP EBre EHyt |
| | ELan EPot EWes LBee LBre LHop |
| | MBro NFla NHar NMen NRoo |
| | SBre SIng SMrm SUsu WAbe |
| | WCom WCot WFar WPat WRus |
| | WWin |
| *albomarginata* | CGra |
| *amoena* hort. | See *P.* x *procumbens* |
| x *arendsii* 'Anja' | WCot WRus |
| ¶ – 'Cathelijne' | WLin |
| – 'Hilda' | CStr |
| – 'Lisbeth' | EBee WCot |
| § – 'Luc's Lilac' | MHlr WCot |
| – 'Suzanne' | NLar WCot |
| *austromontana* | EPot NMen NWCA |
| *bifida* | ITim NHol |
| – 'Alba' | EHyt WAbe WLin |
| – blue | CStr ELan SUsu |
| – 'Colvin's White' | CLyd SBla |
| – 'Minima Colvin' | ECtt EPot |
| – 'Onsted Gem' | Last listed 1996 |
| ✛ 'Petticoat' | CLyd CMea EPot LBee MDHE |
| | NCat SBla SUsu WAbe WLin |
| – 'Ralph Haywood' | CLyd WLin |
| – 'Starbrite' | CLyd ITim MDHE MOne NMen |
| | SBla WFar |
| – 'Sunset' | Last listed 1998 |
| * – 'The Fi' | EWes WAbe WIvy |
| 'Black Buttes' | CLyd NNrd NTow WAbe |
| 'Bleeklila' | WCot |
| *borealis* | ELan EWes GDra ITim |
| * – *arctica* | EPot |
| ♦ *bryoides* | See *P. muscoides* |
| *caespitosa* | CMea EWes GCHN ITim NHed |
| | NMen |
| ♦ – subsp. *condensata* | See *P. condensata* |
| *canadensis* | See *P. divaricata* |
| *carolina* 'Bill Baker' | More than 30 suppliers |
| – 'Magnificence' | EMon EWes GBuc MSte SMrm |
| | SOkh SSvw SUsu SWas |
| – 'Miss Lingard' ♀ | CBos CGle CHea CMGP CSam |
| | EBee EFou EMan GBuc GCal |
| | LRHS MBel MBro MMil MRav |
| | MSte NRoo NSti NTow SChu SCro |
| | SDix SHel SMrm SOkh WHil |
| | WMaN |
| * 'Casablanca' | Last listed 1998 |
| * 'Chanel' | MLan |
| 'Charles Ricardo' | CBos GBuc GMac MBro NTow |
| | SHel SMrm SPla SSca SUsu SWas |
| | SWat WAbe WHoo WPyg WRus |
| 'Chattahoochee' | See *P. divaricata* subsp. *laphamii* |
| * *chonela* 'Nana' | CMea |
| § *condensata* | GCrs IMGH ITim NWCA WAbe |
| ♦ *covillei* | See *P. condensata* |
| 'Daniel's Cushion' | See *P. subulata* 'McDaniel's |
| | Cushion' |
| *diffusa* | Last listed 1998 |
| – NNS 95-46 | Last listed 1998 |
| § *divaricata* ♀ | EHol MRav MSte NPri SBod SHel |
| | SPlb WCot WPer WRus WWin |
| – f. *albiflora* | ELan |
| – 'Blue Dreams' | More than 30 suppliers |
| – 'Blue Perfume' | EFou EMil NBrk |
| – 'Clouds of Perfume' | CHea EBee EFou GBri GMaP NCat |
| | NFla NHol NLar NSti SBla SBod |
| | SCro SMrm SSvw SWat WFar |
| | WRus WSan |
| – 'Dirigo Ice' | CLyd EMan ERav LFis LGre MBel |
| | NBrk NDov NHol SBla WFar WIvy |
| | WRHF WRus |
| – 'Eco Regal' | Last listed 1998 |

| | |
|---|---|
| - 'Eco Texas Purple' | CLAP CRDP EMan MAvo NBrk NHar SIgm SUsu WRus WThi |
| - 'Fuller's White' | CLyd MAvo SUsu |
| § - subsp. *laphamii* | CLyd EWes NDov NSti NVic SBod WCru WFoF WHer WRus WThi |
| - - 'Chattahoochee' ♀ | CBot CHea CSpe EBee ELan EMNN EPot EWes GCrs GMac LBee LHop MBro NHol NWes SBla SBod SIng SLod SMrm SUsu WAbe WCom WMaN WPat WSHC WWin |
| - - 'Chattahoochee Variegated' | EWes LHop LRHS NLar WCot |
| - 'Louisiana Purple' | SWas WThi |
| - 'May Breeze' | CLyd EBrP EBre EMan GMaP GMac LBre LHop MHar MHlr MNrw MSte NBrk NHar NRoo SAga SBla SBre SHel SMrm SWas WCot WElm WFar WIvy WOve WPGP WRHF WRus |
| * - 'White Perfume' | EMil MBrN |
| *douglasii* | NHol NWCA SRms |
| - 'Apollo' | CLyd CPBP EPot GDra NHol NMen SAga WAbe WWin |
| - 'Boothman's Variety' ♀ | CGle CLyd CNic ECha ELan EPar EPot MPla MWat NMen SBod SRms WEas WHoo WWin |
| - 'Concorde' | GDra |
| - 'Crackerjack' ♀ | CLyd ELan EMNN EPot GAbr GDra ITim LBee MPla MWat NHar NMen NRoo SAga SBod SIng WAbe WLin |
| - 'Eva' | CLyd CM&M EBrP EBre ELan EMNN GTou LBre MOne NBir NFla NHar NHol NMen NRoo SBod SBre SMrm WPer WWin |
| - 'Galaxy' | CLyd EWes GDra NHar |
| - 'Holden Variety' | Last listed 1998 |
| - 'Ice Mountain' | ECho ELan NPri SMrm SRot |
| - 'Iceberg' ♀ | CLyd EPot GDra GMaP ITim NHar NMen WWin |
| - 'J.A. Hibberson' | CLyd EPot |
| - Lilac Queen | See *P.douglasii* 'Lilakönigin' |
| § - 'Lilakönigin' | CLyd |
| - 'Millstream Laura' | Last listed 1996 |
| - x *multiflora* var. *depressa* | Last listed 1997 |
| ¶ - 'Ochsenblut' | MDHE |
| - 'Pink Chint' | Last listed 1996 |
| - 'Red Admiral' ♀ | EBrP EBre EMNN EPot ESis EWes GCHN GCrs GDra LBre NHar NHol NLon NMen NRoo SBod SBre SMrm WFar |
| - 'Rose Cushion' | EWes GDra LRHS MDHE MPla NMen |
| - 'Rose Queen' | CLyd CStr GDra |
| - 'Rosea' | EBrP EBre ELan EMNN EPar ESis LBre MBal NMen NRoo SBod SBre SMer SMrm WFar |
| - 'Silver Rose' | GCrs GTou |
| - 'Sprite' | SRms |
| - 'Tycoon' | See *P.subulata* 'Tamaongalei' |
| - 'Violet Queen' | ELan EWes GDra NHar NHol WFar |
| - 'Waterloo' | CLyd CPBP EPot GAri LHop NHar NHol NMen SChu WWin |
| - 'White Drift' | Last listed 1996 |
| *drummondii* | SAga |
| 'Geddington Cross' | MAvo MGed MWgw |
| * 'Herfstsering' | Last listed 1998 |
| * 'Hesperis' | LGre |
| *hirsuta* | NWCA |
| *boodii* | CLyd ECho WAbe |
| * 'Hortensia' | Last listed 1998 |
| 'Kelly's Eye' ♀ | CLyd CM&M CPBP CSam ECha ECtt ELan EMNN EPot GAbr LHop MMil NMen NRoo SBod SIng WFar WPer |
| *kelseyi* | EHyt NWCA |
| - 'Lemhi Purple' | CGra CPBP |
| - 'Rosette' | CLyd EPot NMen WPer |
| *longifolia* | Last listed 1998 |
| ¶ 'Louisiana' | WHil |
| *maculata* | NOrc WPer |
| - 'Alba' | Last listed 1997 |
| - 'Alpha' ♀ | More than 30 suppliers |
| - Avalanche | See *P.maculata* 'Schneelawine' |
| - 'Delta' | CBos CHea EBee EFou LRot MLLN NCut NHol NLon NPri NSti SCro SPla WHil WMaN WRus |
| - 'Good White' | SMrm |
| - 'Natascha' | More than 30 suppliers |
| - 'Omega' ♀ | CHan CHea CMHG EBee EFou EWTr GCHN GMaP LRot MBNS MCAu MUlv NBrk NHol NLar NRoo NSti SChu SMrm SPer SSpi WFar WMaN WRus WSHC |
| - 'Princess Sturdza' | Last listed 1998 |
| ¶ - 'Reine du Jour' | LGre |
| ¶ - 'Rosalinde' | EFou EMan MBel MCAu MRav MSte NCat NHol SChu SCro WLin |
| § - 'Schneelawine' | EBee NCat WRus |
| *mesoleuca* | See *P.nana* subsp. *ensifolia* |
| Mexican hybrids | See *P.nana* |
| 'Millstream' | See *P.x procumbens* 'Millstream' |
| 'Millstream Jupiter' | NHol |
| ¶ 'Miss Wilma' (Springpearl hybrid) | CMGP EBee |
| *missoulensis* | Last listed 1997 |
| 'Mrs Campbell' | See *P.paniculata* 'Elizabeth Campbell' |
| § *muscoides* | EWes |
| § *nana* subsp. *ensifolia* | Last listed 1997 |
| - 'Manzano' | Last listed 1996 |
| ¶ - 'Mary Maslin' | SBla |
| - 'Vanilla Cream' | SBla |
| *nivalis* | NMen |
| - 'Camlaensis' | CLyd ELan EPot ITim LHop WPat |
| - 'Jill Alexander' | Last listed 1997 |
| - 'Nivea' | WLRN |
| ¶ *ovata* | MNrw WRus |
| *paniculata* | CHad EWTr LGre NBid NFor SDix WCot |
| - 'A.E.Amos' | CTri ERou |
| - 'Aida' | CB&S EGar ERou MWat WRus |
| - var. *alba* | CBos GCal SDix WCot |
| - 'Alba Grandiflora' ♀ | MCAu WEas |
| - 'Albert Leo Schlageter' ♀ | ERou SRms |
| - 'Alexander' | Last listed 1998 |
| - 'Amethyst' | CFir CKel CSam EGar EPfP ERou GHCN LFis MBNS MBel NBir |
| - 'Annie Laurie' | Last listed 1997 |
| - 'Anthony Six' | Last listed 1997 |
| - 'Balmoral' | CGle CM&M ECtt EOld LLWP MLLN MRav MSte NSti SMrm SPla SWat WHil WLRN WWal |
| - 'Barnwell' | EFou ELan WMer |
| - 'Betty Symons-Jeune' | ERou |
| - 'Bill Green' | LRHS SMrm |
| - 'Blue Boy' | CM&M EBee EFou ERou MBel NCut WBay WHoo WMer WSan |
| ¶ - 'Blue Evening' | LGre |
| - 'Blue Ice' ♀ | CSev EBee EFou ELan MWat NRoo SMrm WCot WLRN |
| - 'Blue Moon' | GHCN |

| | |
|---|---|
| - 'Blue Paradise' | EFou LGre MBNS MBri MRav MSte SAga SBla SMrm SVil WFar WHil WRus |
| - 'Blushing Bride' | SRms |
| - 'Bonny Maid' | CBla |
| - 'Border Gem' | CB&S EBee EBrP EBre EFou EMon LBre MSte MTis NCut NRoo SBre SMrm SWat WCot |
| - 'Branklyn' | EBrP EBre LBre LGre MArl MRav SBre WFar |
| - 'Bressingham White' | NBrk |
| - 'Brigadier' ♀ | CBla CSam CTri ELan GHCN GMaP MFir MLLN MWat NRoo SMrm SPer SRms SSoC |
| - 'Bright Eyes' ♀ | CBla CBlo CKel COtt EBee EBrP EBre ENot ERic LBre LRHS MArl MBel NRoo SBre |
| - 'Caroline van den Berg' | CTri EGar ERou SMer SRms WCot |
| - 'Cecil Hanbury' | CBlo ERou SRms |
| - 'Charmaine' | CBla |
| - 'Chintz' | MRav SRms |
| - 'Cinderella' | ERou MBel NLar NPri WMer |
| - 'Cool of the Evening' | CBla CBos MRav |
| - 'Count Zeppelin' | See *P. paniculata* 'Graf Zeppelin' |
| ◆ - 'Darwin's Joyce' | See *P. paniculata* 'Norah Leigh' |
| - 'David' | CStr NLak WHil |
| ¶ - 'Discovery' | LBuc |
| - 'Dodo Hanbury Forbes' ♀ | CBla CKel EGar EHol |
| - 'Dresden China' | ERou |
| - 'Düsterlohe' | CPlt CSam CStr GBuc SMrm |
| - 'Eclaireur' | EBee |
| - 'Elie' | EBee LFis MSCN NFai |
| - 'Elizabeth Arden' | EFou ERou MSte WMaN |
| - 'Endurance' | ERou |
| - 'Etoile de Paris' | LGre SUsu SWas |
| - 'Europe' | CB&S CGle EBee EFou ELan EOld ERou MBri MCAu MFir MWat NFai NRoo SMrm SPer WFar WMer WWal |
| - 'Eva Cullum' | CM&M CTri EBrP EBre EFou LBre LHop MArl MLLN MRav NFai NRoo SBre SPer WCot |
| - 'Eventide' ♀ | EBee EBrP EBre ECtt EFou EGar EHal ERic ERou EWTr GChr LBre MArl MCAu NLar NRoo SBre SMrm SPer WCot WViv |
| - 'Excelsior' | CBlo MRav |
| - 'Fairy's Petticoat' | MWat WCot |
| - 'Firefly' | Last listed 1997 |
| - 'Flamingo' | EFou MBNS NLar |
| - 'Franz Schubert' | CHea CTri EBee EBrP EBre ECGP EFou EGar GMac LBre MHlr MTis NLar NRoo NSti SBre WCot WMaN WSan |
| § - 'Frau A. von Mauthner' | LBuc |
| ¶ - 'Frosted Elegance' | EFou |
| § - 'Fujiyama' ♀ | More than 30 suppliers |
| - 'Gaiety' | Last listed 1996 |
| - 'Glamis' | CBla MWat |
| § - 'Graf Zeppelin' | CBla ELan MWat SRms |
| - 'Hampton Court' | NBrk |
| - 'Harewood' | ERou |
| - 'Harlequin' (v) | CKel CMil EBee EBrP EBre ECha GBuc LBre MRav NBid SBre SPla WCot WFar |
| - 'Iceberg' | MFir |
| - 'Iris' | GBuc LGre LPio SMrm SRms SWas |
| - 'Jules Sandeau' | Last listed 1997 |
| § - 'Juliglut' | ELan EMil MWat WCot |
| - July Glow | See *P. paniculata* 'Juliglut' |
| ¶ - 'Kirchenfuerst' | EFou |

| | |
|---|---|
| - 'Kirmesländler' | CB&S ERou MLLN SRPl |
| - 'Lady Clare' | SRms |
| - 'Latest Red' | See *P. paniculata* 'Spätrot' |
| * - 'Laura' | COtt EBee GNau LFis LWoo MSCN NCut SCob WHil WHoo |
| § - 'Lavendelwolke' | ELan LGre |
| - Lavender Cloud | See *P. paniculata* 'Lavendelwolke' |
| - 'Le Mahdi' ♀ | ELan MRav MWat SRms WCot |
| ¶ - 'Lichtspiel' | LGre |
| - 'Lilac Time' | CBla EBee EWll MBel NCat NPla |
| - 'Little Boy' | EBee MSCN NCut WHoo WRus |
| ¶ - 'Little Laura' | EFou |
| - 'Little Lovely' | Last listed 1998 |
| ¶ - 'Lizzy' | MBri |
| - 'Look Again' | ERou |
| ¶ - 'Mary Christine' | EBee |
| - 'Mary Fox' | CSam ERou MRav NRoo |
| - 'Mia Ruys' | EFou EHal ERou MArl MLLN WMer |
| - 'Mies Copijn' | GMaP WMer |
| * - 'Miss Elie' | CMGP EFou LWoo WHil WHoo |
| - 'Miss Holland' | EFou WHoo |
| - 'Miss Jill' | EBee EFou GMaP MSCN NCut NRoo WCot WElm WRus |
| - 'Miss Jo Ellen' | EBee EFou GBri MSCN NRoo |
| - 'Miss Karen' | MSCN NRoo |
| - 'Miss Kelly' | CMGP COtt EBee EFou MSCN NCut WHil WSan |
| - 'Miss Margie' | EBee EFou GBri GMaP MSCN NCut NRoo |
| - 'Miss Mary' | EBee EFou GBri NCut NRoo WRus |
| * - 'Miss Pepper' | EFou EMil LFis MAvo NFai WHil |
| - 'Miss Universe' | EBee EFou LWoo MCCP NCut WHoo |
| * - 'Monica Lynden-Bell' | MHlr NCat WCot |
| - 'Mother of Pearl' ♀ | CBla CGle CHad CKel EBee EBrP EBre ELan LBre MWat NVic SBre SPer WCot |
| - 'Mount Fujiyama' | See *P. paniculata* 'Fujiyama' |
| - 'Mrs A.E. Jeans' | SRms |
| - 'Mrs Fincham' | LFis |
| - 'Newbird' | ERou SRms |
| * - 'Nicky' | EFou LFis MRav WHil |
| - 'Norah Leigh' (v) | More than 30 suppliers |
| - 'Orange Perfection' | CB&S CBlo CM&M EBee EPfP MAvo MBNS MCCP MCli NCut NPri SCob WBay WViv |
| - 'Othello' | CBla |
| - 'Otley Choice' | CBlo CM&M CMil EAst ERic LFis MSte MWat NLak NLar NRoo NSti SCoo SMrm WLRN |
| ¶ - 'P.D. Williams' | WCot |
| - 'Pastorale' | MWat NCat WCot |
| ¶ - 'Pat Coleman' | EFou |
| - 'Pax' | LGre WBay WViv |
| - 'Pike' | WCot |
| ¶ - 'Pink Posie' (v) | LRHS MAsh MBri SPer WCot WWeb |
| ¶ - 'Popeye' | MBri |
| - 'Prime Minister' | CStr NLak |
| - 'Prince of Orange' ♀ | CBla CBlo CElw CGle CMGP CSam EBee EBrP EBre EFou ELan ERou LBre MRav MWat NRoo SAga SBre SMrm SPer SSoC WCot WWal |
| - 'Prospero' ♀ | CBla CSam EOrc LFis MBel MCAu MHlr MRav NRoo SMrm SPer WCot |
| - 'Rapture' | MWat |
| - 'Red Indian' | ERou MWat |
| - 'Rembrandt' | ERou SBla WCot |

- 'Rheinländer' — Last listed 1997
- 'Rijnstroom' — CB&S ECot ERou LFis MBel NCat NFai SMrm WCot WViv WWal
- 'Rosa Pastell' — LGre SAga
- 'Rosa Spier' — WMer
- 'Rougham Supreme' — ERou
- 'Russian Violet' — MRav MWat
- 'San Antonio' — MBel MRav SMrm WCot
- 'Sandringham' — CBlo CSam CTri EBee EBrP EBre ELan EWTr LBre MArl MNrw MRav MSte NBir NLak NRoo NVic SBre SMrm SPer SRPl
- 'Schneerausch' — LGre WCot
- 'Septemberglut' — EBee LWoo WHil
- 'Silver Salmon' — WCot
- 'Sir John Falstaff' — Last listed 1997
- 'Sir Malcolm Campbell' — ERou
- 'Skylight' — EBee MWat NVic SMrm SPer WCot WLRN WLin WWal
- 'Snowball' — Last listed 1997
- 'Snowdrift' — ERou
§ - 'Spätrot' — Last listed 1998
- 'Spitfire' — See *P. paniculata* 'Frau A. von Mauthner'
- 'Starfire' — CB&S CBla CBlo CGle CSam EBee EBrP EBre EFou ELan ENot ERou GMaP LBre LFis LRot MArl MBNS MFir MHlr MRav NRoo NSti SBre SPer SRms WCot WHil WMer WRus
* - 'Steeple Bumpstead' — CMil WCot
- 'Sternhimmel' — ERou LGre
- 'Sweetheart' — Last listed 1998
- 'Tenor' — CBlo CFir CKel CM&M CTri EBee ECGP EFou ERic LRot MBel MSte NCut NFai NPri SMrm WFar
- 'The King' — EBee LRHS WBay WViv
- 'Toits de Paris' — MWat
* - 'Úspech' — EFou LBuc MSte NLak
¶ - 'Utopia' — LGre
- 'Vintage Wine' — CTri MAvo MCli WMer
- 'Violetta Gloriosa' — LGre
¶ - 'Visions' — EBee
- 'White Admiral' ♀ — CB&S CBla CGle CHad CM&M EBee EBrP EBre ELan ENot EWTr GChr GMaP LBre MBNS MBel MRav MUlv MWat NFai NRoo NVic SBre SCob SMrm SPer SRms WMer WMow WWal
- 'William Ramsay' — CTri ELan EOld
- 'Windsor' ♀ — CBla CBlo EFou EPfP ERou EWTr GChr LFis MBel MCAu MLLN MTis NPla NRoo SCoo SMrm SRms

*pilosa* — CMGP EBrP EBre ECha EFou LBre NHol NPro SBre SMrm SUsu WRus
§ x *procumbens* — ELan LHop NDov NTow SAga SBla WThi WWin
'Millstream' ♀
- 'Variegata' — CBot CPBP ECha EHyt ELan EMNN ESis MPla MRav MTho NHol NRoo NWCA SBla SPlb WAbe WCot WFar WLin WPat WWin
*pulchra* 'Eco Pale Moon' — CStr WThi
- 'Eco Place' — CRDP
x *rugellii* — NHol
'Scented Pillow' — LRHS NOla WWeb
¶ *stansburyi* — CPBP
*stolonifera* — EPar GMaP MHar MNrw NPla NPri SAga WCot WMer

- 'Ariane' — CMil EBee ECha ELan EPar LHop MBro MNrw NHar NLar SAga SBla SMrm SWas SWat WAbe WFar WViv WWin
- 'Blue Ridge' ♀ — CFir CHan CPea EBee ECha EGle ELan EMan EPar GBuc GMaP IMGH LFis LHop NHar NLar NRoo SAga SIng SMrm SRms SSca SUsu SWat WSan WWin
* - 'Bob's Motley' (v) — WCot
- 'Bruce's White' — Last listed 1997
- compact form — Last listed 1998
- 'Compact Pink' — LHop NCat SAga SWas WFar
- 'Fran's Purple' — CLAP CLyd EMan NHar NRoo SCro WAbe WFar
- 'Home Fires' — EBee MNrw NHar
- 'Mary Belle Frey' — EBee EBrP EBre EMan EOrc LBre LHop MSte NLar NRoo NSti SAga SBla SBre SCro SMrm SUsu WFar WWin
- 'Pink Ridge' — CLAP GBuc MNrw NCut NHar NLar NRoo
- 'Purpurea' — NHar
- variegated — MHlr MNrw MRav WAbe WCot
- 'Violet Vere' — CLAP CLyd CPBP CSpe CStr EGle GBuc LHop MBro MNrw NHar SAga SBla SLod SMrm WFar WHal WPyg
*subulata* — EPar NWCA
- 'Alexander's Surprise' — CGle CMHG CMea ECtt EPot GAbr GCHN LHop MBal NBir NFla NHol NMen SChu
- 'Amazing Grace' — CTri ELan ESis EWes LHop MOne MPla NMen NPri NRoo NSla SChu SIng WAbe WPer WWin
- 'Apple Blossom' — GAbr GDra GMaP NPri SAga WLRN WRHF
- 'Atropurpurea' — EBrP EBre GCHN LBre MRav NFor NLon SBre WWin
- 'Beauty of Ronsdorf' — See *P. subulata* 'Ronsdorfer Schöne'
- 'Betty' — CTri ECtt EMNN MBNS MDHE NCat NMen NRoo WPer
- 'Blue Eyes' — See *P. subulata* 'Oakington Blue Eyes'
- 'Blue Saucer' — EPot MDHE
- 'Bonita' — CStr EMNN GAri LBee NPri NRoo SMer SMrm WWin
- 'Bressingham Blue Eyes' — See *P. subulata* 'Oakington Blue Eyes'
- 'Brightness' — CTri GCHN GTou SIng
- subsp. *brittonii* 'Rosea' — NHol WPer WRHF
- 'Candy Stripe' — EPfP LRHS NHol
¶ - 'Cavaldes White' — NCat
- 'Christine Bishop' — SAga
- 'Coral Eye' — EPfP
- 'Daisy Hill' — Last listed 1998
- 'Drumm' — See *P. subulata* 'Tamaongalei'
- 'Eco Pale Moon' — Last listed 1998
- 'Emerald Cushion' — CSam EMan EWTr NLon SAga SCob SIng
- 'Emerald Cushion Blue' — CLyd CNic EBrP EBre ELan GTou LBre MBal MMal NHol NMen NRoo SBod SBre SMrm WAbe WPer
- 'Fairy' — SAga WPer
♦ - 'G.F.Wilson' — See *P. subulata* 'Lilacina'
- 'Greencourt Purple' — CMea NCat
* - 'Holly' — EPot MDHE NMen
- 'Jupiter' — SChu
- 'Kimono' — See *P. subulata* 'Tamaongalei'

| | |
|---|---|
| § - 'Lilacina' | CLyd CMea ECha ECtt ELan GTou LGro MBal MWat NFor NMen NRoo NVic SChu WAbe WPer WWin |
| § - 'Maischnee' | CLyd EBrP EBre ECtt ELan EMNN EPot EWTr GAbr LBre LGro LHop MBal MOne MPla MWat NFor NHol NRoo SBre SMrm SUsu WEas WWin |
| - 'Marjorie' | CLyd CMHG ECtt ELan EMNN MBal MBro MHar MMal NMen NPri WEas WHoo WLRN |
| - 'Mauve Queen' | MWat |
| - May Snow = 'Maischnee' | See P.subulata 'Maischnee' |
| § - 'McDaniel's Cushion' ♀ | CLyd EBrP EBre ECha ELan EMNN EPot ESis GTou ITim LBee LBre MMil NFor NHol NLon NMen NRoo SBre SUsu WFar WHoo WPer WWin |
| - 'Mikado' | See P.subulata 'Tamaongalei' |
| - 'Model' | LGro NSla |
| - 'Moonlight' | CLyd ECtt MBro SAga SLod WPer WRHF |
| - 'Nelsonii' | Last listed 1997 |
| - 'Nettleton Variation' (v) | CMea CMil CPBP EDAr ELan EPot ESis EWes GMaP LHop MBro NHol NPri NRoo SAga SIng SPlb SUsu WAbe WCot WPat |
| § - 'Oakington Blue Eyes' | EBrP EBre ECGP EPar GCHN GDra LBre NRoo SBre SMrm SRms WPer |
| ¶ - 'Pink Buttons' | NCat |
| - 'Pink Pearl' | EWes |
| - 'Red Wings' ♀ | CGra CPBP EBrP EBre ECtt GCHN LBre MBal MWgw NFor NMen NPri NRoo SAga SBre SIng SRms WFar |
| § - 'Ronsdorfer Schöne' | EPot LBee NNrd |
| - 'Rose Mabel' | Last listed 1996 |
| - 'Samson' | ELan GTou MHar SBod SMer WPer WWin |
| - 'Scarlet Flame' | CMea CSam EBrP EBre ECha ECtt ELan EMNN LBre LGro MBal MWat NHol SAga SBod SBre SMrm SUsu WPer WWin |
| - 'Schneewittchen' | CLyd |
| - 'Sensation' | GTou SRms |
| - 'Snow Queen' | See P.subulata 'Maischnee' |
| - 'Southcroft' | Last listed 1997 |
| - 'Starglow' | GTou SIng WPer |
| § - 'Tamaongalei' | More than 30 suppliers |
| - 'Temiskaming' | ECha ELan EMNN ENot EWes GCHN GDra LGro MHar NMen NRoo SAga SChu SRms WAbe WCom WEas |
| - violet seedling | CLyd NHol |
| - 'White Delight' | CLyd EBrP EBre ECtt ELan EMNN GCHN GTou LBre NMen NRoo SBod SBre SRms WPer |
| - 'White Swan' | Last listed 1997 |
| - 'Winifred' | Last listed 1996 |
| * 'Sweet William' | Last listed 1998 |
| ¶ 'Tiny Bugles' | CGra |
| 'Vivid' | EDAr MDHE SIgm |

## PHOENICAULIS (Brassicaceae)

| | |
|---|---|
| § cheirantboides | NWCA |

## PHOENIX (Arecaceae)

| | |
|---|---|
| canariensis ♀ | CB&S CBrP CGre CTbh CTrC LPJP LPal MBri MCCP NPal SAPC SArc SEND WMul |
| dactylifera (F) | LPal |
| paludosa | LPal |
| reclinata | CRoM CTrC LPJP NPal |
| roebelenii ♀ | CBrP CRoM LPal MBri NPal WMul |
| rupicola | CRoM LPal |
| sylvestris | LPal |
| theophrasti | LPJP LPal |

## PHORMIUM ✿ (Agavaceae)

| | |
|---|---|
| ¶ 'Amazing Red' | MLov |
| 'Apricot Queen' (v) | CAbb CB&S CDoC EBee GQui IBlr IOrc LRHS MBal NPri SSto WBod WCot |
| Ballyrogan variegated | IBlr |
| * 'Black Edge' | IBlr MRav |
| 'Bronze Baby' | More than 30 suppliers |
| colensoi | See P.cookianum |
| § cookianum ♀ | CAgr CB&S CHan CTrC ECre EMil IBlr IOrc LPal MBal MGos MUlv SAPC SArc SLPl WMul WWat |
| - 'Alpinum Purpureum' | See P.tenax 'Nanum Purpureum' |
| * - 'Flamingo' | EBee ECre IOrc SSto |
| - subsp. bookeri 'Cream Delight' (v) ♀ | CAbb CB&S CDoC CEnd CTrC EBee EHoe ELan ENot IOrc LHil MBal MBlu MGos NArg NFla SAga SPer SRPl WLRN WLeb |
| - - 'Tricolor' ♀ | CDoC CFil CTrC EBee ELan ENot EPla IBlr IOrc MBal SArc SHFr SRms SSpi WCot WDin WLeb WPGP |
| * 'Copper Beauty' | CBlo CDoC COtt EHic NMoo WLRN |
| 'Dark Delight' | CB&S IBlr IOrc MAsh |
| 'Dazzler' (v) | CSpe IBlr IOrc MBal MGos WCot |
| 'Duet' (v) ♀ | CB&S CDoC COtt CTrC EBee EHoe IBlr IOrc SSto WBcn |
| ¶ 'Dusky Chief' | WMul |
| * 'Emerald Pink' | COtt WGer |
| 'Evening Glow' | CTrC ECle EPfP IBlr IOrc LRHS MAsh NOla SPla |
| ¶ 'Firebird' | CB&S |
| ¶ 'Flamingo' | WPat |
| 'Gold Sword' (v) | CB&S COtt EBee IBlr |
| 'Guardsman' (v) | IBlr |
| 'Jack Spratt' (v) | CB&S COtt ECou EHoe IBlr IOrc WLeb |
| 'Jester' | CB&S CDoC CFir COtt CSpe CTrC EHoe ELan ENot EWll GQui IBlr LEdu MAsh MCCP SPla WBcn WBod WCot WLeb |
| § 'Maori Chief' (v) | CFil EHic GQui IBlr IOrc LRHS WCot WLRN WPGP |
| 'Maori Eclipse' | CBlo |
| § 'Maori Maiden' (v) | CB&S CTrC ECre EHic EHoe GQui IOrc MBal MGos MSCN SPla SSto WBod WCot WLeb |
| § 'Maori Queen' (v) | CB&S CDoC GQui IBlr IOrc MAsh MGos SSto WLRN |
| § 'Maori Sunrise' (v) | CB&S CBlo CDoC EBee IBlr IOrc MCCP MGos MSte NPri SAga SSoC WAbe WLRN |
| 'Pink Panther' (v) | CAbb CB&S CBlo CDoC ELan EPfP EWll GQui IBlr IOrc LEdu MAsh MGos NPri SPla WBod WDin WLeb |
| * 'Pink Stripe' | EBee ECle IBlr IOrc WCot |
| ¶ 'Platt's Black' | CB&S EPfP LRHS SMad SVen |
| 'Rainbow Chief' | See P.'Maori Chief' |
| Rainbow hybrids | CSpe MBal |
| 'Rainbow Maiden' | See P.'Maori Maiden' |
| 'Rainbow Queen' | See P.'Maori Queen' |
| 'Rainbow Sunrise' | See P.'Maori Sunrise' |

| | |
|---|---|
| 'Sea Jade' | IBlr |
| ¶ 'Stormy Dawn' | WCot |
| 'Sundowner' (v) ♀ | CB&S CDoC CSpe CTrC EBee ECre ELan EMil ENot EOld GQui IBlr IOrc MBal MGos SLdr SMad SPer SSoC WCot WFar WLeb WStI |
| 'Sunset' (v) | IBlr IOrc |
| 'Surfer' (v) | COtt ECle EHoe IBlr IOrc MCCP WBcn WLeb WWat |
| *tenax* ♀ | More than 30 suppliers |
| - 'Co-ordination' | CAbb ECle IBlr IOrc SSto WBcn |
| ¶ - 'Dark Edge' | ERav |
| * - 'Dwarf' | EMil IBlr |
| * - *lineatum* | SEND |
| § - 'Nanum Purpureum' ♀ | CHad CRDP IBlr MSte SEND SWas WCot |
| - Purpureum Group ♀ | More than 30 suppliers |
| - 'Radiance' (v) | IBlr MBal |
| - 'Rainbow Queen' | See *P.* 'Maori Queen' |
| - 'Rainbow Sunrise' | See *P.* 'Maori Sunrise' |
| - 'Variegatum' ♀ | CFil IBlr LPal LPan MBal SAPC SArc SEND SRms WBrE WMul WPat |
| - 'Veitchianum' (v) | IBlr SPer WPGP |
| - 'Yellow Queen' | Last listed 1997 |
| 'Thumbelina' | CB&S EHoe IOrc MSte WLeb |
| 'Tom Thumb' | IOrc WDin |
| 'Yellow Wave' (v) ♀ | CAbb CB&S CBlo CDoC CEnd CTrC EBee EBrP EBre EHoe ELan EMil ENot IBlr IOrc LBre MAsh MBal MBel SBre SMad SPer SRms WCot WDin |

## PHOTINIA ✿ (Rosaceae)

| | |
|---|---|
| § *arbutifolia* | CPle |
| *beauverdiana* ♀ | CPle CTho SRms WHCr WWat |
| § *davidiana* | CDul CSam EBee ELan EMil GChr GRei IOrc ISea LHop MBal MBar MRav MWat SEas SPer SRPl SRms WFar WNor WWat |
| - 'Palette' (v) | More than 30 suppliers |
| - var. *undulata* | CMHG LRHS MRav WBcn |
| - - 'Fructu Luteo' | CBlo CMHG CSam CTrG EHic EPfP EPla MBri MRav WFar WWat |
| - - 'Prostrata' | ELan EPfP MBar MRav NHol SPer WFar WWat |
| x *fraseri* | CMCN ISea |
| - 'Birmingham' | CBlo CLan EHoe LPan MBal SCob SRms WPyg WSHC WWeb |
| - 'Red Robin' ♀ | More than 30 suppliers |
| - 'Robusta' ♀ | CBlo MBal WShe WWat |
| § - 'Rubens' | ELan MAsh MBri SDry SPer SPla SSta WPat WPyg WWat |
| § *glabra* 'Parfait' (v) | CAbP ELan LHop MAsh MBal MRav SDry SPer SPla WBcn WFar WPat WPyg WWat WWeb |
| - 'Pink Lady' | See *P. glabra* 'Parfait' |
| - 'Rubens' | See *P.* x *fraseri* 'Rubens' |
| - 'Variegata' | See *P. glabra* 'Parfait' |
| *glomerata* | Last listed 1998 |
| *lasiogyna* | CMCN |
| *lindleyana* | CPle |
| *microphylla* SF 92307 | ISea |
| § - 'Redstart' ♀ | CBlo CEnd CPle EPfP MGos SLon SPer SSta SSto WWat |
| § *serratifolia* | CBlo CBot CMHG CPle EPfP MBal SAPC SArc SDry SPer SSta WBod WPGP WPat WPyg WWat |
| *serrulata* | See *P. serratifolia* |
| *villosa* ♀ | CAbP CDul CPle CTho GAri IOrc MBal MBar SSpi |
| - var. *laevis* | Last listed 1998 |

## PHRAGMITES (Poaceae)

| | |
|---|---|
| § *australis* | EMFW GBin NDea SWat |
| - var. *giganteus* | See *P. australis* subsp. *altissimus* |
| - subsp. *pseudodonax* | EMon EPPr LRHS SMad |
| - var. *striatopictus* | EMon |
| - 'Variegatus' | CCuc CInt CRDP CWat EHoe EMFW EMon EPPr EPla IBlr LHil MMoz MRav MTed MWhi NSti SMad SWyc WRus |
| *communis* | See *P. australis* |
| *karka* 'Variegatus' | Last listed 1998 |

## PHUOPSIS (Rubiaceae)

| | |
|---|---|
| § *stylosa* | CElw CLTr CSev EAst ECha ELan EMar MFir MHar MTis NBro NChi NRoo NSti SChu SHFr SMac SRCN SRms SSpe SVil WBea WFar WHal WOve WPer WWhi WWin WWye |
| - 'Purpurea' | CElw ELan MNrw MRav NBrk NCat NChi SChu SDys WByw WCom WFar WGwy WHal |

## PHYGELIUS ✿ (Scrophulariaceae)

| | |
|---|---|
| *aequalis* | CBlo CBot CFee CGle CKno CSev ELan EMil LFis MNrw MWgw SChu SDix SMac WCFE WPer WSHC WSan WWat WWhi |
| - *albus* | See *P. aequalis* 'Yellow Trumpet' |
| - 'Apricot Trumpet' | Last listed 1996 |
| - 'Aureus' | See *P. aequalis* 'Yellow Trumpet' |
| ¶ - Cedric Morris form | CKno |
| - 'Cream Trumpet' | See *P. aequalis* 'Yellow Trumpet' |
| - 'Indian Chief' | See *P.* x *rectus* 'African Queen' |
| * - 'Pink Trumpet' | CLTr EFou NFor NLon SCoo SLon SMac SMrm SOkh WRha |
| § - 'Yellow Trumpet' ♀ | More than 30 suppliers |
| ¶ 'Cabon Flame' | SVen |
| § *capensis* ♀ | More than 30 suppliers |
| - x *aequalis* | See *P.* x *rectus* |
| - *coccineus* | See *P. capensis* |
| - 'Janet's Jewel' (v) | CKno SBid |
| - orange | CKno EGar LHop SVen |
| ¶ - pink | NCat |
| - *roseus* | CTrw |
| - S&SH 50 | CHan SMac |
| 'Golden Gate' | See *P. aequalis* 'Yellow Trumpet' |
| § x *rectus* | EPla |
| § - 'African Queen' ♀ | More than 30 suppliers |
| - 'Devil's Tears' ♀ | CB&S CBrm CDoC CFee CKno CM&M EAst EBee EMil ENot EPla GEil LHop MAsh MBNS MBri MBro NFai NGdn NHol SAga SCro SMac WGwG WHil WHoo WMer WPer WWat WWeb |
| - 'Moonraker' | CChe CDoC CKno CLTr ECtt ELan EMil ESis GOrc LFis MBNS MBro MRav NFai NLar NRoo SMac SMad SRms SUsu WBea WHoo WMer WWat |
| - 'Pink Elf' | CKno ELan ERav ESis GOrc SLon SMac |
| - 'Salmon Leap' ♀ | CKno CM&M EAst EOrc EPla GChr LHil LHop MAsh MBNS MBel MBri NFai SHFr SMac SUsu WFar WHal WHil WOve WPer WWeb |
| - 'Sunshine' | CKno COtt LWoo WWeb |
| § - 'Winchester Fanfare' | More than 30 suppliers |
| - 'Winton Fanfare' | See *P.* x *rectus* 'Winchester Fanfare' |
| ¶ 'Sensation' | CKno MAsh MHlr SBla SCoo SPer |

'Trewidden Pink'

CBrm CCHP CChe CKno CM&M
CPar EBee EHic EMan EPri EWTr
LHil LHop MAvo MBro MMil NFai
NPla SHFr SMac WGwG WHal
WHoo WRus WSan WWat WWol

## PHYLA (Verbenaceae)
§ **canescens** — SUsu WCru WHal WPrP
§ **nodiflora** — CNic ECha EEls NWCA SEND WPer
- 'Alba' — CNic

## PHYLICA (Rhamnaceae)
¶ **arborea** 'Superba' — CB&S CPLG
**ericoides** — CPLG

## x PHYLLIOPSIS (Ericaceae)
'Coppelia' ♀ — EPot GCrs GGGa MAsh MBal MDun NHar NHol SSta WAbe WPat WPyg
**billieri** — Last listed 1996
- 'Askival' — GCrs GGGa WAbe
- 'Pinocchio' — CMHG EPot GCrs GGGa GTou MAsh MBal MDun NHar NHol WAbe WPat WPyg
'Hobgoblin' — EPot MBal NHol WPat
'Mermaid' — GGGa SSta WAbe
'Puck' — WAbe
'Sprite' — GCrs MAsh NHol SSta WAbe WPat
¶ 'Sugar Plum' — SBrw WAbe

## PHYLLITIS See ASPLENIUM

## PHYLLOCLADUS (Phyllocladaceae)
**aspleniifolius** var. **alpinus** CDoC

## PHYLLODOCE (Ericaceae)
**aleutica** — EPot GChr GCrs GGGa MBal MBar NHar WAbe
§ - subsp. **glanduliflora** — EPot GDra MBal NHol
§ - subsp. **glanduliflora** 'Flora Slack' — CMHG GGGa MBal
- - white — See *P. aleutica* subsp. *glanduliflora* 'Flora Slack'
x **alpina** — GDra
**breweri** — GGGa
**caerulea** ♀ — GDra GGGa MBal NHar NHol WAbe
- **japonica** — See *P. nipponica*
¶ - Norwegian form — GCrs
**empetriformis** — GChr GDra GGGa MBal MBar MBri NHar NHed NHol NSla SRms WAbe
**glanduliflora** — See *P. aleutica* subsp. *glanduliflora*
x **intermedia** — GDra MBal
- 'Drummondii' — CMHG
- 'Fred Stoker' — CMHG NHol
§ **nipponica** ♀ — GCrs MBal WAbe
- var. **oblongo-ovata** — WAbe
**tsugifolia** — GCrs

## PHYLLOSTACHYS ✿ (Poaceae - Bambusoideae)
**angusta** — CFil EPla SDry WJun
**arcana** — EPla ISta SDry WJun
- 'Luteosulcata' — EPla SDry
§ **atrovaginata** — EPla SDry
**aurea** ♀ — More than 30 suppliers
- 'Flavescens Inversa' — EPla ERod ISta SDry WJun
- 'Holochrysa' — CB&S EFul EPla ERod ISta SDry WJun
- 'Koi' — EPla ERod MMoz SDry

- 'Variegata' — EFul EPla SDry
**aureosulcata** — EBee EFul EPfP EPla ISta LBlo MMoz NDov SDry WJun
- f.**alata** — EPla SDry
- 'Aureocaulis' — CDoC CFil EFul EPla ISta LJus LPan MMoz SDry WBay WJun WMul WPGP
- 'Harbin' — EPla SDry
¶ - 'Lama Temple' — EPla
- 'Spectabilis' — CDoC CFil EBee EFul EOas EPfP EPla ISta LJus LNet LPan LRHS MBrN MCCP MMoz MWht SDry WBay WJun WPGP
**bambusoides** — CB&S EPla ISta SDix SDry WJun
§ - 'Allgold' — CFil EPla ERod LPan SDry
- 'Castillonis' ♀ — CB&S CFil EFul EPla ERod ISta LEdu LJus LNet MMoz NDov SDix SDry WJun WPGP
- 'Castillonis Inversa' — CFil EPla ERod SDry WJun WPGP
- Holochrysa — See *P. bambusoides* 'Allgold'
- 'Katashibo' — EPla
- 'Kawadana' — EPla SDry
¶ - 'Marliacea' — EPla
- f.**subvariegata** — CFil EPla SDry WPGP
- 'Sulphurea' — See *P. bambusoides* 'Allgold'
- 'Tanakae' — SDry
**bissetii** — CDoC CFil EBee EFul EOas EPla ERod ISta LJus MBrN MCCP MMoz NDov SDry WBay WJun WPGP
**congesta** hort. — See *P. atrovaginata*
**decora** — EPla ISta LJus SDry WJun
**dulcis** — EPla ERod LEdu LPJP WJun
§ **edulis** — CGre EFul EHoe EPla ISta LPan MBal SDry WJun
- 'Bicolor' — SDry
§ - var. **heterocycla** — SDry
- f.**pubescens** — See *P. edulis*
- **subconvexa** — See *P. viridiglaucescens*
**flexuosa** — CFil EBee EFul EPla ISta LNet MDun SCob SDry WBay WJun WPGP
**glauca** — EBee EPla
- 'Yunzhu' — EPla LJus SDry WJun
§ **heteroclada** — SDry
- 'Solid Stem' misapplied — See *P. heteroclada* 'Straight Stem'
§ - 'Straight Stem' — EPla SDry
**heterocycla** — See *P. edulis* var. *heterocycla*
- f.**pubescens** — See *P. edulis*
**humilis** — EBee EPla MCCP MMoz SDry SPer WJun
**iridescens** — EPla SDry WJun
¶ **linearis** — EBee
**lithophila** — WJun
**lofushanensis** — CFil EPla WPGP
**makinoi** — WJun
**mannii** — EPla SDry WJun
**meyeri** — EPla ISta SDry WJun
**nidularia** — EBee EPla ISta LJus SDry WJun
¶ - smooth sheath — EPla
**nigra** ♀ — More than 30 suppliers
- 'Boryana' — CFil EFul EPla ISta LJus LPan NDov SArc SDix SDry WBay WJun WPGP
¶ - 'Fulva' — EPla
¶ - 'Hale' — EPla
- var. **benonis** ♀ — EFul EPla ERod ISta LJus SDry WBay WJun
- 'Megurochiku' — EPla SDry WJun
- f.**nigra** — EPla
- f.**punctata** — CFil EPla ISta LJus MDun MWht SDry WJun WPGP

¶ - 'Tosaensis' — EPla
**nuda** — EPla ISta SDry WJun
  - f. **localis** — SDry
**parvifolia** — EPla ERod
**platyglossa** — CFil WPGP
**praecox** — EPla WJun
**propinqua** — CDoC EOas EPla ISta LJus MCCP MMoz WJun WMul

¶ - 'Bicolor' — EPla
  - 'Li Yu Gai' — CFil EPla WPGP
**purpurata** — See *P.heteroclada*
**rubicunda** — CFil EPla WJun
**rubromarginata** — EPla SDry
**stimulosa** — EPla WJun
♦ **sulphurea** — See *P.bambusoides* 'Allgold'
  - 'Houzeau' — EPla SDry
  - 'Robert Young' — CB&S EPla SDry WJun
  - 'Sulphurea' — See *P.bambusoides* 'Allgold'
§ - var.**viridis** — EPla ERod ISta SDry WJun
  - - 'Mitis' — See *P.sulphurea* var. *viridis*
**violascens** — CB&S CFil EFul EPla ISta LJus SDry WJun WPGP
**virella** — CFil EPla WPGP
§ **viridiglaucescens** ♀ — CB&S CFil EBee EFul EPla ISta LJus LPan MBrN MMoz SArc SCob SDry SEND WBay WCot WJun
**viridis** — See *P.sulphurea* var. *viridis*
**vivax** — EFul EPla ERod ISta MMoz SDry WJun
  - 'Aureocaulis' — CFil EFul EOas EPla ERod ISta LJus LPJP MMoz MWht SDry WBay WJun WPGP
¶ - 'Huanvenzhu' — EPla

## x PHYLLOTHAMNUS (Ericaceae)
**erectus** — GCrs GGGa NHar NHol WAbe WPat WPyg

## PHYMOSIA (Malvaceae)
§ **umbellata** — CBot GGre LCns SOWG

## PHYODINA See CALLISIA

## PHYSALIS (Solanaceae)
**alkekengi** ♀ — CAgr ERav EWTr MLan
  - var.**franchetii** — CArn CB&S EBee ELan ENot EPla GAbr GChr GLil MBri MCAu MCLN NBir NBro NFai NFla NMir NRoo SEas SHel SLon SMad SPer SRPl SRms WFar WOve WPer WWin
¶ - - dwarf — NCut
  - - 'Gigantea' — ECGP GBuc NFor
  - - 'Variegata' — CRDP EBee EPla ERav EWes IBlr MTed NPro
**edulis** (F) — LPVe
**pubescens** (F) — Last listed 1997

## PHYSARIA (Brassicaceae)
¶ **alpina** — NWCA

## PHYSOCARPUS (Rosaceae)
**bracteatus** — Last listed 1996
**capitatus** — Last listed 1996
**opulifolius** — MSal WUnu
  - 'Dart's Gold' ♀ — More than 30 suppliers
  - 'Diabolo' — More than 30 suppliers
¶ - var.**intermedius** — EPla
§ - 'Luteus' — CBot CDoC CMHG CPle EPfP ESis GEil IMGH ISea MBar MGos MRav NFor NLon SPer SRms WBod WDin WFar WMoo

**ribesifolius** 'Aureus' — See *P.opulifolius* 'Luteus'

## PHYSOCHLAINA (Solanaceae)
**orientalis** — CRDP EBee EMan MSal NChi

## PHYSOPLEXIS (Campanulaceae)
§ **comosa** ♀ — CLyd EPot MBro SBla WHoo WPyg

## PHYSOSTEGIA (Lamiaceae)
**angustifolia** — CHan EBee NLak
§ **virginiana** — CTri EAst EBee EWTr GBar GCHN GMaP MBNS MHew NRoo SRms SWat SYvo WByw WFar WRHF
  - 'Alba' — CBot CGle GBri GMaP LNor MSte NLar NOrc NRoo SHel SUsu WEas WRHF
§ - 'Crown of Snow' — CFir CMdw CMil EBee ECoo ECtt EWTr LPVe MBNS MCLN MMal MSCN NArg NHol NLon NMir NPla WCot WHil WPer WRHF WRos
  - dwarf form — Last listed 1998
  - 'Galadriel' — Last listed 1998
  - 'Grandiflora' — CFir SIde WLRN
¶ - 'Grandiflora Rose' — NArg
  - pale pink — EFou SUsu SWat
  - 'Red Beauty' — CFir EBee EHal SMrm SPla WPyg WWin
  - 'Rosea' — CB&S CBot CHar LNor MBel SRPl WOve WPer
  - Schneekrone — See *P.virginiana* 'Crown of Snow'
  - 'Snow Queen' — See *P.virginiana* 'Summer Snow'
  - subsp. **speciosa** — EMon
§ - - 'Bouquet Rose' — CHan EBee ECha EMar ENot EOld LFis LLWP MBri MCAu MFir MRav MSte NCat NFla NMir NPri SChu SPer SSea WElm WFar WHoo WMow WPyg WRos WRus
  - - Rose Bouquet — See *P.virginiana* subsp. *speciosa* 'Bouquet Rose'
§ - - 'Variegata' — CB&S CGle CRDP ECha EFou EHoe ELan EMon LFis LHop MBel MBri MCLN MRav MUlv NOak SOkh SPer SRms WCot WEas WFar WOld WPer WWhi WWin
§ - 'Summer Snow' ♀ — CB&S CKel EAst EBee ECha EFou ELan ENot LHop MBel MBri MCAu MFir MWat NFla NHol SHFr SPer SRms WBea WFar WHoo WOve WRus WWin
  - 'Summer Spire' — ECha ELan EMan MSte NHol SPer WBea WFar
¶ - 'Van Wassenhove' — EBee EMon
  - 'Vivid' ♀ — CGle CMGP CRDP EBee ECha EFou ELan EMon MBro MCLN MMal MRav MWat NFla NHol NOak SDix SMac SPer SRms WCot WEas WHoo WPyg WWal WWin

## PHYTEUMA (Campanulaceae)
**balbisii** — See *P.cordatum*
**betonicifolium** — Last listed 1998
**charmelii** — CPea
**comosum** — See *Physoplexis comosa*
§ **cordatum** — Last listed 1998
**globulariifolium** — Last listed 1997
**halleri** — See *P.ovatum*
**hemisphaericum** — SWas WPat
**humile** — Last listed 1997
**japonicum** — Last listed 1997
**nigrum** — EBee ELan GCal LBee MNrw NBid SSca WMoo WPyg WThi

| | |
|---|---|
| *orbiculare* | ECGN WPyg |
| § *ovatum* | GAri |
| *scheuchzeri* | CNic CPea CRDP EBee ECha ELan |
| | EMan GTou LFis MBro NOrc NPri |
| | SBla SRms SRot SSca WCom |
| | WMoo |
| *sieberi* | ELan GDra NBir |
| *spicatum* | CRDP NBro WWye |
| - subsp. *coeruleum* | GBin |
| *tenerum* | CKin |
| *zahlbruckneri* | WLin |

## PHYTOLACCA (Phytolaccaceae)

| | |
|---|---|
| *acinosa* | CArn EBee IBlr MHew MSal NLar |
| | SWat WHer |
| § *americana* | CArn CSev EBee ECha ELan ELau |
| | EMar GPoy IBlr LHol MBNS MChe |
| | MSal MTis NLar SEND SIde SRms |
| | SWat WByw WEas WFar WHer |
| | WPer WWye |
| *clavigera* | See *P. polyandra* |
| *decandra* | See *P. americana* |
| *dioica* | CPLG |
| *esculenta* | CHid CPLG EBee GBin NLar NPSI |
| - B&SWJ 1000 | WCru |
| § *polyandra* | EBee ECGP ECha GBin GBuc |
| | GCHN NBro NHex SRms WFar |
| | WWye |
| *tibetica* | GPoy MSal |

## PICEA ✿ (Pinaceae)

| | |
|---|---|
| § *abies* | CDul CTri EHul ENot GChr GRei |
| | LBuc LCon MBar MBri MGos |
| | NBee NRoo NWea WDin WMou |
| | WWal |
| - 'Acrocona' | CDoC ECho EHul EOrn LCon |
| | MBar MBri MGos MPla |
| - 'Archer' | CKen |
| - 'Argenteospica' (v) | LCon NHol |
| - 'Aurea' | ECho EOrn IMGH LLin |
| - 'Aurea Magnifica' | LCon |
| - 'Capitata' | CBlo CKen GAri LCon MBar |
| * - 'Cinderella' | MAsh |
| - 'Clanbrassiliana' | CBlo CDoC CKen IMGH LCon |
| | MBar |
| - 'Columnaris' | GAri |
| - 'Compacta' | LBee |
| I - 'Congesta' | CKen |
| - 'Crippsii' | CKen |
| I - 'Cruenta' | CKen |
| - 'Cupressina' | CKen |
| - 'Diffusa' | CBlo CKen LCon MBar |
| - 'Elegans' | LCon MBar |
| - 'Ellwangeriana' | LCon |
| - 'Excelsa' | See *P. abies* |
| ¶ - 'Fahndrich' | CKen |
| - 'Finedonensis' | LCon |
| - 'Formanek' | CKen LCon LLin |
| - 'Four Winds' | CAbP |
| - 'Frohburg' | CDoC COtt GAri LCon MBar MBri |
| | MGos NHol |
| - 'Globosa' | CBlo MBar WStI |
| - 'Globosa Nana' | MGos |
| - 'Gregoryana' | CDoC CKen CMac EGra IMGH |
| | LCon MBar NHed WAbe |
| - 'Humilis' | LCon |
| - 'Hystrix' | LCon |
| - 'Inversa' | CDoC EHul EOrn GAri IOrc LCon |
| | LLin LPan MBar MGos |
| § - 'J.W. Daisy's White' | CDoC CKen EOrn LCon LLin |
| | LRHS MGos NPro SCoo SLim |
| | SMur SPla WGor |

| | |
|---|---|
| - 'Little Gem' ♀ | CBlo CDoC CKen CMac EBrP |
| | EBre EHul EOrn IMGH LBee LBre |
| | LCon LLin MAsh MBar MBri |
| | MGos MPla MWat NBee NRoo |
| | SAga SBre SLim WAbe |
| - 'Mariae Orffiae' | CKen LCon |
| - 'Maxwellii' | EHul MBar MGos |
| - 'Merkii' | GAri |
| - 'Nana' | MBar |
| - 'Nana Compacta' | CKen EHul ESis IMGH LBee LCon |
| | LLin MBar MOne |
| - 'Nidiformis' ♀ | More than 30 suppliers |
| - 'Norrkoping' | CKen |
| - 'Ohlendorffii' | CKen EHul LCon LPan MBar MPla |
| | MWat NHol WStI |
| - 'Pachyphylla' | CKen |
| - 'Pendula Major' | Last listed 1998 |
| - 'Procumbens' | MBar |
| - 'Pseudomaxwellii' | CBlo LCon NHol |
| - 'Pumila' | EOrn NHed |
| - 'Pumila Nigra' | CMac EHul LCon LLin MAsh MBar |
| | MGos MPla NHar SLim |
| - 'Pusch' | CKen |
| - 'Pygmaea' | CKen LCon MBar MGos MPla |
| - 'Reflexa' | EHul IMGH LCon LLin |
| - 'Remontii' | Last listed 1996 |
| - 'Repens' | MBar MBlu MGos NBee |
| - 'Rydal' | LCon MAsh |
| - 'Saint James' | CKen |
| - 'Saint Mary's Broom' | Last listed 1996 |
| - 'Tabuliformis' | MBar |
| - 'Tufty' | EOrn |
| - 'Veitchii' | See *P. abies* 'Gregoryana Veitchii' |
| ¶ - 'Walter Bron' | CKen |
| - 'Waugh' | MBar |
| - Will's Dwarf | See *P. abies* 'Wills Zwerg' |
| § - 'Wills Zwerg' | LCon LPan MAsh |
| § *alcockiana* | Last listed 1996 |
| - 'Prostrata' | LCon MBal MBar NHol |
| *asperata* | ETen |
| § *balfouriana* | CDoC LCon NHol WWes |
| *bicolor* | See *P. alcockiana* |
| *brachytyla* | LCon |
| *breweriana* ♀ | CB&S CDoC CDul EBrP EBre |
| | EHul ENot EOrn GChr GRei |
| | IMGH IOrc ISea LBre LCon LLin |
| | LNet LPan MBar MBri MGos NBee |
| | NHol NWea SBre SLim SPer SSta |
| | WNor |
| * - 'Frühlingsgold' | Last listed 1998 |
| *engelmannii* | CBlo MBar |
| - f. *glauca* | EHul LCon LPan MBar SSta |
| *glauca* | NWea |
| - 'Alberta Blue' | CDoC EOrn LLin LPan SCoo SLim |
| | SSmi WGor WWeb |
| - var. *albertiana* 'Alberta | CBlo CDoC EBrP EBre EHul EOrn |
| Globe' ♀ | EPot GRei IMGH LBee LBre LCon |
| | LLin MAsh MBar MBri MGos MPla |
| | NBee NHed NRoo SAga SBre |
| | SLim SSmi WFar |
| - - 'Conica' ♀ | More than 30 suppliers |
| - - 'Gnome' | CKen |
| - - 'Laurin' | CDoC CKen EBrP EBre EOrn |
| | GPin LBee LBre LCon MAsh MBar |
| | MBri SBre SSmi SSta WAbe |
| - - 'Tiny' | CDoC CKen CNic EHul EOrn |
| | EPot ESis LCon LLin MBar WAbe |
| - 'Arneson's Blue' | CKen LCon MBri SLim |
| ¶ - 'Blue Planet' | CKen |
| - 'Coerulea' | LCon MBar |
| - 'Densata' | Last listed 1998 |
| - 'Echiniformis' ♀ | CKen EHul EPot GAri LBee LCon |
| | MBal MBar MBri |

| | |
|---|---|
| ¶ - 'Goldilocks' | CKen |
| - 'J.W. Daisy's White' | See *P. abies* 'J.W. Daisy's White' |
| - 'Lilliput' | EHul EOrn EPot LCon MBar MGos |
| - 'Nana' | CKen |
| - 'Piccolo' | CKen MBri SLim |
| - 'Rainbow's End' | CKen |
| - 'Sander's Blue' | CKen EOrn MBri |
| - 'Zucherhut' | LRHS MBar MBri |
| ¶ *glehnii* | LCon |
| - 'Sasanosei' | CKen |
| - 'Shimezusei' | CKen |
| *jezoensis* | ETen GAri MGos NWea |
| - subsp. *hondoensis* | WNor |
| *koraiensis* Beijing 176 | Last listed 1996 |
| *kosteri* 'Glauca' | See *P. pungens* 'Koster' |
| § *koyamae* | CBlo ETen LCon |
| *likiangensis* | LCon MBal WWat |
| - var. *balfouriana* | See *P. balfouriana* |
| - var. *purpurea* | See *P. purpurea* |
| *mariana* 'Aureovariegata' | LCon |
| - 'Doumetii' | EOrn |
| - 'Ericoides' | GAri |
| - 'Fastigiata' | CKen EOrn |
| - 'Nana' ♀ | CBlo CDoC CKen CMac EBrP |
| | EBre EGra EHul ELan ESis EWTr |
| | IMGH LBre LCon LLin LNet MBar |
| | MBri MGos MNrw MPla MWat |
| | NBee NHed NHol SBre SLim SSmi |
| | SSta WDin |
| x *mariorika* | MBar |
| § - 'Gnom' | Last listed 1996 |
| - 'Machala' | Last listed 1996 |
| I *obovata* 'Glauca' | LCon |
| *omorika* ♀ | CB&S CDoC CDul CMCN ENot |
| | GRei GAri LBuc LCon LNet MBal MBar |
| | MGos NBee NWea SPer WCFE |
| | WCoo WDin WMou WWat |
| - 'Gnom' | See *P.* x *mariorika* 'Gnom' |
| ¶ - 'Karel' | CKen |
| - 'Nana' ♀ | CMac GAri LBee LCon LNet LPan |
| | MBar NBee SLim |
| - 'Pendula' ♀ | CBlo CDoC IOrc LCon MAsh |
| | MBar SSta |
| - 'Pimoko' | CKen LCon |
| - 'Schneverdingen' | CKen |
| - 'Treblitsch' | CKen |
| *orientalis* ♀ | CLnd ETen GChr LCon LPan MBal |
| | STre WTro |
| § - 'Aurea' ♀ | CDoC CMac EBrP EBre EHul ELan |
| | IOrc LBre LCon LLin LPan MBar |
| | MBri NHol SBre SLim |
| - 'Aureospicata' | CDoC ECho |
| - 'Bergman's Gem' | CKen |
| - 'Early Gold' | Last listed 1996 |
| - 'Gowdy' | MBar |
| - 'Kenwith' | CKen |
| - 'Pendula' | MGos |
| ¶ - 'Professor Langer' | CKen |
| - 'Reynolds' | CKen |
| - 'Skylands' | CBlo CDoC CKen LCon MAsh |
| | MGos SLim |
| *pungens* | GChr MBar NWea WDin WNor |
| - 'Blaukissen' | CKen |
| - 'Blue Trinket' | Last listed 1996 |
| - 'Corbet' | LCon |
| - 'Drayer' | Last listed 1997 |
| - 'Endtz' | Last listed 1996 |
| - 'Erich Frahm' | CDoC EBrP EBre GAri LBre LCon |
| | LLin LNet LPan MBri MGos SBre |
| | SCoo SLim SMad WWeb |
| - 'Fat Albert' | EBrP EBre LBre LNet LPan MBri |
| | SBre |

| | |
|---|---|
| - f. *glauca* | EHul GRei LBee MBal MBar NBee |
| | NWea WDin WMou WStI |
| - 'Glauca Globosa' | See *P. pungens* 'Globosa' |
| - 'Glauca Procumbens' | LNet |
| § - 'Glauca Prostrata' | EHul LCon MBal SLim |
| - 'Globe' | CKen LCon |
| I - 'Globosa' ♀ | CB&S CDoC CKen EBrP EBre |
| | EHul ELan EOrn IOrc LBee LBre |
| | LCon LLin LPan MBar MBri MGos |
| | MWat NBee NHol SBre SLim |
| | SRms WPyg WStI |
| I - 'Globosa Viridis' | EHul |
| - 'Gloria' | CKen LCon |
| - 'Hoopsii' ♀ | CB&S CBlo CDoC CMac EBrP |
| | EBre EHul ELan ENot EOrn GPin |
| | IMGH IOrc LBre LCon LNet LPan |
| | MBal MBar MGos MWat NBee |
| | SBre SLim SPer SPla WDin |
| - 'Hoto' | CDoC EHul EOrn IOrc LCon |
| | MBar WPyg WWeb |
| - 'Hunnewelliana' | EOrn |
| - 'Iseli Fastigiate' | CDoC COtt EBrP EBre LBre LCon |
| | LNet MAsh SBre |
| § - 'Koster' ♀ | CDoC CMac EHul EOrn GRei |
| | IOrc LCon LLin LNet LPan MAsh |
| | MBar MGos NBee NWea SLim |
| | SMad SPer SRms WDin WStI |
| ¶ - 'Koster Fastigiata' | LPan |
| - 'Koster Prostrate' | MBal |
| - 'Lucky Strike' | CKen LCon LLin MAsh MGos |
| - 'Maigold' | CKen |
| - 'Moerheimii' | EHul EOrn LCon LNet MBar |
| | MGos |
| - 'Montgomery' | CBlo CKen LCon MBar NHol |
| ¶ - 'Mrs Cesarini' | CKen |
| - 'Oldenburg' | Last listed 1996 |
| - 'Procumbens' ♀ | CKen LCon |
| - 'Prostrata' | See *P. pungens* 'Glauca Prostrata' |
| - 'Saint Mary's Broom' | CKen |
| - 'Schovenhorst' | EHul EOrn |
| - 'Thomsen' | CKen EHul EOrn LCon MAsh |
| | MBal |
| - 'Thuem' | EHul EOrn LCon MGos |
| - 'Wendy' | CKen |
| § *purpurea* ♀ | LCon |
| *retroflexa* | Last listed 1996 |
| *rubens* | GAri LCon NWea |
| *schrenkiana* | ETen LCon |
| *sitchensis* | CDul GChr GRei LBuc LCon |
| | NWea WMou |
| - 'Nana' | CDoC NHol |
| - 'Papoose' | See *P. sitchensis* 'Tenas' |
| - 'Silberzwerg' | CKen |
| - 'Strypemonde' | CKen |
| § - 'Tenas' | LCon NHol |
| *smithiana* ♀ | CB&S GAri ISea LCon MBal SLim |
| | WFro |
| - CC&McK 363 | Last listed 1996 |

## PICRASMA (Simaroubaceae)
| | |
|---|---|
| *ailanthoides* | See *P. quassioides* |
| § *quassioides* | CMCN |

## PICRIS (Asteraceae)
| | |
|---|---|
| *echioides* | CKin EWFC WHer |

## PICRORHIZA (Scrophulariaceae)
| | |
|---|---|
| *kurrooa* | GPoy |

## PIERIS ✿ (Ericaceae)
| | |
|---|---|
| 'Bert Chandler' | CHig ELan LRHS SPer SSpi |
| 'Flaming Silver' (v) ♀ | More than 30 suppliers |

'Flamingo' — CHig CTrh CTrw MAsh MBal MBar MGos NHed NHol WAbe WBod WFar WPat WPyg

*floribunda* — IOrc LEdu MBal

'Forest Flame' ♀ — More than 30 suppliers

*formosa* — CHig

- B&SWJ 2257 — WCru

- var.*forrestii* — CDoC CTre CTrw GRei ISea NWea SBrw

- - 'Charles Michael' — Last listed 1996

- - 'Fota Pink' — WHar WSHC

- - 'Jermyns' ♀ — CB&S CEnd CHig IOrc MBal

- - 'Wakehurst' ♀ — CB&S CHig CLan CTrG EBee IOrc LHyd MAsh MBal MRav NWea SAPC SBrw SPer SRPl SReu SSta WBod WFar WWal

§ Havila® = 'Mouwsvila' (v) — CDoC IOrc MAsh MBal MBri MGos NHol SBrw WLRN

*japonica* — CB&S CHig CLan CTrw MBal MBar MGos NWea SAPC SArc SReu WDin

- 'Balls of Fire' — CTrh

- 'Bisbee Dwarf' — MBar MBro NHar NHol WAbe WPat WPyg

- 'Blush' ♀ — CHig NHol SBod SEas WSHC

- 'Brookside Miniature' — WPat

- 'Cavatine' ♀ — CMHG LRHS SBod

§ - 'Christmas Cheer' — CLan IOrc MBal MGos NHed SBrw SPer WLRN

- 'Coleman' — Last listed 1998

- 'Compact Crimson' — MBal

- 'Compacta' — NHol WAbe

- 'Crispa' — CHig

- 'Cupido' — CBlo EMil MAsh MBar MGos WLRN

- 'Daisen' — CHig CLan CTrw

§ - 'Debutante' ♀ — CDoC CHig ELan ENot EPfP MAsh MPla NHol SBrw SRPl SSpi WStI WWat

- 'Don' — See *P.japonica* 'Pygmaea'

- 'Dorothy Wyckoff' — CB&S CLan CMHG CTrG NHed NHol SBrw SPer SSta WCwm

- 'Firecrest' ♀ — CB&S CHig CMHG CTrG CTrh ENot IOrc MBal MBri NHed SBrw SSpi WBod WPat

- 'Flaming Star' — ECot

- 'Geisha' — WPat

- 'Glenroy Pink Plenty' — MBal

- 'Grayswood' ♀ — CHig CMHG CSam EPfP IOrc LRHS MBri NHol

- 'Little Heath' (v) ♀ — More than 30 suppliers

- 'Little Heath Green' ♀ — CChe CDoC CHig CMHG CTrG GAri LHyd MAsh MBar MBri MGos NHed SBrw SPer SSta WBrE WFar WPic WWat WWeb

- 'Minor' — MBar NHar NHol WPat WPyg

- 'Mountain Fire' ♀ — More than 30 suppliers

- 'Pink Delight' ♀ — CAbP CB&S CDoC CHig EBee MAsh MBal MBar MGos MPla MRav SBid SBrw SPer SRms WPat

- 'Prelude' ♀ — CChe CWSG GCHN LRHS MBri MRav NHol WPat

- 'Purity' ♀ — CB&S CBlo CDoC CHig CMHG CTrh IOrc MBal MBar MGos NHol SBrw SEas SPer SRPl SReu SSta WBod WDin WFar WLRN WStI

§ - 'Pygmaea' — CMHG GDra MBal MBro NHar NHol WPat WPyg

¶ - red form — CHig

- 'Red Mill' — CAbP CBlo CEnd CHig CMHG EBee EPfP MAsh NHol SBod SPer SSpi WFar WPat

- 'Robinswood' — SBid WBcn

¶ - 'Rosalinda' — WFar

- 'Rosea' — LHyd

- 'Rowallane' — IBlr

- 'Sarabande' ♀ — CHig COtt MBri MGos NHol SBrw SPer WGwG WPat WPyg

- 'Scarlett O'Hara' — CB&S MGos

- 'Select' — MGos

- 'Silver Sword' — Last listed 1996

- 'Snowdrift' — GCHN MSta SPer SSta

- 'Spring Candy' — MGos SBid

- 'Spring Snow' — LRHS

- Taiwanensis Group — CGre CHig CMHG CTre CTrh GCHN GRei IOrc LHyd MBal MBar MRav NHol NWea SPer SRPl SRms SSta WFar WPat WWat

- 'Temple Bells' — CHig EHic ENot SBid SPar

- 'Tickled Pink' — CHig EHic NHol

- 'Tilford' — CDoC CHig MBal MBri MPla NHol SSta WPat

- 'Valley Fire' — CTrh

- 'Valley Rose' — CChe CHig COtt CSam CTrh ENot GCHN MAsh MBal MBel MGos NBee SBid SPer SSpi WGwG WStI

- 'Valley Valentine' ♀ — CDoC CLan COtt EHic ENot EPfP MAsh MBal MBri MGos NHed NHol SBid SBod SBrw SPer SReu SSta WAbe WBod WCwm WPat WStI WWeb

- 'Variegata' hort. — See *P.japonica* 'White Rim'

§ - 'Variegata' (Carrière) Bean — CHig CMHG ELan EPot GRei IOrc LHyd MBal MBar MGos NBee NHed NHol SLdr SPer SReu SSta WAbe WDin WHar WPat WSHC WWat

- 'Wada's Pink' — See *P.japonica* 'Christmas Cheer'

- 'White Cascade' — CHig SBrw

- 'White Pearl' ♀ — CAbP CLan MAsh MBal MBri MGos NBee SPer

§ - 'White Rim' (v) ♀ — CB&S CDoC EBee MAsh MGos MPla SBrw WFar

¶ - 'Whitecaps' — MBal

- 'William Buchanan' — GCrs MBar MBro NHar NHol WPat WPyg

- var.*yakushimensis* — CBlo WSHC

♦ 'Mouwsvila' — See *P.* Havila = 'Mouwsvila'

*nana* — GAri MBal MBar NHar

- 'Redshank' — MBal

## PILEA (Urticaceae)

* 'Anette' — MBri

*cadierei* ♀ — CHal MBri

- 'Minima' ♀ — Last listed 1995

*involucrata* 'Moon Valley' ♀ — Last listed 1992

- 'Norfolk' ♀ — Last listed 1993

*nummulariifolia* — CHal MBri

*peperomioides* ♀ — CHal CSev SRms

*repens* — MBri

## PILEOSTEGIA (Hydrangeaceae)

*viburnoides* ♀ — More than 30 suppliers

- B&SWJ 3565 — WCru

## PILOSELLA (Asteraceae)

§ *aurantiaca* — CLTr CMCo CNic CRow ELan EWFC LNor MBNS MFir MHer MHew MMal NArg NBid NOrc NSti SBea SIde SIng SRms SSmi WCer WCla WElm WHer WOak

§ - subsp.*carpathicola* — GGar

§ *officinarum* — CKin EWFC WGwy

§ x *stoloniflora*     CRow

## PILULARIA (Marsileaceae)
*globulifera*     CNat

## PIMELEA (Thymelaeaceae)
*arenaria*     ECou
*coarctata*     See *P. prostrata*
*drupacea*     ECou
*filiformis*     ECou
*physodes*     Last listed 1998
§ *prostrata*     CLyd CTri ECou EHyt EPot GCrs GNor IMGH MBar NHar NHol NWoo WAbe WPat WPer
   - f. *parvifolia*     ECou
   - Tennyson's form     SBla
*sericeovillosa*     Last listed 1997
*suteri*     Last listed 1997

## PIMPINELLA (Apiaceae)
*anisum*     CArn MSal SIde WHer WSel
¶ *bicknellii*     SIgm WCot
*brachycarpa* B&SWJ 863     Last listed 1998
*major* 'Rosea'     CHan CRDP EMan EMon GBri LHop MHlr SMrm WBro WCot WFar WHal WPGP
*saxifraga*     EWFC

## PINELLIA (Araceae)
*cordata*     CRDP EPot WCru
*pedatisecta*     CRDP CRow EBee MRav SSoC WCot WCru
*pinnatisecta*     See *P. tripartita*
*ternata*     CRDP CRow EPar EPot MSal WCru WWye
   - B&SWJ 3532     WCru
§ *tripartita*     EBee EPot SUsu WCru
   - B&SWJ 1102     WCru
¶ - 'Purple Face' B&SWJ 4850     WCru

## PINGUICULA ✿ (Lentibulariaceae)
*acuminata*     WMEx
*agnata*     WMEx
* 'Ayantla'     Last listed 1996
*crassifolia*     Last listed 1996
*eblersiae*     EFEx WMEx
*emarginata*     WMEx
*esseriana*     EFEx WMEx
*gracilis*     WMEx
*grandiflora*     CRDP CSWC EAnd EFEx EPot GCrs NHar NMen NRya WAbe WHer WMEx WPGP
   - subsp. *coenocantabrica* NWCA
     NS 307
*gypsicola*     WMEx
*hemiepiphytica*     WMEx
'Kewensis'     WMEx
*laueana*     WMEx
*longifolia* subsp. *longifolia* EFEx WPGP
*macrophylla*     WMEx
*moranensis alba*     Last listed 1998
   - var. *caudata*     EFEx WMEx
   - *flos-mulionis*     Last listed 1998
   - 'Kirkbright'     Last listed 1998
   - var. *mexicana*     WMEx
   - *moreana*     EFEx
   - *morelia*     Last listed 1997
   - *superba*     EFEx
*potosiensis*     WMEx
*primuliflora*     EAnd WMEx
*reticulata*     WMEx
*rosea*     Last listed 1996

*rotundifolia*     WMEx
* *santiago* 'Nuyoo Pass'     Last listed 1996
'Sargent'     Last listed 1996
'Sethos'     WMEx
*villosa*     Last listed 1996
*vulgaris*     EFEx WMEx
'Weser'     WMEx
*zecheri*     WMEx

## PINUS ✿ (Pinaceae)
*albicaulis*     WNor
   - 'Flinck'     CKen
   - 'Nana'     See *P. albicaulis* 'Noble's Dwarf'
§ - 'Noble's Dwarf'     CKen
*aristata* Engelm.     CAbP CBlo CDoC CFil CMCN EBrP EBre EHul EOrn GChr LBre LCon LLin MBal MBar MGos MUlv NHol SBre SReu SSta STre WCoo WFro
   - 'Cecilia'     CKen
   - 'Sherwood Compact'     CKen
*armandii*     CB&S CDul CGre CMCN CSWP ETen LCon SFur SMad
   - SF 313     ISea
   - TW 415     Last listed 1997
*attenuata*     STre
*austriaca*     See *P. nigra* subsp. *nigra*
N *ayacahuite*     LCon SMur
*banksiana*     CDul CSam EHul ETen LCon MBal
   - 'Chippewa'     CKen
I    - 'Compacta'     CKen
   - 'H.J. Welch'     CKen
   - 'Manomet'     CKen
   - 'Neponset'     CKen LCon
   - 'Wisconsin'     CKen
*brutia*     See *P. halepensis* subsp. *brutia*
*bungeana*     CAbP CDoC CLnd EHul LCon LLin MBal MBlu MUlv SFur SLPl STre WFro WNor
   - 'Diamant'     CKen
*canariensis* ♀     EHul ISea
*cembra* ♀     CDoC CDul EHul GChr LCon LPan MBal MBar NWea STre WCFE
   - 'Aurea'     See *P. cembra* 'Aureovariegata'
§ - 'Aureovariegata'     CKen LLin
   - 'Barnhourie'     CKen
   - 'Blue Mound'     CKen
   - 'Chalet'     CKen
   - 'Compacta Glauca'     CDoC LRHS MBri
* - 'Griffithii'     WDin
   - 'Inverleith'     CKen
   - 'Jermyns'     CKen
   - 'King's Dwarf'     CKen
   - 'Nana'     See *P. pumila* 'Nana'
   - 'Roughills'     CKen
   - 'Stricta'     CKen
   - Witches' broom     CKen
*cembroides* var. *edulis*     ETen
*contorta*     CB&S CBlo CDoC CTrC GChr GRei Ilve LCon MBal MBar MGos NWea STre WDin WMou
   - 'Asher'     CKen
   - 'Frisian Gold'     CKen
   - var. *latifolia*     CLnd ETen MBal WTro
   - 'Spaan's Dwarf'     CBlo CDoC CKen LCon LLin MBar MBri MGos NHol SLim
*coulteri* ♀     CMCN ETen LCon MBal WNor WPGP
*densiflora*     CDul CMCN EHul ETen LCon MBal SPla STre WFro WNor
   - 'Alice Verkade'     CBlo CDoC EHul LCon LLin LNet LRHS MBri SLim

| | |
|---|---|
| - 'Aurea' | EHul LCon MBar MGos NHol SLim |
| - 'Jane Kluis' | CKen COtt EHul LCon LNet LRHS MBri |
| - 'Oculus Draconis' | CDoC MBar MBri MGos SLim SMur |
| - 'Pendula' | CDoC CKen LLin MBal MBri SLim |
| - 'Pygmy' | CKen |
| * - 'Pyramidalis' | ECho |
| - 'Umbraculifera' | CDoC IGri IMGH IOrc LCon LLin LPan MBar MBri MGos MOne SLim SSta |
| edulis | LCon |
| engelmannii | Last listed 1996 |
| flexilis | CBlo CDul ETen LCon MBal |
| - 'Firmament' | CDoC LCon LLin |
| - 'Glenmore Dwarf' | CKen |
| - 'Nana' | CKen |
| - 'Pendula' | LLin |
| - 'Vanderwolf's Pyramid' | Last listed 1996 |
| - WB No. 1 | CKen |
| - WB No. 2 | CKen |
| gerardiana | LCon MBal |
| greggii | Last listed 1998 |
| griffithii | See P. wallichiana |
| halepensis | CLnd ETen |
| hartwegii | ETen |
| § heldreichii ♀ | CDul CMac ETen LCon LNet MBal MBar SCoo WDin WNor |
| - var. leucodermis | See P. heldreichii |
| - - 'Aureospicata' | LCon LLin MBar SIng |
| - - 'Compact Gem' | CDoC CKen EBrP EBre IOrc LBre LCon LLin LNet LPan MBar MBri MGos SBre SCoo SLim SSta WPyg |
| - - 'Groen' | CKen |
| - - 'Malink' | CKen |
| - - 'Pygmy' | CKen |
| - - 'Satellit' | CDoC EHul EOrn IOrc LBee LLin LPan MGos SLim |
| I - 'Schmidtii' | See P. heldreichii 'Smidtii' |
| § - 'Smidtii' ♀ | CDoC CKen LCon LLin MAsh MBar MBri SLim |
| jeffreyi ♀ | CAgr CDul CLnd CMCN ETen LCon MBal MBar WFro |
| - 'Joppi' | CKen |
| kesiya TW 333 | Last listed 1996 |
| koraiensis | ETen LCon MBal WNor |
| - 'Bergman' | CKen |
| - 'Dragon Eye' | CKen |
| - 'Jack Corbit' | CKen |
| - 'Shibamichi' | CKen |
| - 'Silver Lining' | MAsh |
| ¶ - 'Silveray' | MBri |
| - 'Silvergrey' | CDoC CKen |
| - 'Winton' | CDoC CKen |
| lambertiana | ETen LCon |
| ♦ leucodermis | See P. heldreichii H.Christ |
| - 'Zwerg Schneverdingen' | CKen |
| ¶ longaeva | EPfP |
| magnifica | See P. montezumae |
| massoniana | WNor |
| monophylla | ETen MBal |
| N montezumae | CB&S CGre CLnd CMCN IOrc ISea LCon LLin LPan SAPC SArc WNor |
| monticola | CLnd |
| - 'Pendula' | MBar |
| - 'Pygmy' | See P. monticola 'Raraflora' |
| § - 'Raraflora' | CKen |
| - 'Skyline' | LPan MBar |
| - 'Windsor Dwarf' | CKen |
| mugo | CB&S CBlo CDul CTri EHul ENot GRei LEdu MAsh MBal MBar MGos SRms WDin WFar WStI |

| | |
|---|---|
| * - 'Benjamin' | CKen |
| - 'Bisley Green' | LLin |
| - 'Brownie' | CKen |
| - 'Carsten' | CKen |
| - 'Carsten's Wintergold' | See P. mugo 'Winter Gold' |
| I - 'Columnaris' | Last listed 1998 |
| - 'Corley's Mat' | CKen EBrP EBre LBre LCon LLin MAsh SBre SLim WWeb |
| - 'Gnom' | CBlo CDoC CFee CKen CMac EHul EOrn IMGH LCon LLin LPan MBar MBri MGos MOne NBee WDin WFar |
| - 'Hoersholm' | CKen |
| - 'Humpy' | CFee CKen EBrP EBre EOrn GAri IMGH LBee LBre LCon LLin MAsh MBar MBri MGos MOne NHed NHol SBre SLim WAbe |
| - 'Jacobsen' | CKen |
| - 'Kissen' | CBlo CKen LCon MGos |
| - 'Klosterkotter' | MGos |
| - 'Knapenburg' | NHol |
| - 'Kobold' | CBlo NHol |
| - 'Krauskopf' | CKen |
| - 'Laarheide' | MBri |
| - 'Laurin' | CKen |
| - 'March' | CKen NHol |
| - 'Mini Mops' | CKen |
| - 'Minikin' | CKen |
| - 'Mops' ♀ | CBlo CDoC EBrP EBre EHul GChr LBee LBre LCon LLin LPan MAsh MBar MBri MGos NBee NHol SBre SLim SPer SSta WPyg |
| - 'Mops Midget' | LLin MBri |
| - var. mughus | See P. mugo var. mugo |
| § - var. mugo | CMCN EHic EOrn ESis GRei LPan MBar WWal |
| - 'Mumpitz' | CKen |
| - 'Ophir' | CDoC CKen EBrP EBre EHul EOrn IMGH IOrc LBee LBre LCon LLin LNet MAsh MBar MBri MGos NHol SBre SLim SPer SPla SSta WDin |
| - 'Pal Maleter' | CDoC LCon LLin MBri SLim |
| - 'Piggelmee' | CKen |
| - Pumilio Group ♀ | CBlo CDoC CDul CMac EHul ENot EOrn GRei IOrc LBee LCon LLin LPan MBar MBro MGos NFla NWea STre WNor |
| - var. rostrata | See P. mugo subsp. uncinata |
| - 'Spaan' | CKen |
| - 'Sunshine' | CKen |
| § - subsp. uncinata | ETen GRei LCon NWea |
| ¶ - - 'Grüne Welle' | CKen |
| - - 'Paradekissen' | CKen |
| - 'White Tip' | CKen |
| § - 'Winter Gold' | CKen EBrP EBre EHul EOrn IOrc LBre LCon LLin LPan MAsh SBre SSta |
| - 'Winzig' | CKen |
| - 'Zundert' | CBlo CDoC CKen LLin LNet MBar MBri MGos |
| - 'Zwergkugel' | CKen |
| muricata ♀ | CAbP CDoC CLnd ETen GChr LCon MBal MGos |
| nigra ♀ | CB&S CBlo CDoC CDul ECrN GRei LCon LNet MBar MGos WDin WMou |
| * - 'Asterix' | Last listed 1998 |
| - var. austriaca | See P. nigra subsp. nigra |
| - 'Black Prince' | CBlo CKen EOrn IMGH LBee LCon LLin MBri NHed SCoo SLim |
| N - 'Cebennensis Nana' | CKen |

| | |
|---|---|
| - var. **corsicana** | See *P. nigra* subsp. *laricio* |
| ¶ - 'Frank' | CKen |
| - 'Géant de Suisse' | Last listed 1997 |
| - 'Hornibrookiana' | CKen LCon LPan |
| § - subsp. **laricio** ♀ | CDoC CDul CKen ENot GChr |
| | GRei LBuc LCon MBar MGos |
| | NWea SMad WMou |
| - - 'Bobby McGregor' | CKen LLin SLim |
| - - 'Globosa Viridis' | GAri LLin NHol SLim |
| - - 'Goldfingers' | CKen LLin |
| § - - 'Moseri' ♀ | CKen GAri LCon LLin SLim SSta |
| - - 'Pygmaea' | CKen ECho |
| - - 'Spingarn' | CKen |
| - - 'Talland Bay' | CKen |
| - - 'Wurstle' | CKen |
| - subsp. **maritima** | See *P. nigra* subsp. *laricio* |
| - 'Molette' | Last listed 1998 |
| - 'Nana' | CDoC LPan |
| § - subsp. **nigra** | CDoC CLnd LBuc LPan MGos |
| | NWea WStI |
| - - 'Bright Eyes' | CKen ECho EHul EOrn IMGH |
| | LBee LCon LLin |
| - - 'Helga' | CKen |
| - - 'Schovenhorst' | CKen |
| - - 'Strypemonde' | CKen |
| - - 'Yaffle Hill' | CKen |
| - 'Obelisk' | CKen |
| - subsp. **pallasiana** | LCon |
| - subsp. **salzmannii** | Last listed 1996 |
| * - **serotina** | Last listed 1998 |
| - 'Uelzen' | CKen |
| **palustris** | LCon LLin |
| **parviflora** ♀ | CMCN GAri LCon LPan NWea |
| | STre WDin WNor |
| - 'Adcock's Dwarf' ♀ | CDoC CKen GAri LCon LLin MBar |
| | MGos NHol SLim |
| - 'Aizu' | CKen |
| - 'Al Fordham' | CKen |
| - 'Aoi' | CKen |
| - 'Ara-kawa' | CKen |
| - 'Azuma-goyo' | CKen |
| I - 'Baasch's Form' | CKen |
| - 'Bergman' | CBlo CDoC LCon MAsh MBar |
| ¶ - 'Blue Giant' | ECho |
| - 'Bonnie Bergman' | CKen LLin |
| - 'Brevifolia' | GAri |
| - 'Dai-ho' | CKen |
| - 'Daisetsusan' | CKen |
| ¶ - 'Draijer's Dwarf' | MBri |
| - 'Fukai Seedling' | CKen |
| - 'Fukiju' | CKen |
| - 'Fukushima-goyo' | CKen |
| - 'Fukuzumi' | LLin |
| * - 'Fu-shiro' | CKen |
| - f. **glauca** | CDoC CMac EHul GAri IOrc LCon |
| | LLin MBar MBri MGos NFla |
| I - 'Glauca Nana' | CKen |
| - 'Gyok-kan' | CKen |
| - 'Gyok-ke-sen' | CKen |
| - 'Gyo-ko-haku' | CKen |
| - 'Gyokuei' | CKen |
| - 'Gyokusen Seedling' | CKen |
| - 'Gyo-ku-sui' | CKen |
| - 'Hagaromo Seedling' | CKen |
| - 'Hakko' | CKen |
| ¶ - 'Hatchichi' | CKen |
| - 'Hatsumi' | Last listed 1998 |
| - 'Ibo-can' | CKen |
| - 'Ichi-no-se' | CKen |
| - 'Iri-fune' | CKen |
| - 'Ishizuchi-goyo' | CKen |
| - 'Janome' | Last listed 1996 |
| - 'Jyu-roko-ra-kan' | CKen |
| - 'Ka-ho' | CKen |
| - 'Kanzan' | CKen |
| - 'Kiyomatsu' | CKen |
| - 'Kobe' | CKen |
| - 'Kokonde' | CKen |
| - 'Kokonoe' | CBlo CKen LCon |
| - 'Kokuho' | CKen |
| - 'Koraku' | CKen |
| - 'Kusu-dama' | CKen |
| - 'Meiko' | CKen |
| - 'Michi-noku' | CKen |
| - 'Myo-jo' | CKen |
| - 'Nasu-goyo' | CKen |
| - 'Negishi' | CDoC CKen GAri LCon LPan |
| | MBal MBri |
| - 'Ogonjanome' | CKen |
| ¶ - 'Ossorio Dwarf' | CKen |
| - 'Ryokuho' | CKen |
| - 'Ryuju' | CKen |
| - 'Sanbo' | CDoC CKen LCon MBar |
| § - 'Saphir' | CKen ECho LCon |
| ¶ - 'Seiryoden' | CKen |
| - 'Setsugekka' | CKen |
| - 'Shikashima' | CKen |
| - 'Shiobara' | CKen |
| - 'Shizukagoten' | CKen |
| - 'Shure' | CKen |
| - 'Tempelhof' | COtt GAri LNet LPan MBar SLim |
| I - 'Zelkova' | LLin |
| - 'Zui-sho' | CKen |
| **patula** ♀ | CAbb CB&S CDul CGre CSam |
| | ECre ISea LCon LLin LPan MBal |
| | MBlu SAPC SArc SCoo SIgm SLim |
| | SRPl WWat |
| **peuce** | LCon MBar NWea STre WFro |
| - 'Arnold Dwarf' | CKen |
| **pinaster** ♀ | CB&S CBlo CDoC CDul CLnd |
| | CTrC EHul ISea LCon MBal |
| **pinea** ♀ | CAgr CKen CMac GChr IOrc |
| | LCon LEdu LLin LPan MGos SAPC |
| | SArc SEND WNor |
| - 'Queensway' | CKen |
| **ponderosa** ♀ | CLnd ETen ISea LCon LLin SIgm |
| **pseudostrobus** | MBal |
| **pumila** | CAgr LCon |
| - 'Buchanan' | CKen |
| - 'Draijer's Dwarf' | CDoC EOrn LLin SLim |
| - 'Dwarf Blue' | See *P. pumila* 'Glauca' |
| § - 'Glauca' ♀ | CBlo CKen LCon LLin LNet MBar |
| | MBri |
| - 'Globe' | CDoC LCon LLin LNet MBri |
| - 'Jeddeloh' | CKen |
| - 'Knightshayes' | CKen |
| § - 'Nana' | SRms |
| - 'Säntis' | CDoC CKen |
| - 'Saphir' | See *P. parviflora* 'Saphir' |
| **radiata** ♀ | CB&S CDoC CTrC CTrw ENot |
| | IOrc LCon MBal SAPC SArc STre |
| | WDin |
| - 'Aurea' | CBlo CKen LCon LLin LPan MAsh |
| | MBri SLim SMur |
| - 'Bodnant' | CKen |
| - 'Isca' | CKen |
| - 'Marshwood' | CKen |
| - 'Nana' | Last listed 1996 |
| **resinosa** 'Don Smith' | CKen |
| - 'Joel's Broom' | CKen |
| - 'Nobska' | CKen |
| - 'Quinobequin' | CKen |
| - 'Watnong' | CKen |
| **rigida** | EHul LCon STre |

| | |
|---|---|
| *roxburghii* | CGre |
| *sabineana* | CAgr LCon |
| x *schwerinii* | CDoC LRHS |
| *sibirica* | See *P. cembra* subsp. *sibirica* |
| *strobiformis* | LCon |
| ¶ – 'Fox Tail' | EPfP |
| *strobus* | CB&S CDoC CDul CGre EHul GAri GChr GRei IOrc ISea LCon MBar NWea SEND STre WNor |
| § – 'Alba' | LCon MGos |
| – 'Amelia's Dwarf' | CKen |
| – 'Anna Fiele' | CKen |
| – 'Bergman's Mini' | CKen |
| – 'Bergman's Pendula Broom' | CKen |
| I – 'Bergman's Sport of Prostrata' | CKen |
| * – 'Bloomer's Dark Globe' | CKen |
| – 'Blue Shag' | CBlo CDoC CKen COtt LLin MBri MGos SLim WPyg |
| – 'Contorta' | Last listed 1996 |
| – 'Densa' | CKen |
| – 'Dove's Dwarf' | CKen |
| – 'Fastigiata' | CKen LLin |
| – 'Hillside Gem' | CKen |
| – 'Horsford' | CKen |
| – 'Jericho' | CKen |
| – 'Krügers Lilliput' | LCon LLin MBri SLim |
| – 'Macopin' | MGos |
| – 'Merrimack' | CKen |
| – 'Minima' | CDoC CKen LCon LLin MBar MBlu MBri SLim |
| – 'Minuta' | CKen LCon |
| – 'Nana' | See *P. strobus* 'Radiata' |
| – 'Nivea' | See *P. strobus* 'Alba' |
| – 'Northway Broom' | CKen LLin |
| – 'Pendula' | Last listed 1997 |
| § – 'Radiata' ♀ | CDoC EHul IOrc LNet MBar NBee SLim WAbe |
| – 'Reinshaus' | CKen LCon LLin |
| – 'Sayville' | CKen |
| – 'Sea Urchin' | CKen |
| – 'Uncatena' | CKen |
| – 'Verkade's Broom' | CKen |
| *sylvestris* ♀ | CB&S CDoC CDul CGre CKin CSam ECrN EHul ENot EOrn GChr GRei LBuc LCon LHyr LLin MBal MBar MGos NBee NWea SPer SReu STre WDin WMou WNor WStI |
| – 'Abergeldie' | CKen |
| – 'Andorra' | CKen |
| § – 'Argentea' | LNet |
| § – Aurea Group ♀ | CBlo CDoC CKen CMac EBrP EBre EHul IMGH IOrc LBee LBre LCon LLin LNet MAsh MBal MBar SBre SLim SPer SSta WLRN |
| – 'Aurea' | See *P. sylvestris* Aurea Group |
| – 'Avondene' | CKen |
| – 'Beuvronensis' ♀ | CDoC CKen CMac EOrn GAri IMGH LBee LCon LLin LNet MAsh MGos NHol SLim SSta |
| ¶ – 'Bonna' | LCon |
| – 'Brevifolia' | CBlo LCon MBar NHol |
| – 'Buchanan's Gold' | CKen |
| – 'Burghfield' | CBlo CKen LCon LLin NHol |
| – 'Chantry Blue' | CBlo CDoC EHul EOrn IMGH LBee LCon LLin MAsh MBar MGos SLim |
| – 'Clumber Blue' | CKen |
| – 'Compressa' | GAri |
| – 'Dereham' | CKen LLin |
| – 'Doone Valley' | CKen LLin |
| – 'Edwin Hillier' | See *P. sylvestris* 'Argentea' |
| – 'Fastigiata' | CDoC CEnd CKen EOrn IMGH LCon LLin LPan MAsh MBar MGos SLim |
| – 'Frensham' | CBlo CDoC CKen EOrn IMGH LCon LLin MGos MOne |
| – 'Globosa' | GAri MBri |
| – 'Gold Coin' ♀ | CBlo CDoC CKen EOrn LBee LCon LLin MBri MGos NHol SLim WPyg |
| – 'Gold Medal' | CKen LCon LLin |
| – 'Grand Rapids' | CKen |
| – 'Green Flare' | CKen |
| – 'Hibernia' | Last listed 1997 |
| – 'Hillside Creeper' | CKen LCon LLin SLim |
| – 'Inverleith' (v) | EHul GAri LCon LLin MAsh MBar MGos NHol SLim |
| – 'Jade' | See *P. sylvestris* 'Iceni' |
| – 'Jeremy' | CKen LCon LLin SLim WAbe |
| – 'Kelpie' | CKen |
| – 'Kenwith' | CKen |
| – 'Lakeside Dwarf' | LLin |
| – 'Little Brolly' | CKen |
| – 'Lodge Hill' | CBlo CDoC CKen EBrP EBre EOrn IMGH LBre LCon LLin MAsh MOne SBre SLim WAbe |
| – 'Longmoor' | CDoC CKen |
| – 'Martham' | CKen |
| – 'Moseri' | CDoC ECho MBri |
| – 'Nana' | See *P. sylvestris* 'Watereri' |
| – 'Nana Compacta' | LLin |
| – 'Nisbet' | CKen |
| § – 'Nisbet's Gem' | LLin |
| – 'Padworth' | CKen |
| – 'Pixie' | CKen LCon |
| ¶ – 'Pygmaea' | SLim |
| – 'Pyramidalis Compacta' | NHol |
| – 'Reedham' | LLin |
| – 'Repens' | CKen |
| – 'Sandringham' | CBlo LCon LLin NHol |
| – 'Saxatilis' | CBlo EOrn LCon LLin |
| – 'Scott's Dwarf' | See *P. sylvestris* 'Nisbet's Gem' |
| ¶ – 'Scrubby' | LLin |
| – 'Sentinel' | CKen |
| I – 'Skjak I' | CKen |
| I – 'Skjak II' | CKen |
| – 'Spaan's Slow Column' | CKen |
| – 'Tage' | CKen LLin |
| – 'Tanya' | CKen |
| – 'Tilshead' | CKen |
| – 'Treasure' | CKen |
| – 'Variegata' | Last listed 1998 |
| § – 'Watereri' | CDoC CMac EHul ENot IOrc LBee LCon LLin LNet LPan MAsh MBar MBri MGos NHol SLim WDin WWeb |
| – 'Westonbirt' | CKen EHul LCon |
| – 'Wishmoor' | LLin |
| * – 'Wolf Gold' | CKen |
| * – 'Yaff Hill' | LLin |
| *tabuliformis* | CMCN LCon MBlu SFur |
| ¶ – SF 96040 | ISea |
| *taeda* | Last listed 1997 |
| *taiwanensis* | ISea |
| *thunbergii* | CDoC CDul EHul LCon LLin MBal MGos SEND SPla STre WFro WNor |
| – 'Akame' | CKen |
| ¶ – 'Akame Yatsabusa' | CKen |
| – 'Aocha-matsu' | CKen |
| – 'Banshosho' | CKen |

| | |
|---|---|
| - 'Compacta' | CKen |
| - 'Dainagon' | CKen |
| - 'Iwai' | CKen |
| - 'Kotobuki' | CKen |
| - 'Ko-yo-sho' | Last listed 1998 |
| - 'Kujaku' | CKen |
| ¶ - 'Kyushu' | CKen |
| - 'Miyajuna' | CKen |
| - 'Nishiki-ne' | CKen |
| - var. *oculus draconis* | LLin |
| - 'Ogon' | CKen |
| § - 'Sayonara' | CBlo CKen GAri LCon LLin NHol |
| - 'Senryu' | CKen |
| - 'Shio-guro' | CKen |
| ¶ - 'Suchiro Yatabusa' | CKen |
| - 'Sunsho' | CKen |
| - 'Taihei' | CKen |
| I - 'Thunderhead' | CKen |
| - 'Yatsubusa' | See *P. thunbergii* 'Sayonara' |
| *uncinata* | See *P. mugo* subsp. *uncinata* |
| *virginiana* | MBal |
| - 'Wate's Golden' | CKen |
| § *wallichiana* ♀ | CAbP CBlo CDoC CDul CKen |
| | EHul IOrc LCon LLin LPan MBal |
| | MBar MGos NBee SLim STre |
| | WCoo WGer WNor WTro |
| - CC 1740 | SGre |
| - 'Densa' | MBri |
| - 'Nana' | CKen EHul MBar SLim |
| - 'Umbraculifera' | LRHS MBal MBri |
| - 'Zebrina' (v) | CBlo CDoC LCon MBar MGos |
| *yunnanensis* | CDoC ETen WNor WShe |
| ¶ - SF 96250 | ISea |

## PIPER (Piperaceae)

| | |
|---|---|
| *auritum* | MSal |
| *betle* | CPlN MSal |
| *excelsum* | See *Macropiper excelsum* |
| *methysticum* | Last listed 1998 |
| *nigrum* | MSal |

## PIPTANTHUS (Papilionaceae)

| | |
|---|---|
| *forrestii* | See *P. nepalensis* |
| *laburnifolius* | See *P. nepalensis* |
| § *nepalensis* | CB&S CBot CHan CMac CPMA |
| | CPle ECrN ELan EMil ENot EPla |
| | LHop MBel MGos MWat MWhi |
| | SBra SDix SEND SLon SOWG SPer |
| | SRms SSpi WCru WDin WPat |
| - B&SWJ 2241 | WCru |
| - SF 95180 | ISea |
| *tomentosus* | SDry |

## PISONIA (Nyctaginaceae)

| | |
|---|---|
| *brunoniana* | See *P. umbellifera* |
| § *umbellifera* | Last listed 1998 |
| - 'Variegata' | Last listed 1998 |

## PISTACIA (Anacardiaceae)

| | |
|---|---|
| *chinensis* | CB&S CMCN CPMA ELan EWes |
| | SSpi |
| ¶ *lentiscus* | CB&S |
| *terebinthus* | CFil |

## PISTIA (Araceae)

| | |
|---|---|
| *stratiotes* | MSta |

## PITTOSPORUM ✿ (Pittosporaceae)

| | |
|---|---|
| *anomalum* | ECou SDry |
| - (f) | ECou |
| - (m) | ECou |
| - 'Falcon' | ECou |

| | |
|---|---|
| - 'Raven' (f) | ECou |
| - 'Starling' (m) | ECou |
| * *argyrophyllum* | IOrc |
| 'Arundel Green' | CBlo CDoC LRHS MBri MTed |
| | SDry |
| *bicolor* | CFil CPle ECou GQui SAPC SArc |
| | WPGP |
| *buchananii* | CPle SVen |
| *colensoi* | ECou |
| ¶ - 'Cobb' (f) | ECou |
| - 'Wanaka' | ECou |
| *crassifolium* | CB&S CFil CPle ECou ERea IOrc |
| | WPGP |
| - 'Havering Dwarf' | ECou |
| - 'Napier' | ECou |
| - x *tenuifolium* | ECou |
| - 'Variegatum' | CGre LHil WSPU |
| ¶ 'Craxten' (f) | CPin ECou |
| ¶ *cuneatum* | LHop |
| *dallii* | Last listed 1998 |
| *daphniphylloides* | CFil CGre CPin |
| var. *adaphniphylloides* | |
| - ETE 275 | WPGP |
| *divaricatum* | ECou |
| 'Essex' (v) | ECou |
| *eugenioides* | CB&S CMHG IDee SLon |
| - 'Platinum' | CB&S |
| - 'Variegatum' ♀ | CB&S CCHP CDoC CGre EBee |
| | EPfP GQui IOrc SBid WSHC WSPU |
| 'Garnettii' (v) ♀ | CB&S CCHe CDoC CEnd CLan |
| | CMHG CSam CTrw EBee EBrP |
| | EBre EHoe ELan EMil ENot GOrc |
| | IOrc LBre LHop MBal MGos |
| | MWgw SBre SPer SRPl WAbe |
| | WDin WSHC |
| *heterophyllum* | CPle ECou |
| - variegated | ECou |
| ¶ *buttonianum* | SVen |
| 'Limelight' (v) | CB&S CBlo CGre EMil WWes |
| *lineare* | ECou |
| § 'Margaret Turnbull' (v) | CB&S CTrC ECou EMil LHop |
| | MGos |
| *michiei* | ECou |
| - (f) | ECou |
| - (m) | ECou |
| - 'Jack' (m) | ECou |
| - 'Jill' (f) | ECou |
| 'Nanum Variegatum' | See *P. tobira* 'Variegatum' |
| *obcordatum* | ECou |
| - var. *kaitaiaense* | ECou |
| *omeiense* | CFil CGre |
| *phillyreoides* | CFil |
| *pimeleoides* | ECou |
| var. *reflexum* (m) | |
| *ralphii* | ECou |
| - 'Green Globe' | ECou |
| ¶ - 'Variegatum' | SSpi |
| *revolutum* | Last listed 1998 |
| *rhombifolium* | Last listed 1998 |
| 'Saundersii' (v) | CBlo EBee EMil MBal |
| *tenuifolium* ♀ | CB&S EAst EBee EBrP EBre ECou |
| | ELan EMil ENot GOrc ISea LBre |
| | LHop MBal MBri SArc SBre SPer |
| | SRms STre WAbe WBrE WDin |
| | WSHC WStI WWat |
| - 'Abbotsbury Gold' (v) | CAbb CCHe CDoC CSam CTri |
| | CWSG EBee ECou ELan EMil |
| | EWes GOrc SDry SPer SRPl WSHC |
| - 'Atropurpureum' | CB&S WBcn |
| - 'County Park Dwarf' | ECou WCru |
| - 'Deborah' (v) | CB&S ECou LHop SBid SSto |
| - 'Dixie' | CMHG ECou |

| | |
|---|---|
| § – 'Eila Keightley' (v) | CBlo CMHG CSam IOrc MBal |
| ¶ – 'Elizabeth' | CDoC ECou LRHS |
| * – 'French Lace' | ECou |
| – 'Gold Star' | CB&S CDoC ECou EMil LRHS |
| – 'Golden King' | CB&S CDoC CMHG EBee MBal |
| | MRav SPla SRms |
| ¶ – 'Golden Princess' (f) | ECou |
| * – 'Green Elf' | CHan ECou |
| * – 'Green Thumb' | Last listed 1997 |
| – 'Irene Paterson' (v) ♀ | CAbb CB&S CDoC CGre CMHG |
| | CSam EBee ECou ELan GOrc IOrc |
| | LHop MBal MBri MGos SAga SDry |
| | SLon SPer SPla SRms SSpi SSta |
| | WAbe WSHC |
| – 'James Stirling' | ECou IOrc WSHC |
| – 'John Flanagan' | See P. 'Margaret Turnbull' |
| – 'Katie' | CB&S |
| – 'Loxhill Gold' | CDoC EBee LRHS SEas SSto |
| – 'Marjory Channon' (v) | CB&S SRPl |
| – 'Mellow Yellow' | CAbP LRHS WBcn |
| ¶ – 'Moonlight' | CTrC |
| – 'Nigricans' | CB&S CLan |
| – 'Princess' (f) | Last listed 1998 |
| – 'Purpureum' | CPle CSam CTri CTrw ECou ELan |
| | EPfP IOrc LSpr MBal SDry SPer |
| | SPla SRms WSHC |
| * – 'Silver Dollar' | MBri |
| – 'Silver Magic' | CB&S EMil |
| – 'Silver 'n' Gold' | LRHS |
| ¶ – 'Silver Princess' (f) | ECou |
| – 'Silver Queen' (f/v) ♀ | CB&S CDoC CEnd CMHG CSam |
| | EBee EBrP EBre ECou EHoe ELan |
| | GOrc IOrc LBre MBal MBel MGos |
| | MNrw SBre SPer SPla WAbe WBrE |
| | WSHC WStl WWat |
| – 'Stirling Gold' (v) | CB&S ECou EPfP EWes EWll |
| – 'Sunburst' | See P. tenuifolium 'Eila Keightley' |
| – 'Tiki' | CB&S ECou |
| – 'Tom Thumb' ♀ | More than 30 suppliers |
| – 'Tresederi' (f/m) | CTrw ECou MBal |
| – 'Variegata' | CB&S CDoC ECou EMil |
| ¶ – 'Victoria' | CDoC |
| – 'Warnham Gold' ♀ | CB&S CDoC CHan CMHG COtt |
| | CTrw EBee ECou ELan IOrc SDry |
| | SEas SPla SSpi WAbe WDin WWat |
| – 'Wendle Channon' (v) | CB&S CDoC CEnd CMHG CSam |
| | CWSG EBee ECot ECou LHop |
| | MBal SPer SPla SRPl WSHC WWat |
| – 'Winter Sunshine' | LRHS SSta |
| tobira ♀ | More than 30 suppliers |
| – B&SWJ 4362 | WCru |
| – 'Nanum' | CB&S CDoC EBee ECou EPla |
| | ERea IOrc SArc SBid |
| § – 'Variegatum' ♀ | CB&S CBot CGre CPle ECou ERea |
| | GQui LHop MBri NPal SBid SLon |
| | SPer SSta WCru |
| * – 'Variegatum | Last listed 1998 |
|    Linearifolium' (v) | |
| undulatum | ECou |
| – 'Variegatum' | CGre |

## PITYROGRAMMA (Adiantaceae)

| | |
|---|---|
| triangularis | CFil |

## PLAGIANTHUS (Malvaceae)

| | |
|---|---|
| betulinus | See P. regius |
| divaricatus | CFil CPLG WPGP |
| lyallii | See Hoheria lyallii |
| § regius | ECou GQui LRHS SBid |
| – var. chathamicus | Last listed 1996 |

## PLAGIOMNIUM (Sphagnaceae)

| | |
|---|---|
| affine | Last listed 1996 |

## PLAGIORHEGMA See JEFFERSONIA

## PLANTAGO (Plantaginaceae)

| | |
|---|---|
| alpina | Last listed 1997 |
| argentea | Last listed 1997 |
| asiatica | MSal |
| – 'Variegata' | CRow CSpe EBee EGoo EHoe |
| | GBri GBuc MBNS NBro NEgg |
| | NLar NSti WElm WHer WOut |
| | WRos WSan |
| coronopus | CKin EWFC |
| cynops | LRHS MTho WCot |
| * gaudichaudii | Last listed 1997 |
| lanceolata | EWFC MHew |
| – 'Ballydowling | CNat |
|    Variegated' (v) | |
| – 'Burren Rose' | CNat CRow |
| – 'Freaky' | Last listed 1998 |
| ¶ – 'Martin's Freaky' | WAlt |
| – 'Streaker' (v) | CRow WCot WHal WHer |
| major | EWFC WHbs |
| – 'Atropurpurea' | See P. major 'Rubrifolia' |
| – B&L 12649 | Last listed 1996 |
| – 'Bowles' Variety' | See P. major 'Rosularis' |
| – 'Bract Act' | WAlt |
| – 'Frills' | CNat CRow WCot WHer |
| * – 'Karmozijn' | EGoo |
| § – 'Rosularis' | CArn CInt CRow CSpe EBee |
| | ECha ELan EPla ILis MCAu MFir |
| | MHar MTho NBro NChi NEgg |
| | NLar NRoo NSti WBea WHal |
| | WHer WPer WWye |
| § – 'Rubrifolia' | CArn CHid CKel CRow CSpe |
| | EBee ECha ECoo EPla LFis LNor |
| | MCAu MFir MHar MNrw NBro |
| | NChi NEgg NFla NHar NMir NSti |
| | WBea WCer WHer WPer WRos |
| | WWye |
| – 'Subtle Streak' (v) | WAlt |
| – 'Variegata' | Last listed 1998 |
| maritima | CKin WHer |
| media | CKin EWFC MHew |
| nivalis | CSpe EBee EHyt MBro NNrd |
| | NTow SIng WWin |
| psyllium | CArn GPoy MSal |
| raoulii | WCot |
| rosea | See P. major 'Rosularis' |
| sempervirens | Last listed 1998 |
| ¶ sp. RCB/Eq N-3 | WCot |
| uniflora | See Littorella uniflora |

## PLATANTHERA (Orchidaceae)

| | |
|---|---|
| hologlottis | EFEx |
| metabifolia | EFEx |

## PLATANUS ❀ (Platanaceae)

| | |
|---|---|
| x acerifolia | See P. x hispanica |
| § x hispanica ♀ | CB&S CBlo CDul CKin CLnd |
| | CMCN CTho ECrN EMil ENot |
| | EWTr GChr IOrc LBuc LPan MAsh |
| | MGos NWea SEND SPer WDin |
| | WFar WMou |
| – 'Liberty' | SMad |
| – 'Pyramidalis' | CTho |
| – 'Suttneri' (v) | CBlo CDoC CEnd CLnd CTho |
| | LNet SMad |
| – 'Tremonia' | SMad |
| occidentalis | CDul |

| orientalis ♀ | CLnd CMCN EPfP IOrc SMad WDin WMou |
|---|---|
| - 'Cuneata' | LRHS MBri |
| § - f.*digitata* | CLnd CTho ERod SLPl |
| - 'Laciniata' | See *P. orientalis* f. *digitata* |
| - 'Mirkovec' | CDoC MBri SMad SPer |

## PLATYCARYA (Juglandaceae)
| *strobilacea* | CMCN |
|---|---|

## PLATYCERIUM (Polypodiaceae)
| *alcicorne* hort. | See *P. bifurcatum* |
|---|---|
| § *bifurcatum* ♀ | LCns MBri |
| *grande* hort. | See *P. superbum* |
| § *superbum* ♀ | LCns |

## PLATYCLADUS (Cupressaceae)
| *orientalis* | See *Thuja orientalis* |
|---|---|

## PLATYCODON ✿ (Campanulaceae)
| *grandiflorus* ♀ | CArn CGle CNic EBee ECha ELau LFis LHop MFir MNrw MPEx MSal NBro NFai NOrc NVic SCob SIng WCla WHoo WWye |
|---|---|
| - *albus* | CBro CRDP EAst EBee EOld LHop MBri MBro NBro NFai NOak SCob SPer SPla SSca WHoo WOve WPer |
| - 'Apoyama' ♀ | CLyd EBee LBee MBro MHar MMal SWas WAbe WCot WHoo WPer WWin |
| - *apoyama albus* | LGre MBro NChi SIde SWas WCFE WEas WHoo WPyg |
| - 'Axminster Streaked' | Last listed 1996 |
| - 'Baby Blue' | SRms |
| - 'Blue Haze' | MMHG NCat WLRN |
| - 'Blue Pearl' | WHoo |
| - 'Blue Pygmy' | Last listed 1997 |
| - 'Blue Surf' | Last listed 1998 |
| - 'Florist Blue' | CMdw WMoo |
| - 'Florist Rose' | NBur NOak SSca WMoo WWye |
| - 'Florist Snow' | CMdw NBur NOak WMoo WWye |
| - 'Fuji Blue' | CBlo LIck NLar SUsu |
| - 'Fuji Pink' | CBlo CBro CRDP EAst EBee MRav MTis NLar SCob SMrm SPer SPla SRPl SUsu WAbe WGwG WLin |
| - 'Fuji White' | CBlo CMil MCCP NLar SMrm SPla |
| - 'Hakone' | CRDP EBee EMan LHop MBro MRav NCat SMrm WHoo WPyg WWal |
| ¶ - 'Hakone Blue' | NLar |
| * - 'Hakone Double Blue' | CBro EBee ECGP ERic MCAu MMHG MMll SCro WLRN |
| - 'Hakone White' | EBee ERic MBro MMHG NLar NMen SIng WHoo |
| - 'Mammoth Blue' | Last listed 1998 |
| - 'Mammoth White' | Last listed 1998 |
| - 'Mariesii' ♀ | CBro CGle CLyd CNic EBee EBrP EBre ECtt ENot EWTr GMaP LBre LFis MBal MRav NBir NChi NMen SBre SPer SRms WEas WHoo WPer WWin |
| - *mariesii albus* | EBee MBro WHoo WPyg WWat |
| - 'Misato Purple' | EBee WBay WShe |
| - Mother of Pearl | See *P. grandiflorus* 'Perlmutterschale' |
| - 'Park's Double Blue' (d) | MLLN MTis NOak SSca WHoo WMoo WPyg |
| § - 'Perlmutterschale' | CGle CMil EBee EPfP GMac MBri MCAu SRCN WHoo WPyg WWeb |
| - *pumilus* | EBee MBro MHar NChi NWCA WCFE WHoo WPyg |
| - 'Purple Dwarf' | Last listed 1997 |
| - Purple Princess = 'Hime-murasaki' | Last listed 1997 |
| - *roseus* | MNrw WHoo |
| - 'Sentimental Blue' | EBee NLar SMrm WLRN |
| - 'Shell Pink' | See *P. grandiflorus* 'Perlmutterschale' |
| - 'Zwerg' | EBee LGre |

## PLATYCRATER (Hydrangeaceae)
| ¶ *arguta* | WCru |
|---|---|

## PLECOSTACHYS (Asteraceae)
| § *serpyllifolia* | CHal CLTr |
|---|---|

## PLECTOCOLEA (Jungermanniaceae)
| *hyalina* | Last listed 1996 |
|---|---|

## PLECTRANTHUS (Lamiaceae)
| *amboinicus* | EOHP LHil |
|---|---|
| * - 'Tansania' | EOHP |
| * - 'Variegatus' | EOHP |
| *argentatus* | CHad CPin CSev EHic LHil WKif |
| ¶ - variegated | CSpe |
| § *australis* | CHal EOHP SRCN WEas |
| *behrii* | See *P. fruticosus* |
| *ciliatus* | LHil MBEx |
| *coleoides* 'Marginatus' | See *P. forsteri* 'Marginatus' |
| - 'Variegatus' | See *P. madagascariensis* 'Variegated Mintleaf' |
| *excisus* | EMon |
| § *forsteri* | LHil |
| § - 'Marginatus' | CHal ERea LHil MBEx NFai SVen |
| § *fruticosus* | CHal CHan LHil MBEx |
| ¶ *hirtellus* gold form | MBEx |
| ¶ 'Jan Jaas Veldia' | MBEx |
| § *madagascariensis* | CHal LHil MRav SHFr SRms |
| 'Variegated Mintleaf' | |
| *oertendahlii* ♀ | CHal EBak LHil MBEx |
| ¶ *ornatus* | MBEx |
| *purpuratus* | EOHP |
| * *purpureus* | SVen |
| sp. podena | CArn |
| Swedish ivy | See *P. australis* |
| § *thyrsoideus* | CHal SVen |
| *zatarhendii* | LHil |
| *zuluensis* | LHil MBEx |

## PLEIOBLASTUS ✿ (Poaceae - Bambusoideae)
| *akebono* | EPla SDry |
|---|---|
| § *auricomus* ♀ | More than 30 suppliers |
| - 'Bracken Hill' | EPla SDry WJun |
| - f.*chrysophyllus* | EPla MMoz SDry WJun |
| ¶ - 'Vagans' | EBee |
| ¶ - *variegatus* | CHar |
| § *chino* | EPla ISta MDun SDry WBay |
| § - f.*angustifolius* | LHil MMoz SDry |
| § - var. *argenteostriatus* | EPla |
| ¶ - f.*aureostriatus* (v) | EPla ISta LJus NDov SDry WCru |
| - *chrysanthus* | See *Sasa chrysantha* |
| - f.*elegantissimus* | CEnd CFir COtt EBee EPla ISta LJus LRHS MMoz MWhi NDov SDry WBay WJun |
| ¶ - var. *hisauchii* | EPla |
| - 'Kimmei' | SDry |
| - 'Murakamianus' | EPla SDry |
| *fortunei* | See *P. variegatus* |
| 'Gauntlettii' | See *P. humilis* var. *pumilus* |
| *glaber* 'Albostriatus' | See *Sasaella masamuneana* f. *albostriata* |
| *gramineus* | EPla ISta SDry WJun |
| § *hindsii* hort. | EPla SArc SDry |
| § *humilis* | CBlo ELan |

| | |
|---|---|
| § - var. *pumilus* | CCuc CDoC CRow CTrC EBee |
| | EHoe EPar EPla ISta LJus MBlu |
| | MBri NHol SDry SPlb WJun WNor |
| | WPat WPer |
| *kongosanensis* | EPla SDry |
| 'Aureostriatus' (v) | |
| *linearis* | CB&S CFir EBee EFul EPla ISta |
| | LRHS MMoz SDry WBay WJun |
| *longifimbriatus* | EPla WJun |
| *oleosus* | EPla SDry WJun |
| § *pygmaeus* | More than 30 suppliers |
| § - var. *distichus* | EFul EPPr EPla GBin LHil LJus |
| | MMoz MUlv SArc SDry WJun |
| | WWin |
| * - - 'Mini' | WCot |
| § - 'Mirrezuzume' | EPla GBin WWat |
| *shibuyanus* 'Tsuboi' (v) | CDoC CEnd COtt EBee EPPr EPla |
| | ISta LJus LPJP MBrN MMoz MWhi |
| | NDov SDry WBay WCru WJun |
| § *simonii* | EBee EBrP EBre EFul EPla GBin |
| | ISta LBre MDun MMoz MWhi |
| | NMoo SArc SBre SDry WBay |
| - var. *heterophyllus* | See *P. simonii* f. *variegatus* |
| § - f. *variegatus* | CFil EPla ISta MBar MBlu SDry |
| | SPer WBay WJun |
| § *variegatus* ♀ | More than 30 suppliers |
| - var. *viridis* | SDry |
| *viridistriatus* | See *P. auricomus* |

## PLEIONE ✿ (Orchidaceae)

| | |
|---|---|
| § *albiflora* | SWes |
| § - 'Pinchbeck Diamond' | EEve EPot GCrs |
| **Alishan g.** | CNic EEve EPot GCrs LBut NSpr |
| | SWes |
| - 'Foxhill' | NSpr |
| - 'Merlin' | NSpr |
| - 'Mount Fuji' | LBut |
| - 'Soldier Blue' | LBut |
| **Asama g.** | LBut SWes |
| § *aurita* | EFEx GCrs LAma NSpr SWes |
| **Bandai-san g.** | LBut |
| **Barcena g.** | LBut |
| **Beerenberg g.** | LBut |
| 'Berapi' | EPot LBut SWes |
| **Brigadoon g.** | LBut NSpr |
| - 'Stonechat' | LBut |
| **Britannia g.** | LBut |
| - 'Doreen' | LBut NSpr |
| § *bulbocodioides* | EEve EPot ERos IBlr LBut MBro |
| | MRPP NNrd NSpr WFar |
| - 'Lapwing' | LBut |
| § - Limprichtii Group ♀ | EEve EFEx EPot LBut MRPP NTow |
| | SWes |
| - - 'Primrose Peach' | Last listed 1997 |
| - Pricei Group | See *P. formosana* Pricei Group |
| § - 'Yunnan' | EPot LBut NSpr SWes |
| **Captain Hook g.** | LBut NSpr |
| *chunii* | See *P. aurita* |
| x *confusa* | EEve EFEx EPot GCrs SWes |
| **Cotopaxi g.** | LBut |
| **Danan g.** | LBut SWes |
| **Deriba g.** | LBut |
| **Eiger g.** | EEve EPot ERos LBut NSpr SWes |
| - cream form | EPot ERos GCrs LBut |
| **El Pico g.** | GCrs LBut NSpr SWes |
| - 'Goldcrest' | GCrs LBut |
| - 'Kestrel' | GCrs LBut |
| - 'Pheasant' | LBut |
| - 'Starling' | LBut |
| **Erebus g.** | LBut SWes |
| - 'Quail' | LBut |
| **Erh Hai g.** | NSpr |

| | |
|---|---|
| * **Etna g.** | CNic EEve EPot GCrs LBut SWes |
| ¶ - 'Bullfinch' | GCrs |
| *formosana* ♀ | CNic EFEx EPot ETub GCrs IBlr |
| | LAma NTow SCob SDeJ SIng |
| | SWes |
| - 'Achievement' | LBut |
| I - 'Alba' | EPot GCrs IBlr SIng SWes |
| ¶ - **Arline g.** | EEve |
| - 'Avalanche' | EPot LBut NSpr |
| - 'Ben Nevis' | LBut |
| - 'Blush of Dawn' | EPot GCrs LBut NSpr |
| ¶ - **C.P. Diamond g.** | EEve |
| - 'Cairngorm' | NSpr SWes |
| - 'Christine Anne' | NSpr |
| - 'Clare' | EPot ERos GCrs LBut NSpr |
| - **Eugene g.** | EEve EPot SWes |
| - 'Greenhill' | LBut |
| I - 'Iris' | LBut NSpr |
| - **Kate g.** | EEve EPot |
| - 'Lilac Beauty' | SWes |
| - 'Little Winnie' | EEve EPot SWes |
| - 'Lucy Diamond' | EEve EPot GCrs LBut |
| - **Lulu g.** | EEve EPot SWes |
| - 'Oriental Grace' | EPot LAma LBut SWes |
| - 'Oriental Jewel' | SWes |
| - 'Oriental Splendour' | EPot LBut NSpr SWes |
| ¶ - 'Pitlochry' | LBut |
| - 'Polar Sun' | EEve EPot GCrs NSpr SWes |
| § - Pricei Group | EPot ERos NTow |
| - 'Red Spot' | EEve |
| - 'Serenity' | LBut |
| - 'Snow Cap' | SWes |
| - 'Snow White' | GCrs LBut |
| ¶ - 'Snowy Owl' | LBut |
| *forrestii* | EFEx EPot GCrs LAma SWes |
| **Fuego g.** | LBut NSpr SWes |
| **Fuego g.** 'Wren' | LBut |
| **Fujiyama g.** | LBut |
| ¶ **Gerry Mundey g.** | LBut |
| ¶ *grandiflora* | SWes |
| 'Hallmark' | GCrs |
| **Hekla g.** | EPot GCrs LBut NSpr SWes |
| - 'Partridge' | LBut |
| *hookeriana* | GCrs SWes |
| *humilis* | SDeJ |
| - 'Frank Kingdon Ward' | GCrs SWes |
| **Irazu g.** | GCrs LBut NSpr |
| **Irazu g.** 'Irazu Violet' | GCrs |
| **Jorullo g.** | LBut NSpr SWes |
| - 'Long-tailed Tit' | LBut |
| **Katla g.** | LBut NSpr SWes |
| **Katmai g.** | LBut |
| **Keith Rattray g.** | LBut |
| **Kilauea g.** | EPot LBut SWes |
| ¶ **Kituro g.** | LBut |
| **Krakatoa g.** | Last listed 1998 |
| **Lascar g.** | LBut |
| *limprichtii* mauve | GCrs |
| - pink | GCrs |
| **Lipari g.** | LBut |
| *maculata* | EFEx LAma SWes |
| **Marco Polo g.** | LBut NSpr |
| **Matupi g.** | LBut NSpr |
| 'Mayfield' | GCrs |
| **Mayon g.** | LBut |
| **Mazama g.** | LBut |
| **Myojin g.** | LBut SWes |
| **Novarupta g.** | LBut |
| **Orinoco g.** | LBut SWes |
| - 'Gemini' | LBut |
| ¶ **Orizaba g.** | LBut |
| **Paricutin g.** | LBut |

| | |
|---|---|
| Pavlof g. | LBut |
| *pinkepankii* | See *P. albiflora* |
| Piton g. | EEve EPot GCrs LAma LBut SWes |
| ♦ *pogonioides* Rolfe | See *P. bulbocodioides*, *P. bulbocodioides* Limprichtii Group |
| ♦ - hort. | See *P. speciosa* |
| *praecox* | SWes |
| Rainier g. | LBut |
| Rakata g. | LBut |
| - 'Shot Silk' | LBut |
| Sajama g. | Last listed 1996 |
| San Pedro g. | LBut |
| *scopulorum* | EFEx SWes |
| Shantung g. | EEve EPot GCrs LAma LBut NSpr SWes |
| Shantung g. 'Candyfloss' | NSpr |
| - 'Ducat' | EPot GCrs LAma LBut NSpr |
| - 'Gerry Mundey' | LBut NSpr |
| - 'Golden Jubilee' | NSpr |
| - 'Golden Plover' | LBut |
| - 'Mikki' | NSpr |
| - 'Muriel Harberd' ♀ | CRDP EPot GCrs NSpr |
| - 'R6.7' | NSpr |
| - 'Ridgeway' | EPot GCrs LBut NSpr SWes |
| - 'Stephanie Rose' | Last listed 1998 |
| Sorea g. | LBut |
| Soufrière g. | LBut NSpr SWes |
| § *speciosa* | EEve EPot GCrs LBut MRPP SWes |
| - 'Blakeway Phillips' | NSpr SWes |
| Stromboli g. | EEve EPot GCrs LBut NSpr SWes |
| Stromboli g. 'Fireball' | GCrs LBut NSpr |
| - 'Robin' | LBut |
| Surtsey g. | LBut |
| ¶ - 'Stephanie Rose' | NSpr |
| ¶ Taal g. | LBut |
| Tacana g. | LBut |
| Tambora g. | LBut |
| Tarawera g. | LBut SWes |
| Tolima g. | CNic EEve EPot LAma LBut NSpr SWes |
| - 'Moorhen' | GCrs |
| - 'Nightingale' | Last listed 1996 |
| - 'Tufted Duck' | Last listed 1996 |
| Tongariro g. | EEve EPot ERos GCrs LBut NSpr SWes |
| - 'Jackdaw' | LBut |
| Versailles g. | EEve EFEx EPot LAma LBut NSpr SWes |
| - 'Bucklebury' ♀ | CNic EPot GCrs LBut NSpr |
| - 'Heron' | LBut |
| - 'Muriel Turner' | EEve EPot LAma LBut NSpr |
| Vesuvius g. | EEve EPot LBut NSpr |
| - 'Aphrodite' | EPot |
| - 'Leopard' | LBut |
| * - 'Phoenix' | EPot GCrs LBut NSpr |
| Volcanello g. | GCrs LBut NSpr SWes |
| ¶ Wunzen g. | LBut |
| *yunnanensis* hort. | See *P. bulbocodioides* 'Yunnan' |
| - Rolfe | LAma LBut SWes |
| Zeus Weinstein g. | LBut NSpr |
| Zeus Weinstein g. 'Desert Sands' | LBut |

## PLEOMELE See DRACAENA

## PLEUROCHAETE (Sphagnaceae)

| | |
|---|---|
| *luteoalba* | Last listed 1996 |

## PLEUROSPERMUM (Apiaceae)

| | |
|---|---|
| *brunonis* | EDAr WHal |

## PLEXIPUS (Verbenaceae)

| | |
|---|---|
| *cuneifolius* | Last listed 1996 |
| ¶ *namaquanus* | EBee SIgm |

## PLUMBAGO (Plumbaginaceae)

| | |
|---|---|
| § *auriculata* ♀ | CB&S CDoC CEnd CLTr CPlN CPle CRHN CSpe EBak EBee ELan ERav ERea LBlm LHol LHop MBri MLan MRav NEgg NPal NRog SBra SIde SOWG SPer SRms SYvo WBod |
| - var. *alba* | CB&S CBot CPlN CRHN CSev EBak ELan EMil ERav ERea LBlm LHol MBEx MLan SEND SOWG SPer SYvo |
| * - *aurea* | LIck |
| * - Royal Cape = 'Monott' | ERav |
| *capensis* | See *P. auriculata* |
| § *indica* | CHal CPle SOWG |
| - *rosea* | See *P. indica* |
| *larpentiae* | See *Ceratostigma plumbaginoides* |
| *zeylanica* | Last listed 1997 |

## PLUMERIA (Apocynaceae)

| | |
|---|---|
| forms | Last listed 1996 |
| § *obtusa* | LChe |
| *rubra* | ECon LBlo LChe LRHS SOWG |
| ¶ - f. *acutifolia* | LChe SOWG |
| - f. *lutea* | Last listed 1998 |
| 'Singapore' | See *P. obtusa* |

## PNEUMATOPTERIS See CYCLOSORUS

## POA (Poaceae)

| | |
|---|---|
| *abyssinica* | Last listed 1997 |
| *acicularifolia* | Last listed 1998 |
| *alpina nodosa* | CInt GBin |
| *araratica* | Last listed 1997 |
| *badensis* 'Ingelkissen' | Last listed 1997 |
| *buchananii* | Last listed 1998 |
| *bulbosa* | EPPr |
| *chaixii* | CCuc EHoe EMan EMon EPPr EPla GBin NHol SLPl WFoF |
| *cita* | EWes |
| *colensoi* | CCuc EHoe GChr MCCP MWhi SPla WCot |
| *eminens* | Last listed 1998 |
| - from Magadan, Siberia | EPPr |
| *fawcettiae* | Last listed 1997 |
| *glauca* | Last listed 1997 |
| *hothamensis* | Last listed 1997 |
| *imbecilla* | Last listed 1998 |
| x *jemtlandica* | EHoe NHol |
| *labillardierei* | CBrm CKno ECha EHoe EMan EPPr WCot |
| *nemoralis* | Last listed 1997 |

## PODALYRIA (Papilionaceae)

| | |
|---|---|
| *biflora* | Last listed 1997 |
| *calyptrata* | Last listed 1997 |
| *sericea* | CSpe SIgm |

## PODANTHUS (Asteraceae)

| | |
|---|---|
| *ovatifolius* G&K 4386 | CGre CPLG |

## PODOCARPUS (Podocarpaceae)

| | |
|---|---|
| *acutifolius* | CB&S CDoC ECou EPla MBar STre |
| ¶ - (f) | ECou |
| ¶ - (m) | ECou |
| *andinus* | See *Prumnopitys andina* |

| | |
|---|---|
| 'Autumn Shades' (m) | ECou |
| 'Blaze' (f) | ECou |
| *chilinus* | See *P. salignus* |
| 'Chocolate Box' (f) | ECou |
| 'County Park Fire' (f) | CKen ECou EOrn LCon LLin MGos SLim WGor |
| *cunninghamii* | See *P. hallii* |
| *dacrydioides* | See *Dacrycarpus dacrydioides* |
| *elongatus* | Last listed 1998 |
| *ferrugineus* | See *Prumnopitys ferruginea* |
| 'Golden Dwarf' | See *Prumnopitys ferruginea* 'Golden Dwarf' |
| § *hallii* | ECou WCwm |
| * - 'Kiwi' (f) | ECou |
| - x *nivalis* (f) | ECou |
| - 'Roro' (m) | ECou |
| 'Havering' (f) | ECou |
| *henkelii* | CTrC WMul |
| *latifolius* | CTrC |
| *lawrencei* | CBlo ECho EHul GAri IOrc |
| - (f) | ECou MBar MGos MPla SSmi |
| - 'Alpine Lass' (f) | ECou |
| - 'Blue Gem' (f) | CBlo CDoC ECou EOrn EPla LBee LCon LLin MAsh MBar MBri MGos MOne MUlv SLim WBcn WLRN WWat |
| - 'Kiandra' | ECou |
| *macrophyllus* (m) | ECou |
| - | CDoC CGre EOrn LPan SAPC SArc SMad STre WWat |
| - 'Angustifolius' | SLon |
| ¶ - 'Aureus' | CB&S |
| ¶ 'Maori Prince' (m) | ECou |
| *nivalis* | CMHG CMac EBrP EBre ECou EOrn EPla LBee LLin MBar MPla SBre SIng SPla SRms SSmi WWat |
| - 'Arthur' (m) | ECou |
| - 'Bronze' | EPla |
| - 'Clarence' (m) | ECou |
| - 'Green Queen' (f) | ECou |
| - 'Jack's Pass' (m) | ECou |
| - 'Kaweka' (m) | ECou |
| - 'Little Lady' (f) | ECou |
| - 'Livingstone' (f) | ECou |
| - 'Lodestone' (m) | ECou |
| - 'Moffatt' (f) | ECou |
| - 'Otari' (m) | ECou |
| - 'Park Cover' | ECou |
| - 'Princess' (f) | ECou |
| - 'Ruapehu' | ECou EPla |
| § *salignus* ♀ | CB&S CDoC CGre EPla IOrc ISea SAPC SArc WCoo WSHC |
| - (m) | ECou |
| *spicatus* | See *Prumnopitys taxifolia* |
| 'Spring Sunshine' | ECou |
| *totara* | CGre CHan CMHG ECou LEdu STre WPic |
| - 'Aureus' | CB&S CDoC ECou EPla LLin MBal MBar WLRN |
| - 'Pendulus' | ECou |
| 'Young Rusty' | ECou |

## PODOPHYLLUM (Berberidaceae)

| | |
|---|---|
| *delavayi* | WCru |
| *difforme* | WCru |
| *emodi* | See *P. hexandrum* |
| - var. *chinense* | See *P. hexandrum* var. *chinense* |
| § *hexandrum* | CBos CBro CRDP CRow EOld EPar EPot ERos GAbr GCal GCrs GPoy LAma MBal MBri MSal NChi NHar SBid SSpi WWye |
| - ACE 1894 | Last listed 1996 |

| | |
|---|---|
| § - var. *chinense* | CRow EHyt GBuc IBlr SMad WCru WWat |
| - 'Majus' | EBee WCot WCru |
| ¶ *mairei* | WCru |
| *peltatum* | CArn CBro CRow EBee GPoy IBlr LAma LGre MSal NHar NSti SSpi WCru WThi WViv WWat |
| *pleianthum* | WCru |
| *versipelle* | SSpi WCru |

## PODRANEA (Bignoniaceae)

| | |
|---|---|
| § *ricasoliana* | CPlN ERea LChe SOWG WMul |

## POGONATHERUM (Poaceae)

| | |
|---|---|
| *paniceum* | See *P. saccharoideum* |
| § *saccharoideum* | MBri |

## POGONIA (Orchidaceae)

| | |
|---|---|
| ¶ *japonica alba* | WCot |
| *ophioglossoides* | SSpi |

## POGOSTEMON (Lamiaceae)

| | |
|---|---|
| § *cablin* | CArn GPoy MSal |
| *heyneanus* | MSal |
| *patchouly* | See *P. cablin* |

## POLEMONIUM ✿ (Polemoniaceae)

| | |
|---|---|
| *acutifolium* var. *nipponicum* | See *P. caeruleum* subsp. *nipponicum* |
| 'Apricot Beauty' | See *P. carneum* 'Apricot Delight' |
| N *archibaldiae* | MBro NFai SRms |
| § *boreale* | GGar MNrw MOne NChi NPla SEas WOut |
| * - *album* | NChi |
| *brandegeei* Greene | CHan GAri NArg NBro NRoo STes WByw WPer |
| § - subsp. *mellitum* | CArn GCHN LCot WBea |
| § *caeruleum* | More than 30 suppliers |
| - var. *album* | See *P. caeruleum* subsp. *caeruleum* f. *album* |
| § - subsp. *amygdalinum* | EBee WLin |
| - 'Bambino Blue' | WPer |
| - 'Blue Bell' | ELau MAvo |
| - Brise d'Anjou = 'Blanjou' (v) | COtt EBrP EBre EOrc EWes LBre LRHS MCLN MRav NRoo SBre SCoo SPer WWeb |
| § - subsp. *caeruleum* f. *album* | CBre CGle CHan CHea ECha EFou ELan ELau EOrc EWTr GAbr LHop MBNS MBel MMal MTis NBro NFai NOak SCob SPer SRCN SRms WBea WCla WHen WPer WRos WWin |
| - subsp. *dissectum* f. *album* | CBre |
| - dwarf form | Last listed 1996 |
| ¶ - 'Golden Showers' (v) | CStr MCCP NPro |
| - var. *grandiflorum* | See *P. caeruleum* subsp. *himalayanum* |
| - misapplied Himalayan | See *P. cashmerianum* |
| § - subsp. *himalayanum* | EBee WPer |
| - 'Humile' | See *P.* 'Northern Lights' |
| - 'Idylle' | Last listed 1996 |
| ¶ - 'Larch Cottage Variegated' (v) | NLar |
| - 'Newark Park' | EPPr |
| § - subsp. *nipponicum* | GBin WPer |
| - subsp. *villosum* | CStr EBee |
| *carneum* | CBre CGle CMea EAst ECha EMan EOrc MCCP MFir MNrw MTho NHar SSpi WBea WFar WPer WSan WWin |
| § - 'Apricot Delight' | More than 30 suppliers |

§ *cashmerianum* — CLTr CMdw EBee ECGP GAbr GBuc GCHN MBro NOak WBea WFar WHen WHoo WPyg
  - *album* — Last listed 1997
  *chartaceum* — NWCA
  - NNS 93-650 — MRPP
  'Churchills' — CLAP EBee NFai WBro
  § 'Dawn Flight' — EBee NCat WFar
  'Daydawn' — Last listed 1997
  ◆ *delicatum* — See *P. pulcherrimum* subsp. *delicatum*
  'Eastbury Purple' — CBre CElw CStr
  *elegans* — Last listed 1998
  ¶ 'Elworthy Amethyst' — CElw MAvo NCot WCot
  *eximium* — Last listed 1998
  *flavum* — See *P. foliosissimum* var. *flavum*
  *foliosissimum* A.Gray — CBot CGle EPPr MNrw SRms SUsu WHoo WPer
  - hort. — See *P. archibaldiae*
  - var. *albiflorum* — See *P. foliosissimum* var. *alpinum*
  § - var. *alpinum* — NBir WWal
  § - var. *flavum* — EBee
  'Glebe Cottage Lilac' — CElw CGle CHar CMil LPio WBea WPGP
  ¶ 'Glebe Cottage Violet' — LPio
  'Hannah Billcliffe' — CLAP LCot
  'Hidako White' — Last listed 1998
  § 'Hopleys' — CHan CLAP CStr GBar GBri GCal LFis LHop MAvo NBrk NCot NGdn NRoo SUsu WByw WCot WFar
  x *jacobaea* — WBea WCot
  ◆ 'Katie Daley' — See *P.* 'Hopleys'
  *kiushianum* — EBee
  § 'Lambrook Mauve' ♀ — More than 30 suppliers
  *liniflorum* — EBee
  'Mary Mottram' — CBre EBee
  ◆ *mellitum* — See *P. brandegeei* subsp. *mellitum*
  *mexicanum* — Last listed 1996
  ¶ 'North Tyne' — NChi
  § 'Northern Lights' — EBee ELan EMan EMon EPPr EWes GBri GMaP LGre MBri MCCP MTed WFar
  'Norwell Mauve' — MNrw
  *occidentale* — See *P. caeruleum* subsp. *amygdalinum*
  *pauciflorum* — CFri CGle CHad CMea EAst ECGN EOrc GTou LHop LPio MNrw MTho NBir NMir NOak NSti SRms WBea WCla WElm WHer WMow WPer WWhi WWin WWye
  - form — Last listed 1998
  - subsp. *binckleyi* — NChi
  - silver-leaved — EWTr STes WOve WSan
  § 'Pink Beauty' — CBre CMGP EBee EFou ELan LRHS NCat SCro WBea WCer WWal
  'Pink Pearl' — WWhi
  *pulchellum* Salisbury — See *P. reptans*
  - Willd. — Last listed 1997
  - Turczaninow — See *P. caeruleum*
  *pulcherrimum* Hooker — CHan ELan GAbr GBar GCal GTou LHop NBro NHar NLak NTow WBea WHen WPer WWye
  - *album* — Last listed 1998
  § - subsp. *delicatum* — MHar MTho NChi NHar NWCA
  § - var. *pulcherrimum* — MMal WLin
  - 'Tricolor' — NArg NBus NLak WPrP
  *pulcherrimum* hort. — See *P. boreale*
  - 'Tricolor' — See *P. boreale*
  § *reptans* — CAgr CArn CHea CLTr ECha ECoo ELau GBar GBri GPoy LHol MSal NBro NRoo WBea WFar WPer WWye

- 'Album' — See *P. reptans* 'Virginia White'
- 'Blue Pearl' — CGle CMea EBee EMan EPPr EPar GAri LFis MBel MLLN MNrw NBro NCat NChi NFla NGdn NHol NLon NRoo SCro SHel SOkh SPer SUsu WBea WHen WOve WRHF
- 'Dawn Flight' — See *P.* 'Dawn Flight'
- 'Firmament' — Last listed 1996
- 'Lambrook Manor' — See *P.* 'Lambrook Mauve'
- 'Pink Beauty' — See *P.* 'Pink Beauty'
* - 'Sky Blue' — NBro WShe
§ - 'Virginia White' — CBre EBee LRHS NChi NPri
- 'White Pearl' — LWoo MMow WShe
*richardsonii* Graham — See *P. boreale*
- hort. — See *P.* 'Northern Lights'
'Sapphire' — CBre CDoC GMac MBel MBrN NFai WBea
◆ *scopulinum* — See *P. pulcherrimum* subsp. *delicatum*
'Sonia's Bluebell' — CElw CGle CLAP CMil EBee EWes LGre MAvo MSte NLak WMaN
'Southern Skies' — CBre
'Theddingworth' — MAvo MTed
*viscosum* — EPot GBuc GCHN NTow WHen
- NNS 93-658 — MRPP
*yezoense* — CBre CM&M GBri GCal MNrw WFar WPnP
- *hidakanum* — NRoo
- 'Purple Rain' — CBre CHar CPea CStr EBee EWes GBuc LFis MAvo MCCP MCLN MLLN MNrw MTis MWhi NLon WCot WElm WHer WPrP WRha WSan

## POLIANTHES (Agavaceae)
§ *geminiflora* — LAma
*nelsonii* — CFir
*tuberosa* ♀ — CB&S CSpe EBot NRog
* - 'Marginata' (v) — Last listed 1997
- 'The Pearl' (d) — LAma

## POLIOMINTHA (Lamiaceae)
*bustamanta* — CLon CPlt EBee ELan LGre NBir WCot
*incana* — Last listed 1998

## POLIOTHYRSIS (Flacourtiaceae)
*sinensis* — CAbP CFil CGre MAsh MBri WWes

## POLLIA (Commelinaceae)
¶ *japonica* — EBee

## POLYGALA (Polygalaceae)
*calcarea* — MBro MDun NHar NHol NRya NWCA WAbe WPat
- Bulley's form — LBee SIng
- 'Lillet' ♀ — CLyd EPot GCrs MBro NHar NMen NTow SBla SWas WAbe WFar WPat WWin
*chamaebuxus* ♀ — GCrs GDra IMGH MBal MDun MPla NHar NWoo SRms WLin WWin
- *alba* — LBee MAsh WAbe
§ - var. *grandiflora* ♀ — More than 30 suppliers
- 'Kamniski' — CMHG EPot MAsh NHar NMen
- 'Loibl' — EPot SBla SGre
- 'Purpurea' — See *P. chamaebuxus* var. *grandiflora*
- 'Rhodoptera' — See *P. chamaebuxus* var. *grandiflora*

§ x *dalmaisiana* ♀ — CAbb CLTr CSpe EMil ERea GQui IDee LBlm LHop MAsh MSCN SAga SBla SLon SUsu SVen
'Dolomite' — NHar
*myrtifolia* — LCns MBEx SEND SHFr SMrm WWye
- 'Grandiflora' — See *P.* x *dalmaisiana*
*vayredae* — WPat
*virgata* — ECon EPfP ERea
*vulgaris* — EWFC IOrc

## POLYGONATUM (Convallariaceae)

*acuminatifolium* — Last listed 1998
¶ *alte-lobatum* B&SWJ 286 — WCru
§ *biflorum* — CArn CBro CHid CPou EBla EGar EGol ELan EMan EOrc EPot GCHN IBlr MSal NCat NLar NRoo SSpi WCot WCru
- dwarf form — EPla IBlr WCot
*canaliculatum* — See *P. biflorum*
*cirrbifolium* — CLAP EBee EBla MDun WCru
*commutatum* — See *P. biflorum*
*cryptantbum* — WCru
*curvistylum* — CAvo CMea EBee EBla ECha IBlr LGre SWas WFar WViv
*cyrtonema* hort. — See *Disporopsis pernyi*
- B&SWJ 271 — WCru
§ *falcatum* — CLyd EBee EPla ERav IBlr MBal MDun NOak NWes SIng WHer WWat WWin
* - *nanum* — CAvo
§ - 'Variegatum' — CAvo CHad CLyd CRow CSpe EFou ELan EPar LGre MBel MBri MBro MCLN MDun NDea NFla NHol NSti SBla SCro SMac WHoo WPyg WWat WWhi
'Falcon' — See *P. bumile*
*geminiflorum* — IBlr SWas WFar
*giganteum* — See *P. biflorum*
§ *graminifolium* — CMGP CPBP EPot ERos LGre MSte WCot WCru
- GW 803 — SWas
§ *birtum* — CHid CLAP EMon EPla EPot IBlr NDov WCot WCru WFar
¶ - BM 7012 — EBee
*bookeri* — CBro CLyd EBee EDAr EPot ERos IBlr LBee LGre LHop MBal MTho NHar NHol NMen NNrd NRya NSla NWCA SIng SMac SRot WAbe WHal WHil WLin
§ *bumile* — CGle CHan CLAP CRDP EBee EBla ELan ERos GBri IBlr MBel NHar NMen SBla SSpi SUsu SWas WAbe WCot WCru WHal WRus
§ x *bybridum* ♀ — More than 30 suppliers
¶ - 'Bethberg' — ECha
* - 'Bittenberg' — WCot
- 'Flore Pleno' (d) — Last listed 1998
§ - 'Striatum' (v) — More than 30 suppliers
- 'Variegatum' — See *P.* x *bybridum* 'Striatum'
*inflatum* — Last listed 1998
¶ *involucratum* — WCru
'Langthorns Variegated' (v) — ELan
¶ *lasianthum* — WCru
*latifolium* — See *P. birtum*
*multiflorum* hort. — See *P.* x *bybridum*
- L. — CRow EGar EPla SRms
- *giganteum* hort. — See *P. biflorum*
¶ *nodosum* — WCru
* 'Nymans Variety' — NRar
§ *odoratum* — CAvo CBro CRow CSWP EBee ELau EOHP EPar EPla EPot EWFC EWTr IBlr MSai NLar NRya SMac SSpi

- dwarf form — IBlr
- 'Flore Pleno' (d) ♀ — CLAP CMGP CRow EHrv IBlr NRar SBla SWas WCot WHoo
- 'Grace Barker' — See *P.* x *bybridum* 'Striatum'
- Kew form — EPot
- var. *pluriflorum* — GBuc IBlr SSpi
- - 'Variegatum' — CBro EGol EPla IBlr LGre MBal MBro MCli MRav NLar NRoo WCot WCru WRus WWat WWin
- - 'Variegatum' misapplied — See *P. falcatum* 'Variegatum'
- 'Silver Wings' — ECha
*officinale* — See *P. odoratum*
*oppositifolium* B&SWJ 2537 — WCru
§ *orientale* — CHid
*pluriflorum* — See *P. graminifolium*
♦ *polyanthemum* — See *P. orientale*
*prattii* — Last listed 1998
*pubescens* — Last listed 1998
*pumilum* — See *P. falcatum*
*punctatum* — WCru
- B&SWJ 2395 — WCru
*racemosum* — SIng
*roseum* — WHer
*sibiricum* — IBlr WCru
sp. Himalaya — WCru
¶ *stenophyllum* — CAvo
*stewartianum* — CLAP EPar IBlr NDov
*verticillatum* — CAvo CBro CHid CLyd CMCo CRow EBee ECha EPla EPot IBlr MBal MTho NDov NHol SMad WCot WCru WFar WWat
¶ - CC 1324 — CPLG
- 'Himalayan Giant' — CHid EBee
* - *rubrum* — CArn CBos CHid CRow EGar EHrv EPPr EPar IBlr LGre MSte MTho WCot
- 'Serbian Dwarf' — CHid EBee
¶ aff. *verticillatum* CLD 1308 — EMon

## POLYGONUM ✿ (Polygonaceae)

*affine* — See *Persicaria affinis*
*amplexicaule* — See *Persicaria amplexicaulis*
*aubertii* — See *Fallopia baldschuanica*
¶ *aviculare* — CArn
*baldscbuanicum* — See *Fallopia baldschuanica*
*bistorta* — See *Persicaria bistorta*
*compactum* — See *Fallopia japonica* var. *compacta*
*cuspidatum* — See *Fallopia japonica*
*equisetiforme* hort. — See *P. scoparium*
♦ *filiforme* — See *Persicaria virginiana*
♦ *longisetum* — See *Persicaria longiseta*
*molle* — See *Persicaria mollis*
*multiflorum* — See *Fallopia multiflora*
*odoratum* — See *Persicaria odorata*
*polystacbyum* — See *Persicaria wallichii*
♦ *reynoutria* — See *Fallopia japonica*
*runciforme* — See *Persicaria runcinata*
§ *scoparium* — CRow EPla MFir NFai SDry SDys SVen WCot WWat
♦ *tinctorium* — See *Persicaria tinctoria*
*weyrichii* — See *Persicaria weyrichii*

## POLYLEPIS (Rosaceae)

*australis* — SMad WCot

## POLYMNIA (Asteraceae)

¶ *soncbifolia* — LEdu

## POLYPODIUM ✿ (Polypodiaceae)

'Addison' — Last listed 1996

| | |
|---|---|
| § *aureum* ♀ | Last listed 1994 |
| - ruffled form | Last listed 1997 |
| *australe* | See *P. cambricum* |
| § *cambricum* | EFer NHar NMar WCot WRic |
| § - 'Barrowii' | CCuc NMar WRic |
| - 'Cambricum' ♀ | WRic |
| ¶ - 'Caren Lane' | WRic |
| - 'Cristatum' | WRic |
| - 'Diadem' | WRic |
| - 'Grandiceps Forster' | WRic |
| - 'Grandiceps Fox' ♀ | WRic |
| - 'Hornet' | WRic |
| - 'Oakley' | SWas WAbe WPGP |
| - Omnilacerum Group | Last listed 1998 |
| - 'Omnilacerum Oxford' | WRic |
| - Plumosum Group | Last listed 1998 |
| - 'Prestonii' | WRic |
| - Pulcherrimum Group | EGol NHar SWas |
| ¶ - - bifid form | WRic |
| - 'Pulcherrimum Addison' | WRic |
| ¶ - 'Richard Key' | WRic |
| - Semilacerum Group | NMar WRic |
| - - 'Falcatum O'Kelly' | WRic |
| - - 'Jubilee' | NMar WRic |
| - - 'Robustum' | NMar WRic |
| - 'Wilharris' ♀ | CCuc CFil CLAP WPGP WRic |
| ¶ x *coughlinii* | WRic |
| 'Bifidograndiceps' | |
| *glycyrrhiza* | WRic |
| - Grandiceps Group | WRic |
| - 'Longicaudatum' ♀ | EMon NMar WFib WRic |
| - 'Malahatense' (fertile) | WRic |
| - 'Malahatense' (sterile) | WRic |
| *interjectum* | EBee EFer NMar NOrc NVic WAbe |
| | WFib WRic |
| - 'Bifidograndiceps' | WPGP WRic |
| - 'Cornubiense' ♀ | CFil CLAP CRDP ECha EFer EMon |
| | GCal NBir NBro NHar NHol NMar |
| | NVic SSpi WAbe WPGP WRic |
| - 'Ramosum Hillman' | WRic |
| x *mantoniae* | SWas |
| *scouleri* | NBro |
| *vulgare* | More than 30 suppliers |
| - 'Acutum' | NMar |
| - 'Bifidocristatum' | CLAP EMon GBin GNau NHar |
| | NHol SLon WCot WFib WWat |
| - 'Bifidograndiceps' | NMar SChu SIng |
| - 'Bifidomultifidum' | CBos EBee ETen MBri NBus |
| § - 'Congestum Cristatum' | Last listed 1997 |
| - 'Cornubiense Grandiceps' | CCuc SRms WFib WRic |
| - 'Cornubiense Multifidum' | NHar |
| - 'Crispum Cristatum' | See *P. vulgare* 'Congestum Cristatum' |
| - (Cristatum Group) 'Forster' | CCuc |
| - 'Jean Taylor' | See *P. vulgare* 'Congestum Cristatum' |
| - Ramosum Group | NMar |

## POLYSCIAS (Araliaceae)

| | |
|---|---|
| 'Elegans' | MBri |
| *fruticosa* | MBri |
| *sambucifolia* | SBid |
| *scutellaria* 'Pennockii' (v) | MBri |

## POLYSTICHUM ✿ (Dryopteridaceae)

| | |
|---|---|
| *acrostichoides* | CCuc CLAP EBee GCal GQui IOrc |
| | NHar WCot WRic |
| *aculeatum* ♀ | More than 30 suppliers |
| - Grandiceps Group | EFer NMar |
| *andersonii* | CLAP NHar NHol |
| *braunii* | CB&S EBee EGol MLan NMar |
| | NOak |

| | |
|---|---|
| ¶ - x *proliferum* | NWoo |
| *californicum* | CFil |
| *caryotideum* | See *Cyrtomium caryotideum* |
| *falcatum* | See *Cyrtomium falcatum* |
| *falcinellum* | CFil |
| *fortunei* | See *Cyrtomium fortunei* |
| * *fructuosum* | WRic |
| *imbricans* | CLAP NHar SArc |
| ¶ *lonchitis* | NWoo |
| *makinoi* | CLAP NHol NMar WFib WRic |
| *mehrae* | WRic |
| *mohrioides* | CFil |
| *munitum* ♀ | CBlo CCuc CFil CLAP CMil EBee |
| | EFer IOrc LHil LRot MBri MTed |
| | NBus NFla NHar NHol NOrc |
| | NWoo SAPC SArc SRms SSpi WFib |
| | WPGP WRic WWoo |
| - 'Incisum' | GCal |
| *neolobatum* | WRic |
| *polyblepharum* ♀ | CBlo CCuc CFil CLAP EBee EBrP |
| | EBre EFer ELan EMar EMon EWTr |
| | IOrc LBre MBri NBus NHar NHol |
| | SBre SLdr SPla SRms SWas WFib |
| | WHal WRic WWat |
| *proliferum* (R.Br.) C. Presl. | SWas |
| - hort. | See *P. setiferum* Acutilobum Group |
| * - *plumosum* | NOak |
| *retrorsopaleaceum* | WRic |
| *richardii* | WRic |
| *rigens* | CLAP EBee EHic GCal LHil NHar |
| | NHed NHol NLak NMar SMad |
| | SRms WFib WRic |
| § *setiferum* ♀ | More than 30 suppliers |
| § - Acutilobum Group | CB&S CFil CLAP CMHG CRDP |
| | ECha EHic EPot GAri MBal NCat |
| | NHar NHol NVic SDix SMad SSpi |
| | WAbe WCot WCru |
| - *angulare* | See *P. setiferum* |
| - Congestum Group | CMil CRDP EHic IOrc MBri NHar |
| | NHol NMar SChu SPla SRms WFib |
| | WRic |
| - 'Congestum' | EBee GCal WGor WWat |
| ¶ - Congestum Cristatum Group | EFer |
| § - 'Cristatogracile' | NHar NMar |
| - 'Cristatopinnulum' | CFil EMon NHar NMar WPGP |
| - Cristatum Group | SRms |
| - Cruciatum Group | Last listed 1998 |
| - Dahlem Group | CCuc CDoC CLAP CTrC ECha |
| | ELan MBri MSte NBus SPer WAbe |
| | WRic |
| - Divisilobum Group | CCuc CFee CFil CM&M CMHG |
| | CRow EBee EBrP EBre EFer ELan |
| | EMon EPar LBre LSyl MBro NHol |
| | NMar SApp SBre SMad SPla SRms |
| | WCot WHoo WPGP WRic WWat |
| - - 'Divisilobum Densum' ♀ | CLAP MBal NMar NOrc SSoC SSpi |
| | WCot |
| - - 'Divisilobum Iveryanum' ♀ | NHol SRms |
| - - 'Herrenhausen' | CDoC EBee EBrP EBre ECha EFer |
| | ELan EMar EPfP LBre LHop MBri |
| | MCCP NFla NMar NOrc SBre SPer |
| | WAbe WRic |
| - - 'Madame Patti' | Last listed 1998 |
| - - 'Mrs Goffy' | NMar |
| - - 'Ray Smith' | Last listed 1998 |
| * - 'Divisilobum Latipes' | NMar |
| - 'Divisilobum Laxum' | EPar MHlr SChu |
| - Foliosum Group | EFer |
| - 'Gracile' | MBri MDun WRic |

| | |
|---|---|
| - 'Grandidens' | WRic |
| ¶ - 'Hirondelle' | SRms |
| - Lineare Group | CFil WFib WPGP |
| - Multilobum Group | WRic |
| - Percristatum Group | See *P. setiferum* 'Cristatogracile' |
| ¶ - Perserratum Group | NMar |
| - 'Plumosodensum' | See *P. setiferum* 'Plumosomultilobum' |
| - Plumosodivisilobum Group | CCuc CMil CRow ECha EGol NBid NHar SPla SWas WAbe WCru WFib WWat |
| - - 'Baldwinii' | Last listed 1996 |
| § - 'Plumosomultilobum' | EBee EMon MBri NBus SRms WRic |
| - Plumosum Group | CCuc CLAP CSam MBri NOrc SArc SChu SSoC WFib WStI |
| * - *plumosum grande* 'Moly' | WFib |
| - Proliferum Group | See *P. setiferum* Acutilobum Group |
| * - 'Proliferum Wollaston' | LSyl |
| - 'Pulcherrimum Bevis' ♀ | EMon SDix WFib WPGP WRic |
| * - *ramopinnatum* | NMar |
| * - *ramulosum* | NMar |
| ¶ - Revolvens Group | EFer |
| - Rotundatum Group | CRDP NMar WFib |
| - - 'Cristatum' | Last listed 1998 |
| - 'Wakeleyanum' | SRms |
| N - 'Wollaston' | CLAP GBin MDun NPla WAbe WWoo |
| *silvaticum* | WRic |
| *stenophyllum* | CFil WPGP |
| *triangulum* | NMar |
| *tsussimense* ♀ | CCuc CLAP CRDP EBee EFou GQui MBri MSte NBus NHol NMar NOak SEas SPer SRms WFib WRic |
| ¶ *xiphophyllum* | WRic |
| *yunnanense* | Last listed 1996 |

## POLYXENA (Hyacinthaceae)

| | |
|---|---|
| § *ensifolia* | ERos LBow |
| *odorata* | CLyd WAbe |
| *pygmaea* | See *P. ensifolia* |

## POMADERRIS (Rhamnaceae)

| | |
|---|---|
| *apetala* | Last listed 1998 |
| *elliptica* | Last listed 1998 |

## PONCIRUS (Rutaceae)

| | |
|---|---|
| § *trifoliata* | CAgr CB&S CDoC CFil ELan ENot EPla ERea MBlu MWhi SAPC SArc SBid SLon SMad SPar STre WDin WFar WPGP WSHC WWat |
| - 'Flying Dragon' | CAgr |

## PONERORCHIS (Orchidaceae)

| | |
|---|---|
| *taiwanensis* | Last listed 1997 |

## PONTEDERIA (Pontederiaceae)

| | |
|---|---|
| *cordata* ♀ | CBen CRow CWat ECha ECtt EHon ELan EMFW LPBA MCCP MSta NDea SCoo SLon SPlb SRms SWat SWyc WMAq |
| - *alba* | CRow EMFW SWyc |
| § - var. *lancifolia* | CRow EMFW MSta SWat SWyc |
| - 'Pink Pons' | CRow SWyc |
| *dilatata* | EMFW SWyc |
| *lanceolata* | See *P. cordata* var. *lancifolia* |

## POPULUS ✿ (Salicaceae)

| | |
|---|---|
| x *acuminata* | WMou |
| *alba* | CBlo CDoC CDul CKin CLnd CTri EBrP EBre ECrN ENot EWTr GChr GRei IOrc LBre LBuc MBar NBee NWea SBre SPer WDin WMou WStI |
| - 'Bolleana' | See *P. alba* f. *pyramidalis* |
| § - f. *pyramidalis* | CB&S NBee SRms WMou |
| § - 'Raket' | CBlo CLnd CTho ELan ENot EPfP IOrc MGos NWea SPer |
| - 'Richardii' ♀ | CDul CLnd CTho EBee EBrP EBre ECtt EPla ESis IOrc LBre MBar SBre SPer SRPl WFar WMou |
| - Rocket | See *P. alba* 'Raket' |
| § 'Balsam Spire' (f) ♀ | CDoC CDul CLnd CTho ENot GRei IOrc LBuc NWea WMou |
| § *balsamifera* | CBlo CDoC CTho CTri ELan ENot MGos NWea SPer SRms WCot WDin WHer |
| x *berolinensis* | CDoC |
| x *canadensis* 'Aurea' ♀ | CDoC CLnd CTho EMil ENot MDun MRav SPer WDin WMou |
| - 'Aurea' x *candicans* 'Aurora' | MRav |
| - 'Eugenei' (m) | CTho WMou |
| - 'Robusta' (m) | CDoC CDul CKin CLnd CTri EMil ENot IOrc LBuc NWea WDin WMou |
| - 'Serotina' (m) | CDoC GRei MAsh NWea WDin WMou |
| x *candicans* | WDin |
| - 'Aurora' (v) | More than 30 suppliers |
| x *canescens* | CDoC ELan GChr MBri WDin WMou |
| - 'De Moffart' (m) | ENot |
| - 'Tower' | WMou |
| x *euroamericana* | See *P.* x *canadensis* |
| x *interamericana* 'Beaupré' | CTho WMou |
| *lasiocarpa* ♀ | CDoC CLnd CTho EPfP MBlu MRav SLPl SMad WMou WPGP |
| § - var. *tibetica* | WMou |
| *maximowiczii* | WMou |
| *nigra* | CDul ELan EWTr GChr NWea SPer WDin |
| - (f) | SLPl |
| - (m) | SLPl |
| - subsp. *betulifolia* ♀ | CBlo CCVT CDul CKin CTho LBuc MGos NWea WMou |
| - - (f) | WMou |
| - - (m) | WMou |
| § - 'Italica' (m) ♀ | CBlo CDoC CDul CLnd CTho CTri EBrP EBre ELan ENot EPfP GChr IOrc LBre LBuc MBri MGos NBee NWea SBre SPer SRms WDin |
| - 'Italica Aurea' | See *P. nigra* 'Lombardy Gold' |
| § - 'Lombardy Gold' (m) | CCHP CEnd CTho GRei SRPl WMou |
| ♦ - 'Pyramidalis' | See *P. nigra* 'Italica' |
| *simonii* | Last listed 1997 |
| - 'Fastigiata' | CB&S NSti WMou |
| - 'Obtusata' | WMou |
| *szechuanica* | WMou |
| *tacamahaca* | See *P. balsamifera* |
| 'Tacatricho 32' | See *P.* 'Balsam Spire' |
| *tomentosa* | WMou |
| *tremula* ♀ | CBlo CDul CKin CLnd CTho EBee EBrP EBre ELan ENot GChr GRei IOrc LBre LBuc LHyr NBee NWea SBre SPer WDin WMou |
| § - 'Erecta' | CDul CLnd CTho EBee LPan MBri SMad WMou |
| - 'Fastigiata' | See *P. tremula* 'Erecta' |
| - 'Pendula' (m) | CEnd CLnd CTho EBee SRPl WDin WMou |
| *trichocarpa* | CBlo CDul CTho SPer |
| - 'Fritzi Pauley' (f) | CDul CTho WMou |
| *violascens* | See *P. lasiocarpa* var. *tibetica* |

| | |
|---|---|
| *wilsonii* | WMou |
| *yunnanensis* | CMHG WMou |

## PORTULACA (Portulacaceae)

| | |
|---|---|
| *grandiflora* | MBri |
| *oleracea* | CArn ELau MChe SIde WHer WJek |
| - var. *aurea* | ELau MChe WJek |

## POTAMOGETON (Potamogetonaceae)

| | |
|---|---|
| *crispus* | EHon EMFW SAWi SRms |
| *pectinatus* | EHon |

## POTENTILLA ✿ (Rosaceae)

| | |
|---|---|
| *alba* | CGle CLyd CSev ECha EFou ELan |
| | EMar GCHN LGro MHar MRav |
| | MTho NChi NFai NRoo SCro SPer |
| | SUsu WByw WCot WMow WPer |
| *alchemilloides* | MNrw SMer SOkh WPer |
| *alpicola* | WPer |
| *ambigua* | See *P. cuneata* |
| *andicola* | EBee |
| *anserina* | CArn CKin EEls EGoo EWFC GBar |
| | MHer MHew WHbs WHer |
| - 'Golden Treasure' (v) | EGoo MLLN WHer |
| *anserinoides* | EBee EMan GCal MBel WCot |
| | WMoo WPer WWat |
| *arbuscula* hort. | See *P. fruticosa* 'Elizabeth' |
| - D.Don | See *P. fruticosa* var. *arbuscula* (D. |
| | Don) Maxim. |
| *argentea* | CBlo CSWP CSev ELan LIck LPVe |
| | MBNS MRav MTis NFai NHol SPlb |
| | WBea WCla WCru WPer WWat |
| - 'Calabre' | Last listed 1997 |
| - *glabra* | Last listed 1997 |
| *arguta* | EBee |
| *argyrophylla* | See *P. atrosanguinea* var. |
| | *argyrophylla* |
| * - *insignis rubra* | NChi |
| *atrosanguinea* | CBlo CBos CBrm CGle CHan CInt |
| | ECGN ECha EOrc EWTr GCal |
| | GTou LBlm LHop MBal MBri |
| | MRav NChi NFai NFor NGdn |
| | NRoo NSti SHFr SRms WHoo |
| | WMoo WMow WPyg WWal |
| § - var. *argyrophylla* | CGle CHan EBee ECha ELan ESis |
| | GCHN GCal GTou MBel MCLN |
| | MRav MWat NBir NBro NFai NMir |
| | NNrd NOak SCro SRms WAbe |
| | WByw WCot WFar WMow WPer |
| | WWhi WWin |
| - - SS&W 7768 | GDra MPla MSte NMGW SRms |
| - CC 1384 | CPou |
| - var. *leucochroa* | See *P. atrosanguinea* var. |
| | *argyrophylla* |
| *aurea* | CPea ECtt ELan EMNN MBri |
| | MTho NArg NFla NMen NMir |
| | NOrc NWCA SRms SSmi WRHF |
| - 'Aurantiaca' | CElw GCHN NNrd SBod SRot |
| | SUsu |
| § - subsp. *chrysocraspeda* | NHol NMen NOla |
| § - 'Goldklumpen' | EGar MRav NPro NRoo SCro |
| - 'Plena' (d) | GCHN GDra GTou MBro NHar |
| | NHol SBod WMow |
| 'Blazeaway' | EBee EPPr MBel MBri NCat NHol |
| | SCoo WFar WLRN WMow |
| *brevifolia* | NWCA |
| - NNS 94-25 | Last listed 1998 |
| *calabra* | ECha EDAr EMan EPPr MAvo |
| | SIgm SMer WByw WHer WWin |
| § *cinerea* | CLyd CTri LBee NHar NMen SBla |
| | SIgm SSmi |
| *clusiana* | Last listed 1997 |

| | |
|---|---|
| *collina* | CNic |
| ¶ *concinna bicrenata* | WLin |
| § 'Craigieburn Cochineal' | Last listed 1998 |
| § *crantzii* | CBrm CMea CTri EWFC GCHN |
| | GCrs GMaP GTou LBee MBar |
| | MSte NMen SIng SRms WCla |
| - 'Nana' | See *P. crantzii* 'Pygmaea' |
| § - 'Pygmaea' | ECtt EPfP MOne MTPN NMen |
| § *cuneata* ♀ | CLyd CNic ELan ESis GDra GTou |
| | MPla MTho NHar NMen NRya |
| | NWCA SDys SIng SSmi WPer |
| | WWin |
| aff. *cuneata* CC 1461 | MRPP |
| *delavayi* | MBro MNrw NBus |
| *detommasii* | MHar WPer |
| *dickinsii* | NTow |
| *dombeyi* | GCHN |
| * 'Emilie' | EFou GCal MBri NLar WFar |
| § *erecta* | CAgr CArn CKin EOHP GBar |
| | GPoy LFis MChe MHew MSal |
| | WHbs WOak |
| *eriocarpa* | CLyd EHyt EMNN GCHN GDra |
| | IMGH MBro MHar MPla MWat |
| | NHar NHol NMen NRoo SBod |
| | SSmi WAbe WCla |
| 'Etna' | CBlo CElw CLon CStr ECtt ELan |
| | GAbr GCal GTou LFis LGre MCAu |
| | MNrw NCat NFai NFor NRoo |
| | SAga WBro WByw WCru WHen |
| | WLin WMer WPer WWhi |
| 'Everest' | See *P. fruticosa* 'Mount Everest' |
| 'Fireflame' | ECha LBlm NLar |
| *fissa* | LBlm MNrw MSte NBir NRya |
| | WUnu |
| 'Flambeau' | EBee MGed MRav NLar WRha |
| 'Flamenco' | CB&S CBre CSam CTri EFou ELan |
| | MArl MBri MNrw MRav NRoo |
| | SUsu WAbb WByw WFar WMow |
| *fragiformis* | See *P. megalantha* |
| *fruticosa* | LBuc NMen NWea SHFr |
| - 'Abbotswood' ♀ | More than 30 suppliers |
| - 'Abbotswood Silver' (v) | CBlo CLTr CLyd EAst ECtt ELan |
| | MAsh MBNS MRav NLon SLon |
| | SPla WFar WHar WWal |
| - 'Annette' | CBlo MBri NPro WHCG WWeb |
| - var. *arbuscula* hort. | See *P. fruticosa* 'Elizabeth' |
| - - (D.Don) Maxim. KW 5774 | Last listed 1997 |
| - 'Argentea Nana' | See *P. fruticosa* 'Beesii' |
| - 'Beanii' | NHol SPer WWeb |
| § - 'Beesii' ♀ | CDoC EHyt ELan ESis MAsh MBar |
| | MBlu MPla NHol NRoo SIgm SPer |
| | WAbe WHCG WSHC WWeb WWin |
| - 'Beverley Surprise' | EHol NPro WHCG WWeb |
| ◆ - 'Blink' | See *P. fruticosa* Princess = 'Blink' |
| - 'Buttercup' | CDoC NHol WHCG |
| - 'Cascade' | WBcn WHCG |
| * - 'Chelsea Star' | WHCG |
| * - 'Chilo' | MGos WBcn |
| - 'Clotted Cream' | MBar |
| - var. *dahurica* | WHCG |
| ¶ - - 'Farrer's White' | WWat |
| - - 'Hersii' | See *P. fruticosa* 'Snowflake' |
| - - 'Rhodocalyx' | CPle WHCG WWat |
| - 'Dart's Cream' | MBri MRav |
| - 'Dart's Golddigger' | CTri EBee ECtt ENot MBal NRoo |
| | SLPl WHCG |
| § - 'Dart's Nugget' | WHCG WWeb |
| - 'Daydawn' ♀ | More than 30 suppliers |
| § - 'Donard Gold' | Last listed 1996 |
| - 'Donard Orange' | See *P. fruticosa* 'Donard Gold' |
| - 'Eastleigh Cream' | Last listed 1998 |
| * - 'Eden Lemonlight' | Last listed 1998 |

| | | |
|---|---|---|
| § - 'Elizabeth' ♀ | CB&S CDoC CLan EBee ELan ENot EWTr GDra LGro LHop MBar MBri MGos MWat NFor NHol NLon NWea SPer SRms SSoC WBod WDin WFar WHCG WMoo WWat | |
| - 'Farreri' | See P. fruticosa 'Gold Drop' | |
| - 'Farreri Prostrata' | See P. fruticosa var. pyrenaica | |
| - 'Floppy Disc' | CBlo ELan EPfP MGos NCut NHol NWoo SEas SPer SPla SSta | |
| - 'Frances Lady Daresbury' | MPla | |
| - 'Friedrichsenii' | NHol | |
| - 'Glenroy Pinkie' | CDoC CSam EBee MBal MRav NPro SAga SEas SLon WAbe WHCG WWeb | |
| - 'Glenroy Seashell' | MBal | |
| § - 'Gold Drop' | EHol NHol WHCG WWat WWeb | |
| - 'Golden Dwarf' | MBri MGos | |
| * - 'Golden Nugget' | WLRN | |
| - 'Golden Spreader' | EBrP EBre LBre NPro SBre | |
| - 'Goldfinger' ♀ | CChe CDoC ELan ENot EWTr GChr GOrc GRei IOrc MAsh MBri MGos MRav NMoo SEas SRPl WAbe WDin WHCG WHar WStI WWeb | |
| - Goldkugel | See P. fruticosa 'Gold Drop' | |
| - 'Goldrush' | Last listed 1996 | |
| - 'Goldstar' | CMHG EBee EBrP EBre ENot GAri GCHN IOrc LBre MBri MGos SBre WFar WHCG | |
| - 'Goldteppich' | LBuc MBar | |
| - 'Goscote' | MGos | |
| - 'Hachmann's Gigant' | Last listed 1997 | |
| - 'Hopleys Little Joker' | WPat WPyg | |
| - 'Hopleys Orange' | CChe CDoC CMHG EBee EWes GAri GCHN LHop MBri SAga WGor WHCG WWin | |
| - 'Hurstbourne' | NPro WWeb | |
| - 'Jackman's Variety' | CSam ECtt ENot SPer SRms WBod WStI WWeb | |
| - 'Judith' | Last listed 1997 | |
| - 'Katherine Dykes' ♀ | CChe CDoC EBee ELan ENot EWTr GDra MAsh MBal MBar SLon SPer SRPl SRms WBod WDin WFar WGwG WHar WMoo WStI WWeb | |
| * - 'King Cup' | WWeb | |
| - 'Klondike' ♀ | CB&S CLan EBee ELan EPfP MAsh NFor NWea SBid | |
| § - 'Knap Hill' | EBee ENot GDra GEil NFor WWeb | |
| - 'Knap Hill Buttercup' | See P. fruticosa 'Knap Hill' | |
| - 'Kobold' | CBlo EBee GEil MBar WTro | |
| * - 'Lemon and Lime' | MBlu NPro | |
| ¶ - 'Limelight' | EBee MBri | |
| - 'Logan' | Last listed 1997 | |
| - 'London Town' | CMHG | |
| - 'Longacre Variety' ♀ | CTri GDra MBar NHol NWea WWat WWeb | |
| § - 'Maanelys' ♀ | CTrw ECtt ELan MBal MWat NFla NWea SPer SRms WDin WHCG WMoo WWeb | |
| - 'Macpenny's Cream' | WHCG | |
| § - 'Manchu' | ENot GDra MBar MBri MPla MRav NFla NFor NHol NRoo SChu SPer SRms WWat WWin | |
| § - Marian Red Robin = 'Marrob' | CDoC EAst EBee EBrP EBre ELan ENot EPfP GCHN GRei LBre MAsh MBri MGos MRav MWat NFla NHol NRoo SBre SCoo SPer WDin WStI WWeb | |
| ♦ - 'Marrob' | See P. fruticosa Marian Red Robin = 'Marrob' | |
| - 'Medicine Wheel Mountain' | EHal ELan EWes MAsh MBri MRav NPro NTow SPer WHCG WWeb | |
| - 'Milkmaid' | WWeb | |
| - Moonlight | See P. fruticosa 'Maanelys' | |
| § - 'Mount Everest' | CChe CDoC ELan MBar MWat NCut NHol NWea SLon SRms WHCG WWeb | |
| - 'Nana Argentea' | See P. fruticosa 'Beesii' | |
| - 'New Dawn' | CDoC ECle LRHS MAsh MBri WFar | |
| - 'Northman' | Last listed 1997 | |
| - 'Nugget' | See P. fruticosa 'Dart's Nugget' | |
| - 'Ochroleuca' | Last listed 1997 | |
| - 'Orange Star' | CBlo CCHP WHCG | |
| - 'Orange Stripe' | WWeb | |
| - 'Orangeade' | CBlo MAsh SMur SReu SSta WWeb | |
| - 'Peaches and Cream' | EBee WHCG | |
| * - 'Peachy Proud' | NPro | |
| * - 'Perryhill' | Last listed 1996 | |
| * - 'Pierce Ogon' | Last listed 1998 | |
| ¶ - 'Pink Beauty' | ENot | |
| - 'Pink Glow' | GDra | |
| - 'Pink Pearl' | EBrP EBre LBre SBre WBcn WMoo WWin | |
| - 'Pink Queen' | CDoC WRHF WWeb | |
| - 'Pretty Polly' | CChe CDoC EAst EBee ELan ENot IOrc MBar MBri MGos NHol SPer SSta WAbe WDin WFar WHCG WHar WStI WWal | |
| - 'Primrose Beauty' ♀ | CDoC CLan EAst EBee ELan ENot EWTr MBal MBar MGos MPla MRav NFla NFor NRoo SPlb WAbe WDin WFar WGwG WHCG WHar WMoo WStI WWat WWeb | |
| § - Princess = 'Blink' | CDoC EBee EBrP EBre ELan ENot EWTr GRei LBre MBNS MBal MBar MGos MWat NHol NRoo SBre SPer SReu SRms WDin WFar WHar WStI WWat WWeb | |
| - 'Prostrate Copper' | NPro | |
| - var. pumila | MBro WPat | |
| § - var. pyrenaica | SGre | |
| - Red Ace | CDoC EBrP EBre ELan ENot EWTr GChr GOrc GRei LBre LHop MBar MBri MGos MWat NHol NRoo NWea SBre SPer SRms WDin WFar WHCG WHar WMoo WWal WWeb | |
| - Red Robin | See P. fruticosa Marian Red Robin = 'Marrob' | |
| - 'Royal Flush' | GAri LHop MAsh MBar MBri SAga WHCG WStI | |
| - 'Ruth' | Last listed 1997 | |
| - 'Sandved' | Last listed 1997 | |
| - 'Silver Schilling' | LHop NPro | |
| - 'Snowbird' | EBrP EBre EPfP EPla LBre MBlu MBri MGos NLak NPro SBre WWeb | |
| § - 'Snowflake' | CB&S EWTr WHCG WMoo | |
| § - 'Sommerflor' | ENot | |
| - 'Sophie's Blush' | CChe CLTr EAst EBee MBal MRav NHol NRoo NWea SBid WDin WSHC WWeb | |
| - 'Sunset' | More than 30 suppliers | |
| - 'Tangerine' ♀ | More than 30 suppliers | |
| - 'Tilford Cream' ♀ | More than 30 suppliers | |
| - 'Tom Conway' | WHCG WWeb | |
| § - var. veitchii | EWTr SPer WHCG WStI | |
| - 'Vilmoriniana' | CBot CHad CHar CTri ELan EPfP MRav NFor NLon SBid SIgm SLon SMac SPer SSpi WAbe WGwG WHCG WSHC WWat WWeb | |

- 'Walton Park' MBal
- 'Wessex Silver' CFai WHCG
- 'Whirligig' CFai WHCG
- 'White Rain' CLTr GDra NFor NLon WWeb
- 'Wickwar Trailer' CLyd EPot ESis MBro MPla WHCG
  WHoo
- 'William Purdom' WHCG
- 'Yellow Bird' MGos NOla
- 'Yellow Carpet' WHCG
- 'Yellow Giant' WWeb
*fulgens* See *P. lineata*
'Gibson's Scarlet' ♀ More than 30 suppliers
*glandulosa* CAgr MNrw
'Gloire de Nancy' CBos CLAP EBrP EBre ELan GAri
  GCal LBre MRav NBir SBre SPer
  WElm
'Gold Clogs' See *P. aurea* 'Goldklumpen'
'Grace Darling' CWit ECle GChr GRei MTis NEgg
  NHol WGor WGwG WWeb
*gracilis* CBrm EBee NNrd
§ - var. *glabrata* EPPr
- subsp. *nuttallii* See *P. gracilis* var. *glabrata*
- var. *pulcherrima* Last listed 1996
¶ 'Harlow Cream' NBid
'Helen Jane' CGle EBee EBrP EBre GMac LBre
  LHop LPio MBel MBri MBro MRav
  NBir NBro NGdn NLar NRoo SAga
  SBre SLod WBro WElm WFar
  WHoo WMer WPer
'Herzblut' EPfP GBuc MNrw NLar
x *bopwoodiana* CGle CHad CPlt CPou EPPr LBlm
  LGre MBri MCLN MNrw NBir
  SAga SUsu SWas WAbb WByw
  WLin
* x *hybrida* 'Jean Jabber' EBee EWll GBuc MRav
*byparctica nana* CLyd GCrs LBee MBro NHol SRms
  WAbe WPat WPyg
* 'Limelight' ELan EPla MAsh MRav SPla SRPl
  SSta WFar WHCG
'Mandshurica' See *P. fruticosa* 'Manchu'
'Master Floris' WFar WHer
§ *megalantha* ♀ More than 30 suppliers
¶ - *takedae* MNrw
'Melton' EAst EBee ECoo MNrw NBir NChi
  NOak SAga SIng WHen
* 'Melton Fire' SBea SVen WBea WBro WElm
  WGor
*millefolia klamathensis* Last listed 1996
*miyabei* Last listed 1998
'Monarch's Velvet' See *P. thurberi* 'Monarch's Velvet'
'Monsieur Rouillard' CGle CLon CSam EBrP EBre EPPr
  LBre LFis MBel MNrw MSCN
  MWat NDov NFor NRoo SBre
  SUsu WByw WCru WElm WHoo
  WLin WSan
'Mont d'Or' LRHS MBri MRav
*montana* GCHN MBel NHol WHer WPer
*nepalensis* CSam EBee ECha EDAr GAbr
  IMGH LHop LLWP MFir NBro
  NFor NPro SMac SWas
- 'Craigieburn' Last listed 1998
- 'Craigieburn Cochineal' See *P.* 'Craigieburn Cochineal'
- forms EAst
- 'Kirsten' Last listed 1998
§ - 'Miss Willmott' ♀ More than 30 suppliers
- red WLin
- 'Roxana' CGle EBee ECGP ELan GBuc
  MBNS MBel MRav NBro NFai SHel
  WAbb WByw WFar WMow WPer
- 'Shogran' CPin EBee
§ *neumanniana* EWFC SGre SHel
¶ - *aurea* SRms

- 'Goldrausch' ECha MRav SRms
§ - 'Nana' CInt CSev EMNN EPot ESis LBee
  LHop MBro MLLN MPla MRPP
  MWat NHar NMen NNrd NRoo
  SIng SPlb SRms SSmi WEas WWin
*nevadensis* CLyd CTri ECho SRms WPer
*nitida* NHar NMen SRms
- 'Alannah' Last listed 1998
- 'Alba' EPot
- 'Lissadell' CPBP
- 'Rubra' CLyd CMea CNic GCrs GTou
  IMGH MBro MWat NBir NHol
  NMGW NRoo NTow NWCA SBla
  SRms SSmi WAbe WPat WWin
*nivea* GTou
'Nunk' CBlo MBar WWeb
* 'Olympic Mountains' WPer
*ovina* WPer
*palustris* MSta NLar WCla WGwy WUnu
*pamirica* WUnu
*pedata* LLWP NChi
*peduncularis* WCot
- CC&McK 532 GCHN
'Pheasant Eye' Last listed 1996
'Pink Panther' See *P. fruticosa* Princess = 'Blink'
'Pyrenaica' See *P. fruticosa* var. *pyrenaica*
*recta* CBlo CBrm ELau EMan EWFC
  GTou MCAu MHew SIgm
- 'Alba' CBlo CPea EAst ECoo GMaP LIck
  NDov NFai NPri NRoo SMac WPer
  WWhi
◆ - 'Citrina' See *P. recta* var. *sulphurea*
- HH&K 205 CHan
- 'Macrantha' See *P. recta* 'Warrenii'
§ - var. *sulphurea* ♀ CGle CHad CLon CMil CPea
  CSam ECoo EGoo GCal LHop
  MBNS MBel MCLN MFir MNrw
  MTis NCat NFai NRoo NSti SIgm
  SIng SUsu WHal WHer WHoo
  WLin WPer WPyg
§ - 'Warrenii' CHea CPea EBee EFou GMaP
  MBNS MCAu MCLN MFir MRav
  MTis MWat NFai NMir NOrc
  NRoo SCro SHel SPer SRms WFar
  WHal WHoo WMoo WMow WOve
  WPer WPyg
*reptans* CArn CKin EWFC
- 'Pleniflora' (d) MInt WAlt
*rupestris* CAgr CGle CHan CInt CLTr
  CM&M CTri ECha EMan EWFC
  LFis MCLN MFir MLLN MNrw
  NChi NRoo NSti SUsu WAbe
  WByw WCla WFar WHal WPer
  WUnu WWin
*schillingii* Last listed 1997
¶ sp. CC 1767 MRPP
*speciosa* EHyt EMan
* - var. *discolor* Last listed 1997
- var. *speciosa* Last listed 1998
- - NS 765 MRPP
*sterilis* CHid ELan EWFC
- 'Turncoat' (v) Last listed 1998
'Sungold' ECho ESis WHCG
*tabernaemontani* See *P. neumanniana*
*ternata* See *P. aurea* subsp.
  *chrysocraspeda*
*thurberi* CGle CHid EBee EMan EWes GCal
  LGre LPio MHar MNrw MRav
  NChi NLar WMaN
§ - 'Monarch's Velvet' CBot CHar CLTr CMdw CPou
  CSpe EBee ECGP EWTr MBri MCli
  MRav MTis NArg NDov NFla
  NHed NRoo SBea SSvw SUsu
  WBro WGor WLRN WPrP

| | |
|---|---|
| - 'White Queen' | See *P.* 'White Queen' |
| *tommasiniana* | See *P. cinerea* |
| x *tonguei* ♀ | More than 30 suppliers |
| *tormentilla* | See *P. erecta* |
| *tridentata* | See *Sibbaldiopsis tridentata* |
| *verna* | See *P. neumanniana* |
| - 'Pygmaea' | See *P. neumanniana* 'Nana' |
| 'Versicolor Plena' (d) | CMea |
| *villosa* | See *P. crantzii* |
| 'Volcan' | CMil CPlt EBee EPPr EWes GCal LGre MBNS MBri WAbb WFar WWeb |
| *wallichiana* 'Cream Cracker' | Last listed 1998 |
| * 'White Beauty' | Last listed 1997 |
| § 'White Queen' | CMea EWTr EWll LWoo MNrw NBur SBea WBea WElm WGor |
| 'William Rollison' ♀ | More than 30 suppliers |
| *willmottiae* | See *P. nepalensis* 'Miss Willmott' |
| 'Yellow Queen' | CB&S CTri EMil EPfP LLWP MNrw MRav NFai NRoo NVic SCro SPer SWat WFar WMer WMow WWeb |

## POTERIUM See SANGUISORBA

## PRATIA (Campanulaceae)
| | |
|---|---|
| § *angulata* | GGar NHar |
| - 'Jack's Pass' | GAri NHar |
| - 'Messenger' | ECou |
| - 'Ohau' | Last listed 1997 |
| - 'Tim Rees' | Last listed 1997 |
| § - 'Treadwellii' | ECha ELan LBee MBNS NPro NRoo SLod SPlb SRPl WHal WHen WWin |
| - 'Woodside' | ECou |
| *macrodon* | NNrd WCru |
| § *pedunculata* | CHan CMHG CMea ECha ECou ELan ESis GCHN GMac GTou LBee MBar NFla NLon NRoo NRya NVic SHFr SIng SPlb SRms SSmi SUsu WFar WHen WHoo WPer WWhi WWin |
| - 'Blue Stars' | WCru |
| - 'Clear Skies' | Last listed 1997 |
| - 'County Park' | CInt CMea CSpe CVer ECha ECou ELan EPot ESis GMac MBar NHar NMen NNrd NRoo NWCA SIng SPlb SRms SSmi WFar WHal WHoo WPat WPer WPyg WWin |
| - 'Kiandra' | ECou |
| - 'Kinsey' | Last listed 1997 |
| - 'Tom Stone' | CLTr EPot MBNS NHar NNrd |
| § *perpusilla* | ECou |
| - 'Fragrant Carpet' | ECou WFar |
| - 'Summer Meadows' | ECou WPer |
| § *repens* | ECou |

## PRESLIA (Lamiaceae)
| | |
|---|---|
| *cervina* | See *Mentha cervina* |

## PRESLIA See MENTHA

## PRIMULA ✿ (Primulaceae)
| | |
|---|---|
| *acaulis* | See *P. vulgaris* |
| 'Adrian Jones' (2) | EHyt EPot NHol NNrd SIng WAbe |
| 'Aire Mist' (*allionii* hybrid) (2) | CGra Clyd EHyt EPot GNor MFie NHar NHol WLin |
| § 'Aire Waves' (2) | EHyt GNor |
| 'Alan Robb' (dPrim)(30) | EBee EHic MBNS MBri MBro NHol SIng SPer |
| 'Alexina' (*allionii* hybrid) (2) | EHyt NHar NHol |
| *algida* (11) | CPla ECho NWCA |

| | |
|---|---|
| § *allionii* (2) | EHyt EMNN EPot GTou ITim LBee MBro MFie NCra NHar NHol NNrd NWCA WAbe |
| - 'A.K. Wells' (2) | EPot |
| - 'Aire Waves' | See *P.* 'Aire Waves' |
| - var. *alba* (2) | EMNN NHol |
| * - 'Alexander' (2) | Last listed 1998 |
| - 'Anna Griffith' (2) | CGra EHyt EPot GCHN ITim MFie NHol NNrd NWCA SIng WAbe |
| - 'Anne' (2) | EHyt EPot ITim |
| § - 'Apple Blossom' (2) | CGra EPot GAbr MDHE NNrd NTow |
| - 'Archer' (2) | EMNN NMen WLin |
| - x *auricula* 'Blairside Yellow' (2) | CLyd CPBP GNor |
| - x - 'Old Red Dusty Miller' hort. (2) | MDHE MFie NHar NHol NNrd |
| - 'Austen' (2) | EHyt EPot NHol NMen NNrd WAbe |
| - 'Avalanche' (2) | CLyd EHyt GNor ITim NHar NMen NTow SIng WLin |
| - 'Bill Martin' (2) | EPot |
| - 'Brilliant' KRW 448/69 (2) | EHyt |
| - Burnley form (2) | EPot NHol |
| - CH 1989 (2) | WLin |
| - 'Chris Norton' CCN/03 (2) | ITim |
| - 'Clarence Elliott' | See *P.* 'Clarence Elliott' (2) |
| - 'Claude Flight' (2) | EHyt NHar |
| - x *clusiana* (2) | WLin |
| - 'Crowsley Variety' (2) | CLyd CPBP EHyt EPot NMen NSla NTow NWCA SBla SIng WAbe WLin |
| ¶ - 'Crowsley Variety' x *pubescens* 'The General' (2) | EPot |
| - 'Crusader' (2) | EHyt WLin |
| - 'Crystal' KRW 425/69 (2) | Last listed 1996 |
| * - 'E.G. Watson' | EHyt |
| § - 'Edinburgh' (2) | EHyt EMNN EPot ITim MFie NHol NNrd |
| - 'Edrom' (2) | ITim |
| - 'Elizabeth Baker' (2) | EHyt EMNN GNor MFie WAbe |
| - 'Elizabeth Earle' (2) | EPot NHol NMen WAbe |
| - 'Elliott's Large' | See *P. allionii* 'Edinburgh' |
| - 'Elliott's Variety' | See *P. allionii* 'Edinburgh' |
| - 'Fanfare' (2) | CGra EHyt EPot WGwG |
| - 'Frank Barker' (2) | EPot NHol |
| - 'Gavin Brown' (2) | EHyt EPot |
| - GFS 1984 (2) | CGra |
| § - 'Gilderdale Glow' (2) | MFie NHar |
| - 'Giuseppi's Form' | See *P. allionii* 'Mrs Dyas' |
| - 'Grandiflora' (2) | Last listed 1998 |
| - Hartside 383/12 | See *P. allionii* 'Gilderdale Glow' |
| - Hartside 383/3 (2) | EPot NHol NMen NNrd |
| - Hartside 383/6 | Last listed 1998 |
| - 'Hemswell' (2) | Last listed 1998 |
| - 'Hemswell Blush' | See *P.* 'Hemswell Blush' |
| - 'Hemswell Ember' | See *P.* 'Hemswell Ember' |
| - x *hirsuta* (2) | MFie |
| - 'Hocker Edge' (2) | NNrd |
| - 'Horwood' KD/KRW 397/60 (2) | EHyt |
| - 'Huntsman' | MFie |
| - Ingwersen's form (2) | EPot GTou NHol |
| - JCA 4161/16 (2) | EPot |
| - JCA 4161/21 | See *P. allionii* 'Travellers' JCA 4161/21 |
| - JCA 4161/22 | See *P. allionii* 'Jenny' JCA 4161/22 |
| - JCA 4161/23 | CGra EPot |
| § - 'Jenny' JCA 4161/22 (2) | CGra EHyt EPot |
| - 'Jouster' (2) | Last listed 1996 |
| - 'Julia' JCA 4161/31 | EHyt EPot |

| | |
|---|---|
| - K R W | See *P. allionii* 'Ken's Seedling' |
| § - 'Kath Dryden' (2) | WHil |
| § - 'Ken's Seedling' (2) | CLyd CNic EHyt EPot NHol NNrd WAbe |
| - KRW 1971 (2) | Last listed 1997 |
| - KRW 324/62 (2) | Last listed 1996 |
| - KRW 392/56 (2) | EHyt |
| - KRW 455/70 (2) | EHyt |
| - KRW 461/71 (2) | EHyt |
| - KRW 525/76 (thrum, white) (2) | EHyt |
| - 'Lindisfarne' (2) | EHyt WLin |
| - Lismore 79/7 (2) | WLin |
| - Lismore 81/19/3 | MFie |
| - Lismore P85/16xx (2) | WLin |
| - x 'Lismore Treasure' (2) | CPBP EHyt NWCA WLin |
| - 'Margaret Earle' (2) | NHol WAbe |
| - 'Marion' (2) | EHyt EMNN EPot GNor ITim NHed NHol NMen |
| - 'Marjorie Wooster' KRW 331/52 (2) | EHyt NWCA |
| - 'Martin' (2) | EPot NHol NNrd |
| - 'Mary Berry' (2) | EMNN EPot |
| § - 'Mrs Dyas' (2) | EHyt EMNN ITim NHar NHol NNrd |
| - Nettleton 8824 (2) | EPot |
| - pale clone (2) | WLin |
| - x *pedemontana* | See *P.* x *sendtneri* |
| - 'Peggy Wilson' (2) | EPot EWes NHol |
| - 'Pennine Pink' Hartside 383/7 (2) | EHyt EPot NHol |
| - 'Perkie' | Last listed 1997 |
| - 'Perkie' JCA 4161/12 (2) | EHyt NNrd |
| - 'Phobos' (2) | Last listed 1997 |
| - 'Picton's Variety' (2) | EPot NHed |
| - 'Pink Aire' | See *P.* 'Pink Aire' |
| - 'Pink Beauty' (2) | EPot |
| - 'Pink Gin' (2) | Last listed 1996 |
| - 'Pinkie' KRW 271/51 (2) | CGra |
| - 'Praecox' (2) | EPot MFie NHol NNrd NSla |
| - x *pubescens* 'Harlow Car' (2) | CLyd NHar |
| - x - 'Rosalie' (2) | Last listed 1996 |
| - 'Raymond Wooster' KRW 321/52 (2) | EPot NHol |
| - 'Roger Bevan' (2) | EHyt |
| - x *rubra* (2) | MBro NHol |
| - 'Saint Dalmas' (2) | EPot |
| - 'Scimitar' (2) | EMNN NHar NHol |
| - 'Serendipity' (2) | Last listed 1998 |
| - 'Snowflake' KRW 367/56 (2) | CGra CLyd CPBP EHyt EMNN EPot NHar NTow NWCA WAbe |
| - 'Stanton House' (2) | NHed NHol |
| - 'Stephen' JCA 4161/6 (2) | EHyt EMNN EPot |
| ¶ - 'Stradbrook Mauve Magic' (2) | MFie |
| - 'Sylvia Martinelli' | Last listed 1998 |
| - 'Tranquillity' (2) | WLin |
| - 'Tranquillity' Hartside 383/1 (2) | EHyt MFie NHar NHol NMen NNrd |
| § - 'Travellers' JCA 4161/21 (2) | CGra EPot |
| - 'Viscountess Byng' (2) | EMNN EPot |
| - W 1971 (2) | WLin |
| ¶ - x 'White Linda Pope' (2) | MFie NHol |
| - 'William Earle' (2) | EHyt EMNN EPot MFie NHar NHed NHol NMen NWCA WAbe |
| *alpicola* (26) | CBot CFee CRow CSWP EBrP EBre GAbr GDra GFle LBre LPBA MBal MFie NBro NCra NHed SBre SPer WAbe WRus |
| - var. *alba* (26) | CPla CRow CSWP GBin GMac LSyl MBal MMal MNrw NRoo SWat |
| § - var. *alpicola* | EBee GBuc LSyl MNrw |
| - hybrids (26) | Last listed 1997 |
| - var. *luna* | See *P. alpicola* var. *alpicola* |
| - var. *violacea* (26) | CPla CRow GAbr GDra GMac LSyl MBal MBri MFie MNrw NHar SPer SWat WWhi |
| 'Altaica' | See *P. elatior* subsp. *meyeri* |
| *altaica grandiflora* | See *P. elatior* subsp. *meyeri* |
| * 'Amaranth' | WHil |
| *amoena* | See *P. elatior* subsp. *meyeri* |
| *anisodora* | See *P. wilsonii* var. *anisodora* |
| 'April Rose' (dPrim)(30) | CMea MRav NBid |
| x *arctotis* | See *P.* x *pubescens* |
| *atrodentata* (9) | WAbe |
| *aurantiaca* (4) | CPla GAri GFle LSyl MSta SIng SRms |
| *aureata* (21) | GGGa GGar NCra |
| - subsp. *fimbriata* (21) | GCrs |
| § *auricula* L. (2) ♀ | ELan GCrs GNor GTou MBal MTho NBro NCra NSla NWCA SIng SPer SSmi WAbe WCla WCom |
| ¶ - var. *albocincta* (2) | NWCA |
| - subsp. *auricula* (2) | GTou |
| - subsp. *balbisii* | See *P. auricula* subsp. *ciliata* |
| - subsp. *bauhinii* (2) | MBro |
| ¶ - - var. *albocincta* | WLin |
| § - subsp. *ciliata* (2) | NNrd |
| *auricula* hort. (B) | WLin |
| - 'A.H. Spring' (A) | MFie |
| - 'Adrian' (A) | MFie NCra NNrd SHya SPop |
| - 'Aga Khan' | SHya |
| - 'Agamemnon' | NCra |
| - 'Alamo' | NCra SPop |
| - 'Alan' (A) | Last listed 1996 |
| - 'Alan Ravenscroft' (A) | MFie |
| ¶ - 'Albert Bailey' (S/d) | MCre |
| - 'Albury' (d) | Last listed 1998 |
| - 'Alfred Niblett' (S) | EMNN NNrd |
| - 'Alice Haysom' (S) | ELan MCre MFie NNrd SHya WHil WLin |
| - 'Alicia' (A) | ECGP SHya SPop |
| - 'Alien' (S) | SHya |
| - 'Alison Jane' (A) | CLyd MCre MFie NCra NOak SHya |
| - 'Allansford' | EMNN |
| - 'Almondbury' (S) | NCra SHya |
| - 'Alpine mixed (A) | CNic MMal NCra SRms |
| - 'Amicable' (A) | NCra SHya |
| - 'Andrea Julie' (A) | CNic EMNN MCre MFie MOne NCra NHar NHol NNrd SHya SPop WHil WLin |
| - 'Ann Taylor' (A) | NCra SHya |
| - 'Antoc' (S) | EMNN MFie |
| - 'Anwar Sadat' (A) | EMNN MFie |
| - 'Applecross' (A) | EMNN MCre MFie NCra NHar NNrd SHya WLin |
| - 'Arctic Fox' | NCra |
| - 'Argus' (A) | CLyd MCre MFie NBir NCra NHar NNrd SHya SPop SUsu WHil WLin |
| - 'Arundel Star' | Last listed 1998 |
| - 'Arundell' (S/St) | EMNN MCre NNrd SHya SPop WHil WLin |
| - 'Astolat' (S) | EMNN MCre MFie NCra NNrd NOak SHya SPop SUsu WLin |
| - 'Athur Delbridge' (A) | MFie |
| ¶ - 'Atlantean' | NCra |
| - 'Aurora' (A) | MFie SHya |
| - 'Austin' | NCra |
| - 'Aviemore' (A) | Last listed 1997 |
| - 'Avril Hunter' (A) | MFie SHya |
| - 'Aye Aye' | NCra |
| - 'Bacchus' (A) | MFie |

| | | |
|---|---|---|
| - 'Ballet' (S) | MFie | |
| - 'Banana Split' | Last listed 1996 | |
| - 'Barbara Mason' | NCra | |
| - 'Barbarella' (S) | EMNN MFie WLin | |
| - Barnhaven doubles | CSWP GAbr MCCP | |
| - 'Basuto' (A) | EMNN MFie SHya SPop | |
| - 'Beatrice' (A) | CLyd EMNN GAbr MCre MFie NCra NNrd SHya WLin | |
| - 'Beckjay' (S) | Last listed 1996 | |
| - 'Bedford Lad' (A) | SHya | |
| - 'Beechen Green' (S) | EMNN GNor NNrd SHya | |
| - 'Bellezana' | MFie | |
| - 'Ben Lawers' (S) | SHya SPop | |
| - 'Ben Wyves' (S) | MCre SHya | |
| - 'Bendigo' (S) | SHya WHil | |
| - 'Bernard Smith' (d) | Last listed 1996 | |
| - 'Bilton' (S) | CLyd MFie NCra | |
| - 'Blackfield' (S) | MFie | |
| - 'Blackhill' (S) | EMNN | |
| - 'Blairside Yellow' (B) | CLyd EWes MRPP NHar NHol WAbe | |
| - 'Blossom' (A) | EMNN MFie NCra NNrd SHya WLin | |
| - 'Blue Bonnet' (A) | GNor SPop | |
| - 'Blue Heaven' | NCra | |
| - 'Blue Jean' (S) | EMNN MFie NCra | |
| ¶ - 'Blue Mist' (B) | GAbr GNor | |
| - 'Blue Nile' (S) | EMNN GNor MFie | |
| - 'Blue Ridge' (A) | Last listed 1996 | |
| - 'Blue Steel' (S) | SHya | |
| - 'Blue Velvet' (B) | EMNN MFie NBro SHya SPop WLin | |
| ¶ - 'Blue Wave' (d) | WLin | |
| - 'Bob Lancashire' (S) | EMNN GNor MCre MFie NHar NNrd SHya SPop WHil | |
| - 'Bolero' (A) | SHya | |
| - 'Bookham Firefly' (A) | EMNN GNor MBro MCre MFie NCra NHar NHol NNrd SHya SPop WLin | |
| ¶ - 'Boy Blue' (S) | SHya | |
| - 'Bramshill' (S) | Last listed 1996 | |
| - 'Bravura' | NCra | |
| - 'Brazil' (S) | EMNN GAbr GNor MCre MFie NCra NHol NNrd NOak WHil WLin | |
| - 'Bredon Hill' (S) | Last listed 1997 | |
| - 'Brenda's Choice' (A) | MFie SHya | |
| - 'Bright Eyes' (A) | MFie NCra SHya | |
| - 'Broad Gold' (A) | SHya | |
| - 'Broadwell Gold' (B) | CLyd MFie SHya WLin | |
| - 'Brookfield' (S) | EMNN GCrs MCre MFie NNrd SHya | |
| - 'Broughton' (S) | MFie | |
| - 'Brown Bess' (A) | GNor MFie NCra NNrd SHya WLin | |
| ¶ - 'Brownie' (d) | NCra | |
| - 'Buccaneer' | NCra | |
| - 'Bucks Green' | SPop | |
| - 'Bunty' (A) | MFie | |
| - 'Butterwick' (A) | ECGP MFie NCra NHar NHol NOla NPri SHya SPop WLin | |
| - 'C.F. Hill' (A) | EMNN SHya | |
| - 'C.G. Haysom' (S) | EMNN MCre MFie NCra NHar SHya SPop WLin | |
| - 'C.W. Needham' (A) | EMNN MFie NCra NHol NNrd SHya WHil WLin | |
| I - 'Calypso' (A) | MCre | |
| * - 'Cambodumun' | NCra SPop | |
| - 'Camelot' (d) | CLyd ElAn EMNN GCrs MCre MFie MOne NBro NChi NCra NHar NHol NNrd NPri SHya SPop SUsu WFar WHil | |
| - 'Camilla' (A) | Last listed 1997 | |
| - 'Candida' (d) | SHya SPop | |
| - 'Carole' (A) | MFie WLin | |
| - 'Carreras' | NCra | |
| - 'Catherine' (d) | NCra | |
| - 'Chaffinch' (S) | GNor SHya | |
| - 'Chamois' (B) | Last listed 1997 | |
| - 'Chantilly Cream' (d) | Last listed 1998 | |
| - 'Chelsea Bridge' | EMNN | |
| - 'Cherry' (S) | EMNN GAbr NCra SHya | |
| ¶ - 'Cherry Picker' (A) | MCre WHil | |
| - 'Cherrypicker' (A) | Last listed 1997 | |
| - 'Cheyenne' (S) | EMNN GAbr MCre MFie WLin | |
| - 'Chloë' (S) | SHya | |
| - 'Chloris' (S) | NBir SHya | |
| - 'Chorister' (S) | CLyd ECGP ElAn EMNN GAbr GNor MBro MCre MFie MOne NCra NHed NHol NNrd NOak NPri SHya SPop SUsu WLin | |
| - 'Cicero' (A) | Last listed 1998 | |
| - 'Cindy' (A) | MFie | |
| * - 'Cinnamon' (d) | MCre WHil | |
| * - 'Cinnamon' (S) | SHya | |
| - 'Clare' (S) | MCre SHya | |
| - 'Clatter-Ha' | GCrs | |
| - 'Claudia Taylor' | NHar SHya WHil WLin | |
| - 'Clunie' (S) | GNor WHil | |
| - 'Clunie II' (S) | GCrs SHya WLin | |
| - 'Coffee' (S) | MFie NCra SHya SUsu | |
| - 'Colbury' (S) | MFie NCra NHar SHya WLin | |
| - 'Colonel Champney' (S) | MFie NNrd SHya SUsu WLin | |
| - 'Comet' (S) | MFie NNrd | |
| - 'Commander' (A) | Last listed 1996 | |
| ¶ - 'Connaught Court' (A) | SPop | |
| - 'Connie' (S) | MFie | |
| - 'Conservative' (S) | MFie SHya SUsu | |
| - 'Consett' (S) | EMNN MFie NCra NNrd | |
| - 'Coppernob' (S) | Last listed 1998 | |
| - 'Coral' (S) | MFie NCra | |
| - 'Corona' (S) | Last listed 1998 | |
| - 'Corrie Files' (d) | Last listed 1998 | |
| - 'Cortina' (S) | EMNN GNor MCre MOne NCra NHar NHol NNrd NOak SPop SUsu WLin | |
| - 'County Park Red' (B) | ECou | |
| - 'Craig Vaughan' (A) | MFie NCra NNrd SHya | |
| - 'Creenagh Stripe' (A) | Last listed 1997 | |
| ¶ - 'Crimple' | SHya | |
| - 'Cuckoo Fair' | SPop | |
| ¶ - 'Curry Blend' | GAbr | |
| - 'D.S.J.' (S) | SHya | |
| - 'Daftie Green' (S) | EMNN NNrd | |
| - 'Dakota' (S) | EMNN MFie NCra | |
| ¶ - 'Dales Red' (B) | EBrP EBre LBre NCra NNrd SBre | |
| - 'Daphnis' (S) | Last listed 1997 | |
| - 'Dark Tiger' (St) | SHya | |
| - 'Deep Wilson' | EWes | |
| - 'Delilah' (d) | GAbr GNor MFie WLin | |
| ¶ - 'Denna Snuffer' | EMNN GNor | |
| - 'Devon Cream' (d) | GNor MCre MFie NCra NHol WFar WLin | |
| - 'Diane' | EMNN MFie | |
| - 'Divint Dunch' (A) | MCre SHya SPop | |
| - 'Doctor B. Sharma' (S) | Last listed 1998 | |
| - 'Doctor Duthie' (S) | Last listed 1998 | |
| - 'Doctor Lennon's White' (B) | MFie | |
| - 'Donhead' (A) | MFie SHya WHil | |
| - 'Donna Clancy' (S) | MFie SHya | |
| - 'Doris Jean' (A) | SHya | |
| - 'Dorothy' (S) | Last listed 1997 | |
| - double maroon (d) | Last listed 1998 | |
| - double yellow (d) | Last listed 1998 | |
| - 'Doublet' (d) | CLyd EMNN GAbr MCre MFie NCra NHol NNrd NOak NSla SHya SPop WHil WLin | |

| | | |
|---|---|---|
| | - 'Doubloon' (d) | Last listed 1998 |
| | - 'Doublure' (d) | GAbr MCre SHya |
| | - 'Douglas Black' (S) | SHya |
| | - 'Douglas Green' (S) | MFie SHya |
| ¶ | - 'Douglas Red' | WLin |
| | - 'Douglas White' (S) | EMNN MFie SHya |
| | - 'Dovedale' (S) | SHya |
| | - 'Dowager' (A) | MFie |
| | - 'Dubarii' (A) | NCra |
| * | - 'Dusky' | WLin |
| | - 'Dusky Maiden' (A) | EMNN GNor MCre NCra SHya WLin |
| | - 'Dusky Yellow' (B) | MBro |
| | - 'Dusty Lemon' (d) | Last listed 1998 |
| | - 'Dusty Miller' (B) | NBid |
| | - 'E' | Last listed 1997 |
| | - E82 (S) | Last listed 1997 |
| | - 'Ed Spivey' (A) | Last listed 1998 |
| | - 'Edith Allen' (A) | Last listed 1998 |
| | - 'Eglinton' | NCra |
| | - 'Eileen K' (S) | SHya |
| | - 'Elegance' (S) | SHya |
| | - 'Elizabeth Ann' (A) | EMNN MFie NCra SHya |
| | - 'Ellen Thompson' (A) | MFie NNrd SHya WLin |
| | - 'Elmor Vete' (S) | Last listed 1998 |
| | - 'Elsie' (A) | EMNN MFie |
| | - 'Elsie May' (A) | EMNN GNor MFie NCra NNrd SHya SPop WHil WLin |
| | - 'Embley' (S) | CLyd GNor NCra SHya |
| | - 'Emery Down' (S) | MFie SHya SPop |
| | - 'Enismore' | Last listed 1996 |
| | - 'Enlightened' (A) | NCra SHya |
| | - 'Envy' (S) | Last listed 1996 |
| I | - 'Erica' (A) | EMNN MFie NHar WLin |
| | - 'Error' (S) | SHya |
| | - 'Ethel' | Last listed 1997 |
| | - 'Ettrick' (S) | Last listed 1998 |
| | - 'Eve Guest' (A) | Last listed 1998 |
| | - 'Eventide' (S) | Last listed 1996 |
| | - 'Everest Blue' (S) | SHya SPop SUsu |
| | - 'Eyeopener' | SPop |
| | - 'Fairy' (A) | Last listed 1998 |
| | - 'Falcon' (S) | SHya |
| | - 'Falsefields' (S) | SHya |
| | - 'Fanciful' (S) | CLyd MFie SHya WLin |
| ¶ | - 'Fancy Pin' | NNrd |
| ¶ | - 'Fanfare' (S) | SHya |
| | - 'Fanny Meerbeck' (S) | EMNN GNor MFie NCra NHol NNrd NOak SUsu WHil WLin |
| | - 'Faro' (S) | Last listed 1996 |
| | - 'Favorite' | EMNN NNrd SHya |
| ¶ | - 'Favourite' (S) | MCre SPop |
| | - 'Figaro' (S) | SHya |
| | - 'Finavon' | GCrs |
| | - 'Finchfield' (A) | EMNN MFie SHya SUsu |
| | - 'Firenze' | NCra |
| | - 'Flamingo' (S) | Last listed 1998 |
| | - 'Fleminghouse' (S) | SHya |
| | - 'Forsinard' (S) | Last listed 1998 |
| | - 'Fradley' (A) | SHya |
| | - 'Frank Crosland' (A) | MFie NCra SHya WHil WLin |
| | - 'Frank Faulkner' (A) | Last listed 1998 |
| | - 'Frank Taylor' (S) | SHya |
| | - 'Frittenden Yellow' (B) | WLin |
| | - 'Frosty' (S) | SHya |
| | - 'Fuller's Red' (S) | CLyd MFie |
| | - 'Gaia' (d) | NHol SHya |
| | - 'Galen' (A) | MFie NCra NNrd |
| | - 'Gay Crusader' (A) | EMNN MFie SHya |
| | - 'Gee Cross' (A) | EMNN MFie |
| § | - 'Geldersome Green' (S) | EMNN MCre MFie SHya SPop WLin |

| | | |
|---|---|---|
| | - 'Generosity' (A) | SPop |
| | - 'George Rudd' (S) | SHya |
| | - 'George Swinford's Leathercoat' (B) | SHya |
| | - 'Geronimo' (S) | EMNN GNor MFie |
| | - 'Gizabroon' (S) | CLyd EBrP EBre EMNN LBre MCre MFie NCra NNrd SBre WLin |
| | - 'Gleam' (S) | EMNN GCrs GNor MFie NNrd SHya SPop WLin |
| | - 'Glencoe' (S) | Last listed 1998 |
| | - 'Gleneagles' (S) | MCre SHya |
| | - 'Glenelg' (S) | MCre MFie SHya SPop |
| | - 'Glenluce' (S) | SHya |
| | - 'Gnome' (B) | NHol |
| | - 'Gold Blaze' (S) | Last listed 1996 |
| | - 'Goldcrest' (S) | Last listed 1997 |
| | - 'Golden Chartreuse' (d) | Last listed 1998 |
| | - 'Golden Eagle' | NCra |
| ¶ | - 'Golden Fleece' (S) | GNor |
| | - 'Golden Gleam' (A) | Last listed 1996 |
| ¶ | - 'Golden Hind' (d) | SPop |
| | - 'Golden Splendour' (d) | MCre MFie SHya WLin |
| | - 'Goldilocks' (S) | Last listed 1996 |
| | - 'Goldthorn' (A) | Last listed 1997 |
| | - 'Good Report' | NCra |
| | - 'Gooseberries and Cream' | Last listed 1996 |
| | - 'Gordon Douglas' (A) | MCre MFie NCra SHya SUsu |
| | - 'Gorey' | NCra |
| | - 'Grace' (S) | Last listed 1996 |
| | - 'Grace Ellen' (S) | SHya |
| | - 'Green Isle' (S) | EMNN GAbr MCre MFie NBir NNrd SHya WLin |
| | - 'Green Jacket' (S) | MCre NNrd SHya |
| | - 'Green Mansions' (S) | SHya |
| | - 'Green Mouse' (S) | MFie SHya |
| | - 'Green Parrot' (S) | CLyd EMNN GNor MCre SPop WHil |
| | - 'Green Shank' (S) | GNor MFie NNrd SHya WLin |
| | - 'Greenfinger' (S) | Last listed 1997 |
| | - 'Greenheart' (S) | EMNN GNor SHya |
| | - 'Greenpeace' (S) | LRHS NHar SHya |
| | - 'Greensleeves' (S) | Last listed 1998 |
| | - 'Greta' (S) | ELan EMNN GNor MCre NHar NNrd NOak SHya SPop WHil WLin |
| | - 'Gretna Green' (S) | GNor MFie SHya |
| | - 'Grey Bonnet' (S) | SHya |
| ¶ | - 'Grey Edge' | SUsu |
| | - 'Grey Friar' (S) | SHya |
| | - 'Grey Hawk' (S) | SHya |
| | - 'Grey Lag' | EMNN GNor MFie SHya |
| | - 'Grey Monarch' (S) | GNor MCre MFie SHya |
| | - 'Grey Shrike' (S) | SHya |
| | - 'Grey Tarquin' (S) | Last listed 1998 |
| | - 'Grizedale' (S) | MFie |
| | - 'Guildersome Green' | See P. auricula 'Geldersome Green' |
| | - 'Guinea' (S) | EMNN GAbr MFie NCra NNrd SHya SPop WLin |
| | - 'Gwen' (A) | SHya |
| ¶ | - 'Gwen Baker' (d) | EBrP EBre LBre SBre |
| | - 'Habanera' | NCra SPop |
| | - 'Haffner' (S) | Last listed 1997 |
| | - 'Harmony' (B) | MFie |
| | - 'Harrison Weir' (S) | Last listed 1998 |
| ¶ | - 'Harry Hotspur' (A) | SPop |
| | - 'Harry 'O' (S) | MCre SHya |
| | - 'Harvest Moon' (S) | Last listed 1997 |
| | - 'Haughmond' (A) | EMNN MFie |
| | - 'Hawkwood' (S) | EMNN GNor NCra NHar NNrd SPop WHil |
| | - 'Hawkwood Fancy' (S) | MFie SHya WLin |

| | |
|---|---|
| * - 'Hazel' (A) | GAbr MFie NCra SHya |
| - 'Hazel's Fancy' (S) | SHya |
| - 'Headdress' (S) | MCre MFie |
| - 'Heady' | NCra |
| - 'Hebers' | NCra |
| - 'Helen' (S) | SHya |
| - 'Helen Barter' (S) | SHya |
| - 'Helena' (S) | EMNN GNor MFie NNrd NOak SHya WHil |
| - 'Helena Brown' (S) | SHya |
| - 'Hetty Woolf' | EMNN GNor NNrd |
| - 'Hew Dalrymple' (S) | SHya |
| - 'Hinton Admiral' (S) | SHya WLin |
| - 'Hinton Fields' (S) | GNor MFie SHya |
| - 'Hoghton Gem' (d) | Last listed 1998 |
| - 'Holyrood' (S) | MFie |
| ¶ - 'Hopleys Coffee' | GAbr |
| - 'Hopleys Double Mauve' (d) | Last listed 1998 |
| - 'Humphrey' (S) | SHya |
| - 'Hurstwood Majesty' (S) | Last listed 1996 |
| - 'Hurstwood Midnight' | MBro MFie NHol WLin |
| * - 'Hyacinth' (S) | NWCA |
| - 'Ibis' (S) | MFie SHya |
| - 'Ice Maiden' | NCra |
| - 'Idmiston' (S) | SHya SPop WLin |
| - 'Imber' (S) | Last listed 1997 |
| - 'Immaculate' | SPop |
| - 'Impassioned' (A) | NCra SPop |
| - 'Impeccable' | NCra |
| - 'Indian Love Call' | NCra |
| - 'Jack Dean' (A) | MFie SHya WHil |
| - 'Jack Stant' (S) | SHya |
| - 'James Arnot' (S) | GNor MFie NCra NHar NOak SHya |
| - 'Jane Myers' (d) | MFie |
| - 'Janet' | Last listed 1998 |
| - 'Janie Hill' (A) | SHya |
| - 'Jeanne' (A) | SHya |
| - 'Jeannie Telford' (A) | NCra |
| - 'Jenny' (A) | EMNN GAbr MCre MFie NNrd WHil |
| - 'Jessie' (d) | SHya |
| - 'Jezebel' (B) | SHya |
| - 'Joan Elliott' (A) | CLyd GAbr MFie |
| - 'Joanne' (A) | MCre SHya |
| - 'Joe Perks' | NCra |
| - 'Joel' | MFie |
| - 'Johann Bach' (B) | MFie |
| - 'John Stewart' (A) | EMNN MFie |
| - 'John Wayne' (A) | MFie |
| - 'John Woolf' (S) | Last listed 1998 |
| - 'Joy' (A) | CLyd EMNN GNor MFie NCra NHol NNrd SHya SPop WLin |
| - 'Joyce' | GAbr MCre MFie NBir SHya SPop WLin |
| - 'Julia' (S) | SHya |
| - 'July Sky' (A) | SHya |
| - 'Jupiter' (S) | SHya |
| ¶ - 'K.H.B.' (S) | WLin |
| - 'Karen Cordrey' (S) | WHil WLin |
| - 'Kath Dryden' | See P. allionii 'Kath Dryden' |
| - 'Kathy' (A) | Last listed 1998 |
| - 'Kelso' (A) | MFie |
| - 'Kens Green' (S) | Last listed 1998 |
| - 'Kercup' (A) | MFie NCra NNrd |
| - 'Khachaturian' | NCra |
| - 'Kim' (A) | EMNN MFie NNrd SHya |
| - 'Kincraig' (S) | Last listed 1998 |
| - 'Kingcup' (A) | MFie NCra SHya |
| - 'Kiowa' (S) | MFie |
| - 'Kirklands' (d) | MFie NNrd SPop |
| - 'Königin der Nacht' (St) | SHya |

| | |
|---|---|
| - 'Lady Croft' (S) | Last listed 1997 |
| - 'Lady Daresbury' (A) | EMNN MCre MFie NCra |
| - 'Lady Emma Monson' (S) | SHya |
| - 'Lady Joyful' (S) | SHya |
| - 'Lady Zoë' (S) | MFie NCra |
| - 'Lamplugh' | NNrd |
| - 'Landy' (A) | GCrs MCre |
| - 'Langley Park' (A) | MCre MFie WHil |
| - 'Larkhill' (A) | Last listed 1997 |
| ¶ - 'Lavender Lady' (B) | NCra |
| - 'Laverock' (S) | NBro SHya |
| - 'Laverock Fancy' (S) | EMNN GNor MFie WLin |
| - 'Leather Jacket' | GAbr NHol |
| - 'Lechistan' (S) | EMNN MCre MFie NHar NHol NNrd WHil WLin |
| - 'Lee Paul' (A) | EMNN GNor MCre MFie NCra SHya SPop WLin |
| - 'Lee Sharpe' (A) | SHya |
| - 'Lemon Drop' (S) | SHya |
| - 'Lemon Sherbet' (B) | MFie |
| - 'Lewis Telford' (A) | Last listed 1998 |
| - 'Lich' | EMNN |
| - 'Lichfield' (A) | SHya |
| - 'Light Hearted' | NCra |
| - 'Lilac Domino' (S) | MFie NCra SHya WLin |
| - 'Lillian Hill' (A) | SHya |
| - 'Lime 'n' Lemon' | Last listed 1996 |
| - 'Lincoln Green' (S) | SHya |
| - 'Lindley' (S) | EMNN NHar |
| - 'Lindsey Moreno' (S) | Last listed 1998 |
| - 'Ling' (A) | CLyd EMNN MFie NCra SPop |
| - Lingen seedling No. 1 | Last listed 1998 |
| - 'Lisa' (A) | CLyd MBal MFie NCra NHar NNrd WLin |
| - 'Lisa Clara' (S) | EMNN GNor SHya |
| - 'Lisa's Smile' (S) | MFie NCra |
| - 'Little Rosetta' (d) | WHil |
| ¶ - 'Lord Saye and Sele' (St) | GCrs SHya SPop WLin |
| - 'Louisa' (d) | MFie |
| ¶ - 'Louisa Woolhead' (d) | SPop |
| - 'Lovebird' (S) | EMNN GAbr GNor MFie NCra NHar NNrd SHya SUsu WLin |
| ¶ - 'Lucy Locket' (B) | EBrP EBre LBre NCra SBre |
| - 'Lyn' (A) | Last listed 1996 |
| - 'Madame Gina' (S) | MFie |
| - 'Maggie' (S) | EMNN GNor NNrd SHya |
| - 'Magnolia' (B) | MFie |
| - 'Magpie' (S) | Last listed 1996 |
| - 'Maid Marion' (d) | WLin |
| - 'Mandarin' | SPop |
| - 'Manka' (S) | MFie NCra SHya |
| - 'Mansell's Green' | MFie NNrd SHya |
| - 'Margaret' (S) | SHya |
| - 'Margaret Faulkner' (A) | EMNN GNor MCre MFie NCra SHya |
| - 'Margaret Martin' (S) | GNor SHya WLin |
| - 'Margot Fonteyn' | NCra SPop |
| - 'Marigold' (d) | CLyd NCra WFar |
| - 'Mark' (A) | EMNN MFie NBro NCra NHol |
| - 'Marmion' (S) | SHya |
| - 'Martin Luther King' (S) | MFie |
| - 'Mary' (d) | GNor MFie SHya |
| - 'Mary of Dunoon' (S) | SHya |
| - 'Mary Taylor' (S) | SHya |
| - 'Mary Zac' | NNrd |
| - 'Matley' (S) | Last listed 1996 |
| - 'Matthew Yates' (d) | CHad MCre MFie MOne NChi NCra NHol NPri SPop SUsu WLin |
| - 'Maureen Millward' | EMNN MFie NNrd SPop |
| - 'May Tiger' (S) | SHya |
| - 'Mazetta Stripe' (St) | WLin |
| ¶ - 'McWatt's Blue' (B) | GAbr |

- 'Meadow Lark' — NCra
- 'Mellifluous' — NCra
- 'Merlin' (A) — Last listed 1998
- 'Merlin Stripe' (St) — SHya
- 'Mermaid' — GAbr NCra SHya WHil WLin
- 'Merridale' (A) — EMNN MFie NCra SHya
¶ - 'Mersey Tiger' (S) — GAbr
- 'Metha' — NCra
- 'Mick' (A) — NCra
- 'Midnight' (S) — CLyd EMNN NCra NHar NNrd
- 'Mikado' (S) — MCre MFie SHya SPop WLin
- 'Milkmaid' (A) — Last listed 1996
- 'Millicent' (A) — MFie
- 'Mink' (A) — MFie WHil
- 'Minley' (S) — EMNN GCrs GNor ITim MFie
  NHar NNrd SHya SPop WLin
- 'Minstrel' (S) — SHya
- 'Mipsie Miranda' (d) — SHya
- 'Mirabella Bay' — NCra
- 'Miriam' (A) — Last listed 1998
- 'Mish Mish' (d) — NNrd SHya
- 'Mojave' (S) — EMNN GNor MBro MCre MFie
  NCra NHar NHol SPop WLin
- 'Mollie Langford' — SPop
- 'Moneymoon' (S) — MFie
- 'Monica' (A) — MFie
- 'Monk' (A) — CLyd MFie NNrd SHya WHil
- 'Moonbeam' (S) — Last listed 1996
- 'Moonglow' (S) — EMNN MFie NCra
- 'Moonrise' (S) — EMNN MFie
¶ - 'Moonriver' (A) — SPop
- 'Moonstone' (d) — MFie
- 'Moscow' (S) — MFie
- 'Moselle' (S) — SHya
- 'Mr 'A'' (S) — CLyd GCrs WLin
- 'Mrs L. Hearn' (A) — EMNN MFie NCra NNrd SHya
  SPop WHil WLin
- 'Mrs R. Bolton' (A) — WRha
- 'Murray Lakes' — NCra
- 'Nankenan' — WHil
- 'Neat and Tidy' (S) — CLyd EMNN LRHS MCre MFie
  NCra NHar NNrd NOak SHya
  SPop WLin WLin
- 'Nefertiti' — NCra
- 'Neville Telford' (S) — EMNN GNor MCre MFie
- 'New Baby' (A) — Last listed 1996
- 'Nickity' (A) — SHya WLin
- 'Nigel' (d) — GAbr WLin
- 'Night and Day' (S) — EMNN MFie NCra
- 'Nocturne' (S) — EMNN GNor MCre MFie NBro
  NCra SHya WLin
- 'Nordean' — Last listed 1996
- 'Norma' (A) — MFie NNrd WLin
- 'Notability' (A) — NCra
- 'Oake's Blue' (S) — NCra
- 'Oban' (S) — Last listed 1998
- 'Old Double Green' (d) — Last listed 1998
- 'Old England' (S) — SHya
- 'Old Gold' (S) — SHya SUsu
- 'Old Gold Dusty Miller' (B) — Last listed 1998
- 'Old Irish Blue' (B) — CLyd MBro MFie NHol SHya
- 'Old Irish Scented' (B) — NBro WHil WLin
- 'Old Lilac' (B) — MFie
- 'Old Mustard' — SWas
- 'Old Red Dusty Miller' (B) — ECha MFie NBir SHya
- 'Old Red Elvet' — GNor
- 'Old Suffolk Bronze' (B) — MFie NBro SHya
- 'Old Tawny' (B) — Last listed 1997
- 'Old Wine' (A) — CLyd MFie
- 'Old Yellow Dusty — CLTr CLyd EMNN EWes GAbr
  Miller' (B) — MBro MFie NBro NHol SHya SPop
  WAbe WHil WLin WWin

- 'Olton' (A) — MFie
- 'Orb' (S) — CLyd EBrP EBre EMNN LBre MCre
  MFie SBre SHya WLin
- 'Ordvic' — WLin
- 'Orwell Tiger' (St) — SHya
- 'Osbourne Green' (B) — GNor MFie SPop WHil WLin
- 'Overdale' (A) — Last listed 1998
¶ - 'Paleface' (A) — MCre
- 'Paradise Yellow' (B) — EMNN MFie SHya SPop
- 'Paris' (S) — SHya
- 'Party Dress' (S) — Last listed 1997
- 'Pastiche' (A) — MCre MFie NCra
- 'Pat' (S) — EMNN MFie NCra SHya
- 'Pat Barnard' — Last listed 1997
- 'Patience' (S) — NNrd
- 'Patricia Barras' (S) — SHya
- 'Paula Lewis' — Last listed 1996
- 'Pauline' (A) — MFie SHya
- 'Peggy' (A) — EPot MFie NNrd NWCA
- 'Petite Hybrid' — Last listed 1998
- 'Pharaoh' — NCra SPop
- 'Phyllis Douglas' (A) — EMNN MCre MFie NCra SHya
- 'Pierot' (A) — MFie
- 'Piers Telford' — MCre MFie NCra SPop WHil
- 'Pink Lady' (A) — MFie
- 'Pinstripe' — NNrd
¶ - 'Pioneer Stripe' (S) — NNrd
- 'Pippin' (A) — MFie SHya WLin
- 'Pixie' (A) — SHya
- 'Plush Royal' (S) — MFie
¶ - 'Pop's Blue' (d) — SPop
- 'Portree' (S) — EMNN SHya
- 'Pot o' Gold' (S) — GNor MFie NCra NHar NOak
  SHya SPop
- 'Prague' (S) — MCre MFie NBir SHya SPop
- 'Prince Charming' (S) — MFie SPop
- 'Prince John' (A) — MCre MFie NBro NCra NNrd
  SHya SPop WHil WLin
¶ - 'Purple Dusty Miller' (B) — WLin
- 'Purple Frills' — Last listed 1996
- 'Purple Mermaid' (d) — Last listed 1998
- 'Purple Sage' (S) — EMNN GNor NHar
- 'Purple Velvet' (S) — Last listed 1998
- 'Quality Chase' (A) — Last listed 1996
- 'Queen Bee' (S) — SHya
- 'Queen's Bower' (S) — EMNN
- 'Quintessence' — NCra
- 'Quiquern' (S) — Last listed 1998
- 'Rabley Heath' (A) — CLyd EMNN MFie SHya
- 'Radiance' (A) — Last listed 1996
- 'Radiant' (A) — MFie
¶ - 'Rag Doll' (S) — SHya
- 'Rajah' (S) — ELan GNor MFie NCra NHar SHya
  SPop WHil WLin
- 'Ray Brown' (v) — Last listed 1996
- 'Ray's Grey' (S) — SHya
- 'Red and White Stripe' (St) — WLin
- 'Red Beret' (S) — MFie NCra
- 'Red Gauntlet' (S) — EMNN MFie NCra NHar NNrd
  SHya SPop WCot WLin
- 'Red Mark' (A) — MFie
- 'Red Rum' (S) — MFie NCra
- 'Redstart' (S) — MCre WHil
- 'Redstart' (B) — WHil WLin
- 'Remus' (S) — ELan GAbr MCre MFie NCra NHar
  NHol NNrd NWCA SHya SPop
  SUsu WHil WLin
- 'Renata' (S) — MFie
- 'Rene' — EMNN
- 'Riatty' (d) — MFie
- 'Richard Shaw' (A) — MFie NNrd WLin
- 'Rishworth' (S) — SHya

| | |
|---|---|
| - 'Roberto' (S) | SHya |
| - 'Rock Sand' (S) | EMNN GCrs GNor MFie NHar NNrd |
| - 'Rodeo' (A) | MFie NCra SHya |
| - 'Rolts' (S) | CLyd ELan EMNN GAbr GNor MFie NBir NBro NCra NHar NHol NNrd NOak SHya SPop WHil WLin |
| - 'Rolt's Green Fly' | SSON |
| - 'Rondy' (S) | SHya |
| - 'Ronny Simpson' | NCra |
| - 'Rosalie Edwards' (S) | EMNN MFie NCra NNrd SHya |
| - 'Rosamund' (d) | SHya |
| - 'Rosanna' (S) | Last listed 1997 |
| ¶ - 'Rose Kaye' (A) | GNor |
| - 'Rosebud' (S) | Last listed 1997 |
| - 'Rosemary' (S) | EMNN MCre MFie NNrd |
| - 'Rossiter's Grey' (S) | Last listed 1997 |
| - 'Rowena' (A) | CLyd ECGP EMNN MFie MOne NCra NHar NHol NPri SHya SPop WLin |
| - 'Roxburgh' (A) | EMNN MCre SHya SPop |
| - 'Royal Purple' (S) | Last listed 1997 |
| - 'Royal Velvet' (S) | GAbr NNrd |
| - 'Royalty' (S) | Last listed 1997 |
| - 'Ruby Hyde' (B) | GAbr MFie |
| - 'Rusty Dusty' | GAbr |
| - 'Sailor Boy' (S) | MFie SHya |
| - 'Saint Boswells' (S) | MFie SHya |
| - 'Saint Elmo' (d) | MFie |
| - 'Saint Gerrans'White' (B) | MFie |
| - 'Saint Quentin' (S) | Last listed 1998 |
| - 'Salad' (S) | MFie SHya |
| - 'Sale Green' (A) | SHya |
| - 'Sally' | WHil |
| - 'Salome' (A) | Last listed 1997 |
| - 'Sam Hunter' | NCra |
| - 'Sandhills' (A) | Last listed 1998 |
| - 'Sandmartin' (S) | MFie |
| - 'Sandra' (A) | ELan EMNN GAbr MCre MFie SHya SPop WHil WLin |
| - 'Sandwood Bay' (A) | CLyd EMNN GAbr GNor LRHS MCre MFie NBro NCra NHar NNrd SHya SPop WHil |
| - 'Sarah Lodge' (d) | EMNN GAbr MFie |
| - 'Satchmo' | EMNN |
| - 'Scipio' (S) | SHya |
| - 'Seaton Burn' (S) | Last listed 1998 |
| - 'Serenity' (S) | EMNN GNor MFie SHya |
| - 'Shalford' (d) | MFie NHol SPop WLin |
| - 'Sharman's Cross' (S) | SHya |
| ¶ - 'Sharon Louise' (S) | MCre |
| - 'Sheila' (S) | GAbr MCre MFie NHar NNrd SHya SPop WLin |
| - 'Shere' (S) | EMNN MCre MFie NCra SHya SPop WLin |
| - 'Shergold' (A) | Last listed 1996 |
| - 'Sherwood' | EMNN MFie NHar SHya WHil WLin |
| - 'Shirley Hibberd' (S) | Last listed 1998 |
| - 'Shotley' (A) | EMNN |
| - 'Shrewton' (S) | Last listed 1998 |
| ¶ - 'Sibsey' (d) | SPop |
| - 'Silverway' (S) | MCre SHya |
| - 'Sir Hardy Amies' (S) | SHya |
| - 'Sir John Hall' | NCra |
| - 'Sir Robert Ewbank' (d) | Last listed 1996 |
| ¶ - 'Sirbol' (A) | MCre |
| - 'Sirius' (A) | CLyd GAbr LRHS MCre MFie MOne NCra NHar NHol SHya SPop WHil WLin |
| - 'Slioch' (S) | EMNN GNor MFie NNrd SHya SPop |

| | |
|---|---|
| - 'Snooty Fox' (A) | EMNN MFie NNrd WLin |
| - 'Snooty Fox II' (A) | MCre SHya |
| - 'Snowy Owl' | GNor MFie SHya |
| - 'Soncy Face' | NCra |
| ¶ - 'Sonya' (A) | WLin |
| - 'South Barrow' (d) | EMNN GAbr MCre SUsu WHil |
| - 'Space Age' (S) | Last listed 1997 |
| - 'Splendour' (S) | Last listed 1998 |
| - 'Spring Meadows' (S) | ECGP GAbr MCre MFie MOne NChi NCra NHol NPri NRoo SHya SPop WLin |
| - 'Springtime' | NCra SPop |
| - SS TY 72 (S) | MFie |
| - 'Standish' (d) | GAbr MFie NCra NHol SHya |
| - 'Stant's Blue' (S) | EMNN GNor MFie NBro NHol SHya |
| - 'Star Wars' (S) | SHya |
| - 'Starry' (S) | NHar NHol NNrd WLin |
| - 'Stella' (S) | MFie |
| - 'Stoke Poges' (A) | Last listed 1998 |
| - 'Stoney Cross' (S) | Last listed 1996 |
| - 'Stonnal' (A) | MFie NHar |
| - 'Streamlet' (S) | SHya |
| - 'Stripey' (d) | Last listed 1997 |
| - 'Stubb's Tartan' (S) | NHar WHil |
| - 'Sue' (A) | MFie |
| - 'Sue Douglas' (A) | Last listed 1998 |
| - 'Sugar Plum Fairy' | NNrd |
| - 'Summer Sky' (A) | MCre |
| - 'Sumo' | NCra SPop |
| - 'Sunburst' (S) | GCrs |
| I - 'Sunflower' (S) | MCre MFie NHar NHol WLin |
| - 'Sunsal' (S) | MFie |
| - 'Sunstar' (S) | EMNN MFie |
| - 'Super Para' (S) | EMNN GCrs GNor MFie NNrd SHya |
| - 'Superb' (S) | SHya |
| - 'Susan' (A) | MFie |
| - 'Susannah' (d) | GAbr GNor LRHS MFie MOne NChi NHol NPri SHya SPop WLin |
| - 'Sweet Pastures' (S) | EMNN GNor MFie NCra NHol SHya SPop |
| - 'Swift' (S) | MFie |
| - 'Swinley' (S) | Last listed 1998 |
| - 'Sword' | MCre NNrd SHya |
| - 'Symphony' (A) | SUsu WHil |
| - 'Tall Purple Dusty Miller' (B) | MFie |
| - 'Tally-ho' (A) | SHya |
| - 'Tarantella' (A) | EMNN GNor MFie NCra NNrd SHya WLin |
| - 'Tawny Owl' | NBro |
| ¶ - 'Ted Gibbs' (A) | MCre |
| - 'Ted Roberts' (A) | EMNN MCre MFie NCra SPop WLin |
| - 'Teem' (S) | EMNN MCre MFie NCra SHya WLin |
| - 'Tenby Grey' (S) | MFie WLin |
| - 'The Baron' (S) | GNor MCre MFie MOne NHar WHil WLin |
| - 'The Bishop' (S) | MFie NCra |
| - 'The Bride' (S) | EMNN NCra |
| - 'The Cardinal' (d) | SAsh SUsu |
| - 'The Czar' (A) | SHya |
| - 'The Maverick' (S) | SHya |
| - 'The Raven' (S) | EMNN MFie |
| - 'The Sneeps' | MCre NCra WHil |
| - 'The Snods' (S) | EMNN MFie NCra WHil |
| - 'Thebes' | NCra |
| - 'Thetis' (A) | MCre MFie NCra SHya WHil WLin |
| - 'Thirlmere' (d) | SHya |
| - 'Three Way Stripe' | SHya WHil |

| | |
|---|---|
| - 'Tinkerbell' (S) | MCre MFie SHya WLin |
| - 'Tomato' | WLin |
| - 'Tomboy' (S) | MFie |
| - 'Tomma' | NCra |
| - 'Tosca' (S) | EMNN GCrs GNor MCre NNrd SHya WLin |
| - 'Trojan' (S) | SHya WLin |
| - 'Trouble' (d) | CHad EMNN LPio LRHS MCre MFie MOne NChi NCra NHar SHya SMrm SPop WHil WLin |
| - 'Trudy' (S) | EMNN GAbr GCrs GNor MCre MFie NCra NNrd |
| - 'True Briton' (S) | MFie SHya |
| - 'Trumpet Blue' (S) | MFie |
| - 'Tumbledown' (A) | MFie |
| - 'Tummel' | NCra |
| - 'Tuthmoses' | NCra |
| - 'Two Tone' mauve (d) | WHil |
| - 'Tye Lea' (S) | MFie SHya |
| - 'Typhoon' (A) | MFie WHil |
| - 'Unforgetable' | NCra |
| - 'Upton Belle' (S) | Last listed 1997 |
| - 'V.I. Hinney' | Last listed 1997 |
| - 'Valerie' (A) | MCre MFie NCra NNrd SHya WHil |
| - 'Valerie Clare' | NCra |
| - 'Vee Too' (A) | MFie SHya SPop |
| - 'Velvet Moon' | NCra |
| - 'Venetian' | NCra |
| - 'Vera' (A) | MFie |
| - 'Verdi' (A) | EMNN MFie NCra SHya |
| - 'Victoria' (S) | SHya |
| - 'Victoria de Wemyss' (A) | MCre MFie WHil |
| - 'Vulcan' (A) | MFie NCra SHya SPop |
| - 'Waincliffe Fancy' (S) | Last listed 1997 |
| - 'Waincliffe Red' (S) | MFie |
| - 'Walhampton' (S) | EMNN MFie SHya |
| - 'Walton' (A) | EBrP EBre LBre MCre MFie SBre SHya |
| - 'Walton Heath' (d) | EMNN GAbr MCre MFie SHya SPop WHil WLin |
| - 'Warwick' (S) | SHya |
| - 'Watt's Purple' (d) | Last listed 1997 |
| - 'Wedding Day' (S) | MFie |
| - 'Wendy' | SIng WLin |
| - 'White Ensign' (S) | EMNN GAbr GNor MFie NNrd NOak SHya SPop WLin |
| - 'White Water' | NCra |
| - 'White Wings' (S) | EMNN GNor MFie NCra NNrd SHya WLin |
| - 'Wide Awake' (A) | MFie |
| - 'Wincha' (S) | GCrs MFie SHya |
| - 'Windways Mystery' (B) | MFie |
| - 'Winifrid' (A) | CLyd EMNN LRHS MCre MFie NCra NHar NHol SHya SPop WHil SHya |
| - 'Woodmill' (A) | SHya |
| - 'Woodstock' (S) | Last listed 1997 |
| - 'Wor Jackie' (S) | EMNN MFie NHar |
| - 'Wycliffe Midnight' | GAbr |
| - 'Y.I. Hinney' (A) | EMNN MFie |
| - 'Yelverton' (S) | Last listed 1997 |
| - 'Yorkshire Grey' (S) | MFie NNrd SHya |
| - 'Zambia' (d) | CLyd MFie SHya SUsu WHil WLin |
| *auriculata* (11) | Last listed 1996 |
| 'Barbara Midwinter' (6x30) | CMea NDov |
| Barnhaven Blues Group (Prim)(30) ♀ | GAbr |
| Barnhaven doubles (dPoly)(30) | CSWP |
| Barnhaven Gold-laced Group | See *P.* Gold-laced Group Barnhaven |
| Barnhaven Reds | See *P.* Tartan Reds Group |
| Barnhaven Traditional Group | CSWP |

| | |
|---|---|
| 'Beamish Foam' (Poly)(30) | CVer MDHE NDov |
| 'Beatrice Wooster' (2) | CLyd CNic EHyt EPot MBro MFie NHar NHed NHol NNrd NWCA WAbe |
| 'Beeches' Pink' | GAbr |
| *beesiana* (4) | CInt CMHG CRow EAst EBee EHon ELan EWTr GAbr GCHN GFle LPBA LSyl MBNS MBri MFie MRav MSta MSte NHar NHol NOak SMrm SPer WFar WHil WLin WPer WPyg WWal |
| 'Belinda Red Shades' (Belinda Series) ♀ | Last listed 1995 |
| 'Bellamy's Pride' | CLyd |
| *bellidifolia* (17) | CPla |
| § - subsp. *byacinthina* (17) | Last listed 1998 |
| *beluensis* | See *P.* x *pubescens* 'Freedom' |
| Bergfrühling Julianas Group (Prim)(30) | MFie |
| § x *berninae* 'Windrush' (2) | CLyd EHyt NHar NNrd WAbe |
| 'Betty Green' (Prim)(30) | Last listed 1998 |
| 'Bewerley White' | See *P.* x *pubescens* 'Bewerley White' |
| *bhutanica* | See *P. whitei* 'Sherriff's Variety' |
| x *biflora* (2) | Last listed 1998 |
| 'Big Red Giant' (dPrim)(30) | CBlo EBee LFis MBNS MOne NHar |
| *bileckii* | See *P.* x *forsteri* 'Bileckii' |
| 'Blue Riband' (Prim)(30) | CGle LSur MRav WAbe WFar |
| 'Blue Sapphire' (dPrim)(30) | CBlo GAbr MOne NChi NRoo SLod SUsu |
| Blue Striped Victorians Group (Poly)(30) | GAbr |
| 'Blutenkissen' (Prim)(30) | GAbr GMaP LSur |
| 'Bon Accord Purple' (dPoly)(30) | CGle WFar WRus |
| 'Bonfire' (4) | GDra GGar |
| ¶ 'Bootheosa' (21) | NOla |
| *boothii* (21) | Last listed 1996 |
| - *alba* (21) | GGGa |
| - subsp. *autumnalis* (21) | WAbe |
| - subsp. *repens* (21) | MNrw |
| 'Boothman's Ruby' | See *P.* x *pubescens* 'Boothman's Variety' |
| *boveana* (12) | MFie SBla |
| § *bracteosa* (21) | GCrs ITim NHar WAbe |
| 'Brimstone' (Poly)(30) | CGle |
| 'Broadwell Pink' (2) | EHyt |
| 'Broadwell Ruby' (2) | Last listed 1998 |
| ¶ 'Bronwyn' (Prim)(30) | WCot |
| 'Broxbourne' | CLyd NHar |
| 'Buckland Wine' (Prim)(30) | CVer LSur |
| x *bulleesiana* (4) | CM&M CMGP GFle LFis NBro NHol NPri SMrm SRms SWat WFar WHil WPer WRha |
| - Asthore hybrids (4) | Last listed 1996 |
| - Moerheim hybrids (4) | LIck |
| *bulleyana* (4) ♀ | More than 30 suppliers |
| - ACE 2478 (4) | Last listed 1996 |
| - ACE 2484 (4) | EPot WAbe |
| *burmanica* (4) | CInt CPla EBee GAbr GBuc GDra GFle GGar MBal MSta NCra NDea NHar NPri SRms WCru |
| 'Butterscotch' (Prim)(30) | CGle CSWP |
| 'Caerulea Plena' (dPrim)(30) | GCal |
| *calderiana* (21) | GDra NHar WAbe |
| - subsp. *strumosa* BC 9347 (21) | Last listed 1998 |
| Candelabra hybrids (4) | CBre CBro EMNN EPot NCra WRos |
| Candy Pinks Group (Prim)(30) | GAbr |

*capitata* (5) — CGle CInt CPla CSpe GDra GFle GTou LSyl MBal MBri NCra NHar WAbe WBea WCla WFar WPer

- subsp. *crispata* AGS/ES 407 (5) — Last listed 1998

- dark forms (5) — MFie

¶ - ex CC 2368 (5) — MChR

- KEKE 274 (5) — Last listed 1998

- KEKE 497 (5) — Last listed 1996

- subsp. *mooreana* (5) — CFir CHan CPea EWTr GCan GFle LPBA MCli MMal NLak WCla WHil

- subsp. *sphaerocephala* (5) — NWCA

¶ - - ACE 2092 (5) — EPot

¶ *capitellata* (11) — WAbe

'Captain Blood' (dPrim)(30) — CBos ECGN GAbr NSti SUsu WRha

'Carmen' (Prim)(30) — CLyd

Carnation Victorians Group (Poly)(30) — CSWP GAbr MFie

*carniolica* (2) — Last listed 1996

'Casquet' — CSWP

*cernua* (17) — GCan GDra GFle MFie NHar WAbe WCru WLin

'Charlen' (dPrim)(30) — NHar

Chartreuse Group (Poly)(30) — CGle CSWP GAbr MFie NDov WRha

'Cherry' (Prim)(30) — CVer WHil

§ *chionantha* (18) ♀ — CBot CGle CMHG CPla EAst EWTr GDra GFle GGGa GMaP GTou LBee LSyl MBal MBri MFie MNrw NChi NCra NDea NFor NHar NHed NRoo SLon SPer WFar WGwG WHil WLin

- subsp. *brevicaula* ACE 1689 (18) — Last listed 1997

§ - subsp. *melanops* (18) — CGle CPla GCan GFle GMaP NHar

§ - subsp. *sinoplantaginea* (18) — CPla GAbr WRha

§ - subsp. *sinopurpurea* (18) — CGle CPla EBee EWes GAbr GDra GFle GGGa GTou LSyl MBal MLLN NCra SPer WAbe WFar WLin WPer WWhi

- - ACE 1421 (18) — EPot

'Chocolate Soldier' (dPrim)(30) — GGar MBal

*chungensis* (4) — CGle GFle GGar GLch GTou MBri MLLN NHar SRms SUsu WAbe

§ - x *pulverulenta* (4) — EBrP EBre LBre NLar NPri SBre SMrm WAbe WElm WFar WHil

x *chunglenta* — See *P. chungensis* x *pulverulenta*

§ 'Clarence Elliott' (2) — CGra CLyd EHyt NHar WLin

*clarkei* (11) — CLyd GCrs GFle GGGa GTou NWCA

'Cluny' — Last listed 1996

*clusiana* (2) — GDra MBal NHol NSla

- 'Murray-Lyon' (2) — WLin

*cockburniana* (4) — CInt CRow GAbr GDra GFle GGGa GGar GMac GTou MBal MBri MFie NCra NHar NHed NWCA SMrm SRms WAbe

*concholoba* (17) — CPla GAbr GCan GFle GGGa GGar GTou MFie NHar WAbe

'Corporal Baxter' (dPrim)(30) — MBNS MBri MOne NChi NDov SLod SMrm SUsu WLin WRha

*cortusoides* (7) — CPla GFle MNrw NCra SRms WHil WOve

Cottage Mixed (Prim)(30) — Last listed 1996

Cowichan (Poly)(30) — CInt GAbr NCra NSti

Cowichan Amethyst Group (Poly)(30) — CSWP GAbr

Cowichan Blue Group (Poly)(30) — CMil CSWP EWoo GAbr

Cowichan Garnet Group (Poly)(30) — CSWP EWoo GAbr GCan MFie NDov

Cowichan Venetian Group (Poly)(30) — CSWP GAbr GCan NDov

Cowichan Yellow Group (Poly)(30) — GAbr NDov NWoo WCot

'Craven Gem' (Poly)(30) — GAbr LSur NRoo

Crescendo Series (Poly)(30) — GAbr

'Crimson Cushion' — Last listed 1998

'Crimson Queen' (Prim)(30) — GAbr LSur

'Crimson Velvet' (2) — EMNN GAbr GNor MBro NHol NNrd SRms WLin

*crispa* — See *P. glomerata*

x *crucis* (2) — Last listed 1997

* *cuneata* — GTou

*cuneifolia* (8) — Last listed 1998

* - *alba* (8) — Last listed 1998

'Dales Red' — Last listed 1996

*daonensis* (2) — Last listed 1998

*darialica* (11) — CGle CPla ELan NChi NCra

'David Green' (Prim)(30) — CVer SIng

'David Valentine' — GAbr LSur

'Dawn Ansell' (dPrim)(30) — CElw CGle CRow CSam CSpe EPri GGar LFis LHop MBNS MBal MBri MCAu MCLN MOne MRav NDov NEgg NHar NHol NRoo NSti SLod SPer SSvw SUsu WCot WHer WHil WPnn

Daybreak Group (Poly)(30) — CSWP MFie

*deflexa* (17) — GCrs GFle GGGa LSyl WLin

¶ - ACE 2283 (17) — EHyt EPot

*denticulata* (9) ♀ — More than 30 suppliers

- var. *alba* (9) — CGle EBrP EBre ECha EMNN EPot ERav GAbr GChr GTou LBre LHop MBal MBri MFie MRav MWat NCra NHar NHed NHol NOrc NRoo SBre SCob WHen WPer

- blue (9) — NLar

- 'Bressingham Beauty' (9) — EBrP EBre LBre SBre

- var. *cachemiriana* hort. (9) — EPfP WCla

¶ - CC 2660 (9) — MChR

- 'Glenroy Crimson' (9) — CLAP CRDP MBal SRms SVil

- 'Inshriach Carmine' (9) — Last listed 1998

¶ - 'Karryann' (9/v) — WCot

- lilac (9) — EHon GTou MFie NPri

- purple (9) — GAbr IBlr

- red (9) — CRow EMNN EPar GGar NCut NOrc NPri

- 'Robinson's Red' (9) — EPot GBuc

- 'Ronsdorf' (9) — Last listed 1998

- rose (9) — NCut NHar

- 'Rubinball' (9) — EBrP EBre EPfP GAri LBre NHol NRoo SBre

- ruby (9) — CInt EBee EHon GAbr GTou LNor MBri MCLN MFie NBro NOak SMrm SRms WHen WHil WPer WPyg

- 'Snowball' (9) — MCLN MFir NOak WHen WPyg

*deorum* (2) — CGra WLin

x *deschmannii* — See *P. x vochinensis*

'Desert Sunset' (Poly)(30) — CSWP GAbr MFie

*deuteronana alba* (21) — Last listed 1997

'Devon Cream' (Prim)(30) — ECha GBuc WFar

'Dianne' — See *P. x forsteri* 'Dianne'

'Doctor Lemon's White' — Last listed 1996

'Doctor Mary' (Prim)(30) — GAbr

'Dora' — Last listed 1998

'Dorothy' (Poly)(30) — LSur MRav

'Double Lilac' — See *P. vulgaris* 'Lilacina Plena'

*drummondiana* (21) — Last listed 1998

| | |
|---|---|
| 'Duchess of York' | CLAP CLTr WBro |
| 'Duckyls Red' (Prim)(30) | GBuc |
| 'Dusky Lady' | WFar |
| 'Early Irish Yellow' (Prim)(30) | Last listed 1998 |
| 'Easter Bonnet' (dPrim)(30) | CBlo CMil CSam EPot MCLN MOne NDov NHol NRoo |
| *edelbergii* (12) | MFie |
| *edgeworthii* | See *P. nana* |
| *elatior* (30) ♀ | CGle CKin CNic CPla CRow CSev EMou GFle GLil LFox LSyl MHar MNrw MSal NChi NCra NMen NOrc NRoo NSti SPer SRms SSpi SUsu WCla WFar |
| - hose in hose (30) | GAbr |
| ¶ - hybrids (30) | SIng |
| - subsp. *intricata* (30) | Last listed 1998 |
| - JCA 785.150 (30) | Last listed 1996 |
| * - 'Katy McSporran' (30) | SPer |
| - subsp. *leucophylla* (30) | EBee ECho |
| § - subsp. *meyeri* (30) | Last listed 1997 |
| - subsp. *pallasii* (30) | Last listed 1997 |
| - - JCA 786.500 (30) | Last listed 1996 |
| *elliptica* (11) | Last listed 1997 |
| *ellisiae* (21) | MFie NMen NSla |
| 'Erin's Gem' (Poly)(30) | CGle |
| § *erythra* (26) | Last listed 1998 |
| 'Ethel Barker' (2) | CLyd CNic EPot ITim LFox MBro NHar NHed NHol NNrd SIng WAbe |
| 'Ethel M. Dell' (dPrim)(30) | Last listed 1997 |
| 'Eugénie' (dPrim)(30) | CGle CSpe ECle MOne NChi NDov NHar NHol WCot WLRN WWeb |
| ¶ 'Fairy Rose' KRW 180/48 (2) | EPot WAbe |
| *farinosa* (11) | CLyd CPla GFle MBal MBri MSal NCra NHar NMen NRya WCla WPer |
| - JCA 786.500 (11) | Last listed 1998 |
| *fasciculata* (11) | EDAr EHyt NSla |
| - CLD 345 (11) | IMGH NHar WAbe |
| 'Fife Yellow' (dPoly)(30) | GBuc |
| 'Fire Dance' (Poly)(30) | MFie |
| Firefly Group (Poly)(30) | GAbr LFox NDov |
| *firmipes* (26) | EBee GFle NTow WLRN |
| § *flaccida* (28) ♀ | GDra GFle GGGa MBal NCra NHar WAbe |
| x *flagellicaulis* | See *P.* x *polyantha* |
| Flamingo Group (Poly)(30) | CSWP GAbr MFie |
| § x *floerkeana* (2) | NHol WAbe |
| - f. *biflora alba* (2) | SBla |
| *florida* (29) | GGGa |
| *florindae* (26) ♀ | More than 30 suppliers |
| ¶ - bronze (26) | MFie |
| - hybrids (26) | CVer GAbr LFox MFie MSCN WHil WLin |
| - orange (26) | CSam GMac IBlr LSyl MNrw NChi WCru WFar |
| - 'Ray's Ruby' (26) | GBuc MCLN MNrw NBir WCot WOve WWhi |
| - red (26) | EBee GAbr GGGa LSyl MFie MSta SMrm WFar WPrP |
| Footlight Parade Group (Prim)(30) | CSWP NDov |
| *forrestii* (3) | GGGa GMaP MFie NHar WAbe |
| - ACE 1427* (3) | Last listed 1996 |
| - C&Cu 9431 (3) | Last listed 1998 |
| - CLD 1242 (3) | Last listed 1996 |
| - CLD 738 (3) | Last listed 1996 |
| § x *forsteri* (2) | EMNN NHol WAbe |
| § - 'Bileckii' (2) | EPar EPot GCrs LBee MBal MBro NBro NHar NWCA SRms SSmi WAbe |
| § - 'Dianne' (2) | EHyt EPot GAbr MBro NBro NHar NHol NNrd WAbe WGwG |
| ¶ - 'Dianne' hybrids (2) | MFie |
| 'Freckles' (dPrim)(30) | EBee ECle GGar MOne NHar NHol SPer WHil |
| 'Freedom' | See *P.* x *pubescens* 'Freedom' |
| *frondosa* ♀ | CGle CInt CLyd CPla CSam GCrs GFle LFox LHop MBal MBri MBro MFie NChi NCra NHar NMen NWCA SMrm WAbe WHoo |
| 'Frühlingszauber' (Prim)(30) | Last listed 1997 |
| Fuchsia Victorians Group (Poly)(30) | CSWP MFie |
| Galligaskins Group (Poly)(30) | Last listed 1997 |
| 'Garnet' (*allionii* hybrid) (2) | MFie |
| 'Garryard Guinevere' | See *P.* 'Guinevere' |
| 'Gartenmeister Bartens' (Prim)(30) | Last listed 1997 |
| *gaubana* (12) | MFie |
| *gemmifera* (11) | GFle GGGa NHar |
| - ACE 1375 (11) | Last listed 1998 |
| - ACE 1427 (11) | NHar NWCA WAbe |
| - ACE 1541 (11) | IDac |
| - var. *zambalensis* (11) | WAbe |
| *geraniifolia* (7) | NRoo |
| ¶ - CC 2295 (7) | MChR |
| § 'Gigha' (Prim)(30) | CSpe NDov |
| * *glauca* ML form | Last listed 1996 |
| *glaucescens* (2) | CLyd GFle MBro MFie NHar NSla SIng |
| - subsp. *calycina* | See *P. glaucescens* subsp. *glaucescens* |
| § - subsp. *glaucescens* (2) | NHol |
| - JCA 786.900 (2) | Last listed 1998 |
| 'Glebe Grey' (Prim)(30) | CGle |
| § *glomerata* (5) | CSWP GBuc GCrs GGGa WAbe |
| 'Gloria' (Prim)(30) | LSur |
| 'Gloriosa' (Prim)(30) | LSur |
| 'Glowing Embers' (4) | CGle EBee ELan GFle MFie NBir |
| *glutinosa* Allioni | See *P. allionii* |
| - Lapeyrouse (2) | Last listed 1998 |
| Gold-laced Group (Poly)(30) | CBre CGle CM&M CPla CRDP CSWP EBee ELan EWoo GAbr GMac LFox MBri MBro NChi NCra NHar NWCA SUsu WFar WHer WHil WLin |
| § - Barnhaven | CLAP GAbr LPio MFie |
| - Beeches strain (Poly)(30) ♀ | LSur |
| 'Gordon' | Last listed 1997 |
| *gracilipes* (21) | CGle GFle GGGa GGar MOne NHar SRms WAbe |
| - early form (21) | NHar WAbe |
| - L&S 1 (21) | NHar WAbe |
| - L&S 1166 (21) | NHar |
| - L&S form (21) | Last listed 1996 |
| - late form (21) | NHar WAbe |
| - 'Major' | See *P. bracteosa* |
| - 'Masterton' (21) | Last listed 1997 |
| - 'Minor' | See *P. petiolaris* |
| - 'Winter Jewel' (21) | Last listed 1998 |
| 'Graham' | Last listed 1997 |
| Grand Canyon Group (Poly)(30) | MFie |
| ¶ 'Granny Graham' (Prim)(30) | NOla |
| *griffithii* (21) | GFle GGGa |
| 'Groeneken's Glory' (Prim)(30) | CGle CInt CVer ELan GAbr LSur MBri MRav NBro NCra NFla SIng WFar |
| § 'Guinevere' (Poly)(30) ♀ | More than 30 suppliers |
| 'Hall Barn Blue' | GAbr LSur |

§ *balleri* (11) — CPea CPla GCHN GCan GFle GTou MBal MFie NCra NHar NMen NWCA WAbe WCla
- 'Longiflora' — See *P. balleri*
Harbinger Group (Prim)(30) — CGle NDov
'Harbour Lights' — CSWP MFie
Harlow Carr hybrids (4) — GFle MLLN NDea NHed NRoo WPen
Harvest Yellows Group (Poly)(30) — MFie NDov
x *beeri* (2) — NHol
'Helge' (Prim)(30) — GAbr LSur
*belodoxa* — See *P. prolifera*
§ 'Hemswell Blush' (2) — GNor NHol WLin
§ 'Hemswell Ember' (2) — EHyt EMNN MFie NHar NHed
*beucherifolia* (7) — CPla GCan LFox LSyl MSCN
*birsuta* (2) — CNic GCrs GTou MFie
¶ - from Switzerland (2) — MFie
- 'Lismore Snow' (2) — EHyt NHar
- *nivea* (2) — Last listed 1996
Hose in Hose (Poly)(30) — CGle CSWP MNrw NCra NPri NRoo
'Husky' ♀ —
'Hyacinthia' (2) — CLyd EMNN EPot WAbe
*byacinthina* — See *P. bellidifolia* subsp. *hyacinthina*
*ianthina* — See *P. prolifera*
Indian Reds Group (Poly)(30) — MFie
'Ingram's Blue' (Prim)(30) — CRos WPGP
Inshriach hybrids (4) — CMHG GAbr GCan GDra LHop MBri MFie MSCN MSte NLar SPer WFar WWal
*integrifolia* (2) — GCrs IMGH WAbe WShe
- JCA 787.502 (2) — Last listed 1996
x *intermedia* (2) — Last listed 1998
§ 'Inverewe' (4) ♀ — GAbr GAri GCal GGar NHar NRoo
§ *involucrata* (11) — GCan GFle GGGa NBro NHar NWCA SIng SWat WAbe WHil
* - *alba* CC 1422 (11) — EHyt
- CC 1422 (11) — MRPP
- CC 1812 (11) — MRPP
¶ - CD&R 2409 (11) — WAbe
§ - subsp. *yargongensis* (11) — CGle CInt CLyd CMea CPla EBee EWes GAbr GCHN GCrs GFle GGar GTou MBal MBri MFie MRPP NBro NCra NHar NWCA SBod SRms SWat WAbe WFar WPat
*ioessa* (26) — CPla EWes GGGa MBal MBri NWCA WAbe
- HWJCM 300 (26) — WCru
- hybrids (26) — Last listed 1997
'Iris Mainwaring' (Prim)(30) — CVer EPot GAbr GMaP LSur MDHE NCra NDov
*irregularis* — GCrs GGGa
Jack in the Green Group (Poly)(30) — CGle CMGP CNic CSWP LSur MNrw MRav MWgw NChi NCot NCra WBor WHer WRha WRus
Jackanapes Group (Poly)(30) — Last listed 1998
Jackanapes on Horseback Group (Poly)(30) — Last listed 1997
'Jackaroo' (4) — GFle GGar
'Jackie Richards' (2) — Last listed 1998
*japonica* (4) ♀ — CGle CMHG CRow CSam ECha GFle GTou LPBA MFir NBro NChi NCra NFor NHar NHol NLon NRoo SWat WCla WCru WFar WPer
- 'Alba' (4) — GBin GFle MCAu NPri WAbe WHil WShe
- 'Apple Blossom' (4) — EBee SCob
* - 'Atropurpurea' (4) — SIng

* - 'Carminea' — EWTr LWoo NBro WHil
- 'Fromfield Pink' (4) — Last listed 1998
- 'Fuji' (4) — CSWP CSam GCan GDra GFle MBal MBri MSta NBro
¶ - 'Fuji' hybrids (4) — NLar
- 'Miller's Crimson' (4) — More than 30 suppliers
- 'Oriental Sunrise' (4) — CMil
- 'Postford White' (4) — CBot CGle CPla CRow CSWP CTrw EBrP EBre EHon ELan GMac LBre LPBA LSyl MBri MCLN NCra NDea NSti SBre SCob SPer WCla WFar WGwG WOve WPer WRus WWat WWhi
- red shades (4) — WAbe
- 'Valley Red' (4) — GBin GBuc GFle GMac LSyl NRoo
¶ *jesoana* (7) — EBee GFle
- B&SWJ 618 (7) — WCru
Jewel Group — LSur
'Jill' — CVer LSur
'Joan Hughes' (*allionii* hybrid) (2) — CLyd NHar WAbe
'Johanna' (11) — CGle GFle GGar LSyl NBro NHar NLak NWCA
¶ 'John Fielding' (6x30) — CBos
'Jo-Jo' (2) — CLyd
*juliae* (30) — CGle CPla CRDP GFle LSur MHlr NMen WCot WEas
- white (30) — CGle
x *juribella* (2) — Last listed 1998
'Kate Haywood' — CLyd
'Ken Dearman' (dPrim)(30) — EBee EPot MBNS MBal MCLN MHlr MOne MRav NDov NEgg NHol NSti SIng SMrm
*kewensis* (12) ♀ — EBee MFie NWCA WAbe
'Kinlough Beauty' (Poly)(30) — CVer EPar GAbr LFox LSur NCra NRoo NSti NWCA NWes WEas WLin
*kisoana* (7) — CPla MTho WCru
- *alba* (7) — CLAP CPla GGGa MTho
'Lady Greer' (Poly)(30) ♀ — CGle CInt CPla ECGN ELan GAbr ITim LFox LSur MRav NBir NChi NCra NHar NMen NRoo NRya NSti NWCA SIng SLod SMac SSmi WCom WCot WEas WWat
'Lambrook Lilac' (Poly)(30) — CVer
§ *latifolia* (2) — NCra WLRN
- cream (2) — Last listed 1998
*latisecta* (7) — GGGa
§ *laurentiana* (11) — GFle NWCA
'Lea Gardens' (*allionii* hybrid) (2) — MFie
'Lee Myers' (*allionii* hybrid) (2) — CLyd GNor MFie NHar NHed NNrd
'Lilac Fairy' — NHar
'Lilac Time' — SIng
'Lilian Harvey' (dPrim)(30) — CElw CGle EBee MOne MRav NBir NDov NHol SPer
Limelight Group (Poly)(30) — EWoo GAbr MFie
'Lingwood Beauty' (Prim)(30) — CVer GAbr LSur
'Linnet' (21) — ITim
'Lismore' (2) — EHyt NHol
'Lismore Pink Ice' — Last listed 1998
'Lismore Yellow' (2) — EPot GTou NHar NNrd SBla SIng WAbe
Lissadel hybrids (4) — GMac
'Little Egypt' (Poly)(30) — EWoo
* 'Little Poppet' — GAbr
*littoniana* — See *P. vialii*
§ x *loiseleurii* (2) — EBrP EBre LBre MBro SBre
*longiflora* — See *P. balleri*
'Lopen Red' (Poly)(30) — Last listed 1996
*luteola* (11) — GFle MFie MNrw NHol NPri SRms WFar WHil WWoo

***macrophylla*** (18)  GFle GTou MBal
– H 78 (18)  Last listed 1998
***magellanica*** (11)  WAbe
***malacoides*** (3)  MBri
***marginata*** (2) ♀  EMNN EPot GAbr GCrs GDra
GFle LFox LHop MBro MRPP
NCra NHar NHed NHol SIng SSmi
WAbe WFar
– *alba* (2)  EPot EWes MBro NBro NCra NHar
NHed NHol NNrd SIng SSmi
– 'Amethyst' (2)  EPot
– 'Arthur Branch' (2)  EPot
– 'Baldock's Mauve' (2)  Last listed 1997
– 'Barbara Clough' (2)  CLyd MFie SBla WAbe
– 'Beamish' (2) ♀  CLyd EPot NBro NRya WCom
– 'Beatrice Lascaris' (2)  EPot ITim MBro MFie NHar NHol
SIng WAbe
– 'Beverley Reid' (2)  Last listed 1998
– 'Caerulea' (2)  CLyd EPot WAbe
– 'Clear's Variety' (2)  EMNN EPot NHar NNrd
– 'Correvon's Variety' (2)  CLyd NCra WAbe
– cut-leaved (2)  NHol
– 'Doctor Jenkins' (2)  NHar NHol
– 'Drake's Form' (2)  EPot ITim NHol
¶ – dwarf form (2)  EHyt MFie
– 'Earl L. Bolton' (2)  EPot NHol NNrd WAbe
– 'Elizabeth Fry' (2)  CLyd LFox MBro NNrd
– 'F.W. Millard' (2)  MBro NHar
– 'Grandiflora' (2)  MBro NHar NHol NNrd SIng
– 'Highland Twilight' (2)  CNic CPBP NNrd
¶ – 'Holden Clough'  WCom
– 'Holden Variety' (2)  EHyt EMNN MBal MBro NHar
NHed NHol NNrd WAbe
– 'Hurstwood' (2)  Last listed 1996
– 'Hyacinthia'  See *P.* 'Hyacinthia'
– 'Ivy Agee' (2)  CLyd EPot
– 'Janet' (2)  CLyd EHyt EMNN EPot WCom
– 'Jenkins Variety' (2)  CLyd EPot SIng
– 'Kesselring's Variety' (2)  CLyd EHyt ELan EPot GNor MBro
MRPP NHar NHed NNrd SIng
SSmi WAbe WWin
¶ – 'Laciniata'  WCom
* – 'Lilac' (2)  EHyt LFox NHar NNrd
– 'Lilac Domino'  Last listed 1998
¶ – lilac seedling  MFie
– 'Linda Pope' (2) ♀  CLyd CPBP EMNN EPot ITim
NCra NHar NHol SUsu WAbe
– maritime form (2)  NNrd
– 'Messingham' (2)  EPot
– 'Millard's Variety' (2)  CLyd
– 'Mrs Carter Walmsley' (2)  Last listed 1997
– 'Nancy Lucy' (2)  WAbe
– 'Napoleon' (2)  ITim NHar NHol NNrd
– 'Prichard's Variety' (2) ♀  CLyd ELan EMNN EPot ITim LBee
LFox MBro MFie NCra NHar
NHed NRya SSmi WAbe WCla
WEas
– 'Rheniana' (2)  EPot
– 'Rosea' (2)  EPot NHol SIng
– 'Rubra'  SIng
– 'Sheila Denby' (2)  EMNN NNrd
– small flowered form (2)  Last listed 1997
– 'Snowhite' (2)  WAbe
– 'Violet Form' (2)  EMNN MBro NHar
– 'Waithman's Variety' (2)  EPot GTou
¶ – wild collected  MFie
'Maria Talbot' (*allionii* hybrid) (2)  NNrd
'Marianne Davey' (dPrim)(30)  CGle EPri MRav NMGW

'Marie Crousse' (dPrim)(30)  CGle EBee EHic GAbr LHop LRHS
MBNS MBal MBro MFie MOne
MRav MWgw NDov NHar NHol
SHya SMrm SPer SSvw SUsu WHil
WLin WRha
Marine Blues Group (Poly)(30)  CSWP GAbr MFie
'Mars' (*allionii* hybrid) (2)  EPot GNor MBro NHar NHed
NHol NNrd WLin
'Marven' (2)  CLyd EPot MBro NCra NHol NNrd
NWoo
'Mary Anne'  GAbr LSur
'Mauve Jack in the Green'  LSur
'Mauve Queen' (Prim)(30)  LSur
Mauve Victorians Group  CSWP MFie
'Mauvekissen'  Last listed 1997
'McWatt's Claret' (Poly)(30)  CVer GAbr LSur NCra
'McWatt's Cream' (Poly)(30)  CSWP CVer GAbr GFle GGar
LHop LSur NBro NChi NCra NHol
NMen WLin
***megaseifolia*** (6)  Last listed 1997
***melanops***  See *P. chionantha* subsp.
*melanops*
x ***meridiana*** (2)  EBrP EBre EHyt EPot LBre MFie
NHar SBre WLin
§ – 'Miniera' (2)  CLyd CPBP SBla
'Mexico'  MFie
Midnight Group  CSWP MFie
♦ 'Miniera'  See *P. x meridiana* 'Miniera'
***minima*** (2)  CGra CLyd GFle GTou IMGH MFie
NBro NHar NWCA WAbe
– var. *alba* (2)  CMea GCrs GGGa NSla
– x *glutinosa* (2)  See *P. x floerkeana*
– x *hirsuta* (2)  See *P. x forsteri*
– JCA 788.900 (2)  Last listed 1996
– x *villosa* (2)  See *P. x truncata*
– x *wulfeniana* (2)  See *P. x vochinensis*
'Miss Indigo' (dPrim)(30)  CGle CSam LFis MBNS MBri
MCAu MCLN MOne MRav NDov
NEgg NHar NHol NRoo NSti SIng
SLod SMrm SPer SRPl WCot WEas
WHil WPnn WWol
'Miss Luck'  CVer
***mistassinica alba*** (11)  Last listed 1997
– var. *macropoda*  See *P. laurentiana*
¶ ***miyabeana*** (4)  GCrs GFle
– B&SWJ 3407 (4)  WCru
¶ ***modesta*** (11)  GFle SIng
– *alba* (11)  GFle SUsu
– var. *faurieae* (11)  MFie
– 'Flore Pleno' (d)  CPBP
– var. *samanimontana* (11)  Last listed 1998
***mollis*** (7)  Last listed 1997
'Morton'  Last listed 1998
'Moulin Rouge' (Prim)(30)  Last listed 1996
¶ ***moupinensis*** (21)  EHyt WAbe
¶ – C&H 7038 (21)  GGGa
* 'Mrs Eagland'  Last listed 1998
'Mrs McGillivray' (Prim)(30)  GAbr LSur
Munstead Strain (Poly)(30)  LSur
x ***murettiana*** (2)  WAbe
***muscarioides*** (17)  CGle CPla GAbr GCan GFle GTou
MFie NHar WAbe
Muted Victorians Group (Poly)(30)  CSWP MFie NDov
§ ***nana*** (21)  Last listed 1996
***nepalensis***  See *P. tanneri* subsp. *nepalensis*
¶ 'Netta Dennis'  GCrs
New Pinks Group (Poly)(30)  CSWP GAbr MFie NDov
'Nightingale'  WAbe
***nivalis*** Pallas  See *P. chionantha*
***nutans*** Delavay  See *P. flaccida*

§ – Georgi (25) — Last listed 1998
*obconica* (19) — MBri
'Old Port' (Poly)(30) — GBin MBro WPat
Old Rose Victorians Group (Poly)(30) — CSWP MFie
'Olive Wyatt' (dPrim)(30) — EPri
'Oriental Sunrise' (4) — MBri MFie NDov
Osiered Amber Group (Prim)(30) — CSWP GAbr NDov
'Our Pat' (dPoly)(30) — IBlr WRus
Pagoda hybrids (4) — MBri
*palinuri* (2) — MFie SIng
*palmata* (7) — GFle GGGa NHar WAbe
Pantaloons Group (Poly)(30) — Last listed 1997
'Paris '90' (Poly)(30) — CSWP EWoo GAbr MFie NDov
*parryi* (20) — GCrs MLLN NCra NHar NWCA WFar WHil
'Peardrop' (2) — CGra GAbr NHol WLin
*pedemontana* (2) — MSte NHar NHol NWCA
– 'Alba' (2) — EHyt
'Perle von Bottrop' (Prim)(30) — CLTr GAbr
'Peter Klein' (11) — CNic EPot GAbr GDra GFle ITim MBal NHar WPyg WTin
§ *petiolaris* (21) — EHyt EPar GCHN GCrs GFle GGGa GNor ITim MDun MOne NCra NHar WAbe
– LS&H 19856 — See *P.* 'Redpoll'
'Petticoat' — MOne NHol
§ 'Pink Aire' (2) — EHyt ITim MFie
'Pink Fairy' — EHyt
'Pink Gem' (dPrim)(30) — NWes
'Pink Ice' (*allionii* hybrid) (2) — CGra CLyd CPBP EHyt EPot MDHE MFie NHol NMen NNrd WLin
'Pink Profusion' (Prim)(30) — Last listed 1998
*pinnatifida* (17) — GGGa
*poissonii* (4) — CBot CGle CHar CMHG CPla GAbr GCan GFle GGar GMac IBlr LPBA MBal MFie MSCN WAbe
¶ – ACE 1946 (4) — WCot WCru
¶ – ACE 2407 (4) — EPot WCot
– CLD 1404 (4) — Last listed 1996
– CLD 193 (4) — LSyl
– CLD 485 (4) — Last listed 1996
Polyanthus (30) — NCra WFar
*polyneura* (7) — CBot CNic CPla ECha GFle GMac LSyl MBal MFie MNes MNrw NDea NWCA SRms
– ACE 1429 (7) — EPot
'Port Wine' — GAbr
*praenitens* — See *P. sinensis*
*prenantha* (4) — GCrs GGGa WAbe
'Prince Silverwings' (dPoly)(30) — WEas
§ *prolifera* (4) ♀ — CMHG CTbh CTrw EBee ECha EHon GFle GGGa GGar GMaP GMac LPBA LSyl MFir MLLN MNrw MRav NLak SLon SPer SRms SSpi SWat WAbe WGwy WHil WPer WWat
§ × *pubescens* (2) ♀ — CInt EMan EPot GAbr LFox MBro SMrm SSmi WLRN WPer
– 'Alba' (2) — NHar WAbe
– 'Alison Gibbs' (2) — Last listed 1998
– × *allionii* (2) — NNrd
– 'Apple Blossom' (2) — CLyd EMNN EPot MFie
– 'Balfouriana' (2) — CNic LFox MBro
§ – 'Bewerley White' (2) — ELan EPot MBal MBro MRPP NCra NHed NNrd WWin
– 'Blue Wave' (2) — MFie NNrd

§ – 'Boothman's Variety' (2) — CInt CLyd EMNN EPot ITim MBro MFie MRPP NCra NHar NHed NHol NNrd NWCA SBla SIng SSmi WCla WCom WWin
– 'Carmen' — See *P.* × *pubescens* 'Boothman's Variety'
– 'Chamois' (2) — MFie
– 'Christine' (2) — CLyd EMNN LBee MBro MFie NChi NCra NHar NHed NHol NNrd SBod
– 'Cream Viscosa' (2) — EMNN MBro MFie NHed NHol NMGW NNrd WCom
– 'Deep Mrs Wilson' (2) — EHyt SWas
– 'Ellen Page' (2) — MFie
– 'Elphenor' (2) — NNrd
– 'Faldonside' (2) — CInt CLTr CLyd EHyt EMNN EPot GCHN MBro NCra NHed NHol NMGW NNrd WCom WWin
§ – 'Freedom' (2) — CLyd ELan EMNN EPot GTou ITim MBro MFie NCra NHar NHed NHol NNrd SBod SRms SSmi WCom WEas WWin
– 'George Harrison' (2) — GAbr MFie
– 'Gnome' (2) — Last listed 1996
– 'Greenslacks Yellow' — Last listed 1998
– 'Harlow Car' (2) — CLyd EMNN GMac ITim LFox MBro MFie NHar NHed NNrd WAbe WFar
– 'Henry Hall' (2) — CLyd EWes MFie
– 'Herbert Beresford' (2) — Last listed 1998
– 'Hurstwood Red Admiral' (2) — Last listed 1998
– 'Joan Danger' (2) — CLyd MFie NHol NNrd
– 'Joan Gibbs' (2) — CLyd ELan LBee MBro MFie NCra NHar NNrd
– 'Kath Dryden' (2) — MFie
– 'Lilac Fairy' (2) — NHed
– mixed (2) — Last listed 1997
– 'Mrs J.H. Wilson' (2) — CLyd EHyt ITim MBal MBro MFie NCra NHed NHol WAbe
– 'Pat Barwick' (2) — EMNN LFox MBro MFie NHed NHol
– 'Peggy Fell' (2) — MDHE MFie
– 'Pink Freedom' (2) — NHed
– 'Roseille' (2) — Last listed 1998
– 'Rufus' (2) — CLyd CPBP EHyt GCrs ITim MBal NCra NHol NNrd WTin
– 'S.E. Matthews' (2) — EHyt
– 'Sid Skelton' (2) — EMNN
– 'Snowcap' — CGra EPot
– 'Sonya' (2) — MFie NNrd
– 'The General' (2) — CLyd GNor MBro NCra NNrd WWin
– 'Victoria' (2) — EMNN
§ – 'Wedgwood' (2) — EMNN GNor
– white — Last listed 1997
– × 'White Linda Pope' — Last listed 1998
– 'Winifred' — NHed NHol SSON
*pulchra* (21) — GCrs
*pulverulenta* (4) ♀ — More than 30 suppliers
– Bartley hybrids (4) ♀ — CBot CGle EBee GBuc MFie SMur
– 'Bartley Pink' (4) — CPla GCan LSyl
× *pumila* (2) — Last listed 1996
'Purple Splendour' — LSur
'Purpurkissen' (Prim)(30) — NHol
'Quaker's Bonnet' — See *P. vulgaris* 'Lilacina Plena'
'Rachael Kinnon' (2) — WLin
'Rachel Kinnen' (2) — EHyt MFie SIng
'Ramona' (Poly)(30) — MFie
'Raven' — Last listed 1997
'Ravenglass Vermilion' — See *P.* 'Inverewe'
'Red Sunset' (4) — GDra

| | |
|---|---|
| 'Red Velvet' (dPrim)(30) | CSam EBee LHop MOne SMrm WWeb |
| § 'Redpoll' (21) | GCrs GGar NHar WAbe |
| *reidii* (28) | GFle MBri NCra |
| - var. *williamsii* (28) | EBrP EBre GDra GFle GGGa GTou LBre MBal MBri NHar SBre WLin |
| - - *alba* (28) | GDra GFle MBal MBri |
| *reptans* (16) | GGGa WAbe |
| 'Reverie' (Poly)(30) | EWoo MFie |
| 'Rhubarb and Custard' (Poly)(30) | CGle |
| 'Romeo' (Prim)(30) | CVer LSur NCra |
| 'Rose O'Day' (dPrim)(30) | ECGN GNau MBal MCLN MOne NHol NRoo |
| *rosea* ♀ | CBot CPla CRow EBee EPar GDra GFle GGGa GTou LHop MBal MFie NCra NDea NFla NHar NSti NWes SIng SSpi WEas WFar WWeb |
| - CC&McK 367 (11) | GCHN |
| - 'Delight' | See *P. rosea* 'Micia Visser-de Geer' |
| - 'Gigas' (11) | MSta NHol WFar |
| - 'Grandiflora' (11) | CGle CPea EHon ELan EMNN ENot EPar GCrs GFle LPBA LSyl MBri MRav NHed NMen NRoo SBea SIng SRms WPer |
| * - *splendens* (11) | Last listed 1997 |
| *rotundifolia* | See *P. roxburghii* |
| 'Rowallane Rose' (4) | CBro GBuc GFle MTed SSpi |
| § *roxburghii* (25) | Last listed 1998 |
| 'Roy Cope' (dPrim)(30) | CHad CLTr EHic MBNS MBal MBro MOne MRav NBir NEgg NMoo SIng WPnn |
| 'Roydon Ruby' | MHlr WCot |
| *rubra* | See *P. erythra* |
| *rusbyi* (20) | MFie |
| Rustic Reds Group (Poly)(30) | CSWP MFie NDov |
| ¶ 'Sandy' (21) | NOla |
| 'Sapphire' | EHyt |
| *saxatilis* (7) | MFie |
| *scandinavica* (11) | MFie |
| x *scapeosa* (21) | MBal NHar |
| *scapigera* (21) | Last listed 1996 |
| ◆ 'Schneekissen' (Prim)(30) | See *P.* Snowcushion = 'Schneekissen' |
| *scotica* (11) | EBee GCrs GFle GTou LFox MBal MFie MRPP NCra NSla NWCA WAbe WCla |
| *secundiflora* (26) | CGle CInt CLTr CPla EBee ELan GAbr GDra GFle GGGa GTou LSyl MBal MBro MNrw NChi NCra NMen NRoo NWoo SPer SPlb SRms WAbe WHil WHoo |
| - ACE 1518 (26) | Last listed 1996 |
| - ACE 1820 (26) | Last listed 1996 |
| § x *sendtneri* (2) | MFie |
| ¶ *septemloba* (7) | GFle |
| x *serrata* | See *P.* x *vochinensis* |
| *serratifolia* (4) | GGGa GMaP SBla |
| *sibirica* | See *P. nutans* Georgi |
| *sibthorpii* | See *P. vulgaris* subsp. *sibthorpii* |
| *sieboldii* (7) ♀ | CBre CGle CRow EMNN EPar GFle LFox MBal MBri MNrw NCra NHar NMen NRya NWCA SIng SRms SSpi SUsu WAbe WEas WFar WLin |
| - *alba* (7) | CLAP NBro NDov NMen WCru WFar |
| ¶ - blue shades (7) | NMen |
| - 'Carefree' (7) | NMen NNrd |
| - 'Cherubim' (7) | EBee ECtt GCHN |
| - 'Dancing Ladies' (7) | CGle NOla |
| - 'Galaxy' (7) | CMil WAbe |
| - 'Geisha Girl' (7) | CFir CLAP ECtt GCHN MRav WFar |
| - 'Lilac Sunbonnet' (7) | CGle |
| - 'Manakoora' (7) | CGle MFie |
| - 'Mikado' (7) | CFir ECtt GCHN MFie MRav NNrd |
| - 'Pago-Pago' (7) | CGle CInt CLAP CMea MFie |
| - 'Seraphim' (7) | Last listed 1998 |
| - 'Snowflake' (7) | CGle CMea GCHN NSla WAbe |
| - 'Tah-ni' (7) | Last listed 1998 |
| - 'Winter Dreams' (7) | CGle CInt CLAP MFie NBid |
| § *sikkimensis* (26) | CBot CGle CRow EBee EBrP EBre EHon EMNN ENot EWTr GCHN GCrs GFle GGGa LBre LPBA LSyl MBal MBri MBro MNrw MSta NCra NDea NHar SBre SIng SPer WAbe WRos |
| - ACE 1422 (26) | GBuc WAbe WCru |
| - ACE 1822 (26) | Last listed 1998 |
| - B&SWJ 2471 (26) | WCru |
| - CC&McK 1022 (26) | GTou |
| - crimson and gold (26) | MBro MFie |
| - var. *bopeana* (26) | GCrs GFle |
| - MECC 82 (26) | SGre |
| - 'Tilman Number 2' (26) | EWes GAbr GDra GFle |
| aff. *sikkimensis* ACE 2176 (26) | GBuc |
| Silver-laced Group (Poly)(30) | CGle EPar |
| - 'Silver Lining' (Poly)(30) | LRHS |
| § *sinensis* (27) | MBri |
| ¶ - 'Fanfare Mixed' (27) | MFie |
| *sinoplantaginea* | See *P. chionantha* subsp. *sinoplantaginea* |
| *sinopurpurea* | See *P. chionantha* subsp. *sinopurpurea* |
| 'Sir Bedivere' (Prim)(30) | CElw GAbr |
| *smithiana* | See *P. prolifera* |
| 'Snow Carpet' | See *P.* 'Schneekissen' |
| 'Snow Cushion' | See *P.* 'Schneekissen' |
| 'Snow Queen' | Last listed 1998 |
| 'Snow White' (Poly)(30) | MRav |
| § Snowcushion = 'Schneekissen' | CHid GAbr LSur MBri MBro NChi WHil WRus WViv |
| 'Snowruffles' | Last listed 1997 |
| *sonchifolia* (21) | GGGa MDun |
| *sorachiana* | See *P. yuparensis* |
| sp. ACE 1867 | NWCA |
| sp. B&SWJ 2165 | WCru |
| sp. BC 9331 | Last listed 1998 |
| sp. CLD 1217 (4) | Last listed 1996 |
| sp. CLD 487 (4) | Last listed 1996 |
| *spectabilis* (2) | EHyt GFle NHar |
| - JCA 789.400 (2) | MFie |
| - JCA 789.401 (2) | MFie |
| *speculicola* J&JA 1.768.600 (11) | NWCA |
| Spice Shades Group (Poly)(30) | CSWP EWoo GAbr MFie NDov |
| Springtime Group (Prim)(30) | Last listed 1996 |
| x *steinii* | See *P.* x *forsteri* |
| 'Stradbrook Charmer' (2) | EPot MFie NHol WLin |
| 'Stradbrook Dainty' (2) | EHyt MFie WLin |
| 'Stradbrook Dream' (2) | EPot MFie NHol |
| 'Stradbrook Gem' (2) | EHyt WAbe WLin |
| ¶ 'Stradbrook Lilac Lustre' (2) | MFie |
| 'Stradbrook Lucy' (2) | EHyt ITim NHol |
| ¶ *stricta* (11) | GFle |
| Striped Victorians Group | CMil CSWP GAbr MFie NChi NDov |
| 'Sue Jervis' (dPrim)(30) | CVer EHic EPot GAbr LFis MBro NEgg NHar NSti WHal WHil WRha |
| *suffrutescens* | NWCA SIng WAbe |
| Sunset Group | Last listed 1996 |

'Sunshine Susie' (dPrim)(30) CGle CMil CSam EBee ECGN EPri
GAbr MBNS MBri MCAu MOne
MRav NDov NEgg NHol SIng
SMrm WCot WLRN WPnn
'Sylvia' (Prim)(30) Last listed 1997
¶ *takedana* (24) GGGa
*tanneri* (21) WAbe
§ - subsp. *nepalensis* (21) ITim
- subsp. *tsariensis* GGGa
var. *alba* (21)
'Tantallon' (21) GCrs GGar NHar
'Tawny Port' (Poly)(30) CGle CLTr CMea CVer NBro NCra
SRms
'Techley Red' (Prim)(30) Last listed 1996
'The Grail' (Prim)(30) Last listed 1998
*tibetica* (11) GFle GGGa
¶ 'Tie Dye' (Prim)(30) WCot
'Tinney's Jewel' Last listed 1998
'Tinney's Moonlight' EHyt
'Tipperary Purple' (Prim)(30) GAbr
'Tomato Red' (Prim)(30) CFee CVer GAbr LBee NCra
'Tony' ITim NHar WLin
'Torchlight' (dPrim)(30) Last listed 1998
*tosaensis* (24) Last listed 1998
'Tournaig Pink' (4) GGar
*tschuktschorum* (18) Last listed 1997
*uralensis* See *P. veris* subsp. *macrocalyx*
'Val Horncastle' (dPrim)(30) CHad CSam ECGN MBNS MCAu
MCLN MOne MWgw NDov NEgg
NHar NRoo SMrm SPer SPla WCla
Valentine Victorians (Poly)(30) CSWP MFie
x *variabilis* See *P.* x *polyantha*
*veris* (30) ♀ More than 30 suppliers
* - *alba* Last listed 1998
- subsp. *canescens* JCA Last listed 1997
789.600 (30)
- hybrids (30) WWal
- red (30) WRHF
- red form GFle
* - 'Rhandirmwyn Red' WRha
¶ - 'Sunset Shades' NLar
*vernalis* See *P. vulgaris*
*verticillata* (12) MChR MFie
§ *vialii* (17) ♀ More than 30 suppliers
Victorian shades (Poly)(30) Last listed 1996
§ *villosa* (2) GCrs GFle GTou
- var. *cottica* See *P. villosa*
Violet Victorians Group CSWP MFie NDov
(Poly)(30)
*viscosa* Allioni See *P. latifolia*
§ x *vochinensis* (2) CFee CLyd MBro NHar NHol
NNrd NWCA SIng WAbe
§ *vulgaris* (Prim)(30) More than 30 suppliers
- *alba* (30) CGle CRow WAbe WLin
- 'Alba Plena' (Prim)(30) CGle CHad CRow CSWP GAbr
GBuc GGar IBlr NChi WRus
- Ballyrogan cream edge IBlr
(Prim)(30)
¶ - Barnhaven Gold NDov
- 'Double Sulphur' Last listed 1997
(dPrim)(30)
- green-flowered See *P. vulgaris* 'Viridis'
§ - 'Lilacina Plena' (dPrim)(30) CBot CGle CSam EBee GAbr IBlr
LFis LSur MBNS MCAu MCLN
MRav NChi NDov NSti SIng SMrm
WCla WEas WHil WLin
§ - subsp. *sibthorpii* CGle CMHG GAbr GTou LFox
(Prim)(30) ♀ LSur MBro MRav NBro NChi NCra
NWCA SBla SRms WCot WLin
WPyg
- - *alba* from Lebanon MFie
- - HH&K 265 (Prim)(30) Last listed 1997

- - HH&K 337 (30) Last listed 1997
- - JCA 790.401 (Prim)(30) Last listed 1997
§ - 'Viridis' (Prim)(30) CElw CRow CSWP IBlr
- 'Viridis' semi-double Last listed 1997
(Prim)(30)
- white hose-in-hose Last listed 1998
(Prim)(30)
*waltonii* (26) CPla GCrs GFle MBal MNrw SIng
- hybrids (26) GGar
'Wanda' (Prim)(30) ♀ CGle CRow CVer ELan ENot
GAbr LSur NRoo NSti NVic SBla
SIng SPer SRms WCFE WFar
WHoo WMow
'Wanda Hose in Hose' CGle CVer GAbr LSur NChi WHer
(Prim)(30) WHil
Wanda Jack in the Green CRow MBro MLLN WFar
(Prim)(30)
¶ Wanda Group pale WHil
mauve (30)
*wardii* See *P. involucrata*
*warshenewskiana* MFie NHol
*watsonii* (17) EWes GCan GCrs GGGa GTou
MFie NHar SIng WAbe
'Wedgwood' See *P.* x *pubescens* 'Wedgwood'
'Wharfedale Bluebell' (2) CLyd NHar WGwG
'Wharfedale Butterfly' (2) NHar NHol NNrd
'Wharfedale Crusader' (2) NHol NNrd
'Wharfedale Gem' EHyt GNor MDHE MFie NHar
(*allionii* hybrid) (2) NHol NNrd
'Wharfedale Ling' CGra CPBP EHyt EPot MFie MRPP
(*allionii* hybrid) (2) NHar NHol WAbe
'Wharfedale Superb' MFie NHar NHol NNrd
(*allionii* hybrid) (2)
'Wharfedale Village' (2) CLyd MDHE NHar NHol WGwG
'White Linda Pope' (2) CLyd NHar
¶ 'White Linda Pope' SIng
seedlings (2)
'White Wanda' (Prim)(30) CGle CRow CVer GAbr LSur
NDov WCru
*whitei* (21) CBrd GCrs MBal MDun WAbe
§ - 'Sherriff's Variety' (21) IBlr
*wigramiana* (28) WAbe
'William Genders' (Poly)(30) GAbr LSur
*wilsonii* (4) CPla GBuc GFle GGGa GMac LSyl
MBro MNes MNrw NHed SLon
SWat WAbe WGwy WHer WHoo
WOve WPyg
- var. *anisodora* (4) CPla EBee GCan GFle GMaP MBal
MFie
'Windrush' See *P.* x *berninae* 'Windrush'
'Windward Blue' SBla
'Winter White' See *P.* 'Gigha'
'Wisley Crimson' See *P.* 'Wisley Red'
§ 'Wisley Red' (Prim)(30) NOla
*wollastonii* (28) GGGa
'Woodland Blue' NWoo
*wulfeniana* (2) CGra MBro MFie MRPP NHol
WAbe
*yargongensis* See *P. involucrata* subsp.
*yargongensis*
§ *yuparensis* (11) CInt EBee GFle IDac MChR NMen
WAbe WUnu
'Zenobia' Last listed 1997

## PRINSEPIA (Rosaceae)
*sinensis* CFee CMCN CPle GBin MBlu
¶ *uniflora* CB&S CPLG
*utilis* CTrG

## PRITZELAGO (Brassicaceae)
¶ *alpina* CNic

## PROBOSCIDEA (Pedaliaceae)

| | |
|---|---|
| *fragrans* | Last listed 1996 |
| *louisianica* | EFEx |
| *parviflora* | EFEx |

## PROSOPIS (Mimosaceae)

| | |
|---|---|
| *chilensis* | See *P. glandulosa* |

## PROSTANTHERA (Lamiaceae)

| | |
|---|---|
| *aspalathoides* | CPle ECon ECou LGre WCot WWye |
| *cuneata* ♀ | More than 30 suppliers |
| – 'Alpine Gold' | CB&S CMHG CPle CWSG EHic LHop MSag SBod |
| – 'Fastigiata' | SPan |
| – Kew form | WPGP |
| ¶ 'Eddington Blue' | SBod |
| *incisa* | CTrw EPPr SHDw |
| – 'Rosea' | SChu WSHC |
| *lasianthos* | CB&S CPle CSev ECou LGre SBod SHDw SOWG WWye |
| – var. *subcoriacea* | CPle |
| *melissifolia* | ECon ECre LCns SLod WCot WSel |
| – var. *parvifolia* | CTrw ECre GCHN WAbe WSHC |
| *nivea* | CPle LGre |
| *ovalifolia* | ECou LHil LHop MMil SBod WCot |
| 'Poorinda Ballerina' | CAbb CDoC CLyn CPle CSev CSpe ECon EOrc LHil LHop LRHS MAsh MGos SAga SBod SMur SOWG |
| 'Poorinda Pixie' | Last listed 1996 |
| *rotundifolia* ♀ | CAbb CB&S CInt CPle CSam CSev CTrG CTri EOHP ERea ISea SAga SBod SBrw SEND SMad SOWG SPer WBod WWye |
| ¶ – *alba* | EBee |
| ♦ – 'Chelsea Girl' | See *P. rotundifolia* 'Rosea' |
| § – 'Rosea' | CGre CSpe CTrC CTrG EOHP ERea LHop MLan SAga SBod SHDw SLon WWye |
| *saxicola* var. *montana* | Last listed 1998 |
| *walteri* | CAbb CDoC CPle ECou LGre WHCG |

## PROTEA (Proteaceae)

| | |
|---|---|
| ¶ *acaulos* | CTrC |
| ¶ *aristata* | CTrC |
| ¶ *aurea* | CTrC |
| ¶ *burchellii* | CCpl |
| ¶ *coronata* | CTrF |
| *cynaroides* | CB&S CCpl CTrC CTrF |
| *eximia* | CTrC |
| *grandiceps* | CTrC |
| *lacticolor* | CTrC |
| ¶ *laurifolia* | CTrC |
| *magnifica* | Last listed 1998 |
| ¶ *nana* | CTrC |
| *neriifolia* | CTrC |
| ¶ *repens* | CTrC |
| ¶ *simplex* | CFil |
| ¶ *subvestita* | CCpl CTrC CTrF |
| ¶ *susannae* | CTrF |
| *venusta* | Last listed 1997 |

## PRUMNOPITYS (Podocarpaceae)

| | |
|---|---|
| § *andina* | CDul CGre SLon WWat |
| *elegans* | See *P. andina* |
| § *ferruginea* | Last listed 1998 |
| § – 'Golden Dwarf' | CLTr |
| § *taxifolia* | ECou |

## PRUNELLA (Lamiaceae)

| | |
|---|---|
| § *grandiflora* | CAgr EBot EFer EWTr GBar MNrw MWat NLon SRms SWat WBea WCHb WOve WRos WWye |
| *grandiflora* 'Alba' | CDoC EPfP LPio MCAu NBid NChi NCut NLar NOrc SBea SPla WCHb WOve WWhi |
| – 'Blue Loveliness' | ELan EMan GAbr GTou SPla WCHb |
| ¶ – 'Carminea' | SRPl |
| – 'Little Red Riding Hood' | See *P. grandiflora* 'Rotkäppchen' |
| – 'Loveliness' ♀ | CDoC EAst EBee EBrP EBre ECha ECtt ELan EPar LBre MBel MCAu MRav NBro NMir NSti NVic SBod SBre SPer SPla SPlb WFar WMow WWeb WWin |
| – 'Pagoda' | EAst LIck NBrk NLar NOak WCHb WElm WMoo |
| – 'Pink Loveliness' | CInt EBee EBrP EBre ECha EPar GCHN GTou LBre MBal MWgw NArg NMir SBre SRms WByw WFar WWin WWye |
| – purplish blue | Last listed 1997 |
| – *rosea* | CBlo EPfP MWat WByw WWhi |
| § – 'Rotkäppchen' | CPea ECtt GCHN WMoo |
| ¶ – 'Rubra' | NCut |
| – 'White Loveliness' | EBrP EBre ECha EPar GCHN LBre NBrk NCat NMir SBre SPer SPla WByw WFar WLin WMow WPer WRus WWin WWye |
| *hyssopifolia* | EBee |
| *incisa* | See *P. vulgaris* |
| * 'Inshriach Ruby' | NBir SPla WCHb |
| *laciniata* | CLyd CMCo NChi WCHb |
| – pink form | NChi |
| – white form | NChi |
| § *vulgaris* | CAgr CArn CKin ELan EWFC GAbr GBar GPoy MChe MHew MSal NLan NMir NSti SIde WCHb WCla WHbs WHer WOak WWye |
| – *alba* | WAlt WHer |
| ¶ – 'Gleam' (v) | WAlt |
| – 'Inner Glow' (v) | WAlt |
| – 'Ruth Wainwright' (v) | CNat |
| – 'Saintlow' | Last listed 1998 |
| – 'Voile' | Last listed 1998 |
| x *webbiana* | See *P. grandiflora* |

## PRUNUS ✿ (Rosaceae)

| | |
|---|---|
| 'Accolade' ♀ | CAbP CBlo CDoC CDul CLnd COtt CSam CTho EBee ECrN ECtt ENot IOrc LPan MAsh MBri MRav NBea NWea SEND SPer SSta WDin WJas WStI |
| § 'Amanogawa' ♀ | CB&S CBlo CDul CLnd EBee EBrP EBre ECrN ELan ENot GChr LBre LBuc LHyr LNet LPan MAsh MBal MBar MBri MRav NBea NBee NWea SBre SPer SRPl WFar WHar WJas |
| x *amygdalopersica* 'Pollardii' | CBlo CLnd ENot WJas |
| – 'Spring Glow' | CDoC CDul MAsh MBri WJas |
| *amygdalus* | See *P. dulcis* |
| *armeniaca* 'Alfred' (F) | EMui ERea GTwe MBri SDea |
| – 'Blenheim' (F) | ERea |
| – 'Bredase' (F) | SDea |
| – 'De Nancy' | See *P. armeniaca* 'Gros Pêche' |
| – 'Early Moorpark' (F) | ERea GBon GRei GTwe SDea SFam WWeb |
| – 'Farmingdale' (F) | ERea SDea SKee |

| | |
|---|---|
| - 'Goldcot' (F) | ERea SDea |
| - 'Golden Glow' (F) | GTwe |
| § - 'Gros Pêche' (F) | CMac |
| - 'Hemskirke' (F) | ERea |
| - 'Hongaarse' (F) | SDea |
| ¶ - 'Moniqui' (F) | CGOG |
| - 'Moorpark' (F) ♀ | CEnd EMui ERea GTwe LBuc |
| | MGos NRog SDea SKee WStI |
| - 'New Large Early' (F) | ERea GTwe SDea SEND SKee |
| ¶ - 'Royale' (F) | CMac |
| - 'Tross Orange' (F) | SDea |
| 'Asano' | See *P.* 'Geraldinae' |
| *avium* ♀ | CB&S CBlo CDul CKin CLnd |
| | CSam EBee ECrN ENot EWTr |
| | GChr GRei LBuc LHyr LPan MBar |
| | MBri MGos MRav NBee NRoo |
| | NWea SFam SKee SPer SRPl WDin |
| | WHar WMou WOrn |
| - 'Alba' | Last listed 1996 |
| - 'Amber Heart' (F) | SDea SKee |
| - 'August Heart' (F) | Last listed 1997 |
| - 'Bigarreau Gaucher' (F) | SKee |
| § - 'Bigarreau Napoléon' (F) | GTwe MGos SDea SFam SKee |
| - 'Birchenhayes' | See *P. avium* 'Early Birchenhayes' |
| - 'Black Eagle' (F) | CTho SKee |
| - 'Black Elton' (F) | Last listed 1997 |
| - 'Black Glory' (F) | Last listed 1997 |
| - 'Black Heart' (F) | Last listed 1996 |
| - 'Black Tartarian' (F) | SKee |
| - 'Bottlers' | See *P. avium* 'Preserving' |
| - 'Bradbourne Black' (F) | SKee |
| - 'Bullion' (F) | CEnd CTho |
| - 'Burcombe' (F) | CEnd CTho |
| - 'Caroon' (F) | Last listed 1996 |
| ¶ - 'Celeste' (D) | COtt |
| - 'Cherokee' | See *P. avium* 'Lapins' |
| - 'Circassian' (F) | SKee |
| - 'Colney' (F) | GTwe SFam WJas |
| - 'Dun' (F) | CTho |
| § - 'Early Birchenhayes' (F) | CEnd CTho |
| - 'Early Rivers' (F) | GTwe SDea SKee |
| - 'Elton Heart' (F) | CTho SKee |
| - 'Emperor Francis' (F) | Last listed 1996 |
| - 'Fastigiata' | CTho |
| - 'Fice' (F) | CEnd CTho |
| - 'Florence' (F) | SKee |
| - 'Frogmore Early' (F) | Last listed 1996 |
| - 'Governor Wood' (F) | GTwe |
| - 'Grandiflora' | See *P. avium* 'Plena' |
| - 'Greenstem Black' (F) | CTho |
| - 'Hertford' (F) | SFam SKee |
| - 'Inga' (F) | SFam SKee |
| - 'Ironsides' (F) | SKee |
| - 'Kassins Frühe Herz' (F) | SKee |
| - 'Kent Bigarreau' (F) | Last listed 1997 |
| - 'Kentish Red' (F) | CTho |
| § - 'Lapins' (F) | EMui GTwe SDea SFam SKee |
| | WHar WJas |
| - 'May Duke' | See *P.* x *gondouinii* 'May Duke' |
| - 'Merchant' (F) ♀ | GTwe SKee |
| - 'Mermat' (F) | GTwe |
| - 'Merpet' (F) | GTwe |
| - 'Merton Bigarreau' (F) | Last listed 1997 |
| - 'Merton Bounty' (F) | Last listed 1996 |
| - 'Merton Crane' (F) | SKee |
| - 'Merton Favourite' (F) | SKee |
| - 'Merton Glory' (F) | CDoC GChr GTwe MGos SFam |
| - 'Merton Heart' (F) | Last listed 1997 |
| - 'Merton Late' (F) | Last listed 1997 |
| - 'Merton Marvel' (F) | Last listed 1997 |
| - 'Merton Premier' (F) | SKee |
| - 'Merton Reward' | See *P.* x *gondouinii* 'Merton Reward' |

| | |
|---|---|
| ¶ - 'Nabella' (F) | WJas |
| - 'Napoléon' | See *P. avium* 'Bigarreau Napoléon' |
| - 'Newstar' (F) | EMui |
| - 'Noble' (F) | Last listed 1997 |
| - 'Noir de Guben' (F) | GTwe |
| - 'Nutberry Black' (F) | SKee |
| - 'Old Black Heart' (F) | SKee |
| § - 'Plena' (d) ♀ | CB&S CBlo CLnd CSam CTho |
| | EBee ECrN ELan ENot EPfP GChr |
| | IOrc LBuc LHyr LPan MBal MGos |
| | NBee NWea SFam SPer WDin |
| | WHar WJas WOrn |
| § - 'Preserving' (F) | CTho |
| - 'Ronald's Heart' (F) | Last listed 1997 |
| - 'Roundel Heart' (F) | Last listed 1997 |
| - 'Sasha' (F) | GTwe |
| - 'Small Black' (F) | CTho |
| - 'Smoky Dun' (F) | Last listed 1997 |
| - 'Starking Hardy Giant' (F) | Last listed 1997 |
| - 'Starkrimson' (F) | GTwe |
| - 'Stella' (F) ♀ | CEnd CMac CSam EMui ERea |
| | GBon GChr GRei GTwe LBuc |
| | MBri MGos NBee NRog SDea |
| | SFam SKee SPer WHar WJas |
| | WWeb |
| - 'Stella Compact' (F) | COtt GTwe MBri SDea SKee |
| | WHar |
| - 'Strawberry Heart' (F) | Last listed 1996 |
| ¶ - 'Summer Sun' (D) | EMui |
| - 'Sunburst' (F) | CEnd EMui GTwe LBuc MBri |
| | SDea SFam SKee WJas WWeb |
| - 'Turkish Black' (F) | SKee |
| * - 'Upright' | CTho |
| - 'Van' (F) | GTwe SKee |
| - 'Vega' (F) | GTwe SFam WJas |
| - 'Waterloo' (F) | CTho SKee |
| - 'White Heart' (F) | CTho SKee |
| 'Benden' | CTho |
| * 'Beni-higan' | Last listed 1996 |
| * 'Beni-no-dora' | SMur |
| * 'Beni-yutaka' | CBlo CEnd LBuc MBri |
| *besseyi* | Last listed 1996 |
| * 'Birch Bark' | Last listed 1997 |
| 'Blaze' | See *P. cerasifera* 'Nigra' |
| x *blireana* ♀ | CBlo CDoC CLnd EBee ENot |
| | GChr LPan MAsh MBri MRav |
| | MWat SPer SRPl SSta WHar |
| 'Blushing Bride' | See *P.* 'Shôgetsu' |
| *bucharica* JJH 98807 | NWCA |
| *campanulata* | CTho |
| *capuli* | See *P. salicifolia* |
| *cerasifera* | CAgr CBlo CTri GAri LBuc NWea |
| | SKee WDin WMou |
| - 'Cherry Plum' (F) | SKee |
| - 'Crimson Dwarf' | CDoC |
| * - 'Green Glow' | CBlo |
| - 'Hessei' (v) | CBlo CEnd MBri MGos NMoo |
| - 'Kentish Red' (F) | SKee |
| § - Myrobalan Group (F) | CBlo CKin SDea SKee |
| § - L.H. Bailey 'Nigra' ♀ | CBlo CDoC CDul CLnd CTri EBee |
| | ECrN ELan GChr IOrc LBuc LNet |
| | LPan MAsh MBri MGos MRav |
| | NBea NBee SDea SPer SRms |
| | WDin WHar WOrn WStI |
| - 'Pendula' | Last listed 1997 |
| § - 'Pissardii' | CBlo CTho EBrP EBre GRei LBre |
| | MAsh MBar NBea NFor NWea |
| | SBre SFam SPer WFar WJas |
| - 'Rosea' | MBri |
| - 'Spring Glow' | CEnd |
| ¶ - 'Vesuvius' | SRPl |

*cerasus* 'Montmorency' (F) SKee
- 'Morello' (F) ♀ CMac CSam EBee EBrP EBre EMui
  GBon GChr GRei GTwe LBre
  LBuc MBri MGos NBee NRog SBre
  SDea SFam SKee SPer WJas WWeb
- 'Nabella' (F) Last listed 1997
- 'Rhexii' (d) CBlo CDul MAsh MGos SPer
- 'Wye Morello' (F) SKee
'Cheal's Weeping' See *P.* 'Kiku-shidare-zakura'
§ 'Chôshû-hizakura' ♀ CBlo CLnd GChr GRei IOrc LNet
  MBri SPer WStI
§ x *cistena* ♀ CB&S CBlo EBrP EBre ELan ENot
  IOrc LBre MBar MBri MGos MWat
  NBee SBre SEas SPer SPla WDin
- 'Crimson Dwarf' See *P.* x *cistena*
'Collingwood Ingram' MBri
◆ 'Comet' See *P.* Easter Bonnet = 'Comet'
*conradinae* See *P. hirtipes*
*davidiana* CTho
*domestica* 'Allgroves ERea
  Superb' (D)
- 'Angelina Burdett' (D) ERea GTwe NRog SKee
- 'Anna Späth' (C/D) SKee
- 'Ariel' (C/D) SDea SKee
- 'Autumn Compote' (C) Last listed 1997
- 'Avalon' (C) GTwe SDea SKee
- 'Belgian Purple' (C) SKee
- 'Belle de Louvain' (C) CTho ERea GTwe NRog SDea
  SKee
- 'Birchenhayes' (F) CEnd
◆ - 'Black Diamond' See *P. salicina* 'Black Diamond'
- 'Black Prince' (C) Last listed 1996
- 'Blaisdon Red' (C) Last listed 1996
- 'Blue Imperatrice' (C/D) Last listed 1997
- 'Blue Tit' (C/D) ♀ EMui ERea GTwe SDea SKee
- 'Bonne de Bry' (D) SKee
§ - 'Bountiful' (C) ERea
- 'Brandy Gage' (C/D) SKee
- 'Bryanston Gage' (D) CTho SKee
- 'Burbank' (C/D) SDea
- 'Burcombe' CEnd
- 'Bush' (C) SKee
- 'Cambridge Gage' (D) ♀ CDoC CSam CTho CTri EBrP EBre
  EMui ERea GBon GTwe LBre
  LBuc MBri MGos MWat NBea
  NRog SBre SDea SFam SKee SPer
  WJas WStI WWeb
- 'Chrislin' (F) CTho
- 'Coe's Golden Drop' (D) CTho EMui ERea GTwe MGos
  SCoo SDea SFam SKee
- 'Count Althann's Gage' (D)ERea GTwe NRog SDea SFam
  SKee
- 'Cox's Emperor' (C) SKee
- 'Crimson Drop' (D) ERea SKee
- 'Cropper' See *P. domestica* 'Laxton's
  Cropper'
- 'Curlew' (C) SDea
- 'Czar' (C) ♀ CDoC CSam CTri EBrP EBre EMui
  GTwe IOrc LBre LBuc MGos
  NBea NRog SBre SDea SFam SKee
  SPer WWeb
- 'Delicious' See *P. domestica* 'Laxton's
  Delicious'
- 'Denniston's Superb' See *P. domestica* 'Imperial Gage'
- 'Diamond' (C) SKee
- 'Dittisham Black' (C) CTho
- 'Dittisham Ploughman' (C) CSam CTho SKee
- 'Dunster Plum' (F) CTho
- 'Early Laxton' (C/D) ♀ ERea GTwe SDea SFam SKee
- 'Early Orleans' See *P. domestica* 'Monsieur Hâtif'
- 'Early Prolific' See *P. domestica* 'Rivers's Early
  Prolific'

- 'Early Rivers' See *P. domestica* 'Rivers's Early
  Prolific'
- 'Early Transparent CTho CTri EMui ERea GTwe LBuc
  Gage' (C/D) SDea SFam
- 'Early Victoria' (C/D) SDea
- 'Edwards' (C/D) ♀ GTwe LBuc NBee NRog SDea
  SFam SKee
- 'Excalibur' (D) GTwe SDea
- 'Giant Prune' (C) GTwe NRog SKee
- 'Godshill Blue' (C) SDea
- 'Golden Transparent' (D) CTho ERea GTwe NRog SFam
- 'Goldfinch' (D) GTwe NRog SKee
◆ - Green Gage Group See *P. domestica* Reine-Claude
  Group
◆ - - 'Old Green Gage' See *P. domestica* (Reine-Claude
  Group) 'Reine-Claude Vraie'
- 'Grey Plum' (F) CTho
- 'Grove's Late Victoria' (C/D) SKee
- 'Guthrie's Late Green' (D) SKee
- 'Herman' (C/D) CSam GTwe MBri SDea
- 'Heron' (F) GTwe
- 'Impérial Epineuse' (D) SKee
§ - 'Imperial Gage' (C/D) ♀ CTho EMui ERea GTwe LBuc
  SDea SFam SKee
- subsp. *insititia* See *P. insititia*
- 'Jan James' (F) CEnd
- 'Jefferson' (D) ♀ EMui ERea GTwe NRog SDea
  SFam SKee
- 'Kea' (C) CTho SKee
- 'Kirke's' (D) CTho CWSG ERea GTwe SDea
  SFam SKee
- 'Landkey Yellow' (F) CTho
- 'Late Muscatelle' (D) ERea SKee
- 'Late Transparent Gage' (D) Last listed 1996
- 'Laxton's Bountiful' See *P. domestica* 'Bountiful'
§ - 'Laxton's Cropper' (C) GTwe NRog SKee
§ - 'Laxton's Delicious' (D) GTwe
- 'Laxton's Delight' (D) ♀ GTwe
- 'Laxton's Gage' (D) SDea SKee
- 'Laxton's Supreme' (C/D) Last listed 1996
- 'Manaccan' (C) CTho
- 'Marjorie's Seedling' (C) ♀ CDoC CTho EBrP EBre ECrN
  EMui ERea GBon GTwe LBre
  LBuc MGos MWat SBre SDea
  SEND SFam SKee WJas
- 'McLaughlin' (D) SKee
- 'Merton Gem' (C/D) GTwe SFam SKee
- 'Monarch' (C) GTwe SKee
- 'Olympia' (C/D) Last listed 1996
- 'Ontario' (C/D) SDea
- 'Opal' (D) ♀ CDoC EMui ERea GTwe IOrc
  LBuc MBri MGos MWat SDea
  SEND SFam SKee WWeb
- 'Orleans' (C) SKee
- 'Oullins Gage' (C/D) ♀ CDoC ECrN EMui ERea GBon
  GTwe LBuc MBri MWat NRog
  SDea SFam SKee SPer WJas WWeb
- 'Peach Plum' (D) Last listed 1996
- 'Pershore' (C) ♀ CTho ERea GTwe NRog SDea
  SFam SKee WStI
- 'Pond's Seedling' (C) SDea SKee
- 'President' (C/D) GTwe SDea
- 'Prince Englebert' (C) SKee
- 'Priory Plum' (D) SDea
- 'Purple Pershore' (C) CTri CWSG ERea GTwe NRog
  SDea SFam SKee
- 'Quetsche d'Alsace' See *P. domestica* German Prune
  Group
- 'Reeves' (C) ♀ GTwe SFam SKee
§ - Reine-Claude Group (C/D) EMui GTwe NRog SDea SFam
  SKee SPer
- - 'Reine-Claude de CTho CTri ERea GTwe NRog

|  |  |
|---|---|
| Bavais' (D) | SDea SFam SKee |
| § – – 'Reine-Claude Vraie' (C/D) | EPfP ERea WCFE WJas |
| § – – 'Willingham Gage' (C/D) | ERea GTwe |
| ◆ – 'Reine-Claude Dorée' | See *P. domestica* Reine-Claude Group |
| – 'Reine-Claude Violette' (D) | CTho ERea SKee |
| § – 'Rivers's Early Prolific' (C) | CTho ECrN ERea GTwe MWat NRog SCoo SDea SKee |
| – 'Royale de Vilvoorde' (D) | ERea SKee |
| – 'Sanctus Hubertus' (D) ♀ | GTwe SDea SKee |
| – 'Severn Cross' (D) | GTwe SKee |
| – 'Stint' (C/D) | SKee |
| – 'Swan' (C) | GTwe |
| – 'Thames Cross' (D) | Last listed 1996 |
| – 'Transparent Gage' (D) | ERea SKee |
| – 'Upright' (F) | CEnd |
| – 'Utility' (D) | SKee |
| – 'Victoria' (C/D) ♀ | CMac CSam CTho EBrP EBre EMui ERea GBon GChr GRei GTwe IOrc LBre LBuc MBri MGos MWat NBea NBee NRog SBre SDea SFam SKee SPer WHar WJas WWeb |
| – 'Warwickshire Drooper' (C) | CSam CTho ERea GBon GTwe SDea SFam SKee SPer |
| – 'Washington' (D) | CTho ERea SDea SKee |
| – 'White Magnum Bonum' (C) | CTho SDea |
| ◆ – 'Willingham' | See *P. domestica* (Reine-Claude Group) 'Willingham Gage' |
| – 'Wyedale' (C) | GTwe |
| § *dulcis* | CDul CLnd CTri EMui LHyr MWat NBea NWea SDea SFam SRPl WBay WDin |
| – 'Balatoni' (F) | MBri |
| – 'Macrocarpa' (F) | Last listed 1998 |
| – 'Roseoplena' | CBlo MBri |
| § Easter Bonnet = 'Comet' | LRHS |
| ¶ Fragrant Cloud = 'Shizuka' | MBri |
| *fruticosa* 'Globosa' | CBlo CWSG |
| 'Fudan-zakura' | Last listed 1996 |
| 'Fugenzô' | CBlo |
| § 'Geraldinae' | CLnd MBri WPyg |
| *glandulosa* 'Alba Plena' (d) ♀ | CB&S CBot CEnd CPle CSam EBee ECtt ELan ESis GChr GOrc MBal MGos MPla MTis MWat NBea NBee NHol SPan SPer SPla SReu SRms SSpi SSta WDin WHCG WSHC |
| – 'Rosea Plena' | See *P. glandulosa* 'Sinensis' |
| § – 'Sinensis' (d) ♀ | CBot CEnd CPle ELan ESis GChr GOrc MBal MGos MPla MRav SPan SPer SPla SRPl SReu SRms SSpi SSta WHCG WSHC |
| § x *gondouinii* 'May Duke' (F) | SKee |
| § – 'Merton Reward' (F) | SKee |
| 'Gyoikô' | CTho |
| ¶ 'Hakanagoto' | MBri |
| 'Hally Jolivette' | CEnd COtt ELan MAsh MBri SCoo SPla WBcn |
| 'Hillieri' | ECrN MBar MGos |
| 'Hillieri Spire' | See *P.* 'Spire' |
| 'Hilling's Weeping' | EBee MBri |
| § *hirtipes* | CTho SFam |
| 'Hisakura' | See *P.* 'Chôshû-hizakura' |
| 'Hokusai' | Last listed 1996 |
| Hollywood | See *P.* 'Trailblazer' |
| 'Horinji' | Last listed 1996 |
| 'Imose' | Last listed 1996 |
| *incisa* | CTri GAri IOrc NBea SLPl SPer SSpi |

|  |  |
|---|---|
| – 'Beniomi' | GAri MRav |
| – 'February Pink' | CBlo CPMA LBuc MAsh MBri MPla MRav NPro |
| – 'Fujima' | MAsh NHol SMur WPat WPyg WRHF WWat |
| – 'Kojo-no-mai' | CEnd CHar CMil CPMA EBee EBrP EBre ECtt EPla ESis GAri GBin LBre MAsh MBlu MBri MGos NPro NTow SBre SPan WBay WCot WFar WPat WWeb |
| – 'Mikinori' | CB&S MBri MGos |
| – 'Oshidori' | MBri MGos MRav NHol WFar WPyg WShe |
| * – 'Otome' | MBri WFar |
| ¶ – 'Pendula' | MBri |
| – 'Praecox' ♀ | CTho LRHS MBri |
| – 'The Bride' | CEnd MAsh MBri |
| § – f. *yamadae* | CB&S CEnd LBuc |
| *insititia* 'Blue Violet Damson' (F) | SKee |
| § – 'Bradley's King Damson' (F) | GTwe SKee |
| – Bullace (C) | SDea |
| – 'Dittisham Damson' (C) | CTho |
| – 'Farleigh Damson' (C) | ERea GTwe SDea SFam SKee WJas |
| – 'Godshill Damson' (C) | SDea |
| – 'Golden Bullace' | See *P. insititia* 'White Bullace' |
| – 'King of Damsons' | See *P. insititia* 'Bradley's King Damson' |
| – 'Langley Bullace' (C) | CTho ERea SKee |
| – 'Merryweather Damson' (C) | CDoC CMac CTho EBrP EBre EMui ERea GBon GChr GRei GTwe LBre LBuc MBri NBee NRog SBre SDea SFam SKee SPer WHar WJas WStI WWeb |
| – 'Mirabelle de Nancy' (C) | CTho GTwe SDea SFam SKee |
| – 'Mirabelle de Nancy (Red)' (C) | SDea |
| – 'Mirabelle Petite' | See *P. insititia* 'Mirabelle de Metz' |
| § – 'Prune Damson' (C) ♀ | CSam CTho EMui ERea GBon GTwe LBuc MBri MGos MWat NRog SDea SFam SKee WHar WJas |
| – 'Shepherd's Bullace' (C) | CTho ERea SKee |
| – 'Shropshire Damson' | See *P. insititia* 'Prune Damson' |
| – 'Small Bullace' (C) | SKee |
| § – 'White Bullace' (C) | ERea SKee |
| – 'Yellow Apricot' (C) | ERea SKee |
| § *jamasakura* | CTho |
| 'Jô-nioi' | CEnd CLnd CTho |
| x *juddii* | Last listed 1996 |
| § 'Kanzan' ♀ | CB&S CBlo CDul CLnd CSam EBee EBrP EBre ELan EWTr GRei LBre LBuc LHyr LPan MAsh MBal MBar MBri MGos MRav NBea NBee NWea SBre SPer SSta WFar WJas |
| § 'Kiku-shidare-zakura' ♀ | CB&S CBlo CDul CLnd EBee EBrP EBre ELan ENot GChr GRei LBre LBuc LHyr LNet LPan MAsh MBar MBri MGos MRav NBea NBee NWea SBre SFam SPer WDin WFar WJas WStI |
| Korean Hill Cherry | See *P.* x *verecunda* |
| *kurilensis* | See *P. nipponica* var. *kurilensis* |
| 'Kursar' ♀ | CBlo CDul COtt CTho EBee EMui EPfP GRei IOrc LNet MAsh MBri SFam |
| *laurocerasus* ♀ | CB&S CChe CDul CKin EBee ELan GRei LHyr LNet LPan MRav MWat NBea NFor NWea SEND SPer SRPl SReu WFar WMou WStI |

- 'Aureovariegata' — See *P. laurocerasus* 'Taff's Golden Gleam'
- 'Camelliifolia' — CHan CTri EPla MBlu SMad WDin WHCG WPyg
N - 'Castlewellan' (v) — CBot CDul CHan CLTr CPle CTrw EAst EPla IOrc ISea MBar MGos NBea NHol SEND SPer SPla SSta WGwG WHar WLeb WWat
- 'Caucasica' — MGos
- 'Cherry Brandy' — EGra ENot NPro SPer WCot WLRN WStI
- Dart's Lowgreen™ — See *P. laurocerasus* Low 'n' Green = 'Interlo'
- 'Etna' — EBee LRHS MGos
¶ - 'Golden Splash' — WBcn
- Green Carpet — See *P. laurocerasus* 'Grünerteppich'
- 'Green Marble' (v) — CPMA CTri EBee MUlv WSHC
♦ - 'Interlo' — See *P. laurocerasus* Low 'n' Green = 'Interlo'
§ - 'Latifolia' — EPla SAPC SArc SLPl SMad
§ - Low 'n' Green = 'Interlo' — ENot
- 'Magnoliifolia' — See *P. laurocerasus* 'Latifolia'
¶ - 'Mano' — MGos
- 'Marbled White' — See *P. laurocerasus* 'Castlewellan'
- 'Mischeana' — ENot MBri SLPl
- 'Mount Vernon' — EBee MBar MBri MGos NBee WDin
- 'Otinii' — Last listed 1998
- 'Otto Luyken' ♀ — More than 30 suppliers
¶ - Renault Ace = 'Renlau' — EBee
- 'Reynvaanii' — EPla MBri MGos WBcn
- 'Rotundifolia' — CDoC CTri ELan ENot LBuc MBNS MBar MBri MGos NBea NFla SRms WDin WHar WStI
- 'Rudolf Billeter' — EPla
- 'Schipkaensis' — NFor SPer WCot
§ - 'Taff's Golden Gleam' (v) — CEnd CPMA MGos SMad WCot WWes
- 'Van Nes' — EMil IOrc
N - 'Variegata' — EHic MGos SRms
- 'Zabeliana' — CDoC CLan EBee ENot EPla GChr GRei MBar NWea SPer SRms WDin WPyg WWin

*litigiosa* — Last listed 1996
\* *longipedunculata* — MBri
*lusitanica* ♀ — More than 30 suppliers
- subsp. *azorica* ♀ — EPla SMad SPer WPGP WWat
- 'Myrtifolia' — EBee EPla MBri MRav SMad WShe WWat
- 'Variegata' — CB&S CBot EAst EBee EBrP EBre EHoe ELan ENot EPla IOrc ISea LBre MBal MBri MGos MRav MWat NSti SBre SDix SPer SRPl SSta WDin WFar WSHC WWat

*maackii* — CTho EBee EPfP LPan NBea SEND SSpi WDin WWat
- 'Amber Beauty' — CDul CPMA GChr MBri NBee SLPl WPyg
*mahaleb* — CTho
\* 'Mahogany Lustre' — MBlu
'Mount Fuji' — See *P.* 'Shirotae'
*mume* — NBea WNor
- 'Alboplena' — CChe
§ - 'Beni-chidori' — CB&S CBlo CEnd CPMA EBee EPfP LRHS MBlu MBri MGos NBea SSpi SSta WJas
- 'Beni-shidori' — See *P. mume* 'Beni-chidori'
\* - 'Ken Kyo' — LRHS
\* - 'Kyo Koh' — LRHS SPla
§ - 'Omoi-no-mama' (d) — CEnd CPMA LRHS MAsh MBri MMHG

- 'Omoi-no-wac' — See *P. mume* 'Omoi-no-mama'
- 'Pendula' — CLnd MBri
¶ - 'Yae-kankobane' (d) — LRHS
*myrobalana* — See *P. cerasifera* Myrobalan Group
§ *nipponica* var. *kurilensis* — CB&S MAsh
¶ - var. *kurilensis* 'Brilliant' — MBri MGos
- - 'Ruby' — CDul CEnd GChr LRHS MBri MGos NBee NEgg SMur
- - 'Spring Joy' — MBri
'Ojōchin' — Last listed 1996
'Okame' ♀ — CBlo CLnd CSam CTho EBee EBrP EBre LBre MAsh MBri MGos MRav NBee NWea SBre SPer SRPl
§ 'Okumiyako' — CB&S CBlo CEnd SFam WDin
*padus* — CBlo CDul CKin CLnd ECrN GChr IOrc LBuc LHyr LNet MGos NBea NBee NRoo NWea SSpi WDin WMou
- 'Albertii' — CTho LPan SLPl WJas
- 'Colorata' ♀ — CBlo CDoC CDul CEnd CMHG CSam CTho ECrN ELan GChr IOrc LBuc LNet LPan MGos NBee SPer SSpi WDin WJas
- 'Dropmore' — Last listed 1997
- 'Grandiflora' — See *P. padus* 'Watereri'
- 'Plena' (d) — CTho
- 'Purple Queen' — CBlo CEnd CTho ENot MGos WStI
§ - 'Watereri' ♀ — CB&S CBlo CDoC CDul CLnd CTho EBee ECrN ELan ENot IOrc LPan MGos SPer SRPl WDin WJas
'Pandora' ♀ — CB&S CBlo CLnd EBee ECrN ENot EPfP GChr LHyr LPan MAsh MBal MBri MRav MWat NBea NBee NWea SEND SPer SRPl
§ *pendula* var. *ascendens* — CBlo
'Rosea' —
§ - 'Pendula Rosea' ♀ — CB&S CBlo ENot LPan MAsh SPer WJas
§ - 'Pendula Rubra' ♀ — CBlo CDoC COtt CTho CTri EBee ENot EPfP LNet MAsh MBri MGos SFam SPer
*persica* 'Amsden June' (F) — ERea GTwe SDea SFam
- 'Bellegarde' (F) — ERea GTwe SDea SFam SKee
- 'Bonanza' (F) — EMui ERea
- 'Doctor Hogg' (F) — SDea
- 'Duke of York' (F) ♀ — CTri ERea GTwe SDea SFam SKee WWeb
- 'Dymond' (F) — ERea
- 'Early Alexander' (F) — Last listed 1996
- 'Flat China' (F) — ERea
- 'Francis' (F) — SKee
- 'Garden Anny' (F) — ERea
- 'Garden Lady' (F) — EMui ERea GTwe WWeb
- 'Garden Silver' — Last listed 1997
- 'Hale's Early' (F) — ERea GTwe SEND SFam SKee SPer
¶ - 'Hylands' (F) — SDea
- 'Kestrel' (F) — Last listed 1998
- 'Klara Mayer' (d/F) — CBlo WJas
- 'Melred' — Last listed 1997
♦ - 'Merrill O'Henry' — See *P. persica* 'O'Henry'
- 'Miriam' (F) — Last listed 1996
¶ - 'Natalia' (F) — SDea
- var. *nectarina* Crimson Gold (F) — SDea
- - 'Early Gem' (F) — ERea SDea
¶ - - 'Early Rivers' (F) ♀ — CMac EMui ERea GTwe NRog SDea SFam
- - 'Elruge' (F) — ERea GTwe SDea SEND SFam
- - 'Fantasia' (F) — CGOG ERea SDea
- - 'Fire Gold' (F) — SDea
- - 'Garden Beauty' (F/d) — WWeb

| | |
|---|---|
| - - 'Humboldt' (F) | ERea GTwe SDea |
| - - 'John Rivers' (F) | ERea GTwe SFam |
| - - 'Lord Napier' (F) ♀ | CDoC CWSG EMui ERea LBuc MGos SDea SEND SFam SKee SPer WStI WWeb |
| - - 'Nectared' (F) | GTwe |
| - - 'Nectarella' (F) | EMui ERea GTwe |
| - - 'Pineapple' (F) | CTri ERea GTwe SDea SFam WWeb |
| - - 'Red Haven' (F) | GTwe SDea SKee |
| - - 'Rivers Prolific' (F) | Last listed 1997 |
| - - 'Ruby Gold' (F) | SDea |
| - - 'Terrace Ruby' (F) | WWeb |
| § - 'O'Henry' (F) | CGOG |
| - - 'Peregrine' (F) ♀ | CMac CTri CWSG EMui ERea GBon GRei GTwe LBuc MBri MGos NRog SDea SFam SKee SPer WJas WStI WWeb |
| ¶ - 'Purpurea' | EBee |
| - 'Reliance' (F) | SDea |
| - 'Robin Redbreast' (F) | SDea |
| - 'Rochester' (F) ♀ | CWSG EMui ERea GBon GTwe MBri SDea SEND SFam WStI |
| - 'Royal George' (F) | GTwe NRog SFam |
| - 'Rubira' (F) | Last listed 1998 |
| ¶ - 'Sagami-shidare' | MBri |
| - 'Saturne' (F) | EMui |
| - 'Springtime' (F) | ERea SDea |
| - 'Terrace Amber' | WWeb |
| - 'Terrace Diamond' | WWeb |
| - 'Terrace Garnet' | ENot WWeb |
| - 'Terrace Pearl' | WWeb |
| ¶ - 'White Cascade' | MBri |
| 'Pink Perfection' ♀ | CB&S CBlo CDul CLnd EBee EBrP EBre ENot GChr LBre LHyr LPan MAsh MBri NBee SBre SFam SLon SPer SRPl SSta WFar WJas WOrn |
| 'Pink Shell' ♀ | CBlo CLnd CTho MAsh MBri SFam WStI |
| pissardii | See P. cerasifera 'Pissardii' |
| 'Pissardii Nigra' | See P. cerasifera 'Nigra' |
| * pissardii 'Princess' | CBlo EMui MAsh |
| prostrata | SBla WPat |
| * - 'Anita Kistler' | ECho |
| * - var. discolor | WNor |
| * - 'Pygmaea' | EHyt |
| pseudocerasus | Last listed 1996 |
| 'Cantabrigiensis' | |
| pumila | SEas |
| - var. depressa | CPMA CPle GAri IHar MBar MBlu MRav NPro |
| 'Red Cascade' | SDea |
| ¶ 'Royal Burgundy' | MBri |
| rufa | CTho |
| - FK 40 | Last listed 1997 |
| § salicina 'Black Diamond' (F) | SDea |
| - 'Satsuma' (F) | ERea |
| sargentii ♀ | CB&S CBlo CDoC CDul CLnd CSam CTho EBee ECrN ELan ENot IOrc LBuc LHyr LPan MAsh MBri MGos NBea NWea SFam SPer WDin WJas |
| - 'Columnaris' | MBri |
| - Rancho™ | CLnd ENot SLPl SSta WOrn |
| x schmittii | CLnd CTho ENot SPer WJas |
| 'Sekiyama' | See P. 'Kanzan' |
| serotina | CDul |
| § serrula ♀ | CBlo CDoC CDul CEnd CLnd CSam CTho EBee ECrN ELan ENot GChr IOrc LPan MBal MBar MBlu MBri MGos MRav NBee NBee NBir NWea SMad SPer SSta WDin WNor WWat |

| | |
|---|---|
| - x serrulata | CTho |
| - var. tibetica | See P. serrula |
| serrulata | Last listed 1996 |
| - 'Erecta' | See P. 'Amanogawa' |
| - 'Grandiflora' | See P. 'Ukon' |
| - var. hupehensis | SLPl |
| - 'Longipes' | See P. 'Okumiyako' |
| - 'Miyak' | See P. 'Okumiyako' |
| N - var. pubescens | See P. x verecunda |
| - 'Rosea' | See P. 'Kiku-shidare-zakura' |
| - var. spontanea | See P. jamasakura |
| 'Shidare-zakura' | See P. 'Kiku-shidare-zakura' |
| 'Shimizu-zakura' | See P. 'Okumiyako' |
| 'Shirofugen' ♀ | CB&S CBlo CDoC CLnd CTho EBee EMil IOrc LBuc LPan MAsh MBri MWat SFam SPer SSta WDin WJas WOrn |
| § 'Shirotae' ♀ | CBlo CDoC CEnd CLnd CSam CTho CTri EBee ECrN ELan ENot IOrc LBuc LHyr MAsh MBal MGos MRav NBee NWea SFam SPer SRPl SSta WWeb |
| § 'Shôgetsu' ♀ | CLnd CTho ELan IOrc MBal MBri SFam SPer WDin WStI |
| 'Shosar' | CBlo CEnd CLnd MBri SPer |
| § x sieboldii 'Caespitosa' | Last listed 1996 |
| 'Snow Goose' | MBri |
| spinosa | CDoC CDul CKin CSam CTri ECrN LBuc LHol MBri NBee NWea SPer STre WDin WHer WMou WNor |
| - 'Plena' (d) | CEnd CTho SRPl |
| - 'Purpurea' | MBlu WHCG WMou WPat |
| § 'Spire' ♀ | CBlo CDoC CLnd CTho EBee ENot IOrc LBuc LHyr LPan MGos MRav SPer WFar WJas |
| x subhirtella | WNor |
| - var. ascendens | See P. pendula var. ascendens |
| - 'Autumnalis' ♀ | CB&S CBlo CDul CEnd CLnd CTho EBee EBrP EBre ECrN ELan ENot LBre LPan MAsh MBal MBar MBri MGos MRav NWea SBre SFam SPer SSpi SSta WDin WFar WHar WWat |
| - 'Autumnalis Rosea' ♀ | More than 30 suppliers |
| § - 'Dahlem' | MBri |
| - 'Fukubana' ♀ | CBlo CLnd CTho LPan MAsh MBri |
| - 'Pendula' hort. | See P. pendula 'Pendula Rosea' |
| - 'Pendula Rubra' | See P. pendula 'Pendula Rubra' |
| ♦ - 'Plena' | See P. x subhirtella 'Dahlem' |
| N - 'Rosea' | CLnd MRav SMad |
| - 'Stellata' | See P. pendula 'Stellata' |
| 'Sunset Boulevard' | MBri |
| 'Taihaku' ♀ | More than 30 suppliers |
| 'Takasago' | See P. x sieboldii 'Caespitosa' |
| * takesimensis | CMCN |
| 'Taki-nioi' | Last listed 1996 |
| 'Taoyame' | CLnd MBri WPyg |
| tenella | CB&S CEnd ELan NBee SIng WCot WHCG WWat |
| - 'Fire Hill' ♀ | CEnd CPMA ELan LNet MBar MGos MPla NBee SBod SPer SRPl SSpi SWas WCot WDin WJas WOrn WPat WPyg |
| tibetica | See P. serrula |
| tomentosa | EPla SBod |
| § 'Trailblazer' (C/D) | CBlo CEnd CLnd CTho IOrc LPan MGos NWea SKee SSta WStI |
| triloba | CB&S CBlo LBuc LPan MBar MPla NBee WDin |
| - 'Multiplex' (d) ♀ | EBrP EBre ENot GChr LBre MGos MRav SBre SPer SRms WJas |

|  | |
|---|---|
| - Rosemund | MBri MGos |
| § 'Ukon' ♀ | CB&S CBlo CDoC CDul CLnd |
| | CTho CTri EBee ENot IOrc LBuc |
| | LNet MBal MBar MBri MGos |
| | MRav NBee NWea SFam SPer SRPl |
| | SSta WDin WHar WPyg WStI |
| 'Umineko' | CBlo CDoC CLnd ENot IOrc |
| | MGos SPer |
| § x *verecunda* | CBlo CDoC CLnd GChr NWea |
| | WJas |
| - 'Autumn Glory' | CTho NBea SLPl |
| *virginiana* 'Schubert' | CBlo CDoC CLnd CTho EBee |
| | ENot EPla IOrc LPan SSta WJas |
| 'Wood's Variety' | See *P. cerasifera* 'Woodii' |
| *yamadae* | See *P. incisa* f. *yamadae* |
| § x *yedoensis* ♀ | CLnd CSam CTho ENot NWea |
| | SFam SPer SRPl WDin WJas WOrn |
| | WWat |
| - 'Ivensii' | CB&S CBlo CDoC CDul MAsh |
| | MBri MGos NMoo SFam SPer WStI |
| - 'Moerheimii' | Last listed 1996 |
| - 'Pendula' | See *P. x yedoensis* 'Shidare-yoshino' |
| - 'Perpendens' | See *P. x yedoensis* 'Shidare-yoshino' |
| § - 'Shidare-yoshino' | CBlo CDoC CEnd CLnd CTho |
| | EBee ECrN EPfP GChr LNet MBar |
| | MBri MGos MRav MWat NBee |
| | NWea SPer WOrn WPyg |
| - 'Tsubame' | MBri |
| 'Yoshino' | See *P. x yedoensis* |
| 'Yoshino Pendula' | See *P. x yedoensis* 'Shidare-yoshino' |

## PSEUDERANTHEMUM (Acanthaceae)
| | |
|---|---|
| *reticulatum* 'Eldorado' | LChe |
| ¶ *seticalyx* | ECon |

## PSEUDOCYDONIA (Rosaceae)
| | |
|---|---|
| § *sinensis* | CB&S LNet |

## PSEUDOFUMARIA See CORYDALIS

## PSEUDOLARIX (Pinaceae)
| | |
|---|---|
| § *amabilis* ♀ | CDoC CEnd CFil CGre CMCN |
| | EHul ISea LCon LNet MBal MBar |
| | MBlu MBri SFur STre WCoo WNor |
| | WWat |
| *kaempferi* | See *P. amabilis* |

## PSEUDOMUSCARI See MUSCARI

## PSEUDOPANAX ✿ (Araliaceae)
| | |
|---|---|
| (Adiantifolius Group) 'Adiantifolius' | CB&S CTrC GQui |
| - 'Cyril Watson' ♀ | CB&S |
| *arboreus* | CAbb CB&S |
| *chathamicus* | SAPC SArc |
| *crassifolius* | CAbb CB&S CBot LPan SAPC SArc |
| | SMad |
| ¶ *davidii* | SLon |
| *delavayi* | Last listed 1997 |
| *discolor* | ECou |
| *ferox* | CAbb CB&S LEdu SAPC SArc |
| | SMad |
| *laetus* | CAbb ECou LEdu |
| *lessonii* | CB&S ECou |
| - 'Gold Splash' (v) ♀ | CB&S |
| - hybrids | Last listed 1998 |
| 'Linearifolius' | CTrC |
| 'Purpureus' ♀ | CAbb |

| | |
|---|---|
| 'Sabre' | Last listed 1998 |
| 'Trident' | CTrC SVen |
| *valdiviensis* | Last listed 1998 |

## PSEUDOPHEGOPTERIS (Thelypteridaceae)
| | |
|---|---|
| *levingei* | CCuc EMon |

## PSEUDOPHOENIX (Arecaceae)
| | |
|---|---|
| * *nativo* | MBri |

## PSEUDOSASA (Poaceae - Bambusoideae)
| | |
|---|---|
| § *amabilis* | LJus SDry |
| § - hort. | See *Arundinaria tecta* |
| § *japonica* ♀ | CB&S CBlo EBee EFul EOas EPfP |
| | EPla ISta LBlo LEdu LJus MBal |
| | MBrN MWht NBee NMoo SAPC |
| | SDry SMad SPer WBay WCru |
| | WDin WJun |
| § - 'Akebonosuji' (v) | EFul EPla ISta LJus SDry |
| - 'Tsutsumiana' | CDoC EBee EPla ISta LJus MMoz |
| | SDry WBay WJun |
| - 'Variegata' | See *P. japonica* 'Akebonosuji' |
| *owatarii* | SDry |
| *pleioblastoides* | EPla SDry |
| *usawai* | EPla WJun |

## PSEUDOTSUGA (Pinaceae)
| | |
|---|---|
| § *menziesii* ♀ | CB&S CDoC CDul GChr IOrc |
| | LBuc LCon MBar NWea SRPl |
| | WMou |
| - 'Bhiela Lhota' | CKen |
| - 'Blue Wonder' | CKen MAsh |
| - 'Densa' | CKen |
| - 'Fastigiata' | CKen |
| - 'Fletcheri' | CKen MBar SLim |
| - var. *glauca* | LCon MBar STre |
| - 'Glauca Pendula' ♀ | LCon MBar MGos SMad |
| I - 'Gotelli's Pendula' | CKen |
| - 'Graceful Grace' | CKen |
| - 'Julie' | CKen |
| - 'Little Jamie' | CKen MBar |
| - 'Little Jon' | NHol |
| - 'Lohbrunner' | CKen |
| - 'McKenzie' | CKen |
| - 'Nana' | CKen |
| - Pendula Group | Last listed 1996 |
| - 'Stairii' | CKen |
| - 'Tempelhof Compact' | SLim |
| - f. *viridis* | GRei |
| *taxifolia* | See *P. menziesii* |

## PSEUDOWINTERA (Winteraceae)
| | |
|---|---|
| § *colorata* | CB&S CCHP CDoC CMCN CPla |
| | CTrw IOrc ISea MBlu SLon WCru |
| | WPat WPyg WWat |
| ¶ - 'Mount Congreve' | SSpi SSta |

## PSIDIUM (Myrtaceae)
| | |
|---|---|
| *cattleyanum* | See *P. littorale* var. *longipes* |
| *guajava* (F) | GPoy MPEx |
| *littorale* (F) | ERea |
| § - var. *longipes* (F) | LBlo |

## PSILOSTROPHE (Asteraceae)
| | |
|---|---|
| *tagentinae* | Last listed 1996 |

## PSORALEA (Papilionaceae)
| | |
|---|---|
| *affinis* | Last listed 1998 |
| ¶ *bituminosa* HH&K 174 | CHan |
| *glandulosa* | Last listed 1998 |
| *pinnata* | CTrC CTrG LHil |

## PSYCHOTRIA (Rubiaceae)

| | |
|---|---|
| *capensis* | Last listed 1998 |
| *viridis* | Last listed 1998 |

## PTELEA (Rutaceae)

| | |
|---|---|
| *trifoliata* ♀ | CB&S CFil CLnd CMCN CPMA |
| | ELan LHol MAsh SPer SRms SSpi |
| | WDin WFar WHCG WNor WOrn |
| - 'Aurea' ♀ | CAbP CB&S CBot CDul CEnd |
| | CLnd CPMA CPle ELan ICrw LHol |
| | MBlu MBri MGos SPer SSpi SSta |
| | WHCG WPat WPyg |

## PTERACANTHUS See STROBILANTHES

## PTERIDIUM (Dennstaedtiaceae)

| | |
|---|---|
| *aquilinum* Percristatum | IOrc |
| Group | |

## PTERIDOPHYLLUM (Papaveraceae)

| | |
|---|---|
| *racemosum* | EFEx EPot WCru |

## PTERIS (Pteridaceae)

| | |
|---|---|
| *argyraea* | MBri NMar |
| *bulbifera* | Last listed 1997 |
| *cretica* ♀ | MBri SAPC SArc |
| - var. *albolineata* ♀ | GQui MBri SRms |
| - *cristata* | MBri |
| - 'Gautheri' | MBri |
| - 'Parkeri' | MBri |
| - 'Rivertoniana' | MBri |
| - 'Rowei' | MBri |
| - 'Wimsettii' | MBri |
| *ensiformis* | MBri NMar |
| - 'Arguta' | MBri |
| - 'Victoriae' | MBri |
| *longifolia* | NMar |
| *tremula* | GQui MBri NMar SRms |
| *umbrosa* | MBri |
| *vittata* | SRms |

## PTEROCARYA (Juglandaceae)

| | |
|---|---|
| *fraxinifolia* ♀ | CAgr CB&S CDoC CDul CLnd |
| | CMCN CTho CTrG ECrN ENot |
| | IOrc MBlu WDin WMou |
| - var. *dumosa* | Last listed 1998 |
| x *rehderiana* | CTho WMou |
| *rhoifolia* | Last listed 1998 |
| *stenoptera* | CB&S CFil CLnd CMCN CTho |
| | SLPl SMad WMou |
| - 'Fern Leaf' | SMad WMou |

## PTEROCELTIS (Ulmaceae)

| | |
|---|---|
| *tatarinowii* | CMCN WHCr |

## PTEROCEPHALUS (Dipsacaceae)

| | |
|---|---|
| ¶ *depressus* | WPat |
| *hookeri* | Last listed 1998 |
| *parnassi* | See *P.perennis* |
| § *perennis* | CLyd ELan ESis GCHN LBee MBro |
| | NBir NHar NLon NMen NTow |
| | NWCA SBla SMer SRms WAbe |
| | WCom WEas WHoo WPat WPyg |
| | WWin |
| - subsp. *perennis* | SRms |
| *pinardii* | Last listed 1997 |

## PTEROSTYLIS (Orchidaceae)

| | |
|---|---|
| ¶ *abrupta* | SWes |
| *alata* | SWes |
| Bantam g. | SWes |
| *coccinea* | SSpi SWes |
| - red | SWes |
| *concinna* | SWes |
| - yellow | SWes |
| *curta* | CFil |
| Cutie g. 'Harold's Pride' | SWes |
|    AM-OCSA | |
| Dunkle g. | SWes |
| ¶ *erecta* | SWes |
| *fischii* | SWes |
| Hookwink g. | SWes |
| x *ingens* | SWes |
| Joseph Arthur g. | SWes |
| Marelba g. | SWes |
| Mary Eleanor g. | SWes |
| Nodding Grace g. | SWes |
| ¶ *nutans* white | SWes |
| *obtusa* | SWes |
| *ophioglossa* | SWes |
| ¶ *pedunculata* | SWes |
| *procera* | SWes |
| *revoluta* | Last listed 1996 |
| *robusta* | SWes |
| *russellii* | SWes |
| Sentinel g. | SWes |
| *stricta* | SWes |
| Talhood g. | SWes |
| *taurus* | Last listed 1998 |
| x *toveyana* | SWes |
| *truncata* | SSpi SWes |
| ¶ Trunkfish g. | SWes |

## PTEROSTYRAX (Styracaceae)

| | |
|---|---|
| *corymbosa* | CB&S CMCN SSpi WWat |
| *hispida* ♀ | CB&S CBrd CCHP CFil CLnd |
| | CMCN CPMA CPle CSam EPfP |
| | MBel MBlu MRav SFur SSpi WPGP |
| | WWat |
| *psilophylla* | CMCN CPle |

## PTILIMNIUM (Apiaceae)

| | |
|---|---|
| *capillaceum* | EBee |

## PTILOSTEMON (Asteraceae)

| | |
|---|---|
| ¶ *afer* | CStr EHrv MWgw NChi |
| *casabonae* | Last listed 1998 |
| § *diacantha* | Last listed 1998 |

## PTILOTRICHUM See ALYSSUM

## PUERARIA (Papilionaceae)

| | |
|---|---|
| *montana* var. *lobata* | CAgr CArn CPlN |
| *thunbergiana* | Last listed 1998 |

## PULICARIA (Asteraceae)

| | |
|---|---|
| § *dysenterica* | CArn CKin EWFC MChe MSal |
| | NMir SIde WCHb WJek WOak |
| | WWye |

## PULMONARIA ✿ (Boraginaceae)

| | |
|---|---|
| 'Abbey Dore Pink' | WAbb |
| *affinis* | CElw EMon LRHS |
| ¶ - 'Margaret' | EMon |
| *angustifolia* ♀ | CRow CSam EWTr GDra MBro |
| | MHew MSal NBrk NFla NHol |
| | NOrc SChu SIng SRms WByw |
| | WEas WFar WHil WWat WWin |
| - subsp. *azurea* | CBro CElw COIW CRow CVer |
| | EAst EBee EFou ELan EPla ERav |
| | LNor MBNS MBri MCLN MRav |
| | NBro NRoo NTow SPer SPla SRms |
| | WFar WHoo WWye |

| | Name | Suppliers |
|---|---|---|
| | - 'Blaues Meer' | CBos CFir CSam EBee GBuc LPio MBNS SPla SWas WCru |
| | - 'Blue Pearl' | EBee EMon MBel NHaw NSti |
| | - 'Munstead Blue' | CElw CGle CHea CLAP CWit EBee ECha EFou EHrv EPar LFis LLWP LPio LSpr MTho MWgw NBrk NHol NLon NRya NSti SAga SRms WCru WRus |
| | - 'Rubra' | See P. rubra |
| | 'Apple Frost' | NSti |
| | 'Barfield Regalia' | CGle CLAP CMHG EMon MBro NCat NChi NSti SDys WByw WCer |
| ¶ | 'Benediction' | NSti |
| | 'Berries and Cream' | NSti |
| | 'Beth's Blue' | ECha MBri MGrG WByw WCru WPrP |
| | 'Beth's Pink' | CElw ECha ERav MBel NCat WCHb WCru WFar WPnP |
| | 'Blauer Hügel' | CBel CElw EMon NSti |
| § | 'Blauhimmel' | CLAP EMon MBro WElm WFar WHoo |
| | 'Blue Crown' | CElw CGle CLAP CSev MBri NSti SSpe SWas WBro WCot WHal WPGP |
| | 'Blue Ensign' | More than 30 suppliers |
| | 'Blue Moon' | MBro WElm WHoo WTin |
| ¶ | 'Blue Star' | SWas |
| | 'Botanic Hybrid' | Last listed 1997 |
| | 'British Sterling' | CLAP WGle |
| | 'Buckland' | Last listed 1997 |
| | Cally hybrid | CLAP EBee GCal NSti WCot |
| | 'Cedric Morris' | CElw NSti |
| | 'Chintz' | CLAP CPlt GBuc MAvo WBay WCru WHal |
| | 'Cleeton Red' | NCat NSti SDys WCru |
| | 'Coral Springs' | NSti |
| | 'Corsage' | CElw EBee |
| | 'Crawshay Chance' | SWas WPnP |
| | 'De Vroomen's Pride' | CFir CFri CHid CLAP EAst EBee EMan WWat |
| | 'Diana Chappell' | MBel MSCN NCat SSpi |
| ¶ | 'Diana Clare' | WCot |
| | 'Duke's Silver' | CElw |
| ¶ | 'Elworthy Rubies' | CElw MAvo |
| | 'Esther' | CElw NSti SDys WRus |
| | 'Excalibur' | CElw EBee ECha EMan GBuc NSti |
| | 'Fiona' | NHaw |
| | 'Glacier' | CElw CGle CMea CMil CStr ECha EMon EPPr LPio LRHS MArl MBel NCat NChi NSti SVil WCer WCot WCru WHal |
| | 'Hazel Kaye's Red' | CElw LPio NSti |
| | 'Highdown' | See P. 'Lewis Palmer' |
| | 'Joan's Red' | CElw WCot |
| | 'Lambrook Silver' | Last listed 1996 |
| § | 'Lewis Palmer' ♀ | CBro CGle CMHG CSam EBee EBrP EBre ECtt EOrc GAbr GCHN GCal LBre MBri MCAu NHol NRoo NSti SBla SBre SCro SSpi WByw WCHb WCot WCru WHal WHoo WRus WWat |
| | 'Little Star' | EBee EMon GBuc LRHS MTed WGle |
| | *longifolia* | More than 30 suppliers |
| § | - 'Ankum' | CBos CElw CGle CLAP CSpe CVer EMan EPla GBuc LPio MBel MBrN MBri MRav NSti SBid SCob SSpe SUsu SWas WByw WCot WLin WPnP WRus |
| ¶ | - 'Ballyrogan Blue' | IBlr |
| | - 'Bertram Anderson' | More than 30 suppliers |
| | - subsp. *cevennensis* | MBri SSpi |
| | - 'Coen Jansen' | See P. longifolia 'Ankum' |
| ¶ | - 'Coral Spring' | MBNS |
| | - 'Dordogne' | CGle CLAP CVer EBee ECha EFou EGle GBuc LEdu MGrG MRav SBla SUsu WCot WCru WPGP |
| | - forms | ECha GAbr |
| | - from France | EPPr |
| | - wild-collected | WCot |
| | 'Lovell Blue' | CElw WRus |
| | 'Majesté' | CFil EBee ECha EFou EHoe MBri MHlr SWas WCot WPGP |
| § | 'Margery Fish' ♀ | CBro CGle CLAP COtt EBee LFis LPio MAvo MBri MLLN LBro NChi NRoo NSti NWes SHFr SMer WByw WCHb WCru WEas WMer WPrP WWat WWye |
| | 'Mary Mottram' | CElw CLAP EAst EMan MBel MBri MCLN MLLN MMil NBir NSti SWas WByw WCer WCot WCru WGle WHal WMaN WMoo WPnP |
| | 'Mawson's Blue' | CGle CLAP CMea EBrP EBre ECha EMon LBre LPio MAvo MBel MBri MWat NChi NRoo NSti SBre WCHb WCot WCru WEas WElm WMaN WMoo WOve WRHF WWat |
| | 'Merlin' | CLAP EBee EMon LRHS NSti SSpi WCHb |
| § | 'Milchstrasse' | CLAP NSti |
| ♦ | Milky Way | See P. 'Milchstrasse' |
| | *mollis* | CBel CBot CLAP CSWP EBee EMon EOrc GCal MBri NBrk NCat NSti NWoo SMrm WByw WCot WPrP |
| | - 'Royal Blue' | GCHN MRav SLod WCHb |
| | - 'Samobor' | SCob WCot |
| | *mollissima* | Last listed 1997 |
| ¶ | 'Monksilver' | EMon NSti |
| | 'Moonstone' | CElw CLAP EAst LPio WRus |
| | 'Mournful Purple' | CElw CGle CLAP CRow ECha ERav NBrk SWat WCot WCru WPnP |
| | 'Mrs Kittle' | CElw CMil EBee GBri MBro MCLN MGrG MRav NHaw NSti SDys SSpi WByw WCHb WCot WHal WMer WRus |
| ¶ | 'Netta Statham' | ECha |
| | 'Nürnberg' | EFou EHoe EMon EPPr LFis LRHS MAvo MBel MBro NHaw WCru WHal |
| | *obscura* | EGar EMon LRHS MBel |
| ♦ | 'Ocupol' | See P. Opal = 'Ocupol' |
| | *officinalis* | CArn CBro CGle CHar CRow EHon EMon EOrc EPar EWFC GPoy LHol LLWP MChe MFir MHew NBrk NChi NVic SIde WCru WEas WFar WHal WHbs WOak WWye |
| | - 'Alba' | NCat NLon WByw |
| | - 'Blue Mist' | CElw CMil EBee ECha EGar EMon EOrc GBri MBel NPar NSti SMrm WByw WCru WHal WLin WMoo |
| | - 'Bowles' Blue' | CBel CElw CGle CLAP CVer MMil SSpi WAbb WPGP WRus |
| | - Cambridge Blue Group | CHan EAst EBee ECGN EFou EGar EMon EPla ERav NFai NHol NSti WByw WCru WEas WHal WRus |
| ¶ | - 'Marjorie Lawley' | NPar |
| | - 'Plas Merdyn' | IBlr |
| | - *rubra* | See P. rubra |
| | - 'Sissinghurst White' ♀ | More than 30 suppliers |
| ¶ | - 'Stillingfleet Gran' | LPio NSti |

- 'White Wings'  CElw CHan CHea CLAP CMil EPPr EPla EPri LPio MBNS MBro MCLN NDov NPri NSti SSpi WCHb WEas WFar WMaN
'Oliver Wyatt's White'  EMon
§ Opal = 'Ocupol'  More than 30 suppliers
'Patrick Bates'  MBel WCru
'Paul Aden'  CLAP WGle
¶ 'Pewter'  LPio
¶ 'Purple Haze'  NSti
¶ 'Raspberry Splash'  CElw
* 'Rowlatt Choules'  SSpi
'Roy Davidson'  CElw CGle CLAP CMil CVer EBee EBrP EBre ECGN EPPr LBre LFis MBel MBri MBro NRoo NSti SAga SBla SBre SMrm SWas WCot WCru WGle WHal WRus WWat
§ rubra ♀  CElw CGle CHan CSWP CStr ECha ELan EMar EOrc EWTr LFis LLWP MCAu MFir MSCN NHol NOrc NSti SChu SEas SIng SRms WByw WCHb WCru WElm WFar WRha
- var. alba  See P. rubra var. albocorollata
§ - var. albocorollata  CBel CBre CElw CFil CGle CMHG CVer EAst ECha EHrv EMar EMon LRHS MAvo MBel MBro MCLN MFir MSte NCat NSti SUsu WByw WCru WPrP WRus WWat
- 'Ann'  CBel CElw CLAP EBee EMon IBlr LPio LRHS MBro MWrn NSti SOkh WCru WFar
* - argentea  SCob
- 'Barfield Pink'  CElw CRow EBee ECtt ELan EMon GCal MBel MBro MCLN MMil NBro NLar NRoo NSti SAga SChu SMrm WCHb WCer WCot WCru WHal WLin WPnP WRus
- 'Barfield Ruby'  CLAP EMon GBuc LRHS
- 'Bowles' Red'  CBel CBot CElw CMea CWit EBee EBrP EBre ECtt EHrv ENot ERav EWTr GAbr LBre LHop MWgw NRoo NSti SBre SCro SMrm SPer WFar WHal WMow
- 'David Ward' (v)  More than 30 suppliers
- 'Prestbury Pink'  EMon LLWP
- 'Redstart'  More than 30 suppliers
- 'Warburg's Red'  EMon
§ saccharata  CRow ECha ELan EWTr LGro MBro MCAu MFir NHol SChu SCro SIng SRms WCHb WCru WEas WHoo WPyg WWat WWin
- 'Alba'  CBro CRow ECha EGar GBuc MBel NOak SIng SRms WCru
- Argentea Group ♀  More than 30 suppliers
- 'Blauhimmel'  See P. 'Blauhimmel'
- 'Bofar Red'  Last listed 1997
- 'Brentor'  CElw CRow
¶ - Cambridge Blue Group  NLar
- 'Cotton Cool'  CFil EBee EGar NSti SBid SSpi WCot WCru WMoo WPGP
- 'Dora Bielefeld'  More than 30 suppliers
- 'Frühlingshimmel'  CBel CBro CElw CGle ECha EFou LGre LPio MAvo MBel MRav MUlv NDov NTow SBla SMrm WFar WHal WLin WPnP WPrP WRus
- 'Glebe Cottage Blue'  CElw ECGP LPio NSti
- 'Jill Richardson'  EGar ELan MUlv
- 'Lady Lou's Pink'  LFis WCru
- 'Leopard'  CBos CElw CGle CLAP CMea CSam EBee ECtt GMaP LFis MBel NSti SBid SBla SIng SMrm WCot WCru WHoo WMer WPnP WRus

- 'Mrs Moon'  CWit EBee ECtt EFou ENot GMaP LHop MBNS MCAu MWgw NBrk NBro NFla NHol NOrc SChu SPer WCHb WCru WHen WHil WMow WPnP WPyg WWal
- 'Old Rectory Silver'  CLAP MWrn
- 'Picta'  See P. saccharata
- 'Pink Dawn'  CMHG EMan EOrc LFis MBri NBus NPri NSti WCru
- 'Reginald Kaye'  CElw CRow ECha EHic EMFP ERav EWes MBro NBrk NChi NCot NDov NSti
- 'Snow Queen'  Last listed 1997
- 'South Hayes'  CLAP
- 'White Leaf'  WRus
'Saint Ann's'  CElw CLTr EMon NSti
¶ 'Silver Mist'  MAvo NPar
'Silver Spring'  Last listed 1998
'Skylight'  CElw MAvo
'Smoky Blue'  CBlo CLAP EAst EBee EFou EPfP MBro MCLN NPri NRoo NSti SCob SMer SWat WByw WFar WHal WMer WWat WWeb WWoo WGle
'Snowy Owl'  WGle
¶ 'Spilled Milk'  NSti
'Tim's Silver'  ECha NBrk NPar WBcn
'Ultramarine'  CElw EMon
¶ vallarsae  EAst
- 'Margery Fish'  See P. 'Margery Fish'
* veitchii BQE 1307  SWas
¶ 'Victorian Brooch'  CLAP
'Weetwood Blue'  CBre CElw CLAP CVer EBee MSte
'Wendy Perry'  CElw CFil
'Wisley White'  CElw

## PULSATILLA (Ranunculaceae)

alba  CBro
albana  CBro EHyt GCrs SBla WCom WLin
- 'Lutea'  SBla
- white  Last listed 1998
alpina  CBot NRoo SRms WSan WViv
§ - subsp. apiifolia ♀  CBot CLyd ELan EWTr GTou NHar NRoo WLin WSan
- subsp. sulphurea  See P. alpina subsp. apiifolia
ambigua  EBee ESis SIgm
aurea  GCrs
bungeana  Last listed 1998
campanella  Last listed 1998
caucasica  CBro
cernua  GBuc NDov NLar SIgm
chinensis  Last listed 1998
* czerna  Last listed 1998
dahurica  Last listed 1998
x gayeri  Last listed 1998
georgica  SIgm
halleri ♀  ECGP EMan GLch MMil NHed NSla SIgm
- alba  Last listed 1997
- subsp. slavica ♀  CBro EPot GCrs NNrd NWCA SWas WCom WWin
koreana  CBro LRHS
* lutea  Last listed 1998
montana  EWes SIgm WLin
- var. australis  Last listed 1998
occidentalis  EPot
§ patens  WAbe
- subsp. flavescens  WAbe
- var. multifida NNS 96221  EPot IDac SIgm
- subsp. trisecta  Last listed 1997
* pinnata  Last listed 1998
pratensis  GTou
- subsp. nigricans  CBro EHyt LRHS

¶ *rubra* — CHar
\* *serotina* — Last listed 1998
*turczaninovii* — EBee SIgm
\* *ucrainica* — Last listed 1998
§ *vernalis* ♀ — EPot GCrs GDra GTou NHar NSla NTow NWCA SRms WAbe
§ *vulgaris* ♀ — More than 30 suppliers
- 'Alba' ♀ — More than 30 suppliers
- 'Barton's Pink' — CMil EWes EWll NSla SBla SSON WRus
- Czech Fringed hybrids — Last listed 1997
- 'Eva Constance' — CBro CLyd CRDP EBrP EBre EHyt ESis LBre LHop LRHS SBre SIng SWas WAbe
- 'Flore Pleno' (d) — CNic
- 'Gotlandica' — CLyd GDra NHol SIgm
- subsp. *grandis* — CLAP WLin
- - 'Budapest' — SIng
- - f. *dissecta* — WAbe
- - ex 'Budapest' — GCrs NMen
- Heiler hybrids — EMan SIng SSON
- 'Miss Beveridge' — NOak
- pale pink — NRoo
- 'Papageno' — CBot CGle CSpe EMan GCrs LGre NLar NRoo NSla SIgm SMrm SUsu WHil WViv
- 'Red Clock' — See *P. vulgaris* 'Röde Klokke'
§ - 'Röde Klokke' — LGre MBro MTis NHol NOla WHil
- *rosea* — SCob WHoo
- Rote Glocke — See *P. vulgaris* 'Röde Klokke'
- var. *rubra* — CB&S CGle CSpe EFou EHyt ELan EOrc GAbr LHop MBal MBri MBro NFla NHar NHol NRoo SRms WCom WHoo WPer WRus
¶ - violet blue — SCob
§ - 'Weisse Schwan' — CBlo EHyt EOld LFis MCLN NFla NMen
- White Swan — See *P. vulgaris* 'Weisse Schwan'
\* *wisetonensis* — Last listed 1998

## PULTENAEA (Papilionaceae)
*daphnoides* — Last listed 1998

## PUNICA (Punicaceae)
*granatum* — ECon ERea GAri LPan MPEx SOWG STre WSHC
- var. *nana* — CArn CHal CPle EOHP EPfP ERea GAri LHop LPan MPla SLon SMrm SRCN SRms WPat WWat
- f. *plena* (d) — CB&S MRav WCFE
- - 'Flore Pleno Luteo' (d) — Last listed 1997
¶ - - 'Rubrum Flore Pleno' (d) ♀ — LPan WPat
\* - 'Striata' — SOWG

## PUSCHKINIA (Hyacinthaceae)
*scilloides* — Last listed 1996
§ - var. *libanotica* — CAvo EPar EPot ETub LAma MBal NEgg NRog WPer WShi
- - 'Alba' — CAvo EPar EPot LAma NRog
- - S&L 113 — Last listed 1996
- Polunin 5238 — Last listed 1998

## PUTORIA (Rubiaceae)
*calabrica* — CLyd NWCA

## PUYA (Bromeliaceae)
*alpestris* — CFil CTbh CTrC SAPC SSpi WCot WPGP
*berteroniana* — CTrC WPic
*chilensis* — CAbb CB&S CBrd CDoC CTbh CTrC ECre EOas LEdu SAPC SArc

*coerulea* — CFir EOas GBin SIgm
- var. *coerulea* — SCob
- F&W 8411 — WLRN
- JCA 14371 — IDac
- RB 94100 — LLew
§ - var. *violacea* — Last listed 1998
- - F&W 7911 — WLRN
*conquimbensis* — Last listed 1997
*laxa* — Last listed 1998
*mirabilis* — CTrC LLew WPGP
*mitis* — Last listed 1996
*raimondii* — Last listed 1998
sp. G&P 5036 — Last listed 1996
*venusta* — WPic
- JCA 14369 — IDac
*violacea* — See *P. coerulea* var. *violacea*
*weberbaueri* — Last listed 1998

## PYCNANTHEMUM (Lamiaceae)
¶ *californicum* — WCot
*montanum* — WCot
*muticum* — MRav
*pilosum* — CArn CHal CSev ELau EMan GBar GPoy MHer MSal NLar NPri SIde WGwG WHer WPer WWye
¶ *tenuifolium* — WCot
*virginiana* — ECha

## PYCNOSTACHYS (Lamiaceae)
*urticifolia* — Last listed 1998

## PYGMAEA See CHIONOHEBE

## PYRACANTHA ✿ (Rosaceae)
Alexander Pendula — CBlo EHol ENot GAri LHop MGos MRav SEas SRms WHar WWat
*angustifolia* — CBlo EHic WUnu
§ *atalantioides* — CB&S CBlo CMac CSam SPla WCFE
§ - 'Aurea' — CBlo WWin
'Brilliant' — CB&S EBee EPfP
'Buttercup' — EPla GAri WBcn
◆ 'Cadange' — See *P.* Saphyr® Orange = 'Cadange'
◆ 'Cadaune' — See *P.* Saphyr® Jaune = 'Cadaune'
◆ 'Cadrou' — See *P.* Saphyr® Rouge = 'Cadrou'
*coccinea* — CTrw
§ - 'Lalandei' — CBlo CMac CSam EBee EWTr NFor SPer WGwG WWal
- 'Red Column' — CBlo CChe CMac EBee ECtt ELan EWTr GChr GOrc GRei LBuc MBNS MBar MGos MRav MWat NBee NFla SAga SCoo SEas WBod WDin WGwG WHar WWal
- 'Red Cushion' — CBlo EBee ENot MGos MRav SPer SRms
- 'Rutgers' — SLPl
- 'Telstar' — Last listed 1998
¶ *crenulata* S&SH 385 — CHan
Dart's Red — CBlo EBee MBri WBod WLRN
*gibbsii* — See *P. atalantioides*
- 'Flava' — See *P. atalantioides* 'Aurea'
¶ 'Gold Rush' — WSPU
'Golden Charmer' — CBlo EBee EBrP EBre ECtt ELan ENot EPfP LBre MBal MGos NLon SBre SPer SRms WBod WDin WFar WGwG WHar
'Golden Dome' — SEas
'Golden Glow' — CBlo
'Golden Sun' — See *P.* 'Soleil d'Or'

| | |
|---|---|
| 'Harlequin' (v) | CB&S CBlo ECtt EPla MBal NSti SBid SReu WCot WLeb WSHC WWeb |
| 'John Stedman' | See *P*. 'Stedman's' |
| 'Knap Hill Lemon' | CChe MBlu WSPU |
| 'Mohave' | CB&S CBlo CChe CMac EBee EBrP EBre ELan ENot EWTr LBre MBal MBar MGos MWat NFor NHed SBre SPer SReu SRms WDin WStI WWal |
| 'Mohave Silver' (v) | CBlo EAst ELan MBNS MGos MWat SEas WGwG WWal |
| 'Monrovia' | See *P. coccinea* 'Lalandei' |
| 'Mozart' | WWeb |
| 'Navaho' | CBlo EPfP MPla MRav WBcn |
| 'Orange Charmer' | CB&S CBlo CChe CTri EBee ELan ENot MAsh MBal MGos MWat NBee SPer WRHF WStI WWeb |
| 'Orange Glow' ♀ | CBlo CChe CMac EBee EBrP EBre ECtt ENot EWTr GOrc GRei LBre LBuc MAsh MBar MGos NFla NFor NLon NWea SBre SPer SRPl SRms WDin WFar WHar WStI |
| * 'Red Pillar' | CBlo CDoC SRPl |
| 'Renault d'Or' | SLPl |
| *rogersiana* ♀ | CBlo EBee EHic ENot EPfP MRav WWal |
| - 'Flava' ♀ | CBlo CTri EBee EHol ENot EPfP MAsh MBal MBar MRav NFla NFor NWea SRPl WGwG WWal |
| § Saphyr® Jaune = 'Cadaune' | CBlo CDoC CEnd EBee EPfP IOrc MBNS MGos MRav SPer SSto WLRN WWeb |
| § Saphyr® Orange = 'Cadange' | CBlo CDoC CEnd ECtt EBee EPfP IOrc MBri MRav SBid SPer SSto WLRN WWeb |
| § Saphyr® Rouge = 'Cadrou' | CBlo CDoC CEnd ECtt EBee EPfP IOrc MBri MGos MRav SBid SPer SSto WLRN WWeb |
| 'Shawnee' | CB&S CBlo CMac EBee ECot EHic EPfP MAsh MRav MWat NHed SPla |
| § 'Soleil d'Or' | CBlo CMac CSam EBrP EBre ECtt ELan ENot EWTr LBre LBuc MBar MBri MPla MRav NCut NFor NLon SBre SLPl SLon SPer SReu WDin WFar WHCr WHar WStI |
| 'Sparkler' (v) | CBlo CDoC CMac CPMA EHoe ELan LHop MAsh MBNS MGos NFor NHol NLon SAga SBid SPer WFar WHar |
| § 'Stedman's' | MBri |
| 'Teton' | CMHG CMac EBee ELan ENot EPla ESis LHop MAsh MBar MBri MGos MRav NHed SPla SRms WBod WDin WFar WLRN WStI |
| 'Watereri' ♀ | CBlo SBid SLPl SPer |
| 'Yellow Sun' | See *P*. 'Soleil d'Or' |

## PYRENARIA (Theaceae)
| | |
|---|---|
| * *spectabilis* | EPfP |

## PYRETHROPSIS See RHODANTHEMUM

## PYRETHRUM (Asteraceae)
| | |
|---|---|
| *radicans* | See *Leucanthemopsis pectinata* |
| *roseum* | See *Tanacetum coccineum* |

## PYRETHRUM See TANACETUM

## + PYROCYDONIA (Rosaceae)
| | |
|---|---|
| 'Danielii' (F) | WMou |

## PYROLA (Ericaceae)
| | |
|---|---|
| *rotundifolia* | WHer |

## PYROSTEGIA (Bignoniaceae)
| | |
|---|---|
| *venusta* | CPIN LChe LCns SOWG WMul |

## PYRROCOMA (Asteraceae)
| | |
|---|---|
| *clementis* | EBee |

## PYRROSIA (Polypodiaceae)
| | |
|---|---|
| * *heterophylla* | NMar |
| *lingua* 'Variegata' (v) | EMon |

## PYRUS ✿ (Rosaceae)
| | |
|---|---|
| *amygdaliformis* | CTho |
| - var. *cuneifolia* | CTho |
| *betulifolia* | CMCN MAsh WJas |
| *calleryana* | Last listed 1998 |
| - 'Bradford' | CLnd |
| - 'Chanticleer' ♀ | CB&S CBlo CDoC CDul CEnd CLnd CTho EBee ENot IOrc LHyr LPan MAsh MBlu MGos MRav NBee SPer SSta WDin WJas WOrn WWat |
| ¶ - 'Redspire' | WGer |
| x *canescens* | CTho |
| *communis* (F) | CCVT CKin GChr LBuc MBlu NRog SKee SPer STre WMou |
| - 'Abbé Fétel' (D) | Last listed 1996 |
| - 'Admiral Gervais' (D) | Last listed 1996 |
| - 'Alexandrina Bivort' (D) | Last listed 1996 |
| - 'Autumn Bergamot' (D) | CTho SKee |
| - 'Barland' (Perry) | Last listed 1998 |
| - 'Barnet' (Perry) | CTho |
| - 'Baronne de Mello' (D) | CTho SFam SKee |
| - 'Beech Hill' (F) | CDul CLnd CTho EMil ENot EPfP |
| - 'Belle Guérandaise' (D) | SKee |
| - 'Belle Julie' (D) | SKee |
| - 'Bellissime d'Hiver' (C) | Last listed 1996 |
| - 'Bergamotte d'Automne' (D) | SKee |
| - 'Bergamotte Esperen' (D) | SKee |
| - 'Beth' (D) ♀ | CDoC CWSG EMui GBon GTwe LBuc MBri MGos NBee NRog SDea SFam SKee SPer WHar |
| - 'Beurré Alexandre Lucas' (D) | SKee |
| - 'Beurré Bachelier' (D) | Last listed 1996 |
| - 'Beurré Bedford' (D) | Last listed 1998 |
| - 'Beurré Bosc' (D) | SKee |
| - 'Beurré Clairgeau' (C/D) | SKee |
| - 'Beurré d'Amanlis' (D) | SKee |
| - 'Beurré d'Avalon' (D) | CTho |
| - 'Beurré de Beugny' (D) | SKee |
| - 'Beurré de Jonghe' (D) | Last listed 1996 |
| - 'Beurré de Naghin' (C/D) | SKee |
| - 'Beurré Diel' (D) | Last listed 1996 |
| - 'Beurré Dumont' (D) | SFam |
| - 'Beurré Gris d'Hiver' (D) | Last listed 1997 |
| - 'Beurré Hardy' (D) ♀ | CDoC CTho EMui ERea GTwe MBri MWat NBea NRog SDea SFam SKee |
| - 'Beurré Jean van Geert' (D) | Last listed 1996 |
| - 'Beurré Mortillet' (D) | SKee |
| - 'Beurré Six' (D) | SKee |
| - 'Beurré Superfin' (D) | ERea GTwe SFam SKee |
| - 'Bianchettone' (D) | SKee |
| - 'Bishop's Thumb' (D) | SDea SKee |
| - 'Black Worcester' (C) | GTwe SDea SFam SKee WJas WSPU |
| - 'Blakeney Red' (Perry) | CTho SDea |

- 'Blickling' (D) — SKee
- 'Brandy' (Perry) — CTho SDea
- 'Bristol Cross' (D) — GTwe SKee
- 'Brown Bess' (Perry) — Last listed 1998
- 'Buckland' (F) — Last listed 1996
§ - 'Butirra Precoce Morettini' (D) — SDea
- 'Butt' (Perry) — Last listed 1996
- 'Catillac' (C) ♀ — CTho GTwe NRog SFam SKee
- 'Chalk' — See *P. communis* 'Crawford'
- 'Charles Ernest' (D) — Last listed 1996
- 'Chaumontel' (D) — SKee
- 'Clapp's Favourite' (D) — CTho GTwe IOrc SKee
- 'Colmar d'Eté' (D) — CTho
- 'Comte de Lamy' (D) — SKee
- 'Concorde' (D) ♀ — CDoC CSam CWSG EMui ERea GTwe LBuc MBri MGos NBee NRog SDea SFam SKee WHar WJas WWeb
- 'Conference' (D) ♀ — CDoC CMac CSam CTho CWSG EBrP EBre EMui ERea GBon GChr GRei IOrc LBre LBuc MBri MGos MWat NBea NBee NRog SBre SDea SFam SKee SPer WHar WJas WWeb
- 'Craig's Favourite' (D) — GTwe
- 'Crassane' — CTho
§ - 'Crawford' (D) — SKee
- 'Deacon's Pear' (D) — SDea
¶ - 'Devoe' (D) — SDea
- 'Docteur Jules Guyot' (D) — SDea SKee
- 'Double de Guerre' (C/D) — SKee
- 'Doyenné Boussoch' (D) — SKee
- 'Doyenné d'Eté' (D) — ERea SFam SKee
- 'Doyenné du Comice' (D) ♀ — CDoC CMac CSam CTho CWSG EBrP EBre EMui ERea GBon IOrc LBre LBuc MBri MRav MWat NRog SBre SDea SFam SKee SPer WHar WJas WWeb
- 'Doyenné Georges Boucher' (D) — SKee
- 'Duchesse d'Angoulême' (D) — SKee
- 'Duchesse de Bordeaux' (D) — Last listed 1996
- 'Durondeau' (D) — CTho GTwe NRog SDea SFam SKee
- 'Easter Beurré' (D) — SKee
- 'Emile d'Heyst' (D) — CTho GTwe
- 'English Caillot Rosat' (D) — Last listed 1997
- 'Eva Baltet' (D) — SKee
- 'Fair Maid' (D) — Last listed 1997
- 'Fertility' (D) — Last listed 1996
- 'Fertility Improved' — See *P. communis* 'Improved Fertility'
- 'Fondante d'Automne' (D) — CTho SKee
- 'Forelle' (D) — ERea SKee
- 'Gansel's Bergamot' (D) — CTho
- 'Gin' (Perry) — CTho
- 'Glou Morceau' (D) — CTho EMui GTwe MWat NRog SDea SFam SKee
- 'Glow Red Williams' (D) — SFam
- 'Gorham' (D) — CTho GTwe NBee SFam SKee
- 'Gratiole de Jersey' (D) — CTho
- 'Green Horse' (Perry) — CTho
- 'Green Pear of Yair' (D) — SKee
- 'Hacon's Imcomparable' (D) — SKee
¶ - 'Harrow Delight' (D) — SDea
¶ - 'Harvest Queen' (D/C) — SDea
§ - 'Hellen's Early' (Perry) — Last listed 1996
- 'Hendre Huffcap' (Perry) — Last listed 1998

- 'Hessle' (D) — GTwe NRog SDea SFam SKee
- 'Highland' (D) — SKee
§ - 'Improved Fertility' (D) — CDoC GBon GTwe SDea SKee
- 'Jargonelle' (D) — GTwe NRog SDea SFam SKee
- 'Joséphine de Malines' (D) ♀ — CTho GTwe SDea SFam SKee
- 'Judge Amphlett' (Perry) — Last listed 1998
- 'Laxton's Early Market' (D) — Last listed 1996
- 'Laxton's Foremost' (D) — SKee
- 'Laxton's Satisfaction' (D) — SFam
- 'Le Lectier' (D) — SKee
- 'Louise Bonne of Jersey' (D) — CDoC CTho CTri EMui GTwe MBri MGos NRog SDea SFam SKee
- 'Louise Marillat' (F) — Last listed 1996
- 'Madame Treyve' (D) — Last listed 1997
- 'Maggie Duncan' (F) — GTwe
- 'Marguérite Marillat' (D) — GTwe SDea
- 'Marie-Louise' (D) — SKee
- 'Martin Sec' (C/D) — Last listed 1997
- 'Merton Pride' (D) — CTho GTwe MWat SDea SFam SKee
- 'Merton Star' (D) — SKee
¶ - 'Monarch' (D) — CLnd
¶ - 'Moonglow' (D/C) — SDea
- 'Moorcroft' (Perry) — Last listed 1998
♦ - 'Morettini' — See *P. communis* 'Butirra Precoce Morettini'
- 'Muirfield Egg' (D) — Last listed 1996
- 'Nouveau Poiteau' (C/D) — CTho GTwe SKee
- 'Nouvelle Fulvie' (D) — Last listed 1996
- 'Oldfield' (Perry) — Last listed 1998
- 'Olivier de Serres' (D) — SFam SKee
- 'Onward' (D) ♀ — CLnd EMui GTwe LBuc MGos NBee NRog SDea SFam SKee WHar
- 'Ovid' (D) — Last listed 1996
§ - 'Packham's Triumph' (D) — CDoC GTwe NRog SDea SKee
- 'Parsonage' (Perry) — Last listed 1996
- 'Passe Colmar' (D) — CTho
- 'Passe Crassane' (D) — SKee
- 'Pear Apple' (D) — SDea
- 'Pitmaston Duchess' (C/D) ♀ — CWSG GTwe SDea SKee
- 'Précoce de Trévoux' (D) — Last listed 1996
- 'Red Comice' (D/C) — GTwe SKee
- 'Red Pear' (Perry) — Last listed 1996
- 'Robin' (C/D) — ERea SDea SKee
- 'Roosevelt' (D) — SKee
- 'Santa Claus' (D) — SDea SFam SKee
- 'Seckle' (D) — GTwe SFam SKee
- 'Soleil d'Automne' (F) — SKee
- 'Souvenir du Congrès' (D) — Last listed 1998
- 'Sucrée de Montluçon' (D) — Last listed 1997
- 'Swan's Egg' (D) — CTho SKee
- 'Sweet Huffcap' — See *P. communis* 'Hellen's Early'
- 'Taynton Squash' (Perry) — Last listed 1996
- 'Thompson's' (D) — GTwe SFam
- 'Thorn' (Perry) — CTho
- 'Triomphe de Vienne' (D) — SFam
- 'Triumph' — See *P. communis* 'Packham's Triumph'
- 'Uvedale's St Germain' (C) — CTho SKee
- 'Vicar of Winkfield' (C/D) — GTwe SDea SKee
- 'Williams' Bon Chrétien' (D/C) ♀ — CMac CSam CWSG EBrP EBre EMui ERea GBon GChr GRei IOrc LBre LBuc MBri MGos MWat NBea NRog SBre SDea SFam SKee SPer WHar WJas WStI WWeb
- 'Williams Red' (D/C) — GTwe SKee
- 'Winnal's Longdon' (Perry) — CTho
- 'Winter Christie' (F) — GTwe

- 'Winter Nelis' (D) | CTho GTwe SDea SFam SKee
- 'Zéphirin Grégoire' (D) | Last listed 1997
*cordata* | CTho SKee
*cossonii* | CTho
*elaeagnifolia* | CTho WWat
- var. *kotschyana* | CBlo CEnd MAsh MRav
*nivalis* | CLnd CTho ENot EPfP SLPl SPer
*pashia* CLD 114 | EPla
*pyraster* | Last listed 1998
*pyrifolia* '20th Century' | See *P. pyrifolia* 'Nijisseiki'
- 'Chojura' (F) | IOrc
- 'Kumoi' (F) | LBuc SDea
* - 'Nashi Kumoi' | LPan
§ - 'Nijisseiki' (F) | Last listed 1996
- 'Shinseiki' (F) | EMui SDea SKee
- 'Shinsui' (F) | SDea SKee
*salicifolia* 'Pendula' ♀ | More than 30 suppliers
*ussuriensis* | CBlo CMCN

# Q

## QUERCUS ✿ (Fagaceae)

§ *acuta* | CB&S CMCN
§ *acutissima* | CLnd CMCN SBir WNor WShe
*aegilops* | See *Q. macrolepis*
*affinis* | CMCN SBir
*agrifolia* | CB&S CMCN LEdu SBir
*alba* | CMCN
- f. *elongata* | LRHS
*aliena* | CMCN SBir
¶ - var. *acutiserrata* | CMCN
*alnifolia* | CDul
*arkansana* | CMCN
*austrina* | CMCN
*baloot* | Last listed 1997
♦ x *beadlei* | See *Q.* x *saulii*
*bicolor* | CMCN SBir WDin WNor
*borealis* | See *Q. rubra*
*brantii* | CMCN
♦ *breweri* | See *Q. garryana* var. *fruticosa*
x *bushii* | CMCN MBlu
*canariensis* ♀ | CFil CLnd CMCN CTho CTrG
 | EPfP IDee WMou WTro
*canbyi* | Last listed 1998
*castaneifolia* | CB&S CLnd CMCN LPan WMou
- 'Green Spire' ♀ | CDoC CDul CLnd CMCN EBee
 | EPfP MAsh MBlu MBri SMad SPer
*cerris* ♀ | CB&S CBlo CDoC CDul CKin
 | CLnd CMCN EBee ECrN EMil
 | ENot EWTr IOrc LPan MGos
 | NWea SEND SPer SSta STre WDin
 | WFro WMou WTro
§ - 'Argenteovariegata' | CDul CMCN CTho EPfP MAsh
 | MBlu MBri SMad WMou
* - 'Marmorata' | CLyn
- 'Variegata' | See *Q. cerris* 'Argenteovariegata'
- 'Wodan' | CMCN MBlu
¶ *chapmanii* | CMCN
*chrysolepis* | CMCN SBir
*coccifera* | CDul CFil CMCN WPGP
¶ - subsp. *calliprinos* | CMCN
*coccinea* | CAbP CB&S CDul CLnd CMCN
 | CWSG EHic EPfP GChr IOrc
 | MAsh NBea NBee NWea SBir SPer
 | SSta STre WNor WOrn
- 'Splendens' ♀ | CDoC CDul CEnd CFil CMCN
 | COtt CTho EBee ELan EWTr IOrc
 | LPan MBlu MBri NBee SPer SSpi
 | WDin WPGP

x *comptoniae* | CMCN
*crassipes* | CMCN
*dentata* | CMCN EPfP
- 'Carl Ferris Miller' | CFil CMCN LRHS MBlu SMad
 | WPGP
- 'Pinnatifida' | CMCN MBlu SMad
- 'Sir Harold Hillier' | LRHS
*douglasii* | CAgr CMCN
*dumosa* | CMCN WNor
♦ *durandii* | See *Q. sinuata* var. *sinuata*
*durata* | Last listed 1997
*ellipsoidalis* | CAbP CDoC CDul CMCN SBir
 | WNor WWat WWes
- 'Hemelrijk' | CFil MBlu
*engelmannii* | CMCN
¶ *fabrei* | SBir
*faginea* | CMCN SBir
♦ - subsp. *tlemcenensis* | See *Q. faginea* subsp. *broteroi*
♦ - aff. subsp. *tlemcenensis* | See *Q. faginea* aff. subsp. *broteroi*
*falcata* | CDul CLnd CMCN
♦ - var. *pagodifolia* | See *Q. pagoda*
x *fernaldii* | CMCN
*frainetto* | CDoC CDul CLnd CMCN CTho
 | EBee GChr IOrc LPan MBlu MBri
 | SEND SMad SPer SSpi WDin
 | WMou WNor
¶ - 'Hungarian Crown' ♀ | CMCN
- 'Trump' | MBlu SMad
*fruticosa* | See *Q. lusitanica* Lamarck
*gambelii* | CMCN
- x *macrocarpa* | Last listed 1998
*garryana* | CMCN MBlu
§ - var. *fruticosa* | CMCN
- x *turbinella* | Last listed 1998
*geminata* | Last listed 1997
*georgiana* | CMCN
*gilva* | Last listed 1997
*glabra* | See *Lithocarpus glaber*
*glabrescens* | CB&S
♦ *glandulifera* | See *Q. serrata*
§ *glauca* | CB&S CMCN SAPC SArc SBir
 | WNor
*hartwissiana* | CMCN
x *hastingsii* | CMCN
*hemisphaerica* | CMCN SBir
x *heterophylla* | CDul CMCN SBir
♦ x *heuffelii* | See *Q.* x *haynaldiana*
x *hickelii* | CMCN
*hinckleyi* | WDin
§ x *hispanica* | CLnd WPic
¶ - 'Ambrozyana' | LRHS SMad
¶ - 'Diversifolia' | CMCN MBlu WMou
¶ - 'Fulhamensis' | CMCN
§ - 'Lucombeana' ♀ | CDul CMCN CTho MBlu SPer
 | WMou
¶ - 'Suberosa' | CTho
¶ - 'Wageningen' | CMCN WMou
*ilex* ♀ | More than 30 suppliers
*ilicifolia* | CDul CMCN MBlu WNor WShe
 | WWat
*imbricaria* | CDul CMCN MBlu SBir WWes
*incana* Roxburgh | See *Q. leucotrichophora*
- Bartram | CMCN IOrc MBlu
*infectoria* | CDul
- subsp. *veneris* | CMCN
*ithaburensis* | CMCN
§ - subsp. *macrolepis* | CMCN MBlu
*kelloggii* | CMCN WWes
x *kewensis* | CMCN WMou
♦ *laevigata* | See *Q. acuta*
*laevis* | CMCN MBlu
§ *laurifolia* | CDul CMCN

| | |
|---|---|
| § *leucotrichophora* | CMCN |
| ♦ *liaotungensis* | See *Q. wutaishanica* |
| x *libanerris* | SBir |
| - 'Rotterdam' | CMCN |
| *libani* | CDul CMCN |
| *lobata* | CAgr CMCN |
| ♦ x *lucombeana* | See *Q.* x *hispanica* |
| ♦ - 'William Lucombe' | See *Q.* x *hispanica* 'Lucombeana' |
| x *ludoviciana* | CMCN |
| § *lusitanica* Lamarck | CDul CMCN |
| *lyrata* | CMCN SBir |
| *macranthera* | CMCN EMil EPfP |
| *macrocarpa* | CMCN SBir SMad WDin WNor |
| - x *robur* | Last listed 1998 |
| - x *turbinella* | Last listed 1996 |
| ♦ *macrolepis* | See *Q. ithaburensis* subsp. *macrolepis* |
| *marilandica* | CDul CEnd CMCN EPfP SBir WWes |
| ¶ 'Maurii' | LPan |
| *mexicana* | CMCN |
| *michauxii* | CMCN SBir |
| *mongolica* | Last listed 1996 |
| ¶ - subsp. *crispula* var. *grosseserrata* | CMCN |
| § *montana* | CMCN MBlu |
| *muehlenbergii* | CDul CMCN CTho SBir |
| ♦ *myrsinifolia* | See *Q. glauca* |
| *nigra* | CMCN CMHG MBlu SBir WNor |
| ♦ *nuttallii* | See *Q. texana* |
| ♦ *obtusa* | See *Q. laurifolia* |
| § *pagoda* | CMCN MBlu SBir |
| *palustris* ♀ | CAgr CDul CLnd CMCN CTho IOrc LPan MBal MBri SBir SPer SSpi WDin WNor WOrn |
| * - 'Compacta' | LRHS |
| - 'Pendula' | CEnd CMCN |
| * - 'Swamp Pygmy' | CMCN MBlu |
| *pedunculata* | See *Q. robur* |
| ♦ *pedunculiflora* | See *Q. robur* subsp. *pedunculiflora* |
| § *petraea* ♀ | CDoC CDul CKin CLnd GChr GRei IOrc LBuc MBal NBee NWea SPer WDin WFro WMou WTro |
| - 'Columna' | Last listed 1997 |
| § - 'Insecata' | CDoC CEnd CMCN |
| - 'Laciniata' | See *Q. petraea* 'Insecata' |
| - 'Mespilifolia' | CTho |
| § - 'Purpurea' | CMCN MBlu |
| ♦ - 'Rubicunda' | See *Q. petraea* 'Purpurea' |
| § *phellos* ♀ | CDul CLnd CMCN CTho GChr MAsh MBlu SLPl SLdr SSpi STre WCoo WDin WNor WWat WWes |
| *phillyreoides* | CB&S CDul CMCN SBir SLPl WCoo WNor WWat |
| *planipocula* | CMCN |
| 'Pondaim' | CMCN LRHS |
| *pontica* | CMCN EPfP MBlu |
| *prinoides* | Last listed 1998 |
| * *prinus* L. | CAgr CMCN MBlu |
| * - Engelm. | See *Q. montana* |
| *pubescens* | CDul CMCN |
| *pumila* Walt. | See *Q. phellos* |
| - Michaux | See *Q. montana* |
| *pyrenaica* | CMCN CTho |
| - 'Pendula' | CMCN MBlu |
| § *robur* ♀ | More than 30 suppliers |
| - 'Argenteomarginata' | CDul CMCN MBlu SMad SSta |
| - 'Atropurpurea' | EMil |
| * - 'Compacta' | MBlu |
| - 'Concordia' | CB&S CBlo CEnd CFil CMCN COtt EPfP GChr LRHS MBlu SMad SSpi WPGP |

| | |
|---|---|
| ¶ - 'Contorta' | CMCN |
| - 'Cristata' | CDul CMCN |
| - 'Cucullata' | CMCN |
| * - *dissecta* | CMCN |
| - 'Facrist' | CBlo CDul CEnd |
| - f. *fastigiata* | CBlo CDoC CDul CLnd CTho EBee EMil ENot ERod GChr IOrc LPan MAsh MBar MGos MWat NBee NWea SCoo SLPl SPer WDin WOrn |
| - 'Fastigiata Koster' ♀ | CDul CMCN COtt EMil EPfP LPan MCoo SSta |
| - 'Fastigiata Purpurea' | Last listed 1997 |
| - 'Fennessii' | CMCN MBlu SMad |
| - 'Filicifolia' | See *Q.* x *rosea* 'Filicifolia' |
| - 'Fürst Schwarzenburg' | CMCN MBlu |
| - 'Hentzei' | CMCN |
| - 'Hungaria' | MBlu |
| ¶ - 'Irtha' | EPfP |
| - x *lobata* | Last listed 1998 |
| - x *macrocarpa* x *muehlenbergii* | Last listed 1997 |
| - x *macrocarpa* x *virginiana* | Last listed 1997 |
| - 'Pectinata' | MBlu |
| § - subsp. *pedunculiflora* | CMCN |
| - f. *pendula* | CDul CEnd CMCN CTho |
| - 'Purpurascens' | CEnd CMCN MAsh MBlu |
| - 'Raba' | CMCN |
| - 'Salicifolia Fastigiata' | Last listed 1997 |
| - 'Strypemonde' | CMCN |
| - x *turbinella* | CMCN |
| x *rosacea* 'Filicifolia' | CEnd NBea WMou |
| § *rubra* ♀ | More than 30 suppliers |
| - 'Aurea' | CDul CEnd CFil CMCN EPfP MBlu SMad SSpi |
| * - 'Sunshine' | CMCN LRHS MBlu SMad |
| *rugosa* | CMCN |
| *sadleriana* | CMCN |
| *sartorii* | Last listed 1998 |
| § x *saulii* | CMCN SBir |
| x *schochiana* | CMCN |
| ¶ *schottkyana* | SBir |
| x *schuettei* | Last listed 1997 |
| *semecarpifolia* | ISea |
| § *serrata* | CMCN SBir |
| *sessiliflora* | See *Q. petraea* |
| *shumardii* | CDul CMCN EPfP SBir WDin WNor WWes |
| *stellata* | CMCN |
| *suber* | CB&S CDoC CDul CLnd CMCN CTho GAri GChr ISea SAPC SArc SEND SSpi WDin WPGP |
| § *texana* | CMCN SBir WWes |
| *trojana* | CMCN |
| *turbinella* | CMCN |
| x *turneri* | CDoC CDul CLnd CMCN CTho WMou |
| - 'Pseudoturneri' | CB&S EMil GChr LPan LRHS MBlu MBal |
| *vacciniifolia* | CMCN MBal |
| *variabilis* | CDul CMCN EPfP MBlu WCoo WWes |
| *velutina* | CDul CGre CLnd CMCN SBir WCoo WWat |
| ¶ - 'Albertsii' | MBlu |
| - 'Rubrifolia' | CMCN EPfP |
| ♦ *virgiliana* | See *Q. pubescens* subsp. *pubescens* |
| *virginiana* | CMCN |
| 'Warburgii' | CMCN |
| ¶ *wislizeni* | CMCN IOrc SBir |
| § *wutaishanica* | CMCN |

## QUILLAJA (Rosaceae)

*saponaria*      CGre CPle CTrG

## QUIONGZHUEA (Poaceae - Bambusoideae)
*tumidinoda*      See *Chimonobambusa tumidissinoda*

## QUISQUALIS (Combretaceae)
¶ *indica*      LChe

# R

## RACOPILUM (Sphagnaceae)
*robustum*      Last listed 1996

## RACOSPERMA See ACACIA

## RAMONDA (Gesneriaceae)
| | |
|---|---|
| § *myconi* ♀ | CLAP CPBP EHyt MBro NHar NMen NSla NTow NWCA SBla SIgm SIng SRms WAbe |
| - var. *alba* | WAbe |
| - 'Rosea' | CLAP SBla |
| *nathaliae* ♀ | CLAP CPBP EPot NHar SIgm WAbe |
| - 'Alba' | SBla SWas WAbe |
| *pyrenaica* | See *R. myconi* |
| *serbica* | GCrs SIgm |

## RANUNCULUS ✿ (Ranunculaceae)
| | |
|---|---|
| *abnormis* | SWas |
| *aconitifolius* | CGle EBee ECha EMFP EPar MHlr NSti WCot |
| - 'Flore Pleno' (d) ♀ | CHea CRow EBee EPar EPri GBuc IBlr LGre MBri NBir NPar NTow SBla WByw WHer WHil |
| *acris* | EWFC NLan |
| * - *citrinus* | CElw ECoo EPar EPri EWoo MCAu NRya SMrm WAlt WBea WElm WFar WPrP WRha WSan |
| - 'Cricket' (v) | WAlt |
| - 'Farrer's Yellow' | CRow |
| - 'Flore Pleno' (d) | CAvo CElw CFee CFir CGle CRow EBee ECha ELan EMan EPar GAbr LPio MCAu MInt NBro NChi NFai NHex NHol NRya NSti SMac SRms WAlt WByw WHal WLin WSan WWal |
| - 'Hedgehog' | EMon WCot |
| - 'Stevenii' | CFee CRow SDix WCot |
| - 'Sulphureus' | CBre CGle MSte NCat NSti SMrm WEas WHal |
| *alpestris* | NMen NRya |
| *amplexicaulis* | EBee EPot ERos GCrs GDra GTou MRav NHar NSla SBla WAbe |
| *aquatilis* | CBen EHon EMFW NDea SWat SWyc |
| x *arendsii* | Last listed 1996 |
| ¶ - 'Moonlight' | SWas |
| *asiaticus* | WCot |
| - Accolade | SCoo WStI |
| - red | Last listed 1997 |
| - Tecolote hybrids | LAma |
| - white | SBla |
| - yellow | SBla |
| *auricomus* | CKin |
| *baurii* | Last listed 1998 |
| *bilobus* | WAbe |

| | |
|---|---|
| *brotherusii* CC&McK 745 | Last listed 1996 |
| *bulbosus* | CKin EWFC |
| § - 'F.M. Burton' | CBos CRDP EGar GCal MAvo MCLN NTow SCro SUsu WAlt WCot WHal WRus WWin |
| - *farreri* | See *R. bulbosus* 'F.M. Burton' |
| - 'Speciosus Plenus' | See *R. constantinopolitanus* 'Plenus' |
| *calandrinioides* ♀ | SBla WAbe WCot |
| - dwarf form | Last listed 1998 |
| - SF 37 | WCot |
| § *constantinopolitanus* 'Plenus' (d) | CElw CGle CRDP CRow EBee ECha GCal IHdy MBri MBro MInt MLLN MRav NBro NRoo NRya WCot WEas WFar |
| *cortusifolius* | CFir CRDP NSti WCot WCru WSpi |
| *crenatus* | CLyd EHyt ELan GTou ITim MBal NHar NMen NRya NSla NTow SBla WAbe WHal WHil |
| *creticus* | EMon WCot |
| *eschscholtzii* | IMGH |
| - *oxynotus* | Last listed 1996 |
| - *trisectus* | Last listed 1996 |
| *extorris* 'Flore Pleno' | EMon |
| *ficaria* | CArn CJew CKin CNat CRow EWFC GBar MChe MHew MMal MSal WFar WHbs WHer WShi WWye |
| I - 'Aglow in the Dark' | CNat EBee |
| - var. *albus* | CElw CGle CMil CRow CVer EMon ERos NRya SIng WByw |
| - anemone centred | See *R. ficaria* 'Collarette' |
| - 'Ashen Primrose' | CRow EBee |
| § - var. *aurantiacus* | CMil CNic CRow CVer EBee ECha EMon EPar GDra MBro MRav NHol NMen NNrd NRya SIng SRms SSvw WAbe |
| - 'Blackadder' | CRow |
| ¶ - 'Bosvigo' | CHid |
| - 'Bowles' Double' | See *R. ficaria* 'Double Bronze', 'Picton's Double' |
| - 'Brambling' | CBre CHea CLAP CRow EBee EMon MRav WCot |
| ¶ - 'Brazen Child' | EBee |
| - 'Brazen Daughter' | CRow |
| - 'Brazen Hussy' | More than 30 suppliers |
| - 'Bregover White' | CRow |
| - 'Bunch' (d) | CRow |
| - 'Button Eye' | Last listed 1998 |
| - 'Champernowne Giant' | CRow |
| - 'Chedglow' | Last listed 1998 |
| - 'Chocolate Cream' | CRow |
| § - subsp. *chrysocephalus* | CRow ECha EMon NRya SIng SSvw WCot WHer |
| - 'Coffee Cream' | CRow |
| § - 'Collarette' (d) | CGle CInt CMil CRDP CRow EBee ECha EHyt EMon EPar EPot ERos GAbr GBar GCal GGar MRav MTho NMGW NMen NNrd NRya NSla SBla SIng SMac WAbe WCla WCot WHil |
| - 'Coppernob' | CAvo CHid CRDP CRow CVer LPio SWas WFar WPnP |
| - 'Coy Hussy' (v) | CNat |
| - 'Crawshay Cream' | SWas |
| - 'Cupreus' | See *R. ficaria* var. *aurantiacus* |
| - 'Damerham' | CRow EMon |
| § - 'Double Bronze' (d) | CMil CVer EBee EMon EPar ERos MTho NRya NSti WCot |
| - double cream | See *R. ficaria* 'Double Mud' |
| - double green eye (d) | CRow |
| § - 'Double Mud' (d) | CLAP CMil CRDP CVer EMon ERos MBro MTho NNrd NRya SBla SIng SWas WCot WHal |

| | |
|---|---|
| - double yellow | See *R. ficaria flore-pleno* |
| - 'Dusky Maiden' | CRow EMon WFar |
| - 'E.A. Bowles' | See *R. ficaria* 'Collarette' |
| - 'Elan' (d) | CRow |
| - subsp. *ficariiformis* | EMon |
| § - *flore-pleno* (d) | CAvo CFee CGle CInt CMil CRow |
| | ECha ELan EMar EMon EPar ERos |
| | GAbr GDra IMGH NDea NHol |
| | NNrd NRya NSla NSti SIng SRms |
| | WCot WFar WHil WWin |
| - 'Fried Egg' | CRow |
| - 'Green Petal' | CAvo CElw CMil CRDP CRow |
| | EBee EMon EPar MRav MS&S |
| | MTho NNrd NRya NSla SIng SSvw |
| | SUsu SWas WHal |
| I - 'Holly' | See *R. ficaria* 'Holly Green' |
| § - 'Holly Green' | CRow |
| - 'Hoskin's Miniature' | Last listed 1998 |
| ¶ - 'Hyde Hall' | EMon |
| - 'Inky' | CNat |
| - 'Jane's Dress' | CHid |
| - 'Ken Aslet' (d) | CRow EMon SWas WHal |
| - 'Lemon Queen' | NHol WCot |
| - 'Limelight' | CRow |
| - 'Little Southey' | CRow EBee |
| - subsp. *major* | See *R. ficaria* subsp. |
| | *chrysocephalus* |
| - 'Martin Gibbs' | CNat |
| - 'Mimsey' (d) | CRow |
| - 'Mobled Jade' | CNat |
| - 'Newton Abbot' | CRow |
| - 'Norton' | Last listed 1998 |
| ¶ - 'Orange Sorbet' | EMon |
| - 'Palest Cream' | CNic CSam |
| § - 'Picton's Double' (d) | CGle CRDP CRow CVer EHyt |
| | EMou GBar GCal MTho NNrd |
| | NRya WAbe |
| - 'Primrose' | CRow EMon GGar MRav MTho |
| | NCat NHol NRya WCot |
| - 'Quillet' (d) | CRow |
| - 'Randall's White' | CGle CRDP CRow CSWP ECha |
| | LSyl MRav MTho NTow SSvw |
| | WCom WCot |
| - 'Rowden Magna' | CRow |
| - 'Ruby Baker' | Last listed 1998 |
| - 'Salmon's White' | CAvo CBre CFee CRow CVer ELan |
| | EMar EPPr EPar EPot MRav NNrd |
| | NRya SSvw WFar WHal WHil |
| - 'Sheldon' | CNat |
| - 'Sheldon Silver' | CNat |
| - single cream | EMon |
| - 'Suffusion' | CNat |
| - 'Sutherland's Double' (d) | CRow |
| - 'Sweet Chocolate' | CRow |
| - 'Tortoiseshell' | CHid CRow CVer MAvo MRav |
| | WBro WCot |
| - 'Trenwheal' (d) | CRow |
| ¶ - 'Winkworth' | EMon |
| ¶ - 'Wisley White' | NSti |
| - 'Yaffle' | CBre CRow EBee EMon MRav |
| | SIng WCot |
| x *flabaultii* | Last listed 1996 |
| *flammula* | CArn CBen CKin CRow EHon |
| | EMFW GBar LPBA MSta NDea |
| | SWat SWyc |
| - subsp. *minimus* | CRow |
| *glacialis* | Last listed 1996 |
| *gouanii* | EPot NTow |
| *gramineus* ♀ | More than 30 suppliers |
| - 'Pardal' | SBla WFar |
| 'Granby Cream' | MAvo MGrG |
| *bederaceus* | EMFW SWyc |

| | |
|---|---|
| ¶ *illyricus* | ECha WCru |
| *insignis* | CRDP EHyt |
| *kochii* | EPot |
| *lanuginosus* | WCot |
| - AL&JS 89066YU | EMon |
| *lingua* | CFir CKin ECoo EMFW MCCP |
| | SLon SPlb |
| - 'Grandiflorus' | CBen CRow EHon LPBA MSta |
| | NDea NRya SWat SWyc WMAq |
| | WWye |
| *lyallii* | CPla GCal GNor SIgm SSpi WSan |
| ¶ *macauleyi* | GCrs |
| *macrophyllus* | WCru |
| *millefoliatus* | EHyt ERos MTho NMen NRya |
| | WCot WHil |
| *montanus* | MBal |
| - double form | SBla |
| - 'Molten Gold' ♀ | EPot GCrs MRav MTho NBro |
| | NHar NHol NMen NRya NTow |
| | SBla SIng SRot WLin |
| *muelleri* var. *brevicaulis* | Last listed 1997 |
| *nivicola* | EBee EHyt |
| *ophioglossifolius* | Last listed 1998 |
| *parnassiifolius* | GCrs GTou NHar NTow SBla |
| | WAbe |
| *platanifolius* | CBre LGre |
| ¶ *pyrenaeus* | NSla |
| *repens* | CKin EWFC |
| ¶ - 'Cat's Eyes' (v) | WAlt |
| - 'Dinah Myte' (v) | Last listed 1998 |
| ¶ - 'Gloria Spale' | WAlt |
| ¶ - 'In Vein' (v) | WAlt |
| - 'Joe's Golden' | EHoe EMon NSti WAlt WCer |
| ¶ - 'Justin Time' (v) | WAlt |
| - var. *pleniflorus* (d) | CInt CRow ECha ELan GCal GGar |
| | NSti WAlt WEas WFar |
| - semidouble (d) | WAlt |
| - 'Timothy Clark' (d) | MInt WAlt WHil |
| ¶ *reptans* 'Boraston O.S.' | WCHb |
| *rupestris* | See *R. spicatus* |
| *sceleratus* | WHer |
| ¶ *serbicus* | EBee |
| sp. from Morocco | Last listed 1997 |
| sp. from NE China | Last listed 1998 |
| *speciosus* 'Flore Pleno' | See *R. constantinopolitanus* |
| | 'Plenus' |
| § *spicatus* | CRDP WHil |

## RANZANIA (Berberidaceae)

| | |
|---|---|
| *japonica* | SWas |

## RAOULIA (Asteraceae)

| | |
|---|---|
| *australis* Hooker | CLTr CLyd ECou EHoe ELan |
| | EMNS EPot GAbr GCHN ITim |
| | MBal MBar MRPP MWat NBro |
| | NNrd NRoo NWCA SIng WAbe |
| | WHoo WPyg |
| - 'Calf' | ITim |
| § - Lutescens Group | ECha EPot GAri ITim |
| - 'Saxon's Pass' | GCHN |
| *australis* hort. | See *R. bookeri* |
| *bryoides* | Last listed 1996 |
| *glabra* | ECou GAbr |
| ¶ *grandiflora* | WAbe |
| *baastii* | CLyd ECou |
| § *bookeri* | CLyd ECha ECou ELan EPot |
| | GCHN IMGH ITim LBee NNrd |
| | NTow NWCA SBla SIng SRms |
| | WFar WLin |
| ¶ - var. *apice-nigra* | WAbe |
| - var. *laxa* | EPot EWes |
| x *loganii* | See x *Leucoraoulia loganii* |

| | |
|---|---|
| *lutescens* | See *R. australis* Lutescens Group |
| *monroi* | ELan GCHN ITim NTow |
| * *nova* | ITim |
| *parkii* | Last listed 1996 |
| *petriensis* | GCrs NSla |
| x *petrimia* | CGra EHyt ITim NHar WAbe |
|   'Margaret Pringle' | |
| *subsericea* | CLyd ECou GCrs NMen |
| *tenuicaulis* | ECha ECou GAbr GAri |

## RAOULIA x LEUCOGENES
See x LEUCORAOULIA

## RATIBIDA (Asteraceae)
| | |
|---|---|
| *columnifera* | EBee IIve |
|  - f. *pulcherrima* | LEur SDys |
| *pinnata* | EGar |

## RAUVOLFIA (Apocynaceae)
| | |
|---|---|
| *serpentina* | Last listed 1997 |
| *verticillata* | Last listed 1996 |

## RAVENALA (Strelitziaceae)
| | |
|---|---|
| *madagascariensis* | LBlo LPal WMul |

## RAVENEA (Arecaceae)
| | |
|---|---|
| *rivularis* | LPal WMul |

## RECHSTEINERIA See SINNINGIA

## REGELIA (Myrtaceae)
| | |
|---|---|
| ¶ *ciliata* | SOWG |
| *velutina* | SOWG |

## REHDERODENDRON (Styracaceae)
| | |
|---|---|
| *macrocarpum* | CB&S EPfP |

## REHMANNIA (Scrophulariaceae)
| | |
|---|---|
| *angulata* | See *R. elata* |
| § *elata* | CBot CFri CGle CSev CSpe EBee |
| | ELan GMac LBlm LPio MCLN |
| | MNrw MPEx SCob SLon SMrm |
| | SRPl WBro WCru WFar WPer |
| | WWal WWin WWye |
| ¶ - 'Popstar' | WElm |
| *glutinosa* ♀ | LGre LLew MSal WWye |

## REINECKEA (Convallariaceae)
| | |
|---|---|
| § *carnea* | CHan CHid CSpe ECha EGar ELan |
| | EMan EMar EOrc EPar EPla ERos |
| | EWTr GCal LFis LNor MFir MRav |
| | MUlv NNrd NSti SCob SDys SOkh |
| | SPlb WCot WCru WGwG WPer |
| | WWal |
| - 'Variegata' | WCot |

## REINWARDTIA (Linaceae)
| | |
|---|---|
| § *indica* | CGre CPle LChe LHil |
|  - S&SH  106 | CHan |
| *trigyna* | See *R. indica* |

## RESEDA (Resedaceae)
| | |
|---|---|
| *alba* | EMon MHer |
| *lutea* | CKin EWFC MSal SIde |
| *luteola* | CJew CKin ECGN EWFC GBar |
| | GPoy MChe MHer MHew MSal |
| | SIde WCHb WHer WOak WWye |

## RESTIO (Restionaceae)
| | |
|---|---|
| ¶ *pachystachyus* | CCpl CTrC |
| *quadratus* | WNor |
| *subverticillatus* | See *Ischyrolepis subverticillata* |

| | |
|---|---|
| *tetraphyllus* | Last listed 1996 |

## RETAMA (Papilionaceae)
| | |
|---|---|
| § *monosperma* | Last listed 1997 |

## REYNOUTRIA See FALLOPIA

## RHABDOTHAMNUS (Gesneriaceae)
| | |
|---|---|
| *solandri* | Last listed 1998 |

## RHAGODIA (Chenopodiaceae)
| | |
|---|---|
| ¶ *baccata* | CCpl |
| *triandra* | CPLG ECou |

## RHAMNUS (Rhamnaceae)
| | |
|---|---|
| *alaternus* | CFil SBid WPGP |
|  - var. *angustifolia* | CFil WHCr WPGP WWat |
| § - 'Argenteovariegata' ♀ | More than 30 suppliers |
|  - 'Variegata' | See *R. alaternus* |
| | 'Argenteovariegata' |
| *cathartica* | CCVT CKin GChr LBuc MPEx |
| | WDin WGwy WMou |
| ¶ *daburica* | IIve |
| *frangula* | CArn CCVT CKin CSam ENot |
| | GChr LBuc STre WDin WGwy |
| | WMou |
|  - 'Aspleniifolia' | EBee ENot EPfP EPla GChr LBuc |
| | MBri SMur |
|  - 'Columnaris' | EMil SLPl |
| x *hybrida* 'Billardii' | ESis |
| *japonica* | SPer |
| ¶ *libanotica* | WLin |
| ¶ *pallasii* | WLin |
| *prinoides* | Last listed 1997 |

## RHAPHIOLEPIS (Rosaceae)
| | |
|---|---|
| x *delacourii* | CCHP CMHG EPfP GQui NPal |
| | SBid WBcn WBod WHCG WWat |
|  - 'Coates' Crimson' | CDoC CSPN EHic EMil EPfP GQui |
| | MBlu SBid SBra SLon SOWG SPer |
| | WSHC |
|  - 'Enchantress' | CMHG EBrP EBre ENot LBre SBre |
| | SMur |
|  - 'Spring Song' | EBee |
| ¶ - 'Spring Time' | SPer |
| *indica* | CGre ERom SEND WWat |
| *ovata* | See *R. umbellata* f. *ovata* |
| § *umbellata* ♀ | CAbb CB&S CBot CCHP CSam |
| | CTri EBee GQui LHop MBlu MRav |
| | SAga SBra SBrw SOWG WHCG |
| | WPic WSHC WWat |
| ¶ - f. *ovata* B&SWJ  4706 | WCru |

## RHAPHITHAMNUS (Verbenaceae)
| | |
|---|---|
| *cyanocarpus* | See *R. spinosus* |
| § *spinosus* | CGre CPle EPla ERea SBid WAbe |
| | WBod WPic |

## RHAPIDOPHYLLUM (Arecaceae)
| | |
|---|---|
| *hystrix* | CBrP LPal |

## RHAPIS (Arecaceae)
| | |
|---|---|
| § *excelsa* ♀ | CBrP CTrC LBlo LPal NPal WMul |
| *multifida* | LPal |

## RHAZYA (Apocynaceae)
| | |
|---|---|
| *orientalis* | See *Amsonia orientalis* |

## RHEKTOPHYLLUM See CERCESTIS

## RHEUM ✿ (Polygonaceae)
| | |
|---|---|
| § 'Ace of Hearts' | More than 30 suppliers |

'Ace of Spades'  See *R.* 'Ace of Hearts'
*acuminatum*  CRow EBee GBin MHlr WBay WViv
 - HWJCM 252  WCru
*alexandrae*  GAri GCal IBlr WBay
¶ *altaicum*  IIve
§ *australe*  CArn CRow EBee MBro MLLN MSal NBro NLar SMrm WCot WHoo WPyg
*compactum*  Last listed 1996
N x *cultorum*  See *R.* x *hybridum*
*emodi*  See *R. australe*
¶ *forrestii*  CAgr
 - ACE 2286  Last listed 1997
§ x *hybridum*  NVic
¶ - 'Appleton's Forcing'  GTwe
 - 'Baker's All Season'  GTwe
 - 'Canada Red'  GTwe
 - 'Cawood Delight'  GTwe SEND
 - 'Champagne'  GTwe
 - 'Daw's Champion'  GTwe
 - 'Early Champagne'  GTwe
 - 'Early Cherry'  GTwe
 - 'Fenton's Special'  GTwe
 - 'Fulton's Strawberry Surprise'  GTwe
 - 'German Wine'  GTwe
 - 'Goliath'  GTwe
 - 'Grandad's Favorite'  EBrP EBre LBre SBre
 - 'Greengage'  GTwe
 - 'Hammond's Early'  GTwe SEND
 - 'Harbinger'  GTwe
 - 'Hawke's Champagne'  GTwe
 - 'Mac Red'  GTwe
 - 'Prince Albert'  GTwe
 - 'Red Prolific'  GTwe
 - 'Reed's Early Superb'  GTwe
¶ - 'Saint Kevin'  IIve
 - 'Stein's Champagne'  GTwe
 - 'Stockbridge Arrow'  GTwe
 - 'Stockbridge Bingo'  GTwe
 - 'Stockbridge Emerald'  GTwe
 - 'Stockbridge Guardsman'  GTwe
* - 'Strawberry'  EMui GTwe
 - 'Sutton's Cherry Red'  GTwe
 - 'The Sutton'  GTwe LBuc
 - 'Timperley Early'  CDoC CMac CSam CTri EMui GChr GTwe LBuc NFai SDea
 - 'Tingley Cherry'  GTwe
 - 'Valentine'  GTwe
 - 'Victoria'  GTwe
 - 'Zwolle Seedling'  GTwe
*kialense*  EBee GCal NSti
* *maximum*  Last listed 1998
¶ *nobile*  EBee
 - HWJCM 307  Last listed 1998
 - SF 95170  Last listed 1998
*officinale*  GCal MBri SWat
*palmatum* ♀  CArn CB&S CBlo EBee ECha EHal ELan ERic LPBA MRav MSal NCut NDea NFla NFor NGdn SMac SPer SSpi SWat WBea WPyg WStI WWal
 - 'Atropurpureum'  See *R. palmatum* 'Atrosanguineum'
§ - 'Atrosanguineum'  CBot CRow EBrP EBre ECha EGar ELan EOld EPar EPla GBuc LBre MBri MWgw NBro NFor NHol NLon SBre SCob SRCN SSoC SWat WCru WWin
 - 'Bowles' Crimson'  CHad LRHS MBri SAga SSoC WBay
 - 'Hadspen Crimson'  CHad GVic WCot
¶ - var. *palmatum*  WHil

 - 'Red Herald'  MBri
 - *rubrum*  CDoC COtt EBrP EBre EHic GCHN LBre MCCP MHlr SBre SLon WCot
 - 'Saville'  MBri MLLN
 - var. *tanguticum*  CRow EBee ECha EGar MAvo MBri MCCP MSCN MSal MSta NCat NPri NSti SPer SRms SSoC SWat WCot WHoo
I - - 'Rosa Auslese'  Last listed 1997
*rhaponticum*  CAgr EBee NLar
* *robertianum*  Last listed 1997
*spiciforme*  Last listed 1997
*tataricum*  CAgr EBee EGar GCal LEdu
*tibeticum*  WWoo
 - SEP 20  EPot
*undulatum*  CRow

## RHEXIA (Melastomataceae)
*mariana*  Last listed 1997
 - var. *purpurea*  Last listed 1997

## RHINEPHYLLUM (Aizoaceae)
*broomii*  Last listed 1998

## RHIPSALIS (Cactaceae)
*cassytha*  See *R. baccifera*

## RHODANTHE (Asteraceae)
§ *anthemoides*  ECou IDac

## RHODANTHEMUM (Asteraceae)
§ *atlanticum*  ECho ELan EWes
§ *catananche*  CPBP ECho ELan EPot EWes LHop NTow SMrm WAbe
§ *gayanum*  ELan EMFP EWes LBee MBNS NTow SCro WEas WHen WKif
 - 'Flamingo'  See *R. gayanum*
§ - 'Tizi-n-Test'  LBee SBla
 - 'Tizi-n-Tichka'  CInt CPBP ELan EWes LBee LHop LRHS NBir NTow SBla SIng SLod SUsu
§ *hosmariense* ♀  ECha ELan EPot LFis LHop MBal NNrd SBla SIng SPer SRms SSmi SYvo WAbe WCot WEas WLin WRus
¶ sp. from High Atlas, Morocco  EPot

## RHODIOLA (Crassulaceae)
*alsia*  Last listed 1998
¶ *angusta*  NSla
*arctica*  Last listed 1998
*bupleuroides* CLD 1196  EMon
*crassipes*  See *R. wallichiana*
§ *fastigiata*  EMon GCal NRoo
 - x *kirilovii*  Last listed 1998
*gelida*  Last listed 1998
§ *heterodonta*  ECha EGle ELan LPio MRav SIng WCot
*himalensis*  See *R.* 'Keston'
 - (D. Don) Fu EMAK 331  Last listed 1996
§ *ishidae*  Last listed 1998
§ 'Keston'  SSmi
§ *kirilovii*  GBin GTou
 - var. *rubra*  EBee EBrP EBre LBre NRoo SBre SSmi WFar
*pachyclados*  See *Sedum pachyclados*
*pamiroalaica*  Last listed 1998
§ *primuloides*  CLyd NMen
§ *quadrifida*  Last listed 1998
*recticaulis*  EBee
*rhodantha*  EBee

§ *rosea*   EBee ECha EHoe ELan EMan MBal
MFir NFor NHol NRoo NSla NSti
SCro SIng SRms SSmi STre WAbb
WCot WEas WFar WWhi
§ - subsp. *integrifolia*   WLin
*semenowii*   EBee GAri MHar
sp. CC&McK 158   GCHN
sp. EMAK 0516   Last listed 1998
§ *trollii*   CNic GCrs
§ *wallichiana*   GAri GCrs WCot
§ *yunnanensis*   Last listed 1997

# RHODOCHITON (Scrophulariaceae)
§ *atrosanguineus* ♀   CB&S CEnd CGle CMac CPlN
CRHN CSpe ELan ERea LHop
MHlr MNes NEgg NFai SOWG
SSoC SUsu WEas
*volubilis*   See *R. atrosanguineus*

# RHODOCOMA (Restionaceae)
*arida*   CTrC LHil
¶ *fruticosa*   CTrC
*gigantea*   CTrC IDac LHil WNor

# RHODODENDRON ✿ (Ericaceae)
'A.J. Ivens'   See *R.* 'Arthur J. Ivens'
'Abbot' (EA)   Last listed 1996
'Abegail'   NMun SLdr
'Abendrot'   MBri
*aberconwayi*   IOrc LMil MBal MDun NMun SLdr
SReu
- 'His Lordship'   GGGa LHyd
- McLaren U35a   Last listed 1996
- pink   NMun
'Accomplishment'   CWri
ACE 2256   Last listed 1998
ACE 2384   Last listed 1998
'Achilles'   Last listed 1998
* *acpunctum* SF 313   Last listed 1997
¶ *acrophilum* Argent   GGGa
2768 (V)
'Actress'   IOrc LHyd NMun
'Adamant'   Last listed 1996
'Addy Wery' (EA) ♀   CDoC ENot GHCN IOrc LKna
MBal MBar MGos NMun SBod
SBrw SLdr SPer SReu WBod WStI
Adelaide Group & cl.   Last listed 1998
*adenogynum*   GGGa MDun NMun SLdr
§ - Adenophorum Group   SLdr
- - F 20444   SLdr
- - 'Kirsty'   NMun SLdr
- - R 11471   NMun
- CLD 795   LMil
- PA Cox 6502   GGGa
- white   NMun SLdr
*adenophorum*   See *R. adenogynum*
Adenophorum Group
*adenopodum*   GGGa MDun NMun SLdr SReu
- A.M. form   SLdr
*adenosum*   LMil MDun NHol NMun SLdr
- Kuluense Group   NMun SLdr
- R 18228   GGGa
'Admiral Piet Hein'   SReu
'Adonis' (EA/d)   CMac IOrc MBar SPer
§ 'Adorable' (EA)   IOrc
'Adriaan Koster'   IOrc SLdr
*adroserum* USDAPI 52910   See *R. lukiangense* R 11275
'Advance' (O)   NMun SLdr
*aeruginosum*   See *R. campanulatum* subsp.
*aeruginosum*
*aganniphum*   GGGa NMun SLdr
§ - var. *aganniphum*   GGGa NMun SLdr

Doshongense Group
- - - C&V 9541   GGGa
- - - KW 5863   NMun SLdr
- - F 16472   NMun
- - Glaucopeplum Group   GGGa LHyd
- - Schizopeplum Group   GGGa
- - SSNY 138   GGGa
- CNW 1174   LMil
- EGM 284   LMil
- var. *flavorufum*   GGGa MDun NMun SLdr
- - EGM 160   LMil
- - PA Cox 5070*   GGGa
- - SSNY 143   GGGa
- PA Cox 6003   GGGa
- 'Rusty'   NMun
- SSNY 320a   GGGa
*agapetum*   See *R. kyawii* Agapetum Group
x *agastum*   NMun SLdr
- PW 98   GGGa LMil
¶ 'Ahren's Favourite'   SBrw
'Aida' (R/d)   SReu
'Airy Fairy'   Last listed 1996
'Aksel Olsen'   ECho MBal MBar MDun NHol
'Aladdin' (EA)   CDoC ECho GGGa IOrc SLdr
WFar
Aladdin Group & cl.   CWri SReu
Albatross Group & cl.   LHyd LKna LMil SLdr SPer SReu
SSta
'Albatross Townhill Pink'   LMil
'Albert Schweitzer'   CWri GGGa LMil MBal MBar MBri
SBrw SLdr SReu
*albertsenianum*   Last listed 1998
- F 14195   Last listed 1996
*albiflorum* (A)   GGGa SReu
*albrechtii* (A) ♀   GGGa LHyd LMil MDun SReu
'Alena'   GGGa
'Alex Hill'   Last listed 1997
'Alexander' (EA)   CTrh GQui IOrc LMil MBri MGos
SBod SReu
'Alfred'   LRHS
'Alice' ♀   IOrc LHyd LKna MDun NMun
SBrw SLdr SPer SReu
'Alice' (EA)   LHyd LKna WBod
'Alice Gilbert'   Last listed 1996
'Alice Street'   Last listed 1998
'Alisa Nicole' (V)   Last listed 1998
Alison Johnstone Group & cl.   CB&S GGGa MBal MBri MDun
MLea NMun SLdr SPer SReu WPic
¶ (Alix Group) 'Alix'   SLdr
'Aloha'   CAbP MAsh MBar NHed SReu
'Alpine Dew'   Last listed 1997
Alpine Gem Group   GQui NHol
'Alpine Glow' ♀   NMun SLdr
*alutaceum*   NMun
- var. *alutaceum*   GGGa
§ - - Globigerum Group   LMil
- - - R 11100   GGGa NMun
§ - var. *iodes*   GGGa LMil NMun SLdr
§ - var. *russotinctum*   GGGa LMil SLdr
¶ - - R 158   SLdr
§ - - Triplonaevium Group   Last listed 1997
- - - USDAPI 59442/ R10923   GGGa
§ - - Tritifolium Group   Last listed 1998
- - - R 158*   Last listed 1997
*amagianum* (A)   LMil
Amalfi Group & cl.   Last listed 1996
Amaura Group   WBod
*ambiguum*   CHig LMil SLdr SReu
- 'Jane Banks'   LMil
* - KR 185 select*   GGGa
'America'   CB&S IOrc MBal MBar MGos
SBrw SLdr WFar WWeb

| | |
|---|---|
| *amesiae* | GGGa NMun SLdr |
| 'Amethyst' | LHyd |
| § 'Amethystinum' (EA) | LKna |
| 'Amity' | CDoC CWri ECho |
| § 'Amoenum' (EA/d) | CDoC CMac CTrG CTrh CTrw |
| | IOrc LHyd LKna MBar MGos |
| | NMun SLdr WBod WFar |
| ¶ 'Amoenum Coccineum' | SReu |
| (EA/d) | |
| Amor Group & cl. | LHyd SLdr |
| 'Analin' | See *R.* 'Anuschka' |
| 'Anatta Gold' (V) | Last listed 1998 |
| 'Anchorite' (EA) | GQui LMil SLdr |
| 'Andre' | NMun SLdr SReu |
| * 'Andrea' | NMun |
| Angelo Group & cl. | LHyd LMil MDun SReu |
| Anita Group | SLdr |
| 'Anita Dunstan' | LMil MLea |
| 'Ann Lindsay' | SBrw SReu |
| 'Anna Baldsiefen' ♀ | ENot LMil MBri NHol SBrw SPer |
| | SReu SSta WAbe |
| 'Anna H. Hall' | IOrc MDun |
| 'Anna Rose Whitney' ♀ | CB&S GChr GGGa IOrc LHyd |
| | LKna LMil MAsh MBar MBri |
| | MDun MGos MLea NMun SBrw |
| | SLdr SPer SReu SSta |
| 'Annabella' (K) ♀ | MBri SLdr SReu |
| *annae* | GGGa LMil LRHS MDun NMun |
| | SLdr |
| aff. *annae* C&H 7185 | LMil |
| § - Hardingii Group | NMun |
| 'Anne Frank' (EA) | COtt MGos SReu WBod |
| 'Anne George' | LHyd |
| 'Anne Rothwell' | LHyd |
| 'Anne Teese' | LMil |
| 'Anneke' (K) | MAsh MBar MBri SLdr SReu SSta |
| | WBod |
| 'Anniversary Gold' | GGGa |
| 'Anny' (EA) | IOrc LKna |
| *anthopogon* | LMil SLdr |
| - subsp. *anthopogon* | Last listed 1998 |
| BL&M 332 | |
| - - Sch 2259 | Last listed 1998 |
| - 'Betty Graham' | GGGa LMil |
| - CH&M 2052 | Last listed 1998 |
| § - subsp. *hypenanthum* | LMil MDun |
| - - - 'Annapurna' | GGGa NHol |
| § *anthosphaerum* | GGGa NMun SLdr SReu |
| - Eritimum Group | Last listed 1996 |
| - F 17943 | Last listed 1997 |
| - F 26432 | SLdr |
| ¶ - F 5848 | SLdr |
| - Gymnogynum Group | NMun |
| § - Heptamerum Group | NMun |
| - KW 5684 | NMun |
| § 'Antilope' (Vs) | LMil SReu SSta |
| 'Antje' | Last listed 1997 |
| Antonio Group & cl. | Last listed 1997 |
| ¶ 'Antoon van Welie' | SBrw |
| § 'Anuschka' | MBri SBrw |
| § *anwheiense* (V) ♀ | LHyd LMil MDun NMun SLdr |
| | SReu |
| *aperantum* | GGGa MDun |
| - F 26933 | SLdr |
| - F 27022 | GGGa |
| ¶ - JN 498 | GGGa |
| 'Aphrodite' (EA) | GQui |
| *apodectum* | See *R. dichroanthum* subsp. |
| | *apodectum* |
| 'Apotheose' (EA) | Last listed 1997 |
| ¶ 'Apotrophia' | SLdr |

| | |
|---|---|
| 'Apple Blossom' | CMac CTrh SLdr SReu |
| N 'Appleblossom' | See *R.* 'Ho-o' |
| 'Apricot Fantasy' | LMil SMur |
| 'Apricot Surprise' | Last listed 1997 |
| ¶ 'Apricot Top Garden' | SLdr |
| 'April Chimes' | Last listed 1996 |
| 'April Dawn' | GGGa |
| 'April Gem' | MBri |
| § 'April Glow' | LHyd SLdr |
| ¶ 'April Rose' | MBri |
| 'April Showers' | ENot |
| 'April Snow' (d) | Last listed 1998 |
| 'April White' | MBri |
| 'Arabesque' | MBri SLdr |
| *araiophyllum* | GGGa |
| Arbcalo Group | Last listed 1998 |
| Arblact Group | Last listed 1996 |
| § *arborescens* (A) | GGGa LHyd LKna LMil NMun |
| | SLdr SReu |
| *arboreum* | CB&S GGGa IOrc ISea LMil MDun |
| | NMun SLdr SReu WPic |
| - subsp. *arboreum* KR 966 | NMun |
| - - Sch 1111 | Last listed 1996 |
| - B 708 | MBal |
| ¶ - B&SWJ 2244 | WCru |
| - 'Blood Red' | NMun |
| - C&S 1651 | NMun |
| - C&S 1695 | NMun |
| - subsp. *cinnamomeum* | GGGa NMun SLdr SReu |
| - - var. *album* | SLdr SReu |
| - - var. *cinnamomeum* | MBal |
| BM&W 172 | |
| - - - Campbelliae Group | NMun SLdr |
| - - var. *roseum* | GGGa NMun |
| - - - BB 151* | NMun |
| * - - - *crispum* | SLdr |
| - - - 'Tony Schilling' ♀ | LHyd LMil NMun SLdr |
| § - subsp. *delavayi* | GGGa ISea NMun SLdr |
| - - C&H 7178 | GGGa |
| - - C&S 1515 | NMun |
| - - CNW 994 | LMil |
| - - KW 21796 | NMun |
| - 'Goat Fell' | Last listed 1996 |
| - 'Heligan' | SReu |
| - mid-pink | SLdr |
| * - *nigrescens* | Last listed 1998 |
| § - subsp. *nilagiricum* | GGGa SLdr |
| - var. *roseum* | SLdr |
| - TSS 26 | Last listed 1997 |
| § - subsp. *zeylanicum* | ISea NMun SLdr |
| - - 'Rubaiyat' | NMun |
| 'Arborfield' | Last listed 1998 |
| Arbsutch Group | Last listed 1998 |
| § Arbutifolium Group | SLdr |
| x *arbutifolium* | See *R.* Arbutifolium Group |
| 'Arcadia' (EA) | LKna |
| 'Arctic Regent' (K) | GQui |
| 'Arctic Tern' | See x *Ledodendron* 'Arctic Tern' |
| § *argipeplum* | NMun SLdr |
| - Bhutan form | MDun |
| - Cave 6714 | Last listed 1998 |
| - Eastern form | Last listed 1996 |
| - KR 1231 | Last listed 1997 |
| ¶ - SEH 581 | GGGa |
| 'Argosy' ♀ | LMil NMun SBid SReu |
| *argyrophyllum* | MDun NMun SLdr |
| - subsp. *argyrophyllum* | SLdr |
| var. *cupulare* | |
| ¶ - - KW 772711* | SLdr |
| ¶ - - pink | SLdr |
| ¶ - - W/A 1210 | SLdr |

| | |
|---|---|
| § - subsp. *hypoglaucum* | NMun SLdr |
| § - - 'Heane Wood' | GGGa |
| - subsp. *nankingense* | GGGa IOrc LMil NMun |
| - - 'Chinese Silver' ♀ | LHyd LMil LRHS MDun NMun |
| | SLdr SReu |
| Ariel Group | SLdr |
| § *arizelum* | GGGa LMil MDun NMun SLdr |
| - 'Brodick' | Last listed 1997 |
| - F 21861 | Last listed 1997 |
| - KW 20922 | Last listed 1997 |
| - R 25 | GGGa |
| - Rubicosum Group | NMun SLdr |
| ¶ - - USDAPI 59550/ R 11207 | SLdr |
| 'Arkle' | Last listed 1997 |
| 'Armantine' | LKna |
| Armia Group | Last listed 1996 |
| *armitii* Woods 2518 (v) | GGGa |
| 'Arneson Gem' (M) | CDoC GGGa LMil MDun |
| ¶ 'Arneson Ruby' (K) | CDoC MDun |
| § 'Arpege' (Vs) | MBal SReu |
| 'Arthur Bedford' | CWri GGGa LHyd LKna SBrw |
| | SLdr SReu |
| § 'Arthur J. Ivens' | SLdr |
| 'Arthur Osborn' | CHig GGGa SLdr |
| 'Arthur Stevens' ♀ | SLdr |
| 'Arthur Warren' | LKna |
| 'Asa-gasumi' (EA) | LHyd |
| 'Ascot Brilliant' | SBrw SLdr |
| *asterochnoum* C&H 7051 | GGGa |
| Asteroid Group | SLdr |
| 'Astrid' | ENot |
| *atlanticum* (A) | GAri GGGa LMil NMun SSpi |
| | WWat |
| - 'Seaboard' (A) | LMil SLdr |
| 'Atlantis' | Last listed 1998 |
| 'Audrey Wynniatt' (EA) | MAsh |
| Augfast Group | CB&S CTrw IOrc MBal SBod |
| | WBod |
| 'August Lamken' | MAsh MBri SBid |
| *augustinii* | CB&S CHig CSam CTrG CTrw |
| | CWri GGGa IOrc ISea LHyd LMil |
| | MBal MLea NMun SLdr SPer SSpi |
| | SSta WGer WPic |
| - subsp. *augustinii* C 7008 | GGGa |
| - - C&H 7048 | GGGa |
| - - 'Smoke' | CGre |
| - - Vilmorinianum Group | Last listed 1996 |
| - - W/A 1207 | Last listed 1997 |
| § - subsp. *chasmanthum* | GGGa LMil SLdr |
| - - C&Cu 9407 white | GGGa |
| - - C&Cu 9418 pale pink | Last listed 1998 |
| - Dartington Form | Last listed 1996 |
| § - Electra Group & cl. | GGGa LHyd LMil MDun NMun |
| | SLdr |
| - EN 3527 | Last listed 1998 |
| - Exbury best form | SReu |
| § - subsp. *hardyi* | GGGa SLdr |
| - Reuthe's dark form | Last listed 1996 |
| § - subsp. *rubrum* | GGGa |
| - - 'Papillon' | NMun |
| I - 'Werrington' | SReu |
| § *aureum* | GGGa LMil MDun NMun SLdr |
| *auriculatum* | GGGa LMil MBal NHol NMun |
| | SLdr SReu SSta |
| - compact form | Last listed 1996 |
| - x *degronianum* | Last listed 1997 |
| ¶ - hybrid | SLdr |
| - PW 50 | GGGa |
| - Reuthe's form | SReu |
| *auritum* | GGGa NMun WPic |

| | |
|---|---|
| 'Aurora' (K) | NMun SLdr |
| § *austrinum* (A) ♀ | LMil |
| 'Autumn Gold' | COtt CWri LMil MBal SBrw SLdr |
| | SMur |
| ¶ 'Avalanche' ♀ | LMil |
| Avalanche Group & cl. | SReu |
| Avocet Group | Last listed 1996 |
| 'Award' | LMil |
| 'Ayah' | SReu |
| 'Aya-kammuri' (EA) | LHyd |
| 'Ayton' | Last listed 1996 |
| Azor Group & cl. | CHig LHyd NMun SLdr SReu |
| 'Azorazie' | NMun |
| 'Azuma-kagami' (EA) ♀ | CDoC LHyd LKna LMil |
| 'Azuray' | GGGa |
| 'Azurika' | NHol |
| 'Azurro' | GGGa LMil MDun SMur |
| 'Azurwolke' | Last listed 1997 |
| ¶ 'Babette' | MAsh MBri |
| ¶ 'Babuschka' | GGGa |
| 'Baby Scarlet' | SSta |
| 'Babylon' | Last listed 1998 |
| ¶ 'Bad Eilsen' | SBrw |
| 'Baden-Baden' | CDoC GCHN GChr GCrs LKna |
| | MAsh MBal MBar MDun MGos |
| | NHol NMun NWea SBod SLdr SSta |
| | WFar |
| 'Bagshot Ruby' ♀ | ENot LKna MDun NWea SBod |
| *baileyi* | GGGa LHyd LMil NMun SLdr |
| - LS&H 17359 | NMun |
| *bainbridgeanum* hybrid | LMil |
| - USDAPI 59184/ R11190 | NMun SLdr |
| *bakeri* | See R. cumberlandense |
| *balangense* EN 3530 | GGGa |
| *balfourianum* | GGGa LMil MDun NMun SLdr |
| - var. *aganniphoides* | LMil NMun SLdr |
| - F 16811 | Last listed 1997 |
| ¶ - F 29256* | SLdr |
| - SSNY 224 | GGGa |
| 'Ballerina' (K) | MBal SReu |
| 'Balsaminiflorum' | See R. indicum 'Balsaminiflorum' |
| 'Balzac' (K) | IOrc MBri MGos SBrw SLdr |
| 'Bambi' | LHyd NMun SBrw SLdr SReu |
| 'Bambino' | CAbP COtt LNet MAsh |
| 'Bandoola' | SReu |
| 'Banzai' (EA) | Last listed 1998 |
| 'Barbara Coates' (EA) | LHyd SLdr |
| 'Barbara Reuthe' | SReu |
| *barbatum* | CWri GGGa ISea LHyd LMil |
| | MDun NMun SLdr SReu |
| - B 235* | Last listed 1997 |
| - BB 152 | MBal |
| - BL&M 325 | NMun |
| - DF 525 | MBal |
| - KW 5659* | Last listed 1997 |
| - LS&H 17512 | Last listed 1997 |
| - TSS 30 | Last listed 1997 |
| 'Barbecue' (K) | LMil |
| Barclayi Group | LHyd |
| 'Barclayi Helen Fox' | NMun SLdr |
| 'Barclayi Robert Fox' | NMun SLdr |
| 'Barmstedt' | CWri |
| 'Barnaby Sunset' | GAri GGGa LRHS NHol |
| 'Bashful' ♀ | EPfP GRei IOrc LHyd MAsh MBal |
| | MGos NMun SLdr SReu |
| § *basilicum* | GGGa IDee LMil NMun SLdr |
| - AC 616 | NMun |
| - SF 381 | ISea |
| - TW 368 | Last listed 1997 |

| | | |
|---|---|---|
| 'Basilisk' (K) | Last listed 1996 | |
| 'Bastion' | Last listed 1996 | |
| x *bathyphyllum* | NMun SLdr | |
| – PA Cox 6542 | GGGa | |
| *bauhiniiflorum* | See *R. triflorum* var. *bauhiniiflorum* | |
| *beanianum* | GGGa LMil NMun SLdr | |
| – compact form | See *R. piercei* | |
| – KW 6805 | NMun | |
| 'Beatrice Keir' ♀ | LHyd LMil NMun SLdr SReu | |
| ¶ 'Beattie' (EA) | SLdr | |
| Beau Brummel Group & cl. | LMil | |
| 'Beaulieu' (K) | Last listed 1996 | |
| 'Beaulieu Manor' | GQui | |
| 'Beauty of Littleworth' ♀ | LHyd LKna LMil NMun SLdr SReu | |
| 'Beaver' (EA) | MBri | |
| *beesianum* | GGGa LMil NMun SLdr | |
| – F 10195 | NMun | |
| ¶ – F 16375 | SLdr | |
| – R 176 | Last listed 1997 | |
| ¶ – red bud form | SLdr | |
| – SSNY 250 | GGGa | |
| – SSNY 303 | GGGa | |
| 'Beethoven' (EA) ♀ | CTrG CTrh LHyd MBal NMun SBod SLdr SReu WGor | |
| Belkanto® | ENot | |
| 'Belle Heller' | MBal MBri SLdr WGwG WLRN | |
| 'Belle of Tremeer' | Last listed 1997 | |
| Bellerophon Group | NMun | |
| ¶ 'Ben Morrison' (EA) | SReu | |
| 'Bengal' (Rh) | ISea MBal MBar MBri MDun NHol SReu | |
| 'Bengal Beauty' (EA) | GQui LMil | |
| 'Bengal Fire' (EA) | CMac SLdr | |
| ¶ 'Beni Glasso' (A) | SLdr | |
| § 'Benifude' (EA) | WBod | |
| 'Beni-giri' (EA) | CMac | |
| I 'Benjamen' | GGGa | |
| 'Bergie Larson' | CB&S CDoC CWri LMil MBri MLea | |
| *bergii* | See *R. augustinii* subsp. *rubrum* | |
| 'Berg's Yellow' | CWri GGGa MBri MDun | |
| 'Bernard Shaw' | SReu | |
| 'Berryrose' (K) ♀ | CB&S CTri ENot IOrc LHyd LKna LMil MAsh MBal MBar MBri MDun NMun SBrw SLdr SPer SReu WBod WLRN | |
| Berryrose Group & cl. | Last listed 1996 | |
| 'Bert's Own' | Last listed 1996 | |
| § 'Beryl Taylor' | GGGa NMun | |
| 'Better Half' | Last listed 1998 | |
| 'Betty' (EA) ♀ | CTrG LHyd SLdr SRms | |
| 'Betty Anne Voss' (EA) | LHyd MAsh SCoo SReu | |
| 'Betty Stewart' | Last listed 1998 | |
| 'Betty Wormald' ♀ | CDoC CHig CWri LKna LMil MAsh MBri MGos NMun SBid SBrw SLdr SReu SSta WGer WPic | |
| *beyerinckianum* (V) | CEqu | |
| *bhutanense* | MDun SLdr | |
| – AC 119 | NMun | |
| – AC 124 | NMun | |
| – EGM 077 | GGGa | |
| – KR 1753 | Last listed 1997 | |
| Bibiani Group & cl. | Last listed 1996 | |
| 'Big Punkin' | LMil | |
| 'Bijou de Ledeberg' (EA) | SSta | |
| 'Billy Budd' | LHyd | |
| 'Binfield' | SLdr | |
| 'Birthday Girl' | COtt LMil | |
| 'Birthday Greeting' | NMun SLdr | |

| | | |
|---|---|---|
| 'Biscuit Box' | NMun SLdr | |
| Biskra Group & cl. | GGGa NMun | |
| 'Blaauw's Pink' (EA) ♀ | CChe CDoC CHig CMac CTrh EBee ENot GQui IOrc LHyd LKna LMil MAsh MBar MBri MGos NMun SBod SBrw SLdr SPer SReu SRms WFar | |
| 'Black Hawk' (EA) | CB&S COtt CTrG | |
| ¶ 'Black Knight' (A) | SLdr | |
| 'Black Magic' | COtt CWri LMil | |
| 'Black Satin' | COtt LMil | |
| 'Black Sport' | MLea | |
| Blanc-mange Group & cl. | Last listed 1996 | |
| Blaue Donau | See *R.* 'Blue Danube' | |
| 'Blazecheck' | LRHS MGos SCoo | |
| 'Blewbury' ♀ | CDoC LHyd LMil MDun NMun SLdr SReu SSta | |
| 'Blitz' | Last listed 1998 | |
| 'Blizzard' (EA) | CTrh | |
| 'Blue Bell' | LKna | |
| 'Blue Boy' | LMil SMur | |
| 'Blue Carpet' | Last listed 1998 | |
| 'Blue Chip' | LHyd NMun SLdr | |
| § 'Blue Danube' (EA) ♀ | CChe CDoC CMac CTrG CTrh CTri ENot IOrc LHyd LKna LMil MBal MBar MBri NMun SBod SBrw SLdr SPer SReu SSta WBod WFar WGwG WStI | |
| Blue Diamond Group & cl. | CB&S CBrm CChe CMHG CTrh CWri ENot GRei LHyd LKna MAsh MBal MBar MDun MGos NHol NMun SBod SBrw SLdr SReu SRms WBod WGwG | |
| 'Blue Ensign' | Last listed 1996 | |
| 'Blue Gown' | LKna | |
| 'Blue Haze' | LHyd | |
| 'Blue Jay' | Last listed 1996 | |
| 'Blue Monday' | SLdr WBod | |
| 'Blue Moon' | MBar | |
| 'Blue Mountain' | GDra MBal | |
| 'Blue Pacific' | SBod | |
| 'Blue Peter' ♀ | CDoC CHig CWri ENot GGGa IOrc LHyd LKna MBar MBri MGos NMun SBrw SLdr SPer SReu SSta WStI | |
| 'Blue Pool' | LMil LRHS MBal MBar WBod | |
| Blue Ribbon Group | CMHG CTrw ISea | |
| 'Blue River' | Last listed 1997 | |
| 'Blue Silver' | GGGa NHol | |
| 'Blue Star' | LHyd LRHS MBri MLea NHed SBrw SReu WAbe | |
| ♦ 'Blue Steel' | See *R. fastigiatum* 'Blue Steel' | |
| Blue Tit Group | CB&S CSam CTrG CTre GDra LHyd LKna MAsh MBal MBar NHol NMun SBrw SLdr SReu SSta STre WBod | |
| Bluebird Group & cl. | ECho ENot IOrc LKna MBal MBar MGos SLdr SPer SRms WBod | |
| Bluestone Group | WBod | |
| 'Bluette' | ISea MBal MDun MLea NHed WAbe | |
| 'Blumiria' | GGGa | |
| 'Blurettia' | CWri | |
| 'Blushing Belle' (V) | CEqu | |
| Boadicea Group | Last listed 1996 | |
| ¶ 'Bobbie' | SReu | |
| 'Bob's Blue' | ISea | |
| 'Bob's Choice' (V) | Last listed 1998 | |
| 'Boddaertianum' ♀ | LHyd SReu | |
| *bodinieri* USDAPI | NMun | |

59585/ R11281
'Bodnant Yellow' — CSam
'Bonfire' — SReu
Bonito Group & cl. — Last listed 1997
'Bonnie Babe' — Last listed 1997
Bo-peep Group & cl. — CB&S CHig CSam LHyd LMil MBal MLea NMun SLdr WPic
'Borderer' — Last listed 1998
◆ 'Boskoop Ostara' — See R. 'Ostara'
'Boule de Neige' — MDun SBod SLdr
'Boulodes' — Last listed 1997
'Bounty' — Last listed 1997
'Bouquet de Flore' (G) ♀ — LMil MBar MBri SLdr SPer SReu WGer
'Bow Bells' ♀ — NMun SBrw SLdr WFar WWat
Bow Bells Group & cl. — CSam EBrP EBre IOrc ISea LBre LHyd LKna LMil MAsh MBal MBar MBri MDun MGos MLea SBod SBre SPer SReu SRms
'Bow Street' — LHyd
brachyanthum — GGGa NMun SLdr
- subsp. hypolepidotum — GGGa LMil MBal MDun NMun SLdr
§ - - KW 7038 — NMun
- L&S 2764 — See R. glaucophyllum var. glaucophyllum L&S 2764
brachycarpum — GGGa MBal NMun SLdr
- subsp. brachycarpum Tigerstedtii Group — SLdr SReu
§ - subsp. fauriei — NMun SLdr
¶ - - menota — SLdr
- pink — NMun SLdr
- 'Roseum Dwarf' — GGGa NMun
brachysiphon — See R. maddenii subsp. maddenii
bracteatum CH&M 2586 — Last listed 1997
'Brazier' (EA) — CTrh LHyd NMun SLdr
'Brazil' (K) — LKna SBid SBrw SReu
Break of Day Group & cl. — Last listed 1998
'Bremen' — MOne
'Brentor' — SLdr
'Breslau' (EA) — SBrw SSta
'Brets Own' — NMun SLdr
Bric-a-brac Group & cl. — CB&S CSam CTrw LHyd MBal NMun SLdr SReu SRms
'Bride's Bouquet' (EA/d) — SReu
'Bridesmaid' (O) — ENot SLdr
'Brigadoon' — GGGa
'Bright Forecast' (K) — MDun SLdr WGor
'Brigitte' — CWri GGGa MBri
'Brilliant' — MGos NHol
'Brilliant' (EA) — MGos
'Brilliant Blue' — MAsh
'Brilliant Crimson' — WWeb
'Brilliant Pink' — MAsh WWeb
'Britannia' ♀ — CB&S CSam CWri IOrc ISea LHyd LKna LNet MAsh MBal MBar MBri MGos NMun NWea SBod SBrw SLdr SPer SReu SSta WFar WWeb
'Britannia' x griersonianum — SLdr
'Brocade' ♀ — CSam LHyd LKna LMil MBri NMun SLdr
'Bronze Fire' (A) — SReu
'Brookside' — Last listed 1996
'Broughtonii' — CWri GGGa NMun SLdr
'Brown Eyes' — CWri
'Bruce Brechtbill' — CDoC GGGa GRei LMil MAsh MBal MBri MLea NHol SBrw SLdr SReu SSta
'Bruce Hancock' (Ad) — Last listed 1998
¶ bryophilum (V) — SLdr

'Buccaneer' (EA) — CTrh IOrc LHyd MBal SBod SPer
'Bud Flanagan' — LMil MAsh NMun
'Buketta' — GGGa MBri
Bulbul Group & cl. — Last listed 1996
bullatum — See R. edgeworthii
bulu C&V 9503 — GGGa
'Bungo-nishiki' (EA/d) — CMac SRms
bureaui ♀ — CAbP GGGa IOrc LHyd LMil MBal MDun NMun SLdr SReu SSta
- 'Ardrishaig' — GGGa
- C&H 7158 — GGGa
- CNW 1039 — GGGa
- CNW 957 — GGGa
- CNW 965 — GGGa
- CNW 969 — GGGa
* - cruentum CNW 922 — LMil
- EGM 141 — Last listed 1997
- x Elizabeth Group — SReu
- F 15609 — NMun
I - 'Lem's Variety' — LMil WAbe
- x prattii PA Cox 5066 — Last listed 1998
- R 25439 — NMun
¶ - SF 510 — ISea
- SF 517 — ISea
bureauoides — MDun NMun SReu
- PA Cox 5039 — GGGa
- PA Cox 5076 — GGGa
¶ 'Burma Road' — SLdr
burmanicum ♀ — GGGa LMil MDun NMun SLdr
Burning Bush Group — Last listed 1996
Bustard Group — Last listed 1998
'Butter Brickle' — Last listed 1997
'Butter Yellow' — ECho MBri
'Buttercup' (K) — MBar
'Buttered Popcorn' — Last listed 1998
'Butterfly' — LKna NMun SBrw SLdr
'Buttermint' — CTrh GAri MAsh MBal MBri NMun SLdr SReu SSta
'Buttersteep' — Last listed 1998
'Buttons and Bows' (K) — GGGa LMil
'Buzzard' (K) — LKna LMil
'C.B. van Nes' ♀ — Last listed 1996
'C.I.S.' — MDun NMun SLdr
'Caerhays Lavender' — CB&S IOrc
caesium — GGGa
- F 26798 — Last listed 1996
calendulaceum (A) — LHyd LMil MBal SReu
- yellow — LMil
Calfort Group & cl. — NMun SLdr
caliginis (V) — CEqu
callimorphum — GGGa LMil NMun SLdr
§ - var. myiagrum — Last listed 1996
- - F 21821a — NMun SLdr
- - KW 6962 — NMun
calophytum ♀ — CWri GGGa LHyd LMil MDun NMun SLdr
¶ - var. calophytum W/A 4279 — SLdr
¶ - Grieg's form — SLdr
- Knott 151 — NMun
¶ - var. openshawianum C&H 7055 — GGGa
- - EGM 318 — LMil
¶ - W 1523 — SLdr
- W/V 1523 — Last listed 1997
calostrotum — CHig LMil SRms WAbe
- 'Gigha' ♀ — CDoC CWri GGGa LMil MBri MDun MOne NHar WAbe

§ - subsp. *keleticum* ♀ — CTrG GAri GDra LHyd MBal MBar MDun MGos NHol SBod SBrw SRms WAbe WGer
- - F 19915 — NHol
- - F 21756 — NMun SLdr
- - R 58 — LMil
§ - - Radicans Group — GCrs LHyd LMil MBar MBri MBro MDun MLea NHol SRms WAbe WPat WPyg
- - - mound form — Last listed 1998
- - USDAPI 59182/R 11188 — MLea
- subsp. *riparium* — LMil MBal
- - Calciphilum Group — GGGa MDun WAbe
- - - Yu 19754 — Last listed 1998
§ - - Nitens Group — CDoC GGGa LMil MDun NHed WAbe
- - PA Cox 6157 — Last listed 1998
- - Rock's form R 178 — GGGa NHol
- SF 357 — ISea
- USDAPQ 03954/ R18453 — GGGa
*caloxanthum* — See *R. campylocarpum* subsp. *caloxanthum*
'Calsap' — GGGa
Calstocker Group — Last listed 1998
Calsutch Group — SLdr
*calvescens* var. *duseimatum* — NMun
*camelliiflorum* — GGGa LMil SLdr
- Rump 5696A — Last listed 1997
'Cameronian' (Ad) — LKna
*campanulatum* — COtt IOrc LHyd LKna LMil MDun NMun SLdr SReu WAbe
§ - subsp. *aeruginosum* — GGGa LMil MDun NMun SLdr SReu
¶ - - Airth 10 — GGGa
- - EGM 068 — LMil
- *album* — NMun SLdr
- - SS&W — Last listed 1997
- B&SWJ 2633 — Last listed 1998
- Bu 249 — GGGa
- Bu 258 — GGGa
- subsp. *campanulatum* B 643 — MBal
- - BL&M 283 — NMun
- - 'Roland Cooper' — NMun
- - DF 563 — MBal
¶ - HWJCM 195 — WCru
- 'Knap Hill' ♀ — LHyd NMun SReu
- 'Roland E. Cooper' — SLdr
- SMM 41 — SLdr
- SS&W 9107 — GGGa SLdr
- SS&W 9108 — Last listed 1996
- TSS 11 — NMun SLdr
- TSS 44 — Last listed 1996
- TSS 7 — SLdr
- TW 27 — Last listed 1996
- 'Waxen Bell' — LHyd NMun SLdr
§ 'Campfire' (EA) — SLdr
*campylocarpum* — CHig GGGa LHyd LMil MDun NMun SLdr SReu
- BM&W 150 — MBal
§ - subsp. *caloxanthum* — GGGa IOrc
- - forms — NMun SLdr
- - KR 3516 — LMil
§ - - Telopeum Group — NMun
§ - - - KW 5718B — NMun SLdr
- subsp. *campylocarpum* Elatum Group — MDun NMun
- - TSS 12 — NMun
- - TSS 43 — Last listed 1996

¶ - x *decorum* — SLdr
- DF 558 — MBal
¶ - East Nepal — MDun
¶ - var. *elatum* — SLdr
¶ - x *fortunei* — SLdr
- LS&H 16495* — NMun
- TW 31* — Last listed 1997
*campylogynum* — MGos SLdr SSpi
- 'Album' — See *R.* 'Leucanthemum'
- apricot — Last listed 1998
- 'Beryl Taylor' — See *R.* 'Beryl Taylor'
¶ - Brodick form — SLdr
- Castle Hill form — LMil SReu
- Celsum Group — Last listed 1996
- Charopoeum Group — GCrs GGGa LMil MBal MBar MDun MGos NHar NHol WAbe
- - 'Patricia' — ECho MBal MBri MDun
- claret — ECho GGGa LMil MBal MDun WAbe
- copper — Last listed 1996
§ - Cremastum Group — CTrG GGGa LHyd LMil NHol NMun
- - 'Bodnant Red' — CHig GGGa LHyd MDun NMun SLdr
* - - 'Cerise' — GGGa
- KW 21481 — Last listed 1998
- var. *leucanthum* — See *R.* 'Leucanthemum'
- Myrtilloides Group — CB&S CDoC CHig CTrh CTrw GAri GGGa GQui IOrc LHyd LMil MBal MBri MDun NMun SLdr SReu WAbe
- - Farrer 1046 — GGGa
¶ - PA Cox 6051* — GGGa
¶ - PA Cox 6096 — GGGa
- pink — CTrh MBar WAbe
- plum — GGGa WAbe
- salmon pink — ECho EPot MBal MBri MDun NHar NHol WAbe WBod
- SF 95181 — ISea
*camtschaticum* — GAri GGGa MBal MLea SLdr
- var. *albiflorum* — GGGa
- red — GGGa
*canadense* (A) — GGGa MBal NHol SLdr SReu
- f. *albiflorum* (A) — GGGa LMil
- 'Deer Lake' (A) — SReu
'Canary' — LKna MBal SLdr SReu
'Canby' (K) — MLea
§ x *candelabrum* — NMun
*canescens* (A) — LMil
'Cannon's Double' (K/d) — GGGa LMil
'Canzonetta' (EA) — GGGa MGos
*capitatum* — GGGa
¶ 'Caprice' (EA) — SReu
'Captain Jack' — CWri GGGa SLdr
'Caractacus' — IOrc MBar SBrw WFar
'Carat' — SLdr SReu
Cardinal Group & cl. — Last listed 1996
*cardiobasis* — See *R. orbiculare* subsp. *cardiobasis*
Carex Group & cl. — Last listed 1997
'Carillon Bells' — CEqu
Carita Group — LKna SReu
'Carita Golden Dream' ♀ — LKna LMil NMun SLdr
'Carita Inchmery' ♀ — LHyd LKna NMun SBrw SLdr
'Carmen' ♀ — CSam GChr GDra GGGa ISea LHyd LKna LMil MBal MBar MBri MDun MLea NHar NHol NMun NWea SBod SBrw SLdr SReu SRms WBod
*carneum* — GGGa LMil

'Caroline Allbrook' ♀ CSam CWri GGGa LHyd LMil
MAsh MBri MGos MLea MOne
NHed NHol NMun SBrw SLdr
SReu
'Caroline de Zoete' LHyd
◆ *carolinianum* See *R. minus* var. *minus*
*carringtoniae* (V) Last listed 1996
'Cary Ann' CB&S CSam CWri GCHN GChr
ISea MBal MLea NMun SBid SLdr
SReu
'Cassley' (Vs) LMil LRHS SLdr
¶ 'Castle of Mey' SLdr
*catacosmum* GGGa SLdr
– R 11185 SLdr
§ 'Catalode' SBrw
*catawbiense* CHig GGGa LHyd NMun SLdr
'Catawbiense Album' IOrc
'Catawbiense Boursault' CWri IOrc
'Catawbiense Grandiflorum' CWri IOrc LRHS SBrw
*catawbiense* 'Powell Glass' Last listed 1996
'Catherine Hopwood' NMun SLdr
Cauapo Group Last listed 1996
*caucasicum* LHyd MBal
§ – 'Cunningham's Sulphur' MDun
– ex AC&H GGGa NMun
'Caucasicum Pictum' GGGa LHyd LMil MBar MBri SBrw
SLdr
'Cavalcade' Last listed 1996
'Cayenne' (EA) SLdr
'Cecile' (K) ♀ CB&S GChr GRei LHyd LKna LMil
MAsh MBal MBar MBri MGos
NMun SPer SReu
'Celestial' (EA) CMac
I 'Celtic Cross' CB&S
'Centennial' See *R.* 'Washington State
Centennial'
'Centennial Celebration' IOrc
*cephalanthum* GGGa LMil
– subsp. *cephalanthum* MBal
– – – Crebreflorum Group GAri GGGa LMil LRHS
– – – Week's form Last listed 1997
– – – Nmaiense Group GGGa
C&V 9513
– – SBEC 0751 GGGa
– subsp. *platyphyllum* GGGa
– – CNW 835 LMil
*cerasinum* GGGa ISea LMil MDun NMun
SLdr
– C&V 9504 GGGa
– 'Cherry Brandy' LHyd NMun
– 'Coals of Fire' NMun SLdr
– deep pink NMun SLdr
– x *forrestii* subsp. MBal
*forrestii*
– KW 11011 NMun SLdr
– KW 5830 SLdr
– KW 6923 Last listed 1997
– KW 8258 Last listed 1997
– red form SLdr
'Cetewayo' SBrw SLdr SReu
*chaetomallum* See *R. haematodes* subsp.
*chaetomallum*
'Chaffinch' (K) LKna
*chamaethomsonii* GGGa LMil MBal NHar NMun
SLdr
¶ – CCH&H 8195 GGGa
– var. *chamaedoron* LMil
F 21768
– var. *chamaethauma* LMil
KW 5847

– var. *chamaethomsonii* GGGa
Exbury form L&S
§ – – F 21723 NMun
– – pink forms L&S GGGa
– – Rock form Last listed 1998
'Chameleon' (EA) IOrc
*chameunum* See *R. saluenense* subsp.
*chameunum*
§ 'Champagne' ♀ IOrc LHyd LKna LMil MDun
MGos MLea NMun SBrw SLdr
SReu
*championiae* GGGa
'Chanel' (Vs) SReu SSta
'Chanticleer' (EA) CTrh SBrw SLdr SReu
*chapaense* See *R. maddenii* subsp. *crassum*
*charitopes* GGGa LMil MBal NMun SLdr
– subsp. *charitopes* SReu
F 25570
§ – subsp. *tsangpoense* GGGa GQui LMil NHol
¶ – – C&V 9575* GGGa
'Charlotte Currie' SLdr
* 'Charlotte de Rothschild' (A) Last listed 1998
'Charlotte de Rothschild' ♀ LMil NMun SLdr
Charmaine Group & cl. CSam GGGa MBal MDun NHol
WBod
'Charme La' GGGa
'Charming Valentino' (V) CEqu
*chasmanthum* See *R. augustinii* subsp.
*chasmanthum*
'Checkmate' See *R.* (PJM Group) 'Checkmate'
'Cheer' COtt CWri IOrc LMil MAsh MBal
MBar MBri SBrw SLdr WGor
'Cheerful Giant' (K) CDoC LMil MLea
'Chelsea Reach' (K/d) LKna
'Chelsea Seventy' COtt ENot MBal NMun SLdr SReu
'Chenille' (K/d) LKna
'Cherokee' SLdr
'Chetco' (K) CDoC LMil
'Chevalier Félix de CWri LMil MBri MGos NMun
Sauvage' ♀ SBod SBrw SReu
'Cheyenne' SLdr
'Chicago' (M) LKna
'Chiffchaff' LHyd SLdr WAbe
*chibsinianum* C&H 7189 GGGa
'Chikor' CTrg GGGa LKna MAsh MBal
MBar MBri MDun MGos MLea
NFla NHar NHol NMun SBrw
SLdr SReu SRms WAbe WBod
WFar WSHC
China Group & cl. LKna SBrw SReu
'China A' LKna SBrw SLdr
'Chinchilla' (EA) GQui MBri WGor
'Chink' CB&S CGre CSam ENot LHyd
MAsh MBal MBar MDun NMun
SLdr SPer WBod
'Chionoides' GGGa IOrc LKna SBid SLdr
'Chipmunk' (E/d) Last listed 1997
'Chippewa' (EA) GGGa LMil LRHS MBri
*chlorops* SLdr
'Chocolate Ice' (K/d) LKna
'Chopin' (EA) WBod
'Choremia' ♀ MLea NMun SLdr SReu
'Chorister' (K) LKna
¶ 'Chris' (EA) SLdr
'Chris Bagley' SBrw
*christi* (V) Last listed 1998
– Sandham 61/86 (V) GGGa
'Christina' (EA/d) CMac CTrh GHCN MBri SLdr SPer
SReu WBod WGor WWal
'Christmas Cheer' (EA) See *R.* 'Ima-shojo'

| | |
|---|---|
| 'Christmas Cheer' | CB&S CHig CMac GGGa IOrc ISea LHyd LKna LMil MGos MLea NMun SBrw SLdr SPer SReu WPic |
| 'Christobel Maude' | LHyd |
| § 'Christopher Wren' (K) | ELan GChr MBal SLdr |
| *chrysanthum* | See *R. aureum* |
| *chryseum* | See *R. rupicola* var. *chryseum* |
| *chrysodoron* | GGGa LMil NMun |
| *chrysomanicum* | See *R.* Chrysomanicum Group & cl. |
| § Chrysomanicum Group & cl. | NMun |
| *ciliatum* ♀ | CB&S CSam GGGa IOrc LHyd MBal NMun SLdr WAbe |
| - 'Multiflorum' | See *R.* 'Multiflorum' |
| *ciliicalyx* | Last listed 1996 |
| - subsp. *lyi* | See *R. lyi* |
| - SF 535 | ISea |
| Cilpinense Group | CB&S CHig CSam CWri ENot GGGa IOrc LHyd LKna LMil MAsh MBal MBar MDun NFla NHol NMun SBrw SLdr SPer SRPl SReu WAbe WBod WFar |
| *cinnabarinum* | LMil MBal MDun NMun SLdr |
| ¶ - B&SWJ 2633 | WCru |
| - Bu 268 | Last listed 1998 |
| - Caerhays John Group | Last listed 1996 |
| - 'Caerhays Lawrence' | MBal NMun SLdr |
| - 'Caerhays Philip' | MBal |
| ¶ - subsp. *cinnabarinum* | SLdr |
| - - 'Aestivale' | LMil MDun |
| - - B 652 | MBal |
| - - BL&M 234 | LMil |
| - - Blandfordiiflorum Group | GGGa MBal MDun NMun SLdr |
| § - - 'Conroy' ♀ | GGGa LMil MBal MDun SReu |
| ¶ - - Ghunsa Nepal | MDun |
| - - LS&H 21283 | Last listed 1997 |
| I - - 'Mount Everest' | SLdr |
| - - 'Nepal' ex LS&M 21283 | LMil MDun SLdr |
| - - Roylei Group | GGGa LMil MBal MDun MLea NMun SLdr SReu |
| - - 'Vin Rosé' | LMil MDun |
| - SHE 638 | Last listed 1997 |
| § - subsp. *tamaense* | GGGa NMun |
| - - KW 21003 | NMun |
| - - KW 21021 | GGGa NMun |
| § - subsp. *xanthocodon* ♀ | CHig ISea LMil MBal MLea NMun SLdr WAbe |
| § - - Concatenans Group | CB&S CSam CWri GGGa MDun NMun SLdr |
| - - - 'Amber' | LMil MDun MLea |
| - - - C&V 9523 | GGGa |
| - - - KW 5874 | LHyd LMil |
| - - - LS&T 6560 | NMun |
| - - - mustard form | NMun |
| - - 'Daffodilly' | LHyd |
| - - EGM 88 | LMil |
| - - forms | NMun |
| - - KW 6026 | Last listed 1996 |
| - - KW 8239 | NMun |
| - - Purpurellum Group | GGGa MDun NMun SLdr |
| Cinnkeys Group & cl. | GGGa LMil SLdr |
| Cinzan Group | SReu |
| *citriniflorum* | NMun |
| ¶ - CCH&H 8177 | GGGa |
| - var. *citriniflorum* | LMil |
| - var. *horaeum* | NMun |
| - - F 21850* | GGGa |
| - - F 25901 | NMun SLdr |
| - - R 108 | GGGa |
| 'Clarissa' (EA/d) | IOrc |
| 'Claydian Variegated' | GGGa |
| *clementinae* | GGGa LHyd MDun NMun SLdr SReu |
| - F 25705 | LMil NMun SLdr |
| - F 25917 | Last listed 1997 |
| ¶ - × *pronum* | GGGa |
| ¶ - R 25401 | SLdr |
| 'Cliff Garland' | GQui LMil MDun |
| Clio Group | NMun SLdr |
| 'Coccineum Speciosum' (G) ♀ | GGGa IOrc LHyd LMil MBar MBri SReu SSta |
| 'Cockade' (EA) | LKna |
| 'Cockatoo' (K) | LKna |
| *coelicum* | Last listed 1996 |
| - F 21830 | See *R. pocophorum* var. *pocophorum* F 21830 |
| - F 25625 | GGGa |
| § - KW 21075 | NMun |
| § - KW 21077 | NMun SLdr |
| *coeloneuron* | CB&S GGGa LMil MDun |
| - EGM 108 | Last listed 1997 |
| 'Colin Kenrick' (K/d) | LKna |
| *collettianum* | Last listed 1996 |
| - H&W 8975 | GGGa |
| 'Colonel Coen' | CWri MBal MLea |
| Colonel Rogers Group | LHyd NMun SLdr SReu |
| 'Colyer' (EA) | LHyd SLdr |
| Comely Group | NMun SLdr |
| ¶ - 'Golden Orfe' | SLdr |
| 'Commodore' (EA) | Last listed 1996 |
| *complexum* F 15392 | GGGa |
| - SSNY 296 | Last listed 1998 |
| 'Comte de Gomer' | CB&S |
| *concatenans* | See *R. cinnabarinum* subsp. *xanthocodon* Concatenans Group |
| *concinnum* | CHig CTrw CWri LHyd LMil MBal MDun NMun SLdr |
| - Benthamianum Group | Last listed 1997 |
| - PA Cox 5011 | Last listed 1998 |
| - PA Cox 5085 | Last listed 1998 |
| - Pseudoyanthinum Group ♀ | GGGa GQui LMil MDun NMun SLdr WPic |
| 'Concorde' | LHyd |
| 'Congo' | See *R.* 'Robin Hill Congo' |
| ♦ 'Conroy' | See *R. cinnabarinum* subsp. *cinnabarinum* 'Conroy' |
| 'Consolini's Windmill' | LMil |
| 'Constable' | LHyd NMun SLdr |
| 'Constant Nymph' | LKna |
| 'Contina' | GGGa |
| Conyan Group | LHyd |
| *cookeanum* | See *R. sikangense* Cookeanum Group |
| 'Cora Grant' (EA) | Last listed 1998 |
| 'Coral Beauty' | Last listed 1997 |
| 'Coral Reef' | NMun SLdr SReu |
| 'Coral Sea' (EA) | SReu |
| 'Coral Velvet' | COtt |
| ¶ 'Corany' (A) | SLdr |
| *coriaceum* | GGGa LMil NMun SLdr |
| - F 16364 | Last listed 1997 |
| - F 21843 | Last listed 1997 |
| - PA Cox 6531 | GGGa |
| - R 120 | NMun |
| - SF 348 | Last listed 1998 |
| 'Corneille' (G/d) ♀ | LKna LMil SBid SPer SReu |
| 'Cornish Cracker' | NMun SLdr |
| Cornish Cross Group | LHyd NMun SLdr SReu |

Cornish Early Red Group — See *R.* Smithii Group
'Cornish Red' — See *R.* Smithii Group
Cornsutch Group — Last listed 1996
Cornubia Group — NMun SLdr
'Corona' ♀ — LKna
'Coronation Day' — SLdr SReu
'Coronation Lady' (K) — ENot LKna MBri
Coronet Group — Last listed 1996
'Corringe' (K) ♀ — LMil
'Corry Koster' — LKna SBrw
*coryanum* — GGGa NMun SLdr
- 'Chelsea Chimes' ex KW 6311 — GGGa LMil
'Cosmopolitan' — CWri GChr GGGa IOrc LMil MBar MDun MGos SBrw
'Costa del Sol' — NMun SLdr
'Cotton Candy' — LMil NMun
'Countess of Athlone' — IOrc LKna SBrw SLdr
'Countess of Derby' — IOrc SBrw SLdr SReu
'Countess of Haddington' ♀ — CB&S CWri ISea LMil NMun SLdr
'County of York' — See *R.* 'Catalode'
*cowanianum* — GGGa
Cowslip Group — CSam LHyd LKna LMil MBal MBar MDun MGos NHol NMun SLdr SReu
*coxianum* C&H 475B — GGGa
'Craig Faragher' (V) — CEqu
'Cranbourne' — SReu
'Crane' — GGGa GQui LMil
*crassum* — See *R. maddenii* subsp. *crassum*
'Cream Crest' — GQui ISea MDun WAbe
'Cream Glory' — LHyd SReu
'Creamy Chiffon' — CDoC CWri GCHN GGGa LHyd MBal MBri MGos MLea SLdr SReu SSta WGwG
§ 'Creeping Jenny' ♀ — GGGa LHyd MBal MBar MDun MLea NHol
*cremastum* — See *R. campylogynum* Cremastum Group
§ 'Crest' ♀ — CSam CWri GGGa IOrc ISea LHyd LKna LMil MBal MDun MGos MLea SLdr SPer SReu
'Crete' — COtt LMil LRHS MAsh MDun MGos SReu
'Crimson Glory' — See *R.* 'Natalie Coe Vitetti'
'Crimson Pippin' — GGGa LMil
*crinigerum* — GGGa LMil LRHS MDun NMun SLdr
- bicolored form — SLdr
- var. *crinigerum* KW 7123 — NMun
- - KW 8164 — NMun
- - R 100 — NMun
- - R 38 — NMun
- var. *euadenium* — NMun
'Crinoline' (K) — SBrw SLdr SPer SReu WWeb
¶ 'Crooksbury Gold' — SLdr
Crossbill Group — CB&S CGre MBal SLdr WPic
* *crossium* — SReu
'Crosswater Red' (K) — LMil
'Crown Jewel' (EA/d) — Last listed 1996
'Crowthorne' — Last listed 1997
*cruttwellii* (V) — GGGa
*cubittii* — See *R. veitchianum* Cubittii Group
*cucullatum* — See *R. roxieanum* var. *cucullatum*
cultivar FH 8 — LMil
§ *cumberlandense* (A) — GGGa LMil
- 'Sunlight' (A) — LMil
*cuneatum* — GGGa LMil NMun
- F 27119* — NMun

- R 11392 — NMun
§ - Ravum Group — CHig WPic
'Cunningham's Blush' — GAri GGGa
'Cunningham's Sulphur' — See *R. caucasicum* 'Cunningham's Sulphur'
'Cunningham's White' — CB&S CHig CPMA CSam CWri GChr GGGa GRei IOrc LKna LMil MAsh MBar MBri MDun MGos NMun NWea SBrw SLdr SPer SReu WFar WStI WWeb
'Cupcake' — GGGa
'Curlew' ♀ — CDoC CTrh CWSG EBrP EBre GGGa GRei IOrc LBre LHyd LMil MAsh MBal MBar MBri MGos MLea NHar NHol NMun SBod SBre SIng SLdr SReu WAbe WBod WGwG
'Cutie' — Last listed 1998
*cyanocarpum* — GGGa LMil MDun NMun SLdr
- AC 676 — NMun
- Bu 294 — GGGa
- EN 2458 — Last listed 1998
'Cynthia' ♀ — CB&S CWri ENot GGGa IOrc LHyd LKna LMil MAsh MBal MBar MBri MDun MGos NMun NWea SBod SBrw SLdr SPer SReu SSta WFar
'Dagmar' — Last listed 1997
'Daimio' (EA) — SPer
'Dainty Drops' (V) — CEqu
'Dairymaid' — LHyd LKna NMun SBrw SLdr SReu
*dalhousieae* — GGGa SLdr
§ - var. *rhabdotum* ♀ — GGGa SLdr
Damaris Group — NMun SLdr
'Damaris Logan' — See *R.* 'Logan Damaris'
Damozel Group & cl. — WStI
'Dandy' — LKna
Dante Group — SLdr
'Daphne' — SLdr
'Daphne Jewiss' — SReu
'Daphne Magor' — SLdr
'Daphnoides' — MLea
'Dartmoor Dawn' — MBal
* 'Dartmoor Rose' — Last listed 1998
*dasycladum* — See *R. selense* subsp. *dasycladum*
*dasypetalum* — ECho MBal MBar MBri MDun
*dauricum* — LMil MBal SLdr
- 'Album' — See *R. dauricum* 'Hokkaido'
- 'Arctic Pearl' — GGGa SLdr
- 'Dark St Andrews' — GGGa
- dwarf — LHyd
§ - 'Hokkaido' — GAri LHyd
- 'Hokkaido' x *leucaspis* — GGGa
- 'Midwinter' ♀ — GGGa LHyd LMil MBri SLdr
- 'Nanum' — MBal
- 'Suzuki' — SLdr
'David' ♀ — GGGa LHyd LKna NMun SBrw SLdr SReu
'David Grant' — Last listed 1997
*davidsonianum* ♀ — CB&S CTrw GGGa IOrc ISea LHyd LMil MBal NMun SLdr WBod
- Bodnant Form — LMil
- C&H 7023 — Last listed 1997
- 'Caerhays Pink' — GGGa
- PA Cox 5007 — Last listed 1997
- PA Cox 5091 — Last listed 1997
- 'Ruth Lyons' — LMil

| | |
|---|---|
| 'Daviesii' (G) ♀ | CB&S CTri ENot GGGa LHyd |
| | LKna LMil MAsh MBal MBri MLea |
| | SLdr SPer SReu SSpi WWat WWeb |
| 'Dawn's Delight' | NMun |
| 'Dawn's Glory' (K) | Last listed 1996 |
| * 'Day Dawn' | SReu |
| Day Dream Group & cl. | IOrc LKna SReu |
| 'Daybreak' (K) | GQui MAsh |
| N 'Daybreak' (EA/d) | See R. 'Kirin' |
| 'Dayspring' (EA) | ENot LMil |
| N 'Debutante' | Last listed 1998 |
| x *decipiens* | SLdr |
| *decorum* | COtt IOrc LHyd LMil MDun |
| | NMun SLdr SReu |
| - AC 757 | NMun |
| - BU 286 | NHol |
| ¶ - C&H 7023 | GGGa |
| - CNW 582 | ISea |
| - 'Cox's Uranium Green' | SReu |
| - subsp. *decorum* SBEC 1060 | NMun |
| - - SBEC 181 | NMun |
| - - SBEC 439 | Last listed 1997 |
| § - subsp. *diaprepes* | CWri IOrc LMil NMun |
| ¶ - - 'Forest May Cly' | SLdr |
| - - 'Gargantua' | NMun SLdr SReu |
| - Farrer 979 | NMun |
| - forms | GGGa NMun |
| - x hybrid | Last listed 1997 |
| ¶ - pink | SLdr |
| - R 54021* | Last listed 1997 |
| ¶ - SBEC 106005786 | SLdr |
| ¶ - SBEC 4390516 | SLdr |
| - SF 252 | ISea |
| - TW 384 | Last listed 1997 |
| - TW 388 | Last listed 1997 |
| *degronianum* | GGGa NMun SReu |
| § - subsp. *degronianum* | NMun SLdr |
| * - - 'Gerald Loder' | GGGa LHyd |
| * - - *spontaneum* | SLdr |
| § - subsp. *beptamerum* | GGGa MDun NMun SLdr |
| - - 'Ho Emma' | LMil |
| - - var. *macranthum* | LMil |
| - 'Metternianum' | See R. degronianum subsp. |
| | heptamerum var. kyomaruense |
| - 'Rae's Delight' | LMil |
| *delavayi* | See R. arboreum subsp. delavayi |
| 'Delicatissimum' (O) ♀ | GGGa GQui MAsh MLea SLdr |
| | WWeb |
| 'Delta' | SBrw |
| *dendricola* KW 20981* | GGGa |
| - Taronense Group | Last listed 1996 |
| *dendrocharis* | GGGa |
| - CC&H 4012 | GGGa |
| - PA Cox 5016 | GGGa NHol |
| * 'Denny's Rose' (A) | SReu |
| 'Denny's Scarlet' | SReu |
| 'Denny's White' | SReu |
| *denudatum* C&H 7012 | GGGa |
| - C&H 7118 | GGGa |
| - EGM 294 | LMil |
| 'Desert Orchid' | LHyd |
| 'Desert Pink' (K) | LKna |
| *desquamatum* | See R. rubiginosum |
| | Desquamatum Group |
| x *detonsum* | LMil NMun SLdr |
| - F13784 | SLdr |
| ¶ 'Devisiperbile' (A) | SLdr |
| 'Dexter's Spice' | LMil |
| 'Diabolo' (K) | LKna |

| | |
|---|---|
| 'Diadem' (V) | SBrw |
| Diamant Group (EA) | GAri GGGa |
| - lilac (EA) | GGGa LMil MBri |
| - pink (EA) | ECho GGGa MGos SReu WAbe |
| § - purple (EA) | ECho MGos |
| § - red (EA) | WAbe |
| - rosy red (EA) | COtt ECho GAri GGGa MBri |
| | WGor |
| - white (EA) | ECho SLdr WAbe |
| 'Diamant Purpur' | See R. Diamant Group purple |
| 'Diamant Rot' | See R. Diamant Group red |
| 'Diana Colville' | Last listed 1996 |
| 'Diana Pearson' | LHyd NMun SLdr |
| 'Diana van Herzeele' | SBrw |
| 'Diane' | LKna NMun SBrw SLdr WBod |
| *diaprepes* | See R. decorum subsp. diaprepes |
| Dicharb Group | Last listed 1996 |
| *dichroanthum* | CDoC GGGa IOrc LHyd MBal |
| | MDun NMun SLdr SReu |
| § - subsp. *apodectum* | GGGa LMil MDun NMun SLdr |
| - subsp. *dichroanthum* | NMun |
| F 6781 | |
| - - SBEC 545 | GGGa |
| - - SBEC 601 | GGGa |
| - forms | NMun |
| § - subsp. *scyphocalyx* | GGGa LMil MBal MDun NMun |
| | SLdr |
| - - F 24546 | GGGa |
| - - F 27115 | GGGa |
| - - F 27137 | NMun |
| - - Farrer 1024 | GGGa |
| *dictyotum* | See R. traillianum var. dictyotum |
| 'Dido' | LHyd |
| *didymum* | See R. sanguineum subsp. |
| | didymum |
| 'Dietrich' | SBrw SReu SSta |
| *dignabile* C&V 9569 | GGGa |
| *dimitrum* | MDun |
| 'Diny Dee' | MBal MGos |
| 'Diorama' (Vs) | SLdr SReu SSta |
| *diphrocalyx* | NMun |
| § 'Directeur Moerlands' (M) ♀ | Last listed 1991 |
| 'Direktor E. Hjelm' | SBrw |
| *discolor* | See R. fortunei subsp. discolor |
| Diva Group & cl. | Last listed 1996 |
| 'Doc' ♀ | CB&S ENot GRei IOrc LHyd LMil |
| | MAsh MBal MBar MGos NHed |
| | NMun SBrw SLdr SReu WStI |
| 'Doctor Arnold W. Endtz' | CWri IOrc NMun SBrw |
| 'Doctor Ernst Schäle' | GGGa |
| 'Doctor H.C. Dresselhuys' | IOrc MBar SBrw |
| ¶ 'Doctor Herman | GGGa |
| Sleumer' (V) | |
| 'Doctor M. Oosthoek' (M) ♀ | SReu |
| 'Doctor Stocker' | CWri NMun SLdr |
| 'Doctor Tjebbes' | SBrw |
| 'Doctor V.H. Rutgers' | IOrc MBar MGos SBrw WFar |
| 'Donald Waterer' | SBrw |
| 'Doncaster' | ENot IOrc LKna MAsh MBar |
| | MGos NMun NWea SBod SBrw |
| | SLdr WFar |
| 'Dopey' ♀ | CDoC CSam CWri EBee ENot |
| | GGGa GRei IOrc LHyd LMil MAsh |
| | MBal MBar MBri MDun MGos |
| | MLea NHed NHol NMun SBrw |
| | SLdr SPer SReu WGwG WWeb |
| 'Dora Amateis' ♀ | CB&S COtt CSam GGGa ISea |
| | LHyd LMil MAsh MBal MBar MBri |
| | MGos NHol NMun SBid SBrw |
| | SLdr SPer SReu WAbe WBod |
| | WGwG WPic |

| | |
|---|---|
| Dormouse Group | LMil SBrw SLdr |
| 'Dorothea' | SLdr |
| 'Dorothy Amateis' | Last listed 1997 |
| 'Dorothy Corston' (K) | LKna |
| 'Dorothy Hayden' (EA) | LHyd SLdr |
| *doshongense* | See *R. aganniphum* var. *aganniphum* Doshongense Group |
| 'Double Beauty' (EA/d) | CTrh IOrc LKna SBod SPer SReu SSta WWal |
| 'Double Damask' (K/d) ♀ | LHyd LKna SReu |
| 'Double Date' (d) | GGGa |
| 'Double Delight' (K/d) | GGGa MLea |
| 'Doubloons' | NMun SLdr |
| 'Douglas McEwan' | Last listed 1996 |
| Dragonfly Group | MDun SReu |
| - × *serotinum* | SLdr |
| 'Drake's Mountain' | ECho MBar MBri MDun |
| 'Dreamland' | COtt CWri ENot LHyd LMil MAsh MGos MLea SBid SBrw SLdr SReu |
| 'Driven Snow' (EA) | ENot SBod |
| *drumonium* | See *R. telmateium* |
| 'Drury Lane' (K) | GQui LHyd SLdr |
| *dryophyllum* hort. | See *R. phaeochrysum* var. *levistratum* |
| - Balfour & Forrest | See *R. phaeochrysum* var. *phaeochrysum* |
| 'Duchess of Portland' | SReu |
| 'Duchess of Rothesay' | NMun |
| 'Duchess of Teck' | SReu |
| 'Dusky Dawn' | NMun SLdr |
| 'Dusky Orange' | SReu |
| 'Dusty Miller' | CAbP CDoC COtt ISea LHyd MBal MBar MGos NHed SLdr WAbe |
| 'Earl of Athlone' | LHyd SReu |
| 'Earl of Donoughmore' ♀ | LHyd LKna SBrw SReu SSta |
| 'Early Beni' (EA) | LHyd |
| Early Brilliant Group | LKna |
| ¶ 'Early Gem' | MAsh |
| ¶ early red hybrid | SLdr |
| 'Eastern Fire' | See *R. kaempferi* 'Eastern Fire' |
| 'Ebony Pearl' | CDoC GGGa MDun |
| *eclecteum* | LMil MDun NMun SLdr |
| - var. *bellatulum* | Last listed 1997 |
| - - R 110* | Last listed 1997 |
| - var. *eclecteum* 'Kingdon Come' ex KW 6869 | Last listed 1997 |
| - - R 23512 | Last listed 1997 |
| - PA Cox 6054 | GGGa |
| - 'Rowallane Yellow' | NMun |
| 'Eddy' (EA) | LKna NMun |
| × *edgarianum* | LMil |
| § *edgeworthii* ♀ | GGGa LHyd LMil MBal NMun WAbe WBod |
| - AC 666 | NMun |
| - forms | GGGa WBod |
| - × *leucaspis* | CB&S |
| - × *moupinense* | GGGa |
| - SF 607 | Last listed 1998 |
| - Yu 17431 | Last listed 1997 |
| 'Edith Mackworth Praed' | SReu |
| Edmondii Group | Last listed 1997 |
| 'Edna Bee' (EA) | GQui LMil |
| 'Egret' ♀ | CHig CSam GAri GGGa ITim LHyd MAsh MBal MBar MBri MGos MLea NHar NHol SBid SLdr WAbe WGer |
| 'Ehrengold' | Last listed 1998 |
| 'Eider' | COtt GCHN GGGa ISea MAsh MBal NMun SReu WAbe WFar |

| | |
|---|---|
| 'Eileen' | SReu |
| ¶ 'Eisprinzessin' (EA) | GGGa |
| 'El Alamein' | Last listed 1998 |
| 'El Camino' | COtt CWri MBal MBri MLea |
| 'El Greco' | NMun SLdr WWeb |
| Eldorado Group | NMun SLdr |
| 'Eleanor Habgood' | GQui |
| Eleanore Group & cl. | SLdr |
| Electra Group & cl. | IOrc |
| | See *R. augustinii* Electra Group & cl. |
| 'Elegant Bouquet' (V) | Last listed 1996 |
| *elegantulum* | GGGa LHyd LMil MDun NMun SLdr |
| 'Elfenbein' | Last listed 1997 |
| 'Elfin Gold' | GGGa SReu |
| 'Elisabeth Hobbie' ♀ | GDra GGGa LKna LMil MBal MBar MDun MGos SLdr |
| Elizabeth Group | CB&S CDoC CSam CTrh CTrw CWri EBee GDra GGGa IOrc LHyd LKna LMil MAsh MBal MBar MGos NHol NMun NWea SBod SBrw SLdr SPer SReu WBod WFar |
| N 'Elizabeth' (EA) | ENot IOrc MGos |
| 'Elizabeth de Rothschild' | LMil MDun NMun |
| 'Elizabeth Gable' (EA) | Last listed 1997 |
| 'Elizabeth Jenny' | See *R.* 'Creeping Jenny' |
| 'Elizabeth Lockhart' | CGre GGGa GQui MBal MBar MDun MGos MLea |
| 'Elizabeth of Glamis' | GGGa |
| 'Elizabeth Red Foliage' | GGGa LMil LRHS MAsh MDun NHol SBrw |
| *elliottii* | GGGa NMun SLdr SReu |
| - KW 7725 | NMun |
| Elsae Group & cl. | NMun SLdr SReu |
| 'Else Frye' | GGGa |
| 'Elsie Lee' (EA) | CDoC CGre CTrh GGGa LMil MAsh SBod SBrw SReu SSta |
| 'Elsie Pratt' (K) | MBar MBri SReu SSta |
| 'Elsie Straver' | CWri MBal NHol SBrw SLdr SReu |
| 'Elsie Watson' | GGGa LMil |
| 'Elspeth' | LHyd LKna |
| 'Emanuela' | Last listed 1996 |
| § 'Emasculum' ♀ | CGre COtt CSam LKna SPer SReu |
| 'Ember Glow' | NMun |
| Emerald Isle Group | SReu |
| ¶ 'Emma Williams' | CPin |
| 'Empire Day' | LKna SLdr |
| 'Ems' | Last listed 1998 |
| 'Enborne' | LHyd NMun SLdr |
| 'Endre Ostbo' | Last listed 1998 |
| 'English Roseum' | IOrc SLdr |
| 'Erato' | ENot GGGa LMil |
| *eriogynum* | See *R. facetum* |
| *eritimum* | See *R. anthosphaerum* |
| 'Ernest Inman' | LHyd NMun SLdr |
| *erosum* | GGGa NMun SLdr |
| *erubescens* | See *R. oreodoxa* var. *fargesii* |
| | Erubescens Group |
| § × *erythrocalyx* Panteumorphum Group | NMun |
| N 'Esmeralda' | CMac CTrg SBod |
| Ethel Group & cl. | CHig SLdr |
| 'Etna' | SLdr |
| 'Etoile de Sleidinge' | SBrw |
| 'Etta Burrows' | CWri GGGa MBal MLea |
| 'Euan Cox' | GGGa MBal NHar NHol |
| *euchaites* | See *R. neriiflorum* subsp. *neriiflorum* Euchaites Group |
| *euchroum* | NMun SLdr |

| | |
|---|---|
| *eudoxum* | GGGa MDun NMun |
| - var. *eudoxum* | GGGa |
| PA Cox 6036 | |
| - - R 10950 | See *R. temenium* var. *mesopolium* R 10950 |
| - - R 6c | NMun |
| - KW 5879* | NMun |
| 'Eunice Updike' (EA) | LHyd |
| 'Europa' | SReu |
| *eurysiphon* | NMun SLdr |
| ¶ - Arduaine form | GGGa |
| - KW 21557* | NMun |
| 'Eva Goude' (K) | LKna |
| ¶ 'Evelyn Hyde' (EA) | SLdr |
| 'Evening Fragrance' (A) | SReu |
| 'Evening Glow' | NHol |
| 'Evensong' (EA) | LKna |
| 'Everbloom' (EA) | NMun SLdr |
| 'Everest' (EA) | ENot LHyd |
| 'Everestianum' | IOrc LKna MBar SBrw SLdr |
| *exasperatum* | NMun SLdr |
| - KW 8250 | GGGa |
| 'Exbury Albatross' | LKna |
| 'Exbury Calstocker' | LMil |
| 'Exbury Fabia' | SReu |
| § 'Exbury Lady Chamberlain' | Last listed 1996 |
| 'Exbury May Day' | SReu |
| 'Exbury Naomi' | LHyd LKna LMil NMun SLdr |
| 'Exbury White' (K) | EPfP GQui WWeb |
| *excellens* AC 146 | GGGa |
| - SF 92074 | ISea |
| - SF 92079 | ISea |
| - SF 92303 | ISea |
| *eximium* | See *R. falconeri* subsp. *eximium* |
| ¶ 'Exotic' | MAsh |
| 'Exquisitum' (O) ♀ | CDoC EPfP GGGa LMil LRHS MBri MLea SLdr SReu SSpi WWeb |
| *exquisitum* | See *R. oreotrephes* Exquisitum Group |
| F.C. Puddle Group & cl. | SLdr |
| § *faberi* | GGGa MDun NMun SLdr |
| - EGM 111 | LMil |
| - subsp. *prattii* | See *R. prattii* |
| Fabia Group & cl. | GCHN GGGa IOrc LHyd LKna LMil MDun NMun SBrw SLdr SSpi |
| 'Fabia' x *bureaui* | SLdr |
| 'Fabia Roman Pottery' | MDun |
| § 'Fabia Tangerine' | COtt MBal MDun MLea SReu SRms WBod |
| § *facetum* | GGGa LMil NMun SLdr |
| - CLD 1522* | Last listed 1998 |
| - Farrer 1022 | NMun |
| - SF 315 | ISea |
| - TW 360 | Last listed 1997 |
| 'Faggetter's Favourite' ♀ | LKna LMil NMun SLdr SReu SSta |
| Fairy Light Group | LMil MBri MDun SLdr SRms |
| * 'Fairy Mary' | GGGa |
| 'Falcon' | See *R.* (Hawk Group) 'Hawk Falcon' |
| *falconeri* ♀ | CDoC COtt GGGa IOrc ISea LHyd LMil NMun SAPC SLdr SPer SReu |
| - B&SWJ 2437 | WCru |
| * - Cox's species | SReu |
| - DF 526 | MBal |
| § - subsp. *eximium* | GGGa LMil LRHS MDun |
| - subsp. *falconeri* BM&W 66 | MBal |
| - EGM 55 | Last listed 1997 |
| 'Faltho' | SLdr |
| ¶ 'Fanal' (K) | SLdr |

| | |
|---|---|
| Fandango Group | Last listed 1996 |
| 'Fanny' | See *R.* 'Pucella' |
| 'Fantastica' | CWri GGGa LHyd LMil MAsh MBri MDun SReu |
| *fargesii* | See *R. oreodoxa* var. *fargesii* |
| 'Fashion' | CChe CTrG SLdr |
| *fastigiatum* ♀ | GCrs GDra LMil MBal MBar MBri MDun NMen NMun SLdr WAbe |
| § - 'Blue Steel' | CB&S COtt CPMA CTri CWSG CWri GGGa LMil MAsh MBal MBri MBro MDun NHar NHol NMun SBrw SReu WAbe WPat WPyg |
| ¶ - C&H 7159 | GGGa |
| § - 'Harry White' | SReu |
| - pink | GGGa |
| - SBEC 804/4869 | GGGa MDun NHol |
| - SF#518 | ISea |
| 'Fastuosum Flore Pleno' (d) ♀ | CWri GGGa IOrc ISea LHyd LKna LMil MAsh MBal MBar MBri MGos MLea NMun NWea SBrw SLdr SPer SReu SSta WFar |
| *faucium* | GGGa NMun SLdr |
| - C&V 9508 | GGGa |
| ¶ - K&R 5024 | GGGa |
| § - KW 6401 | NMun |
| aff. *faucium* KW 5732 | NMun |
| 'Faulk Lemon' | Last listed 1998 |
| *fauriei* | See *R. brachycarpum* subsp. *fauriei* |
| 'Favorite' (EA) | CMac CTrw IOrc LHyd LKna MBri NMun SLdr |
| 'Fawley' (K) | Last listed 1996 |
| 'Fedora' (EA) ♀ | CB&S LHyd LKna SLdr SPer |
| 'Fernanda Sarmento' (A) | SReu |
| *ferrugineum* | GGGa LKna LMil MBal MBar MGos NMun SLdr SReu |
| - f. *album* | Last listed 1996 |
| - Ascreavie form | NHol |
| * - *compactum* | ECho |
| - Glenarn form | NHol |
| * - 'Hill of Tarvit' | NHol |
| 'Festive' | LHyd |
| 'Feuerwerk' (K) | SLdr |
| *fictolacteum* | See *R. rex* subsp. *fictolacteum* |
| 'Fidelio' (EA) | Last listed 1997 |
| *fimbriatum* | See *R. hippophaeoides* var. *hippophaeoides* Fimbriatum Group |
| Fire Bird Group | LHyd SLdr |
| 'Fireball' | GRei SLdr WLRN WWal |
| 'Fireball' (K) | CB&S CDoC CTri GGGa LHyd LMil MLea SBrw SPer WWeb |
| Firedrake Group | SReu |
| 'Firefly' (K) | ENot |
| 'Firefly' (EA) | See *R.* 'Hexe' |
| 'Fireglow' | CDoC SLdr WFar |
| 'Fireman Jeff' | CWri MBal |
| 'Flamenco Dancer' (V) | ERea |
| 'Flaming Bronze' | SReu |
| 'Flaming June' (K) | LKna |
| Flamingo Group | Last listed 1996 |
| § *flammeum* (A) | LMil |
| 'Flare' | Last listed 1996 |
| Flashlight Group | Last listed 1998 |
| § Flava Group & cl. | CDoC CWri LMil MBar MGos NHed SReu SSta |
| 'Flava Glendoick' | Last listed 1997 |
| 'Flava Lackblatt' | MBri MLea |
| *flavidum* | GGGa MBal MDun |
| - 'Album' | LHyd LMil MDun SBod |

| | |
|---|---|
| – PA Cox 5064 | MDun |
| – PA Cox 6143 | GGGa |
| *fletcherianum* | MBal NMun SLdr WAbe |
| – R 22302 | NMun SLdr |
| – 'Yellow Bunting' | GGGa |
| ¶ *fleuryi* | LMil |
| – KR 3286 | GGGa |
| § *flinckii* | GGGa LMil MDun NMun |
| – CH&M 3080 | GGGa |
| aff. *flinckii* KR 1755 | Last listed 1996 |
| 'Flirt' | Last listed 1996 |
| *floccigerum* | GGGa LMil NMun SLdr |
| – bicolored | NMun |
| – R 10 | Last listed 1997 |
| – USDAPQ 3966/ R18465 | Last listed 1997 |
| aff. *floccigerum* F 20305 | SLdr |
| 'Floradora' (M) | SReu |
| 'Flora's Garden' | Last listed 1997 |
| 'Flora's Green' | Last listed 1997 |
| 'Florence Archer' | Last listed 1997 |
| 'Floriade' | LHyd LKna |
| *floribundum* | LMil NMun SLdr |
| – PA Cox 5090 | Last listed 1997 |
| ¶ – 'Swinhoe' | SLdr |
| 'Florida' (EA/d) ♀ | CMac CTrh LKna LMil MAsh SBod SBrw SPer SReu SSta WBod WFar WWal |
| *formosanum* | GGGa |
| *formosum* ♀ | CB&S CGre ERea GGGa GQui NMun |
| § – var. *formosum* Iteaphyllum Group | GGGa SLdr |
| – – 'Khasia' C&H 320 | GGGa |
| – var. *inaequale* C&H 301 | GGGa |
| *forrestii* | GGGa LMil NMun |
| – subsp. *forrestii* F 21723 | See *R. chamaethomsonii* var. *chamaethomsonii* F 21723 |
| – – LS&T 5582 | NMun |
| – – Repens Group | GGGa LMil MBal NMun SLdr |
| – Tumescens Group | GGGa NHol NMun SLdr |
| – – C&V 9517 | GGGa |
| Fortorb Group | NMun |
| Fortune Group & cl. | NMun SLdr |
| subsect. *Fortunea* sp. PW 099* | LMil |
| *fortunei* | CB&S COtt GGGa IOrc ISea LHyd LKna LMil MDun NMun SLdr SReu |
| § – subsp. *discolor* ♀ | GGGa LMil NMun SLdr |
| – – 'Hilliers Best' | SLdr |
| § – – Houlstonii Group | LMil NMun SLdr |
| – 'Foxy' | NMun SLdr |
| – 'Lu-Shan' | MDun |
| – McLaren S146 | Last listed 1996 |
| – 'Mrs Butler' | See *R. fortunei* 'Sir Charles Butler' |
| § – 'Sir Charles Butler' | LMil |
| 'Fox Hunter' | LKna |
| *fragariiflorum* C&V 9519 | GGGa |
| – hybrid LS&E 15828 | GGGa |
| 'Fragrantissimum' ♀ | CB&S CDoC CGre CHad CTrG CTre CTrw CWri ELan GGGa IOrc ISea LHyd LMil MBal MDun MRav NMun WAbe |
| 'Francis B. Hayes' | IOrc |
| Francis Hanger (Reuthe's) Group | NMun SLdr SReu |
| 'Frank Baum' | CWri MBal NMun SReu SSta |
| 'Frank Galsworthy' ♀ | LKna LMil SBrw SReu SSta |
| 'Frans van der Bom' (M) | MBri SLdr |
| 'Fraseri' (M) | GGGa |
| ¶ 'Fred Harris' | SLdr |
| 'Fred Nutbeam' (EA) | MGos |
| 'Fred Peste' | CAbP GGGa IOrc LMil MDun SReu |
| 'Fred Rose' | Last listed 1998 |
| 'Fred Wynniatt' ♀ | CWri LHyd LMil MDun NMun SLdr SReu |
| 'Fred Wynniatt Stanway' | See *R.* 'Stanway' |
| 'Freya' (R/d) | LMil |
| 'Fridoline' (EA) | GGGa |
| ¶ 'Frieda' (EA) | SLdr |
| 'Frigate' | WLRN |
| 'Frill' | Last listed 1996 |
| 'Frilled Petticoats' | NMun SLdr SReu |
| 'Frills' (K/d) | LHyd |
| 'Frilly Lemon' (K/d) | CDoC LMil MDun SLdr |
| 'Frome' (K) | LKna |
| 'Frontier' | LMil |
| 'Frosted Orange' (EA) | LMil |
| 'Frosthexe' | GGGa |
| 'Frühlingszauber' | Last listed 1996 |
| 'Fudetsukasi' | Last listed 1998 |
| 'Fuju-kaku-no-matsu' (EA) | MGos |
| 'Fuko-hiko' (EA) | NMun |
| 'Fulbrook' | NMun SLdr |
| 'Fulgarb' | SLdr |
| *fulgens* | GGGa LHyd LMil MDun NMun SLdr SReu |
| – DF 543 | MBal |
| Full House Group | Last listed 1996 |
| *fulvum* ♀ | CDoC GGGa IOrc LHyd LMil MDun NMun SLdr SReu SSta |
| – subsp. *fulvoides* | NMun SLdr |
| – – PA Cox 6026 | GGGa |
| – – PA Cox 6532 | GGGa |
| – – R 143 | NMun |
| – – R 180 | NMun |
| – subsp. *fulvum* F 17636 | Last listed 1996 |
| – – F 24110 | SLdr |
| ¶ – – Farrer 874 | SLdr |
| – TW 379 | Last listed 1997 |
| 'Furnivall's Daughter' ♀ | CWri ENot GChr GGGa IOrc LHyd LKna LMil MBal MBar MBri MGos NMun SBrw SLdr SReu SSta WFar |
| 'Fusilier' ♀ | SLdr |
| Fusilier Group & cl. | LHyd SReu |
| 'Gabriele' (EA) | GQui SSpi |
| 'Gabrielle Hill' (EA) | COtt |
| 'Gaiety' (EA) | IOrc LMil SBrw SReu |
| 'Galactic' | NMun SLdr |
| *galactinum* | LMil NMun SLdr |
| – CC&H 4023 | Last listed 1997 |
| – EN 3537 | GGGa |
| – W/A 4254 | NMun |
| 'Galathea' (EA) | CDoC LMil |
| 'Gallipoli' (K) | Last listed 1998 |
| 'Gandy Dancer' | CDoC CWri MDun |
| 'Garden State Glow' (EA/d) | SBod SReu |
| 'Garnet' | Last listed 1996 |
| 'Gartendirektor Glocker' | CDoC CSam CWri GGGa LMil MDun MLea MOne SBrw SSta WWeb |
| 'Gartendirektor Rieger' | CWri GGGa LMil MAsh MBri MDun NHol SBrw SReu |
| 'Gauche' | GQui SLdr |
| 'Gaugin' | GQui |
| ¶ 'Gauntlettii' x *thomsonii* | SLdr |
| 'Geisha' (EA) | MBar |
| 'Geisha Lilac' (EA) | CDoC COtt ECho MBar MBri WLRN WWeb |

'Geisha Orange' (EA) — CDoC COtt CTrh GGGa MBar MBri MGos NHed SLdr WLRN WWeb
'Geisha Purple' (EA) — COtt MBar MOne WFar
'Geisha Red' (EA) — COtt EPfP MBar MBri STre WAbe WFar
'Gekkeikan' (EA) — CB&S
'Gena Mae' (A/d) — GGGa LMil
'General Eisenhower' — SBrw SReu
'General Eric Harrison' — LHyd NMun SLdr
'General Practitioner' — ENot NMun SLdr
'General Sir John du Cane' — NMun
'General Wavell' (EA) — CMac COtt LKna SLdr
'Gene's Favourite' — SReu
*genestierianum* — Last listed 1996
¶ – CC&H 8080 — GGGa
'Genghis Khan' — NMun
'Geoffroy Millais' — LMil
¶ 'Georg Arends' — SLdr
'George Hardy' — CWri
'George Hyde' (EA) — Last listed 1998
'George Johnstone' (EA) ♀ — MBal
'George Reynolds' (K) — Last listed 1997
'George's Delight' — CWri GGGa MLea
'Georgette' — LHyd NMun SLdr
§ × *geraldii* — SLdr
¶ 'Germania' — MBar
Gertrud Schäle Group — CTri MBal MBar NHol SReu
'Getsutoku' (EA) — GAri SReu
Gibraltar Group — Last listed 1996
'Gibraltar' (K) ♀ — CB&S CDoC CSam EBrP EBre ENot GChr GGGa IOrc LBre LKna LMil MAsh MBal MBar MBri MGos MLea SBre SBrw SPer SReu SSta WBod WWal
*giganteum* — See *R. protistum* var. *giganteum*
'Gigi' — Last listed 1997
'Gilbert Mullier' — MBri
'Ginger' (K) — CDoC EPfP LMil MBal NMun SBrw SLdr WWeb
'Ginny Gee' ♀ — CBrm CDoC COtt CSam CTrh CWri GGGa LHyd LMil MAsh MBal MBar MBri MDun MGos MLea NHar NHol NMun SBrw SReu SSta WAbe WFar WGwG
Gipsy King Group — Last listed 1996
§ 'Girard's Hot Shot' (EA) — CTrh ECho GGGa GQui LMil SBod SBrw SReu SVil
¶ 'Glacier' (EA) — SLdr
'Glad Tidings' — Last listed 1998
Gladys Group & cl. — Last listed 1998
'Glamora' (EA) — LHyd SLdr
*glanduliferum* C&H 7131 — GGGa
– EGM 347 — LMil
*glaucophyllum* — GGGa LHyd LMil NMun SLdr
– var. *album* — GGGa
– BH form — LMil
* – 'Branklyn' — Last listed 1998
§ – var. *glaucophyllum* — LMil
    L&S 2764
– 'Glenarn' — Last listed 1998
§ – subsp. *tubiforme* — NMun SLdr
'Gleam' — Last listed 1996
'Glencora' (EA) — LHyd
'Glenn Dale Adorable' — See *R.* 'Adorable'
¶ 'Glen's Orange' — CWri
*glischroides* — GGGa
*glischrum* — GGGa NMun SLdr
– C&Cu 9316 — GGGa

– CNW 398 — ISea
– subsp. *glischroides* — LMil NMun SLdr
– subsp. *glischrum* — GGGa
§ – subsp. *rude* — GGGa LMil MDun NMun SLdr
– – C&V 9524 — GGGa
*globigerum* — See *R. alutaceum* var. *alutaceum*
    Globigerum Group
'Glockenspiel' (K/d) — LKna
*glomerulatum* — See *R. yungningense*
    Glomerulatum Group
'Gloria' — LMil
¶ 'Gloria Mundi' (G) — SLdr SReu
'Gloriana' — Last listed 1996
'Glory of Leonardslee' — SLdr
'Glory of Penjerrick' — NMun SLdr
'Glowing Embers' (K) — GChr GRei MAsh MBal MBri MDun MLea SBid SBrw SLdr SPer SReu SSpi WBod WFar WWeb
'Gloxineum' — CWri
Goblin Group & cl. — SLdr
'Gog' (K) — LHyd LKna MBal SLdr WLRN
'Gold Crest' (K) — LKna
'Gold Dust' (K) — Last listed 1998
'Gold Mohur' — SBrw SLdr SReu
'Goldball' — See *R.* 'Christopher Wren'
'Goldbukett' — LHyd MBri SBrw
'Golden Bee' — GGGa NHol
'Golden Belle' — CWri LMil MBal SMur
'Golden Coach' — COtt LMil MDun MLea NMun
'Golden Eagle' (K) — COtt GRei MAsh MDun MGos SCoo SLdr
'Golden Eye' (K) — LKna
'Golden Flare' (K) — CB&S CDoC LHyd MAsh SLdr SReu WWeb
'Golden Fleece' — LKna SReu
'Golden Gate' — CDoC LMil MDun NMun SLdr WGor WGwG WWeb
'Golden Horn' (K) — GQui SLdr WGor WWeb
Golden Horn Group & cl. — IOrc MBal NMun SLdr
'Golden Horn Persimmon' — See *R.* 'Persimmon'
'Golden Lights' (A) — GChr LHyd LMil LRHS MLea
'Golden Orfe' ♀ — Last listed 1997
'Golden Oriole' (K) ♀ — LKna SReu
Golden Oriole Group — CB&S NHol NMun
§ – 'Talavera' ♀ — CB&S MBal
'Golden Princess' — COtt LMil MDun NHol
§ 'Golden Queen' — Last listed 1996
¶ 'Golden Ruby' — CDoC
'Golden Splendour' — LMil
'Golden Star' — Last listed 1998
'Golden Sunlight' — See *R.* 'Directeur Moerlands'
'Golden Sunset' (K) — COtt MAsh MBar MBri MGos SBrw
'Golden Torch' ♀ — CAbP CB&S COtt CWri EBee ENot GGGa IOrc ISea LHyd LMil LNet MBal MBri MDun MGos MLea NHed NMun SLdr SPer SReu SSta WWeb
'Golden Wedding' — CB&S COtt CWri LMil LRHS MBal MLea
'Golden Wit' — ECho MBal SBod SBrw SLdr
'Goldfee' — LHyd
'Goldfinch' (K) — LKna
'Goldfinger' — MBal
'Goldflimmer' (v) — ENot GGGa MGos NHol SBrw SReu WWeb
'Goldfort' — CWri LKna SBrw SReu
'Goldika' — LMil
'Goldilocks' — Last listed 1997

| | |
|---|---|
| 'Goldkrone' | CDoC CWri ENot GGGa ISea LHyd LMil MBri MGos MLea NMun SBrw SLdr SReu |
| ¶ 'Goldprinz' | GGGa |
| ¶ 'Goldstrike' | SLdr |
| 'Goldsworth Crimson' | LHyd SBrw |
| 'Goldsworth Orange' | GGGa LHyd LKna MBal MGos NMun SBrw SLdr SPer SReu SSta |
| 'Goldsworth Pink' | LKna SBrw SReu |
| 'Goldsworth Yellow' | CSam LKna MGos SLdr SReu |
| 'Goldtopas' (K) | Last listed 1996 |
| ¶ 'Golfer' | GGGa |
| 'Gomer Waterer' ♀ | CDoC CHig CWri GGGa IOrc LHyd LKna LMil MAsh MBal MBar MBri MDun MGos MLea NMun NWea SBod SBrw SLdr SPer SReu SSta WFar |
| 'Good News' | SLdr |
| 'Goosander' | LHyd |
| 'Gordon Jones' | GGGa |
| 'Gossamer White' (V) | Last listed 1996 |
| 'Govenianum' (Ad) | LKna |
| 'Grace Seabrook' | CDoC COtt CSam CWri GGGa LHyd LMil MAsh MDun MLea SLdr SPer SReu |
| gracilentum (V) | Last listed 1997 |
| 'Graciosum' (O) | LKna SReu |
| 'Graf Zeppelin' | Last listed 1998 |
| 'Grafton' | Last listed 1996 |
| ¶ 'Graham Thomas' | LMil MDun |
| ¶ 'Graham Vivian' | SLdr |
| ¶ 'Grand Slam' | MDun |
| grande | GGGa IOrc LMil NMun SLdr |
| - DF 524 | MBal |
| - EGM 58 | Last listed 1997 |
| - pink | NMun |
| - TSS 37 | NMun |
| § aff. grande KR 13649 | NMun |
| ¶ 'Grandeur Triomphante' (G) | SReu |
| gratum | See R. basilicum |
| 'Grayswood Pink' | CSam |
| 'Graziella' | GGGa |
| 'Green Eye' | Last listed 1996 |
| 'Greensleeves' | LKna LMil |
| 'Greenway' (EA) | CB&S CGre CTre IOrc SLdr SPer |
| Grenadier Group & cl. | SBrw |
| 'Greta' (EA) | LHyd |
| 'Gretzel' | NMun SReu |
| 'Grierdal' | Last listed 1997 |
| Grierocaster Group | Last listed 1997 |
| griersonianum | CB&S GGGa IOrc ISea LHyd MBal MDun NMun SLdr |
| - F 24116 | NMun |
| griffithianum | GGGa LMil MDun NMun SLdr WPic |
| - EGM 101 | Last listed 1997 |
| 'Grilse' | Last listed 1996 |
| 'Grisette' | SLdr |
| 'Gristede' | CDoC COtt GGGa LMil MAsh MOne NHol SBrw SReu |
| groenlandicum | GGGa |
| Grosclaude Group & cl. | NMun SLdr |
| 'Grouse' | MBal MLea NHar |
| 'Grouse' x keiskei 'Yaku Fairy' | ECho MBri MDun |
| 'Grumpy' | CDoC ENot GGGa GRei IOrc LHyd LMil LNet MBal MBar MBri MGos MLea NHed NMun SBrw SLdr SReu |
| Guardsman Group | SLdr |
| § 'Gumpo' (EA) | CMac SLdr |
| 'Gumpo Pink' (EA) | SLdr WAbe |
| 'Gumpo White' (EA) | SBod |
| 'Gwenda' (EA) | LHyd |
| 'Gwillt-king' | Last listed 1998 |
| gymnocarpum | See R. microgynum Gymnocarpum Group |
| 'Gyokushin' (EA) | MBal |
| 'H.H. Hume' (EA) | MBal SLdr |
| 'H.O. Carre' (EA) | CMac |
| 'H.Whitner' | NMun SLdr |
| habrotrichum | GGGa LMil NMun |
| - F 15778 | NMun |
| ¶ 'Hachmann's Bananaflip' | LHyd |
| 'Hachmann's Brasilia' | CWri SBrw |
| 'Hachmann's Charmant' | GGGa LMil |
| 'Hachmann's Feuerschein' | ENot LMil |
| ¶ 'Hachmann's Juanita' (K) | MBri |
| 'Hachmann's Marlis' | ENot LHyd LMil SBrw SReu |
| 'Hachmann's Polaris' | LMil MBri |
| 'Hachmann's Porzellan' | LHyd |
| § 'Hachmann's Rokoko' (EA) | ECho GGGa |
| 'Hachmann's Rosita' | MAsh |
| haematodes | GGGa MBal MDun NMun SLdr SRms |
| - AC 710 | NMun |
| - Bu 290 | GGGa |
| - C&Cu 9445 | Last listed 1998 |
| § - subsp. chaetomallum | GGGa LMil NMun |
| - - F 25601 | NMun |
| - - KW 21077 | See R. coelicum KW 21077 |
| - - KW 5431 | Last listed 1996 |
| - - R 18359 | NMun SLdr |
| - - R 41 | NMun |
| - CLD 1283 | LMil |
| - ex Hobbie | Last listed 1997 |
| - subsp. haemotodes F 6773 | NMun SLdr |
| - - McLaren S124A | NMun SLdr |
| - - SBEC 585 | GGGa |
| ¶ aff. haematodes KW 6955 | SLdr |
| 'Haida Gold' | ISea MBal MGos MLea NMun SLdr SReu SSta WWeb |
| 'Hakurakuten' (EA) | Last listed 1997 |
| Halcyone Group | SLdr |
| 'Halfdan Lem' | CAbP CSam GGGa LHyd LMil MBal MBri MGos MLea NMun SBrw SLdr SReu SSta |
| 'Hallelujah' | CWri MBal SMur WWeb |
| 'Halton' | NMun |
| 'Hamlet' (M) | LMil |
| 'Hammondii' (Ad) | LKna |
| 'Hana-asobi' (EA) | CB&S LHyd SLdr |
| hanceanum | CHig NMun SLdr |
| - 'Canton Consul' | GGGa LHyd |
| - EN 2104 | GGGa |
| - Nanum Group | CB&S GGGa MBal |
| ¶ hancockii SF 464 | ISea |
| 'Handsworth Scarlet' | SLdr |
| 'Hansel' | CDoC MDun |
| § haofui Guiz 75 | GGGa |
| Happy Group | IOrc |
| 'Harbinger' (EA) | SBod SLdr |
| 'Hardijzer Beauty' (Ad) ♀ | IOrc LKna MBal MBri SReu |
| hardingii | See R. annae Hardingii Group |
| 'Hardy Gardenia' (EA/d) | SBrw SReu |
| hardyi | See R. augustinii subsp. hardyi |
| 'Harkwood Friendship' | Last listed 1998 |
| 'Harkwood Moonlight' | WWeb |
| 'Harkwood Premiere' | GGGa LMil MGos |

'Harkwood Red' (EA) CTrh GQui LMil SLdr
¶ 'Harmony' (EA/d) SLdr
'Harry Tagg' CTrG GGGa SLdr
'Harumiji' (EA) Last listed 1998
'Harvest Moon' (K) CSam SCoo SReu
'Harvest Moon' CWri LHyd MBal MBar MDun
MGos SBrw SLdr SReu
'Hatsugiri' (EA) ♀ CHig CMac ENot EPfP IOrc LHyd
LKna LMil MBar MBri SBid SBod
SLdr SReu SSta
(Hawk Group) 'Crest' See *R.* 'Crest'
- 'Hawk Buzzard' SLdr
§ - 'Hawk Falcon' SReu
§ - 'Hawk Merlin' MBal
- 'Jervis Bay' See *R.* 'Jervis Bay'
'Haze' SLdr
'Hazel Fisher' LMil
*headfortianum* See *R. taggianum* Headfortianum
Group
'Heather Macleod' (EA) LHyd SLdr
Hebe Group Last listed 1996
*heftii* NMun
'Heidelberg' (K/d) WAbe
'Heiwa' (EA) Last listed 1997
'Heiwa-no-kagami' (EA) GAri
'Helen Close' (EA) CTrh SLdr
'Helen Curtis' (EA) SReu
'Helene Schiffner' ♀ CWri GGGa NMun SLdr SReu
§ *heliolepis* GGGa IOrc LMil MBal SLdr
– AC 759 NMun
- var. *brevistylum* Last listed 1996
- Bu 292 Last listed 1998
- C&Cu 9313 Last listed 1998
- var. *fumidum* See *R. heliolepis* var. *heliolepis*
§ - var. *heliolepis* SLdr
- - CNW 1038 ISea
- - CNW 944 LMil
§ - - F 6762 NMun
- - SSNY 66 NMun
- SF 489 ISea
- SF 516 ISea
- SSNY 314 Last listed 1998
- Yu 7933* Last listed 1997
*hemidartum* See *R. pocophorum* var.
*hemidartum*
x *hemigynum* NMun SLdr
*hemitrichotum* NMun
§ - F 30940 NMun
- KW 4050 NMun
*hemsleyanum* GGGa IOrc MDun NMun SLdr
- EN 2097 GGGa
- x *ungernii* GGGa
aff. *hemsleyanum* C&H 7189 LMil
'Henry Street' Last listed 1998
*heptamerum* See *R. degronianum* subsp.
*heptamerum*
'Herbert' (EA) CMac
Hesperides Group Last listed 1996
§ 'Hexe' (EA) Last listed 1998
*hidakanum* SReu
'Higasa' (EA) CHig GAri
'High Gold' LMil
'High Summer' LMil
'Highland White Jade' Last listed 1996
'Hilda Margaret' SReu
'Hill Ayah' Last listed 1996
*himantodes* (V) Last listed 1998
'Hino-crimson' (EA) ♀ CDoC CGre CMac CTrG CTrh
CTri EBee IOrc LKna LMil MAsh
MBar MBri MGos SBrw SPer SReu
SSta WFar WLRN WStI WWeb

'Hinode-giri' (EA) ♀ CB&S CDoC CHig CMac CTrw
ENot LHyd LKna NMun SBod
SLdr SReu
'Hinode-no-kumo' (EA) NMun SLdr
'Hinomayo' (EA) ♀ CB&S CMac CTrG CTre GQui
IOrc LHyd LKna LMil MBar NMun
SLdr SPer SReu SSta WBod WPic
WStI
'Hino-scarlet' See *R.* 'Campfire'
'Hino-tsukasa' (EA) NMun SLdr
*hippophaeoides* CB&S CDoC CHig EPfP LMil
MDun NMun SLdr SSta WAbe
WFar
- 'Bei-ma-shan' See *R. hippophaeoides* 'Haba
Shan'
- F 22197A SLdr
§ - 'Haba Shan' ♀ GGGa LMil MBri MDun MOne
§ - var. *hippophaeoides* Last listed 1996
Fimbriatum Group
- var. *occidentale* C&Cu GGGa
9314
- Yu 13845 CDoC GGGa MDun
*hirsutum* GGGa LMil MBal SLdr SReu WPyg
- f. *albiflorum* GGGa
- 'Flore Pleno' (d) ECho GCrs GGGa MBal MBar
MDun MLea WAbe
*hirtipes* GGGa
- C&V 9546 GGGa
- KW 10616 GGGa
- KW 5659 GGGa
- KW 6223 NMun
- LS&E 15765 GGGa
- LS&T 3624 NMun
x *hodconeri* NMun
- LS&H 21296 See *R. hodgsonii* LS&H 21296
- 'pink' NMun
- TSS 9 See *R. hodgsonii* TSS 9
*hodgsonii* GGGa IOrc LMil MDun NMun
SLdr SReu
- B 653 MBal
¶ - B&SWJ 2656 WCru
- BL&M 232 Last listed 1997
- DF 532 MBal
§ - LS&H 21296 NMun
- 'Poet's Lawn' NMun
- SU 323 Last listed 1997
- TSS 42A NMun SLdr
§ - TSS 9 NMun SLdr
aff. *hodgsonii* EGM 81 Last listed 1997
'Hojo-no-odorikarako' (EA) NMun SLdr
'Holden' CWri
'Hollandia' IOrc SBrw
'Homebush' (K/d) ♀ CB&S CDoC CMHG ENot GChr
GGGa IOrc LHyd LKna LMil MBal
MBar MBri MDun MLea SLdr SPer
SReu SSpi SSta
'Honey' LKna NMun SBrw
'Honey Bee' MAsh
'Honeymoon' MAsh NMun SLdr WLRN WWeb
'Honeysuckle' (K) IOrc MBar SLdr SReu WBod
'Hong Kong' COtt MDun
*hongkongense* GGGa NMun
¶ 'Honourable John Boscawen' SBrw
§ 'Ho-o' (EA) CB&S CGre SLdr
*hookeri* NMun SLdr SReu
- 'Golden Gate' Last listed 1996
- KW 13859 NMun
¶ - KW 8238 SLdr
- Tigh-na-Rudha form GGGa
'Hope Findlay' LHyd

| | |
|---|---|
| 'Hoppy' | CWri ENot LMil MAsh MBal MDun MLea NMun SLdr SReu WGwG WWeb |
| 'Horizon Dawn' | Last listed 1997 |
| 'Horizon Lakeside' | GGGa LMil |
| 'Horizon Monarch' | GGGa LMil MDun |
| 'Horizon Snowbird' | Last listed 1997 |
| *borlickianum* | GGGa NMun |
| - KW 9403 | NMun |
| 'Hortulanus H. Witte' (M) | MBri SLdr SReu WFar |
| 'Hot Shot' | See *R.* 'Girard's Hot Shot' |
| 'Hotei' ♀ | CB&S CSam CWri GCHN GChr GGGa ISea LHyd LMil MAsh MBal MBar MBri MDun MGos NMun SLdr SPer SReu SSta WGer WWeb |
| Hotspur Group (K) | ELan GGGa SCoo SPer WLRN WWeb |
| 'Hotspur' ♀ | SLdr |
| 'Hotspur Red' (K) ♀ | CDoC CSam LKna LMil MBri SBrw SReu |
| 'Hotspur Yellow' (K) | SReu |
| *boulstonii* | See *R. fortunei* subsp. *discolor* Houlstonii Group |
| ¶ *buanum* | LMil |
| - C&H 7073 | GGGa |
| - EGM 330 | LMil |
| - EN 4028 | Last listed 1997 |
| 'Hugh Koster' | CB&S IOrc LKna MGos NMun SBrw SLdr SPer |
| Humming Bird Group | CB&S CMHG CSam GGGa ISea LHyd LKna MBal MBar MBri MGos MLea NHol NMun SLdr SPer SReu SRms WBod |
| *bunnewellianum* | GGGa SLdr |
| 'Hurricane' | COtt MAsh SBrw SLdr |
| 'Huzzar' | MDun |
| 'Hyde and Seek' | GQui SBrw |
| 'Hydie' (EA/d) | MGos |
| 'Hydon Ball' | LHyd |
| 'Hydon Ben' | LHyd |
| 'Hydon Comet' | LHyd |
| 'Hydon Dawn' ♀ | CDoC COtt GGGa ISea LHyd LMil MAsh MBri MGos MLea NHed NMun SBrw SLdr SReu SSta |
| 'Hydon Glow' | LHyd NMun SLdr |
| 'Hydon Gold' | LHyd |
| 'Hydon Haley' | LHyd |
| 'Hydon Hunter' ♀ | COtt GGGa IOrc LHyd LMil LNet MBri NHed NMun SBrw SLdr SReu SSta |
| 'Hydon Juliet' | LHyd |
| 'Hydon Mist' | LHyd |
| 'Hydon Pearl' | LHyd |
| 'Hydon Pink' | LHyd |
| 'Hydon Primrose' | LHyd |
| 'Hydon Rodney' | LHyd |
| 'Hydon Salmon' | LHyd NMun |
| 'Hydon Snowflake' | Last listed 1996 |
| 'Hydon Velvet' | LHyd SReu |
| *bylaeum* | NMun |
| - KW 6401 | See *R. faucium* KW 6401 |
| - KW 6833 | NMun |
| *bypenanthum* | See *R. anthopogon* subsp. *hypenanthum* |
| Hyperion Group | LKna LMil SBrw SReu SSta |
| *byperythrum* | GGGa MDun NHol NMun SLdr |
| * - album | NMun |
| - ETOT 183 | ISea |
| - subsp. *fauriei* | Last listed 1997 |
| - pink | NMun SLdr |

| | |
|---|---|
| *bypoglaucum* | See *R. argyrophyllum* subsp. *hypoglaucum* |
| - 'Heane Wood' | See *R. argyrophyllum* subsp. *hypoglaucum* 'Heane Wood' |
| Ibex Group & cl. | NMun |
| Icarus Group | Last listed 1996 |
| 'Ice Cream' | LHyd |
| 'Ice Cube' | Last listed 1998 |
| 'Ice Maiden' | SReu |
| 'Iceberg' | See *R.* 'Lodauric Iceberg' |
| 'Icecream Flavour' | See *R.* 'Flavour' |
| 'Icecream Vanilla' | See *R.* 'Vanilla' |
| Idealist Group & cl. | CWri LHyd NMun SLdr SReu |
| 'Ightham Gold' | SReu |
| 'Ightham Peach' | SReu |
| 'Ightham Purple' | SReu |
| 'Ightham Yellow' | NMun SLdr SReu |
| 'Igneum Novum' (G) | MBri SReu |
| 'Il Tasso' (R/d) | LKna |
| ¶ 'Ilam Louie Williams' (A) | SReu |
| § 'Ilam Melford Lemon' (A) | LMil |
| § 'Ilam Ming' (A) | LMil |
| § 'Ilam Red Velvet' | SLdr |
| 'Ilam Violet' | LKna |
| 'Imago' (K/d) | LKna |
| § 'Ima-shojo' (EA/d) ♀ | GAri LHyd LMil |
| 'Impala' (K) | LKna |
| *impeditum* ♀ | CB&S CHig CSam ELan ENot GGGa GRei ISea LHyd LKna MBal MBar MDun MGos MLea MPla NHar NHol NMun NWea SBrw SLdr SPer SReu SSta WAbe WFar WPic |
| - 'Blue Steel' | See *R. fastigiatum* 'Blue Steel' |
| * - 'Compactum' | Last listed 1997 |
| - dark compact form | LKna |
| - F 20454 | Last listed 1997 |
| § - F 29268 | GGGa NMun |
| - 'Harry White's Purple' | See *R. fastigiatum* 'Harry White' |
| - 'Indigo' | CMHG MAsh MBri NHar |
| - 'Johnston's Impeditum' | LKna |
| - 'Moerheim' | See *R.* 'Moerheim' |
| - 'Pygmaeum' | MBro NHol WPat |
| - Reuthe's form | SReu |
| - 'Russell's Blue' | SBrw SReu |
| ¶ - 'Williams' | SLdr |
| *imperator* | See *R. uniflorum* var. *imperator* |
| Impi Group & cl. | LKna NMun SBrw SLdr WAbe |
| 'Ina Hair' | Last listed 1998 |
| *inconspicuum* (V) | Last listed 1997 |
| 'Independence Day' | CWri GGGa |
| Indiana Group | Last listed 1996 |
| § *indicum* (EA) | MBal WBod |
| § - 'Balsaminiflorum' (EA/d) | CMac |
| - 'Crispiflorum' (EA) | Last listed 1997 |
| - var. *eriocarpum* 'Gumpo' | See *R.* 'Gumpo' |
| 'Indigo Diamant' | See *R.* Diamant Group indigo |
| x *inopinum* | GGGa NMun |
| *insigne* ♀ | CWri GGGa IOrc LHyd LMil MDun NMun SLdr |
| - hybrid | SLdr |
| - Reuthe's form | SReu |
| - x *yakushimanum* | SReu |
| Intermedium Group | MBal |
| x *intermedium* white | GGGa |
| Intrepid Group | SReu |
| *intricatum* | GGGa |
| - KW 4184 | NMun |
| - PA Cox 5060 | Last listed 1998 |

| | |
|---|---|
| Intrifast Group | GAri GGGa LHyd MAsh MBal NHar NHol SLdr WAbe |
| *iodes* | See *R. alutaceum* var. *iodes* |
| Iola Group | Last listed 1996 |
| 'Irene' | SBrw |
| 'Irene Koster' (O) ♀ | CMHG ELan GGGa LHyd LKna LMil MAsh MBri MLea SLdr SPer SReu WWeb |
| 'Irohayama' (EA) ♀ | CDoC CHig CMac CTrw GQui LHyd LKna LMil MBri SLdr SPer SReu SSta |
| *irroratum* | CWri LMil NMun SLdr |
| - C&H 7185 | GGGa |
| - subsp. *irroratum* C&H 7100 | GGGa |
| - subsp. *kontumense* KR 3282 | Last listed 1996 |
| - - var. *ningyuenense* EGM 339 | LMil |
| - KW 5002a | Last listed 1996 |
| - 'Langbianense' KR 3295 | LMil |
| - pale pink | NMun |
| § - subsp. *pogonostylum* | NMun SLdr |
| - - KR 3121 | Last listed 1997 |
| - 'Polka Dot' | GGGa LHyd NMun SLdr |
| - R 72 | See *R. lukiangense* R 72 |
| - SF 384 | ISea |
| - SF 92304 | ISea |
| - white | Last listed 1997 |
| 'Isabel Pierce' ♀ | CWri LMil MBal |
| 'Isabella Mangles' | LHyd |
| 'Ishiyama' (EA) | Last listed 1998 |
| Italia Group | Last listed 1998 |
| *iteaphyllum* | See *R. formosum* var. *formosum* Iteaphyllum Group |
| Ivanhoe Group & cl. | Last listed 1998 |
| 'Ivery's Scarlet' | IOrc |
| 'Ivette' (EA) | CMac LHyd LKna |
| Iviza Group | SReu |
| 'Ivory Coast' | LMil |
| 'Iwato-kagami' (EA) | NMun SLdr |
| 'Izayoi' (EA) | WBod |
| 'J.C. Williams' | CB&S |
| 'J.G. Millais' | Last listed 1997 |
| 'J.M. de Montague' | See *R.* 'The Hon. Jean Marie de Montague' |
| 'Jabberwocky' | LHyd |
| 'Jack' | Last listed 1997 |
| 'Jack A Sand' (K) | Last listed 1998 |
| 'Jack Skelton' | Last listed 1997 |
| ¶ 'Jack Skilton' | SLdr |
| 'Jacksonii' | CWri IOrc ISea LKna MBal MBar NMun SLdr SReu |
| Jacques Group | NMun |
| 'Jade' | Last listed 1998 |
| Jaipur Group | Last listed 1996 |
| Jalisco Group & cl. | NMun SLdr |
| 'Jalisco Eclipse' | LKna SLdr |
| 'Jalisco Elect' ♀ | CWri LKna LMil NMun SLdr |
| 'Jalisco Goshawk' | SLdr |
| 'Jalisco Janet' | NMun |
| 'Jalisco Jubilant' | NMun SLdr |
| 'James Barto' | IOrc LHyd NMun SLdr |
| 'James Burchett' ♀ | GGGa LKna LMil SBrw SLdr SReu |
| 'James Gable' (EA) | MAsh SLdr |
| 'Jan Bee' | MBal SLdr |
| 'Jan Dekens' | SReu |
| 'Jan Steen' (M) | SLdr |
| Jan Steen Group & cl. | NMun |
| 'Jan Wellen' (EA) | IOrc |
| 'Jane Abbott' (A) | GGGa |
| 'Janelle Marie' (V) | CEqu |
| 'Janet Blair' | CDoC CWri MDun MLea |
| 'Janet Ward' | LHyd LKna SReu |
| 'Janine Alexandre Debray' | NMun SLdr |
| *japonicum* (A.Gray)Valcken | See *R. molle* subsp. *japonicum* |
| - Schneider var. *japonicum* | See *R. degronianum* subsp. *heptamerum* |
| - var. *pentamerum* | See *R. degronianum* subsp. *degronianum* |
| *jasminiflorum* (V) | CEqu ERea |
| ¶ 'Jason' | SLdr |
| 'Jasorbit' (V) | CEqu |
| 'Java Light' (V) | CDoC ERea |
| *javanicum* Sands 74 (V) | GGGa |
| - var. *teysmannii* (V) | Last listed 1997 |
| 'Jazz Band' (V) | GGGa |
| Jean Group | Last listed 1997 |
| 'Jean Mary Montague' | See *R.* 'The Hon. Jean Marie de Montague' |
| 'Jean Read' (EA) | LHyd |
| 'Jeanette' (EA) | LKna |
| 'Jeff Hill' (EA) | ECho LRHS MBri MOne SLdr SReu |
| 'Jennie Dosser' | LMil |
| 'Jenny' | See *R.* 'Creeping Jenny' |
| § 'Jervis Bay' ♀ | SReu |
| 'Jingle Bells' | CWri GGGa |
| 'Jo Madden' | Last listed 1997 |
| 'Joan Scobie' | SLdr |
| Jock Group | CB&S CMHG CTrw |
| 'Jock Brydon' (O) | GGGa LMil |
| 'Jock Coutts' | LKna |
| 'Jock's White' | MBal SPer |
| 'Joe Paterno' | Last listed 1997 |
| 'Johann Sebastian Bach' (EA) | WBod WWeb |
| 'Johann Strauss' (EA) | WBod |
| 'Johanna' (EA) | CDoC CTrh GGGa GHCN LMil MAsh MBar MBri SLdr SPer SReu WBod |
| 'John Barr Stevenson' | LHyd NMun SLdr |
| 'John Cairns' (EA) ♀ | CMac LHyd LKna MBal MBar SPer SReu WPic |
| 'John Eichelser' | LMil |
| 'John Holms' | SLdr |
| 'John Keats' | Last listed 1996 |
| ¶ 'John Marchand' | SLdr |
| 'John Tremayne' | SLdr |
| 'John Walter' | MBar MBri MGos SBid SLdr |
| 'John Waterer' | CWri IOrc LKna SBrw WFar |
| Johnnie Johnston Group & cl. | Last listed 1998 |
| 'Johnny Bender' | SLdr |
| 'Johnson's Impeditum' | Last listed 1996 |
| *johnstoneanum* ♀ | CB&S CGre CSam GGGa LMil MBal NMun SLdr WBod |
| - 'Double Diamond' (d) | CB&S CGre CWri LMil |
| - 'Rubeotinctum' KW 7732 | NMun |
| 'Jolie Madame' (Vs) | MBri SLdr SReu |
| 'Jonathan Shaw' | GGGa |
| ¶ 'Joseph Haydn' (EA) | WBod |
| 'Joseph Hill' (EA) | CDoC ECho LMil SReu SSpi WPat |
| 'Joseph Whitworth' | Last listed 1996 |
| ¶ 'Josephine Klinger' (G) | SReu |
| 'Joy's Delight' (Ad) | LKna |
| 'Jubilee' | LKna SLdr |
| Jubilee Queen Group & cl. | SLdr |
| ¶ 'Judy Clarke' | SLdr |
| 'Julischka' | MGos |
| 'June Bee' | GGGa |
| ¶ 'June Fire' (A) | GGGa SReu |

| | |
|---|---|
| ¶ 'June Yellow' | GGGa |
| 'Jungfrau' | Last listed 1996 |
| 'Juwel' | MGos |
| **kaempferi** (EA) ♀ | CGre CHig GGGa LMil |
| - 'Damio' | See *R. kaempferi* 'Mikado' |
| - dark form (EA) | Last listed 1998 |
| § - 'Eastern Fire' (EA) | Last listed 1996 |
| - 'Firefly' | See *R.* 'Hexe' |
| - light form (EA) | Last listed 1998 |
| § - 'Mikado' (EA) | LMil SBod SBrw SPer SReu SSta |
| - orange (EA) | IOrc |
| - pink (EA) | IOrc |
| 'Kaho-no-hikari' (EA) | GAri |
| 'Kakiemon' (EA) | SPer |
| 'Kalinka' | LHyd MDun MGos NHol |
| 'Kantilene' | Last listed 1998 |
| 'Kaponga' | CDoC MGos |
| 'Karen Triplett' | LMil |
| 'Karin' | COtt MBal MDun SBod SLdr |
| ¶ 'Karin Seleger' | GGGa |
| 'Kasane-kagaribi' (EA) | LHyd |
| 'Kate Waterer' ♀ | IOrc LHyd LKna MBar MGos |
| | NMun SBrw SLdr SReu |
| N 'Kathleen' (A) | SLdr |
| ¶ 'Kathleen' pale pink (EA) | LHyd |
| ¶ 'Kathleen' rosy red (EA) | LKna WBod |
| ¶ 'Kathleen' salmon pink (EA) | IOrc |
| 'Katinka' (EA) | GGGa MBal MGos |
| 'Katisha' (EA) | LHyd SLdr |
| ¶ 'Katrina' | SLdr |
| 'Katy Watson' | SReu |
| **kawakamii** (V) | GGGa |
| ¶ 'Keija' | SReu |
| 'Keinohana' (EA) | NMun |
| **keiskei** | CHig LHyd MBal NMun SLdr |
| ¶ - **compactum** | SLdr |
| - 'Cordifolium' | NHol WAbe |
| - 'Ebino' | GGGa NHol WAbe |
| - var. **ozawae** 'Yaku Fairy' ♀ | GAri GGGa LMil LRHS MBal NHar |
| | SReu |
| - - 'Yaku Fairy' | Last listed 1997 |
| x **campylogynum** | |
| - - 'Yaku Fairy' x | NHol |
| **campylogynum** | |
| var. **leucanthum** | |
| - - 'Yaku Fairy' x **lowndesii** | EPot |
| - - 'Yaku Fairy' | Last listed 1998 |
| x **spinuliferum** | |
| Keiskrac Group | Last listed 1996 |
| **keleticum** | See *R. calostrotum* subsp. |
| | **keleticum** |
| § 'Ken Janeck' | GGGa SLdr SMur WWeb |
| § **kendrickii** | GGGa MDun NMun |
| - MH 62 | GGGa |
| ¶ 'Kentucky Colonel' | SLdr |
| 'Kentucky Minstrel' (K) | Last listed 1996 |
| 'Kermesinum' (EA) | COtt GGGa MBar SLdr SReu WPat |
| 'Kermesinum Album' (EA) | GGGa MBar MGos |
| I 'Kermesinum Rose' (EA) | GChr LRHS MBar MBri SLdr SReu |
| * 'Kermesinum Wit' | SReu |
| **kesangiae** AC 110 | NMun |
| - CH&M 3058 | GGGa |
| - CH&M 3099 | GGGa |
| - EGM 061 | LMil |
| - var. **kesangiae** KR 1136 | NMun |
| aff. **kesangiae** KR 1640 | GGGa MDun NMun |
| 'Keston Rose' | Last listed 1996 |
| Kewense Group | See *R.* Loderi Group |
| **keysii** | CB&S GGGa LMil MBal MDun |
| | NMun SLdr |

| | |
|---|---|
| - KR 974 | NMun |
| - KW 8101* | NMun |
| - 'Unicolor' | NMun SLdr |
| 'Kijei' | Last listed 1998 |
| Kilimanjaro Group & cl. | LMil NMun SBrw SLdr SReu SSta |
| 'Kimberly' | GGGa |
| 'Kimbeth' | GGGa |
| 'Kimigayo' (EA) | LHyd |
| 'King Fisher' | NMun |
| 'King George' Loder | See *R.* 'Loderi King George' |
| 'King George' Van Nes | SReu |
| ¶ 'King of Shrubs' | SLdr |
| **kingianum** | See *R. arboreum* subsp. |
| | **zeylanicum** |
| 'Kingston' | MDun |
| § 'Kirin' (EA/d) ♀ | CGre CMac CTrw GHCN IOrc |
| | LHyd LKna LMil SBod SLdr WBod |
| 'Kirishima' (EA) | LKna SRms |
| 'Kiritsubo' (EA) | GAri IOrc LHyd |
| * 'Kitty Cole' | SLdr |
| **kiusianum** (EA) ♀ | GGGa LHyd NMun SReu SRms |
| | WAbe |
| - 'Album' (EA) | GAri LHyd LMil SReu WAbe |
| - 'Amoenum' | See *R.* 'Amoenum' |
| - 'Benichidori' (EA) | Last listed 1996 |
| ¶ - 'Ekubo' (EA) | SReu |
| - 'Hillier's Pink' (EA) | LMil |
| ¶ - var. **kiusianum** | CTrh |
| 'Mountain Gem' (EA) | |
| * - 'Mount Fuji' (EA) | LMil WAbe |
| - 'Mountain Pride' (EA) | Last listed 1996 |
| - var. **sataense** (EA) | Last listed 1997 |
| 'Kiwi Majic' | GGGa LMil |
| 'Klondyke' (K) ♀ | CB&S CTri ELan ENot GChr |
| | GGGa IOrc LMil MAsh MBri |
| | MGos MLea SBrw SLdr SPer SReu |
| 'Kluis Sensation' ♀ | CB&S CWri ENot IOrc LHyd LKna |
| | MDun MGos NMun SBrw SLdr |
| | SReu |
| 'Kluis Triumph' | LKna SBrw SReu |
| 'Knap Hill Apricot' (K) | LKna SMur |
| 'Knap Hill Red' (K) | LKna LMil SLdr SMur |
| 'Kobold' (EA) | NMun SLdr |
| 'Koichiro Wada' | See *R. yakushimanum* 'Koichiro |
| | Wada' |
| 'Kokardia' | SLdr |
| 'Komurasaki' (EA) | NMun |
| **kongboense** | GGGa |
| - C&V 9540 | GGGa |
| aff. **kongboense** KR 3725 | LMil |
| § 'Koningin Emma' (M) | LMil MBri |
| § 'Koningin Wilhelmina' (M) | IOrc SMer WBod |
| **konori** M Black (V) | Last listed 1998 |
| - var. **phaeopeplum** (V) | GGGa |
| 'Koster's Brilliant Red' (M) | ENot MBal SLdr SReu |
| **kotschyi** | See *R. myrtifolium* |
| 'Kozan' (EA) | MBal |
| ¶ 'Kupferberg' | GGGa |
| § 'Kure-no-yuki' (EA/d) ♀ | CMac CTrG LHyd LKna LMil |
| | MAsh SBod |
| 'Kusudama' (EA) | GAri |
| **kyawii** | NMun SLdr |
| § - Agapetum Group | NMun |
| 'Lacs' | Last listed 1998 |
| **lacteum** | LMil MDun NMun SLdr |
| - bright yellow | NMun |
| - C 7164 | GGGa |
| - CNW 930 | GGGa |
| - CNW 936 | GGGa |
| - CNW 966 | GGGa |

| | |
|---|---|
| – forms | NMun |
| – KR 2760 | GGGa |
| – SBEC 345 | GGGa |
| – SF 374 | ISea |
| 'Ladt Decis' | Last listed 1997 |
| 'Lady Adam Gordon' | LHyd SLdr |
| 'Lady Alice Fitzwilliam' ♀ | CB&S CDoC CGre CMHG CTrG GGGa ISea LHyd LMil MBal NMun SLdr WWat |
| 'Lady Annette de Trafford' | LKna |
| 'Lady Armstrong' | CWri |
| Lady Bessborough Group & cl. | SLdr |
| 'Lady Bessborough Roberte' | See *R*. 'Roberte' |
| 'Lady Bowes Lyon' | LHyd NMun SLdr |
| Lady Chamberlain Group & cl. | GGGa LMil MBal NMun SLdr |
| 'Lady Chamberlain Exbury' | See *R*. 'Exbury Lady Chamberlain' |
| 'Lady Chamberlain Golden Queen' | See *R*. 'Golden Queen' |
| 'Lady Chamberlain Salmon Trout' | See *R*. 'Salmon Trout' |
| 'Lady Clairmont' | SBrw |
| 'Lady Clementine Mitford' ♀ | CWri GGGa LHyd LKna LMil MAsh MDun MGos MLea NMun SBid SBrw SLdr SPer SRPl SReu SSta |
| 'Lady Decies' | SReu |
| 'Lady Eleanor Cathcart' ♀ | CHig CWri EPfP GGGa IOrc LKna NMun SBrw SLdr |
| 'Lady Elphinstone' (EA) | LHyd SLdr |
| 'Lady Grey Egerton' | LKna |
| Lady Jean Group | Last listed 1996 |
| Lady Linlithgow Group | Last listed 1998 |
| 'Lady Longman' | LHyd SBrw SSta |
| 'Lady Louise' (EA) | LHyd SLdr |
| Lady Montagu Group & cl. | Last listed 1996 |
| 'Lady Primrose' | SLdr SReu |
| 'Lady Robin' (EA) | LMil |
| 'Lady Romsey' | LMil |
| 'Lady Rosebery' (K) | MAsh MBri |
| Lady Rosebery Group & cl. | MLea NMun SLdr |
| 'Lady Rosebery Pink Delight' | See *R*. 'Pink Lady Rosebery' |
| Ladybird Group & cl. | LMil SReu |
| *laetum* (V) | CEqu GGGa |
| Lamellen Group | LHyd SLdr |
| 'Lampion' | ENot GGGa LHyd |
| 'Lamplighter' ♀ | LMil SReu |
| *lanatoides* | NMun |
| ¶ – C&C 7548 | GGGa |
| ¶ – C&C 7574 | GGGa |
| ¶ – C&C 7577 | GGGa |
| – KW 5971 | NMun |
| *lanatum* | LMil NMun SLdr |
| – 716652 | Last listed 1997 |
| – BB 185b | NMun |
| – C 2148 | Last listed 1997 |
| – Cooper 2148 | SLdr |
| – DF 538 | MBal |
| – dwarf cream | GGGa |
| – Flinckii Group | See *R. flinckii* |
| – KR 873 | Last listed 1998 |
| 'Langmans' | LKna |
| 'Langworth' | CWri ECho LKna LMil MLea SBrw SLdr SReu |
| *lanigerum* | MDun NMun SLdr SReu |
| – C&V 9530 | GGGa |
| ¶ – 'Chapel Wood' | SLdr |
| – KW 6258 | Last listed 1997 |
| – KW 8251 | GGGa |

| | |
|---|---|
| – pink | NMun |
| – red | NMun |
| – 'Round Wood' ex KW 6258 | Last listed 1998 |
| subsect. *Lapponica* | Last listed 1998 |
| ACE 1787 | |
| *lapponicum* | LMil |
| ¶ – Confertissimum Group | GGGa |
| – Japanese | GGGa |
| ¶ – Parvifolium Group from Siberia | GGGa |
| 'Lapwing' (K) | LKna MBri |
| 'Lascaux' | SReu |
| *lasiostylum* ETOT 135 | Last listed 1998 |
| – ETOT 136 | Last listed 1998 |
| 'Late Love' (EA) | CDoC MGos SSpi |
| late pink Inverewe | WBod |
| § *latoucheae* (EA) | MBal |
| – PW 86 (EA) | GGGa |
| *laudandum* var. *temoense* | GGGa LMil MDun |
| Laura Aberconway Group & cl. | SLdr |
| 'Laura Morland' (EA) | LHyd |
| 'Lava Flow' | LHyd NHol |
| ¶ 'Lavender Brilliant' | CTrh |
| 'Lavender Girl' ♀ | GGGa LHyd LKna LMil MBal MGos NMun SBrw SLdr SReu SSta |
| 'Lavender Lady' (EA) | CTrG |
| 'Lavender Princess' | Last listed 1998 |
| 'Lavender Queen' | CWri NMun WWeb |
| / 'Lavendula' | GGGa LMil |
| 'Le Progrès' | SReu |
| 'Lea Rainbow' | MLea |
| ◆ 'Ledifolium' | See *R*. x *mucronatum* |
| ◆ 'Ledifolium Album' | See *R*. x *mucronatum* |
| *ledifolium* 'Bulstrode' | See *R*. 'Bulstrode' |
| – 'Magnificum' | See *R*. 'Magnificum' |
| – 'Ripense' | See *R. ripense* |
| 'Lee's Dark Purple' | CB&S CDoC CWri LMil MBar NMun SBrw SPer WFar WGwG |
| 'Lee's Scarlet' | LKna LMil SLdr |
| 'Lemon Cloud' | GGGa |
| * 'Lemon Drop' (A) | GGGa |
| 'Lemon Grove' | SReu |
| 'Lemon Ice' | Last listed 1997 |
| 'Lemon Lodge' | CB&S CDoC |
| 'Lemon Minuet' (V) | CEqu |
| 'Lemonora' (M) | ELan MBri SLdr |
| 'Lem's Cameo' ♀ | GGGa LHyd LMil NMun SReu SSta |
| 'Lem's Monarch' ♀ | CDoC CWri GGGa LMil LRHS MDun MGos MLea SReu SSta |
| 'Lem's Stormcloud' | SSta |
| 'Lem's Tangerine' | LMil |
| 'Lemur' (EA) | CTrh GChr GGGa MBri MGos SReu WAbe WPat |
| 'Leni' | Last listed 1998 |
| 'Leny' (EA) | NHol |
| 'Leo' (EA) | GQui LHyd LKna LMil NMun SBod SLdr SReu WWeb |
| 'Leo' | EPfP NMun |
| 'Leonardslee Brilliant' | SLdr |
| 'Leonardslee Giles' | SLdr |
| ¶ 'Leonardslee Hybrid' | SLdr |
| 'Leonardslee Pink Bride' | SLdr |
| 'Leonardslee Primrose' | SLdr |
| Leonore Group & cl. | NMun SReu |
| *lepidostylum* ♀ | CB&S CWri GGGa LHyd LMil MBar MBri MDun NHar NMun SLdr SReu WSHC |

| | |
|---|---|
| *lepidotum* | GGGa LHyd LMil MDun NMun WAbe |
| - var. *album* | GGGa |
| - CC&McK 530 | Last listed 1996 |
| - Elaeagnoides Group | GGGa |
| - FMB 279 | MBal |
| - x *lowndesii* | Last listed 1998 |
| - M Black 602 | GGGa |
| - 'Reuthe's Purple' | See *R.* 'Reuthe's Purple' |
| - TW 40 | Last listed 1997 |
| - yellow form | NMun |
| ¶ *leptanthum* (V) | CEqu |
| § *leptocarpum* | GGGa LMil |
| - C&H 420 | NMun |
| *leptothrium* | GGGa NMun |
| Letty Edwards Group & cl. | LKna NMun SLdr SReu |
| § 'Leucanthemum' | CHig GGGa LMil |
| *leucaspis* ♀ | CGre CHig ERea GGGa IOrc ISea LHyd MBal NMun SLdr SReu WAbe |
| - KW 7171 | NMun SLdr |
| 'Leverett Richards' | LHyd SReu |
| *levinei* | GGGa |
| 'Lewis Monarch' | Last listed 1996 |
| 'Lila Pedigo' | CDoC COtt CWri GGGa GRei MBal MLea |
| 'Lilac Time' (EA) | MBar SLdr |
| 'Lilacinum' (EA) | WPic |
| 'Lilacinum' | Last listed 1997 |
| *liliiflorum* Guiz 163 | GGGa |
| 'Lillie Maude' (EA) | CTrh |
| 'Lilliput' | MAsh SBod SPer |
| 'Lily Marleen' (EA) | CDoC CTri SCoo SLdr SReu WGwG |
| 'Lincill' | Last listed 1996 |
| 'Linda' | CSam CTri EBee GChr GGGa GRei MBal MBar MBri MDun MGos SBod SReu WWeb |
| ¶ 'Linda Lee' | SLdr |
| 'Linda R' (EA) | Last listed 1997 |
| *lindleyi* ♀ | GQui LMil NMun |
| - 'Dame Edith Sitwell' | GGGa LMil |
| - L&S | GGGa MBal |
| ◆ 'Linearifolium' | See *R. stenopetalum* 'Linearifolium' |
| 'Linnet' (K/d) | LKna |
| 'Linwood Salmon' (EA/d) | SReu |
| Lionel's Triumph Group & cl. | LMil NMun SLdr |
| 'Lissabon Rosa' | Last listed 1998 |
| *litiense* | See *R. wardii* var. *wardii* Litiense Group |
| 'Little Beauty' (EA) | SLdr |
| 'Little Ben' | ECho MBal MBar MDun WAbe |
| 'Little Bert' | Last listed 1998 |
| 'Little Ginger' (V) | Last listed 1996 |
| 'Little Grace' (V) | CEqu |
| 'Little Jessica' | Last listed 1997 |
| 'Little Jock' | MBal |
| 'Little One' (V) | CEqu |
| 'Littlest Angel' (V) | Last listed 1996 |
| 'Loch Earn' | GGGa |
| 'Loch o' the Lowes' | CDoC GGGa LMil MBri MDun MOne |
| 'Loch Rannoch' | GGGa |
| 'Loch Tummel' | GGGa |
| *lochiae* (V) | CEqu GGGa |
| 'Lochinch Spinbur' | GQui |
| Lodauric Group | SReu |
| § 'Lodauric Iceberg' ♀ | GGGa LKna LMil SBrw SReu |
| 'Lodbrit' | SReu |

| | |
|---|---|
| § Loderi Group | CB&S SLdr |
| 'Loderi Fairy Queen' | NMun SLdr |
| 'Loderi Fairyland' | LHyd MDun NMun SLdr |
| § 'Loderi Game Chick' | CB&S CWri LHyd LMil MBal NMun SLdr SPer SReu SSta |
| 'Loderi Georgette' | NMun SLdr |
| 'Loderi Helen' | NMun SLdr |
| § 'Loderi Julie' | NMun SLdr SReu |
| § 'Loderi King George' ♀ | CB&S CSam CWri GGGa ISea LHyd LKna LMil MBlu MDun MLea NMun SLdr SPer SReu SSta |
| 'Loderi Patience' | LHyd NMun SLdr |
| 'Loderi Pink Diamond' ♀ | LMil |
| 'Loderi Pink Topaz' | LHyd LMil MDun NMun SLdr |
| 'Loderi Pretty Polly' | NMun |
| 'Loderi Princess Marina' | NMun SLdr |
| 'Loderi Sir Edmund' | LHyd NMun SLdr |
| 'Loderi Sir Joseph Hooker' | NMun SLdr |
| 'Loderi Titan' | SReu |
| § 'Loderi Venus' ♀ | CDoC CWri GGGa IOrc LHyd LKna LMil MBal MDun MLea NMun SLdr SPer SReu SSta |
| 'Loderi White Diamond' | LHyd NMun SLdr |
| 'Loder's White' ♀ | CWri ENot GGGa LHyd LKna LMil MBal MLea NMun SBrw SLdr SReu SSta |
| 'Lodestar' | Last listed 1997 |
| § 'Logan Damaris' | LHyd NMun SLdr SReu |
| 'Loki' | SLdr |
| ¶ 'Lollipop' | MLea |
| *longesquamatum* | GGGa LMil NMun SLdr |
| *longipes* var. *chienianum* EN 4074 | GGGa |
| - EGM 337 | LMil |
| - var. *longipes* C&H 7072 | GGGa |
| - - C&H 7113 | GGGa |
| *longistylum* | GGGa NMun |
| 'Longworth' | NMun |
| 'Looking Glass' | Last listed 1998 |
| *lopsangianum* | See *R. thomsonii* subsp. *lopsangianum* |
| - LS&T 5651 | NMun |
| *loranthiflorum* (V) | Last listed 1997 |
| 'Lord Roberts' | CB&S CHig CSam CTri CWri EBee ENot GChr GGGa GRei IOrc LKna LMil MAsh MBal MBar MBri MGos NMun SBrw SLdr SPer SReu SRms WFar WWeb |
| 'Lord Swaythling' | LHyd SLdr |
| 'Lori Eichelser' | CSam LMil MBal MDun MLea NHar NHed |
| 'Lorna' (EA) | ENot GQui LMil |
| 'Louis Pasteur' | SBrw SReu |
| 'Louisa' (EA) | SSpi |
| 'Louise Dowdle' (EA) | CTrh GChr LMil SPer |
| 'Lovely William' | CSam MBal SLdr |
| *lowndesii* | WAbe |
| 'Lucy Lou' | CSam GGGa NHol |
| *ludlowii* | GGGa MBal |
| - x *viridescens* | NHol |
| *ludwigianum* | GGGa |
| *lukiangense* | NMun |
| § - R 11275 | NMun |
| § - R 72 | NMun |
| 'Lullaby' (EA) | LKna SLdr |
| 'Lunar Queen' | LHyd NMun SLdr |
| Luscombei Group | SLdr |

| | |
|---|---|
| ¶ 'Luscombei Splendens' | SLdr |
| *luteiflorum* | LMil |
| – KW 21040 | GGGa NMun |
| – KW 21556 | GGGa |
| – TW 390 | Last listed 1997 |
| *lutescens* | CB&S CGre CHig CTre CWri IBlr |
| | IOrc LMil MBal MDun NMun SLdr |
| | SReu SSta WAbe WBod WWat |
| – 'Bagshot Sands' ♀ | GGGa LHyd LMil LRHS SReu |
| – C&H 7124 | GGGa |
| – 'Exbury' | Last listed 1996 |
| – PA Cox 5092 | GGGa NHol |
| – PA Cox 5100 | GGGa NHol |
| – pink | Last listed 1996 |
| § *luteum* (A) ♀ | CB&S CDoC CMHG CPMA CTrG |
| | CTre CTri CWri GGGa ISea LKna |
| | LMil MAsh MBal MBar MBri MGos |
| | MLea NMun SBrw SLdr SReu |
| | SRms SSta WBod WPic WWat |
| § *lyi* | NMun |
| – KR 2861 | GGGa |
| – KR 2962 | GGGa |
| × *lysolepis* KW 4456 | Last listed 1997 |
| * 'Mac Ovata' | CMac |
| *macabeanum* ♀ | CB&S GGGa LMil MBal MDun |
| | NMun SLdr SReu SSta WHer WPic |
| ¶ – deep cream | SLdr |
| – DT 10 | GGGa |
| – KW 7724 | NMun |
| – Reuthe's form | SReu |
| – × *sinogrande* | MDun SReu |
| *macgregoriae* (V) | CEqu ERea |
| – P Woods 2646 (V) | GGGa |
| *macranthum* | See *R. indicum* |
| 'Macranthum Roseum' (EA) | SBod SReu |
| *macrophyllum* | GGGa |
| *macrosmithii* | See *R. argipeplum* |
| 'Macrostemon' | See *R.* (Obtusum Group) |
| | 'Macrostemon' |
| *maculiferum* | NMun SLdr |
| – subsp. *anwheiense* | See *R. anwheiense* |
| – Guiz 120* | GGGa |
| – Guiz 121 | GGGa |
| – Guiz 148 | Last listed 1997 |
| 'Madame Albert Moser' | LKna |
| 'Madame de Bruin' | LKna MBal NWea SBrw SLdr |
| 'Madame F.V. Chauvin' | Last listed 1998 |
| ¶ 'Madame Ida Rubenstein' | SBrw |
| 'Madame Knutz' | Last listed 1998 |
| 'Madame Masson' | CHig CSam CWri GChr GGGa |
| | LMil MAsh MGos NMun SLdr |
| | SReu SSta WWeb |
| 'Madame van Hecke' (EA) | COtt EPfP MAsh MBri SBrw SLdr |
| | SReu WFar WGor |
| *maddenii* ♀ | CGre LHyd LMil NMun SLdr |
| § – subsp. *crassum* ♀ | CTrw GGGa LMil MBal NMun |
| | SLdr SReu WBod |
| – – AC 708 | NMun |
| § – – Obtusifolium Group | NMun SLdr |
| § – subsp. *maddenii* | NMun |
| § – – Polyandrum Group | CB&S GQui ISea MBal NMun SLdr |
| – pink | Last listed 1996 |
| ¶ 'Madeline's Yellow' | SLdr |
| ¶ 'Mademoiselle Masson' | SBrw WFar |
| 'Maestro' | LHyd |
| I 'Magic Flute' (V) | Last listed 1996 |
| N 'Magnificum' (A) | Last listed 1998 |
| *magnificum* | LMil NMun SLdr SReu |
| 'Maharani' | GGGa MAsh |

| | |
|---|---|
| Mai Group | Last listed 1996 |
| § *makinoi* ♀ | CEqu CHig GGGa LHyd LMil |
| | MDun NMun SLdr SReu SSta |
| *mallotum* | GGGa LHyd LMil MDun NMun |
| | SLdr SReu |
| – F 17853 | Last listed 1997 |
| – Farrer 815 | Last listed 1998 |
| 'Malvaticum' (EA) | Last listed 1998 |
| 'Manda Sue' | MAsh MBal MLea WGor |
| Mandalay Group | SLdr |
| 'Manderley' | MDun SBrw |
| *manipurense* | See *R. maddenii* subsp. *crassum* |
| | Obtusifolium Group |
| 'Manor Hill' | SLdr |
| ¶ 'Marcel Ménard' | SBrw SReu |
| 'Marchioness of Lansdowne' | MGos SBrw |
| 'Marcia' | LHyd SLdr |
| 'Mardi Gras' | GGGa |
| Margaret Dunn Group & cl. | CWri |
| 'Margaret Falmouth' | SReu |
| 'Margaret George' (EA) | LHyd SLdr |
| 'Maria Elena' (EA/d) | Last listed 1998 |
| 'Marianne' (EA/d) | Last listed 1998 |
| ¶ 'Maricee' | SLdr |
| 'Marie' (EA) | CMac |
| Marie Antoinette Group | Last listed 1996 |
| 'Marie Curie' | SReu |
| 'Marilee' (EA) | CDoC MGos MOne |
| Mariloo Group | NMun SLdr |
| 'Marinus Koster' ♀ | LKna MAsh MBri MLea SLdr |
| ¶ 'Marion' | LMil |
| 'Marion Merriman' (K) | LKna |
| 'Marion Street' ♀ | LHyd LMil NMun SLdr SReu |
| ¶ 'Mark Turner' | SReu |
| 'Markeeta's Flame' | MAsh |
| 'Markeeta's Prize' ♀ | CDoC CSam CWri EBee GAri |
| | GGGa LMil MBri MGos MLea |
| | NMun |
| 'Marlene Peste' | CAbP |
| ¶ 'Marley Hedges' | GGGa |
| ¶ 'Marlies' (K) | SLdr |
| ¶ 'Marmot' (EA) | WAbe |
| 'Mars' | SBrw SLdr SReu |
| Marshall Group | Last listed 1996 |
| 'Martha Hitchcock' (EA) | LKna SRms |
| 'Martha Isaacson' (Ad) | MBal MBri MGos MLea SReu |
| 'Martine' (Ad) | LHyd LKna MBri MGos SLdr |
| *martinianum* | NMun SLdr |
| aff. *martinianum* KW 21557 | GGGa |
| ¶ 'Maruschka' (EA) | GGGa |
| 'Mary Drennen' | LMil |
| 'Mary Fleming' | MDun NMun SBod SLdr WLRN |
| 'Mary Forte' | SBrw |
| 'Mary Helen' (EA) | CDoC LHyd LRHS SCoo SReu |
| | WBod |
| 'Mary Meredith' (EA) | LHyd |
| 'Mary Poppins' | LRHS MAsh SCoo |
| 'Maryke' | LMil |
| 'Master Mariner' | Last listed 1997 |
| 'Master of Elphinstone' (EA) | Last listed 1998 |
| Matador Group & cl. | NMun SReu |
| 'Mauna Loa' (K) | LKna |
| 'Maurice Skipworth' | CB&S CDoC |
| 'Mavis Davis' | GGGa |
| *maximum* | GGGa NMun SLdr |
| – 'Weeldon's Red' | GGGa |
| 'Maxine Childers' | LMil |
| § 'Maxwellii' (EA) | CMac SLdr |
| ¶ 'May Day' ♀ | CPin |

| Name | Nurseries |
|---|---|
| May Day Group & cl. | CB&S CSam CTrw CWri ISea LHyd LKna MBal MBri MDun MGos NMun SLdr SReu SSta WBod |
| 'May Glow' | MGos |
| May Morn Group & cl. | SReu |
| 'Mayor Johnstone' | LRHS |
| 'Mazurka' (K) | LKna |
| *meddianum* | GGGa NMun SLdr |
| - var. *atrokermesinum* | NMun SLdr |
| - - F 26476 | NMun |
| - - KW 21006a | GGGa |
| ¶ - var. *meddianum* F 24219 | SLdr |
| ¶ Medea Group | SLdr |
| Medusa Group | GGGa SReu |
| *megacalyx* | GGGa |
| 'Megan' (EA) | GGGa IOrc MAsh SLdr SReu |
| *megaphyllum* | See R. *basilicum* |
| *megeratum* | GGGa NMun SReu |
| - 'Bodnant' | WAbe WBod |
| ¶ - R 18861 | SLdr |
| 'Meicho' (EA) | GAri |
| *mekongense* | GGGa |
| - var. *mekongense* | SReu |
| § - - KW 21079 | Last listed 1997 |
| § - - KW 5829 | NMun SLdr |
| - - Rubroluteum Group | See R. *viridescens* Rubroluteum Group |
| - - Viridescens Group | See R. *viridescens* |
| § - var. *melinanthum* | NMun |
| - var. *rubrolineatum* | NMun |
| 'Melford Lemon' | See R. 'Ilam Melford Lemon' |
| 'Melina' (EA/d) | GGGa |
| *melinanthum* | See R. *mekongense* var. *melinanthum* |
| 'Merganser' ♀ | GGGa LMil MAsh MBal MDun MLea NHol SReu WAbe |
| ¶ 'Merlin' (EA) | SLdr |
| ♦ 'Merlin' misapplied | See R. (Hawk Group) 'Hawk Merlin' |
| Merops Group | Last listed 1996 |
| *metternichii* | See R. *degronianum* subsp. *heptamerum* |
| ♦ - var. *pentamerum* | See R. *degronianum* subsp. *degronianum* |
| 'Mi Amor' | LMil |
| 'Michael Hill' (EA) | CB&S COtt CTrh LHyd MAsh SSpi |
| 'Michael Waterer' ♀ | MDun NMun SBod SLdr |
| 'Michael's Pride' ♀ | CB&S GQui MBal NMun |
| *micranthum* | CGre GGGa MDun NMun SLdr |
| *microgynum* | NMun SLdr |
| - F 14242 | GGGa NMun SLdr |
| § - Gymnocarpum Group | Last listed 1996 |
| *microleucum* | See R. *orthocladum* var. *microleucum* |
| *micromeres* | See R. *leptocarpum* |
| *microphyton* | Last listed 1997 |
| 'Midnight Mystique' | GGGa |
| 'Midori' (EA) | Last listed 1998 |
| 'Midsummer' | SLdr |
| 'Mikado' (EA) | See R. *kaempferi* 'Mikado' |
| 'Mikado' | Last listed 1996 |
| *mimetes* | LMil NMun SLdr |
| § - var. *simulans* | NMun SLdr |
| - - F 20428 | GGGa NMun SLdr |
| 'Mimi' (EA) | CMac LHyd |
| ¶ 'Mimra' | SLdr |
| 'Ming' | See R. 'Ilam Ming' |
| 'Minterne Cinnkeys' | MBal |
| *minus* | GQui |
| § - var. *minus* | SLdr |
| § - - Carolinianum Group | LMil |
| § - - Punctatum Group | MBar |
| 'Misomogiri' | CHig |
| 'Miss Muffet' (EA) | SLdr |
| 'Mizu-no-yamabuki' (EA) | Last listed 1998 |
| § 'Moerheim' ♀ | CSam MAsh MBal MBar MDun MOne NHol SLdr SReu SSta WStI |
| § 'Moerheim's Pink' | LHyd LKna LMil MDun NHol SPer |
| 'Moerheim's Scarlet' | LKna |
| ¶ 'Moffat' | SReu |
| Mohamet Group & cl. | Last listed 1996 |
| 'Moidart' (Vs) | LMil |
| 'Moira Salmon' (EA) | LHyd SLdr |
| 'Molalla Red' (K) | LMil |
| § *molle* subsp. *japonicum* (A) | GGGa LHyd |
| - - JR 871 (A) | GGGa |
| ¶ - subsp. *molle* C&H 7181 (A) | GGGa |
| *mollicomum* | NMun |
| - F 10347 | NMun |
| - F 30940 | See R. *hemitrichotum* F 30940 |
| Mollis orange (M) | MBar SRms |
| Mollis pink (M) | GGGa MBar SRms |
| Mollis red (M) | MBar SRms |
| Mollis salmon (M) | GGGa GQui |
| Mollis yellow (M) | GQui MBar SRms |
| 'Molly Ann' | CDoC GGGa GRei LRHS MDun SReu WGor |
| 'Molly Buckley' | Last listed 1996 |
| 'Molly Miller' | Last listed 1998 |
| 'Monaco' | CWri SLdr |
| ¶ *monanthum* CCH&H 8133 | GGGa |
| 'Monica' | Last listed 1998 |
| 'Monica Wellington' | Last listed 1996 |
| *monosematum* | See R. *pachytrichum* var. *monosematum* |
| *montiganum* | ISea |
| *montroseanum* | LMil MDun NMun SLdr WCru |
| * - 'Baravalla' | CWri GGGa |
| - 'Benmore' | NMun SLdr |
| 'Moon Maiden' (EA) | CDoC GQui LMil SLdr SVil |
| Moonbeam Group | LKna |
| Moonshine Group & cl. | SReu |
| 'Moonshine Bright' | LHyd MDun SLdr SReu |
| 'Moonshine Crescent' | SReu |
| 'Moonshine Supreme' | LKna SReu |
| Moonstone Group | CB&S GAri MBal MBar MDun MLea NMun SLdr |
| - pink-tipped | NHol |
| 'Moonstone Pink' | Last listed 1996 |
| 'Moonstone Yellow' | GGGa |
| 'Moonwax' | CB&S CSam CWri MBal SMur |
| § 'Morgenrot' ♀ | GChr GGGa LMil LRHS MBri MGos SReu |
| *morii* ♀ | CWri GGGa LHyd LMil MDun NMun SLdr |
| - ETOT 90 | ISea |
| - W/A 10955 | SLdr |
| 'Morning Cloud' ♀ | CAbP IOrc LHyd LMil MBar MBri NHed NMun SBrw SLdr SReu |
| 'Morning Magic' | CWri LHyd NMun SBrw SLdr |
| Morning Red | See R. 'Morgenrot' |
| 'Morvah' | SLdr |
| 'Moser's Maroon' | CWri LHyd LKna LMil MGos NMun SBrw SLdr WGwG |
| 'Moser's Strawberry' | LKna |
| 'Motet' (K/d) | LKna |
| 'Moth' | GGGa NHol |
| 'Mother Greer' | GGGa |
| 'Mother of Pearl' | LKna SBrw SLdr SReu |

| | |
|---|---|
| 'Mother Theresa' | LKna |
| § 'Motherly Love' | Last listed 1996 |
| 'Mother's Day' (EA) ♀ | More than 30 suppliers |
| § *moulmainense* | CB&S |
| 'Mount Everest' | LHyd LMil SBrw SLdr SReu SSta |
| 'Mount Rainier' (K) | LMil SReu |
| 'Mount Saint Helens' | GGGa LMil MLea |
| 'Mount Seven Star' (EA) | CHig ECho GGGa LHyd LMil MBri |
| | MBro NHol SLdr SReu WAbe WPat |
| 'Mountain Dew' | Last listed 1996 |
| 'Mountain Star' | SLdr |
| *moupinense* ♀ | CB&S CHig ERea GGGa IDee |
| | LHyd NMun SLdr SPer SReu |
| - C&K 140 | GGGa |
| - pink | GGGa MDun |
| 'Mozart' (EA) | SBod |
| 'Mrs A.T. de la Mare' ♀ | CWri ENot GGGa IOrc LHyd |
| | LKna LMil MBri NMun SBrw SLdr |
| | SReu SSta |
| 'Mrs Anthony Waterer' (O) | LKna |
| 'Mrs Anthony Waterer' | LKna SBrw |
| 'Mrs Ashley Slocock' | SReu |
| 'Mrs Betty Robertson' | CHig EBee MAsh SReu |
| 'Mrs C.B. van Nes' | SReu |
| Mrs C. Whitner Group | NMun SLdr |
| 'Mrs Charles E. Pearson' ♀ | CB&S CWri ENot LHyd LKna LMil |
| | MLea NMun SBrw SLdr SPer SReu |
| 'Mrs Davies Evans' ♀ | LHyd LKna MBar SBrw SReu SSta |
| 'Mrs Dick Thompson' | SReu |
| 'Mrs Donald Graham' | SReu |
| 'Mrs Doorenbos' | CMac |
| 'Mrs E.C. Stirling' | LHyd LKna SRms |
| 'Mrs Emil Hager' (EA) | LHyd |
| 'Mrs Furnivall' ♀ | CB&S CDoC CHig CWri EPfP |
| | GGGa LHyd LKna LMil MAsh |
| | MBri MGos SLdr SReu WGer |
| 'Mrs G.W. Leak' | CB&S CSam CWri ENot EPfP |
| | GGGa ISea LHyd LKna LMil MAsh |
| | MBri MLea NMun SBrw SLdr SPer |
| | SReu SSta |
| 'Mrs Helen Koster' | LKna |
| 'Mrs Henry Agnew' | NMun SLdr |
| 'Mrs J.C. Williams' | LKna LMil NMun SLdr |
| 'Mrs J.G. Millais' | LKna LMil NMun SLdr |
| 'Mrs James Horlick' | NMun SLdr |
| 'Mrs John Kelk' | Last listed 1996 |
| 'Mrs John Waterer' | SBrw |
| 'Mrs Kingsmill' | SLdr |
| 'Mrs Lindsay Smith' | LKna SBrw |
| 'Mrs Lionel de Rothschild' ♀ | NMun |
| Mrs Lionel de Rothschild | LKna SReu |
|   Group & cl. | |
| 'Mrs P.D. Williams' ♀ | LKna SBrw SReu |
| ¶ 'Mrs Peter Koster' (M) | SLdr |
| 'Mrs Philip Martineau' | LKna |
| 'Mrs R.S. Holford' ♀ | LKna NMun SBrw SLdr |
| 'Mrs T.H. Lowinsky' ♀ | CHig CWri EPfP GCHN GGGa |
| | LKna LMil MBri MDun MGos |
| | NMun SBrw SLdr SReu SSta |
| 'Mrs W.C. Slocock' | LKna MBri MDun NMun SBrw |
| | SLdr SPer SReu SSta |
| 'Mrs William Agnew' | LKna SLdr |
| ♦ 'Mucronatum' | See *R.* x *mucronatum* |
| § x *mucronatum* (EA) | CHig NMun SLdr SPer SRms WPic |
| 'Mucronatum Amethystinum' | See *R.* 'Amethystinum' |
| *mucronatum* var. *ripense* | See *R. ripense* |
| *mucronulatum* | GGGa LHyd LMil NMun SLdr |
| | WAbe |
| - B&SWJ 786 | WCru |

| | |
|---|---|
| - var. *chejuense* | See *R. mucronulatum* var. |
| | *taquetii* |
| - 'Cornell Pink' ♀ | GGGa LMil |
| - 'Crater's Edge' | Last listed 1996 |
| - 'Mahogany Red' | GGGa |
| § - var. *taquetii* | GGGa |
| - - 'Dwarf Cheju' | Last listed 1996 |
| - - 'Winter Brightness' ♀ | Last listed 1996 |
| ¶ *multicolor* (V) | CEqu |
| § 'Multiflorum' | SReu |
| 'Muncaster Bells' | NMun |
| 'Muncaster Hybrid' | NMun |
| 'Muncaster Mist' | NMun SLdr |
| 'Muriel' | SLdr |
| 'My Lady' | GGGa |
| *myiagrum* | See *R. callimorphum* var. |
| | *myiagrum* |
| § *myrtifolium* | LMil SLdr |
| 'Mystic' | Last listed 1996 |
| *nakaharae* (EA) | MBal NMun SLdr SReu WAbe |
| § - 'Mariko' (EA) | EPot GGGa LHyd LMil MBal MBar |
| | MBro MGos NHol SLdr WAbe |
| | WPat WPyg |
| § - orange (EA) | LMil LRHS MAsh MOne SBrw SPer |
| | SReu SSta |
| - pink (EA) | CDoC CHig LHyd LMil SBrw SLdr |
| | SPer SReu SSta |
| ¶ - red | SLdr |
| ¶ - 'Scree' | SReu |
| 'Nakahari Orange' | See *R. nakaharae* orange |
| 'Nakahari-mariko' | See *R. nakaharae* 'Mariko' |
| *nakotiltum* | NMun SLdr |
| 'Nancy Buchanan' (K) | Last listed 1996 |
| 'Nancy Evans' | CDoC COtt CWri GGGa GRei |
| | ISea LMil MAsh MBal MDun MLea |
| | SBid SBrw SReu SSpi |
| 'Nancy of Robinhill' (EA) | LHyd |
| 'Nancy Waterer' (G) ♀ | MBri SLdr SReu |
| 'Nanki Poo' (EA) | LHyd SLdr SPer |
| 'Naomi' (EA) | GQui IOrc LKna LMil SLdr |
| Naomi Group & cl. | CSam CWri ISea LKna MLea SReu |
| 'Naomi Astarte' | LKna MDun SLdr |
| 'Naomi Early Dawn' | NMun |
| 'Naomi Glow' | Last listed 1997 |
| (Naomi Group) 'Paris' | See *R.* 'Paris' |
| 'Naomi Stella Maris' | Last listed 1996 |
| 'Narcissiflorum' (G/d) ♀ | CDoC ENot IOrc LHyd LKna LMil |
| | SPer SReu |
| 'Naselle' | GGGa LMil |
| 'Nassau' (EA/d) | Last listed 1998 |
| 'Nelly de Bruin' | SBrw |
| *neriiflorum* | GGGa ISea LMil MDun NMun |
| | SLdr SReu SSpi |
| - Bu 287 | GGGa |
| § - subsp. *neriiflorum* | NMun SLdr |
|   Euchaites Group | |
| - - L&S 1352 | GGGa |
| - - 'Lamellen' | Last listed 1996 |
| § - - Phoenicodum Group | Last listed 1997 |
| - - - Farrer 877 | GGGa NMun |
| § - subsp. *phaedropum* | NMun SLdr |
| - - C&H 422 | NMun |
| ¶ - - CCH&H 8125 | GGGa |
| - - KR 1778 | Last listed 1997 |
| - - KW 6845* | NMun |
| - - KW 6854 | Last listed 1996 |
| - - KW 8521 | Last listed 1998 |
| - SF 366 | ISea |
| - SF 375 | ISea |

| | |
|---|---|
| Neriihaem Group | NMun |
| ***nervulosum*** Sleumer (V) | GGGa |
| 'Nestor' | SReu |
| 'Nettie' (EA) | Last listed 1998 |
| ¶ 'Netty Koster' | MBri SBrw |
| 'New Comet' | LHyd LMil NMun SLdr SReu |
| 'New Moon' | SLdr SReu |
| 'Newcomb's Sweetheart' | LMil MDun SMur |
| 'Niagara' (EA) ♀ | CTrh ENot EPfP GQui LHyd LMil |
| | MBal WBod |
| 'Nichola' (EA) | SBod SBrw SReu |
| 'Nico' (EA) | CMac MAsh MBri SPer WBod |
| | WPat |
| 'Nicoletta' | GGGa LMil |
| 'Night Sky' | CDoC COtt GGGa LHyd LMil |
| | MBri MLea MOne NHol |
| 'Nightingale' | LMil SReu |
| ***nigroglandulosum*** | GGGa |
| ***nigropunctatum*** | See *R. nivale* subsp. *boreale* |
| | Nigropunctatum Group |
| x ***nikomontanum*** | LMil |
| ***nilagiricum*** | See *R. arboreum* subsp. |
| | *nilagiricum* |
| 'Nimbus' | LKna LMil SLdr |
| Nimrod Group | CWri NMun SLdr |
| 'Nishiki' (EA) | CMac |
| ***nitens*** | See *R. calostrotum* subsp. |
| | *riparium* Nitens Group |
| ***nitidulum*** | NMun |
| – var. ***nitidulum*** C 5059 | Last listed 1998 |
| – – C 5107 | Last listed 1998 |
| – var. ***omeiense*** KR 185 | GGGa LMil NHol |
| ***nivale*** | Last listed 1996 |
| – subsp. ***boreale*** | GGGa |
|    Ramosissimum Group | |
| § – – Stictophyllum Group | GGGa LMil |
| – subsp. ***nivale*** Sch 2269 | Last listed 1997 |
| ***niveum*** ♀ | GGGa LMil MBal MDun NMun |
| | SLdr SReu SSta |
| ¶ – 'Clyne Castle' | SLdr |
| – 'Nepal' | LHyd |
| ¶ – 'Tower Court' | SLdr |
| 'Noble Mountain' | LMil SMur |
| ***nobleanum*** | See *R.* Nobleanum Group |
| § Nobleanum Group | GGGa LHyd LKna LMil NMun |
| | SLdr SSta |
| 'Nobleanum Album' | LHyd LKna LMil MBal NMun SLdr |
| | SReu SSta |
| 'Nobleanum Coccineum' | ISea LMil NMun SLdr SReu |
| 'Nobleanum Lamellen' | SLdr |
| 'Nobleanum Venustum' | ISea LHyd LKna LMil SBrw SReu |
| | SSta |
| 'Nofretete' | GGGa |
| ¶ 'Nordlicht' (EA) | SLdr |
| N 'Norma' (R/d) ♀ | ENot LMil MBri SReu |
| Norman Shaw Group & cl. | LHyd |
| ¶ 'Northern Hi-Lights' (A) | SLdr |
| 'Northern Star' | SLdr |
| 'Northlight' | MBri |
| ***notiale*** (V) | Last listed 1998 |
| 'Nova Zembla' | GChr GGGa MAsh MBar MGos |
| | SBrw SLdr SReu SSta WGwG WStI |
| ***nudiflorum*** | See *R. periclymenoides* |
| * ***nummularia*** L&S 17294 | Last listed 1998 |
| ***nuttallii*** ♀ | GGGa LMil MBal |
| 'Oban' | GGGa LMil MLea NHol WAbe |
| Obtusum Group (EA) | LHyd |
| ***obtusum*** f. ***amoenum*** | See *R.* 'Amoenum' |
| ◆ – var. ***amoenum*** 'Splendens' | See *R.* 'Splendens' |
| § (Obtusum Group) | WBod |
|    'Macrostemon' (EA) | |
| ***occidentale*** (A) ♀ | CGre GGGa LMil MBal SLdr SReu |
| – forms (A) | GGGa |
| ***ochraceum*** C&H 7052 | GGGa |
| 'Odee Wright' ♀ | CWri GGGa LMil MAsh MDun |
| | MLea NMun SLdr SPer SReu |
| 'Oh-Too' | SBrw |
| 'Oi-no-mezame' (EA) | LHyd |
| 'Old Copper' | CWri LNet MBri SBrw WGer |
| 'Old Gold' (K) | SReu |
| 'Old Port' | CWri LHyd SBrw SReu SSta |
| Oldenburgh Group | SLdr |
| ***oldhamii*** (EA) | CTre NMun |
| – ETOT 60 (EA) | Last listed 1998 |
| – ETOT 601 (A) | GGGa |
| 'Olga' | LHyd LKna LMil NMun SBrw SLdr |
| | SPer SReu SSta |
| 'Olga Mezitt' | GGGa LHyd NHol |
| 'Olin O. Dobbs' | Last listed 1998 |
| 'Olive' | LHyd LKna LMil |
| 'Olive Judson' | Last listed 1998 |
| 'Oliver Cromwell' | SReu |
| Olympic Lady Group | LHyd MLea SLdr |
| 'Olympic Sunrise' | LMil |
| Omar Group | MBar |
| 'Omurasaki' (EA) | Last listed 1998 |
| § 'One Thousand Butterflies' | COtt CWri GGGa MDun MLea |
| N 'Ophelia' | SLdr |
| 'Oporto' | SLdr |
| 'Optima' (EA) | Last listed 1997 |
| 'Orange Beauty' (EA) ♀ | CDoC CMac CTrh GGGa LHyd |
| | LKna MBal MBar MGos NMun |
| | SBod SLdr SPer SReu SSta WBod |
| | WFar WPic |
| 'Orange King' (EA) | WLRN |
| 'Orange Scout' | SLdr WGor WWal |
| 'Orangeade' (K) | Last listed 1996 |
| 'Orangengold' | GGGa |
| ***orbiculare*** | CWri GGGa IDee LHyd LMil |
| | NMun SLdr SSta |
| – C&K 230 | GGGa |
| § – subsp. ***cardiobasis*** | NMun SLdr |
| – x ***decorum*** | Last listed 1996 |
| – subsp. ***orbiculare*** | NMun |
|    W/V 1519 | |
| – Sandling Park form | SReu |
| ¶ 'Orchid Lights' | SLdr |
| 'Oregon Trail' | Last listed 1997 |
| Oregonia Group | Last listed 1996 |
| Oreocinn Group | MBal |
| ***oreodoxa*** | LMil NMun SLdr SReu |
| § – var. ***fargesii*** ♀ | CB&S GGGa IOrc LMil NMun |
| | SLdr |
| § – – Erubescens Group | NMun SLdr |
| – – Knott 348 | NMun |
| – var. ***oreodoxa*** EN 4212 | GGGa |
| – – W/A 4245 | NMun |
| – var. ***shensiense*** | GGGa |
| ***oreotrephes*** | CB&S IOrc LHyd LMil MBal |
| | MDun NMun SLdr SReu |
| – C&Cu 9449 | GGGa |
| – 'Davidian's Favourite' | Last listed 1997 |
| § – Exquisitum Group | ISea SReu |
| – F 20489 | NMun |
| – F 20629 | NMun |
| – KW 9509 | NMun SLdr |
| – R 96 | Last listed 1997 |
| – R/USDA 59593/ R11300 | Last listed 1996 |
| – SF 640 | ISea |
| – Timeteum Group | SReu |

| | |
|---|---|
| aff. *oreotrephes* C&V 9557 | GGGa |
| ¶ Orestes Group | SLdr |
| *orthocladum* | LHyd LMil MDun |
| § - var. *microleucum* ♀ | GGGa ISea LMil MBal NMun WAbe WPat |
| - var. *orthocladum* F 20488 | GGGa NHol |
| 'Oryx' (O) | LKna |
| 'Osmar' | CB&S GGGa MDun MGos |
| § 'Ostara' | CB&S COtt GGGa MBri MGos |
| ¶ 'Ostbo's Low Yellow' | SLdr |
| 'Ostfriesland' | SRms |
| 'Ouchiyama' | LKna |
| 'Oudijk's Favorite' | MBal MGos |
| 'Oudijk's Sensation' | CDoC CTrh GCHN GGGa LKna MGos MOne |
| ¶ (Our Kate Group) 'Our Kate' | SLdr |
| 'Our Marcia' (V) | Last listed 1996 |
| 'Ovation' | NHol |
| *ovatum* (A) | CB&S NMun WBod |
| - CNW 548 | ISea |
| - red CNW 557 | LMil |
| - W/A 1391 (A) | NMun |
| - white CNW 548 | LMil |
| Oxlip Group | Last listed 1998 |
| 'Oxydol' (K) ♀ | MAsh |
| 'P. Den Ouden' | SBrw |
| x *williamsianum* | |
| P J M Group | CWri MAsh MBal MBri MLea SSta |
| 'P.J. Mezitt' | See *R.* 'Peter John Mezitt' |
| § *pachypodum* | GGGa LMil |
| *pachysanthum* ♀ | CDoC LHyd LMil MDun NMun SMur SPer SReu SSpi |
| - 'Crosswater' | LMil |
| - x *morii* | Last listed 1997 |
| - x *proteoides* | GGGa |
| - RV 72/001 | GGGa NMun SLdr |
| *pachytrichum* | GGGa NMun SLdr |
| - C&K 229 | Last listed 1998 |
| § - var. *monosematum* | ISea SLdr |
| - - CNW 953 | LMil |
| - - CNW 956 | GGGa |
| - - W/V 1522 | NMun |
| - var. *pachytrichum* | LMil |
| 'Sesame' | |
| - - W/A 1203 | NMun |
| 'Palestrina' (EA) ♀ | CB&S CBrm CChe CMac CTrh GHCN IOrc LHyd LKna MBal MGos NMun SBod SBrw SLdr SPer SReu SSta WFar |
| 'Pallas' (G) | MBri SReu |
| 'Palma' | See *R. parmulatum* 'Palma' |
| 'Pamela Miles' (EA) | LHyd |
| 'Pamela-Louise' | Last listed 1997 |
| 'Pancake' | CMac |
| 'Panda' (EA) | CDoC CMac CTrh GGGa LHyd LMil MBar MBri NHed SBrw SCoo SLdr SReu WAbe WGwG |
| *panteumorphum* | See *R.* x *erythrocalyx* Panteumorphum Group |
| 'Papaya Punch' | LMil MDun |
| *papillatum* | NMun SLdr |
| 'Paprika Spiced' | CDoC COtt CWri LMil MBal MBri MDun MLea SLdr |
| 'Parade' (A) | LMil |
| ¶ 'Paradise' (EA) | CTrh |
| 'Paradise Pink' (EA) | ENot |
| ¶ *paradoxum* | SLdr |
| - C&K 228 | GGGa |
| - CC&H 3906 | GGGa |

| | |
|---|---|
| 'Paramount' (K/d) | LKna |
| § 'Paris' | LHyd |
| 'Parisienne' | Last listed 1997 |
| *parmulatum* | LMil MDun NMun SLdr |
| - KW 5875 | NMun |
| - mauve | NMun SLdr |
| - 'Ocelot' | GGGa LHyd MDun NMun SLdr |
| § - 'Palma' | Last listed 1998 |
| - pink | GGGa NMun |
| ¶ *parryae* ♀ | GGGa |
| 'Party Pink' | CWri LMil |
| 'Patricia's Day' | Last listed 1998 |
| 'Patty Bee' ♀ | CB&S CDoC CSam CTrh CWri EPot GChr GGGa LHyd LMil MAsh MBar MBri MDun MGos MLea NHar NHol SBod SReu SSpi SSta WAbe WFar |
| *patulum* | See *R. pemakoense* Patulum Group |
| *pauciflorum* (V) | Last listed 1996 |
| 'Pavane' (K) | LKna |
| 'Peace' | GGGa MBal NMun WAbe |
| 'Peach Blossom' | See *R.* 'Saotome' |
| ¶ 'Peach Lady' | SLdr |
| 'Pearl Diver' | Last listed 1997 |
| 'Peep-bo' (EA) | LHyd SLdr SPer |
| 'Peeping Tom' | CDoC LMil MAsh MDun NMun SBid SReu |
| 'Peggy Bannier' | SBrw |
| ¶ 'Pelopidas' | SBrw |
| *pemakoense* | CTrG GGGa LHyd MBal MBar MGos NHol NMun SLdr SReu SRms WAbe |
| § - Patulum Group | GGGa MBar MBri NHol NMun SLdr WPat WPyg |
| 'Pematit Cambridge' | SBod |
| 'Pematit Oxford' | Last listed 1996 |
| *pendulum* | LMil |
| - CH&M 3094 | GGGa |
| - LS&T 6660 | GGGa |
| Penelope Group | SReu |
| 'Penheale Blue' ♀ | CDoC CTre CTrh GGGa GOrc LMil NHed NHol SLdr WGer |
| Penjerrick Group & cl. | Last listed 1997 |
| 'Penjerrick Cream' | LHyd NMun SLdr |
| 'Penjerrick Pink' | LHyd NMun SLdr |
| *pennivenium* | See *R. tanastylum* var. *pennivenium* |
| ¶ 'Pennywhistle' (V) | CEqu |
| 'Penrose' | CB&S |
| *pentaphyllum* (A) | Last listed 1996 |
| *peramoenum* | See *R. arboreum* subsp. *delavayi* var. *peramoenum* |
| 'Percy Wiseman' ♀ | CB&S CDoC CSam CWri EBee GGGa IOrc LHyd LMil LNet MBal MBar MBlu MBri MDun MGos MLea NHed NHol NMun SBrw SLdr SPer SReu SSta |
| *peregrinum* | NMun SLdr |
| - 'Wilson' | Last listed 1996 |
| 'Perfect' | MBal SPer |
| 'Perfect Lady' | LMil LRHS |
| § *periclymenoides* (A) | GGGa LMil SLdr |
| I 'Periwinkle' (V) | CEqu |
| 'Persil' (K) ♀ | CB&S CSam ELan ENot GChr GGGa LHyd LKna MAsh MBar MBri MGos SBrw SCoo SLdr SPer SReu WBod |
| § 'Persimmon' | LKna NMun SLdr |

'Peter Alan'   Last listed 1998
'Peter Berg'   MGos
§ 'Peter John Mezitt' ♀   LHyd LMil NMun SLdr SReu WGer WLRN
'Peter Koster' ♀   CWri NMun SBrw SLdr SMur WStI WWeb
'Petrouchka' (K)   LKna MAsh MBri
'Pettychaps' (EA)   Last listed 1996
*phaedropum*   See *R. neriiflorum* subsp. *phaedropum*
*phaeochrysum*   GGGa MDun NMun SLdr
– var. *agglutinatum*   GGGa MDun NMun
– – EGM 134   LMil
§ – var. *levistratum*   NMun SLdr SReu
– – EGM 143   LMil
– McLaren cup winner   NMun
§ – var. *phaeochrysum*   Last listed 1996
– – EGM 129   LMil
– – 'Greenmantle'   NMun SLdr
– USDAPI 59029/ R11323   NMun
'Phalarope'   CSam GGGa MAsh MBal MBar MDun MGos NHol SReu WAbe WBod
'Pheasant Tail'   NMun SLdr
'Philomene'   Last listed 1996
'Phoebe'   SReu
*phoenicodum*   See *R. neriiflorum* subsp. *neriiflorum* Phoenicodum Group
♦ *pholidotum*   See *R. heliolepis* var. *heliolepis* F 6762
'Phyllis Korn'   CAbP CHig ISea LHyd LMil MAsh MDun MLea SBrw SLdr SPer
'Piccolo' (K/d)   LKna
§ *piercei*   GGGa LMil MDun NMun SLdr
– KW 11040   GGGa NMun
Pilgrim Group & cl.   LKna NMun
'Pillar Box'   Last listed 1996
*pingianum*   NMun SLdr
– EGM 304   LMil
– KR 150   NMun SLdr
– KR 184   GGGa
'Pink and Sweet' (A)   CDoC LMil MLea
¶ 'Pink Bedspread'   SReu
'Pink Bountiful'   LKna
¶ 'Pink Bride'   SLdr
'Pink Cherub' ♀   CWri ENot LHyd MAsh MBal MBar MOne NMun SLdr SReu
N 'Pink Delight'   ERea LKna SLdr WBod
'Pink Drift'   CTrh ENot GChr ISea LKna MAsh MBal MBar MDun MGos NHar NHol NMun NWea SBod SLdr WAbe WGwG
'Pink Frills'   Last listed 1998
'Pink Ghost'   NMun SLdr
'Pink Gin'   LMil
'Pink Glory'   NMun SLdr
'Pink Leopard'   ISea LMil MDun NMun SBid WWeb
'Pink Pancake' (EA)   CB&S CTrh GQui LMil MGos MOne SReu SSpi SVil WWeb
'Pink Pearl'   CB&S CTri ENot GGGa ISea LHyd LKna LMil MAsh MBal MBar MDun MGos NHol NMun NWea SBod SBrw SLdr SPer SReu SSta WFar
'Pink Pebble' ♀   CTrw LHyd NMun SLdr SReu
'Pink Perfection'   MBar MGos NMun SBrw SLdr SReu WFar
¶ 'Pink Pillow'   SReu

'Pink Poppet' (V)   CEqu
'Pink Rosette'   LKna
N 'Pink Ruffles'   ENot
'Pink Sensation'   MAsh MBri
'Pinkerton'   LKna
'Pintail'   GGGa LMil
'Pipaluk'   NMun
'Pipit'   GGGa MBal WAbe
'Pippa' (EA) ♀   CMac CTrG SRms
'Piquante'   Last listed 1996
§ (PJM Group) 'Checkmate'   Last listed 1997
'PJM Elite'   GGGa
x *planecostatum* (V)   Last listed 1997
*planetum*   Last listed 1998
*pleistanthum*   Last listed 1997
– F 15002   Last listed 1998
– R 11288   See *R. rigidum* R 11288
*pocophorum*   GGGa NMun SLdr
– forms   NMun
§ – var. *hemidartum*   GGGa NMun SLdr
– KW 21075   See *R. coelicum* KW 21075
§ – var. *pocophorum* F 21830   SLdr
– – USDAPI 59190/R11201   NMun
*pogonostylum*   See *R. irroratum* subsp. *pogonostylum*
'Point Defiance'   CWri GGGa LMil MAsh SLdr
'Polar Bear' (EA)   MBal MBar MDun MGos SLdr
Polar Bear Group & cl.   CDoC COtt CSam CWri GAri GGGa ISea LHyd LMil MLea NMun SLdr SReu WGer
'Polar Haven' (EA)   LKna
'Polar Sea'   CTrh SBod
'Polaris'   ENot LMil LRHS MBri MGos SReu
'Polgrain'   Last listed 1998
§ *poluninii*   GGGa
*polyandrum*   See *R. maddenii* subsp. *maddenii* Polyandrum Group
'Polycinn'   Last listed 1997
§ *polycladum*   CSam GGGa LHyd LMil MBal MDun MLea SBrw
– Scintillans Group   GDra MBar MBri MLea NHol NMun SLdr WPic
*polylepis*   GGGa NMun
– C&K 284   GGGa
– EGM 351   LMil
– EN 3619   Last listed 1998
§ *ponticum*   CDoC GChr GGGa ISea LHyd LMil MBar MGos MLea NWea SBrw SLdr SPer WFar WOak
I 'Ponticum'   See *R. ponticum*
*ponticum* (A)   See *R. luteum*
– AC&H 205   GGGa
¶ – 'Aureomarginatum'   SBrw
– 'Cheiranthifolium'   NMun SLdr
– 'Foliis Purpureis'   SReu
¶ – 'Roseum'   SBrw
§ – 'Silver Edge' (v)   LMil SBrw SLdr SMur
– 'Variegatum' (v)   CB&S CHig EBrP EBre ENot GChr GGGa IOrc ISea LBre MBal MBar MBri MGos NMun SBre SPer SReu SRms SSta WGer WWeb
'Pooh-Bah' (EA)   LHyd
'Pook'   LHyd
'Popacatapetl'   SLdr SReu
'Port Knap' (EA)   LKna
'Port Wine' (EA)   LKna
'Potlatch'   GGGa
*poukhanense*   See *R. yedoense* var. *poukhanense*

| | |
|---|---|
| 'Powder Puff' | Last listed 1998 |
| § 'Praecox' ♀ | CB&S CSam CTrw ENot GChr GGGa GRei ISea LHyd LKna LMil MAsh MBal MBar MBri MGos NHol NMun NWea SBod SBrw SLdr SPer SReu SSta WBod WFar WGwG WWat |
| *praecox* | See *R.* 'Praecox' |
| - 'Emasculum' | See *R.* 'Emasculum' |
| *praestans* | GGGa LMil MDun NMun SLdr |
| - KW 13369 | NMun |
| - PA Cox 6025A | GGGa |
| *praeteritum* | Last listed 1998 |
| *praevernum* | GGGa LMil NMun SLdr SReu |
| § *prattii* | CWri LMil MDun NMun SLdr |
| - EGM 147 | LMil |
| 'Prawn' | LKna SReu |
| Prelude Group & cl. | SLdr |
| *preptum* | GGGa SLdr |
| 'President Roosevelt' (v) | IOrc LKna LNet MBal MGos NMun SBrw SLdr SReu SSta WWeb |
| 'Pretty Girl' | LKna |
| ¶ 'Pretty Woman' | GGGa |
| ¶ 'Pride of Leonardslee' | SLdr |
| 'Pridenjoy' | LMil |
| 'Prima Donna' | LMil SReu |
| *primuliflorum* | GGGa LMil LRHS MDun SReu |
| - Cephalanthoides Group | GGGa WAbe |
| - 'Doker-La' | CDoC LMil MDun |
| - KW 4160 | NMun |
| ¶ - PA Cox 6136 white | GGGa |
| 'Prince Camille de Rohan' | LMil SBrw SMur |
| 'Prince of Wales' (EA) | SBrw |
| 'Princess Alice' ♀ | CB&S CGre CHig LHyd MBal NMun SLdr WAbe WPic |
| 'Princess Anne' ♀ | CMHG CSam ENot GDra GGGa GRei LHyd LMil MAsh MBal MBar MDun MGos MLea NMun SBod SBrw SLdr SPer SReu SSta WAbe |
| 'Princess Ida' (EA) | LHyd SLdr |
| 'Princess Juliana' | WGor |
| 'Princess Margaret of Windsor' (K) | GQui |
| ¶ 'Princess Margaret Toth' | LMil |
| *principis* | LMil MDun NMun SLdr |
| - C&V 9547 | GGGa |
| - LS&E 15831 | NMun |
| § - Vellereum Group | NMun SLdr |
| ¶ - - 'Far Horizon' KW 5656 | SLdr |
| - - KW 5656 | NMun |
| § *prinophyllum* (A) | LMil |
| 'Prins Bernhard' (EA) | IOrc LKna MAsh SLdr |
| 'Prinses Juliana' (EA) | SLdr SReu WFar |
| 'Professor Hugo de Vries' ♀ | LKna MGos SBrw SReu |
| 'Professor J.H. Zaayer' | MGos SBrw |
| *pronum* | GGGa |
| - × *proteoides* | GGGa |
| - R 151* | NMun |
| - R.B. Cooke form | GGGa |
| - Towercourt form | GGGa |
| § 'Prostigiatum' | MGos |
| *prostigiatum* | See *R.* 'Prostigiatum' |
| *prostratum* | See *R. saluenense* subsp. *chameunum* Prostratum Group |
| *proteoides* | GGGa |
| * - 'Ascreavie' | GGGa |
| - C 6542a | GGGa |
| - EGM 281 | LMil |
| - KGB 700 | GGGa |
| - R 151 | NMun |
| *protistum* | LMil NMun SLdr |
| § - var. *giganteum* | CWri LMil NMun SLdr SReu |
| - KR 1986 | GGGa |
| - KW 8069 | NMun |
| *pruniflorum* | GGGa NMun SLdr |
| - KW 7038 | See *R. brachyanthum* subsp. *hypolepidotum* KW 7038 |
| *prunifolium* (A) | LMil SLdr |
| - 'Summer Sunset' (A) | NMun |
| *przewalskii* | GGGa NMun SLdr |
| - C&K 370 | GGGa |
| - CH&M 2545 | NHol |
| - subsp. *dabansbanense* | GGGa |
| - PA Cox 5073 | GGGa |
| *pseudochrysanthum* ♀ | CWri GGGa LHyd LMil MBal MDun NMun SLdr SReu SSta |
| - (1956 AM form) AM | Last listed 1996 |
| - ETE 442 | GGGa |
| - ETE 443 | GGGa |
| - ETOT 162 | Last listed 1997 |
| - ETOT 164 | Last listed 1997 |
| - ETOT 167 | ISea |
| Psyche Group | See *R.* Wega Group |
| 'Psyche' (EA) | Last listed 1996 |
| 'Ptarmigan' ♀ | CB&S CDoC GChr GGGa LHyd LMil MBal MBar MDun MGos MLea NHar NHol NMun SBod SBrw SLdr SReu SSta WFar WPat |
| *pubescens* | LMil SLdr |
| - 'Fine Bristles' | Last listed 1996 |
| - KW 3953 | GGGa |
| *pubicostatum* | LMil |
| ¶ - CNW 906 | ISea |
| ¶ - CNW 927 | GGGa |
| § 'Pucella' (G) ♀ | MAsh SLdr SReu |
| *pudorosum* | NMun SLdr |
| - L&S 2752 | GGGa |
| 'Puget Sound' | SLdr |
| ◆ 'Pulchrum MaxwelIii' | See *R.* 'Maxwellii' |
| *pumilum* | GCrs GDra GGGa MBal MDun NMun WAbe |
| 'Puncta' | GGGa NHol |
| *punctatum* | See *R. minus* var. *minus* Punctatum Group |
| * *purdomii* | GGGa SLdr |
| 'Purple Carpeter' | Last listed 1996 |
| 'Purple Diamond' | See *R.* Diamant Group purple |
| 'Purple Emperor' | LKna |
| 'Purple Gem' | NHar NHol |
| purple Glenn Dale | Last listed 1997 |
| 'Purple Heart' | ENot |
| 'Purple Lace' | Last listed 1996 |
| 'Purple Peterli' | GGGa |
| 'Purple Queen' (EA/d) | MAsh |
| 'Purple Splendor' (EA) | CMac CTrh EBee IOrc LKna MGos SLdr |
| 'Purple Splendour' ♀ | CB&S CHig CWri ENot GGGa LHyd LKna LMil MBal MBar MBri MDun MGos MLea NMun NWea SBrw SLdr SPer SReu SSta WFar WWeb |
| 'Purple Triumph' (EA) | CB&S IOrc LKna LMil NMun SLdr SReu SSta |
| 'Purpur Geisha' | GGGa |
| 'Purpurtraum' (A) | GGGa |
| *quadrasianum* var. *rosmarinifolium* (V) | Last listed 1996 |

| | |
|---|---|
| Quaver Group | SRms |
| 'Queen Alice' | MDun |
| 'Queen Anne's' | LMil MBal |
| 'Queen Elizabeth II' ♀ | LHyd LMil SLdr SPer SReu SSta |
| Queen Emma | See *R.* 'Koningin Emma' |
| 'Queen Mary' | MBar SBrw |
| 'Queen Mother' | See *R.* 'The Queen Mother' |
| Queen of Hearts Group & cl. | LHyd NMun SLdr |
| 'Queen Souriya' | SReu |
| Queen Wilhelmina | See *R.* 'Koningin Wilhelmina' |
| *quinquefolium* (A) ♀ | LMil NMun SLdr |
| *racemosum* | CB&S CGre LMil MBar MDun |
| | NMun SLdr SPer SReu SSpi SSta |
| – AC 719 | NMun |
| – ACE 1367 | WAbe |
| – 'Glendoick' | GGGa |
| – 'Rock Rose' ex R 11265 ♀ | EPfP GGGa LHyd LMil MBri |
| | NMun |
| – SF 365 | ISea |
| – SSNY 47 | GGGa |
| – x *tephropeplum* | MBal MBar |
| – x *trichocladum* SBEC | NHol |
| – TW 385 | Last listed 1997 |
| – 'White Lace' | LHyd |
| 'Racil' | HYd LKna MBal MBar MDun |
| | MGos MLea |
| 'Racoon' (EA) | GGGa |
| *radicans* | See *R. calostrotum* subsp. |
| | *keleticum* Radicans Group |
| ¶ 'Radistrotum' | SLdr |
| 'Rainbow' | LKna NMun SLdr |
| 'Ramapo' ♀ | CHig GChr GGGa LMil MAsh |
| | MBal MBar MDun MGos MLea |
| | MOne NHar NHol SBrw SReu SSta |
| | WAbe WBod |
| *ramsdenianum* | GGGa NMun SLdr |
| 'Rangoon' | Last listed 1998 |
| 'Raphael de Smet' (G/d) | SReu |
| ¶ *rarum* (V) | CEqu |
| 'Rashomon' (EA) | LHyd SLdr SReu WBod |
| 'Raspberry Delight' (K/d) | SMur |
| 'Raspberry Ripple' | LKna SReu |
| *ravum* | See *R. cuneatum* Ravum Group |
| 'Razorbill' ♀ | CDoC GGGa LHyd LMil MBri |
| | MGos MLea NHar SReu WAbe |
| *recurvoides* | GGGa LHyd LMil MDun NMun |
| | SReu |
| – Keillour form | GGGa |
| – KW 7184 | NMun SLdr |
| *recurvum* | See *R. roxieanum* var. *roxieanum* |
| Red Admiral Group | NMun |
| Red Argenteum Group | NMun |
| 'Red Bird' (EA) | CMac |
| Red Cap Group | Last listed 1996 |
| 'Red Carpet' ♀ | LMil LRHS NMun SLdr |
| 'Red Delicious' | LMil |
| 'Red Diamond' | See *R.* Diamant Group red |
| 'Red Dragon' | Last listed 1998 |
| 'Red Fountain' (EA) | LMil LRHS MOne WLRN WWeb |
| 'Red Glow' | LHyd NMun SLdr |
| 'Red Jack' | Last listed 1997 |
| 'Red Poll' | Last listed 1997 |
| 'Red Red' | Last listed 1998 |
| 'Red Riding Hood' | CWri LKna |
| 'Red Rum' | Last listed 1997 |
| 'Red Sunset' (EA/d) | Last listed 1997 |
| 'Red Velour' | CAbP |
| 'Red Velvet' | See *R.* 'Ilam Red Velvet' |
| 'Red Wood' | GGGa |

| | |
|---|---|
| 'Redmond' (EA) | LHyd |
| 'Redshank' (K) | MAsh MBri |
| 'Redwing' (EA) | CDoC SLdr SPer |
| 'Reich's Schneewittchen' | GGGa |
| Remo Group | MBal SLdr |
| Remus Group | Last listed 1996 |
| 'Rendezvous' | ENot LMil SReu |
| 'Rennie' (EA) | Last listed 1996 |
| 'Renoir' ♀ | LHyd LMil SLdr SReu |
| Repose Group & cl. | Last listed 1998 |
| *reticulatum* (A) ♀ | GGGa LMil NMun SLdr SReu SSta |
| * – *leucanthum* (A) | GGGa |
| – 'Sea King' (A) | LHyd |
| *retusum* (V) | GGGa |
| § 'Reuthe's Purple' ♀ | GGGa MBal NHol NMun SReu |
| 'Rêve d'Amour' (Vs) | SReu SSta |
| Rêve Rose Group & cl. | Last listed 1997 |
| Review Order Group | Last listed 1996 |
| 'Revlon' | LHyd |
| ¶ 'Rex' (EA) | SLdr |
| *rex* | CB&S COtt CWri GGGa IDee |
| | IOrc LHyd LMil MBal MDun |
| | NMun SLdr |
| ◆ – subsp. *arizelum* | See *R. arizelum* |
| – EGM 295 | LMil |
| § – subsp. *fictolacteum* | GGGa LHyd LMil MBal MDun |
| | NMun SLdr SReu |
| – – 'Cherry Tip' R 11385 | NMun SLdr |
| – – var. *miniforme* F 25512 | GGGa |
| – – SF 649 | ISea |
| – – TW 407 | Last listed 1997 |
| – – USDAPI 59104/ R11043 | NMun |
| – subsp. *rex* 'Quartz' ♀ | Last listed 1995 |
| – Sich 1037 | Last listed 1998 |
| – Sich 1134 | Last listed 1998 |
| – Sich 1154 | Last listed 1998 |
| – Sich 1159 | Last listed 1998 |
| – Sich 1236 | Last listed 1998 |
| – x Sincerity Group | NMun SLdr |
| *rhabdotum* | See *R. dalhousieae* var. |
| | *rhabdotum* |
| 'Ria Hardijzer' | LKna MBri |
| Rickshaw Group | SLdr |
| *rigidum* | LHyd LMil NMun |
| * – *album* | CHig NMun |
| § – R 11288 | Last listed 1997 |
| 'Ring of Fire' | CDoC CWri LMil MDun MLea |
| | SReu |
| ¶ 'Rio Grande' | SLdr |
| 'Ripe Corn' | LKna NMun SLdr SReu |
| Riplet Group | GAri GGGa MLea NHar WAbe |
| ¶ 'Ripples' (EA) | CTrh |
| *ririei* | GGGa LHyd NMun SLdr |
| – Guiz 75 | See *R. haofui* Guiz 75 |
| – W 5254a | Last listed 1996 |
| – W/V 1808 | NMun |
| – W/V 5139 | NMun SLdr |
| 'Rivulet' | Last listed 1996 |
| 'Robert Keir' ♀ | NMun SLdr |
| 'Robert Korn' | LMil MDun |
| 'Robert Seleger' | GGGa LMil NHar WAbe |
| 'Robert Whelan' (A) | SReu |
| § 'Roberte' | SBrw |
| 'Robin Hill Frosty' (EA) | LHyd SLdr |
| 'Robin Hill Gillie' (EA) | LHyd |
| Robin Hood Group | NMun |
| 'Robin Redbreast' | NMun |
| ¶ 'Robinette' | CWri |
| 'Rocket' | CAbP LMil MBri MDun NMun |
| | SLdr WGwG WWeb |

| Name | Reference |
|---|---|
| 'Rokoko' | See *R.* 'Hachmann's Rokoko' |
| Romany Chai Group | LHyd LMil MBal SLdr SPer |
| ¶ 'Romarez' | SLdr |
| 'Romy' | NMun SLdr |
| ¶ 'Rosa Marie' | SLdr |
| 'Rosa Mundi' | ENot |
| * 'Rosabelle' | CEqu |
| ¶ Rosalind Group & cl. | SLdr |
| 'Rosata' (Vs) | MBri SLdr SReu SSta |
| 'Rose Bud' | Last listed 1997 |
| 'Rose Elf' | ECho MBal MDun NHar NHol |
| 'Rose Glow' (A) | SReu |
| ¶ 'Rose Gown' | SReu |
| 'Rose Greeley' (EA) | CDoC CHig CTrh GQui IOrc SBod |
|  | SReu WFar WLRN WWeb |
| 'Rose Haze' (A) | SReu |
| 'Rose Ruffles' (K) | SMur |
| 'Rose Torch' (A) | SReu |
| * *roseatum* F 17227 | GGGa |
| 'Rosebud' (EA/d) ♀ | CB&S CDoC CGre CHig CMac |
|  | CTrh CTrw ECho GGGa GHCN |
|  | IOrc LHyd LKna MBar MGos |
|  | NMun SBod SLdr SPer SReu WBod |
|  | WLRN |
| 'Rosemary Hyde' (EA) | SLdr |
| *roseotinctum* | See *R. sanguineum* subsp. |
|  | *sanguineum* var. *didymoides* |
|  | Roseotinctum Group |
| *roseum* | See *R. prinophyllum* |
| 'Roseum Elegans' | ECho GChr LRHS MBar NMun |
|  | SBrw SLdr |
| 'Rosevallon' | Last listed 1996 |
| * 'Rosie Posie' (V) | CEqu |
| 'Rosiflorum' | See *R. indicum* 'Balsaminiflorum' |
| 'Rosy Bell' | LKna |
| 'Rosy Cream' | SPer |
| 'Rosy Dream' | CAbP COtt CWri LMil MBri MLea |
|  | SMur |
| 'Rosy Fire' (A) | SReu |
| 'Rosy Lea' | MLea |
| 'Rosy Lights' | CTri LMil LRHS |
| 'Rothenburg' | LHyd MAsh SLdr SReu |
| *rothschildii* | GGGa LMil LRHS MDun NMun |
|  | SLdr SMur |
| - C&Cu 9312 | GGGa |
| *roxieanum* | LMil NMun SLdr SReu |
| § - var. *cucullatum* | ISea NMun |
| - - CNW 680 | GGGa |
| - - CNW 690 | LMil |
| - - dwarf Dawyck | GGGa |
| - - R 10920 | NMun |
| - - SBEC 0345 | NMun SLdr |
| § - - SBEC 350 | GGGa |
| - var. *oreonastes* ♀ | CDoC GGGa LHyd LMil LRHS |
|  | MDun NMun SLdr SSta |
| - - CNW 307 | GGGa |
| - - CNW 723 | GGGa |
| - - CNW 740 | GGGa |
| - - CNW 743 | GGGa |
| - - Nymans form | SReu |
| - - USDAPI 59222/ R11312 | GGGa NMun |
| - var. *parvum* | GGGa |
| - R 25422 | NMun SLdr |
| - var. *recurvum* CNW 727 | LMil |
| § - var. *roxieanum* | NMun |
| - - CNW 727 | GGGa |
| - - F 16508 | NMun |
| - USDAPI 59159/ R11141 | NMun SLdr |
| 'Royal Blood' | SLdr |
| 'Royal Command' (K) | COtt LMil MAsh MBar SBrw SLdr |
| Royal Flush Group | ISea |
| - pink | Last listed 1996 |
| - yellow | Last listed 1996 |
| 'Royal Lodge' (K) ♀ | SBid |
| 'Royal Pink' | SBod |
| 'Royal Ruby' (K) | MBri |
| 'Roza Stevenson' ♀ | LHyd NMun SBrw SLdr |
| 'Rozanne Waterer' (K)/d | LKna |
| 'Rubicon' | CWri |
| *rubiginosum* | GGGa IOrc LHyd LMil MBal |
|  | NMun SLdr SReu |
| § - Desquamatum Group | CB&S LHyd NMun SLdr |
| - - EGM 272 | LMil |
| ¶ - pink | LMil |
| - SF 368 | ISea |
| - SF 404 | Last listed 1998 |
| - white | LMil |
| Rubina Group | Last listed 1998 |
| 'Rubinetta' (EA) | LRHS WFar |
| *rubroluteum* | See *R. viridescens* Rubroluteum |
|  | Group |
| 'Ruby F. Bowman' | CWri MDun MGos MLea NMun |
|  | SBrw SLdr SReu |
| 'Ruby Hart' | CB&S GGGa MDun NHol SBrw |
|  | SReu |
| *rude* | See *R. glischrum* subsp. *rude* |
| 'Ruffles and Frills' | CDoC CWri ECho MOne |
| *rufum* | GGGa NMun SLdr |
| ¶ - subsp. *hammel* | SLdr |
| - Hummel 31 | Last listed 1997 |
| - Sich 155 | GGGa |
| - W/V 1808* | Last listed 1998 |
| *rugosum* Sinclair 240 (V) | GGGa |
| 'Rumba' (K) | LKna |
| 'Rumpelstilzchen' | GGGa |
| *rupicola* | CHig GDra MBal NMun |
| § - var. *chryseum* | GGGa LHyd LMil NMun |
| - var. *muliense* | NMun |
| - - Yu 14042 | GGGa |
| *russatum* ♀ | CSam ENot EPot GDra GGGa LMil |
|  | MDun NMun SLdr |
| - blue-black | LMil |
| - C&Cu 9315 | GGGa |
| - 'Purple Pillow' | NHar |
| * - 'Tower Court' | NMun |
| - Waterer form | Last listed 1997 |
| Russautinii Group | Last listed 1996 |
| 'Russellianum' | Last listed 1996 |
| *russotinctum* | See *R. alutaceum* var. |
|  | *russotinctum* |
| ¶ 'Sabina' | CTrh |
| 'Sacko' | CHig CTrh ECho GGGa GRei LMil |
|  | MBri MOne NHol |
| 'Saffron Queen' | CB&S CGre CTrG CTrw MBal |
| 'Sahara' (K) | LKna |
| 'Saint Breward' | CTrG GGGa LHyd MBal MLea |
|  | NHol SBod SLdr SPer WAbe |
| 'Saint Keverne' | SLdr |
| 'Saint Kew' | Last listed 1996 |
| 'Saint Merryn' ♀ | CTrG EBee ENot GAri GGGa |
|  | LHyd MAsh MBri MOne NHol |
|  | NMun SLdr WGer WWeb |
| 'Saint Michael' | SReu |
| 'Saint Minver' ♀ | LHyd SLdr |
| 'Saint Tudy' ♀ | EPfP LHyd LKna MBal NMun SBid |
|  | SLdr SPer WAbe |
| 'Saint Wenn' | Last listed 1996 |
| 'Sakata Red' (EA) | CGre IOrc WBod |
| 'Sakon' (EA) | NMun SLdr |

| | |
|---|---|
| ¶ 'Salmon Bedspread' | SReu |
| 'Salmon Sander' (EA) | SLdr |
| § 'Salmon Trout' | Last listed 1996 |
| 'Salmon's Leap' (EA/v) | CB&S CChe COtt CTrh GQui LMil MAsh SBrw SCoo SLdr SPer SReu WAbe WFar WWeb |
| *saluenense* | GGGa LHyd LMil MBal NMun SLdr |
| § – subsp. *chameunum* ♀ | GGGa LMil MBal NMun SLdr WGer |
| – – PA Cox 6112 | GGGa |
| § – Prostratum Group | GGGa MBal WAbe |
| ¶ – JN 260 | GGGa |
| – subsp. *saluenense* Exbury form R 11005 | LMil |
| – – F 19479 | NMun |
| 'Sammetglut' | CWri SReu |
| 'Samuel Taylor Coleridge' (M) | MBri |
| *sanctum* | LMil |
| 'Sandling' | Last listed 1997 |
| ¶ 'Sandy' (A) | SLdr |
| 'Sang de Gentbrugge' (G) | SReu |
| *sanguineum* | GGGa LMil MDun NMun SLdr SReu |
| § – subsp. *didymum* | GGGa NMun SLdr |
| – var. *himertum* | SLdr |
| – PA Cox 6056 | GGGa |
| – subsp. *sanguineum* var. *cloiophorum* R 10899 | NMun |
| – – – USDAPI 59553/ R11212 | NMun SLdr |
| – – var. *didymoides* Consanguineum Group | NMun SLdr |
| – – – – KW 6831 | LMil |
| § – – – Roseotinctum Group | LMil |
| – – – – USDAPI 59038/ R10903 | GGGa LMil NMun SLdr |
| – – var. *haemaleum* | CWri GGGa LMil NMun SLdr |
| – – – F 21732 | NMun |
| – – – F 21735 | GGGa NMun |
| – – – R 31 | GGGa |
| – – – USDAPI 59303/ R10895 | NMun |
| – – – USDAPI 59453/ R10938 | NMun |
| – – var. *sanguineum* F 25521 | LMil |
| – – – R 10893 | NMun SLdr |
| – – – USDAPI 59096/R11029 | NMun SLdr |
| 'Santa Claus' | Last listed 1996 |
| 'Santa Maria' | CDoC COtt SLdr SReu SSta |
| *santapaui* (V) | Last listed 1998 |
| § 'Saotome' (EA) | LHyd |
| 'Sapphire' ♀ | CTrG LKna MBal MBar SBod SLdr SRms |
| 'Sappho' ♀ | CB&S CWri EBee ENot GGGa IOrc LHyd LKna LMil MBal MBar MGos NMun SBid SBrw SLdr SPer SReu SSta WFar WGer WGwG WWeb |
| 'Sapporo' | GGGa |
| 'Sarah Boscawen' | SReu |
| *sargentianum* ♀ | LMil MLea NMun SLdr WAbe |
| – 'Maricee' | GGGa MBri WGer |
| – 'Whitebait' | GGGa MBro NMun |
| Sarita Loder Group & cl. | SLdr |
| Sarled Group | CB&S GDra GGGa LHyd LMil MAsh MBal NHar NMun SBid SLdr SPer SReu SRms WAbe WWat |
| 'Saroi' (EA) | NMun SLdr |
| 'Saskia' (K) | LKna |

| | |
|---|---|
| 'Satan' (K) ♀ | COtt ELan GAri GGGa LKna MBri SReu |
| 'Satsuki' (EA) | CGre ECho LNet MAsh WWeb |
| ¶ 'Saturnus' (M) | ELan SLdr |
| *scabrifolium* | NMun SLdr |
| § – var. *spiciferum* | GGGa MBal NMun SLdr WPic |
| – – SBEC K 160 | Last listed 1996 |
| ¶ – – SF 502 | ISea |
| ¶ – – SF 534 | ISea |
| 'Scarlet Pimpernel' (K) | Last listed 1996 |
| 'Scarlet Wonder' ♀ | CDoC CMHG CTrh CWri EPot GGGa GRei ISea LKna LMil MBal MBar MBri MGos MLea NHol NMun SBod SBrw SLdr SReu SSta WBod WFar |
| Scarlett O'Hara Group | Last listed 1997 |
| ¶ *schistocalyx* | SLdr |
| – F 17637 | Last listed 1996 |
| *schlippenbachii* (A) ♀ | CB&S CGre GGGa LHyd LMil MBal NMun SLdr SPer SReu SSta WWat |
| – 'Sid's Royal Pink' (A) | LMil MDun |
| ¶ 'Schneeflöckchen' | GGGa |
| 'Schneekrone' | GGGa LMil MBri NHol |
| ¶ 'Schneeperle' (EA) | GGGa |
| Schneespiegel® | ENot |
| 'Schubert' (EA) | MBar MGos SLdr WBod |
| *scintillans* | See *R. polycladum* |
| 'Scintillation' | CDoC CSam CWri EBee GGGa LMil MBal MBar MLea NMun SBid SBrw SLdr |
| *scopulorum* | SLdr |
| – KW 6354 | GGGa |
| – Magor's hardy form | Last listed 1996 |
| *scottianum* | See *R. pachypodum* |
| ¶ 'Scout' (EA) | SLdr |
| *scyphocalyx* | See *R. dichroanthum* subsp. *scyphocalyx* |
| Seagull Group & cl. | NMun SLdr |
| *searsiae* | NMun SLdr |
| – W/A 1343 | Last listed 1997 |
| 'Seashell' | SLdr |
| 'Sea-Tac' | MLea |
| ¶ 'Seb' | SLdr |
| 'Second Honeymoon' | CDoC CWri MLea SBrw SReu WWeb |
| 'Seikai' (EA) | SLdr |
| *seinghkuense* KW 9254 | GGGa |
| *selense* | GGGa LMil NMun SLdr |
| – CNW 690 | Last listed 1998 |
| § – subsp. *dasycladum* | MDun NMun SLdr |
| – – F 11312 | NMun |
| – – KW 7189 | NMun |
| – – R 11269 | NMun |
| – subsp. *jucundum* | GGGa LMil MDun NMun SLdr |
| – – SF 660 | ISea |
| – PA Cox 6041 | GGGa |
| – subsp. *selense* F 14458 | NMun SLdr |
| – – PA Cox 6024 | GGGa |
| – – Probum Group | Last listed 1996 |
| § – subsp. *setiferum* | NMun |
| *semnoides* | GGGa NMun SLdr |
| – F 21870 | NMun |
| – F 25639 | NMun |
| – R 25388 | NMun |
| 'Senator Henry Jackson' | GGGa LMil |
| 'Sennocke' ♀ | GGGa LHyd |
| 'September Morn' | CHig |

| | |
|---|---|
| 'September Song' | CDoC COtt CWri GGGa GRei LHyd LMil MAsh MBal MBri MDun MLea |
| 'Serendipity' | GGGa |
| *serotinum* | LMil NMun SLdr SReu |
| *serpyllifolium* (A) | CB&S GGGa NMun SLdr |
| - var. *albiflorum* (A) | GAri |
| 'Sesterianum' | CMHG SLdr |
| Seta Group & cl. | CB&S CHig LHyd MBal NMun SLdr SReu WAbe |
| *setiferum* | See *R. selense* subsp. *setiferum* |
| *setosum* | GGGa LMil MBal MDun NMun |
| - TW 30 | Last listed 1997 |
| 'Seven Stars' ♀ | MDun NMun SLdr SReu WPyg |
| 'Seville' | Last listed 1996 |
| 'Shamrock' | CB&S CDoC CSam EPfP GCrs ISea MAsh MBal MBar MDun MLea NHar NHol SBrw SLdr SReu WAbe WBod WFar WGwG |
| 'Sham's Candy' | ERea |
| 'Shanty' (K/d) | LKna |
| ¶ 'Sheila' (EA) | CDoC |
| x *sheilae* (V) | CEqu |
| *shepherdii* | See *R. kendrickii* |
| Shepherd's Delight Group | SLdr |
| *sherriffii* | GGGa MDun NMun SLdr |
| - (AM 1966 clone ex L&S 2751) AM | Last listed 1996 |
| - L&S 2751 | NMun |
| Shilsonii Group | NMun SLdr SReu |
| 'Shinimiagagino' (EA) | NMun |
| 'Shinnyo-no-hikari' (EA) | GAri |
| 'Shi-no-noe' (EA) | NMun SBod SLdr |
| 'Shinsei' (EA) | GAri |
| 'Shin-seikai' (EA/d) | CB&S |
| 'Shintoki-no-hagasane' (EA) | LHyd |
| 'Shintsune' (EA) | NMun SLdr |
| Shot Silk Group | NMun SLdr |
| 'Shrimp Girl' | ENot LHyd MBal MGos MLea NMun SLdr SReu |
| 'Shukishima' (EA) | NMun SLdr |
| 'Shuku-fuku' (EA) | GAri |
| *shweliense* | GGGa LMil SReu |
| *sidereum* | GGGa LMil NMun SLdr |
| - KR 2710* | GGGa |
| - KW 13649 | See *R.* aff. *grande* KR 13649 |
| - KW 6792 | NMun SLdr |
| - SF 314 | ISea |
| - SF 318 | ISea |
| - TW 345 | Last listed 1997 |
| - TW 350 | Last listed 1997 |
| *siderophyllum* | SLdr |
| - EGM 346 | LMil |
| *sikangense* | MDun NMun SLdr |
| - C&K 246 | GGGa |
| § - Cookeanum Group | NMun |
| - - CNW 1060 | LMil |
| - EGM 108 | LMil |
| - var. *exquisitum* CNW 958 | LMil |
| - R 18142 | NMun |
| - var. *sikangense* PA Cox 5012 | GGGa |
| - - PA Cox 5105 | GGGa NHol |
| * *sikkimense* SD 1108 | GGGa |
| § 'Silberwolke' | COtt ENot MAsh SBrw SReu |
| 'Silkcap' | WWeb |
| 'Silky' | MBal |
| Silver Cloud | See *R.* 'Silberwolke' |
| ♦ 'Silver Edge' | See *R. ponticum* 'Silver Edge' |

| | |
|---|---|
| 'Silver Glow' (EA) | CMac |
| 'Silver Jubilee' | GGGa LHyd LMil SLdr |
| 'Silver Moon' (EA) | IOrc NMun SBod SLdr SPer |
| 'Silver Queen' | ECho |
| 'Silver Sixpence' ♀ | ENot IOrc MAsh MBal MBar MDun MLea NMun SLdr SReu WWeb |
| 'Silver Skies' | LMil |
| 'Silver Slipper' (K) ♀ | CDoC CGre LHyd LKna LMil MAsh MBal MBar MBri MLea SLdr SReu SSta WGor |
| 'Silverwood' (K) | LMil |
| 'Silvester' (EA) | COtt MBri SLdr WPat |
| 'Silvetta' | Last listed 1996 |
| *simiarum* | GGGa |
| - SF 92304 | Last listed 1996 |
| 'Simona' | CWri SReu |
| *simsii* (EA) | CMac LMil SLdr |
| - SF 431 (EA) | ISea |
| *simulans* | See *R. mimetes* var. *simulans* |
| 'Sinbad' | Last listed 1998 |
| *sinofalconeri* C&H 7183 | GGGa |
| - KR 1992* | Last listed 1996 |
| - SEH 229 | LMil |
| - SF 92142 | ISea |
| *sinogrande* ♀ | CB&S GGGa IOrc LMil MBal NMun SAPC SArc SLdr WPic |
| - KW 21111 | NMun SLdr |
| - SF 327 | ISea |
| - SF 329 | ISea |
| - SF 350 | ISea |
| - TW 341 | Last listed 1997 |
| - TW 383 | Last listed 1997 |
| 'Sir Charles Lemon' ♀ | CDoC CWri LMil MDun NMun SLdr SPer SReu SSta |
| Sir Frederick Moore Group & cl. | Last listed 1997 |
| * 'Sir G.E. Simpson' | NMun |
| ¶ 'Sir George Sansom' | SLdr |
| * 'Sir John Tremayne' | Last listed 1996 |
| 'Sir William Lawrence' (EA) | LKna SReu |
| Siren Group & cl. | MBal |
| 'Sirius' | Last listed 1996 |
| 'Skookum' | ECho LMil MBri MGos SMur |
| 'Sleeping Beauty' | WAbe |
| 'Sleepy' | ENot IOrc NHed NMun SLdr SPer SReu WGwG WLRN |
| *smirnowii* | GGGa LMil MBal NMun SLdr SReu SSta |
| § Smithii Group | CWri SReu |
| *smithii* | See *R. argipeplum* |
| - Argipeplum Group | See *R. argipeplum* |
| 'Sneezy' | CB&S EBee ENot GGGa GRei LHyd LMil MAsh MBal MBar MGos MLea NHol NMun SLdr SReu SSta WGwG |
| 'Snipe' ♀ | CDoC CSam EBee ENot GGGa LHyd LMil MAsh MBal MBar MBri MDun MGos MOne NHar NHol SReu |
| 'Snow' (EA) | CMac MBar SLdr |
| 'Snow Crown' | Last listed 1998 |
| 'Snow Hill' (EA) | GQui LHyd LMil |
| 'Snow Lady' ♀ | ENot EPfP GCrs LMil MAsh MBal MBar MGos MLea NHar NHol SBid SLdr WAbe |
| Snow Queen Group & cl. | LKna LMil SReu WWeb |
| ¶ (Snow Queen Group) | SLdr |
| 'Snow Queen' ♀ | |

| | |
|---|---|
| 'Snowbird' | GGGa |
| 'Snowflake' | See *R.* 'Kure-no-yuki' |
| 'Snowstorm' | CWri ECho MDun |
| 'Soho' (EA) | GAri GQui LNet |
| 'Soir de Paris' (Vs) | CDoC MAsh MBar MBri MLea NMun SLdr SReu SSta WBod |
| 'Soldier Sam' | SBrw SReu SSta |
| 'Solent Queen' | See *R.* (Angelo Group) 'Solent Queen' |
| 'Solidarity' | ECho MBal WLRN |
| 'Solway' (Vs) | LMil |
| 'Sonata' | GAri GGGa MBal MDun SReu |
| 'Songbird' | CSam GCHN GChr GDra LHyd LKna LMil MAsh MBal MBar MBri NMun SBid SLdr SReu WBod |
| 'Songster' | Last listed 1998 |
| 'Sophie Hedges' (K/d) | LKna |
| *sororium* KR 3080 (V) | GGGa |
| - KR 3085 | LMil |
| - var. *wumengense* CNW 990 | LMil |
| Souldis Group | LMil MDun SLdr SMur |
| *souliei* | IOrc LMil NMun SLdr |
| - C&K 371 | Last listed 1998 |
| ¶ - deep pink | GGGa |
| - PA Cox 5056 | Last listed 1998 |
| - white | GGGa |
| 'Southern Cross' | CSam CWri MDun MLea NMun |
| 'Souvenir de Congo' | SBrw |
| 'Souvenir de D.A. Koster' | SLdr |
| 'Souvenir de Doctor S. Endtz' ♀ | CWri LKna MBal MBar SBrw SLdr |
| 'Souvenir du Président Carnot' (G/d) | LKna |
| 'Souvenir of Anthony Waterer' ♀ | LKna SBrw SReu |
| 'Souvenir of W.C. Slocock' | CSam LKna NMun SBrw SLdr SReu SSta |
| 'Sparkler' | CWri MGos MLea WWeb |
| 'Sparkler' (Vs) | GGGa |
| *speciosum* | See *R. flammeum* |
| ¶ 'Spek's Brilliant' (M) | SReu |
| 'Spek's Orange' (M) ♀ | MGos SReu |
| 'Spellbinder' | Last listed 1996 |
| *sperabile* | NMun |
| - var. *sperabile* F 26446 | Last listed 1998 |
| - var. *weihsiense* | GGGa LMil NMun SLdr |
| - - CNW 564 | ISea |
| - - F 26453 | SLdr |
| *sperabiloides* | GGGa NMun |
| - R 125 | NMun |
| *sphaeranthum* | See *R. trichostomum* |
| *sphaeroblastum* | GGGa LMil NMun SLdr |
| - F 17110 | Last listed 1996 |
| - F 20416 | SLdr |
| - KR 1481* | NMun |
| - var. *wumengense* CNW 510 | ISea |
| - - CNW 942 | GGGa |
| - - CNW 963 | GGGa |
| - - CNW 968 | GGGa |
| - - SF 515 | ISea |
| *spiciferum* | See *R. scabrifolium* var. *spiciferum* |
| 'Spicy Lights' | LMil |
| *spilotum* | GGGa NMun SLdr |
| *spinuliferum* | GGGa NMun SLdr |
| - 'Jack Hext' | Last listed 1996 |
| - SF 247 | ISea |

| | |
|---|---|
| - TW 413 | Last listed 1996 |
| - TW 418 | Last listed 1996 |
| 'Spinulosum' | Last listed 1997 |
| 'Spitfire' | MGos SBrw SReu |
| 'Spoonbill' (K) | LKna |
| 'Spring Beauty' (EA) | CMac SReu |
| 'Spring Dawn' | Last listed 1996 |
| 'Spring Dream' | See *R.* 'Frühlingstraum' |
| 'Spring Magic' | LMil NMun SLdr |
| 'Spring Pearl' | See *R.* 'Moerheim's Pink' |
| 'Spring Rose' | NMun SBid SLdr |
| 'Spring Sunshine' | LMil |
| 'Springbok' | LHyd |
| 'Springday' | Last listed 1996 |
| 'Squirrel' (EA) | CDoC COtt GGGa LHyd LMil MAsh MBal MBri MGos NHed SLdr SReu WAbe WBod |
| ¶ 'Squirrel' tall form (EA) | SLdr |
| 'Staccato' | GGGa |
| Stadt Essen Group & cl. | GGGa LMil |
| *stamineum* | NMun |
| - SF 417 | ISea |
| - W/V 887 | NMun |
| ¶ 'Standishii' | SLdr |
| 'Stanley Rivlin' | LHyd SLdr |
| § 'Stanway' | LMil NMun |
| 'Starcross' | Last listed 1997 |
| 'Starfish' | SReu |
| 'Stella' | NMun |
| *stenaulum* | See *R. moulmainense* |
| § *stenopetalum* | CMac ISea LMil NMun SLdr SReu |
| 'Linearifolium' (A) | WAbe |
| ◆ *stenophyllum* | See *R. makinoi* |
| *stewartianum* | GGGa MDun NMun SLdr |
| ¶ - CCH&H 8137 | GGGa |
| - CLD 1300* | LMil |
| - F 26921 | NMun |
| - SF 370 | ISea |
| 'Stewartstonian' (EA) ♀ | CMac CTrh IOrc LHyd LMil MBal MBar MBri SBod SReu SSta WBod WFar |
| *stictophyllum* | See *R. nivale* subsp. *boreale* Stictophyllum Group |
| 'Stoat' (EA) | GQui |
| 'Stranraer' | MAsh MBri |
| 'Strategist' | Last listed 1996 |
| 'Strawberry Cream' | GGGa NHol |
| 'Strawberry Ice' (K) ♀ | CB&S CMHG ENot EPfP GGGa GRei IOrc LKna LMil MAsh MBar MBri MDun MGos SPer SReu SLdr |
| 'Streatley' ♀ | SLdr |
| *strigillosum* | GGGa MDun NMun SLdr |
| - C&H 7035 | GGGa |
| - C&H 7047 | GGGa |
| - EGM 338 | LMil |
| - Reuthe's form | SReu |
| 'Striped Beauty' | MBal |
| 'Suave' | Last listed 1998 |
| *subansiriense* C&H 418 | GGGa NMun SLdr |
| *suberosum* | See *R. yunnanense* Suberosum Group |
| subsect. *Triflora* PW 020* | LMil |
| subsect. *Triflora* PW 097 | LMil |
| *succothii* | GGGa LHyd MDun NMun SLdr |
| - BB 185A | NMun |
| - CH&M 3079 | Last listed 1997 |
| - CH&M 3105 | Last listed 1997 |
| - CH&M 3109 | NHol |
| - CH&M 3125 | Last listed 1997 |

| | |
|---|---|
| – EGM 086 | LMil |
| – KW 13666 | SLdr |
| – LS&H 19850 | Last listed 1997 |
| – LS&H 21295 | NMun SLdr |
| 'Suede' | Last listed 1997 |
| 'Sugar Pink' | LMil LRHS |
| 'Sugared Almond' (K) ♀ | MBal |
| 'Sugi-no-ito' | See *R.* 'Kumo-no-ito' |
| *sulfureum* | CHig NMun |
| – SBEC 249 | GGGa |
| 'Sumatra' | Last listed 1997 |
| 'Summer Blaze' (A) | SReu |
| 'Summer Flame' | SLdr SReu |
| 'Summer Fragrance' (O) ♀ | SReu SSta |
| 'Sun Chariot' (K) ♀ | CB&S LHyd LKna MAsh MBri |
| | MMHG SLdr SReu |
| 'Sunbeam' (EA) | See *R.* 'Benifude' |
| 'Sunbeam' | LKna SReu |
| I 'Sundance' | Last listed 1997 |
| 'Sunny' | Last listed 1996 |
| 'Sunny' (V) | GGGa |
| ¶ 'Sunny Day' | SLdr |
| 'Sunny Splendour' (V) | ERea |
| ¶ (Sunrise Group) 'Sunrise' | SLdr |
| 'Sunset over Harkwood' | Last listed 1997 |
| 'Sunset Pink' (K) | LHyd LMil WWeb |
| 'Sunstruck' | GGGa |
| 'Sunte Nectarine' (K) ♀ | GQui LHyd LMil MBri SCoo |
| *superbum* (V) | GGGa |
| 'Superbum' (O) | SReu |
| 'Surprise' (EA) | CDoC CTrh CTri MAsh NMun |
| | SCoo SLdr |
| 'Surrey Heath' ♀ | CB&S CMHG COtt CWri EBee |
| | ENot GGGa GRei LMil LNet MAsh |
| | MBal MBar MBri MDun MGos |
| | MLea NHed NMun SBrw SLdr |
| | SReu |
| 'Susan' ♀ | CB&S CDoC CHig CWri GGGa |
| | LHyd LKna LMil MAsh MBri |
| | MDun MLea NMun SBrw SLdr |
| | SReu |
| 'Susannah Hill' (EA) | CDoC CTrh LMil SBod SPer SReu |
| 'Sussex Bonfire' | NMun SLdr |
| *sutchuenense* | CHig CWri GGGa IDee LMil |
| | MDun NMun SLdr |
| – var. *geraldii* | See *R.* x *geraldii* |
| 'Swamp Beauty' | CWri GGGa LMil MDun |
| 'Swansdown' | CWri MDun |
| 'Swansong' (EA) | CMac |
| 'Sweet Beatrice' (V) | Last listed 1996 |
| 'Sweet Mac' (V) | CEqu |
| 'Sweet Seraphim' (V) | Last listed 1997 |
| 'Sweet Simplicity' ♀ | LKna MBal SBrw |
| 'Sweet Sixteen' | CWri NMun SLdr |
| 'Sweet Sue' | EBee MAsh MBal NMun SLdr |
| | SReu WLRN |
| 'Swift' | CDoC GGGa GQui MBri MOne |
| 'Sword of State' (K) | Last listed 1998 |
| 'Sylphides' (K) | LKna MBri |
| 'Sylvester' | CDoC MGos SReu |
| • 'Sylvetta' | Last listed 1996 |
| 'Sylvia' (EA/d) | Last listed 1997 |
| *taggianum* | Last listed 1996 |
| – 'Cliff Hanger' ex KW 8546 | LMil |
| ¶ 'Taka' (A) | SLdr |
| 'Takasago' (EA/d) | LHyd LMil |
| 'Talavera' | See *R.* (Golden Oriole Group) |
| | 'Talavera' |
| *taliense* | GGGa LHyd MDun NMun SLdr |

| | |
|---|---|
| – F 6772 | NMun SLdr |
| – KR 2765* | GGGa |
| – SBEC 350 | See *R. roxieanum* var. *cucullatum* |
| | SBEC 350 |
| – SF 92069 | Last listed 1998 |
| – SSNY 352 | GGGa |
| subsect. *Taliensia* CNW 256 | LMil |
| ¶ 'Tally Ho' | SLdr |
| Tally Ho Group & cl. | NMun SLdr SReu |
| *tamaense* | See *R. cinnabarinum* subsp. |
| | *tamaense* |
| 'Tama-no-utena' (EA) | LHyd SLdr |
| 'Tan Crossing' | SReu |
| 'Tanager' (EA) | CDoC CTrh LKna |
| ¶ *tanastylum* | SLdr |
| § – var. *pennivenium* | NMun SLdr |
| – – SF 593 | ISea |
| 'Tangerine' | See *R.* 'Fabia Tangerine' |
| 'Tangiers' (K) | Last listed 1998 |
| *tapetiforme* | GGGa |
| 'Tara' | SLdr |
| Tarantella® | CDoC ENot |
| ¶ Taranto Group | SLdr |
| Tasco Group | SLdr |
| *tashiroi* (EA) | NMun |
| 'Tatjana' | ENot LMil |
| *tatsienense* | GGGa |
| – EGM 321 | LMil |
| 'Taurus' ♀ | COtt CWri GGGa LMil MGos |
| | MLea WGwG WWeb |
| 'Tay' (K) | Last listed 1997 |
| 'Teal' ♀ | CTri GGGa MBal MBar MBri |
| | MGos MLea NHol NMun SLdr |
| | SReu |
| 'Teddy Bear' | CDoC GGGa LMil MDun SLdr |
| | SMur |
| § *telmateium* | NMun |
| *telopeum* | See *R. campylocarpum* subsp. |
| | *caloxanthum* Telopeum Group |
| *temenium* | MDun |
| – var. *dealbatum* | LMil |
| – – EGM 275 | LMil |
| – – Glaphyrum Group | NMun |
| F 21902 | |
| – EGM 274 | LMil |
| – var. *gilvum* 'Cruachan' | GGGa LMil NMun |
| R 22272 | |
| – – R 101 | NMun |
| – – R 22271 | NMun |
| § – var. *mesopolium* R 10950 | NMun |
| – P Cox 6037B | GGGa |
| – R 10909 | NMun |
| – var. *temenium* F 21734 | NMun |
| – – F 21809 | NMun |
| 'Temple Belle' ♀ | CWri MDun |
| Temple Belle Group | CSam LHyd LKna MBal MLea |
| | NHed NMun SLdr |
| 'Tensing' | SLdr |
| § *tephropeplum* ♀ | GGGa NMun SLdr |
| – Deleiense Group | See *R. tephropeplum* |
| – KW 6303 | NMun |
| – SF 92069 | ISea |
| – USDAPQ 3914/R 18408 | GGGa |
| 'Tequila Sunrise' | MBal NMun SLdr |
| 'Terra-cotta' | LKna LMil SMur |
| 'Terra-cotta Beauty' (EA) | CTrG WPat |
| Tessa Group & cl. | CDoC GRei LKna LMil MGos |
| | MOne SBod |
| 'Tessa Bianca' | GGGa |

| | |
|---|---|
| 'Tessa Roza' ♀ | GGGa GQui LHyd |
| *thayerianum* | GGGa NMun SLdr |
| ¶ 'The Dowager' | SLdr |
| § 'The Hon. Jean Marie de | CAbP CWri EPfP IOrc LKna LMil |
| Montague' ♀ | MBal MBri MDun MLea NMun |
| | SBrw SLdr WWeb |
| 'The Master' ♀ | LKna NMun SBrw SLdr SReu |
| § 'The Queen Mother' | LHyd |
| 'The Warrior' | MDun |
| 'Theme Song' | Last listed 1998 |
| Thomdeton Group | Last listed 1996 |
| *thomsonii* | GGGa LHyd LMil MDun NHol |
| | NMun SLdr SReu |
| - AC 113 | NMun |
| ¶ - B&SWJ 2638 | WCru |
| - BL&M 153* | MBal |
| - Bu 270 | GGGa |
| - var. *candelabrum* | See *R.* x *candelabrum* |
| ¶ - 'Davidian' | SLdr |
| - DF 540 | MBal |
| § - subsp. *lopsangianum* | GGGa MDun SLdr |
| § - - LS&T 6561 | NMun |
| - LS&H 1949* | NMun |
| - MH 70 | GGGa |
| - subsp. *thomsonii* | NMun |
| BL&M 228 | |
| - - L&S 2847 | GGGa NMun |
| Thomwilliams Group | MBal |
| Thor Group & cl. | GGGa SBrw SReu |
| 'Thousand Butterflies' | See *R.* 'One Thousand Butterflies' |
| 'Thunderstorm' ♀ | LHyd LKna SReu |
| *thymifolium* | GGGa |
| 'Tiana' | GGGa |
| 'Tibet' | GQui LMil MBal MBar MDun |
| | NHar WWeb |
| 'Tidbit' | GGGa LHyd LKna LMil MAsh |
| | MBal MGos MLea NMun SLdr |
| | WGer |
| 'Tilford Seedling' | LKna |
| 'Timothy James' | LRHS SReu |
| ¶ 'Tinkerbird' | GGGa |
| 'Tiny' (EA/d) | Last listed 1997 |
| 'Tit Willow' (EA) | LHyd LRHS SCoo SPer WGwG |
| 'Titian Beauty' ♀ | CB&S CDoC COtt CWri EBee |
| | GChr GGGa IOrc LNet MBal |
| | MBri MDun MGos MLea NHed |
| | NMun SBrw SLdr SReu WWeb |
| 'Titipu' (EA) | LHyd SLdr |
| 'Toff' (V) | Last listed 1997 |
| 'Tolkien' | SReu SSta |
| 'Tom Williams' | NMun SLdr |
| 'Tomba' | Last listed 1997 |
| 'Tonkonatsu' (EA) | SLdr |
| 'Too Bee' | GGGa MAsh NHol WAbe |
| 'Top Banana' | LMil LRHS MBal MDun MLea |
| | SMur SPer |
| 'Top Brass' | Last listed 1996 |
| 'Top Hat' | Last listed 1998 |
| 'Topaz' | Last listed 1996 |
| 'Topsvoort Pearl' | SReu |
| 'Torch' | LKna MGos |
| 'Toreador' (EA) | CTrG SLdr |
| ¶ 'Torero' | GGGa |
| 'Torridon' (Vs) | LMil SLdr |
| 'Tortoiseshell Biscuit' | Last listed 1996 |
| 'Tortoiseshell Champagne' | See *R.* 'Champagne' |
| 'Tortoiseshell Orange' ♀ | LHyd LKna LMil MBri MDun SBrw |
| | SReu SSta WGer |
| 'Tortoiseshell Pale Orange' | LKna |

| | |
|---|---|
| 'Tortoiseshell Salome' | LKna SBrw SReu |
| 'Tortoiseshell Scarlet' | LKna SReu |
| 'Tortoiseshell Wonder' ♀ | LHyd LKna LMil MBal MGos |
| | NMun SLdr SReu SSta |
| *tosaense* (EA) | Last listed 1997 |
| - 'Ralph Clarke' (EA) | Last listed 1998 |
| 'Totally Awesome' (K) | GGGa MLea |
| 'Tottenham' | MBal |
| 'Tower Beauty' (A) | LHyd |
| 'Tower Dainty' (A) | LHyd |
| 'Tower Daring' (A) | LHyd |
| 'Tower Dexter' (A) | LHyd |
| 'Tower Dragon' (A) | LHyd |
| 'Trail Blazer' | GGGa |
| *traillianum* | GGGa LMil NMun SLdr |
| - CNW 746 | ISea |
| § - var. *dictyotum* | NMun SLdr |
| - - 'Kathmandu' | NMun |
| - F 5881* | NMun SLdr |
| aff. *traillianum* | LMil |
| *aberrans* CNW 747 | |
| 'Travis L' | SPer |
| Treasure Group | GDra IOrc LHyd MBal SLdr |
| 'Trebah Gem' | NMun SLdr |
| 'Tregedna' | NMun SLdr |
| 'Tregedna Red' | SReu |
| 'Tretawn' | SLdr |
| 'Trewithen Orange' | CB&S CDoC CTrw MBal MBar |
| | NMun SLdr SPer |
| 'Trewithen Purple' | CTrw |
| 'Trianon' | LMil NMun |
| *trichanthum* | CHig CWri GGGa IOrc LMil |
| | NMun SLdr |
| - 'Honey Wood' | LHyd LMil SLdr |
| - W/A 1342 | Last listed 1996 |
| *trichocladum* | LMil NMun SLdr |
| - CNW 880 | ISea |
| - KW 21079 | See *R. mekongense* var. |
| | *mekongense* KW 21079 |
| ¶ - SF 661 | ISea |
| ¶ - SF 96179 | ISea |
| § *trichostomum* ♀ | GGGa MDun NMun SSpi WAbe |
| - KW 4465 | NMun |
| - Ledoides Group | LMil NMun SLdr SReu |
| - - 'Collingwood Ingram' | LMil SReu |
| - Radinum Group | SSta |
| *triflorum* | GGGa IOrc ISea LMil MBal MDun |
| | NMun SLdr |
| § - var. *bauhiniiflorum* | CB&S LMil MDun NMun SLdr |
| - C&V 9573 | GGGa |
| ¶ - SF 95149 | ISea |
| - var. *triflorum* | NMun SLdr |
| Mahogani Group | |
| 'Trilby' | SReu |
| *triplonaevium* | See *R. alutaceum* var. |
| | *russotinctum* Triplonaevium |
| | Group |
| *tritifolium* | See *R. alutaceum* var. |
| | *russotinctum* Tritifolium Group |
| 'Troll' (EA) | SLdr SReu |
| 'Troupial' (K) | LKna |
| 'Trude Webster' | CHig CSam GGGa MBri MLea |
| | SReu SSta |
| aff. *tsaii* C&H 7022 | GGGa |
| - H&M 1490 | GGGa |
| *tsangpoense* | See *R. charitopes* subsp. |
| | *tsangpoense* |
| *tsariense* | GGGa LMil NHol NMun |
| - forms | NMun SLdr |

- var. *magnum* — NMun
- Poluninii Group — See *R. poluninii*
- x *proteoides* — GGGa
- var. *trimoense* — GGGa NMun
- var. *tsariense* L&S 2766 — Last listed 1997
- 'Yum Yum' — NMun SLdr
aff. *tsariense* — LMil
§ *tsusiophyllum* — GAri GGGa WAbe
'Tsuta-momiji' (EA) — LHyd
♦ *tubiforme* — See *R. glaucophyllum* subsp. *tubiforme*
¶ 'Tuffet' — SReu
'Tulyar' — LKna
'Tunis' (K) — ECho MAsh
'Turkish Delight' — Last listed 1998
N 'Twilight' (EA) — MBri
'Twilight Pink' — MLea NMun
'Twilight Sky' (A) — ENot SBrw SLdr WWeb
'Tyermannii' ♀ — Last listed 1998
'Ukamuse' (EA/d) — LHyd
'Uki Funei' (EA/v) — LMil
'Umpqua Queen' (K) — MLea
Ungerio Group — NMun SLdr
*ungernii* — CWri GGGa NMun SLdr
*uniflorum* — LMil MDun NHol NMun WAbe
§ - var. *imperator* — LMil
- - KW 6884 — GGGa WAbe
- var. *uniflorum* KW 5876 — NMun SLdr
'Unique' ♀ — CB&S CDoC CHig CSam CWri GChr GGGa LHyd LKna LMil LNet MAsh MBal MBri MDun MLea NMun SBrw SLdr SPer SReu SSta WGwG WWeb
'Unique' (G) — LKna
¶ 'Unique Marmalade' — LMil
'Unknown Warrior' — SBrw SReu
*uvariifolium* — GGGa NMun SLdr
- CNW 127 — ISea
- CNW 1275 — ISea
- var. *griseum* KR 3423 — LMil
- - LS&E 15817 — Last listed 1998
- PA Cox 6519 — GGGa
- 'Reginald Childs' — LMil
- var. *uvariifolium* — NMun
  USDAPI 59623/ R11391
- 'Yangtze Bend' — GGGa
¶ *vaccinioides* CCH&H — GGGa
  8051 (V)
Valaspis Group & cl. — SLdr
'Valentine' (EA) — GGGa
*valentinianum* — CB&S CSam GGGa MBal NMun SLdr WAbe
- F 24347 — NMun
- var. *oblongilobatum* — LMil
  C&H 7186
Valpinense Group & cl. — WBod
'Van Heka' (A) — Last listed 1996
'Van Nes Sensation' — LMil
'Van Weerden Poelman' — SBrw
Vanessa Group & cl. — LMil SReu
'Vanessa Pastel' ♀ — CHig GGGa LHyd LMil MBal MDun MLea NMun SLdr SReu WBod
§ 'Vanilla' — LKna
*vaseyi* (A) ♀ — GGGa LHyd LMil MBal
¶ - white (A) — LMil
¶ 'Vayo' (A) — SLdr
*veitchianum* ♀ — GGGa

§ - Cubittii Group ♀ — GGGa NMun SLdr
- (Cubittii Group) — LHyd
  'Ashcombe'
- KNE Cox 9001 — GGGa
'Veldtstar' — Last listed 1997
*vellereum* — See *R. principis* Vellereum Group
'Velvet Gown' (EA) — ENot IOrc SBid SReu
*venator* — GGGa MDun NMun SLdr
'Venetia' (K) — MBri
'Venetian Chimes' — ENot IOrc ISea MBal NMun SLdr SPer SReu
*vernicosum* — GGGa LMil NMun SLdr
- C&H 7009 — Last listed 1998
- Euanthum Group F 5880 — NMun
- F 5881 — NMun
¶ - JN 180 — GGGa
- McLaren T 71 — NMun SLdr
- SF 416 — ISea
¶ - Yu 13961 — SLdr
- Yu 14694 — Last listed 1997
aff. *vernicosum* C&H 7150 — Last listed 1998
x *verruculosum* — Last listed 1998
'Veryan Bay' ♀ — CB&S LMil
*vesiculiferum* — NMun SLdr
'Vespers' (EA) — CTrh
'Victoria Hallett' — SLdr SReu
'Vida Brown' (EA/d) — CMac ENot LKna LMil MAsh MBri SBid SBod SReu SSta WPat
'Viking' (EA) — LHyd
'Vincent van Gogh' — GGGa LMil
'Vinecourt Duke' (R/d) — ECho MDun
'Vinecourt Troubador' (K/d) — CDoC ECho MDun
'Vinecrest' — Last listed 1996
'Vineland Dream' (K/d) — ECho
'Vineland Fragrance' — CDoC CWri GGGa MDun MLea
* 'Vinestar' AM/T — LHyd LMil
'Vintage Rosé' ♀ — LMil MAsh MBal MLea NMun SLdr SReu
'Violet Longhurst' (EA) — LHyd SLdr
'Violetta' (EA) — GGGa WGwG
*virgatum* — Last listed 1997
- subsp. *oleifolium* — Last listed 1998
  KW 6279
Virginia Richards Group & cl. — CHig GAri GChr GGGa LHyd MBal MDun MGos MLea NMun SLdr SReu SSta WGer
§ *viridescens* — LMil MBal MDun
- 'Doshong La' — LMil
- KW 5829 — See *R. mekongense* var. *mekongense* KW 5829
§ - Rubroluteum Group — GGGa LMil
*viscidifolium* — GGGa NMun
*viscosum* (A) ♀ — GGGa GQui LHyd LKna LMil LRHS SReu
* - *aemulans* (A) — Last listed 1997
- 'Antilope' — See *R.* 'Antilope'
- 'Arpege' — See *R.* 'Arpege'
- 'Grey Leaf' (Vs) — LMil
- var. *montanum* (A) — IBlr
- f. *rhodanthum* (A) — LMil
- 'Roseum' (Vs) — LMil
'Viscount Powerscourt' — ENot SLdr
'Viscy' — CDoC CWri EBee ECho GGGa GQui GRei LHyd LMil MAsh MDun WGer
'Vital Spark' — Last listed 1998
'Vivacious' — MDun
Volker Group — See *R.* Flava Group & cl.

'Vulcan' ♀ — CB&S ENot EPfP GGGa LMil MBal MLea SBrw SLdr
'Vulcan' x *yakushimanum* — SReu
'Vulcan's Flame' — Last listed 1997
'Vuyk's Rosyred' (EA) ♀ — CDoC CHig CMac CTri ENot GChr GQui GRei IOrc LHyd LKna LMil MBar MBri MGos SBod SBrw SLdr SPer SReu WBod WFar WStI WWeb
'Vuyk's Scarlet' (EA) ♀ — CB&S CChe CDoC CMac CTrh GGGa GQui IOrc ISea LHyd LKna LMil MBar MBri MGos NMun SBrw SLdr SPer SReu SSta WFar WWeb
'W.E. Gumbleton' (M) — SReu
W.F.H. Group — CWri LMil NMun SLdr
¶ 'W. Leith' — SLdr
*wadanum* var.*leucanthum* — LMil
'Wagtail' — GGGa NHol WAbe
*wallichii* — GGGa SLdr
¶ – B&SWJ 2633 — WCru
– Bu 249 — Last listed 1998
– Bu 262 — Last listed 1998
– Bu 290 — Last listed 1998
– DM 21 — LMil
– KR 813* — Last listed 1997
– KR 882 — Last listed 1997
– LS&H 17527 — NMun
– TW 32 — Last listed 1997
Walloper Group — NMun SLdr SReu
'Wallowa Red' (K) — ECho LMil
'Wally Miller' — MBri SReu SSta
*walongense* — NMun
aff.*walongense* C&H 373 — GGGa
*wardii* — IDee IOrc ISea LHyd LMil MBal MDun NMun SLdr
– C&V 9558 — GGGa
– C&V 9606 — GGGa
– L&S form* — GGGa SReu
– P Cox 6119 — GGGa
– var.*puralbum* — GGGa NMun
– – F 10616 — NMun
– – Yu 14757 — Last listed 1997
– SHEG 5672 — NMun
– var.*wardii* C&V 9548 — GGGa
– – F 21551 — NMun
– – KW 4170 — Last listed 1997
– – KW 5736 — NMun
§ – – Litiense Group — NMun SLdr
– – LS&E 15764 — NMun
– – LS&T 5679 — NMun
– – LS&T 5686 — NMun
– – LS&T 6591 — NMun
– – R 18333 — Last listed 1997
– – R 25391 — Last listed 1997
– – SSNY 99 — Last listed 1997
– yellow — GGGa
'Ward's Ruby' (EA) — CTrh CTrw
'Warrior' (EA) — SBrw
§ 'Washington State Centennial' (A) — GGGa
*wasonii* — GGGa LHyd LMil MDun NMun
– McLaren AD 106 — Last listed 1997
– f.*rhododactylum* — NMun SLdr SReu
– – KW 1876 — GGGa
– var.*wenchuanense* C 5046 — NHol
– white — SLdr SReu
– yellow form — LMil

'Waterfall' — MBal
*watsonii* — GGGa MDun NMun SLdr SReu
– CC&H 3939 — Last listed 1998
– EGM 109 — LMil
– PA Cox 5075 — GGGa
'Waxwing' — LKna
*websterianum* EGM 146 — LMil
– PA Cox 5123 — GGGa
– PA Cox 5123a — Last listed 1998
'Wee Annie' (V) — CEqu
'Wee Bee' — CDoC EPot GCrs GGGa LMil MAsh MBri MDun MLea NHar NHed NHol SReu SSpi WAbe
§ Wega Group — LHyd
'Wellesleyanum' — Last listed 1998
'Werei' — NMun
'Werrington' — CGre
'Westminster' (O) — LKna LMil
'Weston's Innocence' — Last listed 1998
'Weston's Pink Diamond' — GGGa LMil NHol
'Weybridge' — NMun SLdr
*weyrichii* (A) — GGGa
¶ 'Wheatear' — GGGa
'Whidbey Island' — LMil
'Whisperingrose' — CSam LMil MBal MBri MLea
¶ 'White Cloud' — MAsh
'White Frills' (EA) — LMil MBal SMur
White Glory Group & cl. — NMun SLdr
¶ 'White Grandeur' (EA) — CTrh
'White Jade' (EA) — SLdr
'White Lady' (EA) — LKna MBar SBrw SLdr SRms WGor
'White Lights' (A) — GChr LMil LRHS MLea
'White Olympic Lady' — LKna
¶ 'White Perfume' — SReu
¶ 'White Sport' (A) — SLdr
'White Swan' (K) — Last listed 1996
'White Swan' ♀ — ENot LKna LMil MBal SBrw SReu
'White Wings' — GQui SLdr WAbe WPic
'Whitethroat' (K/d) ♀ — EPfP GQui IOrc LKna LMil MAsh MBri SLdr
'Whitney's Dwarf Red' — SLdr
'Wigeon' — GGGa LMil NHol SPer
*wightii* — GGGa MDun NMun SLdr
– BM&W 153* — MBal
– DF 542 — MBal
– KR 877 — Last listed 1997
'Wilbrit Rose' — SBod
'Wild Affair' — Last listed 1997
'Wilgen's Ruby' ♀ — LKna MBar MGos SBod SBrw SPer WStI
'Willbrit' — CDoC CHig CWri ECho LHyd MAsh MDun MGos MOne WGor
*williamsianum* ♀ — CB&S CDoC CSam CTrG GChr GGGa ISea LHyd LMil MBal MBar MDun MGos MLea NMun NWea SBrw SLdr SPer SReu SRms SSpi WBod WPic WSHC
– Caerhays form — LMil MPla
– pink — WWat
– 'Special' — GGGa
– white — CPMA MBal NMun WWat
'Willy' (EA) — CTrh SLdr
*wilsoniae* — See *R. latoucheae*
Wilsonii Group — CTrG
'Wilsonii' (Ad) — LKna
*wiltonii* — GGGa LMil MDun NMun SLdr
– CC&H 3906 — GGGa
'Windbeam' — SBod

| | | |
|---|---|---|
| 'Windlesham Scarlet' ♀ | ENot LHyd LMil SBrw | |
| ¶ 'Windsor Hawk' | CWri | |
| 'Windsor Lad' | LKna SBrw SReu | |
| Winsome Group & cl. | CB&S CHig CSam CTrw CWri | |
| | GCHN GGGa IOrc LHyd LKna | |
| | MAsh MBal MBar MDun MLea | |
| | NMun SBid SBrw SLdr SPer SSta | |
| | WBod | |
| 'Winston Churchill' (M) | MBar SReu | |
| I 'Winter Green' (EA) | Last listed 1997 | |
| 'Wintergreen' (EA) | COtt CTrh | |
| 'Wishmoor' ♀ | LMil NMun SLdr SReu | |
| 'Witch Doctor' | CDoC ECho LMil SBod SBrw | |
| 'Witchery' | GGGa | |
| 'Wojnar's Purple' | LMil | |
| 'Wombat' (EA) | CDoC COtt CTrh GChr GGGa | |
| | LHyd LMil MBal MBar MGos | |
| | NHed NHol SLdr SReu WAbe | |
| 'Wonderland' | LKna | |
| *wongii* | CSam GGGa GQui LMil NMun | |
| 'Woodcock' | GGGa | |
| 'Woodside' | Last listed 1998 | |
| 'Wren' | CSam GCrs GGGa MAsh MBal | |
| | MBar MBri MDun MLea MOne | |
| | NHar NHol SReu WAbe | |
| 'Wryneck' (K) ♀ | LHyd LMil MBri SReu | |
| *xanthocodon* | See *R. cinnabarinum* subsp. | |
| | *xanthocodon* | |
| *xanthostephanum* | NMun | |
| ¶ – CCH&H 8070 | GGGa | |
| – KR 3095 | LMil | |
| 'Xenophile' | Last listed 1996 | |
| 'Yachiyo Red' | Last listed 1997 | |
| 'Yaku Angel' | MDun | |
| ¶ 'Yaku Incense' | MBri MDun | |
| 'Yaku Prince' | CAbP IOrc MBri SPer | |
| 'Yaku Princess' | CAbP IOrc MLea SPer | |
| 'Yaku Queen' | Last listed 1998 | |
| *yakushimanum* | CB&S CDoC CMHG CSam CWri | |
| | GGGa IOrc LKna LMil MBar MBri | |
| | MDun MGos NHol NMun SBrw | |
| | SLdr SPer SReu SSta WAbe WGer | |
| I – 'Angel' | MLea WWeb | |
| I – 'Beefeater' | SLdr | |
| ¶ – 'Berg' | MDun | |
| – x *bureaui* | MBal MLea SReu | |
| – x *campanulatum* | GGGa | |
| 'Roland Cooper' | | |
| ¶ – x 'Coronation Day' | SLdr | |
| – x *decorum* | GGGa SLdr SReu | |
| – 'Edelweiss' | GGGa | |
| – x 'Elizabeth' | GGGa | |
| – Exbury form | SReu | |
| – FCC form | CPMA EBee SBrw SReu WWat | |
| – x 'Floriade' | SLdr | |
| ¶ – x *griersonianum* | SLdr | |
| § – 'Koichiro Wada' ♀ | GGGa LHyd MBal MGos NMun | |
| | SLdr | |
| – x *lanatum* | GGGa | |
| – subsp. *makinoi* | See *R. makinoi* | |
| – 'Mist Maiden' | MLea | |
| – x *pachysanthum* | GGGa SLdr SReu | |
| – x *ponticum* | GGGa | |
| – x *proteoides* | GGGa | |
| – x *rex* | GGGa SReu | |
| – x 'Sappho' | Last listed 1998 | |
| ¶ – 'Snow Mountain' | SReu | |

| | | |
|---|---|---|
| I – 'Torch' | Last listed 1997 | |
| – Tremeer tall form | Last listed 1996 | |
| – x *tsariense* | GGGa | |
| – subsp. *yakushimanum* | See *R.* 'Ken Janeck' | |
| 'Ken Janeck' | | |
| * 'Yaya' | Last listed 1997 | |
| ¶ 'Yaye' (EA) | CDoC | |
| § *yedoense* var. | SLdr SReu | |
| *poukhanense* | | |
| 'Yellow Cloud' (K) | CDoC ECho | |
| 'Yellow Dane' | GGGa | |
| 'Yellow Hammer' ♀ | CTrG EPfP MDun SBrw | |
| Yellow Hammer Group | CB&S CHig CSam CWri GGGa | |
| | LKna LMil MBal MBar MGos | |
| | NMun SBid SBod SLdr SPer SReu | |
| | SRms SSta WAbe WBod | |
| 'Yellow Petticoats' | MBri MLea | |
| 'Yellow Pippin' | CWri | |
| 'Yellow Rolls Royce' | MDun | |
| 'Yoga' (K) | LKna | |
| ¶ 'Yol' | SLdr | |
| 'Youthful Sin' | MBal | |
| 'Yo-zakura' (EA) | NMun | |
| Yuncinn Group | Last listed 1996 | |
| *yungningense* | LMil NMun WAbe | |
| – F 29268 | See *R. impeditum* F 29268 | |
| *yunnanense* | CB&S CHig GGGa IOrc ISea LHyd | |
| | LMil MDun NMun SLdr | |
| – AC 751 | NMun | |
| – C&H 7145 | GGGa | |
| – 'Diana Colville' | Last listed 1996 | |
| – Hormophorum Group | Last listed 1996 | |
| – KGB 551 | SReu | |
| – KGB 559 | SReu | |
| – 'Openwood' ♀ | GGGa LMil | |
| – pink | GGGa | |
| ¶ – 'Red Throat' | SLdr | |
| – SF 379 | ISea | |
| – SF 400 | ISea | |
| ¶ – SF 96102 | ISea | |
| § – Suberosum Group | NMun | |
| * – 'Tower Court' | Last listed 1996 | |
| – TW 400 | Last listed 1997 | |
| – white | GGGa | |
| aff. *yunnanense* ACE 2097 | Last listed 1998 | |
| Yvonne Group | Last listed 1996 | |
| 'Yvonne Dawn' | NMun | |
| *zaleucum* | MDun | |
| – AC 685 | NMun | |
| – F 15688 | GGGa | |
| – F 27603 | NMun | |
| – Flaviflorum Group | NMun | |
| KW 20837 | | |
| ¶ – SF 347 | ISea | |
| ¶ – SF 578 | ISea | |
| – TW 373 | Last listed 1997 | |
| Zelia Plumecocq Group & cl. | CWri NMun | |
| *zeylanicum* | See *R. arboreum* subsp. | |
| | *zeylanicum* | |
| *zoelleri* (V) | CEqu | |
| Zuiderzee Group | SBrw SLdr | |

# RHODOHYPOXIS (Hypoxidaceae)

| | |
|---|---|
| 'Albrighton' | CAvo CBro CInt CRDP ELan EPot |
| | ERos EWes LAma SBla SIng WAbe |
| | WPat |
| 'Appleblossom' | CAvo EPot ERos EWes GCrs SIng |
| | WAbe |

| | |
|---|---|
| ***baurii*** ♀ | CAvo CElw CHea CInt CNic CRDP ELan EPot GCrs IMGH MBro MTho NNrd NRoo NSla NTow SRms WPyg WWin WWye |
| - 'Alba' | CBro CRDP CTri EDAr WWye |
| - var. ***baurii*** | EPot EWes GCrs LBee |
| - var. ***confecta*** | EPot EWes SIng |
| - 'Dulcie' | EDAr EPot EWes NTow SWas WAbe |
| - forms | Last listed 1997 |
| * - x ***parousia*** | EWes |
| - pink | WCru |
| - 'Pinkeen' | EPot WAbe |
| - var. ***platypetala*** | CRDP EHyt EPot EWes NHol NMen WAbe |
| - - x ***milloides***, Burtt 6981 | EWes |
| - red | WCru |
| - 'Susan Garnett-Botfield' | EPot EWes SIng WAbe |
| - white | WCru |
| 'Betsy Carmine' | Last listed 1997 |
| 'Confusion' | EHyt EWes WAbe |
| 'Dawn' | CAvo EHyt EPot EWes LAma NHol SBla SIng WAbe |
| ***deflexa*** | CGra EHyt EWes GCrs IMGH SIng WAbe |
| 'Donald Mann' | EHyt EWes |
| 'Douglas' | CRDP EHyt EPot LAma NHol NNrd SBla SIng WAbe WLRN WPat WPyg |
| 'Dusky' | EPot |
| 'E.A. Bowles' | EWes GCrs SIng WAbe |
| 'Emily Peel' | EPot EWes WAbe |
| 'Eva-Kate' | EPot ERos EWes LAma SBla SIng WAbe WPat |
| 'Fred Broome' | CBro ELan EPot EWes GCrs LAma NHol NTow SBla SIng WAbe WFar WPat WPyg |
| 'Garnett' | EDAr EPot EWes GCrs SBla WPat |
| 'Great Scott' | ECho EPot EWes WAbe |
| 'Harlequin' | CBro ELan EPot EWes LAma NHol SIng WAbe |
| ♦ 'Hebron Farm Biscuit' | See *Hypoxis parvula* var. *albiflora* 'Hebron Farm Biscuit' |
| ♦ 'Hebron Farm Cerise' | See x *Rhodoxis* 'Hebron Farm Cerise' |
| ♦ 'Hebron Farm Pink' | See x *Rhodoxis hybrida* 'Hebron Farm Pink' |
| § 'Helen' | EPot EWes NHol SBla WAbe |
| hybrids | ELan |
| 'Knockdolian Red' | NHol |
| 'Margaret Rose' | EPot EWes GCrs WAbe |
| ***milloides*** | CPla CRDP EHyt EPot EWes IMGH LBee NHol NMen NWCA SBla SSpi WAbe |
| - 'Claret' | CRDP EWes SBla WAbe |
| - 'Damask' | CRDP EWes SBla |
| - giant form | Last listed 1997 |
| 'Monty' | EPot EWes WAbe |
| 'New Look' | ERos EWes WAbe |
| 'Perle' | EPot ERos EWes NMen NNrd WAbe |
| 'Picta' | CAvo CRDP EHyt EPot EWes GCrs LAma NHol NNrd SBla SSpi WAbe WPat |
| 'Pink Pearl' | EPot EWes NHol |
| 'Pinkeen' | EWes GCrs |
| 'Ruth' | EHyt EPot EWes LAma NHol SBla WAbe |
| 'Shell Pink' | EWes |

| | |
|---|---|
| ¶ 'Starry Eyes' (d) | CRDP |
| 'Stella' | CAvo EPot ERos EWes GCrs NHol SBla SIng WAbe |
| 'Tetra Pink' | EWes SIng |
| 'Tetra Red' | EPot EWes NHol NMen SIng WAbe WWin |
| 'Tetra White' | See *R.* 'Helen' |
| ***thodiana*** | CAvo CRDP EPot EWes SBla SIng SSpi |
| 'True' | Last listed 1996 |

## RHODOHYPOXIS x HYPOXIS (Hypoxidaceae)
| | |
|---|---|
| ♦ *R. baurii* x *H. parvula* | See x *Rhodoxis hybrida* |

## RHODOMYRTUS (Myrtaceae)
| | |
|---|---|
| ***tomentosa*** | Last listed 1997 |

## RHODOPHIALA (Amaryllidaceae)
| | |
|---|---|
| § ***advena*** | EHyt WCot |
| - yellow form | Last listed 1997 |
| ***bakeri*** F&W 7196 | Last listed 1997 |
| § ***bifida*** | LBow |
| - ***spathacea*** | LBow |
| ***chilensis*** | CLAP |
| ***elwesii*** | EHyt |
| ¶ ***montana*** | NWoo |
| ¶ - JCA 14366 | SBla |
| ¶ - JCA 14422 | SBla |

## RHODORA See RHODODENDRON

## RHODOTHAMNUS (Ericaceae)
| | |
|---|---|
| ***chamaecistus*** | GCrs WAbe |

## RHODOTYPOS (Rosaceae)
| | |
|---|---|
| ***kerrioides*** | See *R. scandens* |
| § ***scandens*** | CB&S CBot CDul CHan CPle EPfP GBin MPla MTis NTow SBid SLon SMac SSpi WBod WCru WSHC WWin |

## x RHODOXIS (Hypoxidaceae)
| | |
|---|---|
| § 'Hebron Farm Cerise' | EWes |
| § ***hybrida*** | CRDP EWes SBla SIng WAbe |
| § - 'Hebron Farm Pink' | EWes GCrs SBla SIng WAbe |
| ¶ - 'Hebron Farm Red Eye' | EWes SBla WAbe |

## RHOEO See TRADESCANTIA

## RHOICISSUS (Vitaceae)
| | |
|---|---|
| ***capensis*** ♀ | Last listed 1990 |

## RHOPALOSTYLIS (Arecaceae)
| | |
|---|---|
| ***baueri*** | CBrP LPal |
| ***cheesemanii*** | CBrP |
| ***sapida*** | CBrP ECou LPal |
| ¶ - 'Chatham Island' | CBrP |

## RHUS (Anacardiaceae)
| | |
|---|---|
| ***ambigua*** B&SWJ 3656 | WCru |
| § ***aromatica*** | CAgr CArn CFil ELau EPfP WPGP |
| ***chinensis*** | CDoC EPfP |
| ***copallina*** | EPfP SMur |
| ***cotinus*** | See *Cotinus coggygria* |
| ***glabra*** | CAgr CArn CB&S CDoC NFla SPer WPGP |
| - 'Laciniata' Carrière | Last listed 1997 |
| - 'Laciniata' hort. | See *R.* x *pulvinata* Autumn Lace Group |
| N ***hirta*** | See *R. typhina* |
| ***incisa*** | Last listed 1997 |

| | |
|---|---|
| *integrifolia* | CArn |
| *leptodictya* | Last listed 1997 |
| *pendulina* | CGre |
| *potaninii* | EPfP WWat |
| § x *pulvinata* Autumn Lace Group | CDoC EPfP MGos SDix |
| - (Autumn Lace Group) 'Red Autumn Lace' ♀ | LRHS MBlu MBri SPer |
| *punjabensis* | Last listed 1997 |
| § *radicans* | CArn GPoy |
| ¶ *succedanea* | SSpi |
| *toxicodendron* | See *R. radicans* |
| *trichocarpa* | SLPl SMur SSpi |
| ◆ *trilobata* | See *R. aromatica* |
| N *typhina* ♀ | More than 30 suppliers |
| § - 'Dissecta' ♀ | CB&S CDoC CDul CLnd EBee ELan ENot GRei IOrc MBar MBri MGos MWat NBee NFla NLon SEND SEas SMad SPer WDin WTro |
| - 'Laciniata' hort. | See *R. typhina* 'Dissecta' |
| *verniciflua* | CFil CLnd SSpi |

## RHYNCHELYTRUM See MELINIS

## RHYNCHOSIA (Papilionaceae)
| | |
|---|---|
| ¶ *sordida* | WCot |

## RHYNCHOSPORA (Cyperaceae)
| | |
|---|---|
| § *colorata* | CInt CRow MCCP |

## RIBES ✿ (Grossulariaceae)
| | |
|---|---|
| *alpinum* | CAgr ELan ENot GOrc GRei IOrc LBuc NSti NWea SBid SPer SRms WDin WTro |
| - 'Aureum' | CMHG EBee EHoe ELan EPla NFor NPro WCot WDin WSHC WTro |
| - 'Schmidt' | MBar NFla |
| *amarum* | Last listed 1998 |
| *americanum* | EPla |
| - 'Variegatum' | EBee EHoe ELan EPla EWTr NHol SPan WCom WPat WPyg |
| *atrosanguineum* | See *R. sanguineum* 'Atrorubens' |
| *aureum* hort. | See *R. odoratum* |
| * - 'Roxby Red' | MCoo |
| 'Black Velvet' (F) | CBlo CMac COtt LRHS MBri MCoo SPer |
| *bracteosum* | CPle |
| *californicum* | Last listed 1998 |
| x *culverwellii* Jostaberry (F) | CAgr EMui GTwe LBuc LRHS SDea |
| ¶ *diacanthum* | CFil |
| *divaricatum* | CAgr |
| - 'Worcesterberry' (F) | CMac CWSG EMui MBri MGos NRog SDea SPer |
| *gayanum* | CGre CPle LHop SLPl WHCG |
| *glutinosum* | See *R. sanguineum* var. *glutinosum* |
| x *gordonianum* | CDoC CGre CHan CMHG CMil CPle CWSG EBee EPla GBin LHop MBal MBel MHlr MRav SBid SEND SLon SMrm SPan WCot WHCG WPyg WWat |
| ¶ 'Kathleen' | SApp |
| *laurifolium* | CB&S CBot CFil CPla CPle CSam EBee ELan IOrc MBal MBel MRav SBid SEND SPer SSpi SSta WCot WCru WDin WHCG WPyg WSHC WWal WWat WWin |
| - (f) | CPMA |
| - (m) | CPMA |
| - 'Mrs Amy Doncaster' | EPla |

| | |
|---|---|
| *lobbii* | CPle |
| * *macabeanum* | Last listed 1996 |
| *nigrum* 'Amos Black' (F) | GTwe |
| - 'Baldwin' (F) | CMac GBon SDea SPer WStI WWeb |
| * - 'Barchatnaja' (F) | CAgr |
| - 'Ben Alder' (F) | CBlo SDea |
| - 'Ben Connan' (F) ♀ | COtt EMui GTwe MGos SCoo SDea WLRN |
| - 'Ben Lomond' (F) ♀ | CBlo CTri EBee EMui GBon GChr GRei GTwe LBuc MBri MGos NBee NRog SDea SPer WStI |
| - 'Ben Loyal' (F) | GTwe |
| - 'Ben More' (F) | CBlo GRei GTwe MBri NBee SDea SPer WStI |
| - 'Ben Nevis' (F) | CBlo CTri EBee GTwe SDea |
| - 'Ben Sarek' (F) ♀ | CBlo CSam CSut EBee EBrP EBre EMui ERea GRei GTwe LBre LBuc MBri MGos NRog SBre SDea SPer WWeb |
| - 'Ben Tirran' (F) | CBlo CDoC LBuc MGos |
| - 'Black Reward' (F) | Last listed 1996 |
| - 'Blackdown' (F) | Last listed 1997 |
| - 'Blacksmith' (F) | WLRN |
| - 'Boskoop Giant' (F) | CMac GTwe NRog SPer |
| * - 'Byelorussian Sweet' (F) | CAgr |
| * - 'Cascade' (F) | Last listed 1997 |
| * - 'Cherry' (F) | Last listed 1997 |
| - 'Consort' (F) | CAgr |
| - 'Daniel's September' (F) | GTwe |
| - 'Farleigh' (F) | EMui |
| - 'Foxendown' | EMui |
| * - 'Hystawneznaya' (F) | CAgr |
| - 'Jet' (F) | CBlo GTwe LRHS NRog SPer WLRN |
| * - 'Kosmicheskaya' (F) | Last listed 1998 |
| - 'Laxton's Giant' (F) | GTwe |
| - 'Mendip Cross' (F) | CBlo GTwe |
| - 'Pilot Alexander Mamkin' (F) | Last listed 1998 |
| - 'Seabrook's' (F) | Last listed 1997 |
| - 'Wellington XXX' (F) | CBlo ERea GTwe LBuc MBri NBee NRog WStI WWeb |
| - 'Westwick Choice' (F) | GTwe |
| § *odoratum* | CB&S CBlo CChe CDoC CMHG CPle CSam EBee ECoo ELan ENot EPla EWTr GOrc LHol MBar MBel MGos MPla NLon NWea SEas SPer SRms SSpi SUsu WHCG WSHC WWat WWin |
| - 'Crandall' | Last listed 1998 |
| *praecox* | CB&S MBlu SEND |
| *propinquum* | CPiN |
| *roezlii* | CPle |
| *rubrum* 'Blanka' (W) | CSut |
| - 'Cascade' (R) | Last listed 1998 |
| - 'Fay's New Prolific' (R) | GTwe |
| - 'Hollande Rose' (P) | GTwe |
| - 'Jonkheer van Tets' (R) ♀ | EMui GTwe LRHS MGos SDea WTro |
| - 'Junifer' (R) | CAgr CSut EMui GTwe |
| - 'Laxton's Number One' (R) | CAgr CBlo CSam CTri EBrP EBre EMui GBon GRei GTwe LBre MBri NRog SBre SDea SPer WWeb |
| - 'Laxton's Perfection' (R) | MCoo |
| - 'October Currant' (P) | GTwe |
| - 'Raby Castle' (R) | GTwe |
| - 'Red Lake' (R) ♀ | CBlo CMac CSam EBrP EBre ERea GBon GChr GRei GTwe LBre LBuc MBri MGos NBee NRog SBre SDea SPer WStI |

| | |
|---|---|
| - 'Redstart' (R) | CBlo COtt GTwe LBuc LRHS MBri SDea WWeb |
| - 'Rondom' (R) | SDea |
| - 'Rovada' (R) | CSut EMui |
| - 'Stanza' (R) ♀ | GTwe SDea |
| § - 'Versailles Blanche' (W) | CBlo CDoC CMac CSam CTri EMui GChr GTwe LBuc MBri MGos SDea SPer WWeb |
| - 'White Dutch' (W) | MCoo |
| - 'White Grape' (W) ♀ | CBlo CTri GTwe NRog |
| - 'White Pearl' (W) | CB&S GRei |
| - 'White Transparent' (W) | GTwe |
| - White Versailles | See *R. rubrum* 'Versailles Blanche' |
| - 'Wilson's Long Bunch' (R) | GTwe |
| ***sanguineum*** | CBlo CLTr CPle CSam GChr MBal MBar NCut NFor NLon WStI |
| - 'Albescens' | SLon SPer WBcn |
| - 'Brocklebankii' ♀ | CAbP CBlo EAst EBee EPar EPla LHop MGos MPla SAga SBid SPer SPla WAbe WGwG WSHC |
| - double | See *R. sanguineum* 'Plenum' |
| - 'Elk River Red' | Last listed 1996 |
| - 'Flore Pleno' | See *R. sanguineum* 'Plenum' |
| - 'Giant White' | Last listed 1996 |
| - var. *glutinosum* 'Albidum' | SChu WWat |
| - 'King Edward VII' | CBlo CDoC EBee ECtt GChr LBuc MBar MGos MWat NBee NFor NWea SLon SPer SPla SRPl SReu SRms WDin WFar WGwG WMoo WStI WTro WWeb |
| - 'Koja' | LRHS MBri NPro |
| - 'Lombartsii' | CBlo EPla MRav |
| § - 'Plenum' (d) | CBot |
| - 'Porky Pink' | CLyn EBrP EBre GSki LBre LRHS MAsh MBri MGos MRav SBre |
| - 'Pulborough Scarlet' ♀ | CB&S CBlo CChe CDoC CLTr EBee ELan ENot EWTr GOrc MAsh MGos MPla MRav MWat NBee NBir NFla SPer SPla SRms WFar WWeb |
| - 'Pulborough Scarlet Variegated' | CBlo CPMA LHop MPla SBid |
| - 'Red Pimpernel' | CDoC EAst MBNS MBri WBcn WFar |
| - 'Roseum' | See *R. sanguineum* 'Carneum' |
| - 'Splendens' | Last listed 1997 |
| - 'Taff's Kim' (v) | CPMA EPla |
| - 'Tydeman's White' ♀ | CBlo CChe CPMA CPle EAst ECtt EPfP EPla MBar MBlu SBid SSpi WStI |
| ♦ - 'Ubric' | See *R. sanguineum* White Icicle = 'Ubric' |
| § - White Icicle = 'Ubric' | CBlo CBot CDoC CWSG EBee EBrP EBre ELan GSki LBre MAsh MBri MGos NBir SBre SPla SSto WWat |
| ***speciosum*** ♀ | More than 30 suppliers |
| ***tenue*** | EPla |
| ***uva-crispa*** var. *reclinatum* 'Achilles' (C/D) | GTwe |
| - - 'Admiral Beattie' (F) | GTwe NRog |
| - - 'Alma' (D) | NRog |
| - - 'Annelii' (F) | SDea |
| - - 'Aston Red' | See *R. uva-crispa* var. *reclinatum* 'Warrington' |
| - - 'Australia' (F) | NRog |
| - - 'Bedford Red' (D) | GTwe NRog |
| - - 'Bedford Yellow' (D) | GTwe |
| - - 'Beech Tree Nestling' (F) | GTwe |
| - - 'Bellona' (C) | NRog |
| - - 'Blucher' (F) | NRog |
| - - 'Bright Venus' (D) | GTwe |
| - - 'Broom Girl' (D) | GTwe NRog |
| - - 'Captivator' (F) | GTwe |
| - - 'Careless' (C) ♀ | CBlo CMac CSam CTri EBee EMui ERea GBon GRei GTwe IOrc MBri MGos NBee NRog SDea SPer WStI WWeb |
| - - 'Catherina' (C/D) | Last listed 1997 |
| - - 'Champagne Red' (F) | GTwe |
| - - 'Clayton' (F) | NRog |
| - - 'Cook's Eagle' (C) | GTwe |
| - - 'Cousen's Seedling' (F) | GTwe |
| - - 'Criterion' (C) | GTwe NRog |
| - - 'Crown Bob' (C/D) | GTwe LRHS NRog |
| - - 'Dan's Mistake' (D) | GTwe NRog |
| - - 'Drill' (F) | GTwe |
| - - 'Early Sulphur' (D/C) | CBlo GTwe LRHS NRog SDea WStI |
| - - 'Edith Cavell' (F) | GTwe |
| - - 'Firbob' (D) | GTwe NRog |
| - - 'Forester' (D) | GTwe |
| - - 'Freedom' (C) | GTwe LRHS NRog |
| - - 'Gipsey Queen' (F) | GTwe |
| - - 'Glenton Green' (F) | GTwe |
| - - 'Golden Ball' (D) | SDea |
| - - 'Golden Drop' (D) | GTwe LRHS |
| - - 'Green Gascoigne' | See *R. uva-crispa* var. *reclinatum* 'Early Green Hairy' |
| - - 'Green Gem' (C/D) | GTwe NRog |
| - - 'Green Ocean' (F) | GTwe NRog |
| - - 'Greenfinch' (F) ♀ | CWSG EBee EMui GTwe LRHS MGos SDea |
| - - 'Greengage' (D) | NRog |
| - - 'Gretna Green' (F) | GTwe |
| - - 'Guido' (F) | GTwe NRog |
| - - 'Gunner' (D) | CTri GTwe NRog |
| - - 'Heart of Oak' (F) | GTwe NRog |
| ¶ - - 'Hebburn Prolific' (D) | GTwe |
| - - 'Hedgehog' (D) | GTwe |
| - - 'Hero of the Nile' (C) | GTwe NRog |
| - - 'High Sheriff' (D) | GTwe NRog |
| ¶ - - 'Hinnonmäki' | CAgr |
| ¶ - - 'Hinnonmäki Gul' | SDea |
| ¶ - - 'Hinnonmäki Röd' (F) | GTwe SDea |
| - - 'Howard's Lancer' (C/D) | GTwe NRog SDea |
| - - 'Invicta' (C) ♀ | CBlo CDoC CMac CSut CTri CWSG EBee EBrP EBre EMui GBon GChr GRei LBre LBuc MBri MGos SBre SDea SPer WStI WWeb |
| - - 'Ironmonger' (F) | CBlo GTwe NRog |
| - - 'Jubilee' (C/D) | COtt CTri LBuc MBri MGos NRog WStI |
| - - 'Keen's Seedling' (D) | GTwe |
| - - 'Keepsake' (C/D) | CBlo GTwe LRHS NRog SDea |
| - - 'King of Trumps' (F) | GTwe LRHS NRog |
| - - 'Lancashire Lad' (C/D) | GTwe LRHS NRog |
| - - 'Langley Gage' (D) | GTwe LRHS NRog |
| - - 'Laxton's Amber' (D) | GTwe |
| - - 'Leveller' (C/D) ♀ | CBlo CMac CTri EBrP EBre EMui GBon GChr GTwe LBre LBuc MBri MGos NRog SBre SDea SPer WStI WWeb |
| - - 'London' (C/D) | GTwe LRHS NRog |
| - - 'Lord Derby' (C/D) | CBlo GTwe MBri NRog |
| - - 'Lord Kitchener' (F) | NRog |

- - 'Macherauch's Seedling' NRog
(F)
- - 'Marigold' (F)     NRog
- - 'Matchless' (D)     NRog
- - 'May Duke' (C/D)     LRHS NRog SDea
- - 'Mitre' (C)     GTwe
- - 'Pax'     CDoC CWSG EMui GTwe LBuc
SDea WLRN
- - 'Peru'     GTwe NRog
- - 'Pitmaston Green     GTwe
Gage' (D)
- - 'Plunder' (F)     NRog
- - 'Prince Charles' (F)     GTwe
- - 'Queen of Hearts' (F)     NRog
- - 'Queen of Trumps' (C)     GTwe NRog
- - 'Rifleman' (D)     GTwe
- - 'Rokula'     CDoC EMui GTwe
¶ - - 'Rosebery' (D)     GTwe
¶ - - 'Scotch Red Rough' (D) GTwe
- - 'Scottish Chieftan' (D) GTwe
- - 'Sir George Brown' (D) NRog
- - 'Snowdrop' (C)     GTwe
- - 'Speedwell' (F)     NRog
- - 'Spinefree' (F)     GTwe
- - 'Sultan Juror' (F)     NRog
- - 'Surprise' (C)     GTwe NRog
- - 'Suter Johnny' (F)     NRog
- - 'Telegraph' (F)     GTwe
- - 'The Leader' (F)     NRog
- - 'Tom Joiner' (F)     GTwe
- - 'Trumpeter' (C)     NRog
- - 'Victoria' (F)     GTwe LRHS NRog
§ - - 'Warrington' (D)     GTwe NRog
- - 'Whinham's Industry'     CBlo CMac CSam CSut EMui ERea
(C/D) ♀     GBon GChr GRei GTwe IOrc
LBuc MBri MGos NBee NRog
SDea SPer WStI
- - 'White Eagle' (C)     NRog
- - 'White Lion' (C/D)     GTwe LRHS
- - 'White Transparent' (C) GTwe
- - 'Whitesmith' (C/D)     CTri GTwe LRHS NRog SDea WStI
- - 'Woodpecker' (F)     GTwe LRHS NRog
- - 'Yellow Champagne' (F) GTwe LRHS NRog
viburnifolium     CPle EBee LEdu LRHS SPan SSta
SVen WPGP WWat

## RICHEA (Epacridaceae)
dracophylla     CFil SAPC
milliganii     CFil WPGP
scoparia     CFil SAPC

## RICINUS (Euphorbiaceae)
communis     Last listed 1998
- 'Carmencita' ♀     LBlo
- 'Gibsonii'     EOas LBlo
- 'Impala'     LBlo MLan SSoC
- 'Niger'     WMul
- 'Zanzibariensis'     EOas LBlo WMul

## RIGIDELLA (Iridaceae)
¶ orthantha     CPLG

## RIVINA (Phytolaccaceae)
humilis     Last listed 1997

## ROBINIA (Papilionaceae)
x ambigua 'Bellarosea'     Last listed 1996
- 'Decaisneana'     Last listed 1996
boyntonii     CTho MGos
fertilis     SIgm SSpi WShe

hispida ♀     CCHP CEnd CLnd CTho ELan
EPfP ICrw LNet MBlu MHlr SSpi
SSta WPyg WSHC
- 'Macrophylla'     CBlo CEnd SSpi
N - 'Rosea'     CB&S CBlo CBot EBee ENot LRHS
MGos NFla
kelseyi     CBlo CDul IOrc SPer WPyg
luxurians     Last listed 1996
x margaretta Casque     See R. x margaretta 'Pink
Rouge     Cascade'
§ - 'Pink Cascade'     CBlo CDoC CEnd CTho EBee
LNet LPan MBri MGos MMea SBid
SPer SRPl SSpi WDin WPyg
neomexicana     CAgr CLnd
pseudoacacia ♀     CAgr CB&S CBlo CLnd ELan ENot
GAri LBuc LPan MCoo WFar
WNor
- 'Bessoniana'     CBlo CLnd CTho ENot
- 'Fastigiata'     See R. pseudoacacia 'Pyramidalis'
- 'Frisia' ♀     More than 30 suppliers
- hort. 'Inermis'     See R. pseudoacacia
'Umbraculifera'
- 'Lace Lady'     EBee ELan ENot LPan LRHS MAsh
MBri MGos MRav SCoo SMad
WWes
- 'Lacy Lady'     Last listed 1998
* - 'Mimosifolia'     MBri
§ - 'Pyramidalis'     CTho ENot
- 'Rozynskiana'     CTho SFam
- 'Sandraudiga'     Last listed 1997
- 'Tortuosa'     CBlo CDul CEnd CLnd CTho
EBee ELan EMil EPfP LPan MAsh
MBri MGos MMea SLdr SLon SPar
SPer SRPl
§ - 'Umbraculifera'     CLnd EMil ENot LPan MGos SFam
- 'Unifoliola'     CTho MAsh
x slavinii 'Hillieri' ♀     CBlo CDul CEnd CLnd CTho
EBee ECrN ELan IOrc LPan MAsh
MWat SBid SFam SPer SSpi WWat
* 'Twisty Baby'     EPfP

## ROCHEA See CRASSULA

## RODGERSIA ✿ (Saxifragaceae)
aesculifolia ♀     More than 30 suppliers
¶ - green bud form     IBlr
- 'Irish Bronze'     IBlr LPio
- pink form     IBlr
¶ aff. aesculifolia petaloid IBlr
¶ 'Blickfang'     IBlr
'Die Anmutige'     CRow
¶ 'Elfenbeinturm'     IBlr
henrici     CRow IBlr MCCP MCli SWat
WPnP WRus
- hybrid     GAri NHol NLar SCob WCru
'Kupfermond'     CRow IBlr
¶ 'Maigrün'     IBlr
nepalensis     CFil IBlr
¶ new hybrids     WHil
'Parasol'     CFil CHad ELan GBuc IBlr NHol
SSpi WPGP
§ 'Perthshire Bronze'     IBlr
pinnata     CDoC CGle CHad CHid CRow
EBee EBrP EBre EHon ERav IBlr
LBre MBal MBri MCli MRav MSta
NDea NFla NHol NVic SBre SChu
SCob SMac SPer WHoo WPyg
WWat WWhi
- 'Alba'     IBlr MBri NHol
¶ - 'Buckland Beauty'     IBlr SSpi
¶ - 'Cally Salmon'     GCal
- CLD 432     Last listed 1996

| | |
|---|---|
| - 'Elegans' | CHad EBrP EBre ELan EMan ENot EPar GMaP IBlr LBre MBel MRav MUlv NHol NOrc SBre SChu SMrm SSoC WGer WWat WWin |
| ¶ - L 1670 | SSpi |
| - 'Maurice Mason' | Last listed 1996 |
| ♦ - 'Perthshire Bronze' | See R. 'Perthshire Bronze' |
| ¶ - x *podophylla* 'Koriata' | IBlr |
| - 'Rosea' | IBlr |
| - 'Superba' ♀ | CBos CHad ECha ECtt EOld GAbr IBlr LFis LGro MBNS MBal MBri MBro MCLN MTis MUlv NBee NFla NHar NPer NSti SLon SSpi WAbe WCot WCru WKif |
| - white form | GCal |
| *podophylla* ♀ | CB&S CHad CHan CRow CWit EBrP EBre ECha GMaP LBre NBir NDea NHol NLar SBla SBre SMac SMad SPer SSoC SSpi WCot WCru WEas WGer WPGP WWat |
| ¶ - 'Bronceblad' | IBlr |
| - Donard form | CFil IBlr WCot |
| - 'Rotlaub' | CRow GCal IBlr MBri WCot |
| - 'Smaragd' | CLAP CRow EBee GCal IBlr |
| *purdomii* hort. | CRow IBlr SSpi |
| § 'Reinecke Fuchs' | IBlr |
| I 'Reinicke Fuchs' | See R. 'Reinecke Fuchs' |
| 'Rosenlicht' | CRow |
| ¶ 'Rosenzipfel' | IBlr |
| *sambucifolia* | CB&S CDoC CRow EBee EMan EWTr MBri MCli MFir MUlv NDea NFla NHar NLar NSti SMac SPer SSoC SSpi WCru WFar WGer WHil WMer |
| - dwarf pink-flowered | IBlr |
| - dwarf white-flowered | IBlr |
| - large green-stemmed | IBlr |
| - large red-stemmed | IBlr |
| - x *pinnata* | IBlr |
| - x - 'Panache' | IBlr |
| sp. ACE 2303 | GBuc WAbe |
| sp. CLD 1329 | NHol |
| sp. CLD 1432 | NHol |
| sp. from Castlewellan | IBlr |
| *tabularis* | See *Astilboides tabularis* |

## ROELLA (Campanulaceae)

| | |
|---|---|
| *ciliata* | Last listed 1998 |
| *maculata* | Last listed 1998 |

## ROHDEA ✿ (Convallariaceae)

| | |
|---|---|
| *japonica* | CFil WPGP |
| - 'Gunjaku' | EMon |
| - 'Lance Leaf' | SApp |
| - long-leaved form | WCru WPGP |
| - 'Talbot Manor' (v) | CFil SApp WCot WPGP |
| ¶ - 'Tama-jishi' (v) | WCot |
| - 'Tuneshige Rokujo' | WCot |
| - variegated | WCot |
| *watanabei* B&SWJ 1911 | WCru |

## ROMANZOFFIA (Hydrophyllaceae)

| | |
|---|---|
| § *sitchensis* | CLyd CTri |
| *suksdorfii* E. Greene | See R. *sitchensis* |
| - hort. | See R. *californica* |
| *tracyi* | Last listed 1997 |
| *unalaschcensis* | CNic GTou NBro NWCA SRms SSca WPer WWin |

## ROMNEYA (Papaveraceae)

| | |
|---|---|
| *coulteri* ♀ | CAbb CB&S CBot CHad CPle EBee ELan IBlr LHop MBlu MBri MGos MLan MWgw SBid SBla SBrw SPer SRPl SReu SRms SSta SVil WCot WDin WSHC WSpi WWat WWeb |
| § - var. *trichocalyx* | IBlr SCro SSpi WAbe |
| § - 'White Cloud' | ENot EREa IBlr MRav SMad SSoC SSpi |
| - 'White Sails' | IBlr |
| x *hybrida* | See R. *coulteri* 'White Cloud' |
| ♦ *trichocalyx* | See R. *coulteri* var. *trichocalyx* |

## ROMULEA (Iridaceae)

| | |
|---|---|
| *battandieri* AB&S 4659 | Last listed 1998 |
| *bifrons* AB&S 4359/4360 | Last listed 1998 |
| *bulbocodium* | CBro CNic EHic |
| - var. *clusiana* | LAma |
| - - MS 239 | EHyt |
| - - Serotina Group | EPot |
| - - SF 237 | Last listed 1998 |
| * - 'Knightshayes' | CLAP EHyt |
| * - var. *leichtliniana* MS 784 | EHyt |
| *campanuloides* | Last listed 1998 |
| *columnae* AB&S 4659 | Last listed 1998 |
| *engleri* SF 3 | Last listed 1998 |
| *hirta* | Last listed 1998 |
| *ligustica* var. *rouyana* SF 360 | Last listed 1998 |
| *linaresii* | EPot LAma |
| - var. *graeca* | Last listed 1997 |
| - - CE&H 620 | Last listed 1998 |
| *longituba* | See R. *macowanii* |
| § *macowanii* | WAbe |
| - var. *alticola* | EHyt WAbe |
| *minutiflora* | NRog |
| *monticola* | Last listed 1998 |
| *nivalis* | CAvo LAma LBow |
| *pratensis* | Last listed 1997 |
| *ramiflora* | Last listed 1998 |
| - SF 63 | Last listed 1998 |
| *requienii* | Last listed 1998 |
| - L65 | EHyt |
| *rosea* | NRog |
| *sabulosa* | Last listed 1998 |
| *saldanhensis* | Last listed 1998 |
| sp. SF 367 | Last listed 1998 |
| *tabularis* | Last listed 1997 |
| *tempskyana* | EHyt EPot |
| 'Zahni' | CNic LAma |

## RONDELETIA (Rubiaceae)

| | |
|---|---|
| ¶ *amoena* | LChe |

## RORIPPA (Brassicaceae)

| | |
|---|---|
| *nasturtium-aquaticum* | MHew |

## ROSA ✿ (Rosaceae)

| | |
|---|---|
| § A Shropshire Lad = 'Ausled' (S) | CSam MAus MJon |
| § Aalsmeer Gold® = 'Bekola' (HT) | Last listed 1998 |
| 'Abbandonata' | See R. 'Laure Davoust' |
| § Abbeyfield Rose = 'Cocbrose' (HT) ♀ | ENot GCoc GGre SJus SPer |
| § 'Abbotswood' (*canina* hybrid) | EBls MAus |
| § Aberdeen Celebration = 'Cocmystery' (F) | GCoc |
| § Abigaile® = 'Tanelaigib' (F) | MJon NBat |

'Abington Park
  Northampton' (HT)      Last listed 1998
§ Abraham Darby® =
  'Auscot' (S)      CGro CSam EBee EBrP EBre GGre
           IHar LBre LStr MAus MFry MGan
           MHlr MJon NPri SBre SPer SRPl
           SWCr WAct WHCG WHow WStI
§ Acapulco =
  'Dicblender' (HT)      EBee IDic MFry MJon
§ Ace of Hearts =
  'Korred' (HT)      MBur
  *acicularis*      EPla
  - var. *nipponensis*      EBls
  'Adam' (ClT)      EBls MAus
  'Adam Messerich' (Bb)      EBee EBls MAus SWCr WHCG
  'Adélaïde d'Orléans' (Ra) ♀      CRHN EBls MAus MBri SFam SPer
           SWCr WAct WHCG WPen
§ Admirable = 'Searodney'
  (Min)      MBur
  'Admiral Rodney' (HT)      MGan MJon NBat NRog
  Adolf Horstmann® (HT)      MGan
¶ Adriana = 'Frydesire' (HT)      MFry
  'Adrienne Berman' (HT)      Last listed 1998
  'Agatha' (G)      EBls
§ Agatha Christie =
  'Kormeita' (ClF)      CGre MBri MJon MMat SApu SJus
  'Agathe Incarnata' (DxG)      Last listed 1997
  'Aglaia' (Ra)      WHCG
  'Agnes' (Ru)      EBee EBls ENot EPfP GCoc IHar
           MAus MGan MMat NFla SJus SPer
           SWCr WAct WHCG WOVN
  'Aimée Vibert' (Ra)      EBee EBls MAus MHlr SFam SPer
           SRPl WAct WHCG
§ Air France =
  'Meifinaro' (Min)      Last listed 1997
  'Alain Blanchard' (G)      EBls MAus WHCG
  x *alba* (A)      EBls NRog
§ - 'Alba Maxima' (A) ♀      CHad EBee EBls ENot GChr GCoc
           MAus MHlr MMat NFla SFam SPer
           SRPl WAct WHCG
§ - 'Alba Semiplena' (A) ♀      EBls MAus SJus SPer WAct WGer
           WHCG WHow
◆ - Celestial      See *R.* 'Céleste'
  - 'Maxima'      See *R.* x *alba* 'Alba Maxima'
§ Alba Meidiland® =
  'Meiflopan' (S/GC)      WOVN
  'Albéric Barbier' (Ra) ♀      CHad CSam EBee EBls ENot LHol
           LStr MAus MBNS MBri MFry
           MGan MHlr MJon MMat NRog
           SApu SJus SPer SRPl SSea SWCr
           WAct WHCG WHow WOVN
§ Albert Weedall =
  'Scriveo' (HT)      Last listed 1997
  'Albertine' (Ra) ♀      More than 30 suppliers
  'Alchymist' (S/Cl)      CHad CPou EBee EBls ENot MAus
           MBri MGan MJon MMat SFam
           SPer SWCr WAct WHCG WHow
§ Alec's Red® = 'Cored' (HT)      CB&S CGro EBls GCoc IHar LPlm
           LStr MAus MBri MGan MJon MMat
           NRog SPer SWas WWeb
§ Alex C. Collie =
  'Cococrust' (F)      GCoc
§ Alexander® =
  'Harlex' (HT) ♀      CGro EBls ENot EWTr GCoc
           LGod LPlm LStr MFry MGan MJon
           MMat NRog SApu SPer
  'Alexander Hill Gray' (T)      EBls
  'Alexander von Humboldt'      MGan
  (Cl)
  'Alexandre Girault' (Ra)      CRHN EBee EBls EMFP MAus
           MHlr SPer SWCr WAct WHCG
           WHow
§ 'Alfred Colomb' (HP)      EBls
  'Alfred de Dalmas' misapplied      See *R.* 'Mousseline'

  'Alida Lovett' (Ra)      EBls MAus
§ Alison = 'Coclibee' (F)      GCoc SApu
§ 'Alister Stella Gray' (N) ♀      EBee EBls EMFP MAus MGan
           MHlr SPer SSea SWCr WAct
           WHCG WHow
  'Allen Chandler' (ClHT)      EBls MAus
  Allgold® (F)      CB&S CGro EBls GCoc LStr MAus
           MGan MJon SWas WStI
  'Allison' (F)      Last listed 1997
  'Aloha' (ClHT)      CB&S CGro EBee EBls EBrP EBre
           IHar IOrc LBre LStr MAus MBur
           MFry MGan MJon MMat NBat
           NRog SApu SBre SChu SJus SPer
           SSea SSoC SWCr WAct WHCG
           WHow WSHC
  *alpina*      See *R. pendulina*
  Alpine Sunset® (HT)      CTri EBee EBls EWTr GGre MGan
           SPer
  *altaica* hort.      See *R. pimpinellifolia*
           'Grandiflora'
§ Altissimo® = 'Delmur' (Cl) ♀      CHad EBee EBls EMFP LPlm MAus
           MGan MHlr MJon MMat SPer SSea
           SWCr WAct WGer
  'Amadis' (Bs)      EBls MAus SWCr WHCG
§ Amanda = 'Beesian' (F)      LStr MBri MJon SApu SWCr
  'Amatsu-otome' (HT)      Last listed 1997
  'Amazing Grace' (HT)      GCoc GGre
§ Amber Nectar =
  'Mehamber' (F)      LStr MJon
§ Amber Queen® =
  'Harroony' (F) ♀      CGro EBee EBls ELan GCoc GGre
           LGod LPlm LStr MAus MBri MBur
           MFry MGan MJon MMat NRog
           SApu SJus SPer SRPl SWCr
◆ 'Ambossfunken'      See *R.* Anvil Sparks =
           'Ambossfunken'
§ Ambridge Rose =
  'Auswonder' (S)      MAus MBri
  'Amélia'      See *R.* 'Celsiana'
  'Amelia Louise' (Min)      Last listed 1997
  'American Pillar' (Ra)      CGro CSam EBee EBls EBrP EBre
           ISea LBre LStr MAus MGan MHlr
           MMat NRog SApu SBre SPer SSea
           WAct WHCG
◆ 'America's Junior Miss'      See *R.* Junior Miss = 'America's
           Junior Miss'
  'Améthyste' (Ra)      Last listed 1998
  Amorette      See *R.* Snowdrop = 'Amoru'
◆ 'Amoru'      See *R.* Snowdrop = 'Amoru'
◆ 'Amruda'      See *R.* Red Ace = 'Amruda'
  'Amy Robsart' (RH)      EBls MAus SJus
§ Anabell = 'Korbell' (F)      MGan
  'Anaïs Ségalas' (G)      MAus
◆ 'Andeli'      See *R.* Double Delight = 'Andeli'
§ 'Andersonii' (*canina* hybrid)      EBls MAus WAct
◆ 'Andgeo'      See *R.* Georgie Anderson =
           'Andgeo'
◆ 'Andglo'      See *R.* Glowing Embers =
           'Andglo'
◆ 'Andour'      See *R.* Our Love = 'Andour'
◆ 'Andwit'      See *R.* With Love = 'Andwit'
  'Anemone' (Cl)      EBls MAus
  *anemoniflora*      See *R.* x *beanii*
  *anemonoides*      See *R.* 'Anemone'
  - 'Ramona'      See *R.* 'Ramona'
§ Angela Rippon® =
  'Ocaru' (Min)      MFry MGan MJon SPer SRPl WGer
  'Angela's Choice' (F)      MGan
  'Angèle Pernet' (HT)      EBls
  'Angelina' (S)      EBls
§ Anisley Dickson® =
  'Dickimono' (F) ♀      IDic LGod MGan NBat SApu SPer

◆ Ann — See *R.* Ann = 'Ausfete'
'Ann Aberconway' (F) — MJon MMat
§ Ann = 'Ausfete' — MAus
'Anna de Diesbach' (HP) — EBls
§ Anna Ford® = 'Harpiccolo' — GGre IHar LGod LPlm LStr MAus
(Min/Patio) ♀ — MGan MJon SApu SWCr
§ Anna Livia = 'Kormetter' — EBee ENot MGan MJon MMat
(F) ♀ — SApu SJus
'Anna Olivier' (T) — EBls
'Anna Pavlova' (HT) — EBls
§ Anna Zinkeisen = — WAct WOVN
'Harquhling' (S)
Anne Cocker® (F) — GCoc MGan
'Anne Dakin' (ClHT) — MAus
§ Anne Harkness® = — MAus MGan MJon NRog SPer
'Harkaramel' (F)
§ Anne Moore = — Last listed 1997
'Morberg' (Min)
'Anne of Geierstein' (RH) — EBls MAus MGan
'Anne Watkins' (HT) — EBls
◆ Antique — See *R.* Antique '89® = 'Kordalen'
§ Antique '89® = — EBee EBls MBri MJon MMat SJus
'Kordalen' (ClF) — WGer
'Antoine Rivoire' (HT) — EBls
'Antonia d'Ormois' (G) — EBls
§ Anusheh = 'Payable' (F) — Last listed 1997
§ Anvil Sparks® = — MGan
'Ambossfunken' (HT)
Apothecary's Rose — See *R. gallica* var. *officinalis*
'Apple Blossom' (Ra) — EBls SWCr WHCG
'Applejack' (S) — EBls
'Apricot Garnet' — See *R.* 'Garnette Apricot'
'Apricot Nectar' (F) — LStr MAus MGan SPer SWCr
'Apricot Silk' (HT) — CB&S CGro CTri EBls IHar MAus
— MGan NRog SPer WWeb
§ Apricot Summer® = — ENot GCoc MBri MJon MMat
'Korpapiro' (Patio) — WGer
§ Apricot Sunblaze® = — EBls MJon SJus WWeb
'Savamark' (Min)
'Apricot Wine' (F) — IHar
'April Hamer' (HT) — NBat
§ Arc Angel = 'Fryorst' (HT) — MFry
§ Arcadian = 'Macnewye' (F) — MJon
'Archiduc Joseph' misapplied — See *R.* 'Général Schablikine'
'Archiduchesse Elisabeth — EBls
d'Autriche' (HP)
§ Arctic Sunrise = — Last listed 1997
'Bararcsun' (Min/GC)
'Ardoisée de Lyon' (HP) — EBls
§ Ards Beauty = 'Dicjoy' (F) — IDic MGan SApu SPer
'Ards Rover' (ClHP) — EBls
'Arethusa' (Ch) — EBls
¶ 'Arizona Sunset' (Min) — NBat
*arkansana* × *moyesii* — Last listed 1996
§ - var. *suffulta* — EBls WHCG
§ Armada® = 'Haruseful' (S) — GCoc SApu
◆ 'Arodi' — See *R.* Heidi = 'Arodi'
◆ 'Arokris' — See *R.* Golden Wedding = 'Arokris'
◆ 'Aromikeh' — See *R.* Hotline = 'Aromikeh'
◆ 'Arowillip' — See *R.* Strawberry Fayre = 'Arowillip'
'Arrillaga' (HP) — MAus
§ Artful Dodger = — MBur
'Sabbelief' (Patio)
'Arthur Bell' (F) ♀ — EBls EBrP EBre EWTr GChr GCoc
— GGre IHar LBre LPlm LStr MAus
— MBur MGan NRog SApu SBre SPer
— SRPl SWas WWeb
'Arthur de Sansal' (DPo) — EBls MAus
'Arthur Scargill' (Min) — Last listed 1997

*arvensis* — CCVT CKin EBls LBuc MAus
— NWea WAct
◆ 'Aschermittwoch' — See *R.* Ash Wednesday = 'Aschermittwoch'
§ Ash Wednesday = — EBls
'Aschermittwoch' (Cl)
'Assemblage des — EBls MAus
Beautés' (G)
'Astrid Späth Striped' (F) — EBls
§ Atco Royale = — MFry
'Frywinner' (F)
§ Atlantic Star = 'Fryworld' (F) — MFry MJon
Audrey Gardner (Min/Patio) — Last listed 1998
Audrey Wilcox (HT) — MFry
'August Seebauer' (F) — EBls MAus
'Auguste Gervais' (Ra) — EBls IHar MAus SPer WHCG
§ Auguste Renoir® = — GGre
'Meitoifar' (HT)
'Augustine Guinoisseau' (HT) — EBls MAus
'Augustine Halem' (HT) — EBls
'Aunty Dora' (F) — Last listed 1997
◆ 'Ausapple' — See *R.* Dapple Dawn = 'Ausapple'
◆ 'Ausbath' — See *R.* The Wife of Bath = 'Ausbath'
◆ 'Ausbeam' — See *R.* Moonbeam = 'Ausbeam'
◆ 'Ausbells' — See *R.* Bow Bells = 'Ausbells'
◆ 'Ausbloom' — See *R.* The Dark Lady = 'Ausbloom'
◆ 'Ausblossom' — See *R.* Peach Blossom = 'Ausblossom'
◆ 'Ausblush' — See *R.* Heritage = 'Ausblush'
◆ 'Ausbord' — See *R.* Gertrude Jekyll = 'Ausbord'
◆ 'Ausbreak' — See *R.* Jayne Austin = 'Ausbreak'
◆ 'Ausbrid' — See *R.* Mayor of Casterbridge = 'Ausbrid'
◆ 'Ausbuff' — See *R.* English Garden = 'Ausbuff'
◆ 'Ausburton' — See *R.* Emily = 'Ausburton'
◆ 'Ausbury' — See *R.* Canterbury = 'Ausbury'
◆ 'Ausca' — See *R.* Fair Bianca = 'Ausca'
◆ 'Auscam' — See *R.* Marinette = 'Auscam'
◆ 'Auscat' — See *R.* Winchester Cathedral = 'Auscat'
◆ 'Auscent' — See *R.* John Clare = 'Auscent'
◆ 'Auscer' — See *R.* Chaucer = 'Auscer'
◆ 'Auschar' — See *R.* Charity = 'Auschar'
◆ 'Auschild' — See *R.* Fisherman's Friend = 'Auschild'
◆ 'Ausclough' — See *R.* Sir Clough = 'Ausclough'
◆ 'Ausclub' — See *R.* Kathryn Morley = 'Ausclub'
◆ 'Auscoat' — See *R.* Red Coat = 'Auscoat'
◆ 'Auscomp' — See *R.* Happy Child = 'Auscomp'
◆ 'Auscook' — See *R.* Heather Austin = 'Auscook'
◆ 'Auscot' — See *R.* Abraham Darby = 'Auscot'
◆ 'Auscountry' — See *R.* Country Living = 'Auscountry'
◆ 'Auscress' — See *R.* Cressida = 'Auscress'
◆ 'Auscrim' — See *R.* L.D. Braithwaite = 'Auscrim'
◆ 'Auscross' — See *R.* Windflower = 'Auscross'
◆ 'Auscup' — See *R.* Ellen = 'Auscup'
◆ 'Ausday' — See *R.* The Alexandra Rose = 'Ausday'
◆ 'Ausdimindo' — See *R.* Bibi Maizoon = 'Ausdimindo'
◆ 'Ausdir' — See *R.* Tradescant = 'Ausdir'
◆ 'Ausdoctor' — See *R.* Doctor Jackson = 'Ausdoctor'
◆ 'Ausdor' — See *R.* Mrs Doreen Pike = 'Ausdor'
◆ 'Ausdove' — See *R.* Dove = 'Ausdove'
¶ 'Ausea' — See *R.* Fair Bianca = 'Ausca'

- ◆ 'Auselle'    See *R.* Belle Story = 'Auselle'
- ◆ 'Ausemi'    See *R.* Lucetta = 'Ausemi'
- ◆ 'Ausfin'    See *R.* Financial Times
  Centenary = 'Ausfin'
- ◆ 'Ausfire'    See *R.* Morning Mist = 'Ausfire'
- ◆ 'Ausglisten'    See *R.* Cottage Rose =
  'Ausglisten'
- ◆ 'Ausglobe'    See *R.* Brother Cadfael =
  'Ausglobe'
- ◆ 'Ausgold'    See *R.* Golden Celebration =
  'Ausgold'
- ◆ 'Ausham'    See *R.* Geoff Hamilton = 'Ausham'
- ◆ 'Aushero'    See *R.* Hero = 'Aushero'
- ◆ 'Ausjac'    See *R.* Jacquenetta = 'Ausjac'
- ◆ 'Ausjess'    See *R.* Pretty Jessica = 'Ausjess'
- ◆ 'Ausjo'    See *R.* Jude the Obscure = 'Ausjo'
- ◆ 'Ausjuno'    See *R.* Immortal Juno = 'Ausjuno'
- ◆ 'Ausky'    See *R.* Mistress Quickly = 'Ausky'
- ◆ 'Ausland'    See *R.* Sceptre'd Isle = 'Ausland'
- ◆ 'Auslea'    See *R.* Leander = 'Auslea'
- ◆ 'Ausleaf'    See *R.* English Elegance =
  'Ausleaf'
- ◆ 'Auslean'    See *R.* Cymbeline = 'Auslean'
- ◆ 'Ausleap'    See *R.* Sweet Juliet = 'Ausleap'
- ◆ 'Ausled'    See *R.* A Shropshire Lad =
  'Ausled'
- ◆ 'Ausles'    See *R.* Charles Austin = 'Ausles'
- ◆ 'Auslett'    See *R.* Symphony = 'Auslett'
- ◆ 'Ausli'    See *R.* Lilian Austin = 'Ausli'
- ◆ 'Auslian'    See *R.* Warwick Castle = 'Auslian'
- ◆ 'Auslight'    See *R.* Claire Rose = 'Auslight'
- ◆ 'Auslilac'    See *R.* Lilac Rose = 'Auslilac'
- ◆ 'Auslo'    See *R.* Othello = 'Auslo'
- ◆ 'Auslot'    See *R.* Sophy's Rose = 'Auslot'
- ◆ 'Auslow'    See *R.* Yellow Button = 'Auslow'
- ◆ 'Ausman'    See *R.* The Countryman =
  'Ausman'
- ◆ 'Ausmark'    See *R.* Eglantyne = 'Ausmark'
- ◆ 'Ausmary'    See *R.* Mary Rose = 'Ausmary'
- ◆ 'Ausmas'    See *R.* Graham Thomas =
  'Ausmas'
- ◆ 'Ausmash'    See *R.* Heavenly Rosalind =
  'Ausmash'
- ◆ 'Ausmian'    See *R.* Charmian = 'Ausmian'
- ◆ 'Ausmira'    See *R.* Admired Miranda =
  'Ausmira'
- ◆ 'Ausmit'    See *R.* Saint Cecilia = 'Ausmit'
- ◆ 'Ausmol'    See *R.* Molineux = 'Ausmol'
- ◆ 'Ausmoon'    See *R.* Pegasus = 'Ausmoon'
- ◆ 'Ausmum'    See *R.* Pat Austin = 'Ausmum'
- ◆ 'Ausmurr'    See *R.* Hilda Murrell = 'Ausmurr'
- ◆ 'Ausnun'    See *R.* The Nun = 'Ausnun'
- ◆ 'Ausoil'    See *R.* Troilus = 'Ausoil'
- ◆ 'Ausold'    See *R.* Trevor Griffiths = 'Ausold'
- ◆ 'Auspale'    See *R.* Redouté = 'Auspale'
- ◆ 'Ausperd'    See *R.* Perdita = 'Ausperd'
- ◆ 'Auspero'    See *R.* Prospero = 'Auspero'
- ◆ 'Auspoly'    See *R.* Charlotte = 'Auspoly'
- ◆ 'Auspom'    See *R.* Snow Goose = 'Auspom'
- ◆ 'Ausport'    See *R.* Wise Portia = 'Ausport'
- ◆ 'Ausprima'    See *R.* Sir Edward Elgar =
  'Ausprima'
- ◆ 'Ausquire'    See *R.* The Squire = 'Ausquire'
- ◆ 'Ausram'    See *R.* Francine Austin = 'Ausram'
- ◆ 'Ausreef'    See *R.* Sharifa Asma = 'Ausreef'
- ◆ 'Ausreeve'    See *R.* The Reeve = 'Ausreeve'
- ◆ 'Ausren'    See *R.* Charles Rennie
  Mackintosh = 'Ausren'
- ◆ 'Ausron'    See *R.* Lordly Oberon = 'Ausron'
- ◆ 'Ausroyal'    See *R.* William Shakespeare =
  'Ausroyal'

- ◆ 'Ausrush'    See *R.* Windrush = 'Ausrush'
- ◆ 'Aussal'    See *R.* Radio Times = 'Aussal'
- ◆ 'Aussaucer'    See *R.* Evelyn = 'Aussaucer'
- ◆ 'Aussemi'    See *R.* The Herbalist = 'Aussemi'
- ◆ 'Aussnow'    See *R.* Mountain Snow =
  'Aussnow'
- I    'Ausspry' (1985)    See *R.* Sir Walter Raleigh =
  'Ausspry'
- ◆ 'Austamora'    See *R.* Tamora = 'Austamora'
- ◆ 'Austance'    See *R.* Constance Spry =
  'Austance'
- ◆ 'Austop'    See *R.* Barbara Austin = 'Austop'
- ◆ 'Austream'    See *R.* Rushing Stream =
  'Austream'
-      Austrian Copper    See *R. foetida* 'Bicolor'
-      Austrian Yellow    See *R. foetida*
- ◆ 'Ausuel'    See *R.* Emanuel = 'Ausuel'
- ◆ 'Ausvelvet'    See *R.* The Prince = 'Ausvelvet'
- ◆ 'Auswalker'    See *R.* The Pilgrim = 'Auswalker'
- ◆ 'Ausway'    See *R.* Noble Antony = 'Ausway'
- ◆ 'Auswebb'    See *R.* Mary Webb = 'Auswebb'
- ◆ 'Auswen'    See *R.* Wenlock = 'Auswen'
- ◆ 'Auswhite'    See *R.* Swan = 'Auswhite'
- ◆ 'Auswith'    See *R.* Saint Swithun = 'Auswith'
- ◆ 'Auswonder'    See *R.* Ambridge Rose =
  'Auswonder'
- ◆ 'Ausyel'    See *R.* Yellow Charles Austin =
  'Ausyel'
-      'Autumn' (HT)    NRog
-      'Autumn Bouquet' (S)    EBls
-      'Autumn Delight' (HM)    EBls MAus WHCG
-      Autumn Fire    See *R.* 'Herbstfeuer'
-      'Autumn Sunlight' (ClF)    MGan SPer
-      'Autumn Sunset' (S)    EBls
-      'Autumnalis'    See *R.* 'Princesse de Nassau'
-      Aviateur Blériot' (Ra)    EBls MAus
- ¶    'Avignon' (F)    EBee
- §    Avocet = 'Harpluto' (F)    GGre
- §    Avon = 'Poulmulti' (GC)    EBee ELan ENot GCoc LGod LStr
    MAus MGan MJon SApu SPer
    SWCr WHCG WOVN
- §    Awakening =    EBls WHCG
      'Probuzini' (Cl)
- §    Awareness =    MFry
      'Frybingo' (HT)
-      'Ayrshire Splendens'    See *R.* 'Splendens'
-      'Baby Bio' (F/Patio)    CB&S MBri MGan NRog
-      'Baby Darling' (Min)    MAus MGan
-      'Baby Faurax' (Poly)    MAus
- ◆    Baby Gold Star (Min)    See *R.* 'Estrellita de Oro'
-      'Baby Katie' (Min)    NBat
- §    Baby Love = 'Scrivluv'    MAus MJon MMat
      (yellow) (Min/Patio)
- §    Baby Masquerade® =    CBrm ELan GCoc LGod LPlm
      'Tanba' (Min)    MBur MGan MJon MMat NRog
    SWCr WStI
- §    Baby Sunrise =    MJon SJus
      'Macparlez' (Min)
-      'Bad Neuenahr' (Cl)    MGan
-      'Ballerina' (HM/Poly) ♀    More than 30 suppliers
- §    Ballindalloch Castle =    GCoc
      'Cocneel' (F)
-      'Baltimore Belle' (Ra)    CRHN EBls MAus WHCG
- §    Bangor Cathedral =    MJon
      'Kirmelody' (HT)
-      ***banksiae*** (Ra)    CGre GQui LPan SPer SRms
-      - *alba*    See *R. banksiae* var. *banksiae*
- §    - var. ***banksiae*** (Ra/d)    CBot EPfP ERea LStr MAus SBid
    SBra WWat
-      - 'Lutea' (Ra/d) ♀    More than 30 suppliers
-      - var. ***normalis*** (Ra)    CBot CGre MAus

- 'Purezza' — See *R.* 'Purezza'
- SF 96051 (Ra) — ISea
Bantry Bay® (ClHT) — EBls LStr MGan MMat NFla SJus SPla SSea SWCr
◆ 'Bararcsun' — See *R.* Arctic Sunrise = 'Bararcsun'
§ Barbara Austin = 'Austop' (S) — MAus
'Barbara Carrera' (F) — EBls
§ Barkarole® = 'Tanelorak' (HT) — LStr MJon SApu SJus
'Baron de Bonstetten' (HP) — EBls
'Baron de Wassenaer' (CeMo) — EBls MGan
'Baron Girod de l'Ain' (HP) — EBls MAus MHlr SPer SPla SWCr WAct WHCG WHow
◆ Baron Sunblaze® — See *R.* Baron Meillandina = 'Meitifran'
◆ 'Baroness Rothschild' (HP) — See *R.* 'Baronne Adolph de Rothschild'
◆ 'Baroness Rothschild' (HT) — See *R.* 'Baronne Edmond de Rothschild = 'Meigriso'
§ 'Baronne Adolph de Rothschild' (HP) — EBee EMFP IOrc MGan WHCG
§ Baronne Edmond de Rothschild® = 'Meigriso' (HT) — MAus WAct
'Baronne Henriette de Snoy' (T) — EBls
'Baronne Prévost' (HP) ♀ — EBls MAus SFam WAct WHCG
◆ 'Barout' — See *R.* Tranquility = 'Barout'
§ Barry Fearn = 'Korschwama' (HT) — MMat
◆ 'Barshifle' — See *R.* Snowgoose = 'Barshifle'
'Bashful' (Poly) — MGan
§ Basildon Bond = 'Harjosine' (HT) — IHar MJon
◆ 'Batmercury' — See *R.* Freddie Mercury = 'Batmercury'
§ Battersby Beauty = 'Horbatbeauty' (HT) — NBat
◆ 'Battoo' — See *R.* Myra = 'Battoo'
◆ 'Beacath' — See *R.* Norwich Cathedral = 'Beacath'
◆ 'Beadix' — See *R.* Dixieland Linda = 'Beadix'
◆ 'Beamac' — See *R.* Macmillan Nurse = 'Beamac'
§ x *beanii* (Ra) — EPla SMad
◆ 'Beatwe' — See *R.* Twenty-fifth = 'Beatwe'
'Beau Narcisse' (G) — MAus
'Beauté' (HT) — EBls MAus MGan
§ Beautiful Britain = 'Dicfire' (F) — EBls GGre IDic LStr MAus MBri MGan MJon NRog SJus SWCr
'Beauty of Rosemawr' (CIT) — EBls
Beauty Queen (F) — Last listed 1996
Beauty Star® — See *R.* Liverpool Remembers = 'Frystar'
◆ 'Bedchild' — See *R.* Pudsey Bear = 'Bedchild'
◆ 'Bedone' — See *R.* Happy Times = 'Bedone'
◆ 'Beebop' — See *R.* Cleo = 'Beebop'
◆ 'Beesian' — See *R.* Amanda = 'Beesian'
§ Behold = 'Savahold' (Min) — NBat
◆ 'Bekola' — See *R.* Aalsmeer Gold = 'Bekola'
'Bel Ange' (HT) — MGan
§ Belfast Belle = 'Dicrobot' (HT) — Last listed 1998
*bella* — EBee
§ Bella = 'Pouljill' (S) — GCoc GGre
'Belle Amour' (AxD) — EBls MAus WHCG
'Belle Blonde' (HT) — MGan SPer

'Belle de Crécy' (G) ♀ — EBls GCoc IOrc LStr MAus MHlr MMat SFam SJus SPer SWCr WAct WHCG WHow
'Belle des Jardins' misapplied — See *R.* 'Centifolia Variegata'
§ Belle Epoque = 'Fryyaboo' (HT) — EBee GCoc LStr MBur MFry MGan / MJon MMat SApu
'Belle Isis' (G) — EBls MAus SPer
'Belle Lyonnaise' (CIT) — EBls
'Belle Poitevine' (Ru) ♀ — EBls MAus
'Belle Portugaise' (Cl) — EBls MAus
§ Belle Story® = 'Auselle' (S) — MAus
§ Belle Sunblaze = 'Meidanego' (Min) — IHar
§ Bellevue® = 'Poulena' (HT) — Last listed 1998
§ 'Belvedere' (Ra) — EBls MAus MBri SWCr WHCG
◆ 'Benbid' — See *R.* Biddy = 'Benbid'
◆ 'Benblack' — See *R.* Black Jade = 'Benblack'
◆ 'Benfig' — See *R.* Figurine = 'Benfig'
* 'Bengal Beauty' — WCot WWat
§ Benita® = 'Dicquarrel' (HT) — EBee IDic LGod MJon
◆ 'Benjee' — See *R.* Gee Gee = 'Benjee'
◆ 'Benjen' — See *R.* Jennifer = 'Benjen'
◆ 'Benmagic' — See *R.* Kristin = 'Benmagic'
§ 'Bennett's Seedling' (Ra) — MAus
§ Benson and Hedges Gold® = 'Macgem' (HT) — Last listed 1997
§ Benson and Hedges Special = 'Macshana' (Min) — ELan GGre MAus MJon
§ Berkshire = 'Korpinka' (GC) — ENot LStr MGan MHlr MJon MMat SWCr WOVN WWeb
§ Best Wishes = 'Chesnut' (Cl/v) — COtt GCoc GGre LStr MJon SWCr SWas
§ Bettina® = 'Mepal' (HT) — MAus MGan
§ Betty Driver = 'Gandri' (F) — MBri MGan SPer
§ Betty Harkness = 'Harette' (F) — GCoc SApu
'Betty Prior' (F) — GCoc MGan
'Betty Uprichard' (HT) — EBls
'Beyreuth' (S) — MGan
§ Bianco = 'Cocblanco' (Patio/Min) — GCoc MAus SJus
§ Bibi Maizoon® = 'Ausdimindo' (S) — IHar MAus SPer
§ Biddulph Grange = 'Frydarkeye' (S) — MFry
§ Biddy = 'Benbid' (Min) — Last listed 1997
*biebersteinii* — EBls
'Big Chief' (HT) — MJon NRog
§ Big Purple® = 'Stebigpu' (HT) — MJon SApu
§ Birthday Girl = 'Meilasso' (F) — MJon NPri SApu
§ Birthday Wishes = 'Guesdelay' (HT) — LPlm
'Bishop Darlington' (HM) — EBls
§ Bishop Elphinstone = 'Cocjolly' (F) — GCoc
'Bit o' Sunshine' (Min) — MGan
'Black Beauty' (HT) — MAus MJon
'Black Ice' (F) — MGan
◆ 'Black Jack' (Ce) — See *R.* 'Tour de Malakoff'
§ Black Jack™ = 'Minkco' (Min/Patio) — NBat
§ Black Jade™ = 'Benblack' (Min/Patio) — Last listed 1997
'Black Prince' (HP) — EBls
'Blairii Number One' (Bb) — EBls
'Blairii Number Two' (ClBb) ♀ — EBee EBls EMFP MAus MHlr SFam SPer SWCr WAct WHCG WHow WSHC

'Blanche de Vibert' (DPo) — EBls MAus

'Blanche Double de Coubert' (Ru) ♀ — CHad CSam EBee EBls ELan ENot GCoc IOrc LBuc LHol LStr MAus MFry MGan MHlr MJon MMat NRog SApu SFam SJus SPer SRPl SWCr WAct WHCG WHow WOVN

'Blanche Moreau' (CeMo) — EBls IHar MAus MGan MHlr SPer SWCr WAct

'Blanchefleur' (CexG) — EBls MAus

*blanda* — EBls

'Blaydon Races' (F) — Last listed 1998

§ Blenheim = 'Tanmurse' (GC) — ECle MBur MGan MJon SApu WOVN

Blessings® (HT) ♀ — CB&S CGro EBls EBrP Ebre EWTr GGre LGod LPlm LStr MAus MBri MBur MFry MGan MJon NRog SApu SBre SPer SRPl SWCr SWas WWeb

'Bleu Magenta' (Ra) ♀ — EBee EBls MAus SWCr WHCG

'Bloomfield Abundance' (Poly) — CPou EBee EBls MAus MMat SPer SWCr WHCG WHer WHow

'Bloomfield Dainty' (HM) — EBls

'Blossomtime' (Cl) — NRog SMad SPer

'Blue Diamond' (HT) — MGan

§ Blue Moon® = 'Tannacht' (HT) — CGro EBls EBrP EBre ELan GChr GCoc GGre LBre LGod LPlm MAus MBur MGan MJon NRog SApu SBre SPer WWeb

§ Blue Parfum® = 'Tanfifum' — MAus MJon

§ Blue Peter = 'Ruiblun' (Min) — MFry MJon SApu WWeb

'Blush Boursault' (Bs) — EBls MAus

'Blush Damask' (D) — EBls WHCG

'Blush Noisette' — See *R.* 'Noisette Carnée'

'Blush Rambler' (Ra) — EBee EBls MAus MHlr SPer SPla WHCG WHow

'Blushing Lucy' (Ra) — MAus MTPN SMrm WAct WSHC

'Bob Collard' (F) — Last listed 1998

§ Bob Greaves = 'Fryzippy' (F) — MFry

'Bob Woolley' (HT) — NBat

'Bobbie James' (Ra) ♀ — CHad EBee EBls EBrP EBre LBre LStr MAus MFry MGan MHlr MJon MMat NBat SBre SFam SJus SPer SWas WAct WHCG WHow

'Bobby Charlton' (HT) — MFry MGan NRog

'Bobolink' (Min) — MGan

'Bon Silène' (T) — EBls

Bonfire Night® (F) — CGro ENot MBur MGan

Bonica 82® — See *R.* Bonica = 'Meidomonac'

§ Bonica® = 'Meidomonac' (GC) ♀ — CSam EBee EBls EBrP EBre ELan ENot GCoc IHar LBre LGod LStr MAus MBur MFry MGan MHlr MJon SApu SBre SJus SPer SWCr WAct WHCG WOVN

'Bonn' (HM/S) — CB&S MAus MGan NRog

'Bonnie Scotland' (HT) — MGan

§ Bonsoir = 'Dicbo' (HT) — MGan

'Border Coral' (F) — Last listed 1998

♦ 'Bosanne' — See *R.* Middlesex County = 'Bosanne'

♦ 'Bosgreen' — See *R.* Peppermint Ice = 'Bosgreen'

♦ 'Bosijurika' — See *R.* Preservation = 'Bosijurika'

'Botzaris' (D) — EBls SFam

'Boule de Nanteuil' (G) — EBls

'Boule de Neige' (Bb) — CHad EBls EMFP ENot EWTr GCoc IHar LGod LHol LStr MAus MHlr MMat SFam SJus SPer SPla SWCr WAct WHCG WOVN

'Bouquet d'Or' (N) — EBls MAus WHCG

'Bouquet Tout Fait' misapplied — See *R.* 'Nastarana'

'Bourbon Queen' (Bb) — EBee EBls MAus MHlr SWCr SWas WHCG

§ Bow Bells = 'Ausbells' (S) — MAus MHlr

§ Boy O Boy = 'Dicuniform' (GC) — GCoc IDic

§ Boys' Brigade® = 'Cocdinkum' (Patio) — CGro GCoc MGan SApu

§ *bracteata* — EHol GQui MAus WHCG WWat

§ Brave Heart = 'Horbondsmile' (F) — NBat

§ Breath of Life = 'Harquanne' (ClHT) — CGro CSam EBls ELan GGre IHar LGod LStr MAus MBri MFry MGan MJon NBat SApu SJus SPer SWCr SWas

§ Bredon® = 'Ausbred' (S) — IHar MAus MBri

'Breeze Hill' (Ra) — EBls MAus

'Brenda Colvin' (Ra) — ISea MAus

♦ 'Brennende Liebe' — See *R.* Burning Love = 'Brennende Liebe'

'Brennus' (China hybrid) — EBls

'Briarcliff' (HT) — EBls

§ Bridal Pink™ = 'Jacbri' (F) — MJon

§ Bride = 'Fryyearn' (HT) — GCoc LStr MFry MJon SApu SWCr

§ Bright Fire = 'Peaxi' (Cl) — MBri MJon

§ Bright Smile® = 'Dicdance' (F/Patio) — GCoc IDic IHar LStr MAus MFry MGan SPer SWCr

§ Bright Spark = 'Rubrispa' (Min) — Last listed 1998

'Brindis' (ClF) — MGan

§ Britannia = 'Frycalm' (HT) — MFry

§ Broadlands = 'Tanmirson' (GC) — CSam EBee ECle LGod MAus MBur MGan MJon SApu SChu SRPl WGer WHow

§ Brother Cadfael = 'Ausglobe' (S) — IHar MAus MBNS MBri MHlr MJon SPer SSoC WOVN WWeb

§ Brown Velvet = 'Macultra' (F) — MJon SApu

'Browsholme Rose' (Ra) — Last listed 1998

§ *brunonii* (Ra) — CDoC CHan EBls EWes MAus WLRN

— 'Betty Sherriff' (Ra) — CDoC SSpi

— CC 1235 (Ra) — Last listed 1997

— CC&McK 362 (Ra) — Last listed 1997

§ — 'La Mortola' (Ra) — MAus

§ Bubbles = 'Frybubbly' (GC) — MFry

♦ 'Bucbi' — See *R.* Carefree Beauty = 'Bucbi'

§ Buck's Fizz = 'Poulgar' (F) — EBee GGre MBur MGan SApu SJus

'Buff Beauty' (HM) ♀ — More than 30 suppliers

'Bullata' — See *R. x centifolia* 'Bullata'

♦ 'Burbrindley' — See *R.* Katie Crocker = 'Burbrindley'

§ 'Burgundiaca' (G) — EBee EBls LFis MAus WAct

Burgundian rose — See *R.* 'Burgundiaca'

♦ 'Burkhardt' — See *R.* Grumpy = 'Burkhardt'

'Burma Star' (F) — GCoc

burnet, double pink — See *R. pimpinellifolia* double pink

burnet, double white — See *R. pimpinellifolia* double white

♦ 'Burspec' — See *R.* Good Luck = 'Burspec'

§ Bush Baby = 'Peanob' (Min) — LGod LStr MJon SApu SWCr WStI

¶ 'Buttercup' — WWeb

§ Buttons = 'Dicmickey' (Min/Patio) — IDic

§ By Appointment = 'Harvolute' (F) — GGre

'C.F. Meyer' — See *R.* 'Conrad Ferdinand Meyer'

§ *caesia* subsp.*glauca* — Last listed 1998

'Café' (F) — WBcn

| | |
|---|---|
| 'Cairngorm' (F) | GCoc |
| 'Caledonian' (HT) | NBat |
| *californica* (S) | MAus |
| - 'Plena' | See *R. nutkana* 'Plena' |
| 'Callisto' (HM) | MAus SWCr WHCG |
| § Calypso = 'Poulclimb' (Cl) | EBee ECle |
| 'Camaïeux' (G) | CPou EBee EBls MAus MHlr MMat SPer SWCr SWas WAct WHCG |
| § Cambridgeshire = 'Korhaugen' (GC) | EBee ENot LGod LStr MAus MMat NPri SPer SWCr WWeb |
| 'Camélia Rose' (Ch) | EBls WHCG |
| 'Cameo' (Poly) | EBls IHar MAus MGan |
| Canadian White Star® (HT) | Last listed 1996 |
| ♦ 'Canana' | See *R.* Mary Donaldson = 'Canana' |
| 'Canary Bird' | See *R. xanthina* 'Canary Bird' |
| § Can-can = 'Legglow' (HT) | Last listed 1998 |
| ♦ 'Candide' | See *R.* Goldstar = 'Candide' |
| ♦ 'Candoodle' | See *R.* Lady Rachel = 'Candoodle' |
| § Candy Rose® = 'Meiranovi' (S) | GGre |
| *canina* (S) | CCVT CKin EWFC GChr LBuc MAus MHew NWea SRPl WMou |
| - 'Abbotswood' | See *R.* 'Abbotswood' (*canina* hybrid) |
| - 'Andersonii' | See *R.* 'Andersonii' (*canina* hybrid) |
| - deep pink (S) | MAus |
| - 'Inermis' (S) | Last listed 1998 |
| ♦ 'Canlloyd' | See *R.* Lloyds of London = 'Canlloyd' |
| ♦ 'Canrem' | See *R.* Sally's Rose = 'Canrem' |
| ♦ 'Cansend' | See *R.* Colchester Beauty = 'Cansend' |
| ♦ 'Cansit' | See *R.* Jenny's Rose = 'Cansit' |
| ♦ 'Canson' | See *R.* Dame Wendy = 'Canson' |
| 'Cantabrigiensis' (S) ♀ | EBee EBls ENot GChr MAus MHlr NBus NFla NRog SFam SPer WAct WHCG WOVN WWat |
| § Canterbury = 'Ausbury' (S) | MAus |
| 'Capitaine Basroger' (CeMo) | EBls MAus |
| 'Capitaine John Ingram' (CeMo) ♀ | EBee EBls MAus SPer WHow |
| 'Captain Christy' | See *R.* 'Climbing Captain Christy' |
| § Captain Cook = 'Macal' (F) | Last listed 1998 |
| 'Captain Hayward' (HP) | EBls |
| 'Captain Scarlet' (ClMin) | WWeb |
| 'Cardiff Bay' (HT) | Last listed 1997 |
| 'Cardinal de Richelieu' (G) ♀ | CHad CPou EBee EBls EMFP EWTr GCoc IOrc LStr MAus MFry MHlr MMat SApu SFam SPer WAct WHCG WHow |
| § Cardinal Hume® = 'Harregale' (S) | EBls MGan SApu SPer |
| § Carefree Beauty™ = 'Bucbi' (S) | Last listed 1997 |
| 'Carmen' (Ru) | EBls MAus |
| § 'Carmenetta' (S) | EBls MAus |
| § 'Carol' (Gn) | See *R.* 'Carol Amling' |
| § 'Carol Amling' (Gn) | MJon SWCr |
| *carolina* | CGre LHop WHCG |
| § Caroline de Monaco® = 'Meipierar' (HT) | MJon |
| 'Caroline Testout' | See *R.* 'Madame Caroline Testout' |
| ♦ 'Carol-Jean' | See *R.* Indian Sunblaze = 'Carol-Jean' |
| § Casino® = 'Macca' (ClHT) | CGro CSam EBls IHar LPlm MBur MFry MGan MJon SPer WStI WWeb |
| ¶ Castle Howard Tercentenary (F) | LStr |

| | |
|---|---|
| § Castle of Mey = 'Coclucid' (F) | GCoc MJon |
| § Catherine Cookson = 'Noscook' (HT) | NBat |
| 'Catherine Mermet' (T) | EBls MAus |
| 'Catherine Seyton' (RH) | EBls |
| § 'Cécile Brünner' (Poly) ♀ | CHad EBee EBls ELan EMFP ENot GCoc LHol LStr MAus MGan MHlr MMat NRog SJus SPer SWCr WAct WHCG WHow WOVN WWat |
| 'Cécile Brünner, White' | See *R.* 'White Cécile Brünner' |
| § Cecily Gibson = 'Evebright' (F) | MJon |
| § 'Céleste' (A) ♀ | EBls EMFP ENot GCoc IHar LGod LStr MAus MFry MHlr MMat SApu SFam SJus SPer SWCr WAct WGer WHCG WHow WOVN WWat |
| 'Célina' (CeMo) | EBls MGan |
| 'Céline Forestier' (N) ♀ | CBos EBls MAus SFam SPer WAct WHCG |
| § 'Celsiana' (D) | EBls IHar MAus MHlr SFam SPer SRPl WAct WHCG |
| § Centenaire de Lourdes® = 'Delge' (F) | EBls |
| § Centenary = 'Koreledas' (F) | ENot MMat |
| § x *centifolia* (Ce) | CTri EBls IOrc MAus MHlr NRog SJus SMad WAct WHCG |
| § - 'Bullata' (Ce) | EBls MAus |
| § - 'Cristata' (Ce) ♀ | EBls EMFP ENot EPfP LStr MAus MMat NBus NFla NRog SFam SJus SPer SRPl WAct WHCG |
| § - 'Muscosa' (Ce/Mo) ♀ | CTri EBls EMFP ENot GCoc IOrc MAus MGan MMat NRog SFam SJus WAct |
| - 'Parvifolia' | See *R.* 'Burgundiaca' |
| § 'Centifolia Variegata' (Ce) | EBls MAus MGan |
| 'Cerise Bouquet' (S) ♀ | EBls IHar MAus MMat SJus SPer WAct WHCG WKif WWeb |
| § Cha Cha = 'Cocarum' (Patio/Min) | SApu |
| § Champagne Cocktail = 'Horflash' (F) | GChr GGre MJon NBat SApu |
| § Champagne® = 'Korampa' (F) | MJon |
| 'Champion' (HT) | MAus |
| 'Champneys' Pink Cluster' (China hybrid) | EBls MAus SFam |
| § Champs Elysées® = 'Meicarl' (HT) | MGan |
| 'Chanelle' (F) | EBls GCoc MAus MGan NRog SPer |
| Chapeau de Napoléon | See *R.* x *centifolia* 'Cristata' |
| 'Chaplin's Pink Climber' (Cl) | EBls MBri MGan |
| § Chardonnay = 'Macrealea' (HT) | MJon |
| § Charisma = 'Peatrophy' (F) | Last listed 1997 |
| § Charity = 'Auschar' (S) | MAus MJon SWCr WWeb |
| § Charles Austin® = 'Ausles' (S) | IHar MAus MBri SJus WAct |
| § Charles Aznavour® = 'Meibeausai' (F) | Last listed 1997 |
| 'Charles de Mills' (G) ♀ | CHad EBee EBls ELan EMFP ENot GCoc IHar LGod LStr MAus MFry MHlr MJon MMat SFam SJus SPer SWCr WAct WHCG WHow WWeb |
| 'Charles Gater' (HP) | EBls |
| 'Charles Lefèbvre' (HP) | EBls |
| 'Charles Mallerin' (HT) | EBls |
| § Charles Notcutt = 'Korhassi' (S) | ENot MMat |

§ Charles Rennie | MAus MJon NPri SWCr WGer
Mackintosh® = | WWeb
'Ausren' (S)
§ Charleston '88 = | Last listed 1997
'Meiresty' (HT)
§ Charleston = 'Meiridge' (F) MGan
§ Charlotte = 'Auspoly' (S) | CAbP IHar MAus MHlr MJon SApu
| SWCr WAct
'Charlotte Elizabeth' (F) | Last listed 1996
§ Charmian® = 'Ausmian' (S) MAus
'Charter 700' (F) | MFry
'Château de | MGan
Clos-Vougeot' (HT)
¶ 'Chatsworth Roty 1995' | SRPl
§ Chatsworth = | EBee LGod MBri MFry MGan
'Tanotax' (Patio/F) | MJon SApu SCoo SPer SWas
| WWeb
§ Chaucer® = 'Auscer' (S) | MAus MBri
§ Chelsea Belle = | NBat
'Talchelsea' (Min)
§ Chelsea Pensioner = | LPlm SApu
'Mattche' (Min)
§ Cherry Brandy '85® = | MBur MFry MGan MJon
'Tanryrandy' (HT)
'Cherryade' (S) | MGan
◆ 'Chesdeep' | See *R*. Thank You = 'Chesdeep'
'Cheshire Life' (HT) | MAus MBur MFry MGan MJon
| NPri WStI
◆ 'Chesnut' | See *R*. Best Wishes = 'Chesnut'
◆ 'Chessupremo' | See *R*. Golden Hands =
| 'Chessupremo'
§ Chester Cathedral = | MJon
'Franshine' (HT)
◆ 'Chewallop' | See *R*. Rosalie Coral =
| 'Chewallop'
◆ 'Chewarvel' | See *R*. Laura Ford = 'Chewarvel'
◆ 'Chewaze' | See *R*. Pillar Box = 'Chewaze'
◆ 'Chewbeaut' | See *R*. Donald Davis =
| 'Chewbeaut'
◆ 'Chewell' | See *R*. Iris Webb = 'Chewell'
◆ 'Chewharia' | See *R*. Laura Ashley =
| 'Chewharia'
◆ 'Chewizz' | See *R*. Warm Welcome =
| 'Chewizz'
◆ 'Chewlegacy' | See *R*. Edith Holden =
| 'Chewlegacy'
◆ 'Chewpixcel' | See *R*. Open Arms = 'Chewpixcel'
◆ 'Chewpobey' | See *R*. Pathfinder = 'Chewpobey'
◆ 'Chewpope' | See *R*. Gloriana = 'Chewpope'
◆ 'Chewramb' | See *R*. Little Rambler =
| 'Chewramb'
◆ 'Chewsea' | See *R*. Nice Day = 'Chewsea'
◆ 'Chewsunbeam' | See *R*. Good as Gold =
| 'Chewsunbeam'
◆ 'Chewsunford' | See *R*. Golden Handshake =
| 'Chewsunford'
'Chianti' (S) | EBls MAus MBri WHCG
§ Chicago Peace® = | EBls GGre LGod LPlm MAus
'Johnago' (HT) | MGan MJon NRog SWCr WStI
◆ Child of Achievement | See *R*. Bella = 'Pouljill'
§ Childhood Memories = | MBri
'Ferho' (HM/CI)
§ Child's Play™ = | Last listed 1997
'Savachild' (Min)
§ Chilterns = 'Kortemma' (GC) ENot MMat SWCr
Chinatown® (F/S) ♀ | CB&S CGro EBls EBrP EBre ELan
| GGre LBre LPlm LStr MAus MGan
| MJon NRog SApu SBre SJus SPer
◆ *chinensis* 'Minima' sensu | See *R*. 'Pompon de Paris'
stricto hort.
 - 'Mutabilis' | See *R*. x *odorata* 'Mutabilis'

 - 'Old Blush' | See *R*. x *odorata* 'Pallida'
'Chloris' (A) | EBls EMFP
'Chorus Girl' (F) | MGan
§ Chris = 'Kirsan' (Cl) | LStr MJon MMat SApu
§ Christian Dior = | EBls
'Meilie' (HT)
'Christine Gandy' (F) | MGan
§ Christopher = 'Cocopher' | GCoc
(HT)
§ Christopher Columbus® = | MBri MJon MMat SApu
'Meinronsse' (HT)
§ 'Chromatella' (N) | EBls MAus
'Chrysler Imperial' (HT) | EBls MAus MGan
§ Cider Cup = 'Dicladida' | GChr GCoc GGre IDic LGod LStr
(Min/Patio) ♀ | MAus MFry MJon NBat SApu
'Cinderella' (Min) | MGan
*cinnamomea* | See *R*. *majalis*
'Circus' (F) | MGan
§ City Lights = | LGod MMat
'Poulgan' (Patio)
§ City of Belfast® = | EBls MAus
'Macci' (F)
§ City of Birmingham = | MMat
'Korholst' (S/HT)
'City of Cardiff' (HT) | Last listed 1997
'City of Leeds' (F) | ENot EWTr GGre MGan NRog
| SPer WStI
§ City of London® = | EBls LStr MBur MJon SApu SJus
'Harukfore' (F) ♀ | SPer SRPl SWCr
'City of Newcastle' (HT) | Last listed 1998
'City of Portsmouth' (F) | CB&S MGan
'City of Worcester' (HT) | Last listed 1997
§ City of York = | EBls
'Direktor Benschop' (Cl)
§ Clair Matin = | CHad EBee EBls MAus SPer SPla
'Meimont' (ClS) | WAct
'Claire Jacquier' (N) | EBee EBls MAus SFam SPer WAct
| WHCG
§ Claire Rayner = | LPlm LStr MJon WGer
'Macpandem' (F/Patio)
§ Claire Rose® = | CGro CSam EBee IHar MAus
'Auslight' (S) | MBNS MJon NPri SPer SWCr
§ Claire Scotland = | Last listed 1997
'Cocdimity' (Min/Patio)
§ Clarissa® = | MAus
'Harprocrustes' (Min)
'Clementina Carbonieri' (T) EBls
§ Cleo = 'Beebop' (HT) | MJon
§ Cleopatra = 'Korverpea' (HT) EBee ENot MBur MMat
'Cliff Richard' (F) | Last listed 1997
Climbing Alec's Red® | SPer
(ClHT)
'Climbing Allgold' (ClF) | EBls GGre MGan SWas
'Climbing Arthur Bell' (ClF) CSam CTri NRog SApu SPer
'Climbing Ballerina' (Ra) | MBri SWCr
§ Climbing Bettina® = | EBls MAus
'Mepalsar' (ClHT)
Climbing Blessings® (ClHT) EBls
'Climbing Blue Moon' (ClHT) MGan
§ 'Climbing Captain Christy' EBls MAus
(ClHT)
'Climbing Cécile Brünner' | CHad CHan EBls LGod LStr MAus
(ClPoly) ♀ | SApu SFam SJus SPer SWCr SWas
| WAct WHCG WHow WSHC WWat
'Climbing Château de | EBls MAus
Clos-Vougeot' (ClHT)
'Climbing Cherryade' (ClHT) MGan
'Climbing Christine' (ClHT) MAus
§ 'Climbing Columbia' (ClHT) ERav ERea NRog WHCG

'Climbing Comtesse Vandal' (ClHT) — EBls MAus

'Climbing Crimson Glory' (ClHT) — EBls EMFP GCoc MAus MGan NRog WStI

§ 'Climbing Devoniensis' (CIT) — CPou EBls MAus

'Climbing Ena Harkness' (ClHT) — CB&S CGro CSam CTri EBls GCoc GGre MAus MBNS MBri MBur MGan NRog SPer SPla WStI WWeb

'Climbing Ernest H. Morse' (ClHT) — MGan

'Climbing Etoile de Hollande' (ClHT) ♀ — CPou CSam EBls EBrP EBre EMFP GCoc LBre LHol LStr MAus MGan MHlr MJon MRav NRog SApu SBre SChu SJus SPer SPla SWCr WHCG WHow WOVN WWeb

'Climbing Fashion' (ClF) — EBls

§ Climbing Fragrant Cloud = 'Colfragrasar' (ClHT) — CB&S ELan MGan

§ 'Climbing Frau Karl Druschki' (ClHP) — EBls MGan NRog

'Climbing General MacArthur' (ClHT) — EBls MAus

§ Climbing Gold Bunny = 'Meigro-Nurisar' (ClF) — MJon WGer

§ 'Climbing Golden Dawn' (ClHT) — MAus

'Climbing Grand-mère Jenny' (ClHT) — EBls

'Climbing Home Sweet Home' (ClHT) — MAus

'Climbing Iceberg' (ClF) ♀ — CGro EBls EBrP EBre ELan ENot EWTr GGre LBre LPlm LStr MAus MBri MGan MJon NRog SBre SPer SRPl SWas WHCG WOVN WSHC WWeb

'Climbing Irish Fireflame' (ClHT) — MAus

'Climbing Josephine Bruce' (ClHT) — MAus MGan

'Climbing la France' (ClHT) — CPou MAus

§ 'Climbing Lady Hillingdon' (CIT) ♀ — EBls EBrP EBre EMFP EPfP LBre MAus MGan MHlr SApu SBre SFam SPer SRPl SWCr WAct WHCG WSHC

'Climbing Lady Sylvia' (ClHT) — EBls EMFP EPfP MAus MGan NRog SPer WStI

'Climbing Little White Pet' — See R. 'Félicité Perpétue'

'Climbing Madame Abel Chatenay' (ClHT) — EBls MAus

'Climbing Madame Butterfly' (ClHT) — EBls EBrP EBre EPfP LBre MAus MGan SBre SJus SPer SWas

'Climbing Madame Caroline Testout' (ClHT) — CPou EBls MAus NRog SPer SWCr WBcn WSHC

§ 'Climbing Madame Edouard Herriot' (ClHT) — EBls MAus MGan SPer

'Climbing Madame Henri Guillot' (ClHT) — EBls MAus

'Climbing Maman Cochet' (CIT) — EBls MAus

'Climbing Masquerade' (ClF) — EBls GGre LPlm MAus MGan MJon NRog WStI WWeb

'Climbing McGredy's Yellow' (ClHT) — MGan

§ 'Climbing Mevrouw G.A. van Rossem' (ClHT) — EBls MAus

'Climbing Mrs Aaron Ward' (ClHT) — EBls MAus

'Climbing Mrs G.A. van Rossem' — See R. 'Climbing Mevrouw G.A. van Rossem'

'Climbing Mrs Herbert Stevens' (ClHT) — EBee EBls EMFP MAus MHlr NRog SPer WHCG WHow

'Climbing Mrs Sam McGredy' (ClHT) ♀ — CGro EBls LPlm MAus MBri MGan MJon NRog SPla

'Climbing My Love' (ClHT) — MGan

'Climbing Niphetos' (CIT) — EBls MAus

'Climbing Ophelia' (ClHT) — EBee EBls MAus MHlr SPer SWCr

§ Climbing Orange Sunblaze = 'Meijikatarsar' (ClMin) — LStr MBri MJon NPri SApu SPer

'Climbing Pascali' (ClHT) — CB&S MGan

§ 'Climbing Paul Lédé' (CIT) — CPou EBee EBls EBrP EBre EMFP IHar LBre MAus MHlr SBre WHCG WHow

'Climbing Picture' (ClHT) — EBls MAus MGan

§ 'Climbing Pompon de Paris' (ClMinCh) — CBot CHan EBls LHop MAus MGan MRav SPer SRPl WHCG WSHC

'Climbing Richmond' (ClHT) — EBls MAus

'Climbing Roundelay' (Cl) — EBls

'Climbing Shot Silk' (ClHT) ♀ — EBee EBls MAus MGan SJus SPer

§ 'Climbing Souvenir de la Malmaison' (ClBb) — EBls MAus SPer WAct WHCG

'Climbing Spartan' (ClF) — Last listed 1997

'Climbing Spek's Yellow' (ClHT) — MAus

'Climbing Summer Sunshine' (ClHT) — MBri

§ Climbing Super Star = 'Tangostar' (ClHT) — MAus

'Climbing Sutter's Gold' (ClHT) — MAus MGan

'Climbing Talisman' (ClHT) — EBls

'Climbing The Doctor' (ClHT) — MGan

'Climbing The Queen Elizabeth' (ClF) — EBls MGan

§ Clive Lloyd = 'Kirshow' (HT) — Last listed 1996

'Cloth of Gold' — See R. 'Chromatella'

§ Clydebank Centenary = 'Cocdazzle' (F/Min) — Last listed 1996

♦ 'Cocabel' — See R. Little Jewel = 'Cocabel'

♦ 'Cocabest' — See R. Wee Jock = 'Cocabest'

♦ 'Cocacert' — See R. Vital Spark = 'Cocacert'

♦ 'Cocadilly' — See R. The Coxswain = 'Cocadilly'

♦ 'Cocagold' — See R. Golden Jubilee = 'Cocagold'

♦ 'Cocamond' — See R. Dainty Dinah = 'Cocamond'

♦ 'Cocanelia' — See R. Pink Posy = 'Cocanelia'

♦ 'Cocapeer' — See R. Sweetheart = 'Cocapeer'

♦ 'Cocarum' — See R. Cha Cha = 'Cocarum'

♦ 'Cocasun' — See R. Sunset Song = 'Cocasun'

♦ 'Cocathes' — See R. Crathes Castle = 'Cocathes'

♦ 'Cocavoter' — See R. Sweet Nell = 'Cocavoter'

♦ 'Cocbaden' — See R. Doctor Dick = 'Cocbaden'

♦ 'Cocbamber' — See R. Fyvie Castle = 'Cocbamber'

♦ 'Cocblanco' — See R. Bianco = 'Cocblanco'

♦ 'Cocbonne' — See R. Ena Baxter = 'Cocbonne'

♦ 'Cocbrose' — See R. Abbeyfield Rose = 'Cocbrose'

♦ 'Coccages' — See R. Country Heritage = 'Coccages'

♦ 'Cocceleste' — See R. Rosabell = 'Cocceleste'

♦ 'Cocclare' — See R. Ray of Sunshine = 'Cocclare'

♦ 'Coccord' — See R. Little Prince = 'Coccord'

♦ 'Coccrazy' — See R. Gingernut = 'Coccrazy'

◆ 'Cocdana'          See *R.* Fulton Mackay = 'Cocdana'
◆ 'Cocdandy'         See *R.* Royal Volunteer =
                     'Cocdandy'
◆ 'Cocdapple'        See *R.* Scottish Special =
                     'Cocdapple'
◆ 'Cocdarlee'        See *R.* Coral Reef = 'Cocdarlee'
◆ 'Cocdazzle'        See *R.* Clydebank Centenary =
                     'Cocdazzle'
◆ 'Cocdestin'        See *R.* Remember Me =
                     'Cocdestin'
◆ 'Cocdimity'        See *R.* Claire Scotland =
                     'Cocdimity'
◆ 'Cocdimple'        See *R.* Conservation =
                     'Cocdimple'
◆ 'Cocdinkum'        See *R.* Boys' Brigade =
                     'Cocdinkum'
◆ 'Cocember'         See *R.* Roxburghe Rose =
                     'Cocember'
◆ 'Cocflag'          See *R.* Highland Laddie =
                     'Cocflag'
◆ 'Cocfoster'        See *R.* Regal Red = 'Cocfoster'
◆ 'Cocglen'          See *R.* Honey Bunch = 'Cocglen'
◆ 'Cocgold'          See *R.* Toprose = 'Cocgold'
◆ 'Cocgrand'         See *R.* Myriam = 'Cocgrand'
◆ 'Cocharod'         See *R.* Shirley Spain = 'Cocharod'
◆ 'Cochello'         See *R.* Hello = 'Cochello'
◆ 'Cochunter'        See *R.* Ohshima Rose =
                     'Cochunter'
◆ 'Cocjabby'         See *R.* Gordon's College =
                     'Cocjabby'
◆ 'Cocjojo'          See *R.* UNICEF = 'Cocjojo'
◆ 'Cocjolly'         See *R.* Bishop Elphinstone =
                     'Cocjolly'
§ Cocktail® = 'Meimick' (S)   EBls MGan WAct
◆ 'Coclager'         See *R.* William Quarrier =
                     'Coclager'
◆ 'Coclands'         See *R.* Scotland's Trust =
                     'Coclands'
◆ 'Coclent'          See *R.* Lady MacRobert =
                     'Coclent'
◆ 'Coclibee'         See *R.* Alison = 'Coclibee'
◆ 'Coclucid'         See *R.* Castle of Mey = 'Coclucid'
◆ 'Cocmarris'        See *R.* Wee Cracker = 'Cocmarris'
◆ 'Cocmystery'       See *R.* Aberdeen Celebration =
                     'Cocmystery'
◆ 'Cocneel'          See *R.* Ballindalloch Castle =
                     'Cocneel'
◆ 'Cocnest'          See *R.* Constance Fettes =
                     'Cocnest'
◆ 'Cocnilly'         See *R.* Ray of Hope = 'Cocnilly'
◆ 'Cococrust'        See *R.* Alex C. Collie =
                     'Cococrust'
◆ 'Cocoddy'          See *R.* Greer Garson = 'Cocoddy'
◆ 'Cocopher'         See *R.* Christopher = 'Cocopher'
◆ 'Cocoray'          See *R.* Innocence 97 = 'Cocoray'
◆ 'Cocorona'         See *R.* Heartbeat = 'Cocorona'
◆ 'Cocosimber'       See *R.* President Heidar Aliyev =
                     'Cocosimber'
◆ 'Cocquamber'       See *R.* Home on Time =
                     'Cocquamber'
◆ 'Cocquestrum'      See *R.* Rose 2000 =
                     'Cocquestrum'
◆ 'Cocredward'       See *R.* Marguerite Anne =
                     'Cocredward'
◆ 'Cocrob'           See *R.* Rob Roy = 'Cocrob'
◆ 'Cocty'            See *R.* Curiosity = 'Cocty'
◆ 'Cogamo'           See *R.* My Love = 'Cogamo'
§ Colchester Beauty =   EBee
  'Cansend' (F)
◆ 'Colfragrasar'     See *R.* Climbing Fragrant Cloud =
                     'Colfragrasar'

§ Colibre '79 =                  ELan LStr SWCr
    'Meidanover' (Min)
  Colibre '80                    See *R.* Colibre '79 = 'Meidanover'
§ Colibri = 'Meimal' (Min)       LGod MGan SPer
§ 'Colonel Fabvier'              EBee EBls MAus
◆ colonial white                 See *R.* 'Sombreuil'
§ Colorama = 'Meirigalu' (HT)    Last listed 1998
  'Columbian'                    See *R.* 'Climbing Columbia'
  *colvillei*                    Last listed 1996
§ Colwyn Bay (F)                 MJon
  'Commandant                    EBls MAus SWCr
    Beaurepaire' (Bb)
  'Commemoration'                Last listed 1996
  common moss                    See *R.* x *centifolia* 'Muscosa'
§ Commonwealth Glory             GCoc GGre
    = 'Harclue' (HT)
  Compassion® (ClHT) ♀           More than 30 suppliers
§ 'Complicata' (G) ♀             EBls IHar LEdu LStr MAus MBri
                                 MGan MHlr MMat MRav NRog
                                 SApu SFam SJus SPer SSpi SWCr
                                 WAct WHCG WOVN WSHC
N 'Comte de Chambord'            See *R.* 'Madame Knorr'
    misapplied
  'Comtesse Cécile de            EBls MAus
    Chabrillant' (HP)
  'Comtesse de Lacépède'         See *R.* 'Du Maître d'Ecole'
    misapplied
§ 'Comtesse de Murinais'         EBls IHar MAus SFam SWCr
    (DMo)
§ 'Comtesse du Caÿla' (Ch)       MAus SWas
  'Comtesse Vandal' (HT)         MAus
  'Condesa de Sástago' (HT)      EBls
§ 'Conditorum' (G)               EBls SFam
§ Congratulations =              EBee ENot GCoc GGre LGod
    'Korlift' (HT)               LPlm LStr MFry MGan MJon MMat
                                 NPri SApu SJus SPer SWCr
§ 'Conrad Ferdinand             EBls EWTr MAus MGan SPer WAct
    Meyer' (Ru)
§ Conservation =                 GCoc GGre LStr MBri MJon SApu
    'Cocdimple' (Min/Patio)      WWeb
§ Constance Fettes =             Last listed 1997
    'Cocnest' (F)
§ Constance Spry =               More than 30 suppliers
    'Austance' (CIS) ♀
§ 'Cooperi' (Ra)                 CCHP EBls MAus SLon WAct
                                 WHow WSHC
◆ Cooper's Burmese               See *R.* 'Cooperi'
  'Copenhagen' (ClHT)            EBls MAus MBri
  'Copper Delight' (F)           NRog
§ Copper Pot = 'Dicpe' (F)       MGan SPer
  'Coral Cluster' (Poly)         EBls MAus MGan
  'Coral Creeper' (ClHT)         EBls
  Coral Dawn® (ClHT)             EBls IHar MFry MJon
§ Coral Fiesta®                  See *R.* Maria Teresa de Esteban
                                 = 'Dotrames'
§ Coral Reef = 'Cocdarlee'       GCoc GGre LStr MBri SWCr
    (Min/Patio)
  'Coral Satin' (Cl)             EBls MGan
  'Coralie' (D)                  EBls
  'Coralin' (Min)                MGan
§ Cordon Bleu =                  MBur
    'Harubasil' (HT)
◆ 'Cored'                        See *R.* Alec's Red = 'Cored'
  'Cornelia' (HM) ♀              CB&S CHad CSam EBee EBls ENot
                                 GCoc LHol LStr MAus MBri MFry
                                 MHlr MJon MMat NRog SApu
                                 SFam SJus SPer SRPl SWas WAct
                                 WHCG WOVN WWeb
  'Coronation Gold' (F)          GCoc
  Corso® (HT)                    Last listed 1996

'Coryana'                               EBls
I  'Corylus'                            See R. 'Hazel Le Rougetel'
   *corymbifera*                        EBls
   *corymbulosa*                        EBls
   'Cosimo Ridolfi' (G)                 EBls
§  Cottage Garden =                     Last listed 1998
   'Haryamber' (Patio/Min)
   cottage maid                         See R. 'Centifolia Variegata'
§  Cottage Rose™ =                      MAus MJon NPri SJus SWCr
   'Ausglisten' (S)                     WHow
§  Country Lady =                       MBur SApu SJus
   'Hartsam' (HT)
§  Country Living™ =                    EBls MAus
   'Auscountry' (S)
   'Country Maid' (F)                   Last listed 1997
   'Coupe d'Hébé' (Bb)                  EBls MAus MBri
§  Courage = 'Poulduff' (HT)            GCoc GGre NEgg SWCr
   'Cramoisi Picotée' (G)               EBls MAus
   'Cramoisi Supérieur' (Ch)            EBls MAus WHCG
§  Crathes Castle = 'Cocathes'          GCoc
§  Crazy for You =                      GCoc MJon
   'Wekroath' (F)
   'Creme' (S)                          Last listed 1996
§  Crème de la Crème =                  MGan
   'Gancre' (Cl)
   'Crépuscule' (N)                     EBls WHCG
§  Cressida = 'Auscress' (S)            MAus
   crested moss                         See R. x *centifolia* 'Cristata'
§  Cricri = 'Meicri' (Min)              MAus MGan
§  Crimson Cascade =                    MAus MBri MFry NBat SApu SJus
   'Fryclimbdown' (Cl)                  SWCr
   'Crimson Conquest' (ClHT)            EBls
   crimson damask                       See R. *gallica* var. *officinalis*
   'Crimson Descant' (Cl)               EBee
   'Crimson Gem' (Min)                  MGan
   'Crimson Globe' (Mo)                 MGan
   'Crimson Glory' (HT)                 EBee EBls MBur MGan WAct
   'Crimson Rambler' (Ra)               MAus WBcn
   'Crimson Shower' (Ra)  ♀             EBrP EBre EMFP LBre LPlm MAus
                                        MGan MHlr MJon MMat NRog
                                        SBre SPer SWCr WGer WHCG
                                        WHer WStI
   'Cristata'                           See R. x *centifolia* 'Cristata'
§  Crystal Palace® =                    EBee MJon MMat WHow
   'Poulrek' (Patio)
   cuisse de nymphe                     See R. 'Great Maiden's Blush'
   'Cupid' (ClHT)                       EBee EBls MAus SPer SWCr WAct
§  Curiosity = 'Cocty' (HT/v)           GGre MJon
§  Cymbeline = 'Auslean' (S)            MAus SPer
   'Cynthia Brooke' (HT)                EBls
   'D'Aguesseau' (G)                    EBls MAus
§  Daily Express =                      Last listed 1998
   'Frychambi' (HT)
   'Daily Mail'                         See R. 'Climbing Madame Edouard
                                        Herriot'
§  Daily Post = 'Frytrooper' (F)        MFry
§  Daily Sketch = 'Macai' (F)           MGan
   'Dainty Bess' (HT)                   EBls MAus MRav
§  Dainty Dinah =                       LStr SApu
   'Cocamond' (Min/Patio)
   'Dainty Maid' (F)                    EBls MAus
   'Dairy Maid' (F)                     MAus
   'Daisy Hill' ('Macrantha'            EBls
   hybrid)
§  Dalli Dalli® = 'Tanlilida' (F)       Last listed 1998
   x *damascena* var. *bifera*          See R. x *damascena* var.
                                        *semperflorens*
§  - var. *semperflorens* (D)           EBee EBls EMFP MAus SRPl WAct
                                        WHCG WHow
N - 'Trigintipetala' misapplied         See R. 'Professeur Emile Perrot'

§  - var. *versicolor* (D)              EBee EBls ENot MAus MGan SFam
                                        WAct WHCG
   'Dame Edith Helen' (HT)              EBls
   'Dame of Sark' (F)                   Last listed 1997
§  Dame Wendy = 'Canson' (F)            EBee GCoc LGod MAus MGan
                                        MJon
   'Danaë' (HM)                         CPou EBls EMFP MAus MHlr
                                        WHCG
§  Dancing Pink = 'Hendan' (F)          NBat
   'Danny Boy' (ClHT)                   Last listed 1997
§  Danse des Sylphes® =                 EBls
   'Malcair' (Cl)
   Danse du Feu® (Cl)                   CB&S CGro EBee EBls ELan ENot
                                        EWTr GCoc GGre LGod LPlm LStr
                                        MAus MBri MFry MGan MJon
                                        MMat NRog SApu SPer SSea
                                        WWeb
   'Daphne Gandy' (F)                   MGan
§  Dapple Dawn =                        MAus SPer SWCr
   'Ausapple' (S)
§  Darling Flame =                      ELan GGre MGan SApu
   'Meilucca' (Min)
   'Dart's Defender'                    SLPl
   'Dave Hessayon' (HT)                 Last listed 1997
§  David Whitfield = 'Gana' (F)         MGan MJon
   *davidii*                            EBls MAus
   *davurica*                           Last listed 1996
§  Dawn Chorus =                        CGro EBre EBre GCoc GGre IHar
   'Dicquasar' (HT)                     LBre LGod LPlm LStr MBri MFry
                                        MGan MJon MMat NPri SApu
                                        SBre SJus SPer SRPl WWeb
   'Daybreak' (HM)                      EBls MAus NRog SWCr WAct
                                        WHCG
§  Daylight = 'Interlight' (F)          IDic
§  Dazzler = 'Genpat' (Patio)          MJon
§  De Meaux' (Ce)                       EBls EMFP ENot LFis MAus MMat
                                        SPer SPla SRPl SWCr WHCG
                                        WHow
   'De Meaux, White'                    See R. 'White de Meaux'
§  'De Rescht' (DPo)  ♀                 CBos CPou EBee EBls ENot IHar
                                        LHol MAus MBri MGan MJon
                                        MMat SPer WAct WGer WHCG
                                        WHow
   'Dearest' (F)                        CB&S GGre MGan MJon NRog
                                        SRPl WStI
   'Debbie Thomas' (HT)                 Last listed 1997
§  Deb's Delight =                      ELan MJon
   'Legsweet' (F)
   'Debutante' (Ra)                     EBls MAus MHlr SFam
§  Dee Bennett™ =                       Last listed 1996
   'Savadee' (Min)
   'Deep Secret' (HT)                   CGro CTri EBee EBrP EBre GCoc
                                        GGre LBre LPlm MBur MFry
                                        MGan MJon NRog SApu SBre SJus
                                        SPer SWCr SWas WWeb
♦  'Degenhard'                          See R. Doc = 'Degenhard'
♦  'Deladel'                            See R. Madame Georges
                                        Delbard = 'Deladel'
   'Delambre' (DPo)                     EBls MAus MRav
♦  'Delbrad'                            See R. Royal Baby = 'Delbrad'
♦  'Delge'                              See R. Centenaire de Lourdes =
                                        'Delge'
   'Delicata' (Ru)                      MAus
♦  'Delmur'                             See R. Altissimo = 'Delmur'
♦  'Delpous'                            See R. Fontainebleau = 'Delpous'
♦  'Delpre'                             See R. Happy Anniversary =
                                        'Delpre'
   'Dembrowski' (HP)                    EBls
§  Denman = 'Landen' (HT)               MJon SApu
   'Dentelle de Malines' (S)            EBls MAus MHlr WAct
   'Deschamps' (N)                      EBls

'Desprez à Fleurs Jaunes' (N) ♀ — CPou EBee EBls EMFP IHar MAus NPri SFam SPla SWCr WHCG WHow WSHC

'Deuil de Paul Fontaine' (Mo) — EBls

'Devon Maid' (Cl) — Last listed 1996

♦ 'Devoniensis' (ClT) — See *R.* 'Climbing Devoniensis'

§ Diadem® = 'Tanmeda' (F) — MJon SRPl

'Diamond Jubilee' (HT) — EBls

♦ 'Dicalow' — See *R.* Yellow Ribbon = 'Dicalow'

♦ 'Dicam' — See *R.* Red Devil = 'Dicam'

♦ 'Dicbar' — See *R.* Memento = 'Dicbar'

♦ 'Dicbee' — See *R.* High Summer = 'Dicbee'

♦ 'Dicblender' — See *R.* Acapulco = 'Dicblender'

♦ 'Dicbo' — See *R.* Bonsoir = 'Dicbo'

♦ 'Dicdance' — See *R.* Bright Smile = 'Dicdance'

♦ 'Dicdivine' — See *R.* Pot o' Gold = 'Dicdivine'

♦ 'Dicdrum' — See *R.* Shona = 'Dicdrum'

♦ 'Dicel' — See *R.* Scarlet Queen Elizabeth = 'Dicel'

♦ 'Dicfire' — See *R.* Beautiful Britain = 'Dicfire'

♦ 'Dicgrow' — See *R.* Peek A Boo = 'Dicgrow'

♦ 'Dicinfra' — See *R.* Disco Dancer = 'Dicinfra'

♦ 'Dicjana' — See *R.* Elina = 'Dicjana'

♦ 'Dicjeep' — See *R.* Len Turner = 'Dicjeep'

♦ 'Dicjem' — See *R.* Freedom = 'Dicjem'

♦ 'Dicjoon' — See *R.* Leslie's Dream = 'Dicjoon'

♦ 'Dicjoy' — See *R.* Ards Beauty = 'Dicjoy'

♦ 'Dicjubell' — See *R.* Lovely Lady = 'Dicjubell'

♦ 'Dickerfuffle' — See *R.* Wishing = 'Dickerfuffle'

♦ 'Dickerry' — See *R.* Laughter Lines = 'Dickerry'

♦ 'Dickimono' — See *R.* Anisley Dickson = 'Dickimono'

♦ 'Dickooky' — See *R.* Tall Story = 'Dickooky'

§ Dick's Delight = 'Dicwhistle' — IDic

'Dickson's Flame' (F) — MGan

♦ 'Dicladida' — See *R.* Cider Cup = 'Dicladida'

♦ 'Diclittle' — See *R.* Little Woman = 'Diclittle'

♦ 'Diclulu' — See *R.* Gentle Touch = 'Diclulu'

♦ 'Dicmagic' — See *R.* Sweet Magic = 'Dicmagic'

♦ 'Dicmickey' — See *R.* Buttons = 'Dicmickey'

♦ 'Dicmoppet' — See *R.* Minilights = 'Dicmoppet'

♦ 'Dicnifty' — See *R.* Empress Michiko = 'Dicnifty'

♦ 'Dicnorth' — See *R.* Harvest Fayre = 'Dicnorth'

♦ 'Dicobey' — See *R.* Tequila Sunrise = 'Dicobey'

♦ 'Dicodour' — See *R.* Fragrant Dream = 'Dicodour'

♦ 'Dicogle' — See *R.* Valentine Heart = 'Dicogle'

♦ 'Dicomo' — See *R.* Tear Drop = 'Dicomo'

♦ 'Dicor' — See *R.* Redgold = 'Dicor'

♦ 'Dicpaint' — See *R.* Painted Moon = 'Dicpaint'

♦ 'Dicparty' — See *R.* Party Trick = 'Dicparty'

♦ 'Dicpe' — See *R.* Copper Pot = 'Dicpe'

♦ 'Dicperhaps' — See *R.* Quaker Star = 'Dicperhaps'

♦ 'Dicplay' — See *R.* New Horizon = 'Dicplay'

♦ 'Dicquarrel' — See *R.* Benita = 'Dicquarrel'

♦ 'Dicquasar' — See *R.* Dawn Chorus = 'Dicquasar'

♦ 'Dicqueen' — See *R.* Melody Maker = 'Dicqueen'

♦ 'Dicracer' — See *R.* Sunseeker = 'Dicracer'

♦ 'Dicreason' — See *R.* Our Molly = 'Dicreason'

♦ 'Dicrelax' — See *R.* Flair = 'Dicrelax'

♦ 'Dicrobot' — See *R.* Belfast Belle = 'Dicrobot'

♦ 'Dicroyal' — See *R.* Princess Royal = 'Dicroyal'

♦ 'Dicsun' — See *R.* Mr J.C.B. = 'Dicsun'

♦ 'Dictalent' — See *R.* Shine On = 'Dictalent'

♦ 'Dictator' — See *R.* Pure Bliss = 'Dictator'

♦ 'Dicumpteen' — See *R.* Pretty in Pink = 'Dicumpteen'

♦ 'Dicuncle' — See *R.* Wine and Dine = 'Dicuncle'

♦ 'Dicuniform' — See *R.* Boy O Boy = 'Dicuniform'

♦ 'Dicuptight' — See *R.* Tintinara = 'Dicuptight'

♦ 'Dicvanilla' — See *R.* Happy Ever After = 'Dicvanilla'

♦ 'Dicvintage' — See *R.* Roche Centenary = 'Dicvintage'

♦ 'Dicvood' — See *R.* Glenshane = 'Dicvood'

♦ 'Dicwhistle' — See *R.* Dick's Delight = 'Dicwhistle'

♦ 'Dicwillynilly' — See *R.* Old John = 'Dicwillynilly'

♦ 'Dicwitness' — See *R.* Irish Eyes = 'Dicwitness'

♦ 'Dicwonder' — See *R.* Marry Me = 'Dicwonder'

♦ 'Dicxplosion' — See *R.* Rainbow Magic = 'Dicxplosion'

§ Die Welt® = 'Diekor' (HT) — NBat

♦ 'Diekor' — See *R.* Die Welt = 'Diekor'

'Diorama' (HT) — MAus MGan

'Directeur Alphand' (HP) — EBls WHCG

♦ 'Direktor Benschop' — See *R.* City of York = 'Direktor Benschop'

§ Disco Dancer® = 'Dicinfra' (F) — IDic

§ Dixieland Linda = 'Beadix' (ClHT) — EBls

¶ Dizzy Heights = 'Fryblissful' (Cl) — MFry

§ Doc = 'Degenhard' (Poly) — MGan

'Docteur Andry' (HP) — EBls

'Docteur Grill' (T) — EBls MAus

'Doctor A.J. Verhage' (HT) — MGan

'Doctor Abrahams' (HT) — MJon

§ Doctor Dick = 'Cocbaden' — NBat NRog

'Doctor Edward Deacon' (HT) — EBls

§ Doctor Goldberg = 'Gandol' (HT) — MGan

§ Doctor Jackson™ = 'Ausdoctor' (S) — MAus

'Doctor John Snow' (HT) — MGan

§ Doctor McAlpine = 'Peafirst' (F/Patio) — MBri MJon SWCr

'Doctor W. Van Fleet' (Ra/Cl) — EBls MAus WSHC

¶ 'Doktor Eckener' — EBls IHar MGan

§ Dollie B = 'Trobee' (Min) — Last listed 1996

'Don Charlton' (HT) — NBat

'Don Juan' (Cl) — MGan

§ Donald Davis = 'Chewbeaut' (F) — MJon

§ 'Doncasteri' — EBls MAus

'Dopey' (Poly) — MGan

'Doreen' (HT) — NRog

Doris Tysterman (HT) — CGro EBls EBrP EBre GGre LBre LPlm LStr MAus MGan MJon NRog SBre SPer WWeb

♦ 'Dorneye' — See *R.* Copacabana = 'Dorneye'

'Dorothy Perkins' (Ra) — CGro CTri EBee EBls GChr GGre GOrc LFis LPlm LStr MAus MGan MJon MMat NPer NRog SApu SPer SRPl SWas WHCG

'Dorothy Wheatcroft' (F) — MGan

'Dorothy Whitney Wood' (HT) — MFry

'Dorothy Wilson' (F) — EBls

Dortmund® (ClHScB) — EBee EBls LGod LPlm MAus MGan MMat SPer WAct WHCG

◆ 'Dotrames' — See *R.* Maria Teresa de Esteban = 'Dotrames'

§ Double Delight® = 'Andeli' (HT) — CGro ELan GCoc GGre LPlm LStr MBri MGan MJon NRog SApu SPer

§ Dove® = 'Ausdove' (S) — Last listed 1997

¶ Dr Jo = 'Fryatlan' (F) — MFry

'Dream Girl' (Cl) ♀ — MAus MBri SFam

§ Dream Lover = 'Peayetti' (Patio) — GCoc

'Dream Time' (HT) — Last listed 1997

'Dream Waltz' (F) — Last listed 1997

'Dreamglo' (Min) — Last listed 1998

'Dreaming Spires' (Cl) — MBri MJon MMat SApu SJus SPer

§ Dreamland = 'Träumland' (F) — MFry MGan

'Dresden Doll' (MinMo) — EBls MAus SApu

§ Drummer Boy = 'Harvacity' (F/Patio) — GGre SJus

§ 'Du Maître d'Ecole' (G) ♀ — EBls MAus SWCr WHCG

§ Dublin Bay® = 'Macdub' (Cl) ♀ — CTri EBee EBls EBrP EBre ELan ENot IHar LBre LGod LPlm LStr MBri MBur MFry MGan MJon MMat NRog SApu SBre SPer SRPl SWCr SWas WGer WHow

'Duc de Fitzjames' (G) — EBls SWCr

'Duc de Guiche' (G) ♀ — CPou EBls MAus SFam SPer SWCr WAct WHCG

'Duchess of Portland' — See *R.* 'Portlandica'

Duchess of York — See *R.* Sunseeker = 'Dicracer'

'Duchesse d'Albe' (T) — EBls

'Duchesse d'Angoulême' (G) — EBls MAus SFam

'Duchesse d'Auerstädt' (N) — EBls

'Duchesse de Buccleugh' (G) — EBls MAus

§ 'Duchesse de Montebello' (G) ♀ — EBee EBls MAus MHlr SFam SPer SRms WHCG WHow

'Duchesse de Rohan' (CexHP) — EBls

'Duchesse de Verneuil' (CeMo) — EBls MAus SFam

'Dukat' (Cl) — Last listed 1996

§ Duke Meillandina = 'Meipinjid' (Min) — MBri SApu

'Duke of Edinburgh' (HP) — EBls MAus

'Duke of Wellington' (HP) — EBls WHCG

'Duke of Windsor' (HT) — IHar MGan SPer

'Duke of York' (Ch) — EBls

◆ Duke Sunblaze® — See *R.* Duke Meillandina = 'Meipinjid'

'Dundee Rambler' (Ra) — EBls MAus

'Dupontii' (S) — EBee EBls EWTr MAus SFam SPer WAct WHCG WHow WOVN

'Dupuy Jamain' (HP) — EBls WHCG

'Durham Prince Bishop' (HT) — Last listed 1998

'Dusky Maiden' (F) — EBls MAus WHCG

'Düsterlohe' (Ra) — Last listed 1998

Dutch Gold® (HT) — CGro CTri MAus MGan MJon NRog SPer SRPl SWas

Dwarf King (introduced 1957) — See *R.* 'Zwergkönig'

'E.H. Morse' — See *R.* 'Ernest H. Morse'

'Easlea's Golden Rambler' (Ra) — EBee EBls MAus SWCr WAct WHCG

'Easter Morning' (Min) — ELan MAus MGan MJon SApu SPer

§ Easy Going = 'Harflow' (F) — GCoc

'Eblouissant' (Poly) — MGan

*ecae* — EBls MAus

- 'Helen Knight' — See *R.* 'Helen Knight' (*ecae* hybrid)

'Eclair' (HP) — EBls

'Eddie's Jewel' (*moyesii* hybrid) — EBls IHar MAus MGan

Eden Rose® (HT) — EBls MGan

§ Eden Rose '88 = 'Meiviolin' (ClHT) — MJon SApu SJus SPer

'Edith Bellenden' (RH) — EBls

§ Edith Holden = 'Chewlegacy' (F) — LGod MAus MJon SApu SJus

*eglanteria* — See *R. rubiginosa*

§ Eglantyne = 'Ausmark' (S) — CAbP CSam EBrP EBre IHar LBre LStr MAus MHlr MJon MMat SBre SJus SPer SWCr WWeb

'Egyptian Treasure' (F) — Last listed 1996

'Elegance' (ClHT) — EBls MAus MGan

§ *elegantula* (S) — Last listed 1996

§ - 'Persetosa' (S) — CHad EBls ENot MAus SPer SRPl WAct WHCG

§ Elina® = 'Dicjana' (HT) ♀ — EBee GGre IDic LGod LStr MAus MBur MFry MGan MJon MMat NBat NRog SApu SJus SPer SWCr WHCG

'Eliza Boëlle' (HP) — WHCG

Elizabeth Harkness® (HT) — EBls EWTr MAus MBur MGan SPer

§ Elizabeth Heather Grierson = 'Mattnot' (ClHT) — MMat

§ Elizabeth of Glamis® = 'Macel' (F) — CGro EBls GChr GCoc IHar MBri MGan NRog SPer

'Elizabeth Philp' (F) — LPlm

§ Ellen® = 'Auscup' (S) — MAus MBri

'Ellen Poulsen' (Poly) — MGan

'Ellen Willmott' (HT) — CHad EBee EBls MAus SWCr

'Elmshorn' (S) — CB&S MGan WHCG

'Elsa' (HT) — Last listed 1996

§ Elsie Warren = 'Milsweet' (F) — NBat

§ Emanuel® = 'Ausuel' (S) — MAus SPer

§ Emily = 'Ausburton' (S) — MAus SApu

'Emily Gray' (Ra) — CGro CPou CSam EBls EBrP EBre ENot LBre LStr MAus MBur MGan MHlr MJon NPri NRog SBre SPer SWCr SWas WAct WHCG

§ Emily Louise = 'Harwilla' (Patio) — Last listed 1998

§ Emma Kate = 'Jayemm' (F) — Last listed 1997

'Emma May' (HT) — Last listed 1997

§ Emma Mitchell = 'Horharpdos' (Patio) — Last listed 1998

'Emma Wright' (HT) — MAus

'Emmerdale' (F) — WStI

'Empereur du Maroc' (HP) — EBls MAus MMat WAct WHCG

'Empress Josephine' — See *R.* x *francofurtana*

§ Empress Michiko = 'Dicnifty' (HT) — GCoc IDic SApu WOVN

§ Ena Baxter = 'Cocbonne' (HT) — GCoc GGre

'Ena Harkness' (HT) — CGro EBls ELan GChr GGre MBur MGan NRog WStI

§ 'Enfant de France' (HP) — EBls

x *engelmannii* — EBls

§ English Elegance® = 'Ausleaf' (S) — MAus

§ English Garden® = 'Ausbuff' (S) — EBee EBrP EBre EMFP ENot IHar LBre LStr MAus MBNS MBri MMat SApu SBre SPer SWas WAct WWeb

'English Miss' (F) — EBee EBls LPlm LStr MAus MFry MGan MJon SApu SJus SPer WStI WWeb

'Eos' (*moyesii* hybrid) — EBls MAus

'Erfurt' (HM) — EBls EMFP MAus MGan SRms SWCr WHCG

§ 'Erinnerung an Brod' (S) — WHCG

§ 'Ernest H. Morse' (HT) — CTri EBls GCoc GGre IHar MAus MBur MGan MJon NRog SApu SPer
§ Eroica = 'Erotika' (HT) — Last listed 1998
♦ 'Erotika' — See *R.* Eroica = 'Erotika'
§ Escapade® = 'Harpade' (F) ♀ — EBls MAus MGan
§ Especially for You = 'Fryworthy' (HT) — LGod LStr MBur MFry MJon SApu
§ Esther Ofarim® = 'Korfarim' (F) — Last listed 1997
§ 'Estrellita de Oro' (Min) — LPlm MAus MGan
¶ 'Etain' (Ra) — EBee
§ 'Etendard' — WAct
§ Eternally Yours = 'Macspeego' (HT) — MJon
'Ethel' (Ra) — EBee EMFP
§ Ethel Austin = 'Frymestin' (F) — MFry
'Etoile de Hollande' (HT) — CHad EBee SFam SSea
'Etoile de Lyon' (T) — EBls
'Eugène Fürst' (HP) — EBls WHCG
'Eugénie Guinoisseau' (Mo) — EBls WHCG
§ Euphoria = 'Interup' (GC/S) — ECle GCoc IDic MJon SApu
§ Euphrates = 'Harunique' (*persica* hybrid) — MAus MGan WAct
Europeana® (F) — MAus MGan SWCr
§ Eurostar = 'Poulreb' (F) — ENot MMat SApu
'Eurydice' — Last listed 1996
'Eva' (HM) — EBls
'Evangeline' (Ra) — EBls MAus WAct
♦ 'Evebright' — See *R.* Cecily Gibson = 'Evebright'
§ Evelyn® = 'Aussaucer' (S) — CAbP CSam EBee EBrP EBre EMFP GCoc IHar LBre LGod LStr MAus MFry MHlr MJon MMat SApu SBre SChu SPer SSoC WHow
§ Evelyn Fison = 'Macev' (F) — ELan ENot EPfP GGre MAus MGan MJon NRog SApu SPer
§ Evelyn Grace = 'Horavme' (F) — NBat
'Evelyn Taylor' (F) — Last listed 1996
§ Evening Star® = 'Jacven' (HT) — MAus
'Evening Telegraph' (HT) — Last listed 1997
'Everest Double Fragrance' (F) — EBls
'Excelsa' (Ra) — CTri EBee EBls EMFP GChr GCoc GGre LGod LStr MAus MGan MJon NBus NRog SSea WAct WStI WLRN
Exception (Ru) —
§ Exploit® = 'Meilider' (Cl) — GGre WWeb
§ Eye Paint = 'Maceye' (F) — MAus MGan MJon SMrm
'Eyecatcher' (F) — Last listed 1997
§ Eyeopener = 'Interop' (S/GC) — CGro EBls IDic MGan MJon
'F.E. Lester' — See *R.* 'Francis E. Lester'
§ 'F.J. Grootendorst' (Ru) — EBls GOrc IOrc LGod LStr MAus MGan MJon NRog WAct
'Fabvier' — See *R.* 'Colonel Fabvier'
§ Fair Bianca® = 'Ausca' (S) — IOrc MAus MBri MHlr
§ Fairhope = 'Talfairhope' (Min) — NBat
§ Fairy Changeling = 'Harnumerous' (Poly) — MAus
§ Fairy Damsel = 'Harneaty' (Poly/GC) — EBls MAus MBur
§ Fairy Queen = 'Sperien' (Poly/GC) — IDic SSea

'Fairy Rose' — See *R.* 'The Fairy'
§ Fairy Snow = 'Holfairy' (S) — Last listed 1998
§ Fairygold = 'Frygoldie' (Patio) — MBri MFry
§ Fairyland® = 'Harlayalong' (Poly) — EBls MAus MBur SApu
§ Fancy Pants™ = 'Kinfancy' (Min) — Last listed 1997
'Fantin-Latour' (*centifolia* hybrid) ♀ — CHad CSam EBee EBls ELan ENot GCoc IHar LGod LStr MAus MBri MGan MHlr MMat NFla NRog SApu SFam SJus SPer SRPl WAct WGer WHCG WHow WSHC WWeb
*fargesii* hort. — See *R. moyesii* var. *fargesii*
*farreri* — See *R. elegantula*
- var. *persetosa* — See *R. elegantula* 'Persetosa'
§ Fascination = 'Jacoyel' (HT) — ECle LStr MBri SCoo
§ Fascination = 'Poulmax' (F) — EPfP GCoc LGod LPlm LRHS MFry MGan MMat
'Fashion Flame' (Min) — Last listed 1997
§ Favorite Rosamini = 'Ruifaro' (Min) — Last listed 1998
*fedtschenkoana* hort. — EBls MAus MGan SPer WAct WHCG
Fée des Neiges® — See *R.* Iceberg = 'Korbin'
'Felicia' (HM) ♀ — CHad CSam EBee EBls ELan ENot GCoc IHar LGod LHol LStr MAus MBri MFry MHlr MJon MMat NFla NRog SApu SFam SJus SPer SWCr SWas WAct WHCG WHow WOVN
'Félicité Parmentier' (AxD) ♀ — EBls EWTr MAus SFam SJus SPer WAct WHCG WOVN
§ 'Félicité Perpétue' (Ra) ♀ — CSam EBls ELan EWTr GCoc IHar ISea LHol LStr MAus MBri MGan MHlr MMat NFla SApu SFam SJus SPer SRPl SWCr SWas WAct WHCG WSHC
§ Felicity Kendal = 'Lanken' (HT) — MBri MJon
'Fellenberg' (Ch) — EBls MAus WHCG
§ Fellowship = 'Harwelcome' (F) — GCoc LGod LPlm LStr MAus MBri MBur MFry MGan MJon MMat SJus WGer
'Femina' (HT) — MGan
'Ferdinand Pichard' (Bb) ♀ — CPou EBee EBls EMFP ENot EWTr IHar LFis MAus MBri MGan MHlr MJon MMat NFla SJus SPer WAct WGer WHCG WHow WOVN
§ Ferdy® = 'Keitoli' (GC) — EBls ELan ENot MAus MGan SApu SPer WOVN
§ Fergie = 'Ganfer' (F/Patio) — MGan
♦ 'Ferho' — See *R.* Childhood Memories = 'Ferho'
§ Festival = 'Kordialo' (Patio) — CGro ENot GGre IHar LGod LPlm LStr MAus MBri MGan MJon MMat NPri SApu SPer SWas WGer WOVN WWeb
§ Fiesta = 'Macfirinlin' (Patio) — LStr MJon NBat SWCr
§ Fifi = 'Hanfif' (F) — NBat
§ Figurine™ = 'Benfig' (Min) — Last listed 1997
*filipes* 'Brenda Colvin' — See *R.* 'Brenda Colvin'
§ - 'Kiftsgate' (Ra) ♀ — More than 30 suppliers
§ 'Fimbriata' (Ru) — EBls MAus MBri SPer WAct WHCG
§ Financial Times Centenary = 'Ausfin' (S) — MAus
§ Fine Gold = 'Weegold' (HT) — Last listed 1997
§ Fiona® = 'Meibeluxen' (S/GC) — EBls GGre SApu SWCr WHCG WOVN
'Fire Princess' (Min) — Last listed 1997
'Firecracker' (F) — EBls
§ Firefly® = 'Macfrabro' (Min) — MJon

| | |
|---|---|
| 'First Love' (HT) | EBls MGan |
| 'Fisher and Holmes' (HP) | EBls MAus WAct WHCG |
| § Fisherman's Friend® = 'Auschild' (S) | MAus SPer |
| § Flair = 'Dicrelax' (F) | IDic LStr MJon |
| § Flamenco = 'Poultika' (Cl) | EBee |
| § Flaming Rosamini = 'Ruiflami' (Min) | Last listed 1996 |
| ◆ Flamingo | See *R.* Margaret Thatcher = 'Korflüg' |
| § Flamingo Meidiland = 'Meisolroz' | WOVN |
| 'Fleur Cowles' (F) | MBur |
| 'Flora' (Ra) | CRHN EBls MAus SFam |
| 'Flora McIvor' (RH) | EBls MAus MGan |
| § Florence Nightingale = 'Ganflor' (F) | MBur MGan SApu SPer |
| Flower Carpet™ | See *R.* Pink Flower Carpet = 'Noatraum' |
| ¶ 'Flower Carpet Twilight' (GC) | CGro LRHS |
| § Flower Power = 'Frycassia' (Patio) | GCoc LStr MFry |
| § *foetida* (S) | EBls MAus |
| § - 'Bicolor' (S) | EBee EBls ENot IHar MAus MGan MMat NRog SMad WAct |
| § - 'Persiana' (S) | EBls MAus MGan SPer |
| *foliolosa* | EBls SLPl WHCG |
| 'Forgotten Dreams' (HT) | MJon |
| *forrestiana* | EBls MAus MMat |
| x *fortuneana* (Ra) | EBls |
| Fortune's double yellow | See *R.* x *odorata* 'Pseudindica' |
| 'Fountain' (HT/S) | CSam EBls LStr MAus MGan SApu SPer |
| § Fragrant Cloud = 'Tanellis' (HT) | CGro EBee EBls EBrP EBre EWTr GCoc GGre IHar LBre LStr MAus MBri MBur MFry MJon MMat NBat NRog SApu SBre SPer WWeb |
| Fragrant Delight® (F) ♀ | EBee GCoc LPlm LStr MFry MGan MJon NBat SApu SPer SRPl WWeb |
| § Fragrant Dream = 'Dicodour' (HT) | GGre IDic LStr MBri SApu |
| § Fragrant Gold = 'Tanduft' (HT) | GCoc LStr |
| 'Fragrant Hour' (HT) | MGan |
| 'Francesca' (HM) | EBee EBls LFis MAus MGan SFam SPer SWCr WAct WHCG |
| § Francine Austin® = 'Ausram' (S/GC) | MAus SPer WAct |
| 'Francis Dubreuil' (T) | EBls |
| § 'Francis E. Lester' (HM/Ra) ♀ | CHad CRHN CSam EBee EBls EBrP EBre MAus MBri SBre SFam SPer SWCr SWas WAct WHCG WHow |
| § x *francofurtana* ♀ | CPou EBls MAus MRav SFam WAct WHCG |
| 'François Juranville' (Ra) ♀ | CPou CRHN EBee EBls LStr MAus MBri MGan MHlr MMat NBus NRog SApu SMad SPer SRPl SSoC WAct |
| 'Frank MacMillan' (HT) | Last listed 1997 |
| 'Frank Naylor' (S) | Last listed 1997 |
| ◆ 'Franlac' | See *R.* Road to Freedom = 'Franlac' |
| ◆ 'Franluv' | See *R.* Summer Love = 'Franluv' |
| ◆ 'Franshine' | See *R.* Chester Cathedral = 'Franshine' |
| 'Frau Astrid Späth' (F) | NRog |
| 'Frau Eva Schubert' (Ru) | Last listed 1996 |
| § 'Frau Karl Druschki' (HP) | EBls MAus MGan SWCr WAct |
| 'Fraulein Octavia Hesse' (Ra) | EBls |

| | |
|---|---|
| 'Fred Gibson' (HT) | Last listed 1997 |
| 'Fred Loads' (F/S) ♀ | EBls MAus MGan SApu SWCr |
| § Freddie Mercury = 'Batmercury' (HT) | MJon NBat |
| § Freddy = 'Peaproof' (F) | Last listed 1996 |
| § Free as Air = 'Mehbronze' (Patio) | MBri |
| § Freedom® = 'Dicjem' (HT) ♀ | ENot GCoc GGre IDic IHar LGod LPlm LStr MAus MBur MFry MGan MMat NBat NRog SApu SJus WWeb |
| 'Freiherr von Marschall' (T) | EBls |
| 'Frensham' (F) | CB&S CGro EBls LStr MGan MMat SWas |
| Fresh Pink (Min/Poly) | MGan |
| § Friday's Child = 'Horabi' (HT) | Last listed 1997 |
| § Friend for Life = 'Cocnanne' (F) | GCoc MJon |
| 'Fringette' (Min) | MGan |
| 'Fritz Nobis' (S) ♀ | EBee EBls ENot GCoc IHar LStr MAus MGan MHlr MRav NFla SJus SPer SWCr WAct WHCG WHow |
| 'Frohsinn' (F) | Last listed 1996 |
| § Frothy = 'Macfrothy' (Min) | MJon |
| 'Fru Dagmar Hastrup' (Ru) ♀ | CSam EBee EBls EBrP EBre ELan ENot GChr GCoc GOrc IOrc LBre LBuc LStr MAus MFry MGan MHlr MJon MMat NRog SApu SBre SJus SPer WAct WHCG WOVN |
| 'Frühlingsanfang' (PiH) | EBls MAus MBri WAct WHCG |
| 'Frühlingsduft' (PiH) | EBee EBls NRog |
| 'Frühlingsgold' (PiH) ♀ | CB&S CGro EBee EBls EBrP EBre ELan ENot EWTr GCoc IOrc LBre LStr MAus MBri MFry MGan MMat NRog SApu SBre SJus SPer SWCr WAct WHCG WOVN WWeb |
| 'Frühlingsmorgen' (PiH) | EBee EBls EBrP EBre ENot EWTr GCoc LBre LFis LStr MAus MBri MGan MHlr MMat NRog SApu SBre SJus SMad SPer WAct WHCG WOVN |
| 'Frühlingsschnee' (PiH) | EBls |
| 'Frühlingszauber' (PiH) | EBls |
| ◆ 'Fryaffair' | See *R.* Sightsaver = 'Fryaffair' |
| 'Fryamour' (HT) | MFry |
| ◆ 'Frybingo' | See *R.* Awareness = 'Frybingo' |
| ◆ 'Frybountiful' | See *R.* Phab Gold = 'Frybountiful' |
| ◆ 'Frybright' | See *R.* Razzle Dazzle = 'Frybright' |
| ◆ 'Frybubbly' | See *R.* Bubbles = 'Frybubbly' |
| ◆ 'Frycalm' | See *R.* Britannia = 'Frycalm' |
| ◆ 'Frycassia' | See *R.* Flower Power = 'Frycassia' |
| ◆ 'Frychambi' | See *R.* Daily Express = 'Frychambi' |
| ◆ 'Frycharm' | See *R.* Lions International = 'Frycharm' |
| ◆ 'Fryclimbdown' | See *R.* Crimson Cascade = 'Fryclimbdown' |
| ◆ 'Frydabble' | See *R.* Jack Wood = 'Frydabble' |
| ◆ 'Frydarkeye' | See *R.* Biddulph Grange = 'Frydarkeye' |
| ◆ 'Fryevenest' | See *R.* Evening Sentinel = 'Fryevenest' |
| ◆ 'Frygoldie' | See *R.* Fairygold = 'Frygoldie' |
| ◆ 'Frygran' | See *R.* Johnnie Walker = 'Frygran' |
| ◆ 'Fryjam' | See *R.* The Flower Arranger = 'Fryjam' |
| ◆ 'Fryjasso' | See *R.* Inner Wheel = 'Fryjasso' |
| ◆ 'Fryjingo' | See *R.* The Lady = 'Fryjingo' |

◆ 'Frymartor'          See *R.* Marianne Tudor = 'Frymartor'
◆ 'Frymestin'          See *R.* Ethel Austin = 'Frymestin'
◆ 'Fryminicot'         See *R.* Sweet Dream = 'Fryminicot'
◆ 'Fryministar'        See *R.* Top Marks = 'Fryministar'
◆ 'Fryorst'            See *R.* Arc Angel = 'Fryorst'
◆ 'Fryperdee'          See *R.* Velvet Fragrance = 'Fryperdee'
◆ 'Fryprincess'        See *R.* Julie Cussons = 'Fryprincess'
◆ 'Fryrelax'           See *R.* Pensioner's Voice = 'Fryrelax'
◆ 'Fryrhapsody'        See *R.* Langdale Chase = 'Fryrhapsody'
◆ 'Fryromeo'           See *R.* Scent-sation = 'Fryromeo'
◆ 'Fryshrewby'         See *R.* Shrewsbury Show = 'Fryshrewby'
◆ 'Frystar'            See *R.* Liverpool Remembers = 'Frystar'
◆ 'Frysweetie'         See *R.* Mary Gammon = 'Frysweetie'
◆ 'Frytranquil'        See *R.* Golden Moments = 'Frytranquil'
◆ 'Frytrooper'         See *R.* Daily Post = 'Frytrooper'
◆ 'Fryvivacious'       See *R.* Julie Andrews = 'Fryvivacious'
◆ 'Frywinner'          See *R.* Atco Royale = 'Frywinner'
◆ 'Fryworld'           See *R.* Atlantic Star = 'Fryworld'
◆ 'Fryworthy'          See *R.* Especially for You = 'Fryworthy'
◆ 'Fryxotic'           See *R.* Warm Wishes = 'Fryxotic'
◆ 'Fryxquisite'        See *R.* Sweet Petite = 'Fryxquisite'
◆ 'Fryyaboo'           See *R.* Belle Epoque = 'Fryyaboo'
◆ 'Fryyat'             See *R.* Good Morning = 'Fryyat'
◆ 'Fryyearn'           See *R.* Bride = 'Fryyearn'
◆ 'Fryyeh'             See *R.* Pomona = 'Fryyeh'
◆ 'Fryyippee'          See *R.* Rosie Larkin = 'Fryyippee'
◆ 'Fryyoung'           See *R.* Special Occasion = 'Fryyoung'
◆ 'Fryzebedee'         See *R.* The Cheshire Regiment = 'Fryzebedee'
◆ 'Fryzippy'           See *R.* Bob Greaves = 'Fryzippy'
  'Fulgens'            See *R.* 'Malton' (China hybrid)
§ Fulton Mackay = 'Cocdana' (HT)          GCoc MFry MGan SApu
§ Fyvie Castle = 'Cocbamber' (HT)         GCoc GGre MGan
  'Gail Borden' (HT)   MAus MGan
§ *gallica* (G)        EBls
  - 'Beckett's Single' (G)   Last listed 1996
  - 'Complicata'       See *R.* 'Complicata'
  - 'Conditorum'       See *R.* 'Conditorum'
§ - var. *officinalis* (G) ♀   EBls GCoc GPoy LHol MAus MBri MJon MMat NRog SApu SFam SJus SPer WAct WHCG WHow
  - 'Velutiniflora' (G)   EBls
§ - 'Versicolor' (G) ♀   CHad CSam EBee EBls ELan ENot GChr GCoc GGre LGod LStr MAus MBri MFry MGan MJon NRog SApu SJus SPer SPla SRPl SWas WHCG WHow WWeb
§ Galway Bay® = 'Macba' (ClHT)   CSam EBrP EBre LBre MGan MMat SBre SPer
◆ 'Gana'.              See *R.* David Whitfield = 'Gana'
I 'Gancence'           See *R.* Eminence = 'Gancence'
◆ 'Gancre'             See *R.* Crème de la Crème = 'Gancre'
◆ 'Gandol'             See *R.* Doctor Goldberg = 'Gandol'

◆ 'Gandri'             See *R.* Betty Driver = 'Gandri'
◆ 'Ganfer'             See *R.* Fergie = 'Ganfer'
◆ 'Ganflor'            See *R.* Florence Nightingale = 'Ganflor'
◆ 'Ganhol'             See *R.* Moriah = 'Ganhol'
◆ 'Ganjil'             See *R.* Jill's Rose = 'Ganjil'
◆ 'Ganspa'             See *R.* Spangles = 'Ganspa'
§ Garden News = 'Poulrim' (HT)   GCoc GGre
§ Garden Party™ = 'Kormollis' (F)   ENot MMat
  'Gardener's Delight' (Ra)   Last listed 1996
  'Gardenia' (Ra)      CRHN EBee MHlr SPer WHCG
§ 'Garnette' (Gn)      Last listed 1998
§ 'Garnette Apricot' (Gn)   SPla
  'Garnette Carol'     See *R.* 'Carol Amling'
  'Garnette Golden'    See *R.* 'Golden Garnette'
  'Garnette Pink'      See *R.* 'Carol Amling'
  'Garnette Red'       See *R.* 'Garnette'
§ Gary Lineker = 'Pearobin' (F)   MBri
  'Gary Player' (HT)   NBat
  'Gateshead Festival' (HT)   Last listed 1998
  'Gaujard'            See *R.* Rose Gaujard = 'Gaumo'
◆ 'Gaumo'              See *R.* Rose Gaujard = 'Gaumo'
  'Gavotte' (HT)       Last listed 1997
§ Gee Gee™ = 'Benjee' (Min)   Last listed 1997
  'Gelbe Dagmar Hastrup'   See *R.* Yellow Dagmar Hastrup = 'Moryelrug'
  'Général Galliéni' (T)   EBls
  'Général Jacqueminot' (HP)   EBls MAus MCAu WAct
  'Général Kléber' (CeMo)   EBee EBls MAus SFam SPer SWCr WAct WHCG
§ 'Général Schablikine' (T)   EBee EBls MAus WBcn
◆ 'Genpat'             See *R.* Dazzler = 'Genpat'
N *gentiliana* (Ra)    EBls MAus WHCG
§ Gentle Touch = 'Diclulu' (Min/Patio) ♀   CGro EBls GGre IDic IHar MBri MFry MJon MMat NRog SApu SPer
  'Geoff Boycott' (F)  Last listed 1997
§ Geoff Hamilton™ = 'Ausham' (S)   MAus MBNS MJon SWCr WWeb
§ Geordie Lad = 'Horkorblush' (HT)   NBat
  'Georg Arends' (HP)  EBls MAus
  'George Dickson' (HT)   EBls MAus SRms
  'George R. Hill' (HT)   NBat
  'Georges Vibert' (G)   EBls MAus WHCG
§ Geraldine = 'Peahaze' (F)   MGan SWCr
§ 'Geranium' (*moyesii* hybrid) ♀   CB&S CGro EBee EBrP EBre ELan ENot EPla GCoc IHar IOrc LBre LGod LStr MAus MBri MGan MHlr MJon SApu SBre SPer SRPl SWas WAct WHCG WOVN WSHC WWeb
  Gerbe d'Or           See *R.* Casino = 'Macca'
  'Gerbe Rose' (Ra)    EBls MAus WAct
§ Gertrude Jekyll® = 'Ausbord' (S) ♀   More than 30 suppliers
  'Geschwinds Orden'   Last listed 1996
  'Geschwinds Schönste' (Ra)   Last listed 1996
  'Ghislaine de Féligonde' (Ra/S)   EBls LStr SWCr WHCG
  *gigantea*           EBls ISea
◆ - 'Cooperi'          See *R.* 'Cooperi'
  Gilda                See *R.* The Daily Telegraph = 'Peahigh'
§ Gingernut = 'Coccrazy' (Patio)   GCoc GGre SApu
§ Ginny-Lou = 'Trobinka' (Min)   SJus
  'Ginsky' (F)         Last listed 1996
  Gipsy Boy            See *R.* 'Zigeunerknabe'

§ Glad Tidings = 'Tantide' (F) — CGro GGre LPlm MAus MBri MBur MGan MJon NRog SApu SJus SPer WWeb

§ Glamis Castle = 'Auslevel' (S) — CBlo EBee EBls EBrP EBre IHar LBre LStr MAus MBri MJon NPri SBre SJus SPer WHCG WHow WWeb

◆ 'Glanlin' — See *R.* Lincoln Cathedral = 'Glanlin'

◆ 'Glanmusic' — See *R.* Sir Neville Marriner = 'Glanmusic'

◆ 'Glareabit' — See *R.* Lincolnshire Poacher = 'Glareabit'

§ *glauca* (S) ♀ — More than 30 suppliers

'Glenfiddich' (F) — CGro GChr GGre EHar LPlm LStr MAus MBri MGan MJon NRog SPer SWCr WStI WWeb

¶ 'Glenn Dale' (Cl) — EBee

§ Glenshane = 'Dicvood' (GC/S) — IDic

'Gloire de Bruxelles' (HP) — EBls

'Gloire de Dijon' (ClT) ♀ — More than 30 suppliers

'Gloire de Ducher' (HP) — CPou EBee MAus MGan WAct WHCG

'Gloire de France' (G) — EBee EBls MAus

'Gloire de Guilan' (D) — EBls MAus WAct

'Gloire des Mousseuses' (CeMo) — EBls MAus SFam WAct WHCG

'Gloire du Midi' (Poly) — MAus

'Gloire Lyonnaise' (HP) — EBee EBls WHCG

'Gloria Mundi' (Poly) — EBls MGan

§ Gloriana = 'Chewpope' (ClPatio) — ECle MBri MJon

§ Glowing Amber = 'Manglow' (Min) — NBat

*glutinosa* — See *R. pulverulenta*

'Goethe' (CeMo) — EBls

§ Gold Bunny = 'Meifronuri' (F) — MBri MGan MJon

Gold Crown — See *R.* 'Goldkrone'

'Goldbusch' (RH) — EBls MAus MGan SRms SWas WAct

'Golden Anniversary' (Patio) — GGre NEgg

¶ 'Golden Burrel' (Min) — NBat

§ Golden Celebration™ = 'Ausgold' (S) — CTri EBee EBrP EBre GGre IHar LBre LRHS LStr MAus MBri MGan MHlr MJon NPri SApu SBre SJus SPer SWCr WGer

§ Golden Chersonese = 'Hilgold' (S) — EBls MAus NRog

◆ 'Golden Dawn' (ClHT) — See *R.* 'Climbing Golden Dawn'

§ Golden Days = 'Rugolda' (HT) — MBri MFry

§ 'Golden Garnette' (Gn) — Last listed 1998

'Golden Glow' (Cl) — EBls MGan

§ Golden Halo™ = 'Savahalo' (Min) — Last listed 1997

§ Golden Hands = 'Chessupremo' (Min/Patio) — GGre

§ Golden Handshake = 'Chewsunford' (ClMin/ClPatio) — MBri

§ Golden Hope = 'Mehac' (F) — LStr

Golden Jewel — See *R.* Goldjuwel = 'Tanledolg'

§ Golden Jubilee = 'Cocagold' (HT) — ELan GCoc GGre LPlm LStr MAus MBur

§ Golden Melody = 'Irene Churruca' (HT) — EBls

§ Golden Moments = 'Frytranquil' (HT) — MFry MJon

'Golden Moss' (Mo) — EBls

'Golden Ophelia' (HT) — EBls

§ Golden Penny = 'Rugul' (Min) — MFry MGan MJon WGer

§ Golden Quill = 'Tanellelog' (F) — MJon

'Golden Rambler' — See *R.* 'Alister Stella Gray'

§ Golden Rosamini = 'Intergol' (Min/Patio) — Last listed 1998

'Golden Salmon' (Poly) — MGan

'Golden Salmon Supérieur' (Poly) — EBls

'Golden Shot' (F) — MGan

Golden Showers® (Cl) ♀ — CB&S CGro CSam EBee EBls EBrP EBre ELan GCoc GGre LBre LGod LPlm LStr MAus MBri MBur MFry MGan MJon MMat NRog SApu SBre SPer WAct WHCG WWeb

'Golden Slippers' (F) — CB&S MGan

'Golden Sunblaze' — See *R.* 'Rise 'n' Shine'

§ Golden Symphonie = 'Meitoleil' (Min/Patio) — MJon

Golden Times — See *R.* Kordes' Golden Times = 'Kortime'

§ Golden Treasure = 'Tantasch' (F) — Last listed 1996

§ Golden Wedding = 'Arokris' (F/HT) — EBee EBrP EBre ELan GCoc GGre IHar LBre LGod LPlm LRHS LStr MAus MBri MBur MFry MGan MJon MMat NBat NEgg SApu SBre SJus SPer SRPl WStI WWeb

'Golden Wings' (S) ♀ — CHad EBee EBls EMFP ENot EWTr GCoc IHar LFis LStr MAus MBri MFry MGan MJon MMat NFla SApu SJus SPer SWas WAct WHCG WHow WOVN WWeb

§ Golden Years® = 'Harween' (F) — MAus MJon

'Goldfinch' (Ra) — CHad EBee EBls EMFP GGre IHar LStr MAus MBri MHlr SApu SFam SPer SWCr WAct WHCG WHow

§ Goldfinger = 'Pearoyal' (F) — MBri

'Goldilocks' (F) — NRog

§ Goldjuwel = 'Tanledolg' (F/Patio) — NBat

'Goldkrone' (HT) — Last listed 1997

◆ Goldschatz® — See *R.* Golden Treasure = 'Tantasch'

§ Goldstar = 'Candide' (HT) — EBee MGan SApu

◆ Goldstern® (Cl) — See *R.* Gold Star = 'Tantern'

§ Good as Gold = 'Chewsunbeam' (ClMin) — LStr MBri MFry MJon SApu WGer WOVN

¶ 'Good Life' (HT) — GCoc

§ Good Luck = 'Burspec' (F/Patio) — MJon

§ Good Morning = 'Fryyat' (F) — Last listed 1997

§ Gordon's College = 'Cocjabby' (F) — GCoc SApu

'Grace Abounding' (F) — NBat

'Grace Darling' (T) — EBls

§ Grace de Monaco® = 'Meimit' (HT) — EBls MAus MGan

§ Graceland = 'Kirscot' (Min/Patio) — MJon

§ Graham Thomas = 'Ausmas' (S) ♀ — More than 30 suppliers

Granada (HT) — EBls

§ Grand Hotel® = 'Mactel' (ClHT) — ENot MJon MMat SPer SWCr

§ Grand-mère Jenny =    EBls MGan
   'Grem' (HT)
'Grandpa Dickson' (HT)    EBls EBrP EBre EWTr GGre IHar
                             LBre LGod LPlm MAus MBur
                             MGan MJon NBat NRog SApu
                             SBre SPer WWeb
§ 'Great Maiden's Blush' (A)    EBls GCoc GOrc MFry MMat
                             SFam SRPl WAct
'Great News' (F)    MAus
'Great Ormond Street' (F)    EBls
'Great Western' (Bb)    EBls
'Green Diamond' (Min)    MAus MJon
§ Green Snake® =    Last listed 1996
   'Lenwich' (S/GC)
§ Greenall's Glory =    LStr MAus MJon WHow
   'Kirmac' (F/Patio)
'Greenmantle' (RH)    EBls MAus MGan
§ Greensleeves® =    EBls LStr MAus SPer SWCr
   'Harlenten' (F)
§ Greer Garson =    GCoc
   'Cocoddy' (HT)
§ Greetings = 'Jacdreco' (F)    GCoc IDic
◆ 'Grem'    See R. Grand-mère Jenny =
                             'Grem'
¶ 'Grimpant Cramoisi    EBls
   Supérieur' (ClCh)
'Grootendorst'    See R. 'F.J. Grootendorst'
'Grootendorst Supreme' (Ru)    MAus SPer
N 'Gros Choux de Hollande'    EBls WHCG
   (Bb)
§ Grouse = 'Korimro' (S/GC)    EBls ENot GCoc IHar MAus MHlr
                             MJon MMat SApu SPer WAct
                             WOVN
§ Grumpy = 'Burkhardt' (Poly)    MGan
'Gruss an Aachen' (Poly)    EBls EWTr LStr MAus MBri MGan
                             SPer SWCr WAct WHCG WHow
'Gruss an Teplitz'    CPou EBls LFis MAus SPer SRPl
   (China hybrid)    SWCr WHCG
§ Guernsey Love =    MJon SJus
   'Troblove' (Min)
◆ 'Guesdelay'    See R. Birthday Wishes =
                             'Guesdelay'
'Guinée' (ClHT)    CHad CSam EBls EBrP EBre ELan
                             IHar LBre LStr MAus MBur MGan
                             MMat NPri SBre SChu SPer WHCG
                             WHow
Guletta®    See R. Golden Penny = 'Rugul'
'Gustav Grünerwald' (HT)    EBls MAus
§ Gwent = 'Poulurt' (GC)    EBee EBrP EBre ELan ENot LBre
                             LGod LPlm LStr MFry MGan MHlr
                             MMat NPri SApu SBre SPer WOVN
                             WRHF
§ *gymnocarpa*    EBls ENot MAus MGan MMat SPer
   var. *willmottiae*    WAct WHCG
Gypsy Boy    See R. 'Zigeunerknabe'
'Gypsy Moth' (F)    Last listed 1996
◆ 'Hadangel'    See R. Smooth Angel = 'Hadangel'
◆ 'Hadlady'    See R. Smooth Lady = 'Hadlady'
◆ 'Hadmelody'    See R. Smooth Melody =
                             'Hadmelody'
◆ 'Hadperfume'    See R. Smooth Perfume =
                             'Hadperfume'
◆ 'Hadprince'    See R. Smooth Prince =
                             'Hadprince'
◆ 'Hadromance'    See R. Smooth Romance =
                             'Hadromance'
◆ 'Hadromeo'    See R. Olde Romeo = 'Hadromeo'
◆ 'Hadsatin'    See R. Smooth Satin = 'Hadsatin'
◆ 'Hadvelvet'    See R. Smooth Velvet =
                             'Hadvelvet'
'Hakuun' (F/Patio)    MAus MGan

Hamburger Phönix® (Ra)    CGro EBls MGan SPer WAct
§ Hampshire = 'Korhamp'    ENot MAus MGan MMat SApu
   (GC)
§ Hand in Hand =    MBri MJon
   'Haraztec' (Patio/Min)
§ Handel® = 'Macha' (Cl) ♀    CGro EBls EBrP EBre ELan GGre
                             LBre LGod LPlm LStr MAus MBri
                             MBur MFry MGan MJon MMat
                             NBat NRog SApu SBre SPer SWCr
                             SWas WWeb
◆ 'Hanfif'    See R. Fifi = 'Hanfif'
§ Hannah Gordon =    EBee ENot LStr MBur MGan MJon
   'Korweiso' (F)    MMat NBat NRog SWas
'Hannah Hauwxell' (Patio/F)    NBat NRog
'Hanne' (HT)    IHar NRog
'Hansa' (Ru)    EBls ENot IHar LBuc MAus MGan
                             MMat SPer SWCr WHCG WHow
                             WOVN
'Happy' (Poly)    MGan
§ Happy Anniversary =    CTri GChr GGre LStr MJon NEgg
   'Delpre' (F)    WWeb
'Happy Birthday' (Min/Patio)    GGre NEgg SWCr
§ Happy Child = 'Auscomp' (S)    EBrP EBre IHar LBre MAus MHlr
                             MJon SBre SJus SPer WGer
§ Happy Ever After =    IDic
   'Dicvanilla' (F)
'Happy Thought' (Min)    MJon
§ Happy Times =    GGre
   'Bedone' (Patio/Min)
Happy Wanderer® (F)    Last listed 1997
◆ 'Haraztec'    See R. Hand in Hand = 'Haraztec'
◆ 'Harbabble'    See R. Sunset Boulevard =
                             'Harbabble'
◆ 'Harbella'    See R. Peacekeeper = 'Harbella'
◆ 'Harbilbo'    See R. Saint John = 'Harbilbo'
◆ 'Harbingo'    See R. House Beautiful =
                             'Harbingo'
◆ 'Harbonny'    See R. Ruby Anniversary =
                             'Harbonny'
◆ 'Harcester'    See R. Caroline Davison =
                             'Harcester'
◆ 'Harclue'    See R. Commonwealth Glory =
                             'Harclue'
◆ 'Harcogent'    See R. Saint Christopher =
                             'Harcogent'
◆ 'Harcomp'    See R. Highfield = 'Harcomp'
◆ 'Harcross'    See R. Humanity = 'Harcross'
◆ 'Hardimple'    See R. World Class = 'Hardimple'
◆ 'Hardinkum'    See R. Princess of Wales =
                             'Hardinkum'
◆ 'Hardolly'    See R. Tambourine = 'Hardolly'
◆ 'Hardwell'    See R. Penny Lane = 'Hardwell'
◆ 'Hareast'    See R. Rising Star = 'Hareast'
◆ 'Harelan'    See R. Poetry in Motion =
                             'Harelan'
◆ 'Harencore'    See R. Pride of England =
                             'Harencore'
◆ 'Harette'    See R. Betty Harkness = 'Harette'
§ Harewood =    MJon SApu
   'Taninaso' (Patio/F)
◆ 'Harflow'    See R. Easy Going = 'Harflow'
◆ 'Harhero'    See R. Marjorie Fair = 'Harhero'
§ x *harisonii* 'Harison's    EBls MAus WAct
   Yellow' (PiH) ♀
§ - 'Lutea Maxima' (PiH)    EBls MAus
§ - 'Williams' Double    EBls GChr GCoc MAus
   Yellow' (PiH)
◆ 'Harjosine'    See R. Basildon Bond =
                             'Harjosine'
'Harkaramel'    See R. Anne Harkness =
                             'Harkaramel'

◆ 'Harkinder'    See *R.* Esther's Baby = 'Harkinder'

◆ 'Harking'    See *R.* Judy Garland = 'Harking'

§ Harkness Marigold = Last listed 1996
   'Hartoflex' (F)

◆ 'Harkover'    See *R.* Letchworth Garden City = 'Harkover'

◆ 'Harkreme'    See *R.* Camphill Glory = 'Harkreme'

◆ 'Harkuly'    See *R.* Margaret Merril = 'Harkuly'

◆ 'Harlayalong'    See *R.* Fairyland = 'Harlayalong'

◆ 'Harlenten'    See *R.* Greensleeves = 'Harlenten'

◆ 'Harlex'    See *R.* Alexander = 'Harlex'

◆ 'Harlexis'    See *R.* L'Oréal Trophy = 'Harlexis'

◆ 'Harlightly'    See *R.* Princess Michael of Kent = 'Harlightly'

§ Harlow Carr = 'Kirlyl' (F)    MJon

◆ 'Harmantelle'    See *R.* Mountbatten = 'Harmantelle'

◆ 'Harmark'    See *R.* Hiroshima's Children = 'Harmark'

◆ 'Harmusky'    See *R.* Radox Bouquet = 'Harmusky'

◆ 'Harneaty'    See *R.* Fairy Damsel = 'Harneaty'

◆ 'Harnicely'    See *R.* Fairy Ring = 'Harnicely'

◆ 'Harnougette'    See *R.* Fairy Prince = 'Harnougette'

◆ 'Harnumerous'    See *R.* Fairy Changeling = 'Harnumerous'

◆ 'Haroeluxe'    See *R.* Lilian Baylis = 'Haroeluxe'

§ Harold Macmillan = Last listed 1996
   'Harwestsun' (F)

◆ 'Harpade'    See *R.* Escapade = 'Harpade'

◆ 'Harpiccolo'    See *R.* Anna Ford = 'Harpiccolo'

◆ 'Harpluto'    See *R.* Avocet = 'Harpluto'

◆ 'Harposter'    See *R.* Doctor Darley = 'Harposter'

◆ 'Harprier'    See *R.* Tigris = 'Harprier' (*persica* hybrid)

◆ 'Harprincely'    See *R.* Innoxa Femille = 'Harprincely'

◆ 'Harprocrustes'    See *R.* Clarissa = 'Harprocrustes'

◆ 'Harpurl'    See *R.* Leigh-lo = 'Harpurl'

◆ 'Harquanne'    See *R.* Breath of Life = 'Harquanne'

◆ 'Harquantum'    See *R.* International Herald Tribune = 'Harquantum'

◆ 'Harqueterwife'    See *R.* Paul Shirville = 'Harqueterwife'

◆ 'Harquhling'    See *R.* Anna Zinkeisen = 'Harquhling'

◆ 'Harquibbler'    See *R.* Nigel Hawthorne = 'Harquibbler'

◆ 'Harquillypond'    See *R.* Cosette = 'Harquillypond'

◆ 'Harquince'    See *R.* Wandering Minstrel = 'Harquince'

◆ 'Harquito'    See *R.* Bill Slim = 'Harquito'

◆ 'Harramin'    See *R.* Hollie Roffey = 'Harramin'

◆ 'Harrango'    See *R.* G.P. and J. Baker = 'Harrango'

◆ 'Harregale'    See *R.* Cardinal Hume = 'Harregale'

◆ 'Harronver'    See *R.* Anneka = 'Harronver'

◆ 'Harroony'    See *R.* Amber Queen = 'Harroony'

◆ 'Harrowbond'    See *R.* Rosemary Harkness = 'Harrowbond'

'Harry Maasz' (GC/Cl)    EBls

'Harry Wheatcroft' (HT)    CB&S CGro EBls GGre MAus MBur MGan MJon NRog

◆ 'Harsherry'    See *R.* Sheila's Perfume = 'Harsherry'

◆ 'Harsuma'    See *R.* Suma = 'Harsuma'

◆ 'Hartanna'    See *R.* Princess Alice = 'Hartanna'

◆ 'Hartesia'    See *R.* Beryl Bach = 'Hartesia'

◆ 'Hartillery'    See *R.* Reconciliation = 'Hartillery'

◆ 'Hartoflex'    See *R.* Harkness Marigold = 'Hartoflex'

◆ 'Hartsam'    See *R.* Country Lady = 'Hartsam'

◆ 'Hartwiz'    See *R.* Conqueror's Gold = 'Hartwiz'

◆ 'Harubasil'    See *R.* Cordon Bleu = 'Harubasil'

◆ 'Harubondee'    See *R.* Queen Charlotte = 'Harubondee'

◆ 'Harukfore'    See *R.* City of London = 'Harukfore'

◆ 'Harunique'    See *R.* Euphrates = 'Harunique' (*persica* hybrid)

◆ 'Haruseful'    See *R.* Armada = 'Haruseful'

◆ 'Harvacity'    See *R.* Drummer Boy = 'Harvacity'

◆ 'Harvalex'    See *R.* Christingle = 'Harvalex'

◆ 'Harverag'    See *R.* Samaritan = 'Harverag'

§ Harvest Fayre = CGro IDic LGod LStr MAus MGan
   'Dicnorth' (F)    MMat NRog SApu SPer

◆ 'Harvilac'    See *R.* Gentle Maid = 'Harvilac'

◆ 'Harvintage'    See *R.* Savoy Hotel = 'Harvintage'

◆ 'Harvissa'    See *R.* Juliet Ann = 'Harvissa'

◆ 'Harvolute'    See *R.* By Appointment = 'Harvolute'

◆ 'Harwaderox'    See *R.* Rosy Future = 'Harwaderox'

◆ 'Harwanna'    See *R.* Jacqueline du Pré = 'Harwanna'

◆ 'Harwanted'    See *R.* Many Happy Returns = 'Harwanted'

◆ 'Harween'    See *R.* Golden Years = 'Harween'

◆ 'Harwelcome'    See *R.* Fellowship = 'Harwelcome'

◆ 'Harwellington'    See *R.* High Sheriff = 'Harwellington'

◆ 'Harwesi'    See *R.* Harvest Home = 'Harwesi'

◆ 'Harwestsun'    See *R.* Harold Macmillan = 'Harwestsun'

◆ 'Harwherry'    See *R.* Malcolm Sargent = 'Harwherry'

◆ 'Harwigwam'    See *R.* Indian Summer = 'Harwigwam'

◆ 'Harwilla'    See *R.* Emily Louise = 'Harwilla'

◆ 'Harwolave'    See *R.* Guiding Spirit = 'Harwolave'

◆ 'Harxampton'    See *R.* Remembrance = 'Harxampton'

◆ 'Haryamber'    See *R.* Cottage Garden = 'Haryamber'

◆ 'Haryearn'    See *R.* Lady Mitchell = 'Haryearn'

◆ 'Haryup'    See *R.* High Hopes = 'Haryup'

◆ 'Harzart'    See *R.* Renaissance = 'Harzart'

◆ 'Harzeal'    See *R.* Octavia Hill = 'Harzeal'

◆ 'Harzippee'    See *R.* Perception = 'Harzippee'

◆ 'Harzodiac'    See *R.* The Compassionate Friends = 'Harzodiac'

◆ 'Harzola'    See *R.* L'Aimant = 'Harzola'

◆ 'Harzumber'    See *R.* Welwyn Garden Glory = 'Harzumber'

◆ 'Havam'    See *R.* Amsterdam = 'Havam'

'Hazel Rose' (HT)    Last listed 1997

'Headleyensis'    EBee EBls MAus

'Heart of England' (F)    MBur

§ Heartbeat = 'Cocorona' (F)    NBat

§ Heartbreaker = 'Weksibyl' (Min) — Last listed 1997

§ Heather Austin = 'Auscook' (S) — MAus NPri

§ Heather Honey = 'Horsilbee' (HT) — Last listed 1997

§ 'Heather Muir' (*sericea* hybrid) (S) — EBls EHol MAus

'Heaven Scent' (F) — MJon NBat

§ Heavenly Rosalind = 'Ausmash' (S) — MAus

§ Hebe's Lip' (DxSwB) — EBls MAus WAct

'Hector Deane' (HT) — EBls MBur MGan

'Heidi Jayne' (HT) — MBur

'Heinrich Schultheis' (HP) — EBls

§ 'Helen Knight' (*ecae* hybrid) (S) ♀ — EBee EBls MAus MBri MMat WHCG

§ 'Helen Traubel' (HT) — EBls MGan

§ Helena = 'Poulna' (S) — ECle LPlm

*helenae* — EBls GCal MAus SPer WHCG

¶ - hybrid — WHCG

¶ Helga® (HT/F) — SRPl

♦ 'Helhein' — See *R.* Super Sparkle = 'Helhein'

♦ 'Helkleger' — See *R.* Super Elfin = 'Helkleger'

§ Hello = 'Cochello' (Min/Patio) — Last listed 1998

♦ 'Helsufair' — See *R.* Super Fairy = 'Helsufair'

*hemisphaerica* (S) — EBls MAus WAct

¶ *hemsleyana* — CHid

♦ 'Hendan' — See *R.* Dancing Pink = 'Hendan'

'Henri Fouquier' (G) — EBls

§ 'Henri Martin' (CeMo) ♀ — CTri EBls IOrc MAus NBus NRog SPer SWCr WAct WHCG

'Henry Nevard' (HP) — EBls MAus

'Her Majesty' (HP) — EBls

§ 'Herbstfeuer' (RH) — EBls MAus

§ Heritage® = 'Ausblush' (S) — CGro CSam EBee EBls ELan EMFP ENot GCoc GGre IHar LGod LPlm LStr MAus MBNS MBri MHlr MJon MMat NBat SApu SJus SMad SPer WAct WHCG WHow WOVN

'Hermosa' (Ch) — EBls EMFP LFis MAus MHlr NBus WAct WHCG

§ Hero® = 'Aushero' (S) — MAus

§ Hertfordshire = 'Kortenay' (GC) — EBrP EBre ENot LBre LPlm MMat SBre SPer SWCr WOVN

¶ 'Hi Society' (F) — GCoc

'Hiawatha' (Ra) — EBls MAus WHCG

'Hiawatha Recurrent' (Ra) — Last listed 1996

x *hibernica* — MAus

'Hidcote Gold' (S) — EBls MAus

§ High Hopes = 'Haryup' (Cl) — EBee GGre LGod LStr MBri MBur MFry MGan MJon SApu SJus SWCr WHCG WWeb

'High Noon' (ClHT) — Last listed 1996

§ 'Highdownensis' (*moyesii* hybrid) (S) ♀ — CSam EBls ELan MAus MMat SFam SPer

§ Highfield® = 'Harcomp' (Cl) — IHar LGod MAus MBri MJon SApu SJus SPer

§ Highland Laddie = 'Cocflag' — GCoc

§ Hilda Murrell® = 'Ausmurr' (S) — MAus

♦ 'Hilgold' — See *R.* Golden Chersonese = 'Hilgold'

§ 'Hillieri' (S) — EBls MAus

'Himmelsauge' (Ra) — Last listed 1996

'Hippolyte' (G) — EBls MAus WSHC

§ Hole-in-one = 'Horeagle' (F) — Last listed 1997

♦ 'Holfairy' — See *R.* Fairy Snow = 'Holfairy'

§ Hollie Roffey = 'Harramin' (Min) — Last listed 1996

*bolodonta* — See *R. moyesii* f. *rosea*

holy rose — See *R.* x *richardii*

§ Home on Time = 'Cocquamber' (HT) — GCoc GGre

'Home Sweet Home' (HT) — EBls MAus

§ Home Sweet Home = 'Mailoeur' (Cl/G) — LStr

'Homère' (T) — EBls MAus

§ Honey Bunch® = 'Cocglen' (F) — GCoc LGod LStr MBri MJon NBat SApu

'Honey Favorite' (HT) — MAus

Honeymoon — See *R.* 'Honigmond'

§ 'Honigmond' (F) — GGre NPri

'Honorine de Brabant' (Bb) — CPou EBee EBls IHar LFis MAus MBri MHlr MMat SFam SPer WHCG

¶ 'Hope' (F) — GCoc GGre NEgg

♦ 'Horabi' — See *R.* Friday's Child = 'Horabi'

'Horace Vernet' (HP) — EBls

♦ 'Horavme' — See *R.* Evelyn Grace = 'Horavme'

♦ 'Horbatbeauty' — See *R.* Battersby Beauty = 'Horbatbeauty'

♦ 'Horbondarc' — See *R.* Caroline Clarke = 'Horbondarc'

♦ 'Horbondsmile' — See *R.* Brave Heart = 'Horbondsmile'

♦ 'Horeagle' — See *R.* Hole-in-one = 'Horeagle'

♦ 'Horethel' — See *R.* Isobel Derby = 'Horethel'

♦ 'Horflan' — See *R.* Flanders Field = 'Horflan'

♦ 'Horflash' — See *R.* Champagne Cocktail = 'Horflash'

♦ 'Horharpdos' — See *R.* Emma Mitchell = 'Horharpdos'

♦ 'Horharryplus' — See *R.* Whitley Bay = 'Horharryplus'

♦ 'Horjack' — See *R.* Jack Collier = 'Horjack'

♦ 'Horjemma' — See *R.* Jemma = 'Horjemma'

♦ 'Horkorblush' — See *R.* Geordie Lad = 'Horkorblush'

♦ 'Horlights' — See *R.* Friction Lights = 'Horlights'

♦ 'Hormislac' — See *R.* Ted Gore = 'Hormislac'

*borrida* — See *R. biebersteinii*

♦ 'Horsaddle' — See *R.* Saddlers Gold = 'Horsaddle'

♦ 'Horsilbee' — See *R.* Heather Honey = 'Horsilbee'

♦ 'Horstacey' — See *R.* Stacey's Star = 'Horstacey'

'Horstmanns Rosenresli' (F) — EBls

♦ 'Horsun' — See *R.* Playgroup Rose = 'Horsun'

♦ 'Horsunsmile' — See *R.* Voice of Thousands = 'Horsunsmile'

♦ 'Hortropic' — See *R.* Sir William Leech = 'Hortropic'

♦ 'Hosunpegy' — See *R.* Marjorie May = 'Horsunpegy'

§ Hot Gossip = 'Jacati' (Patio/Min) — GGre

§ Hotline® = 'Aromikeh' (MinMo) — Last listed 1996

§ House Beautiful = 'Harbingo' (Patio) — SJus

'Hugh Dickson' (HP) — EBls MAus SJus SWCr

*bugonis* — See *R. xanthina* f. *bugonis*

♦ - 'Plenissima' — See *R. xanthina* f. *bugonis*

'Hula Girl' (Min) — EWTr LGod MJon

§ Humanity™ = 'Harcross' (F) — Last listed 1998

Hume's — See *R.* x *odorata* 'Odorata'

'Hunslet Moss' (Mo) — EBls

'Hunter' (Ru) — SWCr WAct

'Hutton Village' (HT) — Last listed 1997

*hypoleuca* — Last listed 1996
§ Ice Cream = 'Korzuri' (HT) — CTri ENot GGre LStr MGan MJon MMat NBat SApu SCoo SJus
§ Iceberg = 'Korbin' (F) ♀ — CB&S CGro EBee EBls EBrP EBre ENot EWTr GCoc GGre LBre LFis LGod LStr MAus MFry MGan MJon MMat NRog SApu SBre SJus SPer SRPl SSea WWeb
'Iced Ginger' (F) — MGan SApu SPer
'Idylle' (HT) — Last listed 1996
'Illusion' (Cl/F) — MGan
Ilse Krohn Superior® (Cl) — EBls
§ In the Pink = 'Peaverity' (F) — Last listed 1997
§ Indian Summer = 'Peaperfume' (HT) ♀ — GCoc LGod MBri MFry MJon
§ Indian Sunblaze = 'Carol-Jean' (Min/Patio) — Last listed 1998
'Indigo' (DPo) — EBls MAus WHCG
§ Ingrid Bergman® = 'Poulman' (HT) ♀ — EBee GCoc GGre LGod LStr MAus MBri MBur MFry MGan MJon MMat SApu SJus SWCr
§ Inner Wheel = 'Fryjasso' (F) — MFry
§ Innocence 97 = 'Cocoray' (Patio) — SApu
'Inspiration' (Cl/HT) — Last listed 1996
♦ 'Interall' — See *R.* Rosy Cushion = 'Interall'
♦ 'Interamon' — See *R.* White Diamond = 'Interamon'
♦ 'Intercell' — See *R.* Red Blanket = 'Intercell'
♦ 'Interchimp' — See *R.* Pink Chimo = 'Interchimp'
♦ 'Intereup' — See *R.* Euphoria = 'Intereup'
♦ 'Interfour' — See *R.* Petit Four = 'Interfour'
♦ 'Intergant' — See *R.* Elegant Pearl = 'Intergant'
♦ 'Intergol' — See *R.* Golden Rosamini = 'Intergol'
♦ 'Interim' — See *R.* Red Trail = 'Interim'
♦ 'Interlight' — See *R.* Daylight = 'Interlight'
'Intermezzo' (HT) — MBur MGan
♦ 'Intermunder' — See *R.* Red Dot = 'Intermunder'
§ International Herald Tribune® = 'Harquantum' (F/Patio) — Last listed 1997
♦ 'Interop' — See *R.* Eyeopener = 'Interop'
♦ 'Interrob' — See *R.* Robin Redbreast = 'Interrob'
♦ 'Intersmart' — See *R.* Smarty = 'Intersmart'
§ Intrigue = 'Korlech' (F) — ENot LStr MMat
§ Invincible = 'Runatru' (F) — EBee MFry MGan
'Invitation' (HT) — MBur MGan
'Ipsilanté' (G) — EBls MAus SWCr WAct WHCG
'Irene Av Danmark' (F) — EBls
♦ 'Irene Churruca' — See *R.* Golden Melody = 'Irene Churruca'
'Irène Watts' (Ch) ♀ — EBee EBls EMFP EPfP MAus MHlr SPla WAct WHCG WHow
'Irene's Delight' (HT) — NBat NRog
'Irish Elegance' (HT) — EBls
§ Irish Eyes = 'Dicwitness' (F) — ECle LStr SApu
'Irish Fireflame' (HT) — EBls
'Irish Mist' (F) — Last listed 1996
Irish Wonder — See *R.* Evelyn Fison = 'Macev'
§ Irresistible = 'Tinresist' (Min/Patio) — NBat
§ Isabella = 'Poulisab' (S) — EBee ECle
'Isis' (F) — MBri
Isis® (HT) — See *R.* Silver Anniversary = 'Poulari'
'Isobel' (HT) — Last listed 1996
§ Isobel Derby = 'Horethel' (HT) — MJon

'Ispahan' (D) ♀ — EBls EPfP MAus MHlr SApu SFam SJus SPer SWCr WAct WHCG WSHC
'Ivory Fashion' (F) — EBls
♦ 'Jacati' — See *R.* Hot Gossip = 'Jacati'
♦ 'Jacbed' — See *R.* Red Rascal = 'Jacbed'
♦ 'Jacboy' — See *R.* Tango = 'Jacboy'
♦ 'Jacbri' — See *R.* Bridal Pink = 'Jacbri'
♦ 'Jacdreco' — See *R.* Greetings = 'Jacdreco'
♦ 'Jacel' — See *R.* Graceland = 'Jacel'
♦ 'Jacient' — See *R.* Tournament of Roses = 'Jacient'
§ Jack Collier = 'Horjack' (HT) — Last listed 1998
§ Jack Wood = 'Frydabble' (F) — MFry
§ x *jacksonii* 'Max Graf' (GC/Ru) — EBls ENot MAus MGan MJon NRog WAct
 - Red Max Graf™ — See *R.* Rote Max Graf = 'Kormax'
§ - White Max Graf = 'Korgram' (GC/Ru) — ENot MAus WAct
♦ 'Jaclover' — See *R.* Magic Carpet = 'Jaclover'
Jacobite rose — See *R.* x *alba* 'Alba Maxima'
♦ 'Jacoyel' — See *R.* Fascination = 'Jacoyel'
♦ 'Jacpico' — See *R.* Pristine = 'Jacpico'
♦ 'Jacpur' — See *R.* Purple Tiger = 'Jacpur'
§ Jacqueline du Pré = 'Harwanna' (S) ♀ — EBee GCoc IHar MAus MBri MGan MHlr MJon MMat SApu SChu SJus SPer SWCr WAct WGer WHCG WHow
§ Jacquenetta = 'Ausjac' (S) — MAus
N Jacques Cartier — See *R.* 'Marchesa Boccella'
♦ 'Jacshe' — See *R.* Summer Dream = 'Jacshe'
♦ 'Jacven' — See *R.* Evening Star = 'Jacven'
'James Bourgault' (HP) — EBls
'James Mason' (G) — EBls MAus MBri SWCr
'James Mitchell' (CeMo) — EBls MAus SWCr WHCG
'James Veitch' (DPoMo) — EBls MAus WHCG
¶ 'Jan Guest' (HT) — NRog
§ Jane Asher = 'Peapet' (Min/Patio) — MBri MJon SApu
¶ 'Jane Eyre' — COtt
'Janet's Pride' (RH) — EBls MAus
§ Janina® = 'Tanija' (HT) — MJon
§ Japonica' (CeMo) — MAus
§ Jardins de Bagatelle® = 'Meimafris' (HT) — MBur MJon SApu
'Jason' (HT) — Last listed 1997
♦ 'Jayemm' — See *R.* Emma Kate = 'Jayemm'
§ Jayne Austin = 'Ausbreak' (S) — EBrP EBre LBre MAus MJon SApu SBre SPer SWCr
§ Jazz = 'Poulnorm' (Cl) — EBee SApu
§ Jean Kenneally™ = 'Tineally' (Min) — NBat
'Jean Mermoz' (Poly) — MAus NRog WAct WHCG
'Jean Rosenkrantz' (HP) — EBls
'Jean Sisley' (HT) — EBls
'Jeanie Deans' (RH) — MAus
'Jeanne de Montfort' (CeMo) — EBls MAus
♦ 'Jelbar' — See *R.* Wee Barbie = 'Jelbar'
§ Jemma = 'Horjemma' (Patio) — Last listed 1998
§ Jennie Robinson = 'Trobette' (Min/Patio) — SApu
§ Jennifer™ = 'Benjen' (Min) — Last listed 1997
§ Jenny Charlton = 'Simway' (HT) — NBat
'Jenny Duval' misapplied — See *R.* 'Président de Sèze'
'Jenny Wren' (F) — EBls MAus
'Jenny's Dream' (HT) — Last listed 1997
§ Jenny's Rose = 'Cansit' (F) — EBee
'Jens Munk' (Ru) — WAct
'Jersey Beauty' (Ra) — EBls MAus
§ Jill's Rose = 'Ganjil' (F) — MGan

| | |
|---|---|
| 'Jiminy Cricket' (F) | EBls NRog |
| 'Jimmy Greaves' (HT) | MGan |
| § Joan Ball = 'Troball' (Min) | Last listed 1996 |
| ¶ 'Joan Bell' (HT) | NRog |
| 'Joanna Hill' (HT) | EBls |
| 'Joanna Lumley' (HT) | Last listed 1997 |
| 'Joanne' (HT) | MJon NRog |
| 'Jocelyn' (F) | EBls |
| 'Joe Longthorne' (HT) | Last listed 1998 |
| 'Johanna Röpcke' (Ra) | Last listed 1996 |
| ¶ 'John Cabot' (S) | SSea |
| § John Clare = 'Auscent' | EBrP EBre LBre MAus NPri SBre |
| 'John Hopper' (HP) | EBls MAus |
| § John Keats = 'Meiroupis' (S) | SApu |
| ◆ 'Johnago' | See R. Chicago Peace = 'Johnago' |
| § Johnnie Walker = 'Frygran' (HT) | MFry |
| 'Josephine Bruce' (HT) | CB&S EBls LGod MAus MBur MGan NRog WStI |
| 'Josephine Wheatcroft' | See R. 'Rosina' |
| 'Joseph's Coat' (S/Cl) | EBls LGod LStr MBri MFry MGan |
| 'Journey's End' (HT) | MGan |
| 'Jubilee Celebration' (F) | MJon |
| § Jude the Obscure = 'Ausjo' (S) | CAbP IHar MAus MJon |
| § Judi Dench = 'Peahunder' (F) | MBri |
| 'Judy Fischer' (Min) | LGod |
| § Judy Garland = 'Harking' (F) | SJus |
| 'Julia Mannering' (RH) | MAus |
| Julia's Rose® (HT) | CGro LStr MAus MBur MGan MJon SApu SPer SWCr |
| § Julie Andrews = 'Fryvivacious' (F) | Last listed 1998 |
| § Julie Cussons = 'Fryprincess' (F) | MFry |
| 'Juliet' (HP) | EBls |
| § June Laver™ = 'Lavjune' (Min) | Last listed 1998 |
| 'Juno' (Ce) | EBls MAus WAct WHCG |
| 'Just Jenny' (Min) | NBat |
| Just Joey® (HT) ♀ | CGro EBee EBls ELan GCoc GGre LGod LPlm LStr MAus MBri MBur MFry MGan MJon MMat NRog SApu SJus SPer SSoC WWeb |
| § Just Magic = 'Trobic' (Min) | MJon |
| 'Karl Foerster' (PiH) | EBls MAus |
| 'Kassel' (S/Cl) | EBls MAus SPer WAct |
| 'Katharina Zeimet' (Poly) | EBls MAus MGan NRog WAct WHCG |
| 'Kathleen' (HM) | EBls |
| 'Kathleen Ferrier' (F) | EBls MGan |
| 'Kathleen Harrop' (Bb) | EBee EBls ENot IHar LStr MAus MBur MHlr MMat SFam SPer SRPl WAct WHCG WSHC WWat |
| 'Kathleen O'Rourke' (HT) | Last listed 1997 |
| § Kathleen's Rose = 'Kirkitt' (F) | MJon |
| § Kathryn Mcgredy® = 'Macaucklad' (HT) | MJon |
| § Kathryn Morley = 'Ausclub' (F) | CAbP EBrP EBre IHar LBre MAus MBri MHlr MJon NPri SBre SWCr |
| 'Katie' (ClF) | MGan |
| § Katie Crocker = 'Burbrindley' (F) | MBur |
| 'Kazanlik' misapplied | See R. 'Professeur Emile Perrot' |
| § Keepsake = 'Kormalda' (HT) | ENot LPlm MGan MMat |
| ◆ 'Keitoli' | See R. Ferdy = 'Keitoli' |
| § Kent® = 'Poulcov' (S/GC) | EBee ELan ENot GGre LPlm LStr MHlr MJon MMat NPri SPer SPla SRPl WHCG WOVN WRHF |
| 'Kerrygold' (F) | Last listed 1996 |
| 'Kerryman' (F) | Last listed 1997 |
| 'Kew Rambler' (Ra) | EBee EBls MAus MRav SFam SWCr WHCG |
| 'Kiese' (canina hybrid) | MJon |
| 'Kiftsgate' | See R. filipes 'Kiftsgate' |
| 'Kilworth Gold' (HT) | MGan |
| 'Kim' (Patio) | NRog |
| § Kind Regards = 'Pentiger' (F) | Last listed 1998 |
| ◆ 'Kinfancy' | See R. Fancy Pants = 'Kinfancy' |
| 'Kingig' (Min) | Last listed 1997 |
| King's Ransom® (HT) | CB&S EBls GGre MGan MJon SPer WWeb |
| ◆ 'Kirbill' | See R. Margaret's World = 'Kirbill' |
| ◆ 'Kirkitt' | See R. Kathleen's Rose = 'Kirkitt' |
| ◆ 'Kirlon' | See R. Woman o'th' North = 'Kirlon' |
| ◆ 'Kirlyl' | See R. Harlow Carr = 'Kirlyl' |
| ◆ 'Kirmac' | See R. Greenall's Glory = 'Kirmac' |
| ◆ 'Kirmelody' | See R. Bangor Cathedral = 'Kirmelody' |
| ◆ 'Kirpink' | See R. Owen's Pride = 'Kirpink' |
| ◆ 'Kirsan' | See R. Chris = 'Kirsan' |
| ◆ 'Kirscot' | See R. Graceland = 'Kirscot' |
| ◆ 'Kirshow' | See R. Clive Lloyd = 'Kirshow' |
| ◆ 'Kirshru' | See R. Saint Dunstan's Rose = 'Kirshru' |
| 'Kirsten Poulsen' (Poly) | EBls |
| ◆ 'Kirworjackie' | See R. Wor Jackie = 'Kirworjackie' |
| § Kiss 'n' Tell = 'Seakis' (Min) | MBur |
| 'Kitchener of Khartoum' | See R. 'K of K' |
| 'Kitty Hawk' (Min) | Last listed 1997 |
| x kochiana | EBls |
| 'Köln am Rhein' (Cl) | MGan |
| § Königin von Dänemark' (A) ♀ | CHad EBee EBls EMFP ENot GCoc IHar MAus MBri MMat NFla SApu SJus SPer WAct WHCG WHow |
| ◆ 'Koral' | See R. Bengali = 'Koral' |
| ◆ 'Koralu' | See R. Perfecta = 'Koralu' |
| ◆ 'Korampa' | See R. Champagne = 'Korampa' |
| ◆ 'Korbarkeit' | See R. Yorkshire = 'Korbarkeit' |
| ◆ 'Korbasren' | See R. St Tiggywinkles = 'Korbasren' |
| ◆ 'Korbe' | See R. Heidelberg = 'Korbe' |
| ◆ 'Korbell' | See R. Anabell = 'Korbell' |
| ◆ 'Korbelma' | See R. Simba = 'Korbelma' |
| ◆ 'Korbin' | See R. Iceberg = 'Korbin' |
| ◆ 'Korblue' | See R. Shocking Blue = 'Korblue' |
| ◆ 'Korcelin' | See R. Mandarin = 'Korcelin' |
| ◆ 'Kordadel' | See R. The Valois Rose = 'Kordadel' |
| ◆ 'Kordalen' | See R. Antique '89 = 'Kordalen' |
| ◆ 'Kordapt' | See R. Pheasant = 'Kordapt' |
| ◆ 'Kordehei' | See R. Malverns = 'Kordehei' |
| § Kordes' Golden Times = 'Kortime' (F) | MJon |
| 'Kordes' Robusta' | See R. Robusta = 'Korgosa' |
| ◆ 'Kordialo' (F/Patio) | See R. Festival = 'Kordialo' |
| ◆ 'Koreb' | See R. Diamant = 'Koreb' |
| ◆ 'Koreklia' | See R. Valencia = 'Koreklia' |
| ◆ 'Korelasting' | See R. Summer Breeze = 'Korelasting' |
| ◆ 'Koreledas' | See R. Centenary = 'Koreledas' |
| ◆ 'Korfalt' | See R. Goldmarie = 'Korfalt' |

◆ 'Korfarim'          See *R.* Esther Ofarim = 'Korfarim'
◆ 'Korflot'           See *R.* Ballet = 'Korflot'
◆ 'Korflüg'           See *R.* Margaret Thatcher = 'Korflüg'
◆ 'Korfullwind'       See *R.* Oxfordshire = 'Korfullwind'
◆ 'Korgi'             See *R.* Cologne Carnival = 'Korgi'
◆ 'Korgo'             See *R.* Gold Topaz = 'Korgo'
◆ 'Korgosa'           See *R.* Robusta = 'Korgosa'
◆ 'Korgram'           See *R.* x *jacksonii* White Max Graf = 'Korgram'
◆ 'Korgund'           See *R.* Loving Memory = 'Korgund'
◆ 'Korhamp'           See *R.* Hampshire = 'Korhamp'
◆ 'Korhassi'          See *R.* Charles Notcutt = 'Korhassi'
◆ 'Korhaugen'         See *R.* Cambridgeshire = 'Korhaugen'
◆ 'Korhitom'          See *R.* Perestroika = 'Korhitom'
◆ 'Korholst'          See *R.* City of Birmingham = 'Korholst'
◆ 'Korimro'           See *R.* Grouse = 'Korimro'
◆ 'Korinor'           See *R.* Mandy = 'Korinor'
◆ 'Korizont'          See *R.* Summer Wine = 'Korizont'
◆ 'Korkandel'         See *R.* Warwickshire = 'Korkandel'
◆ 'Korkeltin'         See *R.* Tradition '95 = 'Korkeltin'
◆ 'Korlady'           See *R.* Lady Rose = 'Korlady'
◆ 'Korlanum'          See *R.* Surrey = 'Korlanum'
◆ 'Korlasche'         See *R.* Mary Pope = 'Korlasche'
◆ 'Korlech'           See *R.* Intrigue = 'Korlech'
◆ 'Korlift'           See *R.* Congratulations = 'Korlift'
◆ 'Korlillub'         See *R.* Lichtkönigin Lucia = 'Korlillub'
◆ 'Korlima'           See *R.* Lilli Marlene = 'Korlima'
◆ 'Kormalda'          See *R.* Keepsake = 'Kormalda'
◆ 'Kormarie'          See *R.* Miss Pam Ayres = 'Kormarie'
◆ 'Kormarter'         See *R.* Sunrise = 'Kormarter'
◆ 'Kormasyl'          See *R.* Pink Pearl = 'Kormasyl'
◆ 'Kormat'            See *R.* Australian Gold = 'Kormat'
◆ 'Kormatt'           See *R.* Saint Boniface = 'Kormatt'
◆ 'Kormax'            See *R.* Rote Max Graf = 'Kormax'
◆ 'Kormeita'          See *R.* Agatha Christie = 'Kormeita'
◆ 'Kormetter'         See *R.* Anna Livia = 'Kormetter'
◆ 'Kormixal'          See *R.* Suffolk = 'Kormixal'
◆ 'Kormollis'         See *R.* Garden Party = 'Kormollis'
◆ 'Kormuse'           See *R.* Wiltshire = 'Kormuse'
◆ 'Kornita'           See *R.* Korona = 'Kornita'
◆ 'Korol'             See *R.* Peer Gynt = 'Korol'
§ Korona® = 'Kornita' (F)   MGan NRog
◆ 'Korpapiro'         See *R.* Apricot Summer = 'Korpapiro'
◆ 'Korpatri'          See *R.* Patricia = 'Korpatri'
◆ 'Korpeahn'          See *R.* The Times Rose = 'Korpeahn'
◆ 'Korpinka'          See *R.* Berkshire = 'Korpinka'
◆ 'Korpinrob'         See *R.* The Seckford Rose = 'Korpinrob'
◆ 'Korpriwa'          See *R.* Selfridges = 'Korpriwa'
◆ 'Korquemu'          See *R.* Queen Mother = 'Korquemu'
◆ 'Korred'            See *R.* Ace of Hearts = 'Korred'
  'Korresia' (F)      EBls GCoc GGre IHar LGod LStr MAus MBri MFry MGan MJon MMat NRog SJus SPer SWCr
◆ 'Korsaku'           See *R.* Playtime = 'Korsaku'
◆ 'Korschwana'       See *R.* Barry Fearn = 'Korschwama'
◆ 'Korstacha' (S/ClHT)  See *R.* White Cloud = 'Korstacha'

◆ 'Korstegli'         See *R.* Lancashire = 'Korstegli'
◆ 'Kortat'            See *R.* Tatjana = 'Kortat'
◆ 'Kortemma'          See *R.* Chilterns = 'Kortemma'
◆ 'Kortenay'          See *R.* Hertfordshire = 'Kortenay'
◆ 'Kortersen'         See *R.* Rosarium Uetersen = 'Kortersen'
◆ 'Kortime'           See *R.* Kordes' Golden Times = 'Kortime'
◆ 'Kortingle'         See *R.* Scarlet Patio = 'Kortingle'
◆ 'Kortlitze'         See *R.* Lady Mavis Pilkington = 'Kortlitze'
◆ 'Korverpea'         See *R.* Cleopatra = 'Korverpea'
◆ 'Korweirim'         See *R.* Partridge = 'Korweirim'
◆ 'Korweiso'          See *R.* Hannah Gordon = 'Korweiso'
◆ 'Korwest'           See *R.* Westerland = 'Korwest'
◆ 'Korwisco'          See *R.* The Compass Rose = 'Korwisco'
◆ 'Korwonder'         See *R.* Toynbee Hall = 'Korwonder'
◆ 'Korworm'           See *R.* Romantic Hedgerose = 'Korworm'
◆ 'Korzaun'           See *R.* Royal William = 'Korzaun'
◆ 'Korzuri'           See *R.* Ice Cream = 'Korzuri'
§ Kristin™ = 'Benmagic' (Min)   NBat
§ Kronenbourg® = 'Macbo' (HT)   EBls LPlm MAus
  'Kronprinzessin Viktoria' (Bb)   EBee EBls MAus MHlr WHCG
§ L.D. Braithwaite® = 'Auscrim' (S)   CSam EBrP EBre ELan ENot IHar LBre LGod LPlm LStr MAus MFry MGan MHlr MJon MMat SBre SJus SPer SRPl SSoC SWCr SWas WAct WHCG WHow WWeb
  'La Belle Distinguée' (RH)   EBls MAus WHCG
  'La Belle Sultane'   See *R.* 'Violacea'
  'La Follette' (Cl)   EBls
  'La France' (HT)     EBls MAus
  'La Mortola'         See *R. brunonii* 'La Mortola'
  'La Noblesse' (Ce)   EBls
  'La Perle' (Ra)      CRHN MAus
  'La Plus Belle des Ponctuées' (G)   Last listed 1996
  'La Reine' (HP)      EBls
  'La Reine Victoria'  See *R.* 'Reine Victoria'
  'La Rubanée'         See *R.* 'Centifolia Variegata'
§ La Sévillana = 'Meigekanu' (F/GC)   EBls SApu SPer WOVN
  'La Ville de Bruxelles' (D) ♀   EBls MAus MRav SFam SPer WAct WHCG WHow
  'Lady Alice Stanley' (HT)   EBls
  'Lady Barnby' (HT)   EBls
  'Lady Belper' (HT)   EBls
  'Lady Curzon' (Ru)   EBls MAus SWCr
  'Lady Elgin'         See *R.* Thaïs = 'Memaj'
  'Lady Forteviot' (HT)   EBls
  'Lady Gay' (Ra)      EBee MAus WHCG
  'Lady Godiva' (Ra)   MAus
  'Lady Hillingdon' (T)   MAus WHow
  'Lady Hillingdon' (ClT)   See *R.* 'Climbing Lady Hillingdon'
  'Lady Iliffe' (HT)   MGan
§ Lady in Red = 'Sealady' (Min)   MBur
  'Lady Jane' (HT)     Last listed 1997
  'Lady Love '95' (Patio)   GGre
§ Lady MacRobert = 'Coclent' (F)   GCoc
  'Lady Mary Fitzwilliam' (HT)   EBls
§ Lady Mavis Pilkington = 'Kortlitze' (HT)   MMat
§ Lady Meillandina® = 'Meilarco' (Min)   SApu
  'Lady of Stifford' (F)   Last listed 1997

'Lady Penelope' (MinCl)  WWeb

§ 'Lady Penzance' (RH)  CB&S EBls MAus MFry MGan
SApu SPer WAct

§ Lady Rachel =  EBee
'Candoodle' (F)

'Lady Romsey' (F)  EBls

§ Lady Rose® =  MJon
'Korlady' (HT)

'Lady Seton' (HT)  Last listed 1997

'Lady Stuart' (Ch)  Last listed 1998

◆ Lady Sunblaze  See R. Lady Meillandina =
'Meilarco'

'Lady Sylvia' (HT)  EBee EBls MAus MGan NRog SPer
WHow WStI

§ Lady Taylor = 'Smitling'  IHar MBur
(F/Patio)

'Lady Waterlow' (ClHT)  EBee EBls MAus SPer SWCr
WHCG

*laevigata* (Ra)  EBls MAus
- 'Anemonoides'  See R. 'Anemone'
- 'Cooperi'  See R. 'Cooperi'
'Lafter' (S)  EBls
'Lagoon' (F)  EBls

§ L'Aimant = 'Harzola' (F)  ECle GCoc LGod LStr MFry MJon
MMat SApu SJus

'Lakeland' (HT)  MAus

'Lamarque' (N)  MAus

Laminuette® (F)  MJon

◆ 'Lanbet'  See R. Jennifer-Betty Kenward =
'Lanbet'

§ Lancashire = 'Korstegli' (GC)  ENot GCoc LStr MMat NPri

§ Lancashire Life =  MBri
'Ruilanca' (F)

◆ 'Landen'  See R. Denman = 'Landen'

◆ 'Landia'  See R. Anne Diamond = 'Landia'

◆ 'Landisney'  See R. Snow White = 'Landisney'

◆ 'Landora'  See R. Sunblest = 'Landora'

§ 'Lanei' (CeMo)  EBls

§ Langdale Chase =  MFry
'Fryrhapsody' (F)

§ Langford Light =  Last listed 1997
'Lannie' (Min/GC)

◆ 'Lanican'  See R. Great Expectations =
'Lanican'

◆ 'Lanken'  See R. Felicity Kendal = 'Lanken'

◆ 'Lannie'  See R. Langford Light = 'Lannie'

◆ 'Lantor'  See R. Torvill and Dean = 'Lantor'

§ Laughter Lines =  IDic MGan
'Dickerry' (F)

Laura Anne (HT)  GCoc

§ Laura Ashley =  MAus
'Chewharia' (GC/ClMin)

§ Laura Ford® =  CGro CTri EBrP EBre GGre IHar
'Chewarvel' (ClMin) ♀  LBre LStr MAus MBri MGan MJon
MMat NBat NPri NRog SApu SBre
SJus SWCr WWeb

'Laura Jane' (HT)  MGan

'Laura Louisa' (Cl)  EBls

Laura = 'Meidragelac'  Last listed 1997
(HT)

§ Laurence Olivier® =  Last listed 1998
'Meinagre' (F)

'Lavender Jewel' (Min)  IHar MAus MBur

'Lavender Lace' (Min)  Last listed 1996

'Lavender Lassie' (HM) ♀  CHad EBee EMFP IOrc MAus
MFry MGan MHlr MMat SPer
WHCG WHow

'Lavender Pinocchio' (F)  MAus WAct

§ Lavinia = 'Tanklawi' (Cl) ♀  CTri EBee LGod LStr MBri MGan
SApu SJus SPer

◆ 'Lavjune'  See R. June Laver = 'Lavjune'

'Lawrence Johnston' (Cl)  EBls MAus NPri SFam SWCr WAct

'Le Havre' (HP)  EBls

'Le Rêve' (Cl)  EBls MAus

'Le Vésuve' (Ch)  EBls MAus

§ Leander® = 'Auslea' (S)  MAus MBri

§ Leaping Salmon =  CGro EBee ELan GCoc IHar IOrc
'Peamight' (ClHT)  LGod LStr MAus MBri MGan MJon
SApu SChu SPer SPla WOVN WStI

'Leda' (D)  EBls MAus SFam SPer WAct

◆ 'Leggab'  See R. Pearl Drift = 'Leggab'

◆ 'Legglow'  See R. Can-can = 'Legglow'

◆ 'Legnews'  See R. News = 'Legnews'

◆ 'Legsweet'  See R. Deb's Delight = 'Legsweet'

'Lemon Pillar'  See R. 'Paul's Lemon Pillar'

§ Len Turner = 'Dicjeep' (F)  IDic SApu

◆ 'Lenbrac'  See R. Pink Surprise = 'Lenbrac'

◆ 'Lengra'  See R. Pleine de Grâce = 'Lengra'

◆ 'Lenip'  See R. Pascali = 'Lenip'

◆ 'Lenmacra'  See R. Maria Teresa = 'Lenmacra'

◆ 'Lenmobri'  See R. Rush = 'Lenmobri'

◆ 'Lenramp'  See R. Running Maid = 'Lenramp'

◆ 'Lenwich'  See R. Green Snake = 'Lenwich'

§ Leonidas = 'Meicofum' (HT)  MJon

'Léonie Lamesch' (Poly)  EBls

'Léontine Gervais' (Ra)  CAbP CRHN MAus MHlr SWCr
WAct WHCG

§ Leslie's Dream =  IDic
'Dicjoon' (HT)

'Leuchtstern' (Ra)  EBls

'Leverkusen' (Cl)  CHad EBls MAus MGan MJon SPer
SPla SRPl SSea WAct WHCG
WHow WSHC

'Leveson-Gower' (Bb)  EBls

'Ley's Perpetual' (ClT)  CPou EBee EBls WBcn

¶ x *lheritieriana* (Bs)  EBee

'Lilac Charm' (F)  EBls MAus

§ Lilac Rose™ = 'Auslilac' (S)  MAus

§ Lilian Austin® = 'Ausli' (S)  MAus MBri

§ Liliana = 'Poulsyng' (S)  EBee ECle LPlm

§ Lilli Marlene = 'Korlima' (F)  CB&S CTri EBls GCoc LStr MAus
MGan NPri NRog SPer

'Lily de Gerlache' (HT)  Last listed 1996

'Lily the Pink' (HT)  Last listed 1997

'Lime Kiln' (Ra)  Last listed 1998

§ Lincoln Cathedral =  MGan MJon SPer
'Glanlin' (HT)

§ Lincolnshire Poacher =  NBat
'Glareabit' (HT)

§ Lions International =  MFry
'Frycharm' (HT)

◆ 'Litakor'  See R. Lolita = 'Litakor'

§ Little Artist® =  MJon
'Macmanley' (Min)

§ Little Bo-peep =  ENot MJon MMat
'Poullen' (Min/Patio)

'Little Buckaroo' (Min)  CBrm ELan LGod MGan SPer WStI

'Little Dorrit' (Poly)  NRog WAct

'Little Flirt' (Min)  EWTr MAus MGan SWCr

'Little Gem' (DPMo)  EBls MAus MGan

§ Little Jackie™ =  NBat
'Savor' (Min)

§ Little Jewel =  Last listed 1997
'Cocabel' (Patio)

'Little Len' (Min/Patio)  MJon

§ Little Marvel =  MBri
'Ruigerdan' (Min)

§ Little Prince =  Last listed 1997
'Coccord' (F/Patio)

§ Little Rambler =  MJon MMat SApu
'Chewramb' (MinRa)

§ Little Rascal = | GCoc GGre
'Peaalamo' (Patio/Min)
§ Little Russell = | MJon
'Trobric' (Min)
* 'Little White' | Last listed 1998
'Little White Pet' | See R. 'White Pet'
§ Little Woman = | IDic LStr SApu SWCr
'Diclittle' (Patio)
'Liverpool Echo' (F) | LPlm MJon
§ Liverpool Remembers = | LGod MBri MBur MFry
'Frystar' (HT)
'Living Fire' (F) | MBur MGan NRog
§ Lloyds of London = | Last listed 1996
'Canlloyd' (F)
'Lollipop' (Min) | MGan
'Long John Silver' (Cl) | EBls
*longicuspis* hort. | See R. *mulliganii*
*longicuspis* Bertol. (Ra) | EBls
- B&L 12386 (Ra) | Last listed 1996
§ - var. *sinowilsonii* (Ra) | EBls GCal MAus
§ Longleat = 'Macinca' (Min) | Last listed 1997
§ Lord Byron = | LStr MBri MJon SApu SWCr
'Meitosier' (ClHT)
'Lord Penzance' (RH) | EBee EBls MAus MGan WAct
WHow
§ L'Oréal Trophy = | MAus MJon
'Harlexis' (HT)
'Lorraine Lee' (T) | EBls
'Los Angeles' (HT) | EBls
'L'Ouche' misapplied | See R. 'Louise Odier'
'Louis Gimard' (CeMo) | EBls MAus SPer WAct WHCG
'Louis Philippe' (Ch) | EBls
'Louis XIV' (Ch) | CHad EBls WHCG
'Louise Odier' (Bb) | CBos EBee EBls EBrP EBre EMFP
IHar LBre LFis LStr MAus MBri
MHlr MMat SApu SBre SFam SJus
SPer SPla SRPl WAct WHCG
WOVN
'Love Token' (F) | MBur
§ Lovely Fairy® = | IDic MBri MJon WAct
'Spevu' (Poly)
§ Lovely Lady™ = | CTri EBee IDic LStr MGan MJon
'Dicjubell' (HT) ♀ | SApu SJus SWCr
'Lovers' Meeting' (HT) | GGre LPlm MBri MBur MGan
MJon NBat NRog SApu SPer SWas
WStI
§ Loving Memory = | ENot GCoc GGre LPlm LStr MFry
'Korgund' (HT) | MGan MMat NPri SPer
Loving Touch™ (Min) | Last listed 1997
LU 87 | Last listed 1998
'Lübeck' | See R. 'Hansestadt Lübeck'
§ Lucetta = 'Ausemi' (S) | MAus SPer WAct
*luciae* | EBls
- var. *onoei* | EPot NMen
'Lucilla' (Patio) | NBat
'Lucy Ashton' (RH) | MAus
§ Luis Desamero = | NBat
'Tinluis' (Min)
'Lutea Maxima' | See R. x *harisonii* 'Lutea Maxima'
'Lykkefund' (Ra) | EBls MAus
'Lyon Rose' (HT) | EBls
'Ma Perkins' (F) | EBls
'Ma Ponctuée' (DPMo) | EBls
'Mabel Morrison' (HP) | EBls MAus
◆ 'Macai' | See R. Daily Sketch = 'Macai'
◆ 'Macal' | See R. Captain Cook = 'Macal'
◆ 'Macangeli' | See R. Snowball = 'Macangeli'
◆ 'Macar' | See R. Piccadilly = 'Macar'
Macartney rose | See R. *bracteata*
◆ 'Macaucklad' | See R. Kathryn Mcgredy = 'Macaucklad'

◆ 'Macba' | See R. Galway Bay = 'Macba'
◆ 'Macbern' | See R. Young Quinn = 'Macbern'
◆ 'Macbo' | See R. Kronenbourg = 'Macbo'
◆ 'Macca' | See R. Casino = 'Macca'
◆ 'Maccarpe' | See R. Snow Carpet = 'Maccarpe'
◆ 'Maccatsun' | See R. Phantom = 'Maccatsun'
◆ 'Macci' | See R. City of Belfast = 'Macci'
◆ 'Macclack' | See R. Paddy Stephens = 'Macclack'
◆ 'Macdub' | See R. Dublin Bay = 'Macdub'
◆ 'Macel' | See R. Elizabeth of Glamis = 'Macel'
◆ 'Macesp' | See R. Old Master = 'Macesp'
◆ 'Macev' | See R. Evelyn Fison = 'Macev'
◆ 'Maceye' | See R. Eye Paint = 'Maceye'
◆ 'Macfirnlin' | See R. Fiesta = 'Macfirinlin'
◆ 'Macfirwal' | See R. Tango = 'Macfirwal'
◆ 'Macfrabro' | See R. Firefly = 'Macfrabro'
◆ 'Macfreego' | See R. Penelope Keith = 'Macfreego'
◆ 'Macfrothy' | See R. Frothy = 'Macfrothy'
◆ 'Macgarn' | See R. Kapai = 'Macgarn'
◆ 'Macgem' | See R. Benson and Hedges Gold = 'Macgem'
◆ 'Macgenev' | See R. New Zealand = 'Macgenev'
◆ 'Macha' | See R. Handel = 'Macha'
◆ 'Macinca' | See R. Longleat = 'Macinca'
◆ 'Macio' | See R. Violet Carson = 'Macio'
◆ 'Macir' | See R. Miss Ireland = 'Macir'
◆ 'Macivy' | See R. Singin' in the Rain = 'Macivy'
◆ 'Macjuliat' | See R. Vidal Sassoon = 'Macjuliat'
◆ 'Mackati' | See R. Old Port = 'Mackati'
◆ 'Mackinja' | See R. Maestro = 'Mackinja'
◆ 'Macloupri' | See R. Too Hot to Handle = 'Macloupri'
◆ 'Macman' | See R. Matangi = 'Macman'
◆ 'Macmanley' | See R. Little Artist = 'Macmanley'
◆ 'Macmi' | See R. Mischief = 'Macmi'
§ Macmillan Nurse = | EBls
'Beamac' (S)
◆ 'Macnewye' | See R. Arcadian = 'Macnewye'
◆ 'Macngaura' | See R. Penthouse = 'Macngaura'
◆ 'Macon' | See R. Uncle Walter = 'Macon'
◆ 'Macoranlem' | See R. Oranges and Lemons = 'Macoranlem'
◆ 'Macpa' | See R. Paddy McGredy = 'Macpa'
◆ 'Macpandem' | See R. Claire Rayner = 'Macpandem'
◆ 'Macparlez' | See R. Baby Sunrise = 'Macparlez'
◆ 'Macpic' | See R. Picasso = 'Macpic'
◆ 'Macpow' | See R. Chivalry = 'Macpow'
'Macrantha' (Gallica hybrid) | EBls MAus WAct
x *macrantha* 'Raubritter' | See R. 'Raubritter' ('Macrantha hybrid)
◆ 'Macrat' | See R. Priscilla Burton = 'Macrat'
◆ 'Macrealea' | See R. Chardonnay = 'Macrealea'
◆ 'Macrexy' | See R. Sexy Rexy = 'Macrexy'
*macrophylla* | MAus MMat
- B&SWJ 2603 | WCru
- 'Doncasteri' | See R. 'Doncasteri'
§ - 'Master Hugh' ex SS&W 7822 ♀ | EBls MAus
◆ 'Macros' | See R. Royal Salute = 'Macros'
◆ 'Macsee' | See R. Courvoisier = 'Macsee'
◆ 'Macshana' | See R. Benson and Hedges Special = 'Macshana'
'Macsplash' | See R. Sue Lawley = 'Macsplash'

◆ 'Macspeego'                See *R*. Eternally Yours = 'Macspeego'
◆ 'Mactel'                   See *R*. Grand Hotel = 'Mactel'
◆ 'Mactemaik'                See *R*. The Painter = 'Mactemaik'
◆ 'Mactru'                   See *R*. Trumpeter = 'Mactru'
◆ 'Macultra'                 See *R*. Brown Velvet = 'Macultra'
◆ 'Macwhenu'                 See *R*. Derek Nimmo = 'Macwhenu'
◆ 'Macyefre'                 See *R*. Solitaire = 'Macyefre'
◆ 'Macyou'                   See *R*. Regensberg = 'Macyou'
§ Madam Speaker =            SApu
     'Meizuzes' (HT)
◆ 'Madame A. Meilland'       See *R*. Peace = 'Madame A. Meilland'
  'Madame Abel Chatenay'     EBls MAus
     (HT)
  'Madame Alfred Carrière'   More than 30 suppliers
     (N) ♀
  'Madame Alice Garnier' (Ra) EBee EBls SPer
  'Madame Antoine Mari' (T)  EBls
  'Madame Berkeley' (T)      EBls
  'Madame Bravy' (T)         EBls MAus
  'Madame Butterfly' (HT)    EBee EBls MAus MBur MGan SApu SFam
§ 'Madame Caroline Testout'  EBee MHlr SFam WAct
     (HT)
  'Madame Charles' (T)       EBls
  'Madame d'Arblay' (Ra)     EBls
  'Madame de Sancy de        EBee EBls MAus SFam SWCr
     Parabère' (Bs)          WHCG
  'Madame de Watteville' (T) EBls
  'Madame Delaroche-         EBls MAus WAct WHCG
     Lambert' (DPMo) ♀
  'Madame Driout' (ClT)      EBls WHCG
  'Madame Eliza de           EBls
     Vilmorin' (HT)
  'Madame Ernest Calvat' (Bb) EBls MAus
  'Madame Eugène Résal'      See *R*. 'Comtesse du Caÿla'
     misapplied
  'Madame Gabriel Luizet' (HP) EBls
  'Madame Georges            EBls MAus
     Bruant' (Ru)
§ 'Madame Grégoire           CSam EBee EBls EBrP EBre EMFP
     Staechelin' (ClHT) ♀    ENot EWTr IHar LBre LStr MAus
                             MBri MGan MHlr MJon MMat
                             NFla NRog SApu SBre SChu SFam
                             SJus SPer SRPl WAct WHCG
                             WOVN WWeb
  'Madame Hardy' (ClD) ♀     CPou CSam EBee EBls ENot GCoc
                             IHar LGod LStr MAus MBri MGan
                             MHlr MJon MMat SApu SFam SJus
                             SPer SWas WAct WHCG WHow
                             WOVN
  'Madame Isaac Pereire'     More than 30 suppliers
     (ClBb) ♀
  'Madame Jules              EBls MAus
     Gravereaux' (ClT)
  'Madame Jules Thibaud'     MAus
     (Poly)
§ 'Madame Knorr' (DPo) ♀     CBos CPou EBee EBls EMFP EWTr
                             MAus MMat SJus SPer SWCr SWas
                             WAct WHow WOVN
  'Madame Laurette           EBls MAus WHCG WSHC
     Messimy' (Ch)
  'Madame Lauriol de         EBls MAus MGan SFam SWCr
     Barny' (Bb)             WHCG
  'Madame Legras de Saint    EBee EBls EMFP IHar MAus SFam
     Germain' (AXN)          SJus SPer WAct WHCG
  'Madame Lombard' (T)       EBls
  'Madame Louis Laperrière'  EBls MAus MGan SPer
     (HT)

  'Madame Louis Lévêque'     EBls SWCr WHCG
     (DPMo) ♀
  'Madame Pierre Oger' (Bb)  EBls ENot GCoc LHol LStr MAus
                             MHlr MMat SApu SPer WAct
                             WHCG WWeb
  'Madame Plantier' (AxN)    EBee EBls IHar LHol MAus MHlr
                             MMat SPer WHCG WOVN
  'Madame Scipion Cochet' (T) EBls WHCG
  'Madame Victor Verdier' (HP) EBls
  'Madame Wagram,            EBls
     Comtesse de Turenne' (T)
  'Madame William Paul'      EBls
     (PoMo)
  'Madame Zöetmans' (D)      EBls MAus
  'Madeleine Selzer' (Ra)    EBls MAus MGan
  'Mademoiselle Marie        Last listed 1996
     Dirvon' (Bb)
¶ 'Madge' (HM)               ECha
§ Maestro® =                 MAus
     'Mackinja' (HT)
  'Magenta' (S/HT)           EBls MAus SPer SWCr WAct
                             WHCG
§ Magic Carpet =             EPfP GCoc GGre IDic LGod LPlm
     'Jaclover' (S/GC)       LStr MAus MBri MFry MGan MJon
                             MMat SApu SCoo SJus SPla SRPl
§ Magic Carrousel® =         LPlm MAus NPri WStl
     'Moorcar' (Min)
  'Magna Charta' (HP)        EBls
  'Magnifica' (RH)           EBls MAus MGan
N 'Maiden's Blush' (A)       CSam EBee EBls EBrP EBre ELan
                             EMFP ENot IHar LBre LHol MAus
                             MGan MHlr SApu SBre SChu
                             SFam SJus SPer SWCr WHCG
                             WHow WWeb
  'Maiden's Blush, Great'    See *R*. 'Great Maiden's Blush'
  'Maigold' (ClPiH) ♀        CB&S CGro EBee EBls EBrP EBre
                             ELan ENot GCoc GGre LBre LGod
                             LPlm LStr MAus MBri MGan MJon
                             MMat NBat NFla NRog SApu SBre
                             SJus SPer WAct WHCG WSHC
                             WWeb
◆ 'Mailoeur'                 See *R*. Home Sweet Home = 'Mailoeur'
§ *majalis*                  Last listed 1998
§ Make a Wish =              LStr MBri SWCr
     'Mehpat' (Min/Patio)
  'Malaga' (ClHT)            MMat
◆ 'Malcair'                  See *R*. Danse des Sylphes = 'Malcair'
§ Malcolm Sargent =          SPer
     'Harwherry' (HT)
  Maltese rose               See *R*. 'Cécile Brünner'
§ 'Malton' (China hybrid)    EBls
§ Malverns = 'Kordehei' (GC) ENot MMat
§ Mandarin® = 'Korcelin'     LStr MJon MMat NPri SWCr
     (Min)
  'Manettii' (N)             EBls
◆ 'Manglow'                  See *R*. Glowing Amber = 'Manglow'
  'Manning's Blush' (RH)     EBls MAus WAct WHCG
§ Manou Meilland® =          Last listed 1998
     'Meitulimon' (HT)
  Manuela® (HT)              MGan
  'Manx Queen' (F)           MGan MJon
§ Many Happy Returns =       EBee EBrP EBre ENot GCoc LBre
     'Harwanted' (S/F) ♀     LGod LPlm LStr MAus MBri MBur
                             MFry MGan MJon MMat SApu
                             SBre SJus SPer SWCr WOVN
                             WWeb
  'Marbrée' (DPo)            EBls MAus
  'Marcel Bourgouin' (G)     EBls

| | |
|---|---|
| 'Märchenland' (F/S) | EBls MAus |
| § 'Marchesa Boccella' (DPo) ♀ | CPou EBee EBls EMFP EPfP IHar MAus MGan MMat NPri SJus SPer SPla SWas WAct WWeb |
| 'Marcie Gandy' (HT) | MGan |
| 'Maréchal Davoust' (CeMo) | EBls MAus SFam |
| 'Maréchal Niel' (N) | EBls ERea MAus MGan SPer SWCr WHCG |
| 'Margaret' (HT) | MBur MGan |
| § Margaret Merril = 'Harkuly' (F/HT) ♀ | EBee EBls EBrP EBre GChr GCoc GGre LBre LGod LPlm LStr MAus MBri MBur MFry MGan MJon MMat NBat NRog SApu SBre SJus SPer SWas WHCG WOVN WWeb |
| § Margaret Thatcher = 'Korflüg' (HT) | MJon |
| § Margaret's World = 'Kirbill' (F) | MJon |
| 'Margo Koster' (Poly) | EBls MAus NRog WAct |
| § Marguerite Anne = 'Cocredward' (F) | GCoc NBat SApu |
| 'Marguérite Guillard' (HP) | EBls |
| 'Marguerite Hilling' (S) ♀ | EBee EBls ENot GCoc GGre MAus MBri MGan MHlr MJon MMat NRog SApu SPer SRPl SWCr WAct WHCG WOVN |
| Maria Theresa® (HT) | Last listed 1998 |
| ◆ Maria Therese (HT/S) | See R. Maria Teresa de Esteban = 'Dotrames' |
| x *mariae-graebnerae* | WHCG |
| § Marianne Tudor = 'Frymartor' (HT) | Last listed 1998 |
| 'Marie de Blois' (CeMo) | EBls |
| 'Marie Louise' (D) | EBee EBls IHar MAus SFam WAct WHCG |
| 'Marie Pavič' (Poly) | EBls MAus WHCG |
| 'Marie van Houtte' (T) | EBls MAus |
| 'Marie-Jeanne' (Poly) | EBls MAus |
| 'Marijke Koopman' (HT) | MFry |
| § Marinette = 'Auscam' (S) | MAus MBri MJon NPri SWCr |
| § Marjorie Fair® = 'Harhero' (Poly/S) | EBls LPlm MAus MGan MMat SApu WAct WOVN |
| § Marjorie May = 'Horsunpegy' (HT) | MJon |
| 'Marlena' (F/Patio) | GCoc MAus MGan |
| § Marry Me = 'Dicwonder' (Patio) | ECle IDic MJon SApu |
| 'Martha' (Bb) | EBls MAus |
| 'Martian Glow' (F/S) | MGan |
| 'Martin Frobisher' (Ru) | EBls MAus |
| 'Mary' (Poly) | LStr |
| Mary Campbell = 'Horlovequeen' (F) | Last listed 1996 |
| § Mary Donaldson = 'Canana' (HT) | MGan |
| § Mary Gammon = 'Frysweetie' (Min/Patio) | MFry |
| Mary Hayley Bell = 'Korporalt' (S) | Last listed 1996 |
| 'Mary Manners' (Ru) | EBls SPer SWCr |
| § Mary Pope = 'Korlasche' (HT) | ENot MMat |
| § Mary Rose® = 'Ausmary' (S) | CGro CHad CSam EBee EBls EBrP EBre ELan ENot GCoc GGre LBre LGod LStr MAus MBri MFry MGan MHlr MJon MMat NBat SApu SBre SJus SPer SRPl WAct WOVN |
| 'Mary Wallace' (Cl) | EBls MAus |

| | |
|---|---|
| § Mary Webb® = 'Auswebb' (S) | MAus MBri |
| 'Masquerade' (F) | CB&S CGro EBls LGod LStr MAus MGan MJon NRog WStl |
| ◆ 'Master Hugh' | See R. macrophylla 'Master Hugh' ex SS&W 7822 |
| § Matangi® = 'Macman' (F) | LGod MGan NRog |
| ◆ 'Mattche' | See R. Chelsea Pensioner = 'Mattche' |
| ◆ 'Mattdor' | See R. Northamptonshire = 'Mattdor' |
| ◆ 'Mattgro' | See R. Pink Wave = 'Mattgro' |
| Matthias Meilland® = 'Meifolio' (F) | Last listed 1997 |
| ◆ 'Mattnot' | See R. Elizabeth Heather Grierson = 'Mattnot' |
| ◆ 'Mattwyt' | See R. Tynwald = 'Mattwyt' |
| 'Maurice Bernardin' (HP) | EBls |
| 'Max Graf' | See R. x jacksonii 'Max Graf' |
| 'Maxima' | See R. x alba 'Alba Maxima' |
| *maximowicziana* | Last listed 1996 |
| - CC 541 | WHCr |
| 'May Queen' (Ra) | CPou CRHN EBee EBls EMFP MAus MHlr SFam SPer SWCr WHCG WHow |
| 'May Woolley' (F) | Last listed 1996 |
| § Mayor of Casterbridge = 'Ausbrid' (S) | IHar MAus MJon NPri |
| 'McCartney Rose' (HT) | See R. The McCartney Rose = 'Meizeli' |
| 'McGredy's Sunset' (HT) | NRog |
| 'McGredy's Yellow' (HT) | EBls MBur MGan |
| ◆ 'Meban' | See R. Message = 'Meban' |
| 'Meg' (ClHT) | CHad EBee EBls MAus MBri MGan MHlr SPer SWCr WAct WHCG |
| 'Meg Merrilies' (RH) | EBls MAus MGan SWCr SWas WAct |
| ◆ 'Megabi' | See R. Starina = 'Megabi' |
| ◆ 'Meger' | See R. Baccará = 'Meger' |
| 'Megiddo' (F) | MGan |
| ◆ 'Mehac' | See R. Golden Hope = 'Mehac' |
| ◆ 'Mehamber' | See R. Amber Nectar = 'Mehamber' |
| ◆ 'Mehbronze' | See R. Free as Air = 'Mehbronze' |
| ◆ 'Mehpat' | See R. Make a Wish = 'Mehpat' |
| ◆ 'Mehsherry' | See R. The Holt = 'Mehsherry' |
| ◆ 'Meiarlo' | See R. Allegro = 'Meiarlo' |
| ◆ 'Meibalbika' | See R. IGA '83 München = 'Meibalbika' |
| ◆ 'Meibeausai' | See R. Charles Aznavour = 'Meibeausai' |
| ◆ 'Meibeluxen' | See R. Fiona = 'Meibeluxen' |
| ◆ 'Meibil' | See R. Pink Peace = 'Meibil' |
| ◆ 'Meiblam' | See R. Yorkshire Sunblaze = 'Meiblam' |
| ◆ 'Meibleri' | See R. Alliance = 'Meibleri' |
| ◆ 'Meiburenac' | See R. Swany = 'Meiburenac' |
| ◆ 'Meicarl' | See R. Champs Elysées = 'Meicarl' |
| ◆ 'Meicloux' | See R. Pigalle '84 = 'Meicloux' |
| ◆ 'Meicobius' | See R. Terracotta = 'Meicobius' |
| ◆ 'Meicofum' | See R. Leonidas = 'Meicofum' |
| ◆ 'Meicoublan' | See R. White Meidiland = 'Meicoublan' |
| ◆ 'Meicri' | See R. Cricri = 'Meicri' |
| ◆ 'Meicupag' | See R. Golden Sunblaze = 'Meicupag' |
| ◆ 'Meicurbos' | See R. Zambra = 'Meicurbos' |
| ◆ 'Meidanego' | See R. Belle Sunblaze = 'Meidanego' |

♦ 'Meidanover'　　See *R.* Colibre '79 = 'Meidanover'
♦ 'Meidesi'　　See *R.* Mimi = 'Meidesi'
♦ 'Meido'　　See *R.* Scarlet Gem = 'Meido'
♦ 'Meidomonac'　　See *R.* Bonica = 'Meidomonac'
♦ 'Meifiga'　　See *R.* Pharoah = 'Meifiga'
♦ 'Meifinaro'　　See *R.* Air France = 'Meifinaro'
♦ 'Meiflopan'　　See *R.* Alba Meidiland = 'Meiflopan'
♦ 'Meifronuri'　　See *R.* Gold Bunny = 'Meifronuri'
♦ 'Meigekanu'　　See *R.* La Sévillana = 'Meigekanu'
♦ 'Meigeroka'　　See *R.* Pink La Sevillana = 'Meigeroka'
♦ 'Meiglassol'　　See *R.* Tropico Sunblaze = 'Meiglassol'
♦ 'Meigovin'　　See *R.* Snow Sunblaze = 'Meigovin'
♦ 'Meigriso'　　See *R.* Baronne Edmond de Rothschild = 'Meigriso'
♦ 'Meigro-Nurisar'　　See *R.* Climbing Gold Bunny = 'Meigro-Nurisar'
♦ 'Meihand'　　See *R.* Sarabande = 'Meihand'
♦ 'Meihati'　　See *R.* Sparkling Scarlet = 'Meihati'
♦ 'Meihelvet'　　See *R.* Sweet Promise = 'Meihelvet'
♦ 'Meihimper'　　See *R.* Indian Song = 'Meihimper'
♦ 'Meihirvin'　　See *R.* Thomas Barton = 'Meihirvin'
♦ 'Meijenorsar'　　See *R.* Climbing Soraya = 'Meijenorsar'
♦ 'Meijidiro'　　See *R.* Pink Sunblaze = 'Meijidiro'
♦ 'Meijikatar'　　See *R.* Orange Sunblaze = 'Meijikatar'
♦ 'Meijikatarsar'　　See *R.* Climbing Orange Sunblaze = 'Meijikatarsar'
♦ 'Meijulita'　　See *R.* Chorus = 'Meijulita'
I 'Meikeluxen'　　See *R.* Fiona = 'Meibeluxen'
♦ 'Meikrotal'　　See *R.* Scarlet Meidiland = 'Meikrotal'
♦ 'Meilanein'　　See *R.* Charles de Gaulle = 'Meilanein'
♦ 'Meilarco'　　See *R.* Lady Meillandina = 'Meilarco'
♦ 'Meilasso'　　See *R.* Birthday Girl = 'Meilasso'
♦ 'Meilider'　　See *R.* Exploit = 'Meilider'
♦ 'Meilie'　　See *R.* Christian Dior = 'Meilie'
♦ 'Meilista'　　See *R.* Princess Margaret of England = 'Meilista'
♦ 'Meilivar'　　See *R.* The Children's Rose = 'Meilivar'
§ Meillandina® = 'Meirov' (Min)　　MGan
♦ 'Meilontig'　　See *R.* Repens Meidiland = 'Meilontig'
♦ 'Meilucca'　　See *R.* Darling Flame = 'Meilucca'
♦ 'Meimafris'　　See *R.* Jardins de Bagatelle = 'Meimafris'
♦ 'Meimal'　　See *R.* Colibri = 'Meimal'
♦ 'Meimex'　　See *R.* Fantan = 'Meimex'
♦ 'Meimick'　　See *R.* Cocktail = 'Meimick'
♦ 'Meimit'　　See *R.* Grace de Monaco = 'Meimit'
♦ 'Meimont'　　See *R.* Clair Matin = 'Meimont'
♦ 'Meinagre'　　See *R.* Laurence Olivier = 'Meinagre'
♦ 'Meinastur'　　See *R.* Alpha = 'Meinastur'
♦ 'Meinatac'　　See *R.* Susan Hampshire = 'Meinatac'
♦ 'Meineble'　　See *R.* Red Meidiland = 'Meineble'
♦ 'Meinimo'　　See *R.* Twenty-one Again* = 'Meinimo'

♦ 'Meiparadon'　　See *R.* Antonia Ridge = 'Meiparadon'
♦ 'Meipierar'　　See *R.* Caroline de Monaco = 'Meipierar'
♦ 'Meipinjid'　　See *R.* Duke Meillandina = 'Meipinjid'
♦ 'Meiponal'　　See *R.* Sunny Sunblaze = 'Meiponal'
♦ 'Meipoque'　　See *R.* Pink Meidiland = 'Meipoque'
♦ 'Meiranovi'　　See *R.* Candy Rose = 'Meiranovi'
♦ 'Meiresty'　　See *R.* Charleston '88 = 'Meiresty'
♦ 'Meirevolt'　　See *R.* Toulouse-Lautrec = 'Meirevolt'
♦ 'Meiridge'　　See *R.* Charleston = 'Meiridge'
♦ 'Meiriental'　　See *R.* Paprika = 'Meiriental'
♦ 'Meirigalu'　　See *R.* Colorama = 'Meirigalu'
♦ 'Meiroupis'　　See *R.* John Keats = 'Meiroupis'
♦ 'Meirov'　　See *R.* Meillandina = 'Meirov'
♦ 'Meirutral'　　See *R.* Red Sunblaze = 'Meirutral'
♦ 'Meisar'　　See *R.* Papa Meilland = 'Meisar'
♦ 'Meisolroz'　　See *R.* Flamingo Meidiland = 'Meisolroz'
♦ 'Meitifran'　　See *R.* Baron Meillandina = 'Meitifran'
♦ 'Meitoifar'　　See *R.* Auguste Renoir = 'Meitoifar'
♦ 'Meitoleil'　　See *R.* Golden Symphonie = 'Meitoleil'
♦ 'Meitonje'　　See *R.* Pretty Polly = 'Meitonje'
♦ 'Meitosier'　　See *R.* Lord Byron = 'Meitosier'
♦ 'Meitrisical'　　See *R.* Yellow Sunblaze = 'Meitrisical'
♦ 'Meitulandi'　　See *R.* Hidalgo = 'Meitulandi'
♦ 'Meitulimon'　　See *R.* Manou Meilland = 'Meitulimon'
♦ 'Meivestal'　　See *R.* Spirit of Youth = 'Meivestal'
♦ 'Meivildo'　　See *R.* Royal Brompton Rose = 'Meivildo'
♦ 'Meiviolin'　　See *R.* Eden Rose '88 = 'Meiviolin'
♦ 'Meixerul'　　See *R.* Peach Sunblaze = 'Meixerul'
♦ 'Meizeli'　　See *R.* The McCartney Rose = 'Meizeli'
♦ 'Meizuzes'　　See *R.* Madam Speaker = 'Meizuzes'
　　Melina®　　See *R.* Sir Harry Pilkington = 'Tanema'
　'Melinda' (HT)　　Last listed 1998
§ Melody Maker = 'Dicqueen' (F)　　IDic MAus MBur MGan MJon
♦ 'Memaj'　　See *R.* Thaïs = 'Memaj'
§ Memento® = 'Dicbar' (F)　　IDic MGan MMat
　'Memoriam' (HT)　　MGan
§ Memory Lane = 'Peavoodoo' (F)　　GGre
♦ 'Mepal'　　See *R.* Bettina = 'Mepal'
♦ 'Mepalsar'　　See *R.* Climbing Bettina = 'Mepalsar'
§ Mercedes = 'Merkor' (F)　　MJon
♦ 'Merkor'　　See *R.* Mercedes = 'Merkor'
　'Mermaid' (Cl) ♀　　CB&S CGro EBee EBls ENot GCoc IHar LHop LStr MAus MGan MJon MMat NRog SApu SBra SJus SLPl SPer SSoC WAbe WAct WHCG WWat
　'Merveille de Lyon' (HP)　　EBls
§ Message = 'Meban' (HT)　　MGan
　Meteor® (F/Patio)　　MGan

| | | |
|---|---|---|
| § | 'Mevrouw Nathalie Nypels' (Poly) ♀ | CBos CHad EBee EBls IHar LStr MAus SPer WAct WKif WOVN |
| | 'Mexico' (Min) | LPlm |
| § | Michael Crawford = 'Poulvue' (HT) | LGod |
| | 'Michèle Meilland' (HT) | EBls MAus MGan |
| | *micrantha* | Last listed 1998 |
| x | *microgosa* | EBls MAus |
| | - 'Alba' | EBls MAus |
| I | 'Middlesbrough Football Club (The Boro)' (HT) | NBat |
| § | Middlesex County = 'Bosanne' (F) | NBat |
| ¶ | 'Mike Thompson' (HT) | NBat |
| ◆ | 'Millennium Rose 2000' | See *R*. Rose 2000 = 'Cocquestrum' |
| ¶ | Millionaire = 'Peazara' (F) | GCoc GGre SApu |
| ◆ | 'Milsweet' | See *R*. Elsie Warren = 'Milsweet' |
| § | Mimi = 'Meidesi' (Min) | MGan |
| § | Mini Metro = 'Rufin' (Min) | MFry |
| | Minijet® = 'Meirutego' (Min) | Last listed 1997 |
| § | Minilights = 'Dicmoppet' (Patio) | IDic SApu SPer |
| ◆ | 'Minkco' | See *R*. Black Jack = 'Minkco' |
| | 'Minnehaha' (Ra) | EBls EMFP LGod MAus |
| | Minnie Pearl® = 'Savahowdy' (Min) | Last listed 1997 |
| | *mirifica stellata* | See *R*. stellata var. *mirifica* |
| § | Mischief = 'Macmi' (HT) | EBls GGre MAus MGan NRog SPer |
| | 'Miss Edith Cavell' (Poly) | EBls |
| § | Miss Harp = 'Tanolg' (HT) | MGan NRog |
| § | Miss Ireland = 'Macir' (HT) | Last listed 1998 |
| | 'Miss Lowe' (Ch) | EBls |
| § | Miss Pam Ayres = 'Kormarie' (S) | MMat |
| § | Mister Lincoln® (HT) | EBls EWTr LGod MAus MBri MBur MGan SPer |
| § | Mistress Quickly = 'Ausky' (S) | IHar LStr MAus MJon NPri WWeb |
| ◆ | 'Moersdag' | See *R*. Mother's Day = 'Moersdag' |
| | 'Mojave' (HT) | MAus MGan |
| | Moje Hammarberg® (Ru) | ENot MJon WAct |
| § | Molineux = 'Ausmol' (S) | EBrP EBre GCoc IHar LBre LGod MAus MBri MHlr MJon NPri SBre WHCG WWeb |
| § | *mollis* | Last listed 1998 |
| | Molly McGredy = 'Macmo' (F) | Last listed 1996 |
| | 'Mona Ruth' (Min) | MGan |
| | 'Monique' (HT) | EBls MGan |
| | 'Monsieur Tillier' (T) | EBls |
| | 'Moon Maiden' (F) | Last listed 1998 |
| § | Moonbeam = 'Ausbeam' (S) | MAus |
| | 'Moonlight' (HM) | CTri EBee EBls EWTr IHar MAus MGan MMat NBus NRog SJus SPer SWCr WAct WHCG |
| ◆ | 'Moorcar' | See *R*. Magic Carrousel = 'Moorcar' |
| ◆ | 'Morberg' | See *R*. Anne Moore = 'Morberg' |
| | 'Morgengruss' (Cl) | MGan SPer |
| § | Moriah = 'Ganhol' (HT) | MGan |
| | 'Morlettii' (Bs) | EBls EHol MRav SWCr |
| ◆ | 'Mormyval' | See *R*. My Valentine = 'Mormyval' |
| | Morning Jewel® | GCoc LPlm MAus MFry MJon NRog |
| § | Morning Mist = 'Ausfire' (S) | MAus |
| ◆ | 'Morsheri' | See *R*. Sheri Anne = 'Morsheri' |
| ◆ | 'Moryelrug' | See *R*. Yellow Dagmar Hastrup = 'Moryelrug' |
| | *moschata* (Ra) | EBls MAus MHlr MRav SWCr |
| | - 'Autumnalis' | See *R*. 'Princesse de Nassau' |

| | | |
|---|---|---|
| | - var.*nastarana* | See *R*. 'Nastarana' |
| | - var.*nepalensis* | See *R. brunonii* |
| I | 'Mother's Day' | ELan MJon |
| § | Mother's Day = 'Moersdag' (Poly/F) | NEgg NPri |
| | Mother's Love = 'Tinlove' (Min) | Last listed 1997 |
| § | Mountain Snow = 'Aussnow' (Ra) | MAus MBri |
| § | Mountbatten® = 'Harmantelle' (F) ♀ | CB&S CGro EBls EBrP EBre ELan ENot EWTr GGre LBre LGod LPlm LStr MAus MFry MGan MJon MMat SApu SBre SJus SPer SRPl WWeb |
| § | 'Mousseline' (DPoMo) | EBls EMFP MAus SWCr WAct WHCG |
| | 'Mousseuse du Japon' | See *R*. 'Japonica' |
| | *moyesii* (S) | CPin CSam EBee EBls ELan ENot GCoc IHar IOrc ISea LEdu MAus MFry MGan MJon MMat NRog NWea SPer WAct WOVN |
| | - 'Evesbatch' (S) | WAct |
| § | - var.*fargesii* (S) | EBls |
| | - 'Geranium' | See *R*. 'Geranium' (*moyesii* hybrid) |
| | - 'Highdownensis' | See *R*. 'Highdownensis' (*moyesii* hybrid) |
| | - 'Hillieri' | See *R*. 'Hillieri' |
| | - *holodonta* | See *R*. *moyesii* f. *rosea* |
| § | - f.*rosea* (S) | EBls GCal |
| | - 'Sealing Wax' | See *R*. 'Sealing Wax' (*moyesii* hybrid) |
| | 'Mozart' (HM) | MJon WHCG |
| | 'Mr Bluebird' (MinCh) | MAus MGan WStI |
| | 'Mr Chips' (HT) | MBur |
| § | Mr J.C.B. = 'Dicsun' (S) | IDic |
| | 'Mr Lincoln' | See *R*. Mister Lincoln |
| | 'Mrs Anthony Waterer' (Ru) | EBls MAus SPer WAct WHCG |
| | 'Mrs Arthur Curtiss James' (ClHT) | Last listed 1997 |
| | 'Mrs B.R. Cant' (T) | EBls |
| § | Mrs Doreen Pike = 'Ausdor' (Ru) | MAus WAct |
| | 'Mrs Eveline Gandy' (HT) | MGan |
| | 'Mrs Foley Hobbs' (T) | EBls |
| | 'Mrs Honey Dyson' (Ra) | CHad |
| | 'Mrs John Laing' (HP) | EBee EBls MAus MHlr SJus SPer SWCr WHCG |
| | 'Mrs Oakley Fisher' (HT) ♀ | CHad EBee EBls MAus WAct WCot |
| | 'Mrs Paul' (Bb) | EBls MAus |
| | 'Mrs Pierre S. duPont' (HT) | EBls |
| | 'Mrs Sam McGredy' (HT) | MAus MGan |
| | 'Mrs Walter Burns' (F/Patio) | MGan |
| | 'Mullard Jubilee' (HT) | IHar MGan |
| § | *mulliganii* (Ra) ♀ | CDoC EBee EBls EPfP IHar MAus MJon SBid SJus SPer SPla SRPl WHCG |
| | *multibracteata* ♀ | EBls MAus WHCG |
| | *multiflora* | EBls MAus WPic |
| | - 'Carnea' | EBls |
| | - var.*cathayensis* | EBls |
| § | - 'Grevillei' | EBee EBls MAus WHow |
| | - 'Platyphylla' | See *R. multiflora* 'Grevillei' |
| | - var.*watsoniana* | See *R. watsoniana* |
| | 'München' (HM) | MAus |
| | *mundi* | See *R. gallica* 'Versicolor' |
| | - 'Versicolor' | See *R. gallica* 'Versicolor' |
| | *muriculata* | Last listed 1996 |
| | 'Mutabilis' | See *R*. x *odorata* 'Mutabilis' |
| | 'My Choice' (HT) | MGan SWCr |
| | 'My Joy' (HT) | NBat |

'My Little Boy' (Min)    MBur
§ My Love = 'Cogamo' (HT)    MAus MBur MJon SWCr
§ My Valentine® =    Last listed 1998
   'Mormyval' (Min)
§ Myra = 'Battoo' (HT)    NBat
§ Myriam® = 'Cocgrand' (HT)    GCoc MJon SApu
'Nancy's Keepsake' (HT)    NBat
*nanothamnus*    Last listed 1997
'Narrow Water' (Ra)    EBee EBls LFis WAct WHCG
§ 'Nastarana' (N)    EBls WHCG
'Nathalie Nypels'    See *R.* 'Mevrouw Nathalie Nypels'
'National Trust' (HT)    EBls GGre IHar MGan MJon NRog
   SPer WStI
'Nestor' (G)    EBls MAus
'Nevada' (S) ♀    EBee EBrP EBre ELan ENot GCoc
   GGre IOrc LBre LEdu LGod LStr
   MAus MBri MFry MGan MHlr
   MJon MMat NFla NRog SApu SBre
   SFam SJus SPer WAct WHCG
   WOVN WWeb
Nevertheless = 'Hannev' (F)    Last listed 1996
¶ 'New Arrival' (Patio/Min)    GGre
New Daily Mail = 'Pussta' (F)    Last listed 1997
§ 'New Dawn' (Cl) ♀    More than 30 suppliers
§ New Fashion =    ENot MMat
   'Poulholm' (Patio)
§ New Horizon = 'Dicplay' (F)    IDic
'New Look' (F)    MGan
'New Penny' (Min)    IHar MGan
§ New Zealand =    MJon NBat SApu
   'Macgenev' (HT)
§ News® = 'Legnews' (F)    MAus MGan
§ Nice Day = 'Chewsea'    CGro EBrP EBre ENot GGre LBre
   (ClMin)    LStr MBri MBur MFry MJon MMat
   NBat SApu SBre SJus WOVN
'Nicola' (F)    MGan
§ Nigel Hawthorne =    WAct
   'Harquibbler' (S)
§ Night Light® = 'Poullight'    EBee LPlm MBri MBur MFry
   (Cl)    MGan MJon SApu SJus
Nina Weibull® (F)    MGan
*nitida*    EBee EBls ELan ENot EPla GChr
   MAus NWea SPer SRPl WAct
   WHCG WHer WOVN
   - 'Defender'    Last listed 1997
♦ 'Noaschnee'    See *R.* White Flower Carpet =
   'Noaschnee'
♦ 'Noatraum'    See *R.* Pink Flower Carpet =
   'Noatraum'
§ Noble Antony = 'Ausway' (S)    MAus MJon SWCr WWeb
§ 'Noisette Carnée' (N)    CBos CHad EBls GChr MAus SLPl
   SPer SSea WAct WHCG WHow
   WSHC
'Non Plus Ultra' (Ra)    Last listed 1996
§ Norfolk = 'Poulfolk' (GC)    EBls EBrP EBre ENot GCoc LBre
   LStr MAus MHlr MMat SApu SBre
   SPer SPla WHCG WOVN
'Norma Major' (HT)    Last listed 1997
§ Northamptonshire =    ENot LGod MGan MMat
   'Mattdor' (GC)
Northern Lights® (HT)    GCoc
'Northumberland WI' (HT)    Last listed 1998
'Norwich Castle' (F)    EBls
§ Norwich Cathedral =    EBls
   'Beacath' (HT)
'Norwich Pink' (Cl)    MAus
'Norwich Salmon' (Cl)    MAus
'Norwich Union' (F)    EBls
♦ 'Noscook'    See *R.* Catherine Cookson =
   'Noscook'

♦ 'Nosshef'    See *R.* City of Sheffield =
   'Nosshef'
♦ 'Nossun'    See *R.* Sunderland Supreme =
   'Nossun'
§ Nostalgie® = 'Taneiglat' (HT)    LStr
♦ 'Nostarn'    See *R.* Arnold Greensitt =
   'Nostarn'
'Nova Zembla' (Ru)    EBls MAus
'Nozomi' (ClMin/GC) ♀    CGro EBee EBls ELan ENot EWTr
   GCoc GGre LPlm LStr MAus MFry
   MGan MHlr MJon MMat SApu
   SJus SPer WAct WHCG WOVN
'Nuits de Young' (CeMo)    EBls GCoc IHar MAus MMat SFam
   SWCr WHCG
'Nur Mahal' (HM)    EBls MAus WHCG
*nutkana* (S)    EBls MAus
- var. *hispida* (S)    EBls
§ - 'Plena' (S) ♀    CHan EBls ENot EPfP MAus NFla
   SFam SRPl SWCr WGer WHCG
'Nymphenburg' (HM)    EBls EMFP MAus SPer
'Nypels' Perfection' (Poly)    MAus
'Nyveldt's White' (Ru)    EBls MAus
'Oakington Ruby' (MinCh)    Last listed 1997
♦ 'Ocaru'    See *R.* Angela Rippon = 'Ocaru'
§ Octavia Hill = 'Harzeal' (F/S)    LStr MFry MJon SApu SJus SPer
   SWCr WAct WHCG WHow
'Octet' (S)    Last listed 1996
x *odorata* 'Fortune's    See *R.* x *odorata* 'Pseudindica'
   Double Yellow'
§ - 'Mutabilis' (Ch) ♀    CGre EBee EBls EMFP MAus
   MMat SJus SMrm SPer WAct
   WHCG WHow WOVN WWat
§ - 'Ochroleuca' (Ch)    EBls
§ - 'Odorata' (Ch)    EBls
- Old Crimson China (Ch)    EBls WAct
§ - 'Pallida' (Ch)    EBls EMFP GCoc MAus MMat
   NPri SPla SWCr SWas WHCG
   WHow
§ - 'Pseudindica' (ClCh)    EBls MAus WSHC
§ - Sanguinea Group (Ch)    EBls IDac WHCG
- - 'Bengal Crimson' (Ch)    Last listed 1996
§ - 'Viridiflora' (Ch)    EBls MAus MBur MMat SPer SSoC
   WAct WHCG
'Oeillet Flamand'    See *R.* 'Oeillet Parfait'
'Oeillet Panaché' (Mo)    WAct
§ 'Oeillet Parfait' (G)    EBls MAus
*officinalis*    See *R. gallica* var. *officinalis*
'Ohl' (G)    EBls
§ Ohshima Rose =    GCoc
   'Cochunter' (HT)
'Oklahoma' (HT)    MGan
old blush China    See *R.* x *odorata* 'Pallida'
old cabbage    See *R.* x *centifolia*
Old Glory™ = 'Benday'    Last listed 1996
   (Min/Patio)
§ Old John = 'Dicwillynilly' (F)    ECle IDic MJon
§ Old Master = 'Macesp' (F)    MAus MGan
old pink moss rose    See *R.* x *centifolia* 'Muscosa'
§ Old Port = 'Mackati' (F)    GGre MJon SApu
old red moss    See *R.* 'Henri Martin', *R.* 'Lanei'
old velvet moss    See *R.* 'William Lobb'
old yellow Scotch (PiH)    See *R.* x *harisonii* 'Williams'
   Double Yellow'
§ Olde Romeo =    Last listed 1998
   'Hadromeo' (HT)
§ Oliver Twist =    MBur
   'Sabbyron' (Patio)
Olympiad® =    Last listed 1996
   'Macauck' (HT)
'Omar Khayyám' (D)    EBls ENot MAus NFla
§ 'Ombrée Parfaite' (G)    EBls

omeiensis f.*pteracantha*   See *R. sericea* subsp. *omeiensis* f.
                            *pteracantha*
§ Open Arms =               LGod MFry MJon WGer
   'Chewpixcel' (ClMin)
'Ophelia' (HT)             EBee EBls MAus MBur MGan
'Orange Honey' (Min)       MBur
§ Orange Sensation® (F)    EBls ENot GChr MAus MGan
                            MJon NRog
Orange Star™ =            Last listed 1996
   'Minako' (Min)
§ Orange Sunblaze® =       EBls GGre MGan MJon SJus SPer
   'Meijikatar' (Min)       WWeb
Orange Triumph® (Poly)    EBls
Orangeade (F)             MGan
§ Oranges and Lemons™ =   CGro EBee ENot GCoc GGre
   'Macoranlem' (S/F)       LGod LPlm LStr MBri MBur MFry
                            MGan MJon MMat SApu SJus
                            SWas WGer WWeb
'Oriana' (HT)             Last listed 1998
'Orient Express' (HT)     MJon
'Orpheline de Juillet'    See *R.* 'Ombrée Parfaite'
§ Othello® = 'Auslo' (S)  MAus SApu WAct
¶ Our George =            MJon
   'Kirrush' (Patio)
§ Our Love = 'Andour' (HT) GGre
§ Our Molly =            IDic MGan SApu
   'Dicreason' (GC/S)
Owen's Pride = 'Kirpink' (HT) MJon
§ Oxfordshire =           ENot LStr MMat SJus SWCr
   'Korfullwind' (GC)
§ Paddy McGredy =         CGro GChr MAus MGan MJon
   'Macpa' (F)              NRog
§ Paddy Stephens =        GCoc MFry MJon
   'Macclack' (HT)
§ Painted Moon =          GCoc IDic
   'Dicpaint' (HT)
§ Paint-pot = 'Trobglow' (Min) Last listed 1996
'Pam Ayres'               See *R.* Miss Pam Ayres =
                           'Kormarie'
§ Panache = 'Poultop' (Patio) GGre LStr MJon WGer
Pandora® =
   'Harwinner' (Min)       Last listed 1996
'Panorama Holiday' (F/HT) MBur
'Papa Gontier' (T)        EBls MAus
'Papa Hémeray' (Ch)       EBls
§ Papa Meilland® =        CGro EBls MAus MGan MJon
   'Meisar' (HT)            NRog SApu SPer
'Papillon' (T)            EBls
§ Paprika™ = 'Meiriental' (F) MAus
'Pâquerette' (Poly)       EBls
◆ 'Para Ti'               See *R.* Pour Toi = 'Para Ti'
'Parade' (Cl) ♀           MAus MFry MGan SJus SWCr
                           WHCG
§ Paradise® = 'Weizeip' (HT) MGan
Parkdirektor Riggers® (Cl) CSam EBee EBls LStr MAus MBri
                           MGan SPer WHCG WSHC
Park's yellow China       See *R.* x *odorata* 'Ochroleuca'
'Parkzierde' (Bb)         EBls
Parson's pink China       See *R.* x *odorata* 'Pallida'
§ Partridge = 'Korweirim' (GC) EBls MAus MGan MJon MMat
                           SApu SJus SPer WAct WOVN
Party Girl® (Min)         NBat
§ Party Trick = 'Dicparty' (F) IDic MBri
*parvifolia*              See *R.* 'Burgundiaca'
§ Pascali® = 'Lenip' (HT) CGro EBls EBrP EBre ELan ENot
                           GCoc GGre LBre LStr MAus MBur
                           MGan MJon NRog SBre SPer SRPl
                           SWCr
Passion (Ru)             WLRN
§ Pat Austin = 'Ausmum' (S) CSam MAus MBri MJon NBus SJus
                           SWCr WWeb

§ Pathfinder =           CBrm MJon MMat
   'Chewpobey' (GC)
§ Patricia = 'Korpatri' (F) Last listed 1998
'Paul Crampel' (Poly)    EBls MAus MGan NRog SPer WAct
'Paul Lédé' (ClT)        See *R.* 'Climbing Paul Lédé'
Paul McCartney (HT)      See *R.* The McCartney Rose =
                           'Meizeli'
'Paul Neyron' (HP)       EBls MAus MMat WAct WHCG
'Paul Ricault' (CexHP)   EBls MAus
§ Paul Shirville =        ENot GGre IHar LPlm MAus MFry
   'Harqueterwife' (HT) ♀  MGan MMat NRog SApu SJus SPer
'Paul Transon' (Ra) ♀    CRHN EBee EBls EMFP IHar MAus
                           MBri MHlr SJus SPer SWCr WHow
                           WOVN
'Paul Verdier' (Bb)      EBls
§ 'Paulii' (Ru)           EBls ELan ENot LFis MAus SWCr
                           WAct WHCG WOVN
'Paulii Alba'            See *R.* 'Paulii'
'Paulii Rosea' (Ru/Cl)   EBls MAus WAct WHCG
'Paul's Early Blush' (HP) EBls
'Paul's Himalayan Musk'  CHad CRHN CSam EBee EBls
   (Ra) ♀                   EBrP EBre EMFP EWTr IHar ISea
                           LBre LHol LStr MAus MBri MFry
                           MHlr MJon SApu SBre SFam SJus
                           SPer SWas WAct WHCG WHow
                           WKif WPic
§ 'Paul's Lemon Pillar' (ClHT) CHad EBee EBls EBrP EBre LBre
                           MAus NRog SBre SPer
'Paul's Perpetual White' (Ra) EBls WHCG
'Paul's Scarlet Climber'  CGro EBee EBls ELan ENot GGre
   (Cl/Ra)                 LGod LStr MAus MGan MJon
                           MMat SApu SPer SWCr SWas
                           WWeb
'Pax' (HM)               CPou EBee EBls EMFP MAus SPer
                           SRPl WHCG WKif
◆ 'Payable'               See *R.* Anusheh = 'Payable'
◆ 'Peaalamo'              See *R.* Little Rascal = 'Peaalamo'
§ Peace = 'Madame A.      CB&S CGro EBee EBls ELan EWTr
   Meilland' (HT) ♀         GChr GCoc GGre LGod LPlm LStr
                           MAus MBri MBur MFry MGan
                           MJon MMat NRog SApu SPer SRPl
                           SWas WWeb
Peace Sunblaze (Min)     See *R.* Lady Meillandina =
                           'Meilarco'
§ Peacekeeper = 'Harbella' (F) GGre SJus
§ Peach Blossom =         MAus MHlr SWCr
   'Ausblossom' (S)
§ Peach Sunblaze =        MBri MJon SApu SJus WWeb
   'Meixerul' (Min)
'Peachy White' (Min)     MAus
◆ 'Peafirst'             See *R.* Doctor McAlpine =
                           'Peafirst'
◆ 'Peahaze'              See *R.* Geraldine = 'Peahaze'
◆ 'Peahigh'              See *R.* The Daily Telegraph =
                           'Peahigh'
◆ 'Peahunder'           See *R.* Judi Dench = 'Peahunder'
◆ 'Peamax'              See *R.* Dame Vera Lynn =
                           'Peamax'
◆ 'Peamight'            See *R.* Leaping Salmon =
                           'Peamight'
◆ 'Peanob'              See *R.* Bush Baby = 'Peanob'
◆ 'Peapatio'            See *R.* Royal Flush = 'Peapatio'
◆ 'Peaperfume'          See *R.* Indian Summer =
                           'Peaperfume'
◆ 'Peapet'              See *R.* Jane Asher = 'Peapet'
◆ 'Peapolly'            See *R.* Jimmy Savile = 'Peapolly'
◆ 'Peapost'             See *R.* Carol Ann = 'Peapost'
◆ 'Peaproof'            See *R.* Freddy = 'Peaproof'
§ Pearl Anniversary =     GGre LStr MBri SWCr
   'Whitson' (Min/Patio)
§ Pearl Drift® = 'Leggab' (S) EBls LStr MAus MJon SPer WHCG

◆ 'Pearobin'                See *R.* Gary Lineker = 'Pearobin'
◆ 'Pearoyal'               See *R.* Goldfinger = 'Pearoyal'
◆ 'Peatrophy'              See *R.* Charisma = 'Peatrophy'
  Peaudouce                See *R.* Elina = 'Dicjana'
◆ 'Peavandyke'            See *R.* Stardust = 'Peavandyke'
◆ 'Peaverity'              See *R.* In the Pink = 'Peaverity'
◆ 'Peavoodoo'             See *R.* Memory Lane =
                            'Peavoodoo'
◆ 'Peawinner'             See *R.* Ruby Celebration =
                            'Peawinner'
◆ 'Peaxi'                  See *R.* Bright Fire = 'Peaxi'
◆ 'Peayetti'               See *R.* Dream Lover = 'Peayetti'
§ Peek A Boo =             ELan ENot IDic IHar LGod MFry
   'Dicgrow' (Min/Patio)   MGan SApu SPer WStI
§ Peer Gynt® = 'Korol' (HT) LPlm MGan
§ Pegasus = 'Ausmoon' (S)  IHar LStr MAus MJon NPri SSoC
                            SWCr
  'Peggy Netherthorpe' (HT) Last listed 1997
◆ 'Pekcouliane'           See *R.* Julia = 'Pekcouliane'
  'Pélisson' (CeMo)        EBls
§ *pendulina*             EBls MAus WHCG
  'Penelope' (HM) ♀        More than 30 suppliers
§ Penelope Keith =         MJon SApu
   'Macfreego' (Min/Patio)
  'Penelope Plummer' (F)   EBls
§ Penny Lane =             CGro EBee ECle ENot GCoc LGod
   'Hardwell' (Cl)         LPlm LRHS LStr MBri MFry MGan
                            MJon MMat NBat SApu SJus SPer
                            SWas
§ Pensioner's Voice =      MFry
   'Fryrelax' (F)
§ Penthouse =              MJon
   'Macngaura' (HT)
◆ 'Pentiger'              See *R.* Kind Regards = 'Pentiger'
  x *penzanceana*         See *R.* 'Lady Penzance'
§ Peppermint Ice =         MJon SApu SWCr
   'Bosgreen' (F)
§ Perception™ =            SApu
   'Harzippee' (HT)
§ Perdita® = 'Ausperd' (S) EBee IOrc MAus MBri MHlr MJon
                            SPer SRPl SWCr WAct WHCG
§ Perestroika =            ENot GCoc LStr MJon MMat SApu
   'Korhitom' (F/Min)      SJus WGer
§ Perfecta = 'Koralu' (HT) EBls MGan
  'Perla de Montserrat' (Min) Last listed 1997
  'Perle des Jardins' (T)  EBls MAus
  'Perle des Panachées' (G) EBls
§ 'Perle d'Or' (Poly) ♀    CHad EBee EMFP ENot GCoc
                            MAus MHlr MMat NRog SChu
                            SPer SPla SWCr WAct WHCG
                            WWat
  'Perle von Hohenstein' (Poly) EBls
  Pernille Poulsen® (F)    EBls
  Persian yellow           See *R. foetida* 'Persiana'
  *persica*                MAus
¶ Peter Pan =              MJon
   'Chewpan' (Min)
§ Petit Four® =            SApu
   'Interfour' (Min/Patio)
  'Petite de Hollande' (Ce) EBee EBls MAus SPer SWCr WAct
                            WHCG WHow
  Petite Folie® =          Last listed 1996
   'Meiherode' (Min)
  'Petite Lisette' (CexD)  EBls MAus SPer
  'Petite Orléannaise' (Ce) EBls
§ Phab Gold =              MFry
   'Frybountiful' (F)
§ Phantom =                MBur MJon WGer
   'Maccatsun' (S/GC)
  'Pharisäer' (HT)         EBls

§ Pheasant = 'Kordapt' (GC) ELan ENot GCoc MAus MHlr
                            MJon MMat SJus SPer WAct
                            WOVN
¶ Philippa = 'Poulheart' (S) EBee
  *phoenicia*              EBls
  'Phyllis Bide' (Ra) ♀    EBee EBls EMFP LStr MAus MGan
                            MHlr SJus SPer SRPl SSea WHCG
                            WHow
§ Picasso = 'Macpic' (F)   EBls MAus MGan
§ Piccadilly® = 'Macar' (HT) CB&S CGro EBls GGre IHar LPlm
                            MAus MGan MJon NRog SApu
                            SPer
§ Piccolo = 'Tanolokip'    EBee GGre LStr MBri MFry MJon
   (F/Patio)               SApu SWas WGer WWeb
  'Picture' (HT)           EBls MAus MGan NRog SPer
  'Pierre Notting' (HP)    EBls
  Pierrine™ = 'Micpie' (Min) Last listed 1997
§ Pigalle '84 = 'Meicloux' (F) Last listed 1998
  'Pilgrim'                See *R.* The Pilgrim = 'Auswalker'
§ Pillar Box = 'Chewaze' (F) MGan
§ *pimpinellifolia*        CKin EBls ENot LBuc MAus MGan
                            MMat NFla NRoo NWea SPer SRPl
                            WHCG WOVN
  – 'Altaica' hort.        See *R. pimpinellifolia*
                            'Grandiflora'
§ – 'Andrewsii' ♀          MAus WAct
  – 'Bakewell Scots Briar'  Last listed 1998
§ – double pink            EBls
  – double white           CNat EBls GCoc MAus WAct
  – double yellow          See *R.* x *harisonii* 'Williams'
                            Double Yellow'
§ – 'Dunwich Rose'         EBee EBls EBrP EBre ENot LBre
                            MAus MBri MGan MMat SBre SPer
                            SWCr WAct WHCG
§ – 'Falkland'             EBls MAus
§ – 'Glory of Edzell'      EBls MAus
§ – 'Grandiflora'          EBls MAus SJus
  – 'Harisonii'            See *R.* x *harisonii* 'Harison's
                            Yellow'
  – HH&K 328               CHan
  – var. *hispida*         MAus
  – 'Irish Marbled'        EBls
  – 'Lutea'                See *R.* x *harisonii* 'Lutea Maxima'
  – 'Marbled Pink'         EBls MAus
  – 'Mary, Queen of Scots' EBls MAus SRms WAct
  – 'Mrs Colville'         EBls MAus
  – 'Ormiston Roy'         MAus
  – x *pendulina*          See *R.* x *reversa*
§ – 'Robbie'               MAus WAct
  – 'Single Cherry'        EBls MAus
  – 'Stanwell Perpetual'   See *R.* 'Stanwell Perpetual'
  – 'Variegata'            CArn
  – 'William III'          EBls LHop MAus SChu SLPl
§ Pink Bells® =            CGro EBls ENot GCoc MAus
   'Poulbells' (GC)        MGan MHlr MMat SApu SPer
                            SWCr WAct WHCG WOVN
  'Pink Bouquet' (Ra)      CRHN MAus
§ Pink Chimo® =            IDic
   'Interchimp' (S/GC)
§ Pink Drift =             ENot MMat
   'Poulcat' (Min/GC)
  'Pink Elizabeth Arden' (F) Last listed 1997
  'Pink Favorite' (HT)     MGan NRog SPer
§ Pink Flower Carpet™ =    CTri EBrP EBre ELan GGre IHar
   'Noatraum' (GC) ♀       LBre LRHS MAus MFry MGan
                            MJon MMat SBre SCoo SJus SPer
                            SPla SWCr WWeb
  'Pink Garnette'          See *R.* 'Carol Amling'

'Pink Grootendorst' (Ru) ♀  CB&S EBee EBls ENot IOrc LStr
                            MAus MGan MHlr MJon MMat
                            NFla NRog SPer SWCr WAct
                            WHCG
'Pink Hedgerose'            See *R.* Romantic Hedgerose =
                            'Korworm'
I  'Pink Hedgrose'          See *R.* Romantic Hedgerose =
                            'Korworm'
§  Pink Hit® = 'Poulink'    ENot MMat
   (Min/Patio)
§  Pink La Sevillana® =     Last listed 1998
   'Meigeroka' (F/GC)
§  Pink Meidiland® =        MGan WOVN
   'Meipoque' (GC)
   pink moss                See *R.* x *centifolia* 'Muscosa'
   Pink Panther® =          Last listed 1997
   'Meicapinal' (HT)
'Pink Parfait' (F)          EBls GCoc GGre MAus MGan
                            NRog SPer
§  Pink Peace = 'Meibil' (HT) CB&S GGre
§  Pink Pearl = 'Kormasyl' (HT) MMat SApu
'Pink Perpétué' (Cl)        CGro EBee EBls EBrP EBre ELan
                            ENot GCoc GGre LBre LGod LPlm
                            MAus MBri MBur MFry MGan
                            MJon MMat NBat NFla NRog
                            SApu SBre SPer SRPl SWas WWeb
'Pink Petticoat' (Min)      Last listed 1996
§  Pink Posy =              MAus
   'Cocanelia' (Min/Patio)
'Pink Prosperity' (HM)      EBls MAus
'Pink Showers' (ClHT)       WAct
§  Pink Sunblaze® =         SApu
   'Meijidiro' (Min/Patio)
§  Pink Surprise =          MAus
   'Lenbrac' (Ru)
§  Pink Wave = 'Mattgro' (GC) MMat
§  Pinocchio =              EBls
   'Rosenmärchen' (F)
'Pinta' (HT)                EBls
§  Piroschka® = 'Tanpika' (HT) MJon
   *pisocarpa*              Last listed 1996
'Pixie Rose' (Min)          Last listed 1998
♦  'Pixiree'                See *R.* Free Spirit = 'Pixiree'
§  Playgroup Rose =         IHar NBat
   'Horsun' (F)
§  Playtime =               ENot MMat
   'Korsaku' (GC/Ru)
   Playtime™ =              Last listed 1996
   'Morplati' (F)
§  Pleine de Grâce =        EBls MAus WAct
   'Lengra' (S)
'Plentiful' (F)             EBls
§  Poetry in Motion =       NBat SApu
   'Harelan' (HT)
§  Polar Star =             EBls EWTr GGre LGod LPlm LStr
   'Tanlarpost' (HT)        MFry MGan MJon NRog SApu
                            SPer SRPl WWeb
   x *polliniana*           SLPl
'Polly' (HT)                EBls MGan NRog
   *polyantha grandiflora*  See *R. gentiliana*
   *pomifera*               See *R. villosa*
   - 'Duplex'               See *R.* 'Wolley-Dod'
§  Pomona = 'Fryyeh' (F)    MFry
'Pompon Blanc Parfait' (A)  EBls MAus SFam
'Pompon de Bourgogne'       See *R.* 'Burgundiaca'
§  'Pompon de Paris' (MinCh) EBls SWCr
'Pompon de Paris' (ClMinCh) See *R.* 'Climbing Pompon de
                            Paris'
'Pompon Panaché' (G)        EBls MAus
♦  Porcelain                See *R.* Margaret Thatcher =
                            'Korflüg'

¶  Porcellina (F)           MJon
   Portland Dawn =          Last listed 1997
   'Seatip' (Min)
   Portland rose            See *R.* 'Portlandica'
§  'Portlandica'            EBls MAus SPer WAct WHCG
§  Pot o' Gold =            EBee IDic LStr MAus MFry MGan
   'Dicdivine' (HT)         MJon SApu SPer
♦  'Poulari'                See *R.* Silver Anniversary =
                            'Poulari'
♦  'Poulave'                See *R.* Sussex = 'Poulave'
♦  'Poulbells'              See *R.* Pink Bells = 'Poulbells'
♦  'Poulcat'                See *R.* Pink Drift = 'Poulcat'
♦  'Poulclimb'              See *R.* Calypso = 'Poulclimb'
♦  'Poulcov'                See *R.* Kent = 'Poulcov'
♦  'Poulcub'                See *R.* Tiger Cub = 'Poulcub'
♦  'Pouldra'                See *R.* Princess Alexandra =
                            'Pouldra'
♦  'Poulduce'               See *R.* Tivoli = 'Poulduce'
♦  'Poulduff'               See *R.* Courage = 'Poulduff'
♦  'Poulena'                See *R.* Bellevue = 'Poulena'
♦  'Poulfi'                 See *R.* Elfin = 'Poulfi'
♦  'Poulfolk'               See *R.* Norfolk = 'Poulfolk'
♦  'Poulgan'                See *R.* City Lights = 'Poulgan'
♦  'Poulgar'                See *R.* Buck's Fizz = 'Poulgar'
♦  'Poulholm'               See *R.* New Fashion = 'Poulholm'
♦  'Poulink'                See *R.* Pink Hit = 'Poulink'
♦  'Poulisab'               See *R.* Isabella = 'Poulisab'
♦  'Pouljill'               See *R.* Bella = 'Pouljill'
♦  'Poullack'               See *R.* Lakeland Princess =
                            'Poullack'
♦  'Poullaps'               See *R.* White Knight = 'Poullaps'
♦  'Poullen'                See *R.* Little Bo-peep = 'Poullen'
♦  'Poullight'              See *R.* Night Light = 'Poullight'
♦  'Poulman'                See *R.* Ingrid Bergman =
                            'Poulman'
♦  'Poulmax'                See *R.* Fascination = 'Poulmax'
♦  'Poulmulti'              See *R.* Avon = 'Poulmulti'
♦  'Poulna'                 See *R.* Helena = 'Poulna'
♦  'Poulnoev'               See *R.* Salmo = 'Poulnoev'
♦  'Poulnorm'               See *R.* Jazz = 'Poulnorm'
♦  'Poulnoz'                See *R.* Essex = 'Poulnoz'
♦  'Poulreb'                See *R.* Eurostar = 'Poulreb'
♦  'Poulred'                See *R.* Red Bells = 'Poulred'
♦  'Poulrek'                See *R.* Crystal Palace = 'Poulrek'
♦  'Poulrim'                See *R.* Garden News = 'Poulrim'
♦  'Poulshine'              See *R.* Rutland = 'Poulshine'
♦  'Poulstripe'             See *R.* Christopher Columbus =
                            'Poulstripe'
♦  'Poulsue'                See *R.* Susan = 'Poulsue'
♦  'Poulsun'                See *R.* Sun Hit = 'Poulsun'
♦  'Poulsyng'               See *R.* Liliana = 'Poulsyng'
♦  'Poultika'               See *R.* Flamenco = 'Poultika'
♦  'Poultime'               See *R.* Ragtime = 'Poultime'
   'Poultipe'               See *R.* Pink Hit = 'Poulink'
♦  'Poultop'                See *R.* Panache = 'Poultop'
♦  'Poultumb'               See *R.* Tumbling Waters =
                            'Poultumb'
♦  'Poulurt'                See *R.* Gwent = 'Poulurt'
♦  'Poulvue'                See *R.* Michael Crawford =
                            'Poulvue'
♦  'Poulwhite'              See *R.* White Bells = 'Poulwhite'
♦  'Poulzazz'               See *R.* Pzazz = 'Poulzazz'
♦  'Poumidor'               See *R.* Troika = 'Poumidor'
§  Pour Toi = 'Para Ti' (Min) ENot LPlm MAus MGan MJon
                            SPer
   prairie rose             See *R. setigera*
   *prattii*                Last listed 1996
'Precious Platinum' (HT)    IHar LGod MJon SJus SPer
§  Preservation =           GGre
   'Bosijurika' (S/F)

§ 'Président de Sèze' (G) ♀ — EBee EBls MAus SFam SPer SWCr WAct WHCG WHow
§ President Heidar Aliyev = 'Cocosimber' (HT) — GCoc
'President Herbert Hoover' (HT) — EBls
'Prestige' (S) — NRog
§ Pretty in Pink = 'Dicumpteen' (GC) — IDic MJon
§ Pretty Jessica = 'Ausjess' (S) — MAus MHlr MJon SPer
§ Pretty Lady = 'Scrivo' (F) — ECle LStr MJon
§ Pretty Polly® = 'Meitonje' (Min) — CGro CTri GGre LStr MBri MFry MGan MJon MMat NPri SApu SJus WWeb
§ Pride of England = 'Harencore' (HT) — GCoc
'Prima Ballerina' (HT) — CGro EBls GCoc GGre LPlm LStr MAus MGan MJon NBat NRog SPer
'Primevère' (Cl) — Last listed 1996
primula (S) ♀ — CHad EBls EMFP ENot LHol MAus MJon MMat SPer SWCr WAct WCot WHCG WHow
'Prince Camille de Rohan' (HP) — EBls MAus WHCG
'Prince Charles' (Bb) — EBls MAus MHlr SWCr WHCG
♦ Prince Sunblaze® (Min) — See R. Red Sunblaze = 'Meirutral'
§ Princess Alexandra = 'Pouldra' (S) — EBee ECle
§ Princess Alice = 'Hartanna' (F) — LGod MGan SApu
'Princess Chichibu' (F) — SWCr
§ Princess Margaret of England = 'Meilista' (HT) — Last listed 1997
§ Princess Michael of Kent® = 'Harlightly' (F) — MGan WWeb
'Princess Michiko' (F) — Last listed 1996
§ Princess of Wales = 'Hardinkum' (F) — GCoc LStr MBri MGan SWCr
§ Princess Royal = 'Dicroyal' (HT) — GCoc GGre IDic MBri
'Princesse Adélaïde' (Mo) — EBls
§ 'Princesse de Nassau' (Ra) — EBls MAus WAct WHCG WHow
'Princesse Louise' (Ra) — CRHN MAus SFam
♦ 'Princesse Marie' misapplied — See R. 'Belvedere'
§ Priscilla Burton® = 'Macrat' (F) — MAus
§ Pristine® = 'Jacpico' (HT) — IDic MAus MGan MJon SPer
♦ 'Probuzini' — See R. Awakening = 'Probuzini'
N 'Professor Emile Perrot' (D) — EBee EBls MAus
'Prolifera de Redouté' misapplied — See R. 'Duchesse de Montebello'
'Prosperity' (HM) ♀ — CB&S EBls EMFP ENot GCoc GOrc IOrc MAus MFry MGan MHlr MJon MMat NFla NRog SJus SPer WAct WHCG WHow WOVN WWeb
§ Prospero® = 'Auspero' (S) — MAus MBri WAct
'Prudhoe Peach' (F) — Last listed 1998
♦ x pruhoniciana 'Hillieri' — See R. 'Hillieri'
Prunella = 'Canplant' (F) — Last listed 1996
§ Pudsey Bear = 'Bedchild' (HT) — COtt GGre
§ pulverulenta — EBls
§ Pure Bliss = 'Dictator' (HT) — EBee GCoc IDic MJon NBat
'Purezza' (Ra) — Last listed 1996
¶ 'Purity' (Cl) — SWCr
'Purple Beauty' (HT) — MGan
'Purple Splendour' (F) — MAus
§ Purple Tiger = 'Jacpur' (F) — IDic LPlm MBri MBur MJon SApu

'Purpurtraum' (Ru) — WHCG
§ Pzazz = 'Poulzazz' (Min/Patio) — LStr MJon
§ Quaker Star = 'Dicperhaps' (F) — IDic
quatre saisons — See R. x damascena var. semperflorens
'Quatre Saisons Blanche Mousseuse' (DMo) — EBee EBls IHar
§ Queen Charlotte = 'Harubondee' (HT) — Last listed 1998
Queen Elizabeth — See R. 'The Queen Elizabeth'
§ Queen Mother = 'Korquemu' (Patio) ♀ — EBls ELan ENot GGre LGod LStr MAus MBri MFry MGan MJon MMat NPri SPer SWas
Queen Nefertiti® = 'Ausap' (S) — Last listed 1997
'Queen of Bedders' (Bb) — EBls
Queen of Denmark — See R. 'Königin von Dänemark'
Queen of Hearts — See R. 'Dame de Coeur'
Queen of the Belgians — See R. 'Reine des Belges'
Radiant™ = 'Benrad' (Min) — Last listed 1997
§ Radio Times = 'Aussal' (S) — IHar MAus MJon NPri
§ Radox Bouquet = 'Harmusky' (F) — GCoc
'Radway Sunrise' (S) — Last listed 1997
§ Ragtime = 'Poultime' (Cl) — EBee
'Rainbow' (T) — Last listed 1998
§ Rainbow Magic = 'Dicxplosion' — IDic
Rainbow's End™ = 'Savalife' (Min) — Last listed 1996
'Rambling Rector' (Ra) ♀ — More than 30 suppliers
§ 'Ramona' — EBls MAus WHCG WSHC
§ 'Raubritter' ('Macrantha' hybrid) — EBee EBls MAus MBri SPer SRPl SWCr WAct WHCG
'Ravenswood Village' (HT) — Last listed 1997
§ Ray of Hope = 'Cocnilly' (F) — GCoc GGre NEgg
§ Ray of Sunshine = 'Cocclare' (Patio) — GCoc LStr MBri MFry
'Raymond Chenault' (Cl) — MGan
§ Razzle Dazzle = 'Frybright' (F) — MFry
'Rebecca Claire' (HT) — MJon SApu
§ Reconciliation™ = 'Hartillery' (HT) — GGre SJus
§ Red Ace = 'Amruda' (Min) — EWTr MJon
'Red Beauty' (Min) — Last listed 1996
§ Red Bells® = 'Poulred' (Min/GC) — CGro EBls ENot MAus MGan MMat SPer SWCr WHCG WOVN
§ Red Blanket® = 'Intercell' (S/GC) ♀ — CGro EBls ENot EWTr GCoc IDic MAus MGan SPer SWCr WAct WOVN
§ Red Coat = 'Auscoat' (F) — MAus SWCr
§ Red Dagmar = 'Speruge' (S) — IDic LBuc
'Red Dandy' (F) — MGan
§ Red Devil® = 'Dicam' (HT) — GGre LPlm MAus MGan MJon NBat NRog
§ Red Dot® = 'Intermunder' (S/GC) — IDic WOVN
'Red Elf' (Min) — Last listed 1997
'Red Garnette' — See R. 'Garnette'
'Red Grootendorst' — See R. 'F.J. Grootendorst'
'Red Max Graf' — See R. Rote Max Graf = 'Kormax'
§ Red Meidiland® = 'Meineble' (GC) — WOVN
red moss — See R. 'Henri Martin'
Red New Dawn — See R. 'Etendard'
§ Red Rascal = 'Jacbed' (S/Patio) — IDic MBri MFry MJon SApu
red rose of Lancaster — See R. gallica var. officinalis

¶ Red Splendour = 'Davona' (F) — NRog

§ Red Sunblaze = 'Meirutral' (Min) — MJon WWeb

§ Red Trail = 'Interim' (S/GC) — IDic MJon WOVN

◆ Red Velvet — See *R.* Judi Dench = 'Peahunder'

'Red Wing' (S) — EBls MAus WAct

§ Redgold = 'Dicor' (F) — GGre MGan

§ Redouté = 'Auspale' (S) — CAbP EBrP EBre LBre MAus NPri SBre SJus SPer WWeb

§ Regal Red = 'Cocfoster' (S) — GCoc

§ Regensberg® = 'Macyou' (F/Patio) — CTri ENot GGre LPlm MAus MBri MFry MGan MJon MMat NRog SApu SPer

§ 'Reine des Belges' (Cl) — EBls

'Reine des Centifeuilles' (Ce) — EBls SFam

'Reine des Violettes' (HP) — CHad CPou EBls IHar LGod LStr MAus MHlr SApu SChu SJus SPer WAct WHCG WHow

'Reine Marie Henriette' (ClHT) — EBls

'Reine Victoria' (Bb) — EBls EBrP EBre EMFP EPfP IHar LBre LStr MAus MGan SBre SJus SPer SPla WAct

§ Remember Me® = 'Cocdestin' (HT) ♀ — EBrP EBre GCoc GGre LBre LGod LPlm LStr MBri MFry MGan MJon MMat NBat NRog SApu SBre SJus SPer SWCr

§ Remembrance = 'Harxampton' (F) — LStr MBri SApu SPer SWCr SWas

§ Rémy Martin® = 'Starqueli' (HT) — Last listed 1998

§ Renaissance = 'Harzart' (HT) — ECle EWTr GCoc GGre LStr MBur MFry MJon SJus SWCr SWas

'René André' (Ra) — CRHN EBee EBls MAus

'René d'Anjou' (CeMo) — EBls MAus

§ Repens Meidiland® = 'Meilontig' (S) — WOVN

'Rescht' — See *R.* 'De Rescht'

◆ 'Resland' — See *R.* Dreamland = 'Resland'

'Rest in Peace' (Patio/F) — GGre

'Rêve d'Or' (N) — EBee EBls EMFP MAus SPer WHow WSHC

'Réveil Dijonnais' (ClHT) — EBls MAus

'Reverend F. Page-Roberts' (HT) — EBls

'Rhodes Rose' (S) — Last listed 1998

§ Richard Buckley = 'Smitshort' (F) — MBur

§ x *richardii* — EBls MAus WAct WHCG

§ 'Rise 'n' Shine' (Min) — CGro LGod MGan

§ Rising Star™ = 'Hareast' (F) — SJus

'Ritter von Barmstede' (Cl) — MGan

'Rival de Paestum' (T) — EBls MAus

'River Gardens' — NPer

§ Road to Freedom = 'Franlac' (F) — Last listed 1998

§ Rob Roy® = 'Cocrob' (F) — GCoc MBur MGan SPer

'Robert le Diable' (Ce) — EBls MAus SPer WAct WHCG

'Robert Léopold' (Mo) — EBls

'Robin Hood' (HM) — EBls

§ Robin Redbreast® = 'Interrob' (Min/GC) — EBls IDic IHar MJon SApu SRPl WWeb

§ Robusta® = 'Korgosa' (Ru) — EBls MAus MJon WHow

§ Roche Centenary = 'Dicvintage' (Patio) — IDic

'Roger Lambelin' (HP) — EBls ENot MAus MMat

§ Romance® = 'Tanezamor' (S) — MJon MRav WWeb

§ Romantic Hedgerose = 'Korworm' (F/S) — ENot MMat

§ Rosabell® = 'Cocceleste' (F/Patio) — GCoc GGre LPlm MFry SApu

§ Rosalie Coral = 'Chewallop' (ClMin) — CGro MBri MJon SApu SJus

'Rosamini Gold' — See *R.* Golden Rosamini = 'Intergol'

§ Rosarium Uetersen® = 'Kortersen' (ClHT) — MJon WHow

§ Rose 2000 = 'Cocquestrum' (F) — GCoc NEgg

'Rose à Parfum de l'Haÿ' (Ru) — EBls

§ 'Rose d'Amour' (S) ♀ — EBls ISea MAus SJus WHCG

'Rose de Meaux' — See *R.* 'De Meaux'

'Rose de Meaux White' — See *R.* 'White de Meaux'

'Rose de Rescht' — See *R.* 'De Rescht'

'Rose des Maures' misapplied — See *R.* 'Sissinghurst Castle'

'Rose d'Hivers' (D) — EBls

'Rose d'Orsay' (S) — EBls

'Rose du Maître d'Ecole' — See *R.* 'Du Maître d'Ecole'

'Rose du Roi' (HP/DPo) — EBls MAus WAct WHCG

'Rose du Roi à Fleurs Pourpres' (HP) — EBls MAus

'Rose Edouard' (Bb) — EBls

§ Rose Gaujard® = 'Gaumo' (HT) — EBls GGre LGod LPlm MAus MBur MGan

'Rosecarpe' (HT) — Last listed 1998

§ 'Rose-Marie Viaud' (Ra) — CFee MAus SWCr WHCG

'Rosemary Foster' — SSpi

'Rosemary Gandy' (F) — MGan

§ Rosemary Harkness = 'Harrowbond' (HT) — EWTr LStr MJon MMat SApu SPer

'Rosemary Rose' (F) — EBls NRog SPer

'Rosenelfe' (F) — EBls

◆ 'Rosenmärchen' — See *R.* Pinocchio = 'Rosenmärchen'

'Roseraie de l'Haÿ' (Ru) ♀ — More than 30 suppliers

'Rosette Delizy' (T) — EBls

§ Rosie Larkin = 'Fryyippee' (S) — MFry

§ 'Rosina' (Min) — CBrm MGan

'Rosy Cheeks' (HT) — LPlm MBur MGan

§ Rosy Cushion® = 'Interall' (S/GC) ♀ — ENot EWTr GCoc IDic IHar MAus MGan MHlr SApu SPer SRPl SWCr WAct WHCG WOVN

§ Rosy Future = 'Harwaderox' (F/Patio) — MBri SApu SJus

Rosy Gem = 'Meiradia' (Min) — Last listed 1996

'Rosy Mantle' (Cl) — CB&S GCoc LPlm MGan SPer

§ Rote Max Graf® = 'Kormax' (GC/Ru) — EBls ENot WAct

'Rotkäppchen' (Poly) — Last listed 1996

'Roundelay' (HT) — EBls MAus

§ Roxburghe Rose = 'Cocember' (HT) — GCoc

*roxburghii* (S) — MMat SMad SRPl WAct WHCG

- f. *normalis* (S) — CFee EBls MAus

- 'Plena' — See *R.* roxburghii f. roxburghii

§ - f. *roxburghii* (d/S) — MAus

¶ 'Roy Glow' (F) — NBat

'Royal Albert Hall' (HT) — EBls GCoc

§ Royal Baby = 'Delbrad' (F/Min) — Last listed 1998

§ Royal Brompton Rose = 'Meivildo' (HT) — Last listed 1997

'Royal Conquest' (HT) — SJus

§ Royal Flush = 'Peapatio' (F/Patio) — MBri

'Royal Gold' (ClHT) — EBls ENot LPlm LStr MBri MFry MGan NPri NRog SWas WStI

'Royal Highness' (HT) — EBls MGan NRog

'Royal Occasion' (F)          SPer
§ Royal Romance® =            SJus
  'Rulis' (HT)
§ Royal Salute =              ENot MJon MMat NRog
  'Macros' (Min)
'Royal Smile' (HT)            EBls
Royal Sunblaze® =             Last listed 1996
  'Schobitet' (Min/Patio)
§ Royal Volunteer =           Last listed 1998
  'Cocdandy' (HT)
§ Royal William =             CGro CTri ELan GGre LGod LPlm
  'Korzaun' (HT) ♀            LStr MAus MBur MGan MJon
                             MMat NRog SApu SJus SPer SRPl
§ Royal Worcester =           MJon WGer
  'Trobroy' (S)
'Rubens' (HP)                 EBls
§ rubiginosa ♀               CB&S CKin CSam EBee EBls ENot
                             EWFC GChr GPoy ILis LHol
                             MAus MMat NFla SFam SPer WAct
                             WMou
rubra                         See R. gallica
rubrifolia                    See R. glauca
 - 'Carmenetta'               See R. 'Carmenetta'
◆ 'Rubrispa'                  See R. Bright Spark = 'Rubrispa'
'Rubrotincta'                 See R. 'Hebe's Lip'
rubus (Ra)                    CRHN MAus WAct
 - SF 579 (Ra)                ISea
§ Ruby Anniversary =          CTri LRHS LStr MBri MFry SJus
  'Harbonny' (Patio)          SWCr
§ Ruby Celebration =          GGre LRHS MBri MJon
  'Peawinner' (F)
'Ruby Pendant' (Min)          Last listed 1997
'Ruby Wedding' (HT)           More than 30 suppliers
◆ 'Rufin'                     See R. Mini Metro = 'Rufin'
'Ruga' (Ra)                   EBls MAus
◆ 'Rugolda'                   See R. Golden Days = 'Rugolda'
rugosa (Ru)                   CAgr EBee EWTr GChr ISea LBuc
                             LHol MAus MBri NWea SPlb SWCr
                             WStI
 - 'Alba' (Ru) ♀             CB&S EBee EBls ECGP ELan EMFP
                             ENot GGre LBuc LStr MAus MBri
                             MMat NRoo NWea SJus SPer WAct
                             WHen WOVN
 - var. kamtschatica          See R. rugosa var. ventenatiana
 - 'Rubra' (Ru) ♀            CB&S CTri GGre LBuc MFry
                             MMat NRoo SPer WAct WHen
 - 'Scabrosa'                 See R. 'Scabrosa'
§ - var. ventenatiana (Ru)    Last listed 1996
'Rugosa Atropurpurea' (Ru)    NRog
'Rugspin' (Ru)                WAct
◆ 'Rugul'                     See R. Golden Penny = 'Rugul'
'Ruhm von Steinfurth' (HP)    EBls
◆ 'Ruiblun'                   See R. Blue Peter = 'Ruiblun'
◆ 'Ruico'                     See R. Fresco = 'Ruico'
◆ 'Ruifaro'                   See R. Favorite Rosamini =
                             'Ruifaro'
◆ 'Ruiflami'                  See R. Flaming Rosamini =
                             'Ruiflami'
◆ 'Ruigerdan'                 See R. Little Marvel = 'Ruigerdan'
◆ 'Ruilanca'                  See R. Lancashire Life =
                             'Ruilanca'
◆ 'Ruista'                    See R. Estima = 'Ruista'
◆ 'Rulis'                     See R. Royal Romance = 'Rulis'
Rumba® (F)                    Last listed 1996
◆ 'Runatru'                   See R. Invincible = 'Runatru'
§ Running Maid® =             MAus WAct
  'Lenramp' (S/GC)
§ Rush® = 'Lenmobri' (S)      MAus
§ Rushing Stream =            MAus
  'Austream' (GC)
'Ruskin' (HPxRu)              EBls MAus

'Russelliana' (Ra)            CRHN EBls EMFP MAus SFam
                             WAct WHCG WRha
§ Rutland = 'Poulshine'       ENot MMat SRPl WOVN
  (Min/GC)
◆ 'Rutrulo'                   See R. Yorkshire Bank = 'Rutrulo'
◆ 'Sabbelief'                 See R. Artful Dodger = 'Sabbelief'
◆ 'Sabbyron'                  See R. Oliver Twist = 'Sabbyron'
◆ 'Sabchurchill'              See R. Sweet Bouquet =
                             'Sabchurchill'
'Sadler's Wells' (S)          EBls
'Safrano' (T)                 EBls
§ Saint Boniface =            ENot MMat
  'Kormatt' (F/Patio)
'Saint Catherine' (Ra)        CFee
§ Saint Cecilia® =            CSam EBee ELan MAus MBNS
  'Ausmit' (S)                MHlr MJon SJus
§ Saint Christopher =         SJus
  'Harcogent' (HT)
§ Saint Dunstan's Rose =      MBri MJon SApu SPer
  'Kirshru' (S)
Saint Helena =                Last listed 1997
  'Canlish' (F)
§ Saint John™ =              GGre
  'Harbilbo' (F)
Saint John's rose             See R. x richardii
Saint Mark's rose             See R. 'Rose d'Amour'
'Saint Nicholas' (D)          EBls MAus WHCG
'Saint Prist de Breuze' (Ch)  EBls
§ Saint Swithun = 'Auswith' (S) EMFP GQui MAus MJon SWCr
'Salet' (DPMo)                EBee EBls MAus WHCG
salictorum                    Last listed 1996
¶ Salita® = 'Kormorlet' (Cl)  MJon
Sally Holmes® (S) ♀          CHad EBls ENot GCoc IHar MAus
                             MBri MFry MGan MJon MMat
                             SApu SWCr WAct WHCG
§ Sally's Rose = 'Canrem' (HT) EBee GGre SApu SJus
§ Salmo = 'Poulnoev' (Patio)  MBri MJon MMat
'Salmon' (ClMin)              Last listed 1997
§ Samaritan = 'Harverag' (HT) MAus SApu SJus
◆ 'Sancol'                    See R. Edward Colston = 'Sancol'
sancta                        See R. x richardii
◆ 'Sandaya'                   See R. Enhance = 'Sandaya'
'Sander's White Rambler'      CHad CRHN EBee EBls EBrP EBre
  (Ra) ♀                     EMFP LBre LHol MAus MGan
                             MJon NRog SBre SMad SPer SRPl
                             WAct WHCG WHow WWeb
'Sandringham                  EBls
  Centenary' (HT)
'Sanguinea'                   See R. x odorata Sanguinea
                             Group
◆ 'Sanlilac'                  See R. Lilac Airs = 'Sanlilac'
◆ 'Sanmed'                    See R. Ice Fairy = 'Sanmed'
◆ 'Sanolence'                 See R. Benevolence = 'Sanolence'
◆ 'Sanphyllis'                See R. John Hughes = 'Sanphyllis'
◆ 'Sanroi'                    See R. Corsair = 'Sanroi'
◆ 'Sanrozo'                   See R. Esperanto Jubileo =
                             'Sanrozo'
◆ 'Sanspic'                   See R. Apricot Spice = 'Sanspic'
◆ 'Santor'                    See R. Red Brigand = 'Santor'
§ Sarabande = 'Meihand' (F)   MGan
◆ Sarah® (HT)                 See R. Jardins de Bagatelle =
                             'Meimafris'
Sarah Jo = 'Mehrex' (HT)      Last listed 1997
§ Sarah Robinson =            Last listed 1998
  'Trobinette' (Min)
'Sarah van Fleet' (Ru)        CGro EBee EBls EBrP EBre ENot
                             GCoc LBre LStr MAus MFry MGan
                             MHlr MMat NRog SApu SBre
                             SFam SPer WAct WOVN WWeb
Sarah, Duchess of York        See R. Sunseeker = 'Dicracer'
Satchmo® (F)                  Last listed 1998

◆ 'Savachild'  See *R.* Child's Play = 'Savachild'
◆ 'Savacloud' (Min)  See *R.* White Cloud = 'Savacloud'
◆ 'Savadee'  See *R.* Dee Bennett = 'Savadee'
◆ 'Savahalo'  See *R.* Golden Halo = 'Savahalo'
◆ 'Savahold'  See *R.* Behold = 'Savahold'
◆ 'Savamark'  See *R.* Apricot Sunblaze = 'Savamark'
◆ 'Savaspir'  See *R.* High Spirits = 'Savaspir'
◆ 'Savathree'  See *R.* Acey Deucy = 'Savathree'
◆ 'Savor'  See *R.* Little Jackie = 'Savor'
§ Savoy Hotel = 'Harvintage' (HT) ♀  CTri EBee GCoc GGre LGod LStr MAus MFry MGan MJon MMat SApu SJus SPer SWCr
§ 'Scabrosa' (Ru) ♀  EBls EMFP GCoc MAus MGan MJon MMat WAct WHCG WOVN
Scarlet Fire  See *R.* 'Scharlachglut'
§ Scarlet Gem® = 'Meido' (Min)  ELan MGan
Scarlet Glow  See *R.* 'Scharlachglut'
§ Scarlet Meidiland® = 'Meikrotal' (S/GC)  MGan WOVN
§ Scarlet Patio = 'Kortingle' (Patio)  ENot MMat
'Scarlet Pimpernel'  See *R.* Scarlet Gem = 'Meido'
§ Scarlet Queen Elizabeth® = 'Dicel' (F)  CB&S CGro EBls GGre MBur NPri WStI
'Scarlet Showers' (Cl)  MGan
Scarletta (Min)  Last listed 1998
'Scented Air' (F)  MGan SPer
§ Scent-sation = 'Fryromeo' (HT)  MFry SApu
§ Sceptre'd Isle™ = 'Ausland'  CAbP MAus SPer SWCr WWeb
§ 'Scharlachglut' (ClS) ♀  EBls ELan ENot MAus MGan MMat NFla SApu SPer SWCr WAct WHCG WOVN WSHC
Scherzo® = 'Meipuma' (F)  Last listed 1996
* *schmidtiana*  CFee
'Schneelicht' (Ru)  EBls MAus
Schneewittchen  See *R.* Iceberg = 'Korbin'
§ 'Schneezwerg' (Ru) ♀  EBee EBls ELan ENot GCoc IHar IOrc MAus MBri MGan MJon MMat SApu SPer SRPl SWas WAct WHCG WOVN
'Schoolgirl' (Cl)  CB&S CGro EBee EBls EBrP EBre ELan ENot GChr GGre LBre LPlm LStr MBri MFry MGan MJon MMat NRog MAus SBre SPer SSea WWeb
'Scintillation' (S/GC)  EBls MAus
Scotch rose  See *R.* pimpinellifolia
Scotch yellow (PiH)  See *R.* x harisonii 'Williams' Double Yellow'
'Scotch Yellow' (HT)  MJon
§ Scotland's Trust = 'Coclands' (HT)  Last listed 1998
§ Scottish Special = 'Cocdapple' (Min/Patio)  GCoc MBri
◆ 'Scriveo'  See *R.* Albert Weedall = 'Scriveo'
◆ 'Scrivluv'  See *R.* Baby Love = 'Scrivluv' (yellow) (Min/Patio)
◆ 'Scrivo'  See *R.* Pretty Lady = 'Scrivo'
Sea Foam® (S)  Last listed 1996
Sea of Fire = 'Feuermeer' (F)  Last listed 1996
'Sea Pearl' (F)  ENot MGan
'Seagull' (Ra) ♀  EBee EBls ELan EMFP EWTr GGre LGod LStr MAus MGan MHlr MJon NBus NPri NRog SPer SRPl SWCr WAct WGer WHCG
◆ 'Seakis'  See *R.* Kiss 'n' Tell = 'Seakis'
◆ 'Sealady'  See *R.* Lady in Red = 'Sealady'

¶ Seale Peach  SSea
§ 'Sealing Wax' (*moyesii* hybrid)  EBls MAus MJon WAct
◆ 'Searodney'  See *R.* Admirable = 'Searodney'
Seaspray = 'Macnew' (Min/Patio)  Last listed 1996
§ Selfridges = 'Korpriwa' (HT)  MMat NBat NRog
'Semiplena'  See *R.* x *alba* 'Alba Semiplena'
*sempervirens* (Ra)  Last listed 1996
'Sénateur Amic' (Cl)  EBls
◆ 'Senator Burda'  See *R.* Spirit of Youth = 'Meivestal'
Sentimental® = 'Poultal' (HT)  Last listed 1996
§ *serafinoi*  Last listed 1997
*sericea* (S)  CFee MAus MBal WHCG
– BC 9355 (S)  Last listed 1998
– 'Heather Muir'  See *R.* 'Heather Muir' (*sericea* hybrid)
* – var. *morrisonensis* B&SWJ 1549  Last listed 1998
§ – subsp. *omeiensis* f.*pteracantha* (S)  CHad EBee EBls ELan EMFP ENot MAus MGan MMat NRog SApu SPer WAct WOVN
◆ – 'Red Wing'  See *R.* 'Red Wing'
– SF 505  ISea
* – SF 95049  ISea
'Serratipetala' (Ch)  Last listed 1996
§ *setigera*  EBls MAus
*setipoda*  EBls MAus WAct WHCG WWat MBur
'Seven Seas' (F)  MBur
Seven Sisters rose  See *R.* multiflora 'Grevillei'
§ Sexy Rexy® = 'Macrexy' (F) ♀  CGro EBrP EBre ELan GGre IHar LBre LStr MAus MBri MFry MGan MJon NBat NRog SBre SJus SPer SWCr WWeb
§ 'Shailer's White Moss' (CeMo) ♀  EBls MAus MGan MMat NRog SFam SJus SRPl WHCG
§ Sharifa Asma® = 'Ausreef' (S)  EBee EBrP EBre ENot IHar LBre LStr MAus MHlr MJon MMat NPri SBre SJus SPer WAct
'Sheelagh Baird' (S/Poly)  SWCr
Sheer Delight = 'Harwazzle' (Patio)  Last listed 1997
§ Sheila's Perfume = 'Harsherry' (HT/F)  EBee GCoc GGre LPlm LStr MGan MJon SApu SJus SPer SWCr
'Sheldon'  Last listed 1996
'Shepherd's Delight' (F)  MGan
*sherardii*  Last listed 1998
§ Sheri Anne = 'Morsheri' (Min)  MAus
§ Shine On = 'Dictalent' (Patio)  COtt GCoc IDic MBri MFry MJon SJus WWeb
§ Shirley Spain = 'Cocharod' (F)  GCoc
§ Shocking Blue® = 'Korblue' (F)  EBee ENot LPlm MGan MJon MMat SPer
§ Shona = 'Dicdrum' (F)  IDic
'Shot Silk' (HT)  EBls GCoc MAus MBur MGan
§ Shrewsbury Show = 'Fryshrewby' (HT)  Last listed 1998
'Shropshire Lass' (S)  MAus SPer SWCr
§ Sightsaver = 'Fryaffair' (HT)  MFry SPer
§ Silver Anniversary = 'Poulari' (HT)  EBee ELan EPfP GGre LGod LRHS LStr MAus MFry MGan MJon MMat NEgg SApu SCoo SJus
'Silver Charm' (F)  Last listed 1996

Silver Jubilee® (HT) ♀ — CB&S CGro EBls EBrP EBre ELan ENot EWTr GCoc GGre LBre LGod LPlm LRHS LStr MAus MBri MBur MFry MGan MJon MMat NBat NRog SApu SBre SPer SWas WWeb

'Silver Lining' (HT) — EBls MAus MBur SWCr

'Silver Moon' (Cl) — CRHN EBls MAus

'Silver Tips' (Min) — MAus

'Silver Wedding' (HT) — EBls EBrP EBre GCoc GGre IHar LBre LPlm LRHS MAus MBur MFry MGan MJon NRog SApu SBre SPer SRPl SWCr WOVN

§ Simba = 'Korbelma' (HT) — EBee MGan MMat SApu SJus

§ Simon Robinson = 'Trobwich' (Min/GC) — MJon

♦ 'Simway' — See *R.* Jenny Charlton = 'Simway'

§ Singin' in the Rain = 'Macivy' (F) — MFry MJon SApu

♦ *sinowilsonii* — See *R. longicuspis* var. *sinowilsonii*

'Sir Cedric Morris' (Ra) — EBls ELan SWas

§ Sir Clough = 'Ausclough' (S) — MAus

§ Sir Edward Elgar = 'Ausprima' (S) — EBls EBrP EBre LBre LStr MAus MJon NPri SBre SWCr

'Sir Frederick Ashton' (HT) — EBls

'Sir Joseph Paxton' (Bb) — MAus

'Sir Lancelot' (F) — MGan

§ Sir Neville Marriner = 'Glanmusic' (F) — NBat

§ Sir Walter Raleigh® = 'Ausspry' (S) — MAus MBri

§ Sir William Leech = 'Hortropic' (HT) — NBat

§ 'Sissinghurst Castle' (G) — EBls SBid

'Sleepy' (Poly) — MGan

§ Smarty® = 'Intersmart' (S/GC) — EBls IDic IHar MAus MGan MJon SApu SPer WAct WOVN

♦ 'Smitfirst' — See *R.* Summer Sérénade = 'Smitfirst'

♦ 'Smitling' — See *R.* Lady Taylor = 'Smitling'

♦ 'Smitshort' — See *R.* Richard Buckley = 'Smitshort'

§ Smooth Angel = 'Hadangel' (HT) — CGro ELan LGod LStr MGan NPri SApu

§ Smooth Lady = 'Hadlady' (HT) — CGro ELan LGod LStr MGan NPri

§ Smooth Melody = 'Hadmelody' (F) — MBri SPer

§ Smooth Perfume = 'Hadperfume' (HT) — MBri

§ Smooth Prince = 'Hadprince' (HT) — ELan LGod LStr MBri MGan

§ Smooth Romance = 'Hadromance' (HT) — LStr MBri MGan

§ Smooth Satin = 'Hadsatin' (HT) — Last listed 1998

§ Smooth Velvet = 'Hadvelvet' (HT) — CGro LGod MGan NPri

'Sneezy' (Poly) — MGan

§ Snow Carpet® = 'Maccarpe' (Min/GC) ♀ — CBrm EBls ENot GCoc MAus MFry MJon MMat WAct

'Snow Dwarf' — See *R.* 'Schneezwerg'

§ Snow Goose = 'Auspom' (Cl/S) — MJon

'Snow Queen' — See *R.* 'Frau Karl Druschki'

§ Snow Sunblaze™ = 'Meigovin' (Min) — WWeb

§ Snow White = 'Landisney' (HT) — MJon

§ Snowball = 'Macangeli' (Min/GC) — MJon

'Snowdon' (Ru) — EBls MAus

'Snowdrift' — WHCG

§ Snowdrop = 'Amoru' (Min/Patio) — MFry

'Snowflake' (Ra) — WHCG

§ Snowgoose = 'Barshifle' (F) — MAus

'Snowline' (F) — MGan SPer

'Soldier Boy' (Cl) — WHCG

§ Solitaire® = 'Macyefre' (HT) — MBri MJon SApu WWeb

§ 'Sombreuil' (ClT) — CHad EBee EBls EMFP MAus MHlr MRav SBid SChu SFam SJus SPer SPla SWCr WAct WHCG WHow

♦ Sonia — See *R.* Sweet Promise = 'Meihelvet'

'Sophie's Perpetual' (ClCh) — EBls ENot MAus MGan MHlr MMat SJus SPer SWCr WAct WHCG

§ Sophy's Rose = 'Auslot' (S) — MAus WWeb

*soulieana* (Ra/S) ♀ — EBls MAus MMat WAct WCot WKif

'Soupert et Notting' (DPoMo) — EBls MAus MHlr SBid SPer

§ 'Southampton' (F) ♀ — EBee EBls EWTr GGre IHar LStr MAus MGan NRog SApu SPer

'Souvenir d'Alphonse Lavallée' (ClHP) — EBls WHCG

'Souvenir de Brod' — See *R.* 'Erinnerung an Brod'

'Souvenir de Claudius Denoyel' (ClHT) ♀ — EBee EBls MAus NRog SMad SPer SSoC

'Souvenir de François Gaulain' (T) — EBls

'Souvenir de Jeanne Balandreau' (HP) — EBls

'Souvenir de la Malmaison' (ClBb) — See *R.* 'Climbing Souvenir de la Malmaison'

'Souvenir de la Malmaison' (Bb) — EBls EBrP EBre ENot EWTr GCoc IHar IOrc LBre MAus MGan MHlr MMat SBre SJus SPer SWCr WAct WWeb

'Souvenir de Madame Léonie Viennot' (ClT) — CPou EBls EHol MAus

'Souvenir de Philémon Cochet' (Ru) — EBls MAus

'Souvenir de Pierre Vibert' (DPMo) — EBls

'Souvenir de Saint Anne's' (Bb) ♀ — CHad EBls EWTr IHar MAus SWCr WAct WHCG

'Souvenir d'Elise Vardon' (T) — EBls

'Souvenir di Castagneto' (HP) — MRav

'Souvenir du Docteur Jamain' (ClHP) — CHad CPou EBee EBls LStr MAus MHlr MMat SFam SJus SPer SWCr WAct WHCG

'Souvenir du Président Carnot' (HT) — EBls MAus

'Souvenir d'un Ami' (T) — EBls

sp. CDC 262 — Last listed 1996

*spaldingii* — See *R. nutkana* var. *hispida*

§ Spangles = 'Ganspa' (F) — MBri MBur MGan

'Spanish Beauty' — See *R.* 'Madame Grégoire Staechelin'

§ Sparkling Scarlet = 'Meihati' (ClF) — EBrP EBre ELan LBre LPlm MGan SBre

'Sparrieshoop' (ClS) — Last listed 1997

§ Special Occasion = 'Fryyoung' (HT) — GCoc MFry SApu

'Spectabilis' (Ra) — EBls MAus SFam WHCG

Spek's Centennial (F) — See *R.* Singin' in the Rain = 'Macivy' (F)

'Spek's Yellow' (HT) — EBls

♦ Spellbound — See *R.* Garden News = 'Poulrim'

'Spencer' misapplied — See *R.* 'Enfant de France'
◆ 'Sperien' — See *R.* Fairy Queen = 'Sperien'
◆ 'Speruge' — See *R.* Red Dagmar = 'Speruge'
◆ 'Spevu' — See *R.* Lovely Fairy = 'Spevu'
*spinosissima* — See *R. pimpinellifolia*
§ Spirit of Youth = — SApu
  'Meivestal' (HT)
§ 'Splendens' (Ra) — CHad EBls ELan MAus SLPl WAct
'Spong' (G) — EBls MAus WAct
§ St Tiggywinkles = — ENot MMat
  'Korbasren' (GC)
§ 'Stacey Sue' (Min) ♀ — Last listed 1995
§ Stacey's Star = — Last listed 1998
  'Horstacey' (Patio)
§ 'Stanwell Perpetual' (PiH) — CSam EBee EBls EMFP ENot GCoc
   — LStr MAus MHlr MMat NFla SApu
   — SPer SWCr WAct WHCG WOVN
   — WWeb
Star Child® = — Last listed 1997
  'Dicmadder' (F)
'Star of Waltham' (HP) — WHCG
§ Stardust® = — GGre MJon
  'Peavandyke' (Patio/F)
§ Starina® = 'Megabi' (Min) — MGan
§ Starlight Express = — SCoo SPer
  'Trobstar' (Cl)
§ 'Starqueli' — See *R.* Rémy Martin = 'Starqueli'
'Stars 'n' Stripes' (Min) — LGod LPlm MAus MFry
◆ 'Stebigpu' — See *R.* Big Purple = 'Stebigpu'
Stella (HT) — EBls MGan
*stellata* — MAus
§ - var. *mirifica* — EBls MAus MGan MMat
'Stephanie Diane' (HT) — LPlm
Sterling Silver™ (HT) — EBls LStr MAus MGan
§ Strawberry Fayre = — COtt EBrP EBre GCoc LBre MFry
  'Arowillip' (Min/Patio) — MJon NBat SBre WWeb
'Strawberry Ice' (F) — MJon
*subcanina* — Last listed 1998
*subcollina* — Last listed 1998
§ Sue Lawley = — MGan MJon
  'Macsplash' (F)
Sue Ryder® = 'Harlino' (F) — Last listed 1997
§ Suffolk = 'Kormixal' (S/GC) — EBee EBrP EBre ELan ENot GCoc
   — LBre LPlm LStr MAus MGan MHlr
   — MMat NPri SApu SBre SJus SPer
   — WAct WHow WLRN WOVN WWeb
*suffulta* — See *R. arkansana* var. *suffulta*
§ Suma = 'Harsuma' (GC) ♀ — EPfP GCoc GGre LGod MFry
   — MJon SApu SJus WAct WOVN
§ Summer Breeze = — ENot MMat
  'Korelasting' (Cl)
§ Summer Dream = — LStr MAus MFry SApu SJus SWCr
  'Jacshe' (HT)
§ Summer Fragrance = — GCoc GGre MGan
  'Tanfudermos' (HT)
Summer Holiday® (HT) — MBur SPer
§ Summer Lady® = — MBri MBur MJon SApu
  'Tanydal' (HT)
§ Summer Love = — IHar MJon
  'Franluv' (F)
'Summer Palace' (Patio) — ECle
§ Summer Sérénade® = — Last listed 1998
  'Smitfirst' (F)
§ Summer Snow = — MJon
  'Weopop' (Patio)
'Summer Sunrise' (GC) — EBls
'Summer Sunset' (GC) — EBls
§ Summer Wine = — EBee ENot MBri MGan MJon
  'Korizont' (Cl) ♀ — MMat SApu SJus SPer
§ Sun Hit™ = 'Poulsun' (Patio) — ENot GGre LGod MMat MRav

§ 'Sunblaze' — See *R.* Orange Sunblaze = 'Meijikatar'
§ Sunblest = 'Landora' (HT) — CGro CTri GGre LPlm MBur MFry
   — NRog SWCr
§ Sunderland Supreme = — NBat
  'Nossun' (HT)
Sunmaid® (Min) — MJon
§ Sunny Sunblaze™ = — SJus
  'Meiponal' (Min)
§ Sunrise = 'Kormarter' (Cl) — EBee GCoc MBur MFry MJon
   — MMat SApu WGer
§ Sunseeker = 'Dicracer' — EPfP GGre IDic LGod MJon
  (F/Patio)
§ Sunset Boulevard = — EBee ENot GGre LGod LPlm LStr
  'Harbabble' (F) — MAus MBri MFry MJon NBat SApu
   — SCoo SJus SPer SWCr SWas WWeb
§ Sunset Song = — GCoc
  'Cocasun' (HT)
'Sunshine' (Poly) — MGan
'Sunsilk' (F) — Last listed 1998
§ Super Elfin = — MMat
  'Helkleger' (Ra)
¶ Super Excelsa® = — MGan
  'Helexa' (Ra)
§ Super Fairy = — MMat
  'Helsufair' (Ra)
§ Super Sparkle = — SApu
  'Helhein' (Ra)
§ Super Star® = — CGro EBls EBrP EBre ENot IHar
  'Tanorstar' (HT) — LBre LPlm LStr MAus MGan MJon
   — MMat SBre WWeb
'Super Sun' (HT) — SWCr
§ Surf Rider (S) — Last listed 1997
'Surpasse Tout' (G) — EBls MAus WHCG
§ 'Surpassing Beauty of — EBls WHCG
  Woolverstone' (ClHP)
§ Surrey = 'Korlanum' (GC) ♀ — EBee EBrP EBre ELan ENot GCoc
   — LBre LFis LGod LPlm LStr MAus
   — MFry MGan MHlr MJon MMat
   — SApu SBre SJus SPer SPla WAct
   — WOVN WStI
§ Susan Hampshire = — EBls MGan
  'Meinatac' (HT)
§ Susan = 'Poulsue' (S) — EBee
§ Sussex = 'Poulave' (GC) — EBrP EBre ENot GCoc LBre LPlm
   — LStr MBur MFry MGan MHlr MJon
   — MMat SApu SBre SJus SPer SPla
   — SWCr SWas WHow WOVN
'Sutter's Gold' (HT) — EBls MAus MBur MGan
§ Swan® = 'Auswhite' (S) — MAus MJon
'Swan Lake' (Cl) — EBee EBls EBrP EBre ELan ENot
   — GGre LBre LGod MAus MBur
   — MFry MGan MHlr MMat SBre SPer
   — SRPl SWCr WWeb
'Swanland Gem' (F) — Last listed 1997
§ Swany® = 'Meiburenac' — EBls ELan MAus MGan SApu SPer
  (Min/GC) ♀ — SRPl WAct WHCG WOVN
§ Sweet Bouquet = — MBur
  'Sabchurchill' (HT)
§ Sweet Dream = — CGro EBrP EBre ELan GCoc GGre
  'Fryminicot' (Patio) ♀ — LBre LGod LPlm LStr MAus MBri
   — MBur MFry MGan MJon NBat
   — NRog SApu SBre SJus SPer SWCr
   — WOVN WWeb
'Sweet Fairy' (Min) — LPlm
'Sweet Honesty' (Min) — Last listed 1996
§ Sweet Juliet® = 'Ausleap' (S) — CAbP EBee EBls EBrP EBre IHar
   — LBre LGod LPlm MAus MBri MHlr
   — MJon NBat SApu SBre SJus SPer
   — WAct WHow WOVN

§ Sweet Magic =    CGro EBrP EBre ENot GGre IDic
  'Dicmagic' (Min/Patio) ♀    IHar LBre LGod LPlm LStr MBri
     MFry MGan MJon MMat NBat
     SApu SBre SJus WWeb

§ Sweet Memories =    COtt CTri EBrP EBre EPfP GCoc
  'Whamemo' (Patio)    LBre LStr MJon SBre SCoo SPla
     SWCr WGer

§ Sweet Nell = 'Cocavoter' (F)    Last listed 1997

§ Sweet Petite =    MFry
  'Fryxquisite' (Patio)

§ Sweet Promise =    MGan
  'Meihelvet' (GC)

'Sweet Repose' (F)    MAus MGan

Sweet Symphony (Min)    EBrP EBre ENot LBre MBri MFry
     MJon SBre

¶ Sweet Thoughts (Patio)    LPlm

'Sweet Velvet' (F)    MGan

'Sweet Wonder' (Patio)    COtt

N Sweetheart =    GCoc GGre MGan SWCr
  'Cocapeer' (HT)

*sweginzowii*    GCal MAus MMat

- 'Macrocarpa'    EBls

'Sydonie' (HP)    EBls

Sympathie® (ClHT)    IHar LPlm MFry MGan MJon
     MMat SJus SPer

§ Symphony® = 'Auslett' (S)    MJon WAct

*taiwanensis*    CFil

¶ *taiwanianus* ETE 77    WPGP

♦ 'Talchelsea'    See *R.* Chelsea Belle = 'Talchelsea'

♦ 'Talfairhope'    See *R.* Fairhope = 'Talfairhope'

'Talisman' (HT)    EBls

§ Tall Story® =    EBls IDic MJon SApu WHCG
  'Dickooky' (GC/F) ♀    WOVN

'Tallyho' (HT)    EBls

§ Tambourine = 'Hardolly' (F)    GCoc

§ Tamora = 'Austamora' (S)    MAus

♦ 'Tanal'    See *R.* Allotria = 'Tanal'

♦ 'Tanamola'    See *R.* The Dove = 'Tanamola'

♦ 'Tanba'    See *R.* Baby Masquerade = 'Tanba'

♦ 'Tandereza'    See *R.* Beaulieu = 'Tandereza'

♦ 'Tanduft'    See *R.* Fragrant Gold = 'Tanduft'

♦ 'Taneiglat'    See *R.* Nostalgie = 'Taneiglat'

♦ 'Tanelaigib'    See *R.* Abigaile = 'Tanelaigib'

♦ 'Tanellelog'    See *R.* Golden Quill = 'Tanellelog'

♦ 'Tanellis'    See *R.* Fragrant Cloud = 'Tanellis'

♦ 'Tanelorak'    See *R.* Barkarole = 'Tanelorak'

♦ 'Tanezamor'    See *R.* Romance = 'Tanezamor'

♦ 'Tanfifum'    See *R.* Blue Parfum = 'Tanfifum'

♦ 'Tanfudermos'    See *R.* Summer Fragrance = 'Tanfudermos'

§ Tango = 'Macfirwal' (F) ♀    LPlm MBri MJon NRog

♦ 'Tangostar'    See *R.* Climbing Super Star = 'Tangostar'

♦ 'Tanija'    See *R.* Janina = 'Tanija'

♦ 'Taninaso'    See *R.* Harewood = 'Taninaso'

♦ 'Tanklawi'    See *R.* Lavinia = 'Tanklawi'

♦ 'Tanky'    See *R.* Whisky Mac = 'Tanky'

♦ 'Tanlarpost'    See *R.* Polar Star = 'Tanlarpost'

♦ 'Tanledolg'    See *R.* Goldjuwel = 'Tanledolg'

♦ 'Tanlilida'    See *R.* Dalli Dalli = 'Tanlilida'

♦ 'Tanmeda'    See *R.* Diadem = 'Tanmeda'

♦ 'Tanmirson'    See *R.* Broadlands = 'Tanmirson'

♦ 'Tanmurse'    See *R.* Blenheim = 'Tanmurse'

♦ 'Tannacht'    See *R.* Blue Moon = 'Tannacht'

♦ 'Tanolg'    See *R.* Miss Harp = 'Tanolg'

♦ 'Tanolokip'    See *R.* Piccolo = 'Tanolokip'

♦ 'Tanope'    See *R.* Tip Top = 'Tanope'

♦ 'Tanorstar'    See *R.* Super Star = 'Tanorstar'

♦ 'Tanotax'    See *R.* Chatsworth = 'Tanotax'

♦ 'Tanpika'    See *R.* Piroschka = 'Tanpika'

♦ 'Tanrowise'    See *R.* Wimi = 'Tanrowise'

♦ 'Tanrupeza'    See *R.* Leeds Castle = 'Tanrupeza'

♦ 'Tanryrandy'    See *R.* Cherry Brandy '85® = 'Tanryrandy'

♦ 'Tantasch'    See *R.* Golden Treasure = 'Tantasch'

♦ 'Tantern'    See *R.* Gold Star = 'Tantern'

♦ 'Tantide'    See *R.* Glad Tidings = 'Tantide'

♦ 'Tanydal'    See *R.* Summer Lady = 'Tanydal'

Tapis Jaune®    See *R.* Golden Penny = 'Rugul'

§ 'Tausendschön' (Ra)    EBls

'Tea Rambler' (Ra)    EBls

§ Tear Drop = 'Dicomo'    IDic LStr MFry MGan MJon SApu
  (Min/Patio)    SPer SWCr

¶ Teasing George    WWeb

§ Ted Gore = 'Hormislac' (F)    NBat

♦ 'Teeny'    See *R.* Teeny Weeny = 'Teeny'

§ Teeny Weeny =    MJon
  'Teeny' (Min)

Telford's Promise =    Last listed 1996
  'Chewoz' (GC/S)

'Telstar' (F)    MGan

'Temple Bells' (ClMin/GC)    EBls MAus NRog

Tender Loving Care =    Last listed 1997
  'Bospeabay' (F)

'Tenerife' (HT)    WStI

Tennessee™ =    Last listed 1996
  'Kintenn' (Min)

§ Tequila Sunrise =    CTri GGre IDic IHar LPlm LStr
  'Dicobey' (HT) ♀    MBri MBur MFry MGan MJon
     MMat NRog SApu SJus SPer

§ Terracotta =    MJon
  'Meicobius' (HT)

'Texas Centennial' (HT)    EBls

§ Thaïs = 'Memaj' (HT)    EBls

'Thalia' (Ra)    MAus

§ Thank You =    GGre MJon SWCr
  'Chesdeep' (Patio)

§ The Alexandra Rose =    CSam MAus SWCr WHow
  'Ausday' (S)

'The Bishop' (CexG)    EBls MAus

'The Bride' (T)    EBls

§ The Cheshire Regiment =    MFry
  'Fryzebedee' (HT)

§ The Children's Rose =    SApu
  'Meilivar' (F)

'The Colwyn Rose'    See *R.* Colwyn Bay

§ The Compass Rose =    ENot MMat SApu SPer
  'Korwisco' (S)

§ The Compassionate    SJus
  Friends = 'Harzodiac' (S)

§ The Countryman® =    CAbP EBrP EBre IHar LBre MAus
  'Ausman' (S)    MFry MHlr NPri SBre SJus

§ The Coxswain =    GCoc
  'Cocadilly' (HT)

§ The Daily Telegraph =    Last listed 1996
  'Peahigh' (F)

§ The Dark Lady =    CSam EBrP EBre IHar LBre MAus
  'Ausbloom' (S)    MBri MJon NBus NPri SBre SJus
     SWCr WWeb

'The Doctor' (HT)    EBls MAus MGan SWas

§ The Dove = 'Tanamola' (F)    MGan

'The Ednaston Rose' (Cl)    SRPl WHCG

§ 'The Fairy' (Poly) ♀    CHad EBee EBls EBrP EBre ELan
     ENot EPfP GGre IOrc LBre LGod
     LPlm LStr MAus MBur MFry MGan
     MHlr MJon MMat NRog SApu
     SBre SPer WAct WHCG WOVN
     WSHC

§ The Flower Arranger = 'Fryjam' (F)    MJon

'The Garland' (Ra) ♀    EBee EBls MAus MHlr SFam SPer SPla WAct WHCG

§ The Herbalist™ = 'Aussemi' (S)    MAus

§ The Holt = 'Mehsherry' (F/S)    Last listed 1997

'The Honorable Lady Lindsay' (S)    Last listed 1998

'The Knight' (S)    Last listed 1998

§ The Lady = 'Fryjingo' (S) ♀    EBee LPlm MAus MBur MFry MJon

◆ 'The Margaret Coppola Rose'    See R. 'White Gold'

§ The McCartney Rose = 'Meizeli' (HT)    LStr MJon SApu

'The New Dawn'    See R. 'New Dawn'

§ The Nun = 'Ausnun' (S)    MAus

The Observer = 'Frytango' (HT)    Last listed 1997

§ The Painter = 'Mactemaik' (F)    EBee LStr MBur MFry MJon SApu SWas

§ The Pilgrim = 'Auswalker' (S)    CAbP CHad EBee EBrP EBre IHar LBre LFis MAus MBri MHlr MJon SBre SChu SJus SPer WHCG WHow

§ The Prince® = 'Ausvelvet' (S)    EBrP EBre LBre LStr MAus MBNS MBri MJon NPri SBre SWCr WHow WWeb

'The Prioress' (S)    MAus

§ 'The Queen Elizabeth' (F) ♀    CB&S CGro EBee EBls EBrP EBre ENot EWTr GCoc GGre LBre LGod LPlm LStr MAus MBri MBur MFry MGan MJon MMat NRog SApu SBre SPer SRPl WWeb

§ The Reeve® = 'Ausreeve' (S)    MAus

'The Royal Brompton Rose'    See R. Royal Brompton Rose = 'Meivildo'

§ The Seckford Rose = 'Korpinrob' (S)    ENot MJon MMat

§ The Squire® = 'Ausquire' (S)    MAus WAct

§ The Times Rose = 'Korpeahn' (F) ♀    ENot LGod LStr MGan MJon MMat SJus SPer SRPl

§ The Valois Rose = 'Kordadel' (Min/Patio)    MMat

§ The Wife of Bath = 'Ausbath' (S)    IHar MAus MBri

'Thelma' (Ra)    EBls MAus

'Thérèse Bugnet' (Ru)    EBls

'Thisbe' (HM)    EBls MAus SPer WAct WHCG

§ Thomas Barton® = 'Meihirvin' (HT)    LStr SApu SWas

§ Thora Hird = 'Tonybrac' (F)    MAus

◆ 'Thoresbyana'    See R. 'Bennett's Seedling'

Thousand Beauties    See R. 'Tausendschön'

Threepenny Bit Rose    See R. elegantula 'Persetosa'

'Tiara' (RH)    Last listed 1998

§ Tiger Cub = 'Poulcub' (Patio)    MMat

§ Tigris® = 'Harprier' (persica hybrid) (S)    WAct

'Till Uhlenspiegel' (RH)    EBls

'Tina Turner' (HT)    MBur MJon NBat

◆ 'Tineally'    See R. Jean Kenneally = 'Tineally'

◆ 'Tinluis'    See R. Luis Desamero = 'Tinluis'

◆ 'Tinresist'    See R. Irresistible = 'Tinresist'

§ Tintinara = 'Dicuptight' (HT)    EBee GCoc IDic MFry

Tiny Tot = 'Bentintot' (Min)    Last listed 1996

§ Tip Top® = 'Tanope' (F/Patio)    CB&S CGro CTri ELan EWTr GCoc MBri MGan NRog SPer SWCr WStI

'Tipo Ideale'    See R. x odorata 'Mutabilis'

'Tipsy Imperial Concubine' (T)    EBls

§ Tivoli = 'Poulduce' (HT)    EBee MAus MJon

'Toby Tristam' (Ra)    CRHN WWat

'Tom Foster' (HT)    NBat

*tomentosa*    Last listed 1998

◆ 'Tonybrac'    See R. Thora Hird = 'Tonybrac'

§ Too Hot to Handle = 'Macloupri' (S/Cl)    LStr MJon SApu WGer

§ Top Marks = 'Fryministar' (Min/Patio)    EBrP EBre GCoc LBre LGod LPlm LStr MBri MBur MFry MGan MJon MMat NRog SApu SBre SCoo SJus WStI WWeb

Topaz Jewel    See R. Yellow Dagmar Hastrup = 'Moryelrug'

'Topeka' (F)    Last listed 1998

§ Toprose = 'Cocgold' (F)    EBrP EBre GCoc GGre LBre SBre SJus

Topsi® (F/Patio)    MJon NPri NRog SPer

§ Torvill and Dean = 'Lantor' (HT)    MJon

§ Toulouse-Lautrec® = 'Meirevolt' (S)    SApu

§ 'Tour de Malakoff' (Ce)    EBls IHar MAus MHlr SFam SPer SRPl SWCr WAct WHCG

§ Tournament of Roses = 'Jacient' (HT)    IDic MAus MJon

§ Toynbee Hall = 'Korwonder' (F)    ENot MMat

'Trade Winds' (HT)    MGan

§ Tradescant™ = 'Ausdir' (S)    EBrP EBre IHar LBre MAus MGan MHlr SBre

Tradition    See R. Tradition '95 = 'Korkeltin'

§ Tradition '95® = 'Korkeltin' (Cl)    MBri MMat SJus

§ Tranquility = 'Barout' (HT)    MBur

¶ *transmorrisonensis*    WPGP
   ETE 214

◆ 'Träumland'    See R. Dreamland = 'Träumland'

'Treasure Trove' (Ra)    CRHN EBls EMFP IHar MAus MBur SWCr WAct

§ Trevor Griffiths = 'Ausold' (S)    MAus SWCr

'Tricolore de Flandre' (G)    EBls MAus

Trier® (Ra)    EBee EBls MAus MHlr MMat WHCG

'Trigintepetala' misapplied    See R. 'Professeur Emile Perrot'

'Triomphe de l'Exposition' (HP)    MAus

'Triomphe du Luxembourg' (T)    EBls MAus

*triphylla*    See R. x beanii

◆ 'Troball'    See R. Joan Ball = 'Troball'

◆ 'Trobee'    See R. Dollie B = 'Trobee'

◆ 'Trobette'    See R. Jennie Robinson = 'Trobette'

◆ 'Trobglow'    See R. Paint-pot = 'Trobglow'

◆ 'Trobic'    See R. Just Magic = 'Trobic'

◆ 'Trobinette'    See R. Sarah Robinson = 'Trobinette'

◆ 'Trobinka'    See R. Ginny-Lou = 'Trobinka'

◆ 'Trobland'    See R. Woodland Sunbeam = 'Trobland'

◆ 'Troblove'    See R. Guernsey Love = 'Troblove'

◆ 'Trobric'    See R. Little Russell = 'Trobric'

◆ 'Trobroy'    See R. Royal Worcester = 'Trobroy'

◆ 'Trobstar'    See R. Starlight Express = 'Trobstar'

| | |
|---|---|
| ◆ 'Trobwich' | See *R.* Simon Robinson = 'Trobwich' |
| § Troika® = 'Poumidor' (HT) ♀ | CTri ENot IHar LStr MAus MBur MFry MGan MJon MMat SPer SWCr |
| § Troilus = 'Ausoil' (S) | MAus |
| ◆ 'Tropicana' | See *R.* Super Star = 'Tanorstar' |
| § Tropico Sunblaze = 'Meiglassol' (Min) | Last listed 1998 |
| 'Truly Yours' (HT) | Last listed 1996 |
| § Trumpeter® = 'Mactru' (F) ♀ | EBee ENot GCoc IHar LGod LPlm LStr MAus MBri MFry MGan MJon MMat NBat SApu SPer SWas |
| § Tumbling Waters = 'Poultumb' (F/S) | ENot NFla |
| ¶ 'Tuner Bridge' (S) | GGre |
| * 'Turkestan' | Last listed 1996 |
| 'Tuscany' (G) | GCoc MAus SJus SPer WAct WHCG |
| 'Tuscany Superb' (G) ♀ | CHad CPou EBee EBls EMFP ENot IHar LHol MAus MHlr MMat NFla NPri SPer SWCr WAct WHCG WHow WKif WSHC |
| *tuschetica* | Last listed 1998 |
| § Twenty-fifth = 'Beatwe' (F) | EBls |
| § Twenty-one Again! = 'Meinimo' (HT) | MBri MJon MRav SApu |
| ¶ 'Twilight' | SCoo WWeb |
| § Tynwald = 'Mattwyt' (HT) | LStr MJon MMat SWCr |
| 'Typhoon' (HT) | IHar MBur MJon |
| 'Ulrich Brünner Fils' (HP) | EBls MAus |
| *ultramontana* | Last listed 1996 |
| 'Uncle Bill' (HT) | EBls |
| § Uncle Walter = 'Macon' (HT) | EBls WStI |
| § UNICEF = 'Cocjojo' (F) | GCoc |
| § 'Unique Blanche' (Ce) | EBee EBls MAus WHow |
| § Valencia® = 'Koreklia' (HT) | ENot MJon MJon MMat NBat |
| § Valentine Heart = 'Dicogle' (F) | EBee IDic LGod MFry MJon SApu SJus |
| 'Vanguard' (Ru) | EBls |
| 'Vanity' (HM) | EBls MAus SPer |
| § 'Variegata di Bologna' (Bb) | CHad EBee EBls GOrc LFis MAus MMat SWCr WAct |
| Vatertag® | MJon |
| 'Veilchenblau' (Ra) ♀ | CHad EBls ELan LFis LGod LStr MAus MBur MGan MHlr SApu SJus SPer SSea SWCr WAct WHCG WHow WKif WSHC |
| § Velvet Fragrance = 'Fryperdee' (HT) | EBee GCoc LStr MAus MBri MFry MJon NBat SApu |
| 'Venusta Pendula' (Ra) | EBls MAus |
| 'Verschuren' (HT/v) | ELan |
| *versicolor* | See *R. gallica* 'Versicolor' |
| 'Vesuvius' (HT) | Last listed 1996 |
| 'Vick's Caprice' (HP) | EBls MAus |
| 'Vicomtesse Pierre du Fou' (ClHT) | EBls MAus |
| Victor Hugo® | See *R.* Spirit of Youth = 'Meivestal' |
| 'Victoriana' (F) | MAus |
| § Vidal Sassoon = 'Macjuliat' (HT) | EBee MBur MGan MJon MMat SApu |
| 'Village Maid' | See *R.* 'Centifolia Variegata' |
| *villosa* auct. | See *R. mollis* |
| - L. | EBls MAus MMat WAct |
| - 'Duplex' | See *R.* 'Wolley-Dod' |
| § 'Violacea' (G) | EBee EBls WHCG |
| § Violet Carson = 'Macio' (F) | MAus MGan |
| 'Violette' (Ra) | EBee EBls GOrc MAus WAct WHCG WHer |
| 'Violinista Costa' (HT) | EBls |
| *virginiana* ♀ | EBls ENot GCal GChr IHar MAus MGan MSte NWea SPer SRPl WAct WHCG WHen WOVN |
| - 'Plena' | See *R.* 'Rose d'Amour' |
| 'Virgo' (HT) | EBls |
| 'Viridiflora' | See *R.* x *odorata* 'Viridiflora' |
| § Vital Spark = 'Cocacert' (F) | MGan |
| 'Vivid' (Bourbon hybrid) | EBls |
| § Voice of Thousands = 'Horsunsmile' (F) | NBat |
| *vosagiaca* | See *R. caesia* subsp. *glauca* |
| 'W.E. Lippiat' (HT) | EBls |
| § Wandering Minstrel = 'Harquince' (F) | SApu |
| *wardii* var. *culta* | MAus |
| 'Warley Jubilee' (F) | Last listed 1997 |
| § Warm Welcome = 'Chewizz' (ClMin) ♀ | EBrP EBre GCoc GGre LBre LGod LStr MAus MBri MFry MJon MMat NBat NRog SBre SJus SMad SPer SSea SSoC WWeb |
| § Warm Wishes = 'Fryxotic' (HT) | EBee GCoc GGre LGod LPlm LStr MAus MBur MFry MGan MJon NPri SApu SJus WWeb |
| 'Warrior' (F) | MGan SPer |
| § Warwick Castle® = 'Auslian' (S) | MAus MBNS NBus SPer |
| § Warwickshire = 'Korkandel' (GC) | ENot MHlr MMat NPri SJus WOVN |
| § *watsoniana* | EBls |
| *webbiana* | CBrd EBls MAus WHCG |
| 'Wedding Day' (Ra) | CHad CSam EBee EBls EBrP EBre ELan EWTr IHar LBre LHol LPlm LStr MAus MBNS MBri MBur MFry MGan MJon MMat SApu SBre SJus SPer SSea WAct WHCG WHow WWeb |
| § Wee Barbie = 'Jelbar' (Min) | SApu |
| § Wee Cracker = 'Cocmarris' (Patio) | GCoc GGre |
| § Wee Jock = 'Cocabest' (F/Patio) | GChr GCoc GGre LStr SWCr |
| ◆ 'Weegold' | See *R.* Fine Gold = 'Weegold' |
| 'Weetwood' (Ra) | CRHN MAus SPer |
| 'Weisse aus Sparrieshoop' (S) | MGan |
| ◆ Weisse Wolcke® | See *R.* White Cloud = 'Korstacha' |
| ◆ 'Weizeip' | See *R.* Paradise = 'Weizeip' |
| ◆ 'Wekroath' | See *R.* Crazy for You = 'Wekroath' |
| ◆ 'Weksibyl' | See *R.* Heartbreaker = 'Weksibyl' |
| 'Welcome Guest' (HT) | Last listed 1996 |
| ¶ 'Well Done' (Patio/Min) | GGre |
| § Welwyn Garden Glory™ = 'Harzumber' (HT) | SJus |
| 'Wembley Stadium' (F/HT) | MGan |
| 'Wendy Cussons' (HT) | CB&S CGro EBls GChr GCoc LPlm MAus MBur MGan MJon NRog SApu SPer WWeb |
| § Wenlock® = 'Auswen' (S) | CSam EBrP EBre GGre IHar LBre MAus MBNS SBre SPer |
| ◆ 'Weopop' | See *R.* Summer Snow = 'Weopop' |
| § Westerland™ = 'Korwest' (F/S) ♀ | MGan MJon MMat WGer WHow |
| 'Westfield Star' (HT) | MAus |
| ◆ 'Whamemo' | See *R.* Sweet Memories = 'Whamemo' |
| 'Whisky Gill' (HT) | MGan |
| § Whisky Mac = 'Tanky' (HT) | CB&S CGro EBls EBrP EBre ELan GCoc GGre LBre LGod LPlm MAus MBri MBur MFry MGan MJon MMat NRog SApu SBre SPer SWCr WWeb |
| 'White Bath' | See *R.* 'Shailer's White Moss' |

§ White Bells® =     EBls ENot MAus MGan MMat SPer
  'Poulwhite' (Min/GC)     SRPl SWCr WAct WHCG WOVN

§ 'White Cécile Brünner' (Poly)     EBls MAus WHCG

  'White Christmas' (HT)     MBur MGan

§ White Cloud =     EBee ENot LGod MJon MMat SJus
  'Korstacha' (S/ClHT)

§ White Cloud =     MBri MFry SApu WHow
  'Savacloud' (Min)

  White Cockade® (Cl) ♀     CB&S EBls GCoc LPlm MFry
       MGan SApu SPer WHCG

§ 'White de Meaux' (Ce)     EBls MAus

§ White Diamond® =     IDic MAus SJus
  'Interamon' (S)

§ White Flower Carpet® =     CGro CTri IHar LRHS MFry MMat
  'Noaschnee' (GC)     SCoo SPer WWeb

§ 'White Gold'     GCoc

  'White Grootendorst' (Ru)     EBls MAus WAct

§ White Knight =
  'Poullaps' (ClHT/S)     EBee

  White Max Graf     See R. x jacksonii White Max
       Graf = 'Korgram'

§ White Meidiland® =     MGan WOVN
  'Meicoublan' (S/GC)

  White Moss     See R. 'Comtesse de Murinais', R.
       'Shailer's White Moss'

§ 'White Pet' (Poly) ♀     CHad EBee EMFP ENot GCoc LStr
       MBri MBur MGan MHlr MJon
       SApu SJus SPer SPla SRPl SWas
       WAct WSHC

  White Provence     See R. 'Unique Blanche'

  'White Queen Elizabeth' (F)     EBls SRPl

  White Rose of York     See R. x alba 'Alba Semiplena'

  'White Spray' (F)     EBls

  'White Tausendschön' (Ra)     MAus

  'White Wings' (HT)     CHad EBee EBls MAus MGan
       WAct WHCG WKif

§ Whitley Bay =     Last listed 1998
  'Horharryplus' (F)

♦ 'Whitson'     See R. Pearl Anniversary =
       'Whitson'

N wichurana (Ra)     EBls MAus WHCG

*  - 'Nana'     MRav

  - 'Variegata' (Ra)     CSWP EHoe ELan EPot MAus
       MCCP MJon NHol SCoo SMad
       WPyg

*  - 'Variegata Nana' (Ra)     Last listed 1998

  'Wickham Highway' (F)     Last listed 1998

  'Wickwar' (Ra)     CSWP EBls ELan EPla GCal GOrc
       MBri MSte SSpi WAct WHCG

  Wild Flower = 'Auswing' (S)  Last listed 1996

  'Wilhelm' (HM) ♀     EBls IHar MAus MRav SWCr
       WHCG

  'Will Scarlet' (HM)     MAus

  'Willhire Country' (F)     EBls

  'William Allen     EBls MAus SFam WHCG
    Richardson' (N)

  'William and Mary' (S)     EBls

¶  William Cobbett     SSea

§ 'William Lobb' (CeMo) ♀     CHad CRHN CSam EBls EBrP EBre
       ENot GCoc IHar IOrc LBre LGod
       LStr MAus MGan MHlr MMat NFla
       SApu SBre SChu SJus SPer SSoC
       SWCr WAct WHCG WKif WWeb

§ William Quarrier =     GCoc
  'Coclager' (F)

  'William R. Smith' (T)     EBls

§ William Shakespeare® =     CTri EBee ELan GCoc GGre IHar
  'Ausroyal' (S)     MBri NBus SMad SPer WStI

  'William Tyndale' (Ra)     WHCG

  'Williams' Double Yellow'     See R. x harisonii 'Williams'
       Double Yellow'

willmottiae     See R. gymnocarpa var.
       willmottiae

§ Wiltshire = 'Kormuse' (S/GC)   EBee ENot LFis LStr MFry MJon
       MMat SJus SRPl WHow WOVN

§ Wimi® = 'Tanrowise' (HT)     MGan

§ Winchester Cathedral® =     CHad EBee EBls EBrP EBre EMFP
  'Auscat' (S)     GChr GGre IHar LBre LGod LStr
       MAus MBri MHlr MJon SApu SBre
       SChu SJus SPer SPla SRPl SSoC
       SWCr SWas WOVN

§ Windflower = 'Auscross' (S)   MAus NPri

§ Windrush = 'Ausrush' (S)     IHar MAus MBri MJon SPer SWCr
       WAct WHCG

§ Wine and Dine =     IDic
  'Dicuncle' (GC)

  Winter Magic™ =     Last listed 1997
  'Foumagic' (Min)

  x wintoniensis     WAct WHCG

§ Wise Portia = 'Ausport' (S)   MAus

§ Wishing = 'Dickerfuffle'     IDic IHar MFry MJon SApu SPer
  (F/Patio)     WWeb

§ With Love = 'Andwit' (HT)     GCoc MJon SApu

  'Woburn Abbey' (F)     CGro EBls IHar

§ 'Wolley-Dod' (S)     EBls MAus MRav

  'Woman and Home' (HT)     CBlo

§ Woman o'th' North =     MJon WGer
  'Kirlon' (F/Patio)

*  'Woman's Hour' (F)     EBls

§ Woodland Sunbeam =     MJon
  'Trobland' (Min/Patio)

  'Woodrow's Seedling' (Cl)     Last listed 1997

  Woods of Windsor =     Last listed 1997
  'Korprill' (HT)

§ woodsii     EBls MAus MMat WHCG

  - var. fendleri     See R. woodsii

  'Woolverstone Church Rose'   See R. 'Surpassing Beauty of
       Woolverstone'

§ Wor Jackie =     NBat
  'Kirworjackie' (HT)

§ xanthina 'Canary Bird' (S) ♀  More than 30 suppliers

§ - f. bugonis ♀     EBls ECGP ELan MAus MGan
       MMat NRog SPer WAct WHCG

  - f. spontanea     EBls IHar MGan

  'Xavier Olibo' (HP)     EBls

  yainacensis     Last listed 1996

§ Yellow Button® =     MAus MBri WAct
  'Auslow' (S)

§ 'Yellow Cécile Brünner'     See R. 'Perle d'Or'

§ Yellow Charles Austin® =     MAus MBri
  'Ausyel' (S)

  'Yellow Cushion' (F)     MAus

§ Yellow Dagmar Hastrup =     EBee LFis MAus MBri MGan MHlr
  'Moryelrug' (Ru)     MJon SApu SJus SPer SWCr WAct
       WHCG WOVN

  'Yellow Doll' (Min)     ELan MAus MGan

  'Yellow Pages' (HT)     Last listed 1997

  'Yellow Patio' (Min/Patio)     LStr SWCr SWas

§ Yellow Ribbon =     Last listed 1997
  'Dicalow' (F)

  yellow Scotch     See R. x harisonii 'Williams'
       Double Yellow'

§ Yellow Sunblaze =     WWeb
  Meitrisical' (Min)

  Yesterday® (Poly/F/S) ♀     EBls MAus MGan MMat SWCr

  'Yolande d'Aragon' (HP)     EBls

  York and Lancaster     See R. x damascena var.
       versicolor

§ Yorkshire Bank =     MFry
  'Rutrulo' (HT)

§ Yorkshire =     ENot GCoc LStr MMat NPri
  'Korbarkeit' (GC)

'Yorkshire Lady' (HT)  NBat
§ Yorkshire Sunblaze® =  Last listed 1997
  'Meiblam' (Min)
§ Young Quinn® =  MBur
  'Macbern' (HT)
Young Venturer =  Last listed 1997
  'Mattsun' (F)
Yves Piaget®  See R. Royal Brompton Rose =
  'Meivildo'
'Yvonne Rabier' (Poly) ♀  EBls LStr MAus MHlr SPer SWas
  WAct WHCG
§ Zambra® = 'Meicurbos' (F)  CB&S
'Zenobia' (Mo)  Last listed 1997
'Zéphirine Drouhin' (Bb) ♀  More than 30 suppliers
§ 'Zigeunerknabe' (S) ♀  EBee EBls EMFP GOrc MAus SPer
  SWCr WAct WHCG
Zitronenfalter® (S)  MGan
'Zweibrücken' (Cl)  MGan
§ 'Zwergkönig' (Min)  MAus

# ROSCOEA ✿ (Zingiberaceae)

*alpina*  CBro CPBP EBee EHyt EPot ERos
  GDra IBlr MTho NHol NWCA
  SBea SRms SWas WAbe WCot
  WCru WSan
¶ – CC 1820  WCot
¶ – pink form  LEur MSCN
*auriculata*  CAvo CBro CFir CLAP CRDP EMar
  ETub IBlr LEur MLLN MTho NHar
  NHol SBla SCro WCru WPyg WViv
*australis*  CFir IBlr
'Beesiana'  CAvo CBro CFir CLAP CRDP EBee
  ECha ERos IBlr LAma LEur MBel
  MTho NHar NHol NPri WCru
  WPyg
'Beesiana' white  CLAP EBee MBNS NHol WAbe
*cautleyoides* ♀  More than 30 suppliers
– Blackthorn strain  SBla
– 'Grandiflora'  Last listed 1998
– x *humeana*  IBlr
– hybrid  MLLN WCot
– 'Kew Beauty'  CLAP CRDP EBrP EBre LBre
  MTho SBla SBre
¶ – – seedlings  GCal
– pink  Last listed 1996
*humeana* ♀  CBro CLAP EHyt GCrs LAma
  NHar SBla WCot WCru
¶ 'Jeffery Thomas'  WCot
§ *purpurea*  CBro CGle CRDP EBee EBrP EBre
  ELan EMan ERos GCal LAma LBre
  MFir MRav NBir NHar NHol SBre
  SCob SPer SRms WCru WPyg
  WWin
¶ – var. *gigantea* CC 1757  WCot
¶ – lilac form  LEur
– var. *procera*  See R. purpurea
§ *scillifolia*  CBro CFir CRDP EBee ERos GCal
  LAma LEur MTho NBir NHar
  NMen NRog NTow SWas WCot
  WCru
– pink form  EBee IBlr WViv
*tibetica*  WCru

# ROSMARINUS ✿ (Lamiaceae)
* *calabriensis*  WCHb
*corsicus* 'Prostratus'  See R. officinalis Prostratus
  Group
'Green Ginger'  CFri MChe NCut NPer WElm
  WRHF WShe WWoo
*lavandulaceus* Noë  See R. eriocalyx
– hort.  See R. officinalis Prostratus
  Group

'Loddon Pink'  ERav
*officinalis*  More than 30 suppliers
– var. *albiflorus*  CArn CSev EBee ELau ESis GAbr
  GChr GPoy MBar MChe MPla
  NChi NHHG NLon NSti SChu
  SHDw SMac SPil SRms WCHb
  WEas WHer WOak WSHC WWye
¶ 'Alderney'  MHer
§ – *angustissimus*  CArn GBar GPoy SCro SHDw SIde
  'Corsican Blue'  SPer WPer
– 'Aureovariegatus'  See R. officinalis 'Aureus'
§ – 'Aureus' (v)  CLan CMil CPla IBlr MAsh MHar
  NHHG SDry SEas SMad WByw
  WCHb WEas WHer WSel
§ – 'Benenden Blue'  CGle CMHG CSev EBee ECha
  EGoo ELau GPoy LHop MAsh
  MBNS MChe MGos MUlv MWgw
  NHHG SBid SChu SDix SIde SPan
  SPer STre WEas WGwG WWat
  WWye
– 'Collingwood Ingram'  See R. officinalis 'Benenden Blue'
– 'Corsicus Prostratus'  CB&S ELau SMac
– dwarf blue  ELau
– 'Eden'  Last listed 1996
– 'Fastigiatus'  See R. officinalis 'Miss Jessopp's
  Upright'
– 'Fota Blue'  CBod CSWP CSev ELau GBar
  MHer NHHG NHex NSti SAga
  SCro SHDw SIde SPan SPil WJek
  WWye
– 'Frimley Blue'  See R. officinalis 'Primley Blue'
* – 'Ginger-scented'  WCHb WRus
– 'Guilded'  See R. officinalis 'Aureus'
– 'Gunnel's Upright'  GBar WRha
¶ – 'Iden Blue'  SIde
¶ – 'Iden Blue Boy'  SIde
¶ – 'Iden Pillar'  SIde
– 'Jackman's Prostrate'  CB&S ECtt
– 'Lady in White'  EAst ELan EPfP SPan SPer WGwG
  WRHF WWat
– *lavandulaceus*  See R. officinalis Prostratus
  Group
– 'Lilies Blue'  GPoy
– 'Lockwood Variety'  WPer
– 'Majorca Pink'  CB&S CChe CSam EGoo ELau
  GBar LHol MMal MPla NSti SIde
  SLon SPer SPil SRms SSoC WCHb
  WGwG WPer WWat WWye
– 'McConnell's Blue'  CArn CDoC CLTr EBee EBrP EBre
  ELan ELau EPla GAbr LBre MAsh
  MGos MWat MWgw NRoo SBre
  SDry SHDw SPan WCHb WGer
  WHoo WPer WWat WWye
* – 'Miss Jessopp's Prostrate'  Last listed 1998
§ – 'Miss Jessopp's Upright' ♀  More than 30 suppliers
– 'Mrs Harding'  CBod MHer
§ – 'Primley Blue'  CArn CBrm CJew CSam CSev
  CWSG EBee ELau GBar LHol
  MChe MRav NHHG NSti SBid
  SChu SIde SMer WCHb WHer
  WPer WWye
§ – Prostratus Group ♀  CArn CB&S CChe CDul CLan
  CMHG CSev CTrw EBee ELau
  EMil EWTr MBar MChe NHHG
  NLon NSti NWCA SArc SIde SPer
  SRms SSoC WAbe WGwG WHar
  WPer WRus WWat WWye
¶ – – 'Gethsemane'  SIde
– – 'Trewithen'  Last listed 1998
– f. *pyramidalis*  See R. officinalis 'Miss Jessopp's
  Upright'
– *repens*  See R. officinalis Prostratus
  Group

| – 'Roseus' | CArn CHan CMHG CWit EBee ELan ELau EMil EWTr GChr GPoy LHop MChe NHHG NLon NSti SChu SEas SRPl SSoC WAbe WEas WGwG WHer WOak WPer WWye |
| – 'Russell's Blue' | WHer WWat |
| – 'Severn Sea' ♀ | CArn CB&S CBot CChe CDul CGle CHan CMHG CSev EBee ECtt ELan GOrc GPoy LHol LHop MBNS MGos NFor NSti SIde SLon SPer WAbe WEas WPGP WPer WWat WWeb |
| ¶ – Silver Spires® = 'Wolros' | SIde WFar |
| – 'Sissinghurst Blue' ♀ | CArn CB&S CMGP CSev EBee ECha ELan ELau EMil ERav LHol MAsh MMal MTis SBid SIde SPer SRms WCHb WGwG WRHF WSel WWat WWye |
| ¶ – 'Sissinghurst White' | WGwG |
| – 'Sudbury Blue' | ELau GBar MChe NHHG NLon NRoo NSti SHDw WEas WJek |
| – 'Trusty' | ECtt ELan LHop LRHS WPer |
| – 'Tuscan Blue' | CDoC CSWP CSev EBee ECGP ECot ELau EMil EPri GBar MHer MWat NFla NHex SDry SIde SMer WCHb WHer WJek WPer WRha WWat WWye |
| – 'Variegatus' | See *R. officinalis* 'Aureus' |
| – 'Vicomte de Noailles' | ERea |
| *repens* | See *R. officinalis* Prostratus Group |

## ROSTRINUCULA (Lamiaceae)
| *dependens* Guiz 18 | CBot |

## ROSULARIA ✿ (Crassulaceae)
| *acuminata* | See *R. alpestris* subsp. *alpestris* |
| *adenotricha* subsp. *adenotricha* | Last listed 1996 |
| § *aizoon* | ESis |
| *alba* | See *R. sedoides* |
| *alpestris* | MSte |
| § – subsp. *alpestris* | Last listed 1998 |
| – CC 327 | Last listed 1996 |
| § *chrysantha* | EBur ESis MBro NMen NNrd SIng SPlb WFar WLow |
| – Number 1 | CWil |
| *crassipes* | See *Rhodiola wallichiana* |
| *haussknechtii* | Last listed 1996 |
| *hissarica* K 92.380 | Last listed 1997 |
| § *muratdaghensis* | EBur MBro NNrd SChr |
| *pallida* A. Berger | See *R. chrysantha* |
| – Stapf | See *R. aizoon* |
| *platyphylla* hort. | See *R. muratdaghensis* |
| *rechingeri* | CWil |
| § *sedoides* | CWil ELan GCHN MBar SChu SSmi WPer WWin |
| § – var. *alba* | CWil ELan GCHN MBar NFla NVic SChu SRms WPyg WWin |
| *sempervivum* | CWil EWes NMen |
| – subsp. *amanensis* | Last listed 1996 |
| § – subsp. *glaucophylla* | CWil NTow |
| *serpentinica* | CWil |
| *serrata* | Last listed 1996 |
| *spatulata* hort. | See *R. sempervivum* subsp. *glaucophylla* |
| *turkestanica* | CWil |

## ROTHMANNIA (Rubiaceae)
| *capensis* | SOWG |
| § *globosa* | Last listed 1997 |

## RUBIA (Rubiaceae)
| ¶ *manjith* | GPoy |
| *peregrina* | CArn EHic EWFC GBar GPoy MHew MSal |
| *tinctorum* | CArn ELau GBar GPoy LHol MHew MSal NHex SIde SWat WHer WWye |

## RUBUS ✿ (Rosaceae)
| 'Adrienne' (F) | EMui |
| *alceifolius* | CPMA CStr |
| – Poiret | CGle |
| *arcticus* | CGle CInt MBal MBro MCCP NHar SRms SRot WBea WCot WCru WPat |
| – subsp. *stellarcticus* (F) | Last listed 1998 |
| – – 'Anna' (F) | Last listed 1998 |
| – – 'Beata' (F) | Last listed 1998 |
| – – 'Linda' (F) | Last listed 1998 |
| – – 'Sofia' (F) | Last listed 1998 |
| *australis* | CPIN |
| x *barkeri* | ECou |
| § 'Benenden' ♀ | More than 30 suppliers |
| 'Betty Ashburner' | CAgr CBlo CDoC CHan CWit EPfP EPla GCal GQui LBuc MGos MRav NArg NFla WHCG WTro WWat |
| *biflorus* | CB&S CFil EBee EMon EPla ERav EWes MBlu WPGP WWat |
| 'Boysenberry, Thornless' (F) | EBee EMui GTwe LBuc SDea SPer |
| * *buergeri* 'Variegatus' | EPla GVic WMoo |
| *caesius* 'Sidings' | CNat |
| * *calophyllus* | WCot |
| *calycinoides* | See *R. pentalobus* |
| *canadensis* | Last listed 1996 |
| *chamaemorus* | GPoy |
| ¶ *cissoides* | WCot |
| *cockburnianus* (F) ♀ | CB&S CBlo CGle CPle EBee EBrP EBre ELan ENot EPla GOrc IOrc LBre LBuc MBal MRav MWat NHol NLon NWea SAga SBre SPer SRms WDin WFar WWat |
| – Goldenvale™ = 'Wyego' ♀ | More than 30 suppliers |
| *coreanus* | CFil CPle EPla |
| *crataegifolius* | MBro SMac SPan WPat WWat |
| 'Emerald Spreader' | LRHS MBri SBod WMoo |
| *flagelliflorus* | MBar WHCG |
| *fockeanus* | See *R. pentalobus* |
| *formosensis* B&SWJ 1798 | WCru |
| x *fraseri* | EPla |
| *fruticosus* | CKin |
| ¶ – 'Adrienne' (F) | EMui |
| – 'Ashton Cross' (F) | EMui GRei GTwe LBuc SDea |
| – 'Bedford Giant' (F) | CBlo EBee GChr GTwe MGos SPer WWeb |
| – 'Black Satin' (F) | CBlo CSam GRei MBri SDea SPer WWeb |
| – 'Dart's Ambassador' | ENot EPla |
| – 'Dart's Robertville' | Last listed 1997 |
| – 'Denver Thornless' (F) | Last listed 1997 |
| – 'Fantasia' (F) ♀ | EMui LBuc |
| – 'Godshill Goliath' (F) | SDea |
| – 'Helen' | CSut EMui |
| – 'Himalayan Giant' (F) | CBlo CSam GTwe NRog SDea SPer |
| – 'John Innes' (F) | CTri NRog |
| – 'Loch Ness' (F) ♀ | CBlo COtt CSam EMui GTwe LBuc MBri MGos SDea SPer |
| – 'Merton Thornless' (F) | CBlo GTwe MGos NBee NRog |
| – 'No Thorn' (F) | SDea |
| – 'Oregon Thornless' (F) | CBlo EBee EMui GTwe MBri SDea SPer SRms |

- 'Parsley Leaved' (F) — CBlo SDea
* - 'Sylvan' (F) — MGos
- 'Thornfree' (F) — CBlo SDea WWeb
- 'Variegatus' — CBot CPMA CRDP EPla MBlu NEgg SLod SMad WCot WPat
¶ - 'Veronique' (F) — EMui
- 'Waldo' — CBlo COtt EBee EMui LBuc MGos SDea

**henryi** — CBot CPlN EPla MRav WCot WHCG WWat WWye
- var. **bambusarum** — CCHP CFil CHan CMCN CPlN CPle EBee EHic ElAn EPar EPla ERav SBid SBra WCru WPat WTin WWat

**hupehensis** — SLPl
**ichangensis** — CB&S CBot CHan CMCN CPlN EPPr EPla LEdu MBal

**idaeus** — CKin
* - 'Allgold' (F) — EMui
- 'Augusta' (F) — EMui
- 'Aureus' (F) — ECha EHal ElAn EPla LHop MRav NSti SDry SMac WCot WFar WLin
- Autumn Bliss™ (F) ♀ — CBlo CSam CSut CWSG EMui GChr GTwe LBuc MBri MGos NBee NEgg SDea SPer WBay WWeb
- 'Fallgold' (F) — GTwe
- 'Galante' (F) — EMui
* - 'Glen Ample' (F) — CSut CWSG EMui GRei GTwe LBuc
- 'Glen Clova' (F) — CBlo GTwe NBee NRog SPer WBay WWeb
- 'Glen Coe' (F) — GTwe
- 'Glen Lyon' (F) — GRei GTwe LBuc MBri SCoo WBay
- 'Glen Magna' (F) — CSut CWSG EMui GRei GTwe LBuc SDea
- 'Glen Moy' (F) ♀ — CBlo CSam CSut CWSG EMui GChr GTwe LBuc MGos NBee NRog SDea SPer
- 'Glen Prosen' (F) ♀ — CWSG EMui GTwe LBuc MBri NRog SDea SPer
- 'Glen Rosa' (F) — GTwe
- 'Glen Shee' (F) — GTwe
- 'Golden Everest' (F) — Last listed 1998
- 'Heritage' (F) — EBee SPer WBay
- 'Julia' (F) — GTwe
- 'Leo' (F) ♀ — CBlo EMui GTwe MGos SCoo WBay
- 'Malling Admiral' (F) ♀ — CBlo COtt GTwe MBri NRog SPer
- 'Malling Augusta' — Last listed 1997
- 'Malling Delight' (F) ♀ — CBlo GTwe SCoo SPer WBay
- 'Malling Jewel' (F) ♀ — COtt EMui GRei GTwe LBuc NBee SDea SPer WBay
- 'Malling Joy' (F) — GTwe
- 'Malling Orion' (F) — MGos
- 'Malling Promise' (F) — CBlo
- 'Redsetter' (F) — EMui
- 'Ruby' (F) — EMui
- 'September' (F) — Last listed 1998
- 'Summer Gold' (F) — GTwe
- 'Terri-Louise' (F) — EMui
- 'Tulameen' (F) — EMui
- 'Zefa Herbsternte' (F) — GTwe WWeb
**illecebrosus** (F) — MBro SMac WBea
**intercurrens** — GCal
**irenaeus** — CFil CHan CPlN CPle WPGP WWat
♦ Japanese wineberry — See R. phoenicolasius
'Kenneth Ashburner' — CDoC EPla MBri SLPl WWat
'King's Acre Berry' (F) — EMui
**laciniatus** — EHol EPla
¶ **lambertianus** — CFil

**lineatus** — CAbb CBot CBrd CGre CHan CPle EPla LHop MBal MBlu SDix SDry SMad WCot WCru WDin WPat WWye
(Loganberry Group) — EMui GTwe NRog SDea SPer
'LY 59' (F) ♀ — SRms
- 'LY 654' (F) ♀ — CBlo CSam CSut GChr GRei GTwe LBuc MBri MGos SDea SPer WWeb
- 'New Zealand Black' (F) — SDea
- Thornless (F) — CBlo CTri ECot GTwe NRog SDea
**ludwigii** — LLew WCot
'Margaret Gordon' — CBlo CPMA MRav NPro WHCG
**microphyllus** 'Variegatus' — SBid WPat WWeb
§ **nepalensis** — CAgr CDoC CGle CLTr MBel NHol NPro NWoo
**nutans** — See R. nepalensis
§ Odel = 'Walberton Red' — MBel SPer
**odoratus** — CWit ELan EPfP LBlm NPal SBid SPer WCot WHCG WWat
**palmatus** var. **coptophyllus** — SLPl
¶ **paniculatus** S&SH 386 — CHan
**parviflorus** — CArn
- double form — EMon WCru
- 'Sunshine Spreader' — GAri LHop NPro WPat
**parvus** — ECou
**pectinellus** var. **trilobus** — NDov WCru WMoo
B&SWJ 1669B
**peltatus** — CFil WPGP
§ **pentalobus** — CGle CTri CWit ElAn ENot ESis LHop MBal MBar SMac SPer WAbe WFar WWin
- B&SWJ 3878 — WCru
- 'Emerald Carpet' — CAgr SBod
- 'Green Jade' — GChr WWat
§ **phoenicolasius** — CAgr CB&S EMui EPla GEil GTwe MBlu MBri NHol NRog SDea SPer WAbb WBea WCru WHCG WWat WWye
**rolfei** B&SWJ 3546 — WCru
**rosifolius** 'Coronarius' (d) — CHan CHid CMil CPle EHal ElAn EOrc EPla GMac LHop MBel MHlr MLLN MMil MSCN MWhi NEgg NHaw NHol NLon NPro SBid SMad WCot WOVN WRus
**setchuenensis** — CMCN CSWP
'Silvan' (F) ♀ — CDoC EMui GTwe
¶ sp. RCB/Eq C-1 — WCot
**spectabilis** — CPle CWit ElAn EPla LFis LHop MBal MRav SEas SPan SRms WBor WFar WLin WRha WWat
- 'Flore Pleno' — See R. spectabilis 'Olympic Double'
- 'Gun Hildi' — Last listed 1997
§ - 'Olympic Double' (d) — More than 30 suppliers
* - 'Olympic Flame' — Last listed 1998
**splendidissimus** — WCru
B&SWJ 2361
**squarrosus** — CPle ECou EHol EPla SMad
'Sunberry' (F) — GTwe
**swinhoei** B&SWJ 1735 — WCru
¶ **taiwanicola** — MBlu NPSI SMac SPan
- B&SWJ 317 — CFee NMen WCru
Tayberry Group (F) ♀ — CSam CTri EMui GChr GRei GTwe MBri MGos NRog SPer SRms WWeb
- 'Buckingham' (F) — CSut EMui WLRN
- 'Medana Tayberry' (F) — LBuc SDea

| | |
|---|---|
| § *thibetanus* ♀ | CB&S CBot CDoC CHan CPle EBee ELan EMil ENot GCal MBri MRav NBir NLon NSti SBod SDix SDry SEas SLPl SMac SPer SRPl WBea WCot WDin WHCG WSHC WWat WWye |
| – 'Silver Fern' | See *R. thibetanus* |
| *treutleri* | Last listed 1997 |
| *tricolor* | CAgr CB&S CChe CGle CHan CPlN ELan ENot EPla GBri LGro MBal MRav NFor NHol SDix SLon SPer WBod WDin WEas WHCG WOak WWat WWin WWye |
| – 'Dart's Evergreen' | SLPl |
| – 'Ness' | SLPl |
| x *tridel* 'Benenden' | See *R.* 'Benenden' |
| 'Tummelberry' (F) | GTwe LRHS |
| *ulmifolius* 'Bellidiflorus' (d) | CBot CSev EBee ELan ENot EPla MBal MBlu MRav NFor NLon NSti SBid SChu SMac SPer WAbb WBea WHal |
| 'Veitchberry' (F) | EMui GTwe |
| ♦ 'Walberton Red' | See *R.* Odel = 'Walberton Red' |
| 'Youngberry' (F) | SDea |

## RUDBECKIA ✿ (Asteraceae)

| | |
|---|---|
| Autumn Sun | See *R.* 'Herbstsonne' |
| *californica* | CSam MNrw SSca WPer |
| *deamii* | See *R. fulgida* var. *deamii* |
| *echinacea purpurea* | See *Echinacea purpurea* |
| § *fulgida* var. *deamii* ♀ | More than 30 suppliers |
| § – var. *speciosa* | CM&M CMGP CSam EBee ECGN ECha EHic ELan EPfP EWTr GMac MBel NRoo SHel SPer SRms WCot WFar WOld WPer WRus |
| – var. *sullivantii* | More than 30 suppliers |
| 'Goldsturm' ♀ | |
| ¶ – 'Viette's Little Suzy' | NCat |
| *gloriosa* | See *R. hirta* |
| 'Goldquelle' ♀ | EBee EFou EGar ELan EMan EPfP GMaP LHop MBel MLLN NOrc NPri SCro SMad SMrm SPer SRms WHil WWin |
| § 'Herbstsonne' | CHea CTri EBee ECGN ECGP ECha ECle EWTr LFis MBel MCAu MSCN MWat NFla NOrc NPer NPri NVic SAga SHel SMad SPer SPla SSoC SSvw WBor WEas WMow |
| § *hirta* | IIve |
| – 'Irish Eyes' | Last listed 1998 |
| – var. *pulcherrima* | EBee |
| § 'Juligold' | EBee EFou NCat NHlc NTow SCro SMrm SSpe WWoo |
| July Gold | See *R.* 'Juligold' |
| *laciniata* | CSam CStr ECGN ELan EMan EMon EPPr EPfP EWTr GCal LFis MArl MFir NOrc NSti SMrm WByw WCot |
| – 'Golden Glow' | See *R. laciniata* 'Hortensia' |
| § – 'Hortensia' | EMon MFir WCot |
| *maxima* | CGle EBee ECGN ECha EGar EMan EMon GBin LGre MBri MBro MCCP NChi NLar SAga SMrm SSoC SSvw WCot |
| ¶ – 'Brilliant' | NCut |
| ¶ *missouriensis* | EBee |
| *mollis* | EBee |
| *newmannii* | See *R. fulgida* var. *speciosa* |
| ¶ *nitida* | EWTr WWoo |
| *occidentalis* | EWTr LFis MLLN NLar WFar WLin WPer |

| | |
|---|---|
| – 'Green Wizard' | CM&M CMil EFou EGar EMan EWTr GCal NBro NChi NLar NSti SLon SMad SRCN SSca WCot WElm WHer WSan WWhi WWoo |
| *purpurea* | See *Echinacea purpurea* |
| *speciosa* | See *R. fulgida* var. *speciosa* |
| *subtomentosa* | CHor CPou EBee EFou EGar EMan EMon GCal MNrw NSti WOld |
| * 'Toto' | Last listed 1996 |
| *triloba* | EBee ECGN EFou EMan GBri NCut SGre SMad WBea WCot |
| * *viridis* | Last listed 1996 |

## RUELLIA (Acanthaceae)

| | |
|---|---|
| *amoena* | See *R. graecizans* |
| *caroliniensis* | WCot |
| * 'Chi Chi' | WCot |
| ¶ *ciliata* | WCot |
| *devosiana* | Last listed 1998 |
| § *graecizans* | Last listed 1997 |
| *humilis* | EBee SIgm WCot WLRN |
| * 'Katie' | WCot |
| *makoyana* ♀ | CHal CSev IBlr MBri |
| *strepens* | WCot |

## RUMEX (Polygonaceae)

| | |
|---|---|
| § *acetosa* | CArn CKin CSev ECha ELau GAbr GBar GPoy LHol MChe MHew MMal NBir SIde WHer WSel WWye |
| – 'Crocodile' (v) | Last listed 1998 |
| – 'Redleaf' | See *R. acetosa* subsp. *vineatus* |
| § – subsp. *vineatus* | WCot |
| *acetosella* | IIve MSal WSel |
| *alpinus* | WCot |
| *flexuosus* | CElw CRow EHoe EPPr IBlr |
| *hydrolapathum* | CArn EMFW EWFC LPBA MSta NDea |
| *maritimus* | EWFC |
| *rubrifolius* | SIde |
| *rugosus* | Last listed 1997 |
| *sanguineus* | CHan EMFW EMan GGar LPBA MSCN SIng WCer WFar WGwG WLRN WWal |
| – var. *sanguineus* | CArn CElw CRow CSev EHoe ELan EPar EPla ESis LHol MNrw MTho NBro NHol NLak NSti WHer WOak WPer WSel WWye |
| *scutatus* | CArn CJew CSev ELau GAbr GPoy LHol MChe MHew SIde WCer WHbs WHer WJek WWye |
| – 'Silver Shield' | CJew CRDP CRow ELau EMar EPPr IBlr NSti WCHb WHer WJek WOak WWye |
| *venosus* | MSal |

## RUMOHRA (Davalliaceae)

| | |
|---|---|
| ¶ *adiantiformis* ♀ | WRic |

## RUPICAPNOS (Papaveraceae)

| | |
|---|---|
| *africana* | EPot NWCA SBla |

## RUSCHIA (Aizoaceae)

| | |
|---|---|
| ¶ *karrooica* | SChr |
| ¶ *macowanii* | EOas |
| ¶ *misera* | EOas |
| § *putterillii* | Last listed 1996 |
| – S&SH 64 | CHan SOkh |
| ¶ *rubricaulis* | CTrC |
| *uncinata* | CTrC SChr |

## RUSCUS ✿ (Ruscaceae)

| | |
|---|---|
| *aculeatus* | CArn CTri EBee ENot EPfP GPoy MFir MRav MWhi SAPC SArc SBrw SMac SRCN SRms SSta WBod WDin WHer WPGP WRHF WSpi WStI WWye |
| - (f) | WGwy WMou |
| - hermaphrodite | EPla EWes GCal WWat |
| - (m) | EGoo WMou WWat |
| - var. *angustifolius* (f) | EPla |
| * - 'Wheeler's Variety' (f/m) | CPMA EBee MPla MRav WWat |
| *hypoglossum* | EPla GOrc MTed SAPC SEND WRHF |
| ¶ - WM 9804 | MPhe |
| ¶ *hypophyllum* | MTed MUlv |
| ¶ x *microglossum* | GCal |
| *ponticus* | EPla |
| *racemosus* | See *Danae racemosa* |

## RUSPOLIA (Acanthaceae)

| | |
|---|---|
| *pseuderanthemoides* | Last listed 1997 |

## RUSSELIA (Scrophulariaceae)

| | |
|---|---|
| § *equisetiformis* ♀ | ERea SIgm |
| *juncea* | See *R. equisetiformis* |

## RUTA (Rutaceae)

| | |
|---|---|
| *chalepensis* | CArn WCHb |
| § - 'Dimension Two' | WHer |
| - prostrate form | See *R. chalepensis* 'Dimension Two' |
| *corsica* | CArn |
| *graveolens* | CArn CFri CGle CJew CWSG EFer GPoy MChe MHew NOak SIde SPar WGwG WHer WJek WOak WPer |
| - 'Harlequin' | EOHP SPil |
| - 'Jackman's Blue' ♀ | CGle CSev EBee EBrP EBre ECha EEls EHoe ELan ENot EWTr GChr LBre LGro LHol MBal MPla MRav MWat MWgw NFor NSti SBre SPer SRms WBod WEas WOak WOve WOak |
| * - *prostrata* | WOak |
| - 'Variegata' | CArn CBot ECha ELan GEil MCLN MChe NFor NPer WHer WJek WWye |
| *montana* | Last listed 1998 |
| *prostrata* | See *R. chalepensis* 'Dimension Two' |

## x RUTTYRUSPOLIA (Acanthaceae)

| | |
|---|---|
| 'Phyllis van Heerden' | Last listed 1998 |

## RYTIDOSPERMA (Poaceae)

| | |
|---|---|
| * *arundinaceum* | EBee |

# S

## SABAL (Arecaceae)

| | |
|---|---|
| § *bermudana* | CRoM LPal |
| *etonia* | LPal |
| *mauritiiformis* | Last listed 1997 |
| § *mexicana* | CRoM CTrC NPal |
| *minor* | CRoM CTrC LPal NPal |
| *palmetto* | CArn CRoM CTrC LPal NPal WNor |
| *princeps* | See *S. bermudana* |
| *rosei* | LPal |

| | |
|---|---|
| *texana* | See *S. mexicana* |
| *uresana* | LPal |

## SABATIA (Gentianaceae)

| | |
|---|---|
| ¶ *kennedyana* | EBee |

## SACCHARUM (Poaceae)

| | |
|---|---|
| *ravennae* | EBee EHoe EMon EWes GBin MSte NChi NSti SMad |

## SADLERIA (Blechnaceae)

| | |
|---|---|
| *cyatheoides* | WRic |

## SAGERETIA (Rhamnaceae)

| | |
|---|---|
| § *thea* | STre |
| *theezans* | See *S. thea* |

## SAGINA (Caryophyllaceae)

| | |
|---|---|
| *boydii* | EMNN EWes GNor ITim NHed |
| ¶ *japonica* 'Flore Pleno' | EMon |
| § *subulata* var. | ECha EFer ELan LGro MBNS |
| *glabrata* 'Aurea' | MOne MRav SIng SRms WEas WHal WPer WWin |

## SAGITTARIA (Alismataceae)

| | |
|---|---|
| *japonica* | See *S. sagittifolia* |
| *latifolia* | EMFW LPBA NDea |
| § *sagittifolia* | CBen CRow EHon EMFW LPBA MSta SLon SRms SWat WMAq WShi |
| * - 'Bloomin Baby' | CRow |
| - 'Flore Pleno' (d) | CRow CWat EHon EMFW LPBA MBal MSta SWat |
| - var. *leucopetala* | WMAq |
| *subulata* | CRow |

## SAINTPAULIA (Gesneriaceae)

| | |
|---|---|
| 'Bright Eyes' ♀ | Last listed 1992 |
| 'Colorado' ♀ | Last listed 1992 |
| 'Delft' ♀ | Last listed 1992 |
| 'Fancy Trail' ♀ | Last listed 1995 |
| 'Garden News' ♀ | Last listed 1992 |
| 'Granger's Wonderland' ♀ | Last listed 1995 |
| 'Gredi' ♀ | Last listed 1992 |
| 'Ice Maiden' ♀ | Last listed 1992 |
| 'Maria' ♀ | Last listed 1992 |
| 'Midget Valentine' ♀ | Last listed 1995 |
| 'Moon Kissed' ♀ | Last listed 1995 |
| 'Phoenix' ♀ | Last listed 1992 |
| 'Rococo Pink' ♀ | Last listed 1992 |
| 'Starry Trail' ♀ | Last listed 1992 |
| 'Tomahawk' ♀ | Last listed 1995 |

## SALIX ✿ (Salicaceae)

| | |
|---|---|
| *acutifolia* | ELan EPla IOrc NSti SPla |
| - 'Blue Streak' (m) ♀ | CEnd CMHG EPfP EPla EWes IOrc MAsh MBal MBlu MRav NBir SWat |
| - 'Pendulifolia' (m) | IOrc |
| *adenophylla* Hook. | See *S. cordata* |
| *aegyptiaca* | CDoC CLnd MBlu NWea WMou |
| *alba* | CCVT CKin CLnd EOHP GChr LBuc WDin WMou |
| - f. *argentea* | See *S. alba* var. *sericea* |
| - 'Aurea' | CLnd CTho MRav WMou |
| - subsp. *caerulea* | CLnd ENot LBuc NWea WMou |
| - 'Cardinalis' (f) | Last listed 1996 |
| - 'Chermesina' hort. | See *S. alba* subsp. *vitellina* 'Britzensis' |
| - 'Dart's Snake' | CBlo CEnd EBee ELan ENot MRav SCoo SMad SPer |
| - 'Hutchinson's Yellow' | EPla MBri MGos |
| - 'Liempde' (m) | ENot MRav |

| | |
|---|---|
| - 'Orange Spire' | Last listed 1997 |
| § - var. *sericea* ♀ | CB&S CLnd CMHG CTho ENot EPla IOrc MBal MBlu MRav NFor NLon NWea SMad SPer WDin WGer WMou WTro WWat |
| - 'Splendens' | See *S. alba* var. *sericea* |
| N - 'Tristis' | CDul CLnd CTri ELan GChr MAsh MBri MGos NWea SRms WDin WFar WHar |
| - subsp. *vitellina* ♀ | CBlo CKin ELan GChr LBuc MBNS MBrn NHol NWea SWat WDin WOrn |
| § - - 'Britzensis' ♀ | More than 30 suppliers |
| - 'Vitellina Pendula' | See *S. alba* 'Tristis' |
| - 'Vitellina Tristis' | See *S. alba* 'Tristis' |
| § *alpina* | CLyd EHyt EWes GAri MBal NHol NRoo NWoo |
| *apoda* (m) | CLyd ESis EWes MBal NHar NHol WPer |
| § *arbuscula* | CB&S CBlo CDoC EHyt MBNS MBal MPla NHar NWCA SPan |
| *arctica* var. *petraea* | MBro WPat |
| *aurita* | CDul GChr |
| *babylonica* | CBlo CDul CTrG NBee WDin WMou |
| - 'Annularis' | See *S. babylonica* 'Crispa' |
| § - 'Crispa' | EHic EHyt ELan EPla ERav LHop MRav SMad SPla WLRN |
| - var. *pekinensis* 'Pendula' | MUlv |
| § - - 'Tortuosa' ♀ | CArn CLnd CTho EBee ECrN ELan ENot GChr IOrc LHop LPan MAsh MBal MBar MGos MTis MWat NBea NFor NPer NWea SLon SPer SRms WHar WWat |
| *bockii* | CBlo EBee MBar NWCA WAbe WPer WWat |
| § - 'Bowles' Hybrid' | CAgr LBuc MRav WMou |
| 'Boydii' (f) ♀ | CFee EHyt ELan EPot GDra GTou MAsh MBal MBri MBro MDun MGos MPla NFor NHar NHol NLon NMen NRoo SIng SRms SSmi STre WAbe WPat |
| § 'Boyd's Pendulous' (m) | CFee CLyd EHyt GAri MBal MBar SIng |
| *breviserrata* | CLyd GDra NWCA |
| *burjatica* | Last listed 1996 |
| ¶ *caesia* | SRPl |
| *calyculata* | Last listed 1998 |
| *caprea* | CB&S CCVT CKin CLnd CTri ECrN ENot GChr GRei LBuc LHyr NWea WDin WMou WTro |
| ¶ - 'Black Stem' | CNat |
| - 'Curlilocks' | CBlo COtt EBee MBar MBlu |
| § - 'Kilmarnock' (m) ♀ | CB&S CBlo CDul CLnd EBee ELan EWTr GRei LBuc LHyr LPan MAsh MBar MGos MRav MWat NBea NBee NHol NWea SMad SPer WDin WFar WHar WMou |
| - var. *pendula* (f) | See *S. caprea* 'Weeping Sally' |
| - - (m) | See *S. caprea* 'Kilmarnock' (m) |
| - var. *variegata* | Last listed 1997 |
| § - 'Weeping Sally' (f) | SRPl |
| *capusii* | Last listed 1997 |
| *cashmiriana* | CFai CLyd MBro NHol WPat |
| ¶ *caspica rubra nana* | SWat |
| x *cernua* | NWCA |
| 'Chrysocoma' | See *S.* x *sepulcralis* var. *chrysocoma* |
| *cinerea* | CB&S CDoC CDul CKin ENot GChr GRei NWea WDin |
| - subsp. *oleifolia* | GChr |
| - 'Tricolor' | CArn CDoC GCHN |

| | |
|---|---|
| - 'Variegata' | Last listed 1996 |
| x *cottetii* | CBlo |
| *daphnoides* | CDoC CDul CLnd CSam ELan ENot EPla GRei IOrc LNor MBrN NSti NWea SPer SPla SRms STre WDin WMou WWat |
| - 'Aglaia' (m) ♀ | CB&S CTri EPla MBal WPGP |
| - 'Meikle' | CAgr |
| 'E.A. Bowles' | See *S.* 'Bowles' Hybrid' |
| x *ehrhartiana* | CNat |
| § *elaeagnos* ♀ | CCVT CDoC CPle CTho EBee ENot MBNS MBlu MBrN MRav SPan SPer SWat WDin WMou |
| § - subsp. *angustifolia* | CDul CLnd ELan IOrc LBuc LHop MBal MRav MTis NWea SMad SRms STre WWat WWin |
| ¶ *elbrusensis* | EPla |
| 'Elegantissima' | See *S. pendulina* var. *elegantissima* |
| x *erdingeri* | EPla |
| § 'Erythroflexuosa' | CB&S CBlo CDoC CMHG CTho EBee EBrP EBre ELan EPla LBre MAsh MBar MGos NBea NWea SBre SEas SMad SPla SWat WHer WOak |
| *exigua* | CB&S CDul CTho EBee ELan ENot EWTr EWes IOrc MBar MBlu MBrN MBri MGos MHlr MRav NWea SDry SMad SPer SRPl SSpi WCot WMou WWat |
| *fargesii* | CBot CDoC CEnd CFee CFil CHan EBee ELan EPla GOrc LHop MBal MBlu MDun MGos MRav NHar SDix SSpi WCot WCru WPat WWat |
| § x *finnmarchica* | MBro |
| *formosa* | See *S. arbuscula* |
| *fragilis* | CCVT CDoC CDul CKin CLnd MRav NWea WDin WMou WTro |
| § *fruticulosa* | CGle CInt GAri GCrs GDra GTou MBal NWCA WLin WWat |
| 'Fuiri-koriyanagi' | See *S. integra* 'Hakuro-nishiki' |
| *furcata* | See *S. fruticulosa* |
| *glauca* | CNat |
| *glaucosericea* | EBee EHic WLRN WWat |
| 'Golden Curls' | See *S.* 'Erythroflexuosa' |
| *gracilistyla* | CTho EPla WMou WWat |
| § - 'Melanostachys' (m) ♀ | More than 30 suppliers |
| x *grahamii* (f) | MBal |
| - 'Moorei' (f) | MBal NWCA |
| x *greyi* | CSam EPla NPro |
| 'Hagensis' | See *S.* 'The Hague' |
| *hastata* 'Wehrhahnii' (m) ♀ | More than 30 suppliers |
| *helvetica* ♀ | More than 30 suppliers |
| *herbacea* | ESis GAri GTou MBal NMen WPer |
| *hibernica* | See *S. phylicifolia* |
| x *hirtei* 'Reifenweide' (f) | CDoC GChr |
| *hookeriana* | CMHG CTho ELan EPla MBal MBrN MRav NHol SLPl SSpi WMou WWat |
| *humilis* var. *microphylla* | CBlo |
| *hylematica* | See *S. fruticulosa* |
| *incana* | See *S. elaeagnos* |
| *integra* 'Albomaculata' | See *S. integra* 'Hakuro-nishiki' |
| § - 'Hakuros' (v) | More than 30 suppliers |
| - 'Pendula' (f) | WGer |
| *irrorata* | CBot CDul CLnd IOrc NSti WMou |
| 'Jacquinii' | See *S. alpina* |
| *japonica* hort. | See *S. babylonica* 'Lavalleei' |
| - Thunberg | Last listed 1996 |
| *kinuyanagi* (m) | ELan LHop SMrm |
| 'Kuro-me' | See *S. gracilistyla* 'Melanostachys' |

| | |
|---|---|
| *lanata* ♀ | More than 30 suppliers |
| - hybrid | MBro NHol WAbe WLin WPat |
| - Kew form | Last listed 1997 |
| - 'Mark Postill' | See *S.* 'Mark Postill' |
| - 'Stuartii' | See *S.* 'Stuartii' |
| *lapponum* | GAri GRei MBro SRms WPat |
| x *laurina* (f) | Last listed 1996 |
| § *lindleyana* | CHan CNic EHyt GAri MPla NMen NOak NRoo NSti WWat |
| 'Maerd Brno' (f) | MBlu |
| *magnifica* ♀ | CEnd CFil CLnd CPle EBee EPar EPla IDee MBal MSte SBid SDry SMad SSpi SWat WMou |
| § 'Mark Postill' (f) | CDoC CFil LFis MBNS SPla |
| *matsudana* | See *S. babylonica* var. *pekinensis* |
| - 'Tortuosa' | See *S. babylonica* var. *pekinensis* 'Tortuosa' |
| - 'Tortuosa Aureopendula' | See *S.* 'Erythroflexuosa' |
| 'Melanostachys' | See *S. gracilistyla* 'Melanostachys' |
| *moupinensis* | IOrc WMou |
| x *myricoides* | See *S.* x *bebbii* |
| § *myrsinifolia* | EPla MBlu MRav |
| *myrsinites* | See *S. alpina* |
|   var. *jacquiniana* | |
| *myrtilloides* | CLyd |
| - 'Pink Tassels' (m) | EHyt MBal MBlu NWCA SIng WPat |
| - x *repens* | See *S.* x *finnmarchica* |
| *nakamurana* | CFai CFee GAri MAsh MBal MBro |
|   var. *yezoalpina* | MRav NHol NPro SRms WPat WPyg WWat |
| *nepalensis* | See *S. lindleyana* |
| *nigricans* | See *S. myrsinifolia* |
| *nivalis* | EPot NWCA |
| *occidentalis* | See *S. humilis* |
| * 'Onoga' | Last listed 1998 |
| 'Onusta' (m) | Last listed 1997 |
| x *ovata* | CLyd GCrs NMen |
| § *pendulina* | CTho |
|   var. *elegantissima* | |
| *pentandra* | CBot CDul CKin GChr IOrc NWea WDin WMou WWat |
| § *phylicifolia* | CNat WMou |
| *polaris* | CLyd GAri MBal |
| *procumbens* | See *S. myrsinites* |
| *prunifolia* | See *S. arbuscula* |
| § *purpurea* | CB&S CDul EHic IOrc SRms WDin WMou |
| - 'Dicky Meadows' | CAgr |
| - 'Goldstones' | CAgr |
| - f. *gracilis* | See *S. purpurea* 'Nana' |
| - 'Green Dicks' | CAgr |
| - 'Helix' | See *S. purpurea* |
| - 'Howki' | WMou |
| § - 'Nana' | CLTr CLyd CPle ELan EPfP EPla MBal MWhi SChu SLPl SPer STre WStI WTro WWat |
| - 'Nancy Saunders' (f) | CBos CTho EHoe EPPr EPla GBuc MBNS MBlu MRav MSte NPro NSti SUsu SWas WCot WSHC |
| - 'Pendula' ♀ | CBlo CEnd CTho EBee ENot GOrc LHyr MAsh MBal MBar MBri MRav NWCA NWea SPer WDin WStI |
| - 'Richartii' (f) | NSti WLRN |
| *pyrenaica* | CLyd EWes NWCA |
| *repens* | GAri MBar SRms STre SWat WDin |
| - var. *argentea* ♀ | CGle ENot EPfP GDra IOrc MBal MBar MRav NWea SPer WDin WWat WWin |
| - from Saint Kilda | GCrs MBro WPat |
| - 'Iona' (m) | CBlo CLyd SIng |

| | |
|---|---|
| - *pendula* | See *S.* 'Boyd's Pendulous' (m) |
| - 'Voorthuizen' (f) | EBee EHyt ELan ESis MBar WGer WPyg |
| *reticulata* ♀ | GCrs GDra GTou MBal NHar NMen NRya NWoo WPat |
| *retusa* | CTri EHyt GAri GDra GTou MBro MPla NHar NHol NMen WPat WPyg |
| - x *pyrenaica* | ECho |
| *rosmarinifolia* hort. | See *S. elaeagnos* subsp. *angustifolia* |
| x *rubens* 'Basfordiana' (m) ♀ | CDoC CLnd CTho EPla EWes GChr LNor MBNS MRav SLon WLRN WMou WOrn |
| x *rubra* 'Eugenei' (m) | CDul EPla GQui MBlu SWat WBcn WMou WWat WWin |
| *sachalinensis* | See *S. udensis* |
| *schraderiana* Willd. | See *S. bicolor* Willd. |
| x *sepulcralis* | CDul NWea |
| § - var. *chrysocoma* ♀ | CDoC EBee ENot GAri LBuc LHyr LPan MAsh MBal MGos MWat NBee SCoo SPer SRPl WLRN |
| *serpyllifolia* | CLyd CTri EHyt ESis MBal MBro NHol NMen WPat WPyg |
| - x *retusa* | NWCA |
| *serpyllum* | See *S. fruticulosa* |
| 'Setsuka' | See *S. udensis* 'Sekka' |
| x *simulatrix* | CLyd EHyt ESis GAri MBar NWCA WWat |
| x *smithiana* | See *S.* x *stipularis* |
| § x *stipularis* (f) | CLnd CMHG EPla NWea |
| § 'Stuartii' | CSam ESis GOrc MBar NMen NWCA SRms |
| *subopposita* | CDoC CDul EBee EHic ELan EWes GOrc MBNS MBar MBlu MPla NPro SIng WWat |
| *syrticola* | See *S. cordata* |
| x *tetrapla* 'Hutchinson's Nigricans' | Last listed 1998 |
| *triandra* | WMou |
| - 'Black Hollander' | CAgr |
| - 'Black Maul' | CAgr |
| - 'Semperflorens' | CNat |
| - 'Whissander' | CAgr |
| *tristis* | See *S. humilis* |
| x *tsugaluensis* 'Ginme' (f) | CDul CMHG SLPl WTro WWat |
| § *udensis* | Last listed 1996 |
| § - 'Sekka' (m) | CB&S CLnd CMHG CTho ECtt ELan EPar EPla GChr IOrc MBal NHol NWea STre SWat WMou WPyg |
| *uva-ursi* | CLyd GAri MBal |
| *viminalis* | CAgr CCVT CDul CKin ENot GChr GRei LBuc NWea WDin WMou |
| - 'Bowles' Hybrid' | See *S.* 'Bowles' Hybrid' |
| - 'Brown Merrin' | CAgr |
| - 'Reader's Red' (m) | CAgr |
| - 'Yellow Osier' | CAgr |
| *violescens* | Last listed 1997 |
| *vitellina* 'Pendula' | See *S. alba* 'Tristis' |
| § *waldsteiniana* | MBar |
| x *wimmeriana* | SRms |
| 'Yelverton' | EPla MBri MRav SWat |

## SALVIA ✿ (Lamiaceae)

| | |
|---|---|
| *acetabulosa* | See *S. multicaulis* |
| *aethiopis* | CPle CSev ECoo ELan EMar EOld LGre MLLN MSte NChi SPil WPer WWye |
| *afghanica* | CPle MRav |
| § *africana-caerulea* | CPle LPio WWye |

§ *africana-lutea* — CHal CPle CSev CStr EBee EGar ELan LHil LPio MBEx MMil SBid WCot WPen WPer
- 'Kirstenbosch' — CPle MRav WCot WPer WWye
*agnes* — CPle
*albimaculata* — SBla
*algeriensis* — CPle
*amarissima* — CPle CStr
*ambigens* — See *S. guaranitica* 'Blue Enigma'
\* *amgiana* — Last listed 1996
§ *amplexicaulis* — CPle WPer WWye
*angustifolia* Cavanilles — See *S. reptans*
- Michaux — See *S. azurea*
*apiana* — SAga SIgm SPil WCot
*argentea* ♀ — CArn CB&S CBos CGle CHad CPle EBot EBrP EBre ECha EHol ELan LBre LGre LHop MNrw MWgw SBre SCob SHFr SRCN WCHb WCru WEas WHal WOve WPer WWin WWye
*arizonica* — CPle CStr EBee GCal LIck MLLN
*atrocyanea* — CPle CStr LHil SLod
*aucheri* — CPle EGar GBuc GCal
*aurea* — See *S. africana-lutea*
*austriaca* — CPle MBel SHFr WPer WWye
§ *azurea* — CArn CFri CPle EBee LGre LPio MNrw MSte SMrm SPil
- subsp. *pitcheri* — CStr
- - var. *grandiflora* — EBee
*bacheriana* — See *S. buchananii*
§ *barrelieri* — CHea CPle CStr NChi SHFr SLod
'Belhaven' — Last listed 1998
*bertolonii* — See *S. pratensis* Bertolonii Group
*bicolor* Desfontaines — See *S. barrelieri*
*blancoana* — CArn CBot CHan CPle EBee ECha ELau EMan LEdu LHop MBEx MHer MLLN MSte MWgw NChi SAga SCro SUsu WHal WSel
*blepharophylla* — CPle CSev CSpe EBee GBri LHil LHop MSte MWat SAga WPen WWol WWoo WWye
'Blue Bird' — Last listed 1997
*brachyantha* — CPle EGar
§ *brevilabra* — Last listed 1996
*broussonetii* — Last listed 1998
§ *buchananii* ♀ — CHad CHal CHan CLon CPle CSWP CSam ELan EMil EOrc ERea GBri GQui LHop LIck NPri SAga SBid SCro SMrm SRCN SSoC WOld WPnn WWye
*bulleyana* — CFai CGle CHea CLyd CPle CSev EBee ELan EOrc GBin GCal LHol MNrw NChi NGdn NSti SHFr SPil SSoC WFar WOve WPer WWin WWye
*cacaliifolia* ♀ — CLTr CLon CPle CSpe CStr EEls EOrc GBri LBlm LHil MHar MLLN MNrw MSte MWat SBid SHFr SPer SUsu WCom WCot WEas WHer WWye
*cadmica* — Last listed 1996
*caerulea* L. — See *S. africana-caerulea*
- hort. — See *S. guaranitica* 'Black and Blue'
*caespitosa* — CPle EHyt NWCA SBla SIng
*campanulata* — CPle EBee
- CC&McK 1071 — CFir
aff. *campanulata* ACE 2379 — Last listed 1997
*canariensis* — CPle LHil MSte SAga SHFr WSan WWye

\* - f. *alba* — CPle
- f. *candidissima* — CPle
*candelabrum* ♀ — CHan CLon CMea CMil CPle EOrc LGre MWgw NLak SAga SHFr WCHb WCot WHer WKif WOut WSHC WWye
*candidissima* — Last listed 1998
*canescens* — Last listed 1998
*cardinalis* — See *S. fulgens*
*carduacea* — Last listed 1998
*castanea* — CPle EBee
§ *chamaedryoides* — CCan CPle CStr WHil WWye
- silver — CSpe LGre LHil
*chapalensis* — CPle SAga
*chiapensis* — CPle EOrc
*chinensis* — See *S. japonica*
¶ 'Christine Yeo' — CPle EBee SDys
*cinnabarina* — CPin CPle CStr
*cleistogama* — CStr EBee NBur
*clevelandii* — CArn CPle SPil
*coahuilensis* — LGre SWas WWye
*coccinea* — CBot CGle CPle EWTr GBri MSte NBus SHFr WPer WWye
\* - 'Cherry Blossom' — SWat
- 'Coral Nymph' — CPle EOrc LIck SDys SLod SSoC WRos
- 'Desert Blaze' — Last listed 1996
- 'Indigo' — EBee EGar ELan EPfP GBri WSan
- 'Lactea' — CBot CStr
- 'Lady in Red' ♀ — EOrc LIck SMrm SWat
- pink — Last listed 1998
\* - 'Snow Nymph' — LIck
*columbariae* — Last listed 1998
*compacta* — Last listed 1998
*concolor* Lamb. — CPle CStr GCal LHil
- hort. — See *S. guaranitica*
*confertiflora* — CAbb CHal CPle CSam CSev CSpe CWit ELan EOrc EWTr GBri LHil LHop MBEx MLLN MSCN MSte SAga SBid SDys SLod SMrm WElm WWye
*corrugata* — CPle CSpe CStr EPri GBri LGre LHil MTis SDys SVen WSPU WWye
*cryptantha* — CStr
*cyanescens* — CPle EBee EPot
*darcyi* — CHan CKel CPle EBee LGre LHop SIgm WPen WWye
*davidsonii* — CPle
'Dear Anja' — EFou LGre
*deserta* — See *S. x sylvestris*
*digitaloides* — CPle GBin
*discolor* ♀ — CBot CHad CPle CSev CSpe CStr ELan ERea GQui LBlm LEdu LHil LHop LPio MBEx MBNS MLLN MSCN MTho SRCN SSoC WCHb WWye
\* - nigra — CMdw
*disermas* — CPle CStr WHil
*divinorum* — EOHP
- palatable strain — Last listed 1998
*dolichantha* — CPle
*dolomitica* — CPle
*dombeyi* — Last listed 1998
*dominica* — CPle
*dorisiana* — CPin CPle CSev ELan EOHP LBlm MSte SVen WJek
¶ *dorrii* var. *dorrii* — CStr
*eigii* — Last listed 1998
¶ 'El Salto' — LHil
§ *elegans* — CCan CMHG CPle CSev ELau EPri EWes LBlm LIck MSCN MSte SBid SCro SIde SLon SUsu WCer WOld

| | |
|---|---|
| ¶ - 'Frieda Dixon' | EOHP |
| ¶ - prostrate form | WCot |
| § - 'Scarlet Pineapple' | More than 30 suppliers |
| * - 'Tangerine Sage' | CArn EOHP MMal SPil SRCN WBea WGwG WOak |
| ¶ *eremostachya* | CStr |
| *fallax* | CPle |
| ¶ *farinacea* | EWTr |
| - 'Alba' | Last listed 1998 |
| - 'Blue Victory' ♀ | Last listed 1995 |
| - 'Rhea' | LIck |
| - 'Silver' | Last listed 1998 |
| - 'Strata' | CPle EHic SRCN |
| - 'Victoria' ♀ | CPle ELau LPVe |
| - 'White Victory' ♀ | Last listed 1995 |
| *forreri* CD&R 1269 | CPle CStr |
| *forsskaolii* | CArn CBrm CGle CHal CHan CLTr CLyd CPle CSev EBee ECtt ELan EWTr LFis LLWP MBro MFir MNrw MRav MWrn NHol NSti SChu SHFr WBea WHoo WPer WWin WWye |
| *frigida* | Last listed 1998 |
| § *fruticosa* | CArn CHan CPle EEls ELau SIde SPil |
| § *fulgens* ♀ | CGle CPle CSev CStr CWit ILis LBlm LHil NBro SBid SHFr SIde WCHb WCot WEas WKif WWhi WWye |
| * x *geradit* | NBir |
| *gesneriiflora* | CAbb CPle CSev LHop MSCN MSte SBid SIde SMrm WPer WWye |
| *glutinosa* | CArn CHad CHan CPle CSam EBee ECha ELan GCal LHol MBel MNrw NBro NCat NHex NSti SAga WPer WWye |
| - HH&K 294 | CHan |
| *grahamii* | See *S. microphylla* var. *microphylla* |
| *grandiflora* Etl. HH&K 210 | See *S. tomentosa* Etl. HH&K 210 |
| *greggii* | CFai CHan CPle EWes LPio MBEx MSCN MSte SAga SPer SWat WHil WOve WPer WWin WWye |
| - 'Alba' | CHal CPle CStr LHop LIck SBid |
| - 'Blush Pink' | See *S. microphylla* 'Pink Blush' |
| - CD&R 1148 | LHop LIck SDys |
| ♦ - 'Devon Cream' | See *S. greggii* 'Sungold' |
| - 'Keter's Red' | CPle |
| § - x *lycioides* | CPle CSev EBee LHil LHop LPio SAga SBid SUsu WSHC |
| - 'Peach' ♀ | CPle CSpe EBee EWes LHil LPio MBEx MLLN MSte NBrk SAga SUsu WAbe WFoF WPnn WWye |
| - 'Peach' misapplied | See *S.* x *jamensis* 'Pat Vlasto' |
| - 'Raspberry Royal' | See *S.* 'Raspberry Royale' |
| § - 'Sungold' | CAbP CPle CStr EBee LRHS |
| - yellow | LPio LRHS |
| § *guaranitica* ♀ | CAbb CBot CGle CPle CSpe EBrP EBre ELan LBre LPio MRav SAga SBre SPer SRCN SRPl SUsu WCHb WEas WSan |
| - 'Argentine Skies' | CLon CPle LHil LPio SDys WWye |
| § - 'Black and Blue' | CCan CGle CLTr CPle CSWP CSev EPPr GBri LBlm LIck MSCN MSte MWat SSoC SVen WPer WPnn WWye |
| § - 'Blue Enigma' ♀ | CArn CB&S CBot CCan CHea CLon CSev EBee ECha EGar EMan EMar EOrc EPPr GBri LHil LHop LIck LPio MBel SDix SDys SUsu WEas WPen WWye |

| | |
|---|---|
| *haematodes* | See *S. pratensis* Haematodes Group |
| *heldreichiana* | CPle |
| ¶ *henryi* | CStr |
| *hians* | CFir CGle CHal CHan CPle EBee ECoo EMar EOrc GBri MBro MNrw NLak NWoo SAga SRms WCer WHoo WOve WPer WPyg WWye |
| *hierosolymitana* | CFri CPle CStr SHFr SUsu |
| *hirtella* | CPle |
| *hispanica* hort. | See *S. lavandulifolia* |
| - L. | CPle |
| *horminum* | See *S. viridis* |
| *hypargeia* | EBee ECGN |
| *indica* | SRms |
| 'Indigo Spires' ♀ | CHan CLon CMdw CStr EBee EPPr GBri LBlm LGre LHil MHlr MLLN SAga SBid SMrm SUsu WKif WPen WWye |
| *interrupta* | CPle ECha EHol EOHP EWes GBar LFis SAga SChu SDix WEas WPen |
| *involucrata* ♀ | CFir CHan CPle CSev EBee EOrc GCal GQui LHil NBro SBid SCob SCro SMrm SRCN WEas WSHC WSpi |
| - 'Bethellii' | More than 30 suppliers |
| - 'Boutin' ♀ | CCan CPle LBlm WEas |
| - dark form | MSte |
| § - 'Hadspen' | CBot CCan CHad CSam CStr LIck MAvo |
| - 'Mrs Pope' | See *S. involucrata* 'Hadspen' |
| § - var. *puberula* | CHan CPle |
| - - 'El Butano' | CPle |
| *iodantha* | CPle WWye |
| ¶ x *jamensis* | LHil |
| - 'Cherry Queen' | CPle CStr |
| - 'Devantville' | CPle SBid SLod |
| - 'El Duranzo' | CPle LGre LPio |
| - 'Fuego' | CPle |
| - 'James Compton' | LHil LPio MSte SBid SHFr SIgm |
| - 'La Luna' | CHan CLon CPle CSev EPri LGre LHil LHop LPio MBEx MSCN MSte SLod SSoC SUsu WPen WPnn WSpi WWye |
| - 'La Siesta' | CPle CSev CStr LPio SAga WPnn |
| - 'La Tarde' | CLon CPle EBee LPio MBEx MSte SAga |
| - 'Los Lirios' ♀ | CHan CPle GBri SLod SMrm SSoC |
| * - 'Moonlight Serenade' | CPle CSev CStr |
| § - 'Pat Vlasto' | CLon CPle EBee GBri LGre LIck MSte SAga SBid SMrm WEas WPen WWye |
| - pink seedling | Last listed 1997 |
| ¶ - 'Pleasant Pink' | CPle EBee |
| § *japonica* | CPle WWye |
| *judaica* | CPle CStr EBee EHal MLLN WOut |
| *jurisicii* | CFir CPle CStr EOrc EWll MBro MLLN SBid SHFr SIgm SMrm SRCN SSca SUsu WHoo WPyg |
| *karwinskyi* | Last listed 1998 |
| *keerlii* | Last listed 1998 |
| *koyamae* | Last listed 1998 |
| ¶ *kuznetzovii* | EBee |
| *lanceolata* | See *S. reflexa* |
| *lanigera* | Last listed 1996 |
| § *lavandulifolia* | CArn CBel CPle ECha EFou ELan ELau EMon EPri EWes MHar MMal MRav NLon NSti SIde SPla SUsu WAbe WCHb WHer WHoo WLin WOak WPen WPer WSel WWat WWye |

| | |
|---|---|
| - pink | Last listed 1997 |
| *lemmonii* | See *S. microphylla* var. *wislizenii* |
| *leptophylla* | See *S. reptans* |
| *leucantha* ♀ | More than 30 suppliers |
| - 'Purple Velvet' | CPle |
| *leucophylla* | CStr SIgm SLon |
| *longispicata* | CPle WWye |
| *lycioides* A.Gray | CPle SDys |
| - hort. | See *S. greggii* x *lycioides* |
| *lyrata* | CPle EBee EOHP MSal NSti SHFr SPil SSca STes SUsu WCru WWye |
| *macellaria* | EBee |
| - yellow form | Last listed 1998 |
| *madrensis* | CPle |
| ¶ *marocana* | CStr |
| *mellifera* | CArn CPle LHop WWye |
| ¶ *merjamie* | EBee |
| - 'Mint-sauce' | CElw CPla MAvo MCCP MNrw MWrn NChi NPro NSti STes WBea |
| *mexicana* | CPle GBri LBlm LHil WEas |
| - var. *major* | Last listed 1996 |
| - var. *minor* | CCan CPle LHop WPer |
| - T&K 550 | CBot |
| *microphylla* | CArn CGle CLTr CMHG CPle CWit ELau EOHP EWes GBar LHil MChe MMal MSCN NFai SHFr SOkh SYvo WCru WHCG WPer |
| - *alba* | Last listed 1996 |
| - 'Cerro Potosi' | CHan CLon CSev CStr GBri LHil SHFr WPen |
| * - 'Huntingdon Red' | ELau EOHP |
| - 'Kew Red' ♀ | CPle CStr |
| - 'La Foux' | CBel CHea LGre LHil NLak SDys SMrm |
| - 'Maraschino' | Last listed 1998 |
| § - var. *microphylla* | More than 30 suppliers |
| - - 'Newby Hall' ♀ | CBrm CLon CPle LHil MBEx MBel MSte WEas WPer |
| - var. *neurepia* | See *S. microphylla* var. *microphylla* |
| ¶ - - 'Oxford' | LFis |
| ¶ - 'Oregon Peach' | LRHS |
| ¶ - 'Oxford' | CPle |
| § - 'Pink Blush' ♀ | CAbP CBot CPle ELan EMan EOrc EPri LHil LHop MAsh MLLN MMil MSte SAga SSpi WOve WSHC |
| - 'Pleasant View' ♀ | CPle |
| - purple form | EBee GCal |
| * - 'Raspberry Ice' | LRHS |
| § - 'Ruth Stungo' (v) | CPle SAga |
| ¶ - 'Trebah' | CSpe CTbh LWoo SCoo |
| ¶ - 'Trelissick' | LWoo SCoo WWoo |
| ¶ - 'Trenance' | SCoo WWoo |
| ¶ - 'Trewithen' | LWoo SCoo |
| - 'Variegata' splashed | See *S. microphylla* 'Ruth Stungo' |
| § - var. *wislizenii* | CPle CStr SCro WPer |
| *microstegia* | Last listed 1998 |
| ¶ *miltiorrhiza* | EOHP |
| *miniata* | CPle sUsu |
| *moelleri* | MSCN |
| *moorcroftiana* | CPle EBee NLak WPer |
| ¶ *muelleri* | CSpe |
| § *multicaulis* ♀ | CHan CPle ECha EMan GCal MRav MSCN NLak NTow WCHb WCot WPer WSHC |
| ¶ *munzii* | CStr |
| ¶ *napifolia* | CStr EBee LGre SUsu |
| *nemorosa* | CHan EBee MTPN NLar SHFr SRms |
| - 'Amethyst' ♀ | CHal CLon CPle EFou LGre MBel MBri MLLN SChu SHel SMrm SWas WCot |

| | |
|---|---|
| ¶ - 'Brightness' | EFou |
| - East Friesland | See *S. nemorosa* 'Ostfriesland' |
| - HH&K 246 | CHan |
| - 'Lubecca' ♀ | CPle EBee EFou MLLN MMil NCat NPri SMrm SOkh SPer SUsu WLRN WRus |
| § - 'Ostfriesland' ♀ | More than 30 suppliers |
| - 'Pusztaflamme' ♀ | CHad CStr EBee ECha EMan LGre LRHS MBri MBro MCLN MLLN SCro WCot WHoo |
| - 'Rose Queen' | Last listed 1997 |
| - 'Rosenwein' | EBee GBuc LGre |
| § - subsp. *tesquicola* | CHan CMdw ECha |
| - 'Wesuwe' | CPle ECha |
| *neurepia* | See *S. microphylla* var. *microphylla* |
| *nilotica* | CPle EBee SHFr WHer |
| *nipponica* | CPle WPer |
| ¶ - 'Fuji Snow' (v) | EWes NPro WCot WHil |
| *nubicola* | CPle CStr EHic GPoy SLod WWye |
| *nutans* | Last listed 1998 |
| *officinalis* | CAgr CArn CChe CHal EBee ELau GBar GPoy MBal MBar MBri MChe MGos MMal MWat NFor NPri SHFr SPlb SRCN SRPl WDin WGwG WMow WOak WPer WWat WWye |
| - 'Alba' | See *S. officinalis* 'Albiflora' |
| § - 'Albiflora' | CBot COIW CPle ECha EOHP EWTr GBar LHol LLWP MLLN NLon NSti SIde WJek WPer |
| N - 'Aurea' | EPar GPoy MBar MFir NFla NPri SUsu |
| - 'Berggarten' | CArn EFou EGar EGoo ELau EOHP EPPr EPri GBar GCal LGre LHol LHop LPio MRav NSti SSvw WHer WLin |
| I - 'Blackcurrant' | NPri WGwG |
| § - broad-leaved | CBot CJew CSWP ELau MLLN SIde SWat WGwG WJek WWye |
| - 'Cedric' | Last listed 1998 |
| * - *extrakta* | EOHP |
| * - 'Giant' | SPil |
| I - 'Ginger' | Last listed 1998 |
| - 'Grandiflora' | Last listed 1998 |
| - 'Grete Stolze' | EFou |
| - 'Herrenhausen' | CPle MSte WPen |
| § - 'Icterina' (v) ♀ | More than 30 suppliers |
| - 'Kew Gold' ♀ | EGar ELau EMon GBar LHop MRav WJek |
| - *latifolia* | See *S. officinalis* broad-leaved |
| - 'Minor' | EGoo MHar WHer |
| * - 'Minor Alba' | WHil |
| - narrow-leaved | See *S. lavandulifolia* |
| * - *prostrata* | EOHP |
| - Purpurascens Group ♀ | More than 30 suppliers |
| - 'Purpurascens Variegata' | CStr GBar NSti WEas WJek |
| - 'Robin Hill' | CBod ERic GBar GNau |
| - 'Rosea' | CPle CStr EGoo GBar |
| - 'Selsley Splash' | Last listed 1998 |
| * - tangerine | NPri |
| - Tomentosa Group | CArn |
| - 'Tricolor' (v) ♀ | More than 30 suppliers |
| - 'Variegata' | See *S. officinalis* 'Icterina' |
| *oppositiflora* ♀ | CPle MLLN SAga |
| *oresbia* | Last listed 1997 |
| *pachyphylla* | SIgm |
| *patens* ♀ | CHad CPle CSev CSpe ELan EOrc EPri EWTr LHol LHop NChi NFai NOrc NSti NWes SAga SHFr SOWG SRms SUsu WCHb WEas WOld WPer WRus WSpi WWin WWye |

| | | |
|---|---|---|
| - misapplied 'Alba' | See *S. patens* 'White Trophy' | |
| ¶ - 'Blue Trophy' | LIck | |
| - 'Cambridge Blue' ♀ | CBot CHad CPle CRDP CSev | |
| | CSpe ECha ELan EOHP LBlm LFis | |
| | LHil LHol LHop MHar NPer SAga | |
| | SBla SCro SRCN SUsu WCot WEas | |
| | WMaN WPer WPnn WSpi WWye | |
| - 'Chilcombe' | CHan CPle CStr LBlm LHil LHop | |
| | MBNS MBel SAga SChu SCro SDys | |
| | SHFr SUsu WHoo WPer WPnn | |
| | WWye | |
| - 'Guanajuato' | CPle CSam CStr LGre LHil LHop | |
| | MHar SBid SMrm WHil | |
| - 'Lavender Lady' | CSam MSCN WMaN | |
| - 'Oxford Blue' | Last listed 1997 | |
| - 'Royal Blue' | ECha EGle LPio | |
| ¶ - 'White Trophy' | CLon CPle ELan EOrc EPri LBlm | |
| | LHop LIck MAvo NCut NPri SBid | |
| | SCro SLod SUsu WRus WWye | |
| 'Peaches and Cream' | Last listed 1997 | |
| *penstemonoides* | Last listed 1998 | |
| *polystachya* | CPle WWye | |
| *pomifera* | Last listed 1996 | |
| *populifolia* | Last listed 1997 | |
| *pratensis* | CArn CKin CLon CPle ELan EMon | |
| | GBar LPio MSal NChi WOak WPer | |
| | WWye | |
| - 'Albiflora' | EMon SSvw | |
| § - Bertolonii Group | CHan CPle EBee MBel SEND | |
| § - Haematodes Group ♀ | CHad CPle EBee EBrP EBre ECha | |
| | ELan LBre MBel MBro MNrw | |
| | NBro NBus NLar SBre SRms WBea | |
| | WHoo WOld WOve WPer WPyg | |
| | WRus WWye | |
| - 'Indigo' ♀ | EBrP EBre EFou EWll LBre MRav | |
| | NLar SBre | |
| - 'Lapis Lazuli' | CMil CPle CStr LGre WPGP | |
| - 'Rosea' | CPle | |
| - 'Tenorei' | WPer | |
| *prostrata* | Last listed 1997 | |
| *przewalskii* | CPle CStr EGar MNrw MSal NChi | |
| | SHFr SUsu WPer WWye | |
| - ACE 1157 | WCot WCru | |
| - CLD 247 | Last listed 1998 | |
| *puberula* | See *S. involucrata* var. *puberula* | |
| *pulchella* | Last listed 1998 | |
| 'Purple Majesty' | CLon CPle CStr GBri LPio WWye | |
| *purpurea* | CM&M CPle WShe | |
| § 'Raspberry Royale' ♀ | CLon CPle CSev ELan EPri EWoo | |
| | LHil LHop LIck LRHS MAsh MBel | |
| | SAga SMrm SUsu SWat WPen | |
| | WRus WWoo WWye | |
| *recognita* | CBot CPle CStr EBee GCal LGre | |
| | NBur | |
| § *reflexa* | Last listed 1998 | |
| *regeliana* Trautv. | CHar CPle EGar MLLN NBir NChi | |
| | NTow SSca WPer WRha | |
| - hort. | See *S. virgata* Jacq. | |
| *regla* | CPle CStr | |
| *repens* | CPle CStr WWye | |
| ¶ - var. *repens* | WHil | |
| § *reptans* | CPle CSam CSpe LIck MHar SAga | |
| | SLod WPer | |
| *ringens* | CPle GCHN | |
| § *riparia* | CPle EHal MLLN | |
| *roborowskii* | CPle | |
| *roemeriana* ♀ | CPle NWCA SSca WCru | |
| *rutilans* | See *S. elegans* 'Scarlet Pineapple' | |
| * 'San Antonio' | Last listed 1997 | |
| *scabiosifolia* | CStr EBee EHal | |

| | | |
|---|---|---|
| *scabra* | CFir CPle | |
| *sclarea* | CArn CGle CPle EGoo ELau EWTr | |
| | GPoy LFis LHol MChe MHew | |
| | MWat NChi NFai SIde SRCN WBea | |
| | WCHb WHer WHoo WOak WPer | |
| | WWye | |
| * - 'Alba' | CPle | |
| N - var. *turkestanica* hort. | More than 30 suppliers | |
| § - 'Vatican White' | EBee EBrP EBre EMar LBre SBre | |
| - white-bracted | Last listed 1996 | |
| *scorodoniifolia* | Last listed 1996 | |
| *scutellarioides* | CPle | |
| *semiatrata* Zucc. | CPle SUsu | |
| - hort. | See *S. chamaedryoides* | |
| *sinaloensis* | CPle MSte SAga SIgm | |
| *somalensis* | CPle CStr | |
| *sonomensis* | CPle WWye | |
| *souliei* | See *S. brevilabra* | |
| sp. ACE 2172 | Last listed 1997 | |
| sp. CC&McK 77 | GTou | |
| sp. Iran | Last listed 1998 | |
| *spatbacea* ♀ | CPle LGre SIgm WWye | |
| *spinosa* | Last listed 1998 | |
| *splendens* | Last listed 1998 | |
| *sprucei* | Last listed 1998 | |
| *squalens* | Last listed 1998 | |
| § *staminea* | CPle EBee MNrw SHFr SSca WSan | |
| *stenophylla* | CPle EBee LFis WGwG WPer | |
| *stepposa* | CPle EBee WOut | |
| x *superba* ♀ | CBot CGle CHad CPle EBrP EBre | |
| | ELan EOrc LBre LEdu MBri MBro | |
| | MWat NRoo SBre SCro SDix | |
| | SMrm SRCN SRms SSpe SSvw | |
| | WCot WHoo WWhi WWye | |
| - 'Adrian' | EFou SChu | |
| - 'Forncett Dawn' | CStr EFou SChu | |
| - 'Rubin' ♀ | CBos CStr EFou SChu SMrm | |
| - 'Superba' | CSev ECha EFou EHrv LGre | |
| x *sylvestris* 'Blauhügel' ♀ | More than 30 suppliers | |
| § - 'Blaukönigin' | CGle EBee EWTr GBri GCHN LFis | |
| | LNor MBro MWat NArg NCat | |
| | NLar NMir NOak NRoo SCob | |
| | SIgm SPar SRPl WBea WHoo WPer | |
| | WPyg | |
| - Blue Queen | See *S.* x *sylvestris* 'Blaukönigin' | |
| - 'Lye End' | CStr ECtt GCal LHop MRav WCot | |
| § - 'Mainacht' ♀ | More than 30 suppliers | |
| - May Night | See *S.* x *sylvestris* 'Mainacht' | |
| - 'Rose Queen' | CLon CPle EBee ECGN ECha | |
| | ECoo ECtt EFou ELan EPfP GCHN | |
| | GChr LFis LHop MCLN MSte NFla | |
| | NOak NOrc NRoo SIgm SUsu | |
| | WBea WHil WHoo WPer WPyg | |
| | WRus | |
| - 'Rügen' | CStr EBee LRHS MBri NLak NOla | |
| | WRus | |
| - 'Schneehügel' (v) | EBee EMan EPPr EPfP SCro SHel | |
| | SUsu WLRN WMer WWat WWye | |
| - 'Tänzerin' ♀ | EBee EFou LGre MBel NChi SChu | |
| | SMrm WCot | |
| - 'Viola Klose' | CMil CStr EBee ECGP EFou EMan | |
| | EMar LGre LRHS MBri SUsu | |
| - 'Wissalink' | SUsu | |
| *tachiei* | EBee EOrc MRav | |
| *taraxacifolia* | CPle CStr WWye | |
| *tarayensis* | Last listed 1998 | |
| *tesquicola* | See *S. nemorosa* subsp. | |
| | *tesquicola* | |
| *tiliifolia* | CPle EBee SRms | |
| *tingitana* | CPle | |

| | |
|---|---|
| *tomentosa* | CPle SAga |
| § - Etl. HH&K 210 | CHan |
| *transcaucasica* | See *S. staminea* |
| *transsylvanica* | CArn CFri CHea CPle EBee EWll |
| | MCAu MWgw NChi NLak STes |
| | SWat WCot WOld WPer |
| ¶ 'Trelawney' | SCoo |
| *trijuga* | CPle |
| *triloba* | See *S. fruticosa* |
| *uliginosa* ♀ | More than 30 suppliers |
| - 'African Skies' | NBrk |
| *urica* | CPle |
| *urticifolia* | Last listed 1996 |
| 'Van-Houttei' ♀ | CPle SDys SUsu |
| 'Vatican City' | See *S. sclarea* 'Vatican White' |
| *verbenaca* | CArn CKin CPle EGar EWFC |
| | GCHN MHew MNrw MSal NMir |
| | SPil WCla WOut WPer WWye |
| - pink | Last listed 1998 |
| *verticillata* | CArn CPle CStr EBee ECha EGoo |
| | ELan EOld EPri MBro NFor NSti |
| | SDys SHFr WHoo WOve WPer |
| | WWhi WWye |
| - 'Alba' | CLTr CMGP CMea CPle CSev |
| | EBee ECGN ECha EPfP MBel |
| | MCAu MGed NGdn NSti SBid |
| | SCob SRPl WHer WPer WRus |
| - subsp. *amasiaca* | CPle |
| - HH&K 253 | Last listed 1997 |
| - HH&K 267 | CHan |
| - HH&K 342 | Last listed 1997 |
| - 'Purple Rain' | More than 30 suppliers |
| ¶ - 'White Rain' | EFou |
| *villicaulis* | See *S. amplexicaulis* |
| § *virgata* Jacq. | CPle EBee LCot MBro MNrw SSca |
| | WOut WPer |
| § *viridis* | CArn CPle EMar EWTr LHol LHop |
| | MChe SIde SPil |
| - var. *alba* | Last listed 1998 |
| *viscosa* Sesse & Moc. | See *S. riparia* |
| *viscosa* Jacq. | CPle CStr WWye |
| *wagneriana* | Last listed 1998 |
| *xalapensis* | CPle |

## SALVINIA (Salviniaceae)

| | |
|---|---|
| *braziliensis* | MSta |

## SAMBUCUS ✿ (Caprifoliaceae)

| | |
|---|---|
| *adnata* B&SWJ 2252 | WCru |
| - L 864 | Last listed 1998 |
| *alba* 'Variegata' | WLRN |
| *caerulea* | EPla |
| *canadensis* | Last listed 1997 |
| - 'Adams' (F) | Last listed 1998 |
| - 'Aurea' | IOrc MBar NWea WHar |
| ¶ - 'John's' | CAgr |
| - 'Maxima' | EPfP ERav GCal LGre SBid SMad |
| | SMrm |
| - 'York' (F) | CAgr |
| ♦ *coraensis* | See *S. williamsii* subsp. *coreana* |
| *ebulus* | CKin CRow LGre SMad |
| *formosana* B&SWJ 1543 | WCru |
| § *javanica* | EBee |
| - B&SWJ 4047 | WCru |
| *nigra* | CDul CKin ENot GChr GPoy GRei |
| | LBuc MBri NWea SIde SMrm |
| | WMou |
| - 'Albomarginata' | See *S. nigra* 'Marginata' |
| - 'Albovariegata' | CDul WWeb |
| * - 'Ardwall' | GCal |
| N - 'Aurea' ♀ | CB&S CDul CInt CLnd CRow |
| | EBee ELan EMon ENot EPla ERav |
| | GRei LHol MBar MRav NFla NWea |
| | SPer WDin WFar |

| | |
|---|---|
| - 'Aureomarginata' | CInt EBee ELan EPla GAri MBal |
| | MRav NFor NLon NSti WCFE |
| | WFar |
| ¶ - Black Beauty = 'Gerda' | GChr LHop LRHS MGos SPer |
| | WWeb |
| - 'Cae Rhos Lligwy' | WAlt WHer |
| - 'Cannop' | WAlt |
| - 'Castledean' | SMad WAlt |
| - 'Cool Head' | WAlt |
| - 'Din Dryfol' (v) | Last listed 1998 |
| - 'Flex' (v) | Last listed 1998 |
| * - 'Frances' | CNat EPla WCot |
| ¶ - 'Godshill' | CAgr SDea |
| - 'Golden Locks' | Last listed 1996 |
| - 'Greener Later' (v) | Last listed 1998 |
| ¶ - 'Guincho Purple' ♀ | More than 30 suppliers |
| ¶ - 'Hadspen' | MAsh |
| - 'Heterophylla' | See *S. nigra* 'Linearis' |
| ¶ - 'Ina' | CAgr |
| - f. *laciniata* ♀ | CB&S CDul CMHG CRow EBee |
| | ELan EMon EPla LHol MBal MLLN |
| | NFor NRoo NSti SChu SDix SEas |
| | SLon SMad SPer SSpi SSta WCot |
| | WSHC |
| § - 'Linearis' | CFai EHal EHic ELan EPla MUlv |
| | SMad SPer WWat |
| - 'Long Tooth' | CNat |
| - 'Luteovariegata' | Last listed 1997 |
| - 'Madonna' (v) | CMHG CPMA EBee EPla MAsh |
| | MGos MRav NHol SEas SMad SPer |
| | WCot |
| § - 'Marginata' | CMHG CRow EBee EHoe ELan |
| | GChr GEil GRei IOrc MBar MBri |
| | MGos MLLN MRav NRoo SDix |
| | SLon SPer SRPl WBod WCot WDin |
| | WFar WHar WSHC WWat WWin |
| - mosaic virus | Last listed 1997 |
| - 'Nana' | EMon |
| - 'Party Girl' | Last listed 1996 |
| - 'Pendula' | EPla ERav |
| - 'Plena' (d) | EMon EPla MInt WCot |
| - 'Pulverulenta' (v) | CBrd CDoC CHan CRow ELan |
| | EPar EPla GCal LHop MAsh MHlr |
| | MLLN MRav NSti SEas WCot |
| | WSHC |
| - 'Purple Pete' | CNat |
| - 'Purpurea' | See *S. nigra* 'Guincho Purple' |
| ¶ - 'Pygmy' | EPla |
| - 'Pyramidalis' | EMon EPla SMad WCot |
| ¶ - 'Sambu' (F) | CAgr |
| ¶ - 'Samdal' (F) | CAgr |
| ¶ - 'Samidan' (F) | CAgr |
| ¶ - 'Samnor' (F) | CAgr |
| ¶ - 'Sampo' (F) | CAgr |
| ¶ - 'Samyl' (F) | CAgr |
| * - 'Tenuifolia' | Last listed 1997 |
| - 'Thundercloud' | MAsh MBri NPro WCot WPat |
| - 'Variegata' | See *S. nigra* 'Marginata' |
| ¶ - f. *viridis* | CNat |
| - 'Witches Broom' | EMon |
| *racemosa* | CAgr CDul EPfP GRei NWea |
| | WCot WRha |
| - 'Aurea' | CLnd EHoe GRei |
| - 'Goldenlocks' | EHal MGos NHol NPro SPer |
| | WBcn WPyg |
| - 'Moerheimii' | EPla |
| - 'Plumosa Aurea' | More than 30 suppliers |
| § - var. *sieboldiana* | CHan EMon |
| - 'Sutherland Gold' ♀ | More than 30 suppliers |
| - 'Tenuifolia' ♀ | CMHG CPMA CSWP CWSG EHal |
| | ELan GSki MBro MGos MPla MUlv |
| | NSti SMad SPer WCru WHCG |
| | WPat WPyg |

| | |
|---|---|
| *sieboldiana* | See *S. racemosa* var. *sieboldiana* |
| *tigrina* | WWat |
| *wightiana* | See *S. javanica* |
| § *williamsii* subsp. *coreana* | CMCN EPla WFar |

## SAMOLUS (Primulaceae)
| | |
|---|---|
| *repens* | ECou |

## SANCHEZIA (Acanthaceae)
| | |
|---|---|
| *nobilis* hort. | See *S. speciosa* |
| § *speciosa* | CHal |

## SANDERSONIA (Colchicaceae)
| | |
|---|---|
| *aurantiaca* | LAma LBow NRog |

## SANGUINARIA (Papaveraceae)
| | |
|---|---|
| *canadensis* | CArn CBro CGle CSpe EPot ERos GPoy IBlr IMGH LAma LHop LSyl NRya SLon SMad SPer WAbe WBea WCru WShi WWat WWin |
| - f. *multiplex* (d) | CLAP CRDP EPot NEgg |
| ¶ - 'Paint Creek Double' | SSpi |
| - pink | SWas WThi |
| - 'Plena' (d) ♀ | CBro CEnd CLyd CMea CRDP EHyt EPar EPot IMGH LAma MTho MTis NHar NHol NMen NPar NRya SBla SIgm SSpi SWas WAbe WEas WLin WSan |
| 'Peter Harrison' | LGre |

## SANGUISORBA (Rosaceae)
| | |
|---|---|
| § *albiflora* | CBlo CRow EBee EBrP EBre EFou ELan GAri GBuc LBre MCLN MRav NLar NPro NRoo SBre WFar WWin |
| *armena* | CHan SSvw |
| *benthamiana* | Last listed 1998 |
| *canadensis* | CHan CRow ECha EGar GAbr GCal GPoy MCAu MFir MSte NHex NRoo SPer WCot WFar WOld WWye |
| * *caucasica* | EBee |
| *dodecandra* | Last listed 1996 |
| *hakusanensis* | ECha MNrw NBir NBro WWhi |
| *magnifica alba* | See *S. albiflora* |
| *menziesii* | LGre WCot WPGP |
| § *minor* | CAgr CArn CKin EEls ELau EWFC GPoy LHol MBar MChe MHew NArg NBro NLan NMir SIde WCHb WCla WHbs WHer WOak WPer WWye |
| - subsp. *muricata* | WGwG |
| - - HH&K 289 | CHan |
| *obtusa* | More than 30 suppliers |
| - var. *albiflora* | See *S. albiflora* |
| *officinalis* | CArn CFri CInt ECGN EPfP EWFC GBar GNau MBel MCAu NMir SSca SWat WCla WMoo WWin WWye |
| - 'Arnhem' | LGre |
| - 'Tanna' | CPlt EBee EMon EPPr GCal LGre SLod SMrm SOkh WCot WMaN |
| ♦ *parviflora* | See *S. tenuifolia* var. *parviflora* |
| *pimpinella* | See *S. minor* |
| *sitchensis* | See *S. stipulata* |
| § *stipulata* | CPlt ECGN GCal IBlr |
| *tenuifolia* | EBee NLar WGwy WMoo WWhi |
| - 'Alba' | CBlo GBuc WCot |
| § - var. *parviflora* | EBee |
| - 'Purpurea' | WCot |

## SANICULA (Apiaceae)
| | |
|---|---|
| *arctopoides* | Last listed 1996 |
| *elata* B&SWJ 2250 | WCru |
| *europaea* | EWFC GBar GPoy MSal WHer |

## SANIELLA (Hypoxidaceae)
| | |
|---|---|
| *verna* | ERos NMen |

## SANSEVIERIA ✿ (Agavaceae)
| | |
|---|---|
| *trifasciata* 'Bantel's Sensation' ♀ | Last listed 1995 |
| - 'Craigii' ♀ | Last listed 1995 |
| - 'Gigantea' (v) | Last listed 1996 |
| - 'Golden Hahnii' (v) ♀ | MBri |
| - 'Hahnii' ♀ | Last listed 1995 |
| - 'Laurentii' (v) ♀ | MBri |
| - 'Moonshine' ♀ | Last listed 1993 |

## SANTOLINA ✿ (Asteraceae)
| | |
|---|---|
| § *chamaecyparissus* ♀ | More than 30 suppliers |
| - var. *corsica* | See *S. chamaecyparissus* var. *nana* |
| - 'Double Lemon' | LFis SPla |
| - 'Lambrook Silver' | CDoC EBee ECtt EOHP EPPr ESis LFis NHol SAga SCoo SEas SPla SSvw |
| - 'Lemon Queen' | CArn CB&S CDoC EAst EGoo ELau ESis GBar GOrc MAsh MBal MBel MGos MMal NBir NFla NSti SAga SEas SIde SPla SWat WCHb WFar WOak WPer |
| * - subsp. *magonica* | Last listed 1998 |
| § - var. *nana* ♀ | CB&S CLyd EBee ECha ENot LHop MBar MDun MHer NFai NFor SHFr SPer SRms SWat WPer WWye |
| - *nana* 'Weston' | CLyd EWes |
| - 'Pretty Carol' | CAbP EBee EBrP EBre ELan EMil ESis GOrc LBre MAsh NBrk NFai SAga SBre SEas SIde SRPl WWeb |
| - 'Small-Ness' | CDoC CLyd CSWP EBee EDAr EGoo EPPr ESis EWes LHop MAsh MBlu MBri MBro MSte NHol NMen SIng WAbe WFar WPat WPyg |
| - subsp. *squarrosa* | Last listed 1997 |
| *dentata* | Last listed 1998 |
| *elegans* | Last listed 1997 |
| *incana* | See *S. chamaecyparissus* |
| 'Oldfield Hybrid' | MBel MLan WCot |
| *pectinata* | See *S. rosmarinifolia* subsp. *canescens* |
| § *pinnata* | CArn CSev CTri LHol WPer |
| § - subsp. *neapolitana* ♀ | CArn CSev ECha ELan ENot LHol LHop MBri NFor SDix SIde SPil SSvw WEas WHCG WOak WSel WWye |
| - - cream | See *S. pinnata* subsp. *neapolitana* 'Edward Bowles' |
| § - - 'Edward Bowles' | CGle CLyd CMil EBee ELan EMil ESis GCal GOrc LHil LHop MBNS MCLN MRav MWgw NBir NHol NLon NPer NSti SAga SChu WAbe WBea WHen WHer WSHC |
| - - 'Sulphurea' | CMea EGoo EPfP LGre MBel SPer WKif WPer WTro WWhi |
| *rosmarinifolia* | CArn CDoC CHad CMil ELau ESis GChr MBel MRav MWhi SLon SPan SRms WCHb WRha WSel WWye |

| | |
|---|---|
| § – subsp. *canescens* | LHol LRHS MRav NCut SPan WPer WRHF WWye |
| § – subsp. *rosmarinifolia* | CChe CSev ECha EGoo ELan ENot EOHP GCHN LHol MBri NFai NSti SDix SSvw WCHb WEas WHoo WSHC WTro WWin WWye |
| ¶ – – cream form | NWoo |
| – – 'Primrose Gem' ♀ | CB&S CHar EBee ECha ELau EMil ESis LHop MBal MCLN MPla NChi NSti SBod SEas SPer SPla SRPl WCot WPer WWal WWye |
| *tomentosa* | See *S. pinnata* subsp. *neapolitana* |
| *virens* | See *S. rosmarinifolia* subsp. *rosmarinifolia* |
| *viridis* | See *S. rosmarinifolia* subsp. *rosmarinifolia* |

## SANVITALIA (Asteraceae)

| | |
|---|---|
| ¶ 'Little Sun' | CSpe |

## SAPINDUS (Sapindaceae)

| | |
|---|---|
| *drummondii* | Last listed 1996 |

## SAPIUM (Euphorbiaceae)

| | |
|---|---|
| ¶ *japonicum* | CMCN |

## SAPONARIA (Caryophyllaceae)

| | |
|---|---|
| 'Bressingham' ♀ | CMea EBrP EBre ECha ELan EPot LBee LBre MTho NHar NHol SBla SBod SBre WAbe WPat WPyg WWin |
| *caespitosa* | EPot EWes GTou NMen NNrd WLin |
| x *lempergii* 'Max Frei' | EBee GAbr GBuc LFis LGre SBla SDix SUsu WCot WOVN |
| * 'Lilac Double' | MRav |
| *lutea* | NWCA WGor |
| *ocymoides* ♀ | CB&S CLTr EBee ECha ECtt EHon ELan ELau EMNN ENot ESis GAbr GCHN GTou LGro MWgw NFla NLon NRoo NVic SIng SRms WBea WFar WHoo WPer WStI WWin |
| – 'Alba' | ECha SIng WAbe WFar |
| – 'Rubra Compacta' ♀ | MTho WPyg |
| ¶ – 'Snow Tip' | NHed WHoo |
| *officinalis* | CAgr CArn CBre CKin CRow ELau EWFC GAbr GPoy LEdu LHol MChe MHew MSal NFai SIde SSea WFar WGwG WHer WOak WPer WWal WWye |
| – 'Alba Plena' (d) | CGle CJew CRDP CSam EBee ECha ECoo EMon GBar NBrk NSti WCHb WElm WFar WHer WPer WRha WWin |
| § – 'Dazzler' (v) | ELau MRav NBir NBrk NFai NRoo WBea WCHb WCot WHer |
| – 'Rosea Plena' (d) | More than 30 suppliers |
| – 'Rubra Plena' (d) | CGle CHad CRDP ECha ELan EMon LFis MCLN MSCN NSti WCHb WHer WRha |
| – 'Variegata' | See *S. officinalis* 'Dazzler' |
| x *olivana* ♀ | CLyd EHyt EPot ESis LFis MPla MTho NHol NMen SBla SBod WAbe WPat WPyg WWin |
| *pamphylica* | MNrw |
| *pulvinaris* | See *S. pumilio* |
| § *pumilio* | CLyd GCHN GTou NWCA WLin |
| 'Rosenteppich' | ESis NHol SBla SWas WLin WPat WPyg |
| *sicula* | WMow |

| | |
|---|---|
| *zawadskii* | See *Silene zawadskii* |

## SARCOCAPNOS (Papaveraceae)

| | |
|---|---|
| *baetica* | NWCA |
| *enneaphylla* | Last listed 1997 |

## SARCOCOCCA ✿ (Buxaceae)

| | |
|---|---|
| *confusa* ♀ | More than 30 suppliers |
| ¶ *coriacea* B&SWJ 2585 | WCru |
| *hookeriana* ♀ | CBlo CTrG ECot EPfP ERav GSki IOrc |
| – B&SWJ 2585 | WCru |
| – var. *digyna* ♀ | More than 30 suppliers |
| – – 'Purple Stem' | EHol EPla ERav MGos MRav SCob WCru WDin |
| ¶ – var. *hookeriana* | CDoC |
| – var. *humilis* | More than 30 suppliers |
| ¶ – HWJCM 92 | WCru |
| – Sch 2396 | EPla |
| *orientalis* | CFil CMCN CPMA EPfP EPla MAsh MGos SMac SPla SSpi WWat WWeb |
| 'Roy Lancaster' | See *S. ruscifolia* 'Dragon Gate' |
| *ruscifolia* | CB&S CDoC CPMA CPle CWSG EBee ELan ENot EPla IOrc LEdu LFis LHop MAsh MBel MGos MPla SCob SLon SPer SRms SSpi WAbe WPGP WWat |
| – var. *chinensis* ♀ | CFil CSam EPfP EPla MRav NHol SBid WCru |
| – – L 713 | EPla |
| § – 'Dragon Gate' | CFil ELan EPla LRHS MAsh |
| *saligna* | CB&S CFil CPMA WBod WCru WPGP |

## SARMIENTA (Gesneriaceae)

| | |
|---|---|
| *repens* ♀ | WAbe WCru |

## SARRACENIA ✿ (Sarraceniaceae)

| | |
|---|---|
| x *ahlsii* | WMEx |
| *alata* | CSWC GTro WMEx |
| – 'Citronelle' | WMEx |
| – copper lid | GTro |
| – x *flava* 'Maxima' | WMEx |
| – 'Nicolson' | WMEx |
| – x *oreophila* | Last listed 1996 |
| – pubescent form | WMEx |
| – purple lid | GTro |
| – 'Red Lid' | Last listed 1998 |
| – 'Red Lid' x *flava* red pitcher | WMEx |
| – red x *purpurea* subsp. *venosa* | WMEx |
| – x *willisii* | WMEx |
| x *areolata* | GTro WMEx |
| * x *areolata* (x *areolata* x *alata* red throat) | WMEx |
| x *catesbyi* ♀ | CFil GTro WMEx |
| x *catesbyi* (x *catesbyi* x *flava*) | Last listed 1996 |
| – x *excellens* | WMEx |
| x *catesbyi* x *popei* | Last listed 1996 |
| – red | Last listed 1996 |
| x *catesbyi* x *rubra* | Last listed 1996 |
| x *chelsonii* ♀ | WMEx |
| x *comptonensis* | Last listed 1996 |
| x *courtii* | Last listed 1998 |
| 'Evendine' | Last listed 1996 |
| x *excellens* ♀ | GTro WMEx |
| – x *wrigleyana* | Last listed 1996 |
| x *exornata* | WMEx |
| x *farnhamii* | See *S.* x *readii* 'Farnhamii' |

*flava* ♀    CFil CRDP CSWC EAnd GTro
      WMEx WPGP
- all green giant    WMEx
- 'Burgundy'    GTro WMEx
¶ - var. *cuprea*    GTro
- 'Maxima'    WMEx WNor
- 'Maxima' x *purpurea*    Last listed 1998
   subsp. *venosa*
- 'Maxima' x *rubra*    Last listed 1998
   subsp. *jonesii*
- var. *ornata*    WMEx
- 'Prince George County'    WMEx
- purple tube    WMEx
x *formosa*    Last listed 1997
- x *excellens*    Last listed 1996
'Gulf Rubra'    Last listed 1996
x *harperi*    WMEx
'Judy'    GTro
*leucophylla* ♀    CSWC GTro WMEx
- x *catesbyi*    Last listed 1996
- x *excellens*    Last listed 1998
- x *oreophila*    Last listed 1996
- x *popei*    Last listed 1996
- white pitchers    WMEx
x *melanorhoda*    GTro WMEx
x *miniata*    WMEx
*minor*    CSWC GTro WMEx
- 'Okefenokee Giant'    WMEx
- tall form    WMEx
- x *wrigleyana*    Last listed 1996
x *mitchelliana* ♀    GTro WMEx
x *moorei*    GTro WMEx
- 'Brook's Hybrid'    GTro WMEx
- (*leucophylla* x *moorei*)    WMEx
- 'Marston Select'    Last listed 1996
- (x *moorei* x *catesbyi*)    Last listed 1996
- x *readii*    Last listed 1996
*oreophila*    CSWC GTro WMEx
- x *leucophylla*    Last listed 1998
- x *minor*    Last listed 1996
- x *purpurea*    Last listed 1998
x *popei*    WMEx
* - (x *popei* x *flava* giant)    WMEx
- x *purpurea*    Last listed 1996
   subsp. *venosa*
x *popoei* (x *popei* x *flava*)    Last listed 1996
*psittacina*    CSWC EAnd GTro WMEx
*purpurea*    CFil CSWC
- subsp. *purpurea*    GTro LEdu WMEx
- - f. *heterophylla*    WMEx
- subsp. *venosa*    GTro WMEx
- - x *oreophila*    WMEx
§ x *readii*    GTro WMEx
- x *excellens*    Last listed 1996
- (*leucophylla* x *readii*)    WMEx
x *rehderi*    WMEx
*rubra*    CSWC GTro WMEx
- subsp. *alabamensis*    WMEx
- x *excellens*    Last listed 1996
- subsp. *gulfensis*    WMEx
* - - f. *heterophylla* strong    WMEx
   green form
- subsp. *jonesii*    WMEx
x *swaniana*    GTro WMEx
- x *popei*    WMEx
*willisii* x *flava*    Last listed 1996
- x *minor* 'Giant'    Last listed 1996
x *wrigleyana* ♀    GTro

## SARUMA (Aristolochiaceae)
¶ *henryi*    WCot

## SASA ✿ (Poaceae - Bambusoideae)
*borealis*    See *Sasamorpha borealis*
*chrysantha* hort.    See *Pleioblastus chino*
*disticha* 'Mirrezuzume'    See *Pleioblastus pygmaeus*
      'Mirrezuzume'
*glabra* f. *albostriata*    See *Sasaella masamuneana* f.
      *albostriata*
*kurilensis*    EPla ISta LJus NMoo SDry WJun
- 'Shimofuri' (v)    EPla ERod ISta LJus SDry WJun
- short form    EPla
*megalophylla* 'Nobilis'    SDry
*nana*    See *S. veitchii* f. *minor*
*nipponica*    CEnd EPla SDry WJun
- 'Aureostriata'    SDry
*oshidensis*    EPla
§ *palmata* ♀    CB&S CHad CHan EBee ENot
      GAri GOrc MCCP WHer
- f. *nebulosa*    CFir EFul EOas EPla ISta LJus
      MMoz MUlv NMoo SAPC SArc
      SDry WBay WJun
- 'Warley Place' (v)    SDry
*quelpaertensis*    EPla GAri ISta SDry
*senanensis*    EPla SDry
*tessellata*    See *Indocalamus tessellatus*
*tsuboiana*    CB&S CDoC EBee EPla ISta MMoz
      SDry WBay
§ *veitchii*    CB&S CCuc CGre CWit EBrP EBre
      ECha EHoe EOld EPar EPla IOrc
      ISta LBlo LBre LEdu LJus LNet
      MBri MMoz MWhi SBre SDry SPer
      WBay WFar WJun WWye
§ - f. *minor*    EBee EPla MCCP

## SASAELLA (Poaceae - Bambusoideae)
*bitchuensis* hort.    SDry
*glabra*    See *S. masamuneana*
§ *masamuneana*    EPla
§ - f. *albostriata* (v)    CDoC CFil COtt CPMA EBee EPPr
      EPla EWsh ISta LJus MCCP MMoz
      MUlv MWht SDry WBay WJun
- f. *aureostriata* (v)    COtt EPla GCal LJus MMoz NPal
      SDry
§ *ramosa*    EBee EPla GAri GBin GOrc ISta
      LEdu LJus MBal MCCP MMoz
      MWht NRya SDry WBay

## SASAMORPHA (Poaceae - Bambusoideae)
§ *borealis*    Last listed 1997

## SASSAFRAS (Lauraceae)
*albidum*    CArn CMCN
¶ *tzumu*    SSpi

## SATUREJA (Lamiaceae)
*biflora*    CArn
§ *coerulea* ♀    EWes NBir SIde WFar
¶ *douglasii*    EOHP
*hortensis*    CBod GPoy ILis LHol MChe
      MHew MLan WHbs WHer WJek
      WSel
*montana*    CArn EEls EHyt ELau EWFC GMaP
      GPoy ILis LEdu LHol LLWP MBri
      MChe MPla NMen SDix SIde
      SRms SRob WCHb WCer WHbs
      WHer WOak WPer WWye
* - *citriodora*    EOHP GPoy IIve
- 'Coerulea'    See *S. coerulea*
§ - subsp. *illyrica*    SIgm WThi
- prostrate white    CRDP
- 'Purple Mountain'    GPoy IIve
- *subspicata*    See *S. montana* subsp. *illyrica*

| | |
|---|---|
| *parnassica* | WPer |
| *repanda* | See *S. spicigera* |
| *seleriana* | CInt EOHP IDac NMen |
| *spicata* | CLyd |
| § *spicigera* | CArn CLyd CPBP EDAr ELau EPot |
| | LFis LHol LLWP MHar MHer NBir |
| | NMen NPri NTow SIde WCHb |
| | WSel WWin WWye |
| *thymbra* | CArn EOHP GBar LLWP SHDw |
| | SIde |
| § *viminea* | EOHP |

## SAURAUIA (Actinidiaceae)
| | |
|---|---|
| *subspinosa* | Last listed 1998 |

## SAUROMATUM (Araceae)
| | |
|---|---|
| *guttatum* | See *S. venosum* |
| § *venosum* | LAma MBri WCot WCru |

## SAURURUS (Saururaceae)
| | |
|---|---|
| *cernuus* | CBen CRow CWat EBrP EBre |
| | EHon ELan EMFW LBre LPBA |
| | MSta NDea SBre SRms SWat |
| *chinensis* | CRow WCru |

## SAUSSUREA (Asteraceae)
| | |
|---|---|
| ¶ *albescens* | WCot |
| *auriculata* HWJCM 490 | WCru |
| § *ceratocarpa* | Last listed 1998 |
| – var. *depressa* | Last listed 1998 |
| *chionophylla* | Last listed 1996 |
| ¶ *grandiflora* | EBee |
| ¶ *hypoleuca* | MNrw |
| ¶ *pulchella* | EBee |
| *spathulifolia* ACE 1344 | Last listed 1996 |

## SAXEGOTHAEA (Podocarpaceae)
| | |
|---|---|
| *conspicua* | CB&S CDoC CMCN ECou EPla |
| | LCon LLin SLon SMad WCwm |

## SAXIFRAGA ✿ (Saxifragaceae)
| | |
|---|---|
| 'Aemula' (x *borisii*) (7) | CLyd WAbe |
| *aizoides* var. | MBal MBro |
|   *atrorubens* (9) | |
| *aizoon* | See *S. paniculata* |
| 'Aladdin' (x *borisii*) (7) | NHol |
| 'Alba' (x *apiculata*) (7) | CLyd ELan EMNN EPot GTou |
| | LFox MBal MBro NHol NMen |
| | NSla SBla SChu SIng SSmi WCla |
| | WHoo WPat WWin |
| 'Alba' (x *arco-valleyi*) | See *S.* 'Ophelia' (x *arco-valleyi*) |
| 'Alba' (*oppositifolia*) (7) | CLyd ELan EMNN EWes GTou |
| | NHar NMen WWin |
| 'Albert Einstein' | NMen NNrd |
|   (x *apiculata*) (7) | |
| * 'Albert Hawkins' | NBro |
| 'Albertii' (*callosa*) (8) | CLyd GTou SIng SSmi WWin |
| 'Albida' (*callosa*) (8) | NFla |
| 'Aldebaran' (x *borisii*) (7) | EMNN MDHE NHar NMen |
| 'Alfons Mucha' (7) | EPot MWat |
| ¶ 'Allendale Accord' | NHed |
|   (*diapensioides* | |
|   x *lilacina*) (7) | |
| ¶ 'Allendale Joy' | NMen |
|   (x *wendelacina*) (7) | |
| ¶ 'Allendale Pearl' | CLyd |
|   (x *novacastelensis*) (7) | |
| 'Alpenglow' (7) | MWat NMen |
| *alpigena* (7) | EHyt NSla |
| 'Amitie' (x *gloriana*) (7) | NMen |
| * 'Anagales Sunset' (8) | Last listed 1996 |
| *andersonii* (7) | CLyd EHyt EMNN ITim MBal |
| | MWat NMen NNrd NTow WAbe |

| | |
|---|---|
| *andersonii* McB 1475 (7) | NHol |
| x *andrewsii* (8x11) | MDHE MTho SSmi |
| § *androsacea* (15) | Last listed 1996 |
| x *anglica* 'Peggy | Last listed 1998 |
|   Eastwood' (7) | |
| ♦ *angustifolia* Haw. | See *S. hypnoides* |
| 'Anne Beddall' | CLyd MWat WAbe |
|   (x *goringiana*) (7) | |
| 'Aphrodite' | CLyd EPot |
|   (*sempervivum*) (7) | |
| x *apiculata* sensu | See *S.* 'Gregor Mendel' (x |
|   stricto hort. | *apiculata*) |
| 'Apple Blossom' (15) | GTou MDHE MOne NBro NFla |
| | WGor |
| 'Archfield White' | NNrd |
|   (*callosa*) (8) | |
| § 'Arco' (x *arco-valleyi*) (7) | CLyd EPot MWat NMen NRya |
| x *arco-valleyi* sensu | See *S.* 'Arco' (x *arco-valleyi*) |
|   stricto hort. | |
| x *arendsii* (15) | WEas |
| § 'Aretiastrum' (x *boydii*) (7) | EHyt EPot LFox NHed NMen |
| *aretioides* (7) | GCHN NMen |
| 'Ariel' (x *hornibrookii*) (7) | CNic LFox |
| 'Assimilis' (x *petraschii*) (7) | CLyd |
| 'August Hayek' | MBro MWat NMen NNrd |
|   (x *leyboldii*) (7) | |
| 'Aurantiaca' | Last listed 1996 |
|   (x *luteopurpurea*) (7) | |
| ♦ 'Aurea Maculata' (*cuneifolia*) | See *S.* 'Aureopunctata' (x *urbium*) |
| § 'Aureopunctata' | CMil CPri ECha EGoo ELan EMar |
|   (x *urbium*) (11/v) | EPla GBuc GCal LHop MBal |
| | MWgw NHol NLon NRoo SMrm |
| | SPer SPlb SRms WHen |
| 'Backhouseana' | Last listed 1996 |
|   (*paniculata*) (8) | |
| 'Backhousei' (15) | NHol |
| 'Balcana' | See *S. paniculata* var. *orientalis* |
| 'Baldensis' | See *S. paniculata* var. *baldensis* |
| 'Ballawley Guardsman' (15) | ECho LFox MBNS MBal NRoo |
| | SIng |
| § 'Beatrix Stanley' | EMNN LFox MBal MBro NHar |
|   (x *anglica*) (7) | NMen |
| 'Becky Foster' (x *borisii*) (7) | MWat |
| 'Beechcroft White' (15) | LBee |
| 'Berenika' (x *bertolonii*) (7) | NMen |
| 'Bettina' (x *paulinae*) (7) | GCHN |
| x *biasolettoi* sensu | See *S.* 'Phoenix' (x *biasolettoi*) |
|   stricto hort. | |
| *biflora* (7) | NHol |
| ¶ x *bilekii* (7) | CLyd |
| 'Birch Baby' (15) | SIng |
| 'Birch Yellow' | See *S.* 'Pseudoborisii' (x *borisii*) |
| 'Black Beauty' (15) | ECho LBee MBro MDHE NRoo |
| | SSmi |
| ¶ 'Black Leaf' (*fortunei*) (4) | EAst EMan GNau MBri |
| ¶ 'Black Ruby' (*fortunei*) (4) | WCot |
| ¶ 'Blackberry and Apple | EHic WCot |
|   Pie' (*fortunei*) (4) | |
| * 'Blackhouse White' (8) | Last listed 1998 |
| ¶ 'Blaník' (x *borisii*) (7) | NMen |
| ¶ 'Blanka' (x *borisii*) (7) | NMen |
| 'Blütenteppich' (15) | WPer |
| 'Bob Hawkins' (15/v) | CLyd ELan GCHN GDra LFox |
| | NHar SMer WRHF WWin |
| § 'Bodensee' | WPat |
|   (x *hofmannii*) (7) | |
| 'Bohemia' (7) | CGra CLyd EHyt EPot ITim NMen |
| | SBla WAbe WGle |
| ♦ *boissieri* | See *S. bourgeana* |
| ♦ x *borisii* sensu stricto hort. | See *S.* 'Sofia' (x *borisii*) |
| 'Boston Spa' | CLyd EMNN GCHN MBro NHed |
|   (x *elisabethae*) (7) | NHol NMen NNrd NRoo SChu |
| | WPat |

¶ 'Brendan' — CNic

'Bridget' (x *edithiae*) (7) — CLyd CMea CPBP ELan ESis ITim LFox MBal NHed NMen NRoo SSmi WWin

'Brno' (x *elisabethae*) (7) — NHol NMen

♦ *bronchialis* var. *vespertina* — See S. *vespertina*

'Brookside' (*burseriana*) (7) — EPot NMen SIng

*brunoniana* — See S. *brunonis*

§ *brunonis* (1) — LFox WCru

  - CC&McK 108 (1) — NWCA

*bryoides* (10) — GCrs GTou

x *burnatii* (8) — CLyd LFox MBro NHed NMen NPro SRot WGor

*burseriana* (7) — GCHN MBro WGor WPyg

'Buttercup' (x *kayei*) (7) — CPBP EPot GTou MBro MWat NHed NHol NNrd NWCA WHoo WPat WPyg

*caesia* (8) — NTow SIng SRms

§ *callosa* (8) ♀ — GCHN GTou MBro MWat NHar NHol SBla SRms WAbe WPat WTin

  - var. *bellardii* — See S. *callosa*

§  - subsp. *callosa* var. *australis* (8) — CNic EPot ESis MBro MDHE NBro NHol NMen NNrd

§  - subsp. *catalaunica* (8) — MBro

§  - x *cochlearis* (8) — NHed NNrd

  - var. *lantoscana* — See S. *callosa* subsp. *callosa* var. *australis*

  - *lingulata* — See S. *callosa*

'Cambria Jewel' (15) — NMen NNrd

'Cambridge Seedling' (7) — MWat NMen

§ *camposii* (15) — GAbr SIng

'Camyra' (7) — MWat NHed NNrd

*canaliculata* (15) — MDHE NMen NNrd

♦ x *canis-dalmatica* — See S. x *gaudinii*

§ 'Carmen' (x *elisabethae*) (7) — ELan EMNN ITim MBro MOne NHed NMen NNrd NRya WAbe

'Carniolica' (*paniculata*) (8) — CInt CLyd LBee LFox MBar MDHE NBro NMen NWCA SBla

'Carnival' (15) — Last listed 1997

'Castor' (x *bilekii*) (7) — MWat NHol SIng WAbe

*catalaunica* — See S. *callosa* subsp. *catalaunica*

'Caterhamensis' (*cotyledon*) (8) — WEas

♦ *caucasica* var. *desoulavyi* — See S. *desoulavyi*

*cebennensis* (15) ♀ — CLyd EWes GCrs LFox NMen NRya NTow SIgm SIng

  - dwarf form (15) — NMen

*cespitosa* — MDHE NWCA WAbe

'Chambers' Pink Pride' — See S. 'Miss Chambers' (x *urbium*)

¶ 'Cheap Confections' (*fortunei*) (4) — WCot

§ *cherlerioides* (10) — ELan MBNS NRya NVic WCla WEas

'Cherrytrees' (x *boydii*) (7) — CLyd MBro NMen

'Chetwynd' (*marginata*) (7) — MWat WAbe

'Chez Nous' (x *gloriana*) (7/v) — CLyd NMen

'Christine' (x *anglica*) (7) — LFox MWat NMen NNrd SIng

♦ *chrysospleniifolia* — See S. *rotundifolia* subsp. *chrysospleniifolia* var. *rhodopea*

¶ *cinerea* (7) — WAbe

'Clare' (x *anglica*) (7) — MDHE

'Clare Island' (15) — MDHE SIng

§ 'Clarence Elliott' (*umbrosa*) (11) ♀ — ELan EWes GCal MBro NHol NRya NVic WAbe WCla WHoo WPat WWin

¶ *cliveorum* McB1476 (7) — EHyt

§ 'Cloth of Gold' (*exarata* — CLyd CMea EAst ECha ELan GDra

subsp. *moschata* (15) — GTou LBee MBal MBar MPla MWhi NMen NRoo NRya NWCA SBod SPlb SRms SSmi WAbe WFar WWin

*cochlearis* (8) — CMea ESis LBee MBal MOne MWat NBro NHed NMen SSmi WPer WPyg WWin

'Cockscomb' (*paniculata*) (8) — MDHE NMen SIng

*columnaris* (7) — NSla

'Compacta' (*exarata* subsp. *moschata*) (15) — MBro

*corbariensis* — See S. *fragilis*

'Corona' (x *boydii*) (7) — LFox MDHE MWat NHol NMen

* 'Corrennie Claret' — GTou

'Correvoniana' (*paniculata*) (8) — ECtt ESis GCHN MBro MOne NBus NHed NRya SIng WCom WGor WRHF WWin

§ 'Corrie Fee' (*oppositifolia*) (7) — GCrs GTou NHar NHol SIng

*corsica* subsp. *cossoniana* (15) — Last listed 1998

§ *cortusifolia* (5) — CHid MBal NHar SSpi

  - dwarf form (5) — Last listed 1997

  - var. *fortunei* — See S. *fortunei*

§ *corymbosa* (7) — NMen

*cotyledon* (8) — CLyd GDra LBee NFor NHol SIng WCla WEas WPer

§ 'Cranbourne' (x *anglica*) (7) ♀ — CLyd EBrP EBre EMNN EPot LBre LFox MBro MWat NHar NHol NMen SBla SBre SSmi WAbe WPat

'Cream' (*paniculata*) (8) — SSmi

'Cream Seedling' (x *elisabethae*) (7) — EBrP EBre ESis LBre MDHE MWat NHed NMen SBre

'Crenata' (*burseriana*) (7) — CGra CLyd CNic EPot GCHN LFox MBro MWat NHar NHed NMen NNrd WAbe WHoo

'Crimson Rose' (*paniculata*) (8) — MBro NNrd

§ *crustata* (8) — EHyt GCHN MDHE NMen NWCA SIng

  - var. *vochinensis* — See S. *crustata*

'Crystalie' (x *biasolettoi*) (7) — EPot MBro MDHE NMen WPat

'Cultrata' (*paniculata*) (8) — NBro

'Cumulus' (*iranica* hybrid) (7) ♀ — EHyt NMen SBla WAbe

*cuneata* (15) — NHol

§ *cuneifolia* (11) — CLyd GDra GGar LBee MBal MWat NFla NHed NRoo NSti NWCA SSmi WRos

  - var. *capillipes* — See S. *cuneifolia* subsp. *cuneifolia*

§  - subsp. *cuneifolia* (11) — SGre

*  - var. *subintegra* (3) — ECho

*cuscutiformis* (5) — CInt EBee GCal MHlr MRav NTow SRms WCot WCru WOve

*cymbalaria* (2) — EBur WCla

  - var. *huetiana* (2) — CNic

♦ *daburica* — See S. *cuneifolia*

'Dainty Dame' (x *arco-valleyi*) (7) — CLyd LFox MWat NHed NMen SIng

'Dana' (x *megaseiflora*) (7) — CLyd EMNN MWat NHol NMen

'Dartington Double' (15/d) — CTri EBrP EBre EWes GCHN GDra GTou LBre MBal NHar NNrd SBre WCom

¶ 'Dartington Double White' (15) — WCom

'Dawn' (7) — NNrd

'Dawn Frost' (7) — EHyt

'Delia' (x *hornibrookii*) (7) — CNic NMen

'Denisa' (x *pseudokotschyi*) (7) — MBal NMen

*densa* — See S. *cherlerioides*

§ 'Dentata' (x *polita*) (11) — CHan ECha EPla GAbr GGar NVic SUsu

'Dentata' (x *urbium*) — See *S.* 'Dentata' (x *polita*)

§ *desoulavyi* (7) — GTou WLin

*diapensioides* (7) — CLyd NMen

♦ *discolor* — See *S. adscendens*

'Doctor Clay' (8) — MDHE NMen

'Doctor Ramsey' (8) — ESis EWes GTou ITim LBee MBro MRPP NBro NHed NNrd SIng SSmi WGor WHoo

¶ 'Donald Mann' — EWes

'Dorothy Milne' (7) — Last listed 1996

aff. *doyalana* SEP 45 (7) — CGra EHyt

'Drakula' (*ferdinandi-coburgi*) (7) — CLyd LRHS MDHE MWat NHed NMen

'Dubarry' (15) — ECho EWes MDHE SIng

'Duncan Lowe' (*andersonii*) (7) ♀ — EHyt

'Dwight Ripley' (7) — LFox

'Edgar Irmscher' (7) — LFox MWat NMen

'Edie Campbell' (15) — Last listed 1998

'Edith' (x *edithiae*) (7) — LRHS MBro NNrd

'Edward Elgar' (x *megaseiflora*) (7) — MWat NHol NMen

§ 'Egemmulosa' (*hypnoides*) (15) — MBal

¶ Eleanora Francini Corti (7) — SBla

♦ 'Elf' (7) — See *S.* 'Beatrix Stanley' (x *anglica*)

'Elf' (15) — ELan EMNN LBee NBro NMen NNrd NRoo SIng SRms SSmi WCla WGor

'Eliot Hodgkin' (x *millstreamiana*) (7) — LFox NNrd

♦ x *elisabethae* — See *S.* 'Carmen' (x *elisabethae*)

'Elizabeth Sinclair' (x *elisabethae*) (7) — EPot NMen NNrd

'Ellie Brinckerhoff' (x *hornibrookii*) (7) — CLyd

§ 'Ernst Heinrich' (x *heinrichii*) (7) — NMen

'Esther' (x *burnatii*) (8) — CLyd CMea EBrP EBre EHyt ELan ESis LBee LBre NMen SBla SBre SMer SSmi WHoo

§ 'Eulenspiegel' (x *geuderi*) (7) — CLyd EPot MBro NNrd

*exarata* (15) — ITim LBee LFox NMen

§ - subsp. *moschata* (15) — MDHE

- *pyrenaica* — See *S. androsacea*

fair maids of France — See *S.* 'Flore Pleno' (*granulata*)

'Fairy' (*exarata* subsp. *moschata*) (15) — ELan EPot NFla WCom

'Faldonside' (x *boydii*) (7) ♀ — CLyd LFox MBro MWat NHed NHol NMen SBla SIng WHoo WPat WPyg

'Falstaff' (*burseriana*) (7) — EPot LFox MDHE MWat SBla SIng

♦ x *farreri* hort. (8) — See *S. callosa* x *cochlearis*

§ 'Faust' (x *borisii*) (7) — EMNN NMen SBla SIng WAbe

I *federici-augusti* — See *S. frederici-augusti*

'Ferdinand' (x *hofmannii*) (7) — NMen

*ferdinandi-coburgi* (7) ♀ — CLyd EPot LFox NHed NWCA WAbe

- var. *pravislavii* — See *S. ferdinandi-coburgi* var. *rhodopea*

- var. *radoslavoffii* — See *S. ferdinandi-coburgi* var. *rhodopea*

* - var. *rhodopea* (7) — EPot LRHS NHed NMen SIng

*ferruginea* (4) — Last listed 1997

'Findling' (15) — EPot GCHN LGro MBro MOne NMen NNrd NRoo SBod SIng WAbe WWin

§ *flagellaris* (1) — WAbe

- subsp. *crassiflagellata* CC 298 (1) — Last listed 1996

¶ 'Flamingo' — NMen

'Flavescens' (*paniculata*) (8) — NBro

x *fleischeri* (7) — NMen

§ 'Flore Pleno' (*granulata*) (15/d) — CFir CMil CRDP CVer EBee EWes GAbr GBri LFox MHlr MTed NBir NHar NPro NRya NWoo SUsu WAbe WCot WFar WHil

'Florissa' (*oppositifolia*) (7) — GCHN LRHS WAbe

♦ *florulenta* — See *S. callosa*

'Flowers of Sulphur' — See *S.* 'Schwefelblüte'

§ *fortunei* (5) ♀ — CLTr CMea EBee GMaP MRav NBir NHol SCob SIng SPer SRms SSpi WAbe WCru WMoo

¶ - black leaf form (4) — CSpe EBee

¶ - double flowers (4) — EBee WCot

- var. *incisolobata* (5) — SSpi

¶ - pink (4) — EBee WAbe

* - variegated (4) — EAst EMan GNau WCot

¶ - yellow-green flowered (4) — EBee

'Foster's Gold' (x *elisabethae*) (7) — NMen

'Four Winds' (15) — EGle EWes GAbr LBee NMen SBla SIng SSmi WCom WMoo

♦ *fragosa* — See *S. nidifica*

¶ 'Francesco Redi' (7) — WAbe

'Francis Cade' (8) — ELan ITim

'Franzii' (x *paulinae*) (7) — MDHE NHed NMen

§ *frederici-augusti* (7) — SBla

§ - subsp. *grisebachii* (7) ♀ — GTou NSla NTow WCla

'Friar Tuck' (x *boydii*) (7) — MWat NMen

'Friesei' (x *salmonica*) (7) — CLyd EMNN EPot NHar NHed NMen

§ x *fritschiana* (8) — MDHE NHol NNrd SIng

'Funkii' (x *petraschii*) (7) — MWat NMen

¶ 'Gaertneri' (*mariae-theresiae*) (7) — NMen

'Gaiety' (15) — ECho ELan GDra LBee MDHE NFla NRoo SIng

'Galaxie' (x *megaseiflora*) (7) — CLyd LFox MDHE NHol NMen

'Ganymede' (*burseriana*) (7) — Last listed 1997

§ x *gaudinii* (8) — CLyd ECtt EGoo EMNN ESis GGar GTou LBee MBro NHar NHed NHol NMen SIng WGor WPer

'Gelber Findling' (7) — EPot LRHS MDHE WAbe

'Gem' (x *irvingii*) (7) — EMNN MBro NHar NMen NNrd

♦ 'General Joffre' (15) — See *S.* 'Maréchal Joffre' (15)

'Geoides' — See *S. hirsuta* subsp. *paucicrenata*

*georgei* (7) — EPot NMen WAbe

- ENF 5 (7) — EHyt

- McB 1379 (7) — NHol

*geranioides* (15) — GCHN

'Gertie Pritchard' (x *megaseiflora*) — See *S.* 'Mrs Gertie Prichard'

x *geuderi* sensu stricto hort. — See *S.* 'Eulenspiegel' (x *geuderi*)

§ x *geum* (11) — CHid EBee ECha ELan MRav NWoo SDys WFar

- Dixter form (11) — ECha WFar

* 'Gladys' (15) — Last listed 1998

'Gleborg' (15) — EWes

'Gloria' (*burseriana*) (7) ♀ — CLyd EHyt LFox MBal MBro MRPP NHol NMen NSla SBla SRms WPat

♦ x *gloriana* sensu stricto hort. (7) — See *S.* 'Godiva' (x *gloriana*)

'Gloriosa' (x *gloriana*) (7) — See *S.* 'Godiva' (x *gloriana*)

§ 'Godiva' (x *gloriana*) (7) — EMNN ITim MWat NMen

'Goeblii' (7) — MDHE

'Gold Dust' (x *eudoxiana*) (7) — CLyd CNic EMNN GTou LFox MOne MWat NHar NMen NNrd SBod SIng WWin

'Gold Leaf' (15) — Last listed 1997
'Golden Falls' (15/v) — CMea EWTr EWes GTou LBee LHop MBNS MBro NMen SIng WCom WPat WRHF
Golden Prague (x *pragensis*) — See *S.* 'Zlatá Praha' (x *pragensis*)
'Gothenburg' (7) — CLyd EHyt NMen
♦ 'Grace' (x *arendsii*) (15/v) — See *S.* 'Seaspray' (x *arendsii*)
'Grace Farwell' (x *anglica*) (7) — CLyd CNic EMMN EPot GCHN ITim MBar MBro NHed NHol NMen NWCA SBla SIng WHoo WPyg
'Gracilis' (x *geum*) — See *S.* 'Gracilis' (x *polita*)
§ 'Gracilis' (x *polita*) (11) — CNic
*granulata* (15) — CNic EWFC MHew MMal NMen NRya WCla
'Gratoides' (x *grata*) (7) — Last listed 1998
'Greenslacks Claire' (*oppositifolia*) (7) — Last listed 1998
'Greenslacks Heather' (*oppositifolia*) (7) — Last listed 1998
'Greenslacks Valerie' (*oppositifolia*) (7) — Last listed 1998
§ 'Gregor Mendel' (x *apiculata*) (7) ♀ — CMea ELan EMMN EPot GDra GTou MBal MBro MPla NHed NHol NMen SBla SBod SIng SRms SSmi WCom WHoo WPyg
*grisebachii* — See *S. frederici-augusti* subsp. *grisebachii*
  - subsp. *montenegrina* — See *S. frederici-augusti*
'Gustav Hegi' (x *anormalis*) (7) — Last listed 1998
'Haagii' (x *eudoxiana*) (7) — CInt ELan EMMN GCHN GCrs GTou MBal MBro MOne NHed NMen NNrd SIng SSmi WWin
♦ *ballii* — See *S. marshallii*
'Harlow Car' (7) — CLyd LFox NMen
'Harlow Car' x *poluniniana* (7) — CPBP
¶ 'Harold Bevington' (*paniculata*) (8) — MDHE
♦ *hartii* — See *S. rosacea*
'Hartside Pink' (*umbrosa*) (11) — NWoo
'Hartswood White' (15) — EWTr MDHE MWat SIng
'Hedwig' (x *malbyana*) (7) — MWat NMen
♦ x *heinreichii* sensu stricto hort. — See *S.* 'Ernst Heinrich' (x *heinrichii*)
'Herbert Cuerden' (x *elisabethae*) (7) — NHed NNrd
'Hi-Ace' (15/v) — ELan GTou LFox MBro NBro NRoo NWCA SBla SBod SSmi WFar
'Highdownensis' (8) — MDHE
'Hindhead Seedling' (x *boydii*) (7) — CLyd EMMN LRHS MDHE MWat NHar NHed NMen
*hirsuta* (11) — MDHE NRya WCru
'Hirsuta' (x *geum*) — See *S.* x *geum*
'Hirtella' (*paniculata*) (8) — MDHE
'His Majesty' (x *irvingii*) (7) — EMMN LFox MDHE NHar NMen WAbe
'Hocker Edge' (x *arco-valleyi*) (7) — ITim LFox MWat NHed NMen
'Holden Seedling' (15) — EMMN EPot EWes MDHE
¶ x *hornibrookii* (7) — WPat
*bostii* (8) — CLyd GTou ITim LBee SIng WTin
§ - subsp. *bostii* (8) — MDHE
  - - var. *altissima* (8) — STre
  - subsp. *rhaetica* (8) — MDHE NBro NMen WAbe
¶ 'Hsitou Silver' B&SWJ 1980 hybrid JB 11 — (*stolonifera*) (4)    WCru NMen
§ *bypnoides* (15) — EWFC GAbr MOne NHar SSmi

*hypostoma* (7) — Last listed 1998
'Icelandica' (*cotyledon*) (8) — NHol
'Icicle' (x *elisabethae*) (7) — MWat
'Ingeborg' (15) — ECha LBee MDHE SIng
*iranica* (7) — EHyt EMMN GCHN GCrs MWat NMen
'Irene Bacci' (x *baccii*) (7) — MWat NMen
'Iris Prichard' (x *hardingii*) (7) — CLyd EPot ESis MBro NMen WHoo WPyg
¶ 'Irish' (15) — EPot
*irrigua* (15) — EWes
x *irvingii* sensu stricto hort. — See *S.* 'Walter Irving' (x *irvingii*)
'Ivana' (x *caroliquarti*) (7) — MWat
'James Bremner' (15) — LBee MDHE MOne NBro NFla NOla SBod SIng
'Jason' (x *elisabethae*) (7) — MWat
¶ JB 14/89 — CGra
'Jenkinsiae' (x *irvingii*) (7) ♀ — CFee CLyd EBrP EBre ELan EMMN EPot ESis GTou ITim LBre MBal MBro MPla MRPP NHed NHol NMen NWCA SBla SBre SChu SIng SMer WAbe WHoo WPat WPyg WWin
§ 'Johann Kellerer' (x *kellereri*) (7) — EPot GCrs LFox NHed NSla SBla
'John Tomlinson' (*burseriana*) (7) — NSla WAbe
'Josef Čapek' (x *megaseiflora*) (7) — CLyd EPot NMen
'Josef Mánes' (x *borisii*) (7) — MDHE NMen
'Joy' — See *S.* 'Kaspar Maria Sternberg' (x *petraschii*)
'Judith Shackleton' (x *abingdonensis*) (7) — CLyd EHyt MWat NMen NNrd WAbe
'Juliet' — See *S.* 'Riverslea' (x *hornibrookii*)
§ *juniperifolia* (7) — ELan EMMN GCHN GTou ITim MOne MWat NHar NHed NMen NNrd NRoo NWCA SChu SMer SRms SSmi
♦ - var. *brachyphylla* — See *S. ruprechtiana*
  - var. *macedonica* — See *S. juniperifolia*
♦ - subsp. *sancta* — See *S. sancta* var. *pseudosancta*
'Jupiter' (x *megaseiflora*) (7) — CLyd EMMN MWat NHar NMen NNrd WAbe
§ *karadzicensis* (7) — EMMN NMen
'Karasin' (7) — NNrd
'Karel Čapek' (x *megaseiflora*) (7) — CLyd CMea CNic EHyt EPot MWat NHed NHol NMen NNrd WAbe
'Karel Stivín' (x *edithiae*) (7) — EMMN MWat NMen
'Karlstejn' (x *borisii*) (7) — WAbe
§ 'Kaspar Maria Sternberg' (x *petraschii*) (7) — EMMN GCHN ITim LFox MBro NHar NHol NMen NNrd SIng WPat
'Kath Dryden' (x *anglica*) (7) — CLyd MDHE NHol SIng WAbe
'Kathleen Pinsent' (8) ♀ — EPot MBro NHar NNrd NVic NWCA SIng
'Kathleen' (x *polulacina*) (7) — CLyd EHyt NHol
x *kellereri* sensu stricto hort. — See *S.* 'Johann Kellerer' (x *kellereri*)
'Kestoniensis' (x *salmonica*) (7) — MWat NNrd
¶ 'Kew Gem' (7) — NMen
'Kewensis' (x *kellereri*) (7) — MWat NMen SIng WAbe
'King Lear' (x *bursiculata*) (7) — EPot LFox LRHS MWat NMen SBla SIng
♦ 'Kingii' — See *S.* 'Egemmulosa' (*hypnoides*)
'Kingscote White' (15) — MDHE SIng
¶ 'Kinki Purple' B&SWJ 4972 (*stolonifera*) — WCru
'Klondike' (x *boydii*) (7) — MDHE
'Knapton Pink' (15) — EWTr LBee MDHE NRya SIng SSmi WAbe WCom

'Knapton White' (15) — EWTr LBuc MDHE NBro SIng WCla

§ x *kochii* (7) — EHyt NHar NTow

§ 'Kolbiana' (x *paulinae*) (7) — CLyd MDHE MWat

'Koprvnik' (*paniculata*) (8) — MDHE SIng

*kotschyi* (7) — Last listed 1996

'Krasava' (x *megaseiflora*) (7) — CLyd CPBP EHyt EMNN NHar NHol NMen WAbe

'Kyrillii' (x *borisii*) (7) — NMen

'Labe' (x *arco-valleyi*) (7) — CLyd CNic EPot LRHS NMen SBla SIng WAbe

'Labradorica' (*paniculata*) — See *S. paniculata* subsp. *neogaea*

'Lady Beatrix Stanley' — See *S.* 'Beatrix Stanley' (x *anglica*)

'Lagraveana' (*paniculata*) (8) — ELan NHed WWin

x *landaueri* sensu stricto hort. — See *S.* 'Leonore' (x *landaueri*)

'Lenka' (x *byam-groundsii*) (7) — EHyt EMNN ITim NHar NMen NNrd NSla

'Leo Gordon Godseff' (x *elisabethae*) (7) — MOne NMen SBla SIng

§ 'Leonore' (x *landaueri*) (7) — MDHE MWat SIng WAbe

'Letchworth Gem' (x *urbium*) (11) — GCal

x *leyboldii* (7) — GTou NMen

'Lidice' (7) — EMNN NHar NMen NNrd WAbe

*lilacina* (7) — CLyd EHyt EMNN NHar NHol NMen NNrd WPat

¶ 'Limelight' (*callosa*) (8) — MDHE

'Lindau' (7) — MWat

*lingulata* — See *S. callosa*

'Lismore Carmine' (x *lismorensis*) (7) — CLyd EHyt MWat NMen

* 'Lismore Gem' — EHyt NMen

'Lismore Mist' (7) — EHyt

'Lismore Pink' (x *lismorensis*) (7) — CLyd EHyt EPot MWat NMen NWCA

'Lohengrin' (x *hoerhammeri*) (7) — MWat NNrd

'Lohmuelleri' (x *biasolettoi*) (7) — MWat

*longifolia* (8) — ELan GCrs NMen NSla NWCA SIng WLin

– JJA 861600 (8) — SBla

Love Me — See *S.* 'Miluj Mne' (x *poluanglica*)

'Lowndes' (*andersonii*) (7) — WAbe

¶ *lowndesii* (7) — EHyt

'Ludmila Šubrová' (x *bertolonii*) (7) — Last listed 1998

'Luna' (x *millstreamiana*) (7) — Last listed 1998

'Lusanna' (x *irvingii*) (7) — MDHE NHol

¶ 'Luschtinetz' (15) — MDHE

◆ 'Lutea' (*diapensioides*) — See *S.* 'Wilhelm Tell' (x *malbyana*), 'Primulina' (x *malbyana*)

'Lutea' (*marginata*) — See *S.* 'Faust' (x *borisii*)

'Lutea' (*paniculata*) (8) ♀ — ESis GDra GTou LBee MBal MBro MRPP NBro NHed NMen NNrd NRoo SChu SIng SSmi

'Lutea' (x *stuartii*) (7) — MDHE

§ 'Luteola' (x *boydii*) (7) ♀ — MDHE

*luteoviridis* — See *S. corymbosa*

'Lužníce' (x *poluluteopurpurea*) (7) — MWat NHed NMen

◆ *macedonica* — See *S. juniperifolia*

'Magna' (*burseriana*) (7) — EHyt

'Major' (*cochlearis*) (8) ♀ — LRHS MBro NMen NNrd WGor

'Major Lutea' — See *S.* 'Luteola' (x *boydii*)

*manshuriensis* (4) — Last listed 1998

§ 'Maréchal Joffre' (15) — LBuc MDHE NPri WCom

'Margarete' (x *borisii*) (7) — MWat NHed

*marginata* (7) — CLyd LFox

– var. *balcanica* — See *S. marginata* var. *rocheliana*

– var. *boryi* (7) — EHyt EPot MDHE MWat NMen SIng

– var. *coriophylla* (7) — EPot MDHE NWCA

◆ – var. *karadzicensis* — See *S. karadzicensis*

§ – var. *rocheliana* (7) — CLyd CPBP ELan EPot NMen

'Maria Callas' (x *poluanglica*) (7) — CGra CLyd

'Maria Luisa' (x *salmonica*) (7) — CLyd CNic CPBP EPot GCrs LFox MBro MWat NHed WAbe

'Marianna' (x *borisii*) (7) — CLyd CNic NHed NMen NNrd

'Marie Stivínová' (x *borisii*) (7) — MWat

¶ 'Maroon Beauty' (*stolonifera*) — MAvo WCot

'Mars' (x *elisabethae*) (7) — MWat

◆ 'Marshal Joffre' (15) — See *S.* 'Maréchal Joffre' (15)

§ *marshallii* (4) — GCHN WWin

§ 'Martha' (x *semmleri*) (7) — CLyd EMNN NMen NNrd

*matta-florida* (7) — MWat

'May Queen' (7) — MWat NHol

*media* (7) — CLyd EHyt MWat

x *megaseiflora* sensu stricto hort. — See *S.* 'Robin Hood' (x *megaseiflora*)

¶ 'Melrose' (x *salmonica*) (7) — NMen

*mertensiana* (6) — CLyd GTou NBir WCru

* – var. *bulbifera* (6) — Last listed 1998

'Meteor' (7) — NNrd NRya

*micranthidifolia* (4) — WThi

'Millstream Cream' (x *elisabethae*) (7) — CGra CLyd EPot MDHE MWat NNrd

§ 'Miluj Mne' (x *poluanglica*) (7) — EHyt LFox NHar NNrd

¶ 'Minnehaha' (x *elisabethaea*) (7) — MDHE WAbe

'Minor' (*cochlearis*) (8) ♀ — CInt EMNN ESis GTou LBee LFox MBal MBro MRPP NHol NMen NVic NWCA SChu SIng SSmi WCla WHoo WLin WPat

◆ 'Minor Glauca' (*paniculata*) — See *S. paniculata* subsp. *neogaea*

'Minor' (*paniculata*) — See *S. paniculata* var. *brevifolia*

'Minutifolia' (*paniculata*) (8) — CNic EPot ESis LFox MBal MBro MDHE NHed NWCA SIng

§ 'Miss Chambers' (x *urbium*) (11) — EGoo EMon SUsu WCot

'Mona Lisa' (x *borisii*) (7) — MBro MDHE MWat NHol SIng WAbe WPat

§ 'Mondscheinsonate' (x *boydii*) (7) — NHol

'Moonlight' — See *S.* 'Sulphurea' (x *boydii*)

'Moonlight Sonata' (x *boydii*) — See *S.* 'Mondscheinsonate' (x *boydii*)

*moschata* — See *S. exarata* subsp. *moschata*

'Mother of Pearl' (x *irvingii*) (7) — EMNN NHar NMen

'Mother Queen' (x *irvingii*) (7) — MBro MDHE NHol WHoo WPat WPyg

'Mount Nachi' (*fortunei*) (5) — CFil EBee EHyt EWes NHar NMen SIng SSpi WAbe WCot WFar WPer

'Mrs E. Piper' (15) — LBuc SRms

§ 'Mrs Gertie Prichard' (x *megaseiflora*) (7) — LFox MWat NHol NMen WAbe

'Mrs Helen Terry' (x *salmonica*) (7) — CLyd EPot LRHS MDHE NHed NMen

'Mrs Leng' (x *elisabethae*) (7) — NMen

*mutata* (8) — Last listed 1996

'Myra' (x *anglica*) (7) — EMNN LFox MBro MWat NHol NMen NWCA WHoo WPat WPyg

'Myra Cambria' (x *anglica*) (7) — GCHN MWat NHol NMen NNrd WAbe

'Nancye' (x *goringiana*) (7)    CLyd CPBP EHyt MDHE NMen
§ **nelsoniana** (4)    NHol NNrd
¶ 'Neptun' (7)    CGra
'Niobe' (7)    EHyt
¶ **nishidae** (10)    MDHE
**nivalis** (4)    NHol NWCA
'Norvegica' (*cotyledon*) (8)    CLyd GTou MDHE WWin
'Notata' (*paniculata*) (8)    NMen
'Nottingham Gold'    CLyd EPot MDHE MWat NHol
    (x *boydii*) (7)    NMen NNrd
'Nugget' (7)    SIng
'Obristii' (x *salmonica*) (7)    ITim NHol NMen NNrd
§ **obtusa** (7)    NMen
'Obtusocuneata'    ECho EHyt ELan NHar SBla WAbe
    (*fortunei*) (5)
'Ochroleuca'    CLyd EMNN ITim NMen WAbe
    (x *elisabethae*) (7)
'Odysseus' (*sancta*) (7)    NMen
'Olymp' (*scardica*) (7)    NMen
'Opalescent' (7)    CLyd LFox MWat NMen NNrd
§ 'Ophelia' (x *arco-valleyi*) (7)    MWat NHol
**oppositifolia** (7)    GTou ITim MBNS MOne NSla
    SPlb SRms WAbe WWin
* - var. **asiatica**    Last listed 1998
- x **biflora**    See *S.* x *kochii*
♦ - 'Corrie Fee'    See *S.* 'Corrie Fee' (*oppositifolia*)
* - var. **latina** (7)    CLyd ELan EMNN GCrs GDra
    GGar GTou NHar
'Oriole' (x *boydii*) (7)    NMen
'Orjen' (*paniculata*    NNrd
    var. *orientalis*) (8)
'Pandora' (*burseriana*) (7)    Last listed 1997
§ **paniculata** (8)    CNic ELan ESis GTou LBee LPVe
    MBal MBro MWat NHed NMen
    NRoo NSla NVic SRms WCla
    WHoo WPyg
§ - var. **baldensis** (8)    CLyd ELan GDra GTou ITim MBar
    MBro MWat NBro NHed NHol
    NMen SBla SIgm SPlb SSmi WCla
    WWin
§ - var. **brevifolia** (8)    CNic SIng SSmi
§ - subsp. **cartilaginea** (8)    NHol SBla
- subsp. **kolenatiana**    See *S. paniculata* subsp.
    *cartilaginea*
§ - subsp. **neogaea** (8)    MDHE
§ - var. **orientalis** (8)    MBro MDHE SSmi WCla
**paradoxa** (15)    CLyd EPot SBla WGor
'Parcevalis'    CLyd
    (x *finnisiae*) (7x9)
¶ **parnassifolia** (1)    GCrs
'Parsee' (x *margoxiana*) (7)    NMen
¶ x **patens** (8x9)    EHyt
§ 'Paula' (x *paulinae*)    Last listed 1998
♦ x **paulinae** sensu    See *S.* 'Paula' (x *paulinae*)
    stricto hort.
'Peach Blossom' (7)    CLyd EPot GCrs MWat NMen SBla
    SIng
'Pearl Rose' (x *anglica*) (7)    LFox
'Pearly Gates' (x *irvingii*) (7)    CLyd MWat NMen NSla WAbe
'Pearly Gold' (15)    CMea NRoo NRya SSmi
'Pearly King' (15)    CLyd ECho ELan LBee MBal
    NMen NVic WAbe WFar
x **pectinata**    See *S.* x *fritschiana*
¶ **pedemontana**    MChR
    subsp. **cervicornis** (15)
'Penelope'    CLyd EHyt EPot GCrs ITim MBro
    (x *boydilacina*) (7)    NHed NHol NMen SBla WAbe
    WHoo WPat WPyg
'Peter Burrow'    CLyd CPBP EHyt MDHE NHar
    (x *poluanglica*) (7) ♀    NMen NNrd WAbe

'Peter Pan' (15)    ELan EMNN EPot EWTr GDra
    GTou LFox LGro MBro NFla
    NMen NNrd NRoo SBod SSmi
    WCom WPat
'Petra' (7)    CLyd EPot MBro NHol NMen
    NNrd WAbe
x **petraschii** (7)    ITim
§ 'Phoenix' (x *biasolettoi*) (7)    EHyt LRHS NMen
'Pilatus' (x *boydii*) (7)    MWat NMen SIng
'Pink Pearl' (7)    CMea
'Pixie' (15)    EBrP EBre EMNN LBee LBre MBal
    MPla MWat NFla NMen NNrd
    NRoo NRya SBre SIng SRms SSmi
'Pixie Alba'    See *S.* 'White Pixie'
'Plena' (*granulata*)    See *S.* 'Flore Pleno' (*granulata*)
'Pluto' (x *megaseiflora*) (7)    MDHE
'Pollux' (x *boydii*) (7)    EPot NHol
**poluniniana** (7)    CLyd EMNN ITim LFox NHar
    NHol NMen NWCA WAbe
'Pompadour' (15)    LBee
¶ 'Popelka' (*marginata*) (7)    CLyd
**porophylla** (7)    EHyt GDra
- x **sempervivum** (7)    Last listed 1996
- var. **thessalica**    See *S. sempervivum* f.
    *stenophylla*
aff. **porophylla** (7)    NWCA
'Portae' (*paniculata*) (8)    NNrd SIng
'Primrose Bee'    EHyt EPot
    (x *apiculata*) (7)
'Primrose Dame'    EMNN ESis ITim MBal MWat NHol
    (x *elisabethae*) (7)    NMen SIng WAbe WFar
* x **primulaize** (9x11)    CLyd MBro NMen NRya SRot
I 'Primulaize Salmon' (9x11)    ESis LBee NHed NWoo WCom
    WPer
§ 'Primulina' (x *malbyana*) (7)    LFox NHed
♦ **primuloides**    See *S.* 'Primuloides' (*umbrosa*)
§ 'Primuloides'    CGle GCHN LFox MBro NMen
    (*umbrosa*) (11) ♀    NPri SRms WEas
'Prince Hal' (*burseriana*) (7)    EMNN EPot ESis GCrs ITim
    MDHE NHar NHed NMen NNrd
    SIng
'Princess' (*burseriana*) (7)    EHyt NMen
'Probynii' (*cochlearis*) (8)    EPot MDHE MWat
'Prometheus'    NNrd
    (x *prossenii*)
'Prospero' (x *petraschii*) (7)    MWat NMen
x **prossenii** sensu    See *S.* 'Regina' (x *prossenii*)
    stricto hort.
§ 'Pseudoborisii' (x *borisii*) (7)    EPot ITim
'Pseudofranzii'    NWCA
    (x *paulinae*) (7)
x **pseudokotschyi**    See *S.* 'Denisa' (x *pseudokotschyi*)
    sensu stricto hort.
'Pseudopungens'    Last listed 1996
    (x *apiculata*) (7)
'Pseudosalomonii'    Last listed 1997
    (x *salmonica*) (7)
'Pseudoscardica'    MWat
    (x *wehrhahnii*) (7)
'Pseudovaldensis'    MDHE
    (*cochlearis*) (8)
**pubescens**    EPot NMen
    subsp. **iratiana** (15)
**punctata** Sternbo. (4)    See *S. nelsoniana*
'Pungens' (x *apiculata*) (7)    NHed NHol NMen
'Purpurea' (*fortunei*)    See *S.* 'Rubrifolia' (*fortunei*)
'Purpurteppich' (15)    MDHE WPer
§ 'Pygmalion' (x *webrii*) (7)    CLyd CPBP ESis NHol NMen
    WAbe WPat
'Pyramidalis' (*cotyledon*) (8)    EPiP SRms
'Pyrenaica'    EMNN NHar NMen
    (*oppositifolia*) (7)

| | |
|---|---|
| *quadrifaria* (7) | NHol |
| 'Quarry Wood' | ITim NMen |
| (x *anglica*) (7) | |
| 'Rainsley Seedling' | MDHE NBro NMen |
| (*paniculata*) (8) | |
| *ramulosa* (7) | NMen |
| 'Red Poll' (x *poluanglica*) (7) | CLyd MDHE MWat NMen WAbe |
| § 'Regina' (x *prossenii*) (7) | GCHN ITim NNrd SIng |
| *retusa* (7) | CLyd EHyt EMNN NMen NSla |
| | NWCA SSca |
| 'Rex' (*paniculata*) (8) | GCHN LBuc NHol NMen |
| *rhodopetala* (7) | EHyt |
| § 'Riverslea' | CGle CLyd CPBP LFox MBro |
| (x *hornibrookii*) (7) ♀ | MWat NHar NHol NMen SIng |
| | WAbe WPat |
| § 'Robin Hood' | CLyd EMNN ITim LFox MWat |
| (x *megaseiflora*) (7) | NHar NHol NMen SBla SIng WAbe |
| | WPat |
| 'Rokujô' (*fortunei*) (5) | LRHS MBri WCot WFar |
| *rosacea* subsp. *hartii* (15) | Last listed 1998 |
| 'Rosea' (*cortusifolia*) (5) | CLAP NHar |
| 'Rosea' (*paniculata*) (8) ♀ | GDra GTou LBee MBal MBro |
| | NBro NHed NHol NRoo NSla SBla |
| | SIng SSmi SSmi STre WCla WHoo |
| | WPyg WWin |
| 'Rosea' (x *stuartii*) (7) | NHed NMen WAbe |
| 'Rosemarie' (x *anglica*) (7) | CLyd ITim NHol NMen |
| 'Rosenzwerg' (15) | LBee |
| 'Rosina Sündermann' | NHed NSla WAbe |
| (x *rosinae*) (7) | |
| *rotundifolia* (12) | CLyd EBee GBin NHol SSpi |
| § - subsp. *chrysospleniifolia* | WCot WCru WPer |
| var. *rhodopea* (12) | |
| ¶ - subsp. *rotundifolia* var. | SIng |
| *heucherifolia* (12) | |
| 'Rubella' (x *irvingii*) (7) | MDHE MWat |
| § 'Rubrifolia' (*fortunei*) (5) | CBos CFil CLAP CMil EBee EBrP |
| | EBre ECha LBre NHar NRoo SBre |
| | SSpi WAbe WCot WCru WFar |
| | WGer WSan |
| * 'Ruby Red' | NPro |
| 'Russell Vincent Prichard' | NHol |
| (x *irvingii*) (7) | |
| 'Ruth Draper' | EMNN GCHN NHar NWCA SBla |
| (*oppositifolia*) (7) | WAbe |
| 'Ruth McConnell' (15) | CMea EWTr LBee LBuc WCom |
| 'Sabrina' | CLyd MWat |
| (x *fallsvillagensis*) (7) | |
| 'Saint John's' (*caesia*) (8) | EBur MBro MDHE NNrd WWin |
| 'Saint Kilda' | CLyd GCrs GTou |
| (*oppositifolia*) (7) | |
| ◆ x *salmonica* sensu | See *S.* 'Salomonii' (x *salmonica*) |
| stricto hort. | |
| § 'Salomonii' | CLyd EPot ITim MBro MOne |
| (x *salmonica*) (7) | NHed NMen NNrd SIng SRms |
| *sancta* (7) | CLyd EPot GCHN LFox MBal |
| | NMen SRms SSmi |
| - subsp. *pseudosancta* | See *S. juniperifolia* |
| var. *macedonica* | |
| ¶ *sanguinea* (1) | MDHE |
| 'Sanguinea Superba' | GDra SIng |
| (x *arendsii*) (15) ♀ | |
| 'Sara Sinclair' | Last listed 1998 |
| (x *arco-valleyi*) (7) | |
| *sarmentosa* | See *S. stolonifera* |
| 'Sartorii' | See *S.* 'Pygmalion' (x *webrii*) |
| 'Saturn' (x *megaseiflora*) (7) | MBro MWat NHol NMen WAbe |
| 'Sázava' | ITim MDHE MWat NHed WAbe |
| (x *poluluteopurpurea*) | CPBP EHyt EMNN MBro MDHE |
| (7) | |
| *scardica* (7) | MWat NBro NMen |
| - var. *dalmatica* | See *S. obtusa* |
| * - f. *erythrantha* (7) | NNrd |
| - var. *obtusa* | See *S. obtusa* |
| § 'Schelleri' (x *petraschii*) (7) | NNrd |
| 'Schleicheri' (x *kellereri*) | See *S.* 'Schleicheri' (x *landaueri*) |
| § 'Schleicheri' | Last listed 1998 |
| (x *landaueri*) (7) | |
| 'Schneeteppich' (15) | WPer |
| § 'Schwefelblüte' (15) | GTou LBee MBal NRoo SIng SSmi |
| | WCom WPat |
| *scleropoda* (7) | WLin |
| § 'Seaspray' (x *arendsii*) (15/v) | EWes |
| 'Seissera' (*burseriana*) (7) | EPot NHol |
| x *semmleri* sensu stricto | See *S.* 'Martha' (x *semmleri*) |
| hort. | |
| *sempervivum* (7) | EPot LFox MBro NMen NSla |
| | NWCA WTin |
| - JCA 864.003 (7) | CPBP MBro |
| * - f. *stenophylla* | GCHN GTou MDHE NHed |
| *sibirica* (14) | GTou |
| § 'Silver Cushion' (15/v) | CMea EAst ELan EPot GTou LBee |
| | MBar MBro NRoo SIng SMer SSmi |
| | WAbe WMoo |
| 'Silver Edge' | NMen WAbe |
| (x *arco-valleyi*) (7) | |
| 'Silver Mound' | See *S.* 'Silver Cushion' |
| 'Sir Douglas Haig' (15) | NNrd SIng |
| 'Skye' (*oppositifolia*) (7) | Last listed 1996 |
| 'Snowcap' (*pubescens*) (15) | EHyt GCrs LBee NHed NMen |
| | NNrd NWCA |
| 'Snowdon' (*burseriana*) (7) | MWat |
| 'Snowflake' (8) | MDHE NHed |
| § 'Sofia' (x *borisii*) (7) | EPot LFox NNrd WAbe |
| ¶ 'Somerset Seedling' (8) | MDHE |
| § 'Southside Seedling' (8) ♀ | CLyd CPri ELan EPot ESis GTou |
| | LHop MBar MBro NBro NHar |
| | NHol NMen NNrd NRoo SIng |
| | SRms SSmi WAbe WCla WHoo |
| | WLin WMoo WPat WPyg WWin |
| sp. BM&W 118 | GDra |
| sp. SEP 22 | MWat |
| 'Spartakus' (x *apiculata*) (7) | Last listed 1998 |
| *spathularis* (11) | EPla WCot WEas WWin |
| 'Speciosa' (*burseriana*) (7) | MDHE NHed |
| 'Splendens' (*oppositifolia*) | ELan EMNN ITim LFox MBal |
| (7) ♀ | NHed NHol NMen SMer SRms |
| | SSmi WAbe WGor WPat |
| 'Sprite' (15) | GCHN LBee |
| *spruneri* (7) | EHyt NMen |
| * - var. *deorum* (7) | Last listed 1998 |
| 'Stansfieldii' (15) | EBrP EBre EMNN LBre NMen |
| | NNrd SBod SBre SSmi |
| § 'Stella' (x *stormonthii*) (7) | SBla |
| *stellaris* (4) | GTou |
| ◆ *stenophylla* | See *S. flagellaris* |
| subsp. *stenophylla* | |
| *stolitzkae* (7) | CLyd EMNN EPot GCrs NHed |
| | NMen |
| § *stolonifera* (5) ♀ | CArn CHal CHan ECho ELan GAri |
| | NBro SDix WFar |
| - B&SWJ 1980 (5) | Last listed 1998 |
| 'Stormonth's Variety' | See *S.* 'Stella' (x *stormonthii*) |
| *stribrnyi* (7) | MWat NMen NTow |
| - JCA 861-400 (7) | NWCA |
| 'Sturmiana' (*paniculata*) (8) | MBro NMen SRms |
| aff. *subsessiliflora* (7) | Last listed 1996 |
| 'Suendermannii' | MWat NHed NWCA SIng |
| (x *kellereri*) (7) | |
| 'Suendermannii Major' | CLyd NSla SIng |
| (x *kellereri*) (7) | |
| 'Suendermannii Purpurea' | GCHN |
| (x *kellereri*) (7) | |
| § 'Sulphurea' (x *boydii*) (7) | EMNN ESis LFox MBro NHar |
| | NHed NHol NMen NNrd NWCA |
| | SChu WAbe WHoo WPat WPyg |

'Sun Dance' (x *boydii*) (7)  MDHE NHol
'Superba' (*callosa*  GDra GTou MBro MDHE SGre
  var. *australis*) (8)  SSmi
'Sylva' (x *elisabethae*) (7)  MWat
¶ 'Symons-Jeunei' (8)  MDHE
*taygetea* (12)  NTow
¶ x *tazetta* (?11x12)  WCom
'Theoden'  CPBP EHyt EMNN EPot EWes
  (*oppositifolia*) (7) ♀  GCrs GTou MBro NHar NHol
    NPro NWCA SBla WSan '
'Thorpei' (7)  GCrs ITim NMen SIng
¶ 'Timbalii' (x *gaudinii*) (8)  MSCN SIng
'Timmy Foster'  NHol NSla
  (x *irvingii*) (7)
x *tiroliensis* (8)  Last listed 1998
'Tom Thumb' (15)  MBro NMen NNrd
*tombeanensis* (7)  NMen
'Tricolor' (*stolonifera*) (5) ♀  EBak ELan SYvo
'Triumph' (x *arendsii*) (15)  ECtt EMNN GCHN GDra GTou
    LBee NMen NRoo NVic SBod
'Tully' (x *elisabethae*) (7)  ESis NHol WPat
'Tumbling Waters' (8) ♀  CInt GAbr LHop MBro NMen SIng
    SRms SSca SUsu WAbe WGor
    WPat WWin
§ 'Tvůj Den'  EHyt NHed NMen WAbe
  (x *poluanglica*) (7)
§ 'Tvůj Píseň'  EHyt MDHE NHar NHed WAbe
  (x *poluanglica*) (7)
§ 'Tvůj Polibek'  EHyt MDHE NHar NHed NMen
  (x *poluanglica*) (7)
§ 'Tvůj Přítel'  EHyt MDHE NHar NHed WAbe
  (x *poluanglica*) (7)
§ 'Tvůj Úsměv'  EHyt MDHE MWat NHar NHed
  (x *poluanglica*) (7)  NMen WAbe
§ 'Tvůj Úspěch'  EHyt MDHE NHed NMen SBla
  (x *poluanglica*) (7)  WAbe
'Tycho Brahe'  CLyd NMen
  (x *doerfleri*) (7)
*umbrosa* (11)  CLyd EBee EBrP EBre EMon LBre
    MRav SBre SMac SPer SPlb SRms
    WHen WMoo WWat WWin
♦ - var. *primuloides*  See S. 'Primuloides' (*umbrosa*)
* - *subinteger*  SGre
'Unique'  See S. 'Bodensee' (x *hofmannii*)
x *urbium* (11) ♀  EAst EGoo ELan EPfP GDra LEdu
    LGro MBal NDov NSti SIng WFar
    WPer
♦ - *primuloides*  See S. 'Clarence Elliott' (*umbrosa*)
'Elliott's Variety'
'Vaccariana'  ECho WAbe
  (*oppositifolia*) (7)
'Václav Hollar'  MWat NMen
  (x *gusmusii*) (7)
'Vahlii' (x *smithii*) (7)  WAbe
'Valborg'  See S. 'Cranbourne' (x *anglica*)
'Valentine'  See S. 'Cranbourne' (x *anglica*)
'Valerie Finnis'  See S. 'Aretiastrum' (x *boydii*)
I 'Variegata' (*cuneifolia*) (3)  ECho ECtt ELan ESis GCHN MBar
    MBro NMen NPri NRoo NVic
    SHFr SSmi WCom WMoo WPer
'Variegata' (*umbrosa*)  See S. 'Aureopunctata' (x *urbium*)
I 'Variegata' (x *urbium*) (3)  EAst ELan EPar GDra GGar LBee
    LGro MBal MRav NCat NFor NLar
    NSti SRms SSmi WCla WEas WWal
    WWat WWin
*vayredana* (15)  CLyd WAbe
*veitchiana* (5)  EPla NBro NCat NNrd WCru
'Venetia' (*paniculata*) (8)  MDHE NNrd SSmi
'Vesna' (x *borisii*) (7)  CLyd EMNN GCHN MOne MWat
    NMen NNrd WAbe WWin
§ *vespertina* (10)  CGra
'Vincent van Gogh'  ITim NHol NNrd
  (x *borisii*) (7)

'Vladana'  CLyd EMNN EPot MDHE NHar
  (x *megaseiflora*) (7)  NHol NMen NRya
'Vlasta' (7)  MWat
'Vltava' (7)  Last listed 1998
'W.A. Clark'  MBal WAbe
  (*oppositifolia*) (7)
'Wada' (*fortunei*) (5)  CFil CGle CLAP CWit EAst EBee
    EHic EPar GAbr GCHN MBal NBir
    NHar NRoo SSpi WAbe WCot
    WFar WWin
'Waithman's Variety' (8)  NNrd
§ 'Wallacei' (15)  ECho MDHE
'Walpole's Variety'  NHar NNrd WPer
  (*longifolia*) (8)
§ 'Walter Ingwersen'  SRms
  (*umbrosa*) (11)
♦ 'Walter Ingwersen'  See S. 'Walter Ingwersen'
  (*umbrosa*  (*umbrosa*)
  var. *primuloides*)
§ 'Walter Irving'  EHyt EMNN EPot MDHE NHar
  (x *irvingii*) (7)  NHol NMen NRya WAbe
'Welsh Dragon' (15)  MDHE WAbe
'Welsh Red' (15)  WAbe
'Welsh Rose' (15)  WAbe
*wendelboi* (7)  CLyd EHyt EMNN LFox MWat
    NMen
'Wendrush'  MDHE NMen WAbe
  (x *wendelacina*) (7)
'Wendy'  CLyd CNic NMen
  (x *wendelacina*) (7)
'Wetterhorn'  MBal NMen
  (*oppositifolia*) (7)
'Wheatley Lion'  MDHE NMen
  (x *borisii*) (7)
'Wheatley Rose' (7)  CLyd LRHS NHol
'White Cap' (x *boydii*) (7)  NHol
§ 'White Pixie' (15)  EMNN EPfP LBee LFox LGro
    NNrd NPri SBla SIng SRms SSmi
    WCla
'White Spire' (15)  MBro
♦ 'White Star' (x *petraschii*)  See S. 'Schelleri' (x *petraschii*)
'Whitehill' (8)  CLyd EBrP EBre EGoo ELan ESis
    GCHN GTou LBee LBre LFox
    MBal MBro NBro NEgg NHol
    NMen SBre SIng SSmi SUsu WAbe
    WCom WHoo WPat WPer WPyg
    WTin WWin
'Whitlavei Compacta'  MTPN NMen NWoo
  (*hypnoides*) (15)
§ 'Wilhelm Tell'  NMen
  (x *malbyana*) (7)
'William Boyd'  MDHE MWat
  (x *boydii*) (7)
'Winifred' (x *anglica*) (7)  CLyd EPot GCrs LFox MWat
    NMen WFar
'Winifred Bevington' (8x11)  More than 30 suppliers
'Winston Churchill' (15)  EPfP MBNS MDHE SIng
Winter Fire  See S. 'Winterfeuer' (*callosa*)
§ 'Winterfeuer' (*callosa*) (8)  Last listed 1997
'Winton' (x *paulinae*) (7)  MDHE
'Wisley' (*frederici-augusti*  GCHN MBal MBro NHar NMen
  subsp. *grisebachii*) (7) ♀  WCom WFar WHoo WPat WPyg
'Wisley Primrose'  See S. x 'Kolbiana' (x *paulinae*)
'Woodside Ross' (15)  MOne
'Yellow Rock' (7)  Last listed 1998
Your Day  See S. 'Tvůj Den' (x *poluanglica*)
Your Friend  See S. 'Tvůj Přítel' (x
    *poluanglica*)
Your Good Fortune  See S. 'Tvůj Úspěch' (x
    *poluanglica*)
Your Kiss  See S. 'Tvůj Polibek' (x
    *poluanglica*)

| | |
|---|---|
| Your Smile | See *S.* 'Tvůj Usmev' (x *poluanglica*) |
| Your Song | See *S.* 'Tvůj Písen' (x *poluanglica*) |
| Your Success | See *S.* 'Tvůj Úspěch' (x *poluanglica*) |
| x *zimmeteri* (8x11) | EWes NNrd SSmi |
| § 'Zlatá Praha' (x *pragensis*) (7) | NMen SIng WAbe |
| * *zoblenschaferi* | Last listed 1997 |

## SCABIOSA ✿ (Dipsacaceae)

| | |
|---|---|
| *africana* | WCot |
| *alpina* L. | See *Cephalaria alpina* |
| *anthemifolia* | CHan |
| *atropurpurea* | CLTr EBee SMrm SUsu |
| ¶ - 'Ace of Spades' | LFis WCot |
| - 'Peter Ray' | EWes LRHS MBri |
| *banatica* | See *S. columbaria* |
| * 'Black Prince' | Last listed 1998 |
| § Butterfly Blue® | EMan EPfP MBNS MBri MRav MWgw SCoo SPer WWeb |
| *caucasica* | CSam EAst ECha EPfP EWTr GChr MBro NCat NChi NLak SBla WHoo WPyg WWin |
| - var. *alba* | CBot CM&M EPfP MBri NCut NRoo WHoo |
| - 'Blue Lace' | MBri |
| - Blue Seal = 'Blausiegel' | EBee EBrP EBre LBre SBre |
| - 'Bressingham White' | SAsh |
| - 'Challenger' | MBri |
| - 'Clive Greaves' ♀ | CB&S CMGP CRDP EAst EBee ECha EFou ENot EOld ERic LHop LRot MBri MBro MCAu NFla NFor NMir SMad SPer SRms SUsu WCot WEas WMow |
| - 'Fama' | CFai EBee EMan EWTr MBNS NBir NLar NRoo SMrm SPlb SRms WFar WHoo WPyg |
| - 'Floral Queen' | Last listed 1997 |
| - 'Goldingensis' | EBee EOld MBNS NPri WFar WPer |
| - House's hybrids | NBro NVic SRms WElm WFar WHil WMoo |
| - 'Isaac House' | CBrm EBee SWat |
| - 'Kompliment' | ENot NLar WShe |
| ¶ - 'Lavender Blue' | WFar |
| - 'Miss Willmott' ♀ | CDoC CGle CHad CM&M CRDP CSev EAst EBee ECha EFou EWTr LHop MAvo MBel MBri MBro MCAu NCut NFla SLon SPer SPla SRms SUsu WFar WRus |
| - 'Moerheim Blue' | ECha MBri NFla SPer |
| - 'Moonstone' | Last listed 1996 |
| - 'Mount Cook' | LHop SAsh |
| - 'Nachtfalter' | LRHS MBri |
| - 'Penelope Harrison' | Last listed 1997 |
| - 'Perfecta' | CSpe EBee EOrc GMaP LPio MTis NLar NRoo SWat WWhi |
| - 'Perfecta Alba' | CSpe EMan EWTr GMaP LFis LPio MBro NLar NOrc NPri NTay SCob SWat WOve WPyg WWhi |
| - 'Stäfa' | CDoC EBee LHop MBel MBri MTed SMrm SPer |
| 'Chile Black' | CHan CMea CSam EWes GCal LGre MHlr MSte NCut SUsu WCot WElm WHoo WRus WWoo |
| * 'Chile Red' | GCal |
| *cinerea* | EBee WMoo WWin |
| § *columbaria* | CKin EBee EWFC EWTr MChe MHew MLLN NLan NMir NTow NWCA SIng WCla WHer WHoo WJek WPyg |

| | |
|---|---|
| * - *alba* | Last listed 1998 |
| - 'Nana' | NBir NMen NPri SSmi SUsu WPyg |
| § - var. *ochroleuca* | More than 30 suppliers |
| - subsp. *portae* | EBee |
| ¶ - var. *webbiana* | WLin |
| ¶ *cretica* | EBee |
| 'Crimson Cushion' | CFai |
| 'Dingle Lilac' | Last listed 1996 |
| ¶ *drakensbergensis* | EBee |
| *farinosa* | CBot CHan MHar WPer |
| - 'Schofield's Variegated' | Last listed 1998 |
| *fischeri* | Last listed 1996 |
| *gigantea* | See *Cephalaria gigantea* |
| *graminifolia* | EBee EDAr ELan EMan GBuc LPio NBir NMen NTow NWCA SUsu |
| ¶ - 'Pinkushion' | CStr |
| - *rosea* | EWes |
| *holosericea* | Last listed 1998 |
| *incisa* 'Pink Cheer' | WSPU |
| *japonica* | WPer |
| - var. *alpina* | CHar CInt CLTr EFou ESis GTou LIck MBel MBro NLon SRot WBea WHoo WRha WSan |
| *lacerifolia* | Last listed 1996 |
| *lachnophylla* | EBee GMac |
| *lucida* | CGle EBee ELan EPar GDra GMac GTou LHop MBro MRav NPri SBla SMrm SSpe WCot WEas WMow WPat WPer |
| ¶ *mansenensis* | EMon |
| ¶ *maritima* | EBee |
| ¶ 'Midnight' | CMea |
| *minoana* | Last listed 1998 |
| ♦ *montana* Mill. | See *Knautia arvensis* |
| ♦ - (Bieb.) DC. | See *Knautia tatarica* |
| *ochroleuca* | See *S. columbaria* var. *ochroleuca* |
| *olgae* | Last listed 1996 |
| *parnassi* | See *Pterocephalus perennis* |
| * 'Perfecta Lilac Blue' | CSev |
| ♦ 'Perpetual Flowering' | See *S.* Butterfly Blue |
| ¶ 'Pink Buttons' | EBee ECoo |
| 'Pink Mist' | CGle LPio NBir SCoo SPer SRms WWeb |
| *pterocephala* | See *Pterocephalus perennis* |
| *rhodopensis* | Last listed 1998 |
| ¶ 'Rosie's Pink' | EMan |
| *rumelica* | See *Knautia macedonica* |
| * 'Satchmo' | Last listed 1997 |
| ¶ *silenifolia* | WCot |
| ¶ *stellata* | EWTr |
| *succisa* | See *Succisa pratensis* |
| *tatarica* | See *Cephalaria gigantea* |
| *triandra* | CHan EBee |
| *vestita* | Last listed 1996 |

## SCADOXUS (Amaryllidaceae)

| | |
|---|---|
| 'König Albert' | See *Haemanthus* 'König Albert' |
| *membranaceus* | Last listed 1997 |
| *multiflorus* | LAma MBri NRog |
| § - subsp. *katherinae* ♀ | Last listed 1995 |
| - - 'King Albert' | Last listed 1997 |
| *natalensis* | See *S. puniceus* |
| § *puniceus* | ERea NRog |
| *rigidus* | Last listed 1996 |

## SCAEVOLA (Goodeniaceae)

| | |
|---|---|
| *aemula* 'Alba' | Last listed 1997 |
| ♦ - 'Blue Fan' | See *S. aemula* 'Blue Wonder' |
| § - 'Blue Wonder' | CHal CSpe EMan LHil LHop MBEx SBid SHFr SMrm |
| * - 'New Wonder' | WLRN |

| | |
|---|---|
| - 'Petite' | CHal CLTr LHil |
| *crassifolia* | Last listed 1998 |
| *bookeri* | ECou |
| *suaveolens* | See *S. calendulacea* |

## SCANDIX (Apiaceae)

| | |
|---|---|
| *pecten-veneris* | EWFC |

## SCHEFFLERA (Araliaceae)

| | |
|---|---|
| *actinophylla* ♀ | EBak MBri SRms |
| *arboricola* ♀ | LBlo MBri SEND |
| - 'Compacta' | MBri |
| - 'Gold Capella' ♀ | MBri |
| - 'Jacqueline' | MBri |
| - 'Trinetta' | MBri |
| *digitata* | Last listed 1998 |
| *elegantissima* ♀ | Last listed 1997 |
| *microphylla* B&SWJ 3872 | WCru |

## SCHIMA (Theaceae)

| | |
|---|---|
| *argentea* | See *S. wallichii* subsp. *noronhae* var. *superba* |
| § *wallichii* subsp. *noronhae* var. *superba* | CB&S WWat |
| - subsp. *wallichii* var. *khasiana* | ISea |
| ¶ *yunnanensis* | GGGa |

## SCHINUS (Anacardiaceae)

| | |
|---|---|
| *molle* | IDee |
| *patagonicus* | Last listed 1998 |
| *polygamus* | CGre |
| *terebinthifolius* | SMad |

## SCHISANDRA (Schisandraceae)

| | |
|---|---|
| *arisanensis* B&SWJ 3050 | WCru |
| *chinensis* | CArn CB&S CPlN ETen WNor WSHC |
| ¶ - B&SWJ 4204 | WCru |
| *grandiflora* | ECot ELan EPfP SSta |
| - B&SWJ 2245 | WCru |
| - var. *cathayensis* | See *S. sphaerandra* |
| *henryi* | Last listed 1996 |
| *propinqua* var. *sinensis* | CBot MBlu WCru |
| *rubriflora* | CBar CRHN CWSG EBee EHic EPfP MDun MUlv NOla SLon SSpi |
| - (f) | CB&S CPlN ELan MBlu MGos SBid SBra WSHC WWat |
| - (m) | CPlN EMil NHol |
| § *sphaerandra* | CPlN |
| *sphenanthera* | EBee EHic ELan EMil EPfP ETen MDun NPal SRPl SSto WSHC |

## SCHISTOSTEGA (Sphagnaceae)

| | |
|---|---|
| *pennata* | Last listed 1996 |

## SCHIVERECKIA (Brassicaceae)

| | |
|---|---|
| *doerfleri* | Last listed 1997 |
| *podolica* | Last listed 1996 |

## SCHIZACHYRIUM (Poaceae)

| | |
|---|---|
| § *scoparium* | CBrm EAst EBee EHoe EPPr EWTr EWes GBin SApp SCob |

## SCHIZANTHUS (Solanaceae)

| | |
|---|---|
| *candidus* | Last listed 1997 |
| - RB 94104 | Last listed 1998 |
| *gilliesii* | Last listed 1998 |
| *grahamii* JCA 12365 | Last listed 1998 |

| | |
|---|---|
| *hookeri* | Last listed 1998 |

## SCHIZOCENTRON See HETEROCENTRON

## SCHIZOCODON See SHORTIA

## SCHIZOLOBIUM (Papilionaceae)

| | |
|---|---|
| *parahybum* | LBlo WMul |

## SCHIZOPETALON (Brassicaceae)

| | |
|---|---|
| *walkeri* | Last listed 1996 |

## SCHIZOPHRAGMA (Hydrangeaceae)

| | |
|---|---|
| *corylifolium* | WCru |
| *hydrangeoides* | CB&S CDoC CFil CPlN CPle EBee EBrP EBre ELan EMil GChr LBre MBal MBri MGos NHlc NPal SBra SBre SLon SMur SSpi SSta WCru WDin WSHC |
| - 'Brookside Littleleaf' | WCru |
| - 'Moonlight' (v) | CFil EPfP LRHS MAsh MBlu MBri SBla SPla SSpi SSta WCot WCru |
| - 'Roseum' | CBot CFil EBee MBlu SBla SSpi WCru |
| *integrifolium* ♀ | CB&S CFil CMac CPlN MBal MGos SDix SSpi WSHC WWat |
| - *fauriei* B&SWJ 1701 | WCru |
| * - var. *molle* | CPlN |

## SCHIZOSTACHYUM (Poaceae - Bambusoideae)

| | |
|---|---|
| § *funghomii* | EPla SDry WJun |

## SCHIZOSTYLIS ✿ (Iridaceae)

| | |
|---|---|
| *coccinea* | More than 30 suppliers |
| - f. *alba* | More than 30 suppliers |
| - 'Ballyrogan Giant' | CFir CLAP CMil IBlr WPGP |
| - 'Cardinal' | CPea NPla WFar |
| ¶ - 'Elburton Glow' | WFar |
| - 'Fenland Daybreak' | CHar CLAP EBee EBrP EBre EFou EGar EMan GMac IBlr LBre LIck MLan NHol NLar SBre SSpe WBea WBro WFar WRus |
| - 'Gigantea' | See *S. coccinea* 'Major' |
| - 'Grandiflora' | See *S. coccinea* 'Major' |
| - 'Hilary Gould' | CLAP CRDP GBuc IBlr MAvo NBrk SUsu WBea WFar WHal |
| - 'Jennifer' ♀ | CAvo CBro CGle CLAP CRDP CTri EFou ERos IBlr MBri MRav NHol SApp SCro SRms SUsu WBro WFar WRus WWat |
| - 'Maiden's Blush' | EBee ECGP EFou EHrv EWll GMac LIck LPio MAvo MBel NHol NLar WBro WFar |
| § - 'Major' ♀ | More than 30 suppliers |
| - 'Molly Gould' | EBee MAvo SLod WBro |
| - 'Mrs Hegarty' | More than 30 suppliers |
| - 'November Cheer' | EBee ECot IBlr LIck MSte MUlv NLar NLon NRoo SSpe WBro WOld |
| - 'Pallida' | CMil CSam EBee ECha EGar EHrv ELan EMan EOld GBuc IBlr LHop WBor |
| - 'Professor Barnard' | CFee CGle CSpe EBee GCal GMac IBlr MBri MSte NBrk SApp WFar WOld WPnn WPyg WWat |
| - 'Salmon Charm' | CLAP EBee EFou IBlr |
| - seedling | Last listed 1998 |
| - 'Snow Maiden' | CFai CLAP CRDP EBee IGri LIck LRHS MBNS WBro |

| | |
|---|---|
| § – 'Sunrise' ♀ | CB&S CFee CHea CMHG CRDP CSam ECha ELan GCal LHop LIck MAvo NFor NHol NLon NRoo SIng SLon SOkh SPer SSpi SUsu WAbe WBea WBod WCot WFar WOld WPer WRus |
| – 'Sunset' | See *S. coccinea* 'Sunrise' |
| – 'Tambara' | CLAP CMHG CPou EBee EGar GMac IBlr SApp WElm WFar WHil WOld WPGP WPnP |
| ¶ – 'The Bride' | EBee |
| – 'Viscountess Byng' | CBro CGle CHea EBee EGar EPot GCal MAvo NRog SAga SRms WBea WCot WFar WHal WPer |
| * – 'Zeal Blush' | IBlr |
| – 'Zeal Salmon' | CBro CFee CFir CLAP CPou ECha EGar GMac IBlr NBrk SApp SCro SSpi WFar WHil WMoo |
| * 'Marietta' | CHid |

## SCHOENOPLECTUS (Cyperaceae)

| | |
|---|---|
| § *lacustris* | EMFW MMoz |
| § – subsp. | SRms |
| *abernaemontana* | |
| 'Golden Spear' | |
| – – 'Albescens' (v) | CBen EBrP EBre EHon EMFW LBre LPBA MSta MTed SBre SRms SWat SWyc WCot |
| – – 'Zebrinus' (v) | CBen CBot CInt EBrP EBre EHon ELan EMFW GBin LBre LPBA MSta MTed NDea SBre SLon SWat SWyc WCot WPrP WWeb |
| ¶ *pungens* | MSta |

## SCHOENUS (Cyperaceae)

| | |
|---|---|
| *pauciflorus* | CCuc CFil ECou EHoe EPla GOrn WPGP |

## SCHOTIA (Caesalpiniaceae)

| | |
|---|---|
| *brachypetala* | SOWG |

## SCIADOPITYS (Sciadopityaceae)

| | |
|---|---|
| *verticillata* ♀ | CB&S CDoC CDul CKen EHul IOrc LBee LCon LLin LNet LPan MBar MBlu MBri MDun MGos SLim SSpi WCoo WCwm WDin WNor |
| – 'Firework' | CKen |
| – 'Globe' | CKen |
| – 'Gold Star' | CKen |
| – 'Jeddeloh Compact' | CKen |
| – 'Picola' | CKen |
| – 'Pygmy' | CKen |
| – 'Shorty' | CKen |
| ¶ – 'Stenschnuffe' | CKen |

## SCILLA ✿ (Hyacinthaceae)

| | |
|---|---|
| *adlamii* | See *Ledebouria cooperi* |
| x *allenii* | See *x Chionoscilla allenii* |
| *amethystina* | See *S. litardierei* |
| *amoena* | LAma LRHS |
| *autumnalis* | CAvo EPot EWFC LAma WShi |
| – subsp. *fallax* AB&S 4345 | Last listed 1998 |
| *baurii* | Last listed 1997 |
| *bifolia* ♀ | CAvo CBro EPar EPot LAma NRog WShi |
| ¶ – 'Alba' | EPot |
| – 'Rosea' | EPar EPot LAma NRog WPer |
| *bithynica* | SSpi WShi WWat |
| *campanulata* | See *Hyacinthoides hispanica* |
| *chinensis* | See *S. scilloides* |
| *cilicica* | CBro LAma |

| | |
|---|---|
| *greilhuberi* | Last listed 1996 |
| *hanburyi* S&L 78 | Last listed 1998 |
| *hohenackeri* | CAvo EPot |
| – BSBE 811 | Last listed 1998 |
| *hyacinthoides* | EHyt |
| *italica* | See *Hyacinthoides italica* |
| *japonica* | See *S. scilloides* |
| *libanotica* S&L 113 | Last listed 1998 |
| *liliohyacinthus* | CAvo CBre CBro CRDP CRow EHyt IBlr SSpi |
| – 'Alba' | Last listed 1997 |
| *lingulata* var. *ciliolata* | CBro |
| – MS 320 | Last listed 1998 |
| – S&L 253 | Last listed 1998 |
| – SF 288/281 | Last listed 1998 |
| § *litardierei* | CAvo EPot ERos LAma NEgg WCot |
| – *hoogiana* | Last listed 1997 |
| *mauretanica alba* | Last listed 1998 |
| – SF 65 | Last listed 1998 |
| § *messeniaca* | SHel |
| § *mischtschenkoana* | CAvo CBro EBrP EBre EHyt EPar EPot ETub LAma LBow LBre MBri NRog SBre |
| ¶ – 'Tubergeniana' ♀ | WCot |
| § – 'Zwanenburg' | WCot |
| *monophyllos* | CFil LAma |
| – SB 184 | Last listed 1998 |
| *morrisii* M 4015 | Last listed 1998 |
| *non-scripta* | See *Hyacinthoides non-scripta* |
| *numidica* MS&CL 288 | Last listed 1998 |
| *nutans* | See *Hyacinthoides non-scripta* |
| *obtusifolia* AB&S 4410 | Last listed 1998 |
| *ovalifolia* | See *Ledebouria ovalifolia* |
| *paucifolia* | Last listed 1998 |
| *persica* | CAvo LRHS |
| – BSBE 1054 | Last listed 1998 |
| *peruviana* | CAvo CBro CFee CHad CMil CSpe EPar EPot ERos LAma MTho NRog SMrm SSpi SUsu WAbe WCot WWhi |
| – 'Alba' | CAvo LAma LPio MTho NRog |
| – var. *elegans* | Last listed 1998 |
| – var. *venusta* | Last listed 1998 |
| *pratensis* | See *S. litardierei* |
| *puschkinioides* | LAma |
| *ramburei* | LAma |
| – B&S 406 | Last listed 1998 |
| – MS 417 | Last listed 1998 |
| *reverchonii* | EHyt ERos |
| – MS 418 | Last listed 1998 |
| ¶ *rosenii* | EHyt |
| § *scilloides* | CBro EPot ERos WCot |
| – MSF 782 | SSpi |
| *siberica* ♀ | CAvo ETub LAma NEgg NRog WPer WShi |
| – 'Alba' | CBro EPar EPfP EPot LAma NEgg NRog WPer |
| – subsp. *armena* | Last listed 1998 |
| – 'Spring Beauty' | CAvo CBro EPar EPot LAma MBri NRog SRms |
| – var. *taurica* | ERos |
| – – M&T 4148 | Last listed 1998 |
| *tubergeniana* | See *S. mischtschenkoana* |
| *verna* | ERos WHer WShi |
| – JCA 878.000 | Last listed 1998 |
| – MS 483 | Last listed 1998 |
| *vicentina* | See *Hyacinthoides italica vicentina* |
| *violacea* | See *Ledebouria socialis* |

## SCINDAPSUS (Araceae)

| | |
|---|---|
| *aureus* | See *Epipremnum aureum* |

*pictus* (v) — MBri
- 'Argyraeus' ♀ — Last listed 1990

## SCIRPOIDES (Poaceae)
§ *holoschoenus* — Last listed 1997

## SCIRPUS (Cyperaceae)
*cernuus* — See *Isolepis cernua*
*cespitosus* — See *Trichophorum cespitosum*
§ *fauriei* var. *vaginatus* — CRow EHoe SWyc
♦ 'Golden Spear' — See *Schoenoplectus lacustris* subsp. *tabernaemontana* 'Golden Spear'
*holoschoenus* — See *Scirpoides holoschoenus*
*lacustris* — See *Schoenoplectus lacustris*
♦ - 'Spiralis' — See *Juncus effusus* f. *spiralis*
♦ *maritimus* — See *Bolboschoenus maritimus*
*sylvaticus* — CKin MTed SWyc
*tabernaemontani* — See *Schoenoplectus lacustris* subsp. *tabernaemontani*

## SCLERANTHUS (Caryophyllaceae)
¶ *baldensis* — SPlb
*biflorus* — CPea ECou EGle ELan EWes GMaP MBro SPlb WPer
*brockiei* — Last listed 1996
*perennis* — CNat
*singuliflorus* — ECou NHol WPat WPyg
*uniflorus* — CLyd EWes GAbr GAri NHed NWCA
- CC 466 — NWCA
- CC 556 — MRPP

## SCLEROCHITON (Acanthaceae)
*harveyanus* — Last listed 1996

## SCOLIOPUS (Trilliaceae)
*bigelowii* — GCrs MS&S SWas WFar
*hallii* — SWas

## SCOLOPENDRIUM See ASPLENIUM

## SCOLYMUS See CYNARA

## SCOPOLIA (Solanaceae)
*anomala* — Last listed 1996
*carniolica* — CAvo CFir EGle ELan EMon EPar GCal GDra GPoy MBel MBlu MHar MSal NSti SBea WCru WHal
- forms — ECha IBlr
- from Slovenia — Last listed 1996
- subsp. *bladnikiana* — CAvo EBee EBrP EBre EPPr LBre LSpr SBre SDys WBcn WTin
¶ - - WM 9811 — MPhe
- *podolica* — CMea
- yellow form — MHar
- 'Zwanenburg' — CAvo EBee EPar WCot
*lurida* — MNrw MSal WWye
*physaloides* — MSal
*sinensis* — See *Atropanthe sinensis*

## SCORZONERA (Asteraceae)
*hispanica* — WCot
*humilis* — GPoy
*suberosa* subsp. *cariensis* — EBee NTow SMad

## SCROPHULARIA (Scrophulariaceae)
*aquatica* — See *S. auriculata*
§ *auriculata* — ELau EWFC MHer MSal NDea NOrc WHer WWye
- 'Burdung' (v) — Last listed 1998

§ - 'Variegata' — CArn CGle CRow EBee EHoe ELan ENot LHop LPBA MBri MCLN MSta MWat NRoo NSti SLon SPer SRms WBea WCot WEas WFar WHal WHil WOve WPrP WRus WWin
*buergueriana* 'Lemon and Lime' (v) — EMan EMon WCot WPrP
*canina* subsp. *bicolor* — Last listed 1998
*macrantha* — EBee
*nodosa* — CArn CJew CKin ELau MChe MSal NMir WCla WHbs WHer
- *tracheliodes* — CNat
- *variegata* — See *S. auriculata* 'Variegata'
*sambucifolia* — GBin MNrw NChi
*scopolii* — EBee
*scorodonia* — SRms
*umbrosa* — MSal
*vernalis* — EWFC

## SCUTELLARIA (Lamiaceae)
*albida* — EBee
§ *alpina* — CLyd EBrP EBre GCHN GCrs LBee LBre MAvo NWCA SBla SBre SIng SRms SUsu WGor WPer WWye
- 'Alba' — Last listed 1996
¶ - 'Arcobaleno' — WHil
- 'Greencourt' — EBee
¶ - subsp. *supina* — CPBP
*altissima* — CArn CGle EBee EGar EMan EMar EPPr GBuc LFis MAvo MRav MSal NBro NPla SSca WBea WPer WWin WWye
*baicalensis* — CArn CHan EBee IBlr LHop NCut SBla SIgm WPer WWye
- 'Coelestina' — Last listed 1996
*barbata* — MNrw MSal
*brevibracteata* — MAvo SHFr
*brittonii* — Last listed 1998
*canescens* — See *S. incana*
*columnae* — Last listed 1998
*diffusa* — CPBP WPer WWye
¶ *formosana* — WCot
*galericulata* — CKin EWFC GPoy MHer MHew MSal WGwy WHer WJek WWye
- 'Corinne Tremaine' (v) — WHer
* *glandulosissima* — Last listed 1997
*hastata* — See *S. hastifolia*
§ *hastifolia* — CPBP CTri ECot ECtt EMNN NSti WCot WPer
§ *incana* — CGle EBee ECGN EFou EHrv ELan EMan EPPr LFis LGre MNrw NSti SMrm SUsu WCot WEas WWoo WWye
*indica* var. *japonica* — See *S. indica* var. *parvifolia*
§ - var. *parvifolia* — CPBP EBee EBur EHyt ELan EWes LBee MTho NMen NTow NWCA SBla SSca SUsu WCot WCru WWye
- - 'Alba' — CPBP EHyt LBee
*integrifolia* — Last listed 1998
*lateriflora* — CArn CBod CJew ELau EOHP ESis GBar GPoy LHol MChe MHew MSal NSti SIde WCer WHbs WJek WPer WSel WWye
*minor* — CKin EWFC MSal WGwy WWye
*nana* var. *sapphirina* — CPBP MRPP
- - JJA 1840650 — NWCA
*novae-zelandiae* — ECou EHyt MTho SSca WCot WWye
*orientalis* — CNic EBee LBee NWCA SBla WCot WCru WPat WWin
¶ - subsp. *bicolor* — EHyt

- subsp. *carica*          WWye
- subsp. *pinnatifida*     EHyt MAvo NWCA SUsu WLin
*pontica*                  NWCA WLin
*prostrata*                CMHG ESis SSca WWin
*repens*                   Last listed 1996
*resinosa*                 Last listed 1998
*scordiifolia*             CLyd CMea CMil CSam ECha ELan
                           EPot LFis MBro MNrw NMen
                           NNrd NRya NWCA SBla SIng
                           SRms SUsu WCla WCot WFar
                           WHal WHoo WPyg WRus WWin
                           WWye
- 'Seoul Sapphire'         Last listed 1996
*serrata*                  Last listed 1997
*supina*                   See *S. alpina*
*tournefortii*             WBor

## SECURIGERA See CORONILLA

## SECURINEGA (Euphorbiaceae)
*ramiflora*                CPle

## SEDASTRUM See SEDUM

## SEDUM ✿ (Crassulaceae)
§ 'Abbeydore'              EBee EGoo EMon NSti
*acre*                     CTri ECot EFer ELan GPoy MBar
                           SPlb WLRN
- 'Aureum'                 CInt ELan EPfP MBar MOne MWat
                           NHol NVic SRms WCot WHoo
                           WPat WPyg
- 'Elegans'                ECtt GDra GTou MBal
§ - var. *majus*           CChe SSmi
- 'Minus'                  SSmi WFar
- tetraploid               Last listed 1996
*aggregatum*               See *Orostachys aggregata*
§ *aizoon*                 EPfP SChu SIde WEas WOve WWal
- 'Aurantiacum'            See *S. aizoon* 'Euphorbioides'
§ - 'Euphorbioides'        EBee EBrP EBre ECha ECtt EGoo
                           ELan EMon ESis LBre MBel MRav
                           NFai NPro SBre SPer WCot WFar
♦ *albescens*              See *S. rupestre* f. *purpureum*
§ *alboroseum*             EBee MTho
- 'Frosty Morn'            More than 30 suppliers
§ - 'Mediovariegatum'      CBot EBee EBrP EBre EGoo ELan
                           EMan EMon EOld EWTr LBre
                           LHop MBri MCLN MNrw MRav
                           MSCN NEgg NFai NRoo SBre
                           WEas WFar WPer WWal
§ *album*                  CHal MBNS NBro WPer
- 'Chloroticum'            SSmi
- subsp. *clusianum*       See *S. gypsicola glanduliferum*
- 'Coral Carpet'           CNic ELan EMan EPfP EPot GDra
                           MBar MWat NMen NVic SChu
                           SIng SSmi
- var. *micranthum*        See *S. album* 'Chloroticum'
§ - subsp. *teretifolium*  CTri MBar
  'Murale'
*algidum*                  See *S. alsium*
*alpestre*                 Last listed 1998
§ *alsium*                 Last listed 1998
*altissimum*               See *S. sediforme*
*altum*                    EMon EPPr LGre WFar WPer
*amplexicaule*             See *S. tenuifolium*
§ *anacampseros*           CNic EGoo GCHN NDov NHol
                           SSmi WCla WEas WPer
*anglicum*                 SChr WCla
*anopetalum*               See *S. ochroleucum*
- alpine form              See *S. ochroleucum* subsp.
                           *montanum*
*athoum*                   See *S. album*
*atlanticum*               See *S. dasyphyllum* subsp.
                           *dasyphyllum* var. *mesatlanticum*

*atuntsuense*              Last listed 1998
Autumn Joy                 See *S.* 'Herbstfreude'
*batesii*                  See *S. hemsleyanum*
§ 'Bertram Anderson' ♀     More than 30 suppliers
*beyrichianum* Masters     Last listed 1996
- hort.                    See *S. glaucophyllum*
*bithynicum* 'Aureum'      See *S. hispanicum* var. *minus*
                           'Aureum'
*bodinieri*                Last listed 1998
*brevifolium*              MDHE
- *potsii*                 Last listed 1998
§ - var. *quinquefarium*   Last listed 1998
bronze-leaved              WHil
*caeruleum*                CInt WUnu
'Carl'                     EGoo EMon NCat SMad SUsu
                           WCot
§ *caucasicum*             SUsu WAbb WEas
- DS&T 89001T              EMon
*cauticola* ♀              CLyd CNic CPri GCal LHop MBro
                           MHar MRav NRoo SBod SRms
                           SSca SSmi WCot WElm WWin
- Lida from Lida           ECho
§ - 'Lidakense'            CMea CSam EBrP EBre ELan LBre
                           MBNS MBar MBri MBro MCLN
                           MTis NFai NHar NSla NVic SBla
                           SBre SChu SIng SSmi SUsu WLin
- 'Robustum'               EMon
- x *tatarinowii*          EGoo EWes
¶ 'Cavalier'               EFou
*clusianum*                See *S. gypsicola glanduliferum*
¶ *confusum*               SChr
*crassipes*                See *Rhodiola wallichiana*
*crassularia*              See *Crassula milfordiae*
*cyaneum* hort.            See *S. ewersii* var. *homophyllum*
- Rudolph                  GCHN NMen NWCA
*dasyphyllum*              ELan ESis GTou MBal MBar MOne
                           MRPP MWat NHol NRoo NVic
                           NWCA SRms SSmi WCla WRHF
- subsp. *dasyphyllum*     CHal WCom
  var. *glanduliferum*
¶ - - 'Lilac Mound'        MDHE
- - var. *macrophyllum*    MDHE SSmi
§ - - var. *mesatlanticum* CNic MDHE NBir
- *mucronatis*             See *S. dasyphyllum* subsp.
                           *dasyphyllum* var. *mesatlanticum*
- subsp. *oblongifolium*   Last listed 1998
*debile*                   Last listed 1998
¶ *decumbens*              EOas
*divergens*                Last listed 1998
- large form               Last listed 1998
*douglasii*                See *S. stenopetalum* 'Douglasii'
'Dudley Field'             CLyd GCHN NMen
'Eleanor Fisher'           See *S. telephium* subsp.
                           *ruprechtii*
*ellacombeanum*            See *S. kamtschaticum* var.
                           *ellacombeanum*
*erythrostichum*           See *S. alboroseum*
§ *ewersii*                CNic EBrP EBre EGoo ELan
                           EMNN GCHN GTou LBre MHar
                           NBro NMen SBre SSmi WEas WFar
§ - var. *homophyllum*     CLyd MTPN SSmi
§ *fabaria*                MCLN WCot WEas
*farinosum*                Last listed 1998
*fastigiatum*              See *Rhodiola fastigiata*
*floriferum*               See *S. kamtschaticum*
*forsterianum*             EMFP LGro
  subsp. *elegans*
¶ *frutescens*             STre
*furfuraceum*              NMen
*gracile*                  SSmi
'Green Expectations'       CMil EFou
*gypsicola*                WPer

'Harvest Moon' — EBur

§ 'Herbstfreude' ♀ — More than 30 suppliers

*heterodontum* — See *Rhodiola heterodonta*

*hidakanum* — CLyd EBee EMFP GCrs GTou MBro NBro NHol NMen WHoo WPat

*hillebrandtii* — See *S. urvillei* Hillebrandtii Group

*himalense* — See *Rhodiola* 'Keston'

§ *hispanicum* — CTri ECho SPlb

- 'Albescens' — CNic

- var. *bithynicum* — Last listed 1998

- *glaucum* — See *S. hispanicum* var. *minus*

§ - var. *minus* — ECtt EGoo GAri GTou MBar NNrd NPri NRya SChu SPlb SSmi STre WMoo

§ - - 'Aureum' — ECha MBar MRPP NMen SBod SIng SSmi WMoo

*humifusum* — EBur EHyt NHol NMen NTow SIng SSmi

*hybridum* — Last listed 1998

¶ - 'Immergrünchen' — CPri

*hyperaizoon* — Last listed 1998

*integrifolium* — See *Rhodiola rosea* subsp. *integrifolia*

*ishidae* — See *Rhodiola ishidae*

*jaeschkei* — See *S. oreades*

*japonicum* — Last listed 1998

'Joyce Henderson' — EBee EFou ERav GNau LPio MGrG MSCN NDov SBla SUsu WCom WCot WEas WOld

§ *kamtschaticum* ♀ — ESis MBar

§ - var. *ellacombeanum* ♀ — CNic EGoo ELan ESis NMen

§ - var. *floriferum* — More than 30 suppliers 'Weihenstephaner Gold'

- var. *kamtschaticum* — CPri CTri ELan ESis GCHN LBee 'Variegatum' ♀ — LHop MWat NFla NRoo SBla SBod SRms SSmi WEas WFar WPyg

- var. *middendorffianum* — See *S. middendorffianum*

* - 'Takahira Dake' — Last listed 1998

*kirilovii* — See *Rhodiola kirilovii*

*kostovii* — See *S. grisebachii* subsp. *kostovii*

*lanceolatum* — Last listed 1998

*laxum* — Last listed 1998

- subsp. *beckneri* — Last listed 1998

*lineare* — ELan

- 'Variegatum' — ESis MBri

*litorale* — EBee

§ *lydium* — CLyd CNic CTri EMNN GTou MBal MBar MOne MRPP NRoo SPlb SSmi

- 'Aureum' — See *S. hispanicum* var. *minus* 'Aureum'

- 'Bronze Queen' — See *S. lydium*

¶ 'Lynda Windsor' — CRDP

*makinoi* — Last listed 1996

- 'Variegatum' — EBrP EBre LBre SBre

*maweanum* — See *S. acre* var. *majus*

*maximowiczii* — See *S. aizoon*

*mexicanum* — MBri

§ *middendorffianum* — CLyd ECho EGoo EMon GTou MDHE MWat NMen SBod SRms SRot WHoo WWin

- var. *diffusum* — SSmi

- 'Striatum' — CNic

*monregalense* — Last listed 1998

'Moonglow' — NMen

*moranense* — CHal CNic NTow SSmi

*morganianum* ♀ — CHal EBak LCns MBri

*morrisonense* — Last listed 1998

*multiceps* — SSmi

*murale* — See *S. album* subsp. *teretifolium* 'Murale'

N *nevii* — CLyd EGle

*nicaeense* — See *S. sediforme*

*obcordatum* — Last listed 1998

§ *obtusatum* — CPri EGle MBro NBro NFla NNrd NSla SSmi

§ - subsp. *retusum* — Last listed 1998

*obtusifolium* — Last listed 1998

* - 'Variegatum' — Last listed 1997

§ *ochroleucum* — Last listed 1996

- 'Green Spreader' — SSmi

§ - subsp. *ochroleucum* — Last listed 1998 *glaucum*

*oppositifolium* — See *S. spurium* var. *album*

§ *oreganum* — CInt ECha EMNN ESis GTou MBar MWat NMen NRoo NVic SBod SHel SIng SRms SRot SSmi WPer WPyg WWin

- 'Procumbens' — See *S. oreganum* subsp. *tenue*

§ - subsp. *tenue* — CNic ESis MBro NHol NRya WPat

§ *oregonense* — EBur GTou NMen NNrd

*oryzifolium* — Last listed 1998

- 'Minor' — EBur

¶ *oxypetalum* — STre

§ *pachyclados* — CInt CLyd CNic EBur EGoo EHoe ELan ESis GAbr GTou LBee MBar MDHE MOne NBir NNrd SChu SIng SPlb SRot SSmi WAbe WCla WCom WHoo WPat WPer

*pallidum* — Last listed 1998

*palmeri* — EOas NBir NTow SChr SSmi WCot

'Philip Houlbrook' — Last listed 1996

*pilosum* — EBur NMen NWCA SBla

§ *pluricaule* — EHyt GCHN GDra MBro NMen SBod SChu SRms WCla WRHF

- Rose Carpet — See *S. pluricaule* 'Rosenteppich'

*polytrichoides* — See *Rhodiola komarovii*

*populifolium* — CLyd CMHG CNic ECha EGoo GCHN GCal MBel MHar SDry SSmi STre SUsu WPer

*praealtum* — EOas SChr SEND SPar

*primuloides* — See *Rhodiola primuloides*

*pruinatum* — Last listed 1998

*pruinosum* — See *S. spathulifolium* subsp. *pruinosum*

*pulchellum* — Last listed 1998

*purdyi* — NMen

'Purple Emperor' — CRDP EFou EPPr SUsu WCot

*quadrifidum* — See *Rhodiola quadrifida*

*quinquefarium* — See *S. brevifolium* var. *quinquefarium*

*ramosissimum* — See *Villadia ramosissima*

'Red Bead' — Last listed 1998

*reflexum* L. — See *S. rupestre* L.

*reptans* var. — Last listed 1998 *carinatifolium*

*retusum* — See *S. obtusatum* subsp. *retusum*

*rhodiola* — See *Rhodiola rosea*

*rosea* — See *Rhodiola rosea*

*rubroglaucum* hort. — See *S. oregonense*

- Praeger — See *S. obtusatum*

x *rubrotinctum* — CHal

§ 'Ruby Glow' ♀ — More than 30 suppliers

§ *rupestre* L. — CAgr CNic EBot EGoo ELan EPfP MBNS MBar MWhi SChu SSmi WCla WEas WHer

- 'Minus' — CNic

- 'Monstrosum Cristatum' — MBal NBir SMad

§ - f. *purpureum* — Last listed 1997

*ruprechtii* — See *S. telephium* subsp. *ruprechtii*

*sarcocaule* — See *Crassula sarcocaulis*

*sarmentosum* — SSmi

§ *sediforme* — LHop MBro

| | |
|---|---|
| *- nicaeense* | See *S. sediforme* |
| *selskianum* | CPri EBee GDra GTou MOne NPri |
| *sempervivoides* | EBur |
| *sexangulare* | EMNN ESis GDra MBar MOne NMen SRms SSmi WCom WFar |
| *sibiricum* | WEas |
| *sichotense* | Last listed 1998 |
| § *sieboldii* | CSam LCns LGro MBri MBro SSmi |
| - 'Mediovariegatum' ♀ | EBrP EBre ELan EMan LBre LHop SBre SCro SSmi WEas WPer |
| 'Silver Moon' | EBur EGoo ESis GCHN MDHE SSmi |
| sp. B&SWJ 054 | WCru |
| *spathulifolium* | CAgr ECha ELan ESis GTou MOne MRPP NBus SChu SRCN WEas WMow |
| - 'Aureum' | EBur ECtt GTou MBar MWat SBod |
| - 'Cape Blanco' ♀ | More than 30 suppliers |
| - var. *majus* | Last listed 1996 |
| § - subsp. *pruinosum* | MDHE |
| - 'Purpureum' ♀ | More than 30 suppliers |
| - 'Roseum' | SSmi |
| § *spectabile* ♀ | CArn EBee ELan EPfP EWTr GMaP MRav NBee NPla SHFr SPlb SRms WBea WFar WWin |
| - 'Abendrot' | EMon |
| - 'Album' | WMoo |
| - 'Brilliant' ♀ | CM&M EBee EBrP EBre ECha EFou ELan EMon ENot EWTr GLil LBlm LBre LPio MBri MRav NOrc NRoo SBre SMad SPer SPla SSoC WCot WEas WFar WMoo |
| ¶ - 'Brilliant Variegated' | SCob |
| - 'Iceberg' | CM&M CMHG COIW CRDP CSev EBee ECha EFou EGoo EMan EMon EPPr ERav LBlm LGre LHop MCAu MCLN MMil NHaw NLar SLon SMad SSoC SSpe WCot WHil WRus |
| - 'Indian Chief' | CDoC EBee NRoo SCro SVil WCot WElm WFar WLRN WRus |
| ¶ - 'Lisa' | EMon MTPN |
| - 'Meteor' | CStr EBee EGoo LGre MBNS MLLN MRav MWat NFai SCro WAbe WCot WPer |
| * - 'Mini' | ELan MRav |
| - 'Pink Fairy' | WHil |
| - 'Rosenteller' | EFou EMon SMrm |
| - September Glow | See *S. spectabile* 'Septemberglut' |
| § - 'Septemberglut' | EMan EMon NDov |
| - 'Stardust' | CBlo EBee EGar EGoo EMil EPfP EWTr GLil GMaP LPio MBNS MLLN MTis NCut SCob SPla WCot WFar WGor WViv WWeb |
| - 'Variegatum' | See *S. alboroseum* 'Mediovariegatum' |
| *spinosum* | See *Orostachys spinosa* |
| *spurium* | CAgr EGoo ELan LGro MBNS SBod SRms STre |
| § - var. *album* | EGoo ELan ESis MHar |
| * - 'Atropurpureum' | CLyd ECha NFor NLon NRoo |
| - 'Coccineum' | MBar WUnu |
| - Dragon's Blood | See *S. spurium* 'Schorbuser Blut' |
| - 'Erdblut' | CTri EBrP EBre LBre NFla NMen NRoo SBre |
| - 'Fuldaglut' | CHal CNic CPri EBrP EBre EHoe LBre MBel MWat NHar SBre SChu SMac WMoo WPer WWin |
| - 'Glow' | CTri STre |
| - 'Green Mantle' | CBlo ECha SMer |
| - Purple Carpet | See *S. spurium* 'Purpurteppich' |
| - 'Purpureum' | CHan CInt EGoo ELan GDra SRms |
| § - 'Purpurteppich' | CPri EBrP EBre ESis LBre LGro MRav NBro NHol SBre SHel SRms |
| - 'Roseum' | CLyd SRms |
| - 'Ruby Mantle' | CBlo NPro |
| § - 'Schorbuser Blut' ♀ | CMea EBee ELan EPot LHop MBNS MBal MBro MWat NBro NChi NVic SHel SPlb SRms WEas WFar WHoo WPat WPyg WRHF |
| - 'Splendens Roseum' | LGro |
| - 'Tricolor' | See *S. spurium* 'Variegatum' |
| § - 'Variegatum' | CHan CLyd CNic ECha EGoo EHoe ELan ESis LHop MBar MRav NRoo SBod SHel SIng SPla SSmi STre WBea WCla WCot WEas WFar WOve WPat WPyg WWin |
| *stenopetalum* | Last listed 1998 |
| § - 'Douglasii' | CNic MOne NNrd SRms SSmi |
| *stephanii* | See *Rhodiola crassipes* var. *stephanii* |
| *stevenianum* | Last listed 1996 |
| 'Stewed Rhubarb Mountain' | CLon CMil EGoo EMon GAri MHlr MRav NDov SUsu WBea WCot |
| *stoloniferum* | SSmi |
| 'Strawberries and Cream' | LGre LPio LRHS MBri MRav NCat |
| *stribrnyi* | See *S. urvillei* Stribrnyi Group |
| 'Sunset Cloud' | CLyd CMHG CSam EBee EMon GCal MRav NRoo WOld |
| *takesimense* | Last listed 1998 |
| § *tatarinowii* | CLyd NTow WViv |
| - K 92.405 | Last listed 1997 |
| § *telephioides* | WCot |
| § *telephium* | CAgr CArn EMon EWFC MBNS NBir NSti SRms WCla WCot |
| ♦ - 'Abbeydore' | See *S.* 'Abbeydore' |
| - 'Arthur Branch' | CElw CMil EHal EMon GBuc MNrw MSte MTho NChi SUsu WCot |
| - var. *borderi* | EMon |
| - subsp. *fabaria* | See *S. fabaria* |
| * - 'Hester' | EFou EMan SCob |
| * - 'Leonore Zuutz' | WCot |
| - 'Matrona' | CPou EBee ECha EFou EGoo EMan EMon EWes GBin GMaP LGre LPio MBri SCob SMad SMrm SPer SUsu WCot WFar WGor WMoo WPen WWhi |
| § - subsp. *maximum* | CBrm ECha MBel SChu |
| - - 'Atropurpureum' ♀ | CBot CGle CHad ECha ECoo ELan EMan EMar MFir MRav NLar NRoo SChu WCot WEas WMoo WWhi WWin |
| - - 'Gooseberry Fool' | CLon EBee EGoo EMon EWTr LGre LPio SUsu |
| - 'Mohrchen' | CHad CLon CMGP CRDP EBee EFou EMan LBuc LPio LRHS MBri MLLN MTed NDov NSti SBla SChu SMrm SUsu WCot WOld |
| - 'Munstead Red' | CLyd CMil EBee EFou EGoo EMan EMar EMon ERic LFis LHop MCAu MRav NLar SLon SPla SSpe SSvw SUsu WCot |
| - 'Roseovariegatum' | EMon |
| - 'Roseum' | LHop |
| § - subsp. *ruprechtii* | CLyd CMHG CMil EBee ECha EGoo EMan EMon EOld EOrc LGre MBri MRav SBla SPer SUsu WCot WEas WFar WPer WViv WWhi |
| - subsp. *telephium* 'Lynda et Rodney' | CRDP EGoo EMon |
| - 'Variegatum' | COtt ECoo LFis MBel SPar WHal WWin |

¶ - 'Veluwe se Wakel'               LPio
* - Washfield purple selection   EWes
§ **tenuifolium**                    EBur
§ - subsp. *ibericum*             Last listed 1998
  - subsp. *tenuifolium*          EBur
  **ternatum**                    Last listed 1998
  **trollii**                     See *Rhodiola trollii*
§ 'Vera Jameson' ♀               CLon CLyd EBee ECha EGoo
                                 EHoe EMar ENot MBri MCLN
                                 MFir MHlr MRav MTis NHol NSti
                                 SBla SChu SPer SUsu WEas WMoo
                                 WPer WWat WWhi
  **verticillatum**               Last listed 1998
  'Weihenstephaner Gold'          See *S. kamtschaticum* var.
                                 *floriferum* 'Weihenstephaner
                                 Gold'
  **weinbergii**                  See *Graptopetalum*
                                 *paraguayense*
  **yezoense**                    See *S. pluricaule*
  **yunnanense**                  See *Rhodiola yunnanensis*

## SEEMANNIA See GLOXINIA

## SELAGINELLA ✿ (Selaginellaceae)
  **apoda**                       MBri
  **braunii**                     NMar
  **douglasii**                   NMar
  **emmeliana**                   See *S. pallescens*
  **helvetica**                   NHol NOla
  **involvens**                   WCot
  **kraussiana** ♀                CHal MBal MBri NMar NRya WRic
  - 'Aurea'                       CHal GGar MBri NMar SMad
  - 'Brownii' ♀                   MBri NMar NVic
  - 'Variegata' ♀                 MBri
  **martensii** ♀                 Last listed 1995
  - 'Variegata'                   Last listed 1996
  - 'Watsoniana'                  NMar
§ **pallescens**                  NMar
  - 'Aurea'                       NMar
¶ **sanguinolenta**               SIng
  **tamariscina**                 Last listed 1998
  **uncinata** ♀                  Last listed 1995
  **vogelii**                     NMar

## SELAGO (Selaginellaceae)
  **flanaganii**                  Last listed 1998

## SELINUM (Apiaceae)
  **candollei**                   Last listed 1996
  **carvifolia**                  Last listed 1997
  sp. EMAK 886                    Last listed 1996
◆ **tenuifolium**                 See *S. wallichianum* EMAK 886
  **wallichianum**                CBos CHad CRow EGoo SIgm
                                 SSpi
§ - EMAK 886                      CGle CMil CPou EBee MBri NSti
                                 SDix SMrm WCot WEas

## SELLIERA (Goodeniaceae)
  **radicans**                    SSca
  - forms                         ECou
  - 'Lake Ellerman'               Last listed 1998

## SEMELE (Ruscaceae)
  **androgyna**                   CPIN CRHN

## SEMIAQUILEGIA ✿ (Ranunculaceae)
* **adnata** B&SWJ 1190           WCru
§ **adoxoides**                   CJyd EBee WPer WPrP WViv
  'Early Dwarf'                   NCut
§ **ecalcarata**                  CBot CGle CMil EBrP EBre GBin
                                 LBre LEur MNrw NHar NHol NLar
                                 NOak SBre SIng SMrm SRms
                                 WCru WLin WPGP WPer WPrP
                                 WWhi WWin

- 'Flore Pleno' (d)              EBee ECGN NPSI NRoo SPla
                                 WPrP WRha
  **simulatrix**                  See *S. ecalcarata*

## SEMIARUNDINARIA (Poaceae - Bambusoideae)
§ **fastuosa** ♀                  CDoC EBee EFul EOas EPfP EPla
                                 ERod GOrc ISta LJus MMoz NMoo
                                 SAPC SArc SDry SPlb WBay WJun
                                 WMul
  - var. *viridis*                EPla ERod ISta LPJP SDry WCru
                                 WJun
  **kagamiana**                   CDoC EPla ISta LJus MMoz SDry
                                 WBay WJun
§ **lubrica**                     CFil ISta WPGP
  **makinoi**                     EPla WJun
  **nitida**                      See *Fargesia nitida*
§ **okuboi**                      EPla WJun
  **sinica**                      ISta
  **villosa**                     See *S. okuboi*
  **yamadorii**                   EPla ISta SDry WJun
  - 'Brimscombe'                  EPla SDry
  **yashadake**                   EPla ISta SDry WJun
  - *kimmei*                      CFil EBee EPla ERod ISta LJus
                                 MMoz SDry WJun WPGP

## SEMNANTHE (Aizoaceae)
¶ **lacera**                      CTrF

## SEMPERVIVELLA See ROSULARIA

## SEMPERVIVUM ✿ (Crassulaceae)
  'Abba'                          MOne WHal WPer
  **acuminatum**                  See *S. tectorum* var. *glaucum*
  'Aglow'                         CWil MOne SSmi
¶ 'Albertnellii'                  NHol
  'Alcithoë'                      CWil MOne
  'Aldo Moro'                     CWil MOne NMen SSmi
  **allionii**                    See *Jovibarba allionii*
  'Alluring'                      GAbr
  'Alpha'                         CWil ESis LBee MOne NHol SIng
                                 SSmi STre WHal
  **altum**                       CWil NMen SSmi
  'Amanda'                        CWil MBro MOne NMen SSmi
                                 WHoo WPer
  'Ambergreen'                    CWil ELau NMen SSmi
¶ 'Andorra'                       NHol
  **andreanum**                   CWil ESis MOne NBro NHol SIng
                                 SSmi
  'Apache'                        CWil NNrd SSmi
¶ 'Apollo'                        NHol
  'Apple Blossom'                 CWil NBus SIng SSmi
  **arachnoideum** ♀              CMea CWil EGoo ELan ELau EPot
                                 ESis GAbr LBee MBar MBro MWat
                                 NHed NHol NNrd NRoo NWCA
                                 SBla SIng SSmi WAbe WEas WFar
                                 WHal WHoo WLow WPyg WWin
  - 'Abruzzii'                    SIng
  - var. *bryoides*               CWil GCHN MBro NMen SIng
  - x *calcareum*                 CWil MBro NMen SSmi WTin
  - 'Clairchen'                   CWil MBro NHol NMen
¶ - cristate                      CWil
* - *densum*                      ESis
  - subsp. *doellianum*           See *S. arachnoideum* var.
                                 *glabrescens*
  - 'Form No. 1'                  SSmi
¶ - from Gorges du Valais         SIng
§ - var. *glabrescens*            NMen SSmi
  - - 'Album'                     Last listed 1998
  - 'Gusseri'                     SIng
  - 'Kappa'                       See *S.* 'Kappa'
  - 'Laggeri'                     See *S. arachnoideum* subsp.
                                 *tomentosum*
  - 'Mole Harbord'                Last listed 1996
  - x *nevadense*                 CWil SDys SIng SSmi

| | |
|---|---|
| ¶ - Peña Priefa | NHol |
| t - x *pittonii* | CWil MBro NHol NMen SSmi |
| - 'Red Variety' | NMen |
| - 'Rubrum' | MOne |
| - 'Sultan' | MOne |
| § - subsp. *tomentosum* ♀ | EBrP EBre ECGP EMNN GCHN LBre MBro MOne MRPP NHol NMen NPer NWCA SBre SChu SMer SRms SSmi WPer WWin |
| - - misapplied | See *S. x barbulatum* 'Hookeri' |
| - - 'Minor' | NHol SIng |
| § - - 'Stansfieldii' | GAbr NMen SIng STre WHal |
| *arenarium* | See *Jovibarba arenaria* |
| *armenum* | NMen |
| 'Aross' | CLyd CWil GAbr NMen SSmi |
| 'Arrowheads Red' | MOne SSmi |
| *arvernense* | See *S. tectorum* |
| 'Ashes of Roses' | CWil EGoo ELau EPot ESis MBro MOne NMen SSmi WAbe |
| 'Asteroid' | CWil NMen SSmi |
| *atlanticum* | CWil NMen NNrd SSmi |
| - 'Edward Balls' | CWil MOne SDys SIng |
| - from Oukaimaden | CWil MBro MOne NHol NMen WTin |
| 'Atlantis' | MOne NHol |
| 'Atropurpureum' | CWil ELau GAbr MBro MOne WGor WIvy |
| 'Aureum' | See *Greenovia aurea* |
| *balcanicum* | MBro NMen |
| *ballsii* | CWil GCHN NHed NMen |
| - from Smólikas | MOne NMen SSmi |
| - from Tschumba Petzi | SDys SIng SSmi |
| 'Banderi' | CWil MOne |
| § x *barbulatum* | GCHN MOne NMen SDys SIng SSmi WHoo WPer WPyg |
| § - 'Hookeri' | CWil ESis EWes MOne NHol NRoo SSmi WAbe WPer |
| 'Bascour Zilver' | CWil GAbr SIng WHal |
| ¶ 'Bayan' | MTPN |
| * 'Beaute' | CWil |
| * 'Bedazzled' | CWil |
| 'Bedivere' | CWil MOne NMen SSmi |
| * 'Bedivere Cristate' | CWil NMen |
| 'Bella Meade' | CWil ELau MOne SSmi |
| I 'Belladonna' | CWil MDHE NHol NMen NTow WPer |
| 'Bellotts Pourpre' | CWil MOne NHol |
| 'Bennerbroek' | MDHE |
| 'Bernstein' | CWil MBro NMen SIng WHal |
| 'Beta' | MOne NHol NMen NRoo SSmi WAbe WCom |
| 'Bethany' | NMen WHal |
| 'Bicolor' | EPfP |
| ¶ 'Big Mal' | NHol |
| 'Big Slipper' | NHol SSmi |
| ¶ 'Binstead' | NHol |
| 'Birchmaier' | NMen |
| ¶ 'Black Claret' | NHol |
| 'Black Knight' | COIW ESis LBee SBla WHal |
| 'Black Mini' | CWil MOne NBir NHed NMen |
| 'Black Mountain' | CWil MOne SIng |
| 'Black Prince' | CLyd CMil |
| 'Black Velvet' | CWil MBro MOne SSmi |
| 'Bladon' | WPer |
| 'Blari' | SSmi |
| 'Blood Tip' | CHal CLyd ELau ESis GAbr GCHN LBee MBro NHar NMen NRoo SChu SSmi WGor WHal WHoo WLow |
| 'Blue Boy' | CWil ESis GAbr MOne NHol SIng WCom |
| 'Blue Moon' | ELau MOne |
| 'Blue Time' | MOne |
| 'Blush' | SSmi |
| 'Boissieri' | See *S. tectorum* subsp. *tectorum* 'Boissieri' |
| 'Bold Chick' | SSmi |
| 'Booth's Red' | ELau MOne SIng SSmi |
| *borisii* | See *S. ciliosum* var. *borisii* |
| *borissovae* | CWil NMen SSmi |
| 'Boromir' | CWil MOne SSmi |
| * 'Bowles' Variety' | WPer |
| 'Brock' | CWil MOne MRPP NHol |
| 'Bronco' | CWil ELan MOne NMen SSmi |
| 'Bronze Pastel' | CWil MBro MOne NMen SSmi WTin |
| ¶ 'Bronze Tower' | NHol |
| 'Brown Owl' | CWil MOne NHol |
| 'Brownii' | COIW GAbr MOne NMen SBla WPer |
| * 'Brunette' | GAbr |
| ¶ 'Burgundy' | ELau MOne |
| 'Burnatii' | CWil MOne |
| 'Butterbur' | CWil |
| 'Café' | CWil MBro MOne NHol NMen NNrd SIng SSmi WPer |
| x *calcaratum* | LBee SIng |
| *calcareum* | CWil ELau MBro MOne NBro SSmi WPer |
| * - 'Atropurpureum' | MBro |
| - 'Benz' | SDys |
| ¶ - 'Extra' | CWil |
| ¶ - from Alps, France | CWil MOne |
| - from Benz, Germany | Last listed 1997 |
| ¶ - from Ceuze | CWil |
| ¶ - from Col Bayard, France | CWil |
| - from Colle St Michael | CWil MOne |
| - from Gleize | CWil MOne NMen |
| - from Gorges du Cains | CWil MOne SSmi . |
| - from Guillaumes, Mont Ventoux, France | CWil GAbr MOne NMen |
| - from Mont Ventoux, France | CWil MOne SSmi |
| - from Queyras | CWil MOne SSmi |
| - from Route d'Annôt | CWil MOne SSmi |
| - from Triora | CWil MBro MOne NHol NMen |
| - 'Greenii' | CWil ESis MOne MRPP NHed NHol NMen SSmi |
| § - 'Grigg's Surprise' | CInt CWil MOne NMen |
| - 'Limelight' | CWil ESis EWes MBro NMen SIng SSmi WHal |
| - 'Monstrosum' | See *S. calcareum* 'Grigg's Surprise' |
| - 'Mrs Giuseppi' | ESis GAbr GCHN LBee MBro MOne NOak NRoo SBla SChu SIng SSmi STre WPer |
| - 'Pink Pearl' | CWil MOne NMen WTin |
| - 'Sir William Lawrence' | CPBP CWil ELau ESis NRoo SChu WHal |
| * 'Caldera' | CWil |
| *californicum* | NHed |
| 'Caliph's Hat' | CWil MOne |
| 'Canada Kate' | CWil MOne SSmi WPer |
| 'Cancer' | CLyd SSmi |
| 'Candy Floss' | CWil MOne SSmi |
| *cantabricum* | CWil MDHE SSmi |
| - subsp. *cantabricum* from Leitariegos | CWil MOne NMen |
| - from Lago de Enol | Last listed 1996 |
| - from Navafria | CWil NHol SIng |
| - from Peña Prieta | NMen SSmi |
| - from Piedrafita, Spain | SSmi |
| - from Riaño, Spain | SCWil GAbr |
| - from San Glorio | CWil GAbr MBro NMen |
| - from Santander, Spain | SSmi |

| | |
|---|---|
| – from Ticeros | CWil MOne NMen |
| – from Valvernera | CWil MOne |
| – subsp. *guadarramense* | CWil MBro MOne SSmi |
|    from Lobo No. 1 | |
| – – from Lobo No. 2 | MOne SSmi |
| – – from Navafria No. 1 | SSmi WTin |
| – – from Valvanera No. 1 | NMen SSmi |
| – x *montanum* subsp. | CWil SSmi WEas |
|    *stiriacum* | |
| – subsp. *urbionense* | SSmMBro MOne NMen |
|    from Picos de Urbi | |
| ¶ – subsp. *urbionese* | CWil |
| 'Canth' | CWil |
| 'Caramel' | CWil |
| * 'Carinal' | NBir |
| 'Carmen' | CHal CWil GAbr MBro MOne |
| 'Carneus' | MOne NHol |
| 'Carnival' | CHal MBro MOne SSmi WPer |
| *caucasicum* | CWil MOne NMen SIng SSmi |
| 'Cavo Doro' | CWil GAbr MDHE |
| *charadzeae* | CWil NHol |
| 'Cherry Frost' | MOne NNrd SSmi |
| 'Cherry Tart' | CWil |
| 'Chocolate' | SSmi |
| x *christii* | MOne NHol SSmi |
| ¶ 'Christmas Time' | NHol |
| *chrysanthum* | NMen |
| * *chyodi* | ELau |
| *ciliosum* | CPBP ESis NMen SIng WLow |
| § – var. *borisii* | CNic ESis GCal GTou MBro MRPP |
| | NHed NMen NNrd NRoo SChr |
| | SIng SSmi WHal |
| – x *ciliosum* var. *borisii* | CHal CWil EPot WTin |
| – from Alí Butús | Last listed 1996 |
| * – from Ochrid | CWil NMen |
| – var. *galicicum* 'Mali Hat' | CWil NHol NMen |
| – x *marmoreum* | CWil MBro NMen SSmi |
| 'Cindy' | CWil |
| 'Circlet' | CWil MOne NMen SSmi |
| * *cistaceum* | WEas |
| 'Clara Noyes' | ELau SSmi WPer |
| 'Clare' | MOne NNrd SSmi |
| 'Cleveland Morgan' | CWil NBro NHar SSmi |
| 'Climax' | MOne |
| 'Cobweb Capers' | MOne |
| 'Cobweb Centre' | MOne |
| 'Collage' | CWil NHol |
| 'Collecteur Anchisi' | MOne SDys SSmi |
| 'Commander Hay' ♀ | CLyd ESis EWes LHop MRPP |
| | NMen NPer NTow WEas WFar |
| | WHal WLow |
| 'Compte de Congae' | MOne NMen |
| 'Congo' | CWil MOne SSmi |
| 'Cornstone' | CWil NHol |
| 'Corona' | MOne NHol WPer |
| ¶ 'Coronet' | MOne |
| 'Correvons' | See *S.* 'Aymon Correvon' |
| 'Corsair' | CWil ESis LEdu MBro MOne |
| | NMen SIng WPer |
| 'Cresta' | SSmi |
| 'Crimson Velvet' | CWil MDHE MOne SSmi WPer |
| § 'Crispyn' | CLyd CWil MBro MOne MRPP |
| | NHol NMen SSmi WEas |
| * 'Croky' | SIng |
| 'Croton' | SIng WPer |
| 'Cupream' | CWil MDHE NHed |
| 'Dakota' | CWil |
| 'Dallas' | CWil MOne NHol SSmi |
| 'Damask' | CWil GAbr MBro MDHE SSmi |
| 'Dark Beauty' | CWil MBro MOne NMen NRoo |
| | SIng SSmi WHal WLow |
| 'Dark Cloud' | CWil GAbr MOne |

| | |
|---|---|
| 'Dark Point' | CWil MOne NMen SIng SSmi |
| 'Darkie' | CWil |
| 'Deep Fire' | CWil GBin MOne NHol SSmi |
| x *degenianum* | GAbr MBro |
| ¶ 'Delta' | WTin |
| *densum* | See *S. tectorum* |
| 'Director Jacobs' | CWil GAbr GCHN MOne NHol |
| | NMen SIng SSmi WEas WWin |
| 'Disco Dancer' | CWil |
| ¶ 'Doctor Roberts' | NHol |
| *dolomiticum* | ELau |
| * – from Rif Sennes | CWil |
| – x *montanum* | CWil MOne NBro NHed NMen |
| | SSmi |
| 'Donarrose' | SIng |
| 'Downland Queen' | CWil NHol |
| 'Duke of Windsor' | CWil MOne MRPP NMen SSmi |
| 'Dusky' | CWil SSmi |
| 'Dyke' | CWil GAbr MBro NHol NMen |
| | WHal |
| *dzhavachischvilii* | CWil MOne |
| 'Edge of Night' | CWil NHol |
| 'El Greco' | CWil |
| 'El Toro' | ELau |
| 'Elgar' | CWil MOne SIng |
| 'Elizabeth' | WPer |
| 'Elvis' | CWil GAbr MBro MOne NMen |
| | SSmi |
| 'Emerald Giant' | CWil MOne |
| 'Emerson's Giant' | CWil MOne NMen |
| 'Emma Jane' | MOne |
| 'Engles' | MOne WHal |
| 'Engle's 13-2' | CLyd CWil MOne NBro NHar |
| | NHol SChu |
| 'Engles No. 1' | MBro |
| 'Engle's Rubrum' | CPBP ESis GAbr GTou LBee NHol |
| | NMen |
| *erythraeum* | CWil NMen SIng WAbe WHal |
| – from Pirin, Bulgaria | NMen |
| 'Excalibur' | CWil MBro NMen SSmi |
| 'Exhibita' | CWil MBro SDys SSmi |
| 'Exorna' | CWil ELau MOne NMen SSmi |
| | WEas |
| 'Fair Lady' | CWil MOne NMen SSmi |
| 'Fame' | CWil MDHE MOne NHol |
| x *fauconnettii* | CWil MBro MOne NHol SIng SSmi |
| – *thompsonii* | MOne NHol SSmi |
| ¶ 'Feldmaier' | MOne |
| 'Festival' | CWil NMen |
| 'Feu de Printemps' | Last listed 1998 |
| 'Fiesta' | CWil WHal |
| *fimbriatum* | See *S.* x *barbulatum* |
| 'Finerpointe' | MBro MOne SSmi |
| 'Fire Glint' | CWil GAbr MOne NHol |
| 'Firebird' | CWil NMen |
| 'First Try' | CWil |
| 'Flaming Heart' | CWil MOne NMen SSmi WPer |
| 'Flander's Passion' | ELau LBee WPer |
| 'Flasher' | CWil MBro WEas WPer |
| * 'Fluweel' | CWil |
| 'Fontanae' | MOne |
| 'Forden' | MOne WGor |
| 'Ford's Amability' | CWil ESis SSmi |
| 'Ford's Giant' | CWil |
| 'Ford's Shadows' | SDys SSmi |
| 'Ford's Spring' | CWil MOne NHol SSmi WPer |
| | WWin |
| 'Freckles' | MOne |
| 'Freeland' | WPer |
| 'Frigidum' | NHed |
| ¶ 'Frost and Flame' | NHol |
| 'Frosty' | CWil MOne |

| | |
|---|---|
| 'Fuego' | CWil MOne |
| x *funckii* | CWil ELau MBro NHol NMen SDys SIng WPer |
| 'Fuzzy Wuzzy' | CWil SSmi |
| 'Galahad' | CWil |
| 'Gambol' | NHol |
| 'Gamma' | LBee NHol NMen SChu SDys SIng WEas |
| 'Garnet' | Last listed 1998 |
| 'Gay Jester' | CWil GAbr MBro MOne SIng SSmi WHoo WTin |
| 'Gazelle' | SSmi |
| 'Georgette' | CWil MBro SSmi |
| 'Ginnie's Delight' | CWil SSmi |
| 'Gipsy' | CWil MBro |
| *giuseppii* | CWil MBro MRPP NHol NMen SIng SRms SSmi |
| – from Peña Espigüte, Spain | CWil MOne NHol NMen SSmi |
| – from Peña Prieta, Spain | CWil MOne NMen |
| 'Gizmo' | CWil |
| 'Gleam' | Last listed 1997 |
| 'Gloriosum' | ELau GAbr MBro NBus NRoo SIng SSmi |
| 'Glowing Embers' | CWil MBro MOne SSmi WHal |
| 'Gollum' | MOne SSmi |
| 'Granada' | MBro |
| 'Granat' | CWil GCal NLak WPer |
| 'Granby' | MOne NMen SSmi |
| *grandiflorum* | CWil GCHN MBro MRPP NHed NMen SSmi WPer |
| – x *ciliosum* | CWil MOne NMen |
| – 'Fasciatum' | CWil MOne NMen SSmi |
| – 'Keston' | SSmi |
| 'Grape Idol' | CWil |
| 'Grapetone' | CWil SDys SSmi WHal |
| 'Graupurpur' | CWil |
| 'Gray Dawn' | CWil SSmi |
| 'Green Apple' | CWil GAbr SSmi |
| 'Green Gables' | CWil MBro SSmi |
| ¶ 'Green Giant' | MTPN |
| 'Greenwich Time' | CWil NMen SSmi |
| * *greigii* | NNrd |
| 'Grey Ghost' | CWil |
| 'Grey Green' | CWil NHol |
| 'Grey Lady' | CWil SSmi |
| 'Greyfriars' | CWil MBro NMen SSmi WPer |
| 'Greyolla' | CWil SSmi WPer |
| 'Grunspecht' | Last listed 1998 |
| * 'Hades' | CWil |
| 'Hall's Hybrid' | GAbr NBro NHar NNrd |
| 'Hall's Seedling' | Last listed 1998 |
| 'Happy' | CWil MBro MOne |
| * 'Hart' | CWil NHol |
| 'Haullauer's Seedling' | Last listed 1997 |
| 'Havana' | CWil NMen |
| 'Hayling' | CWil ELau MOne NHol NMen SSmi |
| 'Heigham Red' | CWil ESis MOne NHol SIng SSmi |
| 'Heliotroop' | MOne SDys |
| *helveticum* | See *S. montanum* |
| 'Hester' | CWil ELau ESis GAbr MBro MDHE MOne NBro NHar NMen SIng SSmi |
| 'Hey-Hey' | ELau LBee LEdu MBro NMen WAbe WLow WPer |
| 'Hidde' | CWil SSmi |
| 'Hiddes Roosje' | MOne SSmi |
| *hirtum* | See *Jovibarba hirta* |
| 'Hookeri' | See *S.* x *barbulatum* 'Hookeri' |
| 'Hopi' | CWil MOne NHol |
| 'Hortulanus Smit' | SSmi |
| 'Hot Peppermint' | CWil |
| 'Hot Shot' | CLyd |
| 'Hullabaloo' | MOne |
| 'Hurricane' | MOne |
| 'Icicle' | CWil ELau NBro NHol NMen SIng SSmi WGor |
| *imbricatum* | See *S.* x *barbulatum* |
| 'Imperial' | CWil SSmi |
| *ingwersenii* | MOne SIng SSmi WLow |
| 'Interlace' | CWil SSmi |
| 'Iophon' | SSmi |
| 'Irazu' | CWil GAbr MBro MOne NMen SDys |
| *ispartae* | CWil |
| *italicum* | CWil |
| 'Itchen' | MOne NMen SIng SSmi |
| 'IWO' | CWil GAbr NMen |
| 'Jack Frost' | CWil MOne NBro NMen SChu SSmi |
| 'Jane' | Last listed 1998 |
| 'Jasper' | MOne |
| * 'Jaspis' | CWil |
| 'Jelly Bean' | CWil MOne NMen SSmi |
| 'Jet Stream' | CWil GAbr MOne NMen SDys SSmi |
| 'Jewel Case' | CWil ELau GAbr SSmi |
| 'John T.' | MOne |
| 'Jolly Green Giant' | CWil |
| 'Jo's Spark' | CWil |
| 'Jubilee' | CLyd ELan GAbr NHol NMen NRoo SSmi WEas WGor WPer WWin |
| 'Jubilee Tricolor' | MBro SSmi |
| 'Jungle Fires' | CWil |
| 'Jupiter' | ESis |
| 'Justine's Choice' | CWil |
| 'Kalinda' | MOne NMen |
| § 'Kappa' | CWil MBro MOne NBro NHol SDys SIng SSmi |
| 'Katmai' | CWil |
| 'Kelly Jo' | CWil NBro NHar NMen SIng SSmi |
| 'Kermit' | SSmi |
| 'Kerneri' | Last listed 1996 |
| 'Kibo' | CWil |
| 'Kilt' | CWil |
| 'Kimble' | CWil MOne WPer |
| 'Kimono' | Last listed 1996 |
| *kindingeri* | CWil GTou NMen NWCA SSmi |
| 'King George' | CHal CWil ESis GAbr GBin LBee MBro MOne NMen NPer SChu SSmi WGor WHal WHoo WPer WPyg |
| 'Kip' | CWil NMen SSmi |
| 'Kismet' | CWil MOne SSmi |
| 'Kolibri' | GAbr MDHE |
| *kosaninii* | CWil ELau MBro MOne NMen SIng SSmi WPer |
| – from Koprivnik | MOne NMen SDys SSmi WAbe |
| – from Visitor | CWil MOne |
| 'Krakeling' | CWil MOne |
| 'Kramers Purpur' | CWil |
| 'Kramers Spinrad' | CWil ESis GAbr LEdu MBro MOne NMen SDys SIng SSmi WEas WHoo |
| 'Lady Kelly' | CLyd CWil ESis MOne |
| 'Launcelot' | MOne WPer |
| 'Lavender and Old Lace' | CWil ELau GAbr MOne MRPP NMen NRoo SChu SMer WCot |
| 'Laysan' | CWil |
| Le Clair's hybrid No. 4 | MOne |
| 'Leneca' | SSmi |
| 'Lennik's Glory' | See *S.* 'Crispyn' |
| § 'Lennik's Glory No. 1' | CWil MBro |

'Lennik's Time'          MBro MOne SSmi
'Lentevur'               CWil
'Lentezon'               CWil MOne
'Leocadia's Nephew'      CWil MOne
'Lilac Time'             CWil ELau GAbr MBro MOne
                         NMen NNrd SChu SSmi WHal
I  'Linaria'             MTPN
'Lipari'                 CWil
'Lipstick'               CWil ELau
'Lively Bug'             CWil MBro NNrd SDys SIng SSmi
                         WPer
'Lloyd Praeger'          See *S. montanum* subsp.
                         *stiriacum*
*  'Lonzo'               CWil
'Lou Bastidou'           MOne SSmi
'Lowe's Rubicundum'      Last listed 1998
'Lynne's Choice'         CWil MOne SIng WHal
*macedonicum*            CWil MBro NHed SSmi
 - from Ljuboten         MOne NMen SSmi
'Magic Spell'            CWil MOne
'Magical'                CWil SSmi
'Magnificum'             CWil NMen
*  'Mahogany'            ELau GBin LBee MBro MOne
                         NHol NMen NRoo SBla WGor
                         WHal
'Maigret'                CWil MOne
'Majestic'               CWil NMen SSmi
'Malabron'               CWil MOne
'Malby's Hybrid'         See *S.* 'Reginald Malby'
'Marella'                CWil WPer
'Marijntje'              SSmi
'Marjorie Newton'        CWil
'Marmalade'              SSmi WTin
§  *marmoreum*           CMea CWil ELau LBee NMen STre
                         WEas WHal WPer
 - 'Brunneifolium'       CWil EGoo ESis MBro MOne
                         NHol NMen SChu SSmi WPer
 - from Kanzas Gorge     ELau MOne NHol SSmi
 - from Monte Tirone     CWil SDys SSmi
 - from Okol             CWil MOne NMen SSmi
 - from Sveta Peta       Last listed 1998
 - subsp. *marmoreum*    MBro NMen
     var. *dinaricum*
§ - - 'Rubrifolium'      GCal MRPP
§ - 'Ornatum'            SRms
'Marshall'               MBro
'Mary Ente'              CWil
¶  'Matador'             MOne
'Mate'                   NMen SSmi
'Maubi'                  CPri CWil
'Mauna Kea'              SSmi
'Mavbi'                  NNrd
'Medallion'              CWil MOne
'Meisse'                 MOne SSmi
'Melanie'                CWil WIvy
'Mercury'                CWil ELau MDHE MOne NBro
                         NHol SSmi
¶  'Merkur'              MOne
'Merlin'                 CWil SSmi
'Midas'                  CWil
'Mila'                   CWil
'Mini Frost'             CLyd CWil GAbr MOne NMen
                         SIng
*  'Minuet'              CWil
'Missouri Rose'          Last listed 1996
'Moerkerk's Merit'       CWil GAbr SSmi
'Mondstein'              CWil MOne
¶  'Montage'             MOne
*  'Montague'            CWil
§  *montanum*            CWil ESis LEdu SIng SMer WPer
 - subsp. *burnatii*     SIng SSmi
 - *carpaticum*          MBro MOne NMen

'Cmiral's Yellow'
 - from Anchisis         MBro MOne
 - from Arbizion         CWil MBro MOne
 - from Windachtal       CWil MBro MOne NMen
 - subsp. *montanum*     MRPP WLow
     var. *braunii*
 - 'Rubrum'              See *S.* 'Red Mountain'
§ - subsp. *stiriacum*   CWil ELau MBro MOne NMen
                         SIng
 - - from Mauterndorf, Austria SSmi
 - - 'Lloyd Praeger'     CWil MOne SDys SSmi
'More Honey'             CWil MOne
'Morning Glow'           MOne WGor WHal
'Mount Hood'             CWil MOne WHal
'Mrs Elliott'            Last listed 1998
'Mulberry Wine'          CLyd CWil
'Myrrhine'               CWil
'Mystic'                 CWil MBro NMen NNrd WPer
'Nell'                   MOne
'Neptune'                CWil
*nevadense*              CWil ELau MBro MOne MRPP
                         NMen SRms SSmi
¶ - from Puerto de       MOne
     San Francisco
 - var. *hirtellum*      CWil NMen SSmi
'Nico'                   CWil
'Night Raven'            CLyd CWil NMen SIng SSmi
'Nigrum'                 See *S. tectorum* 'Nigrum'
'Niobe'                  CWil MOne
'Nixes 27'               MOne
'Noir'                   CWil MOne NBro NMen SSmi
'Norbert'                CWil MOne
'Nortofts Beauty'        MOne
'Nouveau Pastel'         CWil MBro MOne WHal
'Octet'                  MOne NMen SIng
*octopodes*              CLyd ESis MDHE NBir
 - var. *apetalum*       CWil GAbr MOne NMen SIng
                         SSmi
'Oddity'                 CPBP CWil ELau NMen WCot
                         WPer
'Ohio'                   ELau
'Ohio Burgundy'          CWil ELau MDHE MOne NHed
                         NMen SSmi WAbe WPer
'Olivette'               MDHE SSmi WPer
'Omega'                  MBro MOne SSmi WPer
'Opitz'                  CLyd CWil WPer
'Ornatum'                MOne SSmi WAbe WEas WHal
*ossetiense*             CWil GAbr MOne NMen SSmi
'Othello'                CHal CMil EBrP EBre ESis GAbr
                         LBre MRPP NBir NLak NVic SBre
'Packardian'             CWil ELau MOne NMen SSmi
'Painted Lady'           CWil SSmi
'Palissander'            CWil MBro MOne SSmi
'Pam Wain'               Last listed 1997
'Paricutin'              CWil SDys
'Pastel'                 CWil ELau MOne NMen SIng SSmi
*patens*                 See *Jovibarba heuffelii*
'Patrician'              CWil EBrP EBre ESis LBee LBre
                         SBre
'Peach Blossom'          CWil
'Pekinese'               CWil ESis EWes MBro NBro NMen
                         NNrd SIng SSmi WEas WPer
                         WWin
'Peterson's Ornatum'     MOne SSmi
'Petsy'                  MOne
'Pilatus'                CWil MOne
'Pilosella'              MOne
'Pink Cloud'             CWil MBro MOne SSmi
'Pink Dawn'              CWil MOne
'Pink Delight'           CWil
'Pink Flamingoes'        SSmi
'Pink Lemonade'          Last listed 1996

| | | |
|---|---|---|
| * | 'Pink Mist' | WPer |
| | 'Pink Puff' | CWil MOne SSmi |
| | 'Pippin' | CWil GAbr MBro WPer |
| | 'Piran' | CWil MOne |
| | *pittonii* | CMea CWil ESis GAbr NLak NMen SSmi WHal |
| | 'Pixie' | CWil MOne NHed NMen |
| | 'Plumb Rose' | CWil MBro MOne NMen SChu |
| | 'Pluto' | CWil SSmi |
| | 'Poke Eat' | MOne SSmi |
| | 'Polaris' | CWil SSmi |
| | 'Poldark' | Last listed 1997 |
| | 'Pottsii' | CWil GAbr MOne |
| | 'Powellii' | Last listed 1998 |
| * | 'Prairie Sunset' | CWil MOne |
| | 'Precious' | CWil SSmi |
| | 'President Arsac' | SSmi |
| | 'Proud Zelda' | CWil MOne NMen SSmi |
| | 'Pruhonice' | CWil MOne |
| | 'Pseudo-ornatum' | EPfP LBee SChu |
| | 'Pumaros' | CWil NMen SDys SSmi |
| | *pumilum* | CWil MBar NMen |
| | – from Adyl Su No. 1 | CWil SSmi |
| | – from Adyl Su No. 2 | SSmi |
| | – from Armchi | CWil MOne MRPP SDys SIng SSmi |
| | – from Armchi x *ingwersenii* | MOne NMen |
| | – from El'brus No. 1 | CWil MRPP NMen SIng SSmi |
| | – from El'brus No. 2 | SSmi |
| | – from Techensis | CWil NMen |
| | – x *ingwersenii* | CWil MBro WLow |
| | 'Purdy' | WAbe |
| | 'Purdy's 50-6' | CWil |
| | 'Purdy's 90-1' | Last listed 1998 |
| | 'Purple Beauty' | CWil MOne |
| | 'Purple King' | CWil |
| | 'Purple Passion' | MBro |
| | 'Purpurriese' | CWil GAbr |
| | 'Queen Amalia' | See *S. reginae-amaliae* |
| | 'Query' | Last listed 1997 |
| | 'Quintessence' | CWil NHol |
| | 'R.H.I.' | Last listed 1998 |
| | 'Racy' | CWil |
| | 'Radiant' | CWil |
| ¶ | 'Ragtime' | MOne |
| | 'Ramses' | MOne |
| | 'Raspberry Ice' | CLyd CWil MBro NBro NHol NMen WAbe WPer |
| | 'Red Ace' | CWil GAbr NBro NMen SSmi |
| | 'Red Beam' | CWil MDHE MOne SIng SSmi |
| | 'Red Delta' | CWil MOne NBir SSmi |
| | 'Red Devil' | CWil ELau MBro MOne NMen SSmi |
| ¶ | 'Red Giant' | MTPN |
| | 'Red Indian' | CWil MOne |
| | 'Red King' | SSmi |
| § | 'Red Mountain' | CHal CWil ELau MBro MOne MWat NLak SRms SSmi |
| | 'Red Prince' | CWil |
| | 'Red Rum' | WPer |
| | 'Red Shadows' | CInt CWil ESis WPer |
| | 'Red Skin' | CWil |
| | 'Red Spider' | MOne NBro |
| | 'Red Wings' | MOne SRms |
| | 'Regal' | MOne |
| | 'Regina' | MOne |
| | *reginae* | See *S. reginae-amaliae* |
| § | *reginae-amaliae* | NHol SSmi STre |
| | – from Kambeecho No. 1 | SSmi |
| | – from Kambeecho No. 2 | MDHE NMen SDys |
| | – from Mavri Petri | CWil MBro MOne SDys SSmi |
| | – from Peristéri, Greece | MBro SSmi |
| | – from Sarpun | CWil MOne NMen SSmi |
| | – from Vardusa | SDys |
| § | 'Reginald Malby' | CWil ITim MDHE |
| | 'Reinhard' | CWil GAbr ITim MOne NMen NNrd NRoo SIng SSmi WHal WPer |
| | 'Remus' | CWil MBro MOne NMen NNrd SDys SIng |
| | 'Rex' | MOne NMen |
| | 'Rhone' | CWil GAbr MBro MOne |
| * | *richardii* | MBar NBus |
| | 'Risque' | CWil WPer |
| | 'Rita Jane' | CLyd CWil MOne NMen SSmi |
| | 'Robin' | CLyd CWil MOne NBro NHol |
| | 'Ronny' | CWil MOne |
| | 'Roosemaryn' | MBro |
| * | 'Rose Splendour' | CWil MOne |
| | x *roseum* 'Fimbriatum' | MBro NHed NHol NLak SSmi WEas |
| | 'Rosie' | CMea CWil GAbr MBro MOne NBus NHol NMen NRoo SIng SSmi WHal WHoo WPer WPyg |
| | 'Rotkopf' | CWil MOne |
| | 'Rotmantel' | SSmi |
| | 'Rotund' | CWil MOne |
| | 'Rouge' | CWil NMen SRms |
| | 'Royal Flush' | CWil SSmi |
| | 'Royal Mail' | Last listed 1997 |
| | 'Royal Opera' | CWil MOne SSmi |
| | 'Royal Ruby' | CWil GCHN LBee MOne NRoo SChu SSmi |
| | 'Rubellum' | MOne |
| | 'Rubikon Improved' | Last listed 1997 |
| | 'Rubin' | EGoo EPfP ESis GAbr MBro MRPP NBir NMen NNrd SSmi WAbe WEas WHoo WPer WPyg |
| | 'Rubrifolium' | See *S. marmoreum* subsp. *marmoreum* 'Rubrifolium' |
| | 'Rubrum Ash' | CWil GAbr MBro MOne NMen |
| | 'Rubrum Ornatum' | Last listed 1997 |
| | 'Rubrum Ray' | CWil MOne SSmi |
| * | 'Ruby Glow' | ESis |
| | 'Ruby Heart' | SSmi |
| | 'Rusty' | CWil WFar |
| | 'Ruth' | MOne |
| | *ruthenicum* | Last listed 1998 |
| | 'Sabanum' | MOne |
| * | 'Safara' | CWil |
| | 'Saffron' | CLyd CWil MOne |
| | 'Saga' | CWil ELau MOne |
| | 'Sanford's Hybrid' | MOne |
| | 'Santis' | MBro |
| | 'Sassy Frass' | MOne |
| | 'Saturn' | CWil GAbr MOne NMen SSmi |
| | *schlebanii* | See *S. marmoreum* |
| | 'Seminole' | CWil MOne SSmi |
| | 'Sharon's Pencil' | CWil |
| | 'Shawnee' | CWil |
| | 'Sheila' | GAbr |
| | 'Shirley's Joy' | CHal CWil GAbr NMen SSmi WEas |
| * | 'Sideshow' | CWil MOne |
| | 'Sigma' | Last listed 1998 |
| | 'Silberkarneol' | See *S.* 'Silver Jubilee' |
| | 'Silberspitz' | CWil NBro NMen WPer |
| § | 'Silver Jubilee' | CWil GAbr MDHE NBro NHed SSmi |
| | 'Silver Spring' | Last listed 1998 |
| | 'Silver Thaw' | CWil NMen |
| | 'Simonkaianum' | See *Jovibarba hirta* |
| | 'Sioux' | CWil MOne NMen SIng SSmi WPer |
| | 'Skrocki's Bronze' | MOne NMen WPer |
| | 'Skrocki's Purple Rose' | CWil |

'Slabber's Seedling'  CWil
'Smokey Jet'  CWil
'Snowberger'  CWil ELau ESis GAbr MOne NHar NMen NRoo WHal WPer
*soboliferum*  See *Jovibarba sobolifera*
'Soothsayer'  CWil MOne
'Sopa'  CWil MOne
*sosnowskyi*  CWil MOne NMen SSmi
sp. from Figaua Dhag  Last listed 1998
¶ sp. from San Glorio  MOne
sp. from Sierra del Cadi  MOne NHol
sp. from Sierra Nova  NHed
'Spanish Dancer'  CWil SSmi
'Spherette'  CWil MBro NMen SSmi WPer
'Spice'  CWil SSmi
'Spinnelli'  MBro MOne
'Spiver's Velvet'  Last listed 1998
'Spode'  SSmi
'Spring Mist'  CWil GCHN MBro MOne NHar WGor WPer
'Sprite'  CLyd CWil GAbr MOne NMen SDys SSmi
*stansfieldii*  See *S. arachnoideum* subsp. *tomentosum* 'Stansfieldii'
'Starion'  CWil MOne SSmi
'Starshine'  CWil MBro MOne NMen SIng SSmi
'State Fair'  CWil MBro SIng SSmi WPer
* 'Strawberry Fields'  CWil MOne
'Strider'  GAbr MBro
'Stuffed Olive'  CWil MOne SDys SSmi
'Sun Waves'  CWil SSmi
'Sunkist'  Last listed 1996
'Super Dome'  CWil
'Superama'  CWil
'Supernova'  CWil
'Syston Flame'  MOne
'Tamberlane'  CWil
'Tambimuttu'  CWil MOne
* 'Tambora'  CWil
'Tarn Hows'  CWil NRoo
'Teck'  CWil MOne
§ *tectorum* ♀  CArn CNic CPri CWil ELan EWFC GAbr GPoy GTou MBar MDHE MMal SIde SIng STre WAbe WJek WOak WWye
* - 'Alp Gasson'  Last listed 1998
- subsp. *alpinum*  CWil MBro NMen SIng SSmi
- 'Atropurpureum'  ELan MOne WCom
- 'Atroviolaceum'  CWil ESis GCal NHol SIng WFar
- from Andorra  Last listed 1996
- from Mont Ventoux  Last listed 1996
- from Sierra del Cadi  SSmi
§ - var. *glaucum*  CWil ESis NHed SSmi
§ - 'Nigrum'  CWil ESis LBee MBro MOne NBro NHol NMen SIng SSmi
- 'Red Flush'  CWil NHar NMen SDys SIng SSmi WGor
- 'Robustum'  MOne
- 'Royanum'  ESis GAbr WEas
- 'Sunset'  CWil ESis MOne NMen SIng SSmi WEas WHal
- subsp. *tectorum*  MOne
§ - - 'Atropurpureum'  CWil SIng SSmi
§ - - 'Boissieri'  CWil MBro MOne SSmi
- - - 'Triste'  CWil ELau ESis LBee MBro MOne SIng SSmi WCom
- 'Violaceum'  MOne SIng WAbe
* 'Telfan'  MOne NMen SSmi
'Thayne'  NMen
*thompsonianum*  CWil ESis MOne MRPP NHed NHol NMen SSmi

'Tiffany'  MOne NHol WPer
'Tiger Bay'  Last listed 1998
'Tina'  MOne WPer
'Titania'  CWil MBro NBro NHar NMen WHal
'Tombago'  CWil MOne
'Topaz'  CWil GAbr LBee MOne SBla SChu
'Tordeur's Memory'  CWil MOne NMen SSmi
'Traci Sue'  CWil ELau SSmi
* 'Trail Walker'  CWil MOne
*transcaucasicum*  CWil MOne SSmi
'Tree Beard'  CWil MOne
'Tristesse'  CWil MOne NMen WGor WGwG
'Tristram'  SSmi
'Truva'  CWil MOne NMen SSmi
'Twilight Blues'  CWil
'Unicorn'  CWil
x *vaccarii*  MOne NMen SSmi
'Vanbaelen'  CWil MOne SDys SSmi
'Vaughelen'  CWil MBro MOne
* 'Velvet Prince'  CWil
x *versicolor*  NHol
*vicentei*  CWil MBro NHed NMen
- from Gaton  MOne
¶ 'Victorian'  MOne
'Video'  CWil MOne NMen SSmi
'Violet Queen'  CWil
'Virgil'  CWil GAbr MBro NMen SDys SIng SSmi WPer
'Virginus'  CWil MBro MOne
'Vulcano'  CWil GAbr MOne
'Watermelon Rind'  MOne
*webbianum*  See *S. arachnoideum* subsp. *tomentosum*
'Webby Flame'  CWil
'Webby Ola'  MOne SSmi
'Weirdo'  CWil
'Wendy'  CLyd CWil MOne NMen
'Westerlin'  CWil GAbr MOne SSmi
'Whitening'  CWil GAbr NMen SSmi
x *widderi*  MOne SSmi
'Wollcott's Variety'  ELau GAbr MOne MRPP NBir NHar WPer
*wulfenii*  CWil NMen
'Zaza'  CWil
*zeleborii*  CHal ELau MOne WHal
'Zenith'  CWil GAbr MOne
'Zenocrate'  CWil WHal
'Zeppelin'  CWil MBro
'Zinaler Rothorn'  Last listed 1997
'Zircon'  NMen
'Zone'  CWil MOne NMen SSmi
'Zulu'  CWil MOne NHed SSmi

# SENECIO (Asteraceae)
§ *abrotanifolius*  EBee NNrd NTow
- var. *tiroliensis*  See *S. abrotanifolius*
*aquaticus*  Last listed 1998
§ *articulatus*  CHal LHil
*aschenbornianus*  GCal
*aureus*  See *Packera aurea*
*bicolor* subsp. *cineraria*  See *S. cineraria*
*bidwillii*  See *Brachyglottis bidwillii*
*buchananii*  See *Brachyglottis buchananii*
*candicans*  See *S. cineraria*
*cannabifolius*  EBee
*canus*  Last listed 1998
*chionophila*  Last listed 1998
*chrysanthemoides*  See *Euryops chrysanthemoides*
§ *cineraria*  IBlr MBri
- 'Alice'  Last listed 1997

| | |
|---|---|
| – 'Ramparts' | LHop WEas |
| – Sch 3129 | Last listed 1997 |
| – 'Silver Dust' ♀ | ENot EWTr |
| – 'White Diamond' ♀ | CLTr ECha LGro |
| *compactus* | See *Brachyglottis compacta* |
| *confusus* | CPIN ECon ERea LCns SOWG WMul |
| *doria* | EBee EPPr SCro WCot WFar WLRN |
| *doronicum* | EMan |
| *elaeagnifolius* | See *Brachyglottis elaeagnifolia* |
| *elegans* | LHil |
| *eminens* | Last listed 1997 |
| ¶ *erucifolius* | SHut |
| *fuchsii* HH&K 293 | Last listed 1997 |
| – HH&K 318 | Last listed 1998 |
| *gilliesii* JJA 12379 | Last listed 1996 |
| *glastifolius* | ERea LHil |
| *grandiflorus* | Last listed 1997 |
| 'Gregynog Gold' | See *Ligularia* 'Gregynog Gold' |
| *greyi* hort. | See *Brachyglottis* (Dunedin Group) 'Sunshine' |
| – Hooker | See *Brachyglottis greyi* |
| *barbourii* RMRP 96596 | IDac |
| *bectoris* | See *Brachyglottis hectoris* |
| *beritieri* DC. | See *Pericallis lanata* |
| *berreanus* | MBri |
| *jacquemontianus* | Last listed 1998 |
| *kirkii* | See *Brachyglottis kirkii* |
| *laciniatus* | Last listed 1998 |
| *laxifolius* hort. | See *Brachyglottis* (Dunedin Group) 'Sunshine' |
| – Buchanan | See *Brachyglottis laxifolia* |
| 'Leonard Cockayne' | See *Brachyglottis* 'Leonard Cockayne' |
| *leucophyllus* | LHil WLin |
| *leucostachys* | See *S. viravira* |
| *macroglossus* | CPIN |
| – 'Variegatus' ♀ | CB&S CHal CPIN ERea |
| *macrospermus* | CTrC WCot |
| *maritimus* | See *S. cineraria* |
| *mikanioides* | See *Delairea odorata* |
| *monroi* | See *Brachyglottis monroi* |
| *nemorensis* | EMan |
| subsp. *fuchsii* | |
| *petasitis* | LHil |
| *polyodon* | CInt EPPr EWes GBri MAvo MCCP MHlr MNrw SUsu WFar |
| – S&SH 29 | CFir CHan CRDP EBee SAga WCru |
| *populifolius* | See *Pericallis appendiculata* |
| *przewalskii* | See *Ligularia przewalskii* |
| *pulcher* | CFil CGle CHan CSam GBri MAvo MMil MNrw MTho NTow SMrm SUsu WCot WCru WPGP |
| *reinboldii* | See *Brachyglottis rotundifolia* |
| *rodriguezii* | Last listed 1997 |
| *rowleyanus* | EBak |
| *scandens* | CB&S CFil CMac CPIN CPle ELan ERea ISea MCCP MNrw MTho SUsu WCwm WHer WPGP |
| *seminiveus* | EBee |
| § *serpens* | CHal MBri |
| § *smithii* | CHan CRDP CRow ELan NChi WBcn WCot WCru |
| *speciosus* | NBir NTow |
| *spedenii* | See *Brachyglottis spedenii* |
| *squalidus* | Last listed 1997 |
| 'Sunshine' | See *Brachyglottis* (Dunedin Group) 'Sunshine' |

| | |
|---|---|
| *takedanus* | See *Tephroseris takedanus* |
| *tamoides* 'Variegatus' | ERea WPyg |
| *tanguticus* | See *Sinacalia tangutica* |
| § *viravira* ♀ | CGle CHan CPle CSam EHol EMFP EMar ERea GBri LIck MBel MLLN MRav MWgw SMac SPer SRPl WCot WEas WOve WSHC WWat |
| *werneriifolius* | See *Packera werneriifolius* |

## SENNA (Caesalpiniaceae)

| | |
|---|---|
| *alexandrina* | CB&S MSal |
| *artemisioides* ♀ | CTrC SOWG |
| § *candolleana* | SPan |
| § *corymbosa* (Lam.) Irwin & Barneby | CB&S CBot CPIN CPle ERea LChe LCns LHil SOWG |
| *didymobotrya* | SOWG |
| x *floribunda* ♀ | Last listed 1995 |
| *bebecarpa* | MSal |
| § *marilandica* | CB&S EBee ELau MSal SIgm WSHC |
| *obtusa* (Roxb.) Wight | CGre SBid |
| – Clos | See *S. candolleana* |
| § *obtusifolia* | CPIN MSal |
| § *siamea* | MSag |
| *tomentosa* | See *S. multiglandulosa* |

## SEQUOIA (Taxodiaceae)

| | |
|---|---|
| *sempervirens* ♀ | CB&S CDoC CDul CGre CMCN CTrG EHul EPfP GChr IOrc LCon LPan SLon WDin WMou WNor |
| – 'Adpressa' | CDoC CMac CSli EBrP EBre EGra EHul EOrn EPla LBre LCon LLin MAsh MBal MBar MBri MGos MPla NWea SAga SBre SLim WPyg |
| – 'Prostrata' | CB&S CSli EBrP EBre EOrn EPla LBee LBre LCon LLin MAsh MBar MBri SBre |

## SEQUOIADENDRON (Taxodiaceae)

| | |
|---|---|
| *giganteum* ♀ | More than 30 suppliers |
| – 'Barabits' Requiem' | LRHS MBlu MBri SMad |
| – 'Glaucum' | CBlo CDoC LCon LPan MBlu MBri SMad |
| * – 'Glaucum Compactum' | MBri |
| – 'Hazel Smith' | MBlu |
| – 'Pendulum' | CBlo CDoC ERod LCon LPan MBlu |
| – 'Variegatum' | Last listed 1998 |

## SERAPIAS (Orchidaceae)

| | |
|---|---|
| *lingua* | CHdy LAma SBla SSpi |

## SERENOA (Arecaceae)

| | |
|---|---|
| *repens* | CRoM LPal NPal |

## SERIPHIDIUM (Asteraceae)

| | |
|---|---|
| *caerulescens* subsp. *gallicum* | EEls MAvo |
| § *canum* | EEls Iive |
| § *ferganense* | EEls |
| § *fragrans* | EEls |
| § *maritimum* ♀ | EWFC GBar GGar GPoy ILis NSti |
| – var. *maritimum* | EEls |
| § *novum* | EEls |
| § *nutans* | EEls MWat WAbe |
| § *tridentatum* | CArn MWgw |
| – subsp. *tridentatum* | EEls |
| – subsp. *wyomingense* | EEls |
| *tripartitum rupicola* | EEls |
| § *vallesiacum* ♀ | CJew EEls SAga WEas |
| *vaseyanaum* | EEls |

## SERISSA (Rubiaceae)

| | |
|---|---|
| *foetida* | See *S. japonica* |
| § *japonica* | STre |
| - *rosea* | STre |
| - 'Variegata' | CHal ECon STre |

## SERRATULA (Asteraceae)

| | |
|---|---|
| *coronata* | Last listed 1998 |
| § *seoanei* | CBos CMea CNic CPla CRDP CSev CTri EBee ECha EDAr EMan EMon LGre LHop MBri MWat SDix SIng SRms SUsu WByw WCot WHil WPat WWin |
| *shawii* | See *S. seoanei* |
| *tinctoria* | CArn CKin ELau EMan GBar MHew MSal |
| - subsp. *macrocephala* | EBee MTPN |
| ¶ *wolffii* | EBee |

## SESAMUM (Pedaliaceae)

| | |
|---|---|
| *indicum* | CArn |

## SESBANIA (Papilionaceae)

| | |
|---|---|
| *punicea* | SOWG |

## SESELI (Apiaceae)

| | |
|---|---|
| *dichotomum* | Last listed 1998 |
| *elatum* subsp. *osseum* | CFil EBee SIgm |
| *globiferum* | SIgm |
| *gummiferum* | CArn CBot CGle CSpe EWes LGre SIng SMrm WCot |
| *hippomarathrum* | CGle |
| *libanotis* | SIgm |
| *pallasii* | EBee SHut SIgm SMrm |
| ¶ *rigidum* | EBee |
| *varium* | SIgm |

## SESLERIA (Poaceae)

| | |
|---|---|
| § *albicans* | EPPr |
| § *argentea* | Last listed 1997 |
| ¶ *autumnalis* | LGre |
| *caerulea* | CCuc CSam EGar EHoe ELan EMon LNor MBel MLLN MMoz MWgw MWhi SCob SSto WCot |
| - subsp. *calcarea* | See *S. albicans* |
| *cylindrica* | See *S. argentea* |
| *glauca* | CInt EHoe MAvo MSCN NOak NPro NSti SChu WBea WPer |
| *heufleriana* | EHoe EMan EMon EPPr EPla LRHS MAvo |
| *insularis* | CMea CSWP EMon EPPr LRHS MAvo |
| *nitida* | CCuc EGar EHoe EMar EMon EPPr LRHS MAvo |
| *sadleriana* | EBee EPPr EWes |

## SETARIA (Poaceae)

| | |
|---|---|
| *palmifolia* | LHil WCot WHal WMul |
| *sphacelata* | EBee LHil |

## SETCREASEA See TRADESCANTIA

## SEVERINIA (Rutaceae)

| | |
|---|---|
| *buxifolia* | SCit |

## SHEPHERDIA (Elaeagnaceae)

| | |
|---|---|
| *argentea* | CAgr CB&S CPle EBee LEdu |
| *canadensis* | CAgr |

## SHERARDIA (Rubiaceae)

| | |
|---|---|
| *arvensis* | EWFC MSal |

## SHIBATAEA (Poaceae - Bambusoideae)

| | |
|---|---|
| *chinensis* | EPla |
| *kumasasa* | CB&S CCuc CDoC CPMA CWit EBee EHoe EPla GCal IOrc ISta LEdu LJus LNet MBal MBrN MCCP MGos MMoz MUlv MWhi SDry WBay WJun WNor |
| - *aureastriata* | EPla ISta SDry |
| *lancifolia* | EPla SDry WJun |

## SHORTIA (Diapensiaceae)

| | |
|---|---|
| *galacifolia* | IBlr |
| *soldanelloides* | IBlr SSpi WCru |
| - f. *alpina* | IBlr |
| - var. *ilicifolia* | IBlr SSpi |
| - - 'Askival' | IBlr |
| - var. *magna* | GCrs IBlr |
| *uniflora* | IBlr |
| - var. *orbicularis* 'Grandiflora' | GCrs IBlr SSpi |

## SIBBALDIA (Rosaceae)

| | |
|---|---|
| *parviflora* NS 668 | Last listed 1997 |

## SIBBALDIOPSIS (Rosaceae)

| | |
|---|---|
| § *tridentata* | NRoo |
| - 'Lemon Mac' | SIng |
| - 'Nuuk' | GAri MGos NLon SRPl |

## SIBIRAEA (Rosaceae)

| | |
|---|---|
| *altaiensis* | See *S. laevigata* |
| § *laevigata* | CFil |

## SIDA (Malvaceae)

| | |
|---|---|
| *hermaphrodita* | EMon |
| *petrophila* | Last listed 1998 |

## SIDALCEA (Malvaceae)

| | |
|---|---|
| 'Brilliant' | CM&M EBee EPfP NFai WFar WMer WMow |
| *candida* | More than 30 suppliers |
| - 'Bianca' | CBot CPea EAst EBee LFis MBel MSte WFar WMow WPer |
| 'Crimson King' | LFis MAvo WFar |
| 'Croftway Red' | CB&S ELan EWTr LFis MFir NRoo SAga SChu SCro SHel SPer WMaN WMow WSan |
| Crown hybrids | CTri |
| ¶ *cusickii* | EBee |
| 'Elsie Heugh' | More than 30 suppliers |
| *hendersonii* | EBee |
| ¶ *hickmanii* subsp. *anomala* | WLin |
| - subsp. *anomala* NNS 95462 | IDac WCot |
| ¶ *hirtipes* | EBee |
| * *integrifolia* | LGre |
| 'Interlaken' | NFla NOrc WMow |
| 'Loveliness' | CGle CRDP ELan EMan MAvo NCat NLar SAga SUsu WCot WMow |
| *malviflora* | EWTr MFir NSti SChu SRms WMow |
| ¶ - 'Alba' | WFar |
| - dark form | GMac WMow WPrP |
| 'Monarch' | NCut |
| 'Mr Lindbergh' | EBee SPer WCot WFar WMow WRus |
| 'Mrs Borrodaile' | CM&M ECGN GBuc MCLN MTis MUlv NHaw WCot WFar WMow WRus |
| 'Mrs Galloway' | LFis WFar WMow |

'Mrs T. Alderson' — WFar WMoo WMow
¶ 'My Love' — LGre LHop
**neomexicana** — EBee GCal NCat SSvw WBea WHil WMow
'Oberon' — CHan GBuc LPio SPer WEas WFar WMoo WMow
**oregana** — CSam NBid
- subsp. **spicata** — Last listed 1998
'Paramount' — Last listed 1996
'Party Girl' — CM&M EBee EBrP EBre ECot ECtt EFou EHal EOld EWTr LBre LPio MMal MPEx MTis NCat NLak NLar NOrc NPri NRoo NVic SBre SCob SHel SPlb WFar WOve WPer
¶ 'Präriebrand' — LGre
'Puck' — Last listed 1996
* **purpetta** — EWTr NChi NCut STes WBea
'Reverend Page Roberts' — CMCo LFis MMHG MRav SMrm WCot WFar WMaN WMow
'Rosaly' — EBee WShe
'Rosanna' — EWTr NCut WBea
'Rose Bouquet' — MHlr WCot
'Rose Bud' — CStr
'Rose Queen' — CGle CMGP ECha ENot ERic EWTr GChr LHop MBel MCAu MCLN MRav NFla NLon NRoo SAga SChu SPer SRms WFar WMow
'Rosy Gem' — CBlo NCat NCut WFar WMow WShe
Stark's hybrids — SRms WBea WMow
'Sussex Beauty' — CRDP EFou LFis MArl MHlr MLLN MRav NCat NGdn NPla SChu SPer WCot WFar WMow
'Sweet Joy' — EFou
'The Duchess' — LFis MAvo WFar WMow
'Twixt' — WMow
'William Smith' ♀ — CHea COtt CRDP CSam EAst EBee EBrP EBre ECha EPfP EWes LBre LFis LHop MCLN MLLN NCat NFla NGdn NHol NOrc NPla SAga SBre SLon SPer SUsu WCot WMow

## SIDERITIS (Lamiaceae)
**candicans** — Last listed 1998
**clandestina** — EBee
**glacialis** — Last listed 1998
**byssopifolia** — Last listed 1997
**macrostachys** — LHil
**scardica** — WLin
**scordioides** — SHFr
**syriaca** — CBot EBot ECha EMan EOHP SHFr SIgm
- subsp. **syriaca** — EBee NDov

## SIEVERSIA (Rosaceae)
§ **reptans** — Last listed 1997

## SILAUM (Apiaceae)
**silaus** — CKin EWFC

## SILENE (Caryophyllaceae)
**acaulis** — ESis GCHN GTou ITim LBee LFis MBro MPla MTho NMen NRoo NWCA SBla SIng SRms SSmi WAbe
§ - subsp. **acaulis** — CGra EPot GDra NCat SRms
- 'Alba' — EPot EWes GDra NHar NLan NNrd WAbe
§ - subsp. **bryoides** — Last listed 1997
- 'Correvoniana' — Last listed 1996

- subsp. **elongata** — See S. acaulis subsp. acaulis
- subsp. **exscapa** — See S. acaulis subsp. bryoides
- 'Frances' — EHyt EPot GAbr GCHN GCrs GTou IMGH ITim NHar NMen NRya NSla NWCA WAbe
- 'Francis Copeland' — ECho ELan
- 'Helen's Double' (d) — EHyt EPot MBro NNrd WAbe
* - **minima** — EPot
- 'Mount Snowdon' — CInt EBrP EBre ELan ESis EWes IMGH LBee LBre MTho NBus NHar NHol NMen NPri NRya NWCA SBre WAbe WPat
- 'Pedunculata' — See S. acaulis subsp. acaulis
- 'Plena' (d) — NBrk
¶ - 'White Rabbit' — CGra
♦ **alba** — See S. latifolia subsp. latifolia
**alpestris** — CM&M CMea ELan EPfP ESis LFis MBar MNrw MPla MTho NLon NNrd NWCA SRms WCla WFar
- 'Flore Pleno' (d) ♀ — ESis EWes LBee NLon WWin
* **andina** — Last listed 1997
**argaea** — CPBP EHyt
x **arkwrightii** — See Lychnis x arkwrightii
**armeria** — EHal EMar WHer
**asterias** — CElw CSam GBuc MBNS MBel MNrw NBrk NBro NSti STes WPer WWin
- NS 657 — NWCA
**bellidioides** — EBee
¶ **californica** — CGra
**campanula** — Last listed 1998
**caroliniana** — EHal EWTr
- subsp. **pensylvanica** — Last listed 1998
**caryophylloides** — Last listed 1997
  subsp. **echinus**
**chungtienensis** — EBee
**ciliata** — Last listed 1998
§ **compacta** — MAvo NLar WCot WEas
**conica** — EWFC
**delavayi** — Last listed 1998
¶ - ACE 2449 — EHyt
  cf. - ACE 2466 — EBee
**densiflora** HH&K 326 — CHan
**dinarica** — Last listed 1998
§ **dioica** — CArn CKin EOld EWFC EWTr MChe MHew NFai NLan NLar SRms SWat WCla WHen WHer WJek WShi
- **alba** — Last listed 1997
- 'Clifford Moor' (v) — EHoe LRHS NSti SCob SCoo WRus
- 'Compacta' — See S. dioica 'Minikin'
- 'Dorset' — Last listed 1998
§ - 'Flore Pleno' (d) — CJew EBee ECha LFis LLWP MNrw MRav MTho NBro NGdn SMrm WByw WEas WFar WHoo WPer WWin
§ - 'Graham's Delight' (v) — EMon GBri NBur WCHb WCot WHer
- 'Inane' — CNat MAvo WAlt WBea WCot WRHF
§ - 'Minikin' — CLyd ECha EMon LRHS MAvo NBrk NCat NDov WAlt WBea WCot WTin
- 'Pat Clissold' (v) — EMon
¶ - 'Pembrokeshire Pastel' (v) — WAlt
- 'Richmond' (d) — GBuc MInt MNrw
§ - 'Rosea Plena' (d) — CBre CGle CM&M EMan EMon MTho SChu SMrm WByw WCot WHer WPer
- 'Rubra Plena' — See S. dioica 'Flore Pleno'
- 'Thelma Kay' (v) — CMil CSev EMon GBuc MAvo MLLN WCHb WHer WMow WPGP

- 'Variegata' — See *S. dioica* 'Graham's Delight'
*elisabethae* — MRPP NWCA
- 'Alba' — WCla
§ *fimbriata* — CBrd CHad CHan EBee EEls ELan EPPr GCal LFis MFir MRav MWat NSti SMrm WAbb WCot WRHF
- 'Marianne' — MNrw
*fortunei* — Last listed 1996
- var. *kiruninsularis* — Last listed 1998
  B&SWJ 296
*frivaldskyana* HH&K 214 — CHan LFis
*gallica* — EWFC
¶ *bifacensis* — LFis
*bookeri* — EMar MTho NMGW NWCA
- Ingramii Group — CGra WAbe
- JCA 1855400 — CPBP
*ingramii* — CPBP MHew
*italica* — EWFC
*keiskei* — ECha NTow WPer
- var. *minor* — EWes MTho NWCA SPlb SSca WAbe WWin
§ *latifolia* subsp. *latifolia* — CArn EWFC NMir WCla WHen WHer WJek
*lerchenfeldiana* — Last listed 1997
*maritima* — See *S. uniflora*
*moorcroftiana* — Last listed 1997
*morrisonmontana* — Last listed 1997
- B&SWJ 3149 — WCru
*multifida* — See *S. fimbriata*
*nigrescens* — Last listed 1996
aff. *nigrescens* ACE 1391 — Last listed 1996
*noctiflora* — EWFC WCla
*nutans* — CArn EWFC MNrw SRms WGwy WHer
\* - var. *salmoniana* — Last listed 1998
\* - var. *smithiana* — Last listed 1998
*orientalis* — See *S. compacta*
\* *parishii* var. *viscida* — MRPP
  NNS 95-474
*parnassica* — Last listed 1997
*pendula* — LLWP
- 'Compacta' — CInt
*petersonii* — NWCA
*pusilla* — CHal CLyd CNic NMen NWCA
*regia* — Last listed 1998
*rotundifolia* — Last listed 1996
*rubra* 'Flore Pleno' — See *S. dioica* 'Flore Pleno'
*rupestris* — Last listed 1996
*saxatilis* — Last listed 1996
*schafta* ♀ — CHal ECha EMNN GCHN MBro MFir MMal MPla MWat NFla NRoo NWCA SRms WCla WFar WHoo WPer WWin
- 'Abbotswood' — See *Lychnis* x *walkeri* 'Abbotswood Rose'
- 'Brilliant' — Last listed 1996
§ - 'Shell Pink' — CInt EPot EWes LHop NWCA WAbe WThi
*sieboldii* — See *Lychnis coronata* var. *sieboldii*
sp. ACE 1320 — Last listed 1996
sp. ACE 1573 — EHyt
*suksdorfii* — EPot MBro WHoo WPyg
\* *surortii* — WPer
*tenuis* ACE 2429 — GBuc
*thessalonica* — EBee EHyt MBro MCCP NCut SBea
*undulata* — Last listed 1998
§ *uniflora* — EGoo ELan EMNN EMar EWFC GCHN MFir MWat NBro NLon NOak NWCA NWoo SBod SRms WCla WHen WHer

- 'Alba Plena' — See *S. uniflora* 'Robin Whitebreast'
§ - 'Druett's Variegated' — More than 30 suppliers
- 'Flore Pleno' — See *S. uniflora* 'Robin Whitebreast'
§ - 'Robin Whitebreast' (d) — CPBP CVer ECha ECtt ELan GCal MBNS MBar MTho MWat MWgw NBid NBro NHol NOak SRPl SRms WCot WEas WHoo WMoo WOve WPer WPyg WWin
- 'Rosea' — CGle CNic ECtt EMNN EMar MRav SMrm SSca SUsu WCot WPer
- 'Silver Lining' (v) — ELan GBuc
- 'Variegata' — See *S. uniflora* 'Druett's Variegated'
- Weisskehlchen — See *S. uniflora* 'Robin Whitebreast'
- 'White Bells' — CMea CTri EBee WBea WHoo WPyg WSHC
*vallesia* — WPer WRHF
¶ *virginica* — EHal
§ *vulgaris* — CKin EWFC EWTr MChe NLan NMir
- subsp. *alpina* — See *S. uniflora* subsp. *prostrata*
- subsp. *maritima* — See *S. uniflora*
- - 'Flore Pleno' (d) — Last listed 1998
*wallichiana* — See *S. vulgaris*
'Wisley Pink' — CHal NMen
*wrightii* — Last listed 1996
§ *zawadskii* — EHal GBuc MBNS MNrw SSca WPer

## SILPHIUM (Asteraceae)
*laciniatum* — CArn EBee ELau SMad WCot
*perfoliatum* — CArn GPoy NSti WCot WFar
¶ *terebinthinaceum* — LGre SMad WCot
*trifoliatum* — Last listed 1996

## SILYBUM (Asteraceae)
*eburneum* — Last listed 1996
*marianum* — CArn CGle CInt ECoo EFer ELan EMan EMar EPar EWFC GPoy LHol MSal MWgw NArg NFai NFla SIde SLon SRCN SSoC WCer WEas WHer WHil WOak WWye
¶ - 'Adriana' — NArg
¶ - white form — EMar

## SIMMONDSIA (Simmondsiaceae)
*chinensis* — ELau MSal

## SINACALIA (Asteraceae)
§ *tangutica* — CGle CHan CRow EBee ELan EMan GGar MBNS MBal MHlr MNrw NBro NDea NSti SDix SMrm WAbb WCot WCru WFar WHil

## SINARUNDINARIA (Poaceae - Bambusoideae)
*anceps* — See *Yushania anceps*
*jaunsarensis* — See *Yushania anceps*
*maling* — See *Yushania maling*
*murieliae* — See *Fargesia murieliae*
*nitida* — See *Fargesia nitida*

## SINNINGIA (Gesneriaceae)
'Arion' — NMos
'Blanche de Méru' — NMos SDeJ
'Blue Wonder' — MBri
'Boonwood Yellow Bird' — NMos
*canescens* ♀ — CHal
§ *cardinalis* — CHal EBak MLan WDib
§ x *cardosa* — MBri

| | |
|---|---|
| 'Cherry Belle' | NMos |
| 'Diego Rose' | MBri |
| 'Duchess of York' | CSut |
| 'Duke of York' | CSut |
| 'Etoile de Feu' | LAma MBri NMos |
| 'Hollywood' | LAma NMos SDeJ |
| 'Island Sunset' | NMos |
| 'Kaiser Friedrich' | LAma MBri NMos |
| 'Kaiser Wilhelm' | LAma MBri NMos |
| 'Medusa' | NMos |
| 'Mont Blanc' | CSut LAma MBri NMos SDeJ |
| 'Pegasus' | NMos |
| 'Princess Elizabeth' | SDeJ |
| 'Red Tiger' | CSut |
| 'Reine Wilhelmine' | SDeJ |
| 'Royal Crimson' | CSut |
| Royal Pink Group | CSut |
| 'Royal Tiger' | CSut |
| Tigrina Group | NMos SDeJ |
| *tubiflora* | Last listed 1998 |
| 'Violacea' | MBri NMos |
| 'Waterloo' | NMos |

## SINOBAMBUSA (Poaceae - Bambusoideae)
| | |
|---|---|
| *intermedia* | EPla LJus |
| *orthotropa* | CFil EPla WPGP |
| *rubroligula* | CFil EPla WPGP |
| *tootsik* | EPla SDry WJun |
| § - f. *albostriata* | SDry |
| - 'Variegata' | See *S. tootsik* f. *albostriata* |

## SINOCALYCANTHUS (Calycanthaceae)
| | |
|---|---|
| *chinensis* | CB&S CMCN CPMA EBee EPfP LNet LRHS SMad SRPl SSpi WWoo |

## SINOFRANCHETIA (Lardizabalaceae)
| | |
|---|---|
| *chinensis* | CPlN WCru |

## SINOJACKIA (Styracaceae)
| | |
|---|---|
| *xylocarpa* | EPfP MBel |

## SINOWILSONIA (Hamamelidaceae)
| | |
|---|---|
| *henryi* | CB&S CMCN |

## SISYMBRIUM (Brassicaceae)
| | |
|---|---|
| § *luteum* | EWTr WHer |

## SISYRINCHIUM ✿ (Iridaceae)
| | |
|---|---|
| x *anceps* | See *S. angustifolium* |
| § *angustifolium* | CHan CMHG EBot EBur ECha ELan EWTr GBin GCHN MBNS MBal MBar MBel MSal MWat NDea NFla NNrd SRms SSmi WCla WEas WPer WWeb WWin |
| - *album* | CInt GMaP MSCN NCut NLar WLin WRHF |
| § *arenarium* | CPBP EBur EHyt EPot MDHE NMen WBea |
| *atlanticum* | CPea ESis MDHE NBro SUsu WPer |
| *bellum* hort. | See *S. idahoense* var. *bellum* |
| *bermudianum* | See *S. angustifolium* |
| - 'Album' | See *S. graminoides* 'Album' |
| I *birameun* | See *S. graminoides* |
| 'Biscutella' | CHad CHan CInt CLyd CMea CPlt EAst EBur ECtt ELan LHop NDea NMen SChu SIng SLod SOkh SPlb SSmi SUsu WCla WEas WGwG WHal WLRN WMoo |
| * 'Blue Ice' | CCuc CInt CMea CPBP CSpe CVer EBur EGar LNor MBro MDHE NCat NHol WAbb WAbe WBro WFar WHal WHoo WPat WPer WPyg |

| | |
|---|---|
| *boreale* | See *S. californicum* |
| *brachypus* | See *S. californicum* Brachypus Group |
| *brevipes* F&W 7946 | Last listed 1998 |
| 'Californian Skies' | More than 30 suppliers |
| § *californicum* | CBen CInt CLon EBur EHon ESis LPBA MBar MFir MSta MWat NBro NMen NNrd SSmi SWyc WCla WPer WWin WWye |
| § - Brachypus Group | CBro CMea EAst ECtt EPot GCHN GTou LPVe MBNS MNrw MOne NDea NLar NMen NWes SPlb SWat WBea WBrE WCer WEas WElm WMoo WOak |
| § *chilense* | SIng |
| *coeleste* | EBur MDHE |
| *coeruleum* | See *Gelasine coerulea* |
| *commutatum* | CInt CMil EDAr EHyt ERos GBuc MBNS MNrw MWgw SRot WBro WElm WWye |
| *convolutum* | NDov |
| *cuspidatum* | See *S. arenarium* |
| *demissum* | CLyd CNic EBur |
| *depauperatum* | CNic EBur EMar ESis NWCA WHer WPer |
| ¶ 'Devon Blue' | WFar |
| 'Devon Skies' | CHid CInt CM&M CMHG EBur MNrw WAbe WFar WSan WWin |
| *douglasii* | See *Olsynium douglasii* |
| 'Dragon's Eye' | EBee SUsu |
| 'E.K. Balls' | CHea CInt CVer EAst EBur ELan EPla LBee LNor MBro MTho MWgw NBro NCat NFai NHol NMen NRya SBla SSmi SSvw SUsu WAbe WBea WCla WHen WMoo WPat WWin |
| *elmeri* | EBur |
| *filifolium* | See *Olsynium filifolium* |
| § *graminoides* | EBur NBro WPer |
| § - 'Album' | EBur GAri NBro WCla WPer |
| - sterile form | LBee |
| *grandiflorum* | See *Olsynium douglasii* |
| 'Hemswell Sky' | CLyd EBur MDHE MMil NOla WBea WWye |
| 'Iceberg' | NCat SDys SUsu SWas |
| *idahoense* | CCuc NRoo SRms |
| § - 'Album' | CGle CHan CPlt CVer EBur ECha EHyt ELan EPot ERos GTou LBee MNrw MTho MWat NDea NEgg NHol NLon NMen SBla SSmi SUsu WAbe WCla WFar WPat WPer WWin WWye |
| § - var. *bellum* | CBro CMHG EBrP EBre EBur ECha ELan EPfP GCHN GTou LBee LBre LEur MBNS MBal MNrw NCut NMen NRya NWCA SBre SRms WBea WCla WHen WPat WPer |
| - - 'Rocky Point' | EBur LBee WPat WWeb |
| - blue | EGra ELan |
| *iridifolium* | See *S. micranthum* |
| *junceum* | See *Olsynium junceum* |
| *littorale* | EBur NLar WCla WPer |
| *macrocarpon* ♀ | CGra CInt CPBP EBur EHyt EPot ERos ESis GTou ITim LBee NMen NWCA SSpi SUsu WCla WHal WHoo WPer WWye |
| 'Marie' | EBur MDHE |
| 'Marion' | CMil NCat NHar SAsh SBla SUsu SWas WWye |
| 'May Snow' | See *S. idahoense* 'Album' |
| § *micranthum* | CBro EBur ECGP EWes |
| *montanum* | EBur ERos WThi |
| - var. *crebrum* | CInt |

| | |
|---|---|
| – var. *montanum* | Last listed 1998 |
| 'Mrs Spivey' | EBur ECtt EMNN ESis MBal MBar |
| | NBro NMen NOak NRoo SIng |
| | WCla WElm WRHF |
| *mucronatum* | EBur |
| *narcissiflorum* | Last listed 1996 |
| 'North Star' | See *S.* 'Pole Star' |
| *nudicaule* | EBur |
| – x *montanum* | CFee CMHG EBur EMNN ESis |
| | ITim MDHE MNrw NHar NHol |
| | NNrd NRya SRot SUsu WAbe |
| | WPer |
| *patagonicum* | EBur ERos GBuc NCat NNrd WCla |
| | WLRN WPer |
| *pearcei* | Last listed 1998 |
| § 'Pole Star' | CFee CInt CLyd CNic CSpe EBur |
| | EMar GTou IBlr MFir NBro NHar |
| | NHol NMen SRPl SSmi SSvw WHal |
| | WPer |
| 'Quaint and Queer' | CHea CInt CM&M CMil EBur |
| | ECha EMar ERav LNor MBel MBrN |
| | MCLN MRav MTho NBro NRoo |
| | SSmi WAbe WBea WLin WPer |
| | WRus WWhi WWin |
| * 'Raspberry' | EBur NHol WAbe |
| *scabrum* | See *S. chilense* |
| 'Sisland Blue' | EBur EHic EWes MDHE |
| sp. from Tierra del Fuego | CRow MAvo |
| 'Stars and Stripes' | LPBA |
| § *striatum* | More than 30 suppliers |
| § – 'Aunt May' (v) | More than 30 suppliers |
| – 'Rushfields' | Last listed 1996 |
| – 'Variegatum' | See *S. striatum* 'Aunt May' |

## SIUM (Apiaceae)

| | |
|---|---|
| *sisarum* | ELau GBar GPoy LHol MHer MSal |
| | SIde WGwy WOak |

## SKIMMIA ✿ (Rutaceae)

| | |
|---|---|
| *anquetilia* | MBar WBod WWat |
| x *confusa* | EHol |
| ¶ – 'Isabella' | SPer |
| – 'Kew Green' (m) ♀ | CB&S CGre CHan CMHG CTrG |
| | EBee ELan ENot EPfP EPla IOrc |
| | LHop MAsh MBal MBar MBri |
| | MGos MRav NHol SAga SCob |
| | SMac SPer SPla SReu SSta WBod |
| | WFoF WPyg WWat |
| *dulcamara* | Last listed 1998 |
| § *japonica* | CLan CMHG CTrw EBrP EBre |
| | EMil ENot GChr GQui LBre MGos |
| | SBre SCob SRPl SReu SSta STre |
| | WFar WGwG WHCG WICI |
| – (f) | CTrG CTri ELan SRms |
| – 'Alba' | See *S. japonica* 'Wakehurst White' |
| ¶ – B&SWJ 5053 | WCru |
| – 'Bowles' Dwarf Female' (f) | CHig CMHG EBee EMon EPla |
| | MBar MBri MPla MRav NHol SCob |
| | SPer WWat |
| – 'Bowles' Dwarf Male' (m) | CMHG EBee EPla MAsh MBar |
| | MBri MPla SBid SCob SPer WWat |
| * – 'Bronze Beauty' | MBri SBid |
| – 'Bronze Knight' (m) | EBee EHic ENot EPla GBin MAsh |
| | MBar MBri MGos MRav NHol SEas |
| | SPan SSta WWat |
| – 'Cecilia Brown' (f) | EPla WWat |
| ¶ – 'Chameleon' | EBee |
| – 'Claries Repens' | EPla MBri SPer |
| – var. *distincte-venulosa* | B&SWJ 3544 WCru |
| – 'Emerald King' | MAsh MBar MBri WBcn |
| N – 'Foremanii' | See *S. japonica* 'Veitchii' |

| | |
|---|---|
| – 'Fragrans' (m) ♀ | CDoC CHig CSam CTrw EBee |
| | ENot EPla IOrc MAsh MBal MBar |
| | MBel MGos MRav NHol SCob |
| | SEas SPer SReu SSta WBod WFar |
| | WWat |
| – 'Fragrantissima' (m) | EPla LRHS MBri WBod |
| – 'Fructu Albo' | See *S. japonica* 'Wakehurst White' |
| – 'Highgrove Redbud' (f) | EBee MBar MBri MGos SSta WBod |
| – 'Keessen' | Last listed 1998 |
| – 'Kew White' (f) | CB&S CBlo CDoC CSam EBrP |
| | EBre EPfP LBre MBal MBel MBri |
| | MGos NHol SBre SLon WHCG |
| | WLRN WWat |
| ¶ – 'Luwain' | NPro |
| – 'Nymans' (f) ♀ | CDoC CEnd CSam EBee EBrP |
| | EBre ELan IOrc LBre MAsh MBal |
| | MBar MBri MRav NHed NHol |
| | SBre SCob SPer SPla SReu SSpi |
| | SSta WStI WWal WWat WWeb |
| – 'Oblata' | MBar MGos |
| – 'Obovata' (f) | EPla |
| – 'Red Princess' (f) | EPla LRHS MBri SCob |
| * – 'Red Riding Hood' | CLyn MBri NHol SPan |
| – 'Redruth' (f) | CB&S CDoC CLan EBee EPla IOrc |
| | MBal MBar MBri MGos NHol SSta |
| | WBcn |
| § – subsp. *reevesiana* | CDoC CPMA CSam EBee EBrP |
| | EBre GQui IOrc ISea LBre MAsh |
| | MBal MBar MBri MGos MPla |
| | MRav NHol SBre SCob SPer SReu |
| | SSpi SSta WBod WDin WStI WWal |
| – – B&SWJ 3763 | WCru |
| – – B&SWJ 3895 | WCru |
| – – 'Chilan Choice' | SAga SPer SSta |
| ¶ – – ETOT 182 | WPGP |
| – – 'Robert Fortune' ♀ | MBar SCoo WWat |
| § – Rogersii Group | CTri IOrc MBal MBar MWat |
| – – 'Dunwood' | MBar |
| – – 'George Gardner' | MBar |
| – – 'Helen Goodall' (f) | MBar |
| § – – 'Nana Femina' (f) | Last listed 1998 |
| § – – 'Nana Mascula' (m) | CTri |
| – – 'Rockyfield Green' | MBar |
| – – 'Snow Dwarf' (m) | EPla LRHS MBar MBri |
| – 'Rubella' (m) ♀ | More than 30 suppliers |
| – 'Rubinetta' (m) | EBee IOrc MAsh MBar MGos |
| | NHol SSto WWeb |
| – 'Ruby Dome' (m) | MBar MBri WBcn WWat |
| – 'Ruby King' | EHic MBal MBar MBri MGos NHol |
| | SSta WBod WStI |
| – 'Scarlet Dwarf' (f) | MBar MBri |
| – 'Stoneham Red' | Last listed 1996 |
| – 'Tansley Gem' (f) | ELan EPfP MAsh MBar MBri |
| – 'Thelma King' | LRHS MBri |
| § – 'Veitchii' (f) | CDoC CTri EBee ENot EPla GRei |
| | MAsh MBar MGos MRav NBee |
| | NHol SCob SEND SPer WBod |
| | WDin WStI WWal WWeb |
| § – 'Wakehurst White' (f) | CMHG CPle CTrw MBar MBri |
| | MPla MRav SAga SLon SPer SPla |
| | SReu SSpi SSta WWat |
| – 'White Gerpa' | MGos |
| – 'Winifred Crook' (f) | EPla MBar WWat |
| – 'Winnie's Dwarf' | CHig |
| – 'Wisley Female' (f) | CDoC CTri ECtt EHic EPla NHol |
| | SEas SPan WWat |
| *laureola* | CDoC CSam EBee ECot EHic |
| | ENot MAsh MBal MRav NHol |
| | SCob SRms WFar WHCG WSHC |
| ¶ – 'Fragrant Cloud' | SCob |
| – HWJCM 544 | WCru |
| – T 132 | WWat |

'Olympic Flame'                    NHol NPro
*reevesiana*                       See *S. japonica* subsp. *reevesiana*
*rogersii*                         See *S. japonica* Rogersii Group

## SMELOWSKIA (Brassicaceae)
**calycina**                       Last listed 1998
- var. **americana**              Last listed 1996
- NNS 94-137                       MRPP

## SMILACINA (Convallariaceae)
**atropurpurea**                   WCru
**formosana** B&SWJ 349            WCru
**forrestii**                      WCru
**fusca**                          WCru
¶ **henryi**                       WCru
**japonica**                       WCru
**paniculata**                     WCru
**racemosa** ♀                     More than 30 suppliers
- var. **amplexicaulis**          GCal
- dwarf form                       Last listed 1997
- 'Emily Moody'                    SSpi
**stellata**                       CAvo CRDP CRow CVer EBee
                                   EMou EPar EPla LHop SIng SLod
                                   SUsu WCot WCru
- BH 319                           MDun

## SMILAX (Smilacaceae)
**asparagoides** 'Nanus'           See *Asparagus asparagoides*
                                   'Myrtifolius'
**aspera**                         CFil CPlN EPla WPGP
**discotis**                       CB&S CPlN CPle
**excelsa**                        CPlN
**glaucophylla** B&SWJ 2971        WCru
**rotundifolia**                   CPlN LEdu
**sagittifolia**                   CPlN
**sieboldii**                      CPlN MRav
- B&SWJ 744                        WCru

## SMITHIANTHA (Gesneriaceae)
'Calder Girl'                      NMos
'Carmel'                           NMos
'Carmello'                         NMos
'Castle Croft'                     NMos
'Cinna Barino'                     NMos
'Corney Fell'                      NMos
'Dent View'                        NMos
'Ehenside Lady'                    NMos
'Harecroft'                        NMos
'Little One'                       NMos WDib
'Matins'                           NMos
'Meadowcroft'                      NMos
'Multiflora'                       NMos
'New Yellow Hybrid'                NMos
'Orange King'                      NMos
'Orangeade'                        NMos
'Pink Lady'                        NMos
'Sandybank'                        NMos
'Santa Clara'                      NMos
'Starling Castle'                  NMos
'Summer Sunshine'                  NMos
'Vespers'                          NMos
'Zebrina Hybrid'                   NMos

## x SMITHICODONIA (Gesneriaceae)
§ 'Cerulean Mink'                  NMos

## SMYRNIUM (Apiaceae)
**olusatrum**                      CArn CGle CSev EBot GBar LHol
                                   MChe MHer MHew MSal SIde
                                   SWat WCer WHbs WHer WOak
                                   WWye
**perfoliatum**                    CGle CRDP EBee ELan EMar EOrc
                                   EPar GBuc MFir NSti WCot

## SOCRATEA (Arecaceae)
**montana**                        LPal

## SOLANDRA (Solanaceae)
**grandiflora**                    CPlN ERea WMul
**hartwegii**                      See *S. maxima*
**longiflora**                     ERea
§ **maxima**                       CB&S ERea LChe WMul

## SOLANUM (Solanaceae)
**aviculare** G.Forst             ERea WCot
* **conchifolium**                 LHil WSPU
**crispum**                        CHan EHol ELan NEgg WDin WStI
- 'Autumnale'                      See *S. crispum* 'Glasnevin'
§ - 'Glasnevin' ♀                  More than 30 suppliers
- 'Variegatum'                     CCHP MPla
**dulcamara**                      CArn EWFC GPoy
- 'Hullavington' (v)               CNat
- 'Variegatum'                     CB&S CMac CTrw EBee EHoe
                                   ELan GOrc IBlr IOrc MAsh MBNS
                                   MBal MBri NEgg NLon NSti SBra
                                   SLon SRms WCot WEas WWeb
¶ 'Gentianoides'                   LHil
**jasminoides**                    CB&S CPlN EBee EPfP LPan NSti
                                   SBra SRms WDin WSHC
- 'Album' ♀                        More than 30 suppliers
- 'Album Variegatum'               EAst ELan EPPr EPfP GQui LHop
                                   MBNS SBra WCot WKif WSHC
* - 'Aureovariegatum'              EBee EPfP SPer SPla
**laciniatum**                     CArn CDoC CGle CInt CLTr CSev
                                   ERea EWes IBlr LHil LHop MBlu
                                   MHar MLLN SAPC SArc SSoC
                                   SVen SYvo WCot WHer
**linearifolium**                  Last listed 1998
**mauritianum**                    SYvo
**muricatum** (F)                  ECon
- 'Lima' (F)                       Last listed 1998
- 'Otavalo' (F)                    Last listed 1998
- 'Quito' (F)                      Last listed 1998
**pseudocapsicum**                 MBri
- 'Ballon'                         MBri
- 'Thurino'                        Last listed 1996
**quitoense** (F)                  LBlo MPEx WMul
* **rantonnetii** 'Variegatum'     ECon
§ -                                CMdw CPle ELan ERea LBlm LHil
                                   LHop LIck MBEx SDix SMrm
                                   SOWG WKif
'Royal Robe'                       CB&S CRHN GQui
**seaforthianum**                  CPlN ECon SOWG
**sessiliflorum** (F)              LBlo
**sisymbriifolium**                CPLG CSev WKif
**wendlandii**                     CB&S CPlN ERea SYvo

## SOLDANELLA (Primulaceae)
**alpina**                         EBee ELan EWTr GTou MBal
                                   MRav MTho MWat NHar NHol
                                   NMen NWCA SBla SIng SRms
                                   WAbe WLin
**austriaca**                      GCrs
**carpatica** ♀                    GTou MBal NCat NNrd NRya
                                   NTow WAbe
- 'Alba'                           EDAr NHar SBla SWas WAbe
**cyanaster**                      EHyt EPot MBal NBir NRya WAbe
**dimoniei**                       CFee EPot ITim NMen SBla WAbe
§ **hungarica**                    CLyd MBal MTho NWCA WAbe
                                   WLin
**minima**                         CLyd NBro NHar NHed NSla SBla
                                   WAbe
- 'Alba'                           Last listed 1998
**montana**                        CLAP CVer GCrs GTou IMGH
                                   MTho NMen NNrd WAbe WRHF
                                   WRha
◆ - subsp. **bungarica**           See *S. hungarica*

| | |
|---|---|
| *pindicola* | EHyt EWes LBee MBal MBro |
| | MOne NHar NHol NMen NNrd |
| | NWCA SIng SSmi WAbe |
| *pusilla* | CNic GDra ITim NRya NSla WAbe |
| - *alba* | Last listed 1996 |
| *villosa* | CLAP CRDP CTri EBee MBal |
| | MTho NHar NNrd NRya NSla |
| | NTow WAbe WFar WRHF WRus |

## SOLEIROLIA (Urticaceae)

| | |
|---|---|
| *soleirolii* | CHal EPot LPBA MBri MCCP SHFr |
| | SIng STre WHer WMow WOak |
| - 'Argentea' | See *S. soleirolii* 'Variegata' |
| § - 'Aurea' | CHal EPot STre WOak |
| - 'Golden Queen' | See *S. soleirolii* 'Aurea' |
| - 'Silver Queen' | See *S. soleirolii* 'Variegata' |
| § - 'Variegata' | CHal WOak |

## SOLENANTHUS (Boraginaceae)

| | |
|---|---|
| ¶ *scardicus* | EBee |

## SOLENOMELUS (Iridaceae)

| | |
|---|---|
| *chilensis* | See *S. pedunculatus* |
| *lechleri* | Last listed 1996 |
| § *pedunculatus* | CFee |
| *segethii* | EBee |
| *sisyrinchium* | Last listed 1998 |
| sp. RB 94117 | Last listed 1997 |

## SOLENOPSIS (Campanulaceae)

| | |
|---|---|
| *axillaris* | See *Laurentia axillaris* |
| - *alba* | CLTr LIck |
| - pink | LIck |
| * 'Fairy Carpet' | Last listed 1998 |
| *fluviatilis* | CLTr ECou WCru |
| sp. white | Last listed 1996 |

## SOLENOSTEMON (Lamiaceae)

| | |
|---|---|
| ¶ 'Annie' | MBEx |
| *aromaticus* | CHal CInt NHor |
| 'Autumn' | CHal MBEx NHor |
| ¶ 'Barnum' | MBEx |
| 'Beauty' (v) | CHal MBEx NHor |
| 'Beauty of Lyons' | MBEx NHor |
| 'Beckwith's Gem' | CHal NHor |
| 'Bizarre Croton' | MBEx NHor |
| ¶ 'Black Dragon' | NHor |
| 'Black Prince' | CHal MBEx NHor WDib |
| 'Blackheart' | MBEx NHor |
| ¶ 'Brightness' (v) | NHor |
| 'Brilliant' (v) | MBEx NHor WDib |
| 'Bronze Gloriosus' | MBEx NHor |
| 'Buttercup' | NHor WDib |
| 'Buttermilk' (v) ♀ | CHal MBEx NHor |
| 'Carnival' (v) | CHal MBEx NHor |
| ¶ 'Carousel' | MBEx |
| 'Chamaeleon' (v) | MBEx NHor WDib |
| ¶ 'City of Liverpool' | NHor |
| ¶ 'Copper Sprite' | NHor |
| ¶ 'Coppersmith' | NHor |
| 'Cream Pennant' (v) | MBEx |
| 'Crimson Ruffles' (v) ♀ | CHal MBEx NHor WDib |
| 'Crimson Velvet' | CHal NHor |
| ¶ 'Crinkly Bottom' | NHor |
| 'Dairy Maid' (v) | MBEx NHor |
| 'Dazzler' (v) | CHal MBEx NHor |
| 'Display' | CHal MBEx NHor |
| ¶ 'Dolly' | MBEx |
| ¶ 'Dracula' | NHor |
| 'Etna' (v) | CHal NHor |
| 'Firebrand' (v) ♀ | CHal MBEx NHor |
| 'Firedance' | MBEx NHor |

| | |
|---|---|
| 'Freckles' (v) | CHal MBEx NHor |
| 'Funfair' (v) | CHal MBEx NHor |
| 'Gloriosus' | CHal MBEx NHor |
| 'Glory of Luxembourg' (v) ♀ | CHal MBEx NHor |
| 'Goldie' | MBEx NHor |
| ¶ 'Harvest Time' | NHor |
| * 'Holly' (v) | MBEx |
| 'Inky Fingers' (v) | MBEx NHor |
| 'Jean' (v) | MBEx |
| 'Jean Falmouth' | Last listed 1996 |
| 'Joseph's Coat' (v) | MBEx NHor |
| 'Juliet Quartermain' | MBEx NHor WDib |
| 'Jupiter' | CHal NHor |
| 'Kentish Fire' | MBEx NHor |
| 'Kiwi Fern' (v) | CHal CInt MBEx NHor WDib |
| 'Klondike' | CHal MBEx NHor |
| 'Laing's Croton' (v) | CHal MBEx NHor |
| 'Lemon Dash' | MBEx |
| 'Lemondrop' | CHal NHor |
| 'Leopard' (v) | MBEx NHor |
| 'Lord Falmouth' ♀ | CHal MBEx NHor WDib |
| 'Luminous' | MBEx NHor |
| 'Melody' | MBEx NHor |
| ¶ 'Midas' | NHor |
| 'Mission Gem' (v) | CHal MBEx NHor |
| 'Mrs Pilkington' (v) | MBEx NHor |
| ¶ 'Muriel Pedley' | NHor |
| 'Nettie' (v) | MBEx NHor |
| 'Ottoman' | CHal NHor |
| 'Paisley Shawl' (v) ♀ | CHal MBEx NHor WDib |
| *pentheri* | CHal |
| 'Percy Roots' | MBEx |
| 'Petunia Gem' | Last listed 1997 |
| ¶ 'Phantom' | MBEx |
| 'Picturatus' (v) ♀ | CHal MBEx NHor WDib |
| 'Pineapple Beauty' (v) ♀ | CHal MBEx WDib |
| 'Pineapplette' ♀ | CHal MBEx NHor WDib |
| ¶ 'Pink Shawl' | NHor |
| 'Pink Showers' | MBEx |
| 'Primrose Cloud' | MBEx NHor |
| 'Primrose Spray' (v) | MBEx |
| ¶ 'Purple Prowes' | NHor |
| 'Raspberry Ripple' | NHor |
| 'Red Croton' | MBEx |
| 'Red Heart' | MBEx |
| 'Red Mars' | MBEx WDib |
| 'Red Nettie' (v) | MBEx NHor |
| ¶ 'Red Stinger' | NHor |
| 'Red Velvet' | MBEx NHor |
| 'Rose Blush' (v) | CHal NHor WDib |
| 'Rosie' | MBEx NHor |
| ¶ 'Roy Pedley' | NHor |
| 'Royal Scot' (v) ♀ | CHal MBEx NHor WDib |
| 'Salmon Plumes' (v) | CHal MBEx NHor |
| ¶ 'Saturn' | NHor |
| 'Scarlet Ribbons' | CHal MBEx |
| *scutellarioides* | MBri |
| 'Speckles' | NHor |
| 'Spire' | MBEx NHor |
| 'Strawberry Blush' | Last listed 1998 |
| 'Surprise' | MBEx |
| *thyrsoideus* | See *Plectranthus thyrsoideus* |
| 'Treales' (v) | CHal MBEx NHor |
| 'Vesuvius' | CHal MBEx NHor |
| 'Walter Turner' (v) ♀ | CHal MBEx NHor WDib |
| 'White Gem' (v) | MBEx |
| 'White Pheasant' (v) | MBEx |
| 'Winsome' (v) | CHal CInt MBEx NHor WDib |
| 'Winter Sun' (v) | CHal MBEx NHor |
| 'Wisley Flame' | MBEx NHor |
| 'Wisley Tapestry' (v) ♀ | MBEx NHor WDib |

'Yellow Croton' — MBEx

## SOLIDAGO (Asteraceae)

| | |
|---|---|
| *altissima* | See *S. canadensis* var. *scabra* |
| Babygold | See *S.* 'Goldkind' |
| *brachystachys* | See *S. cutleri* |
| *caesia* | EBee ECha EGar EMan EMon EWes LRHS WCot |
| *canadensis* | CTri ELan NCut SMac SPlb WByw WFar WHer |
| 'Cloth of Gold' | CB&S COtt GChr MBri NPro NSti WCot WLRN WOld WOve |
| § 'Crown of Rays' | CLyd EBrP EBre ECtt EFou LBre MArl MRav NArg SBre WFar WWin |
| § *cutleri* | CLyd CNic EBee ELan EMon MBar MTho MWat NHol NNrd SIng SPlb SRms WHoo WPat WPer WPyg WWin |
| - *nana* | EPPr EWes |
| 'Early Bird' | EFou |
| 'Early Sunrise' | EFou |
| § *flexicaulis* | GMaP NLon |
| ¶ - 'All Gold' | WCot |
| § - 'Variegata' | CM&M EBee EBrP EBre ECoo EGar ELan EMan EMar EMon ERav GBin LBre LFis LHop MHar NLar NSti SBre SEas SMad SUsu WCot WHer |
| ¶ 'Gardone' | WFar |
| *gigantea* | ECGN EMon EWTr |
| *glomerata* | CHan WPer |
| Golden Baby | See *S.* 'Goldkind' |
| § 'Golden Dwarf' | CDoC SLon |
| 'Golden Falls' | Last listed 1996 |
| 'Golden Fleece' | See *S. sphacelata* 'Golden Fleece' |
| 'Golden Rays' | See *S.* 'Goldstrahl' |
| 'Golden Shower' | CSam MWat |
| 'Golden Thumb' | See *S.* 'Queenie' |
| 'Golden Wings' | CBre MWat |
| 'Goldenmosa' ♀ | EBrP EBre ECGN EHal EMan ENot EPfP GMaP LBre MBel MRav MWat SBre SChu SPer WCot |
| 'Goldilocks' | NPri SRms |
| § 'Goldkind' | CLTr CM&M CTri ECtt EGar EMan ESis GAbr GChr LNor MBri MFir MMal NArg NCut NFai NOak NOrc SCob SPla WBea WByw WRHF |
| § 'Goldstrahl' | WLRN |
| Goldzwerg | See *S.* 'Golden Dwarf' |
| *graminifolia* | EMon |
| ¶ *hispida* | EMon |
| *hybrida* | See x *Solidaster luteus* |
| *latifolia* | See *S. flexicaulis* |
| 'Laurin' | EPfP NFai NHol WHoo WPyg WTin |
| 'Ledsham' | CMGP EMFP MMil WLRN |
| 'Lemore' | See x *Solidaster luteus* 'Lemore' |
| 'Lesden' | Last listed 1996 |
| * *leuvalis* | CStr |
| 'Loddon' | Last listed 1996 |
| *microcephala* | Last listed 1998 |
| 'Mimosa' | Last listed 1996 |
| *multiradiata* | ESis |
| - var. *scopulorum* | Last listed 1996 |
| *odora* | MSal |
| * 'Peter Pan' | Last listed 1998 |
| § 'Queenie' | CHan CPea EBee ECha ELan ESis GCHN MCLN MWat NPro NVic SEas SLon SPer SRms WGwG WHal WLRN |

| | |
|---|---|
| *randii* | Last listed 1998 |
| *rigida* | MRav WCot |
| - subsp. *humilis* | EBee |
| - JLS 88002WI | EMon LFis |
| ¶ *rugosa* | ECha LGre MWgw |
| ¶ - var. *aspera* | EMon |
| - 'Fireworks' | CBre CStr EFou GAri NCat SUsu WCot WOve |
| *sempervirens* | CBlo EBrP EBre EMon LBre SBre WCot |
| *shortii* | NSti |
| ¶ *simplex* var. *nana* | WPer |
| 'Spätgold' | EFou |
| § *sphacelata* 'Golden Fleece' | EBee WLRN WThi WWoo |
| Strahlenkrone | See *S.* 'Crown of Rays' |
| 'Tom Thumb' | EGle MRav SRms WEas WRHF |
| *virgaurea* | CArn CBod CKin EWFC GPoy IIve LHol SIde WHer WJek WPer WSel WWye |
| - subsp. *alpestris* var. *minutissima* | MTPN NHol WPat |
| - var. *cambrica* | See *S. virgaurea* var. *minuta* |
| § - var. *minuta* | GAri WCla |
| - pale yellow | Last listed 1996 |
| - 'Praecox' | CM&M NHol WLRN |
| § - 'Variegata' | EHoe EPla NPro WAlt WLin WOld |
| *vulgaris* 'Variegata' | See *S. virgaurea* 'Variegata' |

## x SOLIDASTER (Asteraceae)

| | |
|---|---|
| *hybridus* | See x *S. luteus* |
| § *luteus* | CHan CMil CTri EFou EWTr GBri MBri NSti SPla SRms WEas WHal WHil WOld |
| § - 'Lemore' ♀ | EBee EBrP EBre ECGN ECha EFou ELan EMan EMon LBre LFis MCLN MCli MRav MWat NBus NSti NVic SBre SEas SPer WCot WFar WMow |
| 'Super' | EFou LGre WCot |

## SOLLYA (Pittosporaceae)

| | |
|---|---|
| *fusiformis* | See *S. heterophylla* |
| § *heterophylla* ♀ | CAbb CB&S CGre CMac CPlN CPle CRHN CSpe EBee EBrP EBre ECou EOrc ERea IOrc LBlm LBre LGre LHop MBEx NSti SBra SBre SOWG SSoC SSta SUsu WHar WOld WSHC |
| - 'Alba' | CB&S LGre |
| - mauve | ECou |
| - pink | CPIN |
| - 'Pink Charmer' | CB&S ERea LRHS SBra WSHC |
| *parviflora* | CPIN ECou EWes |

## SONCHUS (Asteraceae)

| | |
|---|---|
| *palustris* | EMon |
| *platylepsis* | Last listed 1998 |

## SOPHORA (Papilionaceae)

| | |
|---|---|
| § *davidii* | CPle ECou SIgm SOWG SRCN WPGP |
| *flavescens* | Last listed 1998 |
| *japonica* ♀ | CAbP CB&S CDul CLnd CPMA EBee ELan EMil ENot EPfP EWTr IOrc ISea MBlu MPEx MWhi NBee SMad SPer WDin WNor |
| - 'Pendula' | LPan |
| - 'Regent' | LPan |
| § 'Little Baby' | CB&S EPfP ERea LHil MBlu MGos SBod SHFr SMur WBod |
| *macrocarpa* | CFil CHan GQui ISea SBid |
| *microphylla* | CPle CTrC ECou LHop MBel MBlu SAPC SArc SIgm SMad SPar SRCN SVen SVil WPat WWat |

- 'Dragon's Gold'  CDoC ECou ELan EPfP LRHS MAsh
- 'Early Gold'  CB&S ERea GQui SBid
- var. *fulvida*  ECou
- 'Goldilocks'  Last listed 1996
- var. *longicarinata*  ECou
- Sun King = 'Hilsop'  LRHS MGos SCoo WWeb
*prostrata* Buch.  CBot ECou
- misapplied  See *S.* 'Little Baby'
- Pukaki form  ECou
¶ *secundiflora*  CPLG SIgm
*tetraptera* ♀  CAbP CB&S CHan CLnd CMac CWit EBee ECou ECre GQui IOrc ISea LHil LHop MBel MBlu MLan NPSI SEND SIgm SRPl SRms WAbe WWat
- 'Gnome'  Last listed 1998
- 'Goughensis'  WCru
*viciifolia*  See *S. davidii*

---

## SORBARIA (Rosaceae)

*aitchisonii*  See *S. tomentosa* var. *angustifolia*
*arborea*  See *S. kirilowii*
§ *kirilowii*  IOrc SMad SPer
* - 'Glauca'  SMad
*lindleyana*  See *S. tomentosa*
SF 95205  ISea
*sorbifolia*  CAbP CB&S EBee EHic EMil EPla MBar MDun MTis MWhi NPro SEND SLPl SPan SPer STre WCot WDin WFar WWat
- var. *stellipila*  CFil SLPl WPGP
- *stellipila* B&SWJ 776  WCru
§ *tomentosa*  CAbP EBrP EBre LBre SBid SBre WCru WHCG
§ - var. *angustifolia* ♀  CDoC CDul CTri EBee ELan ENot EPfP IMGH MBal MGos MRav SEND SHFr SLon SPer SSta WEas WHer WWat

---

## SORBUS ✿ (Rosaceae)

§ *alnifolia*  CLnd CMCN EPfP LSyl SLPl WWat
*americana*  CLnd NWea
- 'Belmonte'  LSyl MBri
- *erecta*  See *S. decora*
*anglica*  CMCN WMou
'Apricot Lady'  MBri WJas
*arachnoidea*  LSyl
*aria*  CBlo CDul CKin CLnd CTri EBrP EBre GChr GRei LBre LBuc LHyr MBar NRoo NWea SBre WDin WMou WOrn
- 'Aurea'  CLnd MBlu
- 'Chrysophylla'  CDul CLnd CTho CWSG LSyl MAsh MBri NWea SPer SRPl
- 'Decaisneana'  See *S. aria* 'Majestica'
- 'Gigantea'  CDul
- 'Lutescens' ♀  More than 30 suppliers
- 'Magnifica'  CDoC CDul CTho ELan ENot LPan MAsh WDin WJas
§ - 'Majestica' ♀  CDoC CDul CLnd CTho ELan LPan LSyl MAsh MGos NWea SPer WJas WOrn
- 'Mitchellii'  See *S. thibetica* 'John Mitchell'
- var. *salicifolia*  See *S. rupicola*
x *arnoldiana*  CDul MAsh
  'Apricot Queen'
- 'Brilliant Yellow'  MBlu
- 'Chamois Glow'  WJas
*aronioides*  LSyl
*arranensis*  WMou

*aucuparia*  CB&S CDul CKin CLnd CSam EBee ECrN ELan ENot GRei ISea LBuc LHyr LPan MAsh MBal MBar MBri MGos NBee NRoo NWea SReu WDin WFar WHar WMou
- 'Apricot Lady'  LSyl SSta WWat
- 'Aspleniifolia'  CB&S CDul CLnd CTho EBee EBrP EBre ECrN ENot LBre LHyr LPan MGos NBea NBee NWea SBre SPer WDin WFar WJas WOrn
§ - 'Beissneri'  CLnd CTho LSyl MGos WWat
¶ - 'Cardinal Royal'  CBlo GQui WJas
- 'Dirkenii'  CBlo CDul CLnd COtt LSyl MAsh WJas
- 'Edulis' (F)  CDul CLnd CTho IOrc LBuc MGos NBea WDin
§ - 'Fastigiata'  CBlo CDoC CDul CEnd CSam CTho CTri ECrN EPfP EPla IOrc LSyl MAsh MBri MGos NBee WDin WFar WStI
§ - 'Fructu Luteo' ♀  CBlo ENot LSyl MGos NBea NBee WBay
- 'Hilling's Spire'  CBlo CTho MAsh MBri NBea SLPl
- 'Pendula'  CDul EBee
- *pluripinnata*  See *S. scalaris*
- 'Red Copper Glow'  MBlu
- 'Rossica'  Last listed 1997
- 'Rossica Major'  CDoC CDul CTho GQui LSyl
- 'Rowancroft Coral Pink'  CTho LSyl MBar MGos
- 'Scarlet King'  MBlu
- 'Sheerwater Seedling' ♀  CB&S CDoC CDul CLnd CTho EBee EBrP EBre ECrN ELan ENot IOrc LBre LHyr LSyl MGos MRav NBea NBee SBre SCoo SLon SPer SSta WDin WOrn
- 'Winterdown'  CNat
- 'Xanthocarpa'  See *S. aucuparia* 'Fructu Luteo'
*bristoliensis*  CTho LSyl WMou
*caloneura*  CFil LSyl SBid WHCr WPGP
'Carpet of Gold'  CBlo CLnd CTho LSyl NBea
*cascadensis*  Last listed 1996
*cashmiriana* ♀  More than 30 suppliers
- 'Rosea'  LSyl SSpi
- 'Rosiness'  LRHS MBri
*chamaemespilus*  GDra LSyl WPat
'Chinese Lace'  CDul CLnd CTho EBee ECot ECrN LSyl MAsh MBlu MBri MDun MGos NBea SFam SMad SRPl SSpi WBay WGor WJas WOrn WPyg WWat
§ *commixta*  CB&S CDul CEnd CLnd CMCN CTho EBee ECrN IOrc LSyl MBar MBri MGos MRav NBea SPer WDin WJas WOrn
* - 'Creamlace'  CBlo EBee
- 'Embley' ♀  CB&S CBlo CDul CLnd CMCN CSam CTho EBee ECrN ELan ENot LSyl MBar MBri MGos MRav NBea NBee SSpi SSta WOrn
- var. *rufoferruginea*  GChr GQui LSyl MBlu WHCr
* - 'Serotina'  LSyl
*conradinae* hort.  See *S. pohuashanensis* (Hance) Hedlund
- Koehne  See *S. esserteauana*
'Coral Beauty'  CLnd
¶ *croceocarpa*  CNat
*cuspidata*  See *S. vestita*
x *decipiens*  Last listed 1998
§ *decora*  CDul CLnd CTho LSyl SPer
* - 'Grootendorst'  CDul
- var. *nana*  See *S. aucuparia* 'Fastigiata'

| | |
|---|---|
| * *dentata* | Last listed 1996 |
| *devoniensis* | CDul CNat CTho LSyl WMou |
| *discolor* Hedlund | CLnd EBee ELan LSyl MGos MWat |
| | NWea WJas |
| – hort. | See *S. commixta* |
| *domestica* | CAgr CDul CMCN CTho ENot |
| | EPfP LBuc LEdu MAsh SLPl SPer |
| | WMou |
| – 'Maliformis' | See *S. domestica* var. *pomifera* |
| § – var. *pomifera* | EHol WMou |
| § – var. *pyrifera* | WMou |
| – 'Pyriformis' | See *S. domestica* var. *pyrifera* |
| 'Eastern Promise' | CBlo CDul LRHS LSyl MAsh MBri |
| | MWat SSta WJas |
| 'Edwin Hillier' | LSyl |
| * *ellypsoidalis* McLaren C 288 | LSyl |
| *eminens* | WMou |
| ¶ *epidendron* | LSyl |
| § *esserteauana* | CDoC CDul CSam CTho ENot |
| | LSyl |
| – 'Flava' | CTho LSyl WWat |
| – x *scalaris* | LSyl |
| ¶ 'Ethel's Gold' | LSyl |
| *folgneri* | CDoC CEnd CPMA CTho LSyl |
| – 'Lemon Drop' | CBlo CDoC CEnd CLnd CPMA |
| | LRHS LSyl MBlu SMad SSpi |
| ¶ *foliolosa* | CAbP CLnd CTho LSyl |
| * – KR 3518 | LSyl |
| *forrestii* | CDul CTho EHic EPfP LSyl MBlu |
| | NBea NSti SLPl SSpi |
| § *fruticosa* | CEnd CLnd COtt EBee EPfP MBri |
| | MMea NHol NWea SSpi SSta WJas |
| | WPGP WPat |
| * – 'Koehneana' ♀ | GChr LSyl MDun NTow SHFr |
| | WTin |
| – R 13268 | LSyl |
| 'Ghose' | CLnd CTho MBri SPer SSpi |
| *glabrescens* | Last listed 1996 |
| * – 'Roseoalba' | Last listed 1997 |
| 'Golden Wonder' | CLnd LSyl NBea |
| § *gonggashanica* | Last listed 1997 |
| – L 1008 | LSyl |
| *gracilis* | LSyl |
| § *graeca* | CDul CMCN LSyl SEND |
| *barrowiana* 'Bellona' | LSyl |
| 'Harvest Moon' | GQui MBri |
| *bedlundii* | IBlr LSyl NBea WWes |
| ¶ *belenae* | GGGa |
| *bemsleyi* | CLnd LSyl MDun |
| x *bostii* | CLnd ENot MRav SPer |
| § *bupebensis* Schneider ♀ | CB&S CDul CEnd CLnd CMCN |
| | CSam CTho EBee ECrN ISea |
| | LHyr LSyl MAsh MBal MBar NBee |
| | NWea SLPl SPer SRPl SSpi SSta |
| | WDin WJas WNor WOrn WWat |
| * – 'Apricot' | CBlo CEnd |
| § – var. *obtusa* ♀ | CDoC CMCN CSam GAri MBlu |
| | MDun MRav SFam SSpi SSta WWat |
| – 'Pink Pagoda' | CBlo CDoC CDul CLnd EBee |
| | EMui EPfP EWTr GChr GRei LSyl |
| | MAsh MBri MGos MSta MWat |
| | NWea SCoo SLon SPer WDin |
| | WGer WJas WPyg WWat |
| – 'Rosea' | See *S. bupebensis* var. *obtusa* |
| * – *roseoalba* B&L 12545 | LSyl |
| ¶ – SF 96268 | ISea |
| *bybrida* L. | NWea |
| – 'Gibbsii' ♀ | CBlo CDoC CLnd CTho EBee |
| | ELan EPfP LSyl |
| – hort. | See *S.* x *thuringiaca* |
| *insignis* | CDoC SSpi |
| ¶ – SF 96227 | ISea |

| | |
|---|---|
| *intermedia* | CAgr CB&S CDul CKin CLnd |
| | EBee ENot GChr GRei LSyl MBal |
| | MGos NBee NWea SPer WDin |
| | WMou WStI |
| – 'Brouwers' ♀ | ELan NBee |
| 'Joseph Rock' ♀ | More than 30 suppliers |
| § x *kewensis* ♀ | CDul CLnd CTho EBee LSyl SPer |
| | SSpi |
| 'Kirsten Pink' | CBlo CCHP CLnd EBee LSyl MBlu |
| | MGos NEgg |
| *koehneana* hort. | See *S. fruticosa* |
| aff. *koehneana* | LSyl MBri |
| Schneider Harry Smith | |
| 12799 | |
| *kurzii* EGM | LSyl |
| – KR 1501 | Last listed 1996 |
| *lanata* hort. | See *S. vestita* |
| *lancastriensis* | CNat CTho LSyl WMou |
| *latifolia* | CAgr CLnd CTho ENot NWea |
| | WDin WMou |
| * *laxiflora* | Last listed 1998 |
| ¶ – SF 96126 | ISea |
| 'Leonard Messel' | CTho LSyl MBri NBea |
| 'Leonard Springer' | ENot GQui SSta |
| *leyana* | WMou |
| *lingshiensis* | LSyl |
| 'Lombart's Golden Wonder' | CB&S CBlo CDoC CTho LBuc |
| | LPan NWea WJas |
| *longii* | LSyl |
| 'Lowndes' | CLnd |
| *matsumurana* | Last listed 1997 |
| (Makino) Koehne | |
| – hort. | See *S. commixta* |
| *megalocarpa* | CBlo CFil CPMA CSam CTho LSyl |
| | WNor |
| *meliosmifolia* | CSam LSyl WPGP |
| *microphylla* | Last listed 1996 |
| – Yu 13815 | LSyl |
| *minima* | LSyl WMou |
| * 'Molly Sanderson' | IBlr SSta |
| *monbeigii* CLD 311 | LSyl |
| – McLaren D 84 | LSyl |
| *moravica* 'Laciniata' | See *S. aucuparia* 'Beissneri' |
| *mougeotii* | CTho LSyl |
| ¶ *multijuga* Sch 1132 | LSyl |
| 'November Pink' | CBlo CEnd EPfP IOrc MAsh WJas |
| *pallescens* | LSyl |
| *parva* L 937 | LSyl |
| * 'Peachiness' | LSyl |
| 'Pearly King' | CB&S CSam CTho LSyl MBri |
| | NBea WJas |
| *pekinensis* | See *S. reticulata* subsp. |
| | *pekinensis* |
| § 'Pink Pearl' | LSyl |
| 'Pink-Ness' | MBri |
| *pogonopetala* | Last listed 1996 |
| – Yu 14299 | LSyl |
| *pobuasbanensis* hort. | See *S.* x *kewensis* |
| – (Hance) Hedlund | CSam CTho LSyl NWea |
| *porrigentiformis* | CNat CTho LSyl |
| *poteriifolia* | GCrs LSyl MFir NHar |
| – KW 6968 | Last listed 1996 |
| § *prattii* | CTho GAri LSyl NBea WWat |
| – var. *subarachnoidea* | GBin |
| – var. *tatsienensis* | See *S. prattii* |
| *pseudofennica* | LSyl WMou |
| * *pseudovilmorinii* | EMon LSyl |
| ¶ – MF 93044 | SSpi |
| *randaiensis* | LSyl |
| – B&SWJ 3202 | NHol SSpi WCru |
| 'Red Marbles' | LSyl |
| 'Red Tip' | CDoC CDul CLnd CTho LSyl |
| | MBlu NEgg |

| | |
|---|---|
| *reducta* ♀ | CB&S CEnd CLyd CMCN CSWP EBee GAbr GChr GCrs GDra ISea ITim LSyl MBal MBri MBro MFir MPla NHar NHol SMad SPer SSpi SSta WNor WPat WWat |
| *reflexipetala* | See *S. commixta* |
| *rebderiana* | CLnd MBal WNor |
| - 'Pink Pearl' | LSyl |
| § *reticulata* | LSyl |
| subsp. *pekinensis* | |
| ¶ *rhamnoides* SF 96227 | ISea |
| *rinzenii* | LSyl |
| * 'Rowancroft' | Last listed 1996 |
| ¶ *rufopilosa* | LSyl |
| § *rupicola* | CNat CTho GChr LSyl WMou |
| 'Salmon Queen' | CLnd LSyl |
| *sargentiana* ♀ | CDul CEnd CLnd CMCN CSam CTho CTri EBee EBrP EBre ECrN ELan ENot EWTr IMGH LBre LBuc LPan LSyl MAsh MBlu MBri NWea SBre SPer SRPl SSpi WJas WOrn WWat |
| * 'Savill Orange' | LSyl |
| § *scalaris* ♀ | CB&S CBlo CDul CEnd CTho CTri IOrc LSyl MAsh MBri NMoo SPer SSpi WJas WOrn WWat |
| 'Schouten' | ENot MBlu |
| *scopulina* hort. | See *S. aucuparia* 'Fastigiata' |
| *semi-incisa* | LSyl |
| *setschwanensis* | GAri GGGa |
| 'Signalman' | MBri |
| sp. CLD 237 | LSyl |
| sp. Ghose | LSyl |
| sp. Harry Smith 12732 | LSyl |
| sp. KR 3595 | LSyl |
| sp. KR 3733 | LSyl |
| sp. nova | LSyl |
| sp. SEP 492 | Last listed 1996 |
| 'Sunshine' | CDoC EBee LSyl MAsh MBri WJas |
| *thibetica* | LSyl |
| § - 'John Mitchell' ♀ | CDul CLnd CMCN CSam CTho ECrN ENot GChr GQui IMGH LPan LSyl MAsh MBlu MBri MGos MRav NBea NWea SPer WJas WOrn WWat |
| § x *thuringiaca* | LSyl NBea WMou |
| § - 'Fastigiata' | CB&S CDoC CDul CLnd EBee ENot MGos WDin WJas |
| *torminalis* | CAgr CCVT CDul CKin CLnd CSWP CSam CTho CTri LBuc MBri NWea SPer WCoo WDin WGwy WMou |
| *umbellata* var. *cretica* | See *S. graeca* |
| x *vagensis* | CLnd WMou |
| § *vestita* | CLnd CMCN CTho LSyl WWat |
| ¶ *vexans* | CNat |
| *vilmorinii* ♀ | More than 30 suppliers |
| * - 'Pendula' | Last listed 1996 |
| ♦ - 'Robusta' | See *S.* 'Pink Pearl' |
| *wardii* | CB&S CLnd CTho LSyl MBri |
| 'White Wax' | CBlo CDul MGos NEgg WDin |
| 'Wilfrid Fox' | CLnd LSyl SLPl |
| *willmottiana* | WMou |
| *wilsoniana* | LSyl SLon |
| 'Winter Cheer' | LSyl |
| *zablbruckneri* hort. | See *S. alnifolia* |

## SORGHASTRUM (Poaceae)
| | |
|---|---|
| § *avenaceum* | ECha EHoe EMan |

| | |
|---|---|
| - 'Indian Steel' | CBrm EMan MSte |
| *nutans* | See *S. avenaceum* |

## SORGHUM (Poaceae)
| | |
|---|---|
| *halepense* | MSte |
| *nigrum* | Last listed 1998 |

## SPARAXIS (Iridaceae)
| | |
|---|---|
| *bulbifera* | NRog |
| *elegans* | NRog |
| - 'Coccinea' | LBow |
| *fragrans* subsp. *acutiloba* | NRog |
| - subsp. *fimbriata* | LBow |
| ¶ - subsp. *grandiflora* | WCot |
| hybrids | LAma |
| *tricolor* | EPar GSki MBri NRog WCot |
| § *variegata* | LBow NRog |

## SPARGANIUM (Sparganiaceae)
| | |
|---|---|
| § *erectum* | CRow ECoo EHon EMFW LPBA MSta NDea SWat SWyc WHer |
| *ramosum* | See *S. erectum* |

## SPARRMANNIA (Tiliaceae)
| | |
|---|---|
| *africana* ♀ | CAbb CPle ERea GQui LBlm LCns LHil MBEx MBri SAPC SArc WOak |
| - 'Variegata' | ERea LCns |
| *palmata* | See *S. ricinicarpa* |
| § *ricinicarpa* | Last listed 1998 |

## SPARTINA (Poaceae)
| | |
|---|---|
| ¶ *patens* | EHoe |
| *pectinata* | CHan GBin |
| - 'Aureomarginata' | CCuc CInt CRow EBee ECha ECoo EHoe ELan EMon EPar EPla GCHN GCal GOrn LHil MAvo MBar MMoz MSta MSte MWhi NDea NHol NSti SCob SLod SPer WFar WRus WWye |

## SPARTIUM (Papilionaceae)
| | |
|---|---|
| *junceum* ♀ | CB&S CDoC EBee ELan EMil ENot EPla MBal MBri MGos MWat SArc SDix SLon SMad SPer SRCN SRms WBod WGwG WKif |

## SPARTOCYTISUS See CYTISUS

## SPATHANTHEUM (Araceae)
| | |
|---|---|
| *orbignyanum* | WCot |

## SPATHIPAPPUS See TANACETUM

## SPATHIPHYLLUM (Araceae)
| | |
|---|---|
| 'Adagio' | Last listed 1996 |
| 'Mauna Loa' ♀ | Last listed 1990 |
| 'Viscount' | MBri |
| *wallisii* | CHal EOHP MBri |

## SPATHODEA (Bignoniaceae)
| | |
|---|---|
| ¶ *campanulata* | WMul |

## SPEIRANTHA (Convallariaceae)
| | |
|---|---|
| § *convallarioides* | CFil CLAP CRDP EBee NOla WCot WCru WPGP |
| *gardenii* | See *S. convallarioides* |

## SPERGULARIA (Caryophyllaceae)
| | |
|---|---|
| *purpurea* | Last listed 1997 |
| *rupicola* | CKin EWFC MNrw |

## SPHACELE See LEPECHINIA

## SPHAERALCEA (Malvaceae)

| | |
|---|---|
| *ambigua* | ELan MLLN |
| *coccinea* | Last listed 1998 |
| *fendleri* | CB&S CBot CLTr CMHG CSam EOrc MBEx MHlr MSCN SUsu WWye |
| - *venusta* | Last listed 1998 |
| *grossulariifolia* | Last listed 1997 |
| 'Hopleys Lavender' | EMan LHil LHop SUsu |
| 'Hyde Hall' | EHic MCCP MLLN WRus WWeb |
| *incana* | CM&M CPin CSev EBee MCCP MLLN SMrm SRCN WElm |
| *malviflora* | WPer |
| *miniata* | CMHG ELan LGre LHil LHop MLLN SAga SLon SMrm WCot |
| *munroana* | CBot CHar CMHG CSev EBee ELan LHil LHop MCCP MSCN SMrm WEas WSHC |
| - 'Dixieland Pink' | WEas |
| - pale pink | CSpe EBee ECtt EMan LGre LHop SMrm |
| * - 'Shell Pink' | ECGP |
| 'Newleaze Coral' | LHop |
| ¶ 'Newleaze Pink' | LHop |
| *remorta* | MNrw |
| *rivularis* | CGen EBee EMan WMoo |
| *umbellata* | See *Phymosia umbellata* |

## SPHAEROMERIA (Asteraceae)

| | |
|---|---|
| *argentea* | See *Tanacetum nuttallii* |
| § *capitata* | NWCA |
| *compacta* | CPBP |

## SPHAGNUM (Sphagnaceae)

| | |
|---|---|
| *fuscum* | Last listed 1996 |
| *magellanicum* | Last listed 1996 |
| *pulchrum* | Last listed 1996 |

## SPHENOMERIS (Dennstaedtiaceae)

| | |
|---|---|
| ¶ *chinensis* | WRic |

## SPIGELIA (Loganiaceae)

| | |
|---|---|
| *marilandica* | CRDP |

## SPILANTHES (Asteraceae)

| | |
|---|---|
| *acmella* | Last listed 1996 |
| *oleracea* | Last listed 1996 |

## SPIRAEA ✿ (Rosaceae)

| | |
|---|---|
| 'Abigail' | CDoC |
| *albiflora* | See *S. japonica* var. *albiflora* |
| *arborea* | See *Sorbaria kirilowii* |
| *arcuata* | Last listed 1998 |
| § *'Arguta'* | More than 30 suppliers |
| x *arguta* 'Bridal Wreath' | See *S.* 'Arguta' |
| - 'Compacta' | See *S.* x *cinerea* |
| - 'Nana' | See *S.* x *cinerea* |
| *bella* | CPle MBar WHCG |
| *betulifolia* | EBee GEil MRav NLon WHCG WPat WPyg |
| - var. *aemiliana* | CBot CMHG CPle EBrP EBre ECtt EHal EPla ESis LBre LHop MGos MPla MUlv NHol SBre SLPl SPan SSta WWat |
| x *bumalda* | See *S. japonica* 'Bumalda' |
| - 'Wulfenii' | See *S. japonica* 'Walluf' |
| *callosa* 'Alba' | See *S. japonica* var. *albiflora* |
| *canescens* | Last listed 1997 |
| *cantoniensis* | Last listed 1998 |
| § - 'Flore Pleno' (d) | CPle EMon MBlu |

| | |
|---|---|
| - 'Lanceata' | See *S. cantoniensis* 'Flore Pleno' |
| *chamaedryfolia* | CPle |
| § x *cinerea* | EPfP SSta WRHF WShe |
| - 'Grefsheim' ♀ | CB&S CBlo CDoC COtt EBee ECtt ENot GOrc MBri MGos MMil SPer SPla SSta WTro |
| - 'Variegata' | MPla |
| 'County Park' | Last listed 1996 |
| *crispifolia* | See *S. japonica* 'Bullata' |
| *decumbens* | CPle |
| *densiflora* | EPot |
| 'Dingle Apricot' | Last listed 1996 |
| 'Dingle Gold' | Last listed 1996 |
| *douglasii* | GOrc MBar NRoo |
| - subsp. *menziesii* | NLon |
| x *fontenaysii* 'Rosea' | CPle |
| *formosana* | CPle |
| - CC 1597 | CHan |
| § x *foxii* | SLPl |
| *fritschiana* | SLPl SLon SPan WHCG |
| *bendersonii* | See *Petrophytum bendersonii* |
| *benryi* | CPle |
| § *japonica* | CPle SBod |
| - 'Alba' | See *S. japonica* var. *albiflora* |
| - var. *albiflora* | CB&S CEnd CPle ESis MBal MBar MWat NRoo SPer SRms WHCG |
| - 'Allgold' | NBee |
| - 'Alpina' | See *S. japonica* 'Nana' |
| - 'Alpine Gold' | CFai NPro SPan |
| - 'Anthony Waterer' (v) ♀ | CB&S CChe CPle EBee EBrP EBre ELan ENot GRei LBre MBal MBar MBri MGos NBee NFla NRoo NWea SBre SPer SRms WBod WDin WFar WGwG WHar WSHC |
| - 'Blenheim' | SRms |
| § - 'Bullata' | CFee CMHG ELan ESis MBal MBar MPla NFla NHol NRoo NWCA SPan SRms WAbe WHCG |
| § - 'Bumalda' | CCuc WFar |
| - 'Candle Light' | CAbP CB&S CBlo CWSG EAst EBee EBrP EBre ECle EGra EPfP LBre MAsh MGos NHol SBre SCoo SPer SPla WRHF |
| - 'Country Red' | CBlo |
| § - 'Crispa' | CCuc EPfP EPla MBar MBlu MBri NPro WFar |
| - 'Dart's Red' | CBlo GCHN IOrc MAsh MBlu MBri SCoo SEas SSta WWeb |
| - 'Fire Light' | CAbP CB&S CBlo CChe EBee EBrP EBre ELan EPfP LBre MAsh MBri MGos NHol SBre SCoo SPer SPla SSta WWeb |
| - var. *fortunei* 'Atrosanguinea' | WHCG |
| - 'Froebelii' | CCuc ISea LBuc WRHF |
| - 'Glenroy Gold' | MBal SLon WHen |
| - 'Gold Mound' ♀ | CMHG EBee ELan EWTr GChr GOrc MBal MBar MBel MBlu MBri MGos MRav MWat NBee NFor NLon NRoo SEas SHFr SPer SPlb SRms WHar WSHC WTro WWat |
| - 'Gold Rush' | CMHG MBNS WHCG WRHF WRus EHic WHCG |
| - 'Golden Dome' | EHic WHCG |
| - Golden Princess = 'Lisp' | CTri EAst EBrP EBre ELan GRei IOrc LBre MAsh MBal MBar MBlu MGos MPla NHol NRoo SBre SEas SLon SPer SRPl SReu SRms SSta WFar WWeb |
| - 'Goldflame' ♀ | More than 30 suppliers |
| - 'Little Maid' | Last listed 1997 |
| - 'Little Princess' | CB&S CBrm EBee ELan EMil ENot EWTr LHop MAsh MBal MBar MBri MRav MWat NBee NHol NRoo NWCA SPer SRms SSta WAbe WDin WFar WHar WWal WWat |

| | |
|---|---|
| - Magic Carpet = 'Walbuma' | LRHS MAsh SCoo |
| - 'Magnifica' | WHCG WPat |
| - 'Manon Red Princess' | EBee |
| § - 'Nana' ♀ | CMHG EBee EHyt ELan ENot EPla |
| | ESis MBal MBar MBri MPla MRav |
| | MTho NHar SReu SRms WEas |
| | WHCG WPat WPer WPyg |
| - 'Nyewoods' | See S. japonica 'Nana' |
| - 'Pamela Harper' | EHic |
| N - 'Shirobana' ♀ | More than 30 suppliers |
| § - 'Walluf' | CFai COtt CPle EHic GEil NFor |
| | NLon SPan WHCG |
| latifolia | Last listed 1997 |
| 'Margaritae' | NPro SPer |
| mollifolia | Last listed 1998 |
| myrtilloides | CPle |
| nipponica | CB&S MBar |
| - 'Halward's Silver' | CBlo CFai MBri MGos MRav NHol |
| | NPro SLPl WBcn |
| - 'June Bride' | CBlo NHol |
| § - 'Snowmound' ♀ | More than 30 suppliers |
| - hort. var. tosaensis | See S. nipponica 'Snowmound' |
| - (Yatabe) Makino | LHop MWat SReu |
| ◆ palmata elegans | See Filipendula purpurea 'Elegans' |
| § prunifolia (d) | CFai CPle EBee ELan ENot EPla |
| | LHop MBlu SEas SLon SPer WAbe |
| | WHCG WWin |
| ◆ - misapplied (single) | See S. prunifolia f. simpliciflora |
| - 'Plena' | See S. prunifolia |
| ¶ x pseudosalicifolia | CBlo ENot NCut NFor SHFr WWin |
| 'Triumphans' | |
| salicifolia | CPLG WFar |
| ¶ sp. CLD 138 | EMon |
| sp. CLD 1389 | Last listed 1997 |
| stevenii | GAri |
| 'Summersnow' | SLPl |
| ◆ 'Superba' | See S. x foxii |
| tarokoensis | Last listed 1998 |
| thunbergii ♀ | CChe CPle CTri EBee ENot EPla |
| | IOrc LHop MPla MRav NFla NFor |
| | NLon NWea SCoo SMer SPer |
| | SRms WDin WGwG WHCG WWal |
| - 'Mellow Yellow' | WWat |
| - 'Mount Fuji' | CAbP CCHP CFai EBrP EBre EHoe |
| | GSki LBre MBri MGos NLak NPro |
| | SBre SCoo WFar WTro |
| * - rosea | WBcn |
| ¶ - 'Tickled Pink' | CAbP LRHS MAsh SPla |
| * - 'Variegata' | EBee |
| tomentosa | WShe |
| trichocarpa | Last listed 1998 |
| trilobata | WLRN |
| ulmaria | See Filipendula ulmaria |
| vacciniifolia | Last listed 1996 |
| x vanhouttei ♀ | CB&S CTri EBee ELan ENot IOrc |
| | MBal MBar MRav MWat NFla NFor |
| | NLon SHFr SPer SRms WDin WFar |
| | WWal WWat |
| - Pink Ice (v) | CAbP CB&S CDoC CMHG COtt |
| | CPMA CWit EAst EBee ECle EHoe |
| | ELan EMil LHop MAsh MBal MGos |
| | MLLN MPla MTis NLon SEas SPer |
| | SPla SPlb SRPl WDin WFar WHar |
| veitchii | MBal MRav |
| venusta 'Magnifica' | See Filipendula rubra 'Venusta' |
| wilsonii | CHan |
| 'Wyndbrook Gold' | Last listed 1998 |

## SPIRANTHES (Orchidaceae)

| | |
|---|---|
| aestivalis | SWes |
| cernua | EFEx |
| - f. odorata 'Chadd's Ford' | EBee EHic LEur LRHS WCot WSpi |

| | |
|---|---|
| ¶ ochroleuca | SWes |
| spiralis | SSpi WHer |

## SPIRODELA (Lemnaceae)
| | |
|---|---|
| § polyrhiza | MSta |

## SPODIOPOGON (Poaceae)
| | |
|---|---|
| sibiricus | EBee ECha EMan EMon EPPr |
| | LEdu LRHS MSte SApp SSvw |
| | WCot |

## SPOROBOLUS (Poaceae)
| | |
|---|---|
| fertilis | Last listed 1997 |
| heterolepis | EBee EPPr |
| wrightii | Last listed 1997 |

## SPRAGUEA (Portulacaceae)
| | |
|---|---|
| ¶ 'Powder Puff' | LRHS |
| § umbellata | Last listed 1998 |
| § - glandulifera | Last listed 1998 |

## SPREKELIA (Amaryllidaceae)
| | |
|---|---|
| formosissima ♀ | CSpe EBot LAma LBow NRog |

## STACHYS (Lamiaceae)
| | |
|---|---|
| § affinis | CArn CFir ELau GPoy LEdu |
| alopecuros | CMGP WWin |
| alpina | CNat EBee |
| x ambigua | EWFC NSti |
| ¶ atherocalyx | EBee |
| ¶ balansae | NSti |
| betonica | See S. officinalis |
| § byzantina | More than 30 suppliers |
| § - 'Big Ears' | CMGP ECha EGoo EMon LHop |
| | MCAu MCLN SAga SCob SMrm |
| | WCot |
| § - 'Cotton Boll' | CMGP COlW ECha EFou GCal |
| | MCLN MHar MTho MWat NSti |
| | SPer WCot WGwG WWal WWat |
| - 'Countess Helen von Stein' | See S. byzantina 'Big Ears' |
| - gold-leaved | See S. byzantina 'Primrose Heron' |
| - large-leaved | See S. byzantina 'Big Ears' |
| - 'Limelight' | WCot |
| § - 'Primrose Heron' | COtt EBee ECha ECot EMan |
| | GMaP MCAu MFir NLar NOrc NSti |
| | SMer SPer |
| - 'Sheila McQueen' | See S. byzantina 'Cotton Boll' |
| - 'Silver Carpet' | More than 30 suppliers |
| § - 'Striped Phantom' (v) | CHan MBel SAga WCot |
| - 'Variegata' | See S. byzantina 'Striped Phantom' |
| candida | EHyt NMen WThi |
| chrysantha | LGre |
| citrina | CLyd CMea GCal LBee WCot |
| coccinea | CElw CGle CHan CHar CInt CPla |
| | CPle LGre LHop LLWP MBNS |
| | MFir NBir NFai SHFr SMac SSca |
| | WEas WOve WRos WSan WWye |
| - apricot | WEas |
| - 'Avondale Peach' | MAvo |
| - 'Axminster Lemon' | SAga |
| - 'Axminster Variegated' | SAga |
| - 'El Salto' CDR 1384 | SAga |
| § - 'Hidalgo' | LHop |
| cretica | EMan EOrc LEdu SIgm SRCN |
| | WHer |
| densiflora | See S. monieri |
| § discolor | CBos GBri MBri MBro MLLN |
| | WCot WCru WHil WOut WPer |
| germanica | CNat EBee EMan NArg |
| grandiflora | See S. macrantha |
| ¶ heraclea | EBee |

| | |
|---|---|
| ◆ 'Hidalgo' | See *S. coccinea* 'Hidalgo' |
| 'Hopleys Variegated' | Last listed 1996 |
| *iva* | EBee ESis LGre NTow |
| *lanata* | See *S. byzantina* |
| *lavandulifolia* | EBee |
| § *macrantha* | CArn CHea CMCo ECha ECoo |
| | EOld LSpr MBel MBro MHew |
| | MRav NOak NOrc NSti SMrm |
| | SOkh SRms WBea WEas WFar |
| | WHal WLin WMow WOld WOve |
| | WPyg WWin |
| * - 'Hummelo' | EFou EMil SUsu |
| - 'Nivea' | CElw EBee EHrv ELan EMan GCal |
| | NHol WCot WPat WWal WWye |
| § - 'Robusta' ♀ | CGle ELan EPPr MBri NBro NGdn |
| | SCro SHel WCot WRHF WWye |
| - 'Rosea' | EBee EFou ELan GMaP MArl |
| | MCLN MGed NWes SCro SHel |
| | SPlb WEas WOld WPer WRha |
| | WViv WWye |
| - 'Rosea Compacta' | Last listed 1996 |
| - 'Superba' | CGle CHan CRDP EBee EGar |
| | GCHN MBel MBri MCAu NFai |
| | NFla SMrm SPla WByw WCot |
| | WFar |
| - 'Violacea' | CStr |
| ¶ *marrubiifolia* | EBee |
| § *monieri* | CRDP EHal EMan ESis LFis MCLN |
| | NLar SIgm SLon SMrm WCot |
| | WLin WPer |
| - 'Hummelo' | EBee LGre |
| *nivea* | See *S. discolor* |
| § *officinalis* | CArn CKin CSev CStr EBee EWFC |
| | EWTr GPoy MChe MHew MPEx |
| | MSal NLan NMir SIde SIng WBea |
| | WCla WGwG WHal WHbs WHer |
| | WOak WWye |
| - 'Alba' | CArn CGle CJew CMGP CRDP |
| | MCLN NBro NHol SUsu WAlt |
| | WFar WRha WWye |
| - 'Rosea' | WPrP |
| - 'Rosea Superba' | CGle CMil ECha MBel MCAu |
| | MCLN SDix WCot WFar WGwy |
| *olympica* | See *S. byzantina* |
| *palustris* | CKin ECoo LPBA MSta WGwy |
| *plumosa* | Last listed 1998 |
| *saxicola* | Last listed 1997 |
| subsp. *villosissima* | |
| *setifera* | EBee |
| *spicata* | See *S. macrantha* |
| *sylvatica* | CArn CKin EMan EWFC GPoy |
| | MHew WCla WGwy WHer |
| ¶ - 'Hoskin's Variegated' (v) | WAlt |
| ¶ - 'Huskers Variety' | EBee MCCP |
| - 'Shade of Pale' | WAlt |
| *thirkei* | EBee EOrc SSca |
| *tmolea* | Last listed 1996 |
| *tuberifera* | See *S. affinis* |

## STACHYTARPHETA (Verbenaceae)

| | |
|---|---|
| *mutabilis* | SOWG |

## STACHYURUS (Stachyuraceae)

| | |
|---|---|
| *chinensis* | CB&S CMCN CPMA CRos MBri |
| *himalaicus* | CFil WPGP |
| - HWJCM 009 | WCru |
| ◆ *lancifolius* | See *S. praecox* var. *matsuzakii* |
| *leucotrichus* | CPMA |
| 'Magpie' (v) | CFil CPMA EPfP SBid SSpi WCru |
| | WSpi WWat |

| | |
|---|---|
| *praecox* ♀ | CB&S CBot CDoC CEnd CFil |
| | CPMA CPle CRos CSam EBee |
| | ELan EMil ENot IOrc LHyd MBar |
| | MBlu MGos MRav NPal SBrw SPer |
| | SRPl SReu SSpi SSta WCot WDin |
| | WSHC WWat |
| § - var. *matsuzakii* | CFil WPGP |
| ¶ - - B&SWJ 2817 | WCru |
| * - 'Rubriflora' | CPMA ELan EPfP LRHS MAsh SPer |
| ¶ *yunnanensis* | CFil WPGP |

## STANLEYA (Brassicaceae)

| | |
|---|---|
| *albescens* | Last listed 1998 |
| *elata* | Last listed 1998 |
| *integrifolia* | EBee |
| *pinnata* | EBee |

## STAPHYLEA (Staphyleaceae)

| | |
|---|---|
| *bumalda* | CB&S CMCN |
| *colchica* ♀ | CB&S CHan IOrc SPer SRPl WDin |
| | WPGP WSHC WWat |
| *emodi* | CPle |
| *holocarpa* | CB&S CPMA CPle SSpi WWat |
| N - 'Rosea' ♀ | CBot MBlu MGos SMur SSpi |
| | WSHC |
| N - var. *rosea* | CPMA ENot EPfP LHop SMad |
| *pinnata* | CB&S EPfP LEdu WHCr WNor |
| *pringlei* | Last listed 1996 |
| *trifolia* | CAgr CB&S |

## STATICE See LIMONIUM

## STAUNTONIA (Lardizabalaceae)

| | |
|---|---|
| *hexaphylla* | CB&S CPlN CSam EBee EHol EMil |
| | EPfP GQui MDun SBid SBra SLon |
| | SReu SSpi SSta WSHC |
| ¶ - B&SWJ 4858 | WCru |
| *purpurea* B&SWJ 3690 | WCru |

## STEGNOGRAMMA (Thelypteridaceae)

| | |
|---|---|
| ¶ *pozoi* | EFer |

## STEIRODISCUS (Asteraceae)

| | |
|---|---|
| * *euryopoides* | Last listed 1998 |

## STELLARIA (Caryophyllaceae)

| | |
|---|---|
| *graminea* | CKin EWFC NBid |
| *holostea* | CKin EMan EWFC MChe NMir |
| | WHer |
| *ruscifolia* | Last listed 1996 |

## STEMODIA (Scrophulariaceae)

| | |
|---|---|
| *tomentosa* | Last listed 1997 |

## STENANTHIUM (Melanthiaceae)

| | |
|---|---|
| ¶ *occidentale* | SSpi |
| *robustum* | WPGP |

## STENOCARPUS (Proteaceae)

| | |
|---|---|
| *sinuatus* | Last listed 1998 |

## STENOCHLAENA (Blechnaceae)

| | |
|---|---|
| *palustris* | MBri |

## STENOCOELIUM (Apiaceae)

| | |
|---|---|
| ¶ *divaricatum* | IIve |

## STENOGLOTTIS (Orchidaceae)

| | |
|---|---|
| *fimbriata* | GCrs |
| *longifolia* ♀ | GCrs |
| *woodii* | GCrs |

## STENOMESSON (Amaryllidaceae)

| | |
|---|---|
| § *miniatum* | EPot |
| *variegatum* | Last listed 1998 |

## STENOTAPHRUM (Poaceae)

| | |
|---|---|
| *secundatum* 'Variegatum' ♀ | CHal CInt IBlr LHil WMul |

## STENOTUS (Asteraceae)

| | |
|---|---|
| § *acaulis* | Last listed 1997 |

## STEPHANANDRA (Rosaceae)

| | |
|---|---|
| *incisa* | CB&S CBlo CGle CPle GChr IOrc SChu SPla WHCG WWal |
| § - 'Crispa' | CGle CPle EBee ELan EMil ENot GOrc LHop MBar MBlu MRav MWat NFor NHol SHel SPer WCFE WDin WFar WHCG WWat |
| ¶ - 'Dart's Horizon' | SLPl |
| - 'Prostrata' | See *S. incisa* 'Crispa' |
| *tanakae* | CB&S CDoC CGle CMFo CPle EBee ELan IMGH IOrc MBar MBlu MRav MUlv MWat NFla NFor NHol NLon SLPl SLon SMad SPer SPla SRPl STre WDin WFar WHCG WPat |

## STEPHANIA (Menispermaceae)

| | |
|---|---|
| *glandulifera* | CPlN |

## STEPHANOTIS (Asclepiadaceae)

| | |
|---|---|
| *floribunda* ♀ | CB&S EBak GQui LCns MBri SOWG |
| ¶ - *variegata* | LCns |

## STERNBERGIA (Amaryllidaceae)

| | |
|---|---|
| *candida* | CBro GCrs LAma |
| - JCA 933000 | SSpi |
| § *clusiana* | LAma |
| *colchiciflora* | EHyt EPot |
| *fischeriana* | CBro LAma |
| *greuteriana* | EHyt |
| *lutea* | CAvo CBro CHan CTri EBrP EBre EHyt ELan EPot EWes LAma LBre MBri MWat NRog NWCA SBre SDix SRms SSpi WEas |
| - Angustifolia Group | CBro CMea EMon WCot |
| - var. *lutea* MS 971 | Last listed 1998 |
| *macrantha* | See *S. clusiana* |
| *sicula* | CAvo CBro EHyt EPot ETub WCot |
| - Dodona form | Last listed 1997 |
| - var. *graeca* | EHyt EPot |
| - 'John Marr' ex JRM 3186/75 | Last listed 1996 |
| - MS 796 | Last listed 1998 |

## STEVIA (Asteraceae)

| | |
|---|---|
| *rebaudiana* | EOHP GPoy |

## STEWARTIA ✿ (Theaceae)

| | |
|---|---|
| ¶ *gemmata* | WNor |
| 'Korean Splendor' | See *S. pseudocamellia* Koreana Group |
| *koreana* | See *S. pseudocamellia* Koreana Group |
| *malacodendron* | ELan EPfP LRHS MBri SSpi SSta WBod |
| *monadelpha* | CMCN CPMA SSpi WCoo WNor WWat |
| *ovata* | CGre SSpi SSta WWat |
| N - var. *grandiflora* | CB&S LRHS |
| *pseudocamellia* ♀ | CB&S CDoC CGre COtt CPMA ELan GChr ICrw IMGH IOrc LPan MBel MBlu MBri MDun MLan NBea SBrw SMur SPer SReu SSpi SSta WBod WCru WNor WWat |

| | |
|---|---|
| - var. *koreana* | See *S. pseudocamellia* Koreana Group |
| § - Koreana Group ♀ | CB&S CBlo CEnd CGre CMCN MBri SReu SSpi SSta WDin WNor WWat |
| *pteropetiolata* | CB&S CWSG |
| - var. *koreana* | LRHS |
| ¶ *rostrata* | CB&S WNor |
| *serrata* | CGre GOrc LRHS SSpi |
| *sinensis* ♀ | CB&S CPMA EPfP SSpi WNor WPGP |

## STICTOCARDIA (Convolvulaceae)

| | |
|---|---|
| *beraviensis* | CPlN |

## STIGMAPHYLLON (Malpighiaceae)

| | |
|---|---|
| *ciliatum* | CPlN |

## STIPA (Poaceae)

| | |
|---|---|
| ◆ *arundinacea* | See *Calamagrostis arundinacea* |
| *barbata* | CBos CSpe EBee EBrP EBre EGar EGle EPPr EWes LBre LGre SBre SMrm SUsu WCot WHal |
| - 'Silver Feather' | Last listed 1997 |
| *boysterica* | CFee |
| *brachytricha* | See *Calamagrostis brachytricha* |
| § *calamagrostis* | More than 30 suppliers |
| - 'Lemperg' | EMan EPPr |
| *capillata* | CInt EBee ECGN EGle EMan GBin LGre MAvo MMoz SBea SMrm SUsu WCot WHal WOVN WPrP WWye |
| *comata* | Last listed 1997 |
| *elegantissima* | CInt LHil |
| *extremiorientalis* | ECha EGle LGre |
| *gigantea* ♀ | More than 30 suppliers |
| - 'Gold Fontaene' | EMon EWes WCot |
| - 'Variegata' | Last listed 1998 |
| *grandis* | ECha WPer |
| ¶ *joannis* | EBee |
| *lasiagrostis* | See *S. calamagrostis* |
| ¶ *lessingiana* | CPLG GBin |
| *mollis* | Last listed 1997 |
| *offneri* | EWes LGre SBla SIgm |
| ¶ *papposa* | CInt |
| *patens* | CCuc EPPr |
| *pennata* | CB&S ECGN EMan EPPr GBin MAvo MFir NMoo NOak SMad WCot WLRN |
| *pulcherrima* | EPPr GCal SIgm |
| - 'Windfeder' | CFir ECGN SMrm |
| *pulchra* | GBin MCCP |
| *robusta* | SApp |
| § *splendens* | CCuc ECoo EFou EHoe EPPr LEdu MBrN SDix |
| ◆ *stenophylla* | See *S. tirsa* |
| *tenacissima* | CBar EFou EHoe EMon EOld EPPr EPla MHlr WBro |
| *tenuifolia* | CCuc CHad CMea CMil CSam CSpe EBee EGar EMan EPGN MBel MBri MCLN MRav NBir NBro NChi NDov NHol NSti NVic SIng SLon SPla WHal WWat WWoo |
| *tenuissima* | More than 30 suppliers |
| § *tirsa* | EBee |
| *turkestanica* | LGre |
| ¶ *ucrainica* | GBin LGre |

## STOEBE (Asteraceae)

| | |
|---|---|
| *plumosa* | CTrC |

## STOKESIA (Asteraceae)

| | |
|---|---|
| *cyanea* | See *S. laevis* |
| § *laevis* | CDoC CGen CHea CMea EAst EBee ECGP ECha EHic EOld GMac LFis MBro MCAu NBro NFor NLar NLon SAga WBrE WCot WFar WPGP WPer WWeb |
| - 'Alba' | CHan CHea CM&M CMGP CRDP EAst EBee ECGP ECha EPar LGre MBri MCLN MRav NBrk NHol SAga SChu SPer SUsu SVil WMow WRus |
| - 'Blue Star' | CB&S CElw CGle CRDP CSam EBee EFou ELan LGre LHop MBri MCLN MFir MWgw NFla NOak NRoo SChu SEas SPer WMow WRus WWin |
| - 'Mary Gregory' | CElw CFir CHea CPar EAst EBee EHic GCal LHop MCLN MLLN NDov NHol NLar SOkh SWas WCot |
| - mixed | CPou |
| * - 'Omega Skyrocket' | WCot |
| ¶ - 'Purple Parasols' | COtt EHic NDov WCot |
| ¶ - 'Silver Moon' | EHic NDov WCot |
| - 'Träumerei' | CRDP EAst EBee EHic EMan GMac LFis MBro MGrG NHol SLon SOkh WCot WLRN WMow WWal |
| - 'Wyoming' | Last listed 1997 |

## STRANVAESIA See PHOTINIA

## x STRANVINIA See PHOTINIA

## STRATIOTES (Hydrocharitaceae)

| | |
|---|---|
| *aloides* | CBen CWat ECoo EHon EMFW LPBA MSta NDea SAWi SWat SWyc |

## STRELITZIA (Strelitziaceae)

| | |
|---|---|
| *alba* | LBlo WMul |
| ¶ *caudata* | LBlo |
| *nicolai* | LBlo LPal WMul |
| *reginae* ♀ | CAbb CB&S CBrP CTrC ECon ELan ERea GQui IBlr LCns LPal LPan NPal SAPC SArc SRms WMul |
| ¶ - 'Humilis' | LBlo |
| - 'Kirstenbosch Gold' | CTrC LBlo |

## STREPTOCARPELLA See STREPTOCARPUS

## STREPTOCARPUS ✿ (Gesneriaceae)

| | |
|---|---|
| 'Albatross' ♀ | NHor WDib |
| 'Amanda' | NHor WDib |
| 'Anne' | NHor WDib |
| 'Athena' | NHor WDib |
| ¶ *baudertii* | WDib |
| 'Beryl' | WDib |
| 'Bethan' | NHor WDib |
| * 'Black Panther' | NHor WDib |
| 'Blue Angel' ♀ | Last listed 1995 |
| 'Blue Gem' | WDib |
| 'Blue Heaven' | NHor WDib |
| 'Blue Moon' | WDib |
| 'Blue Nymph' | NHor WDib |
| 'Blue Pencil' | CSpe |
| 'Blue Trumpets' | Last listed 1997 |
| ¶ 'Blue Upstart' | CSpe |
| * 'Blushing Bride' | NHor WDib |
| * 'Boysenberry Delight' | CSpe WDib |
| 'Branwen' | NHor WDib |
| *candidus* | WDib |
| 'Carol' | MBri WDib |
| 'Catrin' | WDib |
| *caulescens* | CHal LHil WDib |
| - var. *pallescens* | WDib |
| 'Chorus Line' | NHor WDib |
| 'Clouds' | CSpe |
| 'Cobalt Nymph' | MBri |
| 'Concord Blue' | MBri WDib |
| 'Constant Nymph' | NHor WDib |
| 'Constant Nymph' seedling | Last listed 1996 |
| *cyaneus* | WDib |
| 'Cynthia' ♀ | MBri NHor WDib |
| 'Diana' ♀ | NHor WDib |
| *dunnii* | CFir WDib |
| 'Elsi' | NHor WDib |
| ¶ 'Emma' | WDib |
| 'Falling Stars' ♀ | CSpe MBri NHor WDib |
| 'Festival Wales' | NHor WDib |
| 'Fiona' | NHor WDib |
| *gardenii* | WDib |
| - JCA 3790400 | CPBP |
| *glandulosissimus* | CHal LCns LHil SVen WDib |
| 'Gloria' ♀ | CSpe NHor WDib |
| 'Good Hope' | ERea |
| *grandis* | Last listed 1996 |
| 'Happy Snappy' | NHor WDib |
| 'Heidi' ♀ | MBri NHor WDib |
| 'Helen' ♀ | NHor WDib |
| 'Holiday Blue' ♀ | Last listed 1995 |
| *holstii* | CHal CSpe LHil |
| 'Huge White' | CSpe |
| 'Jennifer' | NHor WDib |
| 'Joanna' | MBri NHor WDib |
| *johannis* ♀ | Last listed 1995 |
| 'Julie' | WDib |
| * 'Karen' | WDib |
| *kentaniensis* | WDib |
| 'Kim' ♀ | CSpe NHor WDib |
| *kirkii* | WDib |
| 'Laura' | NHor WDib |
| 'Lisa' ♀ | MBri NHor WDib |
| ¶ 'Little Gem' | CSpe |
| * 'Louise' | NHor WDib |
| 'Lynette' | WDib |
| 'Lynne' | NHor WDib |
| 'Maassen's White' | ERea NHor WDib |
| 'Mandy' | WDib |
| ¶ 'Margaret' | NHor |
| 'Marie' | NHor WDib |
| * 'Maureen' | CSpe |
| 'Megan' | NHor WDib |
| 'Mini Nymph' | NHor WDib |
| 'Myba' | MBri |
| 'Neptune' | MBri |
| 'Nicola' | MBri NHor WDib |
| 'Olga' | NHor WDib |
| 'Party Doll' | NHor WDib |
| 'Paula' ♀ | MBri NHor WDib |
| *pentherianus* | SBla WDib |
| 'Pink Fondant' | CSpe |
| ¶ 'Pink Souffle' | WDib |
| 'Pink Upstart' | CSpe |
| 'Plum Crazy' | CSpe |
| ¶ *polyanthus* | WDib |
| subsp. *dracomontanus* | |
| *primulifolius* | WDib |
| subsp. *formosus* | |
| * 'Purple Passion' | CSpe |
| *rexii* | WDib |
| * 'Rhiannon' | NHor WDib |

| | |
|---|---|
| 'Rosebud' | NHor WDib |
| 'Rosemary' | WDib |
| 'Royal Mixed' ♀ | Last listed 1995 |
| 'Ruby' ♀ | MBri NHor WDib |
| ¶ 'Ruffled Lilac' | CSpe |
| 'Sally' | NHor WDib |
| 'Sandra' | MBri NHor WDib |
| 'Sarah' ♀ | NHor WDib |
| *saxorum* ♀ | CHal CInt EMan LCns LHil LIck |
| | MBEx MBri NHor NTow SEND |
| | SRms SYvo WDib |
| - compact form | LCns WDib |
| 'Sian' | WDib |
| 'Snow White' ♀ | CSpe NHor WDib |
| * 'Something Special' | NHor WDib |
| 'Stella' ♀ | WDib |
| *stomandrus* | WDib |
| * 'Sugar Almond' | CSpe |
| 'Susan' ♀ | NHor WDib |
| * 'Sweet Violet' | CSpe |
| 'Tina' ♀ | MBri NHor WDib |
| 'Tracey' | NHor WDib |
| 'Upstart' | Last listed 1998 |
| 'Violet Lace' | CSpe |
| ¶ 'Wendy' | WDib |
| 'Wiesmoor Red' | MBri NHor WDib |
| 'Winifred' | NHor WDib |

## STREPTOLIRION (Commelinaceae)
| | |
|---|---|
| *volubile* | CPIN |

## STREPTOPUS (Convallariaceae)
| | |
|---|---|
| *amplexifolius* | Last listed 1998 |
| *roseus* | LAma |

## STREPTOSOLEN (Solanaceae)
| | |
|---|---|
| *jamesonii* ♀ | CHal CPIN CPle CSev EBak ELan |
| | ERea IBlr LCns LHil NRog SYvo |
| | WBod |
| - yellow | ERea MBEx |

## STROBILANTHES (Acanthaceae)
| | |
|---|---|
| *anisophylla* | CSpe WCot |
| *atropurpurea* | CBot CGle CGre CHan CHea CPle |
| | ECGN ECha EFou EHal ELan GCal |
| | LHil LLWP MCAu MHar NSti SUsu |
| | WCot WCru WFar WHer WMow |
| | WOld WPer WWin WWye |
| *attenuata* | SDys SWas WCot WCru WFar |
| | WMoo |
| - subsp. *nepalensis* | WWye |
| - - TSS | CGle CHan EBee EMar WRHF |
| *dyeriana* ♀ | CHal EBak WMul |
| ¶ *rankanensis* | WCru |
| *violacea* | ERea LFis SAga SMac WPer |

## STROMANTHE (Marantaceae)
| | |
|---|---|
| *amabilis* | See *Ctenanthe amabilis* |
| 'Freddy' | MBri |
| *sanguinea* | CHal MBri |
| - var. *spectabilis* ♀ | Last listed 1995 |
| 'Stripestar' | MBri |

## STROPHANTHUS (Apocynaceae)
| | |
|---|---|
| *kombe* | CPIN MSal |
| *preussii* | CPIN |
| *speciosus* | CPIN MSal |

## STRUTHIOPTERIS (Blechnaceae)
| | |
|---|---|
| *niponica* | See *Blechnum niponicum* |

## STRYCHNOS (Loganiaceae)
| | |
|---|---|
| *cocculoides* | LBlo |
| *madagascariensis* | LBlo |
| *spinosa* | LBlo |

## STUARTIA See STEWARTIA

## STYLIDIUM (Stylidiaceae)
| | |
|---|---|
| *crassifolium* ♀ | Last listed 1995 |
| *macranthum* | Last listed 1998 |

## STYLOMECON (Papaveraceae)
| | |
|---|---|
| ¶ *heterophylla* | WBor |

## STYLOPHORUM (Papaveraceae)
| | |
|---|---|
| *diphyllum* | CGen CHan CPBP CPou EBee |
| | ECGN ECha EMar EPar LAma |
| | MBel MRav MSal WCru WWhi |
| *lasiocarpum* | EBee EMar GMac MBel MCCP |
| | NCat NHed SSca WCot WCru |
| | WRos |

## STYPHELIA (Epacridaceae)
| | |
|---|---|
| *colensoi* | See *Cyathodes colensoi* |

## STYRAX (Styracaceae)
| | |
|---|---|
| *americanus* | CB&S |
| *formosanus* | WPGP |
| ¶ - var. *formosana* | WCru |
| B&SWJ 3803 | |
| *hemsleyanus* ♀ | CAbP CB&S CFil CTho EPfP MBlu |
| | SMad SPer SSpi SSta WNor WPGP |
| | WWat |
| *japonicus* ♀ | More than 30 suppliers |
| § - Benibana Group | SReu SSta |
| - (Benibana Group) | CAbP CEnd CMCN CPMA ELan |
| 'Pink Chimes' | EPfP MAsh MBlu MBri NPro SPer |
| | SSta WWat WWes |
| - 'Carillon' | CEnd ELan EPfP LRHS MAsh SPer |
| - 'Fargesii' | LRHS MAsh MBri SSpi SSta WFar |
| - 'Pendulus' | Last listed 1997 |
| - 'Roseus' | See *S. japonicus* Benibana Group |
| *obassia* ♀ | CArn CB&S CGre CMCN CPMA |
| | CTho CWSG EPfP LPan SReu SSpi |
| | SSta WNor WWat |
| *odoratissimus* | CArn |

## SUCCISA (Dipsacaceae)
| | |
|---|---|
| § *pratensis* | CArn CKin CRDP ECoo EMon |
| | EWFC MChe MFir MHew NLan |
| | NLar SSpi SUsu WGwy WHer |
| | WJek |
| - *alba* | SSpi |
| - 'Corinne Tremaine' (v) | WHer |
| - dwarf form | CLyd NTow |
| - 'Peddar's Pink' | EWes |
| - *rosea* | SSpi |

## SUTERA (Scrophulariaceae)
| | |
|---|---|
| ¶ 'African Sunset' | NPri |
| ♦ *breviflora* | See *Jamesbrittenia breviflora* |
| *cordata* | LHop |
| - Knysna Hills® | EHic LIck MBEx |
| - 'Lilac Pearls' | Last listed 1998 |
| - mauve | Last listed 1997 |
| - pale pink | Last listed 1997 |
| - 'Pink Domino' | Last listed 1998 |
| § - 'Snowflake' | CBar CHal CSpe LHil LPVe MBEx |
| | MLan NPri SCoo SMer WCom |
| | WLRN |
| ♦ *grandiflora* | See *Jamesbrittenia grandiflora* |

| | |
|---|---|
| *halimifolia* JCA 3-812 | EBee EHyt |
| ◆ *jurassica* | See *Jamesbrittenia jurassica* |
| – H&B  19148 | CPBP EHyt |
| * *rosea* 'Plena' | Last listed 1997 |

## SUTHERLANDIA (Papilionaceae)

| | |
|---|---|
| *frutescens* | CAbb CSpe CTrC LHop SHFr SWat |
| – Edinburgh strain | LLew |
| – 'Prostrata' | SIgm WCot |
| *microphylla* | Last listed 1998 |
| – S&SH 56/61 | CHan |
| *montana* | CFir SIgm |

## SWAINSONA (Papilionaceae)

| | |
|---|---|
| *formosa* | Last listed 1998 |
| *galegifolia* 'Albiflora' | CPin CSpe SMrm SOWG WCot |
| *macculochiana* | Last listed 1998 |
| *tephrotricha* | Last listed 1998 |

## SWERTIA (Gentianaceae)

| | |
|---|---|
| *kingii* | WThi |

## SYAGRUS (Arecaceae)

| | |
|---|---|
| § *romanzoffiana* | CBrP EOas LPJP LPal WMul |

## x SYCOPARROTIA (Hamamelidaceae)

| | |
|---|---|
| *semidecidua* | CB&S CFil CPMA LRHS MAsh SBid SSta WWat |

## SYCOPSIS (Hamamelidaceae)

| | |
|---|---|
| ¶ *heterophylla* | EBee |
| *sinensis* | EPfP ICrw LRHS SBid SSpi SSta WSHC WWat |

## SYMPHORICARPOS (Caprifoliaceae)

| | |
|---|---|
| *albus* | CChe CDul CKin ENot GChr NWea WDin |
| – 'Constance Spry' | MTed MUlv SRms |
| § – var. *laevigatus* | CB&S ENot GRei LBuc MBar |
| § – 'Taff's White' (v) | WMoo |
| – 'Turesson' | Last listed 1996 |
| – 'Variegatus' | See *S. albus* 'Taff's White' |
| x *chenaultii* 'Hancock' | EBee ELan ENot EPfP MBar MGos MRav MWat NLon NPro SPer WDin WFar |
| x *doorenbosii* 'Magic Berry' | CBlo EBee ENot LBuc MBar NWea |
| – 'Mother of Pearl' | CBlo CDul EBee ECha ELan ENot EPfP LBuc MBar MGos MRav NWea SPer WTro |
| – 'White Hedge' | EBee ELan ENot LBuc NWea SPer |
| *orbiculatus* | CBrm IMGH WGwG |
| – 'Albovariegatus' | See *S. orbiculatus* 'Taff's Silver Edge' |
| – 'Argenteovariegatus' | See *S. orbiculatus* 'Taff's Silver Edge' |
| – 'Bowles' Golden Variegated' | See *S. orbiculatus* 'Foliis Variegatis' |
| § – 'Foliis Variegatis' | CTri EBee EHal EHoe ELan ENot EPla GChr GEil LHop MBal MGos MRav NSti SEas SPer WEas WGwG WHCG WSHC WWal WWat WWin |
| § – 'Taff's Silver Edge' (v) | CB&S CBrm EHoe ELan EPla IOrc MBar MPla NSti WWat |
| – 'Variegatus' | See *S. orbiculatus* 'Foliis Variegatis' |
| *rivularis* | See *S. albus* var. *laevigatus* |

## SYMPHYANDRA ✿ (Campanulaceae)

| | |
|---|---|
| *armena* | CLTr CPea EBur EWTr GBuc MAvo MHar NPer SWat WRha |
| *asiatica* | CHan WWat |

| | |
|---|---|
| *cretica* | CPBP EBee EWll NTow SWat |
| – *alba* | Last listed 1997 |
| *hofmannii* | CGle EBee EBur ELan MBro MTho NBrk NFai NLar NWCA SRms SSca SWat WElm WOve WPer WRha WSan WWin |
| § *ossetica* | CGle MAvo NPla NWoo SSvw WCot WElm WSan |
| § *pendula* | CFir EBee EWTr EWes GBri GBuc MBNS NLar SCro SRot SSca WPer WThi |
| – *alba* | See *S. pendula* |
| * *tianschanica* | Last listed 1997 |
| *wanneri* | EBee EBur EMan EPfP MAvo MCCP NMen WWin |
| *zangezura* | CNic EBee EBur EEls LCot MAvo MHar SWat WRha |

## SYMPHYTUM (Boraginaceae)

| | |
|---|---|
| *asperum* | ECha EGar ELan EMon EPPr MHew MRav MSal MTed NLar WCHb WCer WOak |
| * *azureum* | EAst LRHS MBri MCAu MSte SRPl WCHb WFar WGwy |
| 'Belsay' | GBuc |
| 'Boking' | GAbr |
| *caucasicum* | CBre CElw CHan CMHG CSam ECha ELau EPar GPoy LEdu LHol MBri MHar NFai NSti SIde SSvw WCHb WHer WHil WOak WRha WWye |
| – 'Eminence' | CGle CRDP EBee EGoo WCHb WCot WOve |
| – 'Norwich Sky' | CInt NMir WCHb WPGP |
| 'Denford Variegated' | WCot |
| ¶ 'Empire' | SDys |
| § 'Goldsmith' (v) | More than 30 suppliers |
| *grandiflorum* | See *S. ibericum* |
| 'Hidcote Blue' | CBre CHan CMGP CTri ECha ELan ELau EPla EWTr ILis LHop MBri MCLN MSte NArg NBro NHol NSti SIde SIng SLPl SPer WCru WElm WPrP WWeb WWin |
| § 'Hidcote Pink' | CGle EAst EBee ECha ELau ENot EPla LHol LHop MMal MRav MSte MWgw NFla NRoo NSti SLPl SRPl WCer WFar |
| 'Hidcote Variegated' | CGle WCHb WRha |
| § *ibericum* | CAgr CArn CGle CHan CMHG CNic CSam ECha ELau EPla GPoy LGro LHol MCAu MDun MFir MNrw MWgw NSti SAWi SIde SRms WCHb WOve WWat |
| – 'All Gold' | ECha ELau EMon MBri SLon WCru |
| – 'Blaueglocken' | CBod CSev ECha NCat NRoo WPrP WSan |
| – dwarf form | SGre |
| – 'Gold in Spring' | EBee EGoo EMon WCHb WCer WFar WRha |
| – 'Jubilee' | See *S.* 'Goldsmith' |
| – 'Langthornes Pink' | Last listed 1998 |
| – 'Lilacinum' | MBro SAga WCer WHer WWat |
| – 'Pink Robins' | EMon WCHb |
| – 'Variegatum' | See *S.* 'Goldsmith' |
| – 'Wisley Blue' | ELan EPfP NCat WCer WWoo |
| ¶ 'Lambrook Silver' | SRPl |
| 'Lambrook Sunrise' | CLAP EBee EPPr EPla MRav NBus SCob SUsu WCot WPrP WSan |
| 'Langthorns Pink' | ELan EMar GBar GBri GBuc GCal WCHb WCer |
| 'Mereworth' (v) | EMon WCHb |

| | |
|---|---|
| *officinale* | CArn CKin CSev EPla GPoy LHol MChe MHew MMal MNrw MSal NFai NHex NMir NPer SIde SRms WGwG WHer WOak WWye |
| * - blue | WWat |
| - *ochroleucum* | WCHb WHer |
| *orientale* | CElw CGle EMon WCHb |
| *peregrinum* | See *S.* x *uplandicum* |
| 'Roseum' | See *S.* 'Hidcote Pink' |
| 'Rubrum' | EAst EBee ECot ELan ELau EOrc EPfP EWes MCAu MSte NOrc NRoo SMrm SPer WCru WOve |
| *tuberosum* | CArn CBre CElw CJew CMHG CRDP EGar ELau EOHP GPoy MFir MMal NCat NHol NSti SSvw WCHb WFar WHer WRha WWat WWye |
| - JMH 8106 | MDun |
| § x *uplandicum* | CSev ELan ELau EMar MHew MSal SIde WCHb WCer WGwG WHbs WJck WOak WWye |
| - 'Axminster Gold' (v) | CLAP CPlt CRDP CRow EMan IBlr SAga WCot |
| - 'Bocking 14' | CAgr CBod CJew |
| - 'Denford Variegated' | MInt |
| - 'Jenny Swales' | Last listed 1998 |
| - 'Variegatum' ♀ | CBot CGle CLAP ELau EOrc EWTr EWes GCal GPoy LHop MTho NGdn SCob SSpi WBea WCHb WCot WEas WFar WWat WWin |

## SYMPLOCARPUS (Araceae)

| | |
|---|---|
| *foetidus* | Last listed 1997 |

## SYMPLOCOS (Symplocaceae)

| | |
|---|---|
| *paniculata* | EPla LHyd MBlu |
| *pyrifolia* | CFil WPGP |

## SYNEILESIS (Asteraceae)

| | |
|---|---|
| *aconitifolia* B&SWJ 879 | WCru |
| *intermedia* B&SWJ 298 | WCru |
| *palmata* B&SWJ 1003 | WCru |

## SYNGONIUM (Araceae)

| | |
|---|---|
| 'Jenny' | Last listed 1996 |
| 'Maya Red' | MBri |
| *podophyllum* ♀ | LBlo |
| - 'Emerald Gem' | CHal |
| - 'Silver Knight' | MBri |
| - 'Variegatum' | MBri |
| 'White Butterfly' | CHal MBri |

## SYNNOTIA See SPARAXIS

## SYNTHYRIS (Scrophulariaceae)

| | |
|---|---|
| *missurica* | EBee NRya NTow |
| *pinnatifida* | NWCA |
| - var. *canescens* | Last listed 1998 |
| * - *laciniata* | Last listed 1996 |
| - var. *lanuginosa* | Last listed 1998 |
| - var. *pinnatifida* | Last listed 1998 |
| *reniformis* | IBlr WCot WHil |
| *stellata* | CLAP CRDP EBrP EBre GCal GGar LBre LFis SBre WHal WPGP |

## SYRINGA ✿ (Oleaceae)

| | |
|---|---|
| *afghanica* | See *S. protolaciniata* |
| ◆ *amurensis* | See *S. reticulata* subsp. *amurensis* |
| x *chinensis* | WWat |
| - 'Saugeana' | SPer WPyg |
| 'Correlata' (graft-chimaera) | IOrc |

| | |
|---|---|
| ¶ *debelderorum* subsp. *patula* | SSta |
| *emodi* | CBot WHCG |
| ¶ - 'Aurea' | EPla IHar |
| - 'Aureovariegata' | CEnd CPMA WDin |
| ¶ 'Fountain' | EPla |
| x *henryi* 'Alba' | WBcn |
| x *hyacinthiflora* | WStI |
| - 'Esther Staley' ♀ | ENot MRav SFam WAbe |
| - 'Laurentian' | SSta |
| ¶ - 'Maiden's Blush' | MBri |
| - 'Pocohontas' | Last listed 1997 |
| - 'Sunset' (d) | Last listed 1998 |
| - 'The Bride' | Last listed 1998 |
| ¶ 'Josee' | EBee |
| x *josiflexa* 'Bellicent' ♀ | CEnd CHan CPle CTho ELan ENot ISea MAsh MBal MBar MGos MRav MTis NFla NSti SMur SPer SPla SRms SSta WHCG WPat |
| - 'Lynette' | CTho EPla WBcn |
| - 'Royalt' | Last listed 1997 |
| § - 'Royalty' | COtt |
| *josikaea* | CBlo CPMA CPle MBar SPer WHCG |
| *julianae* | See *S. pubescens* subsp. *julianae* |
| ¶ *komarovii* L 490 | GGGa |
| § - subsp. *reflexa* ♀ | CDul EPfP LBuc MBar MGos MRav WWat |
| § x *laciniata* Miller | CBot CPMA CPle EBee EHol MBri MRav SMrm SMur SPer SSpi WGor WHCG WSHC WWat |
| § *meyeri* var. *spontanea* 'Palibin' ♀ | More than 30 suppliers |
| *microphylla* | See *S. pubescens* subsp. *microphylla* |
| - 'Superba' | See *S. pubescens* subsp. *microphylla* 'Superba' |
| ¶ - 'Minuet' | MGos |
| *oblata* | WWoo |
| - var. *donaldii* | SSta |
| ◆ *palibiniana* | See *S. meyeri* var. *spontanea* 'Palibin' |
| *patula* (Palibin) Nakai | See *S. pubescens* subsp. *patula* |
| - hort. | See *S. meyeri* var. *spontanea* 'Palibin' |
| *pekinensis* | See *S. reticulata* subsp. *pekinensis* |
| x *persica* ♀ | CBlo EPfP ERav ISea MGos MWat SLon SPer SPla WPyg WSpi WWat |
| - 'Alba' ♀ | CBot GQui SPla WHCG WSHC WWat |
| - var. *laciniata* | See *S.* x *laciniata* |
| *pinnatifolia* | CBot CPle WHCG |
| x *prestoniae* 'Agnes Smith' | MGos |
| - 'Audrey' | MGos |
| - 'Coral' | COtt MBri WFar |
| - 'Desdemona' | Last listed 1998 |
| - 'Elinor' ♀ | CBlo CMHG CPMA CPle ENot ISea MRav NSti SPer |
| ¶ - 'Hiawatha' | MGos |
| - 'Isabella' | MGos NFla SLdr |
| ¶ - 'Nocturne' | MGos WFar |
| - 'Redwine' | COtt MBri MGos |
| ◆ - 'Royalty' | See *S.* x *josiflexa* 'Royalty' |
| § *protolaciniata* | CMHG EPla MBlu MPla SSta WAbe WFar |
| § *pubescens* subsp. *microphylla* | MHlr |

§ - subsp. *microphylla* 'Superba' ♀ — CDoC CDul CPle EBee ELan ENot EWTr GChr IOrc MAsh MBel MBri MBro MGos MRav NBee NFla NHol NRoo SBod SPer SPla SSpi SSta WHCG WPat WPyg WSHC WWal WWat

§ - subsp. *patula* — EAst ELan IOrc LNet MBal MRav MWat NBee NRoo SPla WAbe WStI

§ - - 'Miss Kim' ♀ — CBlo EBee EBrP EBre ECle GOrc LBre MAsh MBel MBri MGos MRav NPro NRoo SBre SSta WDin WGwG WHCG WPat WPyg

*reflexa* — See *S. komarovii* subsp. *reflexa*

*reticulata* — Last listed 1997

§ - subsp. *amurensis* — MBal

♦ - var. *mandschurica* — See *S. reticulata* subsp. *amurensis*

§ - subsp. *pekinensis* — CBot CMCN

¶ x *swegiflexa* — CPLG

*sweginzowii* — CSam LBuc MBal SPer WRus WWat

*tomentella* — CDul CPle CWSG NWea SRms

♦ *velutina* — See *S. pubescens* subsp. *patula*

*villosa* — MWhi

*vulgaris* — GOrc LBuc MBar NWea

- 'Adelaide Dunbar' (d) — Last listed 1997

¶ - 'Agincourt Beauty' — MBri

- var. *alba* — MBar

- 'Albert F. Holden' — SSta

§ - 'Andenken an Ludwig Späth' ♀ — CB&S CBot CDoC CDul CTho CTri ENot EWTr IOrc LPan MBar MBri MGos MRav NWea SLon SPer WFar WPyg WWeb

- 'Arthur William Paul' (d) — MRav

- 'Aurea' — EPla MRav WBcn

- 'Avalanche' — SSta

¶ - 'Beauty of Moscow' — MBri

- 'Belle de Nancy' (d) — EHic ELan EWTr MAsh MBri MWat WDin WLRN WPyg

- 'Charles Joly' (d) ♀ — CB&S CBlo CDoC CDul CTho EBee ELan ENot EWTr GChr GRei IOrc LNet MAsh MBal MBar MBri MGos MRav NBee NWea SPer SRPl WDin WFar WStI

- 'Charm' — Last listed 1997

- 'Condorcet' (d) — LNet

- 'Congo' — CDoC EBee EHic ENot NMoo SCoo SPer

- 'Edward J. Gardner' (d) — ENot MBri SPer

- 'Ellen Willmott' (d) — MRav

- 'Firmament' ♀ — ELan ENot SCoo SPer

¶ - 'Glory' — 

- 'Glory of Horstenstein' — See *S. vulgaris* 'Ruhm von Horstenstein'

- 'Katherine Havemeyer' (d) ♀ — CB&S CBot CCbe CDoC CDul CSam CTri EBee ELan ENot EWTr GChr GRei LBuc MAsh MBri MGos MRav SFam SPer SReu WDin WStI

- 'Krasavitsa Moskvy' — Last listed 1998

- 'Lucie Baltet' — MBri

- 'Madame Antoine Buchner' (d) ♀ — ENot

- 'Madame Florent Stepman' — CBlo

- 'Madame Lemoine' (d) ♀ — More than 30 suppliers

- 'Masséna' — ENot MRav SCoo SPer WWeb

- 'Maud Notcutt' — ENot SCoo SPer

- 'Michel Buchner' (d) — CB&S EBee ENot GRei IOrc MAsh MBar MBri MWat

¶ - 'Miss Ellen Willmott' (d) — MBri

- 'Mrs Edward Harding' (d) ♀ — EBee ENot LBuc LNet MBal MBri MGos SPer WLRN

- 'Olivier de Serres' — MBri

¶ - 'Paul Deschanel' (d) — MBri

- 'Paul Thirion' (d) — Last listed 1997

- 'Président Grévy' (d) — CDoC ECle MBri SPer

- 'Primrose' — CBlo CBot CDoC CTho EBee EHic ELan ENot EPfP EPla MBal MRav SPer SSta WDin WLRN

¶ - 'Rochester' — MBri

- 'Romance' — SSta

- 'Sensation' — CBlo CDoC CPle EBee EHic ENot MRav SCoo SLdr SPer SSta

- 'Silver King' — SSta

- 'Souvenir de Louis Spaeth' — See *S. vulgaris* 'Andenken an Ludwig Späth'

- variegated double (d) — MBal WBcn

- 'Vestale' ♀ — CBlo ENot SCoo

*wolfii* — CPle

*yunnanensis* — CTho

- 'Rosea' — Last listed 1998

## SYZYGIUM (Myrtaceae)

¶ *wilsonii* — ECon

# T

## TABERNAEMONTANA (Apocynaceae)

*coronaria* — See *T. divaricata*

§ *divaricata* — Last listed 1996

## TACCA (Taccaceae)

* *nivea* — WMul

## TACITUS See GRAPTOPETALUM

## TAGETES (Asteraceae)

*lemmonii* — SMac

*lucida* — EOHP MSal

## TALBOTIA (Velloziaceae)

*elegans* — WCot

## TALINUM (Portulacaceae)

*calycinum* — Last listed 1998

*okanoganense* — CGra NTow NWCA

*rugospermum* — Last listed 1998

*teretifolium* — WThi

'Zoe' — WFar

## TAMARINDUS (Caesalpiniaceae)

*indica* (F) — ELau LBlo

## TAMARIX (Tamaricaceae)

*africana* — WWin

*gallica* — CBlo ENot GCHN NWea SAPC SArc SEND WSHC

*germanica* — See *Myricaria germanica*

§ *parviflora* — CB&S CBlo EMil IOrc LRHS MGos SSoC WWal

*pentandra* — See *T. ramosissima*

§ *ramosissima* — EBrP EBre ELan EPla GChr LBre MBar SBre SEND SMrm SRms SSoC SSta WDin WSHC WTro WWeb

- 'Pink Cascade' — EBee EMil ENot EPfP GChr MBri MGos MRav SEas SPer WDin WGwG WStI WWal

§ - 'Rubra' ♀ — CBlo CCbe CDoC EBee EMil ENot EPfP IOrc MBlu MGos MMHG SLon WPyg

| | |
|---|---|
| - 'Summer Glow' | See *T. ramosissima* 'Rubra' |
| **tetrandra** ♀ | CB&S EBee EBrP EBre ELan ENot |
| | GChr GOrc LBre LNet LPan MBar |
| | MWat NBee NFor NPer SBre SPer |
| | SReu SRms WBod WBrE WFar |
| | WHar WRHF WStI WTro WWeb |
| - var. **purpurea** | See *T. parviflora* |

**TAMUS** (Dioscoreaceae)

| | |
|---|---|
| **communis** | CArn |

**TANACETUM** ✿ (Asteraceae)

| | |
|---|---|
| § **argenteum** | MRav MTho NTow |
| - subsp. **canum** | ELan EWes MAsh |
| § **balsamita** | CArn ELan ELau EOHP ERav GPoy |
| | MBri MSal WHbs WHer WJek |
| | WOak WPer WSel WWye |
| § - subsp. **balsametoides** | CBod ELau LHol MChe MHer |
| | MRav NPri SIde WJek WWye |
| § - subsp. **balsamita** | EOHP GPoy LHol MRav MSal SIde |
| - var. **tanacetoides** | See *T. balsamita* subsp. |
| | *balsamita* |
| - **tomentosum** | See *T. balsamita* subsp. |
| | *balsametoides* |
| **capitatum** | See *Sphaeromeria capitata* |
| § **cinerariifolium** | CArn CBod CInt EOHP GPoy SPil |
| | SUsu WPer |
| § **coccineum** | CFri GBar GPoy MSal NVic SRms |
| | WWin |
| I - 'Andromeda' | Last listed 1997 |
| - 'Aphrodite' | Last listed 1998 |
| - 'Bees' Pink Delight' | Last listed 1997 |
| - 'Brenda' ♀ | Last listed 1998 |
| * - 'Duplex' | Last listed 1998 |
| - 'Duro' | CMdw GBuc NCut |
| - 'Eileen May Robinson' ♀ | ECot EPfP NCut SMrm |
| - 'Evenglow' | CM&M MRav MTis SMrm |
| - 'H.M. Pike' | Last listed 1998 |
| - 'James Kelway' ♀ | ECot ENot EPfP ERic EWll GChr |
| | MBri MRav NBir NFai SMrm SRms |
| | WSan |
| - 'K.M. Price' | Last listed 1998 |
| - 'Kelway's Glorious' | NCut |
| - 'King Size' | CSam NMir WFar |
| - 'Laurin' | Last listed 1998 |
| - 'Madeleine' (d) | MTis |
| - 'Phillipa' | Last listed 1997 |
| - 'Pink Petite' | Last listed 1997 |
| - 'Queen Mary' | SLon SPla |
| - Robinson's giant flowered | SRms WMoo WRHF |
| - 'Robinson's Pink' | GMaP NOrc NPla NPri NRoo |
| | SMrm SRms |
| - 'Robinson's Red' | GMaP LIck NOrc NPla NPri NRoo |
| | SMrm SPla WRus |
| - 'Salmon Beauty' | Last listed 1998 |
| - 'Scarlet Glow' | Last listed 1998 |
| - 'Snow Cloud' | EBee SMrm |
| - 'Vanessa' | SMrm |
| § **corymbosum** | CGle EBee GCal LFis NCat WCot |
| § - subsp. **clusii** | Last listed 1997 |
| § - 'Festafel' | MRav |
| **densum** | ECho EPot WCFE |
| - subsp. **amani** | EBee ECha ELan EMFP ESis GTou |
| | LBee LGro MPla MWat NRoo |
| | NWCA SEND SRms SSmi WCom |
| | WWin |
| § **haradjanii** | CGle ELan EMNN GCHN MBro |
| | MHar NFor SBla SChu WByw |
| | WEas WHer WHoo WOld WSHC |
| **herderi** | See *Hippolytia herderi* |
| ¶ **huronense** | EBee |
| 'Jackpot' | EWes LRHS WMow |

| | |
|---|---|
| § **macrophyllum** | EMon EPla GCal LGre WCot WPer |
| **niveum** | CArn CHad EBee EGar EOHP |
| | MSal SPil WBea WCot |
| **pallidum** | See *Leucanthemopsis pallida* |
| § **parthenium** | CArn CKin EEls ELau EWFC GBar |
| | GPoy LHol MChe MHew MMal |
| | NFai NHex NPer NRoo SIde SRms |
| | WGwG WHer WOak WWye |
| - 'Aureum' | CHid CM&M CRow ECha EEls |
| | ELan ELau EOld GPoy LGro MBri |
| | MChe MMal NFai NHex SIng SPer |
| | SRms WCot WEas WHer WOak |
| | WOve WPer WWin |
| - 'Ball's Double White' (d) | SRms |
| - double white (d) | CM&M CSWP GBar GPoy NPer |
| | SEND SRms |
| - 'Golden Ball' | NTow SPil WCot |
| - 'Plenum' (d) | EHrv SIng |
| § - 'Rowallane' (d) | EHol ELan GBuc MAvo MBri |
| | WCot |
| - 'Silver Ball' | LPVe |
| - 'Sissinghurst White' | See *T. parthenium* 'Rowallane' |
| - 'Snowball' (d) | SPil |
| - 'White Bonnet' (d) | CGle NBrk WEas |
| **poteriifolium** | LFis |
| § **praeteritum** | LGre |
| - subsp. **massicyticum** | IDac |
|   MP 95277 | |
| **pseudachillea** | Last listed 1997 |
| § **ptarmiciflorum** | SMer WCot |
| - 'Silver Feather' | EPPr SPil |
| sp. CC&McK 460 | GTou |
| **vulgare** | CAgr CArn CKin CSev ECtt EEls |
| | ELau EWFC GPoy LHol MChe |
| | MHar MHew MMal MSal NLan |
| | SIde SPer WCla WOak WWye |
| - var. **crispum** | CJew CStr EBot ELan ELau EOHP |
| | EPla GBar GCal GPoy LFis MAvo |
| | MBri MRav NHex NLon NVic SIde |
| | WBea WCot WFar WGwy WHer |
| | WJek WOak WRha WSel |
| - 'Isla Gold' | CBod CJew EBee EFou EMon |
| | EWes GCal LFis MHar MHlr MMil |
| | SMad SUsu WCHb WCot WFar |
| | WRha WWye |
| - 'Silver Lace' (v) | ECha EMon GBri LFis NBrk NHex |
| | NSti SEND WBea WCHb WCot |
| | WFar WHer |

**TANAKAEA** (Saxifragaceae)

| | |
|---|---|
| **radicans** | WCru |

**TAPEINOCHILOS** (Zingiberaceae)

| | |
|---|---|
| **ananassae** | Last listed 1996 |

**TAPISCIA** (Staphyleaceae)

| | |
|---|---|
| **sinensis** | CLyn |

**TARASA** (Malvaceae)

| | |
|---|---|
| **humilis** | CPBP |

**TARAXACUM** (Asteraceae)

| | |
|---|---|
| **albidum** B&SWJ 509 | EBee |
| ¶ - DJH 452 | WCot |
| **carneocoloratum** | Last listed 1998 |
| I **officinale** | MHew SIde |
| ¶ - **sativum** | IIve |
| - white-flowered | WAlt |
| **pamiricum** JJH 395 | EHyt |

**TASMANNIA** See DRIMYS

**TAXODIUM** (Taxodiaceae)

| | |
|---|---|
| *ascendens* | See *T. distichum* var. *imbricatum* |
| § *distichum* ♀ | CB&S CDoC CDul CLnd CMCN CMac EHul ELan ENot GChr LCon LNet MBal MBar MBlu MBri MRav NPal NWea SPer SReu WDin WFar WFro WGer WHar WNor WWat |
| - var. *imbricatum* | CB&S CEnd IOrc LPan MBlu MBri |
| 'Nutans' ♀ | SMur |
| *mucronatum* | LCon WFro |

**TAXUS** ✿ (Taxaceae)

| | |
|---|---|
| *baccata* ♀ | More than 30 suppliers |
| - 'Adpressa Aurea' | CKen EPla GAri MPla |
| - 'Adpressa Variegata' (m) ♀ | EHul LCon MAsh SLim |
| - 'Aldenham Gold' | CKen |
| - 'Amersfoort' | EOrn EPla LCon SSpi |
| - 'Argentea Minor' | See *T. baccata* 'Dwarf White' |
| § - Aurea Group | CBlo EPot SRms WShe |
| I - 'Aurea Pendula' | EBrP EBre EOrn LBre SBre |
| I - 'Aureomarginata' | CB&S EOrn NMoo WStI |
| - 'Cavendishii' (f) | ECho |
| - 'Compacta' | EOrn EPla |
| - 'Corley's Coppertip' | CBlo CFee CKen CSam EHul EOrn EPot GPin LCon LLin MAsh MBar MBri MOne NHol WGwG WLRN WWal |
| - 'Cristata' | Last listed 1998 |
| - 'David' | LBee |
| - 'Dovastoniana' (f) ♀ | CDoC CMac LCon MBar NWea |
| - 'Dovastonii Aurea' (m/v) ♀ | CDoC CMac EHul EOrn EPla GChr LBee LCon LHol LPan MBar MBri SLim WDin |
| - 'Drinkstone Gold' | EHul EPla WBcn |
| § - 'Dwarf White' (f/v) | EOrn EPla LCon NHol |
| - 'Elegantissima' (f/v) ♀ | EHul EPfP MPla NWea |
| § - 'Erecta' (f) | EHul |
| § - 'Fastigiata' (f) ♀ | More than 30 suppliers |
| - 'Fastigiata Aurea' | CKen CLnd EAst EHul ELan LBuc LEdu LLin LPan MGos NBee NHol NPer NRar NRoo SRms WBrE WFar WHar WLRN |
| - 'Fastigiata Aureomarginata' (m) ♀ | CDoC CKen CMac EAst EBrP EBre EHul EOrn EPot GRei IMGH IOrc ISea LBee LBre LCon LPan MBal MBar MBri MGos MWat NWea SBre SLim SLon WGwG WMou WWal |
| - 'Fastigiata Robusta' (f) | EBrP EBre EPla LBre MBar MBri SBre WGer WPyg |
| ¶ - 'Gemers Gold' | LPan |
| - 'Glenroy New Penny' | MBal |
| ¶ - 'Goud Elsje' | CKen EOrn GPin WLRN |
| ¶ - 'Green Column' | CKen |
| - 'Green Diamond' | CKen WBcn |
| - 'Hibernica' | See *T. baccata* 'Fastigiata' |
| ¶ - 'Icicle' | CB&S LCon LLin MGos |
| - 'Ivory Tower' | CB&S LCon LLin MGos |
| - 'Judith' | Last listed 1996 |
| - 'Melfard' | EHul |
| - 'Nutans' | CKen CNic EHul EOrn ESis IMGH LCon LLin MBar MOne WLRN |
| - 'Overeynderi' | EHul |
| - 'Pendula' | MBal MRav |
| ¶ - 'Prostrata' | CMac |
| - 'Pumila Aurea' | ELan MAsh |
| - 'Pygmaea' | CKen IOrc |
| - 'Repandens' (f) ♀ | CDoC EHul LCon LPan MBar WCFE WFar WGer |

| | |
|---|---|
| I - 'Repens Aurea' (v) ♀ | CDoC CHig CKen EHul ELan EOrn GCHN LCon LLin MAsh MBar MBri MGos MPla NFla NHol NRoo SAga |
| - 'Rushmore' | Last listed 1997 |
| - 'Semperaurea' (m) ♀ | CB&S CMac CSli EBrP EBre EHul ELan EOrn EPla GCHN LBee LBre LBuc LCon LPan MBal MBar MBri MGos NWea SAga SBre SLim SPla WDin WFar |
| - 'Silver Spire' (v) | CB&S CKen |
| - 'Standishii' (f) ♀ | CB&S CDoC CKen CMac CSli EHul ELan EOrn EPla GCHN IMGH IOrc LBee LCon LLin LNet LPan MAsh MBal MBar MBri MGos MRav MWat NHol SAga SLim SSmi WDin |
| - 'Summergold' (v) | CSli EBrP EBre EHul ELan ENot GCHN GChr GRei IOrc LBre LCon MAsh MBar MGos NHol NRoo SBre SLim WPyg WStI |
| - 'Variegata' | See *T. baccata* Aurea Group |
| - 'Washingtonii' (f) | Last listed 1998 |
| - 'White Icicle' | EOrn WWeb |
| *brevifolia* | EPla LCon |
| *cuspidata* | ETen |
| - 'Aurescens' | CKen EPla MAsh SRms |
| - f. *nana* | EHul EOrn GAri LCon MBar WGwG WLRN WWal |
| - 'Robusta' | EHul LLin |
| - 'Straight Hedge' | CDoC EHul GPin IMGH WLRN |
| x *media* 'Brownii' | EHul LBuc |
| - 'Hicksii' (f) ♀ | CEnd CLnd EHul IMGH LBuc LNet MBar NRoo NWea SLim WLRN |
| - 'Hillii' | CBlo MBar |
| ¶ - 'Lodi' | LBee |
| ¶ - 'Viridis' | MGos |

**TECOMA** (Bignoniaceae)

| | |
|---|---|
| ¶ x *alata* | CPIN |
| *capensis* ♀ | CPIN CSev EBak EHol ELan EMil ERea LHil SOWG SSoC SYvo |
| - 'Apricot' | CSpe EHol |
| - 'Aurea' | CSev CSpe ERea SOWG |
| § - 'Coccinea' | CSpe |
| - 'Lutea' | WMul |
| - subsp. *nyassae* | ERea |
| § - 'Salmonea' | CSpe |
| ♦ 'Coccinea' | See *T. capensis* 'Coccinea' |
| *garrocha* | CPIN |
| 'Orange Glow' | SOWG |
| *ricasoliana* | See *Podranea ricasoliana* |
| ♦ 'Salmon' | See *T. capensis* 'Salmonea' |
| *stans* | CPIN |

**TECOMANTHE** (Bignoniaceae)

| | |
|---|---|
| *dendrophila* | CPIN |
| *speciosa* | CPIN ECou |

**TECOMARIA** See TECOMA

**TECOPHILAEA** (Tecophilaeaceae)

| | |
|---|---|
| *cyanocrocus* ♀ | CAvo CBro EHyt EPot LAma LRHS WCot |
| - 'Leichtlinii' ♀ | CAvo CBro EHyt EPot LAma LRHS SSpi |
| - 'Purpurea' | See *T. cyanocrocus* 'Violacea' |
| - Storm Cloud Group | Last listed 1997 |
| § - 'Violacea' | CAvo CBro EPot LRHS |
| *violiflora* | LAma |

**TECTARIA** (Dryopteridaceae)

| | |
|---|---|
| *gemmifera* | GQui NMar |

**TECTONA** (Verbenaceae)

| | |
|---|---|
| ¶ *grandis* | LBlo |

**TELANTHOPHORA** (Asteraceae)

| | |
|---|---|
| *grandifolia* | SAPC SArc |

**TELEKIA** (Asteraceae)

| | |
|---|---|
| § *speciosa* | CHan CNic CSam EBee ELan LFis MCCP MFir MHar MRav NBro NBus NPSI SChr SDix SMac WByw WFar WHer WOld WPer WPrP WRHF |

**TELEPHIUM** (Molluginaceae)

| | |
|---|---|
| ¶ *imperati* | NSla |

**TELESONIX** See BOYKINIA

**TELINE** See GENISTA

**TELLIMA** (Saxifragaceae)

| | |
|---|---|
| *grandiflora* | More than 30 suppliers |
| - 'Delphine' | CElw |
| * - 'Forest Frost' | WCot |
| - Odorata Group | CBre ECha EGoo IHdy MRav NBrk NCat NLak NSti WGwG WHen WPrP WWal WWat WWye |
| - 'Purpurea' | See *T. grandiflora* Rubra Group |
| - 'Purpurteppich' | CGle EBee ECha EGoo EPPr LPio MRav NCat NDov WPrP WWat |
| § - Rubra Group | More than 30 suppliers |

**TELOPEA** (Proteaceae)

| | |
|---|---|
| *mongaensis* | Last listed 1997 |
| *speciosissima* | CTrC |
| *truncata* | CFil ISea SSpi WCru WPGP |

**TEMPLETONIA** (Papilionaceae)

| | |
|---|---|
| *retusa* | ECou SRCN |

**TEPHROSERIS** (Asteraceae)

| | |
|---|---|
| *integrifolia* | WHer |

**TERNSTROEMIA** (Theaceae)

| | |
|---|---|
| *gymnanthera* | See *T. japonica* |
| § *japonica* | EPfP SBid |

**TETRACENTRON** (Tetracentraceae)

| | |
|---|---|
| *sinense* | CFil CGre CPle CWSG EPfP GQui SBid SFur SLon SSpi |

**TETRADIUM** (Rutaceae)

| | |
|---|---|
| § *daniellii* | CFil CMCN EPfP IDee NPal SSpi WPGP WWat |
| § - Hupehense Group | CB&S CMCN EBee GGGa MBri SSpi WDin |
| ¶ *glabrifolium* B&SWJ 3541 | WCru |
| *velutinum* | CMCN |

**TETRAGONOLOBUS** See LOTUS

**TETRANEURIS** (Asteraceae)

| | |
|---|---|
| *acaulis* var. *caespitosa* K 92.258 | Last listed 1996 |
| § *grandiflora* | CPBP |

| | |
|---|---|
| - JCA 11422 | Last listed 1998 |
| § *scaposa* | EPot |

**TETRAPANAX** (Araliaceae)

| | |
|---|---|
| § *papyrifer* ♀ | CTrC SAPC SArc |

**TETRAPATHAEA** See PASSIFLORA

**TETRASTIGMA** (Vitaceae)

| | |
|---|---|
| *voinierianum* ♀ | CPIN ECon GLch LCns MBri SAPC SArc |

**TEUCRIDIUM** (Lamiaceae)

| | |
|---|---|
| *parvifolium* | Last listed 1998 |

**TEUCRIUM** (Lamiaceae)

| | |
|---|---|
| * *ackermannii* | CLyd EGoo EHyt LBee LHop MBro NMen SBla SCro SIng SMac WAbe WHoo WPat |
| * *arabii* | Last listed 1998 |
| *arduinoi* | CPle |
| *aroanium* | CLyd CMea CPBP EGle EPot LBee MBro MWat NMen SBla SHFr WAbe |
| *asiaticum* | CSam EGoo SSca |
| *bicolor* | CPle SSta WWye |
| *botrys* | MHew MSal |
| *canadense* | Last listed 1998 |
| *chamaedrys* hort. | See *T.* x *lucidrys* |
| - L. | CHal CSam EGoo ESis GBar LFis NHol NRoo NWCA SRms SVen WCer WHbs WHoo WSel WTro WWat |
| - 'Nanum' | CLyd MBro WPat WPyg WWye |
| - 'Rose Carpet' | CMGP EGoo EOrc EWTr MHar SUsu |
| - subsp. *tauricola* | IDac |
| - 'Variegatum' | EGoo GBar LLWP MAvo MHar NHol WCHb WCot WOve WPer WRha WSel |
| § *creticum* | WLin |
| *cyprium* | Last listed 1998 |
| * *discolor* | Last listed 1997 |
| *flavum* | WHer WPGP |
| *fruticans* | More than 30 suppliers |
| - 'Album' | CPle |
| - 'Azureum' ♀ | CB&S CBot CHar CM&M CPle CSpe ERav MBro MWhi SAga SBra WAbe WBod WPat WPyg WSpi |
| - 'Collingwood Ingram' | EBee |
| - 'Compactum' | CDoC EGoo EHic EPla ESis LFis LHop SLon SMrm SPer SPla WAbe WBay WSHC WWat |
| - dark form | SMrm |
| *halacysanum* | Last listed 1998 |
| *hircanicum* | CArn CPle CSam EBee ECoo EGoo EHic EHrv ELan EMan EMar EMon EMou GBin LGre LHop LLWP MBro MCCP MFir MNrw MSte NChi NSti SAga WBea WCot WWye |
| § x *lucidrys* | CAgr CArn CChe CMea CSev EAst EBee EGoo EHyt ELan ELau ERea GAbr GPoy IOrc LHol MBal MChe MPla MRav SIde SMad SPer SRCN SRms WCla WEas WGwG WOak WWin |
| *lucidum* | EWTr GBin WCla WOak |
| *majoricum* | See *T. polium* f. *pii-fontii* |
| *marum* | CArn EOHP MSal NMen SIgm SVen WJek |
| *massiliense* L. | EGoo EOrc WHer |

| | |
|---|---|
| - hort. | See *T.* x *lucidrys* |
| *montanum* | CMea |
| *musimonum* | CLyd EHyt NNrd |
| *polium* | CArn CLyd ESis MBro MWat SIgm WPat |
| - *aureum* | NWCA SBla SIng |
| *pulverulentum* | See *T. cossonii* |
| *pyrenaicum* | CHal CMea EGoo GCrs LBee MBro NSla NWCA WPat WPyg WWin WWye |
| *rosmarinifolium* | See *T. creticum* |
| *scordium* | CNat WWhi |
| *scorodonia* | CArn CKin CSev EGoo ELau EWFC GPoy MChe MHer MHew MSal NMir WCla WHer WJek WOak WSel WWye |
| - 'Cae Rhos Lligwy' (v) | Last listed 1996 |
| - 'Crispum' | CB&S CHan CInt ELau EMar EOrc MFir MHar MLLN MSCN MWat MWgw NBro NFai SMrm WBod WCHb WKif WOak WPer WSel WWat |
| * - 'Crispum Aureomarginatum' | MLLN |
| § - 'Crispum Marginatum' (v) | More than 30 suppliers |
| - 'Winterdown' (v) | CMea CNat LHop WAlt WCHb WCot WHer WLin |
| *subspinosum* | CMea ITim LBee MBro NHol NMen NTow SBla WPat WPyg |
| *webbianum* | ECho |

## THALIA (Marantaceae)

| | |
|---|---|
| *dealbata* | LEdu MSta WMAq WMul |

## THALICTRUM ✿ (Ranunculaceae)

| | |
|---|---|
| *actaeifolium* | EBee |
| *adiantifolium* | See *T. minus adiantifolium* |
| ¶ *alpinum* | EBee |
| *angustifolium* | See *T. lucidum* |
| *aquilegiifolium* | More than 30 suppliers |
| - var. *album* | CBot CMil EBee ECGN ECha EFou ELan EPla LFis MBri MBro MCAu MCLN MHlr MNrw MWgw NPSI NSti NTow SCro SSpi WEas WHoo WPer |
| - dwarf form | Last listed 1998 |
| * - 'Hybridum' | CHad EHic WFar WMoo WPer |
| - Purple Cloud | See *T. aquilegiifolium* 'Thundercloud' |
| - 'Purpureum' | CHid CSev EBee ECGN LFis LPio MBro MTis NLar NPSI SPla WCru WHoo |
| § - 'Thundercloud' ♀ | CBro CFir EBrP EBre ECtt EMan GCal LBre MBel MBri MCLN MUlv NHol SBre WCot WMer WPrP |
| *baicalense* | EBee |
| ♦ *bulgaricum* | See *T. flavidum* |
| *calabricum* | Last listed 1998 |
| § *chelidonii* | CElw EBee GMaP |
| ¶ - B&SWJ 2520 | WCru |
| - dwarf form | SLon WPrP |
| *clavatum* | EBee |
| *coreanum* | See *T. ichangense* |
| *coriaceum* | EBee |
| *cultratum* HWJCM 367 | EBee GNau SSpi WCru |
| *dasycarpum* | EMan LFis MLLN |
| § *delavayi* ♀ | More than 30 suppliers |
| - 'Album' | CGle CRDP CSpe EAst ECha EFou LGre LPio MBro NOak WHoo WMaN |
| - 'Hewitt's Double' (d) ♀ | More than 30 suppliers |
| - 'Sternhimmel' | Last listed 1997 |

| | |
|---|---|
| *diffusiflorum* | NHar SBla |
| *dipterocarpum* hort. | See *T. delavayi* |
| *fendleri* | GBuc |
| ¶ - NNS 93-738 | IDac |
| ¶ *filamentosum* | EMon |
| - B&SWJ 777 | WCru |
| *finetii* | Last listed 1998 |
| § *flavidum* | EBee |
| *flavum* | CGle CHan EBee EFou EOld NBro NDea NPri SSpi WRha |
| - 'Chollerton' | See *T.* sp. from Afghanistan |
| I - 'Glauca' | LSyl WCot |
| § - subsp. *glaucum* ♀ | More than 30 suppliers |
| - 'Illuminator' | CHad CHid CSam EBee ECle MArl MBel MBri MCAu MCLN MMil MOne NHol NPri SBid WCot |
| *flexuosum* | See *T. minus* subsp. *minus* |
| *foetidum* | Last listed 1998 |
| *foliolosum* B&SWJ 2705 | WCru |
| ¶ - S&SH 382 | CHan |
| § *ichangense* | CRDP SMrm |
| *isopyroides* | CLTr CLon CPBP CSev CVer EAst EBee EHic EMon EPla GBin LPio MRav NChi NRya SLon SMrm WCru WLRN WLin WPrP |
| *javanicum* B&L 12327 | Last listed 1998 |
| *kiusianum* | More than 30 suppliers |
| - Kew form | CBos CRDP SWas WPat |
| *koreanum* | See *T. ichangense* |
| § *lucidum* | CPou EBee EHal ELan LGre MRav NLar SMrm SSca |
| *minus* | CAgr CHan CMHG EBee ELan EMan GAbr GBuc MBel MBri MNrw MUlv NHol NOak NRoo NSti SPla WHil WPat WPrP WWye |
| § - *adiantifolium* | CMGP EAst EBee EHic EPla LRHS MRav NOak NPSI SCob SMrm SRms WMer WPer WWat |
| - subsp. *minus* | Last listed 1998 |
| - subsp. *olympicum* | WPer |
| - subsp. *saxatile* | See *T. minus* subsp. *olympicum* |
| ¶ *morisonii* | EBee |
| *occidentale* JLS 86255 | EMon MNrw |
| *orientale* | SBla WCot WPat |
| *pauciflorum* | Last listed 1997 |
| *polycarpum* | NHol |
| *polygamum* | EBee EBrP EBre LBre LFis LGre MSal MUlv SBre SUsu WCot |
| *punctatum* B&SWJ 1272 | EBee GBin LGre MBri NSti STes WCru WGwy |
| *ramosum* | Last listed 1998 |
| ¶ *reniforme* B&SWJ 2159 | WCru |
| - B&SWJ 2610 | EBee WCru |
| *rhynchocarpum* | Last listed 1998 |
| *rochebruneanum* | CBos CGle CHan ECGN EMan EWes LFis LGre MBri MLLN MNrw MTed MTis MUlv SMad SMrm SSca WCru WRus WSHC |
| * *rugosum* | GBuc |
| *simplex* | NHol |
| sp. ACE 1612 | EPPr |
| sp. B&SWJ 2159 | Last listed 1996 |
| sp. B&SWJ 2520 | Last listed 1997 |
| sp. B&SWJ 2622 | Last listed 1998 |
| sp. CLD 564 | Last listed 1998 |
| ¶ sp. from Afghanistan | EBee ELan EPot GBuc GTou WCot |
| ¶ *sparsiflorum* | EBee WPrP |
| *speciosissimum* | See *T. flavum* subsp. *glaucum* |
| *sphaerostachyum* | MBri WGer |
| ¶ *squarrosum* | MTed |
| *tuberosum* | CHan CRDP EBee EPot LGre SAga SBla WCot |

| | |
|---|---|
| *uchiyamae* | SBla WCot |
| *venulosum* | EBee |
| *virgatum* B&SWJ 2964 | WCru |

## THAMNOCALAMUS (Poaceae - Bambusoideae)

| | |
|---|---|
| *aristatus* | EPla ISta LJus WBay |
| *crassinodus* | EPla GLch SDry |
| - dwarf from | EPla |
| - 'Kew Beauty' | EFul EPla ERod EWes ISta LJus |
| | MMoz SDry WJun |
| - 'Lang Tang' | EPla WJun |
| - 'Merlyn' | EPla ERod SDry WJun |
| *falcatus* | See *Drepanostachyum falcatum* |
| *falconeri* | See *Himalayacalamus falconeri* |
| *funghomii* | See *Schizostachyum funghomii* |
| *khasianus* | See *Drepanostachyum* |
| | *khasianum* |
| *maling* | See *Yushania maling* |
| *spathaceus* hort. | See *Fargesia murieliae* |
| § *spathiflorus* | CFil EFul EPla ISta SDry WJun |
| ¶ - subsp. *nepalensis* | EPla |
| § *tessellatus* | EFul EOas EPla ISta LJus MMoz |
| | SDix SDry WBay WJun |

## THAMNOCHORTUS (Restionaceae)

| | |
|---|---|
| ¶ *cinereus* | LHil |
| *insignis* | CTrC WNor |
| *lucens* | IDac |
| *rigidus* | CTrC LHil |
| *spicigerus* | CTrC LHil |

## THAPSIA (Apiaceae)

| | |
|---|---|
| *decipiens* | See *Melanoselinum decipiens* |
| *garganica* | SIgm WCot |

## THEA See CAMELLIA

## THELYMITRA (Orchidaceae)

| | |
|---|---|
| *antennifera* | Last listed 1996 |
| 'Goldfingers' 410 | SWes |
| ¶ 'Kay Nesbit' | SWes |
| ¶ *luteocilium* | SWes |
| 'Melon Glow' | SWes |
| *nuda* | SWes |
| *rubra* | SWes |
| 'Spring Delight' 458 | Last listed 1998 |

## THELYPTERIS ✿ (Thelypteridaceae)

| | |
|---|---|
| *limbosperma* | See *Oreopteris limbosperma* |
| *palustris* | CTrC EBee EMon MLan NHol |
| | SRms WFib WRic |
| *phegopteris* | See *Phegopteris connectilis* |

## THEMEDA (Poaceae)

| | |
|---|---|
| *triandra* subs p. *australis* | Last listed 1997 |
| from Adaminaby | |
| - - from Cooma | Last listed 1997 |
| - subsp. *japonica* | Last listed 1996 |

## THERMOPSIS (Papilionaceae)

| | |
|---|---|
| *barbata* | Last listed 1997 |
| - ACE 2298 | Last listed 1996 |
| *caroliniana* | See *T. villosa* |
| *fabacea* | See *T. lupinoides* |
| *lanceolata* | CHad CTri EBee ECGP EMan GBin |
| | LSpr MBel MBri MCAu MLLN |
| | MMil MTis SAga SLon SMac SMrm |
| | SOkh WFar WLin WPer |
| § *lupinoides* | EBee ECha NOrc SLod WCot |
| | WCru WFar WPer |
| *mollis* | EBee MUlv NBid |

| | |
|---|---|
| *rhombifolia* var. *montana* | CGen CMGP CRDP EBee ELan |
| | ERav EWTr GAbr MGed MNrw |
| | NOrc NSti SUsu WAbb WByw |
| | WGwG WLRN WOve WPer WRus |
| | WWal WWat |
| § *villosa* | CGle CHan EBee EMan LWoo |
| | MHlr MLLN MRav MSte NFai NLar |
| | SBla SDix SPer WCot WPGP WRus |

## THEVETIA (Apocynaceae)

| | |
|---|---|
| *peruviana* | MSal SOWG |

## THLADIANTHA (Cucurbitaceae)

| | |
|---|---|
| *dubia* | CPIN SDix |
| *oliveri* (f) | MSCN |

## THLASPI (Brassicaceae)

| | |
|---|---|
| *alpestre* | Last listed 1996 |
| *alpinum* | EPot MPla MWat NMen NNrd |
| | NWCA SRms |
| *arvense* | Last listed 1997 |
| *bellidifolium* | NBir NWCA |
| *biebersteinii* | See *Pachyphragma* |
| | *macrophyllum* |
| *bulbosum* | GTou NWCA |
| *cepaeifolium* | Last listed 1996 |
| subsp. *cenisium* | |
| § - subsp. *rotundifolium* | CCuc GTou MChR |
| - - var. *limoselifolium* | Last listed 1997 |
| *fendleri* | MNrw |
| *montanum* | Last listed 1996 |
| *ochroleucum* | Last listed 1996 |
| ♦ *rotundifolium* | See *T. cepaeifolium* subsp. |
| | *rotundifolium* |
| *stylosum* | Last listed 1998 |

## THRINAX (Arecaceae)

| | |
|---|---|
| ¶ *radiata* | WMul |

## THRYPTOMENE (Myrtaceae)

| | |
|---|---|
| ¶ *saxicola* 'F.C. Payne' | CPLG |

## THUJA ✿ (Cupressaceae)

| | |
|---|---|
| ♦ 'Extra Gold' | See *T. plicata* 'Irish Gold' |
| § *koraiensis* | LCon MBar WCwm WHCr |
| *occidentalis* | NWea WDin |
| - 'Aurea' | MBar |
| - 'Aureospicata' | EHul |
| ¶ - 'Autumn Glow' | WGor |
| - 'Beau Fleur' | LLin |
| - 'Beaufort' (v) | CKen EHul LLin MAsh MBar MPla |
| | WWal |
| - 'Caespitosa' | CBlo CKen CNic CSli ESis LLin |
| | MOne NHol |
| - 'Cristata Aurea' | CKen |
| - 'Danica' ♀ | CMac CSli EBrP EBre EHul ENot |
| | EOrn GRei IOrc LBre LCon LLin |
| | MAsh MBar MGos MPla SBod SBre |
| | SLim SRms WFar WGwG WStI |
| | WWal WWeb |
| - 'Dicksonii' | EHul |
| - 'Douglasii Aurea' | CKen |
| - 'Ellwangeriana Aurea' | LBee MGos |
| - 'Emerald' | See *T. occidentalis* 'Smaragd' |
| - 'Ericoides' | CDoC CTri EHul LCon MAsh MBal |
| | MBar SRms SSmi WStI |
| - 'Europa Gold' | CDoC EHul IOrc LBee MBar |
| | MGos NMoo SLim WLRN |
| - 'Fastigiata' | CDul MBar |
| - 'Filiformis' | CKen EPla |
| - 'Froebelii' | Last listed 1997 |

- 'Globosa' — CBlo CMac MBar SBod WGor WGwG WWal
- 'Globosa Variegata' — CBlo CKen MBar
- 'Golden Gem' — Last listed 1997
- 'Golden Globe' — CBlo CSli EHul ENot EOrn LCon LNet LPan MBar MGos NHol SBod SLim SPla WDin WLRN
* - 'Golden Minaret' — EHul
- 'Hetz Midget' — CBlo CKen EHul EOrn EPfP ESis IMGH LCon LLin MBar MGos MOne NHol SLim SMer WLRN
- 'Holmstrup' ♀ — CDoC CMac CSli EBrP EBre EGra EHul ENot EOrn IOrc LBre LCon LLin MAsh MBar MWat NBee NHol SBre SLim SRms SSmi WFar WStl WWeb
- 'Holmstrup's Yellow' — CBlo CDoC CKen CSli EGra EHul GPin LCon MAsh MOne MPla WCFE WWeb
- 'Hoveyi' — CTri EHul LCon WLRN
- 'Linesville' — CKen
- 'Little Champion' — EHul GRei NHol
- 'Little Gem' — EHul MGos NHol NPro SRms WDin WGor
- 'Lutea Nana' ♀ — CMac EHul EOrn MBal MBar
- 'Malonyana' — WCwm
- 'Marrisen's Sulphur' — CBlo CSli EHul EOrn LCon SLim WBcn WLRN
- 'Meineckes Zwerg' — CKen EPla SSmi
- 'Miky' — CKen WBcn
- 'Milleri' — Last listed 1998
- 'Ohlendorffii' — CBlo CKen EHul EOrn LCon LLin MBar MWat NHol SSmi
- 'Orientalis Semperaurescens' — See T. orientalis 'Semperaurea'
I - 'Pumila Sudworth' — NHol
- 'Pygmaea' — CKen MBar SLon
- 'Pyramidalis Compacta' — EHul LNet WGor
- 'Recurva Nana' — EHul LLin MBal MBar NHol
- 'Rheingold' ♀ — More than 30 suppliers
- 'Silver Beauty' (v) — CMHG
§ - 'Smaragd' ♀ — CDoC CSli EBrP EBre EHul ENot EOrn IOrc LBre LBuc LCon LLin LNet LPan MAsh MBar MGos MPla SBod SBre SPer WCFE WStl
* - 'Smaragd Variegated' — Last listed 1996
- 'Southport' — CBlo CKen CSli MBri
- 'Sphaerica' — MPla
- 'Spiralis' — CBlo EHul IMGH MBar WCFE
§ - 'Stolwijk' — CBlo EHul EOrn GPin MBar MGos SLim WBcn
- 'Sunkist' — CKen CMHG CMac CSli EBrP EBre EHul ENot EOrn GRei IOrc LBre LCon LLin LNet LPan MAsh MBar MGos MPla NHol SBod SBre SLim SPla SRPl WFar WWeb
- 'Suzie' — LLin
¶ - 'Teddy' — LCon SLim
- 'Tiny Tim' — CBlo CDoC CMac CSli EHul ESis IMGH LCon LLin MBar MGos MOne SIng WGor WLRN WWal WWeb
- 'Trompenburg' — CBlo ECho EHul EOrn MAsh WBcn
- 'Wansdyke Silver' (v) — CBlo CMac CSli EHul EOrn EPla LCon MBar MPla SLim SPla
- 'Wareana' — CMac
- 'Wareana Aurea' — See T. occidentalis 'Wareana Lutescens'
§ - 'Wareana Lutescens' — CMac EHul EOrn GRei LCon MBal MBar MGos MPla
- 'Woodwardii' — EHul MBar MOne SMer

- 'Yellow Ribbon' — CBlo CSli EBrP EBre EHul LBee LBre LCon LNet MBar NHol NMoo SBre SLim SMer SPla
§ orientalis — NWea
§ - 'Aurea Nana' ♀ — More than 30 suppliers
- 'Autumn Glow' — CBlo CKen LBee SLim WWeb
- 'Bergmanii' — WWeb
- 'Beverleyensis' — LLin
- 'Blue Cone' — MBar
- 'Carribean Holiday' — MAsh
- 'Collen's Gold' — CDoC CTri EHul EOrn MBar WBcn
- 'Conspicua' — CKen CSli EHul LBee LCon MAsh MBar
- 'Elegantissima' ♀ — CMac CSli EHul EOrn LBee LCon MBar MGos SBod
- 'Flame' — MGos
* - 'Golden Ball' — Last listed 1996
- 'Golden Minaret' — WBcn
¶ - 'Golden Pillar' — EOrn
- 'Golden Pygmy' — CKen EOrn MAsh WBcn
- 'Golden Wonder' — Last listed 1997
- 'Juniperoides' — CBlo EHul LCon LLin MBar WLRN
- 'Madurodam' — LLin MBar
- 'Magnifica' — EHul WCwm
- 'Meldensis' — CDoC CTri EBrP EBre EHul LBre LLin MBal MBar SBre
- 'Miller's Gold' — See T. orientalis 'Aurea Nana'
- 'Minima' — CDoC CSli EHul ESis MWat
- 'Minima Glauca' — CKen MBar SRms
- 'Purple King' — CSli LCon SLim
I - 'Pyramidalis Aurea' — LBee LPan
- 'Rosedalis' — CKen CMac CSli EBrP EBre EHul EOrn ESis GPin LBee LBre LCon LLin MAsh MBal MBar MBri MPla MWat SBod SBre SLim SRms
- 'Sanderi' — CKen MBar WCFE
§ - 'Semperaurea' — CMac IMGH
- 'Shirley Chilcott' — Last listed 1998
- 'Sieboldii' — EHul
- 'Southport' — LBee LCon LLin MAsh
- 'Spaethii' — EHul EOrn
- 'Summer Cream' — CBlo CKen EHul MBar MGos
- 'Westmont' — CKen EOrn WBcn
plicata — CDul EHul GChr GRei IOrc LHyr MBal MBar MGos NWea SBod SLim SPer WFro WMou WTro
- 'Atrovirens' ♀ — CSli CTri EBrP EBre ENot LBee LBre LBuc LCon LPan MAsh MBri MGos SBre SMer SRPl SRms WHar WWal WWeb
- 'Aurea' ♀ — CBlo EHul MAsh SLim SRms
¶ - 'Barabits' — CMCN
¶ - 'Brabant' — LNet
¶ - 'Can-can' — CBlo EPla LCon
I - 'Cole's Variety' — CBlo MBar MBlu
- 'Collyer's Gold' — EGra EHul LCon SRms
- 'Copper Kettle' — CBlo CKen CNic CSli EGra EHul LCon MAsh MBar MBri MPla NPro SLim WGor WLRN
- 'Cuprea' — CKen EHul LLin MBar
- 'Doone Valley' — CKen CMHG CSli EHul EOrn MBar NHol WAbe
- 'Dura' — CDoC
- 'Fastigiata' ♀ — CMac
- 'Gelderland' — EHul
- 'Gracilis Aurea' — CBlo ECho EHul MPla WBcn
¶ - 'Grune Kugel' — CDoC
- 'Hillieri' — EHul MBar
§ - 'Irish Gold' (v) ♀ — CAbP CBlo CDul CMac EPla LCon LLin SAga WBcn

| | |
|---|---|
| – 'Rogersii' | CDoC CKen CMac CSli EBrP EBre EHul EOrn ESis IOrc LBre LCon LLin MAsh MBNS MBar MGos MPla NHol SBod SBre SIng SLim SRms SSmi WAbe |
| – 'Semperaurescens' | Last listed 1998 |
| – x *standishii* | WCwm |
| – 'Stolwijk's Gold' | See *T. occidentalis* 'Stolwijk' |
| – 'Stoneham Gold' ♀ | CDoC CKen CMHG CMac EBrP EBre EHul EOrn IOrc LBee LBre LCon LLin MAsh MBar MBri MGos MPla SBod SBre SLim SMer SPer SRms SSmi WCFE |
| – 'Sunshine' | CKen |
| * – 'Windsor Gold' | EHul |
| – 'Winter Pink' (v) | CBlo CKen |
| – 'Zebrina' (v) | CB&S CBrm CDoC CDul CMHG CMac CSli EHul EOrn LCon LLin MAsh MBal MBar MGos MWat NBee NEgg NWea SBod SLim SPer SRPl WFar WHar WWal WWin |
| ¶ – 'Zebrina' Bedgebury form | CDoC |
| *standishii* | WCwm |

## THUJOPSIS (Cupressaceae)

| | |
|---|---|
| *dolabrata* ♀ | CB&S CGre CTrG EHul IOrc LBee MBar NHed NWea SPer WBrE WCwm WFar WTro WWat |
| – 'Aurea' (v) | CDoC CKen EHul EOrn LCon LLin MBar MGos SAga SLim |
| – 'Laetevirens' | See *T. dolabrata* 'Nana' |
| § – 'Nana' | CDoC CKen CMac EGra EHul EOrn LCon LLin MBar MPla SLim SLon SRms STre WFar |
| – 'Variegata' | CDoC EHul EOrn LCon LLin MBal MBar NHed NHol SHFr SLim WLRN |
| *koraiensis* | See *Thuja koraiensis* |

## THUNBERGIA (Acanthaceae)

| | |
|---|---|
| *alata* | CPlN MBri |
| *coccinea* | CPlN SOWG |
| *erecta* | CPlN ELan ERea LChe LCns SOWG |
| – 'Alba' | Last listed 1998 |
| *fragrans* | CPlN ERea SOWG |
| *grandiflora* ♀ | CPlN ECon ELan ERea LChe LCns SOWG WMul |
| – 'Alba' | CPlN ECon LChe |
| *gregorii* | CPlN CSpe LChe LCns SOWG |
| *laurifolia* | CPlN |
| *mysorensis* ♀ | CPlN ECon ERea LCns SOWG WMul |
| *natalensis* | CHan LChe LLew |
| *petersiana* | CPlN |

## THYMUS ✿ (Lamiaceae)

| | |
|---|---|
| 'Anderson's Gold' | See *T.* x *citriodorus* 'Bertram Anderson' |
| *azoricus* | See *T. caespititius* |
| 'Belle Orchard' | Last listed 1997 |
| 'Caborn Lilac Gem' | LLWP |
| § *caespititius* | CArn CLyd ELau EPot GAbr GPoy ILis LHol LLWP MBro MRPP NHex NMen NRya SDys SPlb SSmi WAbe WCHb WLow WPer |
| *caespitosus* | LLWP NRoo |
| *camphoratus* | CBod CMea ELau EOHP EWes MWat NHex SHDw WAbe WJek SHDw |
| ¶ – x 'Derry' | |
| *carnosus* misapplied | See *T. vulgaris* 'Erectus' |
| – Boiss. | LFis SSmi |

| | |
|---|---|
| 'Carol Ann' (v) | CBod ELau EWes LLWP NLak |
| *cephalotos* | EHyt WAbe |
| *ciliatus* | CMea LLWP WPer |
| *cilicicus* | CLyd EHyt EWes GCHN LBee MChe SBla WAbe WCHb WJek WMow WWye |
| x *citriodorus* | CArn CDoC ELau GAbr GCHN GPoy LGro LLWP MBrN MChe MMal NHex NMen NOak SRms WHen WJek WOak WPer WWye |
| – 'Archer's Gold' | CHar EAst EBrP EBre EHoe ELau EPot ESis GAbr LBee LBre LGro LHop LLWP MBri NHex NSti SBre SChu SIde SMer SRms SSmi WCHb WJek WOak WPat WPer |
| – 'Argenteus' (v) | LLWP MBro |
| § – 'Aureus' ♀ | EBrP EBre EMNN ESis GBar GDra GTou LBre LLWP MBal MBar MBri MBro MMal NFla NMen NRoo NWCA SBla SBre SPlb SRms WHen WHoo WPyg |
| § – 'Bertram Anderson' ♀ | CArn CTri EBrP EBre ECha ELau EMNN GCHN LBee LBre LHol LLWP MBro MMal NHex NHol NMen NNrd NRoo NRya NVic SBla SBre SIde SSmi WAbe WHoo WLin WWin |
| § – 'Golden King' (v) | EBrP EBre ECha ELan LBee LBre LHop LLWP MBar MBri MBro MChe NHex NSti SAga SBre WCHb WHoo WLin WPer WSel WStI |
| § – 'Golden Lemon' (v) | CArn EOHP GPoy LLWP WJek WWye |
| ♦ – 'Golden Lemon' misapplied | See *T.* x *citriodorus* 'Aureus' |
| – 'Golden Queen' (v) | CLTr CMea EOHP EPot ESis GBar MMal NFla NLak NPri NRoo NSla SMrm SRms WRHF WWin |
| – 'Nyewoods' (v) | GAbr |
| – *repandus* | SIde |
| ¶ – 'Silver King' | LLWP |
| – 'Silver Posie' | See *T. vulgaris* 'Silver Posie' |
| – 'Silver Queen' (v) ♀ | CB&S CHar CLyd ECha ELan EOHP GPoy MBal MBar MBro MChe MMal NHex NLon SPlb SSmi WAbe WHoo WPyg WStI |
| * – 'Variegatus' | CJew LGro LHol LHop MBri MBro MChe MPla NMen WEas WFar WOak WWin |
| * – misapplied 'Variegatus' | See *T.* x *citriodorus* 'Golden King' |
| ¶ – 'Villa Nova' | LLWP |
| * – 'Coccineus' ♀ | CArn ECha ELan ELau EMNN ESis GDra GTou LGro LHol LLWP MBal MBar MBri MBro MChe MWat NHol NRoo SBla SIng WCla WHen WHoo WOak WPat WWin |
| *comosus* | CNic LLWP MChe NTow WAbe WPat WPer |
| ¶ 'Creeping Lemon' | ELau LLWP |
| 'Creeping Orange' | LLWP |
| 'Dartmoor' | GCal LLWP |
| 'Desboro' | GAbr LLWP NHex NHol |
| *doerfleri* | CLyd ECha EOHP GBar LLWP NMen SIde SPil WSel WWye |
| – 'Bressingham' | More than 30 suppliers |
| – 'Doone Valley' (v) | More than 30 suppliers |
| *drucei* | See *T. polytrichus* subsp. *britannicus* |
| 'E.B. Anderson' | See *T.* x *citriodorus* 'Bertram Anderson' |
| 'Elf' | MTPN |
| 'Emma's Pink' | LLWP NHex |

| | |
|---|---|
| *erectus* | See *T. vulgaris* 'Erectus' |
| * *ericoides* | Last listed 1998 |
| 'Fragrantissimus' | CArn CFri CJew ELau EOHP ESis GAbr GPoy LHol LLWP MChe MWat NHex NPri NRoo SIde WHen WJek WOak WPer WWye |
| * 'Golden Icing' | Last listed 1998 |
| ¶ 'Hardstoft Red' | MChe |
| § 'Hartington Silver' (v) | More than 30 suppliers |
| *herba-barona* | CArn CHad CTri EBot ECha ELau EOHP ESis GBar GPoy LEdu LHol LLWP MBal NFor NHex NHol NRoo SIde SPil SRms SSmi WOak WPer WWye |
| - *citrata* | See *T. herba-barona* 'Lemon-scented' |
| § - 'Lemon-scented' | CArn ELau GPoy LLWP MHer MOne NHex NHol NLon SHDw SIde WGwG |
| 'Highland Cream' | See *T.* 'Hartington Silver' |
| I *hirsutus minus* | Last listed 1998 |
| *hyemalis* | LLWP |
| *integer* | SBla |
| *lanuginosus* hort. | See *T. pseudolanuginosus* |
| § 'Lavender Sea' | ELau EWes LLWP |
| 'Lemon Caraway' | See *T. herba-barona* 'Lemon-scented' |
| * 'Lemon Variegated' | ELau |
| *leucotrichus* | CLyd ILis MBro SDys WPat |
| 'Lilac Time' | EWes LLWP |
| *longicaulis* | CArn ECha EGoo ELau LLWP MBNS NHex SIde WJek WWye |
| *marschallianus* | See *T. pannonicus* |
| *mastichina* | CArn EBee ESis GBar LHop MChe SBla SChu SMac SSca SUsu WWye |
| - 'Didi' | LLWP MHer NHex |
| *membranaceus* | CLyd EHyt WAbe |
| *micans* | See *T. caespititius* |
| I *minus* | See *Calamintha nepeta* |
| *montanus* Waldstein & Kitaibel | See *T. pulegioides* |
| *neiceffii* | CArn CLyd ECha EGoo ELau GBar LHol LLWP MHer NHex NMen NTow |
| * *nummularius* | ELau LGro SSca |
| *odoratissimus* | See *T. pallasianus* subsp. *pallasianus* |
| 'Onyx' | CLyd NHex NMen |
| *pallasianus* | ELau LLWP |
| § - subsp. *pallasianus* | CBod GBar SIde SPil |
| § *pannonicus* | LLWP NHex WPer |
| 'Peter Davis' | CArn CBod CMea EOHP ESis LHop LLWP MBNS MChe MGed MHer MPla NHex NMen SBla SChu SIde WAbe WJek WLow |
| § 'Pink Ripple' | CBod ELau EWes LLWP MChe |
| 'Pinkushion' | LLWP NHol |
| § *polytrichus* | LLWP NHol NMir |
| § - subsp. *britannicus* | CKin EEls EPot EWFC GPoy LLWP MHew NMen NSti WJek WPer |
| § - - 'Minor' | EPot LLWP SIde WPer |
| § - - 'Thomas's White' ♀ | ELan LBee LLWP |
| ¶ - - variegated | WLin |
| 'Porlock' | CDoC CMea CSev ELau ESis GPoy LLWP MBNS MChe NChi NHex NHol SIde SRms WHoo WJek WOak WPer WPyg |
| ¶ *praecox* | LLWP |
| - subsp. *arcticus* | See *T. polytrichus* subsp. *britannicus* |
| 'Provence' | LLWP |
| § *pseudolanuginosus* | More than 30 suppliers |
| - 'Hall's Variety' | CHal ELau |
| § *pulegioides* | CArn CBod CJew ELau GBar GPoy LHol LLWP MBri MMal NHex NPri NRoo SHDw SIde WGwG WJek WOak WPer WWye |
| - 'Foxley' (v) | CBod ELau LLWP MChe |
| ¶ - 'Sir John Lawes' | LLWP |
| - 'Redstart' | CBod ELau LBee LLWP MChe WOak |
| *richardii* subsp. *nitidus* | LHol WWye |
| ◆ - subsp. *nitidus* 'Compactus Albus' | See *T. vulgaris* 'Snow White' |
| *rotundifolius* | ELau LLWP SIde |
| § 'Ruby Glow' | EBrP EBre ELau EWes LBre LLWP MChe NHex NRoo NWoo SBre |
| *serpyllum* | CArn ELan ELau GAbr GCHN LLWP MBri MChe MPla MWat NOak SIde SPlb SRms WJek WMow WPer |
| - var. *albus* (Ghose & Bhattacharyya) H.B.Naithani | CHal ECha ELau EMNN ENot ESis GDra GPoy GTou LLWP MBal MBro MHar MMal NNrd NRoo NVic SBla SChu SIde SRms WHoo WOak WWye |
| - 'Albus Variegatus' | See *T.* 'Hartington Silver' |
| - 'Annie Hall' | CDoC CHal EBrP EBre ELau EMNN EPot GAbr LBee LBre LGro LHol LLWP MBro MChe NFor NHex NHol NMen NRoo SBod SBre SDys SIde SIng SSmi WOak WPer WWye |
| - *coccineus* 'Major' | GDra SIde WAbe WJek |
| - - 'Minor' | EBrP EBre ELau GAri GTou LBre LLWP MChe NRoo SBre SIde SRms |
| * - - x *zygis sylvestris* | Last listed 1997 |
| - 'East Lodge' | LLWP |
| - 'Elfin' | CArn CLyd EOHP EPot ESis EWes GBar GTou LBee LHol MBri MBro MHar MHer NMen NNrd SBla SPlb WAbe WBea WCla WHoo |
| - 'Flossy' | LLWP NNrd |
| - 'Fulney Red' | EWes LLWP |
| - 'Goldstream' (v) | CDoC CLyd CMea ELau EMNN ESis GAbr LBee LBuc LHop LLWP MBar MBri MChe NHol NNrd NRoo NSti SIde SPlb SRms WCHb WOak WPer |
| - 'Iden' | SIde |
| - subsp. *lanuginosus* | See *T. pseudolanuginosus* |
| - 'Lavender Sea' | See *T.* 'Lavender Sea' |
| - 'Lemon Curd' | CBod CBrm ELau EOHP GAbr GBar LLWP MChe NSti SIde SMer WCHb WJek WOak WRha WSel WWye |
| - 'Minimus' | CArn CBrm CDoC CHal CLyd ECha ELau ESis GAbr LHol LLWP MBri MChe MMal NHol NSti NTow SIde WOak WPat WPer WRHF WSel WWye |
| § - 'Minor' | CArn EMNN GDra LBee LHol MBro MChe NHol NMen NRya NSla SBla SIde SIng SSmi WAbe WCla WGwG WHoo WLin WPyg WWin |
| * - 'Minor Albus' | GBar |
| I - 'Minus' | See *T. serpyllum* 'Minor' |
| - 'Petite' | EWes LLWP |

| | |
|---|---|
| - 'Pink Chintz' ♀ | CHal ECha ELau EMNN ESis GAbr GDra GPoy GTou LGro LHol LLWP MBar MBri NHol NRoo SBla SChu SIng SPlb SSmi WAbe WHoo WLin WOak WPer WPyg WWin WWye |
| - 'Pink Ripple' | See *T.* 'Pink Ripple' |
| - subsp. *pulchellus* | LLWP |
| - 'Rainbow Falls' (v) | CBod EWes GAbr GBar LLWP MChe NCat NHex NRoo SHDw SIde |
| - 'Roseus' | EOHP GBar SIde WOak |
| - 'Ruby Glow' | See *T.* 'Ruby Glow' |
| - 'Russetings' | CDoC CHal CLyd EGoo ELau EMNN EPot ESis LHol LLWP MBar MBro MChe NHex NHol NMen NRoo SIde SRms WOak WWin WWye |
| - 'September' | LLWP NHol |
| - 'Snowdrift' | CArn CHal CMea EGar ELau EOHP GBar LEdu LHol MBar MBro MChe NHex NHol NSti SIde SSmi WAbe WJek WPat WPer WRHF |
| - 'Splendens' | GMaP LLWP |
| - 'Variegatus' | See *T.* 'Hartington Silver' |
| - 'Vey' | EGle EWes GBar LLWP MChe MHer NHex NHol SIng SSmi SUsu WMaN |
| *sibthorpii* | CArn |
| N 'Silver Posie' | See *T. vulgaris* 'Silver Posie' |
| sp. from Turkey | EWes LLWP |
| * *taeniensis* | CArn |
| 'Valerie Finnis' | Last listed 1996 |
| § *villosus* | Last listed 1998 |
| *vulgaris* | CArn CChe CSev ECha ELau GPoy LLWP MBar MBri MChe MHew MMal NFla NHex NRoo NVic SDix SPlb WJek WOak WPer |
| - *albus* | EOHP GBar LLWP NHex SIde WHen |
| * - 'Aureus' hort. | GBar LGro LLWP MChe NRoo WJek WSel |
| * - 'Compactus' | LLWP |
| ¶ - 'Dorcas White' | LLWP WPer |
| - 'English Winter' | Last listed 1998 |
| § - 'Erectus' | CArn CLyd GBar LHol LLWP MHer NTow SRms WPer WWye |
| - French | ELau LLWP |
| - 'French Summer' | SIde |
| ¶ - 'German Winter' | CArn |
| - 'Golden Pins' | CArn EGar EPot GBar SBla |
| - 'Lemon Queen' | ELau |
| - 'Lucy' | GBar LLWP SIde WJek |
| - 'Pinewood' | GPoy LLWP |
| - pink | LLWP |
| - 'Silver Pearl' (v) | EWes LLWP |
| § - 'Silver Posie' | CArn CHad CSev EBrP EBre EHoe ELan ELau GPoy LBre LHol LLWP MBro MMal NFla NHex NMen NRoo NSti SBla SBre SChu SDix SRms WHoo WLin WOak WPer WWye |
| § - 'Snow White' | ELau EWes GBar LLWP MPla NBus NMen SHDw WJek |
| ¶ - 'Widecombe' (v) | LLWP |
| *zygis* | CArn |

## THYSANOTUS (Anthericaceae)

| | |
|---|---|
| *patersonii* | Last listed 1996 |
| *tuberosus* | Last listed 1996 |

## TIARELLA (Saxifragaceae)

| | |
|---|---|
| ¶ 'Bronze Baby' | SCob |
| *collina* | See *T. wherryi* |
| *cordifolia* ♀ | More than 30 suppliers |
| - 'Eco Red Heart' | Last listed 1998 |
| - 'Glossy' | GBuc GCal NDov SDys WCot |
| - 'Oakleaf' | CLAP GCal MLLN NSti SMrm |
| ¶ - 'Running Tapestry' | CLAP |
| - 'Slick Rock' | ECha EPPr WThi |
| ¶ 'Cygnet' | WCot |
| 'Dark Eyes' | NCat WCot |
| ¶ 'Dark Star' | WCot |
| 'Elizabeth Oliver' | CLAP WThi |
| 'Filigree Lace' | WThi |
| ¶ 'Freckles' | WCot |
| ¶ 'Inkblot' | WCot |
| * 'Laciniate Runner' | CLAP |
| 'Martha Oliver' | CLAP WAbe WCot WThi WTin |
| ¶ 'Mint Chocolate' | GBin GNau MBri MMil NDov WCot WWhi |
| § 'Ninja' | CHid CLAP CSpe EAst EBee EHic LFis LRot LWoo MBri MGrG MLLN NDov NHol NLar NPri NPro SCob SMad SSpi WCot WSpi WWhi |
| 'Pinwheel' | EBrP EBre LBre MRav NCat SBre WCot |
| *polyphylla* | ELan EMar EPar GAbr GBin GMac LGro MLLN MRav MWrn NFla NOrc NSti SMac WBea WCla WCru WFar WWhi WWye |
| - 'Axminster Variegated' | Last listed 1996 |
| - 'Filigran' | NLar SCob |
| - 'Moorgrün' | GCal MBel WWat |
| - pink | CGle CLAP CLTr EBee EPar EPPr MBel NDov |
| ¶ 'Skeleton Key' | WCot |
| 'Tiger Stripe' | CHid CLAP COtt EBee EPfP LRHS SCob SPer WCot WThi |
| *trifoliata* | EBee ELan MRav SBla WFar |
| - 'Incarnadine' | Last listed 1998 |
| *unifoliata* | CMCo NCat |
| I 'Vivid Selection' | WTin |
| § *wherryi* ♀ | More than 30 suppliers |
| - 'Bronze Beauty' | CLAP CMea CMil COtt CRDP EBee ECha EPar GBuc MCLN MRav NLak NPro SAga SCob SUsu SWas SWat WAbe WCot WFar WLin WPGP |
| - fig-leaved | WThi |
| - 'George Schenk' | WThi |
| ¶ - 'Montrose' | CLAP |
| - 'Pink Foam' | Last listed 1998 |

## TIBOUCHINA (Melastomataceae)

| | |
|---|---|
| *grandifolia* | LHil |
| *granulosa* | Last listed 1997 |
| *graveolens* | ERea |
| * *holosericea* 'Elsa' | ERea |
| 'Jules' | ECon ERea LChe |
| *laxa* 'Noelene' | Last listed 1998 |
| * - 'Skylab' | Last listed 1997 |
| *organensis* | CB&S ERea GQui LBlm LChe LHil |
| *paratropica* | CLTr CPle CSev ERea LChe LHil |
| *semidecandra* hort. | See *T. urvilleana* |
| § *urvilleana* ♀ | CAbb CB&S CDoC CGre CPIN CSPN CSpe CTbh CWit EBak ECre ELan ERea IOrc ISea LBlm LCns LHop LPan SAPC SArc SBid SLon SOWG SPer SRms SYvo WMul WSan |

| | |
|---|---|
| - 'Edwardsii' | CBar CSev LChe MLan NPSl |
| ¶ - 'Nana' | CDoC |

## TIGRIDIA (Iridaceae)

| | |
|---|---|
| *durangense* | Last listed 1996 |
| hybrids | SDeJ |
| *lutea* | SDeJ |
| *pavonia* | CGre EBot ERea GMac LAma LBow MBri NCut NRog |

## TILIA ✿ (Tiliaceae)

| | |
|---|---|
| *americana* | CLnd CMCN ENot LPan WMou |
| - 'Dentata' | Last listed 1998 |
| - 'Fastigiata' | WMou |
| - 'Nova' | CDoC CTho |
| - 'Redmond' | CTho |
| *amurensis* | CMCN WMou |
| *argentea* | See *T. tomentosa* |
| *begoniifolia* | See *T. dasystyla* |
| 'Chelsea Sentinel' | WMou |
| *chenmoui* | WMou |
| *chinensis* | WMou |
| *chingiana* | CMCN SSta WMou |
| *cordata* ♀ | CDul CKin CLnd ECrN ELan ENot EWTr GChr GRei IOrc LBuc LHyr MBal MWat NBee NWea SPer WDin WMou WStI WWye |
| - 'Erecta' | CDul GChr SLPl |
| - 'Greenspire' ♀ | CDoC CDul CLnd CTho ENot IOrc LPan NBee WMou WOrn |
| - 'Len Parvin' | Last listed 1998 |
| - 'Lico' | WMou |
| - 'Morden' | WMou |
| - 'Plymtree Gold' | CTho WMou |
| - 'Rancho' | Last listed 1998 |
| - 'Roelvo' | Last listed 1998 |
| - 'Swedish Upright' | CTho WMou |
| - 'Umbrella' | Last listed 1998 |
| - 'Westonbirt Dainty Leaf' | WMou |
| - 'Winter Orange' | MBlu SBir WMou |
| § *dasystyla* | CLnd WMou |
| ¶ - subsp. *caucasica* | WMou |
| x *euchlora* ♀ | CDoC CDul CLnd EBee ECrN ENot EPfP GChr LPan MBri MGos MWat NWea SPer SSta WDin WFar WMou WOrn |
| x *europaea* | CDul CLnd ELan WMou |
| - 'Pallida' | CDul CTho WMou |
| - 'Pendula' | WMou |
| - 'Wratislaviensis' ♀ | CBlo CDoC CDul CTho EPfP LBuc MBlu WMou |
| - 'Zwarte Linde' | Last listed 1998 |
| x *flavescens* 'Glenleven' | Last listed 1998 |
| § 'Harold Hillier' | WMou |
| *henryana* | CDul CEnd CLnd CMCN CTho ERod MBlu SMad WMou |
| - var. *subglabra* | WMou |
| § *heterophylla* | CTho WMou |
| - var. *michauxii* | CLnd SSta |
| 'Hillieri' | See *T.* 'Harold Hillier' |
| *insularis* | MBlu WMou |
| *intonsa* | WMou |
| *japonica* | CMCN WMou |
| *kiusiana* | CMCN WMou |
| *koreana* | WMou |
| *laetevirens* | SSta |
| *ledebourii* | WMou |
| *mandshurica* | CMCN |
| *maximowicziana* | SSta WMou |
| *mexicana* | WMou |
| *miqueliana* | CMCN WMou |
| 'Moltkei' | CMCN WMou |

| | |
|---|---|
| *mongolica* ♀ | CDul CLnd CMCN EBee ENot EPfP WMou |
| *monticola* | See *T. heterophylla* |
| *neglecta* | WMou |
| *oliveri* | CDul CMCN WMou |
| 'Orbicularis' | WMou |
| *paucicostata* | Last listed 1998 |
| 'Petiolaris' ♀ | CDoC CDul CEnd CLnd CMCN CTho EBee ELan ENot EPfP EWTr IOrc LHyr MBri NBee NWea SPer SSta WDin WMou |
| *platyphyllos* | CDoC CDul CKin CMCN ENot GChr GRei LBuc NWea SPer WDin WMou |
| - 'Aurea' | CDul CTho WMou |
| - 'Corallina' | See *T. platyphyllos* 'Rubra' |
| - 'Delft' | Last listed 1998 |
| - 'Erecta' | See *T. platyphyllos* 'Fastigiata' |
| § - 'Fastigiata' | CDul CTho ENot MAsh SLPl WMou |
| - 'Grandiflora' | Last listed 1998 |
| - 'Laciniata' | CEnd CMCN CTho WMou |
| - 'Orebro' | SLPl |
| - 'Pannonia' | Last listed 1998 |
| * - 'Pendula' | CTho |
| - 'Prince's Street' | WMou |
| § - 'Rubra' ♀ | CBlo CDoC CDul CLnd CTho EBee ECrN ENot EPfP GChr IOrc LBuc LHyr MBri MGos NBee NWea SLPl WFar WMou |
| - 'Tortuosa' | CBlo SMad WMou |
| - 'Vitifolia' | WMou |
| ¶ *taquetii* | WMou |
| § *tomentosa* | CAgr CDul CLnd CMCN CTho ELan ENot NWea SEND WDin WMou |
| - 'Brabant' ♀ | CDoC ENot EPfP IOrc NBee WMou |
| - 'Erecta' | Last listed 1998 |
| - 'Silver Globe' | Last listed 1998 |
| - 'Szeleste' | Last listed 1998 |
| - 'Van Koolwijk' | MBlu |
| *tuan* | SSta WMou |

## TILLAEA See CRASSULA

## TILLANDSIA (Bromeliaceae)

| | |
|---|---|
| *abdita* | MBri |
| *acostae* | MBri |
| *argentea* | MBri |
| *baileyi* | MBri |
| *balbisiana* | MBri |
| *benthamiana* | See *T. erubescens* |
| *brachycaulos* | MBri |
| - var. *multiflora* | MBri |
| *bulbosa* | MBri |
| *butzii* | MBri |
| *caput-medusae* | MBri |
| *circinnatoides* | MBri |
| *cyanea* | MBri |
| x *erographica* | MBri |
| * *fasciculata* 'Tricolor' (v) | MBri |
| *filifolia* | MBri |
| *flabellata* | MBri |
| *ionantha* | MBri |
| - var. *scaposa* | See *T. kolbii* |
| *juncea* | MBri |
| § *kolbii* | MBri |
| *lindenii* ♀ | Last listed 1995 |
| *magnusiana* | MBri |
| § *matudae* | MBri |
| *oaxacana* | MBri |

| | |
|---|---|
| *polystachia* | MBri |
| *punctulata* | MBri |
| *seleriana* | MBri |
| *sphaerocephala* | MBri |
| *tenuifolia* | See *T. tenuifolia* var. *tenuifolia* |
| var. *surinamensis* | |
| *tricolor* | MBri |
| var. *melanocrater* | |
| *velickiana* | See *T. matudae* |
| *vicentina* | MBri |
| *wagneriana* | MBri |
| *xerographica* | MBri |

## TITHONIA (Asteraceae)
| | |
|---|---|
| *rotundifolia* 'Torch' | SMrm |

## TODEA (Osmundaceae)
| | |
|---|---|
| ¶ *barbara* | WRic |

## TOFIELDIA (Melanthiaceae)
| | |
|---|---|
| *calyculata* | NHol |
| *pusilla* | Last listed 1996 |

## TOLMIEA (Saxifragaceae)
| | |
|---|---|
| 'Goldsplash' | See *T. menziesii* 'Taff's Gold' |
| *menziesii* ♀ | CGle ECha GAri LGro MBNS MBri |
| | MWgw NHol NOrc WByw |
| - JLS 86284CLOR | Last listed 1998 |
| - 'Maculata' | See *T. menziesii* 'Taff's Gold' |
| § - 'Taff's Gold' (v) ♀ | CGle CMHG CRow ECha EHoe |
| | ELan EOHP EPar GMac MBri NFor |
| | NHol NMir NRoo NSti NVic SCob |
| | SHel WBea WByw WEas WHoo |
| | WOve WPyg WWye |
| - 'Variegata' | See *T. menziesii* 'Taff's Gold' |

## TOLPIS (Asteraceae)
| | |
|---|---|
| *barbata* | Last listed 1997 |

## TONESTUS (Asteraceae)
| | |
|---|---|
| § *lyallii* | MHar WLin WMow WPer WWin |

## TOONA (Meliaceae)
| | |
|---|---|
| § *sinensis* | CMCN CTho CTrC EPfP ISea |
| - 'Flamingo' (v) | CB&S CPMA MGos |

## TORENIA (Scrophulariaceae)
| | |
|---|---|
| *concolor formosana* | MBEx WCru |
| B&SWJ 124 | |
| * 'Summerwave' | SCoo |

## TORTULA (Sphagnaceae)
| | |
|---|---|
| *princeps* | Last listed 1996 |
| *ruralis* subsp. | Last listed 1996 |
| *ruraliformis* | |

## TOVARA See PERSICARIA

## TOWNSENDIA (Asteraceae)
| | |
|---|---|
| *condensata* | Last listed 1998 |
| *eximia* | Last listed 1996 |
| *exscapa* | Last listed 1998 |
| - NNS 93-74 | MRPP |
| *florifera* | CLyd |
| *formosa* | CInt CLyd CMea NBir NMen |
| | NNrd WWin |
| *glabella* | Last listed 1996 |
| *hookeri* | CGra |
| *incana* | CGra EHyt WLin |
| *jonesii* var. *tumulosa* | Last listed 1996 |
| *leptotes* | CGra |
| *mensana* | NMen |

| | |
|---|---|
| *montana* | CGra EHyt WLin |
| *nuttallii* | CGra |
| *parryi* | Last listed 1998 |
| § *rothrockii* | CPBP EHyt NMen NWCA |
| sp. from California | CGra |
| *spathulata* | CGra EHyt |
| *wilcoxiana* hort. | See *T. rothrockii* |

## TRACHELIUM (Campanulaceae)
| | |
|---|---|
| § *asperuloides* | CPBP EHyt EPot |
| *caeruleum* ♀ | CLTr EHol ERea SBid WBrE WCot |
| - 'Purple Umbrella' | CSam EMan |
| - 'White Umbrella' | CLTr EMan |
| *jacquinii* | Last listed 1997 |
| - subsp. *rumelianum* | CPBP MBro NTow NWCA WCot |
| | WHoo WPat WPyg |

## TRACHELOSPERMUM (Apocynaceae)
| | |
|---|---|
| § *asiaticum* ♀ | CB&S CBot CDoC CHan CMac |
| | CPlN CRHN EBrP EBre ELan EMil |
| | EPla GOrc GQui LBre LPri MBal |
| | MGos NPal SAPC SArc SBra SBre |
| | SPer SSpi SSta WPGP WPat WSHC |
| | WWat |
| * - 'Aureum' | LRHS |
| - 'Goshiki' | CB&S GQui MGos SPer SSpi |
| - var. *intermedium* | CFil WPGP |
| * *bodinieri* 'Cathayensis' | GCal |
| *jasminoides* ♀ | More than 30 suppliers |
| ¶ - 'Chamaeleon' | CTrC |
| § - 'Japonicum' | CRHN GCal LRHS NSti SBra SLPl |
| | SLon SSpi WWat |
| - 'Major' | CSPN CTrG SSpi |
| * - 'Oblanceolatum' | GCal |
| - 'Tricolor' (v) | CRHN ERav LRHS SMur SSta |
| - 'Variegatum' ♀ | CB&S CBot CDoC CMac COtt |
| | CSam CTrw EBee ELan ERav ERea |
| | GCal GQui LHop MBNS MGos |
| | MRav NHol SAPC SArc SPer SReu |
| | SSpi SSta WCot WPat WSHC WWat |
| | WWat |
| ¶ - 'Waterwheel' | WWat |
| - 'Wilsonii' W 776 | CBot CMac CPlN CPle CRHN |
| | CSPN EBrP EBre EHic ELan EMil |
| | ERav ETen GCal IOrc LBre MCCP |
| | SArc SBre SPer SReu SSpi SSta |
| | WCru WHar WPGP WWat |
| *majus* Nakai | See *T. asiaticum* |
| - hort. | See *T. jasminoides* 'Japonicum' |
| sp. from Nanking, China | Last listed 1998 |

## TRACHYCARPUS (Arecaceae)
| | |
|---|---|
| § *fortunei* ♀ | More than 30 suppliers |
| *latisectus* | CBrP LPJP LPal |
| *martianus* | LPJP LPal |
| *nanus* | LPal |
| *oreophilus* | LPal |
| *takil* | LPJP LPal NPal |
| *wagnerianus* | CBrP EOas LPJP LPal NPal SDry |
| | WMul WPGP |

## TRACHYSTEMON (Boraginaceae)
| | |
|---|---|
| *orientalis* | CBre CGle CHid CRDP CSev EBee |
| | ECha EGol ELan EPar EPla ERav |
| | MFir MRav MUlv NBid NChi NPSl |
| | SCob SIng SLon WCru WHer |
| | WWal WWat WWin |

## TRADESCANTIA (Commelinaceae)
| | |
|---|---|
| *albiflora* | See *T. fluminensis* |
| x *andersoniana* | CAgr ECGN MBro MFir MSal NFor |
| | WEas WPer WWin |

| | |
|---|---|
| – 'Bilberry Ice' | CM&M CMGP CStr EBee EFou EPla LFis MBri MOne MWhi NBro NLar NRoo NTow SSpe WHoo WSan |
| – 'Blaby Blue' | MTed |
| – 'Blue Stone' | CMGP CMea ECha EFou NFai NPri NRya SRms WFar WThi |
| – 'Caerulea Plena' | See *T. virginiana* 'Caerulea Plena' |
| – Carmine Glow | See *T. x andersoniana* 'Karminglut' |
| – 'Charlotte' | EBee EPla LRHS MAvo MGrG MOne NBro NCut NRoo |
| * – 'Concord Grape' | EFou WCot WWhi |
| – 'Croftway Blue' | SCro |
| – 'Domaine de Courson' | CHan LPio |
| ¶ – 'Double Trouble' (d) | WCot |
| – 'Innocence' | CBos CMHG COIW CSpe EBee ECGN ECha ECtt EFou ELan EOrc EPla GCHN GMaP LHop MBel MBri MCLN MTho NCat NFai NOrc NRoo NSti SPer WBro WHoo WMer WPnP WRus |
| – 'Iris Prichard' | CHan CM&M CMGP CMil EBee ELan EPar EPla GMaP LHop NLar NWoo SChu SCro SEas WPnP WWal |
| – 'Isis' ♀ | CB&S CHar CKel CMHG ECGN ECtt EFou ELan EPar EPla GCHN LHop MBel MRav MWgw NFai NGdn NOrc NRoo SChu SPer SSoC SUsu WCer WCot WMow WWin |
| – 'J.C.Weguelin' ♀ | CBlo EMil EPfP MBri NFai SRms WHoo WPnn WPyg |
| § – 'Karminglut' | CB&S ELan EOld EPar GCHN MAvo MNrw MUlv NFla NHol NOrc NRoo NVic WCer WHoo WPnP WRus |
| – 'Leonora' | COIW ENot EPfP NCut NFai SLon SRPl WThi |
| * – 'Little Doll' | CElw EBee EFou EHic EPla MAvo MLLN WCot WWhi |
| – 'Osprey' ♀ | CRDP CSpe CVer EBee ECha EFou ELan ENot EPla GChr LNor MBNS MNrw MRav MTho NBro NDea NOak NOrc NVic NWes SPer SRPl SRms WBro WEas WMer WMow WPnn WWin |
| – 'Pauline' | EBee ECGN ECtt EFou EMan EPla GCHN MBel MNrw MRav NBir NFai NLar NRoo SChu SUsu WCer WHoo WPyg WSan WWal WWin |
| – 'Purewell Giant' | CTri EBee ECot NBro NCat SChu SPer WGor WKif WPyg |
| – 'Purple Dome' | CHan CHar CKel CMGP CNic CRDP CStr ECtt EFou EOld EPla GCHN GMaP MRav NBir NCat NFai NGdn NMir NWes WCer WHoo WMow WPyg |
| ¶ – 'Purple Glow' | EBee |
| * – 'Red Grape' | EFou |
| – 'Rubra' | CMea EBee EPfP EPla LFis MBel MOne MWgw NDea NFai NOrc NPri SChu SCro SLod SRPl SRms WViv |
| – 'Valour' | CBlo EPla NCut WHil WMow WPnP |
| – 'Zwanenburg Blue' | CMGP ECha EFou EOrc GCHN LFis MUlv NBro NFai SEas SLon WMer WPnn |
| 'Blue and Gold' | EBee EMan NPro |
| *bracteata* | NTow |

| | |
|---|---|
| – *alba* | SEas WThi |
| *brevicaulis* | EBee ECha EFou EMFP EPar EPla GBuc GDra MAvo MBel MTho NBro NLar |
| *canaliculata* | See *T. ohiensis* |
| *cerinthoides* | CHal |
| – 'Variegata' ♀ | Last listed 1995 |
| 'Chedglow' | EPla LHop SUsu WHil |
| * 'Double Grape' (d) | WCot |
| *fluminensis* 'Albovittata' | CHal |
| – 'Aurea' ♀ | CHal MBri |
| – 'Laekenensis' (v) | CHal MBri |
| ¶ – 'Maiden's Blush' (v) | CHal CSpe MBEx NCut SVen WFoF |
| – 'Quicksilver' (v) ♀ | CHal MBri |
| ¶ – 'Rosea' | CHal |
| – 'Tricolor Minima' ♀ | Last listed 1995 |
| ¶ *longipes* | WCot |
| *multiflora* | See *Tripogandra multiflora* |
| *navicularis* | See *Callisia navicularis* |
| § *ohiensis* | EMan LPBA WPnP |
| § *pallida* | CHal IBlr |
| ¶ – 'Purpurea' ♀ | MBEx WCot |
| *pendula* | See *T. zebrina* |
| *sillamontana* ♀ | CHal LChe MBri |
| *spathacea* | Last listed 1998 |
| ¶ – 'Vittata' ♀ | CHal |
| – 'Tracey' | CM&M |
| *tricolor* | See *T. zebrina* |
| *virginiana* | CM&M MWhi SMrm |
| – 'Alba' | GCal WPer WThi |
| § – 'Caerulea Plena' (d) | CHan CM&M CMGP EBee EFou ELan EMan EPla LHop NHol NLar SChu SLod SRms WCot WFar WThi WWal |
| – 'Rubra' | CHan CM&M EAst NCut SPlb WThi |
| * 'White Domino' | Last listed 1997 |
| § *zebrina* ♀ | CHal |
| ¶ – *discolor* | CHal |
| – *pendula* | See *T. zebrina* |
| ¶ – 'Purpusii' ♀ | CHal |
| ¶ – 'Quadricolor' (v) ♀ | CHal |

## TRAGOPOGON (Asteraceae)

| | |
|---|---|
| ¶ *crocifolius* | WCot |
| *porrifolius* | CJew ILis NLak |
| *pratensis* | CArn CKin CPou EWFC NMir |
| *roseus* | See *T. ruber* |

## TRAPA (Trapaceae)

| | |
|---|---|
| *natans* | MSta |

## TRAUTVETTERIA (Ranunculaceae)

| | |
|---|---|
| ¶ *carolinensis* var. *japonica* | EBee WCru |

## TRICHOCEREUS (Cactaceae)

| | |
|---|---|
| *pachanoi* | ELau |

## TRICHOCOLEA (Trichocoleaceae)

| | |
|---|---|
| *tomentella* | Last listed 1996 |

## TRICHOPETALUM (Anthericaceae)

| | |
|---|---|
| § *plumosum* | CBro |

## TRICHOPHORUM (Cyperaceae)

| | |
|---|---|
| § *cespitosum* | MBal |

## TRICHOSANTHES (Cucurbitaceae)

| | |
|---|---|
| *cucumerina* | CPIN |

## TRICHOSTEMA (Lamiaceae)

| | |
|---|---|
| *lanatum* | Last listed 1998 |

## TRICUSPIDARIA See CRINODENDRON

## TRICYRTIS (✿) (Convallariaceae)

| | |
|---|---|
| 'Adbane' | CBro CLAP EBee ELan EMan EWTr LEur MBri NLar WCru WFar |
| *affinis* | GBuc LEur |
| – B&SWJ 2804 | LEur WCru |
| ◆ – 'Variegata' | See *T.* 'Variegata' (*affinis* hybrid) |
| ¶ 'Amanagowa' | CLAP |
| *bakeri* | See *T. latifolia* |
| 'Citronella' | Last listed 1997 |
| *dilatata* | See *T. macropoda* |
| 'Emily' | Last listed 1997 |
| ¶ *flava* | WCru |
| *formosana* ♀ | More than 30 suppliers |
| – B&SWJ 306 | LEur WCot WCru |
| – B&SWJ 355 | LEur WCru WFar |
| – B&SWJ 3712 | LEur |
| * – 'Dark Beauty' | EBee GSki LEur MBri WFar |
| – dark form | LEur WFar |
| ¶ – 'Gates of Heaven' | LEur |
| – pale form | WFar |
| ¶ – 'Samurai' | LEur |
| ¶ – 'Seiryu' | LEur |
| – 'Shelley's' | CLAP GCal LEur NBro NTow |
| § – Stolonifera Group | CAvo CB&S CBro CHan CM&M CMHG ECha ELan EOld LEur LHop MBal MRav NDea NFai SCro SLon SPer WBor WFar WOld WThi WWat WWin |
| – 'Variegata' | LEur WCru |
| ¶ 'Harlequin' | LEur |
| § *hirta* | More than 30 suppliers |
| § – *alba* | CBro CHan CSam EBee EHrv ELan GBri LEur MBal MBel MBro MRav MUlv NNrd WCru WFar WThi WWat WWin |
| * – 'Albomarginata' | LEur |
| ¶ – B&SWJ 2827 | WCru |
| ¶ – 'Golden Gleam' | CHea LEur WCot |
| – hybrids | CM&M WCru WFar |
| – 'Kinkazan' | LEur WFar |
| – 'Makinoi Gold' | LEur WCru |
| – var. *masamunei* | LEur WCru |
| – 'Matsukaze' | EBee LEur WFar |
| – 'Miyazaki' | CFir CHan CHea CHid EAst EGar EGle ELan EOld EPar GBuc LEur MBel MBro MUlv NLak NLar SCro WBea WCot WCru WFar WThi |
| ¶ – 'Miyazaki Gold' | LEur |
| * – 'Nana' | ELan WFar |
| – 'Variegata' | CLAP CLon EMon EWes GBuc LEur SCob SMad SUsu WCot WCru WHil |
| – 'White Flame' (v) | WCot |
| N Hototogisu | CLAP CMea EBee EGle EMar EMon EOld EPar MTho SUsu WCot WCru WFar WHil |
| *ishiiana* | LEur WCru |
| ¶ – var. *surugensis* | LEur WCru WFar |
| ¶ Japanese hybrids | WHil |
| *japonica* | See *T. hirta* |
| – 'Kinkazan' | WFar |
| 'Kohaku' | CLAP EBee LEur WCru WFar |
| ¶ *lasiocarpa* B&SWJ 3635 | WCru |
| § *latifolia* | CBro CGle CHad CHan EBee ELan GMaP GNau LEur MBel MNrw NLar WCot WCru WFar WHil WThi |

| | |
|---|---|
| 'Lemon Lime' | LEur LRHS WCru |
| 'Lilac Towers' | CHan EPar LEur WCru WKif |
| *macrantha* | MBal |
| § – subsp. *macranthopsis* | CLAP EBla LEur SWas WCru WFar |
| ◆ *macranthopsis* | See *T. macrantha* subsp. *macranthopsis* |
| * *macrocarpa* | Last listed 1997 |
| N *macropoda* | CGle CLon CPea CSam EGar ELan EMan EPar GBuc GMaP LEur NBus SAga WFar WThi WWat |
| – B&SWJ 1271 | LEur WCru |
| – variegated | WCru |
| *maculata* HWJCM 470 | WCru |
| *nana* | LEur WCru |
| *ohsumiensis* | CGle CHan CLAP EBee ECha ELan EMan EPot GBri LEur MTho SUsu WCot WCru WFar WThi |
| *perfoliata* | EBee LEur SWas WCru WFar WThi |
| 'Shimone' | CBro CHan CHid CLAP ELan GBri GBuc LEur LRHS MBri WCru WFar WKif |
| *stolonifera* | See *T. formosana* Stolonifera Group |
| 'Tojen' | CBro CHan CLAP EBla ECha EGar ELan EOld EWes GBri GBuc LEur LRHS MBri NBro WCru WFar |
| ¶ 'Toki-no-mai' | EBla LEur |
| ¶ 'Tresahor White' | LEur |
| ¶ 'Tresahor Yellow' | LEur |
| § 'Variegata' (*affinis* hybrid) | EBee GBri LEur NDov WCru WFar |
| 'White Towers' | CFee CHid CLAP EBee LEur MBel MBri NBus NCut SAga SCob SSON SWas WCru WFar WSan WThi |
| 'White Towers' spotted form | LEur SDys |

## TRIENTALIS (Primulaceae)

| | |
|---|---|
| *borealis* | Last listed 1996 |
| *europaea rosea* | CNat |

## TRIFOLIUM (Papilionaceae)

| | |
|---|---|
| ¶ *africanum* | EBee |
| *alpinum* | GDra |
| *arvense* | Last listed 1997 |
| *campestre* | CKin |
| *eximeum* | WAbe |
| *incarnatum* | MHer SIde WHer |
| ¶ *macrocephalum* | WCot |
| *medium* | Last listed 1997 |
| ¶ *nanum* | CGra |
| *ochroleucon* | EWFC GLil |
| *pannonicum* | EMon GCal GNau LGre MBel MHlr MLLN MSte SEND SMrm SOkh SUsu WCot WRus |
| *pratense* | EWFC EWTr MHer |
| – 'Chocolate' | See *T. pratense* 'Purple Velvet' |
| – 'Dolly North' | See *T. pratense* 'Susan Smith' |
| – 'Ice Cool' | See *T. repens* 'Green Ice' |
| – 'Nina' | CBre WAlt |
| – 'Speech House' (v) | WAlt |
| – 'Sprite' (v) | Last listed 1998 |
| § – 'Susan Smith' (v) | CElw CLyd CRow ECha EMan EMar EMon EWes IBlr LHop MCLN MLLN MNrw MSCN MTho NSti WAlt WHer WHil WPic WRos |
| *repens* | EWFC EWTr NCat |
| ¶ – 'Arthur's Folly' (v) | WAlt |
| – 'Aureum' | MBal |
| ¶ – 'Douglas Dawson' | CNat |
| – 'Gold Net' | See *T. pratense* 'Susan Smith' |
| – 'Good Luck' | CRow MTho |

| | |
|---|---|
| § - 'Green Ice' | CBre CInt CMea CRow CSev EBee EMan EMar LHop MTho NBir WAlt WByw WCot WHer WRus WWye |
| - 'Harlequin' (v) | CBre EBee WAlt |
| - 'Hiccups' (v) | WAlt |
| * - 'Pale Centre' | WAlt |
| - 'Peach Pink' | NCat WShe |
| - 'Pentaphyllum' | See *T. repens* 'Quinquefolium' |
| - 'Purp' | WAlt |
| - 'Purple Velvet' | EPPr |
| - 'Purpurascens' | CArn CBre CInt CLyd CRow GCal GDra GMac ILis LNor MBNS MBal MBel NHlc NRoo NSti SSea WBea WHen WKif WOak WWhi |
| § - 'Purpurascens Quadrifolium' | CNic EAst ECha ELan EMar EPla EWes MBel NMir NNrd NPer SIde SPer WAlt WFar WOve WPic WRHF WRus WWin WWye |
| - 'Quadrifolium' | EHoe EPar |
| § - 'Quinquefolium' | WPer |
| - 'Shannel Pinnate' | Last listed 1998 |
| - 'Tetraphyllum Purpureum' | See *T. repens* 'Purpurascens Quadrifolium' |
| * - 'Velvet and Baize' (v) | CNat |
| - 'Wheatfen' (v) | CBre CRow EMan EWes MTho NCat NPer SUsu WAlt WCot WRHF WRus |
| *rubens* | EBee ECGN EMan EMar EMon GBri GNau LGre MAvo MSte NLon SMrm SSca SUsu WCot WRus WWeb |
| ¶ - 'Peach Pink' | MAvo WCot WRus |
| ¶ *subterraneum* | EWFC |
| ¶ *uniflorum* | NWCA |

## TRIGONELLA (Papilionaceae)
| | |
|---|---|
| *foenum-graecum* | CArn MSal SIde |

## TRIGONOTIS (Boraginaceae)
| | |
|---|---|
| *rotundifolia* | EBee |

## TRILLIUM ✿ (Trilliaceae)
| | |
|---|---|
| *albidum* | CBro SSpi |
| ¶ *angustipetalum* | CLAP SSpi |
| *apetalon* | WCru |
| ¶ *camschatcense* | CAvo GCrs LAma SSpi WCru |
| § *catesbyi* | CBro EBee EPot GCrs LAma MSal SSON SSpi WCru |
| *cernuum* | EPot GCrs LAma SBid WCru |
| *chloropetalum* | CBro EBrP EBre EPar GDra LBre SBla SBre SSpi WAbb WCru |
| ¶ - var. *albiflorum* | WTin |
| ¶ - *album* | ECha |
| § - var. *giganteum* ♀ | CFil SSpi SWas WPGP |
| ♦ - var. *rubrum* | See *T. chloropetalum* var. *giganteum* |
| *cuneatum* | CB&S CBro EBee EHyt ELan EPar EPot GAbr ITim LAma MDun MTho SBid SCob SDeJ SSpi WAbe WCru |
| - red | GCrs |
| *decumbens* | Last listed 1996 |
| *erectum* ♀ | More than 30 suppliers |
| § - f. *albiflorum* | CBro CRDP EPot LAma MSal SSpi WCru |
| - 'Beige' | Last listed 1997 |
| - f. *luteum* | GCrs LAma SSpi |
| *flexipes* | EPot GCrs |
| ¶ *govanianum* | LAma WCru |
| *grandiflorum* ♀ | More than 30 suppliers |

| | |
|---|---|
| - 'Flore Pleno' (d) ♀ | EBrP EBre EPar GBuc LBre NHar SBre SWas |
| ¶ - 'Roseum' | WThi |
| - 'Snowbunting' (d) | Last listed 1997 |
| 'Hokkaido' | Last listed 1996 |
| *kurabayashii* | SSpi |
| § *luteum* ♀ | CB&S CBro CCuc CHid CLAP EBee EPar EPot GAbr GBuc GCrs IMGH LAma LBow MDun NHar SBid SCob SLod SPer SSpi WCru WFar |
| *nivale* | CGra GCrs |
| *ovatum* | GCrs GDra LAma |
| - var. *hibbersonii* | CBos CBro GBin GBuc GCrs GDra MBal NHar NMen NTow |
| - 'Roy Elliott' | NBir |
| - 'Wayne Roberts' | Last listed 1997 |
| *parviflorum* | GCrs SSpi |
| *pusillum* | EPot SSpi |
| - var. *pusillum* | GCrs NHar |
| - var. *virginianum* | CBro LAma WCru |
| *recurvatum* | CB&S EBee EPar EPot GCrs LAma SSON WCru |
| *rivale* ♀ | CBro CElw CLAP GCrs LAma SBla WAbe |
| - 'Purple Heart' | Last listed 1997 |
| *rugelii* | CLAP EPot GCrs LAma SSpi WCru |
| *sessile* | CCuc CHid CLAP EPot GBuc IMGH LAma LBow NBir NHar SCob SPer WCru WFar WSHC WShi |
| - var. *luteum* | See *T. luteum* |
| - purple | WPGP |
| *smallii* | LAma WCru |
| *stylosum* | See *T. catesbyi* |
| *sulcatum* | CAvo CBro CLAP EPar EPot GCrs GDra MDun SSpi WCru |
| *tschonoskii* | LAma WCru |
| *undulatum* | EBee GCrs LAma SSpi WCru |
| *vaseyi* | CBro CLAP EHyt EPot GCrs LAma SSpi WCru |
| *viride* | WCru WLin |
| ¶ *viridescens* | LAma |

## TRINIA (Apiaceae)
| | |
|---|---|
| * *grandiflora* | Last listed 1997 |

## TRIOSTEUM (Caprifoliaceae)
| | |
|---|---|
| *himalayanum* | EBee |
| ¶ *pinnatifidum* | WCot |

## TRIPETALEIA (Ericaceae)
| | |
|---|---|
| § *bracteata* | Last listed 1997 |

## TRIPOGANDRA (Commelinaceae)
| | |
|---|---|
| § *multiflora* | CHal |

## TRIPTEROSPERMUM (Gentianaceae)
| | |
|---|---|
| *cordifolium* | Last listed 1996 |
| - B&SWJ 081 | WCru |
| *japonicum* B&SWJ 1168 | WCru |
| *lanceolatum* | Last listed 1996 |
| - B&SWJ 085 | WCru |
| *taiwanense* | Last listed 1996 |
| - B&SWJ 1205 | WCru |

## TRIPTERYGIUM (Celastraceae)
| | |
|---|---|
| *regelii* | CFil CPIN |

## TRISETUM (Poaceae)
| | |
|---|---|
| *distichophyllum* | EHoe |
| *flavescens* | CKin |

## TRISTAGMA (Alliaceae)
| | |
|---|---|
| 'Rolf Fiedler' | See *Ipheion* 'Rolf Fiedler' |
| *uniflorum* | See *Ipheion uniflorum* |

## TRISTANIA (Myrtaceae)
| | |
|---|---|
| *conferta* | See *Lophostemon confertus* |
| *laurina* | See *Tristaniopsis laurina* |

## TRISTANIOPSIS (Myrtaceae)
| | |
|---|---|
| § *laurina* | Last listed 1998 |

## TRISTELLATEIA (Malpighiaceae)
| | |
|---|---|
| *australasiae* | CPlN |

## TRITELEIA (Alliaceae)
| | |
|---|---|
| *californica* | See *Brodiaea californica* |
| § 'Corrina' | Last listed 1998 |
| *grandiflora* | WCot |
| *hyacintha* | ERos ETub LAma WBea WCot |
| *ixioides* | CMea EBee ERos |
| - subsp. *ixioides* | Last listed 1997 |
| - var. *scabra* | Last listed 1997 |
| - 'Splendens' | Last listed 1998 |
| - 'Starlight' | CAvo EBee EPot WAbe WCot |
| § *laxa* | CAvo CMea EBee EHic ELan LAma NRog WCot |
| § - 'Koningin Fabiola' | CTri EBee ETub LAma MBri NRog WBea |
| - PJC 951 | Last listed 1997 |
| - Queen Fabiola | See *T. laxa* 'Koningin Fabiola' |
| § *peduncularis* | EBee LAma WCot |
| x *tubergenii* | EBee LAma |
| *uniflora* | See *Ipheion uniflorum* |

## TRITHRINAX (Arecaceae)
| | |
|---|---|
| *acanthocoma* | LPal |
| *campestris* | LPal |

## TRITOMA See KNIPHOFIA

## TRITONIA (Iridaceae)
| | |
|---|---|
| ¶ *crispa* | LBow |
| *crocata* | CPou LBow NRog WHer |
| ¶ - 'Baby Doll' | LBow |
| ¶ - 'Bridal Veil' | LBow |
| - *hyalina* | Last listed 1998 |
| ¶ - 'Pink Sensation' | LBow |
| - 'Prince of Orange' | CPou |
| § *disticha* | CAvo CBro CElw CFil CHan CPou |
| subsp. *rubrolucens* | CSev EBee ECha EGra EMan GCHN GLch MBel MBri MHlr NRoo SAga SOkh SUsu WGer WLin WPGP WPen WRHF WWhi |
| *lineata* | Last listed 1997 |
| 'Orange Delight' | Last listed 1998 |
| ¶ 'Princess Beatrix' | EBee |
| *rosea* | See *T. disticha* subsp. *rubrolucens* |
| *securigera* | Last listed 1998 |
| *squalida* | LBow |

## TROCHETIOPSIS (Sterculiaceae)
| | |
|---|---|
| § *ebenus* | LHil |
| ♦ *melanoxylon* hort. | See *T. ebenus* |

## TROCHOCARPA (Epacridaceae)
| | |
|---|---|
| *gunnii* | Last listed 1996 |
| *thymifolia* | WAbe |

## TROCHODENDRON (Trochodendraceae)
| | |
|---|---|
| *aralioides* | CB&S CDoC CFil CGre CMCN EBee ENot EPfP MBlu MGos SAPC SArc SLon SPer SReu SSpi SSta WCoo WCot WCru WSHC WWat |

## TROLLIUS (Ranunculaceae)
| | |
|---|---|
| *acaulis* | EBee EGle EWes GDra LHop MTho SMrm WPat WPyg |
| *asiaticus* | CRDP GBuc |
| § *chinensis* | CGle EBee ECha GCal LSyl NChi NCut SRms SWat |
| - 'Golden Queen' ♀ | CMHG ECtt ELan EMar ENot EWTr LFis MBNS MCLN MNrw MRav MUlv MWat NFor NHol NMir NRoo NSti SEas SHel SMac SPer WCru WFar WGor WHen WHil WHoo WOve WPer |
| - 'Imperial Orange' | CGle EWal WWin |
| 'Cressida' | EBee |
| x *cultorum* 'Alabaster' | CHea CLAP CLon CRDP CRow ECha GNau MRav NLar WFar WSan WTin WViv |
| - 'Baudirektor Linne' | ECtt GCHN MRav NRoo |
| - Bressingham hybrids | EBrP EBre LBre NRoo SBre |
| - 'Bunce' | NCut |
| - 'Canary Bird' | CHea ELan GBri NFla SMur SRms WRus |
| - 'Cheddar' | COtt EBee EFou EMan GBin GNau MBri MCLN MRav WCot WHil WWat |
| - 'Commander-in-chief' | EMan MUlv NHol |
| - 'Earliest of All' | CGle CSam MBri NGdn NRoo SPer SPla SRms WGor |
| - 'Etna' | EBee MBri NRoo |
| § - 'Feuertroll' | CMGP ECha MBri NPro SMur |
| - Fireglobe | See *T. x cultorum* 'Feuertroll' |
| - 'Golden Cup' | ECot NGdn NRoo |
| - 'Golden Monarch' | CBlo EPar |
| - 'Goldquelle' ♀ | EHon NVic SMur |
| - 'Goliath' | CGle NRoo |
| - 'Helios' | CGle CHea CSam ECha |
| - 'Lemon Queen' | EMan EPar EWTr GCal LSyl MBri MUlv NCut NFor NRoo SCro SWat WCot WRus WWin |
| - 'Maigold' | MBri |
| - new hybrids | WHil |
| - 'Orange Crest' | GCal |
| - 'Orange Globe' | NPri WHil |
| - 'Orange Princess' ♀ | ENot EPfP GCHN LSyl MBal MBel NBro NDea NHol SPer SRms |
| - 'Prichard's Giant' | WCot |
| - 'Salamander' | SMur |
| § - 'Superbus' ♀ | CM&M CMGP CMHG CRDP ELan EPar EPfP MBNS MBri NHol NRoo SLon SPer SSpi WCot WFar |
| - 'T. Smith' | Last listed 1998 |
| *europaeus* | CBot CRow ECha EPot ERic EWFC EWTr LHop LSyl MBal MBro MNrw NDea NMir NRya NSti SRms SUsu SWat WCla WHoo WLin WPer WPyg |
| - 'Superbus' | See *T. x cultorum* 'Superbus' |
| *hondoensis* | EBee GBin NLar WElm WSan |
| *ledebourii* hort. | See *T. chinensis* |
| *pumilus* | CGle ECha ELan LBee MBro NNrd NWCA SIng WFar WViv |
| - ACE 1818 | GBuc WAbe |
| * - *albidus* | Last listed 1998 |
| - 'Wargrave' | EPot NMen |
| ¶ *riederianus* | EBee |

| | |
|---|---|
| *stenopetalus* | EBee ECha EWes |
| *yunnanensis* | CGle GBuc MBal NSti NWoo SMac WAbe |
| - CD&R 2097 | WCru |

## TROPAEOLUM ✿ (Tropaeolaceae)

| | |
|---|---|
| *azureum* | CPla SHFr |
| *brachyceras* | NLar WCot |
| *ciliatum* ♀ | CAvo CB&S CFil CFir CHan CLAP CMHG CPIN CPla CSam EBee EBrP EBre ELan EOrc GCal LBow LBre LEdu MTho NLar SBre SMad WCot WCru WHer WNor WPGP |
| *incisum* | Last listed 1998 |
| *majus* | EMFW LHol SBid WSel |
| - 'Alaska' (v) | CBod SBid SIde WJek WSel |
| - 'Apricot Trifle' | CSpe |
| * - 'Clive Innes' | ERea |
| - 'Crimson Beauty' | CSpe MAvo MLLN MMil |
| - 'Darjeeling Gold' (d) | CSpe LHil WCot WCru |
| ¶ - 'Darjeeling Red' | NPri |
| - 'Empress of India' | SBid WEas WJek |
| ¶ - 'Forest Flame' | LHil |
| - 'Hermine Grashoff' (d) ♀ | CMHG CSWP CSpe ECtt ERea LHil LHop MLLN NPer NPri SBid SLod WEas WHer WLRN |
| * - 'Indian Chief' | Last listed 1996 |
| - 'Margaret Long' (d) | CSpe LHil MLLN NPri WEas WLRN |
| * - 'Peaches and Cream' | WJek |
| - 'Red Wonder' | CHad CSWP CSpe LHil NPri SBid WJek |
| - Tom Thumb mixed | WJek |
| - 'Variegatum' | Last listed 1997 |
| *peltophorum* | Last listed 1998 |
| *pentaphyllum* | CAvo CFil CLAP ECha GCal IBlr MTho WCot |
| *polyphyllum* | CFil CLAP CPIN ECha EHyt GBuc GCrs SDix SWas WCot |
| *sessilifolium* | EHyt |
| *speciosum* ♀ | More than 30 suppliers |
| *sylvestre* | WCru |
| *tricolorum* ♀ | CAvo CFil CLAP CPIN EHyt EPot MTho SDix WCot |
| *tuberosum* | CB&S CGle CMHG GPoy MBal WWye |
| - var. *lineamaculatum* 'Ken Aslet' ♀ | More than 30 suppliers |
| - P.J. Christian's form | Last listed 1998 |
| - var. *piliferum* 'Sidney' | CFil CGle IBlr IHdy WCru |

## TSUGA (Pinaceae)

| | |
|---|---|
| *canadensis* | EHul EWTr GAri GChr LCon MBar NWea WDin |
| - 'Abbot's Dwarf' | CKen LCon MGos |
| § - 'Abbott's Pygmy' | CKen |
| - 'Albospica' | EOrn LBee LCon WGor |
| - 'Aurea' (v) | LCon MBar WAbe |
| - 'Baldwin Dwarf Pyramid' | MBar |
| - 'Bennett' | EHul LCon MBar MUlv |
| - 'Brandley' | CKen |
| § - 'Branklyn' | CKen WBcn |
| - 'Cinnamonea' | CKen |
| - 'Coffin' | CKen |
| - 'Cole's Prostrate' | CKen EBrP EBre EOrn LBre LCon MAsh MBar NHol SBre |
| - 'Curley' | CKen |
| - 'Curtis Ideal' | CKen |
| - 'Dwarf Whitetip' | LCon |
| - 'Everitt Golden' | CKen |
| - 'Fantana' | EHul LBee LCon LLin MBar NHol SBod SLim WAbe WLRN |
| - 'Gentsch Snowflake' | CKen EPla MGos |

| | |
|---|---|
| ¶ - 'Gentsch White' (v) | MGos |
| - 'Golden Splendor' | Last listed 1997 |
| - 'Greenwood Lake' | Last listed 1998 |
| - 'Horsford' | CKen |
| - 'Hussii' | CKen |
| - 'Jacqueline Verkade' | CKen |
| - 'Jeddeloh' ♀ | CDoC CMac CSli EBrP EBre EHul ENot EOrn GChr IMGH LBre LCon LLin MAsh MBal MBar MBri MGos MPla NBee SBre SLim WPyg WStI WWat |
| - 'Jervis' | CKen LCon |
| - 'Kingsville Spreader' | CKen |
| I - 'Lutea' | CKen |
| - 'Minima' | CKen |
| - 'Minuta' | CKen EHul EOrn ESis LBee LCon LLin MBar MGos SLon |
| - 'Nana' | CMac EHul IOrc WLRN |
| - 'Nana Gracilis' | See *T. canadensis* 'Gracilis' |
| - 'Palomino' | CKen MBar |
| - 'Pendula' ♀ | CDoC CKen EHul ENot EOrn LBee LCon MBar MBri MOne NHol SLim WCwm |
| - 'Pincushion' | CKen |
| - 'Prostrata' | See *T. canadensis* 'Branklyn' |
| - 'Pygmaea' | See *T. canadensis* 'Abbott's Pygmy' |
| - 'Rugg's Washington' | CKen |
| - 'Verkade Petite' | CKen |
| - 'Verkade Recurved' | CKen LCon MBar MUlv WBcn |
| - 'Von Helms' | CKen |
| - 'Warnham' | CKen ECho EOrn LBee LCon MAsh MBri |
| ¶ *candanensis* | CKen |
| 'Everitt's Denseleaf' | |
| *caroliniana* | CKen |
| 'La Bar Weeping' | |
| *diversifolia* | LCon |
| - 'Gotelli' | CKen |
| *heterophylla* ♀ | CDul ENot GAri GChr GRei IOrc LBuc LCon MBar NWea SMad SPer STre WDin |
| - 'Iron Springs' | CKen EOrn |
| - 'Laursen's Column' | CKen |
| *menziesii* | See *Pseudotsuga menziesii* |
| *mertensiana* | WCwm |
| ¶ - 'Blue Star' | LCon MGos |
| - dwarf form | Last listed 1996 |
| - 'Elizabeth' | CKen |
| I - 'Glauca Nana' | CKen |
| - 'Quartz Mountain' | CKen |
| *sieboldii* 'Nana' | CKen |

## TSUSIOPHYLLUM (Ericaceae)

| | |
|---|---|
| *tanakae* | See *Rhododendron tsusiophyllum* |

## TUBERARIA (Cistaceae)

| | |
|---|---|
| *guttata* | WCru |
| *lignosa* | CInt CMHG SSpi WAbe WCla |

## TULBAGHIA ✿ (Alliaceae)

| | |
|---|---|
| *acutiloba* | CAvo ERos LLew |
| *alliacea* | CFee ERos WCot |
| *capensis* | CFee LGre LHil |
| *cepacea* | LHil NBir |
| § - var. *maritima* | CAvo ERos LLew |
| *coddii* | CAvo CFee LGre |
| ¶ - x *violacea* | CPin |
| *cominsii* | CAvo EBee LGre |
| - x *violacea* | LHil |
| *dregeana* | LLew |

'Fairy Star'                    ERos WCot
*fragrans*                      See *T. simmleri*
¶ *fragrantissima*              WCot
*galpinii*                      WCot
  - 'John Rider'                CAbb
* 'John May's Special'          WCot
  'John Rider'                  WPer
*leucantha*                     EBee ERos LHil LLew WCot
*ludwigiana*                    EBee WCot
*maritima*                      See *T. cepacea* var. *maritima*
*natalensis*                    CAvo CHan CPou EBee LGre
  - pink                        WCot
§ *simmleri*                    CAvo EBee EWes LAma LBlm LHil
                                LLew LPio WCot
*violacea*                      CB&S CBro CHan CMHG CPea
                                CPou CSev ECha EHrv ERav ETub
                                IBlr LAma LHil LPan MTho SBea
                                SCob SMrm SSpi SWat WCot
                                WPGP
* - 'Alba'                      CPea LLew
  - *pallida*                   CAvo CRDP LGre LHil SLod SMrm
                                WCot
§ - 'Silver Lace' (v)           CAvo CBos CFee CGle CHan
                                CRDP CSWP CSpe ELan EMon
                                ERav ERea EWes LGre LHop LPio
                                MBEx MTho NBir SCob SIgm SSpi
                                WCot WFar WPGP
  - *tricolor*                  Last listed 1998
  - 'Variegata'                 See *T. violacea* 'Silver Lace'

## TULIPA ✿ (Liliaceae)

¶ 'Abba' (2)                    NRog
  'Abu Hassan' (3)              LAma
*acuminata* (15)                CBro EBot ETub LAma LBow
  'Ad Rem' (4)                  LAma NRog
  'Addis' (14)                  LAma
  'African Queen' (3)           LAma
*aitchisonii*                   See *T. clusiana*
  'Aladdin' (6)                 EWal LAma NRog
  'Alaska' (6)                  LAma
*albertii* (15)                 LAma
  'Albino' (3)                  LAma
*aleppensis* (15)               LAma
  'Aleppo' (7)                  LAma
  'Alfred Cortot' (12) ♀        LAma
  'Ali Baba' (14)               MBri
  'Alice Leclercq' (2)          LAma
  'All Bright' (5)              LAma
  'Allegretto' (11)             LAma NRog
*altaica* (15)                  EPot LAma
*amabilis* PF 8955              See *T. boogiana* PF 8955
  'Ancilla' (12) ♀              CBro LAma NRog WShe
  'Angélique' (11)              CAvo ETub EWal LAma MBri NBir
                                NRog
*anisophylla* (15)              Last listed 1998
  'Anne Claire' (3)             LAma
  'Antwerp' (3)                 LAma
  'Apeldoorn' (4)               ETub EWal LAma MBri NRog
  'Apeldoorn's Elite' (4) ♀     EWal LAma NRog
  'Apricot Beauty' (1)          CAvo CHid ETub EWal LAma MBri
                                NBir NRog
  'Apricot Jewel'               See *T. linifolia* (Batalinii Group)
                                'Apricot Jewel'
  'Apricot Parrot' (10) ♀       LAma NRog
  'Arabian Mystery' (3)         CAvo LAma NBir
  'Aristocrat' (5) ♀            LAma
  'Arma' (7)                    LAma
  'Artist' (8) ♀                CAvo LAma NBir
  'Astarte' (3) ♀               Last listed 1991
  'Athleet' (3)                 LAma
  'Attila' (3)                  LAma NRog
*aucheriana* (15) ♀            CBro EHyt EPot ERos LAma LBow

'Aurea'                         See *T. greigii* 'Aurea'
  'Aureola' (5)                 LAma
*australis* (15)                Last listed 1998
  'Baby Doll' (2) ♀             Last listed 1991
*bakeri*                        See *T. saxatilis* Bakeri Group
  'Balalaika' (5)               Last listed 1998
  'Ballade' (6) ♀               LAma NRog
  'Ballerina' (6) ♀             CAvo LAma
*batalinii*                     See *T. linifolia* Batalinii Group
  'Beauty of Apeldoorn' (4)     LAma NRog
¶ Beauty Queen (1)              NRog
  'Belcanto' (3)                LAma
  'Bellflower' (7)              LAma
  'Bellona' (3)                 LAma NRog
  'Berlioz' (12)                LAma
¶ 'Bestseller' (1)              NRog
*biebersteiniana* (15)          LAma
§ *biflora* (15)                CBro LAma NRog
*bifloriformis* (15)            Last listed 1998
  'Big Chief' (4) ♀             LAma MBri NRog
  'Bing Crosby' (3)             ETub LAma
  'Bird of Paradise' (5)        See *T.* 'Mrs Keightley'
  'Black Diamond' (5) ♀         Last listed 1991
  'Black Parrot' (10) ♀         CAvo ETub LAma NRog
  'Blenda' (3)                  ETub
  'Bleu Aimable' (5)            CAvo ETub LAma
  'Blue Heron' (7) ♀            LAma NRog
  'Blue Parrot' (10)            CSWP EWal LAma NRog
  'Blushing Lady' (5)           LAma
  'Bonanza' (11)                LAma
  'Boule de Neige' (2)          LAma
  'Bravissimo' (2)              MBri
  'Brilliant Star' (1)          LAma MBri NRog
  'Burgundy' (6)                ETub LAma
  'Burgundy Lace' (7)           LAma NRog
  'Burns' (7)                   LAma
*butkovii* (15)                 LAma
I 'Calypso' (14)                ETub
§ 'Candela' (13)                LAma NRog
  'Cantata' (13)                CBro LAma
  'Cantor' (5)                  LAma
  'Cape Cod' (14)               LAma NRog
  'Capri' (4) ♀                 Last listed 1995
  'Caprice' (10)                LAma
*carinata* (15)                 LAma
  'Carlton' (2)                 LAma NRog
  'Carnaval de Nice' (11/v)     ETub LAma MBri NRog
  'Cassini' (3)                 LAma
§ 'celsiana' (15)               EBot LAma
  'César Franck' (12)           LAma
  'Charles' (3)                 LAma NRog
  'China Lady' (14) ♀           Last listed 1991
  'China Pink' (6) ♀            CAvo ETub LAma NRog
  'Chopin' (12)                 LAma NRog
¶ 'Christmas Dream' (1)         NRog
  'Christmas Marvel' (1)        ETub LAma NRog
*chrysantha* Boiss.             See *T. montana*
  - Boiss. ex Baker             See *T. clusiana* var. *chrysantha*
  'Clara Butt' (5)              LAma NRog
§ *clusiana* (15)               CBro LAma
§ - var. *chrysantha* (15) ♀    CAvo LAma LBow NRog
  - - 'Tubergen's Gem' (15)     CSWP LAma MBri
  - 'Cynthia' (15)              CAvo CSWP EPot LAma NRog
§ - var. *stellata* (15)        LAma
  'Concerto' (13)               CBro ETub LAma
  'Cordell Hull' (5)            NRog
  'Corona' (12)                 ETub LAma NRog
  'Corsage' (14) ♀              LAma
  'Couleur Cardinal' (3)        EBot ETub EWal LAma NRog
*cretica* (15)                  Last listed 1998
  'Crystal Beauty' (7)          NRog

'Dancing Show' (8)    CAvo CMea LAma
*dasystemon* (15)    LAma MBNS MRPP
¶ 'Daylight' (12)    NRog
'Demeter' (3) ♀    Last listed 1989
'Diana' (1)    LAma NRog
'Diantha' (14)    LAma
*didieri*    See *T. passeriniana*
'Dillenburg' (5)    LAma
¶ 'Diplomate' (4)    NRog
'Dix' Favourite' (3)    LAma
'Doctor Plesman' (3)    LAma
'Doll's Minuet' (8)    LAma
'Don Quichotte' (3) ♀    LAma
'Donna Bella' (14) ♀    LAma
'Douglas Bader' (5)    CAvo LAma NRog
'Dover' (4) ♀    Last listed 1995
'Dreaming Maid' (3)    LAma
¶ 'Dreamland' (5) ♀    NRog
'Dutch Gold' (3)    LAma
'Dyanito' (6)    EWal LAma NRog
'Early Harvest' (12) ♀    LAma NRog
'Easter Parade' (13)    EWal LAma
'Easter Surprise' (14)    LAma
§ *edulis* (15)    EHyt LAma LRHS
*eichleri*    See *T. undulatifolia*
'Electra' (5)    EWal LAma MBri NRog
'Elegant Lady' (6)    ETub
'Elizabeth Arden' (4)    LAma NRog
'Elmus' (5)    Last listed 1998
'Engadin' (14) ♀    Last listed 1995
'Esperanto' (8/v)    LAma NRog
'Estella Rijnveld' (10)    ETub LAma NBir NRog
'Fair Lady' (12)    LAma
'Fancy Frills' (7) ♀    LAma
'Fantasy' (10) ♀    LAma
'Fashion' (12)    LAma NRog
*ferganica* (15)    LAma
'Feu Superbe' (13)    Last listed 1998
'Fidelio' (3) ♀    Last listed 1993
'Fireside'    See *T. 'Vlammenspel'*
'First Lady' (3) ♀    LAma
'Flair' (1)    LAma NRog
'Flaming Parrot' (10)    LAma NRog
'Flying Dutchman' (5)    LAma
*fosteriana* (13)    MBri
'Franz Léhar' (12)    LAma
'Frasquita' (5)    Last listed 1998
'Fresco' (14)    LAma
'Fringed Group (7)    ETub
'Fringed Apeldoorn' (7)    NRog
'Fringed Beauty' (7)    ETub MBri
'Fringed Elegance' (7)    LAma
'Fritz Kreisler' (12)    LAma
'Fulgens' (6)    LAma
'Gaiety' (12)    LAma
'Galata' (13)    LAma
*galatica* (15)    LAma
'Garden Party' (3)    LAma
'Generaal de Wet' (1)    ETub LAma MBri NRog
'General Eisenhower' (4)    LAma
'Georgette' (5)    EWal LAma MBri NRog
¶ 'Gerbrand Kieft' (11)    NRog
'Giuseppe Verdi' (12)    EWal LAma LBow MBri NRog
'Glück' (12)    EWal LAma NRog
'Gold Medal' (11)    LAma MBri
'Golden Age' (5)    LAma
'Golden Apeldoorn' (4)    EWal LAma MBri NRog
'Golden Artist' (8)    LAma MBri NRog
'Golden Emperor' (13)    LAma
'Golden Harvest' (5)    LAma
'Golden Melody' (3)    ETub LAma NRog
'Golden Oxford' (4)    LAma NRog

'Golden Parade' (4)    LAma NRog
'Golden Springtime' (4)    LAma
'Gordon Cooper' (4)    EWal LAma NRog
'Goudstuk' (12)    LAma
'Grand Prix' (13)    LAma
'Green Eyes' (8)    LAma
'Green Spot' (8)    LAma
*greigii* (14)    CBro
§ - 'Aurea' (14)    Last listed 1998
*grengiolensis* (15)    EPot LAma
'Greuze' (5)    LAma
'Grével' (3)    CAvo LAma
'Groenland' (8)    LAma NRog
'Gudoshnik' (4)    LAma NRog
*hageri* (15)    LAma
- 'Splendens' (15)    ETub LAma
'Halcro' (5) ♀    ETub LAma
'Hamilton' (7) ♀    LAma
¶ 'Hans Mayer' (4)    NRog
'Happy Family' (3)    LAma
'Heart's Delight' (12)    CBro ETub EWal LAma LBow
    NRog
'Hibernia' (3)    LAma
'Hit Parade' (13)    LAma
'Hoangho' (2)    LAma NRog
'Hollands Glorie' (4) ♀    LAma
'Hollywood' (8)    LAma NRog
*hoogiana* (15)    LAma
§ - PF 8955 (15)    Last listed 1998
§ *humilis* (15)    CAvo CBro EPar EPot ETub LAma
    LBow MBri WShi
- 'Eastern Star' (15)    LAma MBri
§ - 'Lilliput' (15)    CBro EPot
- 'Odalisque' (15)    EPot LAma
- 'Persian Pearl' (15)    EPot LAma MBri NRog
§ - var. *pulchella*    EPot LAma
    Albocaerulea Oculata
    Group (15)
§ - Violacea Group (15)    CAvo CMea EPar ETub EWal
    LAma MBri
§ - Violacea Group black    CBro LRHS
    base (15)
- Violacea Group yellow    CBro LAma LBow LRHS
    base (15)
'Humming Bird' (8)    LAma NRog
'Hytuna' (11)    LAma NRog
'Ibis' (1)    LAma
'Ile de France' (5)    LAma
'Inferno'    NBir
*ingens* (15)    LAma
'Inzell' (3)    ETub LAma
¶ 'Jacqueline' (6)    NRog
'Jeantine' (12) ♀    LAma
'Jewel of Spring' (4) ♀    LAma
'Jimmy' (3)    NRog
'Jockey Cap' (14)    LAma
'Joffre' (1)    LAma MBri NRog
'Johann Strauss' (12)    CBro EWal LAma MBri NRog
'Johanna' (3)    Last listed 1998
'Juan' (3)    LAma MBri
'Kansas' (3)    LAma
'Karel Doorman' (10)    LAma
'Kareol' (2)    LAma NRog
*kaufmanniana* (12)    CAvo CBro EPot LBow NRog
    SRms
§ 'Kees Nelis' (3)    LAma MBri NRog
'Keizerskroon' (1) ♀    EBot EWal LAma NRog
'Kingsblood' (5) ♀    LAma
◆ 'Kleurenpracht'    See *T. 'Princess Margaret Rose'*
*kolpakowskiana* (15) ♀    LAma MBri NRog
§ 'Koningin Wilhelmina' (4) ♀    Last listed 1993
*kurdica* (15)    LAma

'La Tulipe Noire' (5) LAma
* 'Lady Diana' (14) MBri
*lanata* (15) LAma
'Landseadel's Supreme' (5) ♀ Last listed 1997
'Large Copper' (14) Last listed 1998
'Leen van der Mark' (3) LAma
'Lefeber's Favourite' (4) LAma
'Lilac Time' (6) LAma
'Lilac Wonder' See *T. saxatilis* (Bakeri Group) 'Lilac Wonder'
'Lilliput' See *T. humilis* 'Lilliput'
*linifolia* (15) ♀ CAvo EHyt EPar EPot ETub LAma LBow NRog
§ - Batalinii Group (15) ♀ CBro LAma NRog
§ - (Batalinii Group) CAvo CBro
  'Apricot Jewel' (15)
- (Batalinii Group) CAvo CBro EPot LAma LBow
  'Bright Gem' (15) ♀ MBro NRog SUsu WHoo WPyg
- (Batalinii Group) CAvo CBro CMea CSWP EPot
  'Bronze Charm' (15) LAma
- (Batalinii Group) CBro LAma
  'Red Gem' (15)
- (Batalinii Group) Last listed 1998
  'Red Jewel' (15)
- (Batalinii Group) CBro
  'Yellow Gem' (15)
- (Batalinii Group) EPot LAma
  'Yellow Jewel' (15)
§ - Maximowiczii Group CBro EPot LAma LBow
'London' (4) LAma
'Love Song' (12) Last listed 1997
'Lucifer' (5) EWal LAma
'Lucky Strike' (3) LAma
§ 'Lustige Witwe' (3) EWal LAma
§ 'Madame Lefeber' (13) CBro EWal LBow MBri NRog
'Madame Spoor' (3) Last listed 1997
'Magier' (5) LAma
'Maja' (7) LAma
'Mamasa' (5) LAma
'March of Time' (14) MBri
'Maréchal Niel' (2) LAma
'Mariette' (6) LAma
'Marilyn' (6) ETub LAma NRog
¶ 'Marjolein' (6) ♀ NRog
*marjolletii* (15) CBro LAma NRog
'Mary Ann' (14) LAma
'Maureen' (5) ♀ ETub LAma
*mauritiana* (15) LAma
*maximowiczii* See *T. linifolia* Maximowiczii Group
'Maytime' (6) LAma NRog
'Maywonder' (11) LAma
'Melody d'Amour' (5) Last listed 1998
'Menton' (5) ETub
¶ 'Merry Christmas' (1) NRog
Merry Widow See *T.* 'Lustige Witwe'
'Mickey Mouse' (1) NRog
'Minerva' (3) NRog
'Mirella' (3) ♀ Last listed 1993
'Miss Holland' (3) MBri
'Mona Lisa' (6) LAma NRog
§ *montana* (15) CBro EPot LAma
'Monte Carlo' (2) ♀ EWal LAma NRog
¶ 'Moonshine' (6) NRog
'Most Miles' (3) ♀ Last listed 1994
'Mount Tacoma' (11) ETub EWal LAma MBri NRog
'Mr Van der Hoef' (2) LAma MBri NRog
'Mrs John T. Scheepers' (5) ♀ Last listed 1996
'Murillo' (2) LAma
'My Lady' (4) ♀ LAma
'Negrita' (3) LAma
¶ *neustruevae* (15) CBro EPot ETub

'New Design' (3/v) ETub EWal LAma MBri NRog
'New Look' (7) ETub
'Orange Bouquet' (3) ♀ LAma NRog
'Orange Elite' (14) LAma MBri
'Orange Emperor' (13) LAma MBri NRog
'Orange Favourite' (10) LAma
'Orange Sun' See *T.* 'Oranjezon'
'Orange Toronto' (14) Last listed 1996
'Orange Triumph' (11) MBri
'Oranje Nassau' (2) ♀ LAma MBri NRog
§ 'Oranjezon' (4) ♀ LAma
'Oratorio' (14) LAma MBri
'Oriental Beauty' (14) LAma NRog
'Oriental Splendour' (14) ♀ EWal LAma
*orphanidea* (15) EPot LAma LBow WCot
- 'Flava' (15) CBro ETub LAma
§ - Whittallii Group (15) CAvo CBro CMea LAma NRog
*ostrowskiana* (15) LAma
'Oxford' (4) ♀ LAma NRog
'Oxford's Elite' (4) LAma
'Page Polka' (3) LAma
'Palestrina' (3) LAma
'Pandour' (14) LAma MBri
'Parade' (4) ♀ LAma MBri
'Paris' (3) Last listed 1997
§ *passeriniana* (15) LAma
'Paul Richter' (3) LAma
'Pax' (3) LAma
'Peach Blossom' (2) ETub LAma MBri NRog
'Peerless Pink' (3) LAma
'Perlina' (14) LAma
*persica* See *T. celsiana*
'Philippe de Comines' (5) LAma
'Picture' (5) ♀ LAma
'Pimpernel' (8/v) CAvo LAma
'Pink Beauty' (1) LAma
'Pink Impression' (4) LAma
'Pink Trophy' (1) Last listed 1998
'Pinkeen' (13) LAma
'Pinocchio' (14) EWal NRog
'Plaisir' (14) ♀ LAma MBri
*platystigma* (15) LAma
*polychroma* See *T. biflora*
*praestans* (15) LAma
- 'Fusilier' (15) ♀ CBro EPot EWal LAma LBow MBri NBir NRog
- 'Unicum' (15/v) EWal LAma MBri NRog
- 'Van Tubergen's LAma NRog WShi
  Variety' (15)
'Preludium' (3) LAma
'President Kennedy' (4) ♀ LAma
*primulina* (15) Last listed 1998
'Prince Charles' (3) ♀ Last listed 1989
'Prince Karl Philip' (3) NRog
'Prince of Austria' (1) LAma
'Princeps' (13) CBro EWal LAma MBri
§ 'Princess Margaret Rose' (5) EWal LAma
¶ 'Princesse Charmante' (14) ETub
'Prins Carnaval' (1) Last listed 1997
'Prinses Irene' (3) ♀ CMea ETub LAma MBri NBir NRog
'Professor Röntgen' (10) LAma
'Prominence' (3) Last listed 1997
*pulchella humilis* See *T. humilis*
§ 'Purissima' (13) CAvo CBro ETub EWal LAma LBow NRog
'Queen' (4) LAma
'Queen Ingrid' (14) LAma
'Queen of Bartigons' (5) ♀ LAma NRog
¶ 'Queen of Marvel' (2) NRog
'Queen of Night' (5) CAvo CMea ETub EWal LAma MBri NRog

| | |
|---|---|
| 'Queen of Sheba' (6) ♀ | CAvo LAma NRog |
| 'Queen Wilhelmina' | See *T.* 'Koningin Wilhelmina' |
| 'Recreado' (5) | ETub |
| 'Red Champion' (10) | LAma |
| 'Red Emperor' | See *T.* 'Madame Lefeber' |
| 'Red Georgette' (5) ♀ | MBri |
| 'Red Matador' (4) | LAma |
| 'Red Parrot' (10) | LAma NRog |
| 'Red Riding Hood' (14) ♀ | CBro ETub EWal LAma LBow MBNS MBri NBir NRog |
| 'Red Sensation' (10) | Last listed 1997 |
| 'Red Shine' (6) ♀ | LAma |
| 'Red Surprise' (14) ♀ | Last listed 1995 |
| 'Red Wing' (7) ♀ | LAma |
| 'Reforma' (3) | Last listed 1997 |
| Rembrandt Mix | ETub MBri |
| 'Renown' (5) | Last listed 1997 |
| *rhodopea* | See *T. urumoffii* |
| 'Rijnland' (3) | Last listed 1997 |
| 'Ringo' | See *T.* 'Kees Nelis' |
| 'Rockery Beauty' (13) | Last listed 1997 |
| ¶ 'Rockery Master' (14) | ETub |
| 'Rockery Wonder' (14) | Last listed 1997 |
| 'Rosario' (3) | Last listed 1998 |
| * 'Rose Emperor' (13) | LAma |
| 'Rosy Wings' (3) | LAma |
| ¶ 'Ruby Red' (1) | NRog |
| 'Safari' (14) | ETub |
| *saxatilis* (15) | CAvo CBro LAma MBri NRog |
| § - Bakeri Group (15) | CPou LAma |
| § - (Bakeri Group) | CAvo LAma EPot ETub LAma MBri |
|     'Lilac Wonder' (15) ♀ | NRog |
| - MS 769 (15) | Last listed 1998 |
| ¶ 'Scarlet Baby' (12) | NRog |
| 'Scarlet Cardinal' (2) | Last listed 1997 |
| 'Scarlett O'Hara' (5) | LAma |
| 'Schoonoord' (2) | ETub LAma MBri NRog |
| *schrenkii* (15) | LAma LRHS |
| 'Scotch Lassie' (5) | LAma |
| 'Shakespeare' (12) | CBro LAma LBow NRog |
| 'Shirley' (3) | CAvo ETub EWal LAma MBri NRog |
| 'Showwinner' (12) ♀ | CBro ETub LAma MBri NRog |
| 'Sigrid Undset' (5) | LAma |
| 'Silentia' (3) | LAma |
| 'Smiling Queen' (5) | LAma |
| 'Snowflake' (3) | LAma |
| 'Snowpeak' (5) | LAma |
| *sogdiana* (15) | LAma |
| 'Sorbet' (5) ♀ | LAma |
| 'Sparkling Fire' (14) | LAma |
| 'Spectacular Gold' | See *T.* 'Goldenes Deutschland' |
| *sprengeri* (15) ♀ | CBro CFil CLAP CNic EHyt EPar LAma MRav SDix SSpi WPGP |
| - Trotter's form (15) | WCot |
| 'Spring Green' (8) ♀ | CAvo CMea ETub EWal LAma MBri NRog |
| 'Spring Pearl' (13) | LAma |
| 'Spring Song' (4) | LAma |
| *stellata* | See *T. clusiana* var. *stellata* |
| 'Stockholm' (2) ♀ | LAma NRog |
| 'Stresa' (12) ♀ | CBro LAma NRog |
| 'Striped Apeldoorn' (4) | LAma NRog |
| 'Striped Bellona' (3) | NRog |
| *subpraestans* (15) | EPot LAma |
| 'Success' (3) | Last listed 1997 |
| 'Summit' (13) | LAma |
| 'Sundew' (7) | LAma NRog |
| 'Sunray' (3) | LAma |
| 'Susan Oliver' (8) | LAma |
| 'Swan Wings' (7) | LAma |
| 'Sweet Harmony' (5) ♀ | LAma MBri NRog |

| | |
|---|---|
| 'Sweet Lady' (14) | LAma NRog |
| 'Sweetheart' (13) | CBro LAma NRog |
| 'Sweetheart' (5) | See *T.* 'Princess Juliana' |
| *sylvestris* (15) | CAvo CBro CMea EPar EWFC LAma LBow NRog WCot WShi |
| 'Tamara' (3) | Last listed 1997 |
| 'Tango' (14) | LAma |
| *tarda* (15) ♀ | CAvo CBro CMea EPar EPot ETub EWal LAma LBow MBri MBro NMGW NRog SUsu WPyg WShi |
| 'Teenager' (14) | Last listed 1997 |
| 'Temple of Beauty' (5) ♀ | LAma |
| 'Tender Beauty' (4) | LAma |
| *tetraphylla* (15) | LAma |
| 'Texas Flame' (10) | LAma NRog |
| 'Texas Gold' (10) | LAma NRog |
| 'The First' (12) | CBro LAma |
| 'Toronto' (14) ♀ | LAma MBri |
| 'Toulon' (13) | MBri |
| 'Towa' (14) | LAma |
| 'Trance' (3) | Last listed 1997 |
| 'Trinket' (14) | LAma |
| 'Triumphator' (2) | LAma |
| *tschimganica* (15) | LAma |
| *tubergeniana* (15) | LAma |
| - 'Keukenhof' (15) | LAma |
| *turkestanica* (15) ♀ | CAvo CBro CSWP EPar EPot ETub LAma LBow MBri MBro NMen NRog WBea WCot WHoo |
| 'Uncle Tom' (11) | LAma MBri |
| § *undulatifolia* (15) | CBro LAma |
| 'Union Jack' (5) ♀ | EWal LAma |
| *urumiensis* (15) ♀ | CAvo CBro EHyt EPot LAma MBri MBro NRog WHoo WPyg WShi |
| § *urumoffii* (15) | LAma |
| 'Valentine' (3) | LAma |
| 'Van der Neer' (1) | LAma |
| 'Varinas' (3) | LAma |
| *violacea* | See *T. humilis* Violacea Group |
| 'Viridiflora' (8) | ETub |
| 'Vivaldi' (12) | LAma |
| 'Vivex' (4) | LAma |
| § 'Vlammenspel' (1) | LAma |
| 'Vuurbaak' (2) | LAma |
| *vvedenskyi* (15) | CBro LAma NRog |
| - 'Blanka' (15) | EPot |
| - 'Hanka' (15) | EPot |
| - 'Lenka' (15) | EPot |
| - 'Tangerine Beauty' (15) | MBri |
| 'West Point' (6) ♀ | CAvo ETub EWal LAma NRog |
| * 'White Bouquet' (5) | NRog |
| 'White Dream' (3) | EWal LAma |
| 'White Emperor' | See *T.* 'Purissima' |
| 'White Parrot' (10) | CAvo ETub LAma NRog |
| 'White Swallow' (3) | NRog |
| 'White Triumphator' (6) ♀ | CAvo CMea ETub EWal LAma NBir NRog |
| 'White Virgin' (3) | LAma |
| *whittallii* | See *T. orphanidea* Whittallii Group |
| 'Willem van Oranje' (2) | LAma NRog |
| 'Willemsoord' (2) | LAma MBri NRog |
| *wilsoniana* | See *T. montana* |
| 'Wirosa' (11) ♀ | Last listed 1991 |
| 'Yellow Dawn' (14) | LAma |
| 'Yellow Dover' (4) | Last listed 1997 |
| 'Yellow Emperor' (5) | MBri |
| 'Yellow Empress' (13) | LAma |
| 'Yellow Present' (3) | LAma |
| 'Yellow Purissima' (13) | NRog |
| 'Yokohama' (3) | ETub LAma NRog |
| 'Zampa' (14) ♀ | EWal LAma |

*zenaidae* (15) — Last listed 1998
'Zombie' (13) — LAma
'Zomerschoon' (5) — EBot ETub
'Zwanenburg' (5) — Last listed 1997

## TUNICA See PETRORHAGIA

## TUPISTRA (Convallariaceae)
¶ *aurantiaca* B&SWJ 2267 — WCru

## TURBINA (Convolvulaceae)
*corymbosa* — Last listed 1998

## TURNERA (Turneraceae)
*ulmifolia* — MSal

## TURRAEA (Meliaceae)
*obtusifolia* — CSpe

## TUSSILAGO (Asteraceae)
*farfara* — CArn CJew ELau EWFC GPoy MHew MSal SIde WHer

## TWEEDIA (Asclepiadaceae)
§ *caerulea* ♀ — CFri CGle CInt CM&M CRHN CSev CSpe ELan ERea IBlr LGre LHop LLWP SHFr SLon SPer SYvo WEas WPic

## TYLOPHORA (Asclepiadaceae)
*ovata* — CPlN

## TYPHA (Typhaceae)
*angustifolia* — CBen CKin CRow CWat EHon EMFW GBin LPBA MSta SPlb SWat SWyc WWye
*latifolia* — CAgr CBen CRow CWat EHon EMFW GBin MSta SWat SWyc WHer WMAq WWye
- 'Variegata' — CBen CRow CWat ELan EMFW LEdu LPBA MSta SWyc WCot
§ *laxmannii* — CBen CRow EHon EMFW LPBA MSta SRms
*minima* — CBen CMHG CRDP CRow EHoe EHon EMFW GBin LEdu LPBA MSta NDea SCoo SLon SMad SWat SWyc WFar WMAq
- var. *gracilis* — Last listed 1996
*shuttleworthii* — CRow
*stenophylla* — See *T. laxmannii*

# U

## UGNI (Myrtaceae)
§ *molinae* — CGre CPle CTrC GAri ISea LEdu MBal MBel SHFr SOWG WCHb WJek WPic WSHC WWal WWat WWye

## ULEX (Papilionaceae)
*europaeus* — CCVT CDoC ENot EWFC GRei LBuc MCoo NWea WDin WHar WMou
- 'Aureus' — Last listed 1998
§ - 'Flore Pleno' (d) ♀ — CB&S CDoC CInt CNic CTri EMon ENot EPla GChr MBal MGos SPer WBcn WCot
- 'Plenus' — See *U. europaeus* 'Flore Pleno'
- 'Prostratus' — MBar

*gallii* — IIve
- 'Mizen Head' — EHic ESis GCal GGGa GSki LRHS MPla MWhi NHar SLon SMad WBcn
§ *minor* — EPla
*nanus* — See *U. minor*

## ULLUCUS (Basellaceae)
¶ *tuberosus* — LEdu

## ULMUS ✿ (Ulmaceae)
¶ *davidiana* 'Nire Keyaki' — CPMA
'Dodoens' — LBuc MGos NBee
§ *glabra* — CDul GCHr GRei NWea WDin
- 'Camperdownii' — CTho ELan EWTr LPan NBee SPer
- 'Exoniensis' — CDul CTho SRPl
- 'Gittisham' — CTho
- 'Horizontalis' — See *U. glabra* 'Pendula'
- 'Lutescens' — CTri
- 'Nana' — NHol WPat
§ - 'Pendula' — LPan
x *hollandica* 'Commelin' — EMil
- 'Groeneveld' — EMil
- 'Jacqueline Hillier' — CBar CInt CTre EBrP EBre ELan GEil IMGH LBre LHop MBal MBar MBro MPla NHar NHol SBre SHFr SLon SMad SRms SSpi STre SVil WFar WHCG WPat WPyg
- 'Lobel' — CDul MGos
- 'Wredei' — See *U. minor* 'Dampieri Aurea'
*minor* 'Cornubiensis' — CBlo
§ - 'Dampieri Aurea' — CBot CDul CEnd CLnd EBee ELan LBuc LNet LPan MAsh MBar MBlu NBee SMad SPer SSta WDin WPat
- 'Variegata' — EPot SCoo
*montana* — See *U. glabra*
*parvifolia* — EHal EHic GAri NWea SMad STre WFro WHCr WNor
- 'Frosty' (v) — ECho ELan EPot NOla
- 'Geisha' (v) — CBlo CPMA ELan MGos SBla WCot WPat WPyg
§ - 'Hokkaido' — EHyt LBee MBro NHol SBla WAbe WPat WPyg
- 'Pygmaea' — See *U. parvifolia* 'Hokkaido'
¶ - 'Seiju' — SMad
- 'Yatsubusa' — CLyd EPot ESis EWes MBro SIng STre WGle WPat WPyg
'Plantijn' — Last listed 1997
¶ *procera* — CDul
- 'Argenteovariegata' — SMad
*pumila* — CAgr GAri WNor
'Sapporo Autumn Gold' — MBlu

## UMBELLULARIA (Lauraceae)
*californica* — CAgr CArn CB&S LEdu SAPC SArc WSHC

## UMBILICUS (Crassulaceae)
*erectus* — CRDP
*rupestris* — ELan EWFC GAri GBar IIve NWCA SChr WCla WCot WHer WShi WWye

## UNCINIA (Cyperaceae)
¶ *clavata* — EPla
*divaricata* — Last listed 1996
N *rubra* — More than 30 suppliers
* - 'Dunn Valley' — GBri
sp. from Chile — EPla EWes GCal
*uncinata* — CFil CM&M ECGN ECha EHoe EMan MBal NHol NWCA SUsu

\* - *rubra*            CFir CHar ECot EPGN LRHS
                       MCLN MMHG SCob SMac

**UNIOLA** (Poaceae)
  *latifolia*          See *Chasmanthium latifolium*

**URCEOLINA** (Amaryllidaceae)
  *miniata*            See *Stenomesson miniatum*
  *peruviana*          See *Stenomesson miniatum*
  *urceolata*          Last listed 1997

**URECHITES** See PENTALINON

**URGINEA** (Hyacinthaceae)
  *fugax* SF 62        Last listed 1998
  *maritima*           EBee EBot EOHP GPoy LAma
                       MNrw MSal
  - SF 275             Last listed 1998
  *ollivieri* MS&CL 281  Last listed 1998
  *undulata* SF 2      Last listed 1998

**UROSPERMUM** (Asteraceae)
  *delachampii*        CGle CHan COtt SAga WCot

**URSINIA** (Asteraceae)
¶ *montana*            NWCA
¶ *pilifera*           CTrC WCot

**URTICA** (Urticaceae)
  *dioica*             Last listed 1997
¶ - 'Bradfield Purpler'  CNat
  - 'Brightstone Bitch' (v)  WAlt
  - 'Chedglow' (v)     CNat WAlt
¶ - 'Danae Johnston' (v)  CNat EMon GVic WAlt
  - 'Dusting' (v)      WAlt
¶ - 'Dying for Attention'  WAlt
¶ - 'Good as Gold' (v)  WAlt
¶ - 'Ingdust' (v)      WAlt
¶ - OBG mutant         CNat
¶ - 'Spring Fever'     WAlt
  *galeopsifolia*      CNat
  *pilulifera dodartii*  Last listed 1996

**UTRICULARIA** (Lentibulariaceae)
  *alpina*             CSWC WMEx
  *australis*          EFEx
  *biloba*             GTro
  *bisquamata*         CSWC GTro WMEx
¶ *blancheti*          NCot
  *calcyfida*          GTro WMEx
  *capensis*           WMEx
  *dichotoma*          EFEx GTro WMEx
  *exoleta*            See *U. gibba*
§ *gibba*              EFEx
  *intermedia*         EFEx
  *laterifolia*        EFEx GTro WMEx
  *livida*             EFEx GTro WMEx
  *longifolia*         GTro WMEx
  *menziesii*          EFEx GTro
  *monanthos*          EFEx
  *nephrophylla*       GTro
  *novae-zelandiae*    GTro
  *ochroleuca*         EFEx
  *praelonga*          GTro
  *prehensilis*        GTro WMEx
  *pubescens*          WMEx
  *reniformis*         EFEx GTro WMEx
  - *nana*             EFEx
  *sandersonii*        GTro WMEx
  - blue               GTro
  *subulata*           EFEx WMEx
  *tricolor*           GTro WMEx

*vulgaris*             EFEx SAWi WMEx

**UVULARIA** (Convallariaceae)
§ *caroliniana*        IBlr
  *disporum*           LAma
  *grandiflora* ♀      More than 30 suppliers
¶ - dwarf form         IBlr
  - var. *pallida*     CHid CRDP ECha EMan EPar
                       GBuc IBlr LGre MRav SWas WCru
  *perfoliata*         ECha EDAr EPar EPfP EPla EPot
                       GCrs LAma MBro MRav SIng
                       WAbe WCru WIvy WPGP WWat
  *pudica*             See *U. caroliniana*
§ *sessilifolia*       CRDP EBee EPar EPot GCrs IBlr
                       LAma WCru WIvy

# V

**VACCARIA** (Caryophyllaceae)
§ *hispanica*          MSal
  *segetalis*          See *V. hispanica*

**VACCINIUM** ✿ (Ericaceae)
\* *alpinum*            Last listed 1997
  *arctostaphylos*     SSta
  *caespitosum*        GDra
¶ x 'Cinderella'       SSta
¶ *consanguineum*      LRHS
  *corymbosum* ♀       CB&S CBlo EPfP MBal MBar
                       MGos NBee SReu SSta WDin
                       WGer
  - 'Berkeley' (F)     CTrh GTwe LBuc LRHS SDea
  - 'Bluecrop' (F)     CDoC CMac CTrh EBee ELan
                       EMui GChr GTwe LBuc MBri
                       MGos SDea WStI WWeb
  - 'Bluegold'         CTrh
  - 'Bluejay' (F)      CTrh LRHS
  - 'Bluetta' (F)      CTrh GTwe LRHS
  - 'Concord' (F)      EBee ENot
  - 'Coville' (F)      CTrh EMui SDea
  - 'Duke' (F)         CTrh ELan EPfP LRHS
  - 'Earliblue' (F)    EMui MGos SDea
  - 'Elliott' (F)      CTrh
  - 'Goldtraube' (F)   CDoC MBlu MBri MGos SDea
  - 'Herbert' (F)      CTrh EMui GTwe MGos
  - 'Ivanhoe' (F)      CTrh
  - 'Jersey' (F)       LRHS MGos SDea
  - 'Nelson'           CTrh
  - 'Northland' (F)    GAri GTwe SDea
  - 'Patriot' (F)      CTrh GAri GTwe LRHS MGos
  - 'Pioneer' (F)      MBar
  - 'Spartan' (F)      GAri GTwe LRHS
  - 'Sunrise' (F)      GTwe
  - 'Toro' (F)         GTwe
  - 'Trovor' (F)       Last listed 1998
¶ - 'Weymouth' (F)     SDea
  *crassifolium*       LRHS MAsh SSta
  'Well's Delight' (F)
  *cylindraceum* ♀     EPfP MBro NHol SSta WAbe WBod
                       WPat WPyg
  - 'Tom Thumb'        WAbe
  *delavayi*           EPot GCHN MAsh MBal MBar
                       MBlu NNrd SReu SSpi SSta WAbe
                       WWat
  *donianum*           See *V. sprengelii*
  *dunalianum*         CB&S
  - var. *caudatifolium*  WCru
      B&SWJ 1716

| | |
|---|---|
| *emarginatum* | SSta |
| *floribundum* | CFil CMHG EPfP GDra GSki GTou MAsh MBal SBrw SPer SRPl SSpi SSta WPGP WPic |
| *glaucoalbum* ♀ | CAbP CDoC EPfP GGGa MBar MBlu MRav SPer SReu SSpi SSta WBod WDin |
| – B 173 | MBal |
| § *macrocarpon* (F) | CMac ELan GTwe MAsh MBal MBar MBri SRms |
| – 'CN' (F) | MGos |
| – 'Early Black' (F) | CB&S MGos SLdr |
| – 'Franklin' (F) | EPot |
| – 'Hamilton' (F) | EPot GCrs NHol WAbe WPat WPyg |
| – 'McFarlin' (F) | EMui |
| – 'Pilgrim' (F) | Last listed 1998 |
| * *McMinn* | GAri MBal |
| *moupinense* | IMGH ITim LRHS MAsh MBal MBlu MGos WAbe |
| – small-leaved | MBal |
| – 'Variegatum' | WPyg |
| *myrtillus* | GPoy IIve MBal WDin |
| 'Nimo Pink' | MBar |
| *nummularia* | EPot GDra LRHS MBal NHar SSpi WAbe |
| – LS&H 17294 | Last listed 1997 |
| *ovalifolium* | Last listed 1996 |
| *ovatum* | CB&S CMHG GSki LRHS MBal MBar SSta |
| § *oxycoccos* (F) | CArn |
| – var. *intermedium* | Last listed 1996 |
| * – *rubrum* | LRHS |
| *padifolium* | CFil CGre MBal WPGP |
| *pallidum* | IBlr |
| *palustre* | See *V. oxycoccos* |
| *parvifolium* | Last listed 1996 |
| *praestans* | GAri NHol |
| *retusum* | CGre CTrw LRHS MBal WBod |
| *sikkimense* | GGGa |
| § *sprengelii* | CB&S |
| *vitis-idaea* | CAgr CNic GPoy MBal MBar MGos SReu SRot WPyg |
| – 'Compactum' | EWes MBal NHar |
| – Koralle Group ♀ | EPfP MAsh MBal MBar MBri MGos MRav NHol SPer SReu SSta WAbe WPat WPyg |
| – var. *minus* | EHyt GAri MAsh MBal NMen SSta SVil |
| – 'Red Pearl' | LRHS MAsh MGos SPer |
| * – 'Variegatum' | EWes WPat |
| *wrightii* var. *formosanum* B&SWJ 1542 | WCru |

## VAGARIA (Amaryllidaceae)
| | |
|---|---|
| *ollivieri* SF 266 | Last listed 1998 |

## VALERIANA (Valerianaceae)
| | |
|---|---|
| ♦ 'Alba' | See *Centranthus ruber* 'Albus' |
| *alliariifolia* | EBee EMon GCal NBro NSti WCot |
| *arizonica* | CLyd LFis MSte MTho NCat |
| 'Coccinea' | See *Centranthus ruber* |
| *dioica* | CRDP |
| ¶ *bardwickii* CC 2227 | CPLG |
| *jatamansi* | GPoy |
| *montana* | GTou MBro NBro NRya SRms SWat |
| *officinalis* | CArn CKin CRDP CSev ECha ELau EWFC GPoy ILis LHol MChe MHew MMal NBro NLar SIde SRms SWat WHer WOak WPer WShi WWye |

| | |
|---|---|
| – subsp. *sambucifolia* | CHan CHid SHel |
| * – 'Variegata' | WCHb |
| *phu* 'Aurea' | More than 30 suppliers |
| * – 'Purpurea' | ECoo |
| *pyrenaica* | ECha EHal WCot |
| *saxatilis* | NRoo NRya SRms |
| *supina* | CGra NWCA |
| *tatamana* | WEas |
| ¶ *wallrothii* | WCot |

## VALERIANELLA (Valerianaceae)
| | |
|---|---|
| *eriocarpa* | Last listed 1997 |
| § *locusta* | CAgr GPoy |
| *olitoria* | See *V. locusta* |

## VALLEA (Elaeocarpaceae)
| | |
|---|---|
| *stipularis* | CDoC |
| – var. *pyrifolia* | CGre CPle |

## VALLOTA See CYRTANTHUS

## VANCOUVERIA (Berberidaceae)
| | |
|---|---|
| *chrysantha* | CElw CFil CVer ECha EMon EOld GBuc IBlr MRav NWCA SLod SSpi WCru WSHC |
| *hexandra* | CFil CNic CVer EBee ECha EMan EMon EPar EPla ERos GBuc GCal IBlr LHop MBal NCat NRya NSti SSca SSpi WBea WCru WWin |
| ¶ *planipetala* | IBlr WCru |

## VANIA (Brassicaceae)
| | |
|---|---|
| *campylophylla* | Last listed 1997 |

## VEITCHIA (Arecaceae)
| | |
|---|---|
| *merrillii* | LPal |

## VELTHEIMIA (Hyacinthaceae)
| | |
|---|---|
| § *bracteata* ♀ | CHal CBak ETub IBlr LBow LHil NRog SYvo WCot |
| § *capensis* ♀ | CSev MTPN |
| *viridifolia* Jacquin | See *V. bracteata* |
| – hort. | See *V. capensis* |

## x VENIDIOARCTOTIS See ARCTOTIS

## VENIDIUM See ARCTOTIS

## VERATRUM (Melanthiaceae)
| | |
|---|---|
| *album* | CBot CFil CFir EBee ECha NLar SBla SPer WCru WFar |
| – var. *flavum* | LGre |
| – var. *oxysepalum* | WCru |
| *californicum* | ECha IBlr |
| *caudatum* | Last listed 1997 |
| *formosanum* B&SWJ 1575 | WCru |
| *nigrum* ♀ | CBot CBro CFil CFir EBee EWTr GCal LGre MNrw SChu SWas WCot WFar WTin |
| *stamineum* | WCru |
| *viride* | CBot ECha IBlr SSpi |

## VERBASCUM (Scrophulariaceae)
| | |
|---|---|
| *acaule* | Last listed 1998 |
| * – 'Album' | WCru |
| *adzbaricum* | EBee EWTr EWll MBro SRCN SWat WElm WHoo WOve WSan |
| Allstree hybrids | CFee EHol EHrv |
| 'Arctic Summer' | See *V. bombyciferum* 'Polarsommer' |
| *arcturus* | ESis WPer |
| * *bakerianum* | EBee EBla WEas WMoo |

| | |
|---|---|
| ¶ 'Bill Bishop' | SIng |
| *blattaria* | CGle CHid CPou EBee EBot |
| | ECGN EHrv ELan EMan EPPr |
| | EWFC LIck MGed MHew NBir |
| | SCob SWat WEas WHer WPer |
| | WUnu |
| - f.*albiflorum* | CLon CNic CSpe ECGN EMar |
| | LGre LLWP MBro NSti SUsu WHer |
| | WKif WPer WPyg WRus WUnu |
| - pink | CFri CLTr EGoo EWll GAbr NLak |
| | STes WOve |
| - yellow | EWll SWat WSan |
| 'Bold Queen' | Last listed 1996 |
| § *bombyciferum* ♀ | CSWP CSev EWTr IIve NSti NVic |
| | SRms SSvw WByw WCot WEas |
| | WHer |
| - BSSS 232 | WCru |
| § - 'Polarsommer' | CSam EBrP EBre EMan EWTr |
| | GAbr LBre MBri MHlr MRav NArg |
| | NBir SBre SRms WMow |
| - 'Silver Lining' | NFla NPer SRCN |
| 'Broussa' | See *V. bombyciferum* |
| 'Butterscotch' | Last listed 1998 |
| *chaixii* | CHea EBee ECha EHrv GBuc LRot |
| | NBir NCut WHil WMow WPer |
| | WPyg |
| - 'Album' | More than 30 suppliers |
| - subsp.*austriacum* | EBee |
| - x *phoeniceum* | CHan WIvy |
| 'Clent Sunrise' | |
| (Cotswold Group) 'Boadicea' | Last listed 1997 |
| - 'C.L.Adams' | Last listed 1996 |
| - 'Cotswold Beauty' ♀ | CFai CHad CLon COtt CPar CSpe |
| | EAst EBee EBla EMan MBel MMil |
| | MTis MWat NGdn NLak NLar |
| | SChu SSpe WLRN WPGP |
| - 'Cotswold Gem' | Last listed 1997 |
| - 'Cotswold King' | CGle LPio MHlr WCot WGle WSan |
| - 'Cotswold Queen' | CGle CLon CM&M COlW EBee |
| | EBrP EBre EFou ELan EMan LBre |
| | LPio MCAu MMil MWat NCut |
| | NFla NGdn NSti SBre SChu SMrm |
| | SPer SSpe WEas WPGP WRus |
| | WSan WWin |
| - 'Gainsborough' ♀ | More than 30 suppliers |
| - 'Mont Blanc' | CGle CMil EAst EBee EBrP EBre |
| | ECot EFou EHrv EMan LBre LPio |
| | MLLN NRoo SBre WRus WSan |
| - 'Pink Domino' ♀ | More than 30 suppliers |
| - 'Royal Highland' | CGle CHad CLon EAst EBee ECot |
| | EFou EHrv ELan EMan GBri LPio |
| | MAvo MTis MWat NCut NGdn |
| | NLak NLar NSti SChu SMrm SWat |
| | WCot WRus |
| - 'White Domino' | CFai EBee EFou MBNS MCAu NPri |
| | WRus WViv |
| *creticum* | ECoo EPri NLak WCla WPer |
| § *densiflorum* | CArn ECoo LHol NCut SIde SPer |
| | WCla WPer |
| *dumulosum* ♀ | EDAr EHyt GCal MHar NWCA |
| | SBla WAbe WSan |
| *elegantissimum* | Last listed 1996 |
| 'Ellenbank Rose' | Last listed 1998 |
| 'Frosted Gold' | LGre |
| 'Golden Wings' ♀ | CPBP CPla EPot ITim NMen |
| | NTow WAbe WPat |
| 'Helen Johnson' ♀ | More than 30 suppliers |
| ¶ *hybrida* 'Snow Maiden' | ECoo |
| 'Jackie' | CFai CHar CSpe EAst EHic MBri |
| | NPri SBla SPer STes WCot WRus |

| | |
|---|---|
| 'Letitia' ♀ | CPla EBrP EBre ELan EMan EPot |
| | EWes GCal IMGH LBee LBre |
| | MTho NTow SBla SBre SIng SRms |
| | SSmi WAbe WEas WHoo WKif |
| | WPyg WWin |
| *longifolium* | EBee |
| - var.*pannosum* | See *V. olympicum* |
| *lychnitis* | CArn CLTr EBee LGre WHer |
| ¶ *macrurum* | EBee |
| *nigrum* | CArn CGle CJew EBee EPfP |
| | EWFC EWTr MBNS MCAu MChe |
| | MHew NChi SEND SRCN WHer |
| | WPer |
| - var.*album* | ECGN LPio MBel MBri WWhi |
| § *olympicum* | CGle CLTr CSam EBee ECha EGoo |
| | ELan ENot EWTr MBNS NOak |
| | SCob SEND WCot WPer |
| ¶ *oreophilum* | EBee |
| *phlomoides* | WHil WKif |
| *phoeniceum* | CArn CGle ECoo ELan GMac |
| | MSCN MWgw NBro NCut NMir |
| | NOak SCob SPlb SRms SUsu |
| | WBro WCla WEas WHen WHil |
| | WOve WPer WWin |
| * - 'Album' | CSpe GMac LIck SCob SUsu WShe |
| - 'Candy Spires' | Last listed 1998 |
| - 'Flush of White' | CBot CM&M ECoo EMan EWll |
| | MLLN NCut SMrm SRob WHen |
| | WLin WWhi |
| - hybrids | CBot CSpe EGoo EMan EWTr |
| | NChi NRoo NVic SRms SSea WFar |
| | WGor WPer |
| ¶ - Wild form | NDov |
| *pulverulentum* | CKin EWFC |
| ¶ *pyramidatum* | EBee |
| *rorippifolium* | EMan |
| 'Silberkandelaber' | SSvw |
| *sinuatum* | CArn WCot |
| ¶ 'Southern Charm' | ECoo LRHS WGor |
| * 'Spica' | CGle NCut SSvw WCot |
| *spicatum* | CBot |
| *spinosum* | CGle SHFr SIng |
| * Sunset shades | WGor |
| *thapsiforme* | See *V. densiflorum* |
| *thapsus* | CJew CSev EBot EOld EWFC |
| | GPoy MChe MHew MMal NFor |
| | NLak NMir SRob WOak WSel |
| | WWye |
| 'Vernale' | CBot |
| *virgatum* | Last listed 1996 |
| *wiedemannianum* | CSpe EWll GAbr SIgm SRCN |
| | WHer WLin WPen |

## VERBENA (Verbenaceae)

| | |
|---|---|
| I 'Adonis' | CAsh |
| ¶ 'Adonis Light Blue' | CAsh |
| ¶ 'Adonis Mango' | CAsh |
| 'Aphrodite' | CAsh GPin |
| 'Apple Blossom' | CAsh |
| 'Artemis' | Last listed 1997 |
| 'Aveyron' | CAsh SChu SMrm |
| ¶ 'Babylon Blue' | CAsh |
| ¶ Babylon® Pink = 'Morena' | CAsh |
| * 'Batesville Rose' | WCot |
| 'Blue Cascade' | CAsh LPVe |
| 'Blue Knight' | CAsh |
| ¶ 'Blue Lagoon' | CAsh |
| 'Blue Moon' | CAsh |
| ¶ 'Blue Prince' | CAsh CSpe NFai |
| § *bonariensis* | More than 30 suppliers |
| 'Boon' | CAsh SVil |
| 'Booty' | CAsh SVil |

| | |
|---|---|
| 'Boughton House' | CAsh CSpe MSte |
| 'Bramley' | SChu |
| ***brasiliensis*** | EBee |
| * 'Calcutta Cream' | Last listed 1997 |
| ***canadensis*** | CAsh |
| - 'Perfecta' | CAsh MBNS |
| 'Candy Carousel' | CAsh CElw CSev MBNS NPri SCro SUsu |
| 'Carousel' | CAsh NPri WCom |
| ***chamaedrifolia*** | See *V. peruviana* |
| ¶ 'Claret' | CAsh |
| ¶ 'Cleopatra Pink' | CAsh |
| ¶ 'Cleopatra White' | CAsh |
| ***corymbosa*** | CAsh CM&M ECGP ECha LLWP MAvo MCLN SMrm WCot WPer WRHF |
| - 'Gravetye' | CAsh GBuc GCal GMac NChi NPla WAbe WFar |
| 'Crimson Star' | CAsh |
| 'Cupido' | Last listed 1998 |
| 'Edith Eddleman' | CAsh COtt ECtt LRHS MBEx MGrG MHlr MNrw NFai WCot |
| * ***exaltata*** | CAsh |
| * 'Fiesta' | WCot |
| * 'Foxhunter' | CAsh EMan |
| ¶ 'Freefall' | CAsh |
| ***hastata*** | CAsh CHan CJew CSev EBee EBot ECot EMan EOrc GCal LHol MChe MHew MNrw NChi NSti WCot WFar WHoo WPer |
| - 'Alba' | CAsh EBee EHal EMan EMon GBuc MBel WPer |
| - JLS 88010WI | CAsh |
| - 'Rosea' | CAsh ECGN EFou GBuc SChu SUsu |
| 'Hecktor' | EMan |
| 'Hidcote Purple' | CAsh MBEx MSte WHoo |
| ¶ ***hispida*** | EBee |
| 'Homestead Purple' | More than 30 suppliers |
| 'Huntsman' | CAsh GBuc MSte WEas |
| ¶ 'Imagination' | CAsh |
| ¶ 'Jenny's Wine' | LHil |
| 'Jugend' | Last listed 1998 |
| N 'Kemerton' | CAsh CSev EMan MBEx |
| 'Kurpfalz' | Last listed 1998 |
| * 'La France' | CAsh CElw CSam ECha EMan MRav SChu SDix SMrm SUsu |
| 'Lawrence Johnston' ♀ | CAsh MBEx SYvo WEas WHen |
| ¶ ***litoralis*** | EBee |
| 'Loveliness' | CAsh EHal EMan IBlr SMer SMrm WEas |
| ***macdougalii*** | EBee |
| x ***maonettii*** | CAsh WCot |
| 'Nero' | CAsh NPri |
| ***officinalis*** | CArn CAsh EWFC GPoy LHol MChe MHew MSal SIde WHer WJek WOak WPer WSel WWye |
| 'Ophelia' | CAsh |
| 'Paradiso' | CAsh |
| ***patagonica*** | See *V. bonariensis* |
| * 'Peach Blossom' | WCot |
| 'Peaches and Cream' | CAsh EWTr LIck |
| § ***peruviana*** | CAsh EBrP EBre LBre MAsh MBEx MRav SBre SChu SCro SDix SIng SRms |
| - 'Alba' | MBEx NTow SCro |
| ***phlogiflora*** | MBEx |
| 'Piccolo' | CAsh |
| 'Pink Bouquet' | See *V.* 'Silver Anne' |
| 'Pink Parfait' | CAsh CHal CSpe ELan EMan EOrc LHop MBEx MBNS MRav SCro SMer |

| | |
|---|---|
| 'Pink Pearl' | ECtt |
| * 'Pink Perfection' | Last listed 1998 |
| ***pulchella*** | See *V. tenera* |
| 'Purple Kleopat' | CAsh |
| 'Purple Sissinghurst' | CAsh |
| ¶ 'Quartz Blue' | CAsh |
| ¶ 'Quartz Burgundy' | CAsh |
| ¶ 'Quartz Scarlet' | CAsh |
| 'Raspberry Crush' | CAsh |
| 'Red Cascade' | CAsh |
| 'Red Sissinghurst' | CAsh NPri SBid |
| § ***rigida*** ♀ | CAsh CBrm CFir CHea COlW EBee ECGP ECha EGra MGrG MHlr SRms SUsu WCot WEas WFar WOut WOve |
| ¶ - 'Lilacina' | EWTr |
| - 'Polaris' | CAsh CStr EBee SMrm SUsu |
| * 'Royal Purple' | CAsh EMan |
| Sandy Series ♀ | Last listed 1995 |
| ***scabridoglandulosa*** | CAsh |
| § 'Silver Anne' ♀ | CAsh CB&S CSam EBee ECtt LFis LHop MBEx MRav NFai NPri NTow SChu SCro SDix SMer SMrm SRms SUsu WCot WEas WHen WHoo |
| § 'Sissinghurst' ♀ | CArn CAsh CGle CSam ECtt LFis LHop MBEx NFai NPri SBid SCro SRms SUsu SYvo WEas WHen WHoo WPyg WWin |
| * 'Snow Flurry' | CAsh EWll WCot |
| * ***spicata*** 'Pam' (v) | WCot |
| ***stricta*** | CAsh EMan GBar |
| ♦ 'Sunmariba' | See *V.* Temari Violet = 'Sunmariba' |
| ♦ 'Sunvat' | See *V.* Tapien Pearl = 'Sunvat' |
| ♦ 'Sunver' | See *V.* Tapien Pink = 'Sunver' |
| ♦ 'Sunvop' | See *V.* Tapien Violet = 'Sunvop' |
| ¶ ***supina*** | CAsh |
| Tapien Lilac = 'Sunvil' | CAsh |
| § Tapien Pearl = 'Sunvat' | CAsh GPin |
| § Tapien Pink = 'Sunver' | CAsh GPin LIck |
| § Tapien Violet = 'Sunvop' | CAsh LIck NPri |
| ¶ Temari Coral Pink = 'Sunmariripi' | CAsh |
| Temari Pink = 'Sunmaripi' | CAsh GPin |
| Temari Scarlet = 'Sunmarisu' | CAsh GPin MBNS WWol |
| § Temari Violet = 'Sunmariba' | CAsh GPin |
| ¶ Temari White = 'Sunmaririho' | CAsh |
| § ***tenera*** | CAsh |
| 'Tenerife' | See *V.* 'Sissinghurst' |
| ***tenuisecta*** | CAsh CM&M MBEx WPer |
| - f. ***alba*** | WCot |
| - 'Edith' | CAsh LHop |
| * 'Texas Appleblossom' | Last listed 1997 |
| ***venosa*** | See *V. rigida* |
| 'Violet Profusion' | CAsh |
| 'White Cascade' | CAsh ECtt |
| * 'White Knight' | CAsh MBEx NPri |
| 'White Sissinghurst' | CAsh SBid |

## VERBESINA (Asteraceae)

| | |
|---|---|
| ***alternifolia*** | EMan GVic |

## VERNONIA (Asteraceae)

| | |
|---|---|
| ***crinita*** | CHan ECha GCal LFis SDix SIgm SMad |
| - 'Mammuth' | LGre |
| ***fasciculata*** | EMan GCal |
| ***noveboracensis*** | ECGN SMrm WCot WPer |
| - 'Albiflora' | WCot WPer |

# VERONICA (Scrophulariaceae)

| | |
|---|---|
| *amethystina* | See *V. spuria* |
| *armena* | CLyd EWes LBee MBro MSte MWat NMen SBla SRot |
| § *austriaca* | MLLN SMac SMrm SRPl WMoo |
| – Corfu form | CLyd CMea CPlt EBee EMan EOrc EWes LGre LHop MSCN NBrk SLod SSvw WPer |
| – var. *dubia* | See *V. prostrata* |
| – 'Ionian Skies' | CLon CLyd CPBP CRDP CSpe ESis GBuc LBee MBel MNrw MRav SAga SBla SChu SHel SIgm SPer SUsu SWas WCot WCru WFar WKif |
| § – subsp. *teucrium* | CArn CHan EBee EHal LPVe MLLN MWgw NLon NRoo NWCA SRms WFar WPer |
| – – 'Blue Blazer' | SCro |
| ¶ – – 'Blue Fountain' | LLWP |
| – – 'Crater Lake Blue' ♀ | CHea CKel CLon CRDP ECha ECtt EFou ELan ENot EOrc IMGH LGre MFir MRav NFai NFor NHol NLon SMac SMrm SRms WByw WCot WEas WPat WPer WWin |
| – – 'Kapitän' | ECha EGar ELan GBuc LHop MFir SMrm WFar WPer |
| – – 'Knallblau' | EBee EFou EMil MBri SUsu WLRN |
| – – 'Königsblau' | SGre WBea |
| – – 'Royal Blue' ♀ | CLTr EBee ECot EFou EPfP ESis EWTr GBuc LPio MArl NOak NSti SPla WBea WMoo WPyg |
| – – 'Shirley Blue' | See *V.* 'Shirley Blue' |
| *beccabunga* | CArn CBen CKin CWat EHon ELan EMFW EWFC GPoy LPBA MHew MSta NDea NMir SRms SWat WHer WMAq |
| – 'Don's Dyke' (v) | Last listed 1998 |
| *bellidioides* | CLyd GTou |
| Blue Bouquet | See *V. longifolia* 'Blaubündel' |
| 'Blue Spire' | SWat WPer |
| *bombycina* | EHyt EPot NMen NTow NWCA |
| ¶ – subsp. *bolkardaghensis* | CPBP EHyt NMen |
| ¶ – subsp. *froediniana* | EHyt |
| – Mac&W 5840 | EHyt |
| *bonarota* | See *Paederota bonarota* |
| *caespitosa* | Last listed 1997 |
| – subsp. *caespitosa* | CLyd EHyt NMen |
| – Mac&W 5849 | NTow |
| *candida* | See *V. spicata* subsp. *incana* |
| × *cantiana* 'Kentish Pink' | EGoo GBuc MBel MBro SHel SPla SSca SUsu WHoo WPer |
| * 'Catforth Border Guard' | NCat |
| *caucasica* | EHal ELan EMon LGre MSCN WCru |
| *chamaedrys* | CKin IIve NMir |
| § – 'Miffy Brute' (v) | CHan EBee ELan LFis LHop MHar MLLN MRav NHol NPro WHer WLRN WRus WWeb |
| ¶ – 'Pam' (v) | WAlt |
| – 'Variegata' | See *V. chamaedrys* 'Miffy Brute' |
| – 'Waterrow' | EMon WAlt |
| – 'Yorkley Wood' | WAlt |
| *cinerea* ♀ | CLyd ECha MBro NHol NTow SIgm WEas WPat |
| *coreana* | CLon |
| *dichrus* | EGoo |
| 'Ellen Mae' | MCAu |
| *exaltata* | CBrd EBee ECGN EHal EMFP EMan EMon GBuc LFis LGre LRHS MLLN MNrw MSte NChi WCot WOve WPer |
| – white | CBrd |
| *filifolia* | MHar |
| *filiformis* | MWhi |
| – 'Fairyland' (v) | EWes |
| ♦ *formosa* | See *Parahebe formosa* |
| § *fruticans* | CLyd GTou NMen WCla |
| *fruticulosa* | NWCA |
| * *galactites* | Last listed 1998 |
| *gentianoides* ♀ | More than 30 suppliers |
| – 'Alba' | CMea CRDP EOrc GCal NChi NSti |
| – 'Barbara Sherwood' | EBee GMac MFir MLLN MTed NPla WCot |
| ¶ – 'Lilacina' | EBee |
| – 'Nana' | EOrc MMil |
| – 'Pallida' | EBee EMan EPfP MBrN MRav NPri SSvw |
| – 'Robusta' | EBee ECha GMac NDov |
| – 'Tissington White' | CBos CBre CHan CLon CVer EBee EBla EFou EMar EOld GMaP LRot MCLN MLLN MTis NCut NRoo NWes SAga SBla SHel SOkh SUsu SWat WAbb WBea WBro WLin WPen |
| – 'Variegata' | More than 30 suppliers |
| ¶ 'Goodness Grows' | CMGP EAst EBee LBuc LRHS SChu SPla SSpe |
| ¶ *grandis* | EBee |
| × *guthrieana* | MHar NMen SRms WCru WFar WPer |
| *hendersonii* | See *V. subsessilis hendersonii* |
| *incana* | See *V. spicata* subsp. *incana* |
| * – – 'Candidissima' | Last listed 1997 |
| 'Inspiration' | EFou LGre |
| * *keiskei* pink form | NLar |
| *kellereri* | See *V. spicata* |
| *kiusiana* | CStr EBee EBrP EBre LBre MBel MTis SBre |
| *kotschyana* | Last listed 1998 |
| * – ES 309 | MRPP |
| * 'Lila Karina' | WPer |
| *liwanensis* | ELan ESis EWes GCHN NMen NTow WThi |
| – Mac&W 5936 | EPot |
| *longifolia* | CHan CKel EBee EGar ELan EOld EPfP EWTr MBel MCLN MFir MHar STes WBea WEas WLRN |
| – 'Alba' | CHea EBee EGar ELan EMan EPfP EWTr LFis MBel SIde SSca WBea WMoo |
| § – 'Blaubündel' | EBee EFou EWll NCut NFai |
| – 'Blauer Sommer' | CMGP EBee EFou EGar NFla NHol SLon SPer WRHF |
| § – 'Blauriesin' | CM&M CTri ECtt EMil GMaP MBri MCLN MUlv NCut NSti SCob |
| – Blue Giantess | See *V. longifolia* 'Blauriesin' |
| – 'Fascination' | SMrm |
| – 'Foerster's Blue' | See *V. longifolia* 'Blauriesin' |
| – 'Joseph's Coat' (v) | EBee EMon NBrk WCot |
| ¶ – 'Lila Karina' | WCot |
| – 'Oxford Blue' | WRHF |
| – pink shades | EPfP |
| – 'Rose Tone' | ECha MRav MTis SMrm WMoo WWhi |
| – 'Rosea' | CTri EWTr MBel WCru WPer |
| – 'Schneeriesin' | CMGP EBee ECha ECtt EHrv GMaP MBri MCLN NWoo SCro SPer SSvw |
| *lyallii* | See *Parahebe lyallii* |
| *macrostachya* RMRP 95188 | IDac |
| 'Martje' | LGre SMrm |
| *montana* | CKin |

- 'Corinne Tremaine' (v) — CElw EMan EMar EMon LHop MAvo MLLN SUsu WCot WHer
*morrisonicola* B&SWJ 086 — Last listed 1998
*nipponica* — NChi NLak WPer
* *nivalis nivea* — Last listed 1997
'Noah Williams' (v) — WCot
*nummularia* — WPer
*officinalis* — CArn CKin EWFC IIve WHbs
*oltensis* — CLyd CPBP EHyt ESis EWes NHol NMen WAbe WLin WPat WWin
- JCA 984.150 — CNic NTow
*orientalis* — Last listed 1996
- subsp. *carduchorum* — Last listed 1997
- subsp. *orientalis* — EPot NMen
*ornata* — CB&S WCot WPer
*pectinata* — EHic ESis EWTr GDra MBel NLon SUsu
- 'Rosea' — CMea ESis EWes GDra NBus SHel SUsu WPer WWin
*peduncularis* — CNic EOrc LBee LRHS SBla WEas
- 'Alba' — MHar WPer
§ - 'Georgia Blue' — More than 30 suppliers
- 'Oxford Blue' — See *V. peduncularis* 'Georgia Blue'
*perfoliata* — See *Parahebe perfoliata*
¶ Pershore Gold = 'Perglow' — EBee
*petraea* 'Madame Mercier' — LRHS MMil SMrm
'Pink Damask' — CElw CHad CLon EFou EMil LFis LGre MBri SCob SCro SOkh SSvw WRHF WRus
*pinnata* 'Blue Eyes' — ESis LBee LHop
*prenja* — See *V. austriaca*
§ *prostrata* ♀ — CAgr CLyd CSam CSpe ECGN ELan EMNN EPot ESis GDra LBee MPla MWat NFla NHol NNrd NRoo SIng SRms SSmi SSoC WEas WFar WHoo WMoo WWin
- 'Alba' — CSpe MBro MWat WFar WHoo WPyg
§ - 'Blauspiegel' — CLon CPBP ECGP SBla SIgm SWas WCru
- 'Blue Ice' — SSmi
- Blue Mirror — See *V. prostrata* 'Blauspiegel'
- 'Blue Sheen' — ECtt EHic ESis LGre MBNS NBus SChu SIng SMer WAbe WLin WPer WWin
- 'Loddon Blue' — NVic SBla SMer WPer
- 'Miss Willmott' — See *V. prostrata* 'Warley Blue'
- 'Mrs Holt' — CLyd CMea CSam CStr EBrP EBre EMNN ESis LBre LGre NFla NFor NMen SBla SBre SIng SRms SSmi SWas WAbe WCom WCru WWin
- 'Nana' — EMNN EPot ESis EWes LBee MPla MWat NHol NMen
- 'Rosea' — CLyd ELan ESis MPla MWat SIgm WFar WKif WPer
¶ - 'Rosen' — MWat
* - 'Shirley Holt' — CHar
- 'Silver Queen' — SRms
- 'Spode Blue' ♀ — CLTr CMea ELan LGre LHop MHar MMil NWCA SBla SCob SIng SRms WLin
- 'Trehane' — CHea CLyd EBrP EBre ECha ELan ESis LBee LBre LFis LGro LHop MBro MCCP MWat NHar NNrd NOak NRoo NRya SBre SCob SCro SIng SPlb SRms SSmi SWat WAbe
§ - 'Warley Blue' — CMGP
* 'Red Georgia' — LFis
*repens* — EHal EWTr LNor MMal MOne WPer
'Rosalinde' — CBot GBuc LFis NCat SPla WPer

*rupestris* — See *V. prostrata*
*saturejoides* — CPBP MBro SRms WPer
*saxatilis* — See *V. fruticans*
*schmidtiana* — GTou WPer
- 'Nana' — CLyd EWTr MBro NHol WPat WRHF
- 'Nana Rosea' — Last listed 1997
*selleri* — See *V. wormskjoldii*
*serpyllifolia* — Last listed 1997
§ 'Shirley Blue' ♀ — EBrP EBre EFou EWTr GCHN GChr LBre LFis LNor MBNS MBel MCLN MFir MRav MWat NChi NFla NMir NRoo SBre SHel SPer SRms SWat WHen WMoo WPer WWat WWhi
§ *sieboldiana* — WCot
§ *spicata* — ELan EWTr LEdu LNor MBNS MBro MCAu NFor NLon SCob SRms SSea WCla WCot WOve WPer
- 'Alba' — EBee EMan EMil MBNS MRav NCut SCob SRPl WBea WFar WHil WPer
- 'Barcarolle' — EBee ELan MLLN
§ - 'Blaufuchs' — CBlo CSam MBel NRoo
- Blue Fox — See *V. spicata* 'Blaufuchs'
* - 'Corali' — Last listed 1997
§ - 'Erika' — ECha ECtt GBuc GMac IMGH MBro MLLN MArg NOak NRoo SCob SIde SPer SSca SUsu WCla WHil
- 'Heidekind' — CGle CLon CMea CSam ECha EFou ELan EOrc ESis IMGH LHop MBel MCLN NFor NHar NVic NWCA SBla SHel SIng SWat WCot WEas WOve WWin
- subsp. *hybrida* — WHer
- hybrids — Last listed 1997
§ - 'Icicle' — CLon EFou EOrc LRHS MBri SLod SUsu WCot WPGP WRus
§ - subsp. *incana* ♀ — CGle CHan CHar CLon CSpe ECGN EHoe ELan ENot EWTr GMaP LFis MBro MPEx MWat NFor NMir SBla SCob SPlb SRms WBea WLin WMoo WPer WPyg
- - 'Mrs Underwood' — ECha
- - 'Nana' — ECha ESis SRms
- - 'Saraband' — WPer
- - 'Silver Carpet' — CMil EBee EFou MRav MTis NDov NSti SCoo
- - 'Wendy' ♀ — GCal
- 'Minuet' — Last listed 1998
- 'Nana Blauteppich' — EMan MBNS SCob WBea
- 'Pavane' — Last listed 1997
- red — WBea WHil
- Red Fox — See *V. spicata* 'Rotfuchs'
- 'Romiley Purple' — ECGP EFou LGre MBrN MBro MCAu MLLN MRav MSte NSti SChu SHel SLod WHoo WPyg
- 'Rosalind' — NLar
- *rosea* — See *V. spicata* 'Erika'
- 'Rosenrot' — EMan
§ - 'Rotfuchs' — CGle CStr EBee ECtt EFou ELan EOld EPar EWTr MRav NFla NRoo NSti SCro SMrm SPer WBro WEas WHoo WOve WPer WWin
¶ - 'Sahin's Early' — WCot
- 'Sightseeing' — NArg NBus NCut NRoo SWat
- subsp. *spicata* 'Nana' — SSmi
- *variegata* — MLLN NBir SRob WCot
§ *spuria* — CStr EMon NWes WPer

| | |
|---|---|
| *stelleri* | See *V. wormskjoldii* |
| *subsessilis* 'Blaue Pyramide' | ECGN NCat |
| * – *hendersonii* | EHal |
| *sumilensis* | Last listed 1996 |
| 'Sunny Border Blue' | EBee EPfP SCob WCot |
| *surculosa* | Last listed 1998 |
| *tauricola* | NTow |
| – JJH 92101536 | LGre |
| – Mac&W 5835 | SIgm |
| – MP 93236 | IDac |
| *telephiifolia* | CLyd EGoo EMNN ESis EWes MPla NMen NTow NWCA WPyg WWin |
| *teucrium* | See *V. austriaca* subsp. *teucrium* |
| *thessalica* | NTow |
| *thessalonica* | MTPN |
| *thymoides* subsp. *pseudocinerea* | NWCA |
| – subsp. *thymoides* | ESis |
| * Ulster blue dwarf | WCot |
| *virginica* | See *Veronicastrum virginicum* |
| *waldsteiniana* | CStr |
| 'Waterperry Blue' | EGoo ELan MBel MRav NWoo SBod SMer WPer |
| *wherryi* | WPer |
| 'White Icicle' | See *V. spicata* 'Icicle' |
| 'White Spire' | CBot |
| *whitleyi* | CLyd CNic CTri MHar WWin |
| § *wormskjoldii* | CHan ELan ESis LHop MBrN MBro MHar NFla NMen SBla SHel SRms WCla WPer WWin |
| – 'Alba' | WPer |

## VERONICASTRUM (Scrophulariaceae)

| | |
|---|---|
| § *virginicum* | CArn CHea CPou CRow ECGN ECha EFou EMon MBel MFir MUlv NSti SCob WPer WWhi WWin |
| – 'Alboroseum' | ECGN WCot |
| – *album* | More than 30 suppliers |
| – 'Apollo' | EFou MBri |
| ¶ – 'Diane' | EBee LGre |
| – 'Fascination' | CLon EBee EFou GCal LGre MBri SUsu WCot |
| § – var. *incarnatum* | CLon ECGN EMan GMaP LRHS MCAu MUlv NFla SCro SPer SUsu WCot |
| – 'Lavendelturm' | CLon EBee LGre WCot |
| * – 'Lila Karina' | Last listed 1998 |
| – 'Pink Glow' | EBrP EBre EFou ELan EMil EPfP GNau LBre LGre SBre SMrm SOkh |
| ¶ – 'Pointed Finger' | EFou |
| – *roseum* | See *V. virginicum* var. *incarnatum* |
| – var. *sibiricum* | EMon SCob WCot WMoo |
| – 'Spring Dew' | EFou MBri |
| – 'Temptation' | EFou LGre MBri |

## VESTIA (Solanaceae)

| | |
|---|---|
| § *foetida* ♀ | CB&S CCHP CDoC CGre CHan CPle ELan EPla EREa IBlr IDee MHar MNrw NChi SLod SOWG SUsu WPat WPer WSHC |
| *lycioides* | See *V. foetida* |

## VETIVERIA (Poaceae)

| | |
|---|---|
| *zizanioides* | GPoy MSal |

## VIBURNUM ✿ (Caprifoliaceae)

| | |
|---|---|
| *acerifolium* | CFil CPle WHCG WWat |
| 'Allegheny' | WWat |
| *alnifolium* | See *V. lantanoides* |

| | |
|---|---|
| *atrocyaneum* | CFil CPle WHCG WPGP WPat WWal WWat |
| *awabuki* | CFil EPfP |
| *betulifolium* | CB&S CBrd CFil CMCN CPle CTrw EPfP EPla MBal MBlu SMad SPer WAbe WHCG WPGP WWat |
| *bitchiuense* | CPMA CPle ELan |
| x *bodnantense* | CBot CTri CTrw ELan ENot GRei MRav MWat NFor NHed NLon WHar WStI WWat WWin |
| – 'Charles Lamont' ♀ | CBot CDoC CEnd CSam EBee ECtt ELan EMil IBlr LPan MAsh MBri MGos MPla MRav NHol SEND SPan SPer SSpi SSta SVil WBod WPat WPyg WWat WWeb |
| – 'Dawn' ♀ | More than 30 suppliers |
| – 'Deben' ♀ | EBee ENot EPfP EPla LRHS MBri MRav SPer SSta WCru WDin WFar WWat |
| *bracteatum* | CFil CPle EPfP SLon |
| *buddlejifolium* | CEnd CHan CPle WHCG WWat |
| *burejaeticum* | CPle |
| x *burkwoodii* | More than 30 suppliers |
| – 'Anne Russell' ♀ | CB&S CPMA CTri EBee EBrP EBre ELan EPfP EWes IOrc LBre MAsh MGos MRav NBee NHol NSti SBod SBre SLon SPer SPla WAbe WFar |
| – 'Chenaultii' | ELan EPfP SRPl WCru |
| – 'Fulbrook' ♀ | CMHG EPfP LRHS MBri SSpi WWat |
| – 'Park Farm Hybrid' ♀ | CBlo CPMA CSam CTri EBee EBrP EBre ELan ENot EPla IOrc LBre MAsh MBal MRav SBre SLPl SPan SPer SRms WCru WPat WWat |
| x *carlcephalum* ♀ | More than 30 suppliers |
| * – 'Variegatum' | CPMA |
| *carlesii* | CB&S EBee ENot EPfP GRei IOrc LEdu LHol MBlu NBee SCoo SPer SRPl SReu WStI |
| * – 'Aurea' | LPan |
| – 'Aurora' ♀ | CB&S CDoC CEnd CPMA CSam EBee EBrP EBre ELan ENot IOrc LBre MBar MGos MRav MWat NHol NLon SBre SPer SReu SSpi SSta WBod WDin WHCG WHar WPat WWat |
| – 'Charis' | CPMA LRHS MBri WBod |
| ¶ – 'Compactum' | CPMA |
| – 'Diana' | CBlo CEnd CPMA CRos EPfP LRHS MMil SBid SSpi SSta WPat WWat |
| *cassinoides* | CPle EPfP WPat WWat |
| 'Chesapeake' | CMHG CPMA CPle EWes MTis SBid SEND SSpi WBcn WWat WWes |
| *chingii* | CFil CPle ELan EMon GGGa WPGP WWat |
| *cinnamomifolium* ♀ | CBlo CFil CLan CPle ELan ISea LNet MAsh SAPC SArc SBid SLon SPer SSpi WCot WHCG WLRN WSHC WWat |
| *congestum* | CPle EMon |
| *cotinifolium* | CPle |
| *cylindricum* | CBot CFil CGre CPle ELan EPfP SBid WCru WWat |
| *dasyanthum* | CPle EPla |
| *davidii* ♀ | More than 30 suppliers |
| – (f) | CB&S CBot CDoC ELan EPfP MAsh MBal MGos MUlv SPer SPla SReu SRms SSta WBod WPat WWat WWeb |

| | |
|---|---|
| - (m) | CB&S CBot CDoC ELan EPfP MBal MGos MRav MUlv SPer SPla SReu SRms SSta WBod WPat WWat WWeb |
| *dentatum* | CFil CPle WPGP |
| § - var. *pubescens* | SLon |
| *dilatatum* | ELan LRHS SSpi WWes |
| ¶ - 'Erie' | EPfP |
| *erosum* | CFil |
| *erubescens* | CPle WWat |
| - var. *gracilipes* | CHan CPle EPfP WWat |
| 'Eskimo' | CBlo CEnd CPMA EBee LHop MAsh MBlu MBro MGos MRav NMoo SSpi WPat WPyg WWes |
| § *farreri* ♀ | CB&S CDoC CDul CPle EAst EBee ECtt ELan ENot EOld EPla GRei LBuc LHol MBNS MBal MBar MBri MGos MPla MRav NHol NWea SPer WCFE WDin WGwG WHCG WHar WWat |
| - 'Album' | See *V. farreri* 'Candidissimum' |
| § - 'Candidissimum' | CBot CFil ELan EPfP EPla IMGH LHop MBri MHlr SBid SSpi WBcn WPyg WWat |
| - 'Farrer's Pink' | CPMA WWat |
| - 'Nanum' | CBlo CFil CPMA CPle EBee EPfP EPla LHop MAsh MBar MPla MRav NHol SChu SSta WHCG WPat WPyg WWat |
| *foetidum* | CPle LBuc WHCr |
| - var. *ceanothoides* | Last listed 1998 |
| - var. *rectangulatum* B&SWJ 3637 | WCru |
| *fragrans* Bunge | See *V. farreri* |
| *furcatum* ♀ | EPfP SSpi WHCG WWat |
| x *globosum* 'Jermyns Globe' | CB&S CBlo CDoC CFil CMHG CPle EBee MBar MBri MGos MRav SEas SLon WBod WCru WHCG WWat |
| *grandiflorum* f. *foetens* | EPfP |
| *barryanum* | CFil CMHG CPle EBee EPfP EPla IOrc MBal SOWG WCru WPGP WSHC WWat |
| *benryi* | CFil CPle EPfP WHCG WPat WWat |
| x *billieri* | CAbP CFil CHan CPle MRav MWhi WBcn WHCG WKif WWat |
| - 'Winton' ♀ | CAbP CDoC CGre EBee EPfP ISea MAsh MBri SBid SOWG WBod WCot WCru WFar WWat |
| *japonicum* | CFil CPle CSam EPfP SBid WWat |
| x *juddii* ♀ | More than 30 suppliers |
| *lantana* | CKin CTri EHic ENot IOrc LBuc NWea SPer WDin WMou WTro |
| - 'Aureum' | EHoe EPla MBlu WBcn |
| - 'Mohican' | NPro WWat |
| ¶ - 'Variefolium' (v) | CPMA |
| ¶ - 'Xanthocarpum' | CDoC |
| § *lantanoides* | EPfP SSpi |
| *lentago* | CAbP CPle |
| *lobophyllum* | CPle EPfP |
| *luzonicum* B&SWJ 3930 | WCru |
| *macrocephalum* | CPMA WPGP |
| - f. *keteleeri* | CPMA WWes |
| *mariesii* | See *V. plicatum* 'Mariesii' |
| 'Mohawk' | CAbP CEnd CRos ELan LRHS MAsh MBri SCoo SMad SMur SPla SSpi WBcn WPat |
| *mullaba* | CPle |
| - CC 1241 | Last listed 1997 |
| *nervosum* B&SWJ 2251a | WCru |
| ¶ *nudum* | CPle |
| - 'Pink Beauty' | CPMA MRav WShe WWat |
| *odoratissimum* | CB&S CFil CGre CPle SBid SMad SSpi WSHC WWat |
| *opulus* | CB&S CKin CSam EBee ECtt ELan ENot EWTr GChr GPoy IOrc LBuc MBar MBlu MBri MRav MWat NBee NFor NWea SHFr SMac SPer WDin WFar WHar WMou |
| - 'Aureum' | CChe CMHG CSam EBee EBrP EBre EHoe ELan EMil EPla IOrc LBre MAsh MBal MBar MGos MPla MRav NFla NHol NLon SBre SEas SPer SSta WFar WHCG WPat WWeb |
| - 'Compactum' ♀ | More than 30 suppliers |
| N - 'Fructu Luteo' | ELan SPan |
| - 'Nanum' | CAbP CBlo CPle ELan EPla ESis MBal MBar MBri MPla MRav NHol NMen WDin WHCG WPat WWat |
| - 'Notcutt's Variety' ♀ | CChe ENot EPfP MGos NTow SHFr SMur SRms |
| - 'Park Harvest' | CRos EBee EPla MBri NSti SAga SLPl |
| § - 'Roseum' ♀ | CB&S CBot CDoC CHar CPle EBee ELan ENot IOrc LPan MBar MBlu MBri MGos MPla MRav MWat NFla NWea SPer SPla WCFE WDin WFar WHar WStI WWal |
| - 'Sterile' | See *V. opulus* 'Roseum' |
| N - 'Xanthocarpum' ♀ | More than 30 suppliers |
| N *plicatum* | CB&S ENot MBar WDin |
| - 'Cascade' | EWTr MUlv NHol SSpi |
| - 'Dart's Red Robin' | ECtt EHic GChr MBri MGos NHol WBcn |
| - 'Grandiflorum' ♀ | CBlo CPle EPfP MBar MBri SSta WBcn WHCG |
| - 'Lanarth' | CB&S CDoC CSam CTre EBee ECtt EMil ENot IOrc LHop MGos MHlr NFla NHol NSti SPer SPla SRPl SSta WBod WDin WHCG WPat WWat |
| - 'Magician' | NHol |
| § - 'Mariesii' ♀ | More than 30 suppliers |
| - 'Nanum' | See *V. plicatum* 'Nanum Semperflorens' |
| § - 'Nanum Semperflorens' | CBar CDoC ECtt ESis IOrc LHop MAsh MBal MBlu MGos MPla WFar WHCG WPat WSHC WWal WWat |
| - 'Pink Beauty' ♀ | CAbP CB&S CDoC CEnd CPle ECtt ELan LHop MBal MBlu MBri MGos MPla MRav NBee NHol SPer SSpi SSta WBod WFar WHCG WPat WSHC WWat WWeb |
| ¶ - 'Popcorn' | CAbP LRHS MAsh |
| * - 'Prostratum' | ESis |
| - 'Variefolium' | MBri NHol SRPl |
| - 'Rowallane' ♀ | EPfP MBel WWat |
| - 'Saint Keverne' | NHol SRob |
| N - 'Sterile' | GOrc |
| - 'Summer Snowflake' | EBee ENot EPfP IOrc MAsh MBal MBri MPla NHol SPer SVil WBod WDin WHCG WWat WWeb |
| - f. *tomentosum* | CLan ELan EWTr WDin WHCG WStI |
| - 'Watanabe' | See *V. plicatum* 'Nanum Semperflorens' |
| 'Pragense' ♀ | CB&S CMCN CPle EBee EPfP EPla MBar MGos NHol SLon SPer WHCG WLRN WPat WPyg WWat WWat |
| *propinquum* | WWat |
| - B&SWJ 4009 | WCru |
| *pubescens* | See *V. dentatum* var. *pubescens* |

| | |
|---|---|
| *recognitum* | CPle |
| x *rhytidophylloides* | CPle NFor WWat |
| - 'Dart's Duke' | ENot MBri SLPl |
| *rhytidophyllum* | CBar CDul CLan EBee EBrP EBre ELan ENot GChr ISea LBre LPan MBal MBar MGos NLon SBre SPer SReu SRms SSpi WDin WGwG WWat WWin |
| - 'Holland' | EPla |
| - 'Roseum' | CBot MRav SLPl |
| - 'Variegatum' | CBot CPMA ELan EPla SPer |
| - 'Willowwood' | ELan LRHS MAsh SMad SPer SSpi SSta WPat WWat |
| * *ribesifolium* | Last listed 1997 |
| *rigidum* | CFil CPle |
| *sargentii* | CBlo GBin IOrc |
| - 'Onondaga' ♀ | More than 30 suppliers |
| - 'Susquehanna' | EPfP |
| *semperflorens* | See *V. plicatum* 'Nanum Semperflorens' |
| § *setigerum* | CPle EPfP SLPl SMad SSpi |
| 'Shasta' | CB&S CBlo CDoC CMCN COtt CRos EHic EPfP MBri NHol NPro SSpi SSta |
| *sieboldii* | CB&S CPle |
| - B&SWJ 2837 | WCru |
| *suspensum* | CPle |
| *taiwanianum* B&SWJ 3009 | WCru |
| *theiferum* | See *V. setigerum* |
| *tinus* | More than 30 suppliers |
| - 'Bewley's Variegated' | CB&S CDoC EBee EMil MGos MRav SCoo |
| - 'Compactum' | EHic |
| - 'Eve Price' ♀ | More than 30 suppliers |
| - 'French White' | CBlo CDoC CDul CEnd EBee EHic ELan EPfP EPla MRav SBid SCoo SEas SRms WGwG WWal WWat |
| - 'Gwenllian' ♀ | More than 30 suppliers |
| ¶ - f. *birtum* hort. | CTre |
| - 'Israel' | EBee EHic EMil SPan SPer SPla WWat |
| ¶ - 'Little Bognor' | MAsh NPro |
| - 'Lucidum' | CB&S CBlo CPle CSam MGos SBid SPla WWat |
| - 'Lucidum Variegatum' | CFil CLan CPMA EHol SDry WPGP |
| * - 'Macrophyllum' | LPan |
| * - 'Pink Parfait' | MRav |
| - 'Pink Prelude' | EBee ENot SEas |
| - 'Purpureum' | CB&S EBee EHal EHoe ELan EPla GChr MAsh MRav SBid SEas SLPl SMac SPer SPla WFar WGwG WWal |
| - 'Pyramidale' | See *V. tinus* 'Strictum' |
| - 'Sappho' | Last listed 1998 |
| - subsp. *subcordatum* C 2002 | GGGa |
| - 'Variegatum' | More than 30 suppliers |
| *tomentosum* | See *V. plicatum* |
| *trilobum* | Last listed 1996 |
| *utile* | CPle EPfP EPla WHCG WWat |
| *wrightii* | CPle EPfP MBro NHol WHCG WPat WPyg |
| - var. *bessei* | MUlv |

**VICIA** (Papilionaceae)

| | |
|---|---|
| *angustifolia* | See *V. sativa* subsp. *nigra* |
| *cracca* | CKin EWFC NLan |
| ¶ *narbonensis* | CAgr |
| *orobus* | MSCN NChi |
| § *sativa* subsp. *nigra* | CKin |
| *sepium* | CKin EWFC |
| *sylvatica* | EWFC WGwy |

**VICTORIA** (Nymphaeaceae)

| | |
|---|---|
| *regia* | See *V. amazonica* |

**VIGNA** (Papilionaceae)

| | |
|---|---|
| § *caracalla* | CPlN |

**VIGUIERA** (Asteraceae)

| | |
|---|---|
| *multiflora* | Last listed 1998 |

**VILLADIA** (Crassulaceae)

| | |
|---|---|
| *hemsleyana* | See *Sedum hemsleyanum* |

**VILLARESIA** See CITRONELLA

**VILLARSIA** (Menyanthaceae)

| | |
|---|---|
| *bennettii* | See *Nymphoides peltata* 'Bennettii' |

**VIMINARIA** (Papilionaceae)

| | |
|---|---|
| *juncea* | Last listed 1998 |

**VINCA** ✿ (Apocynaceae)

| | |
|---|---|
| *difformis* | CGle CHar CLTr CTri EBee ECha EPla LBlm LHop LLWP NCat SDix SDry SMac WCru WHer WOak WPic WWat |
| - subsp. *bicolor* 'Alba' | EPla |
| - - 'Jenny Pym' | EBee EMon LHop SCoo SMac SMad SPan SRms WWat |
| - - 'Ruby Baker' | EMon |
| - subsp. *difformis* | EMon |
| - Greystone form | EPla LHop MBNS SCoo SEND WRus |
| - 'Oxford' | SLPl |
| - 'Snowmound' | MRav WWat |
| *herbacea* | Last listed 1997 |
| 'Hidcote Purple' | See *V. major* var. *oxyloba* |
| *major* | CB&S CChe EBee ELan ENot EOrc EWTr GChr GPoy GRei LBuc MBri MFir MGos MWat SBod SIde SPer WDin WGwG WOak WStI |
| - var. *alba* | GBuc IBlr |
| - 'Caucasian Blue' | CFil WPGP |
| - 'Elegantissima' | See *V. major* 'Variegata' |
| § - subsp. *hirsuta* (Boiss.) Stearn | EMon EOrc WWye |
| - var. *hirsuta* hort. | See *V. major* var. *oxyloba* |
| - 'Honeydew' | EMon |
| - 'Jason Hill' | EMon MBel WCot |
| § - 'Maculata' (v) | CDoC EBee EMar EMon ENot EPla LHop MBar MBri MSCN NHol NPla NRoo SDry SPar SPer WCru WHer WMoo WStI WWeb |
| § - var. *oxyloba* | CLyd CNic ECtt ELan EMon EPla GSki LHop MRav SLPl SMac SRms WHen WPic WWat |
| - var. *pubescens* | See *V. major* subsp. *hirsuta* (Boiss.) Stearn |
| - 'Reticulata' | ELan EMon MBel MSCN NSti |
| * - 'Sissinghurst' | Last listed 1996 |
| - 'Starlight' | Last listed 1996 |
| - 'Surrey Marble' | See *V. major* 'Maculata' |
| § - 'Variegata' ♀ | More than 30 suppliers |
| *minor* | CAgr CDoC CKin CLyd ELan ENot EPar EWTr GCHN GChr GPoy GRei MBar MBro MFir MSCN MWat SIde WDin WOak WWye |
| - f. *alba* | CB&S CBot CDoC EAst ECha EGoo ELan EPla LHol LHop MBar MBri MGos NOak SEas SPer STre WCot WOak WStI WWat WWye |

| | |
|---|---|
| – 'Alba Aureavariegata' | See *V. minor* 'Alba Variegata' |
| § – 'Alba Variegata' | CGle EAst EBot EBrP EBre EGoo EHoe EPPr EPla LBre MBar MFir NHol NPro NRoo SBre SPer SRms STre WCot WEas WFar WHer WWat |
| § – 'Argenteovariegata' ♀ | More than 30 suppliers |
| § – 'Atropurpurea' ♀ | More than 30 suppliers |
| – 'Aurea' | SPla WRHF |
| § – 'Aureovariegata' | CB&S CBot CChe EAst EBee ELan EOrc EPla GPoy LHol MBal MBar MFir MGos MRav NFor NHol NRoo WHen WWye |
| ¶ – 'Azurea' | CHid |
| § – 'Azurea Flore Pleno' (d) ♀ | More than 30 suppliers |
| * – 'Blue and Gold' | EGoo |
| – 'Blue Cloud' | MLLN NHol SBod |
| – 'Blue Drift' | CBlo EMon MBNS MLLN NHol SBod WOak |
| – 'Blue Moon' | ECtt EHic NHol SPla |
| – 'Bowles' Blue' | See *V. minor* 'La Grave' |
| – 'Bowles' Variety' | See *V. minor* 'La Grave' |
| – 'Burgundy' | EPar LLWP MBal SMac SRms WWye |
| – 'Caerulea Plena' | See *V. minor* 'Azurea Flore Pleno' |
| – 'Dartington Star' | See *V. major* var. *oxyloba* |
| – 'Dart's Blue' | Last listed 1998 |
| – 'Double Burgundy' | See *V. minor* 'Multiplex' |
| – 'Gertrude Jekyll' ♀ | CDoC CLTr EBee ELan EMon ENot EOld EPla EWTr GChr ILis MAsh MBri MRav NHol NRoo NSti SBod SChu SCoo SEND SPer SVil WElm WHer WWat |
| – Green Carpet | See *V. minor* 'Grüner Teppich' |
| § – 'Grüner Teppich' | EMon SPla |
| § – 'La Grave' ♀ | CChe CDoC CSev EBee ECGP ECha ELan ENot EPla GAbr MBro MRav NHol SBod SPer SRms SSvw STre WElm WPyg WWat |
| – 'Maculata' (v) | EGoo ELan EPPr SCoo WBcn |
| – 'Marion Cran' | CEnd GSki |
| § – 'Multiplex' (d) | EBee ECtt EMon EPPr EPar EPla MBar MInt NHol NLon NRoo SRms WCru WOak WRHF WWat |
| ¶ – 'Oland Blue' | NOla |
| – 'Persian Carpet' | EMon |
| – 'Purpurea' | See *V. minor* 'Atropurpurea' |
| – 'Rubra' | See *V. minor* 'Atropurpurea' |
| – 'Sabinka' | CHid EGoo EMon EPla |
| – 'Silver Service' (v) | CHid EMon EPPr EPla GBuc LBlm MAvo MBel MInt MRav NHol WCot WElm WOak |
| – 'Variegata' | See *V. minor* 'Argenteovariegata' |
| – 'Variegata Aurea' | See *V. minor* 'Aureovariegata' |
| – 'White Gold' | CChe EBee EHic MPla NHol NPro |

## VINCETOXICUM (Asclepiadaceae)

| | |
|---|---|
| *forrestii* ACE 1615 | IDac |
| § *hirundinaria* | EEls GPoy |
| *nigrum* | CPlN NChi WThi WTin |
| *officinale* | See *V. hirundinaria* |
| sp. HH&K 142 | CHan |

## VIOLA ✿ (Violaceae)

| | |
|---|---|
| 'Abigail' (Vtta) | LPVe |
| 'Achilles' (Va) | LPVe |
| 'Adelina' (Va) | GHCN LPVe |
| * 'Admiral' | GMac |
| 'Admiral Avellan' | See *V.* 'Amiral Avellan' |
| 'Admiration' (Va) | CFul EWTr GHCN GMac LPVe WBou |
| *adunca* | NWCA |

| | |
|---|---|
| – 'Alba' | WLRN |
| – var. *minor* | See *V. labradorica* |
| *aetolica* | CInt |
| 'Agnes Cochrane' (ExVa) | GHCN |
| 'Agneta' (Va) | LPVe |
| 'Alanta' (Va) | LGre LPVe SAga WWhi |
| § *alba* | ELan EWes NHol NWes SCro WEas WWin |
| *albanica* | See *V. magellensis* |
| I 'Alcea' (Va) | LPVe |
| 'Alethia' (Va) | LPVe |
| 'Alexander Rayfield' (Va) | LPVe |
| 'Alexia' (Va) | LPVe |
| 'Alice Witter' (Vt) | CDev CGro |
| 'Alice Wood' (ExVa) | GHCN |
| 'Alice Woodall' (Va) | LPVe |
| * – 'Alison' | GMaP GMac WBou WOut WWhi |
| ¶ 'Alison Lofts' (Va) | WCot |
| 'Alma' (Va) | GHCN |
| *altaica* | LPVe |
| 'Alwyn' (Va) | LPVe |
| 'Amelia' (Va) | GMac LPVe WWhi |
| 'Amethyst' (C) | Last listed 1998 |
| § 'Amiral Avellan' (Vt) | CDev CGro NBro WRus |
| 'Andrena' (Va) | LPVe |
| 'Angela' (Va) | LPVe |
| 'Anita' (Va) | LPVe |
| 'Ann' (SP) | GHCN |
| 'Ann Kean' (Vtta) | LPVe NRoo |
| 'Anna' (Va) | LPVe |
| * 'Anna Leyns' (Va) | LPVe |
| 'Annabelle' (Va) | LPVe |
| 'Annaliese' (C) | LPVe |
| 'Anne Mott' (Va) | LPVe |
| 'Annette Ross' (Va) | LPVe |
| I 'Annona' (Va) | LPVe |
| 'Anthea' (Va) | LPVe |
| 'Antique Lace' (Va) | GMac NBrk |
| 'Aphrodite' (Va) | LPVe |
| 'Apollo' (Va) | LPVe |
| 'Apricotta' | NHaw |
| 'Arabella' (Va) | GHCN LBee LPVe SChu SLod SMrm WBou WFar WHer WLRN |
| *arborescens* | MSCN SIng |
| 'Ardross Gem' (Va) | CFul CGle CMHG CSam EBee GCHN GHCN GMac LBee LHop LPVe MCLN MHlr NRoo SUsu WBou WCom WEas WFar WIvy WKif WPer WWat WWhi WWin |
| *arenaria* | See *V. rupestris* |
| 'Arkwright's Ruby' (Va) | CLTr COIW EWTr LPVe MMal SRms WWhi |
| 'Artemis' (Va) | LPVe |
| *arvensis* | Last listed 1997 |
| 'Aspasia' (Va) ♀ | GHCN GMac LBee LPVe WBou |
| 'Astrid' (Va) | LPVe |
| 'Atalanta' (Vtta) | LPVe |
| 'Athena' (Va) | LPVe |
| *athois* | LPVe |
| 'Aurelia' (Va) | LPVe |
| 'Aurora' (Va) | LPVe |
| 'Avril' (Va) | LPVe |
| 'Avril Lawson' (Va) | GHCN GMac MGrG NNrd WBou |
| 'Baby Blue' | Last listed 1998 |
| 'Baby Lucia' (Va) | CElw COIW EWTr NCat |
| 'Barbara' (Va) | GHCN LPVe NCat NRoo WBou |
| 'Barbara Cawthorne' (C) | LPVe |
| ¶ 'Barnsdale Gem' | NDov |
| 'Baronne Alice de Rothschild' (Vt) | CDev WLRN |
| 'Beatrice' (Vtta) | WBou |
| 'Becka' (Va) | LPVe |

| | | |
|---|---|---|
| * | *bella* | EBee EWll LPVe WEas WShe |
| § | 'Belmont Blue' (C) | CBos CFul CLon CLyd CSpe EBee EWes GMac LBee LPVe MBel MCLN MMal MRav NChi NHol NRoo SAga SBla SChu SHel SMrm WBou WFar WOut WSpi |
| § | *bertolonii* | LPVe WBou |
| | 'Beshlie' (Va) ♀ | CElw CMea GMaP GMac LPVe MArl MBNS SChu WBou WEas WKif WOut |
| | 'Bessie Cawthorne' (C) | LPVe SChu |
| | 'Bessie Knight' (Va) | LPVe |
| | *betonicifolia* | LPVe |
| * | – *albescens* | NHar |
| | 'Bettina' (Va) | LPVe |
| | 'Betty' (Va) | GHCN LPVe |
| | 'Bianca' (Vtta) | LPVe |
| | *biflora* | CMHG CPla EOld EPar MTho NChi NRya SRms |
| | 'Bishop's Belle' (FP) | GHCN |
| | 'Bishop's Gold' (FP) | GHCN |
| | 'Black Ace' (Va) | LPVe |
| * | 'Black Beauty' | Last listed 1998 |
| | 'Blue Butterfly' (C) | GMac |
| | 'Blue Carpet' (Va) | GMac |
| | 'Blue Cloud' (Va) | LPVe NChi |
| ¶ | 'Blue Diamond' | EFou |
| | 'Blue Moon' (C) | SChu SDys SMrm WBou WWat |
| | 'Blue Moonlight' (C) | GBuc GMac NChi NSti SMrm SUsu WWat |
| | 'Blue Princess' | Last listed 1996 |
| | 'Blue Tit' (Va) | SChu |
| | 'Bonna Cawthorne' (Va) | LPVe |
| | *bosniaca* | See *V. elegantula bosniaca* |
| | 'Boughton Blue' | See *V.* 'Belmont Blue' |
| | 'Bournemouth Gem' (Vt) | CDev CGro |
| § | 'Bowles' Black' (T) | CArn CDev CHan CSWP ECha ELan GAbr LPVe NBro NLak NRoo SBla SIng SRPl SRms WBea WBou WEas WOve WWat |
| | 'Boy Blue' (Vtta) | EHal LPVe |
| | 'Brenda Hall' (Va) | LPVe |
| | 'Bronwen' (Va) | LPVe |
| ¶ | 'Bruneau' (dVt) | CGro |
| * | 'Bryony' (Vtta) | LPVe WBou |
| | 'Bullion' (Va) | LPVe WBou WMer |
| | 'Burnock Yellow' (Va) | GHCN |
| | 'Buttercup' (Vtta) | CInt GHCN GMac LBee LPVe NHar NRoo SChu WBou WLRN WOut WWin |
| | 'Butterpat' (C) | NBrk NHaw |
| | 'Buxton Blue' (Va) | CFul LPVe WBou |
| | *calaminaria* | LPVe |
| | 'Calantha' (Vtta) | LPVe |
| | *calcarata* | ELan LPVe |
| § | – subsp. *zoysii* | EWes GCHN |
| | 'California' (Vt) | CDev |
| | 'Callia' (Va) | LPVe |
| I | 'Calliandra' (Vtta) | LPVe |
| I | 'Calypso' (Va) | LPVe |
| § | *canadensis* var. *rugulosa* | CRDP |
| | 'Candida' (Vtta) | LPVe |
| | *canina* | CGro CKin NBro |
| * | – *alba* | CBre |
| | 'Carberry Seedling' (Va) | LPVe |
| | 'Carina' (Vtta) | LPVe |
| | 'Carnival' (Va) | NBrk |
| | 'Carola' (Va) | LPVe |
| | 'Caroline' (Va) | SMrm |
| I | 'Cassandra' (Vtta) | LPVe |
| ¶ | 'Catforth Blue Ribbon' | NCat |
| * | 'Catforth Gold' | NCat |

| | | |
|---|---|---|
| * | 'Catforth Suzanne' | NCat |
| | 'Catherine Williams' (ExVa) | GHCN |
| | 'Cat's Whiskers' | CElw GBri GMac NBrk NSti |
| | *cazorlensis* | SBla |
| | *chaerophylloides* | See *V. dissecta* var. *chaerophylloides* |
| | 'Chandler's Glory' (Va) | LPVe |
| | 'Chantal' (Vtta) | LPVe NRoo |
| | 'Chantreyland' (Va) | CMdw COIW EWTr NBir SRms |
| | 'Charity' (Va) | LPVe |
| * | 'Charlotte' | CSam |
| | 'Charlotte Mott' (Va) | LPVe |
| | 'Chelsea Girl' (Va) | SMrm |
| | 'Chloe' (Vtta) | LPVe |
| * | 'Christina' | WLRN |
| | 'Christmas' (Vt) | CDev CGro EBee |
| | 'Christobel' (Va) | LPVe |
| | 'Cinderella' (Va) | CFul GHCN |
| | 'Citrina' (Va) | LPVe |
| | 'Claire' (Va) | LPVe |
| * | 'Clare Harrison' (Va) | LPVe |
| | 'Clementina' (Va) ♀ | CElw GCHN LPVe MRav NRoo |
| | 'Cleo' (Va) | GMac WBou |
| | 'Clive Groves' (Vt) | CDev CGro |
| | 'Clodagh' (Va) | LPVe |
| | 'Clover' (Va) | LPVe |
| | 'Coeur d'Alsace' (Vt) | CDev CGro CHan CMea CNic CPBP EBee EFou ELan EPar GMac LPVe NBro WCot WEas WRus WWhi |
| | 'Colette' (Va) | LPVe |
| | 'Colleen' (Vtta) | LPVe |
| | 'Columbine' (Va) | CBos CElw CGro CInt CLTr CLon CMHG CRDP CSam EBee GHCN GMac LBee LPVe MCLN MHlr NSti NWoo SAga SChu SLod SMrm WBou WCot WEas WLRN WMaN WSpi WWhi |
| § | 'Comte de Brazza' (dPVt) | CDev CTri GBar GMac WRha |
| | 'Comte de Chambord' (dVt) | WRha |
| | 'Connie' (Va) | CBos LPVe |
| | 'Connigar' | CSam |
| | 'Coralie' (Vtta) | LPVe |
| | 'Cordelia' (Va) | CElw EBee LPVe NBro |
| ¶ | 'Cornetto' | EBee MMal |
| | Cornish indigenous mauve | Last listed 1996 |
| * | 'Cornish White' | CDev |
| | *cornuta* ♀ | More than 30 suppliers |
| | – Alba Group ♀ | More than 30 suppliers |
| § | – 'Alba Minor' | CFul CLyd ELan EWes GMac LPVe MBNS MBro MCLN MFir NBro NRoo SChu WAbe WCot WFar WHoo WPyg WWat |
| | – blue | LPVe WWat |
| * | – 'Bluestone Gold' | WCot |
| | – *compacta* | Last listed 1996 |
| | – 'Eastgrove Blue Scented' (C) | CLTr EBee GMac MCLN MHlr WBou WCot WEas WIvy WOut WRHF |
| * | – 'Gypsy Moth' | GMac |
| | – Lilacina Group (C) | CFul CGle ECha EWes GMac LPVe MBro MRav NCat NChi NFla SChu SMrm SWat WFar WHoo |
| | – 'Maiden's Blush' | GMac |
| | – 'Minor' ♀ | CFul CInt CPla CSam GMac LPVe MCLN MFir NBro SBla WAbe WBou WCom WWat |
| | – 'Minor Alba' | See *V. cornuta* 'Alba Minor' |
| * | – 'Paris White' | EBee EPfP |
| ¶ | – 'Purple Gem' | GMac |
| | – Purpurea Group | CMea ECha GBuc SRPl WRus |
| | – 'Rosea' | CFul CLyd LPVe NSti |

| | |
|---|---|
| - 'Seymour Pink' | CFul |
| - 'Variegata' | LPVe WLin |
| * - 'Victoria's Blush' | MOne NHar NRoo NSti SMrm SUsu WBou WPrP WWhi |
| - 'Violacea' | GMac |
| - 'Yellow King' | EFou |
| 'Coronation' | Last listed 1996 |
| *corsica* | CInt LPVe SDys |
| * 'Cottage Garden' (Va) | GHCN NHaw WFar |
| 'Countess of Shaftsbury' (dVt) | CDev |
| 'Cox's Moseley' (ExVa) | GHCN |
| 'Cream Princess' | EPfP |
| ¶ 'Crepuscule' | CGro |
| 'Cressida' (Va) | LPVe |
| § *cucullata* ♀ | CGro SChu SRms WPrP |
| § - 'Alba' | ECGP EPar LFis LLWP NChi NSti |
| - *rosea* | EWes |
| * - 'Striata Alba' | MWgw |
| *cunninghamii* | Last listed 1998 |
| - CC 463 | MRPP |
| *curtisii* | See *V. tricolor* subsp. *curtisii* |
| 'Cyril Bell' (Va) | LPVe |
| § 'Czar' (Vt) | CBre ILis NRya |
| § 'Czar Bleu' (Vt) | CDev |
| 'Daena' (Vtta) | LPVe |
| 'Daisy Smith' (Va) | CFul GHCN GMac NChi SChu WBou |
| ¶ 'Dancing Geisha' (Vt) | WCot |
| 'Dartington Hybrid' (Va) | LPVe |
| 'Daveron' (C) | LPVe NRoo |
| 'David Rhodes' (FP) | GHCN |
| 'David Wheldon' (Va) | GHCN LPVe |
| 'Davina' (Va) | LPVe SChu SDys |
| 'Dawn' (Vtta) | CFul GHCN GMac LPVe WBou |
| 'Deanna' (Va) | LPVe |
| 'Decima' (Va) | LPVe |
| ¶ *declinata* | CGro NChi |
| 'Delia' (Va) | GMac LPVe WBou |
| 'Delicia' (Vtta) | LPVe NChi NRoo WBou |
| 'Delmonden' (Va) | CRDP SAsh |
| 'Delphine' (Va) | LPVe NPla NRoo SChu |
| 'Demeter' (Va) | LPVe |
| 'Desdemona' (Va) | GMac LBee LGre WBou |
| 'Desmonda' (Va) | LPVe SChu |
| 'Devon Cream' (Va) | GMac WBou |
| ¶ *diffusa glabella* | NWCA |
| 'Dimity' (Va) | LPVe |
| 'Dione' (Vtta) | LPVe |
| I 'Diosma' (Va) | LPVe |
| § *dissecta* | GBin WCot WPer |
| § - var. *chaerophylloides* f. *eizanensis* | EHyt MTho NLar NWCA |
| - var. *sieboldiana* | CRDP |
| 'Dobbie's Bronze' (Va) | LPVe |
| 'Dobbie's Buff' (Va) | LPVe |
| 'Dobbie's Red' (Va) | LPVe |
| 'Doctor Smart' (C) | LPVe |
| *doerfleri* | LPVe WAbe |
| 'Dominique' (Va) | LPVe |
| 'Dominy' (Vtta) | LPVe |
| 'Donau' (Vt) | CDev |
| 'Double White' (dVt) | CGle |
| *dubyana* | EBee GBuc MTPN SSca |
| 'Duchesse de Parme' (dPVt) | CDev CGle CGro GBar GMac |
| 'D'Udine' (dVt) | CDev CGro GBar GMac |
| 'Dusk' | WBou |
| 'E.A. Bowles' | See *V. 'Bowles' Black'* |
| 'Eastgrove Elizabeth' (C) | Last listed 1998 |
| ¶ 'Eastgrove Elizabeth Booth' | WEas |
| 'Eastgrove Ice Blue' (C) | WEas |
| 'Eastgrove Twinkle' (C) | WEas |
| *eizanensis* | See *V. dissecta* var. *chaerophylloides* f. *eizanensis* |
| 'Elaine Cawthorne' (C) | LPVe |
| * 'Elaine Quin' | NPla SChu WBou |
| § *elatior* | CElw CHea CMea CPla CSWP EBee EMon EPar EPla GBri LPVe MAvo MBel MHar MNrw NHol SChu SSca SUsu WCot WFar WLin WPer WPrP WWye |
| § *elegantula* | GCrs LPVe SSca |
| § - *bosniaca* | LPVe |
| 'Elisha' (Va) | LPVe NRoo |
| 'Elizabeth' (Va) | GHCN LPVe MMal SChu SMrm SRms WBou WLRN |
| 'Elizabeth Cawthorne' (C) | LPVe |
| 'Elizabeth Lee' | Last listed 1998 |
| 'Elizabeth McCallum' (FP) | GHCN |
| 'Elliot Adam' (Va) | GHCN WBou WOut |
| 'Elsie Coombs' (Vt) | CDev CGro WPer |
| 'Emily Mott' (Va) | LPVe |
| 'Emma' (Va) | CMea LPVe NHar |
| 'Emma Cawthorne' (C) | CLTr GHCN LPVe |
| 'Enterea' (Va) | LPVe |
| *erecta* | See *V. elatior* |
| 'Eris' (Va) | LPVe NRoo |
| 'Eros' (Va) | LPVe NRoo |
| 'Etain' (Va) | CBos ECha ELan EWes GHCN GMaP GMac LGre LPVe MMil MOne NBrk NHaw NPla NRoo SBla WBou WFar WLRN WWhi |
| 'Ethena' (Va) | LPVe |
| 'Etienne' (Va) | LPVe |
| 'Evelyn' (ExVa) | Last listed 1997 |
| 'Evelyn Cawthorne' (C) | LPVe NRoo |
| 'Fabiola' (Vtta) | GMac LBee LPVe NBir WBou |
| 'Felicity' (Va) | LPVe |
| 'Felix' | CFri |
| 'Finola Galway' (Va) | LPVe |
| 'Fiona' (Va) | CBos CLon GHCN GMac LPVe MCLN NBrk NCat NRoo NSti SChu WBou WOut |
| * 'Fiona Lawrenson' (Va) | LPVe |
| ¶ *flettii* | SIng |
| 'Florence' (Va) | LPVe NRoo |
| 'Foxbrook Cream' (C) | CFul CMea GBuc GHCN GMac LPVe MBel NBrk NPla WBou WCot WHoo WRus WSpi |
| 'Frances' (Va) | LPVe |
| 'Francesca' (Va) | LPVe |
| 'Freckles' | See *V. sororia* 'Freckles' |
| 'Gatina' (Va) | LPVe |
| 'Gazania' (Va) | CMea LPVe WBou |
| I 'Gazelle' (Vtta) | LPVe WCom |
| 'Genesta Gambier' (Va) | CSam |
| 'George Lee' | Last listed 1998 |
| 'Georgina' (Va) | LPVe |
| 'Geraldine' (Vtta) | LPVe |
| 'Geraldine Cawthorne' (C) | GHCN LPVe NCat |
| ¶ 'Giant Elk' (Vt) | CGro |
| 'Gina' (Vtta) | LPVe |
| 'Giselle' (Va) | LPVe |
| *glabella* | CLTr SUsu |
| 'Gladys Findlay' (Va) | GHCN GMac LPVe WBou |
| 'Glenroyd Fancy' (ExVa) | GHCN |
| ¶ 'Gloire de Verdon' (PVt) | CGro |
| 'Governor Herrick' (Vt) | CDev CGro NSti WPer WSpi |
| 'Grace' (Va) | NRoo |
| § *gracilis* | CElw ECha ELan LPVe WFar WOut |
| - x *cornuta* | LPVe |
| - 'Lutea' | CLon CSam NRoo SMrm |
| * - 'Magic' | CElw SMrm SWat WCot |
| - 'Major' | WBou |

| | |
|---|---|
| 'Green Jade' (v) | CPla |
| 'Grey Owl' (Va) | CLon CMea EBee LBee LGre LPVe |
| | NBrk SChu SLod SMrm WBou |
| | WKif |
| *grisebachiana* | Last listed 1998 |
| * – *alba* | Last listed 1998 |
| 'Griselda' (Vtta) | LPVe |
| 'Grovemount Blue' (C) | CMea WPen |
| § *grypoceras* var. *exilis* | CInt EHyt EMan EWes GBri NBus |
| | SBla SChu SMad WBor |
| – 'Variegata' | EHoe NBir |
| 'Gustav Wermig' (C) | GAbr LPVe MBel NHaw WBou |
| 'Gwen Cawthorne' (C) | LPVe |
| 'H.H. Hodge' (ExVa) | GHCN |
| 'Hackpen' | CSam |
| 'Hadria Cawthorne' (C) | GHCN LPVe |
| 'Hansa' (C) | CHid NChi WMer |
| 'Haslemere' | See *V.* 'Nellie Britton' |
| 'Hazeldene Blue' | CFri |
| * 'Heaselands' | SMrm |
| I 'Hebe' (Vtta) | LPVe |
| § *hederacea* | CBos CDev CGro CMHG ECou |
| | ELan ESis GCHN GQui LPVe |
| | MNrw NBro NHar NNrd NOak |
| | SRms SUsu WHer WOve WSpi |
| | WWhi WWye |
| – blue | CFee CLTr SIng WPer |
| – 'Putty' | ECou EWes |
| 'Helen W. Cochrane' (ExVa) | GHCN |
| 'Helena' (Va) | LPVe SChu |
| 'Hera' (Va) | LPVe |
| 'Hespera' (Va) | LPVe |
| I 'Hesperis' (Va) | LPVe |
| *heterophylla* | See *V. bertolonii* |
| subsp. *epirota* | |
| 'Hextable' (C) | LPVe |
| *hirta* | CGro CKin MHew WCla |
| *hispida* | LPVe |
| 'Hopleys White' | CGro |
| 'Hudsons Blue' | CElw WEas |
| 'Hugh Campbell' (ExVa) | GHCN |
| 'Huntercombe Purple' (Va) ♀ | CElw CFul CGle GHCN LBee |
| | LPVe MHlr MWat NPla SAga SBla |
| | SChu SRms SUsu WBou WKif |
| 'Hunter's Pride' | SMrm |
| 'Hyperion' (Va) | LPVe |
| 'I.G. Sherwood' | GHCN |
| 'Iantha' (Vtta) | LPVe |
| 'Iden Gem' (Va) | CFul GHCN LPVe WBou |
| 'Inkie' (Va) | CFul |
| 'Inverurie Beauty' (Va) ♀ | GMaP LPVe MFir NBrk NCat SChu |
| | WBou WKif |
| 'Inverurie Mauve' (Va) | LPVe |
| 'Iona' (Va) | LPVe |
| 'Irina' (Va) | LPVe |
| 'Irish Elegance' (Vt) | CDev NBro SChu WHal |
| 'Irish Mary' (Va) | LPVe SChu SUsu |
| 'Irish Molly' (Va) | CBot CElw CFul CLon CSam CSpe |
| | ECha ELan GHCN GMac LPVe |
| | MCLN MMal NRoo SBla SMrm |
| | SRms WBou WEas WHer WRus |
| | WSHC WWhi WWin |
| 'Isata' (Vtta) | LPVe |
| 'Isla' (Vtta) | LGre LPVe |
| 'Isobel' | EWes |
| 'Ita' (Va) | LPVe |
| 'Iver Grove' (Va) | LPVe |
| 'Ivory Queen' (Va) | CFul GHCN GMac LPVe NBrk |
| | WBou WPen |
| 'Ivory White' (Va) | CDev LPVe |
| * 'Jack Sampson' | CDev |
| 'Jack Simpson' | Last listed 1996 |

| | |
|---|---|
| 'Jackanapes' (Va) ♀ | CElw CFul CHid CSam ECha ECtt |
| | ELan GHCN GMac LPVe NBrk |
| | NRoo SMrm SRms WBou WFar |
| | WSpi WWin |
| 'James' | EWes |
| 'James Pilling' (Va) | GHCN GMac |
| 'Jane Askew' (Va) | LPVe |
| 'Jane Mott' (Va) | LPVe |
| 'Janet' (Va) | GHCN LPVe SMrm WLRN |
| 'Janine' (Vtta) | LPVe |
| 'Janna' (Va) | LPVe |
| *japonica* | Last listed 1998 |
| – 'Rodney Davey' | MCCP |
| 'Jean Arnot' | CGro |
| 'Jeannie Bellew' (Va) | GHCN GMac LPVe NHar SChu |
| | WBou WLRN WSpi |
| 'Jemma' (Va) | LPVe |
| 'Jenelle' (Vtta) | LPVe |
| 'Jenny' (Vtta) | LPVe |
| 'Jersey Gem' (Va) | GMac LPVe |
| 'Jessica' (Va) | LPVe |
| 'Jessie East' | WEas |
| 'Jessie Taylor' (FP) | GHCN |
| 'Jimmie's Dark' (ExVa) | GHCN |
| 'Joanna' (Va) | GHCN WBou |
| I 'Jocunda' (Va) | LPVe |
| 'Jodie' (Va) | Last listed 1996 |
| 'Joella' (Va) | LPVe |
| 'John Raddenbury' (Vt) | Last listed 1996 |
| 'John Rodger' (SP) | GHCN |
| 'John Wallmark' (c) | WMer |
| 'John Yelmark' (Va) | LPVe |
| 'John Zanini' (Vtta) | LPVe |
| 'Johnny Jump Up' (T) | EWll |
| Joker Series (P) ♀ | Last listed 1995 |
| *jooi* | CInt CLyd GTou NBir NBro NMen |
| | SBla SIng SRms SSca WCom WRha |
| *jordanii* | LPVe |
| 'Jordieland Gem' (c) | GMac NDov |
| 'Josie' (Va) | GHCN LPVe |
| 'Joyce Gray' (Va) | GHCN GMac NRoo WBou |
| * 'Judy Goring' (Va) | LPVe |
| 'Julia' (Va) | LPVe WBou |
| 'Julian' (Va) | CBos CFul CLTr GHCN GMac |
| | NRoo SBla SRms WBou WIvy |
| | WWat |
| 'June' (SP) | Last listed 1996 |
| 'Juno' (Va) | GMac LPVe |
| 'Jupiter' (Va) | EBee LPVe SMrm |
| 'Kate' (Va) | CElw CFul |
| 'Katerina' (Va) | LPVe |
| 'Kathleen Hoyle' (ExVa) | Last listed 1996 |
| 'Kathy' (Vtta) | LPVe |
| * 'Katie Grayson' (C) | LPVe |
| 'Katinka' (Va) | LPVe |
| *keiskei* | GCHN |
| 'Kerrie' (Va) | LPVe |
| * 'Kerry Girl' | CDev |
| 'Kiki McDonough' (C) | LPVe NBrk SChu SUsu |
| 'Kilruna' (Va) | LPVe |
| * 'King of the Blacks' | ECoo |
| 'King of the Blues' (Va) | LPVe |
| 'Kinvarna' (Va) | LPVe |
| 'Kirsty' (Va) | LPVe |
| 'Kitten' | GMac NCat NRoo NSti SChu |
| | WBou |
| 'Kitty White' (Va) | LPVe |
| *koraiensis* | NWCA |
| *koreana* | See *V. grypoceras* var. *exilis* |
| *kusanoana* | Last listed 1997 |
| § *labradorica* | CGro CHar EMil EOld EWTr GLil |
| | LSyl MRav NPri SMer WFar WSpi |

N – hort.   See *V. riviniana* Purpurea Group
N – *purpurea* misapplied   See *V. riviniana* Purpurea Group
*lactea*   Last listed 1997
¶ 'Lady Hulme Campbell' (PVt)   CGro
'Lady Jane' (Vt)   Last listed 1996
'Lady Saville'   See *V.* 'Sissinghurst'
'Lady Tennyson' (Va)   GMac LPVe SBla
'Lamorna' (Vtta)   LPVe
*lanceolata*   Last listed 1998
'Larissa' (Va)   LPVe
'Latona' (Va)   LPVe
'Laura' (C)   CFul GBuc GMac NBrk
¶ 'Laura Cawthorne'   NDov
'Lavender Lady'   CGro
'Laverna' (Va)   LPVe
'Lavinia' (Va)   EBee GCrs GHCN LBee LPVe
   WBou
'Lawrence' (c)   WMer
'Leander' (Va)   LPVe
'Leda' (Va)   LPVe
¶ 'Lemon Sorbet'   MOne
'Leora' (Vtta)   CFul LPVe NRoo
'Leora Hamilton' (C)   LPVe NPla
'Lerosa' (Vtta)   LPVe
'Leta' (Vtta)   LPVe
'Letitia' (Va)   CFul EFou GHCN GMac LPVe
   MMil SMrm WBou WLRN WSpi
'Leto' (Va)   LPVe
'Lewisa' (Va)   LPVe
'Lianne' (Vt)   CDev CGro WPer
'Lilac Rose' (Va)   CFul GMac SAga WBou
'Liliana' (Va)   LPVe
'Liriopa' (Va)   LPVe
'Lisa Cawthorne' (C)   LPVe
'Little David' (Vtta) ♀   CBos CFul CInt CSam EHal GHCN
   GMac LBee LPVe NRoo WBou
   WEas WOut
'Little Johnny' (Va)   Last listed 1997
¶ 'Little Liz' (Va)   GHCN
'Livia' (Vtta)   LPVe
'Lola' (Va)   LPVe
'Lord Nelson' (Va)   EMou EWll LPVe WMer
'Lord Plunket' (Va)   LPVe WBou
'Lorna' (Va) ♀   LPVe
'Lorna Cawthorne' (C)   CElw GHCN LPVe NCat WOut
'Lorna Moakes' (Va)   LPVe SAga
'Louisa' (Va)   LPVe
'Louise Gemmell' (Va)   LPVe NBrk NHaw SChu
'Love Duet'   Last listed 1996
'Luca' (Va)   LPVe
'Lucinda' (Va)   LPVe
'Lucy' (Va)   LPVe
'Ludy May' (Va)   LPVe
'Luna' (Vtta)   LPVe
§ *lutea*   EBot LPVe WBou WGwy
– subsp. *elegans*   See *V. lutea*
'Luxonne' (Vt)   CBre CGro WLRN
*lyallii*   Last listed 1997
'Lydia' (Va)   LPVe SChu WBou
'Lydia Groves'   CDev CGro
'Lynn' (Va)   GHCN LPVe
'Lysander' (Va)   LPVe
*macedonica*   See *V. tricolor* subsp. *macedonica*
'Macgregor's Moth' (Va)   Last listed 1996
*macloskeyi* var. *pallens*   WLRN
'Madame Armandine   CBre CDev CGro
   Pagès' (Vt)
'Madelaine' (Va)   EBee LPVe
'Madge' (Va)   LPVe
'Maera' (Vtta)   LPVe
*magellanica*   NWoo
§ *magellensis*   NChi

'Magenta Maid' (Va)   CFul MArl
'Maggie' (Va)   LPVe
'Maggie Mott' (Va) ♀   CFul CGle CSam ECha ECtt EOrc
   GHCN GMac LBee LPVe MBri
   MCLN NBrk NChi NHol NRoo
   SBla WBou WEas WFar WKif WRus
   WSpi WWhi WWin WWol
'Magic'   GMac LBee MArl SChu WBou
   WCru
'Maid Marion'   SRms
'Majella' (Vtta)   LPVe
'Malise' (Va)   LPVe
'Malvena' (Vtta)   LPVe
*mandsburica*   CGro LPVe
\* – *triangularis bicolor*   CInt
'Margaret' (Va)   WBou
'Margaret Cawthorne' (C)   LPVe
'Marian' (Va)   LPVe
'Marie-Louise' (dPVt)   CDev CGro CTri EPar
'Marika' (Va)   LPVe
'Mark Talbot' (Va)   GHCN
'Maroon Picotee'   ELan GHCN
'Mars' (Va)   CLon LPVe
'Marsland's Yellow' (Vtta)   LPVe
'Martin' (Va) ♀   CFul CInt CMHG CNic CSam
   ECha EWes GCHN GHCN GMac
   LBee LHop LPVe MRav NBrk
   SChu SDys SUsu WBou WCom
   WFar WIvy WKif WWin
'Mary Cawthorne' (C)   LPVe
'Mary Dawson' (Va)   Last listed 1996
'Mary Ellen' (Va)   CFul GHCN
'Mary Wyllie'   GHCN
'Mauve Beauty' (Va)   LPVe
'Mauve Haze' (Va)   GMac WBou WEas WWat
'Mauve Radiance' (Va)   CFul GMac LPVe NVic WBou
¶ 'Mavis Tuck'   CSam
'May Mott' (Va)   GMac NBrk WBou
'Mayfly' (Va)   GHCN GMac NBrk WBou
'Meena' (Vtta)   LPVe
'Megumi' (Va)   LPVe
'Melinda' (Vtta)   LPVe WBou
\* 'Melissa' (Va)   CFul LPVe SChu WBou
'Mercury' (Va)   GHCN LPVe WCom
'Merry Cheer' (C)   Last listed 1997
¶ *meryame*   WOut
'Midnight Turk' (Va)   GBuc WCot
'Milkmaid' (Va)   CGle ECha EFou EWll GCrs
   GHCN LBee NBir NFla NHaw
   SIng WFar WKif
'Mina Walker' (ExVa)   GHCN
'Minerva' (Va)   LPVe
\* *minor* subsp. *calcarea*   Last listed 1998
'Miranda' (Vtta)   LPVe
'Miss Brookes' (Va)   GHCN GMac LPVe WBou
'Miss Helen Mount'   Last listed 1998
'Mistral' (Va)   LPVe
'Misty Guy' (Vtta)   NChi WBou
'Mitzel' (Vtta)   LPVe NRoo
'Molly Sanderson' (Va) ♀   CGle CMea CSpe ECha ECtt ELan
   ENot EPot EWTr GHCN GMac
   LBee LHop LPVe MMal NRoo
   NWoo SChu SIng SMrm SSoC
   WBou WEas WSpi WWat WWhi
   WWin
I 'Mona' (Va)   LPVe
'Monica' (Va)   LPVe SChu
'Moonlight' (Va) ♀   CFul CMea ECha ELan GCHN
   GMac LBee LHop LPVe MOne
   NRoo NSti SAga SBla SChu WBou
   WCom WMaN WWhi
'Moonraker'   NCat

'Morvana' (Va) — LPVe
'Morwenna' (Va) — LPVe NRoo WWhi
'Moscaria' (Va) — LPVe
'Moseley Ideal' (ExVa) — GHCN
'Moseley Perfection' (Va) — LPVe
'Mother's Day' — Last listed 1996
'Mrs Chichester' (Va) — GHCN GMac LPVe NBrk WBou
¶ 'Mrs Cotterell' — EBee MOne
'Mrs David Lloyd — CDev
    George' (dVt)
'Mrs Lancaster' (Va) — CFul CHid EWes GHCN GMac
    LPVe MCLN NBir NRoo SChu
    SMrm SRms SUsu WBou WLRN
    WSpi
'Mrs M.B. Wallace' (ExVa) — GHCN
'Mrs Pickett' (C) — Last listed 1997
'Mrs Pinehurst' (Vt) — Last listed 1996
'Mrs R. Barton' (Vt) — CDev CGro NBro WLRN
¶ 'Mrs Staples' — EBee
'Myfawnny' (Va) — CBos CElw CMea EBee ELan
    EWes GHCN GMac LBee LPVe
    NPla NRoo SAga SChu SRms
    WBou WFar WKif WLRN
'Mylene' (Va) — LPVe
'Myntha' (Vtta) — LPVe
'Mysie' (Va) — CFul
'Nadia' (Va) — LPVe
'Naomi' (Va) — LPVe
'Natasha' (Va) — LPVe
'Neapolitan' — See V. 'Pallida Plena'
'Nell' (Va) — CFul
§ 'Nellie Britton' (Va) ♀ — CFul CGle GHCN GMac LPVe
    MRav NRoo NSti SChu SRms
    WBou WEas WRus WWin
'Nemesis' (Va) — LPVe
'Neptune' (Va) — LPVe
'Nerena' (Vtta) — LPVe
'Nesta' (Vtta) — LPVe
'Netta Statham' — See V. 'Belmont Blue'
'Nicole' (Va) — LPVe
'Nigra' (Va) — LPVe
'Nina' (Va) — LPVe
'Nona' (Va) — LPVe
'Noni' (Vt) — Last listed 1996
'Nora May' (Va) — GHCN
'Norah Church' (Vt) — CDev CGro EBee
'Norah Leigh' (Va) — NRoo WBou
*obliqua* — See V. *cucullata*
*occulta striata albe* — EMar NBro
'Octavia' (Va) — LPVe
'Odile' (Va) — LPVe
*odorata* — CArn CB&S CDev CGle CGro
    CJew CKin CSWP EGoo EPar
    EWFC GBar GPoy LHol LPVe
    MHew MRav MWat NFla NLak
    NRoo NSti SIde SIng SSea WCla
    WCot WOak WWat WWye
- 'Alba' — CBre CDev CGle CGro CKin
    CSWP CVer EFou ELan EMan
    EOld EPar GMac ILis MWgw NCat
    NOak NRoo SIde SIng WCla
    WOve WRus WWat WWye
- 'Alba Plena' (d) — CVer EBot ELan EPar SBla
- apricot — See V. 'Sulphurea'
¶ - 'Double Foncee de — CGro
    Mme Dumas'
- *dumetorum* — See V. *alba*
- *flore-pleno* — EBot EPar
- pink — EOld EPar WCla
- *rosea* — CBre CGro GBar GMac MRav SIng
    WCot WWhi
* - subsp. *subcarnea* — Last listed 1998

- 'Sulphurea' — See V. 'Sulphurea'
- 'Wellsiana' (Vt) ♀ — Last listed 1996
'Olive Edmonds' (Va) — LPVe
'Olwyn' (Va) — LPVe
¶ 'Opéra' (Vt) — CGro
¶ 'Orchid Pink' (Vt) — CGro
*oreades* — LPVe NTow
'Oriana' (Va) — LPVe
*orphanidis* — LPVe
*ossea* — LPVe
'Painted Lady' (Va) — GMac
§ 'Pallida Plena' (dPVt) — CDev CGro
*palmata* — CPBP LPVe
¶ - × *loveliana* — NChi
'Palmer's White' (Va) — LPVe WBou
*palustris* — CKin EWFC WHer WShi
'Pamela Zambra' (Va) — CDev CGro
'Pam's Fancy' (ExVa) — Last listed 1996
'Pandora' (Va) — LPVe
*papilionacea* — See V. *sororia*
¶ 'Paradise Blue' (Vt) — CGro
'Parme de Toulouse' (dPVt) — CDev CGro
'Pat Creasy' (Va) — GHCN GMac WBou
'Pat Kavanagh' (C) — CMea GHCN GMac LPVe MOne
    MWat NChi SMrm WBou
'Patricia Brookes' (Va) — LPVe
¶ *patrinii* — EBee
*pedata* — CBro CFai EBee EMan EPot MBri
    NHar SPer WAbe WCot
- 'Bicolor' — SBla WAbe
*pedatifida* — ELan MBNS MBel MBro MTho
    NChi NMGW SChu WCom WWye
'Peggy Morgan' — LPVe
'Penelope' (SP) — GHCN
*pensylvanica* — See V. *pubescens* var. *eriocarpa*
'Peppered-palms' — CPla EBee
'Perle Rose' (Vt) — CDev CGro
'Pete' — SChu SUsu
'Petra' (Vtta) — LPVe
'Philippa Cawthorne' (C) — LPVe
'Phoebe' (Va) — LPVe
'Phyllida' (Va) — LPVe
¶ 'Phyllis Dove' — CGro
'Pickering Blue' (Va) — CFul GHCN GMac LPVe WBou
'Pilar' (Va) — LPVe SChu
'Pippa' (Vtta) — LPVe SChu
'Poppy' (Va) — LPVe
'Priam' (Va) — LPVe
'Primrose Cream' (Va) — LPVe
'Primrose Dame' (Va) — GHCN GMac LPVe NBrk WBou
    WMer WOut
'Primrose Pixie' (Va) — WBou
'Prince Henry' (T) — LPVe
'Prince John' (T) — EWTr LPVe
¶ 'Princess Alexandra' (Vt) — CGro
* 'Princess Blue' — Last listed 1997
'Princess Mab' (Vtta) — GHCN LPVe NBrk NRoo WBou
'Princess of Prussia' (Vt) — CBre CDev EBee
'Princess of Wales' — See V. 'Princesse de Galles'
Princess Series ♀ — Last listed 1995
* 'Princess Yellow' — EPfP WRHF
§ 'Princesse de Galles' (Vt) — CB&S CDev CGro CM&M EOld
    EPar NSti WRus
¶ 'Pritchard's Russian' (Vt) — CGro
§ *pubescens* var. *eriocarpa* — CBro
'Purity' (Vtta) — GHCN LPVe NRoo
'Purple Dove' (Va) — SMrm
¶ 'Purple Splash' — WSpi
'Purple Wings' (Va) — GMac WBou
'Putty' — WCru
'Quatre Saisons' (Vt) — Last listed 1996

'Queen Charlotte' (Vt) CDev CFai CGro CM&M EBee GCHN ILis NBro NFai NHar NMen NWCA WCot WGwG WSpi
'Queen Disa' (Vtta) LPVe
'Queen Victoria' See *V.* 'Victoria Regina'
'Quink' (Va) CFul
'R.N. Denby' (ExVa) GHCN
'Ramona' (Va) LPVe
'Rave' (Vtta) GMac
* 'Raven' NCat NHar NRoo SAga SChu WBou WWat WWhi
'Ravenna' (Va) LPVe
'Rawson's White' (Vt) Last listed 1996
'Rebecca' (Vtta) More than 30 suppliers
'Rebecca Cawthorne' (C) LPVe NRoo
'Red Charm' (Vt) CM&M EBee EWll MWgw NBro NCat NPla WElm WLRN
'Red Lion' CDev CGro
'Red Queen' (Vt) NSti
*reichenbachiana* ELan EPar EWFC
'Reine des Blanches' (dVt) EFou WSpi
'Reliance' (Va) GHCN
'Remora' (Vtta) LPVe
*reniforme* See *V. hederacea*
'Rhoda' (Va) LPVe
'Richard Vivian' (Va) LPVe
'Richard's Yellow' (Va) GHCN LPVe
*riviniana* CArn CKin EWFC MCAu MHer MMal NChi WHer WJek WOak WShi
¶ - 'Ed's Variegated' (v) NDov WCot
§ - Purpurea Group More than 30 suppliers
- - x *verecunda* var. *yakusimana* SIng
- white EWes NWoo
'Rodney Davey' (Vt/v) CPla EGar GBri NBro NCut NFai NWes WElm WLRN
'Rodney Marsh' NBir
'Romilly' (Va) LPVe
'Rosalie' (Va) LPVe
* 'Rosanna' CDev
'Roscastle Black' CPlt GMac NPla WBou WCot WWhi
'Rosemary Cawthorne' (C) LPVe
¶ 'Rosine' (Vt) GMac
'Rowan Hood' (ExVa) GHCN
'Rowena' (Va) LPVe
'Royal Delft' GCHN
'Royal Robe' (VT) CDev CGro
'Rubra' (Vt) WPer
*rugulosa* See *V. canadensis* var. *rugulosa*
§ *rupestris* CGro WOak
- blue Last listed 1996
§ - *rosea* CDev CInt CLTr CNic CPla LLWP MNrw NCat NSti NWCA STre WCla WElm WPrP
'Russian Superb' (Vt) WLRN
'Ruth Blackall' (Va) LPVe
'Ruth Elkans' (Va) GHCN GMac LPVe NBrk
'Saint Helena' (Vt) CDev
'Saint Maur' (Va) Last listed 1998
'Sally' (Vtta) LPVe
'Samantha' (Vtta) LPVe
'Sammy Jo' (Va) WBou
* 'Sandra Louise' (C) LPVe
'Sandra Louise' (Va) Last listed 1997
'Sarah' (Va) CFul
'Saughton Blue' (Va) LPVe
*saxatilis* See *V. tricolor* subsp. *subalpina*
'Scottish Yellow' (Va) Last listed 1996
*selkirkii* CInt CPla EHyt LPVe NBro NBus NWCA WOut

- 'Variegata' GBri GBuc NBir NWes WLin
*sempervirens* CInt
*septentrionalis* CRDP ECha ELan MNrw MOne MRav NBro NRya SSmi WHal WWat
- *alba* CHid CM&M CMHG CSWP CVer EBee EFou MRav MWgw NPla WFar WLRN WPer WWat
'Septima' (Va) LPVe
'Serena' (Va) LPVe WBou
'Sheila' (Va) WBou
'Sidborough Poppet' CInt CNic CPBP EWes NHar SSca WAbe WPer
§ *sieberiana* Last listed 1997
'Sigrid' (Va) LPVe
* 'Sir Fred Warner' (Va) LPVe
§ 'Sissinghurst' (Va) GMac LPVe NBir
'Sky Blue' (Va) LPVe
'Smugglers' Moon' SChu SUsu
'Snow Queen' GMac
'Sophie' (Vtta) LPVe SChu
§ *sororia* EBee GCHN GSki LPVe MSCN MWgw WLRN WWal
- 'Albiflora' CSpe EMil EPPr EPar EPfP GMaP GSki MBNS NHar NPro WLin WOut WPer WRus
§ - 'Freckles' More than 30 suppliers
- 'Priceana' CM&M CNic EBee EMan EOrc MAvo NCat NPla SLod SMrm WCot WElm WLRN WPer WWal WWat
'Soula' (Vtta) LPVe
* 'Stacey Proud' (v) NPro
'Steyning' (Va) LPVe
*stojanovii* CMea ELan SBla WEas
*striata* CInt
¶ 'Sugar Plum' GMac
§ 'Sulphurea' (Vt) CBre CDev CPBP CSWP EBee ELan EPar GMaP LPVe MHar MRav SIng SUsu WCot WHil WPer
'Sunshine' (Va) Last listed 1996
'Susan' (SP) Last listed 1996
'Susanah' (Vtta) GHCN GMac LPVe NPla
'Susie' (Va) GHCN WBou
'Swanley White' See *V.* 'Comte de Brazza'
'Sybil' (SP) GHCN
'Sylvia Hart' CPBP EWes MTho
* *takedana* 'Variegata' Last listed 1997
'Talitha' (Va) GMac LPVe
'Tamsin' (Va) LPVe
* 'Tanith' (Vt) CBre CDev EBee
'Tara' (Va) LPVe
'Thalia' (Vtta) CFul LPVe MCLN WBou
'The Czar' See *V.* 'Czar'
* 'The le Gresley Violet' (Vt) CGro
'Thea' (Va) LPVe
'Thelma' (Va) LPVe
'Thetis' (Va) GHCN LPVe
'Thierry' (Va) LPVe
'Tiffany' (Va) LPVe
'Tina' (Va) GHCN LPVe WBou
'Tina Whittaker' (Vt) Last listed 1996
'Titania' (Va) CGro LPVe
'Tom' (SP) GHCN
'Tom Tit' (Va) LPVe WBou
'Tomose' (Va) Last listed 1998
'Tony Venison' (C/v) CElw EHal EHoe LHop MBel MTho NBus NHaw WBou WCot
'Toulouse' LPVe
'Translucent Blue' Last listed 1996

| | |
|---|---|
| *tricolor* | CKin CNic EFer EWFC EWTr GBar GPoy LHol MHew MMal SIde WHer WJek WSel |
| § - subsp. *curtisii* | LPVe |
| § - subsp. *macedonica* | LPVe |
| - 'Sawyer's Blue' | WPer |
| ♦ - subsp. *saxatilis* | See *V. tricolor* subsp. *macedonica* |
| 'Tullia' (Vtta) | LPVe |
| 'Tuscany' (Vt) | Last listed 1996 |
| Ultima Series ♀ | Last listed 1995 |
| 'Una' (Va) | LPVe |
| 'Unity' (Vtta) | LPVe |
| 'Valerie Proud' | NBrk |
| 'Velleda' (Vtta) | LPVe |
| *velutina* | See *V. gracilis* |
| 'Venetia' (Va) | LPVe |
| 'Venus' (Va) | LPVe |
| ¶ *verecunda* B&SWJ 604a | WCru |
| ¶ - var. *semilunaris* | WCot |
| § - var. *yakusimana* | CRDP ESis EWes |
| 'Victoria' | See *V.* 'Czar Bleu' |
| 'Victoria Cawthorne' (C) | CElw CMea GBuc GHCN GMac LPVe MBel MBro MHlr MOne NChi NPla NRoo SBla SChu WBou WHoo WPyg WWat WWhi |
| § 'Victoria Regina' (Vt) | CDev CRow EMon |
| ¶ 'Victoria's Blush' (C) | GHCN NChi |
| 'Violacea' (C) | GHCN LPVe |
| 'Virginia' (Va) | CFul GMac LPVe SChu WBou |
| 'Virgo' (Va) | LPVe |
| 'Vita' (Va) | CFul CLTr CSpe GBuc GMac LBee LGre LPVe MBNS NRoo NSti SBid SBla SChu SRms WBou WIvy WLin WOut WSpi WWhi |
| *vourinensis* | LPVe |
| 'Wanda' (Va) | LPVe |
| ¶ 'Wasp' | GMac |
| 'Wendy' (SP) | GHCN LPVe |
| 'Westacre' (Va) | EWes |
| 'White Czar' (Vt) | Last listed 1996 |
| 'White Gem' (Va) | LBee |
| 'White Ladies' | See *V. cucullata* 'Alba' |
| 'White Pearl' (Va) | GBuc GMac LGre WBou |
| ¶ 'White Perfection' | MBNS |
| 'White Superior' | CB&S |
| 'White Swan' (Va) | CBos GMac LPVe |
| 'William Fife' (ExVa) | GHCN |
| 'William Wallace' (Va) | LPVe |
| 'Windward' (Vt) | NCat |
| 'Winifred Jones' (Va) | GHCN |
| * 'Winifred Warden' (Va) | GHCN MBNS WSpi |
| 'Winifred Wargent' (Va) | LPVe SAgg WLRN WOut |
| 'Winona' (Vtta) | LPVe NRoo |
| 'Winona Cawthorne' (C) | GHCN GMac LPVe NChi NHaw SChu WBou WWhi |
| 'Woodlands Cream' (Va) | GHCN GMac NBrk NPla WBou |
| 'Woodlands Lilac' (Va) | GHCN LPVe SChu WBou |
| 'Woodlands White' (Va) | LPVe WBou |
| 'Xantha' (Va) | LPVe |
| *yakusimana* | See *V. verecunda* var. *yakusimana* |
| *yezoensis* | Last listed 1998 |
| 'Zalea' (Va) | LPVe |
| 'Zara' (Va) | GMaP WBou |
| 'Zenobia' (Vtta) | LPVe |
| 'Zepherine' (Va) | LPVe |
| 'Zeta' (Va) | LPVe |
| 'Ziglana' (Va) | LPVe |
| 'Zoe' (Vtta) | GHCN GMac LPVe NPri NRoo SChu SDys SMrm WBou WFar WLRN |
| 'Zona' (Va) | LPVe |

| | |
|---|---|
| *zoysii* | See *V. calcarata* subsp. *zoysii* |

## VISCARIA (Caryophyllaceae)

| | |
|---|---|
| *vulgaris* | See *Lychnis viscaria* |

## VITALIANA (Primulaceae)

| | |
|---|---|
| § *primuliflora* | CLyd GCrs GTou MBro NSla WHoo WPyg |
| - subsp. *canescens* | Last listed 1998 |
| - subsp. *praetutiana* | EHyt EPot MBro MRPP NHar NHol NMen NNrd NTow NWCA WAbe WFar WLin WPat WPyg |
| - - *chionantha* | EPot |
| - subsp. *tridentata* | EPot NMen NNrd |

## VITEX (Verbenaceae)

| | |
|---|---|
| *agnus-castus* | CAgr CArn CB&S EBee EEls ELan ELau EOas GPoy LHol MHer SBid SIgm SLon SMad SPer SRPl WFar WWye |
| - 'Chaste Tree' | MCCP |
| - var. *latifolia* | MBri |
| - 'Silver Spire' | SBid |
| *lucens* | Last listed 1998 |
| ¶ *mombassae* | LBlo |
| *negundo* | CArn IIve LLew |
| - *cannabifolia* | See *V. incisa* |

## VITIS ✿ (Vitaceae)

| | |
|---|---|
| 'Abundante' (F) | WSuF |
| *amurensis* | CPIN EHic EPfP EPla ETen MBlu WWat |
| ¶ - B&SWJ 4138 | WCru |
| ¶ 'Aurore' Seibel 5279 (W) | WSuF |
| ¶ 'Baco' (R) | SDea |
| 'Baco Noir' (O/B) | GTwe WSuF |
| Black Hamburgh | See *V. vinifera* 'Schiava Grossa' |
| ¶ 'Black Strawberry' (B) | WSuF |
| § 'Boskoop Glory' (F) | CMac GTwe LBuc SCoo SDea WSuF |
| 'Brant' (O/B) ♀ | More than 30 suppliers |
| *californica* (F) | ERea |
| ¶ 'Canadice' | SDea |
| § 'Cascade' (O/B) | ERea MAsh SDea WSuF |
| Castel 19637 (W) | WSuF |
| ¶ 'Cayuga' (W) | WSuF |
| 'Chambourcin' (B) | WSuF |
| *coignetiae* ♀ | CLan CMac CPIN CSam EBee EBrP EBre ELan EMil ENot EPla LBre LPri MBri MGos MWat NEgg NHed SBra SBre SMad SPer SReu SSpi SSta WBod WCot WDin WPat WWat |
| ¶ - B&SWJ 4744 | WCru |
| § - Claret Cloak = 'Frovit' | ELan EPfP LRHS MAsh MCCP SMad SMur SPer SPla SSpi SVil WWat |
| ♦ - 'Frovit' | See *V. coignetiae* Claret Cloak = 'Frovit' |
| * - 'Rubescens' | CPIN |
| - Soja 457 | Last listed 1996 |
| 'Dalkauer' (W) | WSuF |
| *ficifolia* | See *V. thunbergii* |
| 'Fiesta' | WSuF |
| *flexuosa* | Last listed 1996 |
| ¶ - var. *choii* B&SWJ 4101 | WCru |
| § 'Fragola' (O/R) | CAgr CMac CPIN EBee EBrP EBre EHic EPfP EPla ERea GTwe LBre MAsh SBre SDea SEND SRms WSuF WWat |
| *benryana* | See *Parthenocissus henryana* |
| 'Himrod' (O/W) | ERea GTwe SDea WSuF |

*inconstans* — See *Parthenocissus tricuspidata*

¶ 'Kemsey Black' (B) — WSuF

'Kuibishevski' (O/R) — WSuF

*labrusca* 'Concord' (O/B) — ERea

Landot 244 (O/B) — WSuF

'Léon Millot' (O/G/B) — CAgr EMui ERea SDea WSuF

'Maréchal Foch' (O/B) — WSuF

'Maréchal Joffre' (O/B) — GTwe WSuF

Oberlin 595 (O/B) — WSuF

'Orion' — WSuF

¶ *palmata* — WCru

parsley leaved — See *V. vinifera* 'Ciotat'

*parvifolia* — CPlN WPat WShe

'Phönix' (O/W) — WSuF

*piasezkii* — WCru

¶ – B&SWJ 5236 — WCru

* 'Pink Strawberry' (O) — WSuF

'Pirovano 14' (O/B) — ERea GTwe SDea WSuF

§ 'Plantet' (O/B) — WSuF

* 'Polaske Muscat' (W) — WSuF

*pseudoreticulata* — CFil CPlN WPGP

'Pulchra' — WCru

*quinquefolia* — See *Parthenocissus quinquefolia*

Ravat 51 (O/W) — WSuF

*riparia* — CPlN WCru

¶ 'Rondo New Red' — SDea

¶ *rotundifolia* B&SWJ 4707 — WCru

'Schuyler' (O/B) — WSuF

Seibel (F) — EMui GTwe

Seibel 13053 — See *V.* 'Cascade'

Seibel 5455 — See *V.* 'Plantet'

Seibel 7053 — WSuF

Seibel 9549 — WSuF

'Seneca' (W) — WSuF

§ 'Seyval Blanc' (O/W) — ERea GTwe SDea WSuF

Seyve Villard 12.375 — See *V.* 'Villard Blanc'

Seyve Villard 5276 — See *V.* 'Seyval Blanc'

'Tereshkova' (O/B) — ERea SDea WSuF

'Thornton' — WSuF

§ *thunbergii* — WCru

¶ – B&SWJ 4702 — WCru

'Triomphe d'Alsace' (O/B) — CAgr MAsh NPer SDea WSuF

'Trollinger' — See *V. vinifera* 'Schiava Grossa'

§ 'Villard Blanc' (O/W) — WSuF

*vinifera* 'Abouriou' (O/B) — WSuF

¶ – 'Albalonga' (W) — WSuF

§ – 'Alicante' (G/B) — ERea GTwe WSuF

– 'Apiifolia' — See *V. vinifera* 'Ciotat'

– 'Appley Towers' (G/B) — ERea

– 'Auxerrois' (O/W) — WSuF

– 'Bacchus' (O/W) — SDea WSuF

– 'Black Alicante' — See *V. vinifera* 'Alicante'

– 'Black Corinth' (G/B) — ERea

– 'Black Frontignan' (G/O/B) ERea WSuF

– 'Black Hamburgh' — See *V. vinifera* 'Schiava Grossa'

– 'Black Monukka' (G/B) — ERea WSuF

– 'Blauburger' (O/B) — WCru

– 'Blue Portuguese' — See *V. vinifera* 'Portugieser'

– 'Buckland Sweetwater' (G/W) — ERea GTwe MBri SDea WSuF

– 'Cabernet Sauvignon' (O/B) SDea WSuF

– 'Canon Hall Muscat' (G/W) ERea

– 'Cardinal' (O/R) — ERea

– 'Chaouch' (G/W) — ERea

– 'Chardonnay' (O/W) — MAsh NPer SDea WSuF

§ – 'Chasselas' (G/O/W) — CMac EMui ERea MAsh SDea WSuF WWeb

– 'Chasselas d'Or' — See *V. vinifera* 'Chasselas'

– 'Chasselas Rosé' (G/R) — ERea WSuF

– 'Chasselas Vibert' (G/W) — ERea WSuF

– 'Chenin Blanc' (O/W) — WSuF

§ – 'Ciotat' (F) — EHic EPla ERea SDea WCru WSuF WWat

§ – 'Cot' (O/B) — WSuF

– 'Csabyongye' (W) — WSuF

¶ – 'Daitier de Beyrouth' (W) — WSuF

– 'Dornfelder' (O/R) — CWSG EBee WSuF

– 'Dunkelfelder' (O/R) — WSuF

– 'Early Van der Laan' (F) — LHol

– 'Ehrenfelser' (O/W) — WSuF

– 'Elbling' (O/W) — WSuF

¶ – EM 323158B — WSuF

– 'Excelsior' (W) — SDea WSuF

– 'Faber' (O/W) — WSuF

– 'Findling' (W) — WSuF

– 'Forta' (O/W) — WSuF

– 'Foster's Seedling' (G/W) — CBlo ERea GTwe SDea WSuF

– 'Gagarin Blue' (O/B) — CAgr ERea GTwe NPer SDea WSuF

– 'Gamay Hatif' (O/B) — ERea

– 'Gamay Hatif des Vosges' WSuF

– 'Gamay Noir' (O/B) — WSuF

– 'Gamay Teinturier Group' (O/B) — WSuF

– 'Gewürztraminer' (O/R) — MAsh SDea WSuF

– 'Glory of Boskoop' — See *V.* 'Boskoop Glory'

– 'Golden Chasselas' — See *V. vinifera* 'Chasselas'

– 'Golden Queen' (G/W) — ERea

– 'Goldriesling' (O/W) — SDea WSuF

– 'Gros Colmar' (G/B) — ERea

– 'Gros Maroc' (G/B) — ERea

– 'Grüner Veltliner' (O/W) — WSuF

– 'Gutenborner' (O/W) — WSuF

– 'Helfensteiner' (O/R) — WSuF

– 'Huxelrebe' (O/W) — WSuF

– 'Incana' (O/B) — CPlN EPla MRav WCot WCru WPen WSHC

– 'Interlaken' (F) — ERea

– 'Jubiläumsrebe' (O/W) — WSuF

– 'Kanzler' (O/W) — WSuF

– 'Kerner' (O/W) — WSuF

– 'Kernling' (F) — WSuF

– 'King's Ruby' (F) — ERea

– 'Lady Downe's Seedling' (G/B) — ERea

– 'Lady Hastings' (G/B) — ERea

– 'Lady Hutt' (G/W) — ERea

– 'Lucombe' (F) — Last listed 1997

– 'Madeleine Angevine' (O/W) — EBee ERea GTwe MAsh SDea WSuF WWeb

– 'Madeleine Royale' (G/W) ERea WSuF

– 'Madeleine Silvaner' (O/W) EMui ERea GTwe MAsh MGos NPer SDea SPer WSuF

– 'Madresfield Court' (G/B) — ERea GTwe WSuF

– 'Malbec' — See *V. vinifera* 'Cot'

§ – 'Melon de Bourgogne' (O/W) — Last listed 1996

– 'Mireille' (F) — GTwe SDea WSuF

– 'Morio Muscat' (O/W) — WSuF

– 'Mrs Pearson' (G/W) — ERea

– 'Mrs Pince's Black Muscat' (G/B) — ERea

§ – 'Müller-Thurgau' (O/W) — CBlo EBee EMui ERea GTwe MAsh MBri MGos SDea SPer WSuF WWeb

– 'Muscadet' — See *V. vinifera* 'Melon de Bourgogne'

– 'Muscat Blanc à Petits Grains' (O/W) — WSuF

– 'Muscat Bleu' (O/B) — ERea

– 'Muscat Champion' (G/R) ERea

– 'Muscat de Saumur' (O/W) WSuF

- 'Muscat Hamburg' (G/B) EMui ERea MGos NMoo SDea WSuF
- 'Muscat of Alexandria' (G/W) CB&S CMac CRHN CSam EHol EMui ERea MWat SDea SRPl
- 'Muscat of Hungary' (G/W) ERea
- 'Muscat Ottonel' (O/W) WSuF
- 'New York Muscat' (O/B) ERea
- 'No. 69' (W) WSuF
- 'Noir Hatif de Marseilles' (O/B) ERea WSuF
- 'Oliver Irsay' (O/W) ERea WSuF
- 'Optima' (O/W) WSuF
- 'Ortega' (O/W) WSuF
- 'Perle' (O/W) WSuF
- 'Perle de Czaba' (G/O/W) ERea
- 'Perlette' (O/W) WSuF
- 'Pinot Blanc' (O/W) MAsh WSuF
- 'Pinot Gris' (O/B) SDea WSuF
- 'Pinot Noir' (O/B) WSuF
¶ - 'Plavac Mali' (B) WSuF
§ - 'Portugieser' (O/B) WSuF
- 'Précoce de Bousquet' (O/W) WSuF
- 'Précoce de Malingre' (O/W) ERea SDea
- 'Primavis Frontignan' (G/W) WSuF
- 'Prince of Wales' (G/B) ERea
- 'Purpurea' (O/B) ♀ More than 30 suppliers
- 'Reichensteiner' (O/G/W) SDea WSuF
- 'Reine Olga' (O/R) ERea
- 'Rembrant' (R) WSuF
- 'Riesling' (O/W) MAsh WSuF
- Riesling-Silvaner See *V. vinifera* 'Müller-Thurgau'
¶ - 'Rondo' EM 6494-5 (O/B) EMui WSuF
- 'Royal Muscadine' See *V. vinifera* 'Chasselas'
- 'Saint Laurent' (G/O/W) ERea WSuF
- 'Sauvignon Blanc' (O/W) WSuF
- 'Scheurebe' (O/W) WSuF
§ - 'Schiava Grossa' (G/B) CMac CRHN CSam EBee ELan EMui ERea GChr GRei GTwe LBuc LHol MAsh MBlu MBri MGos MWat NBea NPer NRog SPer WSuF
- 'Schönburger' (O/W) SDea WSuF
- Seibel 138315 (R) WSuF
- Seibel 5409 (W) WSuF
- 'Septimer' (O/W) WSuF
- Seyve Villard 20.473 (F) MAsh WSuF
¶ - 'Shiraz' (B) WSuF
- 'Siegerrebe' (O/W) EMui ERea GTwe SDea WSuF WWeb
- 'Silvaner' (O/W) WSuF
- 'Spetchley Red' WCru
- Strawberry Grape See *V.* 'Fragola'
§ - 'Sultana' ERea GTwe SDea WSuF
- 'Syrian' (G/W) ERea
- Teinturier Group (F) ERea
- 'Thompson Seedless' See *V. vinifera* 'Sultana'
- 'Trebbiano' (G/W) ERea
* - 'Triomphe' (O/B) EMui
- 'Wrotham Pinot' (O/B) SDea WSuF
- 'Würzer' (O/W) WSuF
- 'Zweigeltrebe' (O/B) WSuF
* 'White Strawberry' (O/W) WSuF

## VITTADINIA (Asteraceae)
*cuneata* See *V. australis*

## VRIESEA (Bromeliaceae)
*carinata* MBri
*duvaliana* ♀ Last listed 1995

*fosteriana* ♀ Last listed 1990
*hieroglyphica* MBri
x *poelmanii* MBri
x *polonia* MBri
*psittacina* ♀ Last listed 1995
*saundersii* ♀ MBri
*splendens* ♀ MBri
'Vulkana' MBri

## WACHENDORFIA (Haemodoraceae)
*paniculata* Last listed 1997
*thyrsiflora* CFir CTrC IBlr WCot
- Trengwainton Form Last listed 1998

## WAHLENBERGIA (Campanulaceae)
*albomarginata* ECou EHyt EMan GTou NHar NWCA WRHF
- 'Blue Mist' ECou
- white form Last listed 1997
* *albosericea* Last listed 1997
*cartilaginea* Last listed 1997
*ceracea* Last listed 1997
*congesta* LBee WPat WUnu
*gloriosa* CPBP CSpe GCrs LBee MBro SUsu WAbe WFar WPat WPyg WWin
*matthewsii* Last listed 1998
*pumilio* See *Edraianthus pumilio*
*pygmaea* MBro WHoo WUnu
§ *saxicola* CLyd CRow EHyt GTou NWCA SRms SSca WPer
*serpyllifolia* See *Edraianthus serpyllifolius*
*simpsonii* GTou
species ECou
*stricta* Last listed 1997
*tasmanica* See *W. saxicola*
*trichogyna* Last listed 1997
*undulata* CMdw CSpe

## WALDHEIMIA See ALLARDIA

## WALDSTEINIA (Rosaceae)
*fragarioides* EHal NWoo SIng WPer
*geoides* EBee EMan EPPr EPfP NPro SPer WLRN
*ternata* More than 30 suppliers
* - 'Variegata' IBlr SApp

## WALLICHIA (Arecaceae)
*densiflora* LPal
*disticha* LPal

## WASABIA (Brassicaceae)
*japonica* GPoy

## WASHINGTONIA (Arecaceae)
*filifera* ♀ CAbb CBrP CRoM CTbh CTrC LPal MBri SAPC SArc WMul
*robusta* CRoM CTrC LPal WMul

## WATSONIA (Iridaceae)
*aletroides* IDac LLew SIgm
*angusta* IBlr LLew
*ardernei* See *W. borbonica* subsp. *ardernei*
*beatricis* See *W. pillansii*
§ *borbonica* CPin IBlr
§ - subsp. *ardernei* CHan CLAP GCal IBlr SIgm
¶ - subsp. *borbonica* CLAP

| | |
|---|---|
| - pink form | CPou |
| *brevifolia* | See *W. laccata* |
| *bulbillifera* | See *W. merianiae* var. *bulbillifera* |
| *coccinea* Baker | See *W. spectabilis* |
| - Herbert ex Baker | LLew |
| - dwarf form | Last listed 1997 |
| *densiflora* | CB&S CFil CPou LLew WCot |
| *distans* | LLew |
| *fourcadei* | LLew |
| - S&SH 89 | CHan |
| *fulgens* | CHan LLew MSte |
| *galpinii* | CFir IBlr |
| ¶ *gladioloides* | CFil |
| § *humilis* | CFil CHan WPGP |
| *hysterantha* | IBlr |
| 'Indian Orange' | Last listed 1996 |
| § *laccata* | IDac LLew |
| *lepida* | CFil LLew |
| ¶ - JCA 3.192.800 | SSpi |
| *marginata* | CHan CPou EBee GLch LLew |
| | SIgm |
| ¶ *marlothii* | CFil |
| *merianiae* | CFil CHan GCal IBlr LLew WCot |
| * 'Mount Congreve' | Last listed 1998 |
| peach hybrid | Last listed 1996 |
| § *pillansii* | CFil CHan CLAP CPou CTrC IBlr |
| | SBla SIgm SMrm WHil |
| *pyramidata* | See *W. borbonica* |
| *roseoalba* | See *W. humilis* |
| sp. SH 89 | Last listed 1996 |
| § *spectabilis* | Last listed 1997 |
| 'Stanford Scarlet' | CLAP CPou IBlr SBla SChr WPGP |
| | WSHC |
| *stenosiphon* | EBee LLew |
| *tabularis* | CHan IBlr LLew NBur |
| 'Tresco Dwarf Pink' | CLAP CPou GCal WCot |
| *vanderspuyae* | IBlr LLew |
| *versfeldii* | CHan |
| *watsonioides* | Last listed 1998 |
| 'White Dazzler' | Last listed 1997 |
| *wilmaniae* | CFil CPou IBlr |
| ¶ - JCA 3.955.200 | SSpi |
| *wordsworthiana* | Last listed 1997 |

## WATTAKAKA See DREGEA

## WEIGELA ✿ (Caprifoliaceae)

| | |
|---|---|
| 'Abel Carrière' ♀ | CTri ECtt EHic ENot EPfP NFla |
| | SEND SPla WCFE |
| 'Abel Carrière Golden' | Last listed 1996 |
| 'Avalanche' hort. | See *W.* 'Candida' |
| 'Avalanche' Lemoine | See *W. praecox* 'Avalanche' |
| 'Boskoop Glory' | GQui SPer |
| § Briant Rubidor = 'Olympiade' | CDoC EBee ECtt EHoe ENot GRei |
| | IOrc MAsh MBNS MBal MBar |
| | MBel MBri MGos MRav MWhi |
| | NFla NFor SEND SEas SPer WBay |
| | WBod WHCG WStI WWeb |
| 'Bristol Ruby' | CChe CDul CHar EBee ELan ENot |
| | EWTr GChr GRei LHop MBar |
| | MGos MPla MWhi NBee NFor |
| | NLon NRoo NWea SLon SPer |
| | SRms WDin WFar WGwG WMow |
| | WWal WWin |
| § 'Candida' | CTri EAst ELan EWes GEil GSki |
| | MBar MBel MBri NHol SEas SMac |
| | SPer SPla WGor |
| Carnaval = 'Courtalor' | CBlo COtt EBee EHic GAri LPan |
| | MBri WLRN |
| 'Centennial' | MGos |
| ¶ 'Conquête' | GEil |
| *coraeensis* | EHic MBlu |
| ¶ - 'Alba' | GEil |
| ¶ 'Davnik' | MTPN |
| *decora* | CPle GQui |
| 'Duet' | Last listed 1996 |
| 'Eva Rathke' | CBlo CTri EPla ISea NWea SCoo |
| | WRHF |
| * 'Eva Supreme' | EHic |
| 'Evita' | EHic IOrc MBar MGos MPla SEas |
| | SPer |
| ¶ Feline = 'Courtamon' | SPer |
| 'Fiesta' ♀ | Last listed 1995 |
| *florida* | CTrw EPfP MBar MWat SMer |
| - f. *alba* | CB&S MBar |
| § - 'Aureovariegata' | CMHG CTri GQui ISea MBal MRav |
| | SPla SRms |
| - 'Bicolor' | CB&S SPan |
| - 'Bristol Snowflake' | CSWP EHic EPfP MAsh |
| | MBNS MBar MGos WLRN |
| - 'Foliis Purpureis' ♀ | More than 30 suppliers |
| - 'Java Red' | MBri NOla |
| - 'Magee' | Last listed 1996 |
| - 'Pink Princess' | Last listed 1996 |
| - Rubigold | See *W.* Briant Rubidor = |
| | 'Olympiade' |
| - 'Samabor' | WFar |
| - 'Sunny Princess' | NHol |
| - 'Suzanne' (v) | CB&S MBri MGos NPro WWeb |
| - 'Tango' | CPMA ECtt MAsh MBri NPro |
| | WBcn |
| 'Florida Variegata' ♀ | More than 30 suppliers |
| * *florida* 'Variegata Aurea' | See *W. florida* 'Aureovariegata' |
| - 'Versicolor' | CCHP CMHG GQui LHop MBel |
| | SLon |
| 'Gold Rush' | CBlo |
| 'Gustave Malet' | GQui |
| *hortensis* 'Nivea' | CPle MBri NPro |
| *japonica* | Last listed 1998 |
| - Dart's Colourdream | EBee ECtt EHal EHic EPla EWes |
| | GOrc IOrc MBel MCCP MGos |
| | MRav SCoo SEas SLPl SMac |
| 'Jean's Gold' | MGos MRav NPri SBod |
| 'Kosteriana Variegata' | CBlo EHic NHol NRoo WFar |
| | WLRN |
| 'Looymansii Aurea' | CMHG CPle CTri EAst ELan GEil |
| | LHop MPla MRav SEas SMac SPer |
| | SPla WAbe WBod WDin WGwG |
| | WHCG WHar WWal WWat WWin |
| ¶ Lucifer = 'Courtared' | CDoC MBel NHol WLRN |
| 'Marjorie' | IMGH WLRN |
| *maximowiczii* | CPle GOrc GQui GSki WHCG |
| | WLRN |
| § *middendorffiana* | More than 30 suppliers |
| 'Minuet' | CBlo EHic GSki MBar MGos MRav |
| | NPro SBid SEas SPla WPat |
| 'Mont Blanc' ♀ | CBot CDul MMHG SEND |
| ¶ Nain Rouge = 'Courtanin' | CBlo NHol WLRN |
| 'Nana Variegata' | EHal GChr MBar MBri NBee NHol |
| 'Newport Red' | CBlo EBee EHic ENot MBNS MRav |
| | MWat NBee NWea SMer WGwG |
| | WLRN WStI WWal |
| ♦ 'Olympiade' (v) | See *W.* Briant Rubidor = |
| | 'Olympiade' |
| § *praecox* 'Avalanche' | ECtt MRav WStI |
| - 'Espérance' | EPla |
| 'Praecox Variegata' ♀ | CChe CTri ELan EPfP MBri MRav |
| | SMac SPer SPla SRPl SReu SRms |
| | SSta WCru WHCG WSHC WWat |
| 'Red Prince' | CBlo EBee ELan MAsh MBri MGos |
| | SEas SLon |
| * 'Rosabella' | Last listed 1998 |
| Rubidor | See *W.* Briant Rubidor = |
| | 'Olympiade' |

| | |
|---|---|
| Rubidor Variegata | See *W.* Briant Rubidor = 'Olympiade' |
| Rubigold | See *W.* Briant Rubidor = 'Olympiade' |
| ¶ 'Ruby Queen' | CDoC |
| 'Rumba' | EHic EMil GSki MMHG MRav NPro NRoo |
| ¶ 'Samba' | MBri |
| 'Snowflake' | EBee ECtt EPla MPla NLon NPro SEas SRms WDin |
| sp. CC 1279 | Last listed 1998 |
| § *subsessilis* B&SWJ 1056 | WCru |
| – CC 1289 | Last listed 1998 |
| 'Victoria' | CBlo CDoC CLTr CMHG CSWP EBrP EBre ECtt ELan LBre MAsh MBel MBri NRoo SBre SCoo SPer WGor WHar WLRN WWeb |
| * 'Wessex Gold' | CFai WHCG |

## WEINMANNIA (Cunoniaceae)

| | |
|---|---|
| *trichosperma* | CGre IBlr ISea SAPC SArc |

## WELDENIA (Commelinaceae)

| | |
|---|---|
| *candida* | NHar SIng WAbe |

## WERNERIA (Asteraceae)

| | |
|---|---|
| ¶ *crassifolia* | WCot |

## WESTRINGIA (Lamiaceae)

| | |
|---|---|
| *angustifolia* | ECou |
| *brevifolia* | ECou |
| – Raleighii Group | ECou |
| § *fruticosa* ♀ | CB&S CInt CPle LHil SBid SPan WJek |
| – 'Variegata' | CPle GQui SBid WJek WLRN WSHC |
| – 'Wynyabbie Gem' | EMan LHop |
| *longifolia* | Last listed 1997 |
| * *rigida* 'Variegata' | WCot |
| *rosmariniformis* | See *W. fruticosa* |

## WETTINIA (Arecaceae)

| | |
|---|---|
| *kalbreyeri* | LPal |
| *maynensis* | LPal |
| *quinaria* | LPal |

## WIDDRINGTONIA (Cupressaceae)

| | |
|---|---|
| *cedarbergensis* | IBlr |
| *cupressoides* | See *W. nodiflora* |
| § *nodiflora* | IBlr MBri |
| *schwarzii* | CTrC |
| *whytei* | See *W. nodiflora* |

## WIGANDIA (Hydrophyllaceae)

| | |
|---|---|
| *urens* | Last listed 1998 |

## WIKSTROEMIA (Thymelaeaceae)

| | |
|---|---|
| ¶ *gemmata* | SSta |
| *nutans* B&SWJ 4081 | WCru |

## WISTERIA ✿ (Papilionaceae)

| | |
|---|---|
| § *brachybotrys* | CEnd |
| ¶ – 'Okayama' | LNet |
| § – 'Shiro-kabitan' | CB&S CEnd CPMA CTri ELan ENot EPfP LNet MAsh MBri MGos MMea MRav NHol SBra SLon SMad SPer WWat |
| ¶ – 'Violacea Plena' | LRHS |
| * – 'White Silk' | CEnd CPMA |
| * 'Captain Fuji' | CMCN |

| | |
|---|---|
| 'Caroline' | CB&S CDoC CEnd CMCN CPMA CSam EBee ERea GChr GOrc LNet MGos MMea MRav NBea SPer SReu SSpi SSta |
| *floribunda* | CB&S CRHN ELan LPan MAsh SBra WDin WNor |
| § – 'Alba' ♀ | CB&S CBot CDoC CEnd CPMA EBee ELan GChr LNet LPan MAsh MRav NBea NEgg NHol NSti SBra SPer SPla SSpi SSta WDin WStI |
| ¶ – 'Blue Pacific' | LNet |
| ¶ – 'Blue Sapphire' | WBod |
| – 'Burford' | CBlo CEnd CTri EBee LNet MAsh MBri MMea MWat NBea NHol WHar WWeb |
| ¶ – 'Cascade' | CTrC |
| – 'Fragrantissima' | CBlo |
| * – 'Harlequin' | CB&S EBee LNet LRHS MGos MRav |
| – 'Hichirimen' | EBee LNet MMea |
| – 'Honbeni' | See *W. floribunda* 'Rosea' |
| – 'Honko' | See *W. floribunda* 'Rosea' |
| – Jakohn-fuji | See *W. floribunda* 'Reindeer' |
| § – 'Kuchi-beni' | CB&S CPMA CTrC EBee ELan EPfP LNet MGos MMea MRav SBra SPer WBod WWeb |
| * – 'Lavender Lace' | CPMA EPfP LNet MRav WBod |
| ¶ – 'Lawrence' | LNet MGos |
| – 'Lipstick' | See *W. floribunda* 'Kuchi-beni' |
| – 'Longissima Alba' | EBee LPan MBar MGos NMoo |
| – 'Macrobotrys' | See *W. floribunda* 'Multijuga' |
| ¶ – 'Magenta' | LNet |
| § – 'Multijuga' ♀ | CEnd CPMA EBee ELan GOrc IOrc LNet LPan MAsh MBri MGos MMea MRav MWat NBea NHol SBra SLon SMad SPer SPla SRPl SSoC SSpi SSta WSHC WWat WWeb |
| – Murasaki-naga | See *W. floribunda* 'Purple Patches' |
| – 'Murasaki-noda' | MGos |
| – 'Nana Richin's Purple' | CEnd LNet |
| – 'Peaches and Cream' | See *W. floribunda* 'Kuchi-beni' |
| – 'Pink Ice' | See *W. floribunda* 'Rosea' |
| § – 'Purple Patches' | CPMA ELan LNet MGos MMea MWat NPri WWeb |
| * – 'Purple Tassle' | LNet |
| § – 'Reindeer' | CEnd NHol SBra WWeb |
| § – 'Rosea' ♀ | CB&S CEnd CMac CPMA EBee ELan ENot EPfP IOrc LNet MAsh MBar MBri MGos MMea MWat NBea NHol SBra SPer WFar WStI WWat WWeb |
| – 'Royal Purple' | CBlo ERea LNet MMea WGor |
| – Shiro-nagi | See *W. floribunda* 'Snow Showers' |
| ¶ – × *sinensis* 'Burford' | EMui |
| § – 'Snow Showers' | CB&S CHad CPMA ELan EPfP LNet MBri MGos MMea NPri SPer SPla WBod WGer WGor WWeb |
| * – 'Variegata' | CPMA |
| – 'Violacea Plena' (d) | CBlo CDoC EBee LNet LPan MBri MGos MMea NPal SLon SPar SPla |
| × *formosa* | CPMA ETen LNet WFro WWat |
| – Black Dragon | See *W.* × *formosa* 'Kokuryû' |
| – Domino | See *W.* × *formosa* 'Issai' |
| § – 'Issai' | CB&S CBlo CEnd CPMA EBee LNet MAsh MBar MGos MMea MRav NBea NEgg NHol NSti SBra SPer SSta WWat WWeb |

§ - 'Kokuryû' (d) | CB&S CEnd CPMA EBee ELan EPfP GChr IOrc LNet LPan MAsh MGos MMea NHol SBra SMad SPer SPla SReu SSpi SSta WGor WPyg WWat WWeb
*frutescens* | WNor WShe
¶ - 'Magnifica' | LNet
- 'Nivea' | CMCN LNet
♦ 'Kofuji' | See *Millettia japonica*
¶ *macrostachya* | LNet
'Bayou Two O'clock'
¶ - 'Clara Mack' | LNet
¶ - 'Pondside Blue' | LNet
*multijuga* 'Alba' | See *W. floribunda* 'Alba'
'Showa-beni' | CEnd LNet
*sinensis* ♀ | CB&S CMac EBee EBrP EBre ELan ENot GChr GRei ISea LBre LNet LPan MBal MBar MGos MMea MPla MWat NFla SBra SBre SPer SRms SSta WBod WDin WFar WGwG WNor
§ - 'Alba' ♀ | CB&S CBlo CDoC EBee ELan ENot EPfP IOrc ISea LBuc LNet LPan MBar MMea MWat SSto WDin WFar
- 'Amethyst' | CPMA EBee EPfP ERea MGos SBra SLon SPla
- 'Blue Sapphire' | CDoC CPMA
¶ - 'Cookes Special' | LNet
* - 'Imp' | Last listed 1997
¶ - 'Jake' | LNet
¶ - 'Larry's White' | LNet
- 'Plena' (d) | CPMA
- 'Prematura' | MAsh NHol SSto WSHC
- 'Prematura Alba' | Last listed 1996
- 'Prolific' | CB&S CPMA CPIN EBee ELan EPfP LBuc LPan MBri MGos MMea SBra SPer SSpi SSto WPat
* - 'Rosea' | LPan
- Shiro-capital | See *W. sinensis* 'Alba'
♦ *venusta* | See *W. brachybotrys* 'Shiro-kabitan'
♦ - var. *violacea* | See *W. brachybotrys*
¶ *villosa* | WNor

**WITHANIA** (Solanaceae)
*somnifera* | CArn GPoy

**WITTSTEINIA** (Alseuosmiaceae)
*vacciniacea* | WCru

**WODYETIA** (Arecaceae)
*bifurcata* | LPal

**WOODSIA** (Woodsiaceae)
*fragilis* | Last listed 1998
*ilvensis* | Last listed 1996
*intermedia* | NBro
*obtusa* | CLAP EBee GBin GMaP NHar NHol WRic
*polystichoides* ♀ | GQui NHar

**WOODWARDIA** ✿ (Blechnaceae)
*fimbriata* | NHol
*martinezii* | CFil
¶ *orientalis* | WPic
- var. *formosana* | NMar
*radicans* ♀ | CAbb CFil CGre GQui ISea LBlm NMar SAPC SArc SMad WAbe WPic
sp. from Emei Shan, China | Last listed 1996
*unigemmata* | NWoo SSpi WAbe WHal

**WULFENIA** (Scrophulariaceae)
*carinthiaca* | CNic GAbr MOne NBir NMen SLod SRob WMoo

**WYETHIA** (Asteraceae)
*helianthoides* | EMan

# X

**XANTHOCERAS** (Sapindaceae)
*sorbifolium* ♀ | CAbb CAgr CB&S CBlo CBot CFil CLnd CMCN EBee ELan LEdu MBel MRav MTis MWhi SBid SIgm SMad SSpi WCoo WDin WLRN WNor WPGP WWat

**XANTHOPHTHALMUM** (Asteraceae)
*coronarium* | CArn EEls WJek
§ *segetum* | EWFC MHew MMal WHer

**XANTHORHIZA** (Ranunculaceae)
*simplicissima* | CB&S CFil CRow EPfP GCal SDys SSpi WThi WWat

**XANTHORRHOEA** (Xanthorrhoeaceae)
*australis* | CPLG CTrC SRCN WGer
¶ *johnsonii* | NRog
*preisii* | LPan

**XANTHOSOMA** (Araceae)
*lindenii* | See *Caladium lindenii*
*sagittifolium* | Last listed 1998
*violaceum* | LHil WMul

**XERODRABA** (Brassicaceae)
*mendocinensis* | Last listed 1998

**XERONEMA** (Phormiaceae)
*callistemon* | ECou

**XEROPHYLLUM** (Melanthiaceae)
¶ *tenax* | SSpi

**XYLORHIZA** See MACHAERANTHERA

**XYLOSMA** (Flacourtiaceae)
*quichensis* | CPle

**XYSMALOBIUM** (Asclepiadaceae)
¶ *stockenstroemense* | EBee

# Y

**YPSILANDRA** (Melanthiaceae)
*thibetica* | WCru

**YUCCA** ✿ (Agavaceae)
*aloifolia* | CTrC LEdu SAPC SArc SIgm
- 'Variegata' | LPal LPan SAPC SArc
*angustifolia* | See *Y. glauca*
*angustissima* | Last listed 1998
- var. *toftiae* JCA 1993500 | EMon
*arizonica* | CTbh
*baccata* | CTbh EOas
*brevifolia* | CBrP CRoM SRCN

| | |
|---|---|
| *carnerosana* | CTbh |
| ¶ *desmetiana* | CHan |
| *elata* | CTbh EOas |
| § *elephantipes* ♀ | MBri |
| *faxoniana* | Last listed 1998 |
| - x *glauca* | Last listed 1998 |
| *filamentosa* ♀ | More than 30 suppliers |
| - 'Bright Edge' (v) ♀ | CB&S CDoC CMHG CTrC EBee |
| | EBrP EBre ECtt ELan ENot EPla |
| | GChr IOrc LBre LEdu LPan MAsh |
| | MBri MGos MTis MUlv MWat SBre |
| | SPer WAbe WCot WWin |
| - 'Variegata' ♀ | CB&S CBlo CBot ELan ENot IOrc |
| | LHop MBal MGos SAga SPer SRms |
| | WDin WFar WGer |
| *flaccida* | MAsh MCAu NBee NFla SDix |
| | SEND SPar WShe |
| - 'Golden Sword' (v) ♀ | CAbb CDoC CMHG CTrC EBrP |
| | EBre ELan GChr IOrc LBre LHop |
| | LPio MAsh MBal MBri MSCN |
| | NCut NMoo NPSI SBre SCoo SPer |
| | SPla WAbe WBay WCot |
| - 'Ivory' ♀ | More than 30 suppliers |
| x *floribunda* | SAPC SArc |
| 'Garland's Gold' (v) | CB&S CDoC ELan GQui LEdu |
| | MAsh MBri MGos WBod WMul |
| § *glauca* | CB&S CBrP CMHG CTbh CTrC |
| | EHic GCal MBri NCut SAPC SArc |
| *gloriosa* ♀ | CB&S CDoC ENot EOas EPla |
| | EWTr LNet LPan NFla NPal SAPC |
| | SArc SMad SPer SSpi WBrE WStI |
| - 'Aureovariegata' | See *Y. gloriosa* 'Variegata' |
| - 'Nobilis' | SDix |
| - 'Tricolor' | Last listed 1997 |
| § - 'Variegata' ♀ | CBlo CBot CDoC EBrP EBre ELan |
| | ENot EOas LBre LEdu MRav |
| | NMoo NPal SAPC SArc SBre SCro |
| | SDry SEas SRms SSto WCot WFar |
| | WMul WPat WWeb |
| *guatemalensis* | See *Y. elephantipes* |
| *harrimaniae* | CGra CTbh IDac SIgm |
| ¶ - var. *neomexicana* | CTbh |
| *kanabensis* | CTbh |
| *navajoa* | Last listed 1997 |
| *recurvifolia* ♀ | MBal SAPC SArc |
| - 'Variegata' | Last listed 1996 |
| *rigida* | CBrP |
| *rostrata* | CAbb CBrP SAPC SArc |
| *schidigera* | CTbh GCal |
| *schottii* | CAbb CBrP CTbh EOas |
| *thompsoniana* | Last listed 1998 |
| * *torcelli* | CTbh |
| *torreyi* | CTbh CTrC |
| *valida* | Last listed 1997 |
| 'Vittorio Emanuele II' | Last listed 1998 |
| *whipplei* | CAbb CB&S CBot CBrP CDoC |
| | CFil CTrC EOas LEdu SAPC SArc |
| | SRCN SSpi |
| - subsp. *cespitosa* | Last listed 1996 |
| - - JCA 1993600 | EMon |
| - subsp. *parishii* | SIgm |

## YUSHANIA (Poaceae - Bambusoideae)

| | |
|---|---|
| § *anceps* ♀ | CDoC CFil CHad EFul EPla GAri |
| | IOrc ISta LJus MBri MDun MGos |
| | MMoz MUlv MWht NBee SAPC |
| | SArc SDry SPer SPla WBay WCru |
| | WPGP |
| § - 'Pitt White' | CFil EPla SDry WJun |
| *chungii* | CFil EPla WPGP |
| *maculata* | EPla ISta LJus SDry WJun |
| § *maling* | EPla ISta SDry WJun |

# Z

## ZALUZIANSKYA (Scrophulariaceae)

| | |
|---|---|
| ¶ *capensis* | EWTr |
| 'Katherine' | MTPN SIng SRot WPen |
| *ovata* | CPBP EBee EHyt EPot EWes LHop |
| | LPio LSpr MAvo MTho NBir |
| | NWCA SAga SBla SUsu WAbe |
| | WOve WPat |
| * cf. *rostrata* DBG 219 | NTow |
| ¶ sp. from Lesotho | GCal |
| sp. JCA 15665 | EHyt WAbe |
| sp. JCA 15758 | Last listed 1998 |
| ¶ sp. PK 66 from USA | SSpi |

## ZAMIA (Zamiaceae)

| | |
|---|---|
| *floridana* | LPal |
| *furfuracea* | CBrP LPal |
| *muricata* | LPal |
| ¶ *pumila* | CBrP |
| *skinneri* | LPal |
| ¶ *standleyi* | CBrP |
| *vazquezii* | CBrP |

## ZANTEDESCHIA (Araceae)

| | |
|---|---|
| § *aethiopica* ♀ | CBen CTbh CTrC CWat EHon |
| | EOas EWes LAma LCns LPBA |
| | MNrw MSta NDea NOrc NRog |
| | SDix SSoC SSpi SWat WBrE WEas |
| | WFar WMul WPic WWal |
| - 'Apple Court Babe' | CRow SApp |
| - 'Childsiana' | Last listed 1998 |
| - 'Crowborough' ♀ | More than 30 suppliers |
| - 'Gigantea' | Last listed 1998 |
| - 'Green Goddess' ♀ | CB&S CBro CFir CHan CHid |
| | CMHG COtt CRow CTrC EBee |
| | ECha EGar ELan EMFW GQui |
| | LPBA MHlr NPSI SDeJ SLon SPar |
| | SRms SSoC SUsu WCot WFar |
| | WFib WWat |
| - 'Little Gem' | ECha LPio |
| * - 'Pershore Fantasia' | MAvo WSPU |
| - pink | Last listed 1997 |
| - 'Snow White' | Last listed 1998 |
| - 'White Sail' | CLAP CRow GCal GNau MTed |
| | WFib |
| *albomaculata* | CTrC EBee LAma NPSI NRog |
| - S&SH 35 | CHan |
| 'Apricot' | WViv |
| 'Best Gold' | LAma NRog |
| 'Black Eyed Beauty' | LAma NRog WWeb |
| 'Black Magic' | LAma WViv WWeb |
| 'Bridal Blush' | LAma |
| 'Cameo' | CSut LAma WViv |
| *elliottiana* ♀ | CFir CHal CSut EOas GQui LAma |
| | NRog WPnn WViv |
| 'Galaxy' | WViv |
| 'Harvest Moon' | CWit LAma |
| 'Helen O'Connor' | Last listed 1998 |
| 'Kiwi Blush' | CAbP CB&S CFir CLAP CMil |
| | CRow EBee ELan EWll MBri NPSI |
| | SEND SMad SPla SSpi SUsu SVil |
| | WCot WFar WSan |
| 'Lavender Petite' | LAma NRog |
| ¶ 'Lime Lady' | ECha |
| * 'Little Suzy' | WViv |
| 'Majestic Red' | WWeb |
| 'Mango' | Last listed 1998 |
| 'Maroon Dainty' | LAma NRog |
| ¶ 'Moonglow' | WViv |

| | |
|---|---|
| 'Pacific Pink' | LAma |
| *pentlandii* | See *Z. angustiloba* |
| 'Pink Persuasion' | WWeb |
| *rehmannii* ♀ | CB&S GQui LAma MCCP SRms |
| | WHil WViv |
| – 'Alba' | Last listed 1998 |
| ¶ – 'Little Dream' | WViv |
| – 'Superba' | Last listed 1998 |
| * 'Romeo' | Last listed 1998 |
| 'Ruby' | WWeb |
| 'Shell Pink' | LAma NRog |
| 'Solfatare' | LAma WHil |
| * 'Sweet Suzie' | Last listed 1998 |
| 'Treasure' | WWeb |

## ZANTHORHIZA See XANTHORHIZA

## ZANTHOXYLUM (Rutaceae)

| | |
|---|---|
| ¶ *ailanthoides* | CFil |
| ¶ – from Japan | WPGP |
| *americanum* | CFil CLnd WPGP |
| *armatum* | CFil WPGP |
| *coreanum* | CFil WPGP |
| *oxyphyllum* | CFil EPla WPGP |
| *piperitum* | CAgr CFil LEdu WWat |
| *planispinum* | MRav |
| ¶ *schinifolium* | CAgr CB&S LEdu |
| ¶ – B&SWJ 1245 | WCru |
| *simulans* | CB&S |

## ZAUSCHNERIA (Onagraceae)

| | |
|---|---|
| *arizonica* | See *Z. californica* subsp. *latifolia* |
| § *californica* | CBar CGen CMHG EBee GQui |
| | MCCP NDov SLon SYvo |
| – 'Albiflora' | EPot |
| § – subsp. *cana* | CLTr CSam ECGP ECha ELan IOrc |
| | MHar MPla NSla SAga SChu SIgm |
| | WCru WEas |
| – – 'Sir Cedric Morris' | ELan WWat |
| – 'Clover Dale' | EWes LGre |
| § – 'Dublin' ♀ | ECha ELan EPot ERea LHop MBel |
| | MBro MHar MPla MRav MSCN |
| | MWat SBla SChu SHFr SIng SRot |
| | SUsu WAbe WCot WEas WHer |
| | WHil WHoo WOld WPat WSHC |
| | WWin |
| – *etteri* | Last listed 1996 |
| § – subsp. *garrettii* | LHop NWCA SDys |
| – 'Glasnevin' | See *Z. californica* 'Dublin' |
| § – subsp. *latifolia* | LHop MBro NMen NWCA SAga |
| | SIgm WHoo |
| – – RMRF 93-0443 | Last listed 1996 |
| ¶ – – 'Sally Walker' | EWes |
| § – subsp. *mexicana* | CLyd EPot IDac NCat SRms WAbe |
| – 'Olbrich Silver' | EBee ECha EWes LGre LHop |
| | MSCN NWCA SDys SUsu WAbe |
| | WCot WCru WHil WKif WPat |
| | WWin |
| – 'Sierra Salmon' | LGre SDys |
| – 'Solidarity Pink' | CLTr MTho SAga SUsu WKif WPat |
| – 'Western Hills' | CFir EBee LGre LHop MRav |
| | NWCA SAga SBla SIgm SIng SUsu |
| | WAbe WPGP |
| *cana* subsp. *garrettii* | SIgm |
| – *villosa* | See *Z. californica* subsp. |
| | *mexicana* |
| * *septentrionalis* | SBla SIgm |

## ZEBRINA See TRADESCANTIA

## ZELKOVA ✿ (Ulmaceae)

| | |
|---|---|
| *abelicea* | Last listed 1998 |

| | |
|---|---|
| *carpinifolia* | CDul CLnd CMCN CTho LRHS |
| | MAsh WNor WWoo |
| *hyrcana* | SBir |
| *schneideriana* | CMCN WWoo |
| *serrata* ♀ | CB&S CBlo CDul CLnd CMCN |
| | CTho ECrN ELan EMil GChr IOrc |
| | MBal MBar MBel NBea NPal NWea |
| | SBir SPer SRPl SSpi STre WDin |
| | WFro WMou WNor WWat |
| – 'Goblin' | CPMA EPla MBro NHol SSta WPat |
| ¶ – 'Green Vase' | LPan |
| – 'Nira' | WWes |
| – 'Variegata' | CB&S CPMA MBlu MGos SSta |
| | WBcn |
| – 'Yatsubusa' | STre |
| – 'Yrban Ruby' | MGos SSta |
| *sinica* | CB&S CLnd CMCN GAri SSpi STre |
| | WNor |
| x *verschaffeltii* | GAri |

## ZENOBIA (Ericaceae)

| | |
|---|---|
| *pulverulenta* | More than 30 suppliers |
| – f. *nitida* | SSta |

## ZEPHYRANTHES (Amaryllidaceae)

| | |
|---|---|
| *atamasca* | Last listed 1997 |
| *candida* | CAvo CBro EBee EMan EMon |
| | ERea ERos ITim LAma LHop |
| | NMen NRog SApp SDeJ SDix |
| | WCot |
| 'Capricorn' | Last listed 1997 |
| *chlorosolen* | Last listed 1997 |
| *citrina* | ERos LAma NMen NRog |
| *drummondii* | Last listed 1998 |
| *flavissima* | CBro WCot |
| *grandiflora* | Last listed 1997 |
| 'Grandjax' | Last listed 1997 |
| 'La Buffa Rose' | Last listed 1997 |
| x *lancasterae* | Last listed 1998 |
| *macrosiphon* | Last listed 1997 |
| *morrisclintii* | Last listed 1997 |
| 'Panama Pink' | Last listed 1996 |
| 'Prairie Sunset' | Last listed 1997 |
| *primulina* | Last listed 1997 |
| *puertoricensis* | Last listed 1997 |
| *pulchella* | Last listed 1997 |
| *reginae* | Last listed 1997 |
| *robusta* | See *Habranthus robustus* |
| *rosea* | LAma |
| *smallii* | Last listed 1997 |
| *sulphurea* | LAma |
| *traubii* | Last listed 1996 |
| ¶ *verecunda* | SIng |

## ZIGADENUS (Melanthiaceae)

| | |
|---|---|
| *elegans* | CElw EBee EBla EBrP EBre ECha |
| | EHyt EMan EPar GCrs LBre LGre |
| | MBro NDov NHol NWCA SBre |
| | SSpi WCot WPyg WWin |
| *fremontii* | EBee WLin |
| ¶ *glaberrimus* | SSpi |
| *nuttallii* | CLyd EBee EMan ERos LBee LGre |
| | MSte NHol WCot |
| *venenosus* | CHan EBee |

## ZINGIBER (Zingiberaceae)

| | |
|---|---|
| ¶ *mioga* | GPoy |
| *officinale* | GPoy MSal NHex |
| ¶ *zerumbet* | GPoy |

## ZIZANIA (Poaceae)

| | |
|---|---|
| *aquatica* | Last listed 1997 |

| | |
|---|---|
| *caducifolia* | See *Z. latifolia* |
| § *latifolia* | MSta |

## ZIZIA (Apiaceae)

| | |
|---|---|
| *aptera* | Last listed 1996 |
| *aurea* | EBee |

## ZIZIPHUS (Rhamnaceae)

| | |
|---|---|
| § *jujuba* (F) | CAgr LEdu LPan |
| – 'Lang' (F) | CB&S LHol |
| – 'Li' (F) | LHol |
| *sativa* | See *Z. jujuba* |

# SUPPLEMENTARY KEYS TO THE DIRECTORY

## NOMENCLATURE NOTES

These notes refer to plants in the main Plant Directory that are marked with a 'N'. 'Bean Supplement' refers to W.J. Bean *Trees & Shrubs Hardy in the British Isles* (Supplement to the 8th edition) edited by D L Clarke 1988.

*Acer palmatum* var. *coreanum*
This includes but is not synonymous with the plant sold by Hilliers as *A. palmatum* 'Koreanum', that is to be named *A. palmatum* 'Korean Gem'.

*Acer palmatum* 'Sango-kaku' / 'Senkaki'
Two or more clones are offered under these names. *A. palmatum* 'Eddisbury' is similar with brighter coral stems.

*Acer pseudoplatanus* 'Leopoldii'
True 'Leopoldii' has leaves stained with yellowish pink and purple. Plants are often *A. pseudoplatanus* f. *variegatum*.

*Acer pseudoplatanus* 'Spaethii'
Has large leaves with light yellow specks.

*Aconitum autumnale*
A synonym of *A. napellus* and *A. carmichaelii* Wilsonii Group.

*Achillea ptarmica* The Pearl Group / *A. ptarmica* (The Pearl Group) 'The Pearl'
In the current trial of achilleas at Wisley, only one of the several stocks submitted as 'The Pearl' matched the original appearance of this plant according to Graham Stuart Thomas, this being from Wisley's own stock. At rather less than 60cm/2ft this needed little support, being the shortest of the plants bearing this name, with slightly grey, not glossy dark green, leaves and a non-invasive habit. Only this clone should bear the cultivar name 'The Pearl'. The Pearl Group covers all other double-flowered clones of this species, including seed-raised plants which are markedly inferior, sometimes scarcely double, often invasive and usually needing careful staking. It has been claimed that 'The Pearl' was a renaming of Lemoine's 'Boule de Neige' but not all authorities agree: plants of 'Boule de Neige' in the

Wisley trial are not the same clone as Wisley's 'The Pearl'.

*Acorus gramineus* 'Oborozuki' & 'Ogon'
Although these seem to be the same clone in British gardens, 'Oborozuki' is a distinct brighter yellow cultivar in the USA.

*Alchemilla alpina*
The true species is very rare in cultivation. Plants under this name are usually *A. plicatula* or *A. conjuncta*.

*Alchemilla splendens*
The true species is probably not in cultivation in the British Isles.

*Alopecurus pratensis* 'Aureus'
Name applies only to plants with all gold leaves, not to green and gold striped forms.

*Anemone magellanica*
According to *European Garden Flora*, this is a form of the very variable *A. multifida*.

*Anemone nemorosa* 'Alba Plena'
This name is used for several double white forms including *A. nemorosa* 'Flore Pleno' and *A. nemorosa* 'Vestal'.

*Anthemis* 'Grallagh Gold'
The true cultivar of this name has golden yellow flowers. Plants with orange yellow flowers are *A.* 'Beauty of Grallagh'.

*Aquilegia vulgaris* Vervaeneana Group
This covers all *Aquilegia vulgaris* variants with green leaves splashed with gold. Plants sold as 'Woodside' have no characteristic that distinguishes them from this Group.

*Artemisia* 'Faith Raven' & 'Powis Castle'
Most plants labelled 'Faith Raven' are identical with 'Powis Castle'.

*Artemisia granatensis* hort.
Possibly a variant of *A. absinthium*.

*Artemisia ludoviciana* 'Silver Queen'
Two cultivars are grown under this name, one with cut leaves, the other with entire leaves.

*Artemisia ludoviciana* var. *latiloba* / *A. ludoviciana* 'Valerie Finnis'
Leaves of the former are glabrous at maturity, those of the latter are not.

*Artemisia stelleriana* 'Boughton Silver'
This was thought to be the first validly published name for this plant, 'Silver Brocade' having been published earlier but invalidly in an undated publication. However, an earlier valid publication for the cultivar name 'Mori' has subsequently been found for the same plant. A proposal to conserve 'Boughton Silver' has been tabled because of its more widespread use.

*Arum pictum*
This is commonly confused with *A. italicum* subsp. *italicum* 'Marmoratum' (syn. *A. italicum* 'Pictum') but is a distinct species flowering in autumn.

*Aster amellus* Violet Queen
It is probable that more than one cultivar is sold under this name.

*Aster dumosus*
Many of the asters listed under *A. novi-belgii* contain varying amounts of *A. dumosus* blood in their parentage. It is not possible to allocate these to one species or the other and they are therefore listed under *A. novi-belgii*.

*Aster* × *frikartii* 'Mönch'
The true plant is very rare in British gardens. Most plants are another form of *A.* × *frikartii*, usually 'Wunder von Stäfa'.

*Aster novi-belgii*
See note under *A. dumosus*. *A. laevis* is also involved in the parentage of most cultivars.

*Azara paraguayensis*
This is an unpublished name for what seems to be a hybrid between *A. serrata* and *A. lanceolata*.

*Berberis aristata*
Plants so named may be either *B. chitria* or *B. floribunda*.

*Berberis buxifolia* 'Nana' / 'Pygmaea'
See explanation in Bean Supplement.

*Berberis* × *ottawensis* f. *purpurea* / 'Superba'
'Superba' is a clonal selection from f. *purpurea*.

*Berberis* × *ottawensis* 'Superba'
See note in Bean Supplement, p.109.

*Berberis stenophylla* 'Lemon Queen'
This sport from 'Pink Pearl' was first named in 1982. The same mutation occurred again and was named 'Cream Showers'. The older name has priority.

*Bergenia* Ballawley hybrids
The name 'Ballawley' refers only to plants vegetatively propagated from the original clone. Seed-raised plants, which may differ considerably, should be called Ballawley hybrids.

*Betula pendula* 'Dalecarlica'
The true plant of this name is rare in cultivation in the British Isles and is probably not available from nurseries.

*Betula utilis* var. *jacquemontii*
Plants are often the clones *B. utilis* var. *jacquemontii* 'Inverleith' or *B. utilis* var. *jacquemontii* 'Doorenbos'

*Blechnum tabulare*
The true species has an AGM and is grown in Britain but is probably not presently available. This name is often misapplied to *B. chilense*.

*Brachyscome*
Originally published as *Brachyscome* by Cassini who later revised his spelling to *Brachycome*. The original spelling has been internationally adopted.

*Brachyglottis greyi* and *laxifolia*
Both these species are extremely rare in cultivation, plants under these names usually being *B.* 'Sunshine'.

*Buddleja davidii* Petite Indigo™, Petite Plum™, 'Nanho Blue', 'Nanho Purple'
These cultivars or hybrids of *B. davidii* var. *nanhoensis* are claimed by some to be synonyms while others claim the 'Nanho' plants were raised in Holland and the 'Petite' plants in the USA. We are not yet certain whether these names are synonyms and if so which have priority.

*Calamagrostis* × *acutiflora* 'Karl Foerster'
*C.* × *acutiflora* 'Stricta' differs in being 15cm taller, 10-15 days earlier flowering with a less fluffy inflorescence.

*Caltha polypetala*
This name is often applied to a large-flowered variant of *C. palustris*. The true species has more (7-10) petals.

*Camassia leichtlinii* 'Alba'
The true cultivar has blueish-white, not cream flowers.

*Camassia leichtlinii* 'Plena'
This has starry, transparent green-white flowers; creamy-white 'Semiplena' is sometimes offered under this name.

*Camellia* 'Campbellii'
This name is used for five cultivars including 'Margherita Coleoni' but applies correctly to Guichard's 1894 cultivar, single to semi-double full rose pink.

*Camellia* 'Cleopatra'
There are three cultivars with this name.

*Camellia* 'Perfecta'
There are three cultivars of this name. 'Perfecta' of Jury is the plant usually offered by nurseries in the British Isles.

*Campanula lactiflora* 'Alba'
This refers to the pure white flowered clone, not to blueish- or greyish-white flowered plants, nor to seed-raised plants.

*Campanula persicifolia*
Plants under "cup and saucer white" are not definitely ascribed to a particular cultivar. 'White Cup and Saucer' is a cultivar named by Margery Fish.

*Carex morrowii* 'Variegata'
*C. hachijoensis* 'Evergold' is sometimes sold under this name.

*Carya illinoinensis*
The correct spelling of this name is discussed in
*Baileya*, **10**(1) (1962).

*Cassinia retorta*
Now included within *C. leptophylla*. A valid infraspecific epithet has yet to be published.

*Cedrus deodara* 'Prostrata'
The true plant is extremely rare if not lost to
cultivation. Most plants under this name are *C.
deodara* 'Pendula'.

*Ceanothus* 'Italian Skies'
Many plants under this name are not true to
name.

*Chamaecyparis lawsoniana* 'Columnaris Glauca'
Plants under this name might be *C. lawsoniana*
'Columnaris' or a new invalidly named cultivar.

*Chamaecyparis lawsoniana* 'Elegantissima'
This name has been applied to two cultivars,
'Elegantissima' of Schelle and subsequently
(invalidly) 'Elegantissima' of Hillier.

*Chamaecyparis pisifera* 'Squarrosa Argentea'
There are two plants of this name, one (valid) with
variegated foliage, the other (invalid) with silvery
foliage.

*Cistus* x *loretii*
Plants in cultivation under this name are usually
forms of *C.* x *dansereaui*.

*Cistus* x *purpureus*
The cultivar 'Betty Taudevin' does not appear to be
distinct from this hybrid.

*Cistus* 'Silver Pink'
Plants under this name are not usually true
to type. *C.* 'Grayswood Pink', *C.* 'Peggy Sammons'
and *C.* x *skanbergii* are often offered under this
name.

*Clematis chrysocoma*
The true *C. chrysocoma* is a non-climbing erect
plant with dense yellow down on the young
growth, still uncommon in cultivation.

*Clematis heracleifolia* 'Campanile'
Might be *C.* x *bonstedtii* 'Campanile' .

*Clematis heracleifolia* 'Côte d'Azur'
Might be *C.* x *bonstedtii* 'Côte d'Azur'

*Clematis* 'Jackmanii Superba'
Plants under this name are usually *C.* 'Gipsy
Queen'.

*Clematis montana*
This name should refer to the white-flowered form
only. Pink-flowered forms are referable to *C.
montana* var. *rubens.*

*Clematis* 'Victoria'
There is also a Latvian cultivar of this name with
petals with a central white bar.

*Colchicum* 'Autumn Queen'
Entries here might refer to the slightly different *C.*
'Prinses Astrid'.

*Cornus* 'Norman Hadden'
See note in Bean Supplement, p.184.

*Cotoneaster dammeri*
Plants sold under this name are usually *C. dammeri*
'Major'.

*Crataegus coccinea*
Plants might be *C. intricata*, *C. pedicellata* or *C.
biltmoreana.*

*Crocosmia* x *crocosmiiflora* 'Citronella'
The true plant of this name has a dark eye and
grows at Wisley. The plant usually offered may be
more correctly *C.* 'Golden Fleece'.

*Crocosmia* x *crocosmiiflora* 'Honey Angels'
Also wrongly referred to as 'Citronella'.

*Crocosmia* x *crocosmiiflora* 'James Coey'
Has large tomato-red flowers. A smaller flowered
plant similar to *C.* x *crocosmiiflora* 'Carmin
Brillant' is sometimes sold under this name.

*Crocosmia* x *crocosmiiflora* 'Queen Alexandra'
As many as 20 different clones are grown under
this name. It is not clear which is correct.

*Crocus cartwrightianus* 'Albus'
The plant offered is the true cultivar and not *C.
hadriaticus.*

*Dendranthema* 'Anastasia Variegated'
Despite its name, this seems to be derived from
'Mei-kyo', not 'Anastasia'.

*Dianthus* Fringed Pink
*D.* 'Old Fringed Pink' and *D.* 'Old Fringed White'
are also sometimes sold under this name.

*Dianthus* 'Musgrave's Pink' (p)
This is the registered name of this white-flowered
cultivar.

*Diascia* 'Apricot'
Plants under this name are either *D. barberae*
'Hopleys Apricot' or *D. barberae* 'Blackthorn
Apricot'.

*Dryopteris affinis* Polydactyla Group
This Group includes at least three different clones.

*Elymus magellanicus*
Although this is a valid name, Mr Roger Grounds
has suggested that many plants might belong to a
different, perhaps unnamed species.

*Epilobium glabellum* hort.
Plants under this name are not *E. glabellum* but are
close to *E. wilsonii* Petrie or perhaps a hybrid of it.

*Erodium cheilanthifolium*
Most plants under this name are hybrids.

*Erodium glandulosum*
Plants under this name are often hybrids.

*Erodium guttatum*
Doubtfully in commerce; plants under this name
are usually *E. heteradenum*, *E. cheilanthifolium* or
hybrids.

*Erysimum cheiri* 'Baden-Powell'
Plant of uncertain origin differing from *E. cheiri*
'Harpur Crewe' only in its shorter stature.

*Erysimum* 'Variegatum'
This name might refer to any of the variegated
cultivars of *Erysimum.*

*Eucryphia* 'Penwith'
The cultivar name 'Penwith' was originally
given to a hybrid of *E. cordifolia* x *E. lucida*, not
*E.* x *hillieri*.

*Fagus sylvatica* Cuprea Group/Atropurpurea Group
It is desirable to provide a name, Cuprea Group,
for less richly coloured forms, used in historic
landscapes before the purple clones appeared.

*Fagus sylvatica* 'Pendula'
This name refers to the Knap Hill clone, the most
common weeping form in English gardens. Other
clones occur, particularly in Cornwall and Ireland.

*Fascicularia bicolor*
For a discussion of cultivated fascicularias and their
synonymy, see Nelson, E.C. and Zizka, G. (1997).
*The New Plantsman* 4(4).

*Forsythia* 'Beatrix Farrand'
The true plant might not be in cultivation.

*Fragaria chiloensis* 'Variegata', *F. vesca* 'Variegata'
Most, possibly all, plants under these names are *F.*
x *ananassa* 'Variegata'.

*Fuchsia*
All names marked 'N', except the following, refer
to more than one cultivar or species.

*Fuchsia decussata*
A hybrid of *F. magellanica* is also offered under this
name.

*Fuchsia loxensis*
For a comparison of the true species with the
hybrids 'Speciosa' and 'Loxensis' commonly grown
under this name, see Boullemier's Check List (2nd
ed.) p.268.

*Fuchsia minimiflora*
Some plants under this name might be
*F.* x *bacillaris*.

*Fuchsia* 'Pumila'
Plants under this name might be *F. magellanica* var.
*pumila*.

*Gentiana cachemirica*
Most plants sold are not true to type.

*Geum* 'Borisii'
This name refers to cultivars of *G. coccineum*
Sibthorp & Smith, especially *G.* 'Werner Arends'
and not to *G.* x *borisii* Kelleper.

*Halimium alyssoides* and *H. halimifolium*
Plants under these names are sometimes
*H.* x *pauanum* or *H.* x *santae*.

*Hebe* 'C.P. Raffill'
See note in Bean Supplement, p.265.

*Hebe* 'Carl Teschner'
See note in Bean Supplement, p.264.

*Hebe* 'Glaucophylla'
This plant is a green reversion of the hybrid *H.*
'Glaucophylla Variegata'.

*Hedera helix* 'Caenwoodiana'/ 'Pedata'
Some authorities consider these to be distinct
cultivars while others think them different
morphological forms of the same unstable clone.

*Hedera helix* 'Oro di Bogliasco'
Priority between this name and 'Jubiläum
Goldherz' and 'Goldheart' has yet to be finally
resolved.

*Helleborus orientalis* hort.
Plants under this name are hybrids for which the
name *H.* x *hybridus* has been published. Though
this latter might be the most acceptable name for
acaulescent garden hybrid hellebores, the RHS's
Advisory Panel has not yet adopted this name
because of doubts about the technical validity of its
publication.

*Hemerocallis fulva* 'Kwanso', 'Kwanso Variegata',
'Flore Pleno' and 'Green Kwanso'
For a discussion of these plants see *The Plantsman*,
7(2).

*Heuchera micrantha* var. *diversifolia* 'Palace Purple'
This cultivar name refers only to plants with deep
purple-red foliage. Seed-raised plants of inferior
colouring should not be offered under this name.

*Hosta* 'Marginata Alba'
This name is wrongly used both for *H. crispula*
and, more commonly, for *H. fortunei*
'Albomarginata'.

*Hosta montana*
This name refers only to plants long grown in
Europe, which differ from *H. elata*.

*Hydrangea macrophylla* Teller Series
This is used both as a descriptive common name
for Lacecap hydrangeas (German *teller* = plate,
referring to the more or less flat inflorescence) and
for the series of hybrids raised by Wädenswill in
Switzerland bearing German names of birds. It is
not generally possible to link a hydrangea described
by the series name plus a colour description (e.g.
Teller Blau, Teller Rosa, Teller Rot) to a single
cultivar.

*Hypericum fragile*
The true *H. fragile* is probably not available from
British nurseries.

*Hypericum* 'Gemo'
Either a selection of *H. prolificum* or *H. prolificum*
x *H. densiflorum*.

*Ilex* x *altaclerensis*
The argument for this spelling is given by Susyn
Andrews, *The Plantsman*, 5(2) and is not
superceded by the more recent comments in the
Supplement to Bean's Trees and Shrubs.

*Iris*
Apart from those noted below, cultivar names
marked 'N' are not registered. The majority of
those marked 'I' have been previously used for a
different cultivar.

*Iris histrioides* 'Major'
Two clones are offered under this name, the true
one pale blue with darker spotting on the falls, the
incorrect one violet-blue with almost horizontal
falls.

*Iris pallida* 'Variegata'
The white-variegated *I. pallida* 'Argentea Variegata' is sometimes wrongly supplied under this name, which refers only to the gold-variegated cultivar.

*Juniperus* x *media*
This name is illegitimate if applied to hybrids of *J. chinensis* x *J. sabina*, having been previously used for a different hybrid (P.A. Schmidt, *IDS Yearbook* 1993, 47-48). Because of its importance to gardeners, a proposal to conserve its present use was tabled but subsequently rejected.

*Lamium maculatum* 'Chequers'
This name refers to two plants; the first, validly named, is a large and vigorous form of *L. maculatum* with a stripe down the centre of the leaf; the second is silver-leaved and very similar to *L. maculatum* 'Beacon Silver'.

*Lavandula* 'Alba'
Might be either *L. angustifolia* 'Alba' or *L.* x *intermedia* 'Alba'

*Lavandula angustifolia* 'Lavender Lady'/
*L.* 'Cambridge Lady'
Might be synonyms of *L. angustifolia* 'Lady'.

*Lavandula* x *intermedia* 'Arabian Night'
Plants under this name might be *L.* x *intermedia* 'Impress Purple'.

*Lavandula spica*
This name is classed as a name to be rejected (*nomen rejiciendum*) by the *International Code of Botanical Nomenclature*.

*Lavandula* 'Twickel Purple'
Two cultivars are sold under this name, one a form of *L.* x *intermedia*, the other of *L. angustifolia*.

*Lavatera olbia* and *L. thuringiaca*
Although *L. olbia* is usually shrubby and *L. thuringiaca* usually herbaceous, both species are very variable. Cultivars formally ascribed to one species or the other have been shown to be hybrids and are listed by cultivar name alone.

*Lobelia* 'Russian Princess'
This has green, not purple, leaves and rich pink, not purple, flowers.

*Lonicera* x *americana*
Most plants offered by nurseries under this name are correctly *L.* x *italica*. The true *L.* x *americana* is still widely grown but is slow to propagate. See *The Plantsman*, 12(2).

*Lonicera* x *brownii* 'Fuchsioides'
Plants under this name are usually *L.* x *brownii* 'Dropmore Scarlet'.

*Lonicera* x *heckrotii* 'Gold Flame'
This name applies to the original clone. Many plants under this name are a different clone for which the name 'American Beauty' has been proposed.

*Lonicera periclymenum* 'Serotina'
See note in Bean Supplement, p.315.

*Lonicera sempervirens* f. *sulphurea*
Plants in the British Isles usually a yellow-flowered form of *L. periclymenum*.

*Macleaya cordata*
Most, if not all, plants offered are *M.* x *kewensis*.

*Magnolia* x *highdownensis*.
Believed to fall within the range of variation of *M. wilsonii*.

*Mahonia pinnata*
Most plants in cultivation under this name are believed to be *M.* x *wagneri* 'Pinnacle'.

*Malus domestica* 'Dumeller's Seedling'
The phonetic spelling 'Dumelow's Seedling' contravenes the ICBN ruling on orthography, i.e. that commemorative names should retain the original spelling of the person's name (Article 60.11).

*Melissa officinalis* 'Variegata'
The true cultivar of this name was striped with white.

*Narcissus poeticus* 'Plenus'
A name of uncertain application used for *N. poeticus* 'Spalding Double White' and *N. poeticus* 'Tamar Double White'.

*Nemesia caerulea*
The lavender blue clone 'Joan Wilder', described and illustrated in *The Hardy Plant*, 14(1), 11-14, does not come true from seed; it may only be propagated from cuttings.

*Osmanthus heterophyllus* 'Gulftide'
Probably correctly *O.* x *fortunei* 'Gulftide'.

*Papaver orientale* 'Flore Pleno'
*P.* 'Fireball' is sometimes offered under this name.

*Passiflora antioquiensis*
According to National Colection holder John Vanderplank, the true species is not in cultivation in the British Isles. Plants under this name are likely to be clones of *P.* x *exoniensis*.

*Pelargonium* 'Beauty of Eastbourne'
This should not be confused with *P.* 'Eastbourne Beauty', a different cultivar.

*Pelargonium* 'Lass o' Gowrie'
The American plant of this name has pointed, not rounded leaf lobes.

*Pelargonium quercifolium*
Plants under this name are mainly hybrids. The true species has pointed, not rounded leaf lobes.

*Penstemon* 'Taoensis'
This name for a small-flowered cultivar or hybrid of *P. isophyllus* originally appeared as 'Taoense' but must be corrected to agree in gender with *Penstemon* (masculine). Presumably an invalid name (published in Latin form since 1958), it is not synonymous with *P. crandallii* subsp. *glabrescens* var. *taosensis*.

*Pernettya*
Botanists now consider that *Pernettya* (fruit a berry) is not separable from *Gaultheria* (fruit a capsule) because in some species the fruit is

intermediate between a berry and a capsule. For a fuller explanation see D. Middleton, *The Plantsman*, 12(3).

**Picea pungens** 'Glauca Pendula'
This name is used for several different glaucous cultivars.

**Pinus ayacahuite**
*P. ayacahuite* var. *veitchii* (syn. *P. veitchii)* is occasionally sold under this name.

**Pinus montezumae**
Plants propagated from mature trees in British gardens are mostly an un-named long-needled variety of *P. rudis*.

**Pinus nigra** 'Cebennensis Nana'
A doubtful name, possibly a synonym for *P. nigra* 'Nana'.

**Polemonium archibaldiae**
Usually sterile with lavender-blue flowers. A self-fertile white-flowered plant is sometimes sold under this name.

**Polystichum setiferum** 'Wollaston'
Incomplete name which may refer to either of two cultivars.

**Populus nigra** var. *italica*
See note in Bean Supplement, p.393.

**Prunus laurocerasus** 'Castlewellan'
We are grateful to Dr Charles Nelson for informing us that the name 'Marbled White' is not valid because although it has priority of publication it does not have the approval of the originator who asked for it to be called 'Castlewellan'.

**Prunus laurocerasus** 'Variegata'
The true 'Variegata', (marginal variegation), dates from 1811 but this name is also used for the relatively recent cultivar *P. laurocerasus* 'Castlewellan'.

**Prunus serrulata** var. *pubescens*
See note in Bean Supplement, p.398.

**Prunus x subhirtella** 'Rosea'
Might be *P. pendula* var. *ascendens* 'Rosea', *P. pendula* 'Pendula Rosea', or *P. x subhirtella* 'Autumnalis Rosea'.

**Rheum x cultorum**
The name *R. x cultorum* was published without adequate description and must be abandoned in favour of the validly published *R. x hybridum*.

**Rhododendron** (azaleas)
All names marked 'N', except for the following, refer to more than one cultivar.

**Rhododendron** 'Hino-mayo'
This name is based on a faulty transliteration (should be 'Hinamoyo') but the spelling 'Hino-mayo' is retained in the interests of stability.

**Rhus typhina**
Linnaeus published both *R. typhina* and *R. hirta* as names for the same species. Though *R. hirta* has priority, it has been proposed that the name *R. typhina* should be conserved.

**Robinia hispida** 'Rosea'
This name is applied to *R. hispida* (young shoots with bristles), *R. elliottii* (young shoots with grey down) and *R. boyntonii* (young shoots smooth).

**Rosa x damascena** 'Trigintipetala'
The true cultivar of this name is probably not in cultivation in the Britsh Isles.

**Rosa gentiliana**
Plants might be *R. multiflora* 'Wilsonii', *R. multiflora* var. *cathayensis, R. henryi* or a hybrid.

**Rosa** 'Gros Choux de Hollande' (Bb)
It is doubtful if this name is correctly applied.

**Rosa** 'Maiden's Blush'
*R.* 'Great Maiden's Blush' may be supplied under this name.

**Rosa** Jacques Cartier
For a discussion on the correct identity of this rose see *Heritage Rose Foundation News*, Oct. 1989 & Jan. 1990.

**Rosa** 'Professeur Emile Perrot'
For a discussion on the correct identity of this rose see *Heritage Roses*, Nov. 1991.

**Rosa** Sweetheart
This is not the same as the Sweetheart Rose, a common name for *R.* 'Cécile Brünner'.

**Rosa wichurana**
This is the correct spelling according to the ICBN 1994 Article 60.11 (which enforces Recommendation 60C.1c) and not *wichuraiana* for this rose commemorating Max Wichura.

**Salix alba** 'Tristis'
This cultivar should not be confused with *S. tristis*, which is now correctly *S. humilis*. Although this cultivar is distinct in European gardens, most plants under this name in the British Isles are *S. x sepulcralis* var. *chrysocoma*.

**Salvia microphylla** var. *neurepia*
The type of this variety is referable to the typical variety, *S. microphylla* var. *microphylla*.

**Salvia officinalis** 'Aurea'
*S. officinalis* var. *aurea* is a rare variant of the common sage with leaves entirely of gold. It is represented in cultivation by the cultivar 'Kew Gold'. The plant usually offered as *S. officinalis* 'Aurea' is the gold variegated sage *S. officinalis* 'Icterina'.

**Salvia sclarea** var. *turkestanica*
Plants in gardens under this name are not *S. sclarea* var. *turkistaniana* of Mottet.

**Sambucus nigra** 'Aurea'
Plants under this name are usually not *S. nigra*.

**Sedum nevii**
The true species is not in cultivation. Plants under this name are usually either *S. glaucophyllum* or occasionally *S. beyrichianum*.

**Senna corymbosa**
Some plants sold as *S. corymbosa* are *S. x floribunda*.

*Skimmia japonica* 'Foremanii'
  The true cultivar, which belongs to *S. japonica*
  Rogersii Group, is believed to be lost to
  cultivation. Plants offered under this name are
  usually *S. japonica* 'Veitchii'.

*Spiraea japonica* 'Shirobana'
  Shirobana-shimotsuke is the common name for *S. japonica* var. *albiflora*. Shirobana means white-flowered and does not apply to the two-coloured
  form.

*Staphylea holocarpa* var. *rosea*
  This botanical variety has woolly leaves. The
  cultivar 'Rosea', with which it is often confused,
  does not.

*Stewartia ovata* var. *grandiflora*.
  Most, possibly all, plants available from British
  nurseries under this name are not true to
  name but are derived from the improved Nymans
  form.

*Thymus serpyllum* cultivars
  Most cultivars are probably correctly cultivars
  of *T. polytrichus* or hybrids though they will
  remain listed under *T. serpyllum* pending
  further research.

*Thymus* 'Silver Posie'
  The cultivar name 'Silver Posie' is applied to
  several different plants, not all of them *T. vulgaris*.

*Tricyrtis* Hototogisu
  This is the common name applied generally to all
  Japanese *Tricyrtis* and specifically to *T. hirta*.

*Tricyrtis macropoda*
  This name has been used for at least five different
  species.

*Uncinia rubra*
  This name is loosely applied to *U. egmontiana* and
  *U. uncinata*.

*Verbena* 'Kemerton'
  Origin unknown, not from Kemerton.

*Viburnum opulus* 'Fructu Luteo'
  See note below.

*Viburnum opulus* 'Xanthocarpum'
  Some entries under this name might be the less
  compact *V. opulus* 'Fructu Luteo'.

*Viburnum plicatum*
  Entries may include the 'snowball' form, *V. plicatum* 'Sterile'.

*Viola labradorica*
  See Note in *The Garden*, 110(2): 96.

# COLLECTORS' REFERENCES

Abbreviations following a plant name, refer to
the collector(s) of the plant. These abbreviations
are expanded below, with a collector's name or
expedition title. For a fuller explanation, turn
to p.15.

| | |
|---|---|
| A&JW | A. & J. Watson, S America |
| A&L | Ala & Lancaster expedition, N Iran, 1972 |
| AB&S | Archibald, Blanchard & Salmon, Morocco 1980s |
| AC&H | Apold, Cox & Hutchinson, NE Turkey, 1962 |
| AC&W | Albury, Cheese & Watson |
| ACE | Alpine Garden Society expedition, China, 1994 |
| ACL | A.C. Leslie |
| AGS/ES | Alpine Garden Society expedition, Sikkim, 1983 |
| AGSJ | Alpine Garden Society expedition, Japan, 1988 |
| Airth | Murray Airth |
| Akagi | Akagi Botanical Garden |
| AL&JS | Leslie & Sharman, Yugoslavia, 1990 |
| B L. | Beer, Nepal, 1975 |
| B&L | Brickell & Leslie, China |
| B&M | C.D. Brickell & B. Mathew |
| B&S | P. Bird & M. Salmon |
| B&SWJ | B. & S. Wynn-Jones |

| | |
|---|---|
| BB | B. Bartholomew, Bhutan, 1974 |
| BC | B. Chudziak, Kanchenjunga, Nepal, 1993 |
| BC&W | Beckett, Cheese & Watson |
| BL&M | Beer, Lancaster & Morris, E Nepal, 1971 |
| BM | B. Mathew |
| BM&W | Binns, Mason & Wright, Nepal, 1978 |
| BQE | British Qinghai Expedition, Royal Botanic Garden, Edinburgh, 1998 |
| BS | Basil Smith |
| BSBE | Bowles Scholarship Botanical Expedition |
| Bu | S. Bubert |
| C&C | P.A. & K.N.E. Cox, SE Tibet, 1996 |
| C&Cu | K.N.E. Cox & J. Cubey |
| C&H | P.A. Cox & P.C. Hutchison, Assam, NE Frontier & N Bengal, 1965; Sichuan & Yunnan, China, 1995 |
| C&K | Chamberlain & Knott |
| C&R | Christian & Roderick, California, Oregon, Washington |
| C&S | A. Clark & I. Sinclair, Bhutan, 1994 |
| C&V | K.N.E. Cox & S. Vergera, SE Tibet, China, 1995 |
| C&W | M. Cheese & J. Watson |
| CC | C. Chadwell |
| CC&H | D.F. Chamberlain, P.A. Cox & P.C. Hutchison, Sichuan, China, 1989 |
| CC&McK | Chadwell & McKelvie, Nepal, West Himalaya, 1990-92 |

| | |
|---|---|
| CC&MR | C. Chadwell & M. Ramsey, Kashmir, 1985; Himachal Pradesh & W Himalaya, 1989 |
| CCH&H | Chamberlain, Cox, Hootman & Hutchison |
| CD&R | J. Compton, J. D'Arcy & E.M. Rix, China, Drakensburg, Mexico & Korea |
| CDB | C.D. Brickell |
| CDC&C | Compton, D'Arcy, Christopher & Coke |
| CE&H | Christian, Elliott & Hoog, Yugoslavia & Greece, 1982 |
| CEE | Chengdu Edinburgh Expedition, Sichuan, China, 1991 |
| CGW | C. Grey-Wilson |
| CH&M | P.A. Cox, P.C. Hutchinson & D.M. McDonald, Sichuan & Yunnan, China, 1986; Bhutan, 1988 |
| CHP&W | Chadwell, Howard, Powell & Wright, Kashmir, 1983 |
| CL | C. Lovell |
| CLD | Kew, Edinburgh & RHS Expedition, Zhongdian (Chungtien), Lijiang & Dali, China, 1990 |
| CM&W | M. Cheese, J. Mitchel & J. Watson |
| Cooper | R.E. Cooper (1890-1962), Bhutan, 1914 & '15; Punjab, India, 1916; NE Burma |
| CSE | Cyclamen Society Expedition |
| CT | Carla Teune |
| DBG | Denver Botanic Garden, Colorado |
| DF | Derek Fox |
| DJH | Dan Hinkley |
| DJHC | Dan Hinkley, China |
| DM | David Millais |
| DS&T | Drake, Sharman & Thompson, Turkey, 1989 |
| ECN | E. Charles Nelson |
| EGM | E.G. Millais, Bhutan, 1988 (with others); Sichuan & Yunnan, China, 1995 |
| EKB | E.K. Balls |
| EM | East Malling Research Station clonal selection scheme |
| EMAK | Edinburgh Makalu Expedition, Nepal, 1991 |
| EMR | E.M. Rix |
| EN | Edward Needham |
| ES | Euroseeds (Mojmir Pavelka), Nový Jičin, Czech Republic |
| ETE | Edinburgh Expedition, Taiwan, 1993 |
| ETOT | M. Flanagan & T. Kirkham, Taiwan, 1992 |
| F | George Forrest (1873-1932) |
| F&W | A. Flores & J. Watson, Chile, 1992 |
| Farrer | Reginald Farrer (1880-1920) |
| FK | Fergus W. Kinmonth, China; Nepal; Bhutan, 1990; Vietnam, 1991 |
| FMB | F.M. Bailey |
| G | M.F. Gardner |

| | |
|---|---|
| G&K | M.F. Gardner & S.G. Knees |
| G&P | M.F. Gardner & C. Page, Chile, 1992 |
| GG | George Gusman |
| G-W&P | Grey-Wilson & Phillips |
| GS | George Sherriff (1898-1967) |
| Guitt | G.G. Guittonneau |
| Guiz | J.B. Simmons, H. Fliegner & J. Russell, Guizhou, China, 1985 |
| H | Paul Huggins. Oxford University Expedition, Tehri Garhwal, C Himalaya |
| H&B | O. Hilliard & B.L. Burtt |
| H&M | Howick & McNamara |
| H&W | Hedge & Wendelbo, Afghanistan, 1969 |
| Harry Smith | Karl August Harald Smith (1889-1971) |
| Hartside | Hartside Nursery, breeder's number |
| HCM | Heronswood Expedition to Chile, 1998 |
| HH&K | S. & S. Hannay & N. Kingsbury, Bulgaria, 1995 |
| HM&S | B. Halliwell, M. Mason & P. Smallcombe |
| Hummel | D. Hummel, China, 1950 |
| HW&E | Hedge, Wendelbo & Ekberg, Afghanistan, 1982 |
| HWEL | J.M. Hirst & D. Webster, Lesotho |
| HWJCM | Crûg Heronswood expedition, E Nepal, 1995 |
| J&JA | J.C. & J. Archibald |
| JCA | J.C. Archibald |
| JE | Jack Elliott |
| JJ | John Jackson |
| JJ&JH | Josef J. & Jarmila Halda |
| JJH | Josef J. Halda |
| JLS | J.L. Sharman, USA, 1988 |
| JMT | J. Mann Taylor |
| JN | Jens Nielson |
| JR | J. Russell |
| JRM | J.R. Marr, Greece & Turkey, 1975 |
| JW | J. Watson |
| K | G. Kirkpatrick |
| K&E | Kew & Edinburgh Expedition, China, 1989 |
| K&LG | K.D. & L.M. Gillanders, Ecuador, 1994; Yunnan, China, 1993, '94, '96; Vietnam, 1992; Tibet, 1995 |
| K&Mc | G. Kirkpatrick & R. McBeath. |
| KEKE | Kew/Edinburgh Kanchenjunga Expedition, NE Nepal, 1989 |
| KGB | Kunming-Gothenburg Expedition, NW Yunnan, China, 1993 |
| KR | K. Rushforth |
| KRW | K.R. Wooster, breeder's number |
| KW | Frank Kingdon-Ward (1885-1958) |
| L | Roy Lancaster |
| L&S | F. Ludlow (1885-1972) & G. Sherriff (1898-1967) |
| LA | Long Ashton Research Station clonal selection scheme. |
| Lismore | Lismore Nursery, breeder's number |

| | |
|---|---|
| LM&S | Leslie, Mattern & Sharman, Bulgaria, 1994 |
| LP | Hon. W.J.L. Palmer (1894-1971) |
| LS&E | F. Ludlow, G. Sherriff & H. Elliot |
| LS&H | F. Ludlow, G. Sherriff & Hicks, Bhutan, 1949 |
| LS&T | F. Ludlow, G. Sherriff & G. Taylor, SE Tibet, 1938 |
| M&PS | Mike and Polly Stone, Gravelly Range MT 1993 |
| M&T | B. Mathew & J. Tomlinson |
| Mac&W | MacPhail & Watson |
| McB | Ron McBeath, Nepal, 1981, '83 & '90 |
| McLaren | Henry McLaren, 2nd Baron Aberconway (1879-1953) |
| MF | Maurice Foster, Yunnan, China, 1993 & '96 |
| MH | M. Heasman, Bhutan, 1992 |
| MS | M. Salmon |
| MSF | M.S. Fillan, Tenerife, 1988; S Korea, 1989 |
| MS&CL | M. Salmon & C. Lovell |
| NNS | Northwest Native Seeds (R. Ratko), Seattle. |
| NS | Nick Turland (Northside Seeds) |
| Og | Mikinori Ogisu |
| P&C | D.S. Paterson & S. Clarke, WesternUSA, 1991 |
| P&W | Polastri & Watson, Chile |
| PB | Peter Bird |
| PC&H | G. Pattison, P. Catt & M. Hickson, Mexico, 1994 |
| PD | Peter Davis |
| PF | Paul Furse |
| PJC | P.J. Christian |
| PJC&AH | P.J. Christian & A. Hoog, Greece & Yugoslavia, 1985 |
| Pras | Milan Prasil |
| PS&W | Polunin, Sykes & Williams, W Nepal, 1952 |
| PW | Peter Wharton, Guizhou, China, 1994 |
| R | J.F.C. Rock (1884-1962) |
| RB | Ray Brown (Plant World, Devon), Chile, 1994 |
| RCB/Eq | Robert Brown, Ecuador, 1998 |
| RH | R. Hancock |
| RMRP | Rocky Mountain Rare Plants, Denver, Colorado |
| RS | Reinhart Suckow |
| RV | Richard Valder |
| S&B | M. Salmon & J. Blanchard |
| S&F | Salmon & Fillan, Spain & Morocco |
| S&L | I. Sinclair & D. Long, Bhutan, 1984 |
| S&SH | Sheilah & Spencer Hannay, Lesotho, NE Cape Province, 1989 & '91; C Nepal, 1993 |
| SB&L | Salmon, Bird & Lovell, Jordan & Morocco |
| SBEC | Sino-British Expedition, Cangshan, SW China, 1981 |
| SBEL | Sino-British Expedition, Lijiang, Yunnan, China, 1987 |
| SD | Sashal Dayal |
| Sch | A.D. Schilling, Nepal, 1975, '76, '77, '78, '83; Bhutan, 1988 |
| SEH | Steve Hootman |
| SEP | Swedish Expedition to Pakistan |
| SFP. | Forde (Seaforde Gardens), Bhutan, 1990 |
| SH | Spencer Hannay |
| Sich | Simmons, Erskine, Howick & McNamara, Sichuan, China, 1988 |
| SS&W | Stainton, Sykes & Williams, C Nepal, 1954 |
| SSNY | Sino-Scottish Expedition, NW Yunnan, China, 1992 |
| T | Nigel P. Taylor |
| T&K | N.P. Taylor & S. Knees |
| TS&BC | T. Smythe & B. Cherry, Yunnan, China, 1994 |
| TSS | T. Spring-Smyth, E Nepal, 1961-62, '70 |
| TW | Tony Weston (with A.D. Schilling), Nepal, 1985; (with K. Rushforth) SW Yunnan, China 1993 |
| USDAPI | US Dept of Agriculture Plant Index Number |
| USDAPQ | US Dept of Agriculture Plant Quarantine Number |
| USNA | United States National Arboretum |
| VHH | Vernon H. Heywood |
| W | E.H. Wilson (1876-1930) |
| W/A | E.H. Wilson, for Arnold Arboretum, 1906-19 |
| W/V | E.H. Wilson, for Veitch, 1899-1905 |
| WM | Will McLewin |
| Woods | Paddy Woods |
| Wr | David & Anke Wraight |
| Yu | Tse Tsun Yu (1908-86) |

# CLASSIFICATION OF GENERA

Genera including a large number of species or with many cultivars are often subdivided into groups. Please turn to p.15 for a fuller explanation.

## ACTINIDIA

(s-p)    Self-pollinating

## BEGONIA

(C)    Cane
(R)    Rex
(S)    Semperflorens Cultorum
(T)    x *tuberhybrida* (Tuberous)

## CHRYSANTHEMUM

(By the National Chrysanthemum Society)
(1)    Indoor Large (Exhibition)
(2)    Indoor Medium (Exhibition)
(3a)    Indoor Incurved: Large-flowered
(3b)    Indoor Incurved: Medium-flowered
(3c)    Indoor Incurved: Small-flowered
(4a)    Indoor Reflexed: Large-flowered
(4b)    Indoor Reflexed: Medium-flowered
(4c)    Indoor Reflexed: Small-flowered
(5a)    Indoor Intermediate: Large-flowered
(5b)    Indoor Intermediate: Medium-flowered
(5c)    Indoor Intermediate: Small-flowered
(6a)    Indoor Anemone: Large-flowered
(6b)    Indoor Anemone: Medium-flowered
(6c)    Indoor Anemone: Small-flowered
(7a)    Indoor Single: Large-flowered
(7b)    Indoor Single: Medium-flowered
(7c)    Indoor Single: Small-flowered
(8a)    Indoor True Pompon
(8b)    Indoor Semi-pompon
(9a)    Indoor Spray: Anemone
(9b)    Indoor Spray: Pompon
(9c)    Indoor Spray: Reflexed
(9d)    Indoor Spray: Single
(9e)    Indoor Spray: Intermediate
(9f)    Indoor Spray: Spider, Quill, Spoon or Any Other Type
(10a)    Indoor, Spider
(10b)    Indoor, Quill
(10c)    Indoor, Spoon
(11)    Any Other Indoor Type
(12a)    Indoor, Charm
(12b)    Indoor, Cascade
(13a)    October-flowering Incurved: Large-flowered
(13b)    October-flowering Incurved: Medium-flowered
(13c)    October-flowering Incurved: Small-flowered
(14a)    October-flowering Reflexed: Large-flowered
(14b)    October-flowering Reflexed: Medium-flowered
(14c)    October-flowering Reflexed: Small-flowered
(15a)    October-flowering Intermediate: Large-flowered
(15b)    October-flowering Intermediate: Medium-flowered
(15c)    October-flowered Intermediate: Small-flowered
(16)    October-flowering Large
(17a)    October-flowering Single: Large-flowered
(17b)    October-flowering Single: Medium-flowered
(17c)    October-flowering Single: Small-flowered
(18a)    October-flowering Pompon: True Pompon
(18b)    October-flowering Pompon: Semi-pompon
(19a)    October-flowering Spray: Anemone
(19b)    October-flowering Spray: Pompon
(19c)    October-flowering Spray: Reflexed
(19d)    October-flowering Spray: Single
(19e)    October-flowering Spray: Intermediate
(19f)    October-flowering Spray: Spider, Quill, Spoon or Any Other Type
(20)    Any Other October-flowering Type
(22)    Charm
(23a)    Early-flowering Outdoor Incurved: Large-flowered
(23b)    Early-flowering Outdoor Incurved: Medium-flowered
(23c)    Early-flowering Outdoor Incurved: Small-flowered
(24a)    Early-flowering Outdoor Reflexed: Large-flowered
(24b)    Early-flowering Outdoor Reflexed: Medium-flowered
(24c)    Early-flowering Outdoor Reflexed: Small-flowered
(25a)    Early-flowering Outdoor Intermediate: Large-flowered
(25b)    Early-flowering Outdoor Intermediate: Medium-flowered
(25c)    Early-flowering Outdoor Intermediate: Small-flowered
(26a)    Early-flowering Outdoor Anemone: Large-flowered

| | |
|---|---|
| (26b) | Early-flowering Outdoor Anemone: Medium-flowered |
| (27a) | Early-flowering Outdoor Single: Large-flowered |
| (27b) | Early-flowering Outdoor Single: Medium-flowered |
| (28a) | Early-flowering Outdoor Pompon: True Pompon |
| (28b) | Early-flowering Outdoor Pompon: Semi-pompon |
| (29a) | Early-flowering Outdoor Spray: Anemone |
| (29b) | Early-flowering Outdoor Spray: Pompon |
| (29c) | Early-flowering Outdoor Spray: Reflexed |
| (29d) | Early-flowering Outdoor Spray: Single |
| (29e) | Early-flowering Outdoor Spray: Intermediate |
| (29f) | Early-flowering Outdoor Spray: Spider, Quill, Spoon or Any Other Type |
| (29K) | Early-flowering Outdoor Spray: Korean |
| (29Rub) | Early-flowering Outdoor Spray: Rubellum |
| (30) | Any Other Early-flowering Outdoor Type |

## CLEMATIS

| | |
|---|---|
| (A) | Alpina Group (Section Atragene) |
| (D) | Diversifolia Group |
| (Fl) | Florida Group (double-flowered) |
| (Fo) | Forsteri Group |
| (H) | Heracleifolia Group |
| (I) | Integrifolia Group |
| (J) | Jackmanii Group |
| (L) | Lanuginosa Group |
| (P) | Patens Group |
| (T) | Texensis Group |
| (Ta) | Tangutica Group |
| (Vt) | Viticella Group |

## DAHLIA

(By the National Dahlia Society with corresponding numerical classification according to the Royal Horticultural Society's International Register)

| | |
|---|---|
| (Sin) | 1 Single |
| (Anem) | 2 Anemone-flowered |
| (Col) | 3 Collerette |
| (WL) | 4 Waterlily (unassigned) |
| (LWL) | 4B Waterlily, Large |
| (MWL) | 4C Waterlily, Medium |
| (SWL) | 4D Waterlily, Small |
| (MinWL) | 4E Waterlily, Miniature |
| (GD) | 5A Decorative, Giant |
| (LD) | 5B Decorative, Large |
| (MD) | 5C Decorative, Medium |
| (SD) | 5D Decorative, Small |
| (MinD) | 5E Decorative, Miniature |
| (SBa) | 6A Small Ball |
| (MinBa) | 6B Miniature Ball |
| (Pom) | 7 Pompon |
| (GC) | 8A Cactus, Giant |
| (LC) | 8B Cactus, Large |
| (MC) | 8C Cactus, Medium |
| (SC) | 8D Cactus, Small |
| (MinC) | 8E Cactus, Miniature |
| (S-c) | 9 Semi-cactus (unassigned) |
| (GS-c) | 9A Semi-cactus, Giant |
| (LS-c) | 9B Semi-cactus, Large |
| (MS-c) | 9C Semi-cactus, Medium |
| (SS-c) | 9D Semi-cactus, Small |
| (MinS-c) | 9E Semi-cactus, Miniature |
| (Misc) | 10 Miscellaneous |
| (O) | Orchid-flowering (in combination) |
| (B) | Botanical (in combination) |
| (DwB) | Dwarf Bedding (in combination) |
| (Fim) | Fimbriated (in combination) |
| (Lil) | Lilliput (in combination) |

## DIANTHUS

(By the Royal Horticultural Society)

| | |
|---|---|
| (p) | Pink |
| (p,a) | Annual Pink |
| (pf) | Perpetual-flowering Carnation |
| (b) | Border Carnation |
| (M) | Malmaison Carnation |

## FRUIT

| | |
|---|---|
| (B) | Black (*Vitis*) |
| (C) | Culinary (*Malus, Prunus, Pyrus, Ribes*) |
| (Cider) | Cider (*Malus*) |
| (D) | Dessert (*Malus, Prunus, Pyrus, Ribes*) |
| (F) | Fruit |
| (G) | Glasshouse (*Vitis*) |
| (O) | Outdoor (*Vitis*) |
| (P) | Pinkcurrant (*Ribes*) |
| (Perry) | Perry (*Pyrus*) |
| (R) | Red (*Vitis*), Redcurrant (*Ribes*) |
| (W) | White (*Vitis*), Whitecurrant (*Ribes*) |

## GLADIOLUS

| | |
|---|---|
| (B) | Butterfly |
| (Colv) | Colvillei |
| (G) | Giant |
| (L) | Large |
| (M) | Medium |
| (Min) | Miniature |
| (N) | Nanus |
| (P) | Primulinus |
| (S) | Small |
| (Tub) | Tubergenii |

## HYDRANGEA MACROPHYLLA

(H)         Hortensia
(L)         Lacecap

## IRIS

(By the American Iris Society)
(AB)        Arilbred
(BB)        Border Bearded
(Cal-Sib)   Series *Californicae* x Series *Sibiricae*
(CH)        Californian Hybrid
(DB)        Dwarf Bearded (not assigned)
(Dut)       Dutch
(IB)        Intermediate Bearded
(La)        Louisiana Hybrid
(MDB)       Miniature Dwarf Bearded
(MTB)       Miniature Tall Bearded
(SDB)       Standard Dwarf Bearded
(Sino-Sib)  Series *Sibiricae*, chromosome number
            2n=40
(Spuria)    Spuria
(TB)        Tall Bearded

## LILIUM

(Classification according to *The International Lily
Register* (ed. 3, 1982) with amendments from Supp.
10 (1992), Royal Horticultural Society)
(I)         Hybrids derived from *L. amabile,
            L. bulbiferum, L. cernuum, L. concolor,
            L. davidii, L.* x *hollandicum,
            L. lancifolium, L. leichtlinii,
            L.* x *maculatum* and *L. pumilum*
(Ia)        Early flowering with upright flowers,
            single or in an umbel
(Ib)        Outward-facing flowers
(Ic)        Pendant flowers
(II)        Hybrids of Martagon type, one parent
            having been a form of *L. hansonii* or
            *L. martagon*
(III)       Hybrids from *L. candidum,
            L. chalcedonicum* and other related
            European species (excluding
            *L. martagon*)
(IV)        Hybrids of American species
(V)         Hybrids derived from *L. formosanum* &
            *L. longiflorum*
(VI)        Hybrid Trumpet Lilies & Aurelian
            hybrids from Asiatic species, including
            *L. henryi* but excluding those from
            *L. auratum, L. japonicum, L. rubellum*
            and *L. speciosum.*
(VIa)       Plants with trumpet-shaped flowers
(VIb)       Plants with bowl-shaped flowers
(VIc)       Plants with flat flowers (or only the tips
            recurved)
(VId)       Plants with recurved flowers

(VII)       Hybrids of Far Eastern species as
            *L auratum, L. japonicum, L. rubellum*
            and *L. speciosum,*
(VIIa)      Plants with trumpet-shaped flowers
(VIIb)      Plants with bowl-shaped flowers
(VIIc)      Plants with flat flowers
(VIId)      Plants with recurved flowers
(VIII)      All hybrids not in another division
(IX)        All species and their varieties and forms

## MALUS *SEE* FRUIT

## NARCISSUS

(By the Royal Horticultural Society, revised 1998)
(1)         Trumpet
(2)         Large-cupped
(3)         Small-cupped
(4)         Double
(5)         Triandrus
(6)         Cyclamineus
(7)         Jonquilla and Apodanthus
(8)         Tazetta
(9)         Poeticus
(10)        Bulbocodium
(11a)       Split Corona; Collar
(11b)       Split Corona; Papillon
(12)        Miscellaneous
(13)        Species

## NYMPHAEA

(H)         Hardy
(D)         Day-blooming
(N)         Night-blooming
(T)         Tropical

## PAEONIA

(S)         Shrubby

## PELARGONIUM

(A)         Angel
(C)         Coloured Foliage (in combination)
(Ca)        Cactus (in combination)
(d)         Double (in combination)
(Dec)       Decorative
(Dw)        Dwarf
(DwI)       Dwarf Ivy-leaved
(Fr)        Frutetorum
(I)         Ivy-leaved
(Min)       Miniature
(MinI)      Miniature Ivy-leaved
(R)         Regal
(Sc)        Scented-leaved
(St)        Stellar (in combination)

| | |
|---|---|
| (T) | Tulip (in combination) |
| (U) | Unique |
| (Z) | Zonal |

## PRIMULA

(Classification as per W.W. Smith & Forrest (1928) and W.W. Smith & Fletcher (1941-49))

| | |
|---|---|
| (1) | Amethystina |
| (2) | Auricula |
| (3) | Bullatae |
| (4) | Candelabra |
| (5) | Capitatae |
| (6) | Carolinella |
| (7) | Cortusoides |
| (8) | Cuneifolia |
| (9) | Denticulata |
| (10) | Dryadifolia |
| (11) | Farinosae |
| (12) | Floribundae |
| (13) | Grandis |
| (14) | Malacoides |
| (15) | Malvacea |
| (16) | Minutissimae |
| (17) | Muscarioides |
| (18) | Nivales |
| (19) | Obconica |
| (20) | Parryi |
| (21) | Petiolares |
| (22) | Pinnatae |
| (23) | Pycnoloba |
| (24) | Reinii |
| (25) | Rotundifolia |
| (26) | Sikkimensis |
| (27) | Sinenses |
| (28) | Soldanelloideae |
| (29) | Souliei |
| (30) | Vernales |
| (A) | Alpine Auricula |
| (B) | Border Auricula |
| (Poly) | Polyanthus |
| (Prim) | Primrose |
| (S) | Show Auricula |

## PRUNUS *SEE* FRUIT

## PYRUS *SEE* FRUIT

## RHODODENDRON

| | |
|---|---|
| (A) | Azalea (deciduous, species or unclassified hybrid) |
| (Ad) | Azaleodendron |
| (EA) | Evergreen azalea |
| (G) | Ghent azalea (deciduous) |
| (K) | Knap Hill or Exbury azalea (deciduous) |
| (M) | Mollis azalea (deciduous) |

| | |
|---|---|
| (O) | Occidentalis azalea (deciduous) |
| (R) | Rustica azalea (deciduous) |
| (V) | Vireya rhododendron |
| (Vs) | Viscosa azalea (deciduous) |

## RIBES *SEE* FRUIT

## ROSA

| | |
|---|---|
| (A) | Alba |
| (Bb) | Bourbon |
| (Bs) | Boursault |
| (Ce) | Centifolia |
| (Ch) | China |
| (Cl) | Climbing (in combination) |
| (D) | Damask |
| (DPo) | Damask Portland |
| (F) | Floribunda or Cluster-flowered |
| (G) | Gallica |
| (Ga) | Garnette |
| (GC) | Ground Cover |
| (HM) | Hybrid Musk |
| (HP) | Hybrid Perpetual |
| (HT) | Hybrid Tea or Large-flowered |
| (Min) | Miniature |
| (Mo) | Moss (in combination) |
| (N) | Noisette |
| (Patio) | Patio, Miniature Floribunda or Dwarf Cluster-flowered |
| (Poly) | Polyantha |
| (PiH) | Pimpinellifolia hybrid (Hybrid Scots Briar) |
| (Ra) | Rambler |
| (RH) | Rubiginosa hybrid (Hybrid Sweet Briar) |
| (Ru) | Rugosa |
| (S) | Shrub |
| (T) | Tea |

## SAXIFRAGA

(Classification from Gornall, R.D. (1987). *Botanical Journal of the Linnean Society,* 95(4).)

| | |
|---|---|
| (1) | Ciliatae |
| (2) | Cymbalaria |
| (3) | Merkianae |
| (4) | Micranthes |
| (5) | Irregulares |
| (6) | Heterisia |
| (7) | Porphyrion |
| (8) | Ligulatae |
| (9) | Xanthizoon |
| (10) | Trachyphyllum |
| (11) | Gymnopera |
| (12) | Cotylea |
| (13) | Odontophyllae |
| (14) | Mesogyne |
| (15) | Saxifraga |

## TULIPA

(Classification from *Classified List and International Register of Tulip Names* by Koninklijke Algemeene Vereening voor Bloembollenculture 1996)

(1)    Single Early Group
(2)    Double Early Group
(3)    Triumph Group
(4)    Darwinhybrid Group
(5)    Single Late Group (including Darwin Group and Cottage Group)
(6)    Lily-flowered Group
(7)    Fringed Group
(8)    Viridiflora Group
(9)    Rembrandt Group
(10)   Parrot Group
(11)   Double Late Group
(12)   Kaufmanniana Group
(13)   Fosteriana Group
(14)   Greigii Group
(15)   Miscellaneous

## VIOLA

(C)     Cornuta Hybrid
(dVt)   Double Violet
(ExVa)  Exhibition Viola
(FP)    Fancy Pansy
(PVt)   Parma Violet
(SP)    Show Pansy
(T)     Tricolor
(Va)    Viola
(Vt)    Violet
(Vtta)  Violetta

## VITIS *SEE* FRUIT

# REVERSE SYNONYMS

The following list of reverse synonyms is intended to help users find from which genus an unfamiliar plant name has been cross-referred. For a fuller explanation see p.15

Acacia – Racosperma
Acanthocalyx – Morina
Acca – Feijoa
× Achicodonia – Eucodonia
Achillea – Anthemis
Acinos – Calamintha
Acinos – Micromeria
Aethionema – Eunomia
Agapetes – Pentapterygium
Agarista – Leucothoe
Agastache – Cedronella
Aichryson – Aeonium
Ajania – Chrysanthemum
Ajania – Eupatorium
Albizia – Acacia
Alcea – Althaea
Allardia – Waldheimia
Allocasuarina – Casuarina
Aloysia – Lippia
Althaea – Malva
Alyogyne – Hibiscus
Alyssum – Ptilotrichum
× Amarygia – Amaryllis
Amaryllis – Brunsvigia
Amomyrtus – Myrtus
Amsonia – Rhazya
Anaphalis – Gnaphalium

Anchusa – Lycopsis
Androsace – Douglasia
Anemone – Eriocapitella
Anisodontea – Malvastrum
Anomatheca – Lapeirousia
Anredera – Boussingaultia
Antirrhinum – Asarina
Aphanes – Alchemilla
Arctanthemum – Chrysanthemum
Arctostaphylos – Arbutus
Arctotis – × Venidioarctotis
Arctotis – Venidium
Arenga – Didymosperma
Argyranthemum – Anthemis
Argyranthemum – Chrysanthemum
Armoracia – Cochlearia
Arundinaria – Pseudosasa
Asarina – Antirrhinum
Asarum – Hexastylis
Asclepias – Gomphocarpus
Asparagus – Smilax
Asperula – Galium
Asphodeline – Asphodelus
Asplenium – Camptosorus
Asplenium – Ceterach
Asplenium – Phyllitis
Asplenium – Scolopendrium
Aster – Crinitaria
Aster – Microglossa
Asteriscus – Pallenis
Astilboides – Rodgersia
Atropanthe – Scopola

Aurinia – Alyssum
Austrocedrus – Libocedrus
Azorella – Bolax
Azorina – Campanula

Bambusa – Arundinaria
Bashania – Arundinaria
Bellevalia – Muscari
Bellis – Erigeron
Besseya – Veronica
Blechnum – Lomaria
Bolax – Azorella
Bolboschoenus – Scirpus
Borago – Anchusa
Borinda – Fargesia
Bothriochloa – Andropogon
Boykinia – Telesonix
Brachyglottis – Senecio
Bracteantha – Helichrysum
Brimeura – Hyacinthus
Brugmansia – Datura
Brunnera – Anchusa
Buglossoides – Lithospermum
Bulbine – Bulbinopsis
Buphthalmum – Inula

Cacalia – Adenostyles
Caiophora – Loasa
Caladium – Xanthosoma
Calamagrostis – Agrostis
Calamagrostis – Stipa
Calamintha – Clinopodium
Calliergon – Acrocladium
Callisia – Phyodina

Callisia – Tradescantia
Calocedrus – Libocedrus
Calocephalus – Leucophyta
Calomeria – Humea
Caloscordum – Nothoscordum
Calytrix – Lhotzkya
Camellia – Thea
Cardamine – Dentaria
Carpobrotus – Lampranthus
Cassiope – Harrimanella
Catapodium – Desmazeria
Cayratia – Parthenocissus
Centaurium – Erythraea
Centella – Hydrocotyle
Centranthus – Kentranthus
Centranthus – Valeriana
Cephalaria – Scabiosa
Ceratostigma – Plumbago
Cercestis – Rhektophyllum
Cestrum – Iochroma
Chaenomeles – Cydonia
Chaenorhinum – Linaria
Chamaecyparis – Cupressus
Chamaecytisus – Cytisus
Chamaedaphne – Cassandra
Chamaemelum – Anthemis
Chasmanthium – .Uniola
Cheilanthes – Notholaena
Chiastophyllum – Cotyledon
Chimonobambusa – Arundinaria
Chimonobambusa – Gelidocalamus
Chimonobambusa – Quiongzhuea
Chionohebe – Pygmea
x Chionoscilla – Scilla
Chlorophytum – Diuranthera
Chondrosum – Bouteloua
Chrysanthemum – Dendranthema
Cicerbita – Lactuca
Cionura – Marsdenia
Cissus – Ampelopsis
Cissus – Parthenocissus
x Citrofortunella – Citrus
Citronella – Villaresia
Clarkia – Eucharidium
Clarkia – Godetia
Clavinodum – Arundinaria
Claytonia – Calandrinia
Claytonia – Montia
Clematis – Atragene
Cleyera – Eurya
Clinopodium – Acinos
Clinopodium – Calamintha
Clytostoma – Bignonia
Clytostoma – Pandorea
Cnicus – Carduus
Codonopsis – Campanumoea
Colobanthus – Arenaria
Consolida – Delphinium

x Coralia – Carmichaelia x
    Corallospartium
Cordyline – Dracaena
Cornus – Chamaepericlymenum
Cornus – Dendrobenthamia
Coronilla – Securigera
Cortaderia – Gynerium
Corydalis – Fumaria
Corydalis – Pseudofumaria
Cosmos – Bidens
Cotinus – Rhus
Cotula – Leptinella
Crassula – Rochea
Crassula – Sedum
Crassula – Tillaea
Cremanthodium – Ligularia
Crinodendron – Tricuspidaria
Crocosmia – Antholyza
Crocosmia – Curtonus
Crocosmia – Montbretia
Cruciata – Galium
Ctenanthe – Calathea
Ctenanthe – Stromanthe
x Cupressocyparis – Chamaecyparis
Cyathodes – Leucopogon
Cyathodes – Styphelia
Cyclosorus – Pneumatopteris
Cymbalaria – Linaria
Cynara – Scolymus
Cyperus – Mariscus
Cypripedium – Criogenes
Cyrtanthus – Anoiganthus
Cyrtanthus – Vallota
Cyrtomium – Phanarophlebia
Cyrtomium – Polystichum
Cytisus – Argyrocytisus
Cytisus – Genista
Cytisus – Lembotropis
Cytisus – Spartocytisus

Daboecia – Menziesia
Dacrycarpus – Podocarpus
Dactylorhiza – Orchis
Danae – Ruscus
Darmera – Peltiphyllum
Dasypyrum – Haynaldia
Datura – Brugmansia
Datura – Datura
Davallia – Humata
Delairea – Senecio
Delosperma – Lampranthus
Delosperma – Mesembryanthemum
Dendrocalamus – Bambusa
Derwentia – Hebe
Desmodium – Lespedeza
Dichelostemma – Brodiaea
Dicliptera – Barleria
Dicliptera – Justicia

Diervilla – Weigela
Dietes – Moraea
Diplazium – Athyrium
Disporopsis – Polygonatum
Distictis – Phaedranthus
Distylium – Sycopsis
Dolichothrix – Helichrysum
Dracaena – Pleomele
Dracunculus – Arum
Dregea – Wattakaka
Drepanostachyum – Arundinaria
Drepanostachyum –
    Thamnocalamus
Drepanostachyum –
    Chimonobambusa
Drimys – Tasmannia
Duchesnea – Fragaria
Dunalia – Acnistus
Dypsis – Chrysalidocarpus
Dypsis – Neodypsis

Echeveria – Cotyledon
Echinacea – Rudbeckia
Edraianthus – Wahlenbergia
Egeria – Elodea
Elatostema – Pellionia
Eleutherococcus – Acanthopanax
Elliottia – Botryostege
Elliottia – Cladothamnus
Elymus – Agropyron
Elymus – Leymus
Ensete – Musa
Epilobium – Chamaenerion
Epipremnum – Philodendron
Epipremnum – Scindapsus
Episcia – Alsobia
Eranthis – Aconitum
Erigeron – Aster
Erigeron – Haplopappus
Erysimum – Cheiranthus
Eucodonia – Achimenes
Eupatorium – Ageratina
Eupatorium – Ajania
Eupatorium – Ayapana
Eupatorium – Bartlettina
Euphorbia – Poinsettia
Euryops – Senecio

Fallopia – Bilderdykia
Fallopia – Polygonum
Fallopia – Reynoutria
Farfugium – Ligularia
Fargesia – Arundinaria
Fargesia – Sinarundinaria
Fargesia – Thamnocalamus
Fatsia – Aralia
Felicia – Agathaea
Felicia – Aster

Fibigia – Farsetia
Filipendula – Spiraea
Foeniculum – Ferula
Fortunella -- Citrus
Furcraea – Agave

Galium – Asperula
Galtonia – Hyacinthus
Gaultheria – Chiogenes
Gaultheria – x Gaulnettya
Gaultheria – Pernettya
Gelasine – Sisyrinchium
Genista – Chamaespartium
Genista – Cytisus
Genista – Echinospartum
Genista – Teline
Gentianopsis – Gentiana
Gladiolus – Acidanthera
Gladiolus – Anomalesia
Gladiolus – Homoglossum
Gladiolus – Petamenes
Glechoma – Nepeta
Gloxinia – Seemannia
Gomphocarpus – Asclepias
Goniolimon – Limonium
Graptopetalum – Sedum
Graptopetalum – Tacitus
Greenovia – Sempervivum
Gymnospermium – Leontice

Habranthus – Zephyranthes
Hacquetia – Dondia
x Halimiocistus – Cistus
x Halimiocistus – Halimium
Halimione – Atriplex
Halimium – Cistus
Halimium – x Halimiocistus
Halimium – Helianthemum
Halocarpus – Dacrydium
Haplopappus – Aster
Hechtia – Dyckia
Hedychium – Brachychilum
Hedyscepe – Kentia
Helianthella – Helianthus
Helianthemum – Cistus
Helianthus – Heliopsis
Helichrysum – Gnaphalium
Helictotrichon – Avena
Helictotrichon – Avenula
Heliopsis – Helianthus
Hepatica – Anemone
Herbertia – Alophia
Hermodactylus – Iris
Heterocentron – Schizocentron
Heterotheca – Chrysopsis
Hibbertia – Candollea
Hieracium – Andryala
Himalayacalamus – Arundinaria

Himalayacalamus –
    Drepanostachyum
Hippocrepis – Coronilla
Hippolytia – Achillea
Hippolytia – Tanacetum
Hoheria – Plagianthus
Homalocladium –
    Muehlenbeckia
Howea – Kentia
Hyacinthoides – Endymion
Hyacinthoides – Scilla
Hymenocallis – Elisena
Hymenocallis – Ismene
Hyophorbe – Mascarena
Hypochaeris – Hieracium
Hypoxis – Rhodohypoxis

Incarvillea – Amphicome
Indocalamus – Sasa
Iochroma – Acnistus
Iochroma – Cestrum
Iochroma – Dunalia
Ipheion – Tristagma
Ipheion – Triteleia
Ipomoea – Mina
Ipomoea – Pharbitis
Ipomopsis – Gilia
Ischyrolepis – Restio
Ismelia – Chrysanthemum
Isolepis – Scirpus

Jamesbrittenia – Sutera
Jeffersonia – Plagiorhegma
Jovibarba – Sempervivum
Juncus – Scirpus
Jurinea – Jurinella
Justicia – Beloperone
Justicia – Jacobinia
Justicia – Libonia

Kalanchoe – Bryophyllum
Kalanchoe – Kitchingia
Kalimeris – Aster
Kalimeris – Asteromoea
Kalimeris – Boltonia
Kalopanax – Eleutherococcus
Keckiella – Penstemon
Knautia – Scabiosa
Kniphofia – Tritoma
Kohleria – Isoloma
Kunzea – Leptospermum

Lablab – Dolichos
Lagarosiphon – Elodea
Lagarostrobos – Dacrydium
Lallemantia – Dracocephalum
Lamium – Galeobdolon
Lamium – Lamiastrum

Lampranthus –
    Mesembryanthemum
Lampranthus – Oscularia
Laurentia – Hippobroma
Lavatera – Malva
Ledebouria – Scilla
x Ledodendron – Rhododendron
Lepechinia – Sphacele
Lepidothamnus – Dacrydium
Leptinella – Cotula
Leptodactylon – Gilia
Leucanthemella – Chrysanthemum
Leucanthemella – Leucanthemum
Leucanthemopsis –
    Chrysanthemum
Leucanthemopsis – Tanacetum
Leucanthemum – Chrysanthemum
Leucochrysum – Helipterum
Leucophyta – Calocephalus
Leucopogon – Cyathodes
x Leucoraoulia – Raoulia
Leuzea – Centaurea
Leymus – Elymus
Ligularia – Senecio
Ligustrum – Parasyringa
Lilium – Nomocharis
Limonium – Statice
Linanthus – Linanthastrum
Lindelofia – Adelocaryum
Lindera – Parabenzoin
Liriope – Ophiopogon
Lithocarpus – Quercus
Lithodora – Lithospermum
Littorella – Plantago
Lophomyrtus – Myrtus
Lophomyrtus – Myrtus
Lophospermum – Asarina
Lophospermum – Maurandya
Lophostemon – Tristania
Lotus – Dorycnium
Lotus – Tetragonolobus
Ludwigia – Jussiaea
Luma – Myrtus
x Lycene – Lychnis
Lychnis – Agrostemma
Lychnis – Silene
Lychnis – Viscaria
Lycianthes – Solanum
Lytocaryum – Cocos
Lytocaryum – Microcoelum

Macfadyena – Bignonia
Macfadyena – Doxantha
Machaeranthera – Xylorhiza
Mackaya – Asystasia
Macleaya – Bocconia
Mahonia – Berberis
Mandevilla – Dipladenia

Mandragora – Atropa
Marrubium – Ballota
Matricaria – Chamomilla
Matricaria – Tripleurosperum
Maurandella – Asarina
Maurandella – Maurandya
Maurandya – Asarina
Melicytus – Hymenanthera
Melinis – Rhynchelytrum
Mentha – Preslia
Merremia – Ipomoea
Millettia – Wisteria
Mimulus – Diplacus
Minuartia – Arenaria
Modiolastrum – Malvastrum
Moltkia – Lithodora
Moltkia – Lithospermum
Morina – Acanthocalyx
Mukdenia – Aceriphyllum
Muscari – Hyacinthus
Muscari – Leopoldia
Muscari – Leopoldia
Muscari – Muscarimia
Muscari – Pseudomuscari
Myricaria – Tamarix
Myrteola – Myrtus

Naiocrene – Claytonia
Naiocrene – Montia
Nectaroscordum – Allium
Nematanthus – Hypocyrta
Nemesia – Diascia
Neopaxia – Claytonia
Neopaxia – Montia
Neoregelia – Guzmania
Neoregelia – Nidularium
Nepeta – Dracocephalum
Nepeta – Origanum
Nephrophyllidium – Fauria
Nertera – Coprosma
Nipponanthemum –
    Chrysanthemum
Nipponanthemum –
    Leucanthemum
Nymphoides – Villarsia

Oemleria – Osmaronia
Oenothera – Chamissonia
Olearia – Pachystegia
Olsynium – Phaiophleps
Olsynium – Sisyrinchium
Onixotis – Dipidax
Ophiopogon – Convallaria
Orchis – Dactylorhiza
Oreopteris – Thelypteris
Orostachys – Sedum
Osmanthus – × Osmarea
Osmanthus – Phillyrea

Osteospermum – Dimorphotheca
Othonna – Hertia
Othonna – Othonnopsis
Ozothamhus – Helichrysum

Pachyphragma – Cardamine
Packera – Senecio
Paederota – Veronica
Papaver – Meconopsis
Parahebe – Derwentia
Parahebe – Hebe
Parahebe – Veronica
Paraserianthes – Albizia
Paris – Daiswa
Parthenocissus – Ampelopsis
Parthenocissus – Vitis
Passiflora – Tetrapathaea
Paxistima – Pachystema
Pecteilis – Habenaria
Pelargonium – Geranium
Peltoboykinia – Boykinia
Penstemon – Chelone
Pentaglottis – Anchusa
Pentalinon – Urechites
Pericallis – Senecio
Persea – Machilus
Persicaria – Aconogonon
Persicaria – Bistorta
Persicaria – Polygonum
Persicaria – Tovara
Petrocoptis – Lychnis
Petrophytum – Spiraea
Petrorhagia – Tunica
Petroselinum – Carum
Phegopteris – Thelypteris
Phoenicaulis – Parrya
Photinia – Heteromeles
Photinia – Stransvaesia
Photinia – × Stravinia
Phuopsis – Crucianella
Phyla – Lippia
Phymosia – Sphaeralcea
Physoplexis – Phyteuma
Physostegia – Dracocephalum
Pieris – Arcterica
Pilosella – Hieracium
Piper – Macropiper
Pisonia – Heimerliodendron
Plagiomnium – Mnium
Plecostachys – Helichrysum
Plectranthus – Solenostemon
Pleioblastus – Arundinaria
Pleioblastus – Sasa
Podranea – Tecoma
Polianthes – Bravoa
Polygonum – Persicaria
Polypodium – Phlebodium
Polystichum – Phanerophlebia

Poncirus – Aegle
Potentilla – Comarum
Pratia – Lobelia
Prumnopitys – Podocarpus
Prunus – Amygdalus
Pseudocydonia – Chaenomeles
Pseudopanax – Metapanax
Pseudopanax – Neopanax
Pseudopanax – Nothopanax
Pseudosasa – Arundinaria
Pseudotsuga – Tsuga
Pseudowintera – Drimys
Pterocephalus – Scabiosa
Ptilostemon – Cirsium
Pulicaria – Inula
Pulsatilla – Anemone
Pushkinia – Scilla
Pyrethropsis – Argyranthemum
Pyrethropsis – Chrysanthemum
Pyrethropsis – Leucanthemopsis
Pyrethropsis – Leucanthemum
Pyrrocoma – Haplopappus

Reineckea – Liriope
Retama – Genista
Rhapis – Chamaerops
Rhodanthe – Helipterum
Rhodanthemum –
    Chrysanthemopsis
Rhodanthemum – Chrysanthemum
Rhodanthemum –
    Leucanthemopsis
Rhodanthemum – Leucanthemum
Rhodanthemum – Pyrethropsis
Rhodiola – Clementsia
Rhodiola – Rosularia
Rhodiola – Sedum
Rhododendron – Azalea
Rhododendron – Azaleodendron
Rhododendron – Rhodora
Rhodophiala – Hippeastrum
× Rhodoxis – Hypoxis ×
    Rhodohypoxis
× Rhodoxis – Rhodohypoxis
Rosularia – Cotyledon
Rosularia – Sempervivella
Rothmannia – Gardenia
Ruellia – Dipteracanthus
Ruschia – Mesembryanthemum
Rytidosperma – Merxmuellera

Saccharum – Erianthus
Sagina – Minuartia
Salvia – Salvia
Sanguisorba – Dendriopoterium
Sanguisorba – Poterium
Sasa – Arundinaria
Sasa – Pleioblastus

Sasaella – Arundinaria
Sasaella – Pleioblastus
Sasaella – Sasa
Sasamorpha – Sasa
Satureja – Micromeria
Sauromatum – Arum
Saussurea – Jurinea
Scadoxus – Haemanthus
Schefflera – Brassaia
Schefflera – Dizygotheca
Schefflera – Heptapleurum
Schizachyrium – Andropogon
Schizostachyum – Arundinaria
Schizostachyum – Thamnocalamus
Schoenoplectus – Scirpus
Scirpoides – Scirpus
Scirpus – Eriophorum
Sedum – Hylotelephium
Sedum – Rhodiola
Sedum – Sedastrum
Sedum – Villadia
Semiaquilegia – Aquilegia
Semiaquilegia – Paraquilegia
Semiarundinaria – Arundinaria
Semiarundinaria – Oligostachyum
Senecio – Cineraria
Senecio – Kleinia
Senecio – Ligularia
Senna – Cassia
Seriphidium – Artemisia
Shortia – Schizocodon
Sibbaldiopsis – Potentilla
Sieversia – Geum
Silene – Lychnis
Silene – Melandrium
Silene – Saponaria
Sinacalia – Ligularia
Sinacalia – Senecio
Sinarundinaria – Semiarundinaria
Sinningia – Gesneria
Sinningia – Rechsteineria
Sisymbrium – Hesperis
Sisyrinchium – Phaiophleps
× Smithicodonia –
    × Achimenantha
Solanum – Lycianthes
Soleirolia – Helxine
Solenopsis, – Isotoma
Solenostemon, – Coleus
× Solidaster – Aster
× Solidaster – Solidago

Sorbaria – Spiraea
Sparaxis – Synnotia
Sphaeralcea – Iliamna
Sphaeromeria – Tanacetum
Spirodela – Lemna
Spraguea – Calyptridium
Stachys – Betonica
Steirodiscus – Gamolepis
Stenomesson – Urceolina
Stenotus – Haplopappus
Steptocarpus – Streptocarpella
Stewartia – Stuartia
Stipa – Achnatherum
Stipa – Lasiagrostis
Stipa – Oryzopsis
Strobilanthes – Pteracanthus
Succisa – Scabiosa
Sutera – Bacopa
Syagrus – Arecastrum
Syagrus – Cocos

Tanacetum – Achillea
Tanacetum – Balsamita
Tanacetum – Chrysanthemum
Tanacetum – Matricaria
Tanacetum – Pyrethrum
Tanacetum – Spathipappus
Tanacetum – Sphaeromeria
Tecoma – Tecomaria
Tecomaria – Tecoma
Telekia – Buphthalmum
Tephroseris – Senecio
Tetradium – Euodia
Tetraneuris – Actinella
Tetraneuris – Hymenoxys
Tetrapanax – Fatsia
Thamnocalamus – Arundinaria
Thamnocalamus – Sinarundinaria
Thlaspi – Hutchinsia
Thlaspi – Noccaea
Thuja – Platycladus
Thuja – Thujopsis
Thymus – Origanum
Tiarella – × Heucherella
Tonestus – Haplopappus
Toona – Cedrela
Trachelium – Diosphaera
Trachycarpus – Chamaerops
Tradescantia – Rhoeo
Tradescantia – Setcreasea
Tradescantia – Tradescantia

Tradescantia – Zebrina
Trichopetalum – Anthericum
Trichophorum – Scirpus
Tripetaleia – Elliottia
Tripleurospermum – Matricaria
Tripogandra – Tradescantia
Tristagma – Beauverdia
Tristaniopsis – Tristania
Triteleia – Brodiaea
Tritonia – Crocosmia
Tropaeolum – Nasturtium hort.
Tuberaria – Helianthemum
Tulipa – Amana
Tweedia – Oxypetalum

Ugni – Myrtus
Ullucus – Anredera
Ursinia – Euryops
Uvularia – Oakesiella

Vaccinium – Oxycoccus
Verbascum – Celsia
Verbascum –
    × Celsioverbascum
Verbena – Glandularia
Verbena – Lippia
Veronicastrum – Veronica
Vigna – Phaseolus
Villadia – Sedum
Viola – Erpetion
Vitaliana – Androsace
Vitaliana – Douglasia

Weigela – Diervilla
Weigela – Macrodiervilla

Xanthophthalmum –
    Chrysanthemum
Xanthorhiza – Zanthorhiza

Yushania – Arundinaria
Yushania – Sinarundinaria
Yushania – Thamnocalamus

Zantedeschia – Calla
Zauschneria – Epilobium
Zephyranthes – × Cooperanthes
Zephyranthes – Cooperia
Zephyranthes – Habranthus

# THE NAMING OF PLANTS

> 'The question of nomenclature is
> always a vexed one. The only thing
> certain is, that it is impossible to
> please everyone.'
>
> W.J. BEAN - PREFACE TO FIRST EDITION OF
> Trees & Shrubs Hardy in the British Isles.

Following the acquisition of *The Plant Finder* by the Royal Horticultural Society, the Society's Advisory Panel on Nomenclature and Taxonomy was set up to try to establish the agreed list of plant names now held on the RHS horticultural database and used in this and other RHS publications. The panel looks at all recent and current proposals to change or correct names and strives for a balance between the stability of well-known names and botanical and taxonomic correctness according to the codes of nomenclature.

The Panel reports to the Society's Science and Horticultural Advice Committee. Unlike the independent Horticultural Taxonomy Group (Hortax), its aim is to consider individual problems of plant nomenclature rather than general principles. Chaired by Chris Brickell, the panel includes Susyn Andrews (Kew), Dr James Compton (University of Reading), Dr Stephen Jury (University of Reading), Sabina Knees (Edinburgh), Dr Alan Leslie (RHS), Tony Lord, Dr Simon Thornton-Wood (RHS), Piers Trehane (Index Hortensis) and Adrian Whiteley (RHS).

Many name changes proposed by nurseries and users of the *RHS Plant Finder* over the past year have been adopted but others have yet to be considered and approved by the Panel: we hope that all those who have generously told us about wrong names will be patient if the corrections they suggest are not immediately made: all such opinions are much valued but the volume of information is great and must be thoroughly checked before we make changes.

Families and genera used in the *RHS Plant*

*Finder* are almost always those given in Brummitt's *Vascular Plant Families and Genera*. Thus, for the fifth year, there are no major changes to genera in this edition. For spellings and genders of generic names, Greuter's *Names in Current Use for Extant Plant Genera* is being followed; there are rare cases in which this disagrees with some prominent recent publications such as its use of the spelling *Diplarrhena* as opposed to *Diplarrena* in the current *Flora of Australia*. However, the general effect will be to keep names in exactly the same form as they are already known to gardeners.

In some cases the Panel feels that the conflicting views about the naming of some groups of plants will not be easily resolved. Our policy is to wait until an absolutely clear consensus is reached, not to rush to rename plants only to have to change names a second time when opinions have shifted yet again.

As in last year's, this edition contains few major changes to plant names. Many proposals to make further changes have been resisted until the panel has had time to study them more fully. If nomenclatural arguments are finely balanced, we will retain old names in the interests of stability. This does not alter the fact that all involved in the publication of the *RHS Plant Finder* remain committed to the use of plant names that are as correct as possible. As before, gardeners and nurserymen may still choose to differ and use what names they want, many preferring a more conservative and a few a more radical approach to naming. Except for those names in which we have made corrections of a couple of letters to bring them in line with the codes of nomenclature, we are responsible for none of the name changes in this or any other edition of the *RHS Plant Finder*.

Some publications that have been extremely useful during the last year including *The World Checklist and Bibliography of Conifers* and *The International Conifer Register Part 4:* Juniperus, both of which have influenced Piers Trehane's amendments to conifer names in this edition. *The World Checklist and Bibliography of Fagales* has generally been followed except for those taxa not considered distinct by botanists but nevertheless recognised as being horticulturally significant. *The International Daffodil Register and Classified List 1998* has helped verify and standardise names of daffodil cultivars. I was particularly grateful to obtain a copy of *The International Bougainvillea Check List* (1981) from Dr Brijendra Singh of New Delhi, giving information about the origins of most bougainvillea cultivars. A number of names accepted in our previous editions are shown to be synonyms and are now cross-referred to the originals. Saxifrages have been re-classified according to Richard Gornall's system, adopted by the Saxifrage Society in their *Saxifrages: The Complete List of Species*. *Botanica's Roses* is the most useful, comprehensive and well-illustrated publication on roses to appear for many years and has helped resolve some problems of rose naming, though it reveals dozens of cases in which the same name is used for different roses around the world. The *UPOV-ROM Plant Variety Database* has provided the original and legally-binding form of cultivar names of some plants awarded plant variety rights around the world. In a number of cases, this has also provided the link between code names (the true cultivar epithets) and trade designations under which plants are sold.

The internet has occasionally supplied information about new varieties from the world's most active plant breeders, allowing me to verify or correct a number of new names. The web site of Dan Heims' Terra Nova Nurseries in Oregon was particularly impressive, with pictures of lots of new plants (the tiarellas are stunning), a couple of dozen of them appearing in the *RHS Plant Finder* for the first time this year. This shows what a useful medium this is for disseminating information about and arousing interest in new plants world wide. It is a pity that more of the leading introducers of new plants, including those in the British Isles, do not follow such shining examples.

## RULES OF NOMENCLATURE

Throughout the *RHS Plant Finder* we try to follow the rules of nomenclature set out in the *International Code of Botanical Nomenclature 1994* (ICBN) and the *International Code of Nomenclature for Cultivated Plants 1995* (ICNCP). Cultivar names which are clearly not permissible under the latter and for which there seems to be no valid alternative are marked I (for invalid). The commonest sorts of invalid names seem to be those that are wholly or partly in Latin (not permissible since 1959, e.g. 'Pixie Alba', 'Superba', 'Variegata') and those which use a Latin generic name as a cultivar name (e.g. *Rosa* 'Corylus', *Viola* 'Gazania'). If no prior valid name exists, an enterprising nurseryman may publish a new valid name for any

such plant. This would be considered validly published if it appeared in a dated catalogue with a clear description of the plant; the originator, if still alive, must be willing to accept the new name.

Apart from being discourteous to the plants' originators and their countries, the translating of foreign plant names into English is a bad and insular practice that is likely to cause confusion; it is also contrary to Article 28 of the 1995 ICNCP. In this edition as in the previous one, this and other Articles of the new Code are applied strictly. The Code requires that such translations be considered trade designations and not cultivar names and so should be presented in a different font (here sans serif) and not in quotes. It may be years yet before we make sense of the host of German names and apparent English translations for a genus such as *Coreopsis*, many of which must be synonyms. Throughout the *RHS Plant Finder*, we have tried to give preference to the original name in every case, although English translations are also given as trade designations where they are in general use.

The substitution of slick selling names by nurseries which do not like, or have not bothered to find out, the correct names of the plants they sell is sharp practice not expected of any reputable nursery; it is also a probable breach of the Trades Description Act.

The publication of the ICNCP has done a great deal to clarify nomenclature without generally introducing rules that cause destabilising name changes. However, it significantly alters the sort of plant names that are allowed since 1 January 1996: nurseries who name plants are strongly urged to check that the names they want to use are acceptable under the new Code.

One Article of the 1995 Code that affects names published since 1995, is Art. 17.13, dealing in part with the use of botanical or common generic names within a cultivar or group name. This bans names in which the last word of the cultivar name is the common or botanical name of a genus or species. Two sorts of such names are commonly found: those based on colours (ending Lilac, Lavender, Rose, Rosa, Apricot, Peach, Mauve (French for *Malva*)) and those based on personal names (Rosemary, Hazel). These will be marked I in the *RHS Plant Finder* if known to have been published after 1995 or marked with an asterisk if their date of publication is unknown. This rule does not preclude cultivar epithets ending with common names which apply to only part of a genus such as Cerise, Cherry, Lemon, Lime, Orange, Pink, or Violet, each of which refers to more than one species and/or their hybrids.

An Article of the new Code which the Panel has agreed it cannot implement is Art. 17.11, banning cultivar names consisting of solely adjectival words in a modern language, unless one of these words may be considered a substantive or unless the epithet is the recognized name of a colour. As this rule is retroactive, applying to all cultivar names whenever they were published, if applied strictly it could require rejection of several hundred cultivar names in the *RHS Plant Finder*, many of them very well known and widely used. Furthermore, it is difficult to apply: many adjectives also have substantive meanings, albeit sometimes obscure ones, that might or might not justify acceptance of the names; it is not easy to decide which names of colours are accepted and which are not. Our Panel's judgement is that, as currently worded, this Article is unintentionally restrictive and potentially destabilizing; a future edition of the Code is unlikely to be so proscriptive. So for the time being we will not use this Article as a basis for making changes, nor for declaring already established names unacceptable.

## ORTHOGRAPHY

The ruling on orthography (i.e. correct spelling) of commemorative names, re-stated in the 1994 *International Code of Botanical Nomenclature*, has aroused a great deal of debate at Panel meetings. This subject is discussed in the supplement to Bean's *Trees and Shrubs Hardy in the British Isles* (1988) and is given in ICBN Article 60 and the subsequent recommendations 60C.I. The meaning of Article 60.7 Example 10 (which tells us that the epithet *billardierii*, derived from the part-Latinization Billardierius, is unacceptable and must be corrected to *billardierei*) is not absolutely clear. However, my reading of it is that except for full-scale Latinizations of names (e.g. *brunonius* for Brown, thus *Rosa brunonii*), the name of the person commemorated should remain in its original form. Names ending in -er (e.g. Solander, Faber) may become *solandri* (as in pure Latin, because -er is a usual Latin termination) or *solanderi*, if the specific name was originally spelt in this way. If this interpretation is correct, names such as *backhousiana, catesbaei, glazoviana, manescavii* and *bureavii* are not allowed and must be corrected to *backhouseana, catesbyi, glaziouana, manescaui* and *bureaui* respectively. However, not all of the several authors of the Code share the same interpretation.

If my reading of the Code's rulings on orthography is correct, botanical epithets commemorating someone whose name has been transliterated from script other than Roman (e.g. Cyrillic or Japanese) present problems. Though ICNCP tells us which system of transliteration should be used, it is sometimes difficult to apply orthographic corrections to these: botanists whose names were originally in Cyrillic often had a preferred transliteration of their own name, often based on old French systems in the case of pre-Revolutionary Russian names, and it is hard to justify rejecting these; it is therefore difficult to be dogmatic about the orthography of these. However, implementation of this rule has been assisted by another new publication from Kew, *Authors of Plant Names,* which is particularly helpful in giving acceptable transliterations of names that were originally in Cyrillic.

## VERIFICATION OF NAMES

Although we find that many nurseries have greatly improved the accuracy of their plant names, plants which are new entries often appear in their catalogues under a bewildering variety of wrong names and misspellings. This is partly a reflection on the rarity of the plants and nurserymen are not to be blamed for not finding correct names for plants that do not appear in recent authoritative garden literature. Some plants are simply too new for valid names and descriptions yet to have appeared in print.

Although we try to verify every name which appears in these pages, the amount of time which can be allotted to checking each of over 70,000 entries must be limited. There is always a proportion which do not appear in any of the reference sources used and those unverified names for which there may be scope for error are marked with an asterisk. Such errors may occur with species we cannot find listed (possibly synonyms for more recent and better known names) or may include misspellings (particularly of names transliterated from Japanese or Chinese, or commemorating a person). We are especially circumspect about names not known to the International Registrar for a particular genus. We are always grateful to receive information about the naming and origin of any asterisked plant and once we feel reassured about the plant's pedigree, the asterisk will be removed. Of course, many such names will prove to be absolutely correct and buyers can be reassured if they know that the selling nursery takes great care with the naming of its plants. However, although we are able to check that names are valid, correctly styled and spelt, we have no means of checking that nurseries are applying them to the right plant; *caveat emptor!*

We have great sympathy for gardeners who want to find a particular cultivar but are not sure to which species it belongs. The problem is acute for genera such as *Juniperus* and readers must search through all the entries to find their plants; even nurseries seem uncertain of the species of 'Skyrocket'. Because gardeners generally do not know (or disagree) to which species cultivars of hostas and saxifrages should be ascribed, these have been listed by cultivar first, giving the species in parentheses.

## ADJECTIVAL NAMES

Latin adjectival names, whether for species, subspecies, cultivar etc., must agree in gender with the genus, not with the specific name if the latter is a noun (as for *Styrax obassia, Lonicera caprifolium* etc.). Thus azaleas have to agree with *Rhododendron*, their true genus (neuter), rather than *Azalea* (feminine). For French cultivar names, adjectives should agree with whatever is being described; for roses, this is almost always *la rose* (feminine) but on rare occasions *le rosier* (when describing vegetative characteristics such as climbing forms), *l'oeillet* or *le pompon* (all masculine).

It is often the case that gardeners consider two plants to be distinct but botanists, who know of a whole range of intermediates linking the two, consider them to be the same species. The most notable example is for the rhododendrons, many species of which were 'sunk' in Cullen and Chamberlain's revision. In such cases we have always tried to provide names that retain important horticultural entities, even if not botanically distinct, often by calling the sunk species by a Group name, such as *Rhododendron rubiginosum* Desquamatum Group. Group names are also used for swarms of hybrids with the same parentage. These were formerly treated as grex names, a term now only used for orchids; thus grex names for lilies, bromeliads and begonias are now styled as Groups. A single clone from the Group may be given the same cultivar name, e.g. 'Polar Bear'. In many cases nursery catalogues do not specify whether the named clone is being offered or other selections from the hybrid swarm and entries are therefore given as e.g. *Rhododendron* Polar Bear Group & cl.

One new requirement of the new ICNCP is that cultivar-group names used after 1 January 1996 must have been validly published with a description or reference to a previously published description. Such publication is beyond the scope and purpose of the *RHS Plant Finder*. As editor, I may not style the more variable taxa that appear in this and subsequent editions as cultivar-groups unless they have been published elsewhere as Groups. Nevertheless, I still feel it is helpful to gardeners and other plant users to use cultivar names only for those plants that fulfil the Code's definition of a cultivar ('distinct, uniform and stable') in its narrow sense. This applies particularly to mixtures and races of seed-raised plants that embrace significant variation, are often not distinct from similar named

selections and may be changed in character from year to year: Any new entries that are of this nature are here styled neither as cultivars nor as cultivar-groups but simply as epithets or descriptions, without quotation marks and thus beyond the scope of the new Code. This applies especially to plants described as 'strains' or 'hybrids', though the latter term is sometimes merely a provenance rather than a sign of common parentage. Thus plants here appearing as cultivars with their names in quotes have, as far as I can tell, uniform and predictable characteristics. There are a few cases in which it is difficult to tell whether a 'sunk' species remains horticulturally distinct enough to merit a group name, as for many of the rhododendrons; we would be grateful if users would let us know of any plants that we have 'sunk' in synonymy but which still need to be distinguished by a separate name. In many cases, the plants gardeners grow will be the most extreme variants of a species; although one 'end' of the species will seem to be quite a different plant from the other 'end' to the gardener, the botanist will see them as the outer limits of a continuous range of variation and will give them the same species name. We often hear gardeners complain 'How can these two plants have the same name? They are different!' In such cases, although the botanist may have to 'lump' them under the same name, we will always try to provide an acceptable name to distinguish an important horticultural entity, even if it is not botanically distinct.

## TAXONOMIC RANK

In this edition, subspecies, varietas and forma are shown as subsp., var. and f. respectively. Each of these ranks indicates a successively less significant change in the characteristics of the plant from the original type on which the species was based; in general terms, a subspecies may be expected to be more markedly different from the type of a species than a forma which may differ in only one characteristic such as flower colour, hairiness of leaf or habit.

The ICBN requires the rank of each infraspecific botanical epithet to be given. In many cases, it is not at all clear whether a colour form shown as, say, *alba* is a true botanical forma or a cultivar of garden origin. Our inclination here is not to treat such plants as cultivars if they are recorded as being naturally occurring, nor if they embrace considerable variation: forma *alba* would be preferred if a valid publication is recorded, otherwise a previously-published Group name or a simple description. In the absence of conclusive evidence we will leave such names styled as they are at present and so some ranks remain to be added in future editions. In many cases, *alba* is assumed without any proof to be the correct name for a white-flowered variant though research often shows that the validly published name is something quite different such as *albiflora*, *leucantha* or *nivea*.

## AUTHOR CITATIONS

In many cases the same species name has been used by two or more authors for quite different plants. Thus *Bloomingthingia grandiflora* of Linnaeus might be an altogether different species from *B. grandiflora* of gardeners (*B. grandiflora* hort.). In such circumstances it becomes necessary to define whose *Bloomingthingia* we are considering by quoting the author of the name directly after the species name. Generally the more recent name will be invalid and may be cross-referenced to the plant's first validly published name. Author's names appear directly after the species name and if abbreviated follow Brummitt and Powell's *Authors of Plant Names;* abbreviations are also listed in e.g. Mabberley's *The Plant-Book.* Such names appear in a smaller typeface, and neither in quotes nor in sans serif font so should not be confused with cultivar names or trade designations. In this edition we have uncovered yet more muddles resulting from two or more plants being known by the same name; we have, we hoped, resolved these by clearer cross-referencing.

## HYPHENATION

Some items of the ICBN have been 'more honour'd in the breach than in the observance'. One such is the ruling on hyphenation (Article 60.9) which forbids the use of hyphens after a 'compounding form' (i.e. *albo*, *pseudo*, *aureo*, *neo*). Hyphens are still permitted to divide separate words such as *novae-angliae* or *uva-crispa* and following the Tokyo Congress, after a vowel terminating a compounding form when followed by the same vowel (e.g. *Gaultheria semi-infera, Gentiana sino-ornata*).

## TERMINATIONS OF COMMEMORATIVE NAMES

Another item of the code which is often ignored is that covering terminations of commemorative names (Article 60.11, referring to Recommendation 60C). A botanical epithet commemorating Helena must be styled *helenae* whereas one commemorating Helen may be styled either *heleniae* or, following Helena as an established Latin form of the same name or, quite frequently, of Ellen, *helenae*; in such cases when either spelling could be legitimate, the original is followed. When there is no accepted Latin alternative, the -*iae* ending is used and this seems to be more correct for *murieliae* and *edithiae*. The genitive form of commemorative names ending in -*a* is always -*ae*, even if a man is being commemorated (as for *Picea koyamae*). It is this same article which requires that the well known *Crocosmia* be spelt *masoniorum* and not *masonorum* and that *Rosa wichurana* be spelt thus and not *wichuraiana*.

The *RHS Plant Finder* is useful not only as a directory of plant sources but as a 'menu' of plants grown by British gardeners. Such a list is of great value not only to private gardeners; landscapers can use it to check the range of plants they can incorporate in designs; gardeners in countries of the European Union can check which plants they can import by Mail Order; botanists can discover the species grown in Britain, some of them from recorded natural sources; nurserymen can use it to select for propagation first-rate plants that are still not readily available; horticultural authors, who often only want to write about plants the public are able to buy, will find it invaluable. For all such users, the *RHS Plant Finder* can be recommended as a source of standard, up-to-date and reliable nomenclature.

**Tony Lord**
April 1999

# BIBLIOGRAPHY

The following list of bibliographic sources and references is by no means exhaustive but lists some of the more useful and available works used in the preparation of the *RHS Plant Finder*.

## GENERAL

*The New Plantsman* and *The Garden* are published regularly by the Royal Horticultural Society, Vincent Square, London SW1P 2PE.

Altwegg, A., Fortgens, G. & Siebler, E. (eds). (1996). *ISU Yearbook 1965-95*. Internationale Stauden-Union, Windisch, Germany.

Armitage, A.M. (1989). *Herbaceous Perennial Plants*. Varsity Press, Athens, Georgia.

Bailey, L.H., Bailey, E.Z. *et al.* (1976). *Hortus Third*. Macmillan, New York.

Bean, W.J. (1970-1988). *Trees and Shrubs Hardy in the British Isles*. (8th ed. edited Sir George Taylor & D.L. Clarke & Supp. ed. D.L. Clarke). John Murray, London.

Beckett, K.A. (ed.) (1993-94). *Encyclopaedia of Alpines*, 1 & 2. Alpine Garden Society, Pershore, Worcs.

Beckett, K.A. (1987). *The RHS Encyclopaedia of House Plants*. Century Hutchinson, London.

Blundell, M. (1992). *Wild Flowers of East Africa*. Collins, London.

Bond, P. & Goldblatt, P. (1984). Plants of the Cape Flora. *Journal of South African Botany*, supp. vol. 13. Kirstenbosch.

Bramwell, D.& Z. (1974). *Wild Flowers of the Canary Islands*. Stanley Thomas, London.

Brickell, C.D. (ed.). (1989). *RHS Gardeners' Encyclopedia of Plants and Flowers*. Dorling Kindersley, London.

Brickell, C.D. (ed.). (1996). *RHS A-Z Encyclopedia of Garden Plants*. Dorling Kindersley, London.

Brummitt, R.K. & Powell, C.E. (1992). *Authors of Plant Names*. Royal Botanic Gardens, Kew.

Brummitt, R.K. (1992). *Vascular Plant Families and Genera*. Royal Botanic Gardens, Kew.

*Catalogue of Cultivars in the United Kingdom National Fruit Collection*. (1998). Wye College and Brogdale Horticultural Trust, Faversham, Kent.

Chittenden, F.J. (ed.). (2nd ed. 1965). *The Royal Horticultural Society Dictionary of Gardening*. Oxford University Press.

Clausen, R.R. & Ekstrom, N.H. (1989). *Perennials for American Gardens*. Random House, New York.

Clement, E.J. & Foster, M.C. (1994). *Alien Plants of the British Isles*. Botanical Society of the British Isles, London.

Cooke, I. (1998). *The Plantfinder's Guide to Tender Perennials*. David & Charles, Newton Abbot, Devon.

Cronquist, A. *et al.* (eds). (Vols 1, 3-6, 1986-97). *Intermountain Flora: Vascular Plants of the Intermountain West, USA*. New York Botanical Garden.

Davis, B.& Knapp, B. (1992). *Know Your Common Plant Names*. MDA Publications, Newbury, Berks.

Davis, P.H. *et al.* (ed.). (1965-1988). *Flora of Turkey*, vols 1-10. University Press, Edinburgh.

Fabian, A. & Germishuizen, G. (1997). *Wild Flowers of Northern South Africa*. Fernwood Press, Vlaeberg, South Africa.

*Flora of New Zealand*, vols 1-3. (1961-80). Wellington, New Zealand.

Eggli, U. & Taylor, N. (1994). *List of Names of Succulent Plants other than Cacti Published 1950-92*. Royal Botanic Gardens, Kew.

Forrest, M. (ed. Nelson, E.C.). (1985). *Trees and Shrubs Cultivated in Ireland*. Boethius Press for An Taisce, Dublin.

Galbraith, J. (1977). *Field Guide to the Wild Flowers of South-East Australia*. Collins, London.

Gillett, H.J. & Walter, K.S. (1998). *1997 IUCN Red List of Threatened Plants*. IUCN, Gland, Switzerland & Cambridge, England.

Graf, A.B. (2nd ed. 1981). *Tropica*. RToehrs, New Jersey.

Greuter, W. *et al.* (ed.). (1994). *International Code of Botanical Nomenclature (Tokyo Code)*. Koeltz Scientific Books, Königstein, Germany.

Greuter, W., Brummitt, R.K., Farr, E. *et al.* (1993). *N.C.U.3 Names in Current Use for Extant Plant Genera*. Koeltz Scientific Books, Königstein, Germany.

Grierson, A.J.C & Long, D.G. (1983-91) vol. 1(1-3) & vol. 2(1); Noltie, H J (1994) vol. 3(1). *Flora of Bhutan*. Royal Botanic GardenEdinburgh.

Griffiths, M. (ed.) (1994). *RHS Index of Garden Plants*. Macmillan, London.

Harkness, M.G. (2nd ed. 1993). *The Bernard E. Harkness Seedlist Handbook*. Batsford, London.

Heath, R.E. (1981). *Collectors Alpines*. Collingridge, Twickenham, London.

Hickman, J.C. (ed.). (1993). *The Jepson Manual: Higher Plants of California*. University of California Press, Berkeley & Los Angeles.

*Hillier Manual of Trees and Shrubs*. (6th ed. 1991). David & Charles, Newton Abbot, Devon.

Hirose, Y. & Yokoi, M. (1998). *Variegated Plants in Colour*. Varie Nine, Yamate-cho, Iwakuni, Japan.

Hogg, R. (5th ed. 1884). *The Fruit Manual*. Journal of Horticulture Office, London.

Huxley, A. (ed.). (1992). *The New Royal Horticultural Society Dictionary of Gardening.* Macmillan, London.

*Index Kewensis on Compact Disc* (Version 2 1997). Oxford University Press.

Jacobsen, H. (1973). *Lexicon of Succulent Plants.* Blandford, London.

Jellitto, L. & Schacht, W. (3rd ed. 1990). Schacht, W. & Fessler, A. *Hardy Herbaceous Perennials.* Timber Press, Portland, Oregon.

Kelly, J. (ed.). (1995). *The Hillier Gardener's Guide to Trees and Shrubs.* David & Charles, Newton Abbot, Devon.

Krüssmann, G. (English ed. trans. M E Epp). (1984-1986*). Manual of Cultivated Broadleaved Trees & Shrubs,* vols 1-3. Batsford, London.

Laar, H.J. van de. (1989). *Naamlijst van Houtige Gewassen.* Proefstation voor de Boomteelt en het Stedelijk Groen, Boskoop, Holland.

Laar, H.J. van de & Fortgens, Ing. G (1988). *Naamlijst van Vaste Planten.* Proefstation voor de Boomkwekerij, Boskoop, Holland.

Leslie, A.C. (1993). *New Cultivars of Herbaceous Perennial Plants* 1985-1990. Hardy Plant Society.

Mabberley, D.J. (1987). *The Plant-Book.* Cambridge University Press.

McGregor, R.L., Barkley, T.M. *et al.* (1986). *Flora of the Great Plains.* University Press of Kansas.

Metcalf, L.J. (1987). *The Cultivation of New Zealand Trees and Shrubs.* Reed Methuen, Auckland, New Zealand.

Morin, N.R. *et al.* (eds) (Vols 1-3 1993-97). *Flora of North America.* Oxford University Press, New York.

Ohwi, J. (ed F.G. Meyer & E. Walker). (1965). *Flora of Japan.* Smithsonian Institution, Washington.

Phillips, R. & Rix, E.M. (1997). *Conservatory and Indoor Plants,* vols 1 & 2. Macmillan, London.

Phillips, R. & Rix, E.M. (1989). *Shrubs.* Pan Books, London.

Phillips, R. & Rix, E.M. (1991/2). *Perennials.* Pan Books, London.

Phillips, R. & Rix, E.M. (1993). *Vegetables.* Pan Books Ltd, London.

*The New Plantsman.* Royal Horticultural Society, London.

Polunin, O. & Stainton, A. (1984). *Flowers of the Himalaya.* Oxford University Press.

Press, J.R. & Short, M.J. (1994). *Flora of Madeira.* HMSO, London.

Rehder, R. (2nd ed. 1940). *Manual of Cultivated Trees & Shrubs Hardy in North America.* Macmillan, New York.

Stace, C.A. (2nd ed. 1997). *New Flora of the British Isles.* Cambridge University Press.

Stainton, A. (1988). *Flowers of the Himalaya: A Supplement.* Oxford University Press.

Stearn, W.T. (2nd ed. 1973). *Botanical Latin.* David & Charles. Newton Abbot, England.

Stearn, W.T. (1992). *Stearn's Dictionary of Plant Names for Gardeners.* Cassell, London.

Taffler, S. (1988-98). *The Sport.* Hardy Plant Society Variegated Plant Group, South Petherton, Somerset.

Thomas, G.S. (3rd ed. 1990). *Perennial Garden Plants.* J M Dent & Sons, London.

Trehane, R.P. (1989). *Index Hortensis* (Vol. 1: Perennials). Quarterjack Publishing, Wimborne, Dorset.

Trehane, R.P. (1995). *International Code of Nomenclature for Cultivated Plants - 1995.* Quarterjack Publishing, Wimborne, Dorset.

Tutin, T.G. (1964-1980). *Flora Europaea,* vols 1-5. Cambridge University Press.

Tutin, T.G. *et al.* (2nd ed. 1993). *Flora Europaea,* vol 1. Cambridge University Press.

Van der Werff, D. (ed.). (1995-98). *New, Rare and Elusive Plants,* vols 1-3. Aquilegia Publishing, Hartlepool, Co. Durham.

Walters, S.M. (ed.). *et al.* (1984, 1986, 1989, 1995 & 1997). *The European Garden Flora,* vols 1-5. Cambridge University Press.

Willis, J.C. (8th ed. 1973). Revised Airy Shaw, H.K. *A Dictionary of the Flowering Plants and Ferns.* Cambridge University Press.

Wilson, H.D. (1978). *Wild Plants of Mount Cook National Park.* Christchurch, New Zealand.

Zander, R. (1993). *Handwörterbuch der Pflanzennamen.* Ulmer, Stuttgart, Germany.

## GENERA

*Acacia*

Beckett, K.A. (1993). *The Plantsman,* 15(3):131-47.

Simmons, M.H. (2nd ed. 1987). *Acacias of Australia.* Nelson, Melbourne, Australia.

*Acaena*

Yeo, P.F. (1972). The species of *Acaena* with Spherical Heads Cultivated and Naturalized in the British Isles. Green, P. S. (ed.). *Plants Wild and Cultivated* Botanical Society of the British Isles, Middlesex.

*Acer*

De Jong, P.C. *et al. International Dendrology Society Year Book 1990:* 6-50. London.

Gelderen, D.M. van, De Jong, P.C. & Oterdoom, H.J. (1994). *Maples of the World.* Timber Press, Portland, Oregon.

Harris, J.G.S. (1983). *The Plantsman,* 5(1): 35-58.

Vertrees, J.D. (1978). *Japanese Maples.* Timber Press, Oregon.

*Adiantum*

Goudry, C.J. (1985). *Maidenhair Ferns in Cultivation.* Lothian, Melbourne, Australia.

*Aeschynanthus*
Dates, J.D. *The Gesneriad Register 1990*: Check List of Aeschynanthus. American Gloxinia and Gesneriad Society, Galesburg, Illinois.
*Aesculus*
Wright, D. (1985). *The Plantsman*, 6(4): 228-47.
*Agapetes*
Argent, G.C.G. & Woods, P.J.B. (1988). *The Plantsman*, 8(2): 65-85.
*Ajuga*
Adam, C.G. (1982). *Alpine Garden Society Bulletin*, 50(1): 82-84.
*Allium*
Dadd, R. (1997). *The Garden*, 122(9): 658-61.
Davies, D. (1992). *Alliums*. Batsford, London.
Mathew, B. (1996). *A Review of* Allium *section* Allium. Royal Botanic Gardens, Kew.
*Alnus*
Ashburner, K. (1986). *The Plantsman*, 8(3): 170-88.
*Androsace*
Smith, G.F. & Lowe, D.B. (1977). *Androsaces*. Alpine Garden Society.
*Anemone,* Japanese
McKendrick, M. (1990). *The Plantsman*, 12(3): 140-51.
McKendrick, M. (1998). *The Garden*, 123(9): 628-33.
*Anemone nemorosa*
Toubøl, U. (1981). *The Plantsman*, 3(3): 167-74.
*Anthemis tinctoria*
Leslie, A.C. (1997). *The Garden*, 122(8): 552-55.
*Apiaceae (Umbelliferae)*
Ingram, T. (1993). *Umbellifers*. Hardy Plant Society, Pershore, Worcs.
Pimenov, M.G. & Leonov, M.V. (1993). *The Genera of the* Umbelliferae. Royal Botanic Gardens, Kew.
*Aquilegia*
Munz, P.A. (1946). *Aquilegia*: The Cultivated and Wild Columbines. *Gentes Herbarum*, 7(1). Bailey Hortorium, New York.
*Araceae*
Bown, D. (1988). *Aroids*. Century Hutchinson, London.
*Arecaceae (Palmae - palms)*
Jones, D.L. (1997). *Palms Throughout the World*. Reed Books, Chatswood, NSW, Australia.
Uhl, N.J. & Dransfield, J. (1987). *Genera Palmarum*. Alan Press, Lawrence, Kansas.
*Argyranthemum*
Cheek, R. (1993). *The Garden*, 118(8): 350-55.
Humphries, C.J. (1976). A Revision of the Macaronesian Genus *Argyranthemum. The Bulletin of the British Museum (Natural History)*, Botany, 5(4).
*Arisaema*
Gusman, G. (1997). *Alpine Garden Society Bulletin*, 65(1): 105-08 & 65(2): 195-200.
Mayo, J.J. (1982). *The Plantsman*, 3(4): 193-209.

Pradhan, U.C. (2nd ed. 1997). *Himalayan Cobra-lilies* (Arisaema): *Their Botany and Culture*. Primulaceae Books, Kalimpong, West Bengal, India.
*Arum*
Boyce, P. (1993). *The Genus* Arum. HMSO,London.
*Asplenium*
Rickard, M. (1997). *The Garden*, 122(2): 86-92.
*Aster*
Picton, P. (199?). *A Guide to the Asters Grown By Old Court Nurseries*. Old Court Nurseries, Colwall, Worcs.
Ranson, E.R. (1947). *Michaelmas Daisies*. Garden Book Club.
*Aubrieta*
*International Registration Authority Checklist* Weihenstephan.
*Begonia*
Ingles, J. (1990). *American Begonia Society Listing of Begonia Cultivars*. (Revised Edition Buxton Checklist).
Wall, B. (1989). *The Plantsman*, 11(1): 4-14.
Thompson, M.L. & Thompson, E.J. (1981). *Begonias: The Complete Reference Guide*. Times Books, New York.
*Betula*
Ashburner, K. (1980). *The Plantsman*, 2(1): 31-53.
Ashburner, K. & Schilling, A.D. (1985). *The Plantsman*, 7(2): 116-25.
Hunt, D. (ed.) (1993). Betula: *Proceedings of the IDS Betula Symposium*. International Dendrology Society, Richmond, Surrey.
*Bougainvillea*
Bor, N.L. & Raizada, M.B. (2nd ed. 1982). *Some Beautiful Indian Climbers and Shrubs*: 291-304. Bombay Natural History Society.
Choudhury, B. & Singh, B. (1981). *The International Bougainvillea Check List*. Indian Agricultural Research Institute, New Delhi.
Gillis, W.T. (1976). Bougainvilleas of Cultivation. *Baileya* 20(1): 34-41. New York.
Iredell, J. (1990). *The Bougainvillea Grower's Handbook*. Simon & Schuster, Brookvale, Australia.
Iredell, J. (1994). *Growing Bougainvilleas*. Cassell, London.
MacDaniels, L.H. (1981). A Study of Cultivars in *Bougainvillea. Baileya* 21(2): 77-100. New York.
Swithinbank, A. (1995). *The Garden*, 120(10): 634-37.
*Bromeliaceae*
Beadle, D.A. (1991). *A Preliminary Listing of all the Known Cultivar and Grex Names for the* Bromeliaceae. Bromeliad Society, Corpus Christi, Texas.
Luther, H.E. & Sieff, E. (1991). *An Alphabetical List of Bromeliad Binomials*. Bromeliad Society, Orlando, Florida.

Rauh, W. (1979). *Bromeliads*. Blandford Press, Dorset.

**Brugmansia**
Shaw, J.M.H. (1998). *The New Plantsman*, 5(1): 48-60 & 5(3): 192.

**Buddleja**
Maunder, M. (1987). *The Plantsman*, 9(2): 65-80.

**Bulbs**
Bryan, J.E. (1989). *Bulbs*, vols 1 & 2. Christopher Helm, Bromley, Kent.

Du Plessis, N. and Duncan, G. (1989). *Bulbous Plants of Southern Africa*. Tafelberg, Cape Town, South Africa.

Grey-Wilson, C. & Matthew, B. (1981). *Bulbs*. Collins, London.

Rix, M. & Phillips, R. (1981). *The Bulb Book*. Pan Books, London.

Scheepen, J. van (ed.). (1991). *International Checklist for Hyacinths and Miscellaneous Bulbs*. KAVB, Hillegom, Netherlands.

**Buxus**
Batdorf, L.R. (1989). *Checklist of Buxus*. American Boxwood Society.

Braimbridge, E. (1994). *The Plantsman*, 15(4): 236-54.

**Callistemon**
Mitchem, C.M. (1993). *The Plantsman*, 15(1): 29-41.

**Calluna** see **Heathers**

**Calochortus**
Martinelli, S. (1995). *Alpine Garden Society Bulletin*, 63(1 & 2): 71-92, 180-99. Pershore, Worcestershire.

**Camellia**
Gonos, A.A. (ed.) (22nd rev. ed. 1996). *Camellia Nomenclature*. Southern California Camellia Society.

Savige, T.J. (1993, corrected 1994). *The International Camellia Register*. The International Camellia Society, Wirlinga, Australia.

**Campanula**
Lewis, P. & Lynch, M. (2nd ed. 1998). *Campanulas*. Batsford, London

**Carnivorous Plants**
Pietropaulo, J. & Pietropaulo, P. (1986). *Carnivorous Plants of the World*. Timber Press, Oregon.

Slack, A. (1988). Rev. ed. *Carnivorous Plants*. Alphabooks, Sherborne, Dorset.

**Carpinus**
Rushforth, K. (1986). *The Plantsman*, 7(3 & 4): 173-91 & 212-16.

**Caryopteris**
Pattison, G. (1989). *The Plantsman*, 11(1): 15-18.

**Cassiope**
Blake, F.S. (1985). *Alpine Garden Society Bulletin*, 53(1): 61-65.

Starling, B. (1989). *The Plantsman*, 11(2): 106-16.

Stone, M. (1998). *Alpine Garden Society Bulletin*, 66(4): 484-92.

**Ceanothus**
Gardiner, J. (1997). *The Garden*, 122(5): 308-11.

**Cercidiphyllum**
Lancaster, C.R. (1997). *The Garden*, 122(10): 720-21.

**Cestrum**
Beckett, K.A. (1987). *The Plantsman*, 9(3): 129-32.

**Chaenomeles**
Jewell, D. (1998). *The Garden*, 123(2): 90-93.

Weber, C. (1963). Cultivars in the Genus *Chaenomeles*. *Arnoldia*, 23(3): 17-75. Arnold Arboretum, Harvard, Massachusetts.

**Chrysanthemum (Dendranthema)**
Brummitt, R.K. (1997). The Garden, 122(9): 662-63.

Gosling, S.G. (ed.). (1964). *British National Register of names of Chrysanthemums 1964*. National Chrysanthemum Society, Whetstone, London.

McDougall, A. (comp.). (1997). *British National Register of Names of Chrysanthemums: Amalgamated Edition 1964-96*. National Chrysanthemum Society, Amington, Staffs.

**Cimicifuga**
Compton, J. (1992). *The Plantsman*, 14(2): 99-115.

Compton, J. (1997). *Botanical Journal of the Linnean Society*, 123(1): 1-23.

**Cistus**
Page, R.G. (1991). *The Plantsman*, 13(3): 143-56.

Page, R.G. (1996). *The New Plantsman*, 3(3): 184-89.

Page, R.G. (1998). *The New Plantsman*, 5(4): 219-30.

**Citrus**
Davies, F.S. & Albrigo, L.G. (1994). *Citrus*. CAB International, Wallingford, Oxon.

Saunt, J. (1990). *Citrus Varieties of the World*. Sinclair International Ltd., Norwich, England.

**Cladrastis**
Ma, J. & Spongberg, S.A. (1997). *International Dendrology Society Yearbook 1996*: 27-34.

**Clematis**
Evison, R.J. (1998). *The Gardener's Guide to Growing Clematis*. David & Charles, Newton Abbot, Devon.

Evison, R.J. & Matthews, V. (1994). *The New Plantsman*, 1(2): 95-101.

Fisk, J. (1989). *Clematis, the Queen of Climbers*. Cassell, London.

Fretwell, B. (1989). *Clematis*. Collins, London.

Grey-Wilson, C. (1986). *The Plantsman*, 7(4): 193-204.

Hutchins, G. (1990). *The Plantsman*, 11(4): 193-208.

Lloyd, C. & Bennett, T.H. (1989). *Clematis*. Viking, London.

Oviatt-Ham, M. (1996). *The Garden*, 121(3): 140-45.

Snoeijer, W. (1991). *Clematis Index.* Fopma, Boskoop, Netherlands.

Snoeijer, W. (1996). *Checklist of Clematis Grown in Holland.* Fopma, Boskoop, Netherlands.

*Codonopsis*
Matthews, Y.S. (1980). *Alpine Garden Society Bulletin*, 48(2): 96-108.

Grey-Wilson, C. (1990). *The Plantsman*, 12(2): 65-99.

Grey-Wilson, C. (1995). *The New Plantsman*, 2(4): 213-25.

**Conifers**
Farjon, A. (1998). *World Checklist and Bibliography of Conifers.* Royal Botanic Gardens, Kew.

Krüssmann, G. (English trans. M.E. Epp). (1985). *Manual of Cultivated Conifers.* Batsford,London.

Lewis, J. (ed.). Leslie, A.C. (1987 & 1989). *The International Conifer Register*, pt 1 (*Abies* to *Austrotaxus*), pt 2 (*Belis* to *Pherosphaera* (excluding Cypresses and Junipers) & pt 3 (Cypresses). Royal Horticultural Society, London.

Ouden, P. den & Boom, B.K. (1965). *Manual of Cultivated Conifers.* Martinus Nijhorff, The Hague, Netherlands.

Welch, H.J. (1979). *Manual of Dwarf Conifers.* Theophrastus, New York.

Welch, H.J. (1990). *The Conifer Manual*, 1. Kluwer Academic Publishers, Dordrecht, Holland.

Welch, H.J. (1993). *The World Checklist of Conifers.* Landsman's Bookshops Ltd, Bromyard, Herefordshire.

*Coprosma*
Hutchins, G. (1995). *The New Plantsman*, 2(1): 12-37.

*Cornus*
Flanagan, M. (1997). *The Garden*, 123(1): 16-19.

Howard, R.A. (1961). Registration Lists of Cultivar Names in *Cornus* L., *Arnoldia*, 21(2): 9-18. Arnold Arboretum, Harvard, Massachusetts.

*Corokia*
Hutchins, G. (1994). *The Plantsman*, 15(4):225-35.

*Corydalis*
Lidén, M. and Zetterlund, H. (1988). *Alpine Garden Society Bulletin*, 56(2): 146-69.

Lidén, M. and Zetterlund, H. (1997). *Corydalis.* Alpine Garden Society, Pershore, Worcs.

Rix, E.M. (1993). *The Plantsman*, 15(3): 129-30.

*Corylopsis*
Wright, D. (1982). *The Plantsman*, 4(1): 29-53.

*Corylus*
Crawford, M. (1995). *Hazelnuts: Production and Culture.* Agroforestry Research Trust, Dartington, Devon.

Game, M. (1995). *The Garden*, 120(11): 674-77.

*Cotoneaster*
Fryer, J. (1996). *The Garden*, 121(11): 709-15.

Fryer, J. & Hylmö, B. (1998). *The New Plantsman*, 5(3): 132-44.

*Crassulaceae*
Eggli, U. & 't Hart, H. (1995). *Evolution and Systematics of the* Crassulaceae. Backhuys Publishers, Leiden, Netherlands.

*Crocosmia*
Kostelijk, P.J. (1984). *The Plantsman*, 5(4): 246-53.

*Crocus*
Jacobsen, N. Ørgaard, M. & Scheepen, J. van. (1997). *The New Plantsman*, 4(1): 6-38.

Kerdorff, H. & Pasche, E. (1996). *Alpine Garden Society Bulletin*, 64(3): 296-312.

Kerdorff, H. & Pasche, E. (1996). *Alpine Garden Society Bulletin*, 64(4): 459-67.

Mathew, B. (1982). *The Crocus.* Batsford, London

*Cyclamen*
Grey-Wilson, C. (1988). *The Genus* Cyclamen. Christopher Helm, Bromley, Kent.

Grey-Wilson, C. (1991). *The Plantsman*, 13(1): 1-20.

Grey-Wilson, C. (1997). *Cyclamen.* Batsford, London.

*Cypripedium*
Cribb, P. (1997). *The Genus* Cypripedium. Timber Press, Portland, Oregon.

*Cynara*
Wiklund, A. (1992). *The Genus* Cynara. Botanical Journal of the Linnean Society, 109(1): 75-123.

*Cyrtanthus*
Holford, F. (1989). *The Plantsman*, 11(3): 170-75.

*Dahlia*
Pycraft, D. (1969-95) & Hedge, R. (1996&'97). *International Register of Dahlia Names 1969* & supps 1-8. Royal Horticultural Society, London.

*Daphne*
Brickell, C.D. & Mathew, B. (1976). *Daphne.* Alpine Garden Society.

*Delphinium*
Leslie, A.C. (1996). *The International* Delphinium *Register Cumulative Supplement 1970-1995.* Royal Horticultural Society, London.

**Dendranthema** *see* **Chrysanthemum**
*Deutzia*
Taylor, J. (1990). *The Plantsman*, 11(4): 225-40.

*Dianthus*
Leslie, A.C. (2nd ed. & supps 1-13 1983-96). *The International* Dianthus *Register.* Royal Horticultural Society, London.

*Diascia*
Benham, S. (1987). *The Plantsman*, 9(1): 1-17.

Harrison, H. (1996). *The Hardy Plant*, 18(1): 41-48. Hardy Plant Society.

Lord, W.A. (1996). *The Garden*, 121(4): 192-94.

*Dierama*
Hilliard, O.M. & Burtt, B.L. (1990). *The Plantsman*, 12(2): 106-12.

Hilliard, O.M. & Burtt, B.L. (1991). *Dierama.* Acorn Books CC. Johannesburg, South Africa.

*Dionysia*
Grey-Wilson, C. (1988). *The Plantsman*, **10**(2): 65-84.

Grey-Wilson, C. (1989). *The Genus* Dionysia. Alpine Garden Society, Woking, Surrey.

*Dodecatheon*
Mitchem, C.M. (1991). *The Plantsman*, **13**(3): 157-70.

*Dracaena*
Bos, J.J., Graven, P., Hetterscheid, W.L.A. & van de Wege, J.J. (1992). *Edinburgh Journal of Botany*, **10**(3): 311-31.

*Drosera*
Cheek, M. (1993). *Kew Magazine*, **10**(3): 138-44. Blackwell, Oxford.

*Epimedium*
Barker, D.G. (1996). *Epimediums and Other Herbaceous* Berberidaceae. Hardy Plant Society, Pershore, Worcs.

Stearn, W.T. (1995). *Curtis's Botanical Magazine*, **12**(1): 15-25. Royal Botanic Gardens, Kew.

White, R. (1996). *The Garden*, **121**(4): 208-14.

*Episcia*
Arnold, P. *The Gesneriad Register 1977*: Episcia. American Gloxinia and Gesneriad Society, Binghamton, New York.

*Erica see also* **Heathers**
Baker, H.A. & Oliver, E.G.H. (1967). *Heathers in Southern Africa.* Purnell, Cape Town, South Africa.

Kirsten, G. & Schuman, D. (1992). *Ericas of South Africa.* Fernwood Press, Vlaeberg, South Africa.

*Eriogonum*
Elliott, J. (1993). *Alpine Garden Society Bulletin*, **61**(2): 200-14.

*Erodium*
Addyman, M. & Clifton, R. (1992). *Erodiums in Cultivation.* NCCPG, Wisley, Surrey.

Bacon, L. (1990). *Alpine Garden Society Bulletin*, **58**(1): 65-83.

Leslie, A.C. (1980). *The Plantsman*, **2**(2): 117-26.

*Erythronium*
Mathew, B. (1992). A Taxonomic and Horticultural Review of *Erythronium. Botanical Journal of the Linnean Society*, **109**(4): 453-71.

Mathew, B. (1998). *Alpine Garden Society Bulletin*, **66**(3): 308-22.

*Eucalyptus*
Kelly, S. (3rd ed. 1989, 2 vols). Eucalyptus. Viking O'Neil, South Yarra, Victoria, Australia.

*Eucomis*
Compton, J. (1990). *The Plantsman*, **12**(3): 129-39.

*Eucryphia*
Wright, D. (1983). *The Plantsman*, **5**(3): 167-85.

*Euonymus*
Brown, N. (1996). *The New Plantsman*, **3**(4): 238-43.

Lancaster, R. (1981). *The Plantsman*, **3**(3): 133-66.

*Euphorbia*
Turner, R. (1995). *Euphorbias.* Batsford, London.

*Fagales*
Frodin, D.G. & Govaerts, R. (1998). *World Checklist and Bibliography of* Fagales. Royal Botanic Gardens, Kew.

*Fagus*
Wyman, D. (1964). Registration List of Cultivar Names of *Fagus* L., *Arnoldia*, **24**(1): 1-8. Arnold Arboretum, Harvard, Massachusetts.

*Fascicularia*
Nelson, E.C. & Zikka, G. (1997). *The New Plantsman*, **4**(4): 232-39.

**Ferns**
Goudey, C.J. (1988). *A Handbook of Ferns for Australia and New Zealand.* Lothian, Port Melbourne, Victoria, Australia.

Johns, R.J. (1996). *Index Filicum: Supplementum Sextum pro Annis 1976-90.* Royal Botanic Gardens, Kew.

Johns, R.J. (1997). *Index Filicum: Supplementum Septimum pro Annis 1991-95.* Royal Botanic Gardens, Kew.

Kaye, R. (1968). *Hardy Ferns.* Faber & Faber, London.

Johns, R.J. (1991). *Pteridophytes of Tropical East Africa.* Royal Botanic Gardens, Kew.

Jones, D.L. (1987). *Encyclopaedia of Ferns.* Lothian, Melbourne, Australia.

Rush, R. (1984). *A Guide to Hardy Ferns.* The British Pteridological Society, London.

*Festuca*
Wilkinson, M.J. & Stace, C.A. (1991). A new taxonomic treatment of the *Festuca ovina* aggregate in the British Isles. *Botanical Journal of the Linnean Society*, **106**(4): 347-97.

*Ficus carica*
Hendy, J. (1997). *The Garden*, **122**(9): 636-40.

*Filipendula*
Barnes, P.G. (1998). *The New Plantsman*, **5**(3): 145-53.

*Fragaria*
Day, D. (ed.). (1988, revd 1993). *Grower Digest 3: Strawberries.* Nexus Business Communications, London.

*Fremontodendron*
McMillan Browse, P. (1992). *The Plantsman*, **14**(1): 41-44.

*Fritillaria*
Jefferson-Brown, M. & Pratt, K. (1997). *The Gardener's Guide to Growing Fritillaries.* David & Charles, Newton Abbot, Devon.

Turrill, W.B. & Seely, J.R. (1980). Studies in the Genus *Fritillaria*. *Hooker's Icones Plantarum*, **39**(1 & 2). Royal Botanic Gardens, Kew.

*Fuchsia*

Bartlett, G. (1996). *Fuchsias - A Colour Guide*. Crowood Press, Marlborough, Wiltshire.

Boullemier, L.B. (2nd ed. 1991). *The Checklist of Species, Hybrids & Cultivars of the Genus* Fuchsia. Blandford Press, Dorset.

Goulding, E. (1995). *Fuchsias: The Complete Guide*. Batsford, London.

Johns, E.A. (1997). *Fuchsias of the 19th and Early 20th Century*. British Fuchsia Society, Summerfield, Worcs.

Nijhuis, M. (1994). *1000 Fuchsias*. Batsford, London.

Nijhuis, M. (1996). *500 More Fuchsias*. Batsford, London.

*Gaultheria* (inc. *Pernettya*).

Middleton, D.J. (1990/91). *The Plantsman*, **12**(3): 167-77 & **13**(3): 188-89.

Middleton, D.J. (1991). Infrageneric Classification of the Genus *Gaultheria*. *Botanical Journal of the Linnean Society*, **106**(3): 229-58.

*Gentiana*

Bartlett, M. (1975). *Gentians*. Blandford Press, Dorset.

Wilkie, D. (2nd ed. 1950). *Gentians*. Country Life, London.

*Geranium*

Abbott, P. (1994). *A Guide to Scented Geraniaceae*. Hill Publicity Services, Angmering, West Sussex.

Bath, T., & Jones, J. (1994). *The Gardener's Guide to Growing Hardy Geraniums*. David & Charles, Newton Abbot, Devon.

Clifton, R.T.F. (1992). *Geranium Family Species Checklist*, **4**(2): Geranium. The Geraniaceae Group of the British Pelargonium and Geranium Society, Kent.

Jones, J. *et al.* (1992). *Hardy Geraniums for the Garden*. Hardy Plant Society, Pershore, Worcs.

Yeo, P.F. (2nd ed. 1992). *Hardy Geraniums*. Croom Helm, London.

*Gesneriaceae*

Dates, J.D. *The Gesneriad Register 1986: Check List of Intergeneric Hybrids in the tribe* Gloxinieae. American Gloxinia and Gesneriad Society, Sugar Grove, Illinois.

Dates, J.D. *The Gesneriad Register 1987: Check List of* Bucinellina, Columnea, Dalbergaria, Pentadenia, Trichantha *and Intergeneric Hybrids*. American Gloxinia and Gesneriad Society, Galesburg, Illinois.

Dates, J.D. *The Gesneriad Register 1990: Appendix C: Registered Gesneriads 1957-90*. American Gloxinia and Gesneriad Society, Galesburg, Illinois.

*Gladiolus*

*British Gladiolus Society List of Cultivars Classified for Show Purposes 1994*. British Gladiolus Society, Mayfield, Derbyshire.

*British Gladiolus Society List of European Cultivars Classified for Exhibition Purposes 1997*. British Gladiolus Society, Mayfield, Derbyshire.

*British Gladiolus Society List of European Cultivars Classified for Exhibition Purposes 1998*. British Gladiolus Society, Mayfield, Derbyshire.

*British Gladiolus Society List of New Zealand Cultivars Classified for Exhibition Purposes 1997*. British Gladiolus Society, Mayfield, Derbyshire.

*British Gladiolus Society List of New Zealand Cultivars Classified for Exhibition Purposes 1998*. British Gladiolus Society, Mayfield, Derbyshire.

*British Gladiolus Society List of North American Cultivars Classified for Exhibition Purposes 1997*. British Gladiolus Society, Mayfield, Derbyshire.

*British Gladiolus Society List of North American Cultivars Classified for Exhibition Purposes 1998*. British Gladiolus Society, Mayfield, Derbyshire.

Goldblatt, P. (1996). Gladiolus *in Tropical Africa*. Timber Press, Portland, Oregon.

Lewis, G.J., Obermeyer, A.A. & Barnard, T.T. (1972). A Revision of the South African Species of *Gladiolus*. *Journal of South African Botany*, supp. vol. **10**. Purnell, Cape Town.

*Gleditsia triacanthos*

Santamour, F.S.Jr. & McArdle, A.J. (198?). *Checklist of Cultivars of Honeylocust*. USA.

*Grevillea*

Olde, P. & Marriott, N. (1995). *The Grevillea Book (3)*. Kangaroo Press, Kenthurst, NSW, Australia.

*Haemanthus*

Snijman, D. (1984). A Revision of the Genus *Haemanthus*. *Journal of South African Botany*, supp. vol. **12**. National Botanic Gardens, Kirstenbosch, South Africa.

*Halimium*

Page, R.G. (1998). *The New Plantsman*, **5**(4): 219-30.

*Hamamelidaceae*

Wright, D. (1982). *The Plantsman*, **4**(1): 29-53.

*Hamamelis*

Coombes, A.J. (1996). *The Garden*, **121**(1): 28-33.

Lane, C. (1998). *The Garden*, **123**(1): 38-41.

Strand, C. (1998). *The New Plantsman*, **5**(4): 231-45.

**Heathers**

Small, D. & Small, A. (1992). *Handy Guide to Heathers*. Denbeigh Heather Nurseries, Suffolk.

Underhill, T. (1990). *Heaths and Heathers*. David & Charles, Newton Abbot, Devon.

*Hebe*

Hayter, T. (ed.). (1986-98). *Hebe News*. 20 Beech Farm Drive, Macclesfield, Cheshire.

Hutchins, G. (1979). *Hebe and Parahebe Species in Cultivation.* County Park Nursery, Essex.

Hutchins, G. (1997). *Hebes Here and There.* Hutchins & Davies, Caversham, Berks.

Chalk, D. (1988). *Hebes and Parahebes.* Christopher Helm, London.

*Hedera*

McAllister, H. (1988). *The Plantsman,* 10(1): 27-29.

McAllister, H.A. & Rutherford, A. (1990). *Hedera helix* & *H. hibernica* in the British Isles. *Watsonia,* 18. 7-15

Rose, P.Q. (1980). *Ivies.* Blandford Press, Dorset.

Rose, P.Q. (1996). *The Gardener's Guide to Growing Ivies.* David & Charles, Newton Abbot, Devon.

Rutherford, A., McAllister, H.A. & Rill, R.R. (1993). *The Plantsman,* 15(2): 115-28.

*Hedychium*

Schilling, A.D. (1982). *The Plantsman,* 4(3): 129-49.

Spencer-Mills, L. (1996). *The Garden,* 121(12): 754-59.

*Helichrysum*

Hilliard, O.M. & Burtt, B.L. (1987). *The Garden,* 112(6): 276-77.

*Heliconia*

Berry, F. & Kress, W.J. (1991). Heliconia: *An Identification Guide.* Smithsonian Institution Press, Washington.

*Helleborus*

Mathew, B. (1981). *The Plantsman,* 3(1): 1-10.

Mathew, B. (1989). *Hellebores.* Alpine Garden Society, Woking, Surrey.

McLewin, W. & Mathew, B. (1995). *The New Plantsman,* 2(2): 112-22.

McLewin, W. & Mathew, B. (1996). *The New Plantsman,* 3(1): 50-60.

McLewin, W. & Mathew, B. (1996). *The New Plantsman,* 3(3): 170-77.

Rice, G. & Strangman, E. (1993). *The Gardener's Guide to Growing Hellebores.* David & Charles, Newton Abbot, Devon.

*Hemerocallis*

Erhardt, W. (1988). Hemerocallis *Daylilies.* Batsford, London.

Kitchingman, R.M. (1985). *The Plantsman,* 7(2): 68-89.

Munson, R.W. (1989). Hemerocallis, *The Daylily.* Timber Press, Oregon.

Webber, S. (ed.). (1988). *Daylily Encyclopaedia.* Webber Gardens, Damascus, Maryland.

Grenfell, D. (1998). *The Gardener's Guide to Growing Daylilies.* David & Charles, Newton Abbot,

*Hibiscus*

Beers, L. & Howie, J. (2nd ed. 1990). *Growing Hibiscus.* Kangaroo Press, Kenthurst, Australia.

Dickings, I. (1995). *The Garden,* 120(8): 487-91.

*Hippeastrum*

*Alfabetische Lijst van de in Nederland in cultuur zijnde Amaryllis* (Hippeastrum) *Cultivars.* (1980). Koninklijke Algemeene Veereniging voor Bloembollencultur, Hillegom, Netherlands.

Read, R. (1998). *The Garden,* 123(10): 734-37.

*Hosta*

Grenfell, D. (1985). *The Plantsman,* 7(4): 251-54.

Grenfell, D. (1990). *Hosta.* Batsford, London.

Grenfell, D. (1993). *Hostas.* The Hardy Plant Society, Pershore, Worcs.

Grenfell, D. (1996). *The Gardener's Guide to Growing Hostas.* David & Charles, Newton Abbot, Devon.

Grenfell, D. (1993). *The Plantsman,* 15(3): 168-84.

Hensen, K.J.W. (1985). *The Plantsman,* 7(1):1-35.

Schmid, W.G. (1991). *The Genus* Hosta. Timber Press, Oregon.

*Hoya*

Innes, C. (1988). *The Plantsman,* 10(3): 129-40.

*Hyacinthus orientalis*

Stebbings, G. (1996). *The Garden,* 121(2): 68-72.

*Hydrangea*

Haworth-Booth, M. (1975). *The Hydrangeas.* Garden Book Club, London.

Lawson-Hall, T. & Rothera, B. (1995). *Hydrangeas.* Batsford, London.

Mallet, C. (1992 & 1994). *Hydrangeas,* 1 & 2. Centre d'Art Floral, Varengeville-sur-Mer, France

*Hypericum*

Lancaster, C.R. & Robson, N.K.B. (1997). *The Garden,* 122(8): 566-71.

Robson, N.K.B. (1980). *The Plantsman,* 1(4): 193-200.

*Ilex*

Andrews, S. (1983). *The Plantsman,* 5(2): 65-81.

Andrews, S. (1984). *The Plantsman,* 6(3): 157-66.

Andrews, S. (1985). *The Garden,* 110(11): 518-22.

Andrews, S. (1994). *The Garden,* 119(12): 580-83.

Dudley, T.R. & Eisenbeiss, G.K. 1973 & (1992). *International Checklist of Cultivated* Ilex 1: *Ilex opaca;* 2: *Ilex crenata.* USDA, Washington.

Galle, F.C. (1997). *Hollies: the Genus* Ilex. Timber Press, Portland, Oregon.

*Impatiens*

Grey-Wilson, C. (1983). *The Plantsman,* 5(2): 65-81.

Grey-Wilson, C. (1997). *The Garden,* 122(8): 583-87.

*Incarvillea*

Grey-Wilson, C. (1994). *The New Plantsman,* 1(1): 36-52.

Grey-Wilson, C. (1998). *The New Plantsman,* 5(2): 76-98.

*Iochroma*

Shaw, J.M.H. (1998). *The New Plantsman,* 5(3): 154-91.

*Iridaceae*
Innes, C. (1985). *The World of* Iridaceae. Holly Gate International, Sussex.
*Iris*
British Iris Society Species Group. (1997). *A Guide to Species Irises.* Cambridge University Press.
Hoog, M.H. (1980). *The Plantsman,* **2**(3): 141-64.
Mathew, B. (1981). *The Iris.* Batsford, London.
Mathew, B. (1993). *The Plantsman,* **15**(1): 14-25.
Stebbings, G. (1997). *The Gardener's Guide to Growing Irises.* David & Charles, Newton Abbot, Devon.
*Iris* (series Unguiculares)
Service, N. (1990). *The Plantsman,* 12(1): 1-9.
*Juniperus*
Lewis, J. (ed. Leslie, A.C.). (1998). *The International Conifer Register Part 4:* Juniperus. Royal Horticultural Society, London.
*Kalmia*
Jaynes, R.A. (1997). Kalmia: *Mountain Laurel and Related Species.* Timber Press, Portland, Oregon.
Pullen, A. (1997). *The Garden,* **122**(6): 400-03.
*Kniphofia*
Grant-Downton, R. (1997). *The New Plantsman,* **4**(3): 148-56.
Taylor, J. (1985). *The Plantsman,* 7(3): 129-60.
*Kohleria*
Dates, J.D. (ed.). *The Gesneriad Register 1985*: Check List of Kohleria. American Gloxinia and Gesneriad Society, Lincoln Acres, California.
*Lachenalia*
Duncan, G.D. (1988). *The Lachenalia* Handbook. *Annals of Kirstenbosch Botanic Gardens,* 17. South Africa.
*Lantana*
Howard, R.A. (1969). A Check List of Cultivar Names used in the Genus *Lantana. Arnoldia* **29**(11): 73-109. Arnold Arboretum, Harvard, Massachusetts.
*Larix*
Horsman, J. (1988). *The Plantsman,* **10**(1): 37-62.
*Lathyrus*
Norton, S. (1994). *The Garden,* **119**(5): 216-21.
Norton, S. (1994). *The New Plantsman,* **1**(2): 78-83.
Norton, S. (1996). *Lathyrus.* NCCPG, Wisley, Surrey.
*Lavandula*
Tucker, A.O. & Hensen, K.J.W. (1985). The Cultivars of Lavender and Lavandin. *Baileya,* **22**(4): 168-177. New York.
*Leguminosae (Caesalpiniaceae, Mimosaceae & Papilionaceae)*
Lewis, G.P. (1987). *Legumes of Bahia.* Royal Botanic Gardens, Kew.
Lock, J.M. (1989). *Legumes of Africa.* Royal Botanic Gardens, Kew.
Lock, J.M. & Heald, J. (1994). *Legumes of Indo-China.* Royal Botanic Gardens, Kew.

Lock, J.M. & Simpson, K. (1991). *Legumes of West Asia.* Royal Botanic Gardens, Kew.
Roskov, Yu.R., Sytin, A.K. & Yakovlev, G.P. (1996). *Legumes of Northern Eurasia.* Royal Botanic Gardens, Kew.
*Leptospermum*
Dawson, M. (1997). *The New Plantsman,* **4**(1): 51-59 & **4**(2): 67-78.
Nomenclature Committee of the Royal New Zealand Institute of Horticulture. (1963). Check List of *Leptospermum* Cultivars. *Journal of the Royal New Zealand Institute of Horticulture,* **5**(5): 224-30. Wellington, New Zealand.
*Leucojum*
Elliott, J. (1992). *The Plantsman,* **14**(2): 70-79.
*Lewisia*
Elliott, R. (1978). *Lewisias.* Alpine Garden Society, Woking.
Mathew, B. (1989). *The Genus* Lewisia. Christopher Helm, Bromley, Kent.
*Liliaceae sensu lato*
Mathew, B. (1989). *The Plantsman,* **11**(2): 89-105.
*Lilium*
Leslie, A.C. (3rd ed. & supps 1-15 1982-94). *The International Lily Register.* Royal Horticultural Society, London.
*Liriodendron*
Andrews, S. (1993). *IDS Yearbook 1992*: 15-19. London.
*Lonicera*
Bradshaw, D. (1991). *The Plantsman,* **13**(2):106-10.
Bradshaw, D. (1995). *The Garden,* **120**(7): 406-11. Royal Horticultural Society, London.
Wright, D. (1983). *The Plantsman,* **4**(4): 236-55.
*Magnolia*
Callaway, D.J. (1994). *Magnolias.* Batsford, London.
Frodin, D.G. & Govaerts, R. (1998). *World Checklist and Bibliography of* Magnoliaceae. Royal Botanic Gardens, Kew.
Holman, N. (1979). *The Plantsman,* 7(1): 36-39.
Hunt, D. (ed.). (1998). *Magnolias and their Allies.* International Magnolia Society & International Dendrology Society, Sherborne, Dorset.
Treseder, N.G. (1978). *Magnolias.* Faber & Faber, London.
*Malus*
Crawford, M. (1994). *Directory of Apple Cultivars.* Agroforestry Research Trust, Dartington, Devon.
Fiala, Fr J.L. (1994). *Flowering Crabapples.* Timber Press, Portland, Oregon.
Morgan, J. & Richards, A. (1993). *The Book of Apples.* Ebury Press, London.
Parfitt, B. (1965). *Index of the Apple Collection at the National Fruit Trials.* Ministry of Agriculture, Fisheries and Food, Faversham, Kent.
Spiers, V. (1996). *Burcombes, Queenies and Colloggetts.* West Brendon, St Dominic, Cornwall.

Taylor, H.V. (1948). *The Apples of England.* Crosby Lockwood, London.

**Meconopsis**

Cobb, J.L.S. (1989). *Meconopsis.* Christopher Helm, Bromley, Kent.

Cox, P.A. (1996). *The New Plantsman,* **3**(2): 80-83.

Grey-Wilson, C. (1992). *The Plantsman,* **14**(1): 1-33.

Grey-Wilson, C. (1996). *The New Plantsman,* **3**(1): 22-39.

**Mimulus**

Silverside, A.J. (1994). *Mimulus:* 180 Years of Confusion. *The Common Ground of Wild and Cultivated Plants* (eds Perry, A.R. & Ellis, R.G.). National Museum of Wales, Cardiff.

**Moraea**

Goldblatt, P. (1986). *The Moraeas of Southern Africa.* National Botanic Gardens of South Africa.

**Narcissus**

Blanchard, J.W. (1990). *Narcissus.* Alpine Garden Society, Woking, Surrey.

Kington, S. (3rd ed. & supp. 1, 1998). *The International Daffodil Register and Classified List 1998.* Royal Horticultural Society, London.

Throckmorton, T.D. (ed.). (1985). *Daffodils to Show & Grow and Abridged Classified List of Daffodil Names.* Royal Horticultural Society and American Daffodil Society, Hernando, Mississippi.

**Nematanthus**

Arnold, P. *The Gesneriad Register 1978: Check List of Nematanthus.* American Gloxinia and Gesneriad Society.

**Nerium**

Pagen, F.J.J. (1987). *Oleanders.* Agricultural University, Wageningen, Holland.

Toogood, A. (1997). *The Garden,* **122**(7): 488-91.

**Nothofagus**

Hill, R.S. & Read, J. (1991). *Botanical Journal of the Linnean Society,* **105**(1): 37-72.

**Nymphaea**

Davies, R. (1993). *Identification of Hardy Nymphaea.* Stapeley Water Gardens Ltd (for the International Water Lily Society), Cheshire.

Swindells, P. (1983). *Waterlilies.* Croom Helm, London.

**Olearia**

Heads, M. (1998). *Botanical Journal of the Linnean Society,* **127**(3): 239-85.

**Orchidaceae**

Cribb, P. & Bailes, C. (1989). *Hardy Orchids.* Christopher Helm, Bromley, Kent.

Hunt, P.F. & Hunt, D.B. (1996). *Sander's List of Orchid Hybrids: Addendum 1991-1995.* Royal Horticultural Society, London.

**Origanum**

Paton, A. (1994). *Kew Magazine,* **11**(3): 109-17.

White, S. (1998). Origanum: *The Herb Marjoram and its Relatives.* NCCPG, Wisley, Surrey.

**Osteospermum**

Cheek, R.V. (1997). *The Garden,* **122**(7): 506-11.

**Ostrya**

Rushforth, K. (1986). *The Plantsman,* **7**(3 & 4): 173-91 & 212-16.

**Oxalis**

Erskine, P. (1998). *Alpine Garden Society Bulletin,* **66**(3): 345-52.

**Paeonia**

Harding, A. & Klehm, R.G. (1993). *The Peony.* Batsford, London.

Haw, S.G. (1991). *The Plantsman,* **13**(2): 94-97.

Haworth-Booth, M. (1963). *The Moutan or Tree Peony.* Garden Book Club, London.

Kessenich, G.M. (1976). *Peonies.* (Variety Check List, pts **1-3**). American Peony Society.

Rogers, A. (1995). *Peonies.* Timber Press, Portland, Oregon.

**Palmae** *see* **Arecaceae**

**Papaveraceae**

Grey-Wilson, C. (1993). *Poppies.* Batsford, London.

**Papaver orientale**

Grey-Wilson, C. (1998). *The Garden,* **123**(5): 320-25.

**Parahebe**

Heads, M. (1994). *Botanical Journal of the Linnean Society,* **115**(1): 65-89.

**Passiflora**

Vanderplank, J. (2nd ed. 1996). *Passion Flowers.* Cassell, London.

**Pelargonium**

Abbott, P.G. (1994). *A Guide to Scented Geraniaceae.* Hill Publicity Services, Angmering, W. Sussex.

Baggust, H. (1988). *Miniature and Dwarf Geraniums.* Christopher Helm, Bromley, Kent.

*A Checklist and Register of Pelargonium Cultivar Names,* pt **1** (1978) & pt **2** (1985). Australian Geranium Society, Sydney.

Clifford, D. (1958). *Pelargoniums.* Blandford Press, London.

*Complete Copy of the Spalding* Pelargonium *Checklist.* Unpublished. USA.

Miller, D. (1996). *Pelargoniums.* Batsford, London.

Van der Walt, J.J.A. *et al.* (1977-88). *Pelargoniums of South Africa,* **1-3**. National Botanic Gardens, Kirstenbosch, South Africa.

**Penstemon**

Charlesworth, G. (1994). *Alpine Garden Society Bulletin,* **62**(2 & 4): 158-80 & 465-75.

Elliott, J. & Thornton-Wood, S. *The Garden,* **122**(9): 652-55.

James, P. & Way, D. (1998). *The Gardener's Guide to Growing Penstemons.* David & Charles, Newton Abbot, Devon.

Lindgren, D.T. (1992). *List and Description of Named Cultivars in the Genus* Penstemon. University of Nebraska.

*Lord, W.A. (1994). *The Garden,* **119**(7): 304-09.*

**Philadelphus**
Taylor, J. (1990). *The Plantsman,* **11**(4): 225-40.
Wright, D. (1980). *The Plantsman,* **2**(2): 104-16.

**Phlomis**
Mann Taylor, J. (1998). Phlomis: *The Neglected Genus.* NCCPG, Wisley, Surrey.

**Phlox**
Wherry, E.T. (1955). *The Genus* Phlox. Morris Arboretum Monographs III, Philadelphia, Penn.

**Phormium**
Heenan, P.B. (1991). *Checklist of* Phormium *Cultivars.* Royal New Zealand Institute of Horticulture, Canterbury, New Zealand.
McBride-Whitehead, V. (1998). *The Garden,* **123**(1): 42-45.

**Phygelius**
Coombes, A.J. (1988). *The Plantsman,* **9**(4): 233-46.

**Phyllostachys**
Renvoize, S. (1995). *Curtis's Botanical Magazine,* **12**(1): 8-15. Royal Botanic Gardens, Kew.

**Pieris**
Bond, J. (1982). *The Plantsman,* **4**(2): 65-75.
Wagenknecht, B.L. (1961). Registration List of Names in the Genus *Pieris. Arnoldia,* **21**(8). Arnold Arboretum, Harvard, Massachusetts.

**Pinus**
Muir, N. (1992). *The Plantsman,* **14**(2): 80-98.

**Poaceae** (*Gramineae* - **Grasses**)
Clayton, W.D. & Renvoize, S.A. (1986). *Genera Graminum.* HMSO, London.
Grounds, R. (1998). *The Plantfinder's Guide to Ornamental Grasses.* David & Charles, Newton Abbot, Devon.
Grounds, R. (1998). *Grasses.* Hardy Plant Society, Pershore, Worcestershire.

**Podocarpus**
Hutchins, G. (1991). *The Plantsman,* **13**(2): 98-105.

**Polemonium**
Nichol-Brown, D. (3rd ed. 1997). Polemonium. Nichol-Brown, Trimdon, Co. Durham.

**Polypodium**
Leslie, A.C. (1993). *The Garden,* **118**(10): 450-52. Royal Horticultural Society, London.

**Potentilla**
Brearley, C. (1991). *The Plantsman,* **13**(1): 42-53.
Brearley, C. (1992). *Alpine Garden Society Bulletin,* **60**(3 & 4): 321-28 & 428-35.

**Potentilla** (shrubby).
Brearley, C. (1987). *The Plantsman,* **9**(2): 90-109.
Davidson, C.G., Enns, R.J. & Gobin, S. (1994). *A Checklist of* Potentilla fruticosa: *The Shrubby Potentillas.* Agriculture and Agri-Food Canada Research Centre, Morden, Manitoba, Canada.
Davidson, C.G. & Lenz, L.M. (1989). Experimental Taxonomy of *Potentilla fruticosa. Canadian Journal of Botany,* **67**(12): 3520-28.

**Primula**
Fenderson, G.K. (1986). *A Synoptic Guide to the Genus* Primula. Allen Press, Lawrence, Kansas.
Green, R. (1976). *Asiatic Primulas.* The Alpine Garden Society, Woking.
Halda, J.J. (1992). *The Genus* Primula. Tethys Books, Colorado.
Hecker, W.R. (1971). *Auriculas & Primroses.* Batsford, London.
Richards, J. (1993). Primula. Batsford, London.
Smith, G.F., Burrow, B. & Lowe, D.B. (1984). *Primulas of Europe and America.* The Alpine Garden Society, Woking.
Wemyss-Cooke, T.J. (1986). *Primulas Old and New.* David & Charles, Newton Abbot.

**Primula allionii**
Marcham, A.J. (1992). *Alpine Garden Society Bulletin,* **60**(3): 255-67.

**Primula auricula** hort.
Baker, G. & Ward, P. (1995). *Auriculas.* Batsford, London.
Baker, G. (199?). *Double Auriculas.* National Auricula and Primula Society, Midland and West Section.
Baker, G. & Ward, P. (1995). *Auriculas.* Batsford, London.
Hawkes, A. (1995). *Striped Auriculas.* National Auricula and Primula Society, Midland and West Section.
Nicolle, G. (1996). *Border Auriculas.* National Auricula and Primula Society, Midland and West Section.
Telford, D. (1993). *Alpine Auriculas.* National Auricula and Primula Society, Midland and West Section.
Ward, P. (1991). *Show Auriculas.* National Auricula and Primula Society, Midland and West Section.

**Proteaceae**
Rebelo, T. (1995). *Proteas: A Field Guide to the Proteas of Southern Africa.* Fernwood Press, Vlaeberg, South Africa.

**Prunus**
Bultitude, J. *Index of the Plum Collection at the National Fruit Trials.* Ministry of Agriculture, Fisheries & Food, Faversham, Kent.
Crawford, M. (1996). *Plums.* Agroforestry Research Trust, Dartington, Devon.
Crawford, M. (1997). *Cherries: Production and Culture.* Agroforestry Research Trust, Dartington, Devon.
Grubb, N.H. (1949). *Cherries.* Crosby Lockwood, London.
*Index of the Cherry Collection at the National Fruit Trials.* 1986. Ministry of Agriculture, Fisheries & Food, Faversham, Kent.
Jacobsen, A.L. (1992). *Purpleleaf Plums.* Timber Press, Portland, Oregon.

Jefferson, R.M. & Wain, K.K. (1984). *The Nomenclature of Cultivated Flowering Cherries* (Prunus): *The Sato-zakura Group.* USDA, Washington

Smith, M.W.G. (1978). *Catalogue of the Plums at the National Fruit Trials.* Ministry of Agriculture, Fisheries & Food, Faversham, Kent.

Taylor, H.V. (1949). *The Plums of England.* Crosby Lockwood, London.

*Pulmonaria*

Hewitt, J. (1994). *Pulmonarias.* The Hardy Plant Society, Pershore, Worcs.

Hewitt, J. (1999). *The Garden,* **124**(2): 98-105.

Mathew, B. (1982). *The Plantsman,* **4**(2): 100-11.

*Pyracantha*

Egolf, D.R. & Andrick, A.O. (1995). *A Checklist of* Pyracantha *cultivars.* USDA, Washington

*Pyrus*

Crawford, M. (1996). *Directory of Pear Cultivars.* Agroforestry Research Trust, Dartington, Devon.

Parfitt, B. (1981). *Index of the Pear Collection at the National Fruit Trials.* Ministry of Agriculture, Fisheries & Food, Faversham, Kent.

Smith, M.W.G. (1976). *Catalogue of the British Pears.* Ministry of Agriculture, Fisheries & Food, Faversham, Kent

*Quercus*

Ávalos, S.V. (1995). *Contribución al concimiento del género* Quercus (Fagaceae) *en el estado de Guerrero, Mexico.* Facultad de Ciencias, UNAM, Ciudad Universitaria, Mexico.

Miller, H.A.& Lamb, S.H. (1985). *Oaks of North America.* Naturegraph Publishers, Happy Camp, California.

Mitchell, A. (1994). *The Plantsman,* **15**(4): 216-24.

Muir, N. (1996). *The New Plantsman,* **3**(4): 216-36.

*Ranunculus ficaria*

Carter, J.R.L. (1996). *The Garden,* **121**(2): 90-95.

*Raoulia*

Hutchins, G. (1980). *The Plantsman,* **2**(2): 100-03.

*Rhododendron*

Argent, G., Bond, J.D., Chamberlain, D.F., Cox, P.A. & Hardy, G.A. *The Rhododendron Handbook 1998.* Royal Horticultural Society, London.

Argent, G., Fairweather, G. & Walker, K. *Accepted Names in* Rhododendron *section* Vireya. Royal Botanic Garden, Edinburgh.

Chamberlain, D.F. (1982). *Notes from the Royal Botanic Garden, Edinburgh,* **39**(2). HMSO, Edinburgh.

Chamberlain, D.F. & Rae, S.J. (1990). A Revision of *Rhododendron* IV Subgenus *Tsutsusi. Edinburgh Journal of Botany,* **47**(2). HMSO, Edinburgh.

Cox, P.A. & Cox, K.N.E. (1988). *Encyclopaedia of* Rhododendron *Hybrids.* Batsford, London.

Cullen, J. (1980). *Notes from the Royal Botanic Garden, Edinburgh,* **39**(1). HMSO, Edinburgh.

Davidian, H.H. (1982, 1989, 1992 & 1995). *The* Rhododendron *Species,* **1-4**. Batsford, London.

Galle, F.C. (1987). *Azaleas.* Timber Press, Portland, Oregon.

Lee, F.P. (1958). *The Azalea Book.* D. Van Nostrand, New York.

Leslie, A.C. (comp.). (1980). *The Rhododendron Handbook.* Royal Horticultural Society, London.

Leslie, A.C. (1989). *The International Rhododendron Register:* Checklist of Rhododendron Names Registered 1989-1994 & supps 28-36. Royal Horticultural Society, London.

Salley, H.E. & Greer, H.E. (1986). Rhododendron *Hybrids.* Batsford, London.

Tamura, T. (ed.). (1989). *Azaleas in Kurume.* International Azalea Festival '89, Kurume, Japan.

*Rhus*

Coombes, A.J. (1994). *The New Plantsman,* **1**(2): 107-113.

*Ribes*

Crawford, M. (1997). *Currants and Gooseberries: Production and Culture.* Agroforestry Research Trust, Dartington, Devon.

*Index of the Bush Fruit Collection at the National Fruit Trials.* 1987. Ministry of Agriculture, Fisheries & Food, Faversham, Kent.

*Romneya*

McMillan Browse, P. (1989). *The Plantsman,* **11**(2): 121-24.

*Rosa*

Austin, D. (1988). *The Heritage of the Rose.* Antique Collectors' Club, Woodbridge, Suffolk.

Austin, D. (2nd ed. 1996). *English Roses.* Conran Octopus, London.

Beales, P. (1992). *Roses.* Harvill, London.

Beales, P., Cairns, T., Duncan, W. *et al.* (1998). *Botanica's Roses.* Grange Books, Hoo, Kent.

Bean, W.J. (1900-1988). 8th ed. rev. D.L. Clarke & G.S. Thomas. *Rosa* in *Trees and Shrubs Hardy in the British Isles,* **4** & supp.

Dickerson, B.C. (1992). *The Old Rose Advisor.* Timber Press, Portland, Oregon.

Haw, S.G. (1996). *The New Plantsman,* **3**(3): 143-46.

McCann, S. (1985). *Miniature Roses.* David & Charles, Newton Abbot, Devon.

Pawsey, A. (16th ed. 1998). *Find That Rose!* British Rose Growers' Association, Colchester, Essex.

Phillips, R. & Rix, M. (1988). *Roses.* Macmillan, London.

Phillips, R. & Rix, M. (1993). *The Quest for the Rose.* BBC Books, London.

Thomas, G.S. (1995). *The Graham Stuart Thomas Rose Book.* John Murray, London

Verrier, S. (1996). Rosa gallica. *Florilegium,* Balmain, NSW, Australia.

*Roscoea*
Wilford, R. (1999). *Alpine Garden Society Bulletin*, 67(1): 93-101.
*Rosularia*
Eggli, U. (1988). *A monograph study of the genus* Rosularia. Bradleya, 6 suppl. British Cactus & Succulent Society, Bury, Lancs.
*Salix*
Newsholme, C. (1992). *Willows*. Batsford, London.
*Salvia*
Clebsch, B. (1997). *A Book of Salvias*. Timber Press, Portland, Oregon.
Compton, J. (1994). *The Plantsman*, 15(4):193-215.
*Saxifraga*
Horny, R., Webr, K.M. & Byam-Grounds, J. (1986). Porophyllum *Saxifrages*. Byam-Grounds Publications, Stamford, Lincs.
Kohlein, F. (1984). *Saxifrages and Related Genera*. Batsford, London.
McGregor, M. (1995). *Saxifrages: The Complete Cultivars and Hybrids (International Register of Saxifrages*, 1st ed.). The Saxifrage Society.
McGregor, M. & Harding, W. (1998). S*axifrages: The Complete List of Species*. The Saxifrage Society, Driffield, East Yorkshire.
Webb, D.A.& Cornell, R.J. (1989). *Saxifrages of Europe*. Christopher Helm, Bromley, Kent.
*Saxifragaceae*
Stocks, A. (1995). *Saxifragaceae*. Hardy Plant Society.
*Schisandra*
Whiteley, A. (1997). *The New Plantsman*, 4(2): 88-97.
*Sedum*
Evans, R.L. (1983). *Handbook of Cultivated Sedums*. Ivory Head Press Motcombe, Dorset.
Hensen, K.J.W. & Groendijk-Wilders, N. (1986). *The Plantsman*, 8(1): 1-20.
Stephenson, R. (1994). Sedum. Timber Press, Portland Oregon.
*Sempervivum*
Mitchell, P.J. (1985). *International Cultivar Register for* Jovibarba, Rosularia, Sempervivum. The Sempervivum Society, W. Sussex.
*Shortia*
Barnes, P.G. (1990). *The Plantsman*, 12(1): 23-34.
*Sinningia*
Dates, J.D. *The Gesneriad Register 1988: Check List of* Sinningia. American Gloxinia and Gesneriad Society, Galesburg, Illinois.
*Skimmia*
Brown, P.D. (1980). *The Plantsman*, 1(4): 224-59.
*Solenostemon*
Pedley, W.K. & Pedley, R. (1974). *Coleus - A Guide to Cultivation and Identification*. Bartholemew, Edinburgh.
*Sophora*
Hutchins, G. (1993). *The Plantsman*, 15(1): 1-13.

*Sorbus*
McAllister, H. (1985). *The Plantsman*, 6(4): 248-55.
McAllister, H. (1996). *The Garden*, 121(9): 561-67.
Rushforth, K. (1991). *The Plantsman*, 13(2): 111-24.
Rushforth, K. (1992). *The Plantsman*, 13(4): 226-42 & 14(1): 54-62.
Wright, D. (1981). *The Plantsman*, 3(2): 65-98.
*Streptocalyx*
Innes, C. (1993). *The Plantsman*, 15(2): 73-81.
*Streptocarpus*
Arnold, P. *The Gesneriad Register 1979: Check List of* Streptocarpus. American Gloxinia and Gesneriad Society, Binghamton, New York.
*Sutherlandia*
Schrire, B.D & Andrews, S. (1992). *The Plantsman*, 14(2): 65-69.
*Syringa*
Fiala, Fr J.L. (1988). *Lilacs*. Christopher Helm, Bromley, Kent.
Rogers, O.M. (1976). *Tentative International Register of Cultivar Names in the Genus* Syringa. University of New Hampshire.
Taylor, J. (1990). *The Plantsman*, 11(4): 225-40.
Vrugtman, F. (1976-83). *Bulletin of the American Association of Botanical Gardens and Arboreta*.
*Tilia*
Muir, N. (1984). *The Plantsman*, 5(4): 206-42.
Muir, N. (1988). *The Plantsman*, 10(2): 104-27.
*Tillandsia*
Kiff, L.F. (1991). *A Distributional Checklist of the Genus* Tillandsia. Botanical Diversions, Encino, California.
*Tricyrtis*
Chesters, J. & Lanyon, J. (1996). *The Garden*, 121(9): 536-39.
Matthew, B. (1985). *The Plantsman*, 6(4): 193-224.
*Trillium*
Case, F.W. & Case, R.B. (1997). *Trilliums*. Timber Press, Portland, Oregon.
Jacobs, D.L. & Jacobs, R.L. (1997). *American Treasures*. Eco-Gardens, Decatur, Georgia.
Mitchell, R.J. (1989-92). *The Plantsman*, 10(4): 216-31, 11(2 & 3): 67-79 & 132-51, 12(1): 44-60, 13(4): 219-25.
*Tulbaghia*
Benham, S. (1993). *The Plantsman,* 15(2): 89-110.
*Tulipa*
*Classified List and International Register of Tulip Names*. (1987). Royal General Bulbgrowers' Association, Hillegom, Holland.
*Ulmus*
Green, P.S. (1964). Registration of the Cultivar Names in *Ulmus*. Arnoldia, 24(608). Arnold Arboretum, Harvard, Massachusetts.
*Umbelliferae see Apiaceae*

*Veratrum*
Mathew, B. (1989). *The Plantsman*, 11(1): 34-61.
*Viola*
Coombs, R.E. 1981 *Violets.* Croom Helm,
London.
Farrar, E. (1989). *Pansies, Violas & Sweet Violets.*
Hurst Village Publishing, Reading.
Fuller, R. (1990). *Pansies, Violas & Violettas.*
Crowood Press, Marlborough, Wiltshire.
Perfect, E.G. (1996). *Armand Millet and his Violets.*
Park Farm Press, High Wycombe, Bucks.
Zambra, GL. (2nd ed. 1950). *Violets for Garden
and Market.* Collingridge, London.
*Vitis*
Pearkes, G. (1989). *Vine Growing in Britain.* Dent,
London.
Robinson, J. (1986). *Vines, Grapes and Wines.*
Mitchell Beazley, London.
*Watsonia*
Goldblatt, P. (1989). *The Genus* Watsonia.
National Botanic Gardens, South Africa.
*Weigela*
Howard, R.A. (1965). A Check-list of Cultivar
Names in *Weigela. Arnoldia*, 25(9-11). Arnold
Arboretum, Harvard, Massachusetts.

Taylor, J. (1990). *The Plantsman*, 11(4): 225-40.
*Wisteria*
McMillan-Browse, P. (1984). *The Plantsman*, 6(2):
109-22.
Valder, P. (1995). *Wisterias.* Florilegium, Balmain,
N.S.W., Australia.
*Zantedeschia*
Toogood, A. & Mattin, A. (1998). *The Garden*,
123(3): 176-79.
*Zauschneria (Epilobium).*
Raven, P.H. (1976). *Annals of the Missouri Botanic
Garden*, 63 326-340.
*Zelkova*
Ainsworth, P. (1989). *The Plantsman*, 11(2):
80-86.
Hunt, D. (1994). *I.D.S. Yearbook 1993*, 33-41.
International Dendrology Society, Sherborne,
Dorset.
Muir, N. (1991). *The Plantsman*, 13(2): 125-26.

# INTERNATIONAL PLANT FINDERS

## CANADA

Ashley, A. & P. (comp.). (1996/97). *The Canadian
Plant Source Book.* ISBN 0-9694566-2-X. 21,000
hardy plants available at retail and wholesale
nurseries across Canada, including those who ship
to US. English common names & English & French
cross-indexes. Orders: 93 Fentiman Avenue, Ottawa,
ON, Canada, K1S OT7. T (613) 730-0755. F
(613) 730-2095. E-mail apashley@cyberus.ca  $20
(Canadian or US) inc. p&p. Add $5 for airmail.

## GERMANY

Erhardt, A. & W. (comp.). (3rd ed. 1997). *PPP-
Index.* ISBN-3-8001-6621-6. 80,000 plants from
1,200 European nurseries. CD-ROM included.
Orders: *The European Plant Finder*, 10 Market
Street, Lewes, East Sussex, BN7 2NB, UK or Verlag
Eugen Ulmer, PO Box 70 05 61, D-70574
Stuttgart. T (49) 711-4507-121. E-mail
info@ulmer.de DM 58,00.

## ITALY

Feroni, F. C., & Volta, T. (comp.) & Mondadori, G.
(ed.). (1996). *Il Cercapiante.* ISBN 88-374-1366-1.

15,000 plants from 400 nurseries including 100
specialist suppliers; 100 European nurseries; all
Italian botanical and professional Associations, all
Italian Garden Clubs, wide Bibliography. Orders: Via
Andrea Ponti 10, 20143 Milano. T (02) 89166367.
E-mail edgmonga@tin.it  L. 25,000.

## NETHERLANDS

Hart, S. (ed.). (1997/98). *Plantenvinder voor de Lage
Landen.* ISBN 90-6255-732-5. Approx. 45,000
plants and 140 nurseries. Orders: Uitgeverij
TERRA, Postbus 188, 7200AD Zutphen. T (31)
575 525222. F (31) 575 525242. Dfl. 24,50.

## NEW ZEALAND

Gaddum, M. (comp.). (1997). *New Zealand Plant
Finder.* ISBN 1- 86953-375-5. 22,000 plants
(and seeds) listed from 160 nurseries with retail
facilities. Common names included and indexed.
Orders: PO Box 2237, Gisborne. T (64 6) 862
3418. E-mail meg@infogarden.co.nz NZ$29.95
plus postage overseas. Website containing
searchable, up to date database of at least 33,000
plants & seeds: www.infogarden.co.nz
Subscription NZ$40.00.

## UNITED KINGDOM

Pawsey, A. (ed.). (17th ed. 1999). *Find That Rose!*
Covers Autumn 1999 & Spring 2000 and lists
approx. 2,900 varieties with basic type, colour and
fragrance code together with full details of approx
70 growers. Orders: British Rose Growers
Association, 303 Mile End Road, Colchester, Essex
CO4 5EA. Website: www.city2000com/sh/rose-
growers  SAE for info. or £2.50 for a copy.

Platt, K. (ed.). (3rd ed. 1998). *The Seed Search.*
ISBN 0-9528810-2-0. A directory of over 40,000
seeds, including over 6,000 vegetables, with details
and essential information on suppliers from around
the world. Lists seeds of trees, flowers, vegetables,
herbs. Also English common names and hazardous
plants, seeds. Orders: 35 Longfield Road, Crookes,
Sheffield S10 1QW. T/F 0114 268 1700. E-mail
k@seedsearch.demon.co.uk  Website:
www.seedsearch.demon.co.uk  £11.99 (p&p £1.75).

## USA

Isaacson, R. (comp.). (4th ed. 1996). *The Andersen
Horticultural Library's Source List of Plants and Seeds.*
Approx. 59,000 plants and seeds from 450 retail &
wholesale outlets in the US & Canada. All are
prepared to ship interstate. Does not include
Orchids, Cacti or Succulents.

Facciola, S. (ed.). (1998). *Cornucopia II - A Source
Book of Edible Plants.* ISBN 0-9628087-2-5. A very
substantial and comprehensive volume (713 pages)
which documents 3,000 species of edible plants &
7,000 cultivars available in the US and abroad.
Orders: Kampong Publications, 1870 Sunrise
Drive, Vista, California 92084. T (760) 726-0990.
US$40.00.

Barton, B. (comp.). (5th ed. 1997). *Gardening by
Mail.* ISBN 0-395-87770-9. A directory of mail
order resources for gardeners in the USA and
Canada, including seed companies, nurseries,
suppliers of all garden necessaries and ornaments,
horticultural and plant societies, magazines,
libraries and books. E-mail & web addresses
included. Orders: Houghton Miffin Co., 222
Berkeley Street, Boston, MA 02116. T (800) 726-
0600. E-mail tusker@ap.net  US$24.

New England Wild Flower Society. (1999). *Sources
of Propagated Native Plants and Wildflowers.* Source
list of US nurseries selling nursery propagated,
North American native plants and seeds. 75
nurseries listed. US $3.50 plus $1 postage. *New
England Wild Flower Society Seed & Book Catalogue,*
lists for sale 225-250 North American wildflower
seeds. US $2.50 plus $1.75 postage. Orders: New
England Wild Flower Society, Garden in the
Woods, 180 Hemenway Road, Framingham, MA
01701-2699. E-mail newfs.org Website:
http://www.newfs.org

Shank, D. (ed.). (Vol 9, Issues 1&2, 1998). *Hortus
West: A Western North America Native Plant
Directory & Journal.* Issn 1085 7095. Directory lists
2,500 western native species commercially available
through 200 native plant vendors in eleven Western
United States and two Canadian provinces.

# HOW TO USE THE NURSERY LISTINGS

## NURSERY DETAILS BY CODE

The details given for each nursery have been compiled from information supplied to us in answer to a questionnaire. In some cases, because of constraints of space, the entries have been slightly abbreviated and blanks have been left where no information has been provided.

Each nursery is allocated a code, for example SLan. The first letter of each code indicates the main area of the country in which the nursery is situated. In this example, S=Southern England. The remaining three letters reflect the nursery's name, in this case Langley Boxwood Nursery.

In this main listing the nurseries are given in alphabetical order of codes for quick reference from the Plant Directory. All of the nurseries' details, such as address, opening times, mail order service etc., will be found here. If you wish to visit any of these nurseries you can find its location on the relevant map (following p.920), unless the nursery has requested this is not shown (this usually applies to mail order only nurseries).

## OPENING TIMES

The word 'daily' implies every day including Sunday and Bank Holidays. Although opening times have been published as submitted and where applicable, it is always advisable, especially if travelling a long distance, to check with the nursery first.

## MAIL ORDER - UK & EU

Many nurseries provide a mail order service which, in many cases, now extends to all members of the European Union. Where it is shown that there is 'No minimum charge' (Nmc) it should be realised that to send even one plant may involve the nursery in substantial postage and packing costs. Even so, some nurseries may not be prepared to send tender or bulky plants.

## EXPORT

Export refers to mail order beyond the European Union. Nurseries that are prepared to consider exporting are indicated. However, there is usually a substantial minimum charge and, in addition, all the costs of Phytosanitary Certificates and Customs have to be met by the purchaser.

## CATALOGUE COST

Some nurseries offer their catalogue free, or for a few stamps (the odd value quoted can usually be made up from a combination of first or second class stamps), but a large (at least A5) stamped addressed envelope is always appreciated as well. Overseas customers should use an equivalent number of International Reply Coupons (IRCs) in place of stamps.

## WHOLESALE OR RETAIL

All nurseries listed in the *RHS Plant Finder* provide a retail service. Many retailers also have a wholesale trade and would frequently be prepared to offer discounts for large single orders.

## SPECIALIST NURSERIES

This is a new list of nurseries which has been introduced to help those with an interest in finding specialist categories of plant. Nurseries have been asked to classify themselves under one or more headings where this represents the type of plant they *predominantly* or *exclusively* have in stock. For example, if you wish to find a nursery specialising in ornamental grasses, look up 'Grasses' in the new listing where you will find a list of nursery codes. Then turn to the Nursery Details by Code, for details of the nurseries. In all cases, please ensure you ring to confirm the range available, before embarking on a journey to the nursery.

The specialist plant groups listed in this edition are:

| | |
|---|---|
| Alpines/rock | Grasses |
| Aquatics | Ferns |
| Bamboos | Fruit |
| Bulbous plants | Herbs |
| Cactus & succulents | Orchids |
| Carnivorous | Ornamental trees |
| Climbers | Seed |
| Conifers | Wild flowers. |
| Conservatory plants | |

Perennials and shrubs have been omitted as these are considered to be too general and serviced by a great proportion of the nurseries.

## NURSERY INDEX BY NAME

For convenience, an alphabetical index of nurseries is included on p.xxx. This gives the names of all nurseries listed in the book in alphabetical order of nursery name together with their code.

## DELETED NURSERIES

Every year a few nurseries ask to be deleted. This may be because they are about to move or close, or they are changing the way in which they trade. A small number do not reply and, as we have no current information concerning them, they are therefore deleted.

*Please, never use an old edition*

# USING THE THREE NURSERY LISTINGS

Your first reference from the Plant Directory is the Nursery Details by Code listing, which includes all relevant information for each nursery in order of nursery code. The Specialist Nurseries index is to aid those searching for a particular group of plants. The Nursery Index by Name is an alphabetical list for those who know a nursery's name but not its code and wish to check its details in the main list.

## 1 NURSERY DETAILS BY CODE

Once you have found your plant in the Plant Directory, turn to this list to find out the name, address, opening times and other details of the nurseries whose codes accompany the plant.

> ⊠ Mail order to UK or EU
> ⊠ Exports beyond EU
> ⊠ Also supplies Wholesale    ◆ See Display advertisement

**LLin**

*A geographical code is followed by three letters reflecting the nursery's name*

**LINCLUDEN NURSERY** ⊠ EU ⊠ ⊠ ◆
Bisley Green, Bisley, Woking, Surrey,
GU24 9EN
☎ (01483) 797005   **Fax:** (01483) 474015
**Contact:** Mr & Mrs J A Tilbury
**Opening times:** 0930-1630 Mon-Sat all year
exc. B/Hols.
**Min. mail order UK:** No minimum charge
**Min. mail order EU:** Nmc
**Cat. cost:** 3 x 1st class
**Credit cards:** Visa, MasterCard
**Specialities:** Dwarf, slow-growing & unusual
Conifers.
**Map ref:** 3, A1

*Refer to the box at the base of each right-hand page for a key to the symbols*

*A brief summary of the plants available plus any other special characteristics of the nursery*

*The map number is followed by the nursery's grid reference on the map*

## 2 SPECIALIST NURSERIES

A new list of 14 categories under which nurseries have classified themselves if they exclusively, or predominantly, supply this range of plants.

### CONIFERS

CKen CSli ECho EHul EOrn
GChr GPin IMGH LBee
LCon LLin MAsh MBar
MGos NMoo NPoe SCoo
SLim SMer SSmi WBuc
WCwm WDin WGor

## 3 NURSERY INDEX BY NAME

If you seek a particular nursery, look it up in this alphabetical index. Note its code and turn to the Nursery Details by Code list for more information.

| Michael Lewington Gardener-Plantsman | **LLew** |
| Lilliesleaf Nursery | **GLil** |
| Lime Cross Nursery | **SLim** |
| Lincluden Nursery | **LLin** |
| Lingen Nursery and Garden | **WLin** |
| Liscahane Nursery | **ILsc** |
| Lisdoonan Herbs | **ILis** |
| Little Brook Fuchsias | **SLBF** |

# NURSERY DETAILS BY CODE

Please note that all these nurseries are listed in alphabetical order by their code. All nurseries are listed in alphabetical order by their name in the **Nursery Index by Name** on page 912.

## SOUTH WEST ENGLAND

**CAbb**   ABBOTSBURY SUB-TROPICAL
GARDENS ⊠ EU
Abbotsbury, Nr Weymouth, Dorset, DT3 4LA
☎ (01305) 871344/412
**Fax:** (01305) 871344
**Contact:** David Sutton
**Opening times:** 1000-1800 daily mid
Mar-1st Nov. 1000-1500 Nov-mid Mar.
**Min. mail order UK:** £10.00 + p&p
**Min. mail order EU:** £20.00 + p&p
**Cat. cost:** £2 + A4 Sae + 42p stamp
**Credit cards:** Not for telephone orders
**Specialities:** Less common & tender Shrubs
incl. Palms, Tree Ferns, Bamboos, & plants
from Australia, New Zealand & South Africa.
**Map ref:** 2, C2

**CAbP**   ABBEY PLANTS
Chaffeymoor, Bourton, Gillingham, Dorset,
SP8 5BY
☎ (01747) 840841
**Contact:** K Potts
**Opening times:** 1000-1300 & 1400-1700
Tue-Sat Mar-Nov. Dec-Feb by appt.
**Mail order:** None
**Cat. cost:** 2 x 2nd class
**Credit cards:** None
**Specialities:** Flowering Trees & Shrubs. Shrub
Roses incl. many unusual varieties.
**Map ref:** 2, B2

**CAgr**   AGROFORESTRY RESEARCH
TRUST ⊠ UK
46 Hunters Moon, Dartington, Totnes,
Devon, TQ9 6JT
**E-mail:** agrorestr@aol.com
**Web site:** http://members.aol.com/agrorestr/
homepage.html

**Contact:** Martin Crawford
**Opening times:** Not open - mail order only.
**Min. mail order UK:** No minimum charge
**Cat. cost:** 3 x 1st class
**Credit cards:** None
**Specialities:** Mostly Trees, Shrubs &
Perennials. Alnus, Berberis, Amelanchier,
Carya, Elaeagnus, Juglans, Pinus, Quercus &
Salix. Also seeds.

**CArn**   ARNE HERBS ⊠ EU ▣ ▣
Limeburn Nurseries, Limeburn Hill, Chew
Magna, Avon, BS40 8QW
☎ (01275) 333399   **Fax:** (01275) 333399
**E-Mail:** lyman@lymandixon.freeserve.co.uk
**Contact:** A Lyman-Dixon & Jenny Thomas
**Opening times:** Most times - please check first.
**Min. mail order UK:** No minimum charge
**Min. mail order EU:** Nmc
**Cat. cost:** £2.00 UK, 6 x IRC refundable on
first order.
**Credit cards:** None
**Specialities:** Herbs, Wild Flowers & Cottage
Flowers.
**Map ref:** 2, A2

**CAsh**   ASHFIELD COURT NURSERIES ⊠ EU ▣
Farringdon, North Petherton, Somerset,
TA6 6PF
☎ (01278) 663438   **Fax:** (01278) 663438
**Contact:** Michael Michieli
**Opening times:** 1000-1400 Wed, 1430-1700
Sun Apr-Oct. Other times by appt.
**Min. mail order UK:** No minimum charge
**Min. mail order EU:** Nmc
**Cat. cost:** 2 x 1st class
**Credit cards:** None
**Specialities:** Verbena - National Collection.
**Map ref:** 2, B1

**CAvo**   AVON BULBS ⊠ EU ▣
Burnt House Farm, Mid-Lambrook, South
Petherton, Somerset, TA13 5HE
☎ (01460) 242177
**Contact:** C Ireland-Jones
**Opening times:** Thu, Fri, Sat mid Sep-end

C

Oct & mid Feb-end Mar for collection of pre-booked orders.
**Min. mail order UK:** £10.00 + p&p
**Min. mail order EU:** £20.00 + p&p
**Cat. cost:** 4 x 2nd class
**Credit cards:** Visa, Access
**Specialities:** Smaller & unusual Bulbs.
**Map ref:** 2, B1

**CAxe  AXE VALLEY PENSTEMONS**
Blue Firs, Wessiters, Seaton, Devon, EX12 2PJ
☎ (01297) 625342  **Fax:** (01297) 24085
**E-Mail:** Sher.Bluefirs@btinternet.com
**Contact:** Mrs S K Reynolds
**Opening times:** 1400-1700 Thurs mid April-mid Sept. Other times by appt.
**Mail order:** None
**Cat. cost:** Free plant list
**Credit cards:** None
**Specialities:** Penstemons. National Collection of Penstemon cultivars.
**Map ref:** 2, C1

**CB&S  BURNCOOSE & SOUTH DOWN NURSERIES** ⊠ EU ▣ ▣
Gwennap, Redruth, Cornwall, TR16 6BJ
☎ (01209) 861112  **Fax:** (01209) 860011
**E-mail:** burncoose@eclipse.co.uk
**Web site:** http://www.eclipse.co.uk/burncoose
**Contact:** C H Williams & D Knuckey NDH
**Opening times:** 0800-1700 Mon-Sat & 1100-1700 Sun.
**Min. mail order UK:** No minimum charge
**Min. mail order EU:** Nmc*
**Cat. cost:** £1.50 inc p&p
**Credit cards:** Visa, Access, American Express, Switch
**Specialities:** Extensive range of over 3000 Ornamental Trees & Shrubs and Herbaceous. Magnolia, Rhododendron, rare & unusual. Conservatory plants. 30 acre garden. *Note: Individual quotations for EC sales.
**Map ref:** 1, C1

**CBar  BARTERS FARM NURSERIES LTD** ▣
Chapmanslade, Westbury, Wiltshire, BA13 4AL
☎ (01373) 832694  **Fax:** (01373) 832677
**Contact:** D Travers
**Opening times:** 0900-1700 Mon-Sat & 1000-1700 Sun & B/Hols.
**Mail order:** None
**Cat. cost:** A4 Sae
**Credit cards:** Visa, Switch, MasterCard
**Specialities:** Wide range of Shrubs. Ground Cover, Patio plants, container Trees, Ferns, half-hardy Perennials, Grasses, Herbaceous & Climbers.
**Map ref:** 2, A2

**CBdn  ANN & ROGER BOWDEN** ⊠ EU ▣ ◆
Cleave House, Sticklepath, Okehampton, Devon, EX20 2NL
☎ (01837) 840481  **Fax:** (01837) 840482
**E-Mail:** bowdenshosta@eclipse.co.uk
**Contact:** Ann & Roger Bowden
**Opening times:** Appt. only.
**Min. mail order UK:** No minimum charge
**Min. mail order EU:** Nmc
**Cat. cost:** 3 x 1st class
**Credit cards:** Visa, Access, EuroCard, Switch
**Specialities:** Hosta only. National Collection of modern hybrid Hostas.
**Map ref:** 1, B3

**CBel  BELMONT HOUSE NURSERY**
Little Horton, Devizes, Wiltshire, SN10 3LJ
☎ (01380) 860510
**Contact:** Gordon Cottis
**Opening times:** By appt. Please phone.
**Mail order:** None
**Cat. cost:** 2 x 2nd class
**Credit cards:** None
**Specialities:** Helleborus hybrids & true species, Galanthus, Digitalis, Geranium, Pulmonaria, other Hardy Perennials.
**Map ref:** 2, A3

**CBen  BENNETT'S WATER LILY FARM** ⊠ EU ▣
Putton Lane, Chickerell, Weymouth, Dorset, DT3 4AF
☎ (01305) 785150  **Fax:** (01305) 781619
**E-mail:** JB@waterlily.co.uk
**Web site:** http://www.waterlily.co.uk
**Contact:** J Bennett
**Opening times:** Tue-Sun Apr-Aug, Tue-Sat Sep, Oct & Mar.
**Min. mail order UK:** £25.00 + p&p
**Min. mail order EU:** £25.00 + p&p
**Cat. cost:** Sae for price list
**Credit cards:** Visa, Access, MasterCard, Switch
**Specialities:** Aquatic plants. National Collection of Water Lilies.
**Map ref:** 2, C2

**CBla  BLACKMORE & LANGDON LTD** ⊠ EU ▣
Pensford, Bristol, Avon, BS39 4JL
☎ (01275) 332300  **Fax:** (01275) 332300
**Contact:** J S Langdon
**Opening times:** 0900-1700 Mon-Sat, 1000-1600 Sun.
**Min. mail order UK:** No minimum charge
**Min. mail order EU:** Nmc

---

**KEY**
⊠ Mail Order to UK or EU
▣ Exports beyond EU
▣ Also supplies Wholesale  ◆ See Display advertisement

**C**

Cat. cost: Sae
Credit cards: None
Specialities: Phlox, Delphinium & Begonias.
Also seeds.
Map ref: 2, A2

**CBlo** **BLOUNTS COURT NURSERIES**
Studley, Calne, Wiltshire, SN11 9NH
☎ (01249) 812103   Fax: (01249) 812103
Contact: Mrs P E Rendell
Opening times: 1030-1630 Sun, 0900-1700
Nov-Feb, 0900-1800 Apr-Jul, 0900-1730
Mon, Tue, Fri & Sat Aug-Oct.
Mail order: None
Cat. cost: 2 x 1st or 2nd class
Credit cards: Visa, Access, Switch
Specialities: Wide range of Shrubs, Fruit &
Ornamental Trees, Conifers, Roses, container
& open ground. Clematis, Climbers,
Herbaceous, incl. unusual varieties.
Map ref: 2, A2

**CBod** **BODMIN PLANT AND HERB NURSERY**
Laveddon Mill, Laninval Hill, Bodmin,
Cornwall, PL30 5JU
☎ (01208) 72837   Fax: (01208) 76491
Contact: Sarah Wilks
Opening times: 0900-1800 (or dusk if earlier)
daily.
Mail Order: None
Cat. cost: 2 x 1st class for herb and/or hardy
Geranium list.
Credit cards: MasterCard, Visa, Switch, Solo
Specialities: Herbs & Herbaceous plus good
range of Shrubs.
Map ref: 1, B2

**CBos** **BOSVIGO PLANTS**
Bosvigo House, Bosvigo Lane, Truro,
Cornwall, TR1 3NH
☎ (01872) 275774   Fax: (01872) 275774
Contact: Wendy Perry
Opening times: 1100-1800 Thur-Sat
Mar-end Sep.
Mail order: None
Cat. cost: 4 x 2nd class
Credit cards: None
Specialities: Rare & unusual Herbaceous.
Map ref: 1, C1

**CBot** **THE BOTANIC NURSERY** ✉ UK ▣
Bath Road, Atworth, Nr Melksham, Wiltshire,
SN12 8NU
☎ (01225) 706597, 0850 328756 mobile
Fax: (01225) 700953
Contact: T & M Baker
Opening times: 1000-1700 Wed-Mon, Closed
Jan.

Min. mail order UK: 30p Sae for mail order
lists.
Cat. cost: 5 x 1st class
Credit cards: Visa, Access
Specialities: Rare hardy Shrubs & Perennials
for lime soils.
Map ref: 2, A2

**CBra** **BRADLEY BATCH NURSERY** ▣
64 Bath Road, Ashcott, Bridgwater, Somerset,
TA7 9QJ
☎ (01458) 210256
Contact: J E White
Opening times: 1000-1800 Tue-Sun.
Mail order: None
Cat. cost: None issued
Credit cards: None
Specialities: Echeveria, Haworthia, Lithops &
Cacti.
Map ref: 2, B1

**CBrd** **BROADLEAS GARDENS LTD** ▣
Broadleas, Devizes, Wiltshire, SN10 5JQ
☎ (01380) 722035
Contact: Lady Anne Cowdray
Opening times: 1400-1800 Wed, Thu & Sun
Apr-Oct.
Mail order: None
Cat. cost: 1 x 1st class
Credit cards: None
Specialities: General range.
Map ref: 2, A3

**CBre** **BREGOVER PLANTS** ✉ EU
Hillbrooke, Middlewood, North Hill, Nr
Launceston, Cornwall, PL15 7NN
☎ (01566) 782661
Contact: Jennifer Bousfield
Opening times: 1100-1700 Wed-Fri Mar-mid
Oct and by appt.
Min. mail order UK: No minimum charge
Min. mail order EU: Nmc
Cat. cost: 2 x 1st class
Credit cards: None
Specialities: Unusual Hardy Perennials.
Map ref: 1, B2

**CBrm** **BRAMLEY LODGE GARDEN NURSERY**
Beech Tree Lane, Ipplepen, Newton Abbot,
Devon, TQ12 5TW
☎ (01803) 813265
E-mail: bramleylodge@btinternet.com
Web site: http://www.btinternet.com/
~bramleylodge.nursery
Contact: Susan Young
Opening times: 1000-1600 Thur-Sun
Mar-Oct, 1000-1600 Sun Nov-Feb.
Mail order: None

Cat. cost: 3 x 1st class
Credit cards: None
Specialities: Grasses. Also Trees, Shrubs &
Perennials. Several small model themed
gardens.
Map ref: 1, B3

**CBro    BROADLEIGH GARDENS ⊠ EU**
Bishops Hull, Taunton, Somerset, TA4 1AE
☎ (01823) 286231   Fax: (01823) 323646
Contact: Lady Skelmersdale
Opening times: 0900-1600 Mon-Fri for
viewing ONLY.  Orders collected if prior
notice given.
Min. mail order UK: No minimum charge
Min. mail order EU: Nmc
Cat. cost: 2 x 1st class
Credit cards: Visa, Access
Specialities: Two catalogues. (Jan) - Bulbs in
growth, (Galanthus, Cyclamen etc.) &
Herbaceous. (June) - Dwarf & unusual Bulbs.
Map ref: 2, B1

**CBrP   BROOKLANDS PLANTS ⊠ EU 🔲**
25 Treves Road, Dorchester, Dorset,
DT1 2HE
☎ (01305) 265846
Contact: Ian Watt
Opening times: By appt. for collection of
plants only.
Min. mail order UK: £25.00 + p&p
Min. mail order EU: £25.00 + p&p
Cat. cost: 2 x 2nd class
Credit cards: None
Specialities: Palm & Cycad seedlings. Over
100 species grown. Some specimen sized
plants & other distinctive foliage plants also
grown. Hardy & half-hardy, for the
Conservatory & for indoors.
Map ref: 2, C2

**CBur   BURNHAM NURSERIES ⊠ EU 🔳 🔲**
Forches Cross, Newton Abbot, Devon,
TQ12 6PZ
☎ (01626) 352233   Fax: (01626) 362167
Contact: Brian Rittershausen
Opening times: 0900-1700 Mon-Fri &
1000-1600 Sat & Sun.
Min. mail order UK: No minimum charge
Min. mail order EU: £100.00 + p&p
Cat. cost: Large Sae + 31p stamp
Credit cards: Visa, Access, Switch, American
Express
Specialities: All types of Orchid.
Map ref: 1, B3

**CCan   CANNINGTON COLLEGE MAIL ORDER
CENTRE ⊠ UK**
Cannington, Bridgwater, Somerset, TA5 2LS
☎ (01278) 655000   Fax: (01278) 655055
E-mail: admin@cannington.ac.uk
Web site: http://www.cannington.ac.uk
Contact: Peter Elliman
Opening times: 0900-1700 daily Easter-Oct.
Min. mail order UK: £15.00
Cat. cost: Free
Credit cards: None
Specialities: Abutilon, Argyranthemum,
Osteospermum, Salvia, Felicia & Euryops.
Map ref: 2, B1

**CCar   CARTERS SEEDS**
Woodview Road, Paignton, Devon, TQ4 7NG
☎ (01803) 696400   Fax: (01803) 696360
Contact: Sales Support
Mail order: None
Cat. cost: None issued
Credit cards: None
Specialities: General range available from
retail stockists.

**CCAT   CIDER APPLE TREES ⊠ EU 🔲**
(Office) 12 Tallowood, Shepton Mallet,
Somerset, BA4 5QN
☎ (01749) 343368
Contact: Mr J Dennis
Opening times: By appt. only.
Min. mail order UK: £6.00 + p&p
Min. mail order EU: £6.00 + p&p
Cat. cost: Free
Credit cards: None
Specialities: Malus (speciality standard trees).
Note: Nursery is at Corkscrew Lane,
Woolston. Visits by appt. only.
Map ref: 2, B2

**CCha   CHAPEL FARM HOUSE NURSERY**
Halwill Junction, Beaworthy, Devon,
EX21 5UF
☎ (01409) 221594
Contact: Robin or Toshie Hull
Opening times: 0900-1700 Tue-Sat,
1000-1600 Sun & B/Hol Mons.
Mail order: None
Cat. cost: None issued.
Credit cards: None
Specialities: Plants from Japan. Also
Herbaceous. Japanese garden design service
offered.
Map ref: 1, B3

---

K E Y   ⊠ Mail order to UK or EU
        🔳 Exports beyond EU
        🔲 Also supplies Wholesale   ◆ See Display advertisement

**C**

**CChe**    **CHERRY TREE NURSERY** ✉
(Sheltered Work Opportunities), off New
Road Roundabout, Northbourne,
Bournemouth, Dorset, BH10 7DA
☎ (01202) 593537   **Fax:** (01202) 590626
**Contact:** Stephen Jailler
**Opening times:** 0830-1530 Mon-Fri,
0900-1200 most Sats.
**Mail order:** None
**Cat. cost:** A4 Sae + 2 x 2nd class
**Credit cards:** None
**Specialities:** Hardy Shrubs.
**Map ref:** 2, C3

**CCHP**    **COTSWOLD HARDY
PLANTS LTD** ✉ EU ✉ ✉
Wibble Farm, West Quantoxhead, Nr
Taunton, Somerset, TA4 4DD
☎ (01984) 632303   **Fax:** (01984) 633168
**Contact:** Mrs M L Francis
**Opening times:** 0800-1300 & 1400-1700
Mon-Fri, 0900-1230 Sat. All year exc. B/Hols.
**Min. mail order UK:** No minimum charge
**Min. mail order EU:** Nmc
**Cat. cost:** 2 x 1st class
**Credit cards:** MasterCard, Switch, Visa
**Specialities:** Growers of a wide range of Hardy
plants, many rare & unusual.
**Map ref:** 1, A4

**CCol**    **COLD HARBOUR NURSERY** ✉ UK
(Office) 19 Hilary Road, Poole, Dorset,
BH17 7LZ
☎ 01202 696875 evenings
**E-mail:** coldharbour@hilaryroad.freeserve.co.uk
**Contact:** Steve Saunders
**Opening times:** 1000-1730 Tues-Fri & most
weekends 1st Mar-end Oct.
**Min. mail order UK:** £10.00 + p&p
**Cat. cost:** 3 x 2nd class
**Credit cards:** None
**Specialities:** Unusual Herbaceous Perennials,
incl. hardy Geraniums & Grasses. Note:
Nursery is at Bere Road, (opp. Silent Woman
Inn), Wareham, Dorset (no postal address).
**Map ref:** 2, C2

**CCpl**    **CHAPEL-UNY NURSERY** ✉ UK
Brane, Sancreed, Penzance, Cornwall,
TR20 8RD
☎ (01736) 810649
**Contact:** Mr Charles Tricker
**Opening times:** Not open.
**Min. mail order UK:** £20.00 + p&p
**Cat. cost:** 2 x 1st class
**Credit cards:** None
**Specialities:** Banksia, Protea & other
Proteaceae, Agave, Aloe, Aeonium, Restio.
**Map ref:** 1, C1

**CCuc**    **CUCKOO MILL NURSERY**
Rose Ash, South Molton, Devon, EX36 4RQ
☎ (01769) 550530
**Contact:** Peter Woollard
**Opening times:** Most Sun & Wed Apr-Sep
but please phone first.
**Mail order:** None
**Cat. cost:** 3 x 1st class
**Credit cards:** None
**Specialities:** Hardy Ferns, Grasses & Astilbe.
Shade & moisture loving plants.
**Map ref:** 1, A3

**CCVT**    **CHEW VALLEY TREES** ✉ UK ✉
Winford Road, Chew Magna, Bristol,
BS40 8QE
☎ (01275) 333752   **Fax:** (01275) 333746
**Contact:** J Scarth
**Opening times:** 0800-1700 Mon-Fri all year.
0900-1600 Sat 25th Sep-31st May. Other
times by appt.
**Min. mail order UK:** £5.00 + p&p*
**Cat. cost:** Free
**Credit cards:** None
**Specialities:** Native British Trees and Shrubs,
Apple Trees & Hedging. *Note: Max. plant
height for mail order 2.7m.
**Map ref:** 2, A2

**CDev**    **DEVON VIOLET NURSERY** ✉ EU ✉ ✉ ◆
Rattery, South Brent, Devon, TQ10 9LG
☎ (01364) 643033   **Fax:** (01364) 643033
**Contact:** Joan & Michael Yardley
**Opening times:** Oct 1999-June 2000.
Please ring first.
**Min. mail order UK:** 6 plants
**Min. mail order EU:** 6 plants
**Cat. cost:** 2 x 2nd class
**Credit cards:** None
**Specialities:** Violets & Parma Violets.
**Map ref:** 1, B3

**CDob**    **SAMUEL DOBIE & SON** ✉ UK
Long Road, Paignton, Devon, TQ4 7SX
☎ (01803) 696411   **Fax:** (01803) 696450
**Contact:** Customer Services
**Opening times:** 0830-1700 Mon-Fri (office).
Also answerphone.
**Min. mail order UK:** No minimum charge*
**Cat. cost:** Free
**Credit cards:** Visa, MasterCard
**Specialities:** Wide selection of popular Flower
& Vegetable seeds. Also includes young Plants,
summer flowering Bulbs & garden sundries.
*Note: Mail order to UK & Irish Republic
only.

**CDoC   DUCHY OF CORNWALL** ⊠ UK ◆
Penlyne Nursery, Cott Road, Lostwithiel,
Cornwall, PL22 0HW
☎ (01208) 872668  **Fax:** (01208) 872835
**Contact:** Andrew Carthew
**Opening times:** 0900-1700 Mon-Sat,
1000-1700 Sun. Closed B/Hols.
**Min. order UK:** No minimum charge
**Cat. cost:** Cat £2.00 (stamps or cheque)
**Credit cards:** Visa, American Express, Access,
Switch, Delta
**Specialities:** Very wide range of all garden
plants incl. Trees, Shrubs, Conifers, Roses,
Perennials, Fruit & half-hardy Exotics.
**Map ref:** 1, B2

**CDul   DULFORD NURSERIES** ⊠ UK ▣
Cullompton, Devon, EX15 2DG
☎ (01884) 266361  **Fax:** (01884) 266663
**Contact:** David & Mary Barrow
**Opening times:** 0730-1630 Mon-Fri
**Min. mail order UK:** £10.00 + p&p
**Cat. cost:** Free
**Credit cards:** None
**Specialities:** Native, Ornamental & unusual
Trees & Shrubs, incl. Oaks, Maples, Beech,
Birch, Chestnut, Ash, Lime, Sorbus & Pines.
**Map ref:** 1, B4

**CEgg   EGGESFORD GARDENS** ⊠ EU
Eggesford, Chulmleigh, Devon, EX18 7QU
☎ (01769) 580250  **Fax:** (01769) 581041
**Contact:** Jonathon Parish
**Opening times:** 0900-1700 every day exc.
Christmas, Boxing & N.Year's Day.
**Min. mail order UK:** £15.00 + p&p
**Min. mail order EU:** £20.00 + p&p
**Cat. cost:** £3.00 in stamps
**Credit cards:** MasterCard, Visa, Switch, Delta
**Specialities:** Wide General Range. Strong in
Shrubs, Herbaceous, Roses, Clematis & Ivy.
**Map ref:** 1, A3

**CElw   ELWORTHY COTTAGE PLANTS**
Elworthy Cottage, Elworthy, Lydeard St
Lawrence, Taunton, Somerset, TA4 3PX
☎ (01984) 656427
**Contact:** Mrs J M Spiller
**Opening times:** 1030-1700 Tue, Thu & Fri
mid Mar-mid Oct & by appt.
**Mail order:** None
**Cat. cost:** 3 x 2nd class
**Credit cards:** None
**Specialities:** Unusual Herbaceous plants esp.
Hardy Geranium, Geum, Grasses,
Campanula, Erysimum, Pulmonaria,
Origanum, Astrantia & Viola.
**Map ref:** 2, B1

**CEnd   ENDSLEIGH GARDENS** ⊠ UK ▣ ◆
Milton Abbot, Tavistock, Devon,
PL19 0PG
☎ (01822) 870235  **Fax:** (01822) 870513
**Contact:** Michael Taylor
**Opening times:** 0800-1700 Mon-Sat,
1400-1700 Sun. Closed Sun Dec & Jan.
**Min. mail order UK:** £12.00 + p&p
**Cat. cost:** 2 x 1st class
**Credit cards:** Visa, Access
**Specialities:** Choice & unusual Trees &
Shrubs incl. Acer & Cornus cvs. Old Apples
& Cherries. Grafting service.
**Map ref:** 1, B2

**CEqu   EQUATORIAL PLANT CO.
(VIREYAS)** ⊠ EU
The White Cottage, Three Gates, Leigh, Nr
Sherborne, Dorset, DT9 6JQ
☎ (01963) 210309  **Fax:** (01833) 690519
**Contact:** Blair & Jackie Sibun
**Opening times:** By appt.
**Min. mail order UK:** No minimum charge
**Min. mail order EU:** Nmc
**Cat. cost:** Free
**Credit cards:** Visa, Access
**Specialities:** Vireya Rhododendrons

**CFai   FAIRHAVEN NURSERY** ⊠ EU
Clapworthy Cross, Chittlehampton,
Umberleigh, Devon, EX37 9QT
☎ (01769) 540528
**Contact:** Derek & Pauline Burdett
**Opening times:** 1000-1600 all year, but please
check first.
**Min. mail order UK:** £10.00 + p&p
**Min. mail order EU:** £20.00 + p&p
**Cat. cost:** 2 x 1st class
**Credit cards:** None
**Specialities:** Wide selection of more unusual
Hardy Trees, Shrubs & Perennials.
**Map ref:** 1, A3

**CFee   FEEBERS HARDY PLANTS** ◆
1 Feeber Cottage, Westwood, Broadclyst, Nr
Exeter, Devon, EX5 3DQ
☎ (01404) 822118
**Contact:** Mrs E Squires
**Opening times:** 1000-1700 Thur &
1400-1800 Sat Mar-Jul & Sep-Oct
**Mail order:** None
**Cat. cost:** Sae + 36p stamp
**Credit cards:** None

C

Specialities: Plants for wet clay soils, Alpines & Hardy Perennials incl. those raised by Amos Perry.
Map ref: 1, B3

**CFil    FILLAN'S PLANTS ⊠ EU 🖾 📧**
Pound House Nursery, Buckland Monachorum, Yelverton, Devon, PL20 7LJ
☎ (01822) 855050   Fax: (01822) 614351
Contact: Mark Fillan
Opening times: By appt. only.
Min. mail order UK: £20.00 + p&p
Min. mail order EU: £50.00 + p&p
Cat. cost: 3 x 1st class
Credit cards: None
Specialities: Ferns, Hydrangea & less usual plants.
Map ref: 1, B3

**CFir    FIR TREE FARM NURSERY ⊠ UK**
Tresahor, Constantine, Falmouth, Cornwall, TR11 5PL
☎ (01326) 340593   Fax: (01326) 340593
E-mail: ftfnur@aol.com
Web site: http://members.aol.com/ftfnur
Contact: Jim Cave
Opening times: 1000-1700 Thu-Sun 1st Mar-30th Sep.
Min. mail order UK: £25.00 + p&p
Cat. cost: 6 x 1st class
Credit cards: Visa, Access, Delta, Switch
Specialities: Over 2000 varieties of Cottage Garden & rare Perennials & 100 types of Clematis.
Map ref: 1, C1

**CFri    FRIARS WAY NURSERY**
Friars Way Nursery, Church Street, Upwey, Weymouth, Dorset, DT3 5QE
☎ (01305) 813243   Fax: (01305) 813243
Contact: Christina Scott
Opening times: 1100-1700 Thurs, Apr-end Sept.
Mail order: None
Cat. cost: None issued.
Credit cards: None
Specialities: Hardy Perennials.
Map ref: 2, C2

**CFul    RODNEY FULLER ⊠ UK**
Coachman's Cottage, Higher Bratton Seymour, Wincanton, Somerset, BA9 8DA
Contact: Rodney Fuller
Opening times: Not open.
Min. mail order UK: £25.00
Cat. cost: 2 x 1st class
Credit cards: None
Specialities: Violas & Violettas. Buxus 'Suffruticosa'.

**CGen    GENUS PLANTS ⊠ EU**
Startley Hill Nursery, Startley, Chippenham, Wiltshire, SN15 5HQ
☎ (01249) 720674
E-Mail: genusplants@mcmail.com
Web Site: http://www/mcmail/genusplants
Contact: Jeremy Addington
Opening times: Not open to public.
Min. mail order UK: 6 plants (plugs)* + p&p
Min. mail order EU: 6 plants (plugs)* + p&p
Cat. cost: 2 x 1st class
Credit cards: Access, American Express, Connect, Delta, Diners, EuroCard, JCB, MasterCard, Switch, Visa
Specialities: Hardy & tender unusual Perennials. *Note: Mail order of large plugs only.

**CGle    GLEBE COTTAGE PLANTS**
Pixie Lane, Warkleigh, Umberleigh, Devon, EX37 9DH
Fax: (01769) 540554
Contact: Carol Klein
Opening times: 1000-1700 Wed-Fri.
Mail Order: None
Cat. cost: £1.50
Credit cards: None
Specialities: Extensive range of hard-to-find Perennials.
Map ref: 1, A3

**CGOG   GLOBAL ORANGE GROVES UK ⊠ EU 🖾 📧 ◆**
Horton Road, Horton Heath, Wimborne, Dorset, BH21 7JN
☎ (01202) 826244   Fax: (01202) 814651
Contact: P K Oliver
Opening times: 1030-1700 7 days a week, unless exhibiting.
Min. mail order UK: No minimum charge
Min. mail order EU: Nmc
Cat. cost: Sae
Credit cards: None
Specialities: Citrus trees, Citrus fertiliser & book 'Success with Citrus'. Peaches, Apricots, Nectarines, Mangos, Avocados.
Map ref: 2, B3

**CGra    GRAHAM'S HARDY PLANTS ⊠ EU**
Southcroft, North Road, Timsbury, Bath, Avon, BA3 1JN
☎ (01761) 472187
E-mail: graplant@aol.com
Contact: Graham Nicholls
Opening times: 1000-1600 Wed & Thur 1st Apr-30th Sep. Please phone first.
Min. mail order UK: £1.50 + p&p
Min. mail order EU: £1.50 + p&p

Cat. cost: 2 x 1st class or 2 x IRC
Credit cards: None
Specialities: North American Alpines esp.
Lewisia, Eriogonum, Penstemon, Campanula,
Kelseya, Phlox.
Map ref: 2, A2

**CGre  GREENWAY GARDENS ⊠ UK**
Churston Ferrers, Brixham, Devon, TQ5 0ES
☎ (01803) 842382  Fax: (01803) 842383
Contact: Roger Clark (Manager)
Opening times: 1400-1700 (Nov-Feb 1630)
Mon-Fri, 1000-1200 Sat, ex B/Hols. Also by
appt.
Min. mail order UK: No minimum charge*
Cat. cost: 3 x 1st class
Credit cards: None
Specialities: Unusual Trees & Shrubs
particularly from temperate Southern
hemisphere. *Note: Mail order by Carrier
only.
Map ref: 1, C3

**CGro  C W GROVES & SON ⊠ EU ▣**
West Bay Road, Bridport, Dorset, DT6 4BA
☎ (01308) 422654  Fax: (01308) 420888
Contact: C W Groves
Opening times: 0830-1700 Mon-Sat,
1030-1630 Sun.
Min. mail order UK: No minimum charge*
Min. mail order EU: £10.00 + p&p
Cat. cost: 1 x 1st class
Credit cards: Access, Visa, Switch, Delta,
MasterCard
Specialities: Nursery & Garden Centre
specialising in Parma & Hardy Viola.
*Note: Mainly Violets by mail order.
Map ref: 2, C1

**CGrW  THE GREAT WESTERN GLADIOLUS
NURSERY ⊠ EU ▣ ◆**
Moor's Edge, Athelney, Bridgwater, Somerset,
TA7 0SE
☎ (01823) 698996  Fax: (01823) 698090
E-mail: gladioli@aol.com
Contact: Frank Hartnell
Opening times: By appt. only.
Min. mail order UK: No minimum charge
Min. mail order EU: Nmc
Cat. cost: 2 x 1st class (2 catalogues)
Credit cards: None
Specialities: Gladiolus – species & hybrids,
corms & seeds.
Map ref: 2, B1

**CHad  HADSPEN GARDEN & NURSERY**
Hadspen House, Castle Cary, Somerset,
BA7 7NG

☎ (01749) 813707  Fax: (01749) 813707
E-mail: hadspen@compuserve.com
Contact: N & S Pope
Opening times: 1000-1700 Thu-Sun &
B/Hols. 1st Mar-1st Oct. Garden open at the
same time.
Mail order: None
Cat. cost: 3 x 1st class
Credit cards: None
Specialities: Large leaved Herbaceous. Old
fashioned and shrub Roses.
Map ref: 2, B2

**CHal  HALSWAY NURSERY ⊠ UK**
Halsway, Nr Crowcombe, Taunton, Somerset,
TA4 4BB
☎ (01984) 618243
Contact: T A & D J Bushen
Opening times: Most days - please telephone
first.
Min. mail order UK: £2.00 + p&p
Cat. cost: 2 x 1st class*
Credit cards: None
Specialities: Coleus & Begonias (excl.
tuberous & winter flowering). Also good range
of Greenhouse & garden plants. *Note: List
for Coleus & Begonias only, no nursery list.
Map ref: 2, B1

**CHan  THE HANNAYS OF BATH ▣**
Sydney Wharf Nursery, Bathwick, Bath, Avon,
BA2 4ES
☎ (01225) 462230
Contact: Mr V H S & Mrs S H Hannay
Opening times: 1000-1700 Wed-Sun (but
open B/Hols.) 1st Mar-12th Oct or by appt.,
esp in Winter.
Mail Order: None
Cat. cost: £1.00 + 40p p&p
Credit cards: None
Specialities: Uncommon Perennials & Shrubs,
many grown from seed collected abroad by
ourselves. Note: For Export items, Certificates
arranged but collection only.
Map ref: 2, A2

**CHar  WEST HARPTREE NURSERY ⊠ EU ▣ ▣**
Bristol Road, West Harptree, Bath & North
East Somerset, BS40 6HG
☎ (01761) 221370  Fax: (01761) 221989
Contact: Bryn & Helene Bowles
Opening times: Daily from 1000 except
Mondays, 1st Mar-30th Nov.

**C**

Min. mail order UK: No minimum charge
Min. mail order EU: Nmc
Cat. cost: £1 coin or p. order + 1 x 1st class
Credit cards: None
Specialities: Unusual Herbaceous Perennials & Shrubs. Lilies.
Map ref: 2, A2

CHdy **Hardy Orchids Ltd** ⊠ EU ◪ ▣
New Gate Farm, Scotchey Lane, Stour Provost, Gillingham, Dorset, SP8 5LT
☎ (01747) 838368  Fax: (01747) 838308
Contact: N J Heywood
Opening times: 0800-1300 & 1400-1700 Mon-Fri, by appt. only.
Min. mail order UK: £10.00 + p&p
Min. mail order EU: £10.00 + p&p
Cat. cost: 2 x 1st class
Credit cards: None
Specialities: Hardy Orchids – Cypripedium & Dactylorhiza.
Map ref: 2, B2

CHea **Heather Bank Nursery** ⊠ UK
Woodlands, 1 High Street, Littleton Panell, Devizes, Wiltshire, SN10 4EL
☎ (01380) 812739
Contact: Mrs B Mullan
Opening times: 1000-1500 Mon, Wed & Thurs. Other times by appt.
Min. mail order UK: £10.00 + p&p
Cat. cost: 3 x 1st class
Credit cards: None
Specialities: Campanula, Polemonium & Cottage Garden Plants.
Map ref: 2, A3

CHid **Hidden Valley Nursery** ⊠ EU ◪
Umberleigh, Devon, EX37 9BU
☎ 0789 9056168
Contact: Linda & Peter Lindley
Opening times: By appt. only.
Min. mail order UK: No minimum charge
Min. Mail Order EU: Nmc
Cat. cost: 2 x 1st class
Credit cards: None
Specialities: Hardy Perennials, esp. shade lovers.

CHig **The High Garden** ⊠ EU ▣
Courtwood, Newton Ferrers, South Devon, PL8 1BW
☎ (01752) 872528
Contact: F Bennett
Opening times: By appt.
Min. mail order UK: No minimum charge
Min. Mail Order EU: £40.00 + p&p
Cat. cost: 60p

Credit cards: None
Specialities: Pieris & Rhododendron.
Map ref: 1, C3

CHil **Hillside Cottage Plants** ⊠ UK ◆
Hillside, Gibbet Lane, Whitchurch, North East Somerset, BS14 0BX
☎ (01275) 837505
Contact: Josephine Pike
Opening times: Normally here but please phone first in case at show.
Min. mail order UK: £15.00 + p&p
Cat. cost: 4 x 1st class
Credit cards: None
Specialities: Hardy Geraniums (300+ varieties) & wide range of Hardy Perennials.
Map ref: 2, A2

CHor **Horton Vale Nursery**
Horton Heath, Wimborne, Dorset, BH21 7JN
☎ (01202) 813473
Contact: David Wright
Opening times: 0900-1700 daily exc. Wed, Feb-Nov.
Mail order: None
Cat. cost: None issued
Credit cards: None
Specialities: Perennials.
Map ref: 2, C3

CInt **International Animal Rescue Nursery** ◆
Animal Tracks, Ash Mill, South Molton, Devon, EX36 4QW
☎ (01769) 550277  Fax: (01769) 550917
E-mail: i.a.r@eclipse.co.uk
Contact: Jo Hicks
Opening times: 1000-1730 or dusk 365 days a year.
Mail order: None
Cat. cost: 3 x 1st class
Credit cards: None
Specialities: Alpines, Grasses, Hardy Perennials, Cactus & Succulents.
Map ref: 1, A3

CJas **Jasmine Cottage Gardens**
26 Channel Road, Walton St. Mary, Clevedon, Somerset, BS21 7BY
☎ (01275) 871850
E-mail: baron@bologrew.demon.co.uk
Contact: Mr & Mrs M Redgrave
Opening times: Thurdays & daily by appt.
Mail order: None
Cat. cost: None issued
Credit cards: None
Specialities: Rhodochiton, Asarina,

Maurandya, Lophospermum,
Solenopsis/Isotoma/Laurentia.
**Map ref:** 2, A1

**CJew   JEAN JEWELS**
Millmoor Cottage, Burrington, Umberleigh,
Devon, EX37 9EF
☎ (01769) 520285
**Contact:** Jean Jewels & Peter Charnley
**Opening times:** Telephone call first
appreciated.
**Mail order:** None
**Cat. cost:** 3 x 1st class
**Credit cards:** None
**Specialities:** Herbs, culinary, medicinal & dye
plants. Scented foliage plants & plants for the
wild garden.
**Map ref:** 1, A3

**CKel   KELWAYS LTD ⊠ EU ✔ ▣**
Langport, Somerset, TA10 9EZ
☎ (01458) 250521   **Fax:** (01458) 253351
**Contact:** Mr David Root
**Opening times:** 0900-1700 Mon-Fri,
1000-1700 Sat, 1000-1600 Sun.
**Min. mail order UK:** £4.00 + p&p*
**Min. mail order EU:** £8.00 + p&p
**Cat. cost:** Free
**Credit cards:** Visa, Access
**Specialities:** Paeonia, Iris, Hemerocallis &
Herbaceous perennials. *Note: Mail order for
Paeonia, Iris & Hemerocallis only.
**Map ref:** 2, B1

**CKen   KENWITH NURSERY
(GORDON HADDOW) ⊠ EU ✔ ◆**
Blinsham, Nr Torrington, Beaford, Winkleigh,
Devon, EX19 8NT
☎ (01805) 603274   **Fax:** (01805) 603663
**Contact:** Gordon Haddow
**Opening times:** 1000-1630 Wed-Sat Nov-Feb
& by appt. 1000-1630 daily Mar-Oct.
**Min. mail order UK:** £10.00 + p&p
**Min. mail order EU:** £50.00 + p&p
**Cat. cost:** 3 x 1st class
**Credit cards:** Visa, MasterCard, EuroCard
**Specialities:** All Conifer genera. Grafting a
speciality. Many new introductions to UK.
National Collection of dwarf Conifers.
**Map ref:** 1, A3

**CKin   KINGSFIELD CONSERVATION
NURSERY ⊠ UK ▣**
Broadenham Lane, Winsham, Chard,
Somerset, TA20 4JF
☎ (01460) 30070   **Fax:** (01460) 30070
**Contact:** Mrs M White
**Opening times:** Please phone for details.

**Min. mail order UK:** No minimum charge
**Cat. cost:** 31p stamps
**Credit cards:** None
**Specialities:** Native Trees, Shrubs, Wild
flowers & Wild flower Seeds.
**Map ref:** 2, B1

**CKno   KNOLL GARDENS**
Hampreston, Stapehill, Nr Wimborne,
Dorset, BH21 7ND
☎ (01202) 873931   **Fax:** (01202) 870842
**Contact:** N R Lucas
**Opening times:** 1000-1700 daily Apr-Sep.
1000-1600 Wed-Sun Mar & Oct, 1000-1600
Wed-Fri & Sun Nov & Dec (until Xmas).
**Mail Order:** None
**Cat. cost:** 4 x 1st class
**Credit cards:** Visa, MasterCard
**Specialities:** National Collections of deciduous
Ceanothus & Phygelius (list available).
Herbaceous & Grasses. Half-hardy Perennials.
**Map ref:** 2, C3

**CLan   THE LANHYDROCK GARDENS (NT) ▣**
Lanhydrock, Bodmin, Cornwall, PL30 5AD
☎ (01208) 72220   **Fax:** (01208) 72220
**Contact:** Mr N R Teagle
**Opening times:** Daily, Easter (or Apr 1st) -
31st Oct.
**Mail order:** None
**Cat. cost:** Free
**Credit cards:** None
**Specialities:** Shrubs, especially Camellia,
Azalea, Rhododendron, Magnolia &
Ceanothus.
**Map ref:** 1, B2

**CLAP   LONG ACRE PLANTS ⊠ EU ▣**
South Marsh, Charlton Musgrove, Nr
Wincanton, Somerset, BA9 8EX
☎ (01963) 32802   **Fax:** (01963) 32802
**Contact:** Nigel Rowland
**Opening times:** 1000-1700 Wed-Fri Feb-Oct.
Other days by appt.
**Min. mail order UK:** £10.00 + p&p
**Min. mail order EU:** £20.00 + p&p
**Cat. cost:** 3 x 1st class
**Credit cards:** None
**Specialities:** Ferns, Lilies, Woodland Bulbs &
Perennials.
**Map ref:** 2, B2

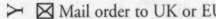

KEY
⊠ Mail order to UK or EU
✔ Exports beyond EU
▣ Also supplies Wholesale   ◆ See Display advertisement

**C**

**CLCN　LITTLE CREEK NURSERY ⊠ EU ▣**
39 Moor Road, Banwell, Weston-super-Mare,
North Somerset, BS29 6EF
☎ (01934) 823739　Fax: (01934) 823739
Contact: Rhys & Julie Adams
Opening times: 1000-1630 Thu & Fri March
& April. Other times by appt. Please ring first.
Min. mail order UK: No minimum charge
Min. mail order EU: Nmc
Cat. cost: 3 x 1st class
Credit cards: None
Specialities: Species Cyclamen (from seed) &
Helleborus.
Map ref: 2, A1

**CLnd　LANDFORD TREES ▣**
Landford Lodge, Landford, Salisbury,
Wiltshire, SP5 2EH
☎ (01794) 390808　Fax: (01794) 390037
E-mail: mo@landford-trees.demon.co.uk
Contact: C D Pilkington
Opening times: 0800-1700 Mon-Fri.
Mail order: None
Cat. cost: Free
Credit cards: None
Specialities: Deciduous ornamental Trees.
Map ref: 2, B3

**CLoc　C S LOCKYER ⊠ EU ▣ ◆**
Lansbury, 70 Henfield Road, Coalpit Heath,
Bristol, BS36 2UZ
☎ (01454) 772219　Fax: (01454) 772219
E-mail: LockyerFuchsias@compuserve.com
Web site: http://ourworld.compuserve.com/
homepages/LockyerFuchsias/
Contact: C S Lockyer
Opening times: Appt. only. (Many open days
& coach parties).
Min. mail order UK: 6 plants + p&p
Min. mail order EU: £12.00 + p&p
Cat. cost: 4 x 1st class
Credit cards: None
Specialities: Fuchsia.
Map ref: 5, C2

**CLon　LONGHALL NURSERY ⊠ EU ▣**
Stockton, Nr Warminster, Wiltshire,
BA12 0SE
☎ (01985) 850914　Fax: (01985) 850914
E-mail: www.designbywire.com
Contact: H V & J E Dooley
Opening times: 0930-1700 Fri-Sat only, from
3rd Fri in Mar-last Sat in Sept.
Min. mail order UK: 10 plants + p&p
Min. mail order EU: 10 plants + p&p
Cat. cost: 3 x 1st class
Credit cards: None
Specialities: Many chalk tolerant plants, esp.
Digitalis, Eryngium, Euphorbia & Salvia.
Map ref: 2, B2

**CLTr　LITTLE TREASURES ⊠ EU**
Wheal Treasure, Horsedowns, Cornwall,
TR14 0NL
☎ (01209) 831978　Fax: (01209) 831978
Contact: Bernadette Jackson
Opening times: 1000-1700 Wed-Sat Mar-end
Sep. Other times by appt. only.
Min. mail order UK: £15.00 + p&p
Min. mail Order EU: £25.00 + p&p
Cat. cost: 4 x 1st class
Credit cards: None
Specialities: Cottage garden plants, Shrubs &
tender Perennials.
Map ref: 1, C1

**CLyd　LYDFORD ALPINE NURSERY ⊠ UK**
2 Southern Cottages, Lydford, Okehampton,
Devon, EX20 4BL
☎ (01822) 820398
Contact: Julie & David Hatchett
Opening times: 1000-1700 Tue & Thu
Apr-Oct & by appt. Nov-Mar by appt. only.
Min. mail order UK: £10.00 + p&p for
Saxifraga only
Cat. cost: 3 x 1st class, Sae for Saxifraga list
only.
Credit cards: None
Specialities: Dianthus, Primula & Saxifraga.
Very wide range of choice & unusual Alpines
in small quantities.
Map ref: 1, B3

**CLyn　LYNASH NURSERIES ⊠ EU**
Culhaven, Wall Ditch Lane, Boozer Pit,
Merriott, Somerset, TA16 5PW
☎ (01460) 76643, (01460) 77764
Fax: (01460) 76643
Contact: Lynn Wallis & Ashley Wallis
Opening times: 0900-1700 Thur-Sat,
1000-1600 Sun.
Min. mail order UK: No minimum charge
Min. mail order EU: £20.00 + p&p
Cat. cost: 4 x 1st class
Credit cards: MasterCard, Visa, Solo, Switch
Specialities: Hebe.
Map ref: 2, B1

**CM&M　M & M PLANTS**
Lloret, Chittlehamholt, Umbesleigh, Devon,
EX37 9PD
☎ (01769) 540448
Contact: Mr M Thorne
Opening times: 0930-1730 Tue-Sat Apr-Oct
& 1000-1600 Tue-Sat Nov-Mar.
Mail order: None
Cat. cost: 4 x 1st class
Credit cards: None
Specialities: Perennials. We also carry a
reasonable range of Alpines, Shrubs, Trees &
Roses.
Map ref: 1, A3

C

**CMac** **MACPENNYS NURSERIES** ⊠ EU
154 Burley Road, Bransgore, Christchurch, Dorset, BH23 8DB
☎ (01425) 672348
**Contact:** T & V Lowndes
**Opening times:** 0800-1700 Mon-Fri, 0900-1700 Sat 1400-1700 Sun.
**Min. mail order UK:** No minimum charge
**Min. mail order EU:** Nmc
**Cat. cost:** A4 Sae with 3 x 1st class
**Credit cards:** Access, American Express, Delta, Access, EuroCard, MasterCard, Visa
**Specialities:** General.
**Map ref:** 2, C3

**CMCN** **MALLET COURT NURSERY** ⊠ EU
Curry Mallet, Taunton, Somerset, TA3 6SY
☎ (01823) 480748 **Fax:** (01823) 481009
**Contact:** J G S & P M E Harris F.L.S.
**Opening times:** 0900-1300 & 1400-1700 Mon-Fri. Sat & Sun by appt.
**Min. mail order UK:** No minimum charge
**Min. mail order EU:** Nmc
**Cat. cost:** 31p Sae
**Credit cards:** MasterCard, Visa
**Specialities:** Maples, Oaks, Magnolia, Hollies & other rare and unusual plants including those from China & South Korea.
**Map ref:** 2, B1

**CMCo** **MEADOW COTTAGE PLANTS**
Pitt Hill, Ivybridge, Devon, PL21 0JJ
☎ (01752) 894532
**Contact:** Mrs L P Hunt
**Opening times:** By appt. only.
**Mail Order:** None
**Cat. cost:** 2 x 2nd class
**Credit cards:** None
**Specialities:** Hardy Geraniums & other Hardy Perennials.
**Map ref:** 1, B3

**CMdw** **MEADOWS NURSERY**
5 Rectory Cottages, Mells, Frome, Somerset, BA11 3PA
☎ (01373) 813025
**Contact:** Sue Lees
**Opening times:** 1000-1800 Tue-Sun 1st Feb-31st Oct & B/Hols.
**Mail order:** None
**Cat. cost:** 2 x 1st class
**Credit cards:** None
**Specialities:** Hardy Cottage garden plants & some Conservatory plants.
**Map ref:** 2, A2

**CMea** **THE MEAD NURSERY**
Brokerswood, Nr Westbury, Wiltshire, BA13 4EG
☎ (01373) 859990
**Contact:** Steve Lewis-Dale
**Opening times:** 0900-1700 Wed-Sat, 1300-1700 Sun, 0900-1700 B/Hols. 1st Feb-10th Oct. Closed Easter Sunday.
**Mail order:** None
**Cat. cost:** 5 x 1st class
**Credit cards:** None
**Specialities:** Perennials & Alpines incl. pot grown Bulbs.
**Map ref:** 2, A2

**CMFo** **MAC FOLIAGE** ⊠ EU ◆
Mac Foliage Plantation & Nursery, Dartmoor National Park, Knapmore Hill, Lounston, Nr. Liverton, Newton Abbot, Devon, TQ12 6LB
☎ (01626) 821006 **Fax:** (01626) 330293
**E-mail:** paul@alexandermacpherson.freeserve.co.uk
**Contact:** Paul Macpherson
**Opening times:** Sat only, by appt.
**Min. mail order UK:** £50.00 + p&p
**Min. mail order EU:** £250.00 + p&p
**Cat. cost:** 4 x 1st class
**Credit cards:** None
**Specialities:** Eucalyptus, Stephanandra, Dodonea.
**Map ref:** 1, B3

**CMGP** **MILTON GARDEN PLANTS** ⊠ EU
Milton-on-Stour, Gillingham, Dorset, SP8 5PX
☎ (01747) 822484 **Fax:** (01747) 822484
**E-mail:** r.w.r.cumming@btinternet.co
**Contact:** Sue Hardy & Richard Cumming
**Opening times:** 0900-1700 Tue-Sat & B/Hol Mons, 1000-1630 Sun. Closed Jan.
**Min. mail order UK:** No minimum charge
**Min. mail order EU:** £30.00 + p&p
**Cat. cost:** £1.50 or 6 x 1st class
**Credit cards:** Visa, Access, Switch, Delta
**Specialities:** Very wide range of Perennials. Ever changing selection of Trees, Shrubs, Conifers, Alpines & Herbs. Emphasis on good information with display gardens alongside.
**Map ref:** 2, B2

**CMHG** **MARWOOD HILL GARDENS**
Barnstaple, Devon, EX31 4EB
☎ (01271) 342528
**Contact:** Dr Smart

KEY
⊠ Mail order to UK or EU
Exports beyond EU
Also supplies Wholesale ◆ See Display advertisement

**C**

Opening times: 1100-1700 daily.
Mail order: None
Cat. cost: 5 x 2nd class
Credit cards: None
Specialities: Large range of unusual Trees & Shrubs. Eucalyptus, Alpines, Camellia, Astilbe & Bog plants.
Map ref: 1, A3

**CMil    MILL COTTAGE PLANTS ⊠ EU**
The Mill, Henley Lane, Wookey, Somerset, BA5 1AP
☎ (01749) 676966
Contact: Sally Gregson
Opening times: 1000-1800 Wed Mar-Sep or by appt. Ring for directions.
Min. mail order UK: £5.00 + p&p
Min. mail order EU: £10.00 + p&p
Cat. cost: 4 x 1st class
Credit cards: None
Specialities: Unusual & period Cottage plants esp. Campanula, Papaver orientale, Hardy Geranium, Euphorbia, Ferns, Pulmonaria & Grasses. Also Hydrangea aspera & H. serrata cvs.
Map ref: 2, A1

**CNat    NATURAL SELECTION ⊠ UK**
1 Station Cottages, Hullavington, Chippenham, Wiltshire, SN14 6ET
☎ (01666) 837369
E-mail: martin@worldmutation.demon.co.uk
Contact: Martin Cragg-Barber
Opening times: Please telephone first.
Min. mail order UK: £8.00 + p&p
Cat. cost: 2 x 1st class
Credit cards: None
Specialities: Unusual British natives, Pelargoniums & others. Also seed.
Map ref: 2, A2

**CNCN    NAKED CROSS NURSERIES ⊠ UK ▣**
Waterloo Road, Corfe Mullen, Wimborne, Dorset, BH21 3SR
☎ (01202) 693256   Fax: (01202) 693256
Contact: Mr P J French & Mrs J E Paddon
Opening times: 0900-1700 daily.
Min. mail order UK: No minimum charge
Cat. cost: 2 x 1st class
Credit cards: Visa, Access, American Express, Switch, not for mail orders
Specialities: Heathers.
Map ref: 2, C2

**CNic    NICKY'S ROCK GARDEN NURSERY**
Broadhayes, Stockland, Honiton, Devon, EX14 9EH
☎ (01404) 881213   Fax: (01404) 881213

Contact: Diana & Bob Dark
Opening times: 0900-dusk daily. Please telephone first to check & for directions.
Mail order: None
Cat. cost: 3 x 1st class
Credit cards: None
Specialities: Plants for Rock gardens, Alpine house, Scree, Troughs, Banks, Walls & front of border & Dwarf Shrubs. Many unusual.
Map ref: 2, C1

**COCH    OTTERS' COURT HEATHERS ⊠ EU ▣**
Otters' Court, West Camel, Yeovil, Somerset, BA22 7QF
☎ (01935) 850285
Contact: Mrs D H Jones
Opening times: By appt. only.
Min. mail order UK: £3.00 + p&p
Min. mail order EU: No minimum charge
Cat. cost: 3 x 1st class
Credit cards: None
Specialities: Lime-tolerant Heathers - Erica, & Daboecia.
Map ref: 2, B2

**COld    THE OLD MILL HERBARY**
Helland Bridge, Bodmin, Cornwall, PL30 4QR
☎ (01208) 841206   Fax: (01208) 841206
Contact: Mrs B Whurr
Opening times: 1000-1700 Thurs-Tues Apr-30th Sept.
Mail order: None
Cat. cost: 6 x 1st class
Credit cards: None
Specialities: Culinary, Medicinal & Aromatic Herbs, Shrubs, Climbing & Herbaceous plants.
Map ref: 1, B2

**COlW    THE OLD WITHY GARDEN NURSERY ⊠ UK**
Cury Cross Lanes, Helston, Cornwall, TR12 7AY
☎ (01326) 240817   Fax: (01326) 241092
Contact: S M Chandler or N D Chandler
Opening times: 1000-1700 Wed-Mon mid Feb-end Oct.
Min. mail order UK: No minimum charge
Cat. cost: 4 x 1st class
Credit cards: None
Specialities: Cottage Garden Plants – Perennials, Biennials & Grasses.
Map ref: 1, C1

**COtt    OTTER NURSERIES LTD**
Gosford Road, Ottery St. Mary, Devon, EX11 1LZ
☎ (01404) 815815   Fax: (01404) 815816

**Contact:** Mrs Pam Poole
**Opening times:** 0800-1730 Mon-Sat,
1030-1630 Sun. Closed Xmas & Boxing Day
& Easter Sun.
**Mail order:** None
**Cat. cost:** Free
**Credit cards:** Visa, Access, American Express,
Diners, Switch
**Specialities:** Large Garden Centre & Nursery
with extensive range of Trees, Shrubs,
Conifers, Climbers, Roses, Fruit & hardy
Perennials.
**Map ref:** 2, C1

**CPar    PARKS PERENNIALS**
242 Wallisdown Road, Wallisdown,
Bournemouth, Dorset, BH10 4HZ
☎ (01202) 524464
**Contact:** S Parks
**Opening times:** Apr-Oct most days, please
phone first.
**Mail order:** None
**Cat. cost:** None issued.
**Credit cards:** None
**Specialities:** Hardy Herbaceous Perennials.
**Map ref:** 2, C3

**CPas    PASSIFLORA (NATIONAL COLLECTION)**
⊠ EU ⊠ ⊠
Lampley Road, Kingston Seymour, Clevedon,
North Somerset, BS21 6XS
☎ (01934) 833350   **Fax:** (01934) 877255
**E-mail:** passion@3wa.co.uk
**Contact:** John Vanderplank or Jane
Lindsay
**Opening times:** 0900-1300 & 1400-1700
Mon-Sat
**Min. mail order UK:** No minimum charge
**Min. mail order EU:** £20.00 + p&p
**Cat. cost:** 3 x 1st class
**Credit cards:** Visa, Access, EuroCard
**Specialities:** Passiflora. National Collection of
over 200 species & varieties. Note: Retail
nursery now at Kingston Seymour.
**Map ref:** 2, A1

**CPBP    PARHAM BUNGALOW PLANTS ⊠ EU**
Parham Lane, Market Lavington, Devizes,
Wiltshire, SN10 4QA
☎ (01380) 812605
**E-mail:** jjs@pbplants.freeserve.co.uk
**Contact:** Mrs D E Sample
**Opening times:** Please ring first.
**Min. mail order UK:** No minimum charge
**Min. mail order EU:** Nmc
**Cat. cost:** Sae
**Credit cards:** None
**Specialities:** Alpines & dwarf Shrubs.
**Map ref:** 2, A3

**CPea    PEAR TREE COTTAGE PLANTS ⊠ EU ⊠**
Pear Tree Cottage, Prestleigh, Shepton Mallet,
Somerset, BA4 4NL
☎ (01749) 831487
**Contact:** PJ & PM Starr
**Opening times:** 0900-1900 Tue-Sun
1st Mar-31st Oct.
**Min. mail order UK:** £15.00 + p&p
**Min. mail order EU:** £20.00 + p&p
**Cat. cost:** 3 x 1st class
**Credit cards:** None
**Specialities:** Wide General Range with many
unusual plants.
**Map ref:** 2, B2

**CPev    PEVERIL CLEMATIS NURSERY**
Christow, Exeter, Devon, EX6 7NG
☎ (01647) 252937
**Contact:** Barry Fretwell
**Opening times:** 1000-1300 & 1400-1730
Fri-Wed, 1000-1300 Sun. Dec-Mar by appt.
**Mail order:** None
**Cat. cost:** 2 x 1st class
**Credit cards:** None
**Specialities:** Clematis.
**Map ref:** 1, B3

**CPhi    ALAN PHIPPS CACTI ⊠ EU**
62 Samuel White Road, Hanham, Bristol,
BS15 3LX
☎ (0117) 9607591
**Contact:** A Phipps
**Opening times:** All times, but prior phone
call ESSENTIAL to ensure a greeting.
**Min. mail order UK:** £5.00 + p&p
**Min. mail order EU:** £20.00 + p&p
**Cat. cost:** Sae or 2 x IRC (EC)
**Credit cards:** None
**Specialities:** Rebutia, Mammillaria,
Astrophytum & Ariocarpus.
**Map ref:** 2, A2

**CPin    PINE COTTAGE PLANTS ⊠ EU ⊠ ⊠**
Pine Cottage, Fourways, Eggesford,
Chulmleigh, Devon, EX18 7QZ
☎ (01769) 580076   **Fax:** (01769) 580076
**Contact:** Dick Fulcher
**Opening times:**
**Min. mail order UK:** £15.00 + p&p
**Min. mail order EU:** £20.00 + p&p
**Cat. cost:** 2 x 1st class
**Credit cards:** None
**Specialities:** Agapanthus – National
Collection.
**Map ref:** 1, A3

**C**

**CPla   PLANT WORLD BOTANIC GARDENS** ⊠ UK 🖰 ◆
St Marychurch Road, Newton Abbot, South Devon, TQ12 4SE
☎ (01803) 872939   **Fax:** (01803) 872939
**Contact:** Ray Brown
**Opening times:** 0930-1700 open 6 days (incl. Sun), closed Weds. Easter-end Sept.
**Min. mail order UK:** *
**Cat. cost:** 3 x 1st class or $2
**Credit cards:** Visa, Access, EuroCard, MasterCard
**Specialities:** Alpines & unusual Herbaceous plants. 4 acre world botanic map. National Collections of Primula. *Note: Mail order for seed only.
**Map ref:** 1, B3

**CPle   PLEASANT VIEW NURSERY** ⊠ EU
Two Mile Oak, Nr Denbury, Newton Abbot, Devon, TQ12 6DG
☎ (01803) 813388 answerphone
**Contact:** Mrs B D Yeo
**Opening times:** 1000-1700 Wed-Sat mid Mar-mid Oct. (Closed for lunch 1245-1330). Garden open 1400-1700 Wed & Fri May-Sep.
**Min. mail order UK:** £20.00 + p&p
**Min. mail order EU:** £20.00 + p&p (Salvias only)
**Cat. cost:** 5 x 2nd class or 2 x IRC
**Credit cards:** None
**Specialities:** Salvia & unusual shrubs for garden & conservatory incl. Buddleja, Viburnum, Ceanothus, Berberis, Lonicera, Spiraea. National Collections of Salvia & Abelia. 2 books on Salvias – the first to be devoted to the genus. Off A381 at T.M. Oak Cross towards Denbury.
**Map ref:** 1, B3

**CPLG   PINE LODGE GARDENS**
Cuddra, St Austell, Cornwall, PL25 3RQ
☎ (01726) 73500   **Fax:** (01726) 73500
**E-mail:** pine@thin-end.co.uk
**Web site:** http://www.thin-end.co.uk/pinehome.html
**Contact:** Ray & Shirley Clemo
**Opening times:** 1400-1700 Wed-Sun Apr-Sep, & B/Hols.
**Mail order:** None
**Cat. cost:** 4 x 2nd class
**Credit cards:** None
**Specialities:** Rare & unusual Shrubs & Herbaceous, some from seed collected on plant expeditions each year. National Collection of Grevillea.
**Map ref:** 1, C2

**CPIN   THE PLANTSMAN NURSERY** ⊠ EU 🖰
North Wonson Farm, Throwleigh, Okehampton, Devon, EX20 2JA
☎ (01647) 231699   **Fax:** (01647) 231157
**E-mail:** pnursery@aol.com
**Web site:** http://www.plantsman.com
**Contact:** Guy & Emma Sisson
**Opening times:** Mail order & strictly by appt.
**Min. mail order UK:** £25.00 + p&p
**Min. mail order EU:** £45.00 + p&p
**Cat. cost:** £2.00 refundable from purchase*
**Credit cards:** MasterCard, Access, American Express, Delta, Diners, EuroCard, Switch, Visa
**Specialities:** Unusual hardy & tender Climbers. Also seeds for non-EU countries. *Note: Seed list available for non-EU countries.
**Map ref:** 1, B3

**CPlt   PLANTAHOLICS**
Hillside, Coombe Street, Pen Selwood, Wincanton, Somerset, BA9 8NF
☎ (01747) 840852
**Contact:** Jane Edmonds
**Opening times:** Usually 1000-1600 Fri & Sat, last Fri Mar-last Sat Oct, but please ring first.
**Mail order:** None
**Cat. cost:** 2 x 2nd class
**Credit cards:** None
**Specialities:** Small nursery concentrating mainly on High Performance Perennials for various situations. Many unusual.
**Map ref:** 2, B2

**CPMA   P M A PLANT SPECIALITIES** ⊠ EU 🖰 🖰
Lower Mead, West Hatch, Taunton, Somerset, TA3 5RN
☎ (01823) 480774   **Fax:** (01823) 481046
**Contact:** Karan or Nick Junker
**Opening times:** Strictly by appt. only.
**Min. mail order UK:** No minimum charge
**Min. mail order EU:** Nmc
**Cat. cost:** 5 x 2nd class
**Credit cards:** None
**Specialities:** Choice & unusual Shrubs incl. grafted Acer palmatum cvs, Cornus cvs, Magnolia cvs. and a wide range of Daphne.
**Map ref:** 2, B1

**CPor   PORTH VEOR FUCHSIAS** ⊠ UK
54 Arundel Way, Newquay, Cornwall, TR7 3AG
☎ (01637) 877207
**Contact:** Mrs Mavis Morris
**Opening times:** By appt.

Min. mail order UK: £6.00 + p&p
Cat. cost: 2 x 1st class
Credit cards: None
Specialities: Fuchsia.
Map ref: 1, B1

**CPou** POUNSLEY PLANTS ⊠ EU ⬛
Poundsley Combe, Spriddlestone, Brixton,
Plymouth, Devon, PL9 0DW
☎ (01752) 402873  Fax: (01752) 402873
Contact: Mrs Jane Hollow
Opening times: Normally 1000-1700
Mon-Sat but please phone first.
Min. mail order UK: £10.00 + p&p*
Min. mail order EU: £20.00 + p&p
Cat. cost: 2 x 1st class
Credit cards: None
Specialities: Unusual Herbaceous Perennials
& 'Cottage plants'. Selection of Clematis
& Old Roses. *Note: Mail order Nov-Feb
only.
Map ref: 1, C3

**CPri** DAVID PRICE ⊠ UK
24 Crantock Drive, Almondsbury, Bristol,
BS12 4HG
☎ (01454) 615578, 0378 959285
Contact: David Price
Opening times: Not open.
Min. mail order UK: £10.00 +p&p
Cat. cost: 2 x 1st class
Credit cards: None
Specialities: Wide range of Rock &
Herbaceous plants, some unusual, incl.
Dianthus, Helianthemum, Lavender, Hebe.
Map ref: 2, A2

**CQua** QUALITY DAFFODILS ⊠ EU ⬛ ⬛
14 Roscarrack Close, Falmouth, Cornwall,
TR11 4PJ
☎ (01326) 317959
Contact: R A Scamp
Opening times: Mail order only.
Min. mail order UK: No minimum charge
Min. mail order EU: Nmc
Cat. cost: 3 x 1st class
Credit cards: None
Specialities: Narcissus Hybrids & Species.
Map ref: 1, C1

**CRde** ROWDE MILL NURSERY
Rowde, Devizes, Wiltshire, SN10 1SZ
☎ (01380) 723016  Fax: (01380) 723016
Contact: Mrs J Cholmeley
Opening times: 1000-1700 Thur-Sun &
B/Hol Mon Apr-Sep.
Mail order: None
Cat. cost: None issued

Credit cards: None
Specialities: Wide range of Hardy Perennials –
all grown on the nursery.
Map ref: 2, A2

**CRDP** R D PLANTS
Homelea Farm, Chard Road, Tytherleigh,
Axminster, East Devon, EX13 7BG
☎ (01460) 220206 ONLY 0830-0930
Contact: Rodney Davey & Lynda Windsor
Opening times: 0900-1300 & 1400-1700
Mon-Fri & most weekends, Mar-end Aug.
Please check first. Feb by appt. for Hellebores.
Mail order: None
Cat. cost: 4 x loose 2nd class
Credit cards: None
Specialities: Choice & unusual Herbaceous,
retentive shade & woodland plants,
Helleborus, plus rarities.
Map ref: 2, C1

**CRea** REALLY WILD FLOWERS ⊠ EU ⬛ ⬛
H V Horticulture Ltd, Spring Mead,
Bedchester, Shaftesbury, Dorset, SP7 0JU
☎ (01747) 811778  Fax: (01747) 811499
E-mail: rwflowers@aol.com
Web site: http://members.ad.com/rwflowers/
go/htm
Contact: Grahame Dixie
Opening times: Not open to public.
Min. mail order UK: £40.00 + p&p
Min. mail order EU: £100.00 + p&p
Cat. cost: 3 x 1st class
Credit cards: None
Specialities: Wild flowers for Grasslands,
Woodlands, Wetlands & Heaths.

**CRHN** ROSELAND HOUSE NURSERY ⊠ UK
Chacewater, Truro, Cornwall, TR4 8QB
☎ (01872) 560451
Contact: C R Pridham
Opening times: 1200-1800 Mon & Tue
Mar-Aug.
Min. mail order UK: £10.00 + p&p
Cat. cost: 2 x 1st class
Credit cards: None
Specialities: Climbing & Conservatory Plants.
Map ref: 1, C1

**CRoM** ROSEDOWN MILL NURSERY
Hartland, Bideford, Devon, EX39 6AH
☎ (01237) 441527  Fax: (01237) 441470
E-mail: huwcol@aol.com

| KEY | |
|---|---|
| ⊠ | Mail order to UK or EU |
| ⬛ | Exports beyond EU |
| ⬛ | Also supplies Wholesale  ◆ See Display advertisement |

**C**

Web site: http://www.treetops.u-net.com
Contact: Huw Collingbourne
Opening times: By appt. only during 1st
Jun-31st Oct 1999 & 1st May-31st Oct 2000.
Mail order: None
Cat. cost: Sae for list
Credit cards: None
Specialities: Palms, Cycads.
Map ref: 1, A2

CRos  ROYAL HORTICULTURAL
SOCIETY'S GARDEN
Rosemoor, Great Torrington, Devon,
EX38 8PH
☎ (01805) 624067  Fax: (01805) 622422
Contact: Plant Sales Manager
Opening times: 1000-1800 Apr-Sep,
1000-1700 Oct-Mar.
Mail order: None
Cat. cost: None issued
Credit cards: Visa, Access, American Express
Specialities: National Collections of Cornus
and part Ilex. Many rare & unusual plants.
Map ref: 1, A3

CRow  ROWDEN GARDENS ⊠ EU ☑ ☑
Brentor, Nr Tavistock, Devon, PL19 0NG
☎ (01822) 810275  Fax: (01822) 810275
Contact: John R L Carter
Opening times: 1000-1700 Sat-Sun & B/Hols
26th Mar-end Sep. Other times by appt.
Min. mail order UK: No minimum charge
Min. mail order EU: Nmc
Cat. cost: £1.50
Credit cards: None
Specialities: Aquatics, Damp Loving &
Associated plants incl. rare & unusual
varieties. National Collections of Polygonum
& Ranunculus ficaria.
Map ref: 1, B3

CRsw  ROSEWARNE COLLECTIONS ⊠ UK
Duchy College, Rosewarne, Camborne,
Cornwall, TR14 0AB
☎ (01209) 710077  Fax: (01209) 719754
E-mail: r.smith@cornwall.ac.uk
Contact: Ros Smith or Marshall Hutchens
Opening times: By appt. only.
Min. mail order UK: £10.00 + p&p
Cat. cost: 2 x 1st class
Credit cards: None
Specialities: Escallonia species and hybrids.
Map ref: 1, C1

CSam  SAMPFORD SHRUBS ⊠ UK
Sampford Peverell, Tiverton, Devon,
EX16 7EW
☎ (01884) 821164

Web site: http://freespace.virgin.net/martin.h
Contact: M Hughes-Jones & S Proud
Opening times: 0900-1700 (dusk if earlier)
Thu, Fri, Sat. 1000-1600 Sun. Closed
Dec-Jan except for mail order.
Min. mail order UK: £15.00 + p&p
Cat. cost: Sae
Credit cards: None
Specialities: Extensive range of good common
& uncommon plants including Herbaceous,
Shrubs, Trees & Fruit.
Map ref: 1, A4

CSCl  SCOTT'S CLEMATIS ⊠ EU ☑
Birchbrook, Birch Lane, Landkey, N Devon,
EX32 7PE
☎ (01271) 831032, Mobile 0411 594241
Contact: John & Marianne McLellan-Scott
Opening times: Birchbrook site not open, see
below for opening times at Tapeley Park Gdns.
Min. mail order UK: £20.00 + p&p
Min. mail order EU: £40.00 + p&p
Cat. cost: A5 Sae
Credit cards: None
Specialities: Clematis only. Note: 2nd site,
Scott's Clematis Direct, is at Tapeley Park
Gdns, Instow, nr. Bideford, N Devon. Open
1000-1700 daily exc. Sat, Mar-Oct.
Map ref: 1, A3

CSev  LOWER SEVERALLS NURSERY
Crewkerne, Somerset, TA18 7NX
☎ (01460) 73234  Fax: (01460) 76105
Contact: Mary R Cooper
Opening times: 1000-1700 Fri-Wed,
1400-1700 Sun 1st Mar-20th Oct.
Mail order: None
Cat. cost: 4 x 1st class
Credit cards: None
Specialities: Herbs, Herbaceous &
Conservatory plants.
Map ref: 2, B1

CSil  SILVER DALE NURSERIES ⊠ EU ◆
Shute Lane, Combe Martin, Illfracombe,
Devon, EX34 0HT
☎ (01271) 882539
Contact: Roger Gilbert
Opening times: 1000-1800 daily
Min. mail order UK: No minimum charge
Min. mail order EU: Nmc
Cat. cost: 3 x 1st class
Credit cards: Visa, MasterCard, EuroCard
Specialities: Fuchsia.
Map ref: 1, A3

**CSla  SLADE'S COUNTRYWISE LTD** ▣
Turks Head Corner, Exeter Road, Honiton,
Devon, EX14 8AZ
☎ (01404) 42720, (01404) 45966
Fax: (01404) 46316
Contact: Colin Dunford
Opening times: 0830-1800 Mon-Sat,
1000-1600 Sun excl. Xmas, Boxing &
New Year's Day & Easter Sun.
Mail order: None
Cat. cost: None issued
Credit cards: Access, Delta, Diners, EuroCard,
JCB, MasterCard, Switch, Visa
Specialities: Roses, Shrubs & Trees,
ornamental & fruit.
Map ref: 2, C1

**CSli  SLIPPS GARDEN CENTRE**
Butts Hill, Frome, Somerset, BA11 1HR
☎ (01373) 467013   Fax: (01373) 467013
Contact: James Hall
Opening times: 0900-1730 Mon-Sat,
1000-1630 Sun.
Mail order: None
Cat. cost: None issued
Credit cards: Visa, Access, MasterCard, Delta,
Switch
Specialities: Conifers. Achillea.
Map ref: 2, A2

**CSpe  SPECIAL PLANTS** ✉ EU
Hill Farm Barn, Greenways Lane, Cold
Ashton, Chippenham, Wiltshire, SN14 8LA
☎ (01225) 891686
E-mail: derry@sclegg.demon.co.uk
Web site: http://www.sclegg.demon.co.uk/
cat.html
Contact: Derry Watkins
Opening times: 1100-1500 daily Mar-Sep.
Other times please ring first to check.
Min. mail order UK: £10.00 + p&p*
Min. mail order EU: £10.00 + p&p
Cat. cost: 4 x 2nd class
Credit cards: None
Specialities: Tender Perennials, Felicia,
Diascia, Lotus, Pelargonium, Salvia,
Streptocarpus, Osteospermum etc. New
introductions of South African plants. *Note:
Mail order Sep-Mar only.
Map ref: 2, A2

**CSPN  SHERSTON PARVA
NURSERY LTD** ✉ EU ⊠
Malmesbury Road, Sherston, Wiltshire,
SN16 0NX
☎ (01666) 841066  Fax: (01666) 841132
E-mail: clematis@sherston-parva.prestel.co.uk
Contact: Martin Rea

Opening times: 1000-1700 every day.
Min. mail order UK: No minimum charge
Min. mail order EU: Nmc
Cat. cost: £2.60 cheque or 10 x 1st class
Credit cards: MasterCard, Delta, Visa
Specialities: Clematis, wall Shrubs &
Climbers. Colour catalogue.
Map ref: 5, C2

**CStr  SUE STRICKLAND PLANTS**
The Poplars, Isle Brewers, Taunton, Somerset,
TA3 6QN
☎ (01460) 281454  Fax: (01460) 281808
Contact: Sue Strickland
Opening times: 0930-1430 Mon-Wed
Apr-Jul & Sep. Other times by appt.
Mail order: None
Cat. cost: 2 x 1st class
Credit cards: None
Specialities: Salvia & unusual Herbaceous
Perennials incl. Nepeta, Helianthus,
Origanum & Monarda.
Map ref: 2, B1

**CSut  SUTTONS SEEDS** ✉ UK
Woodview Road, Paignton, Devon, TQ4 7NG
☎ (01803) 696321  Fax: (01803) 696345
Contact: Customer Services
Opening times: (Office) 0830-1700 Mon-Fri.
Answerphone also.
Min. mail order UK: No minimum charge
Cat. cost: Free
Credit cards: Visa, MasterCard
Specialities: Over 1,000 varieties of flower &
vegetable seed, bulbs, plants & sundries.

**CSWC  SOUTH WEST CARNIVOROUS
PLANTS** ✉ EU ⊠ ▣
2 Rose Cottages, Culmstock, Cullompton,
Devon, EX15 3JJ
☎ (01884) 841549  Fax: (01884) 841549
E-mail: flytraps@swcarnplants.force9.co.uk
Web site: http://www.littleshopofhorrors.co.uk
Contact: Jenny Pearce & Alistair Pearce
Opening times: By appt.
Min. mail order UK: £10.00 + p&p
Min. mail order EU: £20.00 + p&p
Cat. cost: 4 x 2nd class
Credit cards: MasterCard, Visa
Specialities: Cephalotus, Nepenthes, Dionea,
Drosera, Darlingtonia, Sarracenia, Pinguicula
& Utricularia. Specialists in hardy
Carnivorous plants & Dionea muscipula
cultivars.
Map ref: 1, A4

---

**C**

**CSWP**  SONIA WRIGHT PLANTS ✉ EU ☑
Grove Farm, Stitchcombe, Marlborough,
Wiltshire, SN8 2NG
☎ (01672) 514003  **Fax:** (01672) 541047
**Contact:** Anyas Simon
**Opening times:** 1000-dusk Tue-Sat all year.
**Min. mail order UK:** £15 Primulas only
**Min. mail order EU:** £15 Primulas only
**Cat. cost:** 4 x 1st class
**Credit cards:** None
**Specialities:** Barnhaven Polyanthus &
Primula. Grasses, grey-leaved plants, Iris,
Euphorbia, Penstemon, old Roses.
**Map ref:** 2, A3

**CTbh**  TREBAH ENTERPRISES LTD
Trebah, Mawnan Smith, Falmouth, Cornwall,
TR11 5JZ
☎ (01326) 250448  **Fax:** (01326) 250781
**E-mail:** mail@trebah-garden.co.uk
**Web site:** http://www.trebah-garden.co.uk
**Contact:** Plant Sales Staff
**Opening times:** 1030-1700 every day
of the year.
**Mail order:** None
**Cat. cost:** None issued
**Credit cards:** Visa, Access, EuroCard,
American Express, Switch, Delta, Electron,
MasterCard, Solo
**Specialities:** Agave, Tree Ferns, Palms,
Camellias, Gunnera & Conservatory
Climbers.
**Map ref:** 1, C1

**CTho**  THORNHAYES NURSERY ✉ EU ☑ ☑
St Andrews Wood, Dulford, Cullompton,
Devon, EX15 2DF
☎ (01884) 266746  **Fax:** (01884) 266739
**E-mail:** trees@thornhayes.demon.co.uk
**Contact:** K D Croucher
**Opening times:** By appt. only.
**Min. mail order UK:** No minimum charge
**Min. mail order EU:** Nmc
**Cat. cost:** 5 x 1st class
**Credit cards:** None
**Specialities:** A broad range of forms of
Broadleaved, Ornamental, Amenity & Fruit
Trees, including West Country Apple varieties.
**Map ref:** 1, B4

**CThr**  THREE COUNTIES NURSERIES ✉ UK ☑
Marshwood, Bridport, Dorset, DT6 5QJ
☎ (01297) 678257  **Fax:** (01297) 678257
**Contact:** A & D Hitchcock
**Opening times:** Not open.
**Min. mail order UK:** No minimum charge
**Cat. cost:** 2 x 2nd class
**Credit cards:** None
**Specialities:** Pinks & Dianthus.

**CTor**  THE TORBAY PALM FARM ✉ EU ☑ ☑
St Marychurch Road, Coffinswell, Nr Newton
Abbot, South Devon, TQ12 4SE
☎ (01803) 872800  **Fax:** (01803) 322533
**Contact:** T A Eley
**Opening times:** 0900-1730 Mon-Fri,
1030-1700 Sat & Sun.
**Min. mail order UK:** £3.50 + p&p
**Min. mail order EU:** Poa
**Cat. cost:** Free
**Credit cards:** None
**Specialities:** Cordyline australis, Trachycarpus
fortuneii & new varieties of Cordyline.
**Map ref:** 1, B3

**CTrC**  TREVENA CROSS NURSERIES ✉ EU ☑
Breage, Helston, Cornwall, TR13 9PS
☎ (01736) 763880  **Fax:** (01736) 762828
**Contact:** Graham Jeffery
**Opening times:** 0900-1700 Mon-Sat,
1030-1630 Sun.
**Min. mail order UK:** No minimum charge
**Min. mail order EU:** Nmc
**Cat. cost:** A5 Sae with 2 x 1st class
**Credit cards:** Access, Visa
**Specialities:** South African & Australasian
Plants, Aloe, Protea, Tree Ferns, Palms, wide
range of Hardy Exotics. Restios.
**Map ref:** 1, C1

**CTre**  TREWIDDEN ESTATE NURSERY ✉ EU ☑
Trewidden Gardens, Penzance, Cornwall,
TR20 8TT
☎ (01736) 362087  **Fax:** (01736) 3331470
**E-mail:** bolitho@ckd.co.uk
**Web site:** http://www.trewidden-nursery.
co.uk
**Contact:** Mr M G Snellgrove
**Min. mail order UK:** No minimum charge
**Min. mail order EU:** Nmc
**Cat. cost:** 2 x 1st class
**Credit cards:** None
**Specialities:** Camellia & unusual Shrubs.
**Map ref:** 1, C1

**CTrF**  TRESIDDER FARM PLANTS ✉ EU ☑ ☑
Tresidder Farm, St. Buryan, Penzance,
Cornwall, TR19 6EZ
☎ (01736) 810656
**Contact:** N Milligan
**Opening times:** By appt. Please ring.
**Min. mail order UK:** £15.00 + p&p
**Min. mail order EU:** £15.00 + p&p
**Cat. cost:** Plant & seed lists available.
**Credit cards:** None
**Specialities:** Proteaceae, Aloeaceae, large Aloe
collection, unusual Succulents.
**Map ref:** 1, C1

**C**TrG   **TREGOTHNAN NURSERY** ⊠ EU ⊠ ⊡
Estate Office, Tregothnan, Truro, Cornwall,
TR2 4AN
☎ (01872) 520584   **Fax:** (01872) 520291
**E-mail:** bigplants@mailcity.com
**Contact:** Jonathon Jones
**Opening times:** By appt. for collection only.
**Min. mail order UK:** No minimum charge
**Min. mail order EU:** Nmc
**Cat. cost:** Sae
**Credit cards:** MasterCard, Visa, Delta,
EuroCard
**Specialities:** Unusual and rare plants from
own stock. Extra large specimens available for
instant effect. Known wild origin plants.
**Map ref:** 1, C2

**C**Trh   **TREHANE CAMELLIA
NURSERY** ⊠ EU ⊠ ⊡
J Trehane & Sons Ltd, Stapehill Road,
Hampreston, Wimborne, Dorset, BH21 7NE
☎ (01202) 873490   **Fax:** (01202) 873490
**Contact:** Chris, Lorraine or Jeanette
**Opening times:** 0900-1630 Mon-Fri all year
(ex. Xmas & New Year) 1000-1600 Sat-Sun
late Feb-May, & by special appt.
**Min. mail order UK:** No minimum charge
**Min. mail order EU:** Nmc
**Cat. cost:** Cat/Book £1.70
**Credit cards:** Visa, Access, MasterCard
**Specialities:** Extensive range of Camellia
species, cultivars & hybrids. Many new
introductions. Evergreen Azalea, Pieris,
Magnolia, Blueberries & Cranberries.
**Map ref:** 2, C3

**C**Tri   **TRISCOMBE NURSERIES** ◆
West Bagborough, Nr Taunton, Somerset,
TA4 3HG
☎ (01984) 618267
**Contact:** S Parkman
**Opening times:** 0900-1300 & 1400-1730
Mon-Sat. 1400-1730 Sun & B/Hols.
**Mail order:** None
**Cat. cost:** None issued
**Credit cards:** None
**Specialities:** Trees, Shrubs, Roses, Fruit,
Clematis, Herbaceous & Rock plants.
**Map ref:** 2, B1

**C**Trw   **TREWITHEN NURSERIES** ⊡
Grampound Road, Truro, Cornwall,
TR2 4DD
☎ (01726) 882764   **Fax:** (01726) 882301
**Contact:** M Taylor
**Opening times:** 0800-1630 Mon-Fri.
**Mail order:** None
**Cat. cost:** £1.25

**Credit cards:** None
**Specialities:** Shrubs, especially Camellia &
Rhododendron.
**Map ref:** 1, C2

**C**Tuc   **EDWIN TUCKER & SONS** ⊠ EU
Brewery Meadow, Stonepark, Ashburton,
Newton Abbot, Devon, TQ13 7DG
☎ (01364) 652403   **Fax:** (01364) 654300
**Contact:** Geoff Penton
**Opening times:** 0800-1700 Mon-Fri,
0800-1600 Sun.
**Min. mail order UK:** No minimum charge
**Min. mail order EU:** Nmc
**Cat. cost:** Free
**Credit cards:** Visa, MasterCard, Switch
**Specialities:** Over 70 varieties of Seed
Potatoes. Wide range of Vegetables, Flowers,
Green Manures & sprouting seeds in packets.
All not treated.
**Map ref:** 1, B3

**C**Ver   **VERYANS PLANTS** ⊠ UK ⊡
The Barn, Coryton House, Coryton,
Okehampton, Devon, EX20 4PA
☎ (01822) 860302 day*
**Contact:** Miss R V Millar
**Opening times:** Essential to telephone first for
appt. *Note: (01822) 860130 evenings.
**Min. mail order UK:** No minimum charge
**Cat. cost:** 3 x 1st class
**Credit cards:** None
**Specialities:** Range of hardy Perennials inc.
Aster, Ornamental Grasses, Geranium & large
selection of Primroses, many rare.
**Map ref:** 1, B3

**C**Wat   **THE WATER GARDEN** ⊠ UK
Hinton Parva, Swindon, SN4 0DH
☎ (01793) 790558   **Fax:** (01793) 791298
**E-mail:** waterg@dircon.co.uk
**Contact:** Mike & Anne Newman
**Opening times:** 1000-1700 Wed-Sun.
**Min. mail order UK:** £10.00 + p&p
**Cat. cost:** 4 x 1st class
**Credit cards:** Visa, Access, Switch
**Specialities:** Water Lilies, Marginal &
Moisture plants, Oxygenators & Alpines.
**Map ref:** 2, A3

**C**WDa   **WESTDALE NURSERIES** ⊠ EU ⊠ ⊡
Holt Road, Bradford-on-Avon, Wiltshire,
BA15 1TS

---

**K E Y**   ⊠ Mail order to UK or EU
⊠ Exports beyond EU
⊡ Also supplies Wholesale   ◆ See Display advertisement

**C**

☎ (01225) 863258   **Fax:** (01225) 863258
**Contact:** Mr Clarke
**Opening times:** 0900-1800 7 days a week.
**Min. mail order UK:** £10.00 + p&p
**Min. mail order EU:** £10.00 + p&p
**Cat. cost:** 4 x 1st class
**Credit cards:** MasterCard, Visa
**Specialities:** Bougainvillea, Geranium,
Conservatory Plants.
**Map ref:** 2, A2

**CWdb   WOODBOROUGH GARDEN CENTRE**
Nursery Farm, Woodborough, Nr Pewsey,
Wiltshire, SN9 5PF
☎ (01672) 851249   **Fax:** (01672) 851249
**Contact:** Els M Brewin
**Opening times:** 0900-1700 Mon-Sat,
1100-1700 Sun.
**Mail order:** None
**Cat. cost:** None issued
**Credit cards:** Access, Diners, EuroCard,
MasterCard, Switch, Visa
**Specialities:** Wide range of Shrubs, Trees,
Herbaceous, Alpines & Herbs. Large selection
of Climbers, esp. Clematis, & spring Bulbs.
**Map ref:** 2, A3

**CWhi   WHITEHOUSE IVIES ⊠ EU**
Eggesford Gardens, Chulmleigh, Devon,
EX18 7QU
☎ (01769) 580250   **Fax:** (01769) 581041
**Contact:** Joan Burks
**Opening times:** 0900-1700 daily exc. Xmas,
Boxing and N.Year's Day.
**Min. mail order UK:** £17.70 + p&p
**Min. mail order EU:** £17.70 + p&p
**Cat. cost:** £1.50 or 6 x 1st class
**Credit cards:** Visa, MasterCard, Switch, Delta
**Specialities:** Ivy – over 350 varieties.
**Map ref:** 1, A3

**CWil   HOWARD & SALLY WILLS ⊠ EU ▣**
Fernwood, Peters Marland, Torrington,
Devon, EX38 8QG
☎ (01805) 601446   **Fax:** (01805) 601446
**E-mail:** hjwills@houseleeks.freeserve.co.uk
**Web site:** http://www.houseleeks.freeserve.co.uk/
**Contact:** Howard Wills & Sally Wills
**Opening times:** Any time by appt.
Please phone first.
**Min. mail order UK:** No minimum charge
**Min. mail order EU:** Nmc
**Cat. cost:** 3 x 1st class
**Credit cards:** None
**Specialities:** Sempervivum, Jovibarba &
Rosularia. National Collections of all.
**Map ref:** 1, A3

**CWin   WINFRITH HOSTAS ⊠ UK ▣**
5 Knoll Park, Gatemore Road, Winfrith
Newburgh, Dorchester, Dorset, DT2 8LD
☎ (01305) 852935
**Contact:** John Ledbury
**Opening times:** By appt.
**Min. mail order UK:** No minimum charge
**Cat. cost:** 2 x 1st class
**Credit cards:** None
**Specialities:** Hostas.
**Map ref:** 2, C2

**CWit   WITHLEIGH NURSERIES**
Quirkhill, Withleigh, Tiverton, Devon,
EX16 8JG
☎ (01884) 253351
**Contact:** Chris Britton
**Opening times:** 0900-1730 Mon-Sat
Mar-Jun, 0900-1730 Tue-Sat Jul-Feb.
**Mail order:** None
**Cat. cost:** None issued
**Credit cards:** None
**Specialities:** Shrubs & Herbaceous.
**Map ref:** 1, A3

**CWoo   IAN AND ROSEMARY WOOD ⊠ UK**
Newlands, 28 Furland Road, Crewkerne,
Somerset, TA18 8DD
☎ (01460) 74630
**Contact:** Ian and Rosemary Wood
**Opening times:** By appt. only. Primarily mail
order service.
**Min. mail order UK:** No minimum charge
**Cat. cost:** 1 x 1st class
**Credit cards:** None
**Specialities:** Erythronium.
**Map ref:** 2, B1

**CWri   NIGEL WRIGHT RHODODENDRONS ▣**
The Old Glebe, Eggesford, Chulmleigh,
Devon, EX18 7QU
☎ (01769) 580632
**Contact:** Nigel Wright
**Opening times:** By appt. only.
**Mail order:** None
**Cat. cost:** 2 x 1st class
**Credit cards:** None
**Specialities:** Rhododendron only. 200 varieties
field grown. Root-balled, not potted – for
collection only. Specialist grower.
**Map ref:** 1, A3

**CWSG   WEST SOMERSET GARDEN
CENTRE ⊠ EU**
Mart Road, Minehead, Somerset, TA24 5BJ
☎ (01643) 703812   **Fax:** (01643) 706470
**E-mail:** wsgardencentre@compuserve.com
**Contact:** Mrs J K Shoulders

**Opening times:** 0800-1700 Mon-Sat,
1100-1700 Sun (Winter times vary, please
phone).
**Min. mail order UK:** No minimum charge
**Min. mail order EU:** Nmc
**Cat. cost:** Please phone for availability.
**Credit cards:** Access, Visa
**Specialities:** Wide general range.
**Map ref:** 1, A3

**C**WtG  **THE WATER GARDENS**
Highcroft, Moorend, Wembworthy,
Chumleigh, Devon, EX18 7SG
☎ (01837) 83566
**Contact:** J M Smith
**Opening times:** Garden open to the public
1000-1700 Fri, Sun & Mon incl. B/Hols
April-Sept.
**Mail order:** None
**Cat. cost:** None issued
**Credit cards:** None
**Specialities:** Water/Bog/Perennials/Ferns for
sale in the Garden. Entrance fee £2.00.
(Nursery closed.)
**Map ref:** 1, A3

# EASTERN ENGLAND

**E**And  **ANDERS NURSERY** ☒ UK
20 East Hall, Lodge Road, Feltwell, Thetford,
Norfolk, IP26 4DP
☎ (01842) 827676
**E-mail:** timothy.anders@virgin.net
**Contact:** Timothy Anders
**Opening times:** Please call for appt.
**Min. mail order UK:** £10.00 + p&p
**Cat. cost:** Sae
**Credit cards:** None
**Specialities:** Carnivorous plants.
**Map ref:** 8, C2

**E**Ast  **ASTERBY NURSERIES**
Dairy Farm, Church Lane, Asterby, Louth,
Lincolnshire, LN11 9UF
☎ (01507) 343549
**E-mail:** nursery@asterby.freeserve.co.uk
**Web site:** http://www.asterby.freeserve.co.uk
**Contact:** Edwin & Elizabeth Aldridge
**Opening times:** Generally open but please
phone first if making a special journey.
**Mail order:** None
**Cat. cost:** 2 x 1st class
**Credit cards:** Visa, MasterCard, Switch
**Specialities:** Hardy Shrubs & Herbaceous.
**Map ref:** 8, A1

**E**Bak  **B & H M BAKER** 🅐
Bourne Brook Nurseries, Greenstead Green,
Halstead, Essex, CO9 1RJ
☎ (01787) 472900/476369
**Contact:** B, HM and C Baker
**Opening times:** 0800-1630 Mon-Fri,
0900-1200 & 1400-1630 Sat & Sun.
**Mail order:** None
**Cat. cost:** 20p + stamp
**Credit cards:** MasterCard, Delta, Visa, Switch
**Specialities:** Fuchsia & Conservatory Plants.
**Map ref:** 6, B3

**E**Bee  **BEECHES NURSERY** ☒ EU
Village Centre, Ashdon, Saffron Walden,
Essex, CB10 2HB
☎ (01799) 584362  **Fax:** (01799) 584362
**E-mail:** beenurs@argonet.co.uk
**Contact:** Alan Bidwell/Kevin Marsh
**Opening times:** 0830-1700 Mon-Sat,
1000-1700 Sun incl. B/Hols.
**Min. mail order UK:** No minimum charge
**Min. mail order EU:** Nmc
**Cat. cost:** 3 x 2nd class
**Credit cards:** Visa, Access, MasterCard,
EuroCard, Switch
**Specialities:** Herbaceous specialists &
extensive range of other garden plants.
**Map ref:** 6, B2

**E**Bla  **BLACKSMITHS COTTAGE
NURSERY** ☒ UK
Langmere Green Road, Langmere, Diss,
Norfolk, IP21 4QA
☎ (01379) 740982, Tel/Fax (01379) 741917
(nursery)  **Fax:** (01379) 741917
**Contact:** Ben Potterton
**Opening times:** 1000-1700 Fri-Sun all year,
or by appt.
**Min. mail order UK:**
**Cat. cost:** 2 x 1st class
**Credit cards:** None
**Specialities:** Hardy Geranium, Digitalis,
Heuchera, Crocosmia & Siberian Iris. Large
selection of unusual herbaceous plants.
**Map ref:** 6, A4

**E**Bls  **PETER BEALES ROSES** ☒ EU 🗷
London Road, Attleborough, Norfolk,
NR17 1AY
☎ (01953) 454707  **Fax:** (01953) 456845
**E-mail:** sales@classicroses.co.uk
**Web site:** http://www.classicroses.co.uk

E

Contact: Customer advisors
Opening times: 0900-1700 Mon-Fri, 0900-1630 Sat, 1000-1600 Sun. Jan closed Sun.
Min. mail order UK: No minimum charge
Min. mail order EU: Nmc
Cat. cost: £2.00
Credit cards: Visa, MasterCard, Access, Switch, Solo, Delta, JCB
Specialities: Old fashioned Roses & Classic Roses.
Map ref: 8, C3

**EBot    BOTANICUS ⊠ EU**
The Nurseries, Ringland Lane, Old Costessey, Norwich, NR8 5BG
☎ (01603) 742063
Contact: Anthony Murphy
Opening times: 1000-1700 Fri-Sun & B/Hol Mons Apr-Oct. 1000-1600 Sats Nov & Mar.
Min. mail order UK: £15.00 + p&p
Min. mail order EU: £50.00 + p&p
Cat. cost: £2.50
Credit cards: None
Specialities: Historic garden plants grown in Britain from Roman times to 1850, particularly Bulbs, Herbaceous Perennials & Shrubs.
Map ref: 8, C4

**EBre    BRESSINGHAM PLANT CENTRE**
Bressingham, Diss, Norfolk, IP22 2AB
☎ (01379) 687464/688133
Fax: (01379) 688034
Contact: Tony Fry
Opening times: 0900-1730 daily. (Direct retail Plant Centre.)
Mail Order: None
Cat. cost: None issued
Credit cards: Visa, Delta, Switch, MasterCard
Specialities: Very wide general range. Many own varieties. Focus on Hardy Ornamental plants & grasses.
Map ref: 6, A3

**EBrP    BRESSINGHAM PLANT CENTRE**
Elton, Peterborough, PE8 6SH
☎ (01832) 280058   Fax: (01832) 280081
Contact: Tom Green
Opening times: 0900-1730 daily. (Direct retail Plant Centre.)
Mail order: None
Cat. cost: None issued
Credit cards: Delta, Switch, MasterCard, Visa
Specialities: Very wide general range. Many own varieties. Focus on Hardy Ornamental plants & Grasses.
Map ref: 8, C1

**EBSP    BRIAN SULMAN ⊠ EU**
54 Kingsway, Mildenhall, Bury St Edmunds, Suffolk, IP28 7HR
☎ (01638) 712297   Fax: (01638) 515052
Contact: Brian Sulman
Opening times: Mail order only. Special open weekend 12/13th June 1999.
Min. mail order UK: £12.00 + p&p
Min. mail order EU: £12.00 + p&p
Cat. cost: 2 x 1st class
Credit cards: None
Specialities: Regal Pelargoniums.
Map ref: 6, A3

**EBur    JENNY BURGESS ⊠ EU ▣**
Alpine Nursery, Sisland, Norwich, Norfolk, NR14 6EF
☎ (01508) 520724
Contact: Jenny Burgess
Opening times: Any time by appt.
Min. mail order UK: £5.00 + p&p*
Min. mail order EU: £10.00 + p&p
Cat. cost: 3 x 1st class
Credit cards: None
Specialities: Alpines, Sisyrinchium & Campanula. National Collection of Sisyrinchium. *Note: Only Sisyrinchium by mail order.
Map ref: 8, C4

**ECGN    THE CONTENTED GARDENER - NURSERY ▣**
The Garden House, 42 Wragby Road, Bardney, Lincolnshire, LN3 5XL
☎ (01526) 397307   Fax: (01526) 397280
Contact: Lee Heykoop
Opening times: By appt.
Mail order: None
Cat. cost: A4 Sae + 2 x 1st class
Credit cards: None
Specialities: Perennials & Grasses for naturalistic planting in dry and damp and woodland edge.
Map ref: 8, A1

**ECGP    CAMBRIDGE GARDEN PLANTS**
The Lodge, Clayhithe Road, Homingsea, Cambridgeshire, CB5 9JD
☎ (01223) 861370
Contact: Mrs Nancy Buchdahl
Opening times: 1100-1730 Thu-Sun mid Mar-31st Oct. Other times by appt.
Mail order: None
Cat. cost: 4 x 1st class
Credit cards: None
Specialities: Hardy Perennials incl. wide range of Geraniums, Alliums, Euphorbia, Penstemons, Digitalis. Some Shrubs, Roses & Clematis.
Map ref: 6, A2

**E**

**ECha    THE BETH CHATTO GARDENS LTD ⊠ EU**
Elmstead Market, Colchester, Essex,
CO7 7DB
☎ (01206) 822007   **Fax:** (01206) 825933
**Contact:** Beth Chatto
**Opening times:** 0900-1700 Mon-Sat
1st Mar-31st Oct. 0900-1600 Mon-Fri
1st Nov-1st Mar. Closed Sun & B/Hols.
**Min. mail order UK:** See cat. for details
**Min. mail order EU:** Ask for details
**Cat. cost:** £3.00 incl. p&p
**Credit cards:** Visa, Access, Switch
**Specialities:** Predominantly Herbaceous. Many
unusual for special situations.
**Map ref:** 6, B3

**ECho    CHOICE LANDSCAPES ⊠ EU ◪**
Priory Farm, 101 Salts Road, West Walton,
Wisbech, Cambs, PE14 7EF
☎ (01945) 585051   **Fax:** (01945) 585051
**Contact:** Michael Agg & Jillian Agg
**Opening times:** By appt. only.
**Min. mail order UK:** No minimum charge
**Min. mail order EU:** £10.00 + p&p
**Cat. cost:** 4 x 1st class
**Credit cards:** None
**Specialities:** Dwarf Conifers, Heathers,
Alpines, Acers & Rhododendrons.
**Map ref:** 8, C2

**EChP    CHOICE PLANTS**
83 Halton Road, Spilsby, Lincs, PE23 5LD
☎ (01790) 752361
**Contact:** Joan Gunson
**Opening times:** 1000-1700 Wed-Sun &
B/Hol Mon mid Mar-mid Oct.
**Mail order:** None
**Cat. cost:** 3 x 1st
**Credit cards:** None
**Specialities:** Hardy Geranium, Crocosmia,
Hemerocallis, Iris & a good selection of
unusual Hardy Perennials.
**Map ref:** 8, A2

**ECle    CLEY NURSERIES LTD ⊠ UK**
Holt Road, Cley-Next-the-Sea, Holt, Norfolk,
NR25 7TX
☎ (01263) 740892   **Fax:** (01263) 741138
**Contact:** Alec or Gill Mellor
**Opening times:** 1000-1600 daily.
**Min. mail order UK:** £10.00 + p&p
**Cat. cost:** List 2 x 1st class
**Credit cards:** Visa, Access, Switch
**Specialities:** Roses.
**Map ref:** 8, B3

**ECon    CONSERVATORY PLANTLINE ⊠ EU ◪ ◩**
Nayland Road, West Bergholt, Colchester,
Essex, CO6 3DH
☎ (01206) 242533   **Fax:** (01206) 242530
**E-mail:** 100724.3432@compuserve.com
**Contact:** Jane Wells & Paul Holt
**Opening times:** By appt. only.
**Min. mail order UK:** No minimum charge
**Min. mail order EU:** Nmc
**Cat. cost:** £2.00
**Credit cards:** MasterCard, EuroCard, Visa,
WorldWide
**Specialities:** Conservatory Plants.
**Map ref:** 6, B3

**ECoo    PATRICIA COOPER**
Magpies, Green Lane, Mundford, Norfolk,
IP26 5HS
☎ (01842) 878496
**Contact:** Patricia Cooper
**Opening times:** 0900-1700 Mon, Tue, Thu &
Fri 1200-1700 Sat & Sun.
**Mail order:** None
**Cat. cost:** Free
**Credit cards:** None
**Specialities:** Unusual hardy Perennials,
Grasses, Wild Flowers, Bog, Aquatic & Foliage
plants.
**Map ref:** 8, C3

**ECot    COTTAGE GARDENS**
Langham Road, Boxted, Colchester, Essex,
CO4 5HU
☎ (01206) 272269
**Contact:** Alison Smith
**Opening times:** 0800-1730 daily Spring &
Summer. 0800-1730 Thu-Mon Sept-Feb.
**Mail order:** None
**Cat. cost:** Free
**Credit cards:** Visa, Access
**Specialities:** 400 varieties of Shrubs, 390
varieties of Herbaceous. Huge range of Trees,
Alpines, Herbs, Hedging – all home grown.
Garden antiques.
**Map ref:** 6, B3

**ECou    COUNTY PARK NURSERY**
Essex Gardens, Hornchurch, Essex,
RM11 3BU
☎ (01708) 445205
**Contact:** G Hutchins
**Opening times:** 0900-dusk Mon-Sat ex Wed,
1000-1700 Sun Mar-Oct.

**E**

Nov-Feb by appt. only.
**Mail order:** None
**Cat. cost:** 3 x 1st class
**Credit cards:** None
**Specialities:** Alpines & rare and unusual plants from New Zealand, Tasmania & Falklands. National Collection of Coprosma & Parahebe.
**Map ref:** 6, C2

**ECre  CREAKE PLANT CENTRE**
Nursery View, Leicester Road, South Creake, Fakenham, Norfolk, NR21 9PW
☎ (01328) 823018
**Contact:** Mr T Harrison
**Opening times:** 1000-1300 & 1400-1730 every day exc. Xmas.
**Mail order:** None
**Cat. cost:** None issued
**Credit cards:** None
**Specialities:** Unusual Shrubs, Herbaceous, Conservatory Plants. Huge selection of Hardy Geraniums.
**Map ref:** 8, B3

**ECrN  CROWN NURSERY** ⊠ UK ▣
High Street, Ufford, Woodbridge, Suffolk, IP13 6EL
☎ (01394) 460755   **Fax:** (01394) 460142
**Contact:** Jill Proctor
**Opening times:** 0900-1700 Mon-Sat
**Min. mail order UK:** No minimum charge
**Cat. cost:** 2 x 1st class
**Credit cards:** Visa, Delta, MasterCard, EuroCard, JCB, Switch
**Specialities:** Mature & semi-mature Native & Ornamental Trees.
**Map ref:** 6, A4

**ECtt  COTTAGE NURSERIES** ⊠ UK ▣
Thoresthorpe, Alford, Lincolnshire, LN13 0HX
☎ (01507) 466968   **Fax:** (01507) 463409
**Contact:** W H Denbigh
**Opening times:** 0900-1700 daily 1st Mar-31st Oct, 1000-1600 Thu-Sun Nov-Feb.
**Min. mail order UK:** £5.00 + p&p
**Cat. cost:** 3 x 1st class
**Credit cards:** None
**Specialities:** Wide general range.
**Map ref:** 8, A2

**EDAr  D'ARCY & EVEREST** ⊠ EU ▣
(Office) St Ives Road, Somersham, Huntingdon, Cambridgeshire, PE17 3ET
☎ (01487) 843650   **Fax:** (01487) 840096
**E-mail:** angalps@martex.com.uk
**Contact:** Barry Johnson

**Opening times:** By appt. only.
**Min. mail order UK:** £10.00 + p&p
**Min. mail order EU:** £50.00 + p&p
**Cat. cost:** 5 x 1st class
**Credit cards:** None
**Specialities:** Alpines & Herbs.
**Map ref:** 6, A2

**EDrk  JOHN DRAKE** ⊠ EU ▣
Hardwicke House, Fen Ditton, Cambridgeshire, CB5 8TF
☎ (01223) 292246   **Fax:** (01223) 292246
**Contact:** John Drake
**Opening times:**
**Min. mail order UK:** £12.50
**Min. mail order EU:** £12.50
**Cat. cost:** 70p*
**Credit cards:** None
**Specialities:** Aquilegia – National Collection. Seed only. *Note: Seed catalogue available Aug.

**EElm  ELM HOUSE NURSERY** ⊠ UK
Freepost, PO Box 25, Wisbech, Cambridgeshire, PE13 2BR
☎ (01945) 581511   **Fax:** (01945) 588235
**Contact:** Customer Services
**Opening times:**
**Min. mail order UK:** No minimum charge
**Cat. cost:** Free
**Credit cards:** Access, Visa
**Specialities:** Chrysanthemums & cutting raised plants.

**EEls  ELSWORTH HERBS** ⊠ EU
Avenue Farm Cottage, 31 Smith Street, Elsworth, Cambridgeshire, CB3 8HY
☎ (01954) 267414   **Fax:** (01954) 267414
**Contact:** Drs J D & J M Twibell
**Opening times:** Advertised weekends & by appt. only.
**Min. mail order UK:** £10.00 + p&p
**Min. mail order EU:** £10.00 + p&p
**Cat. cost:** 3 x 1st class
**Credit cards:** None
**Specialities:** Herbs. National Collections of Artemisia & Nerium oleander. Cottage garden plants.
**Map ref:** 6, A2

**EEmo  EMORSGATE SEED** ⊠ EU ▣ ▣
Limes Farm, Tilney All Saints, Kings Lynn, Norfolk, PE34 4RT
☎ (01553) 829028   **Fax:** (01553) 829803
**Contact:** Mark Schofield
**Opening times:** 0800-1700 Mon-Fri.
**Min. mail order UK:** No minimum charge
**Min. mail order EU:** £20.00 + p&p

E

Cat. cost: Free
Credit cards: None
Specialities: Wild British Flowers & Grasses –
Seed only.

**EEve** R G & A EVENDEN ⊠ EU ☑ ▣
25 Penway Drive, Pinchbeck, Spalding,
Lincolnshire, PE11 3PJ
☎ (01775) 767857  Fax: (01775) 713878
Contact: Richard Evenden
Opening times: By appt. only, weekends
May-Jul.
Min. mail order UK: No minimum charge
Min. mail order EU: Nmc
Cat. cost: Sae
Credit cards: None
Specialities: Bletilla species & hybrids.
Pleiones.
Map ref: 8, B1

**EFam** FAMECHECK SPECIAL
PLANTS ⊠ EU ☑ ▣ ◆
Hilltrees, Wandlebury Hill (A1307),
Cambridge, Cambridgeshire, CB2 4AD
☎ (01223) 243734 long ring or after dark
Contact: Miss F Cook N.D.H.
Opening times: 1100-dusk Mar & Apr.
Other times by appt.
Min. mail order UK: £5.00 + p&p
Min. mail order EU: £5.00 + p&p
Cat. cost: 2 x 1st class for list.
Credit cards: None
Specialities: Daffodils. Long-lasting &
weatherproof cut-flower varieties. Also bearded
Iris & Orange Violets.
Map ref: 6, A2

**EFer** THE FERN NURSERY ⊠ EU ▣
Grimsby Road, Binbrook, Lincolnshire,
LN8 6DH
☎ (01472) 398092
Contact: R N Timm
Opening times: 0900-1700 Sat & Sun
Apr-Oct or by appt.
Min. mail order UK: No minimum charge
Min. mail order EU: Nmc
Cat. cost: 2 x 1st class
Credit cards: None
Specialities: Ferns & Hardy Perennials.
Map ref: 9, C4

**EFEx** FLORA EXOTICA ⊠ EU ☑ ▣
Pasadena, South-Green, Fingringhoe,
Colchester, Essex, CO5 7DR
☎ (01206) 729414
Contact: J Beddoes
Opening times: Not open to the public.
Min. mail order UK: No minimum charge

Min. mail order EU: Nmc
Cat. cost: 4 x 1st class
Credit cards: None
Specialities: Exotica Flora incl. Orchids.

**EFlo** FLOR DO SOL
Copenore Lodge, South Hanningfield Road,
Wickford, Essex, SS11 7PF
☎ (01268) 710499
Contact: Mrs M Heaton
Opening times: By appt. only from
1st Apr- 31st Oct
Mail order: None
Cat. cost: Sae + 1 x 1st class
Credit cards: None
Specialities: Conservatory plants esp. Nerium
oleanders.
Map ref: 6, C3

**EFot** MR FOTHERGILL'S SEEDS LTD ⊠ UK ▣
Gazeley Road, Kentford, Newmarket, Suffolk,
CB8 7QB
☎ (01638) 552512  Fax: (01638) 750468
Contact: Mail order Dept.
Opening times: 0900-1700 Mon-Fri.
Min. mail order UK: £5.00 + p&p
Cat. cost: Free
Credit cards: Visa, Access, MasterCard, Switch
Specialities: Annuals, Biennials, Perennials,
Herbs, Vegetables, Potatoes, Onion sets, soft
Fruit and Garden Sundries.
Map ref: 6, A3

**EFou** FOUR SEASONS ⊠ EU
Forncett St Mary, Norwich, Norfolk,
NR16 1JT
☎ (01508) 488344  Fax: (01508) 488478
E-mail: mail@fsperennials.co.uk
Web site: http://www.fsperennials.co.uk
Contact: J P Metcalf & R W Ball
Opening times: No callers.
Min. mail order UK: £15.00 + p&p
Min. mail order EU: £15.00 + p&p
Cat. cost: Free
Credit cards: Visa, MasterCard, Switch
Specialities: Herbaceous Perennials.
Aconitum, Anemone, Aster, Campanula,
Chrysanthemum, Digitalis, Erigeron,
Geranium, Helenium, Iris, Salvia & Grasses.

**EFul** FULBROOKE NURSERY ⊠ EU
Home Farm, Westley Waterless, Newmarket,
Suffolk, CB8 0RG

KEY
⊠ Mail order to UK or EU
☑ Exports beyond EU
▣ Also supplies Wholesale  ◆ See Display advertisement

E

☎ (01638) 507124  **Fax:** (01638) 507124
**E-mail:** fulbrook@clara.net
**Web site:** http://www.fulbrook.clara.net
**Contact:** Paul Lazard
**Opening times:** By appt. most times incl. weekends.
**Min. mail order UK:** £6.00 + p&p
**Min. mail order EU:** £6.00 + p&p
**Cat. cost:** 2 x 1st class
**Credit cards:** None
**Specialities:** Bamboos & Grasses.
**Map ref:** 6, A2

**EGar**  **GARDINER'S HALL PLANTS** ✉ EU ✉
Braiseworth, Eye, Suffolk, IP23 7DZ
☎ (01379) 678285  **Fax:** (01379) 678192
**Contact:** Raymond Mayes or Joe Stuart
**Opening times:** 1000-1800 Wed-Sat
1st Apr-31st Oct.
**Min. mail order UK:** £15.00 + p&p
**Min. mail order EU:** £15.00 + p&p
**Cat. cost:** 5 x 1st class
**Credit cards:** None
**Specialities:** Herbaceous Perennials, incl.
Crocosmia, Euphorbia, Kniphofia, Monarda
& Grasses.
**Map ref:** 6, A4

**EGle**  **GLEN CHANTRY**
Ishams Chase, Wickham Bishops, Essex,
CM8 3LG
☎ (01621) 891342
**Contact:** Sue Staines & Wol Staines
**Opening times:** 1000-1600 Fri 27th Mar-mid
Oct. Also Sun & Mon on NGS open days.
**Mail order:** None
**Cat. cost:** 4 x 1st class
**Credit cards:** None
**Specialities:** A wide & increasing range of
Perennials & Alpines, many unusual.
**Map ref:** 6, B3

**EGln**  **GLENHIRST CACTUS NURSERY** ✉ EU ✉
Station Road, Swineshead, Nr Boston,
Lincolnshire, PE20 3NX
☎ (01205) 820314  **Fax:** (01205) 820614
**E-mail:** glenhirstcacti@lineone.net
**Web site:**
http://website.lineone.net/~glenhirstcacti
**Contact:** N C & S A Bell
**Opening times:** 1000-1700 Thu-Sat &
B/Hols 1st Apr-30th Sep, other times by
arrangement, please phone. Mail order all
year.
**Min. mail order UK:** No minimum charge
**Min. mail order EU:** Nmc
**Cat. cost:** 2 x 1st class
**Credit cards:** Visa, MasterCard, American

Express, EuroCard, Discover, Novus
**Specialities:** Extensive range of Cacti &
Succulent plants & seeds, inc. Christmas Cacti
& Orchid Cacti. Hardy & half-hardy desert
plants. All stock fully described on lists.
Display gardens.
**Map ref:** 8, B1

**EGol**  **GOLDBROOK PLANTS** ✉ EU ✉
Hoxne, Eye, Suffolk, IP21 5AN
☎ (01379) 668770  **Fax:** (01379) 668770
**Contact:** Sandra Bond
**Opening times:** 1030-1800 or dusk if earlier,
Thu-Sun Apr-Sep; Sat & Sun Oct-Mar, or by
appt. Closed during Jan, & Chelsea &
Hampton Court shows.
**Min. mail order UK:** £15.00 + p&p
**Min. mail Order EU:** £100.00 + p&p
**Cat. cost:** 4 x 1st class
**Credit cards:** None
**Specialities:** Very large range of Hosta (over
700), Hemerocallis & Bog Iris.
**Map ref:** 6, A4

**EGoo**  **ELISABETH GOODWIN
NURSERIES** ✉ UK
Elm Tree Farm, 1 Beeches Road, West Row,
Bury St. Edmunds, Suffolk, IP28 8NP
☎ (01638) 713050
**Contact:** Elisabeth Goodwin
**Opening times:** Open days 1000-1700 1st
Sun monthly Apr-Oct, or any time by prior
arrangement.
**Min. mail order UK:** No minimum charge
**Cat. cost:** £1 coin or 4 x 1st class*
**Credit cards:** None
**Specialities:** Drought tolerant plants for both
sun & shade especially Dianthus,
Helianthemum, Sedum, Teucrium & Vinca.
*Note: New mail order catalogue each
Autumn.
**Map ref:** 6, A2

**EGou**  **GOULDINGS FUCHSIAS** ✉ EU ✉
West View, Link Lane, Bentley, Nr Ipswich,
Suffolk, IP9 2DP
☎ (01473) 310058  **Fax:** (01473) 310058
**Contact:** Mr E J Goulding
**Opening times:** Closed to visitors from end of
June 1999 on.
**Min. mail order UK:** See cat. for details
**Min. mail order EU:** See cat. for details.
**Cat. cost:** 4 x 1st class
**Credit cards:** None
**Specialities:** Fuchsia – new introductions,
Basket, Hardy, Upright, Terminal flowering
(Triphylla), Species, Encliandras &
Paniculates.
**Map ref:** 6, B4

**E**

**EGra** **GRASMERE PLANTS** ✉ UK
Grasmere, School Road, Terrington St John,
Wisbech, Cambs, PE14 7SE
☎ (01945) 880514
E-mail: fleming@tstjohn.freeserve.co.uk
Web site: http://www.tstjohn.freeserve.co.uk
Contact: Angela Fleming
Opening times: 1000-1700 Thur-Tue
Apr-July & Sept; 1000-1700 Sat & Sun Oct,
Nov, Feb & Mar. Other times by appt.
Garden open.
Min. mail order UK: £10.00 + p&p
Cat. cost: 2 x 1st class
Credit cards: None
Specialities: Hardy Perennials incl. Geraniums
& Grasses; Shrubs incl. Cytisus, dwarf &
hedging Conifers.
Map ref: 8, C2

**EHal** **HALL FARM NURSERY**
Harpswell, Nr Gainsborough, Lincolnshire,
DN21 5UU
☎ (01427) 668412   Fax: (01427) 667478
E-mail: hfnursery@aol.com
Web site: http://members.aol.com/hfnursery
Contact: Pam & Mark Tatam
Opening times: 0930-1730 daily. Please
telephone in winter to check.
Mail order: None
Cat. cost: 5 x 2nd class
Credit cards: Visa, MasterCard, Access, Switch
Specialities: Wide range of Shrubs, Perennials
& old Roses.
Map ref: 8, A1

**EHan** **HANGING GARDENS NURSERIES LTD**
(Office) 15 Further Meadow, Writtle,
Chelmsford, Essex, CM1 3LE
☎ (01245) 421020   Fax: (01245) 422293
Contact: Jim Drake & Louisa Drake
Opening times: 0900-1800 daily Apr-Nov,
0900-1700 daily Dec-Mar.
Mail order: None
Cat. cost: None issued
Credit cards: Access, American Express, Delta,
EuroCard, MasterCard, Switch, Visa
Specialities: Clematis, David Austin Roses,
Basket & Patio plants, excellent range of hardy
nursery stock. Note: Nursery is at Ongar Road
West, (A414) Writtle By Pass, Writtle,
Chelmsford.
Map ref: 6, C2

**EHic** **HICKLING HEATH NURSERY**
Sutton Road, Hickling, Norwich, Norfolk,
NR12 0AS
☎ (01692) 598513
Contact: Brian & Cindy Cogan

Opening times: 0930-1700 Tue-Sun & B/Hol
Mons. Please ring before visiting.
Mail order: None
Cat. cost: 4 x 1st class
Credit cards: Visa, Delta, MasterCard,
EuroCard
Specialities: Shrubs & Herbaceous, many
unusual inc. wide variety of Diascia,
Hydrangea, Lonicera & Penstemon.
Map ref: 8, B4

**EHoe** **HOECROFT PLANTS** ✉ EU ◆
Severals Grange, Holt Road, Wood Norton,
Dereham, Norfolk, NR20 5BL
☎ (01362) 684206   Fax: (01362) 684206
Contact: M Lister
Opening times: 1000-1600 Thur-Sun
1st Apr-1st Oct.
Min. mail order UK: No minimum charge
Min. mail order EU: Nmc
Cat. cost: 5 x 2nd class/£1coin
Credit cards: None
Specialities: 240 varieties of Variegated and
300 varieties of Coloured-leaved plants in all
species. 220 Grasses.
Map ref: 8, B3

**EHof** **HOFFLANDS DAFFODILS** ✉ EU ▣
Bakers Green, Little Totham, Maldon, Essex,
CM9 8LT
☎ (01621) 788678   Fax: (01621) 788445
E-mail: sales@hoffdaff.kemc.co.uk
Contact: John Pearson
Opening times: By appt. only. Normally mail
order only.
Min. mail order UK: No minimum charge
Min. mail order EU: Nmc
Cat. cost: Free
Credit cards: MasterCard, Visa
Specialities: Narcissus.

**EHol** **HOLKHAM GARDENS**
Holkham Park, Wells-next-the-Sea, Norfolk,
NR23 1AB
☎ (01328) 711636   Fax: (01328) 711117
Contact: Tim Leese
Opening times: 1000-1700 (or dusk if earlier)
daily. Closed Xmas & Boxing Day.
Mail order: None
Cat. cost: 2 x 1st class
Credit cards: Access, Visa, Switch
Specialities: Wide range of Shrubs,
Herbaceous Perennials & Alpines, many
unusual.
Map ref: 8, B3

| | |
|---|---|
| K E Y | ✉ Mail order to UK or EU |
| | ▣ Exports beyond EU |
| | ▣ Also supplies Wholesale   ◆ See Display advertisement |

**E**

**EHon**  **HONEYSOME AQUATIC NURSERY** ⊠ UK 🖾
The Row, Sutton, Nr Ely, Cambridgeshire, CB6 2PF
☎ (01353) 778889
Contact: D B Barker & D B Littlefield
Opening times: At all times by appt. only.
Min. mail order UK: No minimum charge
Cat. cost: 2 x 1st class
Credit cards: None
Specialities: Hardy Aquatic, Bog & Marginal.
Map ref: 6, A2

**EHrv**  **HARVEYS GARDEN PLANTS** ⊠ EU 🖾
Mulberry Cottage, Bradfield St George, Bury St Edmunds, Suffolk, IP30 0AY
☎ (01284) 386777  Fax: (01284) 386777 & answerphone
Contact: Roger Harvey
Opening times: Please phone first.
Min. mail order UK: £15.00 + p&p
Min. mail order EU: Please enquire
Cat. cost: 5 x 2nd class
Credit cards: None
Specialities: Helleborus, Epimedium, Euphorbia, Eryngium, Astrantia & other Herbaceous Perennials.
Map ref: 6, A3

**EHul**  **HULL FARM** ⊠ UK 🖾
Spring Valley Lane, Ardleigh, Colchester, Essex, CO7 7SA
☎ (01206) 230045  Fax: (01206) 230820
Contact: J Fryer & Sons
Opening times: 1000-1600 daily ex Xmas.
Min. mail order UK: £30.00 + p&p
Cat. cost: 5 x 2nd class
Credit cards: MasterCard, Visa
Specialities: Conifers.
Map ref: 6, B3

**EHyt**  **HYTHE ALPINES** ⊠ EU 🖾
Methwold Hythe, Thetford, Norfolk, IP26 4QH
☎ (01366) 728543  Fax: (01366) 728543
Contact: Mike Smith
Opening times: 1000-1700 Tue & Wed, Mar-Oct inclusive.
Min. mail order UK: No minimum charge
Min. mail order EU: Nmc
Cat. cost: 6 x 1st class, 4 x IRCs
Credit cards: None
Specialities: Rare & unusual Alpines, Rock garden plants & Bulbs for enthusiasts & exhibitors. Note: Export of dry Bulbs only.
Map ref: 8, C2

**EJWh**  **JILL WHITE** ⊠ UK 🖾
St. Davids', Recreation Way, Brightlingsea, Essex, CO7 ONJ
☎ (01206) 303547
Contact: Jill White
Opening times: By appt. only
Min. mail order UK: No minimum charge
Cat. cost: Sae
Credit cards: None
Specialities: Cyclamen species especially Cyclamen parviflorum. Also seed.
Map ref: 6, B3

**EKMF**  **KATHLEEN MUNCASTER FUCHSIAS** ⊠ EU 🖾
18 Field Lane, Morton, Gainsborough, Lincolnshire, DN21 3BY
☎ (01427) 612329
E-mail: 101713.730@compuserve.com
Contact: Kathleen Muncaster
Opening times: 1000-dusk Thur-Mon incl. After mid-July please phone for opening times.
Min. mail order UK: See cat. for details*
Min. mail order EU: See cat.
Cat. cost: 2 x 1st class
Credit cards: None
Specialities: Fuchsia. *Note: Mail Orders to be received before April 1st.
Map ref: 9, C3

**ELan**  **LANGTHORNS PLANTERY**
High Cross Lane West, Little Canfield, Dunmow, Essex, CM6 1TD
☎ (01371) 872611  Fax: (01371) 872611
Contact: P & D Cannon, P Seymour
Opening times: 1000-1700 or dusk (if earlier) daily excl. Xmas fortnight & Easter Sun.
Mail order: None
Cat. cost: £1.50
Credit cards: Visa, Access, Switch, MasterCard
Specialities: Wide general range with many unusual plants.
Map ref: 6, B2

**ELau**  **LAUREL FARM HERBS** ⊠ UK
Main Road, Kelsale, Saxmundham, Suffolk, IP13 2RG
☎ (01728) 668223
Contact: Chris Seagon
Opening times: 1000-1700 Wed-Mon 1st Mar-31st Oct. 1000-1500 Wed-Fri only 1st Nov-28th Feb.
Min. mail order UK: Please phone for details.*
Cat. cost: 4 x 1st class, refund with first order.
Credit cards: None

**Specialities:** Herbs, esp. Rosemary, Thyme, Lavender, Mint, Comfrey & Sage. *Note: Mail order from May.
**Map ref:** 6, A4

**EMan    MANOR NURSERY** ⊠ UK
Thaxted Road, Wimbish, Saffron Walden, Essex, CB10 2UT
☎ (01799) 513481   **Fax:** (01799) 513481
**E-mail:** flora@gardenplants.co.uk
**Web site:** http://www.gardenplants.co.uk
**Contact:** William Lyall
**Opening times:** 0900-1700 Summer. 0900-1600 Winter. Closed Xmas.
**Min. mail order UK:** 10 plants
**Cat. cost:** 4 x 1st class
**Credit cards:** Visa, Access, Switch, American Express, EuroCard, MasterCard
**Specialities:** Uncommon Perennials, Grasses, Fuchsia, Hardy Geraniums, Pulmonaria, Sedum & Cottage Garden Plants.
**Map ref:** 6, B2

**EMar    LESLEY MARSHALL** ⊠ UK
Islington Lodge Cottage, Tilney All Saints, King's Lynn, Norfolk, PE34 4SF
☎ (01553) 765103
**Contact:** Lesley & Peter Marshall
**Opening times:** 0930-1800 Fri-Sun Mar-Oct. Other times by appt.
**Min. mail order UK:** 4 plants
**Cat. cost:** £1 refundable. £1 coin/4 x 1st class
**Credit cards:** None
**Specialities:** Uncommon garden plants, Hardy Perennials & plants for Foliage effect.
**Map ref:** 8, B2

**EMcA    S M McARD (SEEDS)** ⊠ EU 🄖
39 West Road, Pointon, Sleaford, Lincolnshire, NG34 0NA
☎ (01529) 240765   **Fax:** (01529) 240765
**E-Mail:** s.mcard.seeds@ndirect.co.uk
**Contact:** Susan McArd
**Opening times:** Not open.
**Min. mail order UK:** No minimum charge
**Min. mail order EU:** Nmc
**Cat. cost:** 2 x 2nd class
**Credit cards:** None
**Specialities:** Unusual & giant Vegetables. Seeds & Plants.

**EMFP    MILLS' FARM PLANTS & GARDENS** ⊠ EU 🄖
Norwich Road, Mendlesham, Suffolk, IP14 5NQ
☎ (01449) 766425   **Fax:** (01449) 766425
**Contact:** Peter & Susan Russell
**Opening times:** 0900-1730 daily except Tue.

(Closed Jan).
**Min. mail order UK:** No minimum charge*
**Min. mail order EU:** Nmc
**Cat. cost:** 5 x 2nd class
**Credit cards:** Access, Visa, Switch
**Specialities:** Pinks, Old Roses, Wide general range. *Note: Mail order for Pinks & Roses only.
**Map ref:** 6, A3

**EMFW    MICKFIELD FISH & WATERGARDEN CENTRE** ⊠ EU 🄧 🄖
Debenham Road, Mickfield, Stowmarket, Suffolk, IP14 5LP
☎ (01449) 711336   **Fax:** (01449) 711018
**E-mail:** mike@mickfield.co.uk
**Web site:** http://www.mickfield.co.uk
**Contact:** Mike & Yvonne Burch
**Opening times:** 0930-1700 daily
**Min. mail order UK:** No minimum charge
**Min. mail order EU:** £25.00 + p&p
**Cat. cost:** £1.00
**Credit cards:** Visa, Access, MasterCard
**Specialities:** Hardy Aquatics, Nymphaea & moisture lovers.
**Map ref:** 6, A4

**EMic    MICKFIELD HOSTAS** ⊠ EU
The Poplars, Mickfield, Stowmarket, Suffolk, IP14 5LH
☎ (01449) 711576   **Fax:** (01449) 711576
**Contact:** Mr & Mrs R L C Milton
**Opening times:** By appt. only.
**Min. mail order UK:** See cat. for details
**Min. mail order EU:** See cat.
**Cat. cost:** 4 x 1st class*
**Credit cards:** See catalogue for details
**Specialities:** Hosta, over 425 varieties (subject to availability) mostly from USA. *Note: Catalogue cost refundable with order.
**Map ref:** 6, A4

**EMil    MILL RACE NURSERY** 🄖
New Road, Aldham, Colchester, Essex, CO6 3QT
☎ (01206) 242521   **Fax:** (01206) 241616
**Contact:** Bill Mathews
**Opening times:** 0900-1730 daily.
**Mail Order:** None
**Cat. cost:** Sae + 2 x 1st class
**Credit cards:** Access, Visa, Diners, Switch
**Specialities:** Over 400 varieties of Herbaceous & many unusual Trees, Shrubs & Climbers.
**Map ref:** 6, B3

| K E Y | |
|---|---|
| ⊠ | Mail order to UK or EU |
| 🄧 | Exports beyond EU |
| 🄖 Also supplies Wholesale | ◆ See Display advertisement |

**E**

**EMNN    MARTIN NEST NURSERIES** ✉ EU ☑ ☑
Grange Cottage, Harpswell Lane, Hemswell,
Gainsborough, Lincolnshire, DN21 5UP
☎ (01427) 668369   Fax: (01427) 668080
E-mail: mary@martin-nest.demon.co.uk
Web site: http://www.martin-nest.
demon.co.uk
Contact: M & M A Robinson
Opening times: 1000-1600 daily
Min. mail order UK: No minimum charge
Min. mail order EU: £30.00 + p&p
Cat. cost: 3 x 2nd class
Credit cards: Visa, Access, Switch,
MasterCard, American Express
Specialities: Alpines especially Primula,
Auricula & Saxifraga. National Collection of
Show & Alpine Auriculas.
Map ref: 9, C4

**EMon    MONKSILVER NURSERY** ✉ EU
Oakington Road, Cottenham,
Cambridgeshire, CB4 8TW
☎ (01954) 251555   Fax: (01223) 502887
E-mail: monksilver@dial.pipex.com
Web site:
http://dialspace.dial.pipex.com/monksilver/
Contact: Joe Sharman & Alan Leslie
Opening times: 1000-1600 Fri & Sat 1st
Mar-30th Jun, 19th Sept, & Fri & Sat Oct.
Min. mail order UK: £15.00 + p&p
Min. mail order EU: £30.00 + p&p
Cat. cost: 8 x 1st class
Credit cards: None
Specialities: Herbaceous plants, Grasses,
Anthemis, Arum, Helianthus, Lamium,
Nepeta, Monarda, Salvia, Vinca, Sedges &
Variegated plants. Many NCCPG 'Pink Sheet'
plants. Ferns.
Map ref: 6, A2

**EMor    JOHN MORLEY** ✉ EU
North Green Only, Stoven, Beccles, Suffolk,
NR34 8DG
E-mail: snowdrops@compuserve.com
Contact: John Morley
Opening times: By appt. only.
Min. mail order UK: Details in cat.
Min. mail order EU: Details in cat.
Cat. cost: 6 x 1st class
Credit cards: None
Specialities: Galanthus, a comprehensive range
of cultivars. Also seed.

**EMou    FRANCES MOUNT PERENNIAL
PLANTS** ✉ EU
1 Steps Farm, Polstead, Colchester, Essex,
CO6 5AE
☎ (01206) 262811

Contact: Frances Mount
Opening times: 1000-1700 Tue Wed & Sat.
1400-1800 Fri. Check weekends & hols.
Min. mail order UK: £5.00 + p&p
Min. mail order EU: £5.00 + p&p
Cat. cost: 3 x 1st class
Credit cards: None
Specialities: Hardy Geraniums.
Map ref: 6, B3

**EMsh    S E MARSHALL & CO LTD.** ✉ EU
Regal Road, Wisbech, Cambridgeshire,
PE13 2RF
☎ (01945) 583407 (24 hours)
Fax: (01945) 588235
Contact: Customer Services
Min. mail order UK: No minimum charge
Min. mail order EU: £15.00 + p&p
Cat. cost: Free
Credit cards: Access, Visa
Specialities: Vegetables.

**EMui    KEN MUIR** ✉ UK ☑
Honeypot Farm, Rectory Road, Weeley
Heath, Essex, CO16 9BJ
☎ (01255) 830181   Fax: (01255) 831534
E-mail: ken.muir@farmline.com
Contact: Ken Muir
Opening times: 1000-1600,
Min. mail order UK: No minimum charge
Cat. cost: 3 x 1st class
Credit cards: Visa, Access, Switch
Specialities: Fruit.
Map ref: 6, B4

**ENor    NORFOLK LAVENDER** ✉ EU ☒
Caley Mill, Heacham, King's Lynn, Norfolk,
PE31 7JE
☎ (01485) 570384   Fax: (01485) 571176
E-mail: admin@norfolk-lavender.co.uk
Web site: http://www.norfolk-lavender.co.uk
Contact: Henry Head
Opening times: 0930-1700 daily.
Min. mail order UK: £15.00 + p&p
Min. mail order EU: £15.00 + p&p
Cat. cost: 2 x 1st class
Credit cards: Visa, Access, Switch
Specialities: National Collection of Lavandula.
Map ref: 8, B2

**ENot    NOTCUTTS NURSERIES** ✉ EU ☑ ☑
Woodbridge, Suffolk, IP12 4AF
☎ (01394) 383344   Fax: (01394) 445440
E-mail: sales@notcutts.co.uk
Web site: http://www.notcutts.co.uk
Contact: Plant Adviser
Opening times: Garden centres vary between
0830-1800 Mon-Sat & 1030-1630 Sun.

E

Min. mail order UK: £150.00 + p&p
Min. mail order EU: £300.00 + p&p
Cat. cost: £4.00 + £1.00 postage
Credit cards: Visa, Access, Switch, Connect
Specialities: Wide general range. Specialist list
of Syringa. National Collection of Hibiscus.
Map ref: 6, A4

**EOas    OASIS ⊠ EU**
42 Greenwood Avenue, South Benfleet, Essex,
SS7 1LD
☎ (01268) 757666  Fax: (01268) 795646
E-mail: exotic@globalnet.co.uk
Web site: http://www.user.globalnet.co.uk/
~exotic
Contact: Paul Spracklin
Opening times: Strictly by appt. only.
Min. mail order UK: No minimum charge
Min. mail order EU: Nmc
Cat. cost: 2 x 1st class
Credit cards: None
Specialities: Small nursery offering a range of
Hardy & Half-hardy Exotic plants esp.
Bamboos, Palms, Tree Ferns, Bananas &
unusual Xerophytes.
Map ref: 6, C3

**EOHP    OLD HALL PLANTS ⊠ UK**
1 The Old Hall, Barsham, Beccles, Suffolk,
NR34 8HB
☎ (01502) 717475
Contact: Janet Elliott
Opening times: By appt. most days – please
phone first.
Min. mail order UK: No minimum charge*
Cat. cost: 4 x 1st class
Credit cards: None
Specialities: Herbs, over 550 varieties grown.
*Note: Mail order of rare herbs only.
Map ref: 8, C4

**EOld    OLD MILL HOUSE GARDEN NURSERY**
Guithavon Valley, Witham, Essex, CM8 1HF
☎ (01376) 512396  Fax: (01376) 512396
Contact: Kirsty Bishop & Sheila Bates
Opening times: 1000-17.30 (dusk in winter)
all year except 25th Dec-31st Jan. Garden
open as nursery.
Mail order: None
Cat. cost: 2 x 1st class
Credit cards: None
Specialities: Herbaceous Perennials, plus large
range of Shrubs, Alpines, Herbs, Bog & Water
Plants; also Seasonal Bedding.
Map ref: 6, B3

**EOrc    ORCHARD NURSERIES**
Tow Lane, Foston, Grantham, Lincolnshire,
NG32 2LE
☎ (01400) 281354  Fax: (01400) 281354
Contact: Margaret Rose
Opening times: 1000-1800 Wed-Mon
1st Feb-30th Sep.
Mail order: None
Cat. cost: 5 x 2nd class
Credit cards: None
Specialities: Small flowered Clematis, unusual
Herbaceous esp. Geranium, Hellebores, Hosta,
Salvia. Sae for seed list, mainly Hellebores.
Map ref: 8, B1

**EOrn    ORNAMENTAL CONIFERS ⊠ UK ◆**
22 Chapel Road, Terrington St Clement,
Kings Lynn, Norfolk, PE34 4ND
☎ (01553) 828874  Fax: (01553) 828874
Contact: Peter Rotchell
Opening times: 0930-1700 7 days a week,
1st Feb-20th Dec.
Min. mail order UK: £30.00 + p&p
Cat. cost: New A4 colour cat. supplied at cost
£2.50, refundable with first order + 4 x 1st class.
Credit cards: None
Specialities: Conifers & Heathers.
Map ref: 8, B2

**EPar    PARADISE CENTRE ⊠ EU ▨**
Twinstead Road, Lamarsh, Bures, Suffolk,
CO8 5EX
☎ (01787) 269449  Fax: (01787) 269449
E-mail: hedy@paradisecentre.com
Web site: http://www.paradisecentre.com
Contact: Cees & Hedy Stapel-Valk
Opening times: 1000-1700 Sat-Sun & B/Hols
or by appt. Easter-1st Nov.
Min. mail order UK: £7.50 + p&p
Min. mail order EU: £25.00 + p&p
Cat. cost: 5 x 1st class
Credit cards: Visa, Access, Diners
Specialities: Unusual bulbous & tuberous
plants including shade & bog varieties. Also
some seeds.
Map ref: 6, B3

**EPfP    THE PLACE FOR PLANTS**
East Bergholt Place, East Bergholt, Suffolk,
CO7 6UP
☎ (01206) 299224  Fax: (01206) 299224
E-mail: placeforplants@martex.net
Contact: Rupert & Sara Eley

---

Y  ⊠ Mail order to UK or EU
E  ▨ Exports beyond EU
K  ▣ Also supplies Wholesale  ◆ See Display advertisement

**E**

Opening times: 1000-1700 (dusk if earlier) daily. Closed Xmas fortnight. Garden open Mar-Oct.
Mail order: None
Cat. cost: Free list
Credit cards: Visa, Access, MasterCard, EuroCard, Delta, Switch
Specialities: Wide range of specialist & popular plants. 15 acre mature garden.
Map ref: 6, B4

**EPGN   PARK GREEN NURSERIES ⊠ EU ⌧**
Wetheringsett, Stowmarket, Suffolk, IP14 5QH
☎ (01728) 860139   Fax: (01728) 861277
E-mail: pgn@btconnect.com
Contact: Richard & Mary Ford
Opening times: 1000-1700 daily Mar-Sep.
Min. mail order UK: No minimum charge
Min. mail order EU: Nmc
Cat. cost: 4 x 1st class
Credit cards: Visa, MasterCard, Delta, Switch
Specialities: Hosta, Astilbe, ornamental Grasses & Herbaceous.
Map ref: 6, A4

**EPla   P W PLANTS ⊠ EU ◆**
Sunnyside, Heath Road, Kenninghall, Norfolk, NR16 2DS
☎ (01953) 888212   Fax: (01953) 888212
Contact: Paul Whittaker
Opening times: Every Friday & last Saturday in every month.
Min. mail order UK: No minimum charge
Min. mail order EU: Nmc
Cat. cost: 5 x 1st class
Credit cards: Visa, MasterCard, Switch, JCB
Specialities: Bamboos, Grasses, Choice Shrubs & Perennials, Climbers (incl. wide selection of Hedera).
Map ref: 8, C3

**EPln   THE PLANT LOVERS ▣**
Candesby House, Candesby, Spilsby, Lincolnshire, PE23 5RU
☎ (01754) 890256   Fax: (01754) 890594
Contact: Tim Wilson
Opening times: Daily – but please phone first.
Mail order: None
Cat. cost: None issued
Credit cards: None
Specialities: Sempervivum (Houseleeks) & wide range of Cacti and other Succulents. Brochure available.

**EPot   POTTERTON & MARTIN ⊠ EU ⌧ ▣**
Moortown Road, Nettleton, Caistor, Lincolnshire, LN7 6HX

☎ (01472) 851714   Fax: (01472) 852580
E-mail: pottin01@globalnet.co.uk
Web site: http://www.users.globalnet.co.uk/ ~pottin01
Contact: Mr or Mrs Potterton
Opening times: 0900-1700 daily.
Min. mail order UK: No minimum charge
Min. mail order EU: Nmc
Cat. cost: £1 in stamps only
Credit cards: Electron, MasterCard, Delta, Switch, Solo, JCB, Maestro
Specialities: Alpines, Dwarf Bulbs, Conifers & Shrubs. Hardy Orchids & Pleione. Seed list sent out in November.
Map ref: 9, C4

**EPPr   THE PLANTSMAN'S PREFERENCE ⊠ EU**
Lynwood, Hopton Road, Garboldisham, Diss, Norfolk, IP22 2QN
☎ (01953) 681439
Contact: Jenny & Tim Fuller
Opening times: 0900-1700 Fri & Sun Mar-Oct. Other times by appt.
Min. mail order UK: No minimum charge
Min. mail order EU: Nmc
Cat. cost: 4 x 1st class
Credit cards: None
Specialities: Hardy Geraniums, Grasses and unusual & interesting Perennials.
Map ref: 6, A3

**EPri   PRIORY PLANTS ⊠ UK**
1 Covey Cottage, Hintlesham, Nr Ipswich, Suffolk, IP8 3NY
☎ (01473) 652656
Contact: Sue Mann
Opening times: 0930-1700 Fri, Sat, Sun & B/Hol Mon 1st Mar-31st Oct, or by appt.
Min. mail order UK: £10.00 + p&p
Cat. cost: 3 x 1st class
Credit cards: None
Specialities: Penstemon, Hardy Geranium, Euphorbia, Campanula, Salvia & Grasses.
Map ref: 6, B3

**EPts   POTASH NURSERY**
Cow Green, Bacton, Stowmarket, Suffolk, IP14 4HJ
☎ (01449) 781671
Contact: M W Clare
Opening times: 1000-1700 Fri-Sun & B/Hol Mons mid Feb-end June.
Mail order: None
Cat. cost: 3 x 1st class
Credit cards: None
Specialities: Fuchsia.
Map ref: 6, A3

**E**

**ER&R   RHODES & ROCKLIFFE** ⊠ EU ✈
2 Nursery Road, Nazeing, Essex, EN9 2JE
☎ (01992) 463693  **Fax:** (01992) 440673
**Contact:** David Rhodes or John Rockliffe
**Opening times:** By appt.
**Min. mail order UK:** £2.50 + p&p
**Min. mail order EU:** £5.00 + p&p
**Cat. cost:** 2 x 1st class
**Credit cards:** None
**Specialities:** Begonia species & hybrids.
**Map ref:** 6, C2

**ERav   RAVENINGHAM GARDENS** ⊠ EU ◆
Norwich, Norfolk, NR14 6NS
☎ (01508) 548222
**Fax:** (01508) 548958/548149
**Contact:** Carol Clutten
**Opening times:** Mail order only. Plants for
sale when gardens are open – Sun & B/Hol
Mon May-July. Please phone for details.
**Min. mail order UK:** No minimum charge
**Min. mail order EU:** Nmc
**Cat. cost:** Large Sae.
**Credit cards:** None
**Specialities:** Plants noted for Foliage.
Variegated & coloured leaf plants,
Herbaceous, Snowdrops, Pulmonaria & Hardy
Agapanthus.
**Map ref:** 8, C4

**ERea   READS NURSERY** ⊠ EU ✈
Hales Hall, Loddon, Norfolk, NR14 6QW
☎ (01508) 548395  **Fax:** (01508) 548040
**E-mail:** plants@readsnursery.co.uk
**Web site:** http://www.readsnursery.co.uk
**Contact:** Stephen Read
**Opening times:** 1000-1700 (or dusk if earlier)
Tue-Sat, 1100-1600 Sun & B/Hols Easter-end
Sep & by appt.
**Min. mail order UK:** £10.00 + p&p
**Min. mail order EU:** £10.00 + p&p
**Cat. cost:** 4 x 1st class
**Credit cards:** Visa, Access, Diners, Switch
**Specialities:** Conservatory plants, Vines,
Citrus, Figs & unusual Fruits & Nuts. Wall
Shrubs & Climbers. Scented & Aromatic
Hardy plants. Box & Yew hedging & topiary.
UK grown. National Collections of Citrus,
Figs, Vines.
**Map ref:** 8, C4

**ERic   J W RICKEARD**
The Gables, Station Road, Yoxford,
Saxmundham, Suffolk, IP17 3LA
☎ (01728) 668451
**Contact:** Michael Rickeard
**Opening times:** 0900-1800 daily except
Thurs, Xmas & New Year.

**Mail order:** None
**Cat. cost:** None issued
**Credit cards:** None
**Specialities:** Hardy Perennials, particularly
Geraniums.
**Map ref:** 6, A4

**ERob   ROBIN SAVILL CLEMATIS
SPECIALIST** ⊠ EU ✈ ▣
(Office) 2 Bury Cottages, Bury Road, Pleshey,
Chelmsford, Essex, CM3 1HB
☎ (01245) 237380  **Fax:** (01245) 603882
**E-mail:** robin.savill@virgin.net
**Contact:** Robin Savill
**Opening times:** Mail order only. Visitors by
appt. only.
**Min. mail order UK:** 1 plant + p&p
**Min. mail order EU:** 1 plant + p&p
**Cat. cost:** £1.50 or 6 x 1st class
**Credit cards:** None
**Specialities:** Over 650 varieties of Clematis,
incl. many unusual species & cultivars from
around the world. National Collection of
Clematis viticella.

**ERod   THE RODINGS PLANTERY** ⊠ EU ✈ ▣
Plot 3, Anchor Lane, Abbess Roding, Essex,
CM5 0JW
☎ (01279) 876421
**Contact:** Jane & Andy Mogridge
**Opening times:** By appt. only. Occasional
Open Days, please phone for details.
**Min. mail order UK:** £15.00 + p&p
**Min. mail order EU:** £500.00 + p&p
**Cat. cost:** 3 x 1st class
**Credit cards:** None
**Specialities:** Bamboo. Rare & unusual Trees.
**Map ref:** 6, C2

**ERom   THE ROMANTIC GARDEN** ⊠ EU ✈ ▣ ◆
Swannington, Norwich, Norfolk, NR9 5NW
☎ (01603) 261488  **Fax:** (01603) 871668
**Contact:** John Powles
**Opening times:** 1000-1700 Wed, Fri & Sat all
year.
**Min. mail order UK:** £5.00 + p&p
**Min. mail order EU:** £30.00 + p&p
**Cat. cost:** 4 x 1st class
**Credit cards:** Visa, Access, American Express
**Specialities:** Half-hardy & Conservatory.
Buxus topiary, Ornamental standards, large
specimen.
**Map ref:** 8, B4

---

**E**

**ERos**   ROSEHOLME NURSERY ⊠ EU 🔳 🔳
Roseholme Farm, Howsham, Lincoln,
Lincolnshire, LN7 6JZ
☎ (01652) 678661   Fax: (01472) 852450
Contact: P B Clayton
Opening times: By appt. for collection of
orders.
Min. mail order UK: No minimum charge
Min. mail order EU: Nmc
Cat. cost: 2 x 2nd class
Credit cards: None
Specialities: Underground Lines – Bulbs,
Corms, Rhizomes & Tubers (esp. Crocus,
Iris).
Map ref: 9, C4

**ERou**   ROUGHAM HALL NURSERIES ⊠ EU 🔳 🔳
Ipswich Road, Rougham, Bury St. Edmunds,
Suffolk, IP30 9LZ
☎ (01359) 270577   Fax: (01359) 271149
E-mail: kelvin-harbutt@msn.com
Contact: A A & K G Harbutt
Opening times: 1000-1600 Thu-Mon
Easter-31st Oct.
Min. mail order UK: No minimum charge
Min. mail order EU: Nmc
Cat. cost: 5 x 1st class
Credit cards: MasterCard, Visa
Specialities: Hardy Perennials esp. Aster (n-a,
n-b & species), Delphinium, Hemerocallis,
Iris, Kniphofia, Papaver & Phlox. National
Collection of Delphinium & Gooseberry.
Please note Delphiniums for collection only –
no mail order.
Map ref: 6, A3

**ERsn**   SUE ROBINSON
21 Bederic Close, Bury St Edmunds, Suffolk,
IP32 7DN
☎ (01284) 764310   Fax: (01284) 764310
Contact: Sue Robinson
Opening times: By appt. only.
Mail order: None
Cat. cost: None issued
Credit cards: None
Specialities: Variegated & Foliage plants.
Garden open. Lectures at Clubs & Societies,
group bookings welcome.

**ESCh**   SHEILA CHAPMAN CLEMATIS
Crowther Nurseries, Ongar Road, Abridge,
Romford, Essex, RM4 1AA
☎ (01708) 688090   Fax: (01708) 688677
Contact: Sheila Chapman
Opening times: 0930-1700 daily Summer,
0930-1700 or dusk daily Winter, excl. Xmas
week.
Mail order: None

Cat. cost: 4 x 1st class
Credit cards: Visa, Access, Switch, Connect,
Delta, Discover, EuroCard, Electron, JCB,
Laser, MasterCard
Specialities: Over 450 varieties of Clematis.
Map ref: 6, C2

**ESis**   SISKIN PLANTS ⊠ EU
April House, Davey Lane, Charsfield,
Woodbridge, Suffolk, IP13 7QG
☎ (01473) 737567   Fax: (01473) 737567
E-mail: siskinplants@btinternet.com
Contact: Chris & Valerie Wheeler
Opening times: 1000-1700 Tue-Sat Feb-Oct.
Min. mail order UK: No minimum charge
Min. mail order EU: Nmc
Cat. cost: £1.00
Credit cards: Access, Visa
Specialities: Alpines, miniature Conifers &
dwarf Shrubs, esp. plants for Troughs.
National Collection of dwarf Hebe. Also
seeds.
Map ref: 6, A4

**ESou**   SOUTHFIELD NURSERIES ⊠ EU 🔳
Bourne Road, Morton, Nr Bourne,
Lincolnshire, PE10 0RH
☎ (01778) 570168
Contact: Mr & Mrs B Goodey
Opening times: 1000-1230 & 1330-1600
daily except for Nov-Jan open by appt. only.
Min. mail order UK: No minimum charge
Mail order EU: Nmc
Cat. cost: 1 x 1st class
Credit cards: None
Specialities: A wide range of Cacti &
Succulents including some of the rarer
varieties all grown on our own nursery.
Map ref: 8, B1

**ESul**   PEARL SULMAN ⊠ EU
54 Kingsway, Mildenhall, Bury St Edmunds,
Suffolk, IP28 7HR
☎ (01638) 712297   Fax: (01638) 515052
Contact: Pearl Sulman
Opening times: Not open. Mail order only.
Open weekend 12/13th June 1999.
Min. mail order UK: £9.00 + p&p
Min mail order EU: £9.00 + p&p
Cat. cost: 4 x 1st class
Credit cards: None
Specialities: Miniature, Dwarf, Scented-leaf &
Angel Pelargoniums.
Map ref: 6, A3

**ET&M**   THOMPSON & MORGAN
(UK) LTD ⊠ EU 🔳 🔳
Poplar Lane, Ipswich, Suffolk, IP8 3BU

☎ (01473) 688821  **Fax:** (01473) 680199
**E-mail:** tmseeds_enquiries@compuserve.com
**Web site:** http://www.thompson-morgan.com
**Contact:** Martin Thrower
**Opening times:** Weekend of 31 July/1 Aug 1999
**Min. mail order UK:** No minimum charge
**Min. mail order EU:** Nmc
**Cat. cost:** Free
**Credit cards:** Visa, Access, Switch
**Specialities:** Largest illustrated Seed catalogue in the world.
**Map ref:** 6, B4

**ETen    TENNYSON NURSERIES** ⊠ EU ☑ ▣
Chantry Farm, Campsea Ashe, Wickham Market, Suffolk, IP13 0PZ
☎ (01728) 747113  **Fax:** (01728) 747725
**Contact:** Jon Rose
**Opening times:** 1000-1700 daily British Summer time, 0900-1600 daily Winter time.
**Min. mail order UK:** No minimum charge
**Min. mail order EU:** £20.00 + p&p
**Cat. cost:** 3 x 1st class
**Credit cards:** None
**Specialities:** Range of rare & unusual Hardy Plants.
**Map ref:** 6, A4

**ETho    THORNCROFT CLEMATIS NURSERY** ⊠ EU ☑
The Lings, Reymerston, Norwich, Norfolk, NR9 4QG
☎ (01953) 850407  **Fax:** (01953) 851788
**Contact:** Ruth P Gooch
**Opening times:** 1000-1630 Thu-Tue 1st March-31st Oct.
**Min. mail order UK:** No minimum charge
**Min. mail order EU:** Nmc
**Cat. cost:** 5 x 2nd class
**Credit cards:** MasterCard, Solo, Visa, Delta, Switch
**Specialities:** Clematis.
**Map ref:** 8, C3

**ETub    VAN TUBERGEN UK LTD** ⊠ EU ▣
Bressingham, Diss, Norfolk, IP22 2AB
☎ (01379) 688282  **Fax:** (01379) 687227
**E-mail:** sales@vantub.flexnet.co.uk
**Web site:** http://www.vantubergen.co.uk
**Contact:** General Manager
**Opening times:** Not open to the public.
**Min. mail order UK:** Nmc*
**Min. mail order EU:** No minimum charge
**Cat. cost:** Free
**Credit cards:** Visa, Access, MasterCard, Switch
**Specialities:** Bulbs. *Note: Rretail & wholesale sales by mail order only (wholesale bulbs not listed in Plant Finder).

**EWal    J WALKERS BULBS** ⊠ EU ▣
Washway House Farm, Holbeach, Spalding, Lincolnshire, PE12 7PP
☎ (01406) 426216  **Fax:** (01406) 425468
**E-mail:** walkers@taylors-bulbs.com
**Contact:** J W Walkers
**Opening times:** Not open to the public.
**Min. mail order UK:** See cat. for details
**Min. mail order EU:** See cat.
**Cat. cost:** 2 x 1st class
**Credit cards:** Visa, Access
**Specialities:** Daffodils & Fritillaria.

**EWes    WEST ACRE GARDENS** ⊠ UK
West Acre, Kings Lynn, Norfolk, PE32 1UJ
☎ (01760) 755562/755989
**Fax:** (01760) 755989
**Contact:** J J Tuite
**Opening times:** 1000-1700 daily 15th Feb-15th Nov. Other times by appt.
**Min. mail order UK:** No minimum charge
**Cat. cost:** 4 x 1st class
**Credit cards:** None
**Specialities:** Unusual Shrubs, Herbaceous & Alpines. Large selection of Rhodohypoxis & Grasses.
**Map ref:** 8, B3

**EWFC    THE WILD FLOWER CENTRE** ⊠ UK
Church Farm, Sisland, Loddon, Norwich, Norfolk, NR14 6EF
☎ (01508) 520235  **Fax:** (01508) 528294
**Contact:** D G Corne
**Opening times:** 0900-1700 Fri, Sat, Sun & Tue. By appt. please.
**Min. mail order UK:** £3.80 + p&p
**Cat. cost:** 2 x 2nd class
**Credit cards:** None
**Specialities:** British native and naturalised Wild Flower plants. 283+ varieties.
**Map ref:** 8, C4

**EWll    THE WALLED GARDEN** ◆
Park Road, Benhall, Saxmundham, Suffolk, IP17 1JB
☎ (01728) 602510  **Fax:** (01728) 602510
**E-mail:** jim@thewalledgarden.co.uk
**Contact:** J R Mountain
**Opening times:** 0930-1700 Tue-Sun Mar-Oct, Tue-Sat Nov-Feb.
**Mail order:** None
**Cat. cost:** 2 x 1st class

KEY  ⊠ Mail order to UK or EU
☑ Exports beyond EU
▣ Also supplies Wholesale  ◆ See Display advertisement

**G**

Credit cards: Visa, MasterCard, Switch
Specialities: Tender & hardy Perennials & wall Shrubs.
Map ref: 6, A4

EWoo WOOTTEN'S PLANTS
Wenhaston, Blackheath, Halesworth, Suffolk, IP19 9HD
☎ (01502) 478258
Contact: M Loftus
Opening times: 0930-1700 daily.
Mail order: None
Cat. cost: £2.50 illus.
Credit cards: Access, Visa, American Express, Switch
Specialities: Pelargonium, Penstemon, Auricula, Salvia & Grasses.
Map ref: 6, A4

EWsh WESTSHORES NURSERIES
82 West Street, Winterton, North Lincs, DN15 9QF
☎ (01724) 733940  Fax: (01724) 733940
E-mail: westshnur@aol.com
Contact: Gail & John Summerfield
Opening times: 0930-1830 (dusk when earlier) Wed-Mon 1st Mar-mid Nov.
Mail order: None
Cat. cost: 2 x 1st class
Credit cards: None
Specialities: Ornamental Grasses & Herbaceous Perennials.
Map ref: 9, C4

EWTr WALNUT TREE GARDEN NURSERY ✉ UK
Flymoor Lane, Rocklands, Attleborough, Norfolk, NR17 1BP
☎ (01953) 488163  Fax: (01953) 483187
E-mail: jimnclare@aol.com
Contact: Jim Paine & Clare Billington
Opening times: 0900-1800 Tue-Sun Feb-Nov.
Min. mail order UK: No minimum charge
Cat. cost: 2 x 1st class
Credit cards: Visa, MasterCard, Switch, Solo
Map ref: 8, C3

EYou ROY YOUNG SEEDS ✉ EU 🗺 🖼
23 Westland Chase, West Winch, King's Lynn, Norfolk, PE33 0QH
☎ (01553) 840867  Fax: (01553) 840867
Contact: Mr Roy Young
Opening times: Not open.
Min. mail order UK: £3.00 + p&p
Min. mail order EU: £3.00 + p&p*
Cat. cost: 1 x 1st class or 3 x IRCs
Credit cards: None
Specialities: Cactus & Succulent seeds only,

for wholesale and retail purchase. 24pg catalogue listing app. 2,000 species, varieties & forms (Retail). 18 pg A5 listing (Wholesale). *Note: £25 min Wholesale order charge.

# SCOTLAND

GAbr ABRIACHAN NURSERIES ✉ EU
Loch Ness Side, Inverness, Invernesshire, Scotland, IV3 8LA
☎ (01463) 861232  Fax: (01463) 861232
Contact: Mr & Mrs D Davidson
Opening times: 0900-1900 daily (dusk if earlier) Feb-Nov.
Min. mail order UK: No minimum charge
Min. mail order EU: Nmc
Cat. cost: 4 x 1st class
Credit cards: None
Specialities: Herbaceous, Primula, Helianthemum, Hardy Geranium & Sempervivum.
Map ref: 10, B2

GAri ARIVEGAIG NURSERY ✉ UK° 🖼
Aultbea, Acharacle, Argyll, Scotland, PH36 4LE
☎ (01967) 431331  Fax: (01967) 431331
E-Mail: arivegaignursery@btinternet.com
Contact: E Stewart
Opening times: 0900-1700 daily Easter-end Oct.
Min. mail order UK: £10.00 + p&p
Cat. cost: 4 x 1st class
Credit cards: None
Specialities: A wide range of unusual plants, including those suited for the milder parts of the country.
Map ref: 10, A3

GAul AULTAN NURSERY ✉ UK
Newton of Cairnhill, Cuminestown, Turriff, Aberdeenshire, Scotland, AB53 5TN
☎ (01888) 544702  Fax: (01888) 544702
E-mail: rlking@globalnet.co.uk
Contact: Richard King
Opening times: 1100-1600 Mon, 1330-1800 Sat, 1000-1800 Sun, Apr-Oct. Other times please phone first.
Min. mail order UK: No minimum charge
Cat. cost: 2 x 1st class
Credit cards: None
Specialities: Herbaceous Perennials & Shrubs, mostly grown in peat-free composts. A very wide range including many unusual items.
Map ref: 10, C2

GBal BALLAGAN NURSERY
Gartocharn Road, Nr Balloch, Alexandria, Strathclyde, G83 8NB

**G**

☎ (01389) 752947  **Fax:** (01389) 711288
**E-mail:** ballagan@dircon.co.uk
**Contact:** Mr G Stephenson
**Opening times:** 0900-1800 daily.
**Mail order:** None
**Cat. cost:** None issued
**Credit cards:** Visa, Access, Switch
**Specialities:** Home grown bedding and general
nursery stock.
**Map ref:** 10, B3

**GBar**  BARWINNOCK HERBS ✉ EU ☒
Barrhill, by Girvan, Ayrshire, Scotland,
KA26 0RB
☎ (01465) 821338  **Fax:** (01465) 821338
**E-mail:** 101344.3413@compuserve.com
**Contact:** Dave & Mon Holtom
**Opening times:** 1000-1800 daily 1st April-
31st Oct.
**Min. mail order UK:** No minimum charge
**Min. mail order EU:** Nmc
**Cat. cost:** 3 x 1st class
**Credit cards:** None
**Specialities:** Culinary, Medicinal & fragrant
leaved plants organically grown.
**Map ref:** 10, A4

**GBin**  BINNY PLANTS ✉ UK
West Lodge, Binny Estate, Ecclesmachen
Road, Nr Broxbourn, West Lothian, Scotland,
EH52 6NL
☎ (01506) 858931  **Fax:** (01506) 858931
**E-mail:** binnycrag@aol.com
**Contact:** Billy Carruthers
**Opening times:** 1000-1700 Thur-Mon
18th Mar-18th Oct 1999.
**Min. mail order UK:** No minimum charge*
**Cat. cost:** 3 x 1st class
**Credit cards:** Visa, MasterCard, EuroCard
**Specialities:** Perennials inc. Euphorbia,
Geranium, Hosta. Plus large selection of Grasses
& Ferns. *Note: Mail order Oct-Mar only.
**Map ref:** 10, B3

**GBon**  BONHARD NURSERY
Murrayshall Road, Scone, Perth, Tayside,
Scotland, PH2 7PQ
☎ (01738) 552791  **Fax:** (01738) 552791
**Contact:** Mr & Mrs Hickman
**Opening times:** 1000-1800, or dusk if earlier,
daily.
**Mail order:** None
**Cat. cost:** Free (fruit trees & roses)
**Credit cards:** Access, American Express,
EuroCard, MasterCard, Switch, Visa
**Specialities:** Herbaceous, Conifers & Alpines.
Fruit & ornamental Trees. Shrub & species
Roses.
**Map ref:** 10, B3

**GBri**  BRIDGE END NURSERIES
Gretna Green, Dumfries & Galloway,
Scotland, DG16 5HN
☎ (01461) 800612  **Fax:** (01461) 800612
**Contact:** R Bird
**Opening times:** 0930-1700 all year. Evenings
by appt.
**Mail order:** None
**Cat. cost:** None issued
**Credit cards:** None
**Specialities:** Hardy cottage garden Perennials.
Many unusual & interesting varieties.
**Map ref:** 10, B4

**GBuc**  BUCKLAND PLANTS ✉ EU
Whinnielig014, Kirkcudbright, Scotland,
DG6 4XP
☎ (01557) 331323  **Fax:** (01557) 331323
**Contact:** Rob or Dina Asbridge
**Opening times:** 1000-1700 Thu-Sun
Mar-Nov.
**Min. mail order UK:** £15.00 + p&p
**Min. mail order EU:** £50.00 + p&p
**Cat. cost:** 3 x 1st class
**Credit cards:** None
**Specialities:** A very wide range of scarce
Herbaceous & Woodland plants incl.
Anemone, Cardamine, Crocosmia,
Erythronium, Hellebore, Meconopsis, Tricyrtis
& Trillium etc.
**Map ref:** 10, B4

**GCal**  CALLY GARDENS ✉ EU ☒
Gatehouse of Fleet, Castle Douglas, Scotland,
DG7 2DJ
**Fax:** (01557) 815029. Also information line.
**Contact:** Michael Wickenden
**Opening times:** 1000-1730 Sat-Sun,
1400-1730 Tue-Fri 3rd Apr-26th Sep.
**Min. mail order UK:** £15.00 + p&p
**Min. mail order EU:** £50.00 + p&p
**Cat. cost:** 3 x 1st class
**Credit cards:** None
**Specialities:** Unusual Perennials. Agapanthus,
Crocosmia, Eryngium, Euphorbia, Hardy
Geraniums & Grasses. Some rare Shrubs,
Climbers & Conservatory plants.
**Map ref:** 10, B4

**GCan**  CANDACRAIG GARDENS ✉ UK
Strathdon, Aberdeenshire, Scotland, AB3 8XT
☎ (01975) 651226  **Fax:** (01975) 651391
**E-mail:** candacraig@buchanan.co.uk

**G**

Contact: Mrs E M Young
Opening times: 1000-1700 Mon-Fri &
1400-1800 Sat & Sun May-Sep or by appt.
Min. mail order UK: No minimum charge
Cat. cost: Sae or 1st class for list.
Credit cards: None
Specialities: A wide variety of Hardy
Perennials, Meconopsis & Primula.
Also seeds.
Map ref: 10, B2

**GCHN   CHARTER HOUSE NURSERY ⊠ EU**
2 Nunwood, Dumfries, Dumfries & Galloway,
Scotland, DG2 0HX
☎ (01387) 720363
Contact: John Ross
Opening times: 0900-1700 Tue-Sat Mar-Sep.
Other times by appt.
Min. mail order UK: No minimum charge
Min. mail order EU: Nmc
Cat. cost: 3 x 1st class
Credit cards: None
Specialities: Aquilegia, Geranium, Erodium,
Saxifraga and Campanula. National Collection
of Erodium.
Map ref: 10, B4

**GChr   CHRISTIE ELITE NURSERIES ⊠ UK ▣**
The Nurseries, Forres, Moray, Scotland,
IV36 3TW
☎ (01309) 672633   Fax: (01309) 676846
E-mail: celite@globalnet.co.uk
Contact: Dr S Thompson
Opening times: 0800-1700 daily.
Min. mail order UK: No minimum charge
Cat. cost: Free
Credit cards: Visa, Access
Specialities: Hedging & screening plants.
Woodland & less common Trees, Shrubs &
Fruit.
Map ref: 10, B2

**GCoc   JAMES COCKER & SONS ⊠ EU ▣**
Whitemyres, Lang Stracht, Aberdeen,
Scotland, AB9 2XH
☎ (01224) 313261   Fax: (01224) 312531
Contact: Alec Cocker
Opening times: 0900-1730 daily.
Min. mail order UK: No minimum charge
Min. mail order EU: £4.35 + p&p
Cat. cost: Free
Credit cards: Visa, MasterCard
Specialities: Roses.
Map ref: 10, C2

**GCrs   CHRISTIE'S NURSERY ⊠ EU ▣ ◆**
Downfield, Westmuir, Kirriemuir, Angus,
Scotland, DD8 5LP

☎ (01575) 572977   Fax: (01575) 572977
E-mail: christiealpines@btinternet.com
Web site: http://www.btinternet.com/
~christiealpines
Contact: Ian & Ann Christie & Ian Martin
Opening times: 1000-1700 daily except Tue
(closed) & 1300-1700 Sun, 1st Mar-31st Oct.
Min. mail order UK: 5 plants + p&p
Min. mail order EU: On request
Cat. cost: 2 x 1st class
Credit cards: Access, Delta, EuroCard, JCB,
MasterCard, Switch, Visa
Specialities: Alpines, esp. Gentians, Cassiope,
Primula, Lewisia, Orchids, Trillium &
Ericaceous.
Map ref: 10, B3

**GDra   MESSRS. JACK DRAKE ⊠ EU ▣ ▣**
Inshriach Alpine Nursery, Aviemore,
Invernesshire, Scotland, PH22 1QS
☎ (01540) 651287   Fax: (01540) 651656
Contact: John Borrowman
Opening times: 0900-1700 Mon-Fri, 0900-
1600 Sat & B/Hol Suns mid Feb-mid Nov.
Min. mail order UK: £10.00 + p&p
Min. mail order EU: £50.00 + p&p
Cat. cost: £1.50
Credit cards: None
Specialities: Rare and unusual Alpines & Rock
plants. Especially Primula, Meconopsis,
Gentian, Heathers etc.
Map ref: 10, B2

**GEil   EILDON PLANTS ⊠ EU ▣**
Lowood Nurseries, Melrose, Roxburghshire,
Scotland, TD6 9BJ
☎ (01896) 755530   Fax: (01896) 755530
Contact: R Sinclair
Opening times: 1000-1700 daily
Easter-mid Oct.
Min. mail order UK: No minimum charge
Min. mail order EU: Nmc
Cat. cost: 1 x 1st class
Credit cards: None
Specialities: Shrubs & Shrub Roses. South of
Scotland's best selection.
Map ref: 10, C4

**GFle   FLEURS PLANTS ⊠ EU**
2 Castlehill Lane, Abington Road, Symington,
Biggar, Scotland, ML12 6SJ
☎ (01889) 308528
Contact: Jim Elliott
Opening times: Please phone to arrange a visit.
Min. mail order UK: £8.00 + p&p
Min. mail order EU: £20.00 + p&p
Cat. cost: Sae
Credit cards: None

Specialities: Primula.
Map ref: 10, B4

**G**Gar   GARDEN COTTAGE NURSERY ⊠ UK
Tournaig, Poolewe, Achnasheen, Highland,
Scotland, IV22 2LH
☎ (01445) 781339  Fax: (01445) 781777
E-mail: rrushbrooke@easynet.co.uk
Web site: http://easyweb.easynet.co.uk/
rrushbrooke/
Contact: R & L Rushbrooke
Opening times: 1200-1900 Mon-Sat
mid Mar-mid Oct or by appt.
Min. mail order UK: £10.00 + p&p
Cat. cost: 4 x 2nd class
Credit cards: None
Specialities: Large range of Herbacous &
Alpines esp. Primula, Hardy Geraniums &
moisture lovers. Range of West Coast Shrubs.
Map ref: 10, A2

**G**GGa   GLENDOICK GARDENS LTD ⊠ EU ▧
Glencarse, Perth, Scotland, PH2 7NS
☎ (01738) 860205  Fax: (01738) 860630
E-mail: sales@glendoick.com
Web site: http://www.glendoick.com
Contact: P A, E P & K N E Cox
Opening times: By appt. only. Garden Centre
open 7 days.
Min. mail order UK: £35.00 + p&p
Min. mail order EU: £100.00 + p&p
Cat. cost: £1.50 or £1 stamps
Credit cards: Visa, MasterCard, Delta, Switch,
JCB
Specialities: Rhododendron, Azalea and
Ericaceous, Primula & Meconopsis. Many
catalogue plants available at Garden Centre.
Map ref: 10, B3

**G**Gre   GREENHEAD ROSES ⊠ EU ▧
Greenhead Nursery, Old Greenock Road,
Inchinnan, Renfrew, Strathclyde, PA4 9PH
☎ (0141) 812 0121  Fax: (0141) 812 0121
Contact: C N Urquhart
Opening times: 1000-1700 daily.
Min. mail order UK: No minimum charge*
Min. mail order EU: Nmc
Cat. cost: Sae
Credit cards: Visa, Switch
Specialities: Roses. Wide general range, dwarf
Conifers, Trees, Heathers, Azalea,
Rhododendron, Shrubs, Alpines, Fruit, hardy
Herbaceous & Spring & Summer bedding.
*Note: Mail order for bush roses only.
Map ref: 10, B3

**G**HCN   HIGHCROFT NURSERY ⊠ UK ▧
By Coylton, Ayrshire, Scotland, KA6 6LX

☎ (01292) 570209
Contact: Rose & Malcolm Macgregor
Opening times: 0900-1700 Mon-Sat &
1000-1700 Sun Apr-Aug. Other times by
arrangement.
Min. mail order UK: No minimum charge
Cat. cost: 2 x 1st class
Credit cards: None
Specialities: Pansies & Violas, plus range of
quality Shrubs.
Map ref: 10, A4

**G**Lch   LOCH LEVEN PLANTS
The Grange, Leslie Road, Scotlandwell,
Kinross, Scotland, KY13 7JE
☎ (01592) 840220,  Fax: (01592) 840220
Contact: Sandy or Sharon Fraser
Opening times: 1000-1300 Thur-Sat &
1000-1700 Sun 1st May-30th Sep.
Mail order: None
Cat. cost: None issued
Credit cards: None
Specialities: Southern hemisphere Shrubs &
Climbers, Bamboos & Grasses, select range of
unusual Perennials.
Map ref: 10, B3

**G**Lil   LILLIESLEAF NURSERY ⊠ EU ▧
Garden Cottage, Linthill, Melrose,
Roxburghshire, Scotland, TD6 9HU
☎ (01835) 870415  Fax: (01835) 870415
Contact: Teyl de Bordes
Opening times: 0900-1700 Mon-Sat, 1000-
1600 Sun. In Dec-Feb please phone first.
Min. mail order UK: No minimum charge*
Min. mail order EU: Nmc
Cat. cost: 2 x 1st class
Credit cards: Visa, Access
Specialities: Epimedium & wide range of
common & uncommon plants. National
Collection of Epimedium. *Note: Mail order
of Epimedium only.
Map ref: 10, C4

**G**Mac   ELIZABETH MACGREGOR ⊠ EU ▧
Ellenbank, Tongland Road, Kirkcudbright,
Dumfries & Galloway, Scotland, DG6 4UU
☎ (01557) 330620
Contact: Elizabeth MacGregor
Opening times: Please phone.
Min. mail order UK: 6 plants £12.00 + p&p
Min. mail order EU: £40.00 + p&p
Cat. cost: 4 x 1st class or 5 x 2nd class

**G**

Credit cards: None
Specialities: Violets, Violas & Violettas, old and new varieties. Campanula, Geranium, Penstemon & other unusual Herbaceous.
Map ref: 10, B4

**GMaP** MACPLANTS
Berrybank Nursery, 5 Boggs Holdings, Pencaitland, E Lothian, Scotland, EH34 5BA
☎ (01875) 341179 Fax: (01875) 340842
E-mail: sales.macplants@virgin.net
Contact: Claire McNaughton
Opening times: 1030-1700 daily mid-March-Oct
Mail order: None
Cat. cost: 4 x 2nd class
Credit cards: None
Specialities: Herbaceous Perennials, Alpines, Hardy Ferns, Violas & Grasses.
Map ref: 10, B3

**GNau** NAUGHTON CASTLE GARDEN
Naughton, Wormit, Fife, Scotland, DD6 8RN
☎ (01382) 330603 Fax: (01382) 330565
E-Mail: JamesCrawford1@compuserve.com
Contact: Dr Britt-Marie Crawford
Opening times: 1100-1700 Fri-Sun & B/Hol Mon Mar-Oct.
Mail order: None
Cat. cost: 2 x 1st class
Credit cards: None
Specialities: Herbaceous display garden with a wide variety of plants seen growing for sale. Euphorbia, Geranium, Hosta, Ferns, Heuchera, Aconitum. Many new introductions.
Map ref: 10, B3

**GNor** SHEILA NORTHWAY AURICULAS ⊠ EU
Balmaclellan, Castle Douglas, Kirkcudbrightshire, Scotland, DG7 3QR
☎ (01644) 420661
Contact: Sheila Northway
Opening times: Mail order and by appt. only.
Min. mail order UK: £10.00 + p&p
Min. mail order EU: £10.00 + p&p (normally 48 hr priority rate).
Cat. cost: A4 Sae
Credit cards: None
Specialities: Primula allionii & P. auricula, & a limited range of Alpines largely grown from wild seed.
Map ref: 10, B4

**GOrc** ORCHARDTON NURSERIES
Gardeners Cottage, Orchardton House, Auchencairn, Castle Douglas, Kircudbrightshire, DG7 1QL

☎ (01556) 640366
Contact: Fred Coleman
Opening times: 1200-1800 Sun, Mon & Tues Apr-end Oct.
Mail order: None
Cat. cost: None issued
Credit cards: None
Specialities: Unusual Shrubs & Climbers.
Map ref: 10, B4

**GOrn** ORNAMENTAL GRASSES ⊠ EU
14 Meadowside of Craigmyle, Kemnay, Inverurie, Aberdeenshire, Scotland, AB51 5LZ
☎ (01467) 643544
Contact: John & Lois Frew
Opening times: By appt.
Min. mail order UK: No minimum charge
Min. mail order EU: Nmc
Cat. cost: 3 x 1st class
Credit cards: None
Specialities: Ornamental Grasses.
Map ref: 10, C2

**GPin** PINEGROVE NURSERY
Oakley Road, Cairneyhill, Dunfermline, Fife, Scotland, KY12 8HE
☎ (01383) 881493 Fax: (01383) 880784
Contact: Peter Millican
Opening times: 1000-1700 7 days.
Mail order: None
Cat. cost: Available Autumn 1999
Credit cards: MasterCard, Access, Visa
Specialities: Wide range of Conifers, Patio & basket plants, bedding plants.
Map ref: 10, B3

**GPlc** PLANTIECRUB GROWERS LTD ⊠ EU
Gott, Shetland, ZE2 9SH
☎ (01595) 840600 Fax: (01595) 840600
Contact: Olaf Isbister
Opening times: 0830-1700
Min. mail order UK: No minimum charge
Min. mail order EU: Nmc
Cat. cost: 1 x 1st class
Credit cards: None
Specialities: Bedding, Perennials, Basket & Patio Plants, Indoor Plants, Glasshouse Fruits & Salads. Nurserymen & landscape contractors.
Map ref: 10, C1

**GPoy** POYNTZFIELD HERB NURSERY ⊠ EU
Nr Balblair, Black Isle, Dingwall, Ross & Cromarty, Highland, Scotland, IV7 8LX
☎ (01381) 610352* Fax: (01381) 610352
Contact: Duncan Ross
Opening times: 1300-1700 Mon-Sat 1st Mar-30th Sep, 1300-1700 Sun June-Aug.

**G**

Min. mail order UK: £5.00 + p&p
Min. mail order EU: £10.00 + p&p
Cat. cost: 4 x 1st class
Credit cards: None
Specialities: Over 350 popular, unusual &
rare Herbs, esp. Medicinal. Also seeds. *Note:
Phone only 1200-1300 & 1800-1900.
Map ref: 10, B2

**G**Qui    QUINISH GARDEN NURSERY ⊠ EU ▣
Dervaig, Isle of Mull, Argyll, Scotland,
PA75 6QL
☎ (01688) 400344   Fax: (01688) 400344
Contact: Nicholas Reed
Opening times: By appt. only.
Min. mail order UK: No minimum charge
Min. mail order EU: Nmc
Cat. cost: 2 x 1st class
Credit cards: None
Specialities: Specialist garden Shrubs &
Conservatory plants.
Map ref: 10, A3

**G**Rei    BEN REID AND CO ⊠ UK ▣
Pinewood Park, Countesswells Road,
Aberdeen, Grampian, Scotland, AB15 7AL
☎ (01224) 318744   Fax: (01224) 310104
Contact: John Fraser
Opening times: 0900-1700 Mon-Sat,
1000-1700 Sun.
Min. mail order UK: £10.00 + p&p
Cat. cost: Free
Credit cards: Visa, Access, Switch
Specialities: Trees & Shrubs.
Map ref: 10, C2

**G**Ski    SKIPNESS PLANTS ⊠ EU ▣
The Gardens, Skipness, Nr Tarbert, Argyll,
Scotland, PA29 6XU
☎ (01880) 760201   Fax: (01880) 760201
E-mail: skipnessplants@geocities.com
Web site: http://www.geocities.com/
eureka/7627/
Contact: Bill & Joan McHugh
Opening times: 0900-1800 Mon-Fri,
0900-1600 Sat-Sun, Feb-Nov.
Min. mail order UK: No minimum charge
Min. mail order EU: Nmc
Cat. cost: £1.00*
Credit cards: None
Specialities: Unusual Herbaceous Perennials,
Shrubs, Climbers & Grasses. *Note: Catalogue
cost refundable on first order.
Map ref: 10, A3

**G**Tou    TOUGH ALPINE NURSERY ⊠ EU ▣ ▣
Westhaybogs, Tough, Alford, Aberdeenshire,
Scotland, AB33 8DU

☎ (01975) 562783   Fax: (01975) 563561
E-mail: fred@alpines.co.uk
Web site: http://www.alpines.co.uk
Contact: Fred & Monika Carrie
Opening times: 1st Mar-31st Oct. Please
check first.
Min. mail order UK: £15.00 + p&p
Min. mail order EU: £15.00 + p&p
Cat. cost: 3 x 2nd class
Credit cards: None
Specialities: Alpines
Map ref: 10, C2

**G**Tro    TROPIC HOUSE ⊠ EU ▣
Langford Nursery, Carty Port, Newton
Stewart, Wigtownshire, Scotland, DG8 6AY
☎ (01671) 402485, (01671) 404050
Contact: Mrs A F Langford
Opening times: 1000-1700 daily Easter-end
Sept. Other times by appt.
Min. mail order UK: No minimum charge
Min. mail order EU: £20.00 + p&p
Cat. cost: Sae
Credit cards: None
Specialities: Carnivorous.
Map ref: 10, A4

**G**Twe    J TWEEDIE FRUIT TREES ⊠ UK ◆
Maryfield Road Nursery, Maryfield, Nr Terregles,
Dumfries, Dumfrieshire, Scotland, DG2 9TH
☎ (01387) 720880
Contact: John Tweedie
Opening times: Please ring for opening times.
Collections by appt.
Min. mail order UK: No minimum charge
Cat. cost: Sae
Credit cards: None
Specialities: Fruit trees & bushes. A wide
range of old & new varieties.
Map ref: 10, B4

**G**Uzu    UZUMARA ORCHIDS ⊠ EU ▣
9 Port Henderson, Gairloch, Rosshire,
Scotland, IV21 2AS
☎ (01445) 741228   Fax: (01445) 741228
E-mail: i.la_croix@virgin.net
Contact: Mrs I F La Croix
Opening times: By appt. only.
Min. mail order UK: No minimum charge
Min. mail order EU: Nmc
Cat. cost: Sae
Credit cards: None
Specialities: African & Madagascan Orchids.

**G**

**GVic    VICTORIA GARDENS** ⊠ EU ▣ ◆
(Office) 5 Islands View Road, Kirkwall,
Orkney, KW15 1YP
☎ (01856) 873189   **Fax:** (01856) 870892
**Contact:** Mr R Rendall & Mr R Shearer
**Opening times:** 0900-1730 Mon-Sat.
**Min. mail order UK:** £10.00 + p&p
**Min. mail order EU:** £50.00 + p&p
**Cat. cost:** £1.50 refundable with order.
**Credit cards:** None
**Specialities:** Extensive range of Hardy
Perennials, many rare, incl. Geranium, Hosta,
Grasses, Ferns & Seed. Britain's most
northerly mail order nursery where the
weather tests plants to their limits. Note:
Nursery is at Victoria Street, Kirkwall.
**Map ref:** 10, A1

# N. IRELAND & REPUBLIC

**IBal    BALLYDORN BULB FARM** ⊠ EU ▣
Killinchy, Newtownards, Co. Down,
N Ireland, BT23 6QB
☎ (01238) 541250   **Fax:** (01238) 542276
**E-mail:** ringdaff@dnet.co.uk
**Contact:** Sir Frank & Lady Harrison
**Opening times:** Not open.
**Min. mail order UK:** £15.00 + p&p
**Min. mail order EU:** £25.00 + p&p
**Cat. cost:** 4 x 1st class
**Credit cards:** None
**Specialities:** New Daffodil varieties for
Exhibitors and Hybridisers.

**IBlr    BALLYROGAN NURSERIES** ⊠ EU ▣
The Grange, Ballyrogan, Newtownards,
Co. Down, N Ireland, BT23 4SD
☎ (01247) 810451 eves
**Contact:** Gary Dunlop
**Opening times:** Only open, by appt., for
viewing of national collections of Crocosmia,
Celmisia & Euphorbia.
**Min. mail order UK:** £10.00 + p&p
**Min. mail order EU:** £20.00 + p&p
**Cat. cost:** 2 x 1st class
**Credit cards:** None
**Specialities:** Choice Herbaceous. Agapanthus,
Celmisia, Crocosmia, Euphorbia, Hardy
Geraniums, Meconopsis, Rodgersia, Grasses &
Iris.
**Map ref:** 11, C1

**IBro    BROOKWOOD NURSERIES** ⊠ EU
18 Tonlegee Road, Coolock, Dublin 5,
Rep. of Ireland
☎ 00 353 (0)1 847 3298
**Contact:** Jim Maher

**Opening times:** For collection only. 1st Feb-
30th Apr.
**Min. mail order UK:** £5.00 + p&p
**Min. mail order EU:** £5.00 + p&p
**Cat. cost:** 2 x 1st class
**Credit cards:** None
**Specialities:** Hybrid Crocosmia rarities &
hardy Cyclamen.
**Map ref:** 11, C3

**ICar    CARNCAIRN DAFFODILS** ⊠ EU ▣ ▣
Broughshane, Ballymena, Co. Antrim,
N Ireland, BT43 7HF
☎ (01266) 861216   **Fax:** (01266) 862842
**Contact:** Mr & Mrs R H Reade
**Opening times:** 1000-1700 Mon-Fri. Please
phone in advance.
**Min. mail order UK:** No minimum charge
**Min. mail order EU:** Nmc
**Cat. cost:** Free
**Credit cards:** None
**Specialities:** Old and new Narcissus cultivars,
mainly for show.
**Map ref:** 11, C1

**IClo    CLONMEL GARDEN CENTRE** ▣
Glenconnor House, Clonmel, Co. Tipperary,
Rep. of Ireland
☎ 00 353 (0)522 3294
**Fax:** 00 353 (0)522 9196
**E-mail:** clonmelgc@tinet.ie
**Contact:** C E & T Hanna
**Opening times:** 0900-1800 Mon-Sat,
1200-1800 Sun, 1000-1800 B/Hols.
**Mail order:** None
**Credit cards:** Visa, Access, MasterCard, Laser
**Specialities:** Wide range of plants incl. many
less common varieties. The Garden Centre is
situated in the grounds of a Georgian Country
House with extensive gardens.
**Map ref:** 11, B3

**ICro    CROCKNAFEOLA NURSERY** ▣
Killybegs, Co. Donegal, Rep. of Ireland
☎ 00 353 (0)73 51018
**Fax:** 00 353 (0)73 51018
**Contact:** Andy McKenna
**Opening times:** 0900-1900 Mon-Sat & 1200-
1800 Sun in Summer, until dusk in Winter;
closed Dec-Feb.
**Mail order:** None
**Cat. cost:** None issued
**Credit cards:** None
**Specialities:** Hardy Shrubs, Trees & Hedging
suitable for exposed areas.
**Map ref:** 11, B1

**ICrw**  CAREWSWOOD GARDEN
CENTRE ✉ EU ✪ ◆
Carewswood House, Castlemartyr, Co. Cork,
Rep. of Ireland
☎ 00 353 (0)21 667283
Fax: 00 353 (0)21 667673
E-mail: carewgc@tinet.ie
Contact: Gillian Hornibrook
Opening times: 0900-1800 Mon-Sat &
1200-1800 Sun.
Min. mail order UK: £20.00 + p&p
Min. mail order EU: £20.00 + p&p
Cat. cost: £2.50
Credit cards: Visa, Access, American Express
Specialities: Rare & unusual Shrubs, Alpines
& Herbaceous plants.
Map ref: 11, B4

**IDac**  DACUS PLANTS ✉ EU ✪ ✪
P O Box No. 5326, Dunlaoghaire, Co.
Dublin, Ireland
Fax: 00 353 (0)1 2809602
E-mail: dacusc.indigo.ie
Contact: Carl Dacus
Opening times: Not open to public.
Min. mail order UK: £10.00 + p&p
Min. mail order EU: £10.00 + p&p
Cat. cost: Free
Credit cards: None
Specialities: Alpines, Perennials & Shrubs,
many rare & unusual, growing from collected
seed. South American & South African plants
etc.

**IDee**  DEELISH GARDEN CENTRE ✉ EU
Skibbereen, Co. Cork, Rep. of Ireland
☎ 00 353 (0)28 21374
Fax: 00 353 (0)28 21374
Contact: Bill & Rain Chase
Opening times: 1000-1300 & 1400-1800
Mon-Sat, 1400-1800 Sun.
Min. mail order UK: IR£50.00 + p&p
Min. mail order EU: IR£100.00 + p&p
Cat. cost: Sae
Credit cards: Visa, Access
Specialities: Unusual plants for the mild
coastal climate of Ireland. Conservatory
plants. Sole Irish agents for Chase Organic
Seeds.
Map ref: 11, A4

**IDic**  DICKSON NURSERIES LTD ✉ EU ✪ ✪
Milecross Road, Newtownards, Co. Down,
N Ireland, BT23 4SS
☎ (01247) 812206   Fax: (01247) 813366
Contact: A P C Dickson OBE, Linda Stewart
Opening times: 0800-1230 & 1300-1700
Mon-Thur. 0800-1230 Fri.

Min. mail order UK: One plant
Min. mail order EU: £25.00 + p&p
Cat. cost: Free
Credit cards: None
Specialities: Roses, especially modern Dickson
varieties.
Map ref: 11, C2

**IDun**  BRIAN DUNCAN ✉ EU ✪ ✪
Novelty & Exhibition Daffodils,
15 Ballynahatty Road, Omagh, Co. Tyrone,
N Ireland, BT78 1PN
☎ (01662) 242931   Fax: (01662) 242931
E-mail: 113125.1005@compuserve.com
Contact: Brian Duncan
Opening times: By appt. only.
Min. mail order UK: £20.00 + p&p
Min. mail order EU: £20.00 + p&p
Cat. cost: £1.00 inc p&p
Credit cards: None
Specialities: New hybrid & Exhibition
Daffodils & Narcissus.
Map ref: 11, B2

**IGri**  GRIFFINS GARDEN CENTRE ✉ EU
Dripsey, Co. Cork, Ireland
☎ 00 353 (0)21 334286   Fax: (0)21 334508
Contact: Margaret Griffin
Opening times: 0900-1830 Mon-Sat,
1230-1800 Sun, 0900-1800 B/Hols.
Min. mail order UK: £10.00 + p&p
Min. mail order EU: £15.00 + p&p
Cat. cost: Free
Credit cards: Visa, Access, MasterCard, Laser
Specialities: Award winning garden centre
with wide range of plants, some unusual.
Map ref: 11, B4

**IHar**  HARRY BYRNE'S GARDEN
CENTRE ✉ UK
Castlepark Road, Sandycove, Dublin, Eire
☎ 00 353 (0)1 2803887   Fax: (0)1 2801077
E-mail: dburn@indigo.ie
Contact: H Byrne
Opening times: 0900-1730 Mon-Sat
1200-1730 Sun & Public Hols.
Min. mail order UK: £20.00 + p&p*
Cat. cost: £1.00 Roses & Clematis only.
Credit cards: Visa, MasterCard
Specialities: Roses, Clematis, Patio & Basket
Plants. Wide variety of Trees, Shrubs,
Herbaceous, Alpines. *Note: Mail order to UK
& Eire only.
Map ref: 11, C3

KEY: ✉ Mail order to UK or EU
✪ Exports beyond EU
✪ Also supplies Wholesale  ◆ See Display advertisement

**I**

**IHdy  HARDY PLANT NURSERY ✉ UK**
Ridge House, Ballybrack, Co. Dublin, Ireland
☎ 00 353 (0)1 2826973
**Contact:** Declan Hooke & Paul Cox
**Opening times:** 0900-1700 Sat Apr-May &
Sep-Oct. Wed-Fri by appt.
**Min. mail order UK:** £30.00 + p&p*
**Cat. cost:** 2 IRCs
**Credit cards:** None
**Specialities:** Wide range of Herbaceous plants,
some grown from wild collected seed. *Note:
Mail order to UK & Ireland only.
**Map ref:** 11, C3

**IIve  IVERNA HERBS ✉ EU ▣**
Glenmalure, Rathdrum, Co. Wicklow, Rep. of
Ireland
**Contact:** Peter O'Neill
**Opening times:** Mail Order, or write for appt.
**Min. mail order UK:** No minimum charge
**Min. mail order EU:** Nmc
**Cat. cost:** Free
**Credit cards:** None
**Specialities:** A rapidly growing selection of
Herbs, Wild Flowers & unusual Vegetables.
Rare medicinal plants from east & west. Free
delivery to UK.
**Map ref:** 11, C3

**ILis  LISDOONAN HERBS ✉ UK ▣**
98 Belfast Road, Saintfield, Co. Down,
N Ireland, BT24 7HF
☎ (01232) 813624
**E-mail:** b.pilcher@pop.dial.pipex.com
**Contact:** Barbara Pilcher
**Opening times:** Most days – please phone to
check.
**Min. mail order UK:** No minimum charge
**Cat. cost:** 2 x 1st class
**Credit cards:** None
**Specialities:** Aromatics, Herbs, kitchen garden
plants, some native species. Freshly cut herbs
& salads.
**Map ref:** 11, C2

**ILsc  LISCAHANE NURSERY**
Ardfert, Tralee, Co. Kerry, Rep. of Ireland
☎ 00 353 (0)66 7134222
**Fax:** 00 353 (0)66 7134600
**Contact:** Dan Nolan/Bill Cooley
**Opening times:** 0900-1800 Tue-Sat &
1400-1800 Sun Summer. 0900-1700 Thur-Sat
& Sun afternoon/Winter. Closed Mon.
**Mail order:** None
**Cat. cost:** None issued
**Credit cards:** Visa, Access
**Specialities:** Coastal shelter plants, Eucalyptus.
**Map ref:** 11, A4

**IMGH  M G H NURSERIES**
50 Tullyhenan Road, Banbridge, Co. Down,
N.Ireland, BT32 4EY
☎ (01820) 622795  **Fax:** (01820) 622795
**Contact:** Miss M G Heslip
**Opening times:** 1000-2000 Tue-Fri Apr-Sep,
1000-1700 Sat Apr-Sep, 1230-dusk Oct-Mar.
**Mail order:** None
**Cat. cost:** 3 x 1st class
**Credit cards:** None
**Specialities:** Alpines, grafted Conifers, Holly,
Japanese Maples, Flowering Trees & Shrubs.
**Map ref:** 11, C2

**IMuc  MUCKROSS GARDEN CENTRE ✉ EU**
Muckross, Killarney, Co. Kerry, Rep. of
Ireland
☎ 00 353 (0)64 34044
**Fax:** 00 353 (0)64 37388
**E-mail:** fullerj@indigo.ie
**Contact:** John R Fuller B.Ag.Sc.(Hort.)
**Opening times:** 1000-1800 Tue-Sat &
1415-1800 Sun. Jan & Feb please check first.
**Min. mail order UK:** IR£50.00 + p&p
**Min. mail order EU:** IR£50.00 + p&p
**Cat. cost:** Please enquire
**Credit cards:** Visa, Access
**Specialities:** Many rare & unusual plants.
Azalea, Hydrangea, Rhododendron &
Camellia.
**Map ref:** 11, A4

**IOrc  ORCHARDSTOWN NURSERIES ✉ EU ▣**
4 Miles Out, Cork Road, Waterford, Rep. of
Ireland
☎ 00 353 (0)51 384273
**Fax:** 00 353 (0)51 384422
**E-mail:** otown@iol.ie
**Contact:** Ron Dool
**Opening times:** 0900-1800 Mon-Sat,
1400-1800 Sun.
**Min. mail order UK:** No minimum charge*
**Min. mail order EU:** Nmc
**Cat. cost:** List £1.50
**Credit cards:** None
**Specialities:** Unusual hardy plants incl.
Shrubs, Shrub Roses, Trees, Climbers,
Rhododendron species & Water plants. *Note:
Only some plants mail order.
**Map ref:** 11, C4

**IRya  RYANS NURSERIES**
Lissivigeen, Killarney, Co. Kerry, Rep. of
Ireland
☎ 00 353 (0)64 33507
**Fax:** 00 353 (0)64 37520
**E-mail:** tlryan@tinet.ie
**Contact:** Mr T Ryan

**Opening times:** 0900-1800 Mon-Sat
1400-1800 Sun.
**Mail order:** None
**Cat. cost:** None issued
**Credit cards:** Visa
**Specialities:** Camellia, Pieris, Azalea, Acacia,
Eucalyptus, Dicksonia & many tender & rare
plants.
**Map ref:** 11, A4

ISea    SEAFORDE GARDENS ⊠ EU ⊠ ◪
Seaforde, Co. Down, N Ireland, BT30 8PG
☎ (01396) 811225   **Fax:** (01396) 811370
**Contact:** P Forde
**Opening times:** 1000-1700 Mon-Fri all year.
1000-1700 Sat & 1300-1800 Sun mid
Feb-end Oct.
**Min. mail order UK:** No minimum charge
**Min. mail order EU:** Nmc
**Cat. cost:** Free
**Credit cards:** None
**Specialities:** Over 700 varieties of self-
propagated Trees & Shrubs. National
Collection of Eucryphia.
**Map ref:** 11, C2

ISsi    SEASIDE NURSERY ⊠ EU ◪
Claddaghduff, Co. Galway, Rep. of Ireland
☎ 00 353 (0)954 4687
**Fax:** 00 353 (0)954 4761
**E-mail:** seaside@anu.ie
**Web site:** http://www.anu.ie/seaside/
**Contact:** Charles Dyck
**Opening times:** 0900-1300 & 1400-1800
Mon-Sat, 1400-1800 Sun.
**Min. mail order UK:** No minimum charge
**Min. mail order EU:** Nmc
**Cat. cost:** £3.00
**Credit cards:** Visa, American Express
**Specialities:** Plants & Hedging suitable for
seaside locations. Rare plants originating from
Australia & New Zealand, esp Phormium,
Astelia.
**Map ref:** 11, A2

ISta    STAM'S NURSERIES ⊠ ◪
The Garden House, Cappoquin, Co.
Waterford, Rep. of Ireland
☎ 00 353 (0)585 4787
**Fax:** 00 353 (0)585 2083
**E-mail:** stam@iol.ie
**Web site:** http://www.se_growers.ie
**Contact:** Peter Stam
**Opening times:** By appt. only.
**Mail order:** None
**Cat. cost:** Sae
**Credit cards:** None
**Specialities:** Bamboos. Note: Export for large
orders only.
**Map ref:** 11, B4

ITim    TIMPANY NURSERIES ⊠ EU ◪
77 Magheratimpany Road, Ballynahinch,
Co. Down, N Ireland, BT24 8PA
☎ (01238) 562812   **Fax:** (01238) 562812
**Contact:** Susan Tindall
**Opening times:** 1030-1730 Tue-Sat, 1400-
1700 Sun Summer. Closed Mon exc. B/Hols.
**Min. mail order UK:** No minimum charge
**Min. mail order EU:** £30.00 + p&p
**Cat. cost:** 75p in stamps
**Credit cards:** Visa, Access, MasterCard
**Specialities:** Celmisia, Androsace, Primula,
Saxifraga, Helichrysum, Dianthus & Cassiope.
**Map ref:** 11, C2

# LONDON AREA

LAma   JACQUES AMAND ⊠ EU ⊠ ◪
The Nurseries, 145 Clamp Hill, Stanmore,
Middlesex, HA7 3JS
☎ (0181) 420 7110   **Fax:** (0181) 954 6784
**E-mail:** john.amand@btinternet.com
**Contact:** Stuart Chapman, John Amand or
Martine de Groot.
**Opening times:** 0900-1700 Mon-Fri,
0900-1400 Sat-Sun. Limited Sun opening in
Dec & Jan.
**Min. mail order UK:** No minimum charge
**Min. mail order EU:** Nmc
**Cat. cost:** 1 x 1st class
**Credit cards:** Visa, Access
**Specialities:** Rare and unusual species Bulbs
especially Arisaema, Trillium.
**Map ref:** 6, C1

LAyl    AYLETT NURSERIES LTD ◪
North Orbital Road, London Colney, St
Albans, Hertfordshire, AL2 1DH
☎ (01727) 822255   **Fax:** (01727) 823024
**E-mail:** aylett_nurseries@compuserve.com
**Contact:** Roger S Aylett
**Opening times:** 0830-1730 Mon-Fri,
0830-1700 Sat, 1030-1600 Sun.
**Mail order:** None
**Cat. cost:** Free
**Credit cards:** MasterCard, Switch, Visa,
Connect
**Specialities:** Dahlias.
**Map ref:** 6, C1

LBee    BEECHCROFT NURSERY ◪
127 Reigate Road, Ewell, Surrey, KT17 3DE
☎ (0181) 393 4265   **Fax:** (0181) 393 4265

KEY
⊠ Mail order to UK or EU
⊠ Exports beyond EU
◪ Also supplies Wholesale   ◆ See Display advertisement

**L**

Contact: C Kimber
Opening times: 1000-1700 May-Sept.
1000-1600 Oct-Apr, B/Hols & Suns. Closed
Xmas-New Year & August.
Mail order: None
Cat. cost: 2 x 1st class
Credit cards: Visa, Access, Switch
Specialities: Conifers & Alpines.
Map ref: 3, A2

**LBlm  BLOOMSBURY ⊠ UK**
Upper Lodge Farm, Padworth Common,
Reading, Berkshire, RG7 4JD
☎ (0118) 970 0239
Contact: Susan Oakley
Opening times: By appt.
Min. mail order UK: £15.00 + p&p
Cat. cost: 5 x 1st class
Credit cards: None
Specialities: Selected range of good
Conservatory and Garden Perennials, esp.
Geranium, Iris, Salvia, White flowers &
borderline-hardy Exotics.
Map ref: 2, A4

**LBlo  TERENCE BLOCH - PLANTSMAN ⊠ UK**
9 Colberg Place, Stamford Hill, London,
N16 5RA
☎ (0181) 802 2535
Contact: Mr T Bloch
Opening times: Mail order only.
Min. mail order UK: £15.00 + p&p
Cat. cost: £3.30 incl p&p. Cheque/postal
order only*
Credit cards: None
Specialities: Tropical Plants for the
conservatory/home; Rarer Tropical fruiting
species for the conservatory/greenhouse. Plants
for sub-tropical Summer bedding. *Note:
Each season a new, A4 sized, fully descriptive
& colour catalogue is produced.

**LBow  RUPERT BOWLBY ⊠ EU**
Gatton, Reigate, Surrey, RH2 0TA
☎ (01737) 642221  Fax: (01737) 642221
Contact: Rupert Bowlby
Opening times: Sat & Sun pm in Mar &
Sep-Oct.
Min. mail order UK: No minimum charge
Min. mail order EU: Nmc
Cat. cost: 3 x 2nd class
Credit cards: None
Specialities: Unusual Bulbs & Corms.
Map ref: 3, A2

**LBra  S & N BRACKLEY ⊠ EU ▣ ▣**
117 Winslow Road, Wingrave, Aylesbury,
Buckinghamshire, HP22 4QB

☎ (01296) 681384  Fax: (01296) 681384
Contact: Mrs S Brackley/Mrs K Earwicker
Opening times: Please phone for appt.
Min. mail order UK: No minimum charge*
Min. mail order EU: Nmc
Cat. cost: 1st class Sae.
Credit cards: MasterCard, Visa
Specialities: Sweet Pea Plants (for collection
only). *Note: Onion & Leek Plants by mail
order. Seeds only by mail to EU.
Map ref: 6, B1

**LBre  BRESSINGHAM PLANT CENTRE**
Dorney, Windsor, Buckinghamshire, SL4 6QP
☎ (01628) 669999  Fax: (01628) 669693
Contact: Peter Freeman
Opening times: 0900-1730 daily. (Direct
retail Plant Centre.)
Mail order: None
Cat. cost: None issued
Credit cards: Delta, Switch, MasterCard, Visa
Specialities: Very wide general range. Many
own varieties. Focus on Hardy Ornamental
plants & Grasses.
Map ref: 3, A1

**LBro  MRS P J BROWN ⊠ EU ▣ ▣**
V H Humphrey-The Iris Specialist, Westlees
Farm, Logmore Lane, Westcott, Dorking,
Surrey, RH4 3JN
☎ (01306) 889827  Fax: (01306) 889371
Contact: Mrs P J Brown
Opening times: Regret, no open days or visits
during 1999.
Min. mail order UK: No minimum charge
Min. mail order EU: Nmc
Cat. cost: Sae or 3 x 1st class. 1997/98 cat.
remains current for 1999.
Credit cards: None
Specialities: Bearded, Spuria, Siberian, Pacific
Coast, species & Japanese Iris.
Map ref: 3, A1

**LBuc  BUCKINGHAM NURSERIES ⊠ EU ♦**
14 Tingewick Road, Buckingham,
Buckinghamshire, MK18 4AE
☎ (01280) 813556  Fax: (01280) 815491
E-mail: enquiries@bucknur.com
Contact: R J & P L Brown
Opening times: 0830-1730 (1800 in summer)
Mon-Fri, 1000-1600 Sun.
Min. mail order UK: No minimum charge
Min. mail order EU: Nmc
Cat. cost: Free
Credit cards: Visa, MasterCard, Switch
Specialities: Bare rooted and container grown
hedging. Trees, Shrubs, Herbaceous
Perennials, Alpines, Grasses & Ferns.
Map ref: 5, B4

**LBut** **BUTTERFIELDS NURSERY** ✉ EU ✈ 🅦
Harvest Hill, Bourne End, Buckinghamshire,
SL8 5JJ
☎ (01628) 525455
Contact: I Butterfield
Opening times: 0900-1300 & 1400-1700.
Please telephone beforehand in case we are
attending shows.
Min. mail order UK: No minimum charge
Min. mail order EU: £30.00 + p&p
Cat. cost: 2 x 2nd class
Credit cards: None
Specialities: Only Pleione by mail order.
Dahlia for collection. National Collection of
Pleione.
Map ref: 6, C1

**LCha** **CHASE ORGANICS (GB) LTD** ✉ EU
Riverdene Estate, Molesey Road, Addlestone,
Hersham, Surrey, KT12 4RG
☎ (01932) 253666  Fax: (01932) 252707
E-mail: chaseorg@aol.com
Contact: M Hedges
Opening times: 0930-1630 Mon-Fri.
Min. mail order UK: 80p p&p under £15.00*
Min. mail order EU: No minimum charge
(seed only).
Cat. cost: Free
Credit cards: Visa, Access, Switch
Specialities: 'The Organic Gardening
Catalogue' offers Vegetable, Herb & Flower
seeds & garden sundries especially for Organic
gardeners. *Note: Mail order of plants only to
UK, seeds to EU.
Map ref: 3, A1

**LChe** **CHESSINGTON NURSERIES LTD** ✉ EU
Leatherhead Road, Chessington, Surrey,
KT19 2NG
☎ (01372) 725638  Fax: (01372) 740859
Contact: Jim Knight
Opening times: 0900-1800 Mon-Sat,
1000-1600 Sun.
Min. mail order UK: No minimum charge
Min. mail order EU: Nmc
Cat. cost: 6 x 1st class
Credit cards: MasterCard, Visa
Specialities: Conservatory plants esp. Citrus,
Hoya & Passiflora.
Map ref: 3, A2

**LChw** **CHADWELL SEEDS** ✉ EU ✈
81 Parlaunt Road, Slough, Berkshire, SL3 8BE
☎ (01753) 542823
Contact: Chris Chadwell
Opening times:
Min. mail order UK: No minimum charge
Min. mail order EU: Nmc

Cat. cost: 3 x 2nd class
Credit cards: None
Specialities: Seed collecting expedition to the
Himalaya. Separate general Seed list of
Japanese, N. America & Himalayan plants.

**LCla** **CLAY LANE NURSERY**
3 Clay Lane, South Nutfield, Nr Redhill,
Surrey, RH1 4EG
☎ (01737) 823307
Contact: K W Belton
Opening times: 0900-1700 Thur-Sun 1st
Feb-31st Aug. Other times by appt.
Please phone before travelling.
Mail order: None
Cat. cost: 2 x 1st class
Credit cards: None
Specialities: Fuchsia.
Map ref: 3, A2

**LCns** **THE CONSERVATORY** ✉ EU
Gomshall Gallery, Gomshall, Surrey,
GU5 9LB
☎ (01483) 203019  Fax: (01483) 203282
Contact: Marceline Siddons
Opening times: 1000-1730 Mon-Sat all year;
1400-1700 Sun Apr-Oct. Ring to check Xmas
& B/Hols.
Min. mail order UK: No minimum charge
Min. mail order EU: Nmc
Cat. cost: 3 x 2nd class
Credit cards: Visa, MasterCard
Specialities: Wide range of Conservatory &
House plants incl. Citrus & Bougainvillea
Map ref: 3, B1

**LCon** **THE CONIFER GARDEN** ✉ UK
Hare Lane Nursery, Little Kingshill, Great
Missenden, Buckinghamshire, HP16 0EF
☎ (01494) 862086 (0900-1800)
Fax: (01494) 862086
Web site: http://www.powel.freeserve.co.uk/
conifer/
Contact: Mr & Mrs M P S Powell
Opening times: Usually 1100-1600 Tue-Sat &
B/Hol Mons. (1100-1300 Dec/Jan &
July/Aug.) Please phone first.
Min. mail order UK: No minimum charge
Cat. cost: 2 x 1st class
Credit cards: None
Specialities: Conifers only – over 500 varieties
always in stock.
Map ref: 6, C1

KEY  ✉ Mail order to UK or EU
✈ Exports beyond EU
🅦 Also supplies Wholesale  ◆ See Display advertisement

**LCot**   **COTTAGE GARDEN PLANTS**
9 Buckingham Road, Newbury, Berkshire,
RG14 6DH
☎ (01635) 31941
Contact: Mrs Hannah Billcliffe
Opening times: 1000-1700 Wed-Sat Mar-Jul
& Sep-Oct.
Mail order: None
Cat. cost: Sae + 1 x 1st class
Credit cards: None
Specialities: Wide range of unusual Perennials.
Map ref: 2, A4

**LCTD**   **CTDA** ☒ EU ☒
174 Cambridge Street, London, SW1V 4QE
☎ (0171) 976 5115
Contact: Basil Smith
Opening times: Not open.
Min. mail order UK: £10.00 + p&p
Min. mail order EU: £20 + p&p
Cat. cost: Free
Credit cards: None
Specialities: Hardy cyclamen for the garden,
named Helleborus, Dierama & Aquilegia
species. Also seeds.

**LCtg**   **COTTAGE GARDEN NURSERY** ◆
Barnet Road, Arkley, Barnet, Hertfordshire,
EN5 3JX
☎ (0181) 441 8829   Fax: (07070) 715170
Contact: David and Wendy Spicer
Opening times: 0930-1700 Wed-Sat
Mar-Oct, 0930-1600 Wed-Sat Nov-Feb,
1000-1600 Sun throughout year.
Mail order: None
Cat. cost: None issued.
Credit cards: Visa, Access, MasterCard,
Switch, Solo, Delta
Specialities: General range of Hardy Shrubs,
Trees & Perennials – Architectural & Exotics,
Fuchsia, seasonal Bedding, Patio plants.
Map ref: 6, C1

**LDea**   **Derek Lloyd Dean** ☒ EU ☒
8 Lynwood Close, South Harrow, Middlesex,
HA2 9PR
☎ (0181) 864 0899
Contact: Derek Lloyd Dean
Opening times: Mail order only.
Min. mail order UK: £2.50 + p&p
Min. mail order EU: £2.50 + p&p
Cat. cost: 2 x 1st class
Credit cards: None
Specialities: Regal, Angel, Ivy & Scented Leaf
Pelargoniums.

**LEar**   **EARLSTONE NURSERY** ☒ UK ☒
Earlstone Manor Farm, Burghclere, Newbury,
Berkshire, RG15 9NG
☎ (01635) 278648   Fax: (01635) 278672
E-mail: ginsberg@dial.pipex.com
Contact: B C Ginsberg
Opening times: By appt.
Min. mail order UK: £30.00 + p&p
Cat. cost: Free
Credit cards: None
Specialities: All varieties of Buxus. Topiary.
Map ref: 2, A4

**LEdu**   **EDULIS** ☒ EU ☒
1 Flowers Piece, Ashampstead, Berkshire,
RG8 8SG
☎ (01635) 578113   Fax: (01635) 578113
E-mail: edulis2000@hotmail.com
Contact: Paul Barney
Opening times: Mail order only.
Min. mail order UK: £30.00 + p&p
Min. mail order EU: £50.00 + p&p
Cat. cost: 6 x 1st class
Credit cards: None
Specialities: Unusual edibles, Architectural
plants, Permaculture plants.
Map ref: 2, A4

**LEur**   **THE EUROPA NURSERY** ☒ EU
PO Box 17589, London, E1 4YN
☎ (0171) 265 8131   Fax: (0171) 366 9892
E-mail: europanurs@aol.com
Web Site: http://www.europa-nursery.co.uk
Contact: Tim Branney & Adam Draper
Opening times: Not open.
Min. mail order UK: No minimum charge
Min. mail order EU: Nmc
Cat. cost: 2 x 1st class
Credit cards: None
Specialities: Extensive range of Aquilegia,
Codonopsis, Digitalis, Epimedium & Tricyrtis.

**LFis**   **KAYTIE FISHER NURSERY** ☒ UK
South End Cottage, Long Reach, Ockham,
Surrey, GU23 6PF
☎ (01483) 282304   Fax: (01483) 282304
Contact: Kaytie Fisher
Opening times: 1000-1700 Wed-Sun,
0800-2000 Thur Apr-Jun. 1000-1700 Wed-
Fri Mar & Jul-Oct. Nov-Feb by appt. only.
Min. mail order UK: £11.95. Courier up to
20kg.
Cat. cost: 3 x 1st class
Credit cards: None
Specialities: Mainly hardy Herbaceous,
Alpines, Clematis species, Shrubs. Old Shrub
Roses & Climbing Roses. Nursery 1 mile
South East of RHS Wisley.
Map ref: 3, A1

**L**

**LFli  FLITTVALE GARDEN CENTRE & NURSERY**
Flitwick Road, Westoning, Bedfordshire, MK45 5AA
☎ (01525) 712484  **Fax:** (01525) 718412
**Contact:** Bernie Berry
**Opening times:** 0830-1800 Mon-Sat, 1030-1630 Sun.
**Mail order:** None
**Cat. cost:** 5 x 1st class
**Credit cards:** Visa, Access, Switch, Delta, MasterCard
**Specialities:** Fuchsia.
**Map ref:** 6, B1

**LFol  FOLIAGE SCENTED & HERB PLANTS**
Walton Poor Cottage, Crocknorth Road, Ranmore Common, Dorking, Surrey, RH5 6SX
☎ (01483) 282273  **Fax:** (01483) 282273
**Contact:** Mrs Prudence Calvert
**Opening times:** 1000-1700 Wed-Sun Apr-Sep & B/Hols. 1000-1700 Thu & Fri or by appt. remainder of year.
**Mail order:** None
**Cat. cost:** 3 x 2nd class
**Credit cards:** None
**Specialities:** Herbs, aromatic & scented plants.
**Map ref:** 3, A1

**LFox  FOXGROVE PLANTS** ⊠ EU
Foxgrove, Enborne, Nr Newbury, Berkshire, RG14 6RE
☎ (01635) 40554
**Contact:** Miss Louise Vockins
**Opening times:** 1000-1700 Wed-Sun & B/Hols.
**Min. mail order UK:** No minimum charge*
**Min. mail order EU:** Nmc
**Cat. cost:** £1.00
**Credit cards:** None
**Specialities:** Hardy & unusual plants. Alpines & good selection of Saxifraga & Galanthus.
*Note: Mail order for Galanthus only.
**Map ref:** 2, A3

**LGod  GODLY'S ROSES** ⊠ EU 🅆
Redbourn, St Albans, Hertfordshire, AL3 7PS
☎ (01582) 792255  **Fax:** (01582) 794267
**Contact:** Colin Godly
**Opening times:** 0900-1900 Summer, 0900-dusk Winter Mon-Fri. 0900-1800 Sat & Sun.
**Min. mail order UK:** £4.50 + p&p
**Min. mail order EU:** £50.00 + p&p
**Cat. cost:** Free
**Credit cards:** Visa, Access, American Express, Switch
**Specialities:** Roses.
**Map ref:** 6, B1

**LGre  GREEN FARM PLANTS**
Bury Court, Bentley, Farnham, Surrey, GU10 5LZ
☎ (01420) 23202  **Fax:** (01420) 22382
**Contact:** M Christopher & J Coke
**Opening times:** 1000-1800 Thur-Sat 18th Mar-30th Oct 1999, 23rd Mar-28th Oct 2000.
**Mail order:** None
**Cat. cost:** 3 x 1st class
**Credit cards:** Visa, MasterCard, JCB, Switch, Visa, Delta, Electron, Solo
**Specialities:** Small Shrubs, Sub-shrubs & Perennials. Many uncommon. Cistus, Prostanthera, Achillea, Eryngium, Monarda, Phlox, Grasses.
**Map ref:** 3, B1

**LGro  GROWING CARPETS** ⊠ UK ◆
Christmas Tree House, High Street, Guilden Morden, Nr Royston, Hertfordshire, SG8 0JP
☎ (01763) 852705
**Contact:** Mrs E E Moore
**Opening times:** 1100-1700 Mon-Sat 14th Mar-31st Oct 1998. (Closed 2nd-4th May incl.) 1100-1700 Mon-Sat 13th Mar-30th Oct 1999. (Closed 3rd-5th May incl.)
**Min. mail order UK:** £5.00 + p&p
**Cat. cost:** 5 x 2nd class
**Credit cards:** None
**Specialities:** Wide range of Ground-covering plants.
**Map ref:** 6, B2

**LHer  HERONS BONSAI** ⊠ UK 🅆
Wiremill Lane, Newchapel, Lingfield, Surrey, RH7 6HJ
☎ (01342) 832657  **Fax:** (01342) 832025
**E-mail:** herons.bonsai@virgin.net
**Contact:** Peter Chan
**Opening times:** 0930-1730 Mon-Sat, 1030-1600 Sun.
**Min. mail order UK:** £20.00 + p&p
**Cat. cost:** Sae
**Credit cards:** Visa, MasterCard
**Specialities:** Japanese Maple varieties, Japanese Cherries, Wisterias, Japanese Iris, Bamboos & esp. Bonsai.
**Map ref:** 3, B2

**LHil  BRIAN HILEY** ⊠ EU
25 Little Woodcote Estate, Wallington, Surrey, SM5 4AU
☎ (0181) 647 9679

---

**KEY**
⊠ Mail order to UK or EU
🅆 Exports beyond EU
🄰 Also supplies Wholesale  ◆ See Display advertisement

**L**

**Contact:** Brian & Heather Hiley
**Opening times:** 0900-1700 Wed-Sat
(ex B/Hols). Please check beforehand.
**Min. mail order UK:** No minimum charge
**Min. mail order EU:** Nmc
**Cat. cost:** 3 x 1st class
**Credit cards:** None
**Specialities:** Penstemon, Salvia, Canna,
Pelargoniums, tender & unusual plants.
Ornamental Grasses & Ferns.
**Map ref:** 3, A2

**LHkn**  R HARKNESS & CO. LTD. ⊠ UK ☒ ▣
The Rose Gardens, Cambridge Road, Hitchin,
Hertfordshire, SG4 0JT
☎ (01462) 420402  **Fax:** (01462) 422170
**E-mail:** roses@cocoon.co.uk
**Web site:** http://www.roses.co.uk
**Contact:** Owen Pope
**Opening times:** 0900-1730 Mon-Fri.
**Min. mail order UK:**
**Cat. cost:** Free
**Credit cards:** American Express, Visa, Access,
Switch, Delta
**Specialities:** Roses.
**Map ref:** 6, B1

**LHol**  HOLLINGTON NURSERIES ⊠ EU ▣
Woolton Hill, Newbury, Berkshire,
RG20 9XT
☎ (01635) 253908  **Fax:** (01635) 254990
**E-mail:** hollington@herb-garden.co.uk
**Web site:** http://www.herb-garden.co.uk
**Contact:** S & J Hopkinson
**Opening times:** 1000-1700 Mon-Sat,
1100-1700 Sun & B/Hols Mar-Sep.
Please enquire for winter hours.
**Min. mail order UK:** No minimum charge*
**Min. mail order EU:** Nmc
**Cat. cost:** 3 x 2nd class
**Credit cards:** Visa, Access, American Express,
Switch
**Specialities:** Herbs, Thymes, Old fashioned
Roses, Salvia & Lavandula. *Note: Ltd mail
order service.
**Map ref:** 2, A3

**LHop**  HOPLEYS PLANTS LTD ⊠ UK ▣
High Street, Much Hadham, Hertfordshire,
SG10 6BU
☎ (01279) 842509  **Fax:** (01279) 843784
**E-mail:** hopleys@compuserve.com
**Contact:** Aubrey Barker
**Opening times:** 0900-1700 Mon & Wed-Sat,
1400-1700 Sun. Closed Jan & Feb.
**Min. mail order UK:** No minimum charge*
**Cat. cost:** 5 x 1st class
**Credit cards:** Visa, Access, Switch

**Specialities:** Wide range of Hardy & Half -
hardy Shrubs & Perennials. *Note: Mail order
in Autumn only.
**Map ref:** 6, B2

**LHos**  THE HOSTA GARDEN ⊠ EU ☒
47 Birch Grove, London, W3 9SP
☎ (0181) 248 1300  **Fax:** (0181) 248 1300
**E-mail:** hostagarden@hotmail.com
**Web site:** http://www.bcity.com/ thehostagarden
**Contact:** Ian Toop
**Opening times:** Mail order only.
**Min. mail order UK:** No minimum charge
**Min. mail order EU:** £20.00 + p&p
**Cat. cost:** 4 x 1st class
**Credit cards:** None
**Specialities:** Hosta.
**Map ref:** 6, C1

**LHyd**  HYDON NURSERIES ⊠ EU ☒ ▣ ◆
Clock Barn Lane, Hydon Heath, Godalming,
Surrey, GU8 4AZ
☎ (01483) 860252  **Fax:** (01483) 419937
**Contact:** A F George, Rodney Longhurst &
Mrs A M George
**Opening times:** 0800-1245 & 1400-1700
Mon-Sat. Sun during May and by appt. Open
B/Hols.
**Min. mail order UK:** No minimum charge
**Min. mail order EU:** £25.00 + p&p
**Cat. cost:** £1.50 or 6 x 1st class or 8 x 2nd
class
**Credit cards:** None
**Specialities:** Large and dwarf Rhododendron,
Yakushimanum hybrids, Azaleas deciduous &
evergreen, Camellias & other Trees & Shrubs.
**Map ref:** 3, B1

**LHyr**  HYRONS TREES ▣
The Green, Sarratt, Rickmansworth,
Hertfordshire, WD3 6BL
☎ (01923) 263000  **Fax:** (01923) 270625
**E-mail:** peiser@hyronstrees.demon.co.uk
**Contact:** Graham Peiser
**Opening times:** 0900-1300 Mon-Fri, but
please check first. Other times by appt.
**Mail order:** None
**Cat. cost:** 4 x 1st class
**Credit cards:** Delta, Switch
**Specialities:** Broadleaved Trees (from Whips to
Extra Heavy Standards), Topiary (incl. Bay &
Box) and Hedging - all in containers.
**Map ref:** 6, C1

**LIck**  LOWER ICKNIELD FARM
NURSERIES ⊠ UK ◆
Meadle, Princes Risborough, Aylesbury,
Buckinghamshire, HP17 9TX

☎ (01844) 343436
**Contact:** S Baldwin
**Opening times:** 0900-1730 daily ex.
Xmas-New Year
**Min. mail order UK:** See below.*
**Cat. cost:** 2 x 1st class for Argy. list
**Credit cards:** None
**Specialities:** Argyranthemum - National
Collection. Patio & Basket plants. Tender &
hardy Perennials. *Note: Mail order collection
of 10 Argyranthemums £13.50, send 2 x 1st
class stamps for list.
**Map ref:** 5, C4

**L**Iri   THE IRIS GARDEN ⊠ EU ◆
47 Station Road, New Barnet, Hertfordshire,
EN5 1PR
☎ (0181) 441 1300   **Fax:** (0181) 441 1300
**E-mail:** iris1992@aol.com
**Contact:** Clive Russell
**Opening times:** Show Garden at Roan
Cottage, Dukes Kiln Drive, Gerrards Cross,
Bucks SL9 7HD. Open by appt. only from
mid-May-mid June.*
**Min. mail order UK:** £15.00 + p&p
**Min. mail order EU:** £25.00 + p&p
**Cat. cost:** £1.50 inc. Full colour
**Credit cards:** None
**Specialities:** Modern Tall Bearded Iris from
breeders in UK, USA, France & Australia.
*Note: Tel. for Garden appt. (01753) 884308
after 1700.
**Map ref:** 6, C1

**L**Jus   JUST BAMBOO LTD ⊠ EU ☒ ▣
109 Hayes Lane, Bromley, Kent, BR2 9EF
☎ (0181) 462 1800, **Mobile** 07071 226266
**Fax:** (0181) 462 1800
**E-mail:** mike_james_justbamboo@
compuserve.com
**Web site:** http://www.rsl.ox.ac.uk/users/djh/
ebs/ebsgbn.htm
**Contact:** Mike James
**Opening times:** Thurs-Sun – by appt. please.
**Min. mail order UK:** £20.00 + p&p
**Min. mail order EU:** £60.00 + p&p
**Cat. cost:** Sae + 2 x 1st class
**Credit cards:** None
**Specialities:** Bamboo.
**Map ref:** 3, A2

**L**Kna   KNAP HILL & SLOCOCK
NURSERIES ⊠ EU ☒ ▣
Barrs Lane, Knaphill, Woking, Surrey,
GU21 2JW
☎ (01483) 481214/5   **Fax:** (01483) 797261
**Contact:** Mrs Joy West

**Opening times:** 0900-1700 Mon-Fri by appt.
only
**Min. mail order UK:** No minimum charge
**Min. mail order EU:** Nmc
**Cat. cost:** 3 x 1st class
**Credit cards:** Visa, Access
**Specialities:** Wide variety of Rhododendron &
Azalea.
**Map ref:** 3, A1

**LL**ew   MICHAEL LEWINGTON GARDENER -
PLANTSMAN ⊠ UK ▣
12a Tredown Road, Sydenham, London,
SE26 5QH
☎ (0181) 778 4201   **E-mail:** brugmansia
@mlewington.freeserve.co.uk
**Contact:** Michael Lewington
**Opening times:** May-Oct by appt. only.
**Min. mail order UK:** Please phone for details.
**Cat. cost:** 3 x 1st class
**Credit cards:** None
**Specialities:** Datura & Brugmansia. Rare
Perennials, Shrubs, Conservatory plants &
South African Bulbs.
**Map ref:** 3, A2

**LL**in   LINCLUDEN NURSERY ⊠ EU ☒ ▣ ◆
Bisley Green, Bisley, Woking, Surrey,
GU24 9EN
☎ (01483) 797005   **Fax:** (01483) 474015
**Contact:** Mr & Mrs J A Tilbury
**Opening times:** 0930-1630 Mon-Sat all year
exc. B/Hols.
**Min. mail order UK:** No minimum charge
**Min. mail order EU:** Nmc
**Cat. cost:** 3 x 1st class
**Credit cards:** Visa, MasterCard
**Specialities:** Dwarf, slow-growing & unusual
Conifers.
**Map ref:** 3, A1

**LL**WP   L W PLANTS ⊠ UK
23 Wroxham Way, Harpenden, Hertfordshire,
AL5 4PP
☎ (01582) 768467
**E-mail:** lwplants@orangenet.co.uk
**Contact:** Mrs M Easter
**Opening times:** 1000-1700 most days, but
please phone first.
**Min. mail order UK:** £15.00 + p&p*
**Cat. cost:** A5 Sae + 5 x 2nd class**
**Credit cards:** None

**KEY**   ⊠ Mail order to UK or EU
☒ Exports beyond EU
▣ Also supplies Wholesale   ◆ See Display advertisement

**Specialities:** Unusual Hardy Perennials & Herbs esp. Diascia, Geranium, Penstemon & Thymus. National Collection of Thymus. *Note: Mail order late Sept-April. **Sae for list.
**Map ref:** 6, B1

**LMap**  **MAPLEASH PLANTS**
Ashcombe Cottage, Ranmore Common, Dorking, Surrey, RH5 6SP
☎ (01306) 881599
**Contact:** Beryl Davis
**Opening times:** Open most days but by appt. only. Also ring for directions.
**Mail order:** None
**Cat. cost:** None issued
**Credit cards:** None
**Specialities:** Less usual Hardy Perennials. Garden open to visitors & groups.
**Map ref:** 3, A2

**LMil**  **MILLAIS NURSERIES** ⊠ EU ▨ ▨ ◆
Crosswater Lane, Churt, Farnham, Surrey, GU10 2JN
☎ (01252) 792698   **Fax:** (01252) 792526
**E-mail:** sales@rhododendrons.co.uk
**Web site:** http://www.rhododendrons.co.uk
**Contact:** David Millais
**Opening times:** 1000-1300 & 1400-1700 Mon-Fri. Sats Spring & Autumn. Also daily in May.
**Min. mail order UK:** £25.00 + p&p
**Min. mail order EU:** £60.00 + p&p
**Cat. cost:** 4 x 1st class
**Credit cards:** Visa, Access
**Specialities:** Rhododendron & Azalea.
**Map ref:** 3, B1

**LMor**  **MOREHAVENS** ⊠ UK ▨
Sandpit Hill, Buckland Common, Tring, Hertfordshire, HP23 6NG
☎ (01494) 758642
**Contact:** B Farmer
**Opening times:** Only for collection.
**Min. mail order UK:** £10.50 incl. p&p
**Cat. cost:** Free
**Credit cards:** None
**Specialities:** Camomile 'Treneague'.
**Map ref:** 6, C1

**LNet**  **NETTLETONS NURSERY** ▨ ◆
Ivy Mill Lane, Godstone, Surrey, RH9 8NF
☎ (01883) 742426   **Fax:** (01883) 742426
**Contact:** Jonathan Nettleton
**Opening times:** 0900-1300 & 1400-1700 Mon, Tue, Thu-Sat.
**Mail order:** None
**Cat. cost:** 2 x 1st class
**Credit cards:** Visa, Access

**Specialities:** Trees & Shrubs. Especially Conifers, Azalea, Camellia, Rhododendron, Climbers. 100 Japanese Acer. 35 Wisteria.
**Map ref:** 3, A2

**LNor**  **NORTHVIEW PERENNIALS** ⊠ EU ▨
27 Clifton Road, Henlow, Bedfordshire, SG16 6BL
☎ (01462) 814509   **Fax:** (01462) 814509
**Contact:** N K Wake
**Opening times:** By appt. only.
**Min. mail order UK:** No minimum charge
**Min. mail order EU:** Nmc
**Cat. cost:** 4 x 1st class
**Credit cards:** None
**Specialities:** Herbaceous Perennials.
**Map ref:** 6, B1

**LPal**  **THE PALM CENTRE** ⊠ EU ▨ ▨
Ham Central Nursery, opposite Riverside Drive, Ham Street, Ham, Richmond, Surrey, TW10 7HA
☎ (0181) 255 6191
**Fax:** (0181) 255 6192/6193
**E-mail:** mail@palmcentre.co.uk
**Web Site:** http://www.palmcentre.co.uk
**Contact:** Martin Gibbons
**Opening times:** 1000-1800 daily (until dusk in winter).
**Min. mail order UK:** £10.00 + p&p
**Min. mail order EU:** £10.00 + p&p
**Cat. cost:** £1.95
**Credit cards:** Visa, MasterCard
**Specialities:** Palms & Cycads, exotic & sub-tropical, hardy, half-hardy & tropical. Seedlings to mature trees. Also Bamboo, Tree Ferns & other Exotics. Colour catalogue £1.95.
**Map ref:** 3, A1

**LPan**  **PANTILES PLANT & GARDEN CENTRE** ⊠ EU ▨ ▨ ◆
Almners Road, Lyne, Chertsey, Surrey, KT16 0BJ
☎ (01932) 872195   **Fax:** (01932) 874030
**Contact:** Brendan Gallagher
**Opening times:** 0900-1730 Mon-Sat, 0900-1700 Sun.
**Min. mail order UK:** £100.00 + p&p
**Min. mail order EU:** £100.00 + p&p
**Cat. cost:** Free
**Credit cards:** Visa, Switch, MasterCard
**Specialities:** Large Trees, Shrubs, Conifers & Climbers in containers. Australasian & other unusual plants.
**Map ref:** 3, A1

**L**PBA  PAUL BROMFIELD -
AQUATICS ⊠ EU 🗷 🗹
Maydencroft Lane, Gosmore, Hitchin,
Hertfordshire, SG4 7QD
☎ (01462) 457399  **Fax:** (01462) 422652
**Contact:** P Bromfield
**Opening times:** 0900-1300 & 1400-1730
daily Feb-Oct. 1000-1300 Sat-Sun Nov-Jan.
Please ring first.
**Min. mail order UK:** £10.00 incl.
**Min. mail order EU:** £50.00 incl.
**Cat. cost:** 2 x 1st class
**Credit cards:** Visa, MasterCard, Delta, JCB,
Switch
**Specialities:** Water Lilies, Marginals & Bog.
**Map ref:** 6, B1

**L**Pen  PENSTEMONS BY COLOUR ⊠ EU 🗹
76 Grove Avenue, Hanwell, London, W7 3ES
☎ (0181) 840 3199  **Fax:** (0181) 840 6415
**E-mail:** kimhughes1@compuserve.com
**Contact:** Debra Hughes
**Opening times:** Any time by appt.
**Min. mail order UK:** £5.00 + p&p
**Min. mail order EU:** £10.00 + p&p
**Cat. cost:** Free
**Credit cards:** None
**Specialities:** Penstemons.
**Map ref:** 3, A1

**L**Pio  PIONEER NURSERY ⊠ EU 🗹
Baldock Lane, Willian, Letchworth,
Hertfordshire, SG6 2AE
☎ (01462) 675858  **Fax:** (01462) 675596
**E-mail:** pioneer@nursery.dircon.co.uk
**Contact:** Nick Downing
**Opening times:** 0930-1800 Tue-Sun Feb-Dec.
**Min. mail order UK:** £20.00 + p&p
**Min. mail order EU:** 30 Euro
**Cat. cost:** Free
**Credit cards:** MasterCard, Visa
**Specialities:** Salvia, tender Perennials, Nerium
oleander. Wide range of hard-to-find
Perennials & Bulbs.
**Map ref:** 6, B1

**L**PJP  PJ's PALMS AND EXOTICS ⊠ EU
41 Salcombe Road, Ashford, Middlesex,
TW15 3BS
☎ (01784) 250181  **Fax:** (01784) 250181
**Contact:** Peter Jenkins
**Opening times:** Mail order only. Visits by
arrangement.
**Min. mail order UK:** No minimum charge
**Min. mail order EU:** Nmc
**Cat. cost:** 2 x 1st class
**Credit cards:** None

**Specialities:** Palms and other Exotic Foliage
plants, hardy & half hardy.
**Map ref:** 3, A1

**L**Plm  A J PALMER & SON ⊠ EU 🗹
Denham Court Nursery, Denham Court
Drive, Denham, Uxbridge, Middlesex,
UB9 5PG
☎ (01895) 832035  **Fax:** (01895) 832035
**Contact:** Sheila Palmer
**Opening times:** 0900-dusk daily Jul-Oct,
Rose field viewing. 0900-1700 Mon-Sat,
1000-1300 Sun Nov. Dec-Jun phone.
**Min. mail order UK:** No minimum charge
**Min. mail order EU:** Nmc
**Cat. cost:** Free
**Credit cards:** None
**Specialities:** Roses.
**Map ref:** 6, C1

**L**Pri  PRIORSWOOD CLEMATIS ⊠ EU 🗷 🗹
Priorswood, Widbury Hill, Ware,
Hertfordshire, SG12 7QH
☎ (01920) 461543  **Fax:** (01920) 461543
**Contact:** G S Greenway
**Opening times:** 0800-1700 Tue-Sun & B/Hol
Mondays.
**Min. mail order UK:** £10.00 + p&p
**Min. mail order EU:** £30.00 + p&p
**Cat. cost:** Free plant list;
catalogue/growing guide £2.
**Credit cards:** Visa, Access
**Specialities:** Clematis & other climbing
plants. Lonicera, Parthenocissus, Solanum,
Passiflora, Vitis etc.
**Map ref:** 6, B2

**L**PVe  PLANTA VERA ⊠ EU 🗷 🗹
Lyne Hill Nursery, Farm Close, Lyne Crossing
Road, Chertsey, Surrey, KT16 0AT
☎ (01932) 563011  **Fax:** (01932) 563011
**Contact:** Morris May
**Opening times:** 1000-1600 7 days mid Apr-
mid June. Otherwise ring for an appt.
**Min. mail order UK:** £24.00 (12 plants)
**Min. mail order EU:** £24 (12 plants)
**Cat. cost:** 5 x 2nd class
**Credit cards:** None
**Specialities:** 415 named Violas & Violettas.
NCCPG status (provisional).
**Map ref:** 3, A1

---

Y  ⊠ Mail order to UK or EU
E  🗷 Exports beyond EU
K  🗹 Also supplies Wholesale  ◆ See Display advertisement

**L**

**LRHS**   **WISLEY PLANT CENTRE ◆**
RHS Garden, Wisley, Woking, Surrey,
GU23 6QB
☎ (01483) 211113   **Fax:** (01483) 212372
**Opening times:** 1000-1800 Mon-Sat
1100-1700 Sun Summer, 1000-1730 Mon-Sat
1000-1600 Sun Winter. Closed Easter Sun.
**Mail order:** None
**Cat. cost:** None issued
**Credit cards:** MasterCard, Access, American
Express, Switch, Visa
**Specialities:** Very wide range, many rare &
unusual.
**Map ref:** 3, A1

**LRot**   **ROTHERSTONE PLANTS** ⊠ EU
70 Long Lane, Tilehurst, Reading, Berkshire,
RG31 6YJ
☎ (01189) 615889
**Contact:** J H Over
**Opening times:** 1000-1800 all year.
Please ring first.
**Min. mail order UK:** No minimum charge
**Min. mail order EU:** Nmc
**Cat. cost:** Free
**Credit cards:** None
**Specialities:** Perennials, Grasses & Ferns
**Map ref:** 2, A4

**LSee**   **SEEDS BY SIZE** ⊠ EU ▣
45 Crouchfield, Boxmoor, Hemel Hempstead,
Hertfordshire, HP1 1PA
☎ (01442) 251458
**E-mail:** john-robert-size@seeds-by-size.co.uk
**Web site:** http://www.seeds-by-size.co.uk
**Contact:** Mr John Robert Size
**Opening times:** Not open
**Min. mail order UK:** No minimum charge
**Min. mail order EU:** Nmc
**Cat. cost:** Sae
**Credit cards:** None
**Specialities:** Flowers & Vegetables. 1,400
varieties of Vegetable, (175 Cabbage,
99 Cauliflower, 70 Onion, 100 Tomatoes)
& 4,900 flowers such as 291 varieties of Sweet
Pea, 100 Herbs.

**LSiH**   **SINO-HIMALAYAN PLANT ASSOCIATION**
81 Parlaunt Road, Slough, Berkshire, SL3 8BE
☎ (01753) 542823   **Fax:** (01753) 542823
**Contact:** Chris Chadwell
**Mail order:** None
**Cat. cost:** None issued
**Credit cards:** None
**Specialities:** Seed available for exchange to
Members. Please apply for membership.

**LSpr**   **SPRINGLEA NURSERY**
Springlea, Seymour Plain, Marlow, Bucks,
SL7 3BZ
☎ (01628) 473366
**Contact:** Mary Dean
**Opening times:** 1000-1700 Tue-Sun Mar-Oct.
Please check before visiting. Garden open, see
NGS for details.
**Mail order:** None
**Cat. cost:** None issued
**Credit cards:** None
**Specialities:** Wide range of rare & unusual
Shrubs & Perennials incl. Hardy Geranium,
Pulmonaria, Primula, Bog plants, Ground
Cover & Shade loving plants.
**Map ref:** 6, C1

**LStr**   **HENRY STREET NURSERY** ⊠ EU ▣
Swallowfield Road, Arborfield, Reading,
Berkshire, RG2 9JY
☎ (0118) 9761223   **Fax:** (0118) 9761417
**Contact:** Mr M C Goold
**Opening times:** 0900-1730 Mon-Sat,
1000-1600 Sun.
**Min. mail order UK:** No minimum charge
**Min. mail order EU:** Nmc
**Cat. cost:** Free
**Credit cards:** Visa, Access, Switch
**Specialities:** Roses.
**Map ref:** 3, A1

**LSur**   **SURREY PRIMROSES** ⊠ EU
Merriewood, Sandy Lane, Milford,
Godalming, Surrey, GU8 5BJ
☎ (01483) 416747
**Contact:** Val & Geoff Yates
**Opening times:** Not open to the public.
**Min. mail order UK:** No minimum charge
**Min. mail order EU:** Nmc
**Cat. cost:** Sae
**Credit cards:** None
**Specialities:** Primroses, old named varieties.
**Map ref:** 3, B1

**LSyl**   **SYLVATICA NURSERY** ⊠ UK
Crosswater Farm, Crosswater Lane, Churt,
Farnham, Surrey, GU10 2JN
☎ (01252) 792775   **Fax:** (01252) 792526
**Contact:** John Millais
**Opening times:** By appt.
**Min. mail order UK:** No minimum charge
**Cat. cost:** 5 x 1st class
**Credit cards:** None
**Specialities:** Sorbus & Woodland Perennials.
**Map ref:** 3, B1

**M**

**LToo    TOOBEES EXOTICS ⊠ EU ▣**
(Office) 20 Inglewood, St Johns, Woking,
Surrey, GU21 3HX
☎ (01483) 797534 (nursery)
Fax: (01483) 751995
E-mail: bbpotter@compuserve.com
Web site: http://www.cactus-mall.com/toobees
Contact: Bob Potter
Opening times: 1000-1700 Wed-Sun
27th Feb-3rd Oct 1999 (incl. B/Hol Mons).
Min. mail order UK: No minimum charge
Min. mail order EU: Nmc
Cat. cost: Sae
Credit cards: MasterCard, Visa, Delta, Switch
Specialities: South African & Madagascan
Succulents – many rare & unusual species.
Palms, Tree Ferns, Air plants, Carnivorous
plants, Euphorbia, Pachypodium.
Note: Nursery is at Blackhorse Road,
Brookwood, Woking, Surrey GU22 0QT.
Map ref: 3, A1

**LTor    TORHILL NURSERY ⊠ EU ▣**
3 The Avenue, Hertford, Hertfordshire,
SG14 3DG
☎ (01992) 503311   Fax: (01992) 534310
E-mail: torhill.topiary@dial.pipex.com
Web site: http://www.yew.co.uk or
http://www.torhill.co.uk
Contact: Chris Gates
Opening times: By appt. only.
Min. mail order UK: No minimum charge
Min. mail order EU: Nmc
Cat. cost: Free
Credit cards: None
Specialities: Yew (Taxus) Hedging & Topiary,
Box (Buxus) Hedging, Gunnera manicata.

**LVER    THE VERNON GERANIUM
         NURSERY ⊠ EU**
Cuddington Way, Cheam, Sutton, Surrey,
SM2 7JB
☎ (0181) 393 7616   Fax: (0181) 786 7437
E-mail: mrgeranium@aol.com
Contact: Philip James & Liz Sims
Opening times: 0930-1730 Mon-Sat,
1000-1600 Sun, 1st Mar-31st July.
Min. mail order UK: No minimum charge
Min. mail order EU: Nmc
Cat. cost: £2.00 UK*
Credit cards: Visa, MasterCard, Switch
Specialities: Pelargonium & Fuchsia. *Note:
Illustrated colour catalogue. £2.50 for
overseas.
Map ref: 3, A2

**LWoo    WOODBURY NURSERY ◆**
14 Box End Road, Kempston, Bedfordshire,
MK43 8RR
☎ (01234) 856232   Fax: (01234) 856232
Contact: G J Savage or Helen Rawlins
Opening times: 0830-1800 summer,
0830-1700 winter, exc Xmas & Boxing Day.
Mail order: None
Cat. cost: 4 x 1st class
Credit cards: None
Specialities: Extensive range of Perennials,
Alpines, Trees, Shrubs & basket plants.
Catalogue covers Perennials & Grasses only.
Map ref: 6, A1

## MIDLANDS

**MAAq    AVON AQUATICS ⊠ UK ▣**
Sweet Knowle Farm, Preston-on-Stour,
Stratford-upon-Avon, Warwickshire,
CV37 8NR
☎ (01789) 450638   Fax: (01789) 450967
E-mail: avonaquatics@btinternet.com
Web site: http://www.avonaquatics.com
Contact: Rex & Rosemary Harding
Opening times: 1000-1600 Oct-Feb, 1000-
1800 Mar-Sep.
Min. mail order UK: £50.00 + p&p
Cat. cost: Free
Credit cards: Visa, MasterCard, Switch
Specialities: Water Lilies (70 varieties of
Nymphaea), Marginals (native), Oxygenators
& Bog plants. Note: Nursery is at Ilmington
Road Wimpstone, Stratford upon Avon.
Map ref: 5, A3

**MAld    ALDERTON PLANT NURSERY**
Spring Lane, Alderton, Towcester,
Northamptonshire, NN12 7LW
☎ (01327) 811253
Contact: Tom Hutchinson
Opening times: 1000-1630 Tue-Sun & B/Hol
Mons. Closed Jan 1998.
Mail order: None
Cat. cost: 2 x 1st class
Credit cards: None
Specialities: Fuchsia.
Map ref: 5, A4

**MArl    ARLEY HALL NURSERY**
Northwich, Cheshire, CW9 6NA
☎ (01565) 777479/777231
Fax: (01565) 777465

---

**KEY**
⊠ Mail order to UK or EU
▣ Exports beyond EU
▣ Also supplies Wholesale   ◆ See Display advertisement

**M**

E-mail: janefoster@btinternet.com
**Contact:** Jane Foster
**Opening times:** 1200-1730 Tue-Sun Easter to
end Sept. Also B/Hol Mons.
**Mail order:** None
**Cat. cost:** 4 x 1st class
**Credit cards:** None
**Specialities:** Wide range of Herbaceous incl.
many unusual varieties.
**Map ref:** 7, A2

**MAsh   ASHWOOD NURSERIES LTD ⊠ UK 🖾**
Greensforge, Kingswinford, West Midlands,
DY6 0AE
☎ (01384) 401996   **Fax:** (01384) 401108
**Contact:** John Massey & Philip Baulk
**Opening times:** 0900-1800 Mon-Sat &
1100-1700 Sun. ex Xmas & Boxing day.
**Min. mail order UK:** *
**Cat. cost:** 4 x 1st class
**Credit cards:** Visa, Access
**Specialities:** Large range of hardy plants &
dwarf Conifers. National Collection of Lewisia
& Cyclamen species. Hellebores. *Note: Mail
order for seeds, & special offers only.
**Map ref:** 7, C2

**MAsk   ASKEW'S NURSERY ⊠ UK**
South Croxton Road, Queniborough,
Leicestershire, LE7 3RX
☎ (01664) 840557
**Contact:** Mrs Longland
**Opening times:** 0900-1800 Mon-Fri Feb-Sep.
1000-1800 Sat & Sun. Oct-Jan please
telephone first.
**Min. mail order UK:** No minimum charge
**Cat. cost:** 3 x 1st class
**Credit cards:** None
**Specialities:** Fuchsia.
**Map ref:** 7, C4

**MAus   DAVID AUSTIN ROSES LTD ⊠ EU 🖾 🖾**
Bowling Green Lane, Albrighton,
Wolverhampton, West Midlands, WV7 3HB
☎ (01902) 376300   **Fax:** (01902) 372142
**E-mail:** retail@davidaustin.simplyonline.co.uk
**Contact:** Office Reception
**Opening times:** 0900-1700 Mon-Fri,
1000-1800 Sat, Sun & B/Hols. Until dusk
Nov-Mar.
**Min. mail order UK:** No minimum charge
**Min. mail order EU:** Nmc
**Cat. cost:** Free
**Credit cards:** Access, Switch, Visa
**Specialities:** Roses. National Collection of
English Roses. Also hardy perennials at Claire
Austin Hardy Plants at same site.
**Map ref:** 7, C2

**MAvo   AVONDALE NURSERY**
(Office) 3 Avondale Road, Earlsdon,
Coventry, Warwickshire, CV5 6DZ
☎ (01203) 673662
**Contact:** Brian Ellis
**Opening times:** 1000-1230, 1400-1700 daily
Mar-Oct. Closed Sun pm July-Aug. Other
times by appt.
**Mail order:** None
**Cat. cost:** 4 x 1st class
**Credit cards:** None
**Specialities:** Rare & unusual Perennials, esp.
Campanula, Centaurea, Eryngium,
Leucanthemum, Geum, Crocosmia,
Pulmonaria & Grasses. Note: Nursery is at
Smith's Nursery, 3 Stoneleigh Road, Baginton,
Nr Coventry CV8 3BA.
**Map ref:** 5, A3

**MBal   BALLALHEANNAGH GARDENS**
Glen Roy, Lonan, Isle of Man, IM4 7QB
☎ (01624) 861875   **Fax:** (01624) 861114
**Contact:** Clif & Maureen Dadd
**Opening times:** 1000-1300 & 1400-1700
or dusk if earlier in Winter. Closed w/ends
Nov-Mar. Please telephone first.
**Mail order:** None
**Cat. cost:** £1.50
**Credit cards:** None
**Specialities:** Rhododendron & Ericaceous
Shrubs. Small number of rare trees and shrubs
not in catalogue.
**Map ref:** 4, A1

**MBar   BARNCROFT NURSERIES ⊠ UK 🖾**
Dunwood Lane, Longsdon, Nr Leek,
Stoke-on-Trent, Staffordshire, ST9 9QW
☎ (01538) 384310   **Fax:** (01538) 384310
**Contact:** S Warner
**Opening times:** 0900-1900 or dusk if earlier
Fri-Sun.
**Min. mail order UK:** £20.00 + p&p
**Cat. cost:** None issued
**Credit cards:** None
**Specialities:** Large range of Heathers, Conifers,
Shrubs, Climbers & Rhododendrons. Display
garden containing 400 Heather cvs.
**Map ref:** 7, A2

**MBee   BEES OF CHESTER ⊠ UK**
Freepost 980, Sealand Road, Chester, CH1 6ZT
☎ (01945) 466660   **Fax:** (01945) 475255
**Contact:** Customer Services
**Min. mail order UK:** No minimum charge
**Cat. cost:** Free
**Credit cards:** Access, Visa
**Specialities:** Spring Flowering Bulbs &
Perennial Plants.

**MBel**    **BELLHOUSE NURSERY**
Bellhouse Lane, Moore, Nr Warrington,
Cheshire, WA4 6TR
☎ (01925) 740874   **Fax:** (01925) 740672
**Contact:** Elaine Soens & Doreen Scott
**Opening times:** 1000-1700 Wed-Mon
Mar-Oct. 1000-1600 Wed-Mon Feb.
Closed Nov-Jan & every Tue.
**Mail order:** None
**Cat. cost:** £1.00
**Credit cards:** None
**Specialities:** Wide range of Herbaceous plants
& Shrubs. Good selection of unusual varieties.
**Map ref:** 7, A1

**MBEx**    **BROCKINGS EXOTICS** ⊠ UK 🗷
Rosedene, Nottingham Road, Woodborough,
Nottingham, , NG14 6EH
☎ (0115) 847 9359/(0115) 956 9970,
(07970) 866832
**Contact:** Ian & Joy Cooke
**Opening times:** Strictly by appt. Apr-Sep.
**Min. mail order UK:** £15.00 + p&p
**Cat. cost:** 3 x 1st class
**Credit cards:** None
**Specialities:** Tender Perennials, Canna,
Coleus, Conservatory & exotic plants.
**Map ref:** 7, B4

**MBir**    **BIRCHWOOD FARM NURSERY**
Portway, Coxbench, Derbyshire, DE21 5BE
☎ (01332) 880685   **Fax:** (01332) 880685
**Contact:** Mr & Mrs S Crooks
**Opening times:** 0900-1700 Mon, Tue, Thu,
Fri, Sat Mar-Oct or by appt.
**Mail order:** None
**Cat. cost:** None issued
**Credit cards:** None
**Specialities:** Unusual Hardy Perennials & Shrubs.
**Map ref:** 7, B3

**MBlu**    **BLUEBELL NURSERY** ⊠ EU 🗷
Annwell Lane, Smisby, Nr Ashby de la Zouch,
LE65 2TA
☎ (01530) 413700   **Fax:** (01530) 417600
**E-mail:** castell@bigfoot.com
**Web site:** http://www.bluebellnursery.com
**Contact:** Robert & Suzette Vernon
**Opening times:** 0900-1700 Mon-Sat &
1030-1630 Sun Mar-Oct, 0900-1600 Mon-Sat
(not Sun) Nov-Feb. Closed 24th Dec-4th Jan.
**Min. mail order UK:** No minimum charge
**Min. mail order EU:** Nmc
**Cat. cost:** £1.00 + 2 x 1st class
**Credit cards:** Visa, Access, Switch
**Specialities:** Uncommon Trees & Shrubs.
Display Garden & Arboretum.
**Map ref:** 7, C3

**MBNS**    **BARNSDALE GARDENS**
Exton Avenue, Exton, Oakham, Rutland,
LE15 8AH
☎ (01572) 813200   **Fax:** (01572) 813346
**E-mail:** info@barnsdalegardens.co.uk
**Web site:** http://www.barnsdalegardens.co.uk
**Contact:** Nick or Sue Hamilton
**Opening times:** 1000-1700 1st Mar-31st Oct
Gardens & Nursery, 1000-1600 1st Nov-
28/29th Feb Nursery only. Closed Xmas &
New Year.
**Mail order:** None
**Cat. cost:** A5 + 5 x 2nd class
**Credit cards:** Visa, Access, MasterCard,
Switch, Delta
**Specialities:** Choice & unusual Garden Plants.
Over 70 varieties of Penstemon, large
collection of Hemerocallis.
**Map ref:** 8, C1

**MBon**    **BONACCORD GLADS** ⊠ EU
1 Nagington Drive, Penkridge, Staffordshire,
ST19 5TA
☎ (01785) 715813
**E-mail:** bongladpenkridge@cwcom.net
**Contact:** John Anderson
**Opening times:** Not open.
**Min. mail order UK:** £5.00 + p&p
**Min. mail order EU:** £50.00 + p&p
**Cat. cost:** £1 or 5 x 2nd class
**Credit cards:** None
**Specialities:** American Gladioli corms. Wide
variety of colours. All sizes from miniature to
grandiflora.

**MBre**    **BRETBY NURSERIES** 🗷 ◆
Bretby Lane, Burton-on-Trent, Staffordshire,
DE15 0QS
☎ (01283) 703355   **Fax:** (01283) 704035
**Contact:** Mr David Cartwright
**Opening times:** 0900-1700 Mon-Sat,
1030-1630 Sun.
**Mail order:** None
**Cat. cost:** Info. on request
**Credit cards:** Visa, American Express, Diners,
EuroCard, Switch, Delta, Electron
**Specialities:** Wide range of shrubs.
**Map ref:** 7, B3

**MBri**    **BRIDGEMERE NURSERIES** 🗷 ◆
Bridgemere, Nr Nantwich, Cheshire,
CW5 7QB
☎ (01270) 521100   **Fax:** (01270) 520215

**M**

| K E Y | ⊠ Mail order to UK or EU |
| | 🗷 Exports beyond EU |
| | 🗷 Also supplies Wholesale   ◆ See Display advertisement |

Contact: Keith Atkey
Opening times: 0900-2000 Mon-Sat,
1000-2000 Sun summer, until 1700 in winter.
Mail order: None
Cat. cost: None issued
Credit cards: Visa, Access, MasterCard, Switch
Specialities: Perennials, Shrubs, Trees, Roses,
Climbers, Rhododendrons & Azaleas, Alpines,
Heathers, Ferns, Grasses, Aquatics &
Houseplants.
Map ref: 7, B2

**M**

**MBrN  BRIDGE NURSERY** ▣
Tomlow Road, Napton-on-the-hill, Nr Rugby,
Warwickshire, CV23 8HX
☎ (01926) 812737
Contact: Christine Dakin & Philip Martino
Opening times: 1000-1600 Fri-Sun Apr-July,
Sept & Oct. Other times by appt.
Mail order: None
Cat. cost: 3 x 1st class
Credit cards: None
Specialities: Ornamental Grasses, Sedges &
Bamboos. Also range of Shrubs & Perennials.
Note: Nursery has moved from Cambs where
it was called Simply Plants.
Map ref: 5, A3

**MBro  BROADSTONE NURSERIES**
13 The Nursery, High Street, Sutton
Courtenay, Abingdon, Oxfordshire,
OX14 4UA
☎ (01235) 847557 (day/eve)
Contact: J Shackleton
Opening times: 1400-1700 Tue, 1400-1800
Sat (except Show days). By appt. on other
days/times.
Mail order: None
Cat. cost: 3 x 1st class
Credit cards: None
Specialities: Plants for rock garden, scree,
troughs & borders. Lime tolerant hardy
Alpines, Perennials & unusual plants.
Map ref: 5, C4

**MBur  BURROWS ROSES** ✉ EU
Meadow Croft, Spondon Road, Dale Abbey,
Derby, Derbyshire, DE7 4PQ
☎ (01332) 668289  Fax: (01332) 668289
Contact: Stuart & Diane Burrows
Opening times: Mail order only.
Min. mail order UK: £4.00 + p&p
Min. mail order EU: £4.00 + p&p
Cat. cost: 2 x 1st class
Credit cards: None
Specialities: Roses.

**MCAu  CLAIRE AUSTIN HARDY
PLANTS** ✉ EU ▣
Bowling Green Lane, Albrighton,
Wolverhampton, West Midlands, WV7 3HB
☎ (01902) 376333  Fax: (01902) 372142
E-mail: ken@david-austin.simplyonline.co.uk
Contact: Office Reception
Opening times: 0900-1700 Mon-Fri.
Min. mail order UK: No minimum charge
Min. mail order EU: £50.00 + p&p
Cat. cost: Free
Credit cards: MasterCard, Visa, Switch
Specialities: Paeonia, Iris, Hemerocallis &
hardy plants.
Map ref: 7, C2

**MCCP  COLLECTORS CORNER
PLANTS** ✉ UK ◆
33 Rugby Road, Clifton-under-Dunsmore,
Rugby, Warwickshire, CV23 0DE
☎ (01788) 571881
Contact: Pat Neesam
Opening times: By appt. only.
Min. mail order UK: No minimum charge
Cat. cost: 6 x 1st class
Credit cards: None
Specialities: General range of choice
Herbaceous Perennials, Grasses, Shrubs, Palms
& Ferns.
Map ref: 5, A4

**MChe  CHESHIRE HERBS** ▣ ◆
Fourfields, Forest Road, Nr Tarporley,
Cheshire, CW6 9ES
☎ (01829) 760578  Fax: (01829) 760354
Contact: Mr & Mrs Ted Riddell
Opening times: 1000-1700 daily 3rd Jan-
24th Dec.
Mail order: None
Cat. cost: 1 x 1st class
Credit cards: Access, Visa, Switch
Specialities: Display Herb garden &
Elizabethan knot garden.
Map ref: 7, A1

**MChR  CHESHIRE ROSS LTD** ✉ EU ▣ ▣
Astley Nursery, Sole End House, Astley Lane,
Bedworth, Warwickshire, CV12 0NE
☎ (01203) 643121  Fax: (01203) 643121
Contact: Mr D Cheshire
Opening times: 0900-1630 Sat, 1000-1500
Sun 1st Mar-31st Nov.
Min. mail order UK: £7.50 + p&p
Min. mail order EU: £15.00 + p&p
Cat. cost: Free (stamps appreciated)
Credit cards: None
Specialities: Herbaceous & Alpine plants.
Map ref: 7, C3

**MCli** CLIPSTON NURSERY
Naseby Road, Clipston, Market Harborough,
Leicestershire, LE16 9RZ
☎ (01858) 525567  **Fax:** (01858) 525567
**Contact:** Kate Hayward
**Opening times:** 1000-1800 daily Mar-Sep.
**Mail order:** None
**Cat. cost:** 2 x 2nd class
**Credit cards:** None
**Specialities:** Perennials including many
unusual varieties.
**Map ref:** 5, A4

**MCLN** COUNTRY LADY NURSERY
Lilac Cottage, Chapel Lane, Gentleshaw, Nr
Rugeley, Staffordshire, WS15 4ND
☎ (01543) 675520  **Fax:** (01543) 675520
**Contact:** Mrs Sylvia Nunn
**Opening times:** 1000-1700 Wed-Sun &
B/Hol Mons beginning Mar-end Oct. Other
times by appt.
**Mail order:** None
**Cat. cost:** A5 Sae + 2 x 1st class
**Credit cards:** None
**Specialities:** Wide range of unusual Perennials,
incl. Hardy Geranium, Heuchera, Penstemon
& Primula. 1 acre show garden.
**Map ref:** 7, C2

**MCol** COLLINWOOD NURSERIES ⊠ UK
Mottram St. Andrew, Macclesfield, Cheshire,
SK10 4QR
☎ (01625) 582272
**Contact:** A Wright
**Opening times:** 0830-1730 Mon-Sat
1300-1730 Sun. Closed Sun in Jan-Mar.
**Min. mail order UK:** No minimum charge
**Cat. cost:** 1 x 1st class
**Credit cards:** None
**Specialities:** Chrysanthemums
(Dendranthema).
**Map ref:** 7, A2

**MCoo** COOL TEMPERATE ⊠ EU ▣
5 Colville Villas, Nottingham, , NG1 4HN
☎ (0115) 947 4977  **Fax:** (0115) 947 4977
**Contact:** Phil Corbett
**Opening times:** Not open.
**Min. mail order UK:** No minimum charge
**Min. mail order EU:** Nmc
**Cat. cost:** Sae
**Credit cards:** None
**Specialities:** Tree Fruit, Soft Fruit, Nitrogen-
fixers, Hedging, own-root Fruit Trees.

**MCre** CRESCENT PLANTS ⊠ UK
34 The Crescent, Cradley Heath, West
Midlands, B64 7JS

☎ (0121) 550 2628  **Fax:** (0121) 550 2732
**E-mail:** ian@thecrescent.prestel.co.uk
**Contact:** Ian Goddard
**Opening times:** By appt.
**Min. mail order UK:** No minimum charge
**Cat. cost:** 2 x 1st class
**Credit cards:** None
**Specialities:** Named varieties of Primula
auricula incl. Show, Alpine, Double, Striped
& Border types.

**MDHE** DHE PLANTS ⊠ UK
(Office) Rose Lea, Darley House Estate,
Darley Dale, Matlock, Derbyshire, DE4 2QH
☎ (01629) 732512
**Contact:** Peter M Smith
**Opening times:** 1000-1700 Tue-Sat,
1030-1630 Sun. Advance telephone call
desirable – see note below.
**Min. mail order UK:** No minimum charge*
**Cat. cost:** 2 x 1st class
**Credit cards:** None
**Specialities:** Alpines; esp. Erodium,
Helianthemum, Saxifraga & Sisyrinchium.
*Note: Mail order Oct-Mar only. Nursery
stock is at Robert Young garden centre,
Bakewell Rd, Matlock.
**Map ref:** 7, A3

**MDun** DUNGE VALLEY GARDENS
Windgather Rocks, Kettleshulme, High Peak,
SK23 7RF
☎ (01663) 733787  **Fax:** (01663) 733787
**E-mail:** xon74@dial.pipex.com
**Contact:** David Ketley
**Opening times:** 1030-1800 daily 1st
Apr-31st Aug or by appt.
**Mail order:** None
**Cat. cost:** A4 Sae
**Credit cards:** None
**Specialities:** Rhododendron species & hybrids.
Trees, Shrubs & Perennials, some rare & wild
collected. Meconopsis & Trillium.
**Map ref:** 7, A2

**MFie** FIELD HOUSE NURSERIES ⊠ EU ▣
Leake Road, Gotham, Nottinghamshire,
NG11 0JN
☎ (0115) 9830278  **Fax:** (0115) 9830278
**Contact:** Doug Lochhead & Valerie A Woolley
**Opening times:** 0900-1700 Fri-Wed
or by appt.
**Min. mail order UK:** No minimum charge*

**M**

| KEY | | |
|---|---|---|
| ⊠ | Mail order to UK or EU | |
| ▨ | Exports beyond EU | |
| ▣ | Also supplies Wholesale  ◆ See Display advertisement | |

Min. mail order EU: 4 plants
Cat. cost: 4 x 1st or 4 x IRCs
Credit cards: Visa, Access
Specialities: Auriculas, Primula, Alpines &
Rock plants. *Note: Mail order for Auriculas,
Primula & Seeds only. 3 National Collections
of Primula/Auricula.
Map ref: 7, B4

**MFir   THE FIRS NURSERY**
Chelford Road, Henbury, Macclesfield,
Cheshire, SK10 3LH
☎ (01625) 426422
Contact: Fay J Bowling
Opening times: 1000-1700 Mon/Tue Fri/Sat,
1000-1900 Thur Mar-Sep.
Mail order: None
Cat. cost: 2 x 1st class
Credit cards: None
Specialities: Wide range of Herbaceous
Perennials, many unusual.
Map ref: 7, A2

**MFry   FRYER'S NURSERIES LTD ⊠ EU ▣ ▣**
Manchester Road, Knutsford, Cheshire,
WA16 0SX
☎ (01565) 755455   Fax: (01565) 653755
E-mail: garethfryer@fryers-roses.co.uk
Web site: http://www.fryers-roses.co.uk
Contact: Gareth Fryer
Opening times: 0900-1730 Mon-Sat &
1030-1630 Sun & 1000-1730 B/Hols.
Min. mail order UK: No minimum charge
Min. mail order EU: Nmc
Cat. cost: Free
Credit cards: Visa, Access, Switch
Specialities: Extensive Rose Nursery &
Garden Centre producing over half a million
bushes annually. Rose fields in bloom
Jun-Oct.
Map ref: 7, A2

**MGan   GANDY'S (ROSES) LTD ⊠ EU ▣**
North Kilworth, Nr Lutterworth,
Leicestershire, LE17 6HZ
☎ (01858) 880398   Fax: (01858) 880433
Contact: Miss R D Gandy
Opening times: 0900-1700 Mon-Sat &
1400-1700 Sun.
Min. mail order UK: No minimum charge
Min. mail order EU: £25.00 + p&p
Cat. cost: Free
Credit cards: None
Specialities: 580 Rose varieties.
Map ref: 5, A4

**MGas   LINDA GASCOIGNE WILD
FLOWERS ⊠ EU**
17 Imperial Road, Kibworth Beauchamp,
Leicestershire, LE8 0HR
☎ 0116 2793959
Contact: Linda Gascoigne
Opening times: By appt. only.
Min. mail order UK: £5.00 + p&p
Min. mail order EU: £10.00 + p&p
Cat. cost: 3 x 1st class
Credit cards: None
Specialities: Wide range of Wild Flowers &
plants to attract wildlife. No peat used.
Map ref: 7, C4

**MGed   GEDDINGTON GARDENS**
The Spinney, Grafton Road, Geddington,
Northants, NN14 1AJ
☎ (01536) 461020
Contact: Christine Sturman
Opening times: 1000-1700 Wed-Sun
3rd Mar-31st Oct 1999.
Mail order: None
Cat. cost: 2 x 1st class
Credit cards: None
Specialities: Hardy Perennials, Cottage
Garden plants.
Map ref: 5, A4

**MGos   GOSCOTE NURSERIES LTD ⊠ EU ◆**
Syston Road, Cossington, Leicestershire,
LE7 4UZ
☎ (01509) 812121   Fax: (01509) 814231
Contact: D C Cox & F J Toone
Opening times: 7 days a week.
Min. mail order UK: £10.00 + p&p
Min. mail order EU: £50.00 + p&p
Cat. cost: 5 x 1st class
Credit cards: Visa, Access, MasterCard, Delta,
Switch
Specialities: Japanese Maples, Rhododendron,
Azalea, Magnolia, Camellia, Pieris & other
Ericaceae. Ornamental Trees & Shrubs,
Conifers, Fruit, Heathers, Alpines, Clematis &
unusual Climbers. Showground to visit.
Map ref: 7, C4

**MGrG   GRANBY GARDENS**
Granby House, 8 Long Acre, Bingham,
Nottinghamshire, NG13 8BG
☎ (01949) 837696   Fax: (01949) 837696
Contact: Maureen Gladwin
Opening times: Mon-Wed, other times please
ring first.
Mail order: None
Cat. cost: 2 x 2nd class
Credit cards: None

Specialities: A wide range of Herbaceous Perennials, Shrubs & Climbers. Some rare & unusual.
Map ref: 7, B4

**MHar   HARTS GREEN NURSERY**
89 Harts Green Road, Harborne, Birmingham, B17 9TZ
☎ (0121) 427 5200
Contact: B Richardson
Opening times: 1400-1730 Wed Apr-July & Sep. Closed Aug. Other times by appt.
Mail order: None
Cat. cost: 2 x 1st class
Credit cards: None
Specialities: Alpines & Hardy Perennials.
Map ref: 5, A2

**MHel   HELDON NURSERIES ⊠ EU ⊠**
Ashbourne Road, Spath, Uttoxeter, Staffordshire, ST14 5AD
☎ (01889) 563377   Fax: (01889) 563377
Contact: Mrs J H Tate
Opening times: 1000-sunset daily.
Min. mail order UK: £2.00 + p&p
Min. mail order EU: £50.00 + p&p
Cat. cost: Sae
Credit cards: None
Specialities: Cactus & Succulents.
Map ref: 7, B3

**MHer   THE HERB NURSERY ◆**
Thistleton, Oakham, Rutland, LE15 7RE
☎ (01572) 767658   Fax: (01572) 768021
Contact: Peter Bench
Opening times: 0900-1800 (until dusk in winter). 7 days excl. Xmas-New Year.
Mail order: None
Cat. cost: A5 Sae.
Credit cards: None
Specialities: Herbs, Wild Flowers, Cottage Garden Plants, Scented-leaf Pelargoniums.
Map ref: 8, B1

**MHew   HEWTHORN HERBS & WILD FLOWERS ⊠ EU**
82 Julian Road, West Bridgford, Nottingham, NG2 5AN
☎ (0115) 981 2861
Contact: Julie Scott
Opening times: By appt. only.
Min. mail order UK: No minimum charge
Min. mail order EU: £10.00 + p&p
Cat. cost: 3 x 1st class
Credit cards: None
Specialities: Native Wild Flowers, Dye Plants, Native Medicinal Herbs. All organically grown.
Map ref: 7, B4

**MHlr   THE HILLER GARDEN ◆**
Dunnington, Nr Alcester, Warwickshire, B49 5PD
☎ (01789) 490991   Fax: (01789) 490439
Contact: David Carvill & Brian Meredith
Opening times: 1000-1700 daily.
Mail order: None
Cat. cost: 2 x 1st class
Credit cards: Visa, Access, Switch
Specialities: Two acre garden displaying Herbaceous Perennials, Old-fashioned & Shrub Roses, & Shrubs. All available for sale during the season.
Map ref: 5, A3

**MInt   INTAKES FARM**
Sandy Lane, Longsdon, Stoke-on-Trent, Staffordshire, ST9 9QQ
☎ (01538) 398452
Contact: Mrs Kathleen Inman
Opening times: By appt. only.
Mail order: None
Cat. cost: None issued
Credit cards: None
Specialities: Double, Variegated & unusual forms of British natives & Cottage Garden plants.
Map ref: 7, B2

**MJac   JACKSON'S NURSERIES ⊠**
Clifton Campville, Nr Tamworth, Staffordshire, B79 0AP
☎ (01827) 373307   Fax: (01827) 373307
Contact: N Jackson
Opening times: 0900-1800 Mon Wed-Sat, 1000-1700 Sun.
Mail order: None
Cat. cost: 2 x 1st class
Credit cards: None
Specialities: Fuchsia.
Map ref: 7, C3

**MJon   C & K JONES ⊠ EU ⊠ ⊠**
Golden Fields Nurseries, Barrow Lane, Tarvin, Cheshire, CH3 8JF
☎ (01829) 740663   Fax: (01829) 741877
Web site: http://www.compulink.co.uk/~kyue/roses
Contact: Keith Jones/P Woolley
Opening times: 0900-1700 Fri-Mon and by appt.
Min. mail order UK: 1 plant + p&p
Min. mail order EU: 1 plant + p&p

**M**

KEY  ⊠ Mail order to UK or EU
     ⊠ Exports beyond EU
     ⊠ Also supplies Wholesale  ◆ See Display advertisement

**M**

Cat. cost: £1.00
Credit cards: MasterCard, Delta, Switch, Visa
Specialities: Roses.
Map ref: 7, A1

**MKay    KAYES GARDEN NURSERY**
1700 Melton Road, Rearsby, Leicestershire,
LE7 4YR
☎ (01664) 424578
Contact: Hazel Kaye
Opening times: 1000-1700 Tues-Sat &
B/Hols 1000-1200 Sun Mar-Oct. 1000-1600
Fri & Sat Nov, Dec & Feb. Closed Jan.
Mail order: None
Cat. cost: 2 x 1st class
Credit cards: None
Specialities: Herbaceous, Climbers & Aquatic
plants.
Map ref: 7, C4

**MLan    LANE END NURSERY**
Old Cherry Lane, Lymm, Cheshire,
WA13 0TA
☎ (01925) 752618
E-mail: sawyer@laneend.u-net.com
Contact: I Sawyer
Opening times: 0930-1730 Thu-Tue
Mar-Dec.
Mail order: None
Cat. cost: None issued
Credit cards: None
Specialities: Award of Garden Merit plants
with a wide range of choice & unusual
Shrubs, Trees, Perennials & Ferns.
Map ref: 7, A2

**MLea    LEA RHODODENDRON
GARDENS LTD ⊠ EU 🖂**
Lea, Matlock, Derbyshire, DE4 5GH
☎ (01629) 534380/534260
Fax: (01629) 534260
Contact: Jon Tye
Opening times: 1000-1900 daily
20th Mar-July. Out of season by appt.
Min. mail order UK: £15.00 + p&p
Min. mail order EU: £15.00 + p&p
Cat. cost: 30p + Sae
Credit cards: None
Specialities: Rhododendron & Azalea.
Map ref: 7, A3

**MLit    LITTLEWOOD FARM NURSERY**
Cheddleton, Nr Leek, Staffordshire,
ST13 7LB
☎ (01538) 360478
Contact: Nanette Bloore
Opening times: 1000-1800 Tue-Sun &
B/Hols Apr-Oct

Mail order: None
Cat. cost: 3 x 1st class
Credit cards: None
Specialities: Unusual Hardy Herbaceous
plants, incl. Hardy Geranium, Campanula,
Hosta & Pulmonaria. Also Grasses & Alpines.
Map ref: 7, B2

**MLLN    LODGE LANE NURSERY & GARDENS**
Lodge Lane, Dutton, Nr Warrington,
Cheshire, WA4 4HP
☎ (01928) 713718   Fax: (01928) 713718
Contact: Rod or Diane Casey
Opening times: 1000-1700 Wed-Sun &
B/Hols, mid Mar-early Oct.
Mail order: None
Cat. cost: 3 x 1st class
Credit cards: None
Specialities: Unusual Perennials & Shrubs.
Many Aquilegia, Allium, Aster, Campanula,
Diascia, Nepeta, Penstemon & Salvia. Also
seeds.
Map ref: 7, A1

**MLov    LOVERS KNOT NURSERY ⊠ EU**
Woodside, Langley Road, Langley,
Macclesfield, Cheshire, SK11 0DG
☎ (01260) 253308   Fax: (01260) 253308
Contact: Ian Coppack
Opening times: Mail order only.
Min. mail order UK: £5.00 + p&p
Min. mail order EU: £5.00 + p&p
Cat. cost: 2 x 1st class
Credit cards: None
Specialities: Hostas.

**MMal    MALCOFF COTTAGE
GARDEN NURSERY ⊠ UK**
Malcoff, Chapel-en-le-Frith, High Peak,
Derbyshire, SK23 0QR
☎ (01663) 751969   Fax: Please phone first
E-mail: malcoffcot@aol.com
Contact: Julie Norfolk
Opening times: 1200-1700 Fri-Wed
Mar-Sept. Other times by appt.
Visitors please phone for directions.
Min. mail order UK: £10.00 + p&p
Cat. cost: 3 x 1st class
Credit cards: None
Specialities: Herbs, Wild Flowers & hardy
Cottage Garden plants incl. some old Roses.
Map ref: 7, A3

**MMat    MATTOCK'S ROSES ⊠ EU 🖂 🖂**
Freepost, The Rose Nurseries, Nuneham
Courtenay, Oxford, Oxfordshire, OX44 9PY
☎ (01865) 343265, (0345) 585652 (retail
order line)   Fax: (01865) 343166

E-mail: roses@mattocks.co.uk
Web site: http://www.mattocks.co.uk
Contact: Sales Office
Opening times: 0900-1730 Mon-Sat,
1100-1700 Sun. Closes 1700 Nov-Feb.
Min. mail order UK: No minimum charge
Min. mail order EU: Nmc
Cat. cost: Free
Credit cards: Visa, MasterCard
Specialities: Roses.
Map ref: 5, C4

**MMea    MEARS ASHBY**
**NURSERIES LTD** ⊠ UK ⊠ ⊠
Glebe House, Glebe Road, Mears Ashby,
Northamptonshire, NN6 0DL
☎ (01604) 812371/811811
Fax: (01604) 812353
E-mail: 106612.1047@compuserve.com
Contact: John B & J E Gaggini
Opening times: 0800-1730 Mon-Fri
(Wholesale & Retail). 0900-1730 Sat & Sun
(Retail only).
Min. mail order UK: £8.00 + p&p*
Cat. cost: £1.00**
Credit cards: Visa, Access, Switch,
MasterCard, Diners
Specialities: Specialist growers of container
Trees, Shrubs, Conifers & Fruit, esp. Wisteria.
*Note: Mail order for Wisteria only. **Please
state retail or w/sale catalogue.
Map ref: 5, A4

**MMHG    MORTON HALL GARDENS** ⊠ EU
Morton Hall, Ranby, Retford, Nottingham,
DN22 8HW
☎ (01777) 702530
Contact: Gill McMaster
Opening times: 0900-1600 Mon-Fri,
1400-1700 Sat-Sun & B/Hols, Mar-Nov incl.
Min. mail order UK: £5.00 + p&p
Min. mail order EU: £10.00 + p&p
Cat. cost: 3 x 1st class
Credit cards: None
Specialities: Shrubs & Perennials.
Map ref: 7, A4

**MMil    MILL HILL PLANTS** ⊠ UK ◆
Mill Hill House, Elston Lane, East Stoke,
Newark, Nottinghamshire, NG23 5QJ
☎ (01636) 525460
Contact: G M Gregory
Opening times: 1000-1800 Wed-Sun &
B/Hols Mar-Sep, Fri-Sun in Oct & by appt.
Min. mail order UK: No minimum charge*
Cat. cost: Sae for Iris list.
Credit cards: None

Specialities: Hardy Perennials – many unusual
& Bearded Iris. Also, National Collection of
Berberis. *Note: Mail order for Iris only.
Map ref: 7, B4

**MMiN    MILLFIELD NURSERIES** ⊠ EU ⊠
Mill Lane, South Leverton, Nr Retford,
Nottinghamshire, DN22 0DA
☎ (01427) 880422   Fax: (01427) 880422
Contact: Mr S G Clark
Opening times: By appt. only.
Min. mail order UK: £10.00 + p&p
Min. mail order EU: £25.00 + p&p.
Eurocheques accepted at current rate of
exchange.
Cat. cost: £1.00*
Credit cards: None
Specialities: Hosta. *Note: Catalogue cost
discounted against any order placed.
Map ref: 7, A4

**MMoz    MOZART HOUSE NURSERY**
**GARDEN** ⊠ UK ◆
84 Central Avenue, Wigston, Leicestershire,
LE18 2AA
☎ (0116) 288 9548
Contact: Des Martin
Opening times: By appt. only.
Min. mail order UK: £15.00 + p&p
Cat. cost: 5 x 2nd class
Credit cards: None
Specialities: Bamboo, Ornamental Grasses,
Rushes & Sedges, Hosta.
Map ref: 7, C4

**MNan    NANNEY'S BRIDGE NURSERY** ⊠
Church Minshull, Nantwich, Cheshire,
CW5 6DY
☎ (01270) 522239   Fax: (01270) 522523
Contact: D Dickinson
Opening times: By appt. only.
Mail order: None
Cat. cost: 3 x 1st class
Credit cards: None
Specialities: Geraniums, Penstemons, Salvias
& Ornamental Grasses.
Map ref: 7, A2

**MNes    NESS GARDENS**
Univ. of Liverpool Botanic Gdns., Ness,
Neston, South Wirral, Cheshire, L64 4AY
☎ (0151) 353 0123   Fax: (0151) 353 1004
E-mail: peter.cunnington@liverpool.ac.uk

---

⊠ Mail order to UK or EU
⊠ Exports beyond EU
⊠ Also supplies Wholesale   ◆ See Display advertisement

**M**

Web site: http://www.merseyworld.com/
nessgardens/
Contact: D Maher
Opening times: 0930-1700 Apr-Oct,
1000-1600 Nov-Mar daily.
Mail order: None
Cat. cost: None issued
Credit cards: Delta, Switch, Visa
Specialities: Rhododendron, Primula,
Meconopsis, Penstemon & Camellia.
Map ref: 7, A1

**MNew NEWINGTON NURSERIES** ⊠ UK
Newington, Wallingford, Oxfordshire,
OX10 7AW
☎ (01865) 400533  Fax: (01865) 891766
E-mail: newington.nurseries@btinternet.com
Contact: Mrs A T Hendry
Opening times: 1000-1700 Tues-Sun Mar-
Oct, 1000-1600 Tues-Sun Nov-Feb.
Min. mail order UK: Please enquire for details.
Cat. cost: 4 x 1st class
Credit cards: Access, MasterCard, Visa, Switch
Specialities: Unusual cottage garden plants,
old-fashioned Roses, Conservatory Plants &
Herbs. Provisional National Collection of
Alocasia (Araceae).
Map ref: 5, C4

**MNrw NORWELL NURSERIES** ⊠ UK 🖪 ◆
Woodhouse Road, Norwell, Newark,
Nottinghamshire, NG23 6JX
☎ (01636) 636337
E-mail: wardha@aol.com
Contact: Dr Andrew Ward
Opening times: 1000-1700 Mon, Wed-Fri &
Sun (daily exc. Tue during May & June). By
appt. in Aug & 20th Oct-1st Mar.
Min. mail order UK: £10.00 + p&p
Cat. cost: 3 x 1st class
Credit cards: None
Specialities: A large collection of unusual &
choice Herbaceous Perennials & Alpines esp.
Penstemon, hardy Geranium, Campanula,
Geum, summer Bulbs & Grasses. Gardens open.
Map ref: 7, A4

**MOke OKELL'S NURSERIES** 🖪
Duddon Heath, Nr Tarporley, Cheshire,
CW6 0EP
☎ (01829) 741512  Fax: (01829) 741587
Contact: Tim Okell
Opening times: 0900-1730 daily.
Mail order: None
Cat. cost: Free
Credit cards: Visa, Access, MasterCard,
American Express, Switch
Specialities: Heathers & Alpines.
Map ref: 7, A1

**MOne ONE HOUSE NURSERY** ⊠ UK ◆
Buxton New Road, Macclesfield, Cheshire,
SK11 0AD
☎ (01625) 427087
Contact: Miss J L Baylis
Opening times: 1000-1700 Tue-Sun Mar-Oct
& B/Hol Mons. Nov-Feb ring for opening
times.
Min. mail order UK: No minimum charge*
Cat. cost: 3 x 1st class
Credit cards: None
Specialities: Alpines & Perennials. Good range
of Primula, Sempervivum, Dwarf
Rhododendron, Dwarf Conifers, Bulbs &
Gentians  *Note: Mail order for
Sempervivums & Double Primroses only.
Map ref: 7, A2

**MOsc OSCROFT'S DAHLIAS** ⊠ EU 🖪
Woodside, Warwick Road, Chadwick End, Nr
Solihull, West Midlands, B93 0BP
☎ (01564) 782450
Contact: June & Fred Oscroft
Opening times: 0900-1700 daily.
Min. mail order UK: 6 plants or 2 tubers.
Min. mail order EU: Tubers only, Nmc.
Cat. cost: 1 x 1st class
Credit cards: None
Specialities: Dahlias. Note: Second nursery at
Sprotborough Road, Doncaster, S.Yorks, DN5
8BE. Tel (01302) 785026.
Map ref: 5, A3

**MPet PETER GRAYSON
(SWEET PEA SEEDSMAN)** ⊠ EU 🖪 🖪
34 Glenthorne Close, Brampton, Chesterfield,
Derbyshire, S40 3AR
☎ (01246) 278503  Fax: (01246) 278503
E-mail: matthewfry@cableinet.co.uk
Web site: http://www.igarden.co.uk/
petergrayson/
Contact: Peter Grayson
Opening times: Not open, mail order only.
Min. mail order UK: No minimum charge
Min. mail order EU: Nmc
Cat. cost: A5 Sae (20p stamp)
Credit cards: None
Specialities: Lathyrus species & cultivars.
World's largest collection of Old-Fashioned
Sweet Peas & 100 Spencer Sweet Peas incl. our
own cultivars.

**MPEx PLANTA EXOTICA** ⊠ EU 🖪
11 Heath Close, Banbury, Oxon, OX15 4RZ
☎ (01295) 721989  Fax: (01295) 721989
Contact: Mrs M Hill
Opening times: Mar-Sept by appt.
Min. mail order UK: £3.95 + p&p

Min. mail order EU: £3.95 + p&p
Cat. cost: 2 x 1st class
Credit cards: Visa, MasterCard
Specialities: Rainforest plants, Alpines.
Map ref: 5, B3

**M**Phe    PHEDAR NURSERY ⊠ EU ✈ ▣
Bunkers Hill, Romiley, Stockport, Cheshire,
SK6 3DS
☎ (0161) 430 3772   Fax: (0161) 430 3772
Contact: Will McLewin
Opening times: Frequent, esp. in spring but
very irregular. Please telephone to arrange
appt.
Min. mail order UK: No minimum charge
Min. mail order EU: Nmc
Cat. cost: A5 Sae + 1 x 1st class
Credit cards: None
Specialities: Helleborus, Paeonia. Note: Non-
EU exports subject to destination.
Map ref: 7, A2

**M**Pla    E L F PLANTS
Cramden Nursery, Harborough Road North,
Northampton, Northamptonshire, NN2 8LU
☎ (01604) 846246 Eve.
Contact: E L Fincham-Nichols
Opening times: 1000-1700 Thu-Sat ex Nov,
Dec & Jan.
Mail order: None
Cat. cost: 3 x 1st class
Credit cards: None
Specialities: Dwarf and slow growing Shrubs
& Conifers, many unusual. Some Alpines,
Daphne & Heathers.
Map ref: 5, A4

**M**Rav    RAVENSTHORPE NURSERY ⊠ EU
6 East Haddon Road, Ravensthorpe,
Northamptonshire, NN6 8ES
☎ (01604) 770548   Fax: (01604) 770548
Contact: Jean & Richard Wiseman
Opening times: 1000-1800 (dusk if earlier)
Tue-Sun. Also B/Hol Mons.
Min. mail order UK: No minimum charge
Min. mail order EU: Nmc
Cat. cost: 4 x 1st class
Credit cards: Visa, MasterCard
Specialities: Over 2,600 different Trees,
Shrubs, & Perennials with many unusual
varieties. Search & delivery service for large
orders – winter months only.
Map ref: 5, A4

**M**RPP    R P P ALPINES
6 Bentley Road, Bushbury, Wolverhampton,
West Midlands, WV10 8DZ
☎ (01902) 784508
Contact: R Smallwood
Opening times: By appt. only this year.
Mail order: None
Cat. cost: None issued this year.
Credit cards: None
Specialities: Rare & choice Alpines from
Europe, Himalaya & other regions. A
selection of Hardy plants & Bulbs. All in
small quantities but ever changing. For
collection only.
Map ref: 7, C2

**M**S&S    S & S PERENNIALS
24 Main Street, Normanton Le Heath,
Leicestershire, LE67 2TB
☎ (01530) 262250
Contact: Shirley Pierce
Opening times: Afternoons only – otherwise
please telephone.
Mail order: None
Cat. cost: 2 x 1st class
Credit cards: None
Specialities: Erythronium, Fritillaria, hardy
Cyclamen, dwarf Narcissus, Hepatica,
Anemone & Ranunculus.
Map ref: 7, C3

**M**Sag    SAGE GARDEN PRODUCTS &
NURSERY ⊠ EU ✈ ▣
(Office) 4 Cambrian Way, Swadlincote,
Derbyshire, DE11 9DT
☎ (01283) 217377   Fax: (01283) 217377
Contact: Aubrey Wood
Opening times: Please enquire first.
Min. mail order UK: £15.00 + p&p
Min. mail order EU: £25.00 + p&p
Cat. cost: 2 x 1st class (2 x 1st for seed
catalogue)
Credit cards: MasterCard, Access, Visa
Specialities: Australian Plants, Shrubs & Trees.
Also 800 seed varieties (minimum order £5).
Note: Nursery is at Lowlands Nursery, Linton,
Derbyshire.
Map ref: 7, B3

**M**Sal    SALLEY GARDENS ⊠ EU ✈
32 Lansdowne Drive, West Bridgford,
Nottinghamshire, NG2 7FJ
☎ (0115) 9233878 evenings

**M**

**M**

**Contact:** Richard Lewin
**Opening times:** By appt.
**Min. mail order UK:** No minimum charge
**Min. mail order EU:** Nmc
**Cat. cost:** Sae
**Credit cards:** None
**Specialities:** Medicinal plants, esp. from North America & China. Dye plants, Herbs, Spices, Seeds.
**Map ref:** 7, B4

**MSCN    STONYFORD COTTAGE NURSERY** ▣
Stonyford Lane, Cuddington, Northwich, Cheshire, CW8 2TF
☎ (01606) 888128
**E-mail:** sales@stonyford.u-net.com
**Contact:** F A Overland
**Opening times:** 1000-1730 Tues-Sun & B/Hol Mons 1st Mar-30th Nov.
**Mail order:** None
**Cat. cost:** 4 x 1st class
**Credit cards:** None
**Specialities:** Wide range of Herbaceous Perennials, Diascia, Salvia & Hardy Geranium.
**Map ref:** 7, A1

**MSta    STAPELEY WATER GARDENS LTD** ⊠ EU ⊠ ▣
London Road, Stapeley, Nantwich, Cheshire, CW5 7LH
☎ (01270) 623868    **Fax:** (01270) 624919
**E-mail:** stapeleywg@btinternet.com
**Contact:** Mr Dean Barratt
**Opening times:** Open 0900 Mon-Fri, 1000 Sat, Sun & B/Hols all year. Please check closing times (Closed Xmas day).
**Min. mail order UK:** No minimum charge
**Min. mail order EU:** Nmc
**Cat. cost:** £1.00
**Credit cards:** Visa, Access, MasterCard, Switch
**Specialities:** World's largest Water Garden Centre. Full range of Hardy & Tropical Water Lilies, Aquatic, Bog & Poolside plants. Also large general stock. National Collection of Nymphaea (UK & France).
**Map ref:** 7, B2

**MSte    STEVENTON ROAD NURSERIES** ⊠ EU ▣
Steventon Road, East Hanney, Wantage, Oxfordshire, OX12 0HS
☎ (01235) 868828    **Fax:** (01235) 763670
**Contact:** John Graham
**Opening times:** 1000-1630 Mon-Fri, 1000-1700 Sat & Sun 6th Mar-31st Oct 1999, 4th Mar-5th Nov 2000.
**Min. mail order UK:** £15.00 + p&p
**Min. mail order EU:** £30.00 + p&p

**Cat. cost:** 4 x 1st class
**Credit cards:** None
**Specialities:** Tender & Hardy Perennials.
**Map ref:** 5, C3

**MStw    STEWART'S (NOTTM.) LTD** ⊠ EU
3 George Street, Nottingham, NG1 3BH
☎ (0115) 9476338
**Contact:** Brenda Lochhead
**Opening times:** 0900-1730 Mon-Sat.
**Min. mail order UK:** No minimum charge
**Min. mail order EU:** Nmc
**Cat. cost:** 2 x 1st class
**Credit cards:** Visa, MasterCard, Switch
**Specialities:** Large general range esp. Vegetable seeds. Also seed Potatoes & Grasses.
**Map ref:** 7, B4

**MTed    TED BROWN UNUSUAL PLANTS**
1 Croftway, Markfield, Leicester, LE67 9UG
☎ (01530) 244517
**Contact:** Ted Brown
**Opening times:** From 1000 Sat, Sun & B/Hols Mar-Nov. Other times by appt.
**Mail order:** None
**Cat. cost:** None issued
**Credit cards:** None
**Specialities:** Mainly Herbaceous – many unusual. Bamboos.
**Map ref:** 7, C4

**MTho    A & A THORP**
Bungalow No 5, Main Street, Theddingworth, Leicestershire, LE17 6QZ
☎ (01858) 880496
**Contact:** Anita & Andrew Thorp
**Opening times:** Dawn to Dusk all year.
**Mail order:** None
**Cat. cost:** 50p + Sae
**Credit cards:** None
**Specialities:** Unusual plants or those in short supply.
**Map ref:** 7, C4

**MTis    TISSINGTON NURSERY**
Tissington, Nr Ashbourne, Derbyshire, DE6 1RA
☎ (01335) 390650    **Fax:** (01335) 390693
**Contact:** Mrs Sue Watkins
**Opening times:** 1000-1800 Wed-Sun Mar-Oct & B/Hols.
**Mail order:** None
**Cat. cost:** 2 x 1st class
**Credit cards:** Visa, MasterCard
**Specialities:** Perennials, Shrubs & Climbers incl. unusual varieties.
**Map ref:** 7, B3

**M**

**MTPN  THE PLANT NURSERY ⊠ UK**
Sandy Hill Lane, Off Overstone Road,
Moulton, Northampton, NN3 7JB
☎ (01604) 491941 after 6pm
Contact: Mrs B Jeyes
Opening times: 1000-1700 Thur-Sun & B/Hols
Mar-Oct. 1000-1600 Sun only Nov & Dec.
Min. mail order UK: No minimum charge*
Cat. cost: 2 x 1st class
Credit cards: None
Specialities: Wide range of Herbaceous,
Alpines, Shrubs, Grasses, Hardy Geranium,
Sempervivum & Succulents. *Note: Mail
order of Sempervivum, Succulents only.
Map ref: 5, A4

**MUlv  ULVERSCROFT GRANGE NURSERY 🅆**
Priory Lane, Ulverscroft, Markfield,
Leicestershire, LE67 9PB
☎ (01530) 243635
Contact: David Sewell
Opening times: From 1000 Tue-Sun
Mar-Nov. Other times by appt.
Mail order: None
Cat. cost: None issued
Credit cards: None
Specialities: Wide range of Shrubs, Bamboos,
Grasses & Hardy Perennials – many unusual.
Map ref: 7, C4

**MWar  WARD FUCHSIAS ⊠ UK**
5 Pollen Close, Sale, Cheshire, M33 3LS
☎ (0161) 282 7434
Contact: K Ward
Opening times: 0930-1700 Tue-Sun Feb-Jun
incl B/Hols.
Min. mail order UK: No minimum charge
Cat. cost: Free*
Credit cards: None
Specialities: Fuchsia. *Note: Catalogue
includes cultural information.
Map ref: 7, A2

**MWat  WATERPERRY GARDENS LTD ⊠ UK**
Waterperry, Nr Wheatley, Oxfordshire,
OX33 1JZ
☎ (01844) 339226/254
Fax: (01844) 339883
Contact: Mr R Jacobs
Opening times: 0900-1730 Mon-Fri, 0900-
1800 Sat & Sun Summer. 0900-1700 Winter.
Min. mail order UK: No minimum charge*
Cat. cost: 75p
Credit cards: None
Specialities: General plus National Collection
of Saxifraga (Porophyllum). *Note: Ltd mail
order, please phone for further information
and credit card facilities.
Map ref: 5, C4

**MWeb  A & S WEBB ⊠ UK 🅆**
154 Percival Road, Rugby, Warwickshire,
CV22 5JX
☎ (01788) 565276
Contact: A & S Webb
Opening times: By appt. only.
Min. mail order UK: No minimum charge
Cat. cost: 2 x 1st class
Credit cards: None
Specialities: Ornamental Grasses.

**MWgw  WINGWELL NURSERY ⊠ UK**
Top Street, Wing, Oakham, Rutland,
LE15 8SE
☎ (01572) 737727  Fax: (01572) 737788
Contact: Rose Dejardin
Opening times: 1000-1700 Wed-Sun &
B/Hol Mons Mar-Dec exc. August.
Mail Order Oct-Mar.
Min. mail order UK: No minimum charge
Cat. cost: £1 for descriptive cat. please.
Credit cards: None
Specialities: Herbaceous Perennials.
Map ref: 8, C1

**MWhe  A D & N WHEELER**
Pye Court, Willoughby, Rugby, Warwickshire,
CV23 8BZ
☎ (01788) 890341  Fax: (01788) 890341
Contact: Mrs N Wheeler
Opening times: 1000-1630 daily mid Feb-late
Jun. Other times please phone first for appt.
Mail order: None
Cat. cost: 3 x 1st class
Credit cards: None
Specialities: Fuchsia, Pelargonium & Hardy
Geranium.
Map ref: 5, A4

**MWhi  WHITEHILL FARM NURSERY ⊠ EU**
Whitehill Farm, Burford, Oxon, OX18 4DT
☎ (01993) 823218  Fax: (01993) 822894
Contact: P J M Youngson
Opening times: 0900-1800 daily
1st Feb-31st Nov.
Min. mail order UK: £5.00 + p&p
Min. mail order EU: £5.00 + p&p
Cat. cost: Free
Credit cards: None
Specialities: Grasses & Bamboos, less
common Shrubs, Perennials & Trees.
Map ref: 5, B3

---

KEY  ⊠ Mail order to UK or EU
     🅇 Exports beyond EU
     🅆 Also supplies Wholesale  ◆ See Display advertisement

M

**MWht    WHITELEA NURSERY**
Whitelea Lane, Tansley, Matlock, Derbyshire,
DE4 5FL
☎ (01629) 55010
E-mail:whitelea@nursery-stock.freeserve.co.uk
Web site: http://www.nursery-stock.
freeserve. co.uk
Contact: David Wilson
Opening times: By appt.
Mail order: None
Cat. cost: 1 x 2nd class or Sae.
Credit cards: None
Specialities: Bamboo, Ivies.
Map ref: 7, A3

**MWll    THE WALLED GARDEN ⊠ UK ▣**
2 Castle Road, Shirburn, Watlington,
Oxfordshire, OX9 5DJ
☎ (01491) 612882, (01491) 612117
evenings
Contact: Bridget Gaisburgh-Watkyn
Opening times: 1000-1800 Thur-Tue
Mar-Nov.
Min. mail order UK: £5.00 + p&p
Cat. cost: 4 x 1st class
Credit cards: None
Specialities: Wild Flowers, unusual Herbaceous
Perennials & white flowering herbaceous plants.
Map ref: 5, C4

**MWoo    WOODFIELD BROS ⊠ UK ▣**
Wood End, Clifford Chambers, Stratford-on-
Avon, Warwickshire, CV37 8HR
☎ (01789) 205618
Contact: B Woodfield
Opening times: 1000-1630 Mon-Fri,
1000-1600 Sat & 0900-1200 Sun for plant
collection ONLY.
Min. mail order UK: See list for details
Cat. cost: Sae
Credit cards: None
Specialities: Lupins & Delphinium, plants
& seeds.
Map ref: 5, A3

**MWrn    WARREN HILLS NURSERY**
Warren Hills Cottage, Warren Hills Road,
Coalville, Leicestershire, LE67 4UY
☎ (01530) 812350
Contact: Penny Waters or Bob Taylor
Opening times: By appt. only.
Mail order: None
Cat. cost: 2 x 1st class
Credit cards: None
Specialities: Astrantia, Campanula, Geranium,
Aquilegia, Penstemon, Salvia, Heuchera,
Pulmonaria.
Map ref: 7, C3

# NORTHERN ENGLAND

**NArc    ARCADIA NURSERIES LTD ⊠ EU ▣**
Brasscastle Lane, Nunthorpe,
Middlesborough, Cleveland, TS8 9EB
☎ (01642) 310782   Fax: (01642) 300817
Contact: Mr P Birch
Opening times: Garden Centre 0900-1700
Spring-Autumn, 0900-1500 Winter.
Mail order office 0900-1700 all year.
Min. mail order UK: 6 plants or 1 collection
Min. mail order EU: 6 plants or £2 handling
charge.
Cat. cost: 4 x 1st class
Credit cards: Visa, Access, EuroCard, Switch,
MasterCard
Specialities: Fuchsia & Auricula.
Map ref: 9, A3

**NArg    ARGHAM VILLAGE NURSERY ⊠ EU**
Argham Grange, Grindale, Bridlington, East
Yorkshire, YO16 4XZ
☎ (01723) 892141   Fax: (01723) 892141
Contact: Geoff Pickering
Opening times: 1000-1700 daily Mar-Oct,
1130-1500 daily Nov-Feb.
Min. mail order UK: £20.00 + p&p
Min. mail order EU: £50.00 + p&p
Cat. cost: 4 x 1st class
Credit cards: None
Specialities: Herbaceous Perennials.
Map ref: 9, B4

**NBat    BATTERSBY ROSES ⊠ EU**
Peartree Cottage, Old Battersby, Great Ayton,
Cleveland, TS9 6LU
☎ (01642) 723402
Contact: Eric & Avril Stainthorpe
Opening times: 1000-dusk most days.
Min. mail order UK: No minimum charge
Min. mail order EU: Nmc
Cat. cost: Sae
Credit cards: None
Specialities: Exhibition Roses incl. some
American miniatures.
Map ref: 9, A3

**NBea    BEAMISH CLEMATIS NURSERY ⊠ UK**
Burntwood Cottage, Stoney Lane, Beamish,
Co. Durham, DH9 0SJ
☎ (0191) 370 0202   Fax: (0191) 370 0202
Contact: Colin Brown or Jan Wilson
Opening times: 0900-1700 daily Feb-Nov.
Min. mail order UK: £50.00 + p&p
Cat. cost: 3 x 1st class
Credit cards: None
Specialities: Clematis, Climbers, Shrubs &
Ornamental Trees.
Map ref: 10, C4

**NBee  BEECHCROFT NURSERIES ✉ UK**
Bongate, Appleby-in-Westmorland, Cumbria,
CA16 6UE
☎ (01768) 351201  **Fax:** (01768) 351201
**Contact:** Roger Brown
**Opening times:** 0900-1700 every day.
**Min. mail order UK:** No minimum charge*
**Cat. cost:** Sae for tree list.
**Credit cards:** None
**Specialities:** Hardy field-grown Trees & Shrubs.
*Note: Mail order Trees Nov-Mar only.
**Map ref:** 9, A2

**NBid  BIDE-A-WEE COTTAGE
GARDENS ✉ UK**
Stanton, Netherwitton, Morpeth,
Northumberland, NE65 8PR
☎ (01670) 772262
**E-mail:** bideaweecg@aol.com
**Contact:** Mark Robson
**Opening times:** 1330-1700 Sat 1st May-31st
Aug.
**Min. mail order UK:** £10.00 + p&p
**Cat. cost:** 3 x 1st class
**Credit cards:** None
**Specialities:** Unusual Herbaceous Perennials,
Primula, Grasses.
**Map ref:** 10, C4

**NBir  BIRKHEADS COTTAGE
GARDEN NURSERY**
Nr Causey Arch, Sunniside, Newcastle upon
Tyne, Tyne & Wear, NE16 5EL
☎ (01207) 232262  **Fax:** (01207) 232262
**Contact:** Mrs Christine Liddle
**Opening times:** 1000-1700 daily Apr-end
Oct. Winter opening 1000-1500 (please ring
first). Groups by appt.
**Mail order:** None
**Cat. cost:** None issued
**Credit cards:** None
**Specialities:** Hardy Herbaceous Perennials,
Grasses, Bulbs & Herbs. Allium, Campanula,
Digitalis, Euphorbia, Geranium, Meconopsis,
Primula.
**Map ref:** 10, C4

**NBrk  T H BARKER & SONS ✉ UK ◆**
Baines Paddock Nursery, Haverthwaite,
Ulverston, Cumbria, LA12 8PF
☎ (015395) 58236
**E-mail:** rachel@thbarker.demon.co.uk
**Contact:** W E Thornley
**Opening times:** 0930-1730 Wed-Sun
1st Feb-30th Nov.
**Min. mail order UK:** 2 plants + p&p
**Cat. cost:** £1.00 (Clematis & Climbers)
**Credit cards:** None

**Specialities:** Clematis, Lonicera, Passiflora &
other climbers; Cottage Garden Plants esp.
Hardy Geranium, Aster, Ranunculus, Iris &
Viola. Many rare. Most stock grown on the
nursery.
**Map ref:** 9, B1

**NBro  BROWNTHWAITE HARDY PLANTS**
Fell Yeat, Casterton, Kirkby Lonsdale,
Lancashire, LA6 2JW
☎ (015242) 71340 after 1800.
**Contact:** Chris Benson
**Opening times:** Tue-Sun 1st Apr-30th Sep.
**Mail order:** None
**Cat. cost:** 3 x 1st class
**Credit cards:** None
**Specialities:** Herbaceous Perennials & Grasses
incl. Geranium, Campanula, Iris, Primula &
Penstemon. *Note: Tel. No. (015242) 71340
after 1800.
**Map ref:** 9, B2

**NBur  BURTON AGNES HALL NURSERY ✉ EU**
Burton Agnes Hall Preservation Trust Ltd,
Estate Office, Burton Agnes, Driffield, East
Yorkshire, YO25 0ND
☎ (01262) 490324  **Fax:** (01262) 490513
**Contact:** Mrs S Cunliffe-Lister
**Opening times:** 1100-1700 Apr-Oct.
**Min. mail order UK:** £15.00 + p&p*
**Min. mail order EU:** £15.00 + p&p
**Cat. cost:** 4 x 1st class
**Credit cards:** None
**Specialities:** Large range Perennials & Alpines.
Many unusual varieties esp. Penstemon,
Osteospermum, Digitalis, Anemone,
Geranium. National Collection of Campanula.
*Note: Mail order Nov-Mar only.
**Map ref:** 9, B4

**NBus  BUSH GREEN COTTAGE
NURSERY ✉ UK ▣**
Foxfield Road, Broughton-in-Furness,
Cumbria, LA20 6BY
☎ (01229) 716724
**Contact:** Jim Haunch
**Opening times:** 1000-1700 Tues, Sun &
B/Hols. Garden open at same time.
**Min. mail order UK:** No minimum charge
**Cat. cost:** 4 x 1st class
**Credit cards:** None
**Specialities:** Hardy Geraniums, Hostas,
interesting Hardy Perennials & Ferns.
**Map ref:** 9, B1

N

**N**

**NCat    CATFORTH GARDENS**
Roots Lane, Catforth, Preston, Lancashire,
PR4 0JB
☎ (01772) 690561/690269
Contact: Judith Bradshaw & Chris Moore
Opening times: 1030-1700 13th Mar 1999-
12th Sep 1999.
Mail order: None
Cat. cost: 5 x 1st class
Credit cards: None
Specialities: National Collection of hardy
Geranium. 3 Gardens open every day. Over
1500 varieties of Herbaceous plants.
Map ref: 9, C1

**NChi    CHIPCHASE CASTLE NURSERY**
Chipchase Castle, Wark, Hexham,
Northumberland, NE48 3NT
☎ (01434) 230083
Contact: Suzanne Newell & Janet Beakes
Opening times: 1000-1700 Thu-Sun &
B/Hol Mons from Easter (1st Apr)-mid Oct.
Mail order: None
Cat. cost: A5 Sae for list
Credit cards: None
Specialities: Unusual Herbaceous esp. Erodium,
Eryngium, Geranium, Penstemon & Viola.
Map ref: 10, C4

**NChl    CHILTERN SEEDS ⊠ EU ⊠ ◆**
Bortree Stile, Ulverston, Cumbria, LA12 7PB
☎ (01229) 581137 (24 hrs)
Fax: (01229) 584549
E-mail: chilternseeds@compuserve.com
Opening times: Normal office hours,
Mon-Fri.
Min. mail order UK: No minimum charge
Min. mail order EU: Nmc
Cat. cost: 3 x 2nd class
Credit cards: Visa, Access, American Express,
Switch, MasterCard, EuroCard
Specialities: Almost 4,600 items of all kinds –
Wild Flowers, Trees, Shrubs, Cacti, Annuals,
Houseplants, Vegetables & Herbs.

**NCLN    CRAGS LEWISIA NURSERY ⊠ EU ⊠**
Rosley, Wigton, Cumbria, CA7 8DD
☎ (016973) 42527   Fax: (016973) 42527
Contact: E & E Parkinson
Opening times: By arrangement.
Please phone.
Min. mail order UK: £10.00 + p&p
Min. mail order EU: £10.00 + p&p
Cat. cost: 2 x 2nd class
Credit cards: None
Specialities: Lewisia Cotyledon Crags hybrids.
Map ref: 9, A1

**NCot    COTTAGE GARDEN PLANTS**
1 Sycamore Close, Whitehaven, Cumbria,
CA28 6LE
☎ (01946) 695831
E-mail: jeanp@compuserve.com
Contact: Mrs J Purkiss
Opening times: By appt. only
Mail order: None
Cat. cost: None issued.
Credit cards: None
Specialities: Hardy Perennials incl. Corydalis,
Dicentra, Geranium, Meconopsis,
Polemonium, Primula & Pulmonaria.
Map ref: 9, A1

**NCra    CRAVEN'S NURSERY ⊠ EU ⊠ ⊠**
1 Foulds Terrace, Bingley, West Yorkshire,
BD16 4LZ
☎ (01274) 561412   Fax: (01274) 561412
Contact: S R Craven & M Craven
Opening times: By appt. only.
Min. mail order UK: £10.00 + p&p
Min. mail order EU: £50.00 + p&p
Cat. cost: 4 x 1st class
Credit cards: None
Specialities: Show Auricula, Primula, Pinks,
Alpines, Sempervivum, Jovibarbas and
specialist Seeds.
Map ref: 9, C2

**NCro    CROSTON CACTUS ⊠ EU**
43 Southport Road, Eccleston, Chorley,
Lancashire, PR7 6ET
☎ (01257) 452555
E-mail: desert.plants@lineone.net
Contact: John Henshaw
Opening times: 0930-1700 Wed-Sat &
by appt.
Min. mail order UK: £5.00 + p&p
Min. mail order EU: £10.00 + p&p
Cat. cost: 2 x 1st or 2 x IRCs
Credit cards: None
Specialities: Mexican Cacti, Echeveria hybrids
& some Bromeliads & Tillandsia.
Map ref: 9, C1

**NCut    CUTTING EDGE NURSERY ◆**
Highfield Farm, Knowle Road, off Upper
Sheffield Road, Barnsley, Yorkshire, S70 4AW
☎ (01226) 730292   Fax: (01226) 280256
Contact: Brian B Cockerline
Opening times: 0900-1700 daily all year.
Mail order: None
Cat. cost: 2 x 1st class
Credit cards: None
Specialities: Wide selection of Perennials &
Shrubs, many uncommon.
Map ref: 9, C3

**NDea**  **DEANSWOOD PLANTS**
Potteries Lane, Littlethorpe, Ripon, North
Yorkshire, HG4 3LF
☎ (01765) 603441
Contact: Jacky Barber
Opening times: 1000-1700 Tue-Sun
1st Apr-30th Sep.
Mail order: None
Cat. cost: List 2 x 25p
Credit cards: None
Specialities: Pond, Marginals & Bog plants.
Map ref: 9, B3

**NDov**  **DOVE COTTAGE PLANTS** ⊠ UK
23 Shibden Hall Road, Halifax,
West Yorkshire, HX3 9XA
☎ (01422) 203553
Contact: Stephen & Kim Rogers
Opening times: 1000-1800 Tues-Sun &
B/Hols Feb-Nov.
Min. mail order UK: No minimum charge
Cat. cost: Sae + 2 x 1st class
Credit cards: None
Specialities: Helleborus, Pulmonaria,
Epimedium, Hardy Geranium, Bamboo,
Hosta & Grasses & other Perennials.
Map ref: 9, C2

**NEgg**  **EGGLESTON HALL**
Barnard Castle, Co. Durham, DL12 0AG
☎ (01833) 650403   Fax: (01833) 650378
Contact: Mrs R H Gray
Opening times: 1000-1700 daily
Mail order: None
Cat. cost: £1.50 + Sae
Credit cards: None
Specialities: Rare & Unusual plants with
particular emphasis to Flower Arrangers.
Map ref: 9, A2

**NEqu**  **EQUATORIAL PLANT CO.** ⊠ EU ▣ ▣
7 Gray Lane, Barnard Castle, Co. Durham,
DL12 8PD
☎ (01833) 690519   Fax: (01833) 690519
E-mail: equatorialplants@onyxnet.co.uk
Contact: Richard Warren PhD
Opening times: By appt. only.
Min. mail order UK: No minimum charge
Min. mail order EU: Nmc
Cat. cost: Free
Credit cards: Visa, Access
Specialities: Laboratory raised Orchids only.

**NFai**  **FAIRY LANE NURSERIES**
Fairy Lane, Sale, Greater Manchester,
M33 2JT
☎ (0161) 905 1137, (0161) 969 5594
Contact: Mrs J Coxon

Opening times: 1200-1700 Thur-Mon
Mar-Oct.
Mail order: None
Cat. cost: None issued.
Credit cards: Access, Visa
Specialities: Hardy & tender Perennials,
Herbs, Hebe & less usual Shrubs. National
garden gift tokens.
Map ref: 7, A2

**NFir**  **FIR TREES PELARGONIUM
NURSERY** ⊠ EU
Stokesley, Middlesbrough, Cleveland,
TS9 5LD
☎ (01642) 713066   Fax: (01642) 713066
E-mail: firtre@globalnet.co.uk
Web site: http://www.users.global.co.uk/
~firtre
Contact: Helen Bainbridge
Opening times: 1000-1600 daily 15th Mar -
30th Sep, 1000-1600 Mon-Fri 1st Oct-15th Mar.
Min. mail order UK: £2.00 + p&p
Min. mail order EU: £2.00 + p&p
Cat. cost: 4 x 1st class
Credit cards: MasterCard, Visa
Specialities: All types of Pelargonium: Fancy
Leaf, Regal, Decorative Regal, Oriental Regal,
Angel, Miniature, Zonal, Ivy Leaf, Stellar,
Scented, Dwarf, Unique, Golden Stellar &
species.
Map ref: 9, A3

**NFla**  **FLAXTON HOUSE NURSERY** ⊠ UK
Flaxton, York, North Yorkshire, Y060 7RJ
☎ (01904) 468753
Contact: Mrs H Williams
Opening times: 1000-1700 Tues-Sun
1st Mar-31st Oct.
Min. mail order UK: £3.50 + p&p
Cat. cost: 2 x 1st class
Credit cards: None
Specialities: Wide General Range of Shrubs &
Herbaceous with many unusual plants.
Map ref: 9, B3

**NFor**  **FORD NURSERY** ◆
Castle Gardens, Ford, Berwick-upon-Tweed,
Northumberland, TD15 2PZ
☎ (01890) 820379   Fax: (01890) 820594
Contact: Marjorie Spark & Roy Harmeston
Opening times: 1000-1800 daily Mar-Oct,
1000-1630 Mon-Fri Nov-Feb.
Mail order: None

N

**N**

Cat. cost: £1.00 PO/Chq.
Credit cards: Visa, Access
Specialities: Over 1200 different species of container grown hardy ornamental Shrubs, Perennials, Trees & Herbs.
Map ref: 10, C4

**NFvw    FAIRVIEW FARM NURSERY ⊠ UK**
Robin Hood Road, Ravenscar, Nr Scarborough, N. Yorks, YO13 0ES
☎ (01723) 870616
Contact: Mrs J Johnson
Opening times: By appt. only.
Min. mail order UK: £10.00 + p&p
Cat. cost: 2 x 1st class
Credit cards: None
Specialities: Alpines incl. Campanula, Erodium, Geranium, Lewisia, Saxifraga, Sedum & Sempervivum. Herbs incl. Eryngium, Centaurea, Geranium, Potentilla, Primula & Viola.
Map ref: 9, A4

**NGdn    GARDEN HOUSE NURSERIES**
The Square, Dalston, Carlisle, Cumbria, CA5 7LL
☎ (01228) 710297
Contact: David Hickson
Opening times: 0900-1700 daily Mar-Oct.
Mail order: None
Cat. cost: None issued.
Credit cards: None
Specialities: Geranium, Hosta, Hemerocallis & Iris.
Map ref: 9, A1

**NHal    HALLS OF HEDDON ⊠ EU ⊠ ⊠**
(Office) West Heddon Nurseries, Heddon-on-the-Wall, Newcastle-upon-Tyne, Northumberland, NE15 0JS
☎ (01661) 852445
Contact: Judith Lockey
Opening times: 0900-1700 Mon-Sat 1000-1700 Sun.
Min. mail order UK: No minimum charge*
Min. mail order EU: £25.00 + p&p**
Cat. cost: 3 x 2nd class
Credit cards: None
Specialities: Chrysanthemum & Dahlia. Wide range of Herbaceous. *Note: Mail order Dahlia & Chrysanthemum only. **EU & Export Dahlia tubers only.
Map ref: 10, C4

**NHar    HARTSIDE NURSERY GARDEN ⊠ EU ⊠**
Nr Alston, Cumbria, CA9 3BL
☎ (01434) 381372   Fax: (01434) 381372

Contact: S L & N Huntley
Opening times: 0930-1630 Mon-Fri, 1230-1600 Sat, Sun & B/Hols, 1st Mar-31st Oct. By appt. 1st Nov-28th Feb.
Min. mail order UK: No minimum charge
Min. mail order EU: £50.00 + p&p
Cat. cost: 4 x 1st class or 3 x IRC
Credit cards: Visa, Access, American Express
Specialities: Alpines grown at altitude of 1100 feet in Pennines. Primula, Ferns, Gentian & Meconopsis.
Map ref: 9, A2

**NHaw    THE HAWTHORNES NURSERY ⊠**
Marsh Road, Hesketh Bank, Nr Preston, Lancashire, PR4 6XT
☎ (01772) 812379
Contact: Irene & Richard Hodson
Opening times: 0900-1800 daily 1st Mar-30th Jun, Thur-Sun July-Oct. Gardens open for NGS.
Mail order: None
Cat. cost: 5 x 1st class
Credit cards: None
Specialities: Bedding & Basket plants. Fuchsia, Clematis, Diascia, Penstemon, Argyranthemum, Osteospermum & other Perennials.
Map ref: 9, C1

**NHed    HEDGEROW NURSERY ⊠ EU ⊠ ⊠**
24 Braithwaite Edge Road, Keighley, West Yorkshire, BD22 6RA
☎ (01535) 606531
Contact: Nigel Hutchinson
Opening times: 1000-1700 Wed-Sun & B/Hols.
Min. mail order UK: No minimum charge
Min. mail order EU: Nmc
Cat. cost: 4 x 2nd class
Credit cards: Visa, MasterCard, American Express, EuroCard, Switch
Specialities: National Collection of dwarf Hebe. Saxifraga, Primula, Rhododendron & Conifers.
Map ref: 9, B2

**NHer    HERTERTON HOUSE GARDEN NURSERY**
Hartington, Cambo, Morpeth, Northumberland, NE61 4BN
☎ (01670) 774278
Contact: Mrs M Lawley & Mr Frank Lawley
Opening times: 1330-1730 Mon Wed Fri-Sun 1st April-end Sep. (Earlier or later in the year weather permitting.)
Mail order: None
Cat. cost: None issued
Credit cards: None

**N**Hex **HEXHAM HERBS**
Chesters Walled Garden, Chollerford,
Hexham, Northumberland, NE46 4BQ
☎ (01434) 681483   **Fax:** (01434) 681483
**Contact:** Susie & Kevin White
**Opening times:** 1000-1700 Mar-end Oct
daily. Please phone for Winter opening times.
**Mail order:** None
**Credit cards:** None
**Specialities:** Extensive range of Herbs.
National Collections of Thymus & Origanum.
Wild flowers, Grasses & unusual Perennials,
esp. Geranium, Epilobium & Variegated
plants.
**Map ref:** 10, C4

**N**HHG **HARDSTOFT HERB GARDEN**
Hall View Cottage, Hardstoft, Pilsley, Nr
Chesterfield, Derbyshire, S45 8AH
☎ (01246) 854268
**Contact:** Lynne & Steve Raynor
**Opening times:** 1000-1700 daily 15th
Mar-15th Sep. Closed Tues except for Easter
& B/Hol weeks.
**Mail order:** None
**Cat. cost:** Free
**Credit cards:** None
**Specialities:** Very wide range of Herb Plants.
Over 40 Lavenders & 12 Rosemary. Scented
Pelargoniums.
**Map ref:** 7, A3

**N**Hlc **HALECAT NURSERIES**
Witherslack, Grange over Sands, Cumbria,
LA11 6RU
☎ (01539) 552229
**Contact:** Carl Harrison
**Opening times:** 0900-1630 Mon-Fri all year,
1400-1600 Sun Apr-Oct. Parties by appt.
**Mail order:** None
**Cat. cost:** None issued
**Credit cards:** Visa
**Specialities:** Hosta, Hydrangea, Euphorbia,
grey foliage and perennial border plants.
**Map ref:** 9, B1

**N**Hol **HOLDEN CLOUGH
NURSERY** ⊠ EU ⊠ ⊠ ◆
Holden, Bolton-by-Bowland, Clitheroe,
Lancashire, BB7 4PF
☎ (01200) 447615   **Fax:** (01200) 447615
**Contact:** P J Foley
**Opening times:** 0900-1630 Mon-Sat all year
(closed some Fri), 0900-1630 B/Hol Mons,

**Specialities:** Achillea, Aquilegia, Geum,
Polemonium. Country garden flowers.
**Map ref:** 10, C4

1300-1630 Easter Sun & 2nd Sun in May
each year.
**Min. mail order UK:** No minimum charge
**Min. mail order EU:** Nmc
**Cat. cost:** £1.40
**Credit cards:** MasterCard, Visa
**Specialities:** Large general list incl. Primula,
Saxifraga, Sempervivum, Pulmonaria, Astilbe,
Grasses, Hosta, Heathers & Rhododendron.
**Note:** Closed 24th Dec-2nd Jan 2000 &
Good Friday.
**Map ref:** 9, B2

**N**Hor **HORN'S GARDEN CENTRE** ⊠ UK
Dixon Estate, Shotton Colliery, Nr Peterlee,
Co. Durham, DH6 2PX
☎ (0191) 5262987   **Fax:** (0191) 5262987
**Contact:** G Horn & Theresa Horn
**Opening times:** 0900-1730 Mon-Sat
1000-1600 Sun, all year exc. Easter Mon.
**Min. mail order UK:** £6.25 + p&p
**Cat. cost:** 2 x 1st class
**Credit cards:** Visa, EuroCard, MasterCard,
Access, Switch, American Express, Delta
**Specialities:** Coleus (Solenostemon),
Streptocarpus, Fuchsia & Pelargonium.
**Map ref:** 9, A3

**N**Lak **LAKES' HARDY PLANTS** ⊠ EU ⊠
(Office) 4 Fearns Buildings, Penistone,
Sheffield, South Yorkshire, S30 6BA
☎ (01226) 370574
**Contact:** Dr P A Lake
**Opening times:** Nursery moving, mail order
only this year.
**Min. mail order UK:** No minimum charge
**Min. mail order EU:** Nmc
**Cat. cost:** 4 x 1st class/Sae for list
**Credit cards:** None
**Specialities:** Unusual Herbaceous & Cottage
garden plants esp. Diascia, Digitalis,
Eryngium, Euphorbia, Penstemon & Grasses.
**Note:** Nursery is at Royd Moor Garden
Nursery, Mill House Green.
**Map ref:** 9, C3

**N**Lan **LANDLIFE WILDFLOWERS LTD** ⊠ UK ⊠
National Wildflower Centre, Court Hey Park,
Liverpool, Merseyside, L16 3NA
☎ (0151) 737 1819   **Fax:** (0151) 737 1820
**E-mail:** info@landlife.u-net.com
**Web site:** http://www.merseyworld.com/
landlife

Contact: Gillian Watson
Opening times: By appt. for collection only.
Min. mail order UK: £14.00
Cat. cost: Sae + 2 x 2nd class
Credit cards: Visa, American Express, Delta,
MasterCard
Specialities: Wild herbaceous plants and seeds.
Map ref: 7, A1

**NLar**  LARCH COTTAGE NURSERIES ⊠ UK ◆
Melkinthorpe, Penrith, Cumbria, CA10 2DR
☎ (01931) 712404  Fax: (01931) 712727
Contact: Joanne McCullock or Briony Stott
Opening times: 1000-1900 daily.
Min. mail order UK:
Cat. cost: 6 x 2nd class
Credit cards: Visa, Access, Switch, Delta,
American Express, Solo
Specialities: Unusual & Old fashioned
Perennials. Rare & dwarf Conifers. Unusual
Shrubs & Trees. Aquatics & Water Lilies.
Map ref: 9, A1

**NLon**  LONGFRAMLINGTON GARDENS 🖾 ◆
Swarland Road, Longframlington, Morpeth,
Northumberland, NE65 8DB
☎ (01655) 570382  Fax: (01655) 570382
Contact: Hazel Huddleston
Opening times: 0900-1900 (or dusk) daily all
year, or by appt.
Mail order: None
Cat. cost: £2.50 incl. (available late 1998)
Credit cards: Access, Visa
Specialities: Hardy Ornamental Trees, Shrubs,
Perennials, Herbs, Ground cover & Alpines.
Map ref: 10, C4

**NMar**  J & D MARSTON ⊠ EU ◆
Culag, Green Lane, Nafferton, Driffield, East
Yorkshire, YO25 0LF
☎ (01377) 254487
Contact: J & D Marston
Opening times: 1350-1700 Easter-mid Sep,
Sat, Sun & other times by appt.
Min. mail order UK: £15.00 + p&p
Min. mail order EU: Price on application
Cat. cost: 5 x 1st class
Credit cards: None
Specialities: Hardy & Greenhouse Ferns only.
Map ref: 9, B4

**NMen**  MENDLE NURSERY ⊠ EU
Holme, Scunthorpe, DN16 3RF
☎ (01724) 850864
Contact: Mrs A Earnshaw
Opening times: 1000-1600 Tues-Sun.
Min. mail order UK: No minimum charge
Min. mail order EU: Nmc

Cat. cost: 3 x 2nd class
Credit cards: None
Specialities: Many unusual Alpines esp.
Saxifraga & Sempervivum.
Map ref: 9, C4

**NMGW**  MGW PLANTS ⊠ UK
45 Potovens Lane, Lofthouse Gate, Wakefield,
Yorkshire, WF3 3JE
☎ (01924) 820096
Contact: Michael G Wilson
Opening times: 1000-dusk Wed-Sat 1st
Feb-31st Oct.
Min. mail order UK: £10.00 + p&p
Cat. cost: 1 x 1st class
Credit cards: None
Specialities: Alpines incl. Campanula &
Geranium. Bulbs incl. Colchicum & Crocus.
Herbaceous incl. Geranium & Iris.
Map ref: 9, C3

**NMir**  MIRES BECK NURSERY ⊠ EU 🖾
Low Mill Lane, North Cave, Brough, North
Humberside, HU15 2NR
☎ (01430) 421543
Contact: Irene Tinklin & Martin Rowland
Opening times: 1000-1600 Thur-Sat
1st Mar-31st July. 1000-1500 Thur-Fri
1st Aug-28th Feb & by appt.
Min. mail order UK: £15.00 + p&p
Min. mail order EU: £15.00 + p&p
Cat. cost: 3 x 1st class
Credit cards: None
Specialities: Wild flower plants of Yorkshire
provenance.
Map ref: 9, C4

**NMoo**  MOOR MONKTON NURSERIES ⊠ UK ◆
Moor Monkton, Nr York, North Yorkshire,
YO25 8JJ
☎ (01904) 738319  Fax: (01904) 738319
Contact: Peter Owen
Opening times: 0900-1700.
Min. mail order UK: £20.00 + p&p
Cat. cost: None issued yet.
Credit cards: None
Specialities: Bamboos, Palms, unusual Trees,
Shrubs & Perennials.
Map ref: 9, B3

**NMos**  STANLEY MOSSOP ⊠ EU 🖾 🖾
Boonwood Garden Centre, Gosforth, Seascale,
Cumbria, CA20 1BP
☎ (01946) 725330  Fax: (01946) 725829
Contact: Stanley & Gary Mossop.
Opening times: 1000-1700 daily.
Min. mail order UK: No minimum charge
Min. mail order EU: £50.00 + p&p

Cat. cost: Free
Credit cards: None
Specialities: Achimenes, Achimenantha, Eucodonia, Gloxinia (incl. species) & Smithiantha.
Map ref: 9, A1

**NMun    MUNCASTER CASTLE ⊠ EU ✈**
Ravenglass, Cumbria, CA18 1RQ
☎ (01229) 717357   Fax: (01229) 717010
E-mail: acrhodos@globalnet.co.uk
Web site: http://www.users.globalnet.co.uk/~acrhodos
Contact: Susan Clark
Opening times: 1000-1700 daily 1st Apr-31st Oct. All other times by appt.
Min. mail order UK: £20.00 + p&p
Min. mail order EU: £50.00 + p&p
Cat. cost: 3 x 1st class
Credit cards: Access, Visa, Not for telephone orders
Specialities: Rhododendron & Azalea.
Map ref: 9, A1

**NNew    NEWTON HILL ALPINES ✦**
335 Leeds Road, Newton Hill, Wakefield, Yorkshire, WF1 2JH
☎ (01924) 377056
Contact: Sheena Vigors
Opening times: 0900-1700 Fri-Wed all year. Closed Thur. Please phone first.
Mail order: None
Cat. cost: 2 x 1st class
Credit cards: None
Specialities: Alpines, esp. Saxifraga, also Erica, Conifers & dwarf Shrubs.
Map ref: 9, C3

**NNrd    NORDEN ALPINES ⊠ EU ✦**
Hirst Road, Carlton, Nr Goole, Humberside, DN14 9PX
☎ (01405) 861348
Contact: Norma & Denis Walton
Opening times: 1000-1700 Fri-Mon incl. or by appt.
Min. mail order UK: £10.00 + p&p
Min. mail order EU: £10.00 + p&p
Cat. cost: 3 x 2nd class
Credit cards: None
Specialities: Many unusual Alpines – over 2000 esp. Auricula, Campanula, Primula & Saxifraga.
Map ref: 9, C3

**NOaD    OAK DENE NURSERIES ⊠ UK**
10 Back Lane West, Royston, Barnsley, Yorkshire, S71 4SB
☎ (01226) 722253   Fax: (01226) 722253

Contact: J Foster or Mr G Foster
Opening times: 1000-1600 1st Apr-30th Sep, 0900-1800 1st Oct-31st Mar. (Closed 12.30-13.30.)
Min. mail order UK: Please phone for further info.
Cat. cost: None issued.
Credit cards: None
Specialities: Cacti, Succulents & South African Lachenalia Bulbs.
Map ref: 9, C3

**NOak    OAK TREE NURSERY ⊠ UK**
Mill Lane, Barlow, Selby, North Yorkshire, YO8 8EY
☎ (01757) 618409
Contact: Gill Plowes
Opening times: 1000-1630 Tue-Sun mid Mar-end Sep.
Min. mail order UK: £10.00 + p&p
Cat. cost: 2 x 1st class
Credit cards: None
Specialities: Cottage Garden plants, Grasses & Ferns.
Map ref: 9, C3

**NOla    OLAND PLANTS**
Sawley Nursery, Risplith, Ripon, North Yorkshire, HG4 3EW
☎ (01765) 620622   Fax: (01765) 620487
Contact: Leslie & Jane Oland
Opening times: 0900-1700 daily 1st Mar-31st Oct and by appt. Plant centre at Harlow Carr open all year.
Mail order: None
Cat. cost: None issued.
Credit cards: MasterCard, Delta, Diners, EuroCard, Switch, Visa
Specialities: Very wide range of good garden Perennials, Shrubs, Climbers, Alpines & Conservatory plants. Sales also at Harlow Carr (all year) & Newby Hall (summer).
Map ref: 9, B3

**NOrc    ORCHARD HOUSE NURSERY ✦**
Orchard House, Wormald Green, Nr Harrogate, North Yorks, HG3 3PX
☎ (01765) 677541   Fax: (01765) 677541
Contact: Mr B M Corner
Opening times: 0800-1630 Mon-Fri.
Mail order: None
Cat. cost: £1.00
Credit cards: None

---

KEY
⊠ Mail order to UK or EU
✈ Exports beyond EU
✦ Also supplies Wholesale   ◆ See Display advertisement

Specialities: Herbaceous Perennials, Ferns, Grasses, Water Plants & unusual cottage garden plants.
Map ref: 9, B3

**NPal** THE PALM FARM ⊠ EU ☒ ▣
Thornton Hall Gardens, Station Road, Thornton Curtis, Nr Ulceby, Humberside, DN39 6XF
☎ (01469) 531232　Fax: (01469) 531232
Contact: W W Spink
Opening times: 1400-1700 daily ex Winter when advised to check by phone first.
Min. mail order UK: £11.00 + p&p
Min. mail order EU: £25.00 + p&p
Cat. cost: 1 x 2nd class
Credit cards: None
Specialities: Hardy & half-Hardy Palms, unusual Trees, Shrubs & Conservatory plants.
Map ref: 9, C4

**NPar** GERRY PARKER PLANTS ⊠ EU
9 Cotherstone Road, Newton Hall, Durham, DH1 5YN
☎ (0191) 386 8749
Contact: G Parker
Opening times: Not open.
Min. mail order UK: No minimum charge
Min. mail order EU: Nmc
Cat. cost: 3 x 1st class
Credit cards: None
Specialities: Woodland plants, Bulbs, Border plants – all suited to clay soils.

**NPer** PERRY'S PLANTS ◆
The River Garden, Sleights, Whitby, North Yorkshire, YO21 1RR
☎ (01947) 810329　Fax: (01947) 810940
Contact: Pat & Richard Perry
Opening times: 1000-1700 Easter to October.
Mail order: None
Cat. cost: Large (A4) Sae
Credit cards: None
Specialities: Lavatera, Malva, Erysimum, Euphorbia, Anthemis, Osteospermum & Hebe. Also uncommon Hardy & Container plants.
Map ref: 9, A3

**NPin** PINKS & CARNATIONS ⊠ EU ▣ ◆
22 Chetwyn Avenue, Bromley Cross, Bolton, Lancashire, BL7 9BN
☎ (01204) 306273　Fax: (01204) 306273
Contact: R & T Gillies
Opening times: Appt. only.
Min. mail order UK: No minimum charge
Min. mail order EU: £15.00 + p&p
Cat. cost: 1 x 1st class

Credit cards: Visa, MasterCard
Specialities: Pinks, Perpetual Flowering Carnations. Also seeds.
Map ref: 9, C2

**NPla** PLANTATIONS PERENNIALS
Cicely's Cottage, 43 Elmers Green, Skelmersdale, Lancashire, WN8 6SG
☎ (01695) 720790/724448
Contact: Maureen Duncan/Jennifer Madeley
Opening times: By appt. only. Please phone.
Mail order: None
Cat. cost: 4 x 1st class
Credit cards: None
Specialities: Perennials & Shrubs incl. Diascia, Osteospermum, Penstemon, Viola, Hedera & Hebe.
Map ref: 9, C1

**NPoe** POETS COTTAGE SHRUB NURSERY ◆
Lealholm, Whitby, North Yorkshire, YO21 2AQ
☎ (01947) 897424
Contact: Hilda Rees
Opening times: 0900-1700 daily Mar-Dec, 1200-1500 daily Jan-Feb.
Mail order: None
Cat. cost: None issued.
Credit cards: None
Specialities: Dwarf Conifers, Acers & Herbaceous.
Map ref: 9, A3

**NPri** PRIMROSE COTTAGE NURSERY ◆
Ringway Road, Moss Nook, Wythenshawe, Manchester, M22 5WF
☎ (0161) 437 1557　Fax: (0161) 499 9932
E-mail: caroline@primrosenursery. freeserve. co.uk
Web site: http://www.primrosenursery.freeserve. co.uk
Contact: Caroline Dumville
Opening times: 0815-1800 Mon-Sat, 0930-1730 Sun.
Mail order: None
Cat. cost: 1 x 1st class
Credit cards: Visa, Access, Switch
Specialities: Hardy Herbaceous Perennials, Alpines, Herbs, Roses, Patio & Hanging Basket Plants.
Map ref: 7, A2

**NPro** PROUDPLANTS
Shadyvale Nurseries, Ainstable, Carlisle, Cumbria, CA4 9QN
☎ (01768) 896604
Contact: Roger Proud
Opening times: 0900-1800 daily Mar-Nov.

Other times by appt.
**Mail order:** None
**Cat. cost:** None issued
**Credit cards:** None
**Specialities:** Interesting & unusual Shrubs &
Perennials esp. Dwarf & Ground cover plants.
**Map ref:** 9, A1

**NPSI**  PLANTS OF SPECIAL INTEREST ◆
4 High Street, Braithwell, Nr Rotherham,
South Yorkshire, S66 7AL
☎ (01709) 790642  **Fax:** (01709) 790342
**Contact:** Rita Ann Dunstan
**Opening times:** 1000-1700 Tue-Sun
Mar-Dec.
**Mail order:** None
**Cat. cost:** 3 x 1st class
**Credit cards:** Access, Switch
**Specialities:** Wide selection of Herbaceous
plants esp. Zantedeschia & Grasses. Also
specimen Trees & Shrubs.
**Map ref:** 9, C3

**NRar**  RARER PLANTS
Ashfield House, Austfield Lane, Monk
Fryston, Leeds, North Yorkshire, LS25 5EH
☎ (01977) 682263
**Contact:** Anne Watson
**Opening times:** 1000-1600 Sat & Sun 1st
Feb-1st May.
**Mail order:** None
**Cat. cost:** Sae
**Credit cards:** None
**Specialities:** Helleborus & unusual plants.
**Map ref:** 9, C3

**NRob**  W ROBINSON & SONS LTD ⊠ EU ✈ 🏢
Sunny Bank, Forton, Nr Preston, Lancashire,
PR3 0BN
☎ (01524) 791210  **Fax:** (01524) 791933
**Contact:** Miss Robinson
**Opening times:** 0900-1700 7 days Mar-Jun,
0800-1700 Mon-Fri Jul-Feb.
**Min. mail order UK:** No minimum charge
**Min. mail order EU:** Nmc
**Cat. cost:** Free
**Credit cards:** Visa, Access, American Express,
Switch
**Specialities:** Mammoth Vegetable seed.
Onions, Leeks, Tomatoes & Beans.
**Map ref:**

**NRog**  R V ROGER LTD ⊠ EU 🏢
The Nurseries, Malton Road (A.169),
Pickering, North Yorkshire, YO18 7HG
☎ (01751) 472226  **Fax:** (01751) 476749
**E-mail:** ian@clivia.demon.co.uk
**Web site:** http://www.ian@clivia.demon.co.uk

**Contact:** J R, A G & I M Roger
**Opening times:** 0900-1700 Mon-Sat,
1300-1700 Sun. Closed Dec 25th-Jan 2nd.
**Min. mail order UK:** No minimum charge
**Min. mail order EU:** Nmc
**Cat. cost:** £1.50
**Credit cards:** Visa, Access, Switch
**Specialities:** General list, hardy in North
of England.
**Map ref:** 9, B3

**NRoo**  ROOKHOPE NURSERIES
Rookhope, Upper Weardale, Co. Durham,
DL13 2DD
☎ (01388) 517272
**Contact:** Karen Blackburn
**Opening times:** 0900-1600 mid Mar-end Sep.
**Mail order:** None
**Cat. cost:** 3 x 1st class
**Credit cards:** Visa, Access, MasterCard
**Specialities:** Wide range of Hardy plants
grown at 1100 feet in the northern Pennines.
**Map ref:** 9, A2

**NRya**  RYAL NURSERY ⊠ EU 🏢
East Farm Cottage, Ryal, Northumberland,
NE20 0SA
☎ (01661) 886562  **Fax:** (01661) 886918
**E-mail:** alpines@ryal.freeserve.co.uk
**Contact:** R F Hadden
**Opening times:** Mar-Jul: 1300-1600 Mon
& Tue (please phone first), 1000-1600 Sun
& by appt.
**Min. mail order UK:** £5.00 + p&p
**Min. mail order EU:** £5.00 + p&p
**Cat. cost:** Sae
**Credit cards:** None
**Specialities:** Alpine & Woodland plants.
**Map ref:** 10, C4

**NSla**  SLACK TOP ALPINES 🏢
Hebden Bridge, West Yorkshire, HX7 7HA
☎ (01422) 845348
**Contact:** M R or R Mitchell
**Opening times:** 1000-1800 daily excl. Mon
& Tue, plus B/Hol Mons 1st Mar-31st Oct.
**Mail order:** None
**Cat. cost:** Sae
**Credit cards:** None
**Specialities:** Alpine & Rockery plants.
**Map ref:** 9, C2

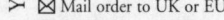

K E Y
⊠ Mail order to UK or EU
✈ Exports beyond EU
🏢 Also supplies Wholesale  ◆ See Display advertisement

**NSpr**  SPRINGWOOD PLEIONES ✉ EU
35 Heathfield, Leeds, W Yorkshire, LS16 7AB
☎ (0113) 261 1781
Contact: Ken Redshaw
Opening times: By appt. only.
Min. mail order UK: £3.00 + p&p
Min. mail order EU: £3.00 + p&p
Cat. cost: 1 x 1st class
Credit cards: None
Specialities: Pleione.
Map ref: 9, B3

**NSti**  STILLINGFLEET LODGE
NURSERIES ✉ UK
Stillingfleet, Yorkshire, YO19 6HP
☎ (01904) 728506   Fax: (01904) 728506
E-mail: vanessa.cook@still-lodge.freeserve.
co.uk
Contact: Vanessa Cook
Opening times: 1000-1600 Tue Wed Fri &
Sat 1st Apr-18th Oct.
Min. mail order UK: No minimum charge
Cat. cost: 7 x 2nd class
Credit cards: None
Specialities: Foliage & unusual perennials. Hardy
Geraniums, Pulmonaria, variegated plants &
Grasses. National Collection of Pulmonaria.
Map ref: 9, B3

**NTay**  TAYLORS NURSERIES ✉ UK ▣ ◆
Sutton Road, Sutton, Doncaster, Yorkshire,
DN6 9JZ
☎ (01302) 700716   Fax: (01302) 708415
Contact: Julie Taylor
Opening times: 0800-1800 Summer,
0800-1700 Winter daily. Closed Xmas
& Boxing day & New Year's day.
Min. mail order UK: 2 plants + p&p
Cat. cost: 5 x 1st class
Credit cards: Visa, Access, MasterCard
Specialities: Clematis (over 250 varieties) &
Herbaceous Perennials.
Map ref: 9, C3

**NTow**  TOWN FARM NURSERY ✉ EU
Whitton, Stockton on Tees, Cleveland,
TS21 1LQ
☎ (01740) 631079
Contact: F D Baker
Opening times: 1000-1800 Fri-Mon
Mar-Oct.
Min. mail order UK: £5.00 + p&p
Min. mail order EU: £20.00 + p&p
Cat. cost: Sae
Credit cards: None
Specialities: Unusual Alpines, Border
Perennials & Shrubs. Also seed.
Map ref: 9, A3

**NVic**  THE VICARAGE GARDEN ✉ UK ▣
Carrington, Urmston, Manchester, M31 4AG
☎ (0161) 775 2750   Fax: (0161) 775 3679
Contact: Mr R Alexander
Opening times: All year 0900-1700 (closed
1215-1330 Sep-Mar). 1000-1630 Sun.
Closed Thur.
Min. mail order UK: £10.00 + p&p
Cat. cost: 5 x 1st class
Credit cards: Visa, Access
Specialities: Herbaceous, Alpines, Grasses,
Ferns. Free admission to 7 acre gardens.
Map ref: 9, C2

**NWCA**  WHITE COTTAGE ALPINES ✉ EU ◆
Sunnyside Nurseries, Hornsea Road,
Sigglesthorne, East Yorkshire, HU11 5QL
☎ (01964) 542692   Fax: (01964) 542692
E-mail: NWCA@whitcottalpines.demon.co.uk
Contact: Sally E Cummins
Opening times: 1000-1700 (or dusk) Thu-
Sun & B/Hol Mons. Closed Dec & Jan.
Min. mail order UK: £7.50 + p&p
Min. mail order EU: £15.00 + p&p
Cat. cost: 4 x 1st class
Credit cards: Visa, MasterCard, Switch, JCB
Specialities: Alpines & Rockery plants. Over
500 species incl. American, dwarf Salix &
Helichrysum.
Map ref: 9, B4

**NWea**  WEASDALE NURSERIES ✉ EU
Newbiggin-on-Lune, Kirkby Stephen,
Cumbria, CA17 4LX
☎ (01539) 623246   Fax: (01539) 623277
E-mail: sales@weasdale.com
Web site: http://www.weasdale.com
Contact: Andrew Forsyth
Opening times: 0900-1700 Mon-Fri.
Closed w/ends, B/Hols, Xmas-New Year.
Min. mail order UK: No minimum charge
Min. mail order EU: Nmc
Cat. cost: £1 (£1.50 by credit card) or
5 x 2nd or 4 x 1st class
Credit cards: Visa, MasterCard, Switch, Delta,
Access, Solo
Specialities: Hardy forest trees, hedging,
broadleaved & conifers. Specimen Trees &
Shrubs grown at 850 feet. Mail order a
speciality.
Map ref: 9, A2

**NWes**  WESTWINDS PERENNIAL PLANTS ✉ EU
Filpoke Lane, High Hesleden, Hartlepool,
Cleveland, TS27 4BT
☎ (0191) 518 0225   Fax: (0191) 518 0225
E-mail: westwinds@btinternet.co.uk
Contact: Harry Blackwood

**Opening times:** Dawn until Dusk Sun & Mon and by appt.
**Min. mail order UK:** No minimum charge*
**Min. mail order EU:** £20.00 + p&p
**Cat. cost:** 2 x 1st class
**Credit cards:** None
**Specialities:** Hosta, Hemerocallis, Geranium & Heuchera. *Note: Mail order for Hostas only.
**Map ref:** 9, A3

**NWoo    WOODLANDS COTTAGE NURSERY**
Summerbridge, Harrogate, North Yorkshire, HG3 4BT
☎ (01423) 780765  **Fax:** (01423) 781390
**E-mail:** j.stark@btinternet.com
**Contact:** Mrs Ann Stark
**Opening times:** 1030-1800 Mon, Wed, Fri, Sat mid Mar-end Sep.
**Mail order:** None
**Cat. cost:** 2 x 1st class
**Credit cards:** None
**Specialities:** Herbs, plants for Shade & Hardy Perennials.
**Map ref:** 9, B2

**NYoL    YORKSHIRE LAVENDER**
The Yorkshire Lavender Farm, Terrington, York, N Yorks, YO60 6QB
☎ (01653) 648430, (01653) 648008
**Fax:** (01653) 648430
**Contact:** Nigel W B Goodwill
**Opening times:** 1030-1630 daily Easter-30th Sept.
**Mail order:** None
**Cat. cost:** None issued
**Credit cards:** None
**Specialities:** Lavandula.
**Map ref:** 9, B3

**NZep    ZEPHYRWUDE IRISES ⊠ EU**
48 Blacker Lane, Crigglestone, Wakefield, West Yorkshire, WF4 3EW
☎ (01924) 252101
**Contact:** Richard L Brook
**Opening times:** Viewing only 0900-dusk daily May-early June, peak late May.
Phone first, 0900-2300.
**Min. mail order UK:** £15.00 + p&p
**Min. mail order EU:** £15.00 + p&p
**Cat. cost:** 1 x 1st class
**Credit cards:** None
**Specialities:** Bearded Iris, 1970s-80s hybrids only. Mainly 12" dwarf & intermediate, a few tall. Catalogue available Apr-Sep 15th.
Delivery Aug-Oct only.
**Map ref:** 9, C3

# SOUTHERN ENGLAND

**SAft    AFTON PARK NURSERY**
Newport Road, Afton, Freshwater, Isle of Wight, PO40 9XR
☎ (01983) 755774, 0966 543031 mobile
**Fax:** (01983) 756661
**E-mail:** barney@skyroots.demon.co.uk
**Web site:** http://www.skyroots.demon.co.uk
**Contact:** Chris Barnes
**Opening times:** 0930-1700 Mon-Sat, 1030-1630 Sun Feb-Dec.
**Mail order:** None
**Cat. cost:** 4 x 1st class
**Credit cards:** Visa, MasterCard
**Specialities:** Wide general range, emphasis on unusual Perennials and Coastal Shrubs. Grasses, Wild Flowers & plants for Mediterranean gardens.
**Map ref:** 2, C3

**SAga    AGAR'S NURSERY**
Agars Lane, Hordle, Lymington, Hampshire, SO41 0FL
☎ (01590) 683703
**Contact:** Mrs Diana Tombs
**Opening times:** 1000-1700 Fri-Wed Mar-Oct, 1000-1600 Fri-Wed Nov, Dec & Feb.
**Mail order:** None
**Cat. cost:** None issued
**Credit cards:** None
**Specialities:** Penstemon & Salvia. Also wide range of Hardy plants inc. Shrubs, Climbers & Herbaceous.
**Map ref:** 2, C3

**SAll    ALLWOOD BROS ⊠ EU ✈ ✪**
London Road, Hassocks, West Sussex, BN6 9NB
☎ (01273) 844229  **Fax:** (01273) 846022
**Contact:** Sue James
**Opening times:** 0900-1600 Mon-Fri.
**Min. mail order UK:** No minimum charge
**Min. mail order EU:** Nmc
**Cat. cost:** 2 x 1st class
**Credit cards:** Access, Visa
**Specialities:** Dianthus, incl Hardy Border Carnations, Pinks, Perpetual & Allwoodii, some available as seed. Note: Exports seed only.
**Map ref:** 3, B2

S

| KEY | |
|---|---|
| ⊠ | Mail order to UK or EU |
| ✈ | Exports beyond EU |
| ✪ | Also supplies Wholesale ◆ See Display advertisement |

**S**

**SAPC**   ARCHITECTURAL PLANTS (CHICHESTER) LTD ⊠ EU ⊠ ⊠ ◆
Lidsey Road Nursery, Westergate, Nr Chichester, West Sussex, PO20 6SU
☎ (01243) 545008   Fax: (01243) 545009
Web Site: http://members.aol.com/gshaw 29868/archplnt.htm
Contact: Christine Shaw
Opening times: 1000-1600 Sun-Fri throughout the year, closed Sat.
Min. mail order UK: No minimum charge
Min. mail order EU: £150.00 + p&p
Cat. cost: Free
Credit cards: Visa, Access, EuroCard, Switch, Delta, Electron, JCB, MasterCard
Specialities: Architectural plants & hardy Exotics, esp. evergreen broadleaved trees, & seaside exotics. Note: Second nursery near Horsham, Code SArc.
Map ref: 3, C1

**SApp**   APPLE COURT ⊠ EU ◆
Hordle Lane, Hordle, Lymington, Hampshire, S041 0HU
☎ (01590) 642130   Fax: (01590) 644220
E-mail: applecourt@btinternet.com
Web site: http://www.applecourt.com
Contact: Diana Grenfell, Roger Grounds & Jenny
Opening times: Daily exc. Wed Mar-Oct. Closed Nov-Feb.
Min. mail order UK: £15.00 + p&p
Min. mail order EU: £50.00 + p&p
Cat. cost: 4 x 1st class
Credit cards: None
Specialities: Hosta, Grasses, Ferns, Hemerocallis. National Collection of Woodwardia, Rohdea, & Hosta.
Map ref: 2, C3

**SApu**   APULDRAM ROSES ⊠ EU ⊠
Apuldram Lane, Dell Quay, Chichester, Sussex, PO20 7EF
☎ (01243) 785769   Fax: (01243) 536973
E-mail: d.sawday@virgin.net
Web site: http://www.gardening-uk.com/apuldram/
Contact: Mrs Sawday
Opening times: 0900-1700 Mon-Sat, 1030-1630 Sun & B/Hols. ex. Dec 23rd-Jan 5th.
Min. mail order UK: £4.50 + p&p
Min. mail order EU: £4.50 + p&p
Cat. cost: 2 x 1st class
Credit cards: Switch, MasterCard, Visa
Specialities: Roses.
Map ref: 3, C1

**SArc**   ARCHITECTURAL PLANTS ⊠ EU ⊠ ⊠
Cooks Farm, Nuthurst, Horsham, West Sussex, RH13 6LH
☎ (01403) 891772   Fax: (01403) 891056
Contact: Sarah Chandler & Monique Gudgeon
Opening times: 0900-1700 Mon-Sat.
Min. mail order UK: No minimum charge
Min. mail order EU: £150.00 + p&p
Cat. cost: Free
Credit cards: Visa, Access, EuroCard, Switch, Delta, Electron, JCB
Specialities: Architectural plants & hardy Exotics. Note: Second nursery near Chichester, Code SAPC.
Map ref: 3, B2

**SAsh**   ASHENDEN NURSERY
Cranbrook Road, Benenden, Cranbrook, Kent, TN17 4ET
☎ (01580) 241792
Contact: Kevin McGarry
Opening times: By appt. Please telephone.
Mail order: None
Cat. cost: Sae + 1 x 1st class
Credit cards: None
Specialities: Rock garden plants, Perennials & Ornamental Grasses.
Map ref: 3, B3

**SAWi**   ANTHONY ARCHER-WILLS LTD ⊠ UK ⊠
Broadford Bridge Road, West Chiltington, West Sussex, RH20 2LF
☎ (01798) 813204   Fax: (01798) 815080
Contact: Anthony Archer-Wills
Opening times: By appt. only - Please telephone.
Min. mail order UK: £15.00 + p&p
Cat. cost: £1.00 + 2 x 2nd class
Credit cards: None
Specialities: Ponds, Lakes & Water garden plants.
Map ref: 3, B1

**SBai**   STEVEN BAILEY LTD ⊠ EU ⊠ ⊠
Silver Street, Sway, Lymington, Hampshire, SO41 6ZA
☎ (01590) 682227   Fax: (01590) 683765
Contact: Fiona Whittles
Opening times: 1000-1300 & 1400-1630 Mon-Fri all year. 1000-1300 & 1400-1600 Sat Mar-Jun ex B/Hols.
Min. mail order UK: Quotation
Min. mail order EU: Quotation
Cat. cost: 2 x 2nd class
Credit cards: Visa, Access
Specialities: Carnations, Pinks & Alstroemeria.
Map ref: 2, C3

**SBea    BEAN PLACE NURSERY** 🔲
(Office) 52 Gladstone Road, South
Willesborough, Ashford, Kent, TN24 0BY
☎ (01233) 631550  **Fax:** (01233) 631550
**Contact:** Miss A Jefford
**Opening times:** 1000-1600 Sun-Tue
1st Mar-1st Nov. Other times by appt.
**Mail order:** None
**Cat. cost:** 3 x 1st class
**Credit cards:** None
**Specialities:** Ornamental Grasses, Herbaceous
Perennials & Cottage Garden plants. Note:
Nursery is at Bean Place, Ashford Road,
Bethersden.
**Map ref:** 3, B4

**SBid    BIDDENDEN NURSERY AT GARDEN
CRAFTS** ⊠ EU 🔲 🔲
Sissinghurst Road, Biddenden, Kent, TN27 8EJ
☎ (01580) 292100  **Fax:** (01580) 292 097
**Contact:** Gerald Bedrich
**Opening times:** 0900-1700 Mon-Fri,
1000-1700 Sat & Sun.
**Min. mail order UK:** No minimum charge
**Min. mail order EU:** Nmc
**Cat. cost:** 3 x 1st class
**Credit cards:** Visa, Access, American Express,
Switch
**Specialities:** Wide range of unusual Shrubs,
esp. Ceanothus, Hydrangea & Viburnum.
Rare & unusual Herbaceous. Comprehensive
range of 'Sissinghurst' plants.
**Map ref:** 3, B3

**SBir    BIRCHFLEET NURSERY** ⊠ EU 🔲 🔲
Nyewood, Petersfield, Hampshire, GU31 5JQ
☎ (01730) 821636  **Fax:** (01730) 821636
**E-mail:** gammoak@aol.com
**Contact:** John & Daphne Gammon
**Opening times:** By appt. only.
Please telephone.
**Min. mail order UK:** £20.00 + p&p
**Min. mail order EU:** £30.00 + p&p
**Cat. cost:** Sae
**Credit cards:** None
**Specialities:** Oaks, Liquidambar – National
Collection.
**Map ref:** 3, B1

**SBla    BLACKTHORN NURSERY**
Kilmeston, Alresford, Hampshire, SO24 0NL
☎ (01962) 771796  **Fax:** (01962) 771071
**Contact:** A R & S B White
**Opening times:** 1999: 0900-1700 Fri & Sat
5th Mar-26th Jun. 2000: 0900-1700 1st
Thur-Sun of Feb, Mar, Apr, May & Jun.
**Mail order:** None
**Cat. cost:** Info. sheets available at nursery.

**Credit cards:** None
**Specialities:** Choice Perennials & Alpines, esp.
Daphne, Epimedium, Helleborus & Hepatica.
**Map ref:** 2, B4

**SBod    BODIAM NURSERY** ⊠ UK 🔲
Ockham House, Bodiam, Robertsbridge, East
Sussex, TN32 5RA
☎ (01580) 830811/830649
**Fax:** (01580) 830071
**Contact:** Richard Biggs and Mike Gornett
**Opening times:** 0900-1700 or by appt.
**Min. mail order UK:** £15.00 + p&p
**Cat. cost:** 4 x 1st class
**Credit cards:** Visa, MasterCard, EuroCard,
American Express
**Specialities:** Heathers, herbaceous Perennials,
Grasses, Conifers, Azalea, Camellia &
Climbers.
**Map ref:** 3, B3

**SBra    J BRADSHAW & SON** ⊠ EU 🔲 ◆
Busheyfield Nursery, Herne, Herne Bay, Kent,
CT6 7LJ
☎ (01227) 375415  **Fax:** (01227) 375415
**Contact:** D J Bradshaw & Martin Bradshaw
**Opening times:** 1000-1700 Tue-Sat 1st
Mar-31st Oct. Other times by appt. only.
**Min. mail order UK:** 2 plants + p&p
**Min. mail order EU:** 2 plants + p&p
**Cat. cost:** Sae + 2 x 1st class
**Credit cards:** None
**Specialities:** Clematis, Climbers & Wall
plants. National Collection of climbing
Lonicera & Clematis montana.
**Map ref:** 3, A4

**SBre    BRESSINGHAM PLANT CENTRE**
Borde Hill, Haywards Heath, West Sussex,
RH16 1XP
☎ (01379) 687464/688133 (Norfolk site
temporarily)  **Fax:** (01379) 688034 (Norfolk
site temporarily)
**Contact:** Nathan Berrisford (or Tony Fry by
phone/fax at the Norfolk site)
**Opening times:** 0900-1730 daily. (Direct
retail Plant Centre.)
**Mail order:** None
**Cat. cost:** None issued
**Credit cards:** Delta, Switch, MasterCard, Visa
**Specialities:** Very wide general range. Many
own varieties. Focus on Hardy Ornamental
plants & Grasses.
**Map ref:** 3, B2

S

| KEY | |
|---|---|
| ⊠ | Mail order to UK or EU |
| 🔲 | Exports beyond EU |
| 🔲 | Also supplies Wholesale  ◆ See Display advertisement |

**SBrk**   **BROOKSIDE NURSERY** ⊠ EU ▣
Elderberry Farm, Bognor Road, Rowhook,
Horsham, West Sussex, RH12 3PS
☎ (01403) 790996   **Fax:** (01403) 790195
**E-mail:** alanbutler1@compuserve.com
**Web site:** http://www.cactus-mall.com
/nursery/brooksid.html
**Contact:** A J Butler
**Opening times:** 1000-1700 Thur-Sun; open
B/Hol Mons. Please phone first.
**Min. mail order UK:** No minimum charge
**Min. mail order EU:** Nmc
**Cat. cost:** 1 x 1st class
**Credit cards:** Visa, MasterCard, Switch
**Specialities:** Cactus & Succulent plants.
National Collection of Sansevieria.
**Map ref:** 3, B1

**SBrw**   **BROADWATER PLANTS**
Fairview Lane, Tunbridge Wells, Kent, TN3 9LU
☎ (01892) 534760   **Fax:** (01892) 534760
**E-mail:** broadwater@coblands.co.uk
**Contact:** John Moaby
**Opening times:** 0900-1630 Mon-Fri,
0900-1600 Sat 1st Mar-30th June.
**Mail order:** None
**Cat. cost:** 3 x 1st class
**Credit cards:** MasterCard, Visa
**Specialities:** Rhododendron, Camellia &
Ericaceous plants incl. many unusual species.
Many field grown Rhododendrons (Hardy
Hybrids) available at specimen sizes.
Minimum delivered value in home counties
£100, other areas Poa.
**Map ref:** 3, B2

**SChr**   **JOHN CHURCHER PLANTS** ⊠ EU ▣
47 Grove Avenue, Portchester, Fareham,
Hampshire, PO16 9EZ
☎ (01705) 326740
**Contact:** John Churcher
**Opening times:** By appt. only. Please phone.
**Min. mail order UK:** No minimum charge
**Min. mail order EU:** Nmc
**Cat. cost:** Sae for list
**Credit cards:** None
**Specialities:** Opuntia, Agave, Succulents, Palms
plus small general range, hardy & half hardy.
Note: Exports seed only.
**Map ref:** 2, C4

**SChu**   **CHURCH HILL COTTAGE
GARDENS** ⊠ UK
Charing Heath, Ashford, Kent, TN27 0BU
☎ (01233) 712522   **Fax:** (01233) 712522
**Contact:** Mr M & J & Mrs M Metianu
**Opening times:** 1000-1700 1st Feb-30th Nov
Tue-Sun & B/Hol Mons. Other times by appt.

**Min. mail order UK:** £10.00 + p&p
**Cat. cost:** 3 x 1st class
**Credit cards:** None
**Specialities:** Unusual hardy plants, Dianthus,
Hosta, Ferns & Viola. Alpines & Shrubs.
**Map ref:** 3, A3

**SCit**   **THE CITRUS CENTRE** ⊠ EU ▣ ▣
West Mare Lane, Marehill, Pulborough, West
Sussex, RH20 2EA
☎ (01798) 872786   **Fax:** (01798) 874880
**E-mail:** enquiries@citruscentre.co.uk
**Web site:** http://www.citruscentre.co.uk
**Contact:** Amanda & Chris Dennis
**Opening times:** 0930-1730 Wed-Sun &
B/Hols. Closed Xmas & Boxing Day.
**Min. mail order UK:** No minimum charge
**Min. mail order EU:** Nmc
**Cat. cost:** Sae
**Credit cards:** Visa, Access
**Specialities:** Citrus & Citrus relatives.
**Map ref:** 3, B1

**SCko**   **COOKOO BOX NURSERY** ⊠ EU ▣ ▣
Longfield, 63 Charlesford Avenue,
Kingswood, Maidstone, Kent, ME17 3PH
☎ (01622) 844866
**Contact:** Mr P Cook
**Opening times:** 1000-1630 daily Mar-Dec.
Sun Jan-Feb by appt. only.
**Min. mail order UK:** No minimum charge
**Min. mail order EU:** Nmc
**Cat. cost:** 2 x 1st class
**Credit cards:** None
**Specialities:** A new family run nursery with an
increasing range of Grasses, Cottage Garden
Perennials, Salvia, Phlox, Hosta, Penstemon
(some unusual), & Spring, Summer &
Autumn Bedding.
**Map ref:** 3, A3

**SCob**   **COBLANDS NURSERY** ▣
(Office) Trench Road, Tonbridge, Kent,
TN10 3HQ
☎ (01732) 770999   **Fax:** (01732) 770271
**E-mail:** plants@coblands.co.uk
**Contact:** Nick Coslett
**Opening times:** 0830-1600 Mon-Fri.
**Mail order:** None
**Cat. cost:** W/Sale Cat only
**Credit cards:** Visa, MasterCard
**Specialities:** General range, esp. Herbaceous –
common & unusual, many in large quantities.
Bamboos, Grasses & Ferns. Note: Nursery is
at Back Lane, Ivy Hatch, Ightham, Sevenoaks,
Kent.
**Map ref:** 3, A3

**S**Cog **COGHURST NURSERY** ✉ EU 🖾
Ivy House Lane, Near Three Oaks, Hastings,
East Sussex, TN35 4NP
☎ (01424) 756228
**Contact:** J Farnfield & L A Edgar
**Opening times:** 1100-1600 Tue, Wed & Fri,
1000-1630 Sun.
**Min. mail order UK:** No minimum charge
**Min. mail order EU:** Nmc
**Cat. cost:** 1 x 2nd class for availability list.
**Credit cards:** None
**Specialities:** Camellia.
**Map ref:** 3, B3

**S**Con **CONNOISSEURS' CACTI** ✉ EU 🖾 🖾
(Office) 51 Chelsfield Lane, Orpington, Kent,
BR5 4HG
☎ (01689) 837781
**Contact:** John Pilbeam
**Opening times:** 1030-1430 but please
phone first.
**Min. mail order UK:** No minimum charge
**Min. mail order EU:** Nmc
**Cat. cost:** Sae or IRC
**Credit cards:** None
**Specialities:** Mammillaria, Sulcorebutia,
Gymnocalycium, Rebutia, Haworthia etc.
**Note:** Nursery is at Woodlands Farm, Shire
Lane, Nr Farnborough, Kent.
**Map ref:** 3, A2

**S**Coo **COOLING'S NURSERIES LTD**
Rushmore Hill, Knockholt, Sevenoaks, Kent,
TN14 7NN
☎ (01959) 532269   **Fax:** (01959) 534092
**Contact:** M Hooker
**Opening times:** 0900-1700 Mon-Sat &
1000-1630 Sun.
**Mail order:** None
**Cat. cost:** 4 x 1st class
**Credit cards:** Visa, Access, Switch, Electron,
Delta
**Specialities:** Large range of Perennials,
Conifers & Bedding plants. Some unusual
Shrubs.
**Map ref:** 3, A2

**S**Cou **COOMBLAND GARDENS** ✉ EU 🖾 ♦
Coombland, Coneyhurst, Billingshurst, West
Sussex, RH14 9DG
☎ (01403) 741727   **Fax:** (01403) 741079
**Contact:** David Browne
**Opening times:** 1400-1600 Mon-Fri Mar-end
Oct. B/Hols & other times by appt. only.
**Min. mail order UK:** £20.00 + p&p
**Min. mail order EU:** 8 plants + p&p*
**Cat. cost:** 5 x 1st class
**Credit cards:** None

**Specialities:** Hardy Geranium – National
Collection – & choice Herbaceous. Also seeds.
*Note: Hardy Geraniums only to EU.
**Map ref:** 3, B1

**S**Cro **CROFTWAY NURSERY** ✉ EU 🖾
Yapton Road, Barnham, Bognor Regis, West
Sussex, PO22 0BH
☎ (01243) 552121   **Fax:** (01243) 552125
**E-mail:** croftway@aol.com
**Web site:** http://members.aol.com/croftway/
**Contact:** Graham Spencer
**Opening times:** 0900-1700 Mon-Sat,
1000-1600 Sun. Closed 1st Dec-28th Feb
except by appt.
**Min. mail order UK:** No minimum charge*
**Min. mail order EU:** Nmc*
**Cat. cost:** 4 x 1st class
**Credit cards:** Visa, Access, Switch
**Specialities:** Wide general range, emphasis on
Perennials. Specialists in Iris & Hardy Geranium.
*Note: Mail order for Iris & Geranium only.
**Map ref:** 3, C1

**S**Dad **J DADSWELL**
4 Marle Avenue, Burgess Hill, West Sussex,
RH15 8JG
☎ (01444) 232874
**Contact:** Judith Dadswell
**Opening times:** By appt. only & for collection
of orders.
**Mail order:** None
**Cat. cost:** Free on written request.
**Credit cards:** None
**Specialities:** Geranium.

**S**Day **A LA CARTE DAYLILIES** ✉ EU ♦
Little Hermitage, St. Catherine's Down, Nr
Ventnor, Isle of Wight, PO38 2PD
☎ (01983) 730512
**Contact:** Jan & Andy Wyers
**Opening times:** By appt. only
**Min. mail order UK:** No minimum charge
**Min. mail order EU:** Nmc
**Cat. cost:** 3 x 1st class
**Credit cards:** None
**Specialities:** Hemerocallis
**Map ref:** 2, C4

**S**Dea **DEACON'S NURSERY** ✉ EU 🖾 🖾 ♦
Moor View, Godshill, Isle of Wight, PO38 3HW
☎ (01983) 840750 (24 hrs), (01983) 522243
**Fax:** (01983) 523575

---

| KEY | | |
|---|---|---|
| ✉ | Mail order to UK or EU | |
| 🖾 | Exports beyond EU | |
| 🖾 | Also supplies Wholesale | ♦ See Display advertisement |

**S**

Contact: G D & B H W Deacon
Opening times: 0800-1600 Mon-Fri
May-Sep, 0800-1700 Mon-Fri 0800-1300 Sat
Oct-Apr.
Min. mail order UK: No minimum charge
Min. mail order EU: Nmc
Cat. cost: Stamp appreciated.
Credit cards: Visa, Access
Specialities: Over 300 varieties of Apple, old
& new. Plus Pears, Plums, Gages, Damsons,
Cherries etc. Fruit & Nut trees, triple Peaches,
Ballerinas. Modern Soft Fruit. Grapes, Hops.
Family Trees – Blueberries/Nuts/Asparagus.
Map ref: 2, C4

**SDeJ**  DE JAGER & SONS ⊠ EU 🖾 🖾
The Nurseries, Marden, Kent, TN12 9BP
☎ (01622) 831235  Fax: (01622) 832416
Contact: Mrs J Croucher
Opening times: 0900-1700 Mon-Fri.
Min. mail order UK: £15.00 + p&p
Min. mail order EU: £15.00 + p&p
Cat. cost: Free
Credit cards: Visa, Access
Specialities: Wide general range, esp. Bulbs.
Lilium, Tulipa, Narcissus species &
miscellaneous. Large range of Perennials.
Map ref: 3, B3

**SDix**  GREAT DIXTER NURSERIES ⊠ EU
Northiam, Rye, East Sussex, TN31 6PH
☎ (01797) 253107  Fax: (01797) 252879
E-mail: greatdixter@compuserve.com
Web site: http://www.entertainnet.co.uk/
greatdixter/index/html
Contact: K Leighton
Opening times: 0900-1230 & 1330-1700
Mon-Fri, 0900-1200 Sat all year. Also
1400-1700 Sat, Sun & B/Hols Apr-Oct.
Min. mail order UK: £15.00 + p&p
Min. mail order EU: £15.00 + p&p
Cat. cost: 4 x 1st class
Credit cards: Access, Switch, Visa
Specialities: Clematis, Shrubs and Plants.
Gardens open.
Map ref: 3, B3

**SDnm**  DENMANS GARDEN,
(JOHN BROOKES LTD)
Clock House, Denmans, Fontwell, Nr
Arundel, West Sussex, BN18 0SU
☎ (01243) 542808  Fax: (01243) 544064
Contact: John Brookes
Opening times: 0900-1700 daily 4th Mar-
31st Oct.
Mail order: None
Cat. cost: £2.50
Credit cards: Visa, MasterCard

Specialities: Rare and unusual plants.
Map ref: 3, C1

**SDow**  DOWNDERRY NURSERY ⊠ EU 🖾 🖾
Pillar Box Lane, Hadlow, Nr Tonbridge, Kent,
TN11 9SW
☎ (01732) 810081  Fax: (01732) 811398
E-mail: simon@downderrynursery.
demon.co.uk
Contact: Dr S J Charlesworth
Opening times: 1000-1700 Wed-Sat &
1100-1700 Sun & B/Hols May-3rd Oct,
and by appt.
Min. mail order UK: No minimum charge
Min. mail order EU: Nmc
Cat. cost: 3 x 1st class
Credit cards: Delta, MasterCard, Switch, Visa
Specialities: Lavandula – National Collection.
Map ref: 3, A3

**SDry**  DRYSDALE GARDEN EXOTICS ⊠ EU
Bowerwood Road, Fordingbridge, Hampshire,
SP6 1BN
☎ (01425) 653010
Contact: David Crampton
Opening times: 0930-1730 Wed-Fri, 1000-
1730 Sun. Closed 24th Dec-2nd Jan incl.
Min. mail order UK: £10.00 + p&p
Min. mail order EU: £15.00 + p&p
Cat. cost: 3 x 1st class
Credit cards: None
Specialities: Plants for exotic & foliage effect.
Plants for Mediterranean gardens. National
Collections of Bamboos.
Map ref: 2, B3

**SDys**  WILLIAM T DYSON ⊠ UK
Great Comp Nursery, Comp Lane, Platt,
Borough Green, Kent, TN15 8QS
☎ (01732) 886154
Contact: William Dyson
Opening times: 1100-1800 daily
1st Apr-31st Oct. Other times by appt.
Min. mail order UK: £15.00 + p&p
Cat. cost: 2 x 1st class
Credit cards: None
Specialities: Wide range of choice & unusual
plants esp. Salvia, Sempervivum, Geranium &
Pulmonaria.
Map ref: 3, A3

**SEas**  EASTFIELD PLANT CENTRE
Paice Lane, Medstead, Alton, Hampshire,
GU34 5PR
☎ (01420) 563640  Fax: (01420) 563640
Contact: D M & P Barton
Opening times: 0900-1700 daily
1st Feb-20th Dec or by appt.

Mail order: None
Cat. cost: None issued
Credit cards: None
Speciality: General range.
Map ref: 2, B4

**SEND  EAST NORTHDOWN FARM** 🔲 ◆
Margate, Kent, CT9 3TS
☎ (01843) 862060  **Fax:** (01843) 860206
**Contact:** Louise & William Friend
**Opening times:** 0900-1700 Mon-Sat,
1000-1700 Sun all year. Closed Xmas week &
Easter Sun.
**Mail order:** None
**Cat. cost:** None issued.
**Credit cards:** Visa, Access, Switch
**Specialities:** Chalk & Coast-loving plants.
**Map ref:** 3, A4

**SFam  FAMILY TREES** ⊠ EU ◆
Sandy Lane, Shedfield, Hampshire, SO32 2HQ
☎ (01329) 834812
**Contact:** Philip House
**Opening times:** 0930-1230 Wed & Sat
mid Oct-mid Apr.
**Min. mail order UK:** No minimum charge
**Min. mail order EU:** Nmc
**Cat. cost:** Free
**Credit cards:** None
**Specialities:** Fruit & Ornamental trees. Trained
Fruit Tree specialists ie. standards, espaliers,
cordons etc. Also other Trees & Old Roses.
**Map ref:** 2, B4

**SFur  FURZEY GARDENS NURSERY** ⊠ EU 🔲 🔲
(Office) The Minstead Training Project,
Minstead Lodge, Minstead, Nr Lyndhurst,
Hampshire, SO43 7FT
☎ (01703) 814134  **Fax:** (01703) 812297
**Contact:** Peter White
**Opening times:** (Nursery) 1000-1700 daily
Mar-Dec. Mail order all year.
**Min. mail order UK:** £20.00 + p&p
**Min. mail order EU:** £20.00 + p&p
**Cat. cost:** 1 x 2nd class
**Credit cards:** None
**Specialities:** Acers. Note: Nursery is at Furzey
Gardens, Minstead, Nr Lyndhurst.
**Map ref:** 2, B3

**SGre  GREENWOOD PLANTS** ⊠ EU
The Old Post House, Christchurch Road,
Downton, Lymington, Hampshire, SO41 0LA
☎ (01590) 642409
**E-mail:** jgplants@aol.com
**Contact:** Jeremy Greenwood
**Opening times:** 0900-1700 Sat & Sun
Mar-June by arrangement, please phone first.

**Min. mail order UK:** £10.00 + p&p
**Min. mail order EU:** £20.00 + p&p
**Cat. cost:** 4 x 1st class
**Credit cards:** None
**Specialities:** Alpines esp. Saxifrages,
uncommon Hardy Perennials many from wild
collected seed.
**Map ref:** 2, C3

**SHar  HARDY'S COTTAGE GARDEN
PLANTS** ⊠ EU 🔲
Freefolk Priors, Freefolk, Whitchurch,
Hampshire, RG28 7NJ
☎ (01256) 896533  **Fax:** (01256) 896572
**E-mail:** hardy@cottagegarden.demon.co.uk
**Contact:** Rosy Hardy
**Opening times:** 1000-1700 daily
1st Mar-31st Oct.
**Min. mail order UK:** No minimum charge
**Min. mail order EU:** Nmc
**Cat. cost:** 5 x 1st class.
**Credit cards:** Visa, Access
**Specialities:** Hardy Geranium & other
Herbaceous both old & new.
**Map ref:** 2, A4

**SHay  HAYWARD'S CARNATIONS** ⊠ EU 🔲
The Chace Gardens, Stakes Road, Purbrook,
Waterlooville, Hampshire, PO7 5PL
☎ (01705) 263047  **Fax:** (01705) 263047
**Contact:** A N Hayward
**Opening times:** 0930-1700 Mon-Fri.
**Min. mail order UK:** £10.00 + p&p
**Min. mail order EU:** £50.00 + p&p
**Cat. cost:** 1 x 1st class
**Credit cards:** None
**Specialities:** Hardy Pinks & Border
Carnations (Dianthus). Greenhouse perpetual
Carnations.
**Map ref:** 2, B4

**SHDw  HIGHDOWN NURSERY** ⊠ EU 🔲 🔲
New Hall Lane, Small Dole, Nr Henfield,
West Sussex, BN5 9YH
☎ (01273) 492976  **Fax:** (01273) 492976
**Contact:** A G & J H Shearing
**Opening times:** 0900-1700 daily
**Min. mail order UK:** £10.00 + p&p
**Min. mail order EU:** £10.00 + p&p
**Cat. cost:** 3 x 1st class
**Credit cards:** Visa, MasterCard, Delta, JCB,
EuroCard
**Specialities:** Herbs.
**Map ref:** 3, B2

KEY: ⊠ Mail order to UK or EU
🔲 Exports beyond EU
🔲 Also supplies Wholesale  ◆ See Display advertisement

**S**

**SHel**    **HELLYER'S GARDEN PLANTS** ✉ UK ◆
Orchards, off Wallage Lane*, Rowfant,
Nr Crawley, Sussex, RH10 4NJ
☎ (01342) 718280
**Contact:** Penelope Hellyer
**Opening times:** 1000-1700 Wed-Sat
Mar-Oct & by prior appt.
**Min. mail order UK:** No minimum charge
**Cat. cost:** 3 x 1st + A5 Sae. Mail order list
1 x 1st + A5 Sae.
**Credit cards:** None
**Specialities:** Unusual hardy plants for sun/shade.
Small selection of Climbers & Shrubs. Over 100
varieties of hardy Geraniums. *Note: Wallage
Lane is off the B2028 equidistant Crawley Down
& Turners Hill.
**Map ref:** 3, B2

**SHFr**    **SUE HARTFREE** ✉ EU 🖥
25 Crouch Hill Court, Lower Halstow,
Nr Sittingbourne, Kent, ME9 7EJ
☎ (01795) 842426
**Contact:** Sue Hartfree
**Opening times:** Any time by appt.
Please phone first.
**Min. mail order UK:** £15.00 + p&p*
**Min. mail order EU:** £30.00 + p&p*
**Cat. cost:** A5 Sae + 4 x 1st class
**Credit cards:** None
**Specialities:** Unusual & interesting Shrubs,
Hardy & Half-hardy Perennials incl. Salvia,
Lobelia, Penstemon & Lysimachia. All can be
seen growing in the garden. *Note: Mail order
Oct-March.
**Map ref:** 3, A3

**SHHo**    **HIGHFIELD HOLLIES** ✉ UK ◆
Highfield Farm, Hatch Lane, Liss, Hampshire,
GU33 7NH
☎ (01730) 892372   **Fax:** (01730) 894853
**E-mail:** louise@bendall.prestel.co.uk
**Contact:** Mrs Louise Bendall
**Opening times:** By appt.
**Min. mail order UK:** No minimum charge
**Cat. cost:** 2 x 1st class
**Credit cards:** None
**Specialities:** Ilex. Over 100 species & cultivars
incl. many specimen trees & topiary.
**Map ref:** 3, B1

**SHmp**    **HAMPSHIRE CARNIVOROUS
PLANTS** ✉ EU 🖥 🖥
Ya-Mayla, Allington Lane, West End,
Southampton, Hampshire, SO30 3HQ
☎ (01703) 473314, 0403 258296 (mobile)
**Fax:** (01703) 473314
**E-mail:** matthew@msoper.freesave.co.uk
**Contact:** Matthew Soper
**Opening times:** By appt. only.
**Min. mail order UK:** No minimum charge
**Min. mail order EU:** £50.00 + p&p
**Cat. cost:** 2 x 2nd class
**Credit cards:** None
**Specialities:** Carnivorous plants esp.
Nepenthes, Heliamphora, Sarracenia.

**SHol**    **HOLLY GATE CACTUS
NURSERY** ✉ EU 🖥
Billingshurst Road, Ashington, West Sussex,
RH20 3BB
☎ (01903) 892 930
**E-mail:** hollygate@tmh.globalnet.co.uk
**Web site:** http://www.users.globalnet.
co.uk/tmh
**Contact:** Mr T M Hewitt
**Opening times:** 0900-1700 daily.
**Min. mail order UK:** £5.00 + p&p
**Min. mail order EU:** £10.00 + p&p
**Cat. cost:** 2 x 1st class
**Credit cards:** Visa, Access, American Express
**Specialities:** Cactus & Succulents, plants &
seeds. World famous Cactus Garden.
**Map ref:** 3, B1

**SHut**    **THE HUT**
Stream Hill, Dallington, Heathfield, East
Sussex, TN21 9NE
☎ (01435) 831002
**Contact:** Mrs M Buss
**Opening times:** By appt. only.
**Mail order:** None
**Cat. cost:** 4 x 2nd class, available early June.
**Credit cards:** None
**Map ref:** 3, B3

**SHvs**    **HARVEST NURSERIES** ✉ EU
Harvest Cottage, Boonshill Farm, Iden,
Nr Rye, E Sussex, TN31 7QA
☎ (01797) 230583
**Contact:** D A Smith
**Opening times:** Mail order only.
**Min. mail order UK:** No minimum charge
**Min. mail order EU:** £20.00 + p&p
**Cat. cost:** 2 x 1st class
**Credit cards:** None
**Specialities:** Epiphyllums & wide range of
Succulents. Descriptive catalogue.

**SHya**    **BRENDA HYATT** ✉ EU
1 Toddington Crescent, Bluebell Hill,
Chatham, Kent, ME5 9QT
☎ (01634) 863251
**Contact:** Mrs Brenda Hyatt
**Opening times:** Appt. only.
**Min. mail order UK:** No minimum charge
**Min. mail order EU:** Nmc
**Cat. cost:** £1.00

**Credit cards:** None
**Specialities:** Show Auricula.
**Map ref:** 3, A3

**SIde    IDEN CROFT HERBS** ✉ EU ✉ ◆
Frittenden Road, Staplehurst, Kent,
TN12 0DH
☎ (01580) 891432  **Fax:** (01580) 892416
**E-mail:** idencroft.herbs@dial.pipex.com
**Web site:** http://www/oxalis.co.uk/ic.htm
**Contact:** Rosemary & D Titterington
**Opening times:** 0900-1700 Mon-Sat all year.
1100-1700 Sun & B/Hols 1st Mar- 30th Sep.
**Min. mail order UK:** No minimum charge
**Min. mail order EU:** Nmc
**Cat. cost:** 4 x 1st class for descriptive list.
**Credit cards:** Visa, Access, American Express,
Delta, JCB, EuroCard, Switch
**Specialities:** Herbs, Aromatic & Wild flower
plants & plants for bees & butterflies.
National Collections of Mentha & Origanum.
Note: Exports seed only.
**Map ref:** 3, B3

**SIgm    TIM INGRAM**
Copton Ash, 105 Ashford Road, Faversham,
Kent, ME13 8XW
☎ (01795) 535919
**Contact:** Dr T J Ingram
**Opening times:** 1400-1800 Tue-Fri & Sat-Sun
Mar-Oct. Nov-Feb by appt.
**Mail order:** None
**Cat. cost:** 4 x 1st class
**Credit cards:** None
**Specialities:** Unusual Perennials, alpines &
plants from Mediterranean-type climates incl.
Lupins, Penstemons, Salvias & Umbellifers.
**Map ref:** 3, A4

**SIng    W E TH. INGWERSEN LTD**
Birch Farm Nursery, Gravetye, East Grinstead,
West Sussex, RH19 4LE
☎ (01342) 810236
**Contact:** M P & M R Ingwersen
**Opening times:** 0900-1300 & 1330-1600
daily 1st Mar-30th Sep. 0900-1300 &
1330-1600 Mon-Fri Oct-Feb.
**Mail order:** None
**Cat. cost:** 2 x 1st class
**Credit cards:** None
**Specialities:** Very wide range of hardy plants
mostly alpines. Also seed.
**Map ref:** 3, B2

**SJus    JUST ROSES** ✉ EU
Beales Lane, Northiam, Nr Rye, East Sussex,
TN31 6QY
☎ (01797) 252355

**Contact:** Mr J Banham
**Opening times:** 0900-1200 & 1300-1700 Tue-
Fri & 0900-1200 & 1300-1600 Sat & Sun.
**Min. mail order UK:** 1 plant + p&p
**Min. mail order EU:** No minimum charge
**Cat. cost:** Free
**Credit cards:** None
**Specialities:** Roses.
**Map ref:** 3, B3

**SKCa    KENT CACTI** ✉ EU
(Office) 35 Rutland Way, Orpington, Kent,
BR5 4DY
☎ (01689) 836249, **Mobile** 0467 881981
**Fax:** (01689) 830157
**Contact:** Mr D Sizmur
**Opening times:** 1000-1700 most days.
Please phone first.
**Min. mail order UK:** No minimum charge
**Min. mail order EU:** Nmc
**Cat. cost:** A5 Sae
**Credit cards:** None
**Specialities:** Agave, Astrophytum,
Conophytum, Crassula, Echeveria, small
Opuntia, Mammillaria etc. Note: Nursery is at
Woodlands Farm, Shire Lane, Farnborough,
Kent, BR6 7HH.
**Map ref:** 3, A2

**SKee    KEEPERS NURSERY** ✉ UK ◆
Gallants Court, Gallants Lane, East Farleigh,
Maidstone, Kent, ME15 0LE
☎ (01622) 726465  **Fax:** (01622) 726465
**E-mail:** keepers@email.infotrade.co.uk
**Contact:** Hamid Habibi
**Opening times:** All reasonable hours by appt.
**Min. mail order UK:** £10.00 + p&p
**Cat. cost:** 2 x 1st class
**Credit cards:** None
**Specialities:** Old & unusual Top Fruit
varieties. Top Fruit propagated to order.
**Map ref:** 3, A3

**SKen    KENT STREET NURSERIES** ✉
Sedlescombe, Battle, East Sussex, TN33 0SF
☎ (01424) 751134  **Fax:** (01424) 751499
**Contact:** Mrs D Downey
**Opening times:** 0900-1800 daily all year.
**Mail order:** None
**Cat. cost:** A5 Sae with 2 x 1st class*
**Credit cards:** MasterCard, Visa, Delta
**Specialities:** Fuchsia, Pelargonium, Bedding &
Perennials. *Note: Separate Fuchsia &
Pelargonium lists – please specify which required.
**Map ref:** 3, B3

KEY
✉ Mail order to UK or EU
✉ Exports beyond EU
▣ Also supplies Wholesale  ◆ See Display advertisement

**SLan**    LANGLEY BOXWOOD
NURSERY ⊠ EU ▨ ▨ ◆
Rake, Nr Liss, Hampshire, GU33 7JL
☎ (01730) 894467  **Fax:** (01730) 894703
**E-mail:** langbox@msn.com.uk
**Web site:** http://www.boxwood.co.uk
**Contact:** Elizabeth Braimbridge
**Opening times:** Weekdays; Sat – please ring
first. Please phone for directions.
**Min. mail order UK:** £20.00 + p&p
**Min. mail order EU:** £100.00 + p&p
**Cat. cost:** 4 x 1st class
**Credit cards:** None
**Specialities:** Buxus species, cultivars &
hedging. Good range of topiary. Taxus.
National Collection of Buxus.
**Map ref:** 3, B1

**SLau**    THE LAURELS NURSERY ▨
Benenden, Cranbrook, Kent, TN17 4JU
☎ (01580) 240463  **Fax:** (01580) 240463
**Contact:** Peter or Sylvia Kellett
**Opening times:** 0800-1700 Mon-Thu, 0800-
1600 Fri, 0900-1200 Sat, Sun by appt. only.
**Mail order:** None
**Cat. cost:** Free
**Credit cards:** None
**Specialities:** Open ground & container
Ornamental Trees, Shrubs & Climbers incl.
Flowering Cherries, Birch & Wisteria.
**Map ref:** 3, B3

**SLay**    LAYHAM NURSERIES ⊠ EU ▨
Summerfield, Staple, Nr Canterbury, Kent,
CT3 1LD
☎ (01304) 611380 (office)
**Fax:** (01304) 615349
**Contact:** L W Wessel
**Opening times:** 0900-1700 Mon-Sat
0900-1700 Sun.
**Min. mail order UK:** £10.00 + p&p
**Min. mail order EU:** £25.00 + p&p
**Cat. cost:** Free
**Credit cards:** Visa, American Express, Switch
**Specialities:** Roses, Herbaceous, Shrubs, Trees,
Conifers, Liners & Whips. Aquatic plants,
Hedging plants.
**Map ref:** 3, A4

**SLBF**    LITTLE BROOK FUCHSIAS ▨
Ash Green Lane West, Ash Green,
Nr Aldershot, Hampshire, GU12 6HL
☎ (01252) 329731
**Contact:** Carol Gubler
**Opening times:** 0900-1700 Wed-Sun
1st Jan-4th Jul.
**Mail order:** None
**Cat. cost:** 40p + Sae

**Credit cards:** None
**Specialities:** Fuchsia old & new.
**Map ref:** 3, A1

**SLdr**    LODER PLANTS ⊠ EU ▨ ▨
Market Garden, Lower Beeding, West Sussex,
RH13 6PX
☎ (01403) 891412  **Fax:** (01403) 891336
**E-mail:** loder@rhododendrons.com
**Web site:** http://www.rhododendrons.com
**Contact:** Chris Loder
**Opening times:** Daily by appointment only.
This is so we can give you our undivided
attention.
**Min. mail order UK:** No minimum charge
**Min. mail order EU:** £100.00 + p&p
**Cat. cost:** 2 x 1st class
**Credit cards:** Visa, Access
**Specialities:** Rhododendron & Azalea in all
sizes. Camellia, Acer.
**Map ref:** 3, B2

**SLim**    LIME CROSS NURSERY ▨ ▨ ◆
Herstmonceux, Hailsham, East Sussex,
BN27 4RS
☎ (01323) 833229  **Fax:** (01323) 833944
**E-mail:** LimeCross@aol.com
**Contact:** J A Tate, G Monk
**Opening times:** 0830-1700 Mon-Sat &
0930-1700 Sun.
**Mail order:** None
**Cat. cost:** 5 x 2nd class
**Credit cards:** Visa, MasterCard, Delta, Switch
**Specialities:** Conifers, Trees & Shrubs,
Climbers. Note: Export for large orders only.
**Map ref:** 3, B3

**SLod**    THE LODGE NURSERY ⊠ UK
Cottage Lane, Westfield, Nr Hastings, East
Sussex, TN35 4RP
☎ (01424) 870186
**Contact:** Mrs Sandra Worley
**Opening times:** 1030-1700 Wed-Sun
mid Mar-end Oct, & all B/Hols.
**Min. mail order UK:** No minimum charge
**Cat. cost:** 4 x 1st class
**Credit cards:** None
**Specialities:** Small nursery with a wide variety
of mainly Herbaceous Perennials.
**Map ref:** 3, B3

**SLon**    LONGSTOCK PARK NURSERY ◆
(Office) 1 Valley View, Longstock,
Stockbridge, Hampshire, SO20 6EF
☎ (01264) 810894  **Fax:** (01264) 810894
**Contact:** Peter Moore
**Opening times:** 0830-1630 Mon-Sat all year exc.
Xmas & New Year, & 1400-1700 Sun Mar-Oct.

Mail order: None
Cat. cost: £2 cheque includes postage.
Credit cards: Visa, Access, Switch, MasterCard
Specialities: A wide range, over 2000 varieties,
of Trees, Shrubs, Perennials, Climbers,
Aquatics & Ferns. Increasing range of
Daphne. National Collection of Buddleja.
Note: Nursery is at Longstock, Nr
Stockbridge, Hants SO20 6EH.
Map ref: 2, B3

**SLPl    LANDSCAPE PLANTS** ✉ EU ✍ ◪
Cattamount, Grafty Green, Maidstone, Kent,
ME17 2AP
☎ 01622 850245   Fax: 01622 858063
Contact: Tom La Dell
Opening times: By appt. only.
Min. mail order UK: £100.00 + p&p
Min. mail order EU: £200.00 + p&p
Cat. cost: 2 x 1st class
Credit cards: None
Specialities: Low maintenance Shrubs.
Map ref: 3, A3

**SMac    MACGREGORS PLANTS** ✉ UK ◪
Carters Clay Road, Lockerley, Romsey,
Hampshire, SO51 0GL
☎ (01794) 340256   Fax: (01794) 341828
Contact: Irene & Stuart Bowron
Opening times: 1000-1600 Fri-Sun & B/Hol
Mons Mar-Oct & at other times by appt.
Min. mail order UK: No minimum charge
Cat. cost: 3 x 1st class
Credit cards: None
Specialities: Phygelius - National Collection.
Less common Shrubs & Perennials,
particularly for shade.
Map ref: 2, B3

**SMad    MADRONA NURSERY** ✉ EU
Pluckley Road, Bethersden, Kent, TN26 3DD
☎ (01233) 820100   Fax: (01233) 820091
Contact: Liam MacKenzie
Opening times: 1000-1700 Sat-Tue
20th Mar-2nd Nov. Closed 6th-30th Aug.
Min. mail order UK: No minimum charge
Min. mail order EU: Nmc
Cat. cost: Free
Credit cards: Visa, MasterCard, American
Express, JCB, Switch
Specialities: Unusual Shrubs, Conifers &
Perennials.
Map ref: 3, B3

**SMcB    MCBEANS ORCHIDS** ✉ EU ✍ ◪
Cooksbridge, Lewes, Sussex, BN8 4PR
☎ (01273) 400228   Fax: (01273) 401181
Contact: Jim Durrant

Opening times: 1030-1600 daily ex. Xmas &
Boxing day, New Year & Good Friday.
Min. mail order UK: £29.95 incl.
Min. mail order EU: £100.00 + p&p
Cat. cost: Free
Credit cards: Visa, American Express, Access
Specialities: Orchids – Cymbidium,
Odontoglossum, Phalaenopsis, Paphiopedilum,
Miltonia, Cattleya & other genera.

**SMer    MERRYFIELD NURSERIES
(CANTERBURY) LTD** ✉ UK
Stodmarsh Road, Canterbury, Kent, CT3 4AP
☎ (01227) 462602
Contact: Mrs A Downs
Opening times: 1000-1600 Mon, 0900-1730
Tue-Sat, 1000-1700 Sun, & B/Hol Mons.
Min. mail order UK: £10.00 + p&p
Cat. cost: None issued at present.
Credit cards: Access, Visa, Switch
Specialities: Herbaceous & Conifers.
Map ref: 3, A4

**SMrm    MERRIMENTS GARDENS**
Hawkhurst Road, Hurst Green, East Sussex,
TN19 7RA
☎ (01580) 860666   Fax: (01580) 860324
E-mail: info@merriments@.co.uk
Web site: http://www.merriments.co.uk
Contact: Mark & Amanda Buchele
Opening times: 1000-1730 daily.
Mail order: None
Cat. cost: £1.00 + 2 x 1st class
Credit cards: Visa, Access, American Express
Specialities: Unusual Shrubs. Tender & Hardy
Perennials.
Map ref: 3, B3

**SMur    MURRELLS PLANT & GARDEN CENTRE**
Broomers Hill Lane, Pulborough, West Sussex,
RH20 2DU
☎ (01798) 875508   Fax: (01798) 872695
Contact: Clive Mellor
Opening times: 0900-1730 summer,
0900-1700 winter, 1000-1600 Sun.
Mail order: None
Cat. cost: 3 x 1st class
Credit cards: Switch, MasterCard, Visa, Solo
Specialities: Shrubs, Trees & Herbaceous
Plants incl. many rare & unusual varieties.
Map ref: 3, B1

S

**S**

**SNut   NUTLIN NURSERY**
Crowborough Road, Nutley, Nr Uckfield,
Sussex, TN22 3BG
☎ (01825) 712670   **Fax:** (01825) 712670
**Contact:** Mrs Morven Cox
**Opening times:** Ring in the evening before
visiting.
**Mail order:** None
**Cat. cost:** 1 x 1st class
**Credit cards:** None
**Specialities:** Hydrangea & Wisteria.
**Map ref:** 3, B2

**SOkh   OAKHURST NURSERY**
Mardens Hill, Crowborough, East Sussex,
TN6 1XL
☎ (01892) 653273   **Fax:** (01892) 653273
**E-mail:** baileyp4@compuserve.com
**Contact:** Stephanie Colton
**Opening times:** 1100-1700 most days mid
Apr-mid Sep. Other times and if travelling
please phone first, especially at weekends.
**Mail order:** None
**Cat. cost:** 2 x 1st class
**Credit cards:** None
**Specialities:** Common & uncommon
Herbaceous Perennials.
**Map ref:** 3, B2

**SOWG   THE OLD WALLED GARDEN ▣**
Oxonhoath, Hadlow, Kent, TN11 9SS
☎ (01732) 810012   **Fax:** (01732) 810012
**E-mail:** amyrtle@aol.com
**Contact:** John & Heather Angrave
**Opening times:** 0900-1700 Mon-Fri.
Weekends by appt.
**Mail order:** None
**Cat. cost:** 2 x 1st class
**Credit cards:** None
**Specialities:** Many rare & unusual Shrubs. Wide
range of Conservatory plants esp. Australian.
**Map ref:** 3, A3

**SPan   PANDORA NURSERY**
(Office) 17 Quail Way, Horndean,
Waterlooville, Hampshire, PO8 9YN
☎ (01705) 597323, 0467 606053/54 mobile
**Contact:** Paul & Amanda O'Carroll
**Opening times:** 1000-1600 Wed-Fri Mar-end
Oct. Also by appt.
**Mail order:** None
**Cat. cost:** 6 x 2nd class & C5 Sae.
**Credit cards:** None
**Specialities:** Cistus & Euphorbias, plus
expanding range of gardenworthy Shrubs &
Climbers. Note: Nursery is at The Walled
Garden, Bury Lodge Estate, West Street,
Hambledon, Hants.
**Map ref:** 2, B4

**SPar   THE PARADISE GARDEN ▣ ◆**
The Courtyard at, Stable Antiques, 46 West
Street, Storrington, West Sussex, RH20 4EE
☎ (01903) 744404   **Fax:** (01903) 740441
**Contact:** Clive Parker
**Opening times:** 1000-1800 7 days British
summer time, 1000-dusk Fri-Sun winter.
Please phone before visiting.
**Mail order:** None
**Cat. cost:** 2 x 1st class
**Credit cards:** Visa, MasterCard, Access,
American Express, Switch, Delta
**Specialities:** Architectural & Foliage plants.
**Map ref:** 3, B1

**SPer   PERRYHILL NURSERIES ✉**
Hartfield, East Sussex, TN7 4JP
☎ (01892) 770377   **Fax:** (01892) 770929
**Contact:** P J Chapman (Manager)
**Opening times:** 0900-1700 daily March 1-
Oct 31.  0900-1630 Nov 1-Feb 28.
**Mail order:** None
**Cat. cost:** £1.65
**Credit cards:** Visa, Access, MasterCard,
EuroCard, Switch
**Specialities:** Wide range of Trees, Shrubs,
Conifers, Rhododendron etc. Over 1300
Herbaceous varieties, over 500 varieties of
Roses. Note: Export for large orders only.
**Map ref:** 3, B2

**SPil   PILGRIM HOUSE HERBS ✉ EU**
Pilgrim House, Coles Dane, Stede Hill,
Harrietsham, Maidstone, Kent, ME17 1NP
☎ (01622) 859371   **Fax:** (01622) 859371
**E-mail:** kdgoss@msn.com
**Contact:** Diana Goss
**Opening times:** By appt. only between
1st Apr-31st Oct.
**Min. mail order UK:** No minimum charge
**Min. mail order EU:** Nmc
**Cat. cost:** 1 x 1st class
**Credit cards:** None
**Specialities:** Herbs incl. Digitalis, Mentha,
Oenothera, Salvia, Tanacetum.
**Map ref:** 3, A3

**SPla   PLAXTOL NURSERIES ✉ EU**
The Spoute, Plaxtol, Sevenoaks, Kent,
TN15 0QR
☎ (01732) 810550   **Fax:** (01732) 810550
**Contact:** Tessa, Donald & Jenny Forbes
**Opening times:** 1000-1700 daily. Closed two
weeks from Xmas eve.
**Min. mail order UK:** £10.00 + p&p*
**Min. mail order EU:** £30.00 + p&p
**Cat. cost:** 2 x 1st class
**Credit cards:** Visa, American Express, MasterCard

**Specialities:** Hardy Shrubs & Herbaceous esp. for Flower Arranger. Old-fashioned Roses, Ferns & Climbers. *Note: Mail order Nov-Mar only.
**Map ref:** 3, A3

**SPlb** PLANTBASE ▣
(Office) 37 Forest Road, Hawkenbury, Tunbridge Wells, Kent, TN2 5AL
☎ (01892) 527434   **Fax:** (01892) 527434
**Contact:** Graham Blunt
**Opening times:** 1000-1700 daily Mar-Nov.
**Mail order:** None
**Cat. cost:** 2 x 1st class
**Credit cards:** Visa, MasterCard, Delta, American Express
**Specialities:** A wide range of Alpines, Perennials, Shrubs, Climbers, Waterside plants, Herbs & Australasian Shrubs. Note: Nursery is at Plantbase, The Vineyard Nursery, Penshurst Vineyards, Grove Hill, Penshurst, Nr Tonbridge, Kent TN11 8DU.
**Map ref:** 3, B3

**SPop** POPS PLANTS ⊠ EU ▣ ▣
Greenfield Farm, North Gorley, Fordingbridge, Hampshire, SP6 2PL
☎ (01725) 511421   **Fax:** (01425) 653472
**Contact:** G Dawson
**Opening times:** 1000-1600 daily exc Sun am & Mon Easter-mid Sept.
**Min. mail order UK:** No minimum charge
**Min. mail order EU:** Nmc
**Cat. cost:** 1 x 1st class
**Credit cards:** Visa, Switch, MasterCard, mail order only
**Specialities:** Primula auricula.
**Map ref:** 2, B3

**SRCN** ROSE COTTAGE NURSERY ⊠ EU ▣
Rose Cottage, Kingsley Common, Nr Bordon, Hampshire, GU35 9NF
☎ (01420) 489071   **Fax:** (01420) 476629
**E-mail:** elliot@cena.demon.co.uk
**Contact:** Ian Elliot
**Opening times:** Open by appt. Mar-Oct.
**Min. mail order UK:** No minimum charge
**Min. mail order EU:** £20.00 + p&p
**Cat. cost:** 3 x 1st class
**Credit cards:** None
**Specialities:** Drought tolerant plants, mainly fully hardy. Suit most conditions but ideal for Mediterranean or gravel gardens.
**Map ref:** 3, B1

**SReu** G REUTHE LTD ⊠ EU ▣
Crown Point Nursery, Sevenoaks Road, Ightham, Nr Sevenoaks, Kent, TN15 0HB

☎ (01732) 810694   **Fax:** (01732) 862166
**Contact:** C Tomlin & P Kindley
**Opening times:** 0900-1630 Mon-Sat. (1000-1630 Sun & B/Hols during Apr & May only. Occasionally in June; please check.) Closed Aug.
**Min. mail order UK:** £25.00 + p&p
**Min. mail order EU:** £500.00*
**Cat. cost:** £2.00
**Credit cards:** Visa, Access
**Specialities:** Rhododendron, Azalea, Trees, Shrubs & Climbers. *Note: Certain plants only to EU & Export.
**Map ref:** 3, A2

**SRGP** ROSIE'S GARDEN PLANTS ⊠ EU ▣
Rochester Road, Aylesford, Kent, ME20 7EB
☎ (01622) 715777   **Fax:** (01622) 715777
**Contact:** J C A'violét
**Opening times:** 1000-1700 Wed-Sat 1st April-25th Sept.
**Min. mail order UK:** No minimum charge
**Min. mail order EU:** Nmc
**Cat. cost:** 2 x 1st class
**Credit cards:** Visa, MasterCard, Switch
**Specialities:** Hardy Geranium.
**Map ref:** 3, A3

**SRiv** RIVER GARDEN NURSERIES ⊠ EU ▣
Troutbeck, Otford, Sevenoaks, Kent, TN14 5PH
☎ (01959) 525588   **Fax:** (01959) 525810
**E-mail:** alban@atlas.co.uk
**Contact:** Jenny Alban Davies
**Opening times:** By appt. only.
**Min. mail order UK:** £10.00 + p&p
**Min. mail order EU:** £50.00 + p&p
**Cat. cost:** 2 x 1st class
**Credit cards:** None
**Specialities:** Buxus species, cultivars & hedging. Buxus topiary.
**Map ref:** 3, A2

**SRms** RUMSEY GARDENS ⊠ EU ◆
117 Drift Road, Clanfield, Waterlooville, Hampshire, PO8 0PD
☎ (01705) 593367
**Contact:** Mr N R Giles
**Opening times:** 0900-1700 Mon-Sat & 1000-1700 Sun & B/Hols.
**Min. mail order UK:** No minimum charge
**Min. mail order EU:** Nmc
**Cat. cost:** None issued

---

**K E Y**
⊠ Mail order to UK or EU
▣ Exports beyond EU
▣ Also supplies Wholesale   ◆ See Display advertisement

Credit cards: None
Specialities: Wide general range. National Collection of Cotoneaster.
Map ref: 2, B4

**SRob   ROBINS NURSERY**
Coldharbour Road, Upper Dicker, Hailsham, East Sussex, BN27 3PY
☎ (01323) 844734
E-mail: robnurse@robnurse.free-online.co.uk
Web site: http://www.robnurse.free-online.co.uk
Contact: Stuart Dye
Opening times: 0930-1730 Tue-Sat, 1000-1600 Sun & B/Hol Mon 1st Mar-31st Oct. Limited opening Feb & Nov.
Mail order: None
Cat. cost: 2 x 1st class
Credit cards: MasterCard, Visa
Specialities: Small retail nursery specialising in Herbaceous plants & Shrubs incl. Aquilegia, Alcea, Digitalis, Viburnum & Verbascum, plus a good selection of Kitchen Herbs.
Map ref: 3, C2

**SRos   ROSEWOOD DAYLILIES ⊠ UK**
70 Deansway Avenue, Sturry, Nr Canterbury, Kent, CT2 0NN
☎ (01227) 711071
Contact: Chris Searle
Opening times: By appt. only. Please telephone.
Min. mail order UK: No minimum charge
Cat. cost: 2 x 1st class
Credit cards: None
Specialities: Hemerocallis, mainly newer American varieties.
Map ref: 3, A4

**SRot   ROTHERVIEW NURSERY ⊠ EU**
Ivy House Lane, Three Oaks, Hastings, East Sussex, TN35 4NP
☎ (01424) 717141   Fax: (01424) 428944
E-mail: rothalps@camellias.demon.uk
Contact: Ray Bates
Opening times: 1000-1700 daily Mar-Oct, 1000-1530 daily Nov-Feb.
Min. mail order UK: £10.00 + p&p
Min. mail order EU: £20.00 + p&p
Cat. cost: 2 x 1st class
Credit cards: None
Specialities: Alpines.
Map ref: 3, B3

**SRPl   ROGER PLATTS GARDEN DESIGN & NURSERIES**
Stick Hill, Edenbridge, Kent, TN8 5NH
☎ (01732) 863318   Fax: (01732) 863318

E-mail: plattsgdn@aol.com
Contact: Patricia Marchant
Opening times: 0900-1700 daily.
Mail order: None
Cat. cost: Available shortly
Credit cards: Access, Visa, American Express
Specialities: Perennials, Roses, Shrubs, Specimen sized plants.
Map ref: 3, B2

**SSad   MRS JANE SADLER**
Ingrams Cottage, Wisborough Green, Billingshurst, West Sussex, RH14 0ER
☎ (01403) 700234   Fax: (01403) 700234
Contact: Mrs Jane Sadler
Opening times: Irregular. Please phone first.
Mail order: None
Cat. cost: Sae
Credit cards: None
Specialities: Small nursery specialising in less common varieties, esp. Auriculas, Lavenders & Pelargoniums.
Map ref: 3, B1

**SSca   SCALERS HILL NURSERY**
Scalers Hill, Cobham, Nr Gravesend, Kent, DA12 3BH
☎ (01474) 822856, (0468) 906770
Contact: Mrs Ann Booth
Opening times: 0900-1600 Wed-Sat or by appt. Mid Mar-end Oct.
Mail order: None
Cat. cost: 2 x 1st class
Credit cards: None
Specialities: Unusual Perennials & Alpines.
Map ref: 3, A3

**SSea   SEALE NURSERIES ⊠ EU ◆**
Seale Lane, Seale, Farnham, Surrey, GU10 1LD
☎ (01252) 782410   Fax: (01252) 783038
E-mail: plants@sealenurseries.demon.co.uk
Web site: http://www.sealenurseries.demon.co.uk
Contact: David May
Opening times: 0900-1700 daily
Min. mail order UK: £10.00 + p&p
Min. mail order EU: £10.00 + p&p
Cat. cost: 2 x 2nd class
Credit cards: Visa, Switch, Access
Specialities: Pelargonium, Fuchsia, Roses, Herbaceous.
Map ref: 3, B1

**SSmi   ALAN C SMITH ⊠ UK**
127 Leaves Green Road, Keston, Kent, BR2 6DG
☎ (01959) 572531

S

Contact: Alan C Smith
Opening times: Appt. only.
Min. mail order UK: No minimum charge
Cat. cost: 50p
Credit cards: None
Specialities: Sempervivum & Jovibarba.
Map ref: 3, A2

**SSmt   PETER J SMITH ⊠ EU ▣**
Chanctonbury Nurseries, Rectory Lane,
Ashington, Pulborough, Sussex, RH20 3AS
☎ (01903) 892870   Fax: (01903) 893036
Contact: Sales Dept.
Opening times: 1000-1300 Mon-Fri
1st Apr-30th Sept.
Min. mail order UK: £6.00 + p&p
Min. mail order EU: £30.00 + p&p
Cat. cost: 1 x 1st class
Credit cards: Visa, Access, MasterCard
Specialities: The Princess & Little Princess
range of hybrid Alstroemeria for conservatory
& garden. Also hybrid Limonium & Freesias.
Gipsy Dianthus.

**SSoC   SOUTHCOTT NURSERY**
Southcott, South Street, Lydd, Romney
Marsh, Kent, TN29 9DQ
☎ (01797) 321848   Fax: (01797) 321848
Contact: Suzy Clark
Opening times: 1200-1730 Mon-Fri.
Mail order: None
Cat. cost: 3 x 1st class
Credit cards: None
Specialities: Unusual Hardy & Half Hardy
Perennials & Shrubs.
Map ref: 3, B4

**SSON   STONE OAK NURSERY ⊠ UK ▣**
Flood Street, Mersham, Nr Ashford, Kent,
TN25 6NX
☎ (01233) 720925
Contact: Mrs D E Saunders & Mr G M
Saunders
Opening times: 1000-1700 Sun & B/Hols
Feb-Nov. Other times by appt. only.
Min. mail order UK: £10.00 +p&p
Cat. cost: 3 x 1st class
Credit cards: None
Specialities: Herbaceous & Woodland plants.
Map ref: 3, B4

**SSpe   SPELDHURST NURSERIES**
Langton Road, Speldhurst, Tunbridge Wells,
Kent, TN3 0NR
☎ (01892) 862682   Fax: (01892) 862682
Contact: Christine & Stephen Lee
Opening times: 1000-1700 Wed-Sat excl. Jan.
1000-1600 Sun Mar-Jul & Sep-Oct.

Mail order: None
Cat. cost: 4 x 1st class for list.
Credit cards: MasterCard, Visa, Switch, Delta,
American Express
Specialities: Herbaceous.
Map ref: 3, B2

**SSpi   SPINNERS GARDEN**
Boldre, Lymington, Hampshire, SO41 5QE
☎ (01590) 673347
Contact: Peter Chappell & Kevin Hughes
Opening times: 1000-1700 Tue-Sat, Sun &
Mon by appt. only.
Mail order: None
Cat. cost: 3 x 1st class
Credit cards: None
Specialities: Less common Trees and Shrubs
esp. Acer, Magnolia, species & lace-cap
Hydrangea. Woodland & Bog Plants. National
Collection of Trillium.
Map ref: 2, C3

**SSpr   SPRINGBANK NURSERIES ⊠ EU ▣**
Winford Road, Newchurch, Sandown, Isle of
Wight, PO36 0JX
☎ (01983) 865444   Fax: (01983) 868688
Contact: K Hall
Opening times: Daily Sept & Oct. Collections
by appt. Specific open days to be advertised.
Min. mail order UK: £10.00 + p&p
Min. mail order EU: £25.00 + p&p
Cat. cost: £1.50
Credit cards: None
Specialities: Nerine sarniensis hybrids (over
600 varieties), & some species. Interesting
National Collection.
Map ref: 2, C4

**SSta   STARBOROUGH NURSERY ⊠ EU ▣**
Starborough Road, Marsh Green, Edenbridge,
Kent, TN8 5RB
☎ (01732) 865614   Fax: (01732) 862166
Contact: C Tomlin & P Kindley
Opening times: 1000-1600 Mon-Sat. Closed
Jan & Jul, & occasional Weds.
Min. mail order UK: £25.00 + p&p*
Min. mail order EU: £500.00
Cat. cost: £2.00
Credit cards: Visa, Access
Specialities: Rare and unusual Shrubs
especially Daphne, Acer, Rhododendron,
Azalea, Magnolia & Hamamelis. *Note:
Certain plants only to EU & Export.
Map ref: 3, B2

S

**S**

**SStn** **STONEHURST NURSERIES** ✉ EU 🖅 🖼
Selsfield Road, Ardingly, Haywards Heath,
Sussex, RH17 6TN
☎ (01444) 892488  **Fax:** (01444) 892488
**E-mail:** stonehurst@compuserve.com
**Web site:** http://www.stonehurstnurseries.com
**Contact:** Cherry Smith
**Opening times:** 0900-1300 & 1400-1700
Tue.-Sun.
**Min. mail order UK:** £5.00 + p&p
**Min. mail order EU:** £5.00 + p&p
**Cat. cost:** 2 x 1st class
**Credit cards:** Visa, MasterCard
**Specialities:** Orchids & Camellias.
**Map ref:** 3, B2

**SSto** **STONE CROSS NURSERIES &
GARDEN CENTRE** 🖼 ◆
Rattle Road, Pevensey, Sussex, BN24 5EB
☎ (01323) 763250  **Fax:** (01323) 763195
**E-mail:** stonex@farmline.com
**Contact:** Mr & Mrs G F Winwood
**Opening times:** 0830-1730 Mon-Sat &
1000-1600 Sun & B/Hols.
**Mail order:** None
**Cat. cost:** None issued
**Credit cards:** Visa, Access, Switch
**Specialities:** Hebe & Clematis, Evergreen
Shrubs. Lime tolerant & coastal Shrubs &
Plants.
**Map ref:** 3, C3

**SSvw** **SOUTHVIEW NURSERIES** ✉ UK ◆
Chequers Lane, Eversley Cross, Hook,
Hampshire, RG27 0NT
☎ (0118) 9732206
**Contact:** Mark & Elaine Trenear
**Opening times:** 0900-1300 & 1400-1630
Wed-Sat 1st Mar-31st Oct. Nov-Feb by appt.
only.
**Min. mail order UK:** No minimum charge
**Cat. cost:** Free
**Credit cards:** None
**Specialities:** Unusual Hardy plants,
specialising in Old Fashioned Pinks & period
plants. National Collection of Old Pinks.
**Map ref:** 3, A1

**STes** **TEST VALLEY NURSERY**
Stockbridge Road, Timsbury, Romsey,
Hampshire, SO51 0NG
☎ (01794) 368881
**Contact:** Julia Benn
**Opening times:** 1030-1600 Mon-Fri, 1100-
1700 Sat & Sun Mar-Nov exc. Mon & Thur.
**Mail order:** None
**Cat. cost:** 2 x 2nd class
**Credit cards:** None

**Specialities:** Small nursery with range of
Herbaceous Perennials, specialising in unusual
& new varieties.
**Map ref:** 2, B3

**STil** **TILE BARN NURSERY** ✉ EU 🖅 🖼
Standen Street, Iden Green, Benenden, Kent,
TN17 4LB
☎ (01580) 240221  **Fax:** (01580) 240221
**Contact:** Peter Moore
**Opening times:** 0900-1700 Wed-Sat.
**Min. mail order UK:** £10.00 + p&p
**Min. mail order EU:** £25.00 + p&p
**Cat. cost:** Sae
**Credit cards:** None
**Specialities:** Cyclamen species.
**Map ref:** 3, B3

**STre** **PETER TRENEAR** ✉ EU
Chantreyland, Chequers Lane, Eversley Cross,
Hampshire, RG27 0NX
☎ 0118 9732300
**Contact:** Peter Trenear
**Opening times:** 0900-1630 Mon-Sat.
**Min. mail order UK:** £5.00 + p&p
**Min. mail order EU:** £10.00 + p&p
**Cat. cost:** 1 x 1st class
**Credit cards:** None
**Specialities:** Trees, Shrubs, Conifers & Pinus.
**Map ref:** 3, A1

**SUsu** **USUAL & UNUSUAL PLANTS**
Onslow House, Magham Down, Hailsham,
East Sussex, BN27 1PL
☎ (01323) 840967  **Fax:** (01323) 844725
**E-mail:** jennie@onslow.clara.net
**Contact:** Jennie Maillard
**Opening times:** 0930-1730 daily
Mar-31st Oct. Closed Tue & Wed.
Thu-Sun only during Aug.
**Mail order:** None
**Cat. cost:** Sae + 50p
**Credit cards:** None
**Specialities:** Small quantities of a wide variety
of unusual perennials, esp. Diascia, Erysimum,
Euphorbia, Hardy Geranium, Salvia &
Grasses.
**Map ref:** 3, B3

**SVen** **VENTNOR BOTANIC GARDEN**
Undercliff Drive, Ventnor, Isle of Wight,
PO38 1UL
☎ (01983) 852198  **Fax:** (01983) 856154
**E-mail:** simon@vbg1.demon.co.uk
**Web site:** http://botanic.co.uk
**Contact:** Simon Goodenough & Jan Wyers
**Opening times:** 1000-1700 7 days a week
Mar-Oct.

Mail order: None
Cat. cost: n/a
Credit cards: MasterCard, Visa
Map ref: 2, C4

**SVil  THE VILLAGE NURSERIES ◆**
Sinnocks, West Chiltington, Pulborough,
West Sussex, RH20 2JX
☎ (01798) 813040  Fax: (01798) 813040
Contact: Peter Manfield
Opening times: 0900-1800 or dusk, daily.
Mail order: None
Cat. cost: Free plant list
Credit cards: Visa, Delta, MasterCard, Switch
Specialities: Wide range of Shrubs &
Perennials with many unusual plants.
Map ref: 3, B1

**SWas  WASHFIELD NURSERY**
Horn's Road (A229), Hawkhurst, Kent,
TN18 4QU
☎ (01580) 752522
Contact: Elizabeth Strangman
Opening times: 1000-1700 Wed-Sat. Closing
end June 1999.
Mail order: None
Cat. cost: 5 x 1st class
Credit cards: None
Specialities: Alpine, Herbaceous & Woodland,
many unusual & rare. Helleborus,
Epimedium, Hardy Geranium.
Map ref: 3, B3

**SWat  WATER MEADOW NURSERY ⊠ EU ▣ ▣**
Cheriton, Nr Alresford, Hampshire,
SO24 0QB
☎ (01962) 771119, (01962) 771895
Fax: (01962) 771895
E-mail: watermeadowplants@msn.com
Contact: Mrs Sandy Worth
Opening times: 0900-1700 Wed-Sat,
Mar-Oct or by appt.
Min. mail order UK: £10.00 + p&p
Min. mail order EU: £50.00  + p&p
Cat. cost: 4 x 1st class
Credit cards: None
Specialities: Water Lilies, extensive Water
Garden plants, unusual Herbaceous
Perennials, aromatic & hardy Shrubs &
Climbers.
Map ref: 2, B4

**SWCr  WYCH CROSS NURSERIES**
Wych Cross, Forest Row, East Sussex,
RH18 5JW
☎ (01342) 822705  Fax: (01342) 825329
E-mail: wychcross@martex.co.uk
Contact: J Paisley

Opening times: 0900-1730 Mon-Sat.
Mail order: None
Cat. cost: Free catalogue
Credit cards: Visa, MasterCard, Delta, Switch
Specialities: Roses.
Map ref: 3, B2

**SWes  WESTWOOD NURSERY ⊠ EU**
65 Yorkland Avenue, Welling, Kent,
DA16 2LE
☎ (0181) 301 0886  Fax: (0181) 301 0886
Contact: Mr S Edwards
Opening times: Not open.
Min. mail order UK: No minimum charge
Min. mail order EU: £50.00 + p&p
Cat. cost: Sae
Credit cards: None
Specialities: Pleiones & Hardy Orchids.
Alpine House & Garden Orchids.

**SWyc  WYCHWOOD WATERLILY &
CARP FARM ⊠ EU ▣**
Farnham Road, Odiham, Hook, Hampshire,
RG29 1HS
☎ (01256) 702800  Fax: (01256) 701001
E-mail: cnhenley@aol.com
Contact: Reg, Ann & Clair Henley
Opening times: 1000-1800 daily
Min. mail order UK: £1.00 + p&p
Min. mail order EU: £1.00 + p&p
Cat. cost: 2 x 2nd class
Credit cards: Visa, Access, Switch, Solo
Specialities: Aquatics. Nymphaea, Moisture
loving, Marginals & Oxygenating plants.
Moist & Water Iris inc. American ensata.
National Collection of Nymphaea.
Map ref: 3, A1

**SYvo  YVONNE'S PLANTS**
66 The Ridgway, Woodingdean, Brighton,
E Sussex, BN2 6PD
☎ (01273) 300883
Contact: Yvonne Law
Opening times: Mar-Oct by appt. only.
Mail order: None
Cat. cost: None issued.
Credit cards: None
Specialities: Conservatory, Tender &
Herbaceous Perennials.
Map ref: 3, C2

KEY: ⊠ Mail order to UK or EU
▣ Exports beyond EU
▣ Also supplies Wholesale  ◆ See Display advertisement

# WALES &
# WESTERN ENGLAND

**WAba   ABACUS NURSERIES** ⊠ EU ▣
Drummau Road, Skewen, Neath, Wales,
SA10 6NW
☎ (01792) 817994 (evenings)
E-mail: abacus.dahlias@swig-online.co.uk
Web site: http://www.swigonline.co.uk/
abacus/
Contact: David Hill
Opening times: Not open to the public.
Collection by arrangement.
Min. mail order UK: No minimum charge
Min. mail order EU: Nmc
Cat. cost: 1 x 2nd class
Credit cards: None
Specialities: Dahlias.
Map ref: 4, B4

**W   WAbb   ABBEY DORE COURT GARDENS**
Abbeydore, Nr Hereford, Herefordshire,
HR2 0AD
☎ (01981) 240419   Fax: (01981) 240419
Contact: Mrs C Ward
Opening times: 1100-1800 Thu-Tue from
1st Mar-3rd Sun in Oct.
Mail order: None
Cat. cost: None issued
Credit cards: None
Specialities: Shrubs & hardy Perennials, many
unusual, which may be seen growing in the
garden. Some Seeds available from garden.
Map ref: 5, B1

**WAbe   ABERCONWY NURSERY**
Graig, Glan Conwy, Colwyn Bay, Conwy,
Wales, LL28 5TL
☎ (01492) 580875
Contact: Dr & Mrs K G Lever
Opening times: 1000-1700 daily Feb-Oct.
W/ends only Nov-Jan.
Mail order: None
Cat. cost: 2 x 2nd class
Credit cards: Visa, MasterCard
Specialities: Alpines, including specialist
varieties, esp. Autumn Gentian, Saxifraga &
dwarf ericaceous. Shrubs, Conifers &
Woodland plants incl. Hellebores &
Epimediums.
Map ref: 4, C1

**WAct   ACTON BEAUCHAMP ROSES** ⊠ EU ▣
Acton Beauchamp, Worcester, Hereford &
Worcester, WR6 5AE
☎ (01531) 640433   Fax: (01531) 640802
Contact: Lindsay Bousfield

Opening times: 1000-1800 Summer,
1000-1600 Winter Tue-Sat, B/Hol Mon, Sun
June-July.
Min. mail order UK: No minimum charge
Min. mail order EU: Nmc
Cat. cost: 3 x 1st class appreciated.
Credit cards: Visa, MasterCard, EuroCard
Specialities: Species Roses, Old Roses, modern
shrub, English, climbers, ramblers & ground-
cover Roses.
Map ref: 5, A2

**WAlt   ALTERNATIVES** ⊠ UK
The Brackens, Yorkley Wood, Nr Lydney,
Gloucestershire, GL15 4TU
☎ (01594) 562457
E-mail: altern@lineone.net
Contact: Mrs Rosemary Castle
Opening times: Mail order only.
Min. mail order UK: No minimum charge
Cat. cost: 3 x 1st class
Credit cards: None
Specialities: Unusual forms of common
British natives such as variegated, double &
pale-flowered forms.

**WAul   AULDEN FARM**
Aulden, Leominster, Herefordshire, HR6 0JT
☎ (01568) 720129
Contact: Alun & Jill Whitehead
Opening times: 1200-1700 Tue & Thur
Apr-Sept.
Mail order: None
Cat. cost: Sae
Credit cards: None
Specialities: Hardy Herbaceous Perennials &
some Shrubs
Map ref: 5, A1

**WBaG   BALMER GROVE PLANTS**
Welshampton, Shropshire, SY12 0PP
☎ (01948) 710403
Contact: Nick & Gill Eleftheriou
Opening times: 0930-1800 most days
Mar-Oct, please phone to check times.
Mail order: None
Cat. cost: None issued
Credit cards: None
Specialities: Selected unusual hardy garden
plants, mainly herbaceous perennials, all
carefully home grown in loam-based compost.
Map ref: 7, B1

**WBay   BAYLEYS GARDEN CENTRE**
Bayston Hill Nurseries, Shrewsbury,
Shropshire, SY3 0DA
☎ (01743) 874261   Fax: (01743) 874208
Contact: Information Desk

**Opening times:** 0830-1800 Mon-Sat
Mar-Dec. 0830-1730 Mon-Sat Jan-Feb.
1100-1700 Sun all year. Open 'til 2000 Fri.
**Mail order:** None
**Cat. cost:** Free plant list
**Credit cards:** Visa, Switch, MasterCard
**Specialities:** Wide range of Trees, Shrubs,
Herbaceous Perennials, Fruit, Climbing &
Wall plants, Roses, Bamboos.
**Map ref:** 7, C1

**WBcn    BEACON'S NURSERIES**
Tewkesbury Road, Eckington, Nr Pershore,
Worcestershire, WR10 3DE
☎ (01386) 750359
**Contact:** Jonathan Beacon
**Opening times:** 0900-1300 & 1400-1700
Mon-Sat & 1400-1700 Sun. (Closed 25th
Dec-1st Jan.)
**Mail order:** None
**Cat. cost:** 4 x 1st class
**Credit cards:** None
**Specialities:** Shrubs, Camellias, Herbaceous,
Aquatics, Conifers, Climbing Plants & Roses.
**Map ref:** 5, B2

**WBea    BEACONS' BOTANICALS ⊠ UK**
Banc-y-Felin, Carregsawdde, Llangadog,
Carmarthenshire, Wales, SA19 9DA
☎ (01550) 777992
**Contact:** Mrs S H Williams
**Opening times:** Most weekdays, please
telephone first.
**Min. mail order UK:** £10.00 + p&p
**Cat. cost:** None issued
**Credit cards:** None
**Specialities:** Hardy Geranium, Allium,
Campanula, Persicaria, Veronica. Extensive
range of rare & unusual Herbaceous plants.
**Map ref:** 4, B3

**WBet    BETWYS-Y-COED GARDEN NURSERY**
Betwys-Y-Coed, Conwy, Wales,
☎ (01690) 710870
**Contact:** John Thompson
**Opening times:** New nursery opened Apr 98.
1000-1700 Mon-Sat, 1000-1600 Sun.
**Mail order:** None
**Cat. cost:** None issued.
**Credit cards:** None
**Specialities:** Grasses, Bamboos, Perennials &
some unusual hardy plants.
**Map ref:** 4, C1

**WBod    BODNANT GARDEN
NURSERY LTD ⊠ EU ✉**
Tal-y-Cafn, Colwyn Bay, Clwyd, Wales,
LL28 5RE

☎ (01492) 650731    **Fax:** (01492) 650863
**E-mail:** sales@bodnant.co.uk
**Web site:** http://www.bodnant.co.uk
**Contact:** Mr Ian Shutes & Ms Sian Grindley
**Opening times:** All year.
**Min. mail order UK:** No minimum charge
**Min. mail order EU:** Nmc
**Cat. cost:** Free
**Credit cards:** Visa, MasterCard, Switch,
Connect, American Express
**Specialities:** Rhododendron, Camellia &
Magnolia. Wide range of unusual Trees & shrubs.
**Map ref:** 4, C1

**WBor    BORDERVALE PLANTS**
Nantyderi, Sandy Lane, Ystradowen, Cowbridge,
Vale of Glamorgan, Wales, CF71 7SX
☎ (01446) 774036
**Contact:** Claire E Jenkins
**Opening times:** 1000-1700 Fri-Sun & B/Hols
Apr-Sep. 1000-1700 Sat & Sun Oct. Other
times by appt.
**Mail order:** None
**Cat. cost:** 1st class Sae.
**Credit cards:** None
**Specialities:** Unusual Herbaceous Perennials
and Cottage Garden Plants, many displayed in
the garden.
**Map ref:** 4, C4

**WBou    BOUTS COTTAGE NURSERIES ⊠ EU**
Bouts Lane, Inkberrow, Worcestershire,
WR7 4HP
☎ (01386) 792923
**Contact:** M & S Roberts
**Opening times:** Not open to the public.
**Min. mail order UK:** No minimum charge
**Min. mail order EU:** Nmc
**Cat. cost:** Sae
**Credit cards:** None
**Specialities:** Viola.

**WBrE    BRON EIFION NURSERY ⊠ UK**
Bron Eifion, Criccleth, Gwynedd, LL52 0SA
☎ (01766) 522890
**Contact:** Suzanne Evans
**Opening times:** 1000-dusk 7 days a week.
**Min. mail order UK:** £30.00 + p&p
**Cat. cost:** 4 x 2nd class
**Credit cards:** None
**Specialities:** Kalmia, Embothrium, Plants for
Coastal Regions & wide range of Hardy plants.
**Map ref:** 4, B1

KEY
⊠ Mail order to UK or EU
✉ Exports beyond EU
▨ Also supplies Wholesale    ◆ See Display advertisement

**W**

**WBro  BROOK FARM PLANTS ⊠ UK**
Boulsdon Lane, Newent, Gloucestershire,
GL18 1JH
☎ (01531) 822534
**Contact:** Mrs S E Keene
**Opening times:** 1400-1700 Wed- Sat
Apr-Oct. Most other times by appt.
**Min. mail order UK:** No minimum charge
**Cat. cost:** 2 x 2nd class
**Credit cards:** None
**Specialities:** Digitalis, Papaver, Schizostylis &
other unusual Perennials.
**Map ref:** 5, B2

**WBuc  BUCKNELL NURSERIES ◪**
Bucknell, Shropshire, SY7 0EL
☎ (01547) 530606  **Fax:** (01547) 530699
**Contact:** A N Coull
**Opening times:** 0800-1700 Mon-Fri &
1000-1300 Sat.
**Mail order:** None
**Cat. cost:** Free
**Credit cards:** None
**Specialities:** Bare rooted hedging Conifers &
forest Trees.
**Map ref:** 5, A1

**WByw  BYEWAYS**
Daisy Lane, Whittington, Oswestry,
Shropshire, SY11 4EA
☎ (01691) 659539
**Contact:** Barbara Molesworth
**Opening times:** By appt. only. Please phone
first.*
**Mail order:** None
**Cat. cost:** Sae + 1 x 2nd class
**Credit cards:** None
**Specialities:** Aster, Campanula, Hardy
Geranium & Pulmonaria. *Note: Also at
Newtown Market on Tue.
**Map ref:** 7, B1

**WCel  CELYN VALE EUCALYPTUS
NURSERIES ⊠ EU ◪ ◪ ◆**
Carrog, Corwen, Clwyd, LL21 9LD
☎ (01490) 430671  **Fax:** (01490) 430671
**Contact:** Andrew McConnell & Paul Yoxall
**Opening times:** 0900-1600 Mon-Fri Mar-end
Oct. Please telephone first outside these days.
**Min. mail order UK:** 3 plants + p&p
**Min. mail order EU:** 3 plants + p&p
**Cat. cost:** 2 x 1st class
**Credit cards:** Visa, MasterCard
**Specialities:** Hardy Eucalyptus & Acacia.
**Map ref:** 4, C1

**WCer  CERNEY HOUSE GARDENS**
North Cerney, Cirencester, Gloucestershire,
GL7 7BX
☎ (01285) 831205  **Fax:** (01285) 831676
**E-mail:** cerneygardens@hotmail.com
**Contact:** Barbara Johnson
**Opening times:** Tue, Wed & Fri Apr-Sep,
or by appt.
**Mail order:** None
**Cat. cost:** A4 Sae + 6 x 1st class
**Credit cards:** None
**Specialities:** Herbs, Hardy Geraniums, Ajuga,
Pulmonaria, Vinca, Tradescantia &
Symphytum.
**Map ref:** 5, C2

**WCFE  CHARLES F ELLIS**
(Office) Barn House, Wormington, Nr
Broadway, Worcestershire, WR12 7NL
☎ (01386) 584077 (nursery)
**Contact:** Charles Ellis
**Opening times:** 1000-1600 daily
1st Apr- 30th Sep.
**Mail order:** None
**Cat. cost:** None issued.
**Credit cards:** None
**Specialities:** Wide range of more unusual
Shrubs, Conifers & Climbers. Note: Nursery
is at Oak Piece Farm Nursery, Stanton,
Broadway, Worcs.
**Map ref:** 5, B3

**WCGr  CARROB GROWERS ⊠ EU**
The Old Post House, How Caple,
Herefordshire, HR1 4TE
☎ (01989) 740235
**Contact:** R & C Boyle
**Opening times:** Not open.
**Min. mail order UK:** No minimum charge
**Min. mail order EU:** Nmc
**Cat. cost:** 1 x 1st class
**Credit cards:** None
**Specialities:** Old & modern varieties of
Peonies of particular garden worthiness.

**WCHb  THE COTTAGE HERBERY**
Mill House, Boraston, Nr Tenbury Wells,
Worcestershire, WR15 8LZ
☎ (01584) 781575  **Fax:** (01584) 781483
**Contact:** K & R Hurst
**Opening times:** 1000-1800 Sun and by appt,
May-end July.
**Mail order:** None
**Cat. cost:** 4 x 2nd class
**Credit cards:** None

**Specialities:** Over 400 varieties of Herbs. Aromatic & scented foliage plants, esp. Symphytum, Pulmonaria, Lamium, Monarda, Ajuga, Salvia, Lobelia & Crocosmia. Also seeds.
**Map ref:** 5, A1

**WChG   CHENNELS GATE GARDENS & NURSERY**
Eardisley, Herefordshire, HR3 6LJ
☎ (01544) 327288
**Contact:** Mark Dawson
**Opening times:** 1000-1700 daily Mar-Dec.
**Mail order:** None
**Cat. cost:** 2 x 2nd class
**Credit cards:** None
**Specialities:** Interesting & unusual Cottage Garden plants, Grasses, Hedging & Shrubs.
**Map ref:** 5, A1

**WCil   CILWERN PLANTS**
Cilwern, Talley, Llandeilo, Carms, Wales, SA19 7YH
☎ (01558) 685526
**Contact:** Anne Knatchbull-Hugessen
**Opening times:** 1100-1800 daily. Closed Mon exc. B/Hols.
**Mail order:** None
**Cat. cost:** Sae for list
**Credit cards:** None
**Specialities:** Hardy Perennials esp. Geranium.
**Map ref:** 4, B3

**WCla   JOHN CLAYFIELD** 🔲
Llanbrook Alpine Nursery, Hopton Castle, Clunton, Shropshire, SY7 0QG
☎ (01547) 530298
**Contact:** John Clayfield
**Opening times:** Daily, - but please check first.
**Mail order:** None
**Cat. cost:** None issued
**Credit cards:** None
**Specialities:** Alpines & Wildflowers. Cottage garden & Herbaceous plants.
**Map ref:** 5, A1

**WClu   CLUN HILLS NURSERY**
Crossways, Newcastle on Clun, Craven Arms, Shropshire, SY7 8QT
☎ (01686) 670890
**Contact:** R G Smith or P J Smith
**Opening times:** 1400-1700 Sun, other times by prior appt.
**Mail order:** None
**Cat. cost:** 2 x 1st class
**Credit cards:** None
**Specialities:** Hardy Perennials esp. Geraniums. Nursery is at 1400 feet.
**Map ref:** 4, C2

**WCom   COMPTON LANE NURSERIES** ⊠ UK 🔲
Little Compton, Moreton-in-Marsh, Gloucestershire, GL56 0SJ
☎ (01608) 674578   **Fax:** (01295) 721459
**Contact:** Chris Brown
**Opening times:** 1000-1700 Wed, Thur & Sat Mar-Oct.
**Min. mail order UK:** £15.00 + p&p*
**Cat. cost:** 5 x 1st class, Sae for separate mail order list.
**Credit cards:** None
**Specialities:** Mainly Alpines/Herbaceous & a few unusual Shrubs. Saxifraga, Primula, Cyclamen, Viola, Philadelphus, Hebe. *Note: Mail order Oct-Mar.
**Map ref:** 5, B3

**WCoo   MRS SUSAN COOPER** ⊠ UK
Firlands Cottage, Bishop Frome, Worcestershire, WR6 5BA
☎ (01885) 490358
**Contact:** Mrs Susan Cooper
**Opening times:** Appt. only.
**Min. mail order UK:** £20.00 + p&p
**Cat. cost:** Small Sae
**Credit cards:** None
**Specialities:** Rare & unusual Trees & Shrubs. Provenances on request at time of order.
**Map ref:** 5, A2

**WCot   COTSWOLD GARDEN FLOWERS** ⊠ EU 🔳 🔲
Sands Lane, Badsey, Evesham, Worcestershire, WR11 5EZ
☎ (01386) 47337 (office), (01386) 833849 (nursery)   **Fax:** (01386) 47337
**E-mail:** cgf@star.co.uk
**Web site:** http://www.cgf.net
**Contact:** Bob Brown/Vicky Parkhouse/ John McLeod
**Opening times:** 0800-1630 Mon-Fri all year. 1000-1800 Sat & Sun Mar-Sep, Sat & Sun Oct-Feb by appt.
**Min. mail order UK:** No minimum charge
**Min. mail order EU:** Nmc
**Cat. cost:** Free
**Credit cards:** None
**Specialities:** Easy & unusual Perennials for the Flower Garden.
**Map ref:** 5, B2

**W**

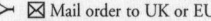

**W**

**WCru** CRÛG FARM PLANTS ▣ ◆
Griffith's Crossing, Nr Caernarfon, Gwynedd,
Wales, LL55 1TU
☎ (01248) 670232  Fax: (01248) 670232
E-mail: bleddyn&sue@crug-farm.demon.co.uk
Web site: http://www.crug-farm.demon.co.uk
Contact: Mr B and Mrs S Wynn-Jones
Opening times: 1000-1800 Thu-Sun last Sat
Feb-last Sun Sept, plus B/Hols.
Mail order: None
Cat. cost: Sae + 2 x 2nd class
Credit cards: Visa, Access, Delta, MasterCard
Specialities: Shade plants, climbers, Hardy
Geranium, Pulmonaria, rare Shrubs,
Tropaeolum, Herbaceous & bulbous incl. self-
collected new introductions from the Far East.
Map ref: 4, B1

**WCwm** CWMRHAIADR NURSERY
Glaspwll, Machynlleth, Powys, Wales, SY20 8UB
☎ (01654) 702223
Contact: Glynne Jones
Opening times: By appt. only. Please phone.
Mail order: None
Cat. cost: 2 x 2nd class
Credit cards: None
Specialities: Rarer Conifer species & clones.
Magnolias. Trees & shrubs for autumn colour.
Increasing range of rarer trees & shrubs from
seed.
Map ref: 4, B2

**WDib** DIBLEY'S NURSERIES ✉ EU ▣ ◆
Llanelidan, Ruthin, Clwyd, LL15 2LG
☎ (01978) 790677  Fax: (01978) 790668
Contact: R Dibley
Opening times: 0900-1700 daily Apr-Sept.
Min. mail order UK: No minimum charge
Min. mail order EU: £20.00 + p&p
Cat. cost: Free
Credit cards: Visa, Access, Switch, Electron,
Solo
Specialities: Streptocarpus, Columnea,
Solenostemon & other Gesneriads & Begonia.
Map ref: 4, C1

**WDin** DINGLE NURSERIES ▣
Welshpool, Powys, Wales, SY21 9JD
☎ (01938) 555145  Fax: (01938) 555778
Web site: http://www.arik.co.uk/
dinglenurseries
Contact: Kerry Hamer
Opening times: 0900-1700 Wed-Mon.
(Wholesale Mon-Sat only).
Mail order: None
Cat. cost: Free plant list
Credit cards: MasterCard, Switch, EuroCard,
Delta, Visa

Specialities: Trees, Shrubs & Conifers.
Herbaceous, Forestry & Hedging Trees.
Map ref: 4, C2

**WEas** EASTGROVE COTTAGE
GARDEN NURSERY
Sankyns Green, Nr Shrawley, Little Witley,
Worcestershire, WR6 6LQ
☎ (01299) 896389
Web site: http://www.hughesmedia.co.uk/
eastgrove/
Contact: Malcolm & Carol Skinner
Opening times: 1400-1700 Thu-Mon
1st Apr-31st July. (Closed Aug.) 1400-1700
Thu, Fri & Sat 1st Sep-9th Oct. Also
1400-1700 Sun 19th Sept & Sun 3rd Oct.
Mail order: None
Cat. cost: 5 x 2nd class
Credit cards: None
Specialities: Unique garden & Arboretum
open. Nursery lists over 1000 varieties incl.
very wide range of Viola, Iris, Hardy
Chrysanthemum, Dianthus. Also Pelargonium
& many exciting Tender/Conservatory plants.
Map ref: 5, A2

**WElm** THE GARDEN AT THE ELMS NURSERY
Frenchlands Lane, Lower Broadheath,
Worcestershire, WR2 6QU
☎ (01905) 640841  Fax: (01905) 640675
Contact: Emma Stewart
Opening times: 1400-1700 Wed-Sat
31st Mar-2nd Oct.
Mail order: None
Cat. cost: 3 x 1st class
Credit cards: None
Specialities: Unusual hardy plants & cottage
garden favourites, most grown on the nursery
from stock in an old farmhouse garden which
is open by appt.
Map ref: 5, A2

**WFar** FARMYARD NURSERIES ✉ EU ▣ ▣ ◆
Llandysul, Dyfed, Wales, SA44 4RL
☎ (01559) 363389, (01267) 220259
Fax: (01559) 362200
E-mail: farmyard.nurseries@btinternet.com
Web site: http://www.btinternet.com/
~farmyard.nurseries
Contact: Richard Bramley
Opening times: 1000-1700 daily except
Christmas, Boxing & New Years Day.
Min. mail order UK: No minimum charge
Min. mail order EU: £50.00 + p&p
Cat. cost: 4 x 1st class
Credit cards: Visa, Switch
Specialities: Excellent general range, esp.
Helleborus, Hosta, Tricyrtis & Schizostylis.

General Shrubs, Trees, Climbers, Alpines, and especially Herbaceous.
**Map ref:** 4, B3

**WFib    FIBREX NURSERIES LTD** ⊠ EU 🄰
Honeybourne Road, Pebworth, Stratford-on-Avon, Warwickshire, CV37 8XP
☎ (01789) 720788   **Fax:** (01789) 721162
**Contact:** H M D Key & R L Godard-Key
**Opening times:** 1030-1700 Mon-Fri, 1200-1700 Sat & Sun Mar-Jul. 1030-1700 Mon-Fri Aug-Feb. Office hours 0930-1700 Mon-Fri all year excl. last 2 weeks Dec & first week Jan.*
**Min. mail order UK:** £10.00 + p&p*
**Min. mail order EU:** £20.00 + p&p
**Cat. cost:** 2 x 2nd class
**Credit cards:** MasterCard, Visa
**Specialities:** Ivies (Hedera), Ferns & Pelargonium & Helleborus. *Note: Plant collections subject to time of year; please check by phone.
**Map ref:** 5, B3

**WFoF    FLOWERS OF THE FIELD** 🄰
Field Farm, Weobley, Herefordshire, HR4 8QJ
☎ (01544) 318262   **Fax:** (01544) 318262
**Contact:** Kathy Davies
**Opening times:** 0900-1900 daily
**Mail order:** None
**Cat. cost:** 2 x 1st class
**Credit cards:** None
**Specialities:** Traditional & unusual Perennials, Shrubs, Trees & Herbs. Summer & Winter Bedding & Hanging Baskets. Cut Flowers & Ornamental Grasses.
**Map ref:** 5, A1

**WFro    FRON NURSERY** ⊠ EU 🄳 🄰
Fron Issa, Rhiwlas, Oswestry, Shropshire, SY10 7JH
☎ (01691) 600605 evenings
**Contact:** Thoby Miller
**Opening times:** By appt. only. Please phone first.
**Min. mail order UK:** £20.00 + p&p
**Min. mail order EU:** £50.00 + p&p
**Cat. cost:** 2 x 1st class
**Credit cards:** None
**Specialities:** Rare and unusual Trees, Shrubs & Perennials.
**Map ref:** 4, C2

**WGei    W G GEISSLER**
Winsford, Kingston Road, Slimbridge, Gloucestershire, GL2 7BW
☎ (01453) 890340   **Fax:** (01453) 890340
**E-mail:** w.geissler@virgin.net

**Web site:** http://www.t.mann.taylor.clara.net/ptero.html
**Contact:** W G Geissler
**Opening times:** 0900-1700 (2000 in summer) Mar-Nov.
**Mail order:** None
**Cat. cost:** None issued.
**Credit cards:** None
**Specialities:** Hardy Cacti & Succulents & related books. National Collections of Opuntia (sect. Tephrocacti) & Pterocacti.
**Map ref:** 5, C2

**WGer    GERDDI FRON GOCH**
Pant Road, Llanfaglan, Caernarfon, Gwynedd, LL54 5RL
☎ (01286) 672212   **Fax:** (01286) 678912
**Contact:** RA & Mrs V Williams
**Opening times:** 0900-1800 Mon-Sat all year round. 1000-1600 Sun.
**Mail order:** None
**Cat. cost:** None issued
**Credit cards:** MasterCard, Switch, Visa
**Specialities:** Wide range of Trees, Shrubs, Conifers and Herbaceous Perennials, some Ferns & Grasses; emphasis on plants for coastal & damp sites
**Map ref:** 4, B1

**WGle    GLEBE GARDEN NURSERY**
Kidnappers Lane, Leckhampton, Cheltenham, Gloucestershire, GL53 0NR
☎ (01242) 521001
**Contact:** Miss T K Budden
**Opening times:** 0900-1700 daily.
**Mail order:** None
**Cat. cost:** 1 x 2nd class
**Credit cards:** None
**Specialities:** Herbaceous, incl. unusual Hemerocallis, Liriope, Paeonia & Heuchera.
**Map ref:** 5, B2

**WGor    GORDON'S NURSERY**
1 Cefnpennar Cottages, Cefnpennar, Mountain Ash, Mid Glamorgan, Wales, CF45 4EE
☎ (01443) 474593   **Fax:** (01443) 475835
**E-mail:** 101716.2661@compuserve.com
**Contact:** D A Gordon
**Opening times:** 1000-1800 1st Mar-31st Oct daily. 1100-1600 1st Nov-28th Feb Sat & Sun only.
**Mail order:** None

**W**

| | |
|---|---|
| **K E Y** | ⊠ Mail order to UK or EU |
| | 🄳 Exports beyond EU |
| | 🄰 Also supplies Wholesale   ◆ See Display advertisement |

Cat. cost: 3 x 1st class
Credit cards: Visa, MasterCard
Specialities: Shrubs, Perennials, Alpines -
especially Lewisias – and Dwarf Conifers.
Map ref: 4, C4

**WGra    GRANGE FARM NURSERY ◆**
Guarlford, Malvern, Worcestershire,
WR13 6NY
☎ (01684) 562544   Fax: (01684) 562544
Contact: Mrs C Nicholls
Opening times: 0900-1730 daily Summer.
0900-1700 daily Winter, ex Xmas & 2 weeks
in Jan.
Mail order: None
Cat. cost: Free pamphlet
Credit cards: Visa, Access, Switch
Specialities: Wide general range of container
grown hardy Shrubs, Trees, Conifers,
Heathers, Alpines & Herbaceous. Shrub,
climbing & bush Roses.
Map ref: 5, B2

**WGwG    GWYNFOR GROWERS ✉ UK**
Gwynfor, Pontgarreg, Llangranog, Llandysul,
Ceredigion, Wales, SA44 6AU
☎ (01239) 654151   Fax: (01239) 654152
Contact: Anne & Bob Seaman
Opening times: 1000-1600 Tues-Sun Winter,
1000-1800 7 days rest of the year.
Min. mail order UK: £30.00 + p&p
Cat. cost: 4 x 1st class
Credit cards: None
Specialities: Good general range specialising
in Herbaceous plants, Fuchsia & Herbs.
Map ref: 4, B3

**WGWT    GRAFTED WALNUT TREES ✉ UK ▣**
Bramley Cottage, Wyck Rissington,
Cheltenham, Glos, GL54 2PN
☎ (01451) 822098
Contact: George Latham
Opening times: Not open.
Min. mail order UK: No minimum charge
Cat. cost: 3 x 1st class
Credit cards: None
Specialities: Grafted Walnut Trees incl. nut
bearing varieties of English Walnut,
ornamental forms of English & Black Walnut,
most minor Walnut species & hybrids.
Map ref: 5, B3

**WGwy    GWYDIR PLANTS**
Plas Muriau, Betws-y-coed, North Wales,
LL24 0HD
☎ (01690) 750379   Fax: (01690) 750379
Contact: Mrs D Southgate
Opening times: 1000-1730 Mon, Tue, Fri &

Sat 15th Mar-30th Oct 1999, or strictly by appt.
Mail order: None
Cat. cost: 2 x 1st class
Credit cards: None
Specialities: Hardy Perennials, Wild Flowers,
Native Trees & Shrubs, Herbs; incl. many
noteworthy but hard-to-find plants.
Note: Gwydir Plants will not be at this
address in 2000 but same tel/fax.
Map ref: 4, C1

**WHal    HALL FARM NURSERY**
Vicarage Lane, Kinnerley, Nr Oswestry,
Shropshire, SY10 8DH
☎ (01691) 682135
Contact: Mrs C Ffoulkes-Jones
Opening times: For 1999: 1000-1700
Tue-Sat 2nd Mar-9th Oct. 2000 may differ.
Mail order: None
Cat. cost: 4 x 1st class
Credit cards: None
Specialities: Unusual Herbaceous plants incl.
Hardy Geranium, Pulmonaria, Grasses &
many others.
Map ref: 7, B1

**WHar    HARLEY NURSERY**
Harley, Shropshire, SY5 6LP
☎ (01952) 510241   Fax: (01952) 510222
Contact: Duncan Murphy
Opening times: 0900-1730 Mon-Sat,
1000-1750 Sun & B/Hols.
Mail order: None
Cat. cost: 2 x 1st class
Credit cards: Visa, Access
Specialities: Wide range of Ornamental &
Fruit Trees. Also own grown Shrubs, Climbing
& Hedging plants. Many unusual varieties.
Map ref: 7, C1

**WHbs    HERBS AT MYDDFAI**
Beiliglas, Myddfai, Nr Llandovery,
Carmarthenshire, SA20 0QB
☎ (01550) 720494
Contact: Gill Swan
Opening times: 1400-1800 Tue-Sat Apr-Oct,
or by appt.
Mail order: None
Cat. cost: 2 x 1st class
Credit cards: None
Specialities: Herbs & Wild Flowers. Organic.
Map ref: 4, C3

**WHCG    HUNTS COURT GARDEN & NURSERY**
North Nibley, Dursley, Gloucestershire,
GL11 6DZ
☎ (01453) 547440   Fax: (01453) 547440
Contact: T K & M M Marshall

**W**

Opening times: Nursery & Garden
0900-1700 Tue-Sat ex Aug. Also by appt.*
Mail order: None
Cat. cost: 5 x 2nd class
Credit cards: None
Specialities: Old Rose species & climbers.
Hardy Geraniums. Shrubby Potentilla,
Penstemon & unusual shrubs. *Note: See
NGS for Sunday openings.
Map ref: 5, C2

WHCr  HERGEST CROFT GARDENS
Kington, Herefordshire, HR5 3EG
☎ (01544) 230160  Fax: (01544) 230160
Contact: Stephen Lloyd
Opening times: 1330-1830 daily Apr-Oct.
Mail order: None
Cat. cost: None issued
Credit cards: None
Specialities: Acer, Betula & unusual woody
plants.
Map ref: 5, A1

WHen  HENLLYS LODGE PLANTS
Henllys Lodge, Beaumaris, Anglesey,
Gwynedd, Wales, LL58 8HU
☎ (01248) 810106
Contact: Mrs E Lane
Opening times: 1100-1700 Mon, Wed, Fri,
Sat, Sun & by appt. Apr-Oct.
Mail order: None
Cat. cost: 2 x 1st class
Credit cards: None
Specialities: Hardy Geranium, Ground cover
& cottage style Perennials.
Map ref: 4, B1

WHer  THE HERB GARDEN & HISTORICAL
PLANT NURSERY ✉ EU
Pentre Berw, Gaerwen, Anglesey, Wales,
LL60 6LF
Contact: Corinne & David Tremaine-Stevenson
Opening times: 0900-1700 daily exc. Tues.
Open all B/Hols.
Min. mail order UK: £15.00 + p&p
Min. mail order EU: £50.00 + p&p
sterling only.
Cat. cost: List £2.00 in stamps
Credit cards: None
Specialities: Wide range of Herbs, rare Natives
& Wild Flowers; rare & unusual Perennials,
Scented Pelargoniums & Old Roses.
Map ref: 4, B1

WHil  HILLVIEW HARDY PLANTS ✉ EU ✈ 🏵
Worfield, Nr Bridgnorth, Shropshire,
WV15 5NT
☎ (01746) 716454  Fax: (01746) 716454

E-mail: hillview_hardy_plants@
compuserve.com
Contact: Ingrid Millington
Opening times: 0900-1700 Mon-Sat Mar-mid
Oct. At all other times, please phone first.
Min. mail order UK: £10.00 + p&p
Min. mail order EU: £10.00 + p&p
Cat. cost: 4 x 2nd class
Credit cards: None
Specialities: Choice Herbaceous Perennials
incl. Auricula, Primula, Phlox, Grasses &
Ferns. Contract growing for wholesale.
Map ref: 7, C2

WHoo  HOO HOUSE NURSERY 🏵 ◆
Hoo House, Gloucester Road, Tewkesbury,
Gloucestershire, GL20 7DA
☎ (01684) 293389  Fax: (01684) 293389
Contact: Robin & Julie Ritchie
Opening times: 1400-1700 Mon-Sat.
Mail order: None
Cat. cost: 3 x 1st class
Credit cards: None
Specialities: Wide range of Herbaceous &
Alpines – many unusual – incl. Campanula,
Geranium & Penstemon. National Collections
of Platycodon & Gentiana asclepiadea CVs.
Map ref: 5, B2

WHow  HOW CAPLE COURT GARDENS
How Caple Court, How Caple, Herefordshire,
HR1 4SX
☎ (01989) 740626  Fax: (01989) 740611
Contact: Mrs V Lee
Opening times: 0930-1700 all year.
Mail order: None
Cat. cost: None issued.
Credit cards: None
Specialities: English & old Rose varieties.
Map ref: 5, B1

WIvy  IVYCROFT PLANTS
Upper Ivington, Leominster, Herefordshire,
HR6 0JN
☎ (01568) 720344
Contact: Roger Norman
Opening times: 0900-1600 Wed & Thur
Mar-Sep. Other times by appt., please phone.
Mail order: None
Cat. cost: 2 x 1st class
Credit cards: None
Specialities: Cyclamen, Violas, Alpines and
Herbaceous.
Map ref: 5, A1

KEY
✉ Mail order to UK or EU
✈ Exports beyond EU
🏵 Also supplies Wholesale  ◆ See Display advertisement

**W**

**W**Jas    PAUL JASPER - FRUIT &
ORNAMENTAL TREES ✉ EU ☎
The Lighthouse, Bridge Street, Leominster,
Herefordshire, HR6 8DX
Fax: (01568) 616499 for orders
E-mail: pjasper253@aol.com
Contact: Paul Jasper
Opening times: Not open for retail sales.
Min. mail order UK: £30.00 + p&p
Min. mail order EU: £100.00 + p&p
Cat. cost: 2 x 1st class
Credit cards: None
Specialities: Full range of Fruit & Ornamental
Trees. Over 100 modern and traditional apple
varieties plus 120 others all direct from the
grower. Many unusual varieties of Malus
domestica.
Map ref: 5, A1

**W**Jek    JEKKA'S HERB FARM ✉ EU ☎ ☎
Rose Cottage, Shellards Lane, Alveston,
Bristol, Avon, BS35 3SY
☎ (01454) 418878   Fax: (01454) 411988
E-mail: farm@jekkasherb.demon.co.uk
Web site: http://www.jekkasherb.demon.co.uk
Contact: Jekka McVicar
Opening times: By appt. only
Min. mail order UK: No minimum charge
Min. mail order EU: Nmc*
Cat. cost: 4 x 1st class
Credit cards: Visa, MasterCard
Specialities: Culinary, Medicinal, Aromatic
Decorative Herbs, Native Wild Flowers.
*Note: Individual quotations for EU Sales.
Organic Food Federation Symbol.
Map ref: 5, C2

**W**Jun    JUNGLE GIANTS ✉ EU ☎ ☎
Burford House Gardens, Tenbury Wells,
Worcestershire, WR15 8HQ
☎ (01584) 819885   Fax: (01584) 819779
Contact: Michael Brisbane & Maria Nolan
Opening times: Daily - by appt. only please.
Min. mail order UK: £20.00 + p&p
Min. mail order EU: £25.00 + p&p
Cat. cost: £5.75*
Credit cards: None
Specialities: Bamboo. *Note: Full descriptive
information pack incl. p&p.
Map ref: 5, A1

**W**Kif    KIFTSGATE COURT GARDENS
Kiftsgate Court, Chipping Camden,
Gloucestershire, GL55 6LW
☎ (01386) 438777   Fax: (01386) 438777
Contact: Mrs J Chambers
Opening times: 1400-1800 Wed, Thu & Sun
Apr 1st-Sep 30th & B/Hol Mons.

Also Sats in Jun & Jul.
Mail order: None
Cat. cost: None issued
Credit cards: None
Specialities: Small range of unusual plants.
Map ref: 5, B3

**W**Kin    KINGSTONE COTTAGE PLANTS ✉ EU
Weston-under-Penyard, Ross-on-Wye,
Herefordshire, HR9 7NT
☎ (01989) 565267
E-mail: kingstone@wyenet.co.uk
Contact: Mr M Hughes
Opening times: By appt. and as under
National Garden Scheme.
Min. mail order UK: No minimum charge
Min. mail order EU: Nmc
Cat. cost: 2 x 1st class
Credit cards: None
Specialities: Dianthus – National Collection.
Map ref: 5, B2

**W**Knf    KINGFISHER NURSERIES
Catshill, Bromsgrove, Worcestershire,
B61 0BW
☎ (01527) 835084   Fax: (01527) 578070
Contact: Gary Booker
Opening times: 0900-1730 Mon-Sat,
(0900-2000 Wed), 1000-1700 Sun all year.
Mail order: None
Cat. cost: None issued
Credit cards: Visa, Access, Switch
Specialities: Half-hardy Perennials for Patio
gardening. Annual flowering plants.
Map ref: 5, A2

**W**Leb    LEBA ORCHARD - GREEN'S
LEAVES ✉ UK ☎
Lea Bailey, Nr Ross-on-Wye, Herefordshire,
HR9 5TY
☎ (01989) 750303
Contact: Paul Green
Opening times: By appt. only, weekends
preferred.
Min. mail order UK: £10.00 + p&p
Cat. cost: 2 x 2nd class
Credit cards: None
Specialities: Ivies, ornamental Grasses &
Sedges. Increasing range of rare & choice
Shrubs, also some Perennials.
Map ref: 5, B2

**W**Lin    LINGEN NURSERY AND
GARDEN ✉ EU ☎
Lingen, Nr Bucknell, Shropshire, SY7 0DY
☎ (01544) 267720   Fax: (01544) 267720
E-mail: kim&maggie@lingen.freeserve.co.uk
Contact: Kim W Davis

Opening times: 1000-1700 daily Feb-Oct.
Fri-Sun Nov-Jan by appt.
Min. mail order UK: No minimum charge
Min. mail order EU: £20.0 + p&p
Cat. cost: 3 x 1st class
Credit cards: None
Specialities: Alpines, Rock Plants &
Herbaceous esp. Androsace, Aquilegia,
Campanula, Iris, Primula, Auricula &
Penstemon. National Collection of herbaceous
Campanula & housing that of Iris sibirica.
Map ref: 5, A1

**WLow    LOWER SPRING NURSERY** ▣
Kenley, Shrewsbury, Shropshire, SY5 6PA
☎ (01952) 510589
Contact: Bob Hemmings
Opening times: Sat & Sun Mar-Sep. Winter
w/ends by arrangement.
Mail order: None
Cat. cost: 2 x 1st class
Credit cards: None
Specialities: A good range of Cacti & Succulents,
plus Herbaceous, Alpines & Shrubs.
Map ref: 7, C1

**WLRN    LITTLE RHYNDASTON NURSERIES**
Hayscastle, Haverfordwest, Pembrokeshire,
SA62 5PT
☎ (01437) 710656
Contact: D A & P Baster
Opening times: 0900-1700 Mon-Sat,
1100-1700 Sun. Closed August.
Mail order: None
Cat. cost: None issued
Credit cards: Visa, MasterCard, Switch
Specialities: Herbaceous Perennials, Conifers,
Shrubs, Alpines, Climbers, Patio plants, many
suitable for coastal locations.
Map ref: 4, A3

**WMal    MARSHALL'S MALMAISON** ⊠ EU ▣ ▣
4 The Damsells, Tetbury, Gloucestershire,
GL8 8JA
☎ (01666) 502589
Contact: J M Marshall
Opening times: By appt. only.
Min. mail order UK: £16.50 incl. p&p
Min. mail order EU: £16.50 incl p&p
Cat. cost: 1st class Sae
Credit cards: None
Specialities: Malmaison Carnations.
Map ref: 5, C2

**WMaN    THE MARCHES NURSERY** ⊠ EU
Presteigne, Powys, Wales, LD8 2HG
☎ (01544) 260474   Fax: (01544) 260474
Contact: Jane Cooke

Opening times: Mail order only, mainly in
Spring.
Min. mail order UK: No minimum charge
Min. mail order EU: Nmc
Cat. cost: 2 x 1st class
Credit cards: None
Specialities: An increasing range of choice
Perennials, many uncommon, incl. Achillea,
Chrysanthemum, Erysimum, Geranium,
Papaver, Penstemon & Phlox.

**WMAq    MEREBROOK WATER PLANTS** ⊠ EU
Merebrook Farm, Hanley Swan, Worcester,
Worcestershire, WR8 0DX
☎ (01684) 310950   Fax: (01684) 310034
E-mail: lily@merebrk.demon.co.uk
Contact: Roger Kings
Opening times: 1000-1700 Thu-Tue
Easter-Sep.
Min. mail order UK: No minimum charge
Min. mail order EU: Nmc
Cat. cost: 1 x 2nd class
Credit cards: None
Specialities: Nymphaea (Water Lilies) & other
Aquatic plants.
Map ref: 5, B2

**WMer    MERTON NURSERIES**
Holyhead Road, Bicton, Shrewsbury,
Shropshire, SY3 8EF
☎ (01743) 850773   Fax: (01743) 850773
E-mail: jessica@mertonnursery.freeserve.co.uk
Contact: Jessica Pannett
Opening times: 0900-1730 daily ex.
Christmas & New Year
Mail order: None
Cat. cost: 2 x 1st class
Credit cards: Access, Visa
Specialities: Hardy Perennials, Hosta.
Map ref: 7, C1

**WMEx    MARSTON EXOTICS** ⊠ EU ▣ ▣
Brampton Lane, Madley, Herefordshire,
HR2 9LX
☎ (01981) 251140   Fax: (01981) 251649
Web site: http://freespace.virgin.net/
carnivorous.connection/
Contact: Paul Gardner
Opening times: 0800-1630 Mon-Fri all year,
1300-1700 Sat & Sun Mar-Oct.
Min. mail order UK: See list for details
Min. mail order EU: £50.00 + p&p
Cat. cost: List 3 x 1st class*

Credit cards: Visa, MasterCard, Switch, Solo
Specialities: Carnivorous plants. National
Collection of Sarracenia. Also seeds.
*Note: Price list & Growers Guide £2.85.
Map ref: 5, B1

**WMoo    MOORLAND COTTAGE PLANTS ⊠ UK**
Rhyd-y-Groes, Brynberian, Crymych,
Pembrokeshire, Wales, SA41 3TT
☎ (01239) 891363
Contact: Jennifer Matthews
Opening times: 1000-1800 daily except Wed
from end Feb-mid Oct. Other times by appt.
Min. mail order UK: See cat. for details.
Cat. cost: 4 x 1st class
Credit cards: None
Specialities: Traditional & unusual Hardy
Perennials incl. Geranium, Campanula,
Geum, Persicaria, Veronica, cottage garden
plants & colourful ground cover.
Map ref: 4, A3

**WMou    MOUNT PLEASANT TREES ▣**
Rockhampton, Berkeley, Gloucestershire,
GL13 9DU
☎ (01454) 260348
Contact: P & G Locke
Opening times: By appt. only.
Mail order: None
Cat. cost: 3 x 2nd class
Credit cards: None
Specialities: Wide range of Trees for forestry,
hedging, woodlands & gardens esp. Tilia &
Populus.
Map ref: 5, C2

**WMow    MOW COTTAGE GARDEN PLANTS**
The Mow, Aston Rogers, Nr Westbury,
Shropshire, SY5 9HQ
☎ (01743) 891479   Fax: (01743) 891479
Contact: Tony Faulkner
Opening times: 1000-1600 Wed.
Other times by appt. please.
Mail order: None
Cat. cost: None issued.
Credit cards: None
Specialities: Hardy herbaceous – Campanula,
Geranium, Sidalcea, Potentilla, Papaver,
Geum.
Map ref: 7, C1

**WMul    MULU NURSERIES ⊠ EU ▣ ▣**
Burford House, Tenbury Wells,
Worcestershire, WR15 8HQ
☎ (01584) 811592   Fax: (01584) 810673
E-mail: plants@mulu.co.uk
Web site: http://www.mulu.co.uk

Contact: Andy Bateman
Opening times: 1000-1800 or dusk if earlier
7 days. Phone first Nov-Mar.
Min. mail order UK: No minimum charge
Min. mail order EU: £25.00 + p&p
Cat. cost: 4 x 1st class
Credit cards: None
Specialities: Exotic plants, hardy & tender,
incl. Bananas, Gingers, Palms, Tree Ferns,
Aroids etc. Note: Credit cards pending, please
phone.
Map ref: 5, A1

**WNor    NORFIELDS ▣ EU ▣**
Llangwm Arboretum, Usk, Monmouthshire,
NP5 1NQ
☎ (01291) 650306   Fax: (01291) 650306
Contact: Andrew Norfield
Opening times: Not open.
Min. mail order UK: £3.00 + p&p
Min. mail order EU: £3.00 + p&p
Cat. cost: 1 x 1st class
Credit cards: None
Specialities: Wide range of Tree seedlings for
growing on. Acer, Betula, Stewartia &
pregerminated seed.

**WOak    OAK COTTAGE WALLED
HERB GARDEN ⊠ UK ◆**
Uffington, Nr Shrewsbury, Shropshire,
SY4 4TG
☎ (01939) 210219   Fax: (01939) 210219
Contact: Jane & Edward Bygott.
Opening times: 1100-1700 most days Easter
to mid-Sept. Other times by appt. If making a
special journey please phone first.
Min. mail order UK: No minimum charge
Cat. cost: 3 x 1st class
Credit cards: None
Specialities: Beneficial plants, Herbs, Wild
Flowers. Vegetable plants to Soil Association
standard.
Map ref: 7, C1

**WOld    OLD COURT NURSERIES ⊠ EU**
Colwall, Nr Malvern, Worcestershire,
WR13 6QE
☎ (01684) 540416   Fax: (01684) 565314
E-mail: picton@dircon.co.uk
Web site: http://www.picton.dircon.co.uk/
Contact: Paul & Meriel Picton
Opening times: 1100-1730 Wed-Sun
Apr-Oct. 2nd week Sep-2nd week Oct only
1100-1730 daily.
Min. mail order UK: No minimum charge*
Min. mail order EU: Nmc
Cat. cost: £2.50. Price list free.
Credit cards: None

**W**

Specialities: National Collection of
Michaelmas Daisies. Herbaceous Perennials.
*Note: Mail order for Aster only.
Map ref: 5, B2

**W**Orn   ORNAMENTAL TREE
NURSERIES ⊠ UK
Broomy Hill Gardens, Cobnash, Kingsland,
Herefordshire, HR6 9QZ
☎ (01568) 708016  Fax: (01568) 709022
Contact: Russell Mills
Opening times: 0900-1700 Mon-Sat.
Min. mail order UK: No minimum charge
Cat. cost: Sae
Credit cards: Visa, Switch, MasterCard,
Access, Delta
Specialities: Ornamental Trees.
Map ref: 5, A1

**W**Out   OUT OF THE COMMON WAY ⊠ EU
(Office) Penhyddgan, Boduan, Pwllheli,
Gwynedd, Wales, LL53 8YH
☎ (01758) 721577 (Office),
(01407) 720431 (Nursery)
Contact: Joanna Davidson (nursery) Margaret
Mason (office & mail order)
Opening times: By arrangement.
Min. mail order UK: No minimum charge
Min. mail order EU: Nmc
Cat. cost: Sae
Credit cards: None
Specialities: Nepeta, Geranium, Salvia, Viola
etc. Note: Nursery is at Pandy Treban,
Bryngwran, Anglesey, LL65 3YW.
Map ref: 4, B1

**W**Ove   OVERCOURT GARDEN NURSERY
Sutton St Nicholas, Hereford, HR1 3AY
☎ (01432) 880845
E-mail: harpover@wbsnet.co.uk
Contact: Nicola Harper
Opening times: 0930-1630 Mon-Sat
1st Mar-31st Oct.
Mail order: None
Cat. cost: 3 x 2nd class
Credit cards: None
Specialities: Hardy Perennials, many unusual.
Garden open under NGS & by appt.
Map ref: 5, B1

**W**OVN   THE OLD VICARAGE NURSERY ⊠ UK
Lucton, Leominster, Herefordshire, HR6 9PN
☎ (01568) 780538  Fax: (01568) 780818
Contact: Mrs R M Flake
Opening times: 1000-1700 most days, but
please telephone first to be sure.
Min. mail order UK: No minimum charge
Cat. cost: 2 x 1st class (specify Rose or plant cat.)

Credit cards: None
Specialities: Roses – old roses, climbers &
ramblers, species & ground cover. Euphorbia
& half-hardy Salvia.
Map ref: 5, A1

**W**Pat   CHRIS PATTISON
Brookend, Pendock, Gloucestershire,
GL19 3PL
☎ (01531) 650480  Fax: (01531) 650480
E-mail: cpplants@redmarley.freeserve.co.uk
Web site: http://www.redmarley.
freeserve.co.uk
Contact: Chris Pattison
Opening times: 0900-1700 Mon-Fri.
Weekends by appt. only.
Mail order: None
Cat. cost: 3 x 1st class
Credit cards: None
Specialities: Choice & rare Shrubs and
Alpines. Grafted Stock esp. Japanese Maples &
Liquidambar. Wide range of Viburnum,
Dwarf Willows & Dwarf Ericaceous Shrubs.
Map ref: 5, B2

**W**PeH   PENHOW NURSERIES ⊠ EU
St Brides Netherwent, Penhow, Nr Newport,
Gwent, NP4 3AU
☎ (01633) 400419  Fax: (01633) 400419
Contact: David Jones
Opening times: 0900-1800 7 days.
Min. mail order UK: £16.00
Min. mail order EU: £16.00
Cat. cost: 1 x 1st class
Credit cards: None
Specialities: Diascia & Perennial Nemesia.
Map ref: 5, C1

**W**Pen   PENPERGWM PLANTS
Penpergwm Lodge, Abergavenny, Gwent,
Wales, NP7 9AS
☎ (01873) 840422/840208
Fax: (01873) 840470/840208
Contact: Mrs J Kerr/Mrs S Boyle
Opening times: 1999: 25th Mar-3rd Oct,
2000: 23rd Mar-1st Oct.
Mail order: None
Cat. cost: 2 x 1st class
Credit cards: None
Specialities: Hardy Perennials.
Map ref: 5, B1

**W**

**W**

**WPer    PERHILL NURSERIES** ✉ UK 🖳
Worcester Road, Great Witley, Worcestershire,
WR6 6JT
☎ (01299) 896329  **Fax:** (01299) 896990
**Contact:** Duncan & Sarah Straw
**Opening times:** 0900-1700 Mon- Sat,
1000-1600 Sun, 1st Feb-15th Oct & by appt.
**Min. mail order UK:** No minimum charge
**Cat. cost:** 6 x 2nd class
**Credit cards:** None
**Specialities:** Over 2500 varieties of rare &
unusual Alpines & Herbaceous Perennials incl.
Penstemon, Campanula, Salvia, Thyme, Herbs
& Veronica.
**Map ref:** 5, A2

**WPGP    PAN-GLOBAL PLANTS** ✉ UK
Spoonbed Nursery, Rococo Garden,
Painswick, Glos, GL6 6TH
☎ (01452) 814242  **Fax:** (01452) 813204
**Contact:** N Macer
**Opening times:** 1100-1700 Wed-Sun 2nd
Wed in Jan-30th Nov. Also B/Hols.
**Min. mail order UK:** £100.00 + p&p
**Cat. cost:** 3 x 1st class
**Credit cards:** MasterCard, Visa
**Specialities:** Rare, unusual & hard to find
Trees, Shrubs & Herbaceous esp. Hydrangea
& Magnolia, many collected in the wild.
**Map ref:** 5, B2

**WPhl    JUST PHLOMIS** ✉ EU
Sunningdale, Grange Court, Westbury-on-
Severn, Gloucestershire, GL14 1PL
☎ (01452) 760268  **Fax:** (01452) 760268
**E-mail:** j.mann.taylor@clara.co.uk
**Contact:** J Mann Taylor
**Opening times:** Appt. only.
**Min. mail order UK:** £7.50 + p&p
**Min. mail order EU:** £7.50 + p&p
**Cat. cost:** 2 x 2nd class
**Credit cards:** None
**Specialities:** Phlomis from the National
Collection.
**Map ref:** 5, B2

**WPic    THE PICTON CASTLE
TRUST NURSERY** 🖳
Picton Castle, Haverfordwest, Pembrokeshire,
SA62 4AS
☎ (01437) 751326  **Fax:** (01437) 751326
**Contact:** D L Pryse Lloyd
**Opening times:** 1030-1700 daily except Mon
Apr-Oct. Other times by arrangement.
**Mail order:** None
**Cat. cost:** 1 x 1st class
**Credit cards:** None

**Specialities:** Woodland & unusual Shrubs.
Herbs.
**Map ref:** 4, A4

**WPnn    THE PERENNIAL NURSERY**
Rhosygilwen, Llanrhian Road, St Davids,
Pembrokeshire, SA62 6DB
☎ (01437) 721954  **Fax:** (01437) 721954
**Contact:** Mrs Philipa Symons
**Opening times:** 0930-1730 Wed-Mon
Mar-Oct. Nov-Apr by appt.
**Mail order:** None
**Cat. cost:** None issued.
**Credit cards:** None
**Specialities:** Herbaceous Perennials & Alpines,
esp. Erodium.
**Map ref:** 4, A3

**WPnP    PENLAN PERENNIALS** ✉ EU 🖳
Penlan Farm, Penrhiwpal, Llandysul,
Ceredigion, Wales, SA44 5QH
☎ (01239) 851244  **Fax:** (01239) 851244
**E-mail:** penlanperennials@penlanfm.
freeserve.co.uk
**Contact:** Richard & Jane Cain
**Opening times:** 0930-1730 Wed-Sun
Mar-Oct & B/Hols.
**Min. mail order UK:** No minimum charge
**Min. mail order EU:** Nmc
**Cat. cost:** 3 x 1st class
**Credit cards:** None
**Specialities:** Hardy Geraniums (160). Dry &
Moist Shade lovers & Woodland plants. New
nursery relocated from Market Harborough,
was Hill Farmhouse (MHFP).
**Map ref:** 4, B3

**WPrP    PRIME PERENNIALS** ✉ EU
Llety Moel, Rhos-y-Garth, Llanilar, Nr
Aberystwyth, Ceredigion, SY23 4SG
☎ (01974) 241505
**Contact:** Elizabeth Powney
**Opening times:** Not open to public.
**Min. mail order UK:** £14.00 + p&p or
6 plants
**Min. mail order EU:** £40.00 + p&p
**Cat. cost:** 4 x 1st class
**Credit cards:** None
**Specialities:** Unusual Perennials. Hardy
Geraniums, Thalictrum, Pulmonaria &
Grasses.
**Map ref:** 4, B3

**WPry    THE PRIORY**
Kemerton, Tewkesbury, Gloucestershire,
GL20 7JN
☎ (01386) 725258  **Fax:** (01386) 725258
**Contact:** Mrs P Healing

Opening times: 1400-1900 Thurs afternoons.
Mail order: None
Cat. cost: None issued
Credit cards: Visa, Access, American Express, Diners
Specialities: Daturas, Rare & unusual plants.
Map ref: 5, B2

**WPyg   THE PYGMY PINETUM**
Cannop Crossroads, Nr Coleford, Forest of Dean, Gloucestershire, GL15 7EQ
☎ (01594) 833398  Fax: (01594) 810815
Contact: Keith Parker
Opening times: 0900-1800 daily all year.
Mail order: None
Cat. cost: 3 x 2nd class
Credit cards: Visa, MasterCard, Switch
Specialities: Unusual Shrubs, Alpines & Herbaceous. Wide range of Trees, Heathers, Ferns, Top Fruit, Water plants & Climbers.
Map ref: 5, C1

**WRha   RHANDIRMWYN PLANTS ✉ EU 🛒**
(Office) 8 Pannau Street, Rhandirmwyn, Nr Llandovery, Carmarthenshire, Wales, SA20 0NP
☎ (01550) 760220  Fax: (01550) 760398
Contact: Sara Fox/Thomas Sheppard
Opening times: 1000-1700 Sat & Sun Apr-end Sep.
Min. mail order UK: No minimum charge
Min. mail order EU: Nmc
Cat. cost: 2 x 1st class
Credit cards: None
Specialities: Old-fashioned Cottage Garden plants, over 400 varieties. Geranium, Helleborus, Primula (double), Pulmonaria, Salvia. Note: Nursery is at Pwyllpriddog Farm, Rhandirmwyn SA20 0NT.
Map ref: 4, B3

**WRHF   RED HOUSE FARM**
Flying Horse Lane, Bradley Green, Nr Redditch, Worcestershire, B96 6QT
☎ (01527) 821269  Fax: (01527) 821674
Contact: Mrs Maureen Weaver
Opening times: 0900-1700 daily all year.
Mail order: None
Cat. cost: 2 x 1st class
Credit cards: None
Specialities: Cottage Garden Perennials.
Map ref: 5, A2

**WRic   RICKARD'S HARDY FERNS ✉ EU**
Kyre Park, Kyre, Tenbury Wells, Worcestershire, WR15 8RP
☎ (01885) 410282, (01885) 410729
Fax: (01885) 410729

Contact: Martin Rickard
Opening times: Wed-Mon all year but appt. advisable Nov-Feb.
Min. mail order UK: £20.00 + p&p
Min. mail order EU: £50.00 + p&p
Cat. cost: 5 x 1st class*
Credit cards: None
Specialities: Ferns, hardy & half-hardy, Tree-ferns. National Collections of Polypodium, Cystopteris & Thelypteroid ferns. *Descriptive list.
Map ref: 5, A1

**WRos   ROSEMARY'S FARMHOUSE NURSERY**
Llwyn-y-moel-gau, Llanfihangel, Llanfyllin, Powys, SY22 5JE
☎ (01691) 648196  Fax: (01691) 648196
Contact: Rosemary Pryce
Opening times: 1000-1700 most days all year, but advisable to telephone to confirm.
Mail order: None
Cat. cost: None issued.
Credit cards: None
Specialities: Fuchsia paniculata, unusual Perennials & Cottage plants, Grasses & Herbs.
Map ref: 4, C2

**WRus   RUSHFIELDS OF LEDBURY 🛒**
Ross Road, Ledbury, Herefordshire, HR8 2LP
☎ (01531) 632004  Fax: (01531) 632004
E-mail: rush01531@aol.com
Contact: B & J Homewood
Opening times: 1100-1700 Wed-Sat. Other times by appt.
Mail order: None
Cat. cost: A5 Sae 31p + £1.00
Credit cards: Visa, Access, American Express
Specialities: Unusual Herbaceous, incl. Euphorbia, Hardy Geranium, Helleborus, Hosta, Osteospermum, Penstemon, Primroses & Grasses.
Map ref: 5, B2

**WSan   SANDSTONES COTTAGE GARDEN PLANTS ✉ EU**
58 Bolas Heath, Great Bolas, Shropshire, TF6 6PS
☎ (01952) 541657  Fax: (01952) 541657
E-mail: pbrelsforth@mcmail.com
Web site: http://www.sandstonesplants.mcmail.com
Contact: Joanne Brelsforth
Opening times: Tues & Wed May-Sept or by appt.

Min. mail order UK: £10.00 + p&p
Min. mail order EU: £25.00 + p&p
Cat. cost: 4 x 1st class
Credit cards: MasterCard, Visa
Specialities: Unusual & interesting Hardy
Perennials. Also large range of variegated varieties.
Map ref: 7, B2

**WSel    SELSLEY HERB FARM**
Waterlane, Selsley, Stroud, Gloucestershire,
GL5 5LW
☎ (01453) 766682   Fax: (01453) 753674
Contact: Rob Wimperis
Opening times: 1000-1700 Tue-Sat,
1400-1700 Sun & B/Hols Apr-Sep.
Mail order: None
Cat. cost: None issued.
Credit cards: None
Specialities: Culinary, Aromatic & Medicinal
Herbs & selected garden plants.
Map ref: 5, C2

**W**

**WSHC    STONE HOUSE COTTAGE NURSERIES**
Stone, Nr Kidderminster, Worcestershire,
DY10 4BG
☎ (01562) 69902   Fax: (01562) 69960
E-mail: louisa@netsmith.demon.co.uk
Contact: J F & L N Arbuthnott
Opening times: 1000-1730 Wed-Sat.
For Sun opening see NGS 'Yellow Book'.
Appt. only mid-Oct-Mar.
Mail order: None
Cat. cost: Sae
Credit cards: None
Specialities: Small general range, especially
wall Shrubs, Climbers and unusual plants.
Map ref: 5, A2

**WShe    SHERBORNE GARDENS** ▣
Sherborne, Cheltenham, Gloucestershire,
GL54 3DW
☎ (01451) 844522, (01451) 844248
Fax: (01451) 844695
E-mail: sherborne.gardens@dial.pipex.com
Contact: John E.M. Hill
Opening times: 0800-1700 Mon-Sat
Mar-Oct, & Mon-Fri Nov-Feb.
Mail order: None
Cat. cost: 2 x 1st class
Credit cards: None
Map ref: 5, B3

**WShi    JOHN SHIPTON (BULBS)** ✉ EU ▣ ▣
Y Felin, Henllan Amgoed, Whitland, Dyfed,
Wales, SA34 0SL
☎ (01994) 240125   Fax: (01994) 241180
E-mail: bluebell@zoo.co.uk
Contact: John Shipton

Opening times: By appt. only.
Min. mail order UK: No minimum charge
Min. mail order EU: Nmc
Cat. cost: Sae
Credit cards: None
Specialities: Native British Bulbs & Bulbs and
Plants for naturalising.
Map ref: 4, A3

**WSpi    SPINNEYWELL NURSERY** ✉ EU ▣ ▣ ◆
Waterlane, Oakridge, Bisley, Glos, GL6 7PH
☎ (01452) 770092   Fax: (01452) 770151
E-mail: imminent-goto.nu-spinneywell
Web site: http://www.imminent-goto.nu-
spinneywell
Contact: Wendy Asher
Opening times: 1000-1700 daily Mar-Dec,
1000-1600 daily winter.
Min. mail order UK: £10.00 + p&p
Min. mail order EU: £30.00 + p&p
Cat. cost: 6 x 1st class
Credit cards: None
Specialities: Buxus, Taxus & Unusual
Herbaceous & Shrubs.
Map ref: 5, C2

**WSPU    SPECIALIST PLANT UNIT**
**& PLANT CENTRE** ▣
Pershore College of Hort., Avonbank,
Pershore, Worcestershire, WR10 3JP
☎ (01386) 561385   Fax: (01386) 555601
Contact: Lucy Allum (Plant Centre)
Opening times: (Plant Centre) 0900-1700
Mon-Sat, 1000-1600 Sun.
Mail order: None
Cat. cost: £1.00
Credit cards: Visa, Access
Specialities: National Collection of
Penstemon. Open for viewing 0800-1630
Mon-Fri. Also South African plants.
Map ref: 5, B2

**WStl    ST ISHMAEL'S NURSERIES**
Haverfordwest, Pembrokeshire, SA62 3SX
☎ (01646) 636343   Fax: (01646) 636343
Contact: Mr D & Mrs H Phippen
Opening times: 0900-1730 daily Summer.
0900-1700 daily Winter.
Mail order: None
Cat. cost: None issued
Credit cards: Visa, Diners, Access, Switch,
Delta, MasterCard, EuroCard
Specialities: Wide general range.
Map ref: 4, A4

**WSuF    SUNNYBANK VINE NURSERY** ✉ EU ▣ ▣
Sunnybank, Pontrilas, Herefordshire,
HR2 0BX

☎ (01981) 240256
**Contact:** B R Edwards
**Opening times: Mail Order only.**
**Min. mail order UK:** £6.00 incl. p&p
**Min. mail order EU:** £6.00 incl. p&p*
**Cat. cost:** Sae
**Credit cards:** None
**Specialities:** Vines. *Note: EU sales by arrangement.
**Map ref:** 5, B1

**WThi   39 STEPS**
Grove Cottage, Forge Hill, Lydbrook, Gloucestershire, GL17 9QS
☎ (01594) 860544
**E-mail:** graham@39steps8844.freeserve.co.uk
**Contact:** Graham Birkin
**Opening times:** By appt. only.
**Mail order:** None
**Cat. cost:** 3 x 1st class
**Credit cards:** None
**Specialities:** Shade lovers, Helleborus & Iris.
**Map ref:** 5, B1

**WTin   TINPENNY PLANTS**
Tinpenny Farm, Fiddington, Tewkesbury, Glos, GL20 7BJ
☎ (01684) 292668
**Contact:** Elaine Horton
**Opening times:** 1200-1700 Tue-Thur or by appt.
**Mail order:** None
**Cat. cost:** 2 x 1st class
**Credit cards:** None
**Specialities:** Wide range of Hardy garden worthy plants esp. Helleborus, Iris & Sempervivum.
**Map ref:** 5, B2

**WTre   TREASURES OF TENBURY LTD ⊠ EU**
Burford House Gardens, Tenbury Wells, Worcestershire, WR15 8HQ
☎ (01584) 810777   **Fax:** (01584) 810673
**E-mail:** treasures@burford.co.uk
**Contact:** Mr Charles Chesshire
**Opening times:** 1000-1800 daily. Until dusk in Winter
**Min. mail order UK:** No minimum charge
**Min. mail order EU:** Nmc
**Cat. cost:** Free Clematis list
**Credit cards:** Visa, Access, Switch
**Specialities:** Clematis and Herbaceous, Conservatory plants, Bamboos, Trees & Shrubs.
**Map ref:** 5, A1

**WTro   TROED-Y-RHIW TREES & SHRUBS ⊠ UK**
Abercregan, Cymmer, Port Talbot, West Glamorgan, SA13 3LG

☎ (01639) 850503
**E-mail:** joseph.latham@btinternet.com
**Contact:** F A Latham
**Opening times:** By arrangement.
**Min. mail order UK:** £10.00 + p&p
**Cat. cost:** 2 x 1st class
**Credit cards:** None
**Specialities:** Hardy Trees & Shrubs.
**Map ref:** 4, C4

**WTus   MARTIN TUSTIN ☒**
Bowers Hill Nursery, Willersey Road, Badsey, Nr Evesham, Worcestershire, WR11 5HG
☎ (01386) 832124   **Fax:** (01386) 832124
**Contact:** Martin Tustin
**Opening times:** 0900-1800 daily ex Xmas week.
**Mail Order:** None
**Cat. cost:** 2 x 1st class
**Credit cards:** None
**Specialities:** Lavenders.
**Map ref:** 5, B3

**WUnu   UNUSUAL PLANTS ◆**
Mork Road, St Briavels, Lydney, Gloucestershire, GL15 6QE
☎ (01594) 530561
**Contact:** Norman D Heath
**Opening times:** 1100-dusk Sat, Sun & B/Hols. Evenings by arrangement.
**Mail order:** None
**Cat. cost:** None issued
**Credit cards:** None
**Specialities:** Hardy Perennials, Alpines and Rockery Plants.
**Map ref:** 5, C1

**WViv   VIV MARSH POSTAL PLANTS ⊠ UK ☒ ◆**
PO Box 115, Shrewsbury DO, Shropshire, SY4 2WD
☎ (01939) 291475   **Fax:** (01939) 290743
**Contact:** Mr Viv Marsh
**Opening times:** Not open to public.
**Min. mail order UK:** £5.00 + p&p
**Cat. cost:** 5 x 1st class
**Credit cards:** Visa, MasterCard, Switch
**Specialities:** Rare & routine Herbaceous Perennials.

**WWal   THE WALLED GARDEN AT PIGEONSFORD ⊠ UK ☒**
Llangranog, Llandysul, Ceredigion, Wales, SA44 6AF

| KEY | |
|---|---|
| ⊠ | Mail order to UK or EU |
| ☒ | Exports beyond EU |
| ☒ | Also supplies Wholesale   ◆ See Display advertisement |

**W**

☎ (01239) 654360  **Fax:** (01239) 654360
**Contact:** David & Hilary Pritchard
**Opening times:** 1000-1800 Easter-end Oct.
Telephone for appt. Nov-Easter.
**Min. mail order UK:** £6.00 + p&p
**Cat. cost:** 4 x 1st class
**Credit cards:** None
**Specialities:** Good general range specialising
in Herbaceous plants esp. Hardy Geranium &
Primula.
**Map ref:** 4, B3

**WWat    WATERWHEEL NURSERY ◆**
Bully Hole Bottom, Usk Road, Shirenewton,
Chepstow, Monmouthshire, Wales, NP6 6SA
☎ (01291) 641577  **Fax:** (01291) 641851
**Contact:** Desmond & Charlotte Evans
**Opening times:** 0900-1800 Tue-Sat incl. all
year. Also B/Hol Mons Mar-Sep.*
**Mail order:** None
**Cat. cost:** 2 x 1st class
**Credit cards:** None
**Specialities:** Unusual & choice
'Gardenworthy' plants, esp. Shrubs. Also
Trees, Climbers, Perennials, Grasses etc. Over
1600 in all. *Note: Do write for list with map
or phone for directions, before visiting.
**Map ref:** 5, C1

**WWeb    WEBBS OF WYCHBOLD 🖾 ◆**
Wychbold, Droitwich, Worcestershire,
WR9 0DG
☎ (01527) 861777  **Fax:** (01527) 861284
**E-mail:** claire@webbsofwychbold.demon.co.uk
**Contact:** David Smith/Jim Teague
**Opening times:** 0900-1800 Mon-Fri Winter.
0900-2000 Mon-Fri Summer. 0900-1800 Sat
& 1030-1630 Sun all year.
**Mail order:** None
**Cat. cost:** None issued
**Credit cards:** Visa, Access, American Express
**Specialities:** Hardy Trees & Shrubs, Climbers,
Conifers, Alpines, Heathers, Herbaceous,
Herbs, Roses, Fruit & Aquatics.
**Map ref:** 5, A2

**WWes    WESTONBIRT ARBORETUM 🖂 UK**
(Forest Enterprise), Tetbury, Gloucestershire,
GL8 8QS
☎ (01666) 880544  **Fax:** (01666) 880386
**Contact:** Glyn R Toplis
**Opening times:** 1000-1800 daily Summer,
1000-1700 Winter.
**Min. mail order UK:** No minimum charge*
**Cat. cost:** None issued.
**Credit cards:** Visa, Access
**Specialities:** Trees & Shrubs, many choice &
rare. *Note: Mail Order Nov-Mar only.
**Map ref:** 5, C2

**WWhi    WHIMBLE NURSERY**
Kinnerton, Presteigne, Powys, LD8 2PD
☎ (01547) 560413
**Contact:** Liz Taylor
**Opening times:** 1100-1730 Wed-Sun mid
Apr-end Sep. Other times by appt.
**Mail order:** None
**Cat. cost:** 5 x 1st class*
**Credit cards:** None
**Specialities:** Mainly Herbaceous, some
unusual. Small collections of Achillea,
Campanula, Dianthus, Geranium, Penstemon,
Viola. *Note: Send SAE for plant list (no
descriptions).
**Map ref:** 5, A1

**WWin    WINTERGREEN NURSERIES 🖂 UK**
Bringsty Common, Worcestershire, WR6 5UJ
☎ (01886) 821858 eves.
**Contact:** S Dodd
**Opening times:** 1000-1730 Wed-Sun
1st Mar-31st Oct & by appt.
**Min. mail order UK:**
**Cat. cost:** 2 x 2nd class
**Credit cards:** None
**Specialities:** General, especially Alpines &
Herbaceous.
**Map ref:** 5, A2

**WWol    WOOLMANS PLANTS LTD 🖂 EU 🖾**
The Plant Centre, Knowle Hill, Evesham,
Worcestershire, WR11 5EN
☎ 01386 833022  **Fax:** 01386 832915
**E-mail:** woolman@compuserve.com
**Contact:** John Woolman
**Opening times:** 0900-1700 Mon-Sun.
**Min. mail order UK:** No minimum charge
**Min. mail order EU:** Nmc
**Cat. cost:** Free
**Credit cards:** MasterCard, Visa, Switch
**Specialities:** Chrysanthemum, Hanging Basket
& Patio Plants, Dahlias.
**Map ref:** 5, B3

**WWoo    WOODLANDS NURSERIES 🖾**
Woodlands View, Blakemere, Herefordshire,
HR2 9PY
☎ (01981) 500306  **Fax:** (01981) 500184
**Contact:** Larry & Mal Lowther
**Opening times:** By appt. only.
**Mail order:** None
**Cat. cost:** 2 x 1st class
**Credit cards:** None
**Specialities:** Common & unusual Herbaceous
Perennials, Shrubs, Ferns, Trees & Grasses.
**Map ref:** 5, B1

**WWst   WESTONBIRT PLANTS ⊠ EU**
9 Westonbirt Close, Worcester,
Worcestershire, WR5 3RX
☎ (01905) 350429 (answerphone)
**Contact:** Garry Dickerson
**Opening times:** Not open, strictly mail order
only.
**Min. mail order UK:** No minimum charge
**Min. mail order EU:** Nmc
**Cat. cost:** 2 x 1st class
**Credit cards:** None
**Specialities:** Iris, Fritillaria, Erythronium,
particular interest in Iris species.

**WWye   WYE VALLEY PLANTS ◆**
The Nurtons, Tintern, Chepstow, Gwent,
Wales, NP6 7NX
☎ (01291) 689253   **Fax:** (01291) 689909
**Contact:** Adrian & Elsa Wood
**Opening times:** 1030-1700 Wed-Mon (closed
Tues) 1st Mar-mid Oct. Other times by appt.
**Mail order:** None
**Cat. cost:** 3 x 1st class
**Credit cards:** None
**Specialities:** Wide range of unusual Perennials,
Aromatic and Medicinal Herbs, Salvia,
Origanum, Grasses & Sedges.
**Map ref:** 5, C1

# ABROAD

**XB&T   B & T WORLD SEEDS ⊠ EU ⊠ ⊠**
Paguignan, 34210 Olonzac, France
☎ (0033) 0468912963
**Fax:** (0033)0468913039
**E-mail:** ralph@b-and-t-world-seeds.com
**Web site:** http://www.b-and-t-world-seeds.com
**Contact:** Lesley Sleigh & Ralph Wheatley
**Min. mail order UK:** £5.00
**Min. mail order EU:** £5.00
**Cat. cost:** £10 Europe, £14 elsewhere.
**Credit cards:** Visa, MasterCard
**Specialities:** Master list contains over 40,000
items. 199 Sub-lists available. Lists to
specification. Note: Exports seed only.

**XBoe   J BOEHM ⊠ EU ⊠ ⊠**
Kirchhof 3, 66424 Homburg, Germany
☎ (0049) + 6841 630733, 06841 3157
**Fax:** (0049) + 6841 630733, 0511 851714
**E-mail:** cyps@compuserve.com
**Contact:** Juergen Boehm
**Opening times:** By appt.
**Min. mail order UK:** No minimum charge
**Min. mail order EU:** Nmc
**Cat. cost:** 1 x IRC for pricelist
**Credit cards:** None
**Specialities:** Cypripedium & Hardy Orchids;
seedlings from in-vitro culture.

**XFro   FROSCH EXCLUSIVE
PERENNIALS ⊠ EU ⊠ ⊠**
Am Brunnen 14, 85551 Kirchheim, Germany
☎ (0049-89) 9043190
**Fax:** (0049-89) 9037683
**E-mail:** michael_weinert@t-online.de
**Contact:** Michael Weinert
**Opening times:** Mail order only. 0700-2200.
**Min. mail order UK:** £120.00 + p&p
**Min. mail order EU:** £120.00 + p&p
**Cat. cost:** None issued.
**Credit cards:** None
**Specialities:** Cypripedium hybrids.

**XJel   JELITTO PERENNIAL SEED ⊠ EU ⊠ ◆**
PO Box 1264, D-29685 Schwarmstedt,
Germany
☎ (0049) 5071 9829 0
**Fax:** (0049) 5071 9829 27
**Contact:** Ulrich Schamp, Georg Uebelhart
**Min. mail order EU:** £32.00 + p&p
**Cat. cost:** Free
**Credit cards:** Visa, MasterCard
**Specialities:** Seeds of Alpines, Perennials,
Herbs, Wildflowers, Ornamental Grasses;
more than 2500 varieties.

**XPab   PABIANICE BOTANICAL
GARDEN ⊠ UK ⊠**
PL-95-200, Pabianice, Box 6, Poland
☎ Please write for catalogue
**Contact:** Roman Plaskota
**Opening times:** Please write for catalogue.
**Min. mail order UK:** See cat. for details
**Cat. cost:** 2 x IRC
**Credit cards:** None
**Specialities:** Botanical garden offering wide
range of Seed: Lilies, Day Lilies, Perennials,
Herbs, Shrubs, Trees, Climbers.

# SPECIALIST NURSERIES

Nurseries have classified themselves under the following headings where they *exclusively* or *predominantly* supply this range of plants. Plant groups are set out in alphabetical order. Refer to **Nursery Details by Code** on page 796 for details of the nurseries whose codes are listed under the plant group which interests you.

## ALPINES/ROCK PLANTS

CAvo CCha CGra CInt
CLyd CMea CNic CPBP
CPri CWil EBur ECho EGle
EHyt EMNN EPot ESis
GCHN GCrs GDra GFle
GMaP GTou IBlr IMGH
ITim LBee LFox LGro MBro
MChR MDHE MOne
MRPP MTho MWat NBro
NCra NFvw NHar NHed
NMen NNew NNrd NRoo
NRya NSla NTow NWCA
SAsh SIgm SIng SMer SRot
SSmi WAbe WCla WCom
WGor WHoo WPat WPer
WUnu XPab

## AQUATICS

CBen CRow CWtG EHon
EMFW LPBA MAAq MKay
MSta NOrc SAWi SLon SWat
SWyc WMAq

## BAMBOOS

CFil CTrG EFul EOas EPla
ERod ISta LEdu LHer LJus
MBrN MCCP MMoz MTed
MWht NMoo SCob WBet
WJun

## BULBOUS PLANTS

CAvo CBro CGrW CLAP
CMea CWoo EBot EFam
EHyt EMui EPar EPot ERos
GCrs IBlr LAma LBlo LBow
MBon MNrw MS&S MStw
MTho NBir NOaD NRog
SDeJ STil WBea WShi
WWst

## CACTI & SUCCULENTS

CBra CCpl CCpl CHal CInt
CPhi CTrF EGln ELau EOas
EPln ESou EYou LToo MHel
NCro NOaD SBrk SChr
SCon SHol SHvs SKCa WGei
WLow

## CARNIVOROUS PLANTS

CSWC EAnd EFEx GTro
SHmp SKCa WMEx

## CLIMBERS

CFir CJas CPlN CRHN CSCl
CSPN CWhi ECot EHic
EOrc EPla ERea ERob ESCh
ETho GSki LPri MBar MBlu
MGos MKay MNew NBea
NTay SApu SBra SLau SLay
SLon SPla WBuc WSHC
WTre

## CONIFERS

CKen CSli ECho EHul EOrn
GChr GPin IMGH LBee
LCon LLin MAsh MBar
MGos NMoo NPoe SCoo
SLim SMer SSmi WBuc
WCwm WDin WGor

## CONSERVATORY PLANTS

CBrP CCpl CGOG CHal
CPlN CRHN CRoM CSpe
CTrF CTrG CWDa EBSP
EBak ECon EEls ERea ERom
LBlm LBlo LChe LCns LDea
LToo MNew MSag NFir SHol
SOWG SStn SYvo WDib
WHer WMal WRic

## FERNS

CCuc CFil CLAP CWtG EFer
GBin GMaP GVic LHil
MCCP NBus NHar NHed
NMar NOrc SApp SCob SLon
SPla SSON WRic

## FRUIT

CAgr CCAT CSla CTho CTri
EMui ERea ERod GChr GTwe
LBlo LEdu MCoo MWat
NRog SDea SFam SKee WHar
WJas WOrn WSuF

## GRASSES

CBrm CCuc CFir CInt CKno
CMea CVer ECot EFot EFul
EGle EPPr EPla EWsh GBin
GCHN GMaP GOrn GSki
GVic LEdu LFox LGre LHil
MBrN MCCP MMoz MNan
MWeb NBid NBir NBro
NHex NMoo NOrc NPSI
NSti SApp SAsh SBea SCob
SLay SPla SSON WBet
WChG WHal WLeb WOve
WRus WWye

## HERBS

CAgr CArn CBod CCha CJew
CSev EBot EEls ELau EOHP
GBar GPoy IIve ILis LFol LGro
LHol LLWP MChe MHer
MHew MNew MWat NHHG
NHex NRob NWoo SHDw
SIde SPil SWat WBea WBet
WCHb WChG WGwG WGwy
WHbs WHer WJek WOak
WOve WPer WPic WSel WTus
WUnu WWye XPab

## Orchids

CBur CHdy EEve EFEx GCrs
GUzu NEqu NSpr SMcB SStn
SWes XBoe XFro

## Ornamental Trees

CAgr CDul CEnd CFil CLnd
CMFo CRoM CSla CTho
CTrG CTri ECho ECot ECrN
EMui ERom GChr IMGH
LHer LHyr LPan MBlu MGos
NBea NBee NPSI NRog SFam

SFur SLau SLay WBuc WCel
WCwm WDin WHar WJas
WMou WNor WOrn WPat
WWes

## Seeds

CCar CDob CGrW CJas CKin
CLyd CPhi CPla CSut CTrF
CTuc EDrk EEmo EFot EMcA
EMsh EPot ET&M EYou
GDra GVic LBra LCTD LCha
LChw LSee LSiH MAsh MBee
MChe MPet MPhe MSag

MStw NChl NLan NMir
NRob SCou SHvs SIde SIng
SWyc WJek WNor XB&T XJel
XPab

## Wild Flowers

CArn CJew CKin CNat CRea
EEmo EWFC IIve ILis MGas
MHer MHew MInt MWll
NHHG NHex NLan NMir
SIde SPil SWat WAlt WCla
WGwy WHbs WHer WJek
WOak WOve WShi WUnu

# NURSERY INDEX BY NAME

Nurseries that are included in the *RHS Plant Finder* for the first time this year (or have been reintroduced) are marked in **bold type**. Full details of the nurseries will be found in **Nursery Details by Code** on page 796. For a key to the geographical codes, see the reverse of the card insert at the start of **Nurseries**.

| | | | |
|---|---|---|---|
| 39 Steps | **WThi** | Aylett Nurseries Ltd | **LAyl** |
| A La Carte Daylilies | **SDay** | B & T World Seeds | **XB&T** |
| **Abacus Nurseries** | **WAba** | Steven Bailey Ltd | **SBai** |
| Abbey Dore Court Gardens | **WAbb** | B & H M Baker | **EBak** |
| Abbey Plants | **CAbP** | Ballagan Nursery | **GBal** |
| Abbotsbury Sub-Tropical Gardens | **CAbb** | Ballalheannagh Gardens | **MBal** |
| Aberconwy Nursery | **WAbe** | Ballydorn Bulb Farm | **IBal** |
| Abriachan Nurseries | **GAbr** | Ballyrogan Nurseries | **IBlr** |
| Acton Beauchamp Roses | **WAct** | Balmer Grove Plants | **WBaG** |
| **Afton Park Nursery** | **SAft** | T H Barker & Sons | **NBrk** |
| Agar's Nursery | **SAga** | Barncroft Nurseries | **MBar** |
| Agroforestry Research Trust | **CAgr** | Barnsdale Gardens | **MBNS** |
| Alderton Plant Nursery | **MAld** | Barters Farm Nurseries Ltd | **CBar** |
| Allwood Bros | **SAll** | Barwinnock Herbs | **GBar** |
| Alternatives | **WAlt** | Battersby Roses | **NBat** |
| Jacques Amand | **LAma** | Bayleys Garden Centre | **WBay** |
| Anders Nursery | **EAnd** | Beacons' Botanicals | **WBea** |
| Apple Court | **SApp** | Beacon's Nurseries | **WBcn** |
| Apuldram Roses | **SApu** | Peter Beales Roses | **EBls** |
| Arcadia Nurseries Ltd | **NArc** | Beamish Clematis Nursery | **NBea** |
| Anthony Archer-Wills Ltd | **SAWi** | **Bean Place Nursery** | **SBea** |
| Architectural Plants | **SArc** | Beechcroft Nursery | **LBee** |
| Architectural Plants (Chichester) Ltd | **SAPC** | Beechcroft Nurseries | **NBee** |
| **Argham Village Nursery** | **NArg** | Beeches Nursery | **EBee** |
| Arivegaig Nursery | **GAri** | Bees of Chester | **MBee** |
| Arley Hall Nursery | **MArl** | Bellhouse Nursery | **MBel** |
| Arne Herbs | **CArn** | **Belmont House Nursery** | **CBel** |
| Ashenden Nursery | **SAsh** | Bennett's Water Lily Farm | **CBen** |
| Ashfield Court Nurseries | **CAsh** | Betwys-Y-Coed Garden Nursery | **WBet** |
| Ashwood Nurseries Ltd | **MAsh** | Biddenden Nursery at Garden Crafts | **SBid** |
| Askew's Nursery | **MAsk** | **Bide-A-Wee Cottage Gardens** | **NBid** |
| Asterby Nurseries | **EAst** | Binny Plants | **GBin** |
| **Aulden Farm** | **WAul** | Birchfleet Nursery | **SBir** |
| Aultan Nursery | **GAul** | Birchwood Farm Nursery | **MBir** |
| **Claire Austin Hardy Plants** | **MCAu** | Birkheads Cottage Garden Nursery | **NBir** |
| David Austin Roses Ltd | **MAus** | Blackmore & Langdon Ltd | **CBla** |
| **Avon Aquatics** | **MAAq** | Blacksmiths Cottage Nursery | **EBla** |
| Avon Bulbs | **CAvo** | Blackthorn Nursery | **SBla** |
| Avondale Nursery | **MAvo** | Terence Bloch - Plantsman | **LBlo** |
| Axe Valley Penstemons | **CAxe** | Bloomsbury | **LBlm** |

| | | | |
|---|---|---|---|
| Blounts Court Nurseries | CBlo | Carncairn Daffodils | ICar |
| Bluebell Nursery | MBlu | Carrob Growers | WCGr |
| Bodiam Nursery | SBod | Carters Seeds | CCar |
| Bodmin Plant and Herb Nursery | CBod | Catforth Gardens | NCat |
| Bodnant Garden Nursery Ltd | WBod | Celyn Vale Eucalyptus Nurseries | WCel |
| **J Boehm** | XBoe | Cerney House Gardens | WCer |
| **Bonaccord Glads** | MBon | Chadwell Seeds | LChw |
| Bonhard Nursery | GBon | **Chapel-Uny Nursery** | CCpl |
| Bordervale Plants | WBor | **Chapel Farm House Nursery** | CCha |
| Bosvigo Plants | CBos | Sheila Chapman Clematis | ESCh |
| The Botanic Nursery | CBot | Charter House Nursery | GCHN |
| Botanicus | EBot | Chase Organics (GB) Ltd | LCha |
| Bouts Cottage Nurseries | WBou | The Beth Chatto Gardens Ltd | ECha |
| Ann & Roger Bowden | CBdn | Chennels Gate Gardens & Nursery | WChG |
| Rupert Bowlby | LBow | Cherry Tree Nursery | CChe |
| S & N Brackley | LBra | Cheshire Herbs | MChe |
| Bradley Batch Nursery | CBra | **Cheshire Ross Ltd** | MChR |
| J Bradshaw & Son | SBra | Chessington Nurseries Ltd | LChe |
| **Bramley Lodge Garden Nursery** | CBrm | Chew Valley Trees | CCVT |
| Bregover Plants | CBre | Chiltern Seeds | NChl |
| Bressingham Plant Centre | EBre | Chipchase Castle Nursery | NChi |
| Bressingham Plant Centre | LBre | Choice Landscapes | ECho |
| Bressingham Plant Centre | EBrP | **Choice Plants** | EChP |
| Bressingham Plant Centre | SBre | Christie Elite Nurseries | GChr |
| Bretby Nurseries | MBre | Christie's Nursery | GCrs |
| Bridge End Nurseries | GBri | Church Hill Cottage Gardens | SChu |
| Bridge Nursery | MBrN | **John Churcher Plants** | SChr |
| Bridgemere Nurseries | MBri | Cider Apple Trees | CCAT |
| Broadleas Gardens Ltd | CBrd | Cilwern Plants | WCil |
| Broadleigh Gardens | CBro | The Citrus Centre | SCit |
| Broadstone Nurseries | MBro | Clay Lane Nursery | LCla |
| Broadwater Plants | SBrw | John Clayfield | WCla |
| Brockings Exotics | MBEx | Cley Nurseries Ltd | ECle |
| Paul Bromfield - Aquatics | LPBA | Clipston Nursery | MCli |
| Bron Eifion Nursery | WBrE | Clonmel Garden Centre | IClo |
| Brook Farm Plants | WBro | **Clun Hills Nursery** | WClu |
| Brooklands Plants | CBrP | Coblands Nursery | SCob |
| Brookside Nursery | SBrk | James Cocker & Sons | GCoc |
| Brookwood Nurseries | IBro | Coghurst Nursery | SCog |
| Mrs P J Brown | LBro | Cold Harbour Nursery | CCol |
| Ted Brown Unusual Plants | MTed | Collectors Corner Plants | MCCP |
| Brownthwaite Hardy Plants | NBro | Collinwood Nurseries | MCol |
| Buckingham Nurseries | LBuc | **Compton Lane Nurseries** | WCom |
| Buckland Plants | GBuc | The Conifer Garden | LCon |
| Bucknell Nurseries | WBuc | Connoisseurs' Cacti | SCon |
| Jenny Burgess | EBur | The Conservatory | LCns |
| Burncoose & South Down Nurseries | CB&S | Conservatory PlantLine | ECon |
| Burnham Nurseries | CBur | The Contented Gardener - Nursery | ECGN |
| Burrows Roses | MBur | **Cookoo Box Nursery** | SCko |
| **Burton Agnes Hall Nursery** | NBur | Cool Temperate | MCoo |
| Bush Green Cottage Nursery | NBus | Cooling's Nurseries Ltd | SCoo |
| Butterfields Nursery | LBut | Coombland Gardens | SCou |
| Byeways | WByw | Patricia Cooper | ECoo |
| Cally Gardens | GCal | Mrs Susan Cooper | WCoo |
| Cambridge Garden Plants | ECGP | Cotswold Garden Flowers | WCot |
| Candacraig Gardens | GCan | **Cotswold Hardy Plants Ltd** | CCHP |
| Cannington College Mail Order Centre | CCan | **Cottage Garden Nursery** | LCtg |
| Carewswood Garden Centre | ICrw | **Cottage Garden Plants** | NCot |

Cottage Garden Plants          LCot
Cottage Gardens                ECot
The Cottage Herbery            WCHb
Cottage Nurseries              ECtt
Country Lady Nursery           MCLN
County Park Nursery            ECou
Crags Lewisia Nursery          NCLN
Craven's Nursery               NCra
Creake Plant Centre            ECre
**Crescent Plants**            MCre
Crocknafeola Nursery           ICro
Croftway Nursery               SCro
Croston Cactus                 NCro
Crown Nursery                  ECrN
Crûg Farm Plants               WCru
CTDA                           LCTD
Cuckoo Mill Nursery            CCuc
Cutting Edge Nursery           NCut
Cwmrhaiadr Nursery             WCwm
Dacus Plants                   IDac
J Dadswell                     SDad
D'Arcy & Everest               EDAr
De Jager & Sons                SDeJ
Deacon's Nursery               SDea
Derek Lloyd Dean               LDea
Deanswood Plants               NDea
Deelish Garden Centre          IDee
Denmans Garden, (John Brookes Ltd)  SDnm
Devon Violet Nursery           CDev
DHE Plants                     MDHE
Dibley's Nurseries             WDib
Dickson Nurseries Ltd          IDic
Dingle Nurseries               WDin
Samuel Dobie & Son             CDob
Dove Cottage Plants            NDov
Downderry Nursery              SDow
Messrs. Jack Drake             GDra
John Drake                     EDrk
Drysdale Garden Exotics        SDry
Duchy of Cornwall              CDoC
Dulford Nurseries              CDul
Brian Duncan                   IDun
Dunge Valley Gardens           MDun
William T Dyson                SDys
E L F Plants                   MPla
Earlstone Nursery              LEar
East Northdown Farm            SEND
Eastfield Plant Centre         SEas
Eastgrove Cottage Garden Nursery  WEas
**Edulis**                     LEdu
Eggesford Gardens              CEgg
Eggleston Hall                 NEgg
**Eildon Plants**              GEil
Charles F Ellis                WCFE
Elm House Nursery              EElm
The Garden at The Elms Nursery  WElm
Elsworth Herbs                 EEls
Elworthy Cottage Plants        CElw

**Emorsgate Seed**             EEmo
Endsleigh Gardens              CEnd
Equatorial Plant Co.           NEqu
Equatorial Plant Co. (Vireyas)  CEqu
**The Europa Nursery**         LEur
R G & A Evenden                EEve
Fairhaven Nursery              CFai
**Fairview Farm Nursery**      NFvw
Fairy Lane Nurseries           NFai
**Famecheck Special Plants**   EFam
Family Trees                   SFam
Farmyard Nurseries             WFar
Feebers Hardy Plants           CFee
The Fern Nursery               EFer
Fibrex Nurseries Ltd           WFib
Field House Nurseries          MFie
Fillan's Plants                CFil
Fir Tree Farm Nursery          CFir
**Fir Trees Pelargonium Nursery**  NFir
The Firs Nursery               MFir
Kaytie Fisher Nursery          LFis
Flaxton House Nursery          NFla
Fleurs Plants                  GFle
Flittvale Garden Centre & Nursery  LFli
Flor do Sol                    EFlo
Flora Exotica                  EFEx
Flowers of the Field           WFoF
Foliage Scented & Herb Plants  LFol
Ford Nursery                   NFor
Mr Fothergill's Seeds Ltd      EFot
Four Seasons                   EFou
Foxgrove Plants                LFox
Friars Way Nursery             CFri
Fron Nursery                   WFro
Frosch Exclusive Perennials    XFro
Fryer's Nurseries Ltd          MFry
Fulbrooke Nursery              EFul
Rodney Fuller                  CFul
**Furzey Gardens Nursery**     SFur
Gandy's (Roses) Ltd            MGan
Garden Cottage Nursery         GGar
**Garden House Nurseries**     NGdn
Gardiner's Hall Plants         EGar
Linda Gascoigne Wild Flowers   MGas
Geddington Gardens             MGed
W G Geissler                   WGei
Genus Plants                   CGen
Gerddi Fron Goch               WGer
Glebe Cottage Plants           CGle
Glebe Garden Nursery           WGle
Glen Chantry                   EGle
Glendoick Gardens Ltd          GGGa
Glenhirst Cactus Nursery       EGln
Global Orange Groves UK        CGOG
Godly's Roses                  LGod
Goldbrook Plants               EGol
Elisabeth Goodwin Nurseries    EGoo
Gordon's Nursery               WGor

| | | | |
|---|---|---|---|
| Goscote Nurseries Ltd | **MGos** | The High Garden | **CHig** |
| Gouldings Fuchsias | **EGou** | Highcroft Nursery | **GHCN** |
| Grafted Walnut Trees | **WGWT** | Highdown Nursery | **SHDw** |
| Graham's Hardy Plants | **CGra** | Highfield Hollies | **SHHo** |
| Granby Gardens | **MGrG** | Brian Hiley | **LHil** |
| Grange Farm Nursery | **WGra** | The Hiller Garden | **MHlr** |
| Grasmere Plants | **EGra** | Hillside Cottage Plants | **CHil** |
| Peter Grayson (Sweet Pea Seedsman) | **MPet** | Hillview Hardy Plants | **WHil** |
| Great Dixter Nurseries | **SDix** | Hoecroft Plants | **EHoe** |
| **The Great Western Gladiolus Nursery** | **CGrW** | Hofflands Daffodils | **EHof** |
| Green Farm Plants | **LGre** | Holden Clough Nursery | **NHol** |
| Greenhead Roses | **GGre** | Holkham Gardens | **EHol** |
| Greenway Gardens | **CGre** | Hollington Nurseries | **LHol** |
| Greenwood Plants | **SGre** | Holly Gate Cactus Nursery | **SHol** |
| **Griffins Garden Centre** | **IGri** | Honeysome Aquatic Nursery | **EHon** |
| C W Groves & Son | **CGro** | Hoo House Nursery | **WHoo** |
| Growing Carpets | **LGro** | Hopleys Plants Ltd | **LHop** |
| Gwydir Plants | **WGwy** | **Horn's Garden Centre** | **NHor** |
| Gwynfor Growers | **WGwG** | Horton Vale Nursery | **CHor** |
| Hadspen Garden & Nursery | **CHad** | The Hosta Garden | **LHos** |
| **Halecat Nurseries** | **NHlc** | How Caple Court Gardens | **WHow** |
| Hall Farm Nursery | **EHal** | Hull Farm | **EHul** |
| Hall Farm Nursery | **WHal** | Hunts Court Garden & Nursery | **WHCG** |
| Halls of Heddon | **NHal** | **The Hut** | **SHut** |
| Halsway Nursery | **CHal** | Brenda Hyatt | **SHya** |
| **Hampshire Carnivorous Plants** | **SHmp** | Hydon Nurseries | **LHyd** |
| Hanging Gardens Nurseries Ltd | **EHan** | Hyrons Trees | **LHyr** |
| The Hannays of Bath | **CHan** | Hythe Alpines | **EHyt** |
| Hardstoft Herb Garden | **NHHG** | Iden Croft Herbs | **SIde** |
| Hardy Orchids Ltd | **CHdy** | Tim Ingram | **SIgm** |
| **Hardy Plant Nursery** | **IHdy** | W E Th. Ingwersen Ltd | **SIng** |
| Hardy's Cottage Garden Plants | **SHar** | Intakes Farm | **MInt** |
| **R Harkness & Co. Ltd.** | **LHkn** | International Animal Rescue Nursery | **CInt** |
| Harley Nursery | **WHar** | The Iris Garden | **LIri** |
| Harry Byrne's Garden Centre | **IHar** | Iverna Herbs | **IIve** |
| Sue Hartfree | **SHFr** | Ivycroft Plants | **WIvy** |
| Harts Green Nursery | **MHar** | Jackson's Nurseries | **MJac** |
| Hartside Nursery Garden | **NHar** | Jasmine Cottage Gardens | **CJas** |
| Harvest Nurseries | **SHvs** | Paul Jasper - Fruit & Ornamental Trees | **WJas** |
| **Harveys Garden Plants** | **EHrv** | Jekka's Herb Farm | **WJek** |
| The Hawthornes Nursery | **NHaw** | **Jelitto Perennial Seed** | **XJel** |
| Hayward's Carnations | **SHay** | Jean Jewels | **CJew** |
| Heather Bank Nursery | **CHea** | C & K Jones | **MJon** |
| Hedgerow Nursery | **NHed** | Jungle Giants | **WJun** |
| Heldon Nurseries | **MHel** | Just Bamboo Ltd | **LJus** |
| Hellyer's Garden Plants | **SHel** | Just Phlomis | **WPhl** |
| Henllys Lodge Plants | **WHen** | Just Roses | **SJus** |
| The Herb Garden & Historical Plant | **WHer** | Kayes Garden Nursery | **MKay** |
|   Nursery | | Keepers Nursery | **SKee** |
| **The Herb Nursery** | **MHer** | Kelways Ltd | **CKel** |
| **Herbs at Myddfai** | **WHbs** | Kent Cacti | **SKCa** |
| Hergest Croft Gardens | **WHCr** | Kent Street Nurseries | **SKen** |
| **Herons Bonsai** | **LHer** | Kenwith Nursery (Gordon Haddow) | **CKen** |
| Herterton House Garden Nursery | **NHer** | Kiftsgate Court Gardens | **WKif** |
| Hewthorn Herbs & Wild Flowers | **MHew** | Kingfisher Nurseries | **WKnf** |
| Hexham Herbs | **NHex** | Kingsfield Conservation Nursery | **CKin** |
| Hickling Heath Nursery | **EHic** | Kingstone Cottage Plants | **WKin** |
| Hidden Valley Nursery | **CHid** | Knap Hill & Slocock Nurseries | **LKna** |

| | | | |
|---|---|---|---|
| Knoll Gardens | **CKno** | S E Marshall & Co Ltd. | **EMsh** |
| L W Plants | **LLWP** | Marshall's Malmaison | **WMal** |
| Lakes' Hardy Plants | **NLak** | J & D Marston | **NMar** |
| Landford Trees | **CLnd** | Marston Exotics | **WMEx** |
| Landlife Wildflowers Ltd | **NLan** | Martin Nest Nurseries | **EMNN** |
| Landscape Plants | **SLPl** | Marwood Hill Gardens | **CMHG** |
| Lane End Nursery | **MLan** | Mattock's Roses | **MMat** |
| Langley Boxwood Nursery | **SLan** | S M McArd (Seeds) | **EMcA** |
| Langthorns Plantery | **ELan** | McBeans Orchids | **SMcB** |
| The Lanhydrock Gardens (NT) | **CLan** | The Mead Nursery | **CMea** |
| Larch Cottage Nurseries | **NLar** | Meadow Cottage Plants | **CMCo** |
| **The Laurels Nursery** | **SLau** | Meadows Nursery | **CMdw** |
| Laurel Farm Herbs | **ELau** | Mears Ashby Nurseries Ltd | **MMea** |
| Layham Nurseries | **SLay** | Mendle Nursery | **NMen** |
| Lea Rhododendron Gardens Ltd | **MLea** | Merebrook Water Plants | **WMAq** |
| Leba Orchard - Green's Leaves | **WLeb** | Merriments Gardens | **SMrm** |
| Michael Lewington Gardener-Plantsman | **LLew** | Merryfield Nurseries (Canterbury) Ltd | **SMer** |
| Lilliesleaf Nursery | **GLil** | Merton Nurseries | **WMer** |
| Lime Cross Nursery | **SLim** | Mickfield Fish & Watergarden Centre | **EMFW** |
| Lincluden Nursery | **LLin** | Mickfield Hostas | **EMic** |
| Lingen Nursery and Garden | **WLin** | Mill Cottage Plants | **CMil** |
| Liscahane Nursery | **ILsc** | Mill Hill Plants | **MMil** |
| Lisdoonan Herbs | **ILis** | Mill Race Nursery | **EMil** |
| Little Brook Fuchsias | **SLBF** | Millais Nurseries | **LMil** |
| Little Creek Nursery | **CLCN** | Millfield Nurseries | **MMiN** |
| Little Rhyndaston Nurseries | **WLRN** | Mills' Farm Plants & Gardens | **EMFP** |
| Little Treasures | **CLTr** | Milton Garden Plants | **CMGP** |
| Littlewood Farm Nursery | **MLit** | Mires Beck Nursery | **NMir** |
| Loch Leven Plants | **GLch** | Monksilver Nursery | **EMon** |
| C S Lockyer | **CLoc** | **Moor Monkton Nurseries** | **NMoo** |
| Loder Plants | **SLdr** | Moorland Cottage Plants | **WMoo** |
| Lodge Lane Nursery & Gardens | **MLLN** | Morehavens | **LMor** |
| The Lodge Nursery | **SLod** | John Morley | **EMor** |
| Long Acre Plants | **CLAP** | Morton Hall Gardens | **MMHG** |
| Longframlington Gardens | **NLon** | Stanley Mossop | **NMos** |
| Longhall Nursery | **CLon** | Frances Mount Perennial Plants | **EMou** |
| **Longstock Park Nursery** | **SLon** | Mount Pleasant Trees | **WMou** |
| Lovers Knot Nursery | **MLov** | Mow Cottage Garden Plants | **WMow** |
| Lower Icknield Farm Nurseries | **LIck** | Mozart House Nursery Garden | **MMoz** |
| Lower Severalls Nursery | **CSev** | Muckross Garden Centre | **IMuc** |
| **Lower Spring Nursery** | **WLow** | Ken Muir | **EMui** |
| Lydford Alpine Nursery | **CLyd** | Mulu Nurseries | **WMul** |
| Lynash Nurseries | **CLyn** | Muncaster Castle | **NMun** |
| M & M Plants | **CM&M** | Kathleen Muncaster Fuchsias | **EKMF** |
| **M G H Nurseries** | **IMGH** | Murrells Plant & Garden Centre | **SMur** |
| MGW Plants | **NMGW** | Naked Cross Nurseries | **CNCN** |
| **Mac Foliage** | **CMFo** | Nanney's Bridge Nursery | **MNan** |
| Elizabeth MacGregor | **GMac** | Natural Selection | **CNat** |
| MacGregors Plants | **SMac** | **Naughton Castle Garden** | **GNau** |
| Macpennys Nurseries | **CMac** | Ness Gardens | **MNes** |
| Macplants | **GMaP** | Nettletons Nursery | **LNet** |
| Madrona Nursery | **SMad** | Newington Nurseries | **MNew** |
| Malcoff Cottage Garden Nursery | **MMal** | Newton Hill Alpines | **NNew** |
| Mallet Court Nursery | **CMCN** | Nicky's Rock Garden Nursery | **CNic** |
| Manor Nursery | **EMan** | Norden Alpines | **NNrd** |
| MapleAsh Plants | **LMap** | Norfields | **WNor** |
| The Marches Nursery | **WMaN** | Norfolk Lavender | **ENor** |
| Lesley Marshall | **EMar** | Northview Perennials | **LNor** |

| | | | |
|---|---|---|---|
| Sheila Northway Auriculas | GNor | Peveril Clematis Nursery | CPev |
| Norwell Nurseries | MNrw | Phedar Nursery | MPhe |
| Notcutts Nurseries | ENot | Alan Phipps Cacti | CPhi |
| Nutlin Nursery | SNut | The Picton Castle Trust Nursery | WPic |
| Oak Cottage Walled Herb Garden | WOak | Pilgrim House Herbs | SPil |
| Oak Dene Nurseries | NOaD | **Pine Cottage Plants** | CPin |
| Oak Tree Nursery | NOak | **Pine Lodge Gardens** | CPLG |
| Oakhurst Nursery | SOkh | **Pinegrove Nursery** | GPin |
| Oasis | EOas | Pinks & Carnations | NPin |
| Okell's Nurseries | MOke | **Pioneer Nursery** | LPio |
| **Oland Plants** | NOla | The Place for Plants | EPfP |
| Old Court Nurseries | WOld | The Plant Lovers | EPln |
| Old Hall Plants | EOHP | The Plant Nursery | MTPN |
| The Old Mill Herbary | COld | Plant World Botanic Gardens | CPla |
| Old Mill House Garden Nursery | EOld | Planta Exotica | MPEx |
| The Old Vicarage Nursery | WOVN | Planta Vera | LPVe |
| The Old Walled Garden | SOWG | **Plantaholics** | CPlt |
| **The Old Withy Garden Nursery** | COlW | Plantations Perennials | NPla |
| One House Nursery | MOne | **Plantbase** | SPlb |
| Orchard House Nursery | NOrc | Plantiecrub Growers Ltd | GPlc |
| Orchard Nurseries | EOrc | Plants of Special Interest | NPSI |
| Orchardstown Nurseries | IOrc | The Plantsman Nursery | CPlN |
| Orchardton Nurseries | GOrc | The Plantsman's Preference | EPPr |
| Ornamental Conifers | EOrn | **Roger Platts Garden Design** | SRPl |
| Ornamental Grasses | GOrn | **& Nurseries** | |
| Ornamental Tree Nurseries | WOrn | Plaxtol Nurseries | SPla |
| Oscroft's Dahlias | MOsc | Pleasant View Nursery | CPle |
| Otter Nurseries Ltd | COtt | **Poets Cottage Shrub Nursery** | NPoe |
| Otters' Court Heathers | COCH | Pops Plants | SPop |
| **Out of the Common Way** | WOut | Porth Veor Fuchsias | CPor |
| Overcourt Garden Nursery | WOve | Potash Nursery | EPts |
| P M A Plant Specialities | CPMA | Potterton & Martin | EPot |
| P W Plants | EPla | Pounsley Plants | CPou |
| **Pabianice Botanical Garden** | XPab | Poyntzfield Herb Nursery | GPoy |
| The Palm Centre | LPal | David Price | CPri |
| The Palm Farm | NPal | Prime Perennials | WPrP |
| A J Palmer & Son | LPlm | Primrose Cottage Nursery | NPri |
| PJ's Palms and Exotics | LPJP | Priorswood Clematis | LPri |
| Pan-Global Plants | WPGP | Priory Plants | EPri |
| Pandora Nursery | SPan | The Priory | WPry |
| Pantiles Plant & Garden Centre | LPan | ProudPlants | NPro |
| Paradise Centre | EPar | The Pygmy Pinetum | WPyg |
| The Paradise Garden | SPar | Quality Daffodils | CQua |
| Parham Bungalow Plants | CPBP | Quinish Garden Nursery | GQui |
| Park Green Nurseries | EPGN | R D Plants | CRDP |
| **Gerry Parker Plants** | NPar | R P P Alpines | MRPP |
| **Parks Perennials** | CPar | Rarer Plants | NRar |
| Passiflora (National Collection) | CPas | Raveningham Gardens | ERav |
| Chris Pattison | WPat | Ravensthorpe Nursery | MRav |
| Pear Tree Cottage Plants | CPea | Reads Nursery | ERea |
| Penhow Nurseries | WPeH | Really Wild Flowers | CRea |
| **Penlan Perennials** | WPnP | Red House Farm | WRHF |
| Penpergwm Plants | WPen | Ben Reid and Co | GRei |
| Penstemons by Colour | LPen | G Reuthe Ltd | SReu |
| The Perennial Nursery | WPnn | Rhandirmwyn Plants | WRha |
| Perhill Nurseries | WPer | Rhodes & Rockliffe | ER&R |
| Perryhill Nurseries | SPer | Rickard's Hardy Ferns | WRic |
| Perry's Plants | NPer | J W Rickeard | ERic |

| | |
|---|---|
| River Garden Nurseries | SRiv |
| Robin Savill Clematis Specialist | ERob |
| **Robins Nursery** | SRob |
| W Robinson & Sons Ltd | NRob |
| Sue Robinson | ERsn |
| The Rodings Plantery | ERod |
| R V Roger Ltd | NRog |
| The Romantic Garden | ERom |
| Rookhope Nurseries | NRoo |
| Rose Cottage Nursery | SRCN |
| **Rosedown Mill Nursery** | CRoM |
| Roseholme Nursery | ERos |
| Roseland House Nursery | CRHN |
| Rosemary's Farmhouse Nursery | WRos |
| **Rosewarne Collections** | CRsw |
| Rosewood Daylilies | SRos |
| Rosie's Garden Plants | SRGP |
| Rotherstone Plants | LRot |
| Rotherview Nursery | SRot |
| Rougham Hall Nurseries | ERou |
| **Rowde Mill Nursery** | CRde |
| Rowden Gardens | CRow |
| Royal Horticultural Society's Garden | CRos |
| Rumsey Gardens | SRms |
| Rushfields of Ledbury | WRus |
| Ryal Nursery | NRya |
| Ryans Nurseries | IRya |
| S & S Perennials | MS&S |
| Mrs Jane Sadler | SSad |
| **Sage Garden Products & Nursery** | MSag |
| St Ishmael's Nurseries | WStI |
| Salley Gardens | MSal |
| Sampford Shrubs | CSam |
| Sandstones Cottage Garden Plants | WSan |
| Scalers Hill Nursery | SSca |
| Scott's Clematis | CSCl |
| Seaforde Gardens | ISea |
| Seale Nurseries | SSea |
| Seaside Nursery | ISsi |
| Seeds by Size | LSee |
| Selsley Herb Farm | WSel |
| Sherborne Gardens | WShe |
| Sherston Parva Nursery Ltd | CSPN |
| John Shipton (Bulbs) | WShi |
| Silver Dale Nurseries | CSil |
| Sino-Himalayan Plant Association | LSiH |
| Siskin Plants | ESis |
| Skipness Plants | GSki |
| Slack Top Alpines | NSla |
| **Slade's Countrywise Ltd** | CSla |
| **Slipps Garden Centre** | CSli |
| Alan C Smith | SSmi |
| Peter J Smith | SSmt |
| **South West Carnivorous Plants** | CSWC |
| Southcott Nursery | SSoC |
| Southfield Nurseries | ESou |
| Southview Nurseries | SSvw |
| Special Plants | CSpe |
| Specialist Plant Unit & Plant Centre | WSPU |
| Speldhurst Nurseries | SSpe |
| Spinners Garden | SSpi |
| Spinneywell Nursery | WSpi |
| Springbank Nurseries | SSpr |
| Springlea Nursery | LSpr |
| Springwood Pleiones | NSpr |
| Stam's Nurseries | ISta |
| Stapeley Water Gardens Ltd | MSta |
| Starborough Nursery | SSta |
| Steventon Road Nurseries | MSte |
| Stewart's (Nottm.) Ltd | MStw |
| Stillingfleet Lodge Nurseries | NSti |
| Stone Cross Nurseries & Garden Centre | SSto |
| Stone House Cottage Nurseries | WSHC |
| Stone Oak Nursery | SSON |
| **Stonehurst Nurseries** | SStn |
| Stonyford Cottage Nursery | MSCN |
| Henry Street Nursery | LStr |
| Sue Strickland Plants | CStr |
| Brian Sulman | EBSP |
| Pearl Sulman | ESul |
| Sunnybank Vine Nursery | WSuF |
| Surrey Primroses | LSur |
| Suttons Seeds | CSut |
| Sylvatica Nursery | LSyl |
| Taylors Nurseries | NTay |
| Tennyson Nurseries | ETen |
| **Test Valley Nursery** | STes |
| Thompson & Morgan (UK) Ltd | ET&M |
| Thorncroft Clematis Nursery | ETho |
| Thornhayes Nursery | CTho |
| A & A Thorp | MTho |
| Three Counties Nurseries | CThr |
| Tile Barn Nursery | STil |
| Timpany Nurseries | ITim |
| Tinpenny Plants | WTin |
| Tissington Nursery | MTis |
| Toobees Exotics | LToo |
| The Torbay Palm Farm | CTor |
| Torhill Nursery | LTor |
| Tough Alpine Nursery | GTou |
| Town Farm Nursery | NTow |
| Treasures of Tenbury Ltd | WTre |
| Trebah Enterprises Ltd | CTbh |
| Tregothnan Nursery | CTrG |
| Trehane Camellia Nursery | CTrh |
| Peter Trenear | STre |
| **Tresidder Farm Plants** | CTrF |
| Trevena Cross Nurseries | CTrC |
| Trewidden Estate Nursery | CTre |
| Trewithen Nurseries | CTrw |
| Triscombe Nurseries | CTri |
| Troed-y-Rhiw Trees & Shrubs | WTro |
| Tropic House | GTro |
| Edwin Tucker & Sons | CTuc |
| Martin Tustin | WTus |
| J Tweedie Fruit Trees | GTwe |

| | | | |
|---|---|---|---|
| Ulverscroft Grange Nursery | MUlv | **Westshores Nurseries** | EWsh |
| Unusual Plants | WUnu | Westwinds Perennial Plants | NWes |
| Usual & Unusual Plants | SUsu | Westwood Nursery | SWes |
| Uzumara Orchids | GUzu | A D & N Wheeler | MWhe |
| Van Tubergen UK Ltd | ETub | Whimble Nursery | WWhi |
| Ventnor Botanic Garden | SVen | White Cottage Alpines | NWCA |
| The Vernon Geranium Nursery | LVER | Jill White | EJWh |
| Veryans Plants | CVer | Whitehill Farm Nursery | MWhi |
| The Vicarage Garden | NVic | Whitehouse Ivies | CWhi |
| **Victoria Gardens** | GVic | **Whitelea Nursery** | MWht |
| The Village Nurseries | SVil | The Wild Flower Centre | EWFC |
| Viv Marsh Postal Plants | WViv | Howard & Sally Wills | CWil |
| J Walkers Bulbs | EWal | Winfrith Hostas | CWin |
| The Walled Garden | EWll | Wingwell Nursery | MWgw |
| **The Walled Garden** | MWll | Wintergreen Nurseries | WWin |
| The Walled Garden at Pigeonsford | WWal | Wisley Plant Centre | LRHS |
| **Walnut Tree Garden Nursery** | EWTr | Withleigh Nurseries | CWit |
| Ward Fuchsias | MWar | Ian and Rosemary Wood | CWoo |
| **Warren Hills Nursery** | MWrn | Woodborough Garden Centre | CWdb |
| Washfield Nursery | SWas | **Woodbury Nursery** | LWoo |
| The Water Garden | CWat | Woodfield Bros | MWoo |
| The Water Gardens | CWtG | Woodlands Cottage Nursery | NWoo |
| Water Meadow Nursery | SWat | Woodlands Nurseries | WWoo |
| Waterperry Gardens Ltd | MWat | Woolmans Plants Ltd | WWol |
| Waterwheel Nursery | WWat | Wootten's Plants | EWoo |
| Weasdale Nurseries | NWea | Nigel Wright Rhododendrons | CWri |
| **A & S Webb** | MWeb | Sonia Wright Plants | CSWP |
| Webbs of Wychbold | WWeb | Wych Cross Nurseries | SWCr |
| West Acre Gardens | EWes | Wychwood Waterlily & Carp Farm | SWyc |
| West Harptree Nursery | CHar | Wye Valley Plants | WWye |
| West Somerset Garden Centre | CWSG | Yorkshire Lavender | NYoL |
| Westdale Nurseries | CWDa | Roy Young Seeds | EYou |
| Westonbirt Arboretum | WWes | **Yvonne's Plants** | SYvo |
| **Westonbirt Plants** | WWst | Zephyrwude Irises | NZep |

# INDEX MAP

The maps on the following pages show the approximate location of the nurseries whose details are listed in this directory.

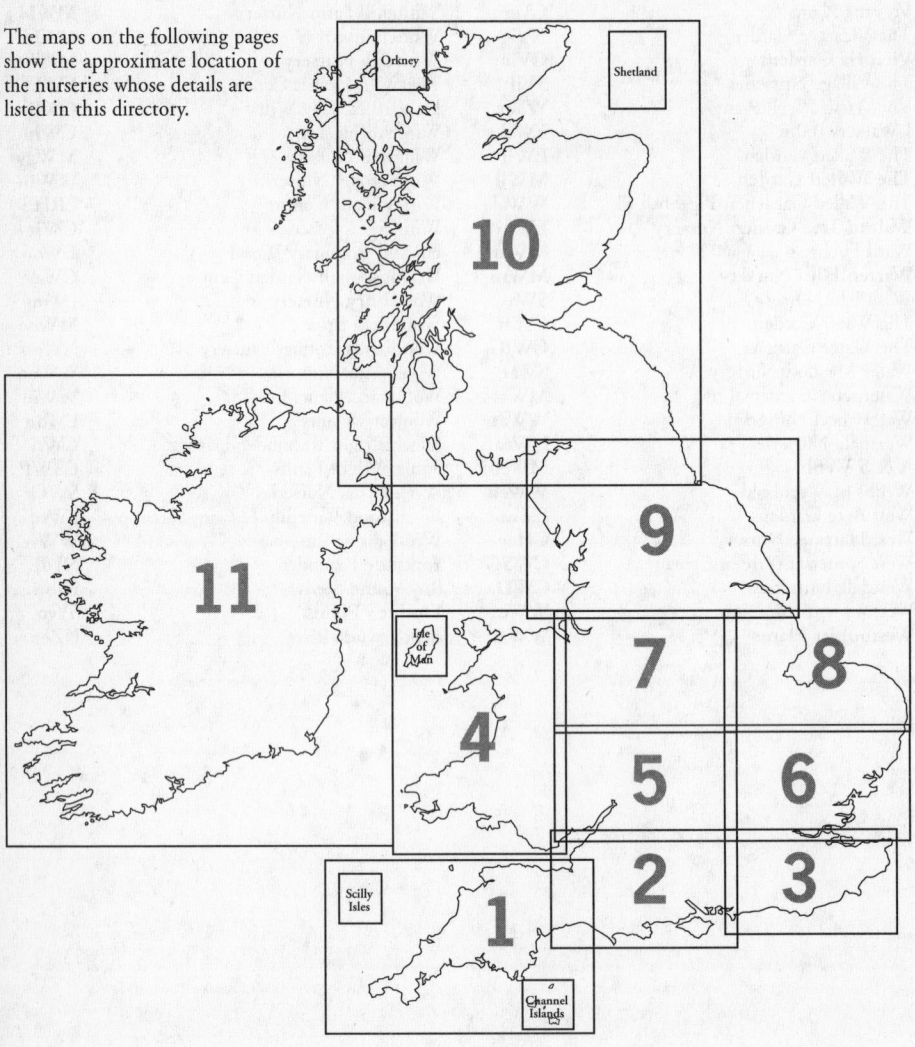

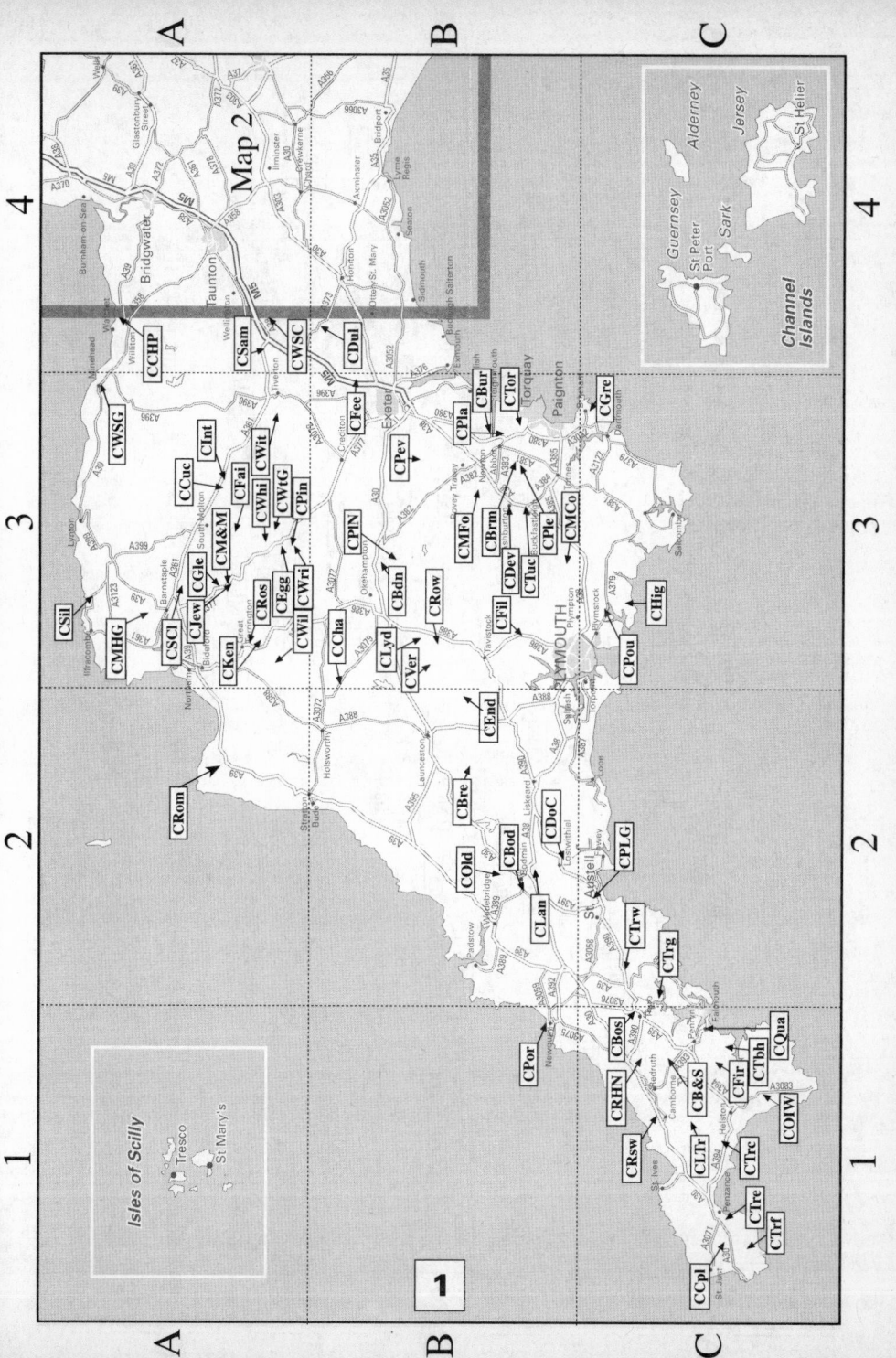

**1**

Map 2

Channel Islands

Isles of Scilly

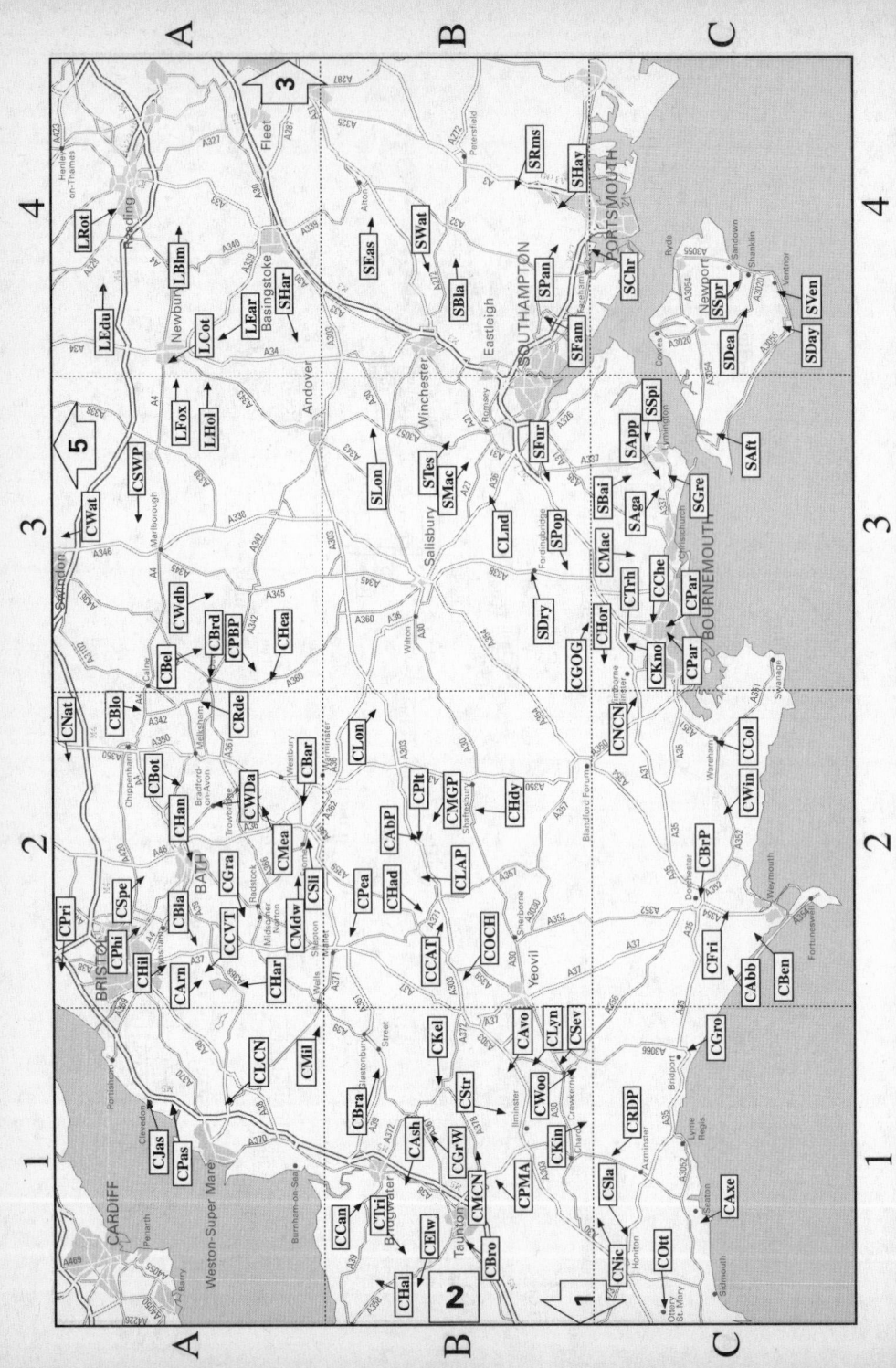

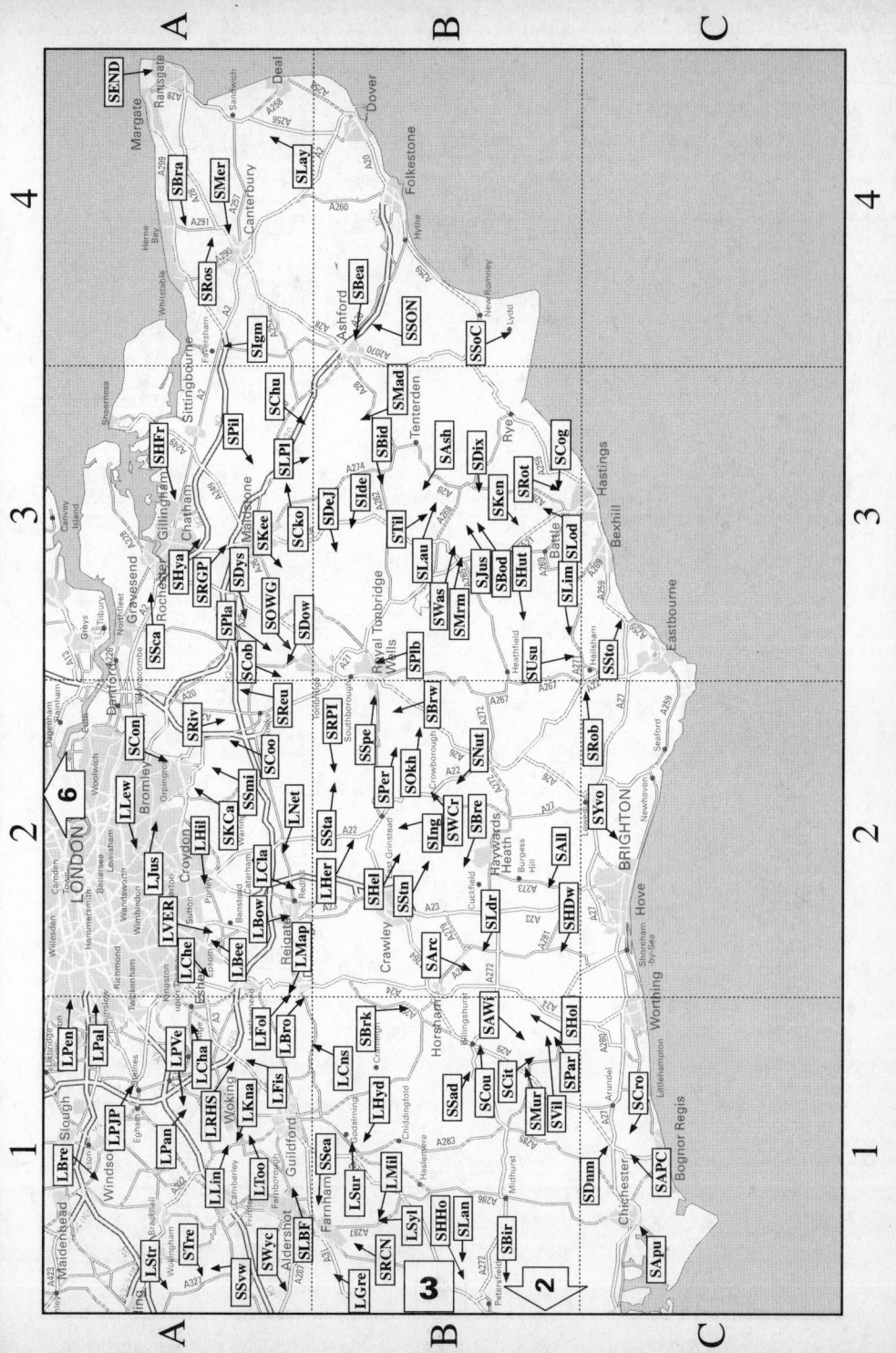

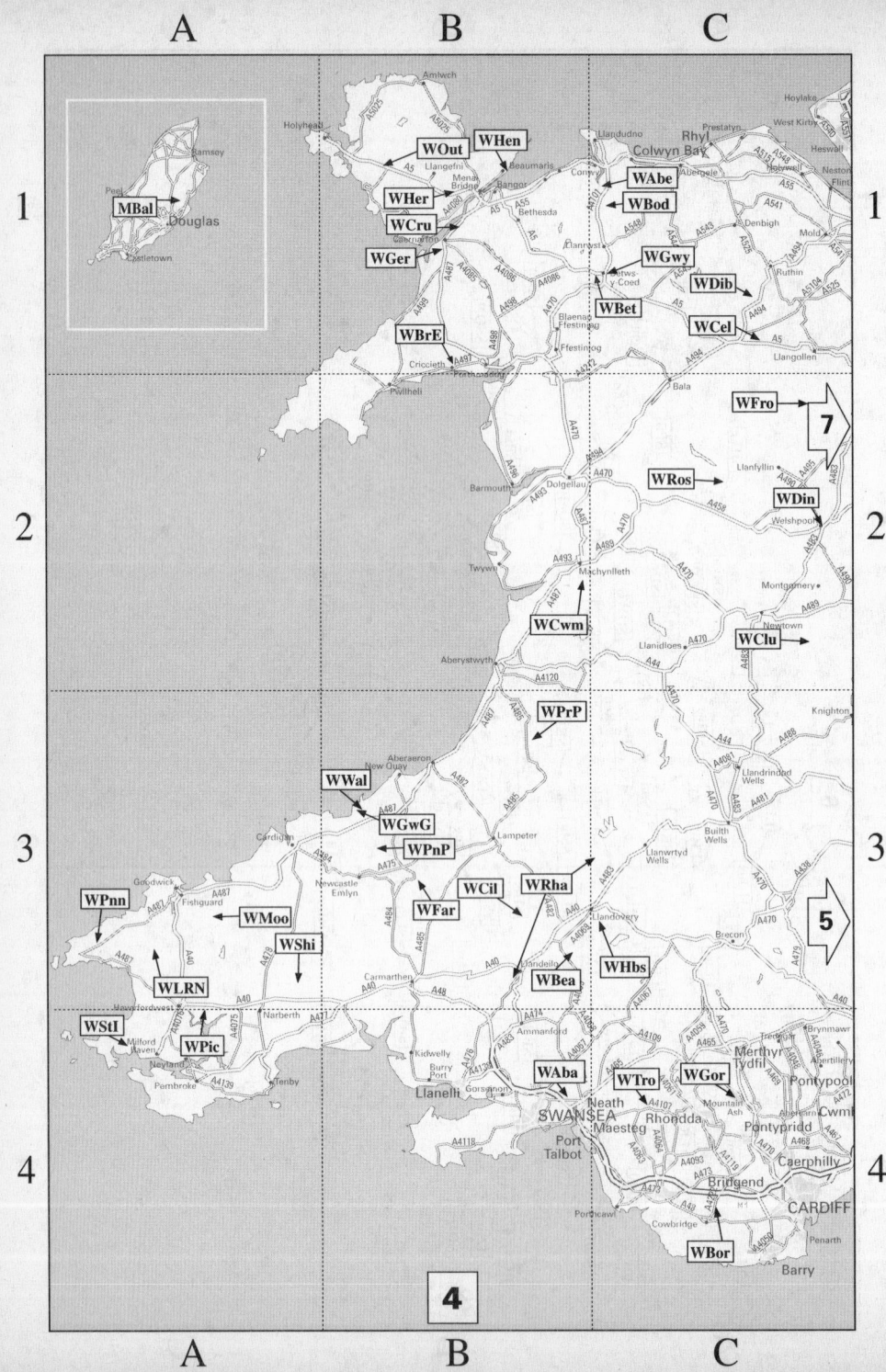

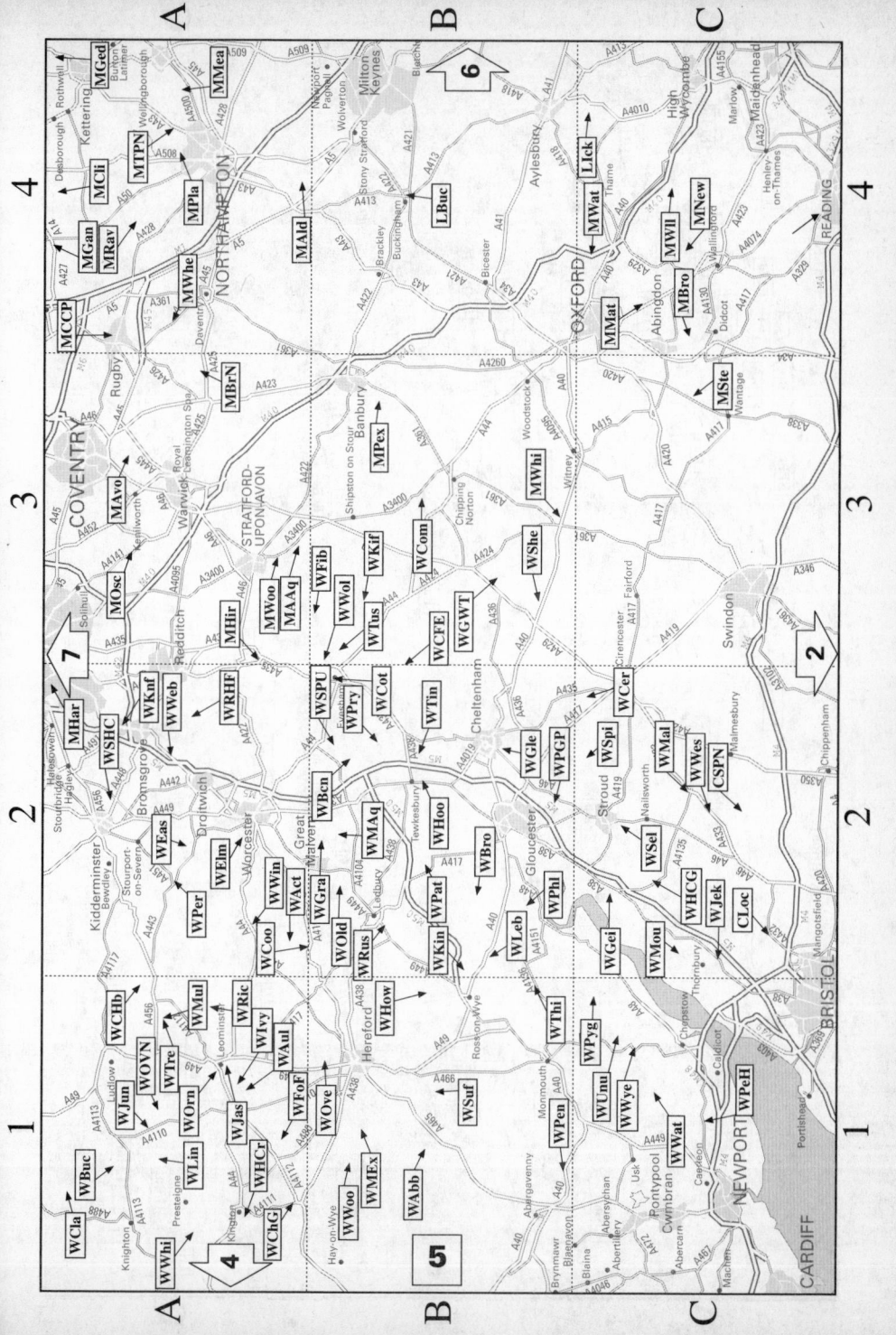

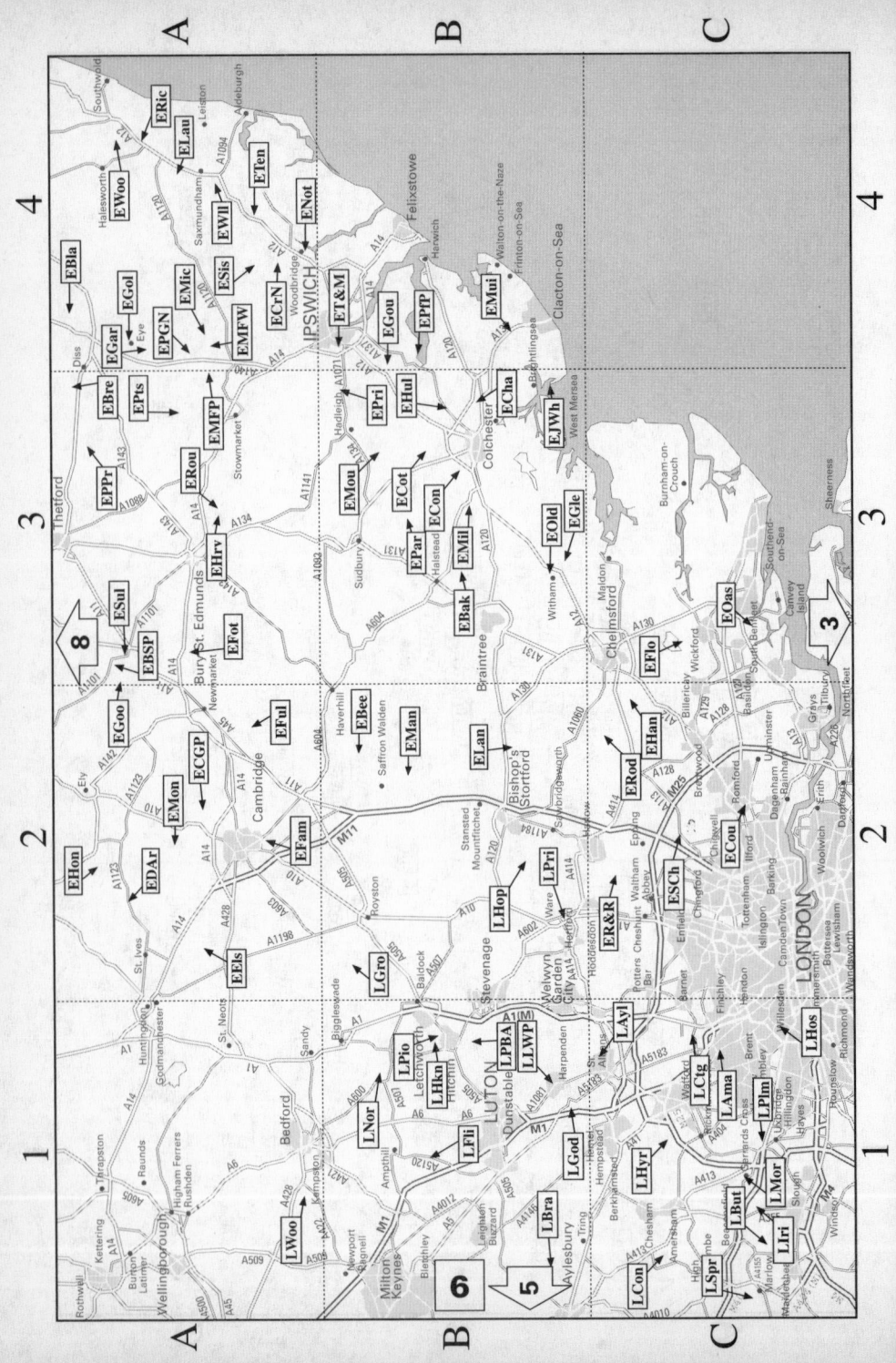

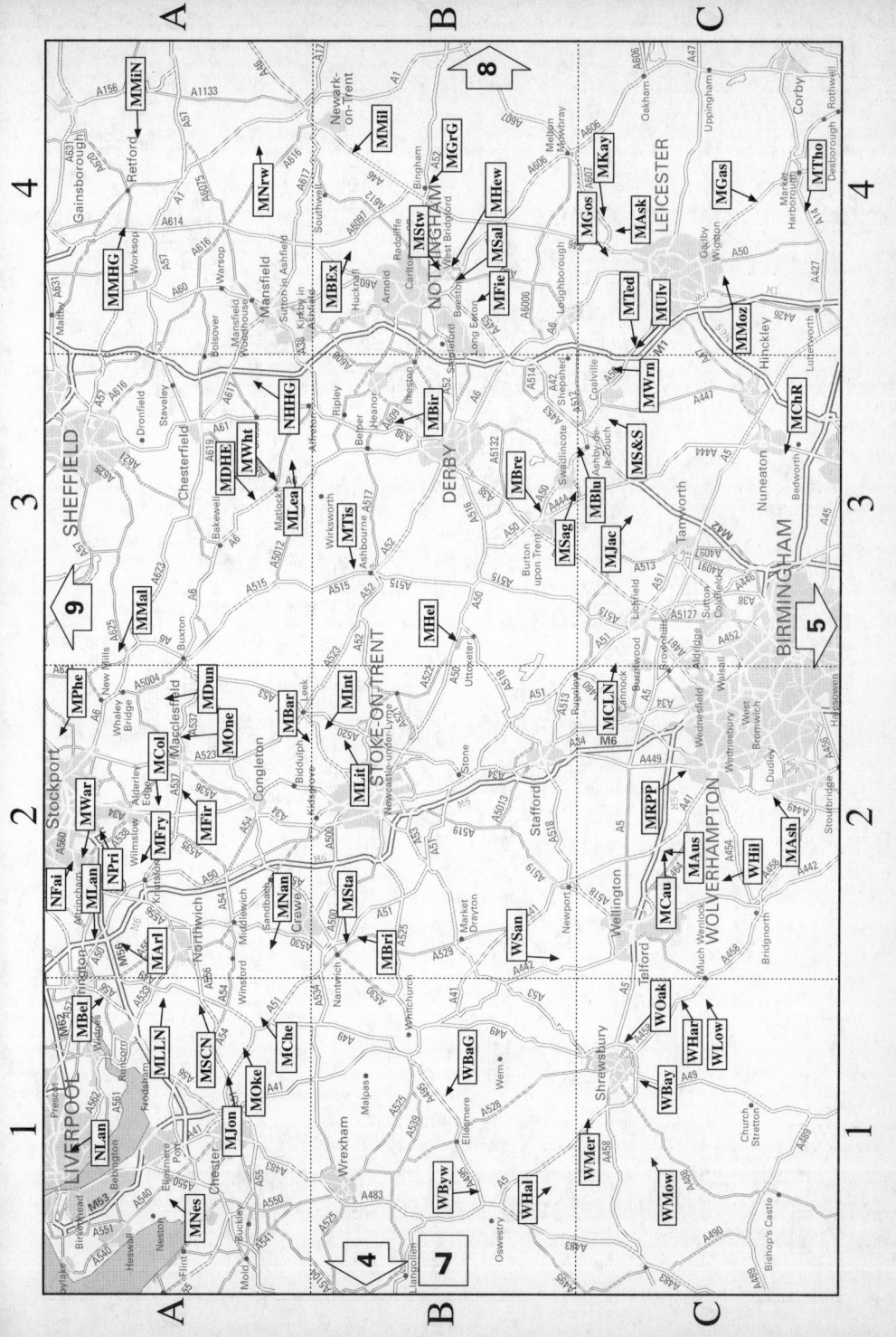

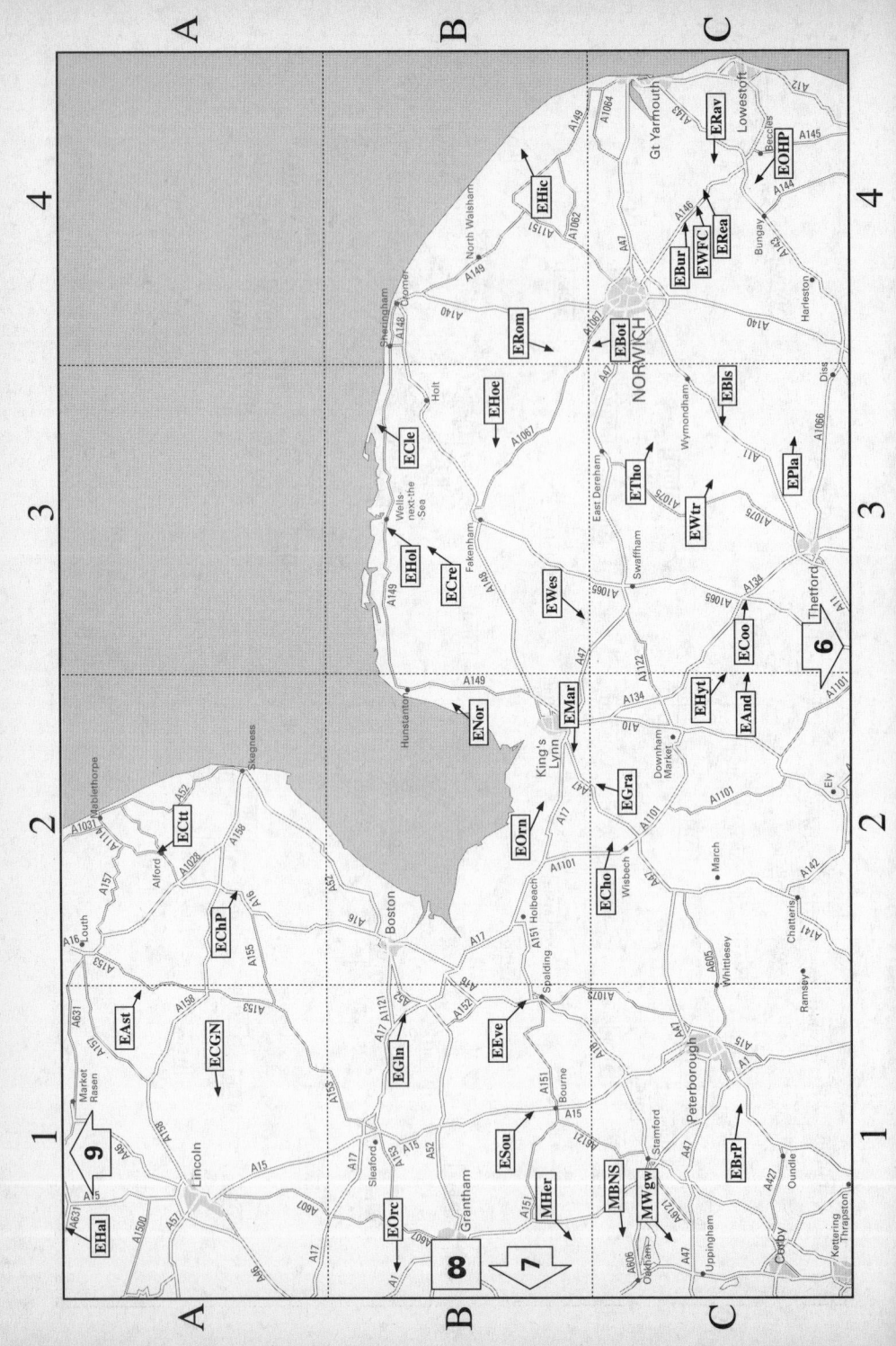

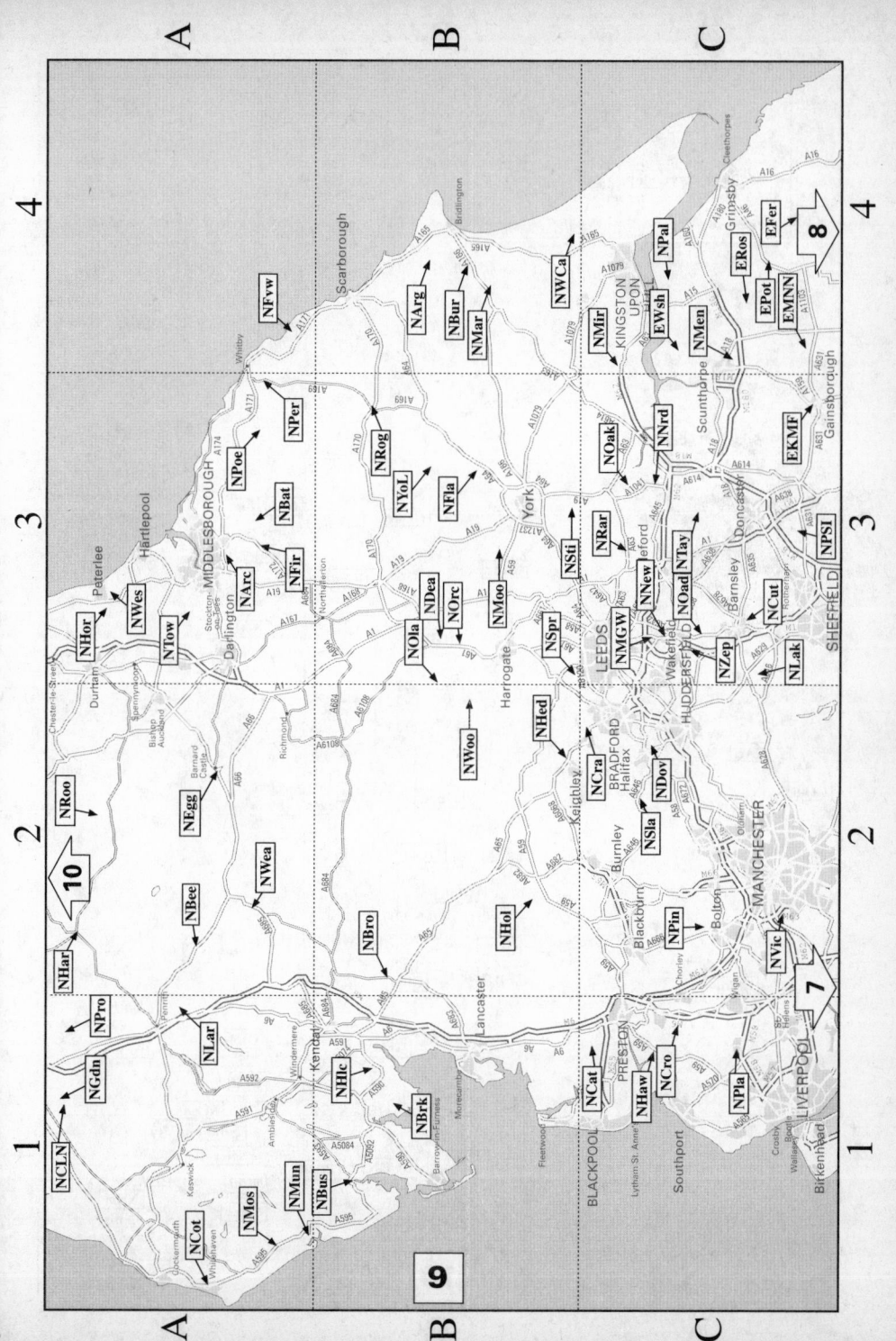

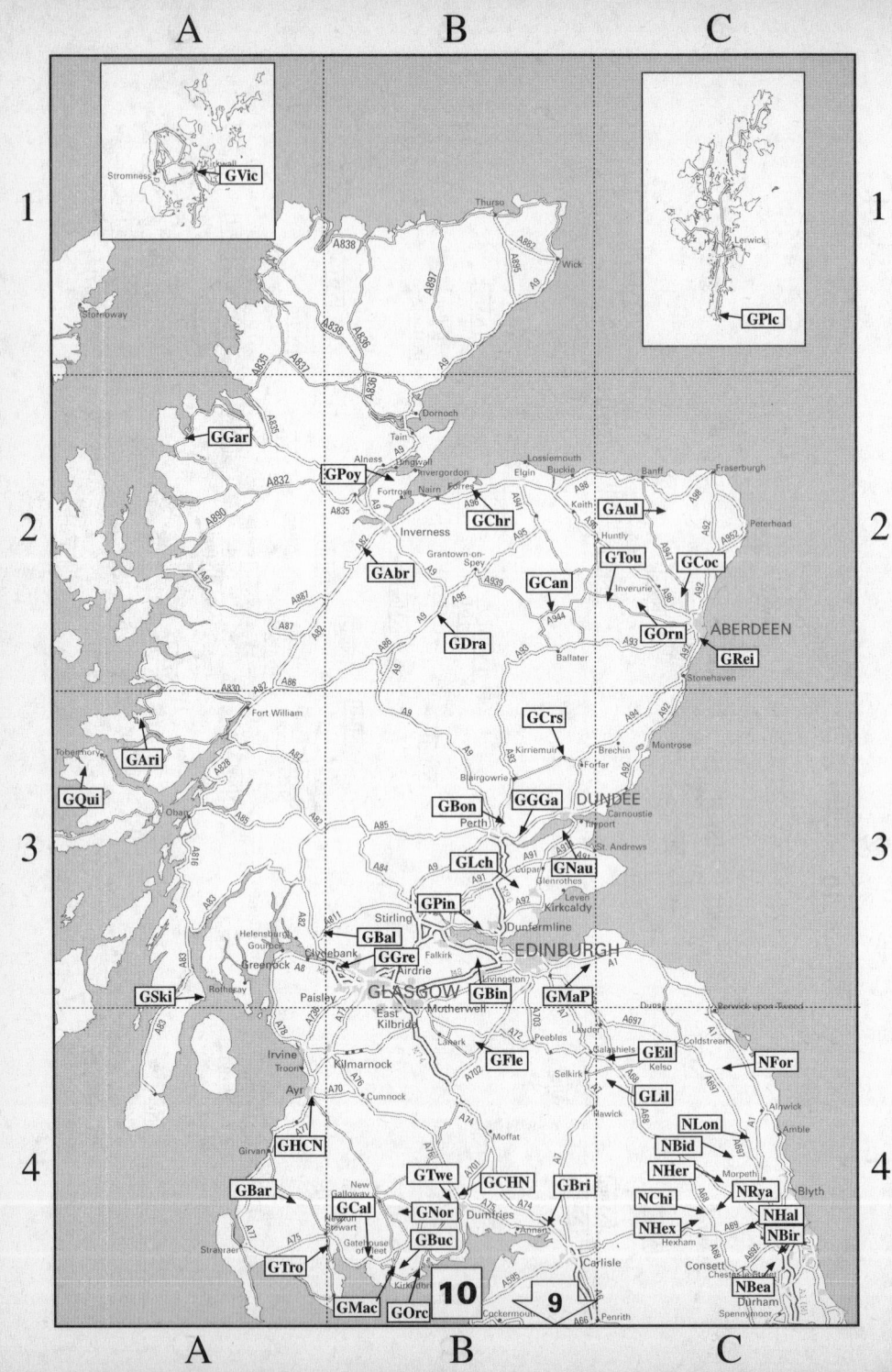

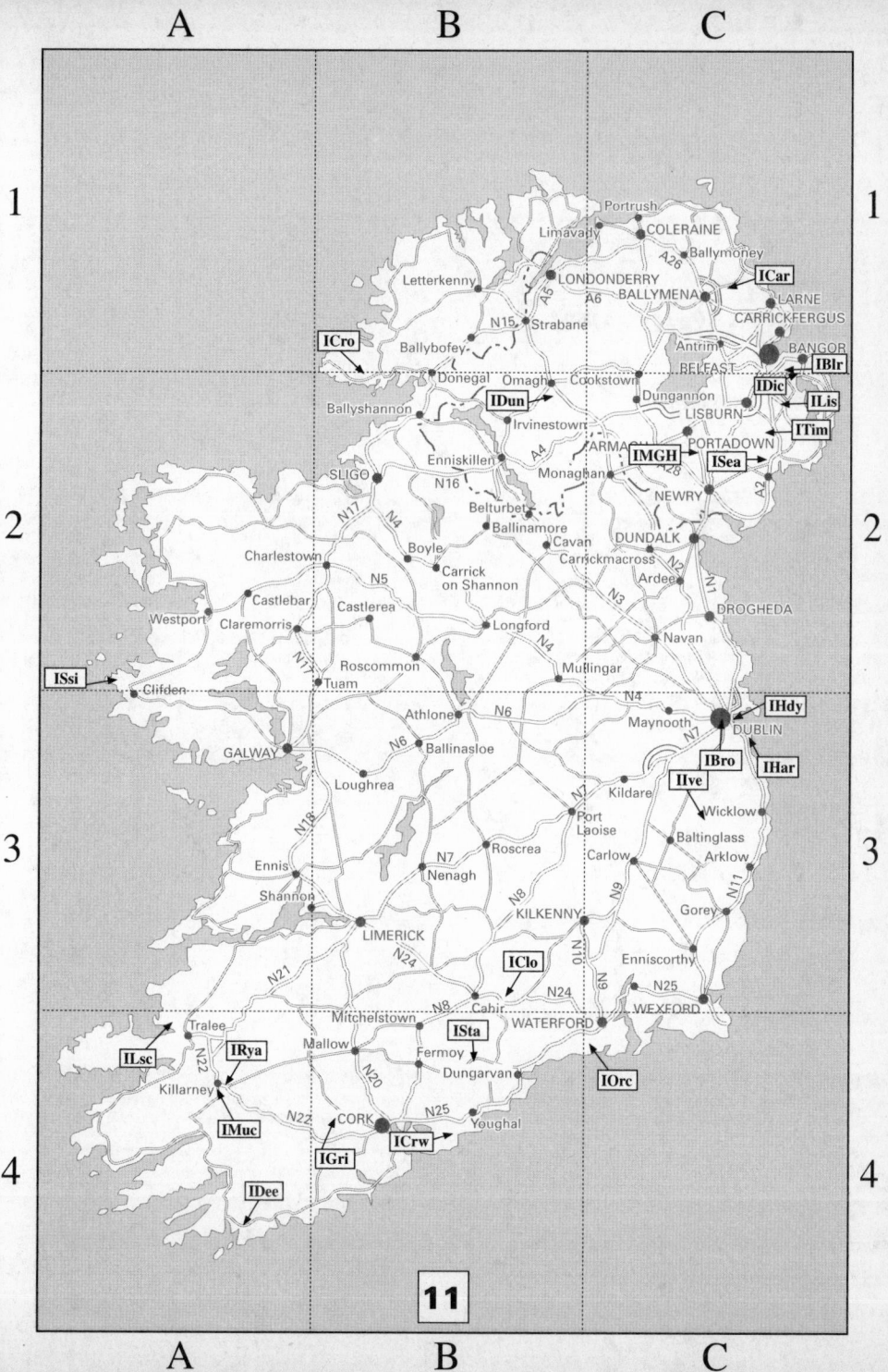

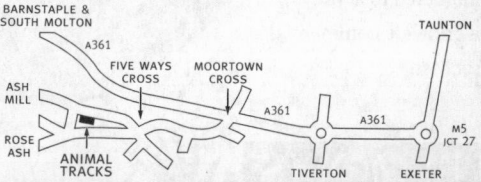

III

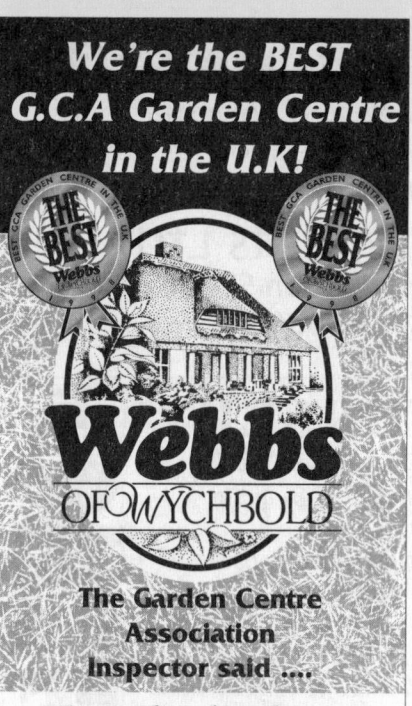
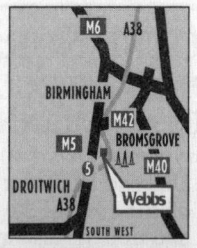

X

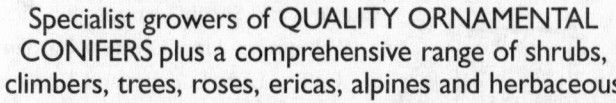
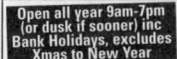

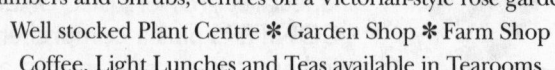

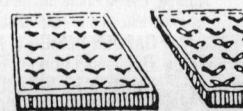

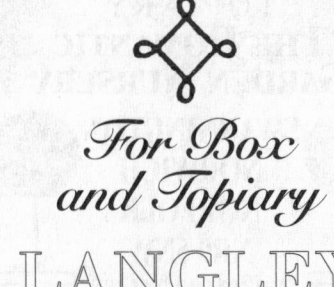

# INDEX OF ADVERTISERS

## A

| | |
|---|---|
| A La Carte Daylilies | XXI |
| Animal Tracks International Animal Rescue | I |
| Applecourt | XVIII |
| Architectural Plants* | XX |

## B

| | |
|---|---|
| Blooms of Bressingham | II |
| Bretby Nurseries | XVIII |
| Bradley Gardens Nursery | XIV |
| Bridgemere Garden World | V |
| Buckingham Nurseries | XXI |

## C

| | |
|---|---|
| Careswood Garden Centre | XVIII |
| Celyn Vale Nurseries | XVII |
| Cheshire Herbs | XII |
| Chiltern Seeds | XIX |
| Christies Nursery | XXII |
| Collectors Corner Plants | XXIII |
| Coombland Garden | XXIII |
| Cottage Garden Nursery | XXI |
| Crug Farm Plants | X |
| Cutting Edge Nursery | XXIII |

## D

| | |
|---|---|
| Deacons Nurseries | III |
| Devon Violet Nurseries | XXIII |
| Dibleys Nurseries | XI |
| Duchy of Cornwall Nursery | V |

## E, F

| | |
|---|---|
| East Northdown Nursery | XX |
| Endsleigh Gardens | XXII |
| Famecheck Special Plants | XIX |
| Family Trees | XIX |
| Farmyard Nurseries | VI |
| Feebers Hardy | XXI |
| Ford Nursery | XIV |

## G

| | |
|---|---|
| Gillies, R. & T. | XVI |
| Global Orange Groves UK | XVIII |
| Goscote Nurseries Ltd | VIII |
| Grange Farm Nursery | IX |
| Great Western Gladiolus | XIX |
| Grove House Nursery | VIII |
| Growing Carpets | XXIII |

## H

| | |
|---|---|
| Hellyers Garden Plants | XII |
| Highfield Hollies | XX |
| Hiller Garden and Plant Centre | XII |
| Hillside Cottage Plants | XXIII |
| Hoecroft Plants | XXII |
| Holden Clough Nurseries | XIII |
| Hoo House Nursery | XXIII |
| Hostas, Anne and Roger Bowden | IX |
| Hydon Nurseries | XVI |

## I, J

| | |
|---|---|
| Iden Croft Herbs | XXIII |
| J. & D. Marston | XXII |
| J. Bradshaw & Son | XVI |
| J. Tweedie | IV |
| Jelitto | IFC |

## K

| | |
|---|---|
| Keepers Nursery | XXI |
| Kenwith Nursery | XI |

## L

| | |
|---|---|
| Langley Boxwood Nursery | XVII |
| Larch Cottage Nurseries | XVII |
| Lime Cross Nursery | XI |
| Lincluden Nursery | X |
| Lockyer, Mr C.S. | XIX |
| Longframlington Gardens | XI |
| Longstock Park Nursery | XII |
| Lower Icknield Farm Nursery | VI |

## M

| | |
|---|---|
| Mac Foliage Plantation | XIV |
| Mill Hill Plants | XXI |
| Millais Nurseries | XV |
| Moor Monkton Nurseries | XIV |
| Mozart House Nursery Garden | XX |

## N, O

| | |
|---|---|
| Nettletons Nursery | XX |
| Norwells Nurseries | XIX |
| Oak Cottage Herb Garden | XXIII |
| One House Nursery | X |

## P

| | |
|---|---|
| P. & S. Rotchell | VII |
| PW Plants | VII |
| Pantiles Plant and Garden Centre | VIII |
| Perry Plants | XXIII |
| Plant World | XVI |
| Plants of Distinction | IBC |
| Plants of Special Interest Nursery | XVIII |
| Poets Cottage Shrub Nursery | XX |
| Primrose Cottage Nursery & Garden Centre | XIII |

## R

| | |
|---|---|
| Raveningham Farms Ltd | XXII |
| RHS Enterprises Ltd | IV |
| Romantic Garden Nursery | XVIII |
| Rumsey Gardens | XIII |

## S

| | |
|---|---|
| Seale Nurseries | XIX |
| Sheen Developments | X |
| Silver Dale Nurseries | XXI |
| Southview Nurseries | XXIII |
| Spinneywell Nursery | XXII |
| Stone Cross Nurseries Garden Centre | XIII |

## T

| | |
|---|---|
| T.H. Barker & Son | XXIII |
| Taylors Nurseries | XXII |
| The Herb Nursery | XXIII |
| The Iris Garden | XIX |
| The Old Manor Nursery | XX |
| The Paradise Garden | XV |
| The Village Nurseries | XV |
| The Walled Gardenn | XX |
| Triscombe Nurseries | XV |

## U, V

| | |
|---|---|
| Unusual Plants | XXIII |
| Viv Marsh Postal Plants | XVII |

## W

| | |
|---|---|
| Waterwheel Nursery | XXIII |
| Webbs of Wychbold | IX |
| White Cottage Alpines | XXIII |
| Woodbury Nurseries | XIV |
| Wye Valley Herbs | XXI |

# THE HARDY PLANT SOCIETY

The Hardy Plant Society was formed to foster interest in hardy herbaceous plants on the widest possible scale. It aims to give its members information about the wealth of both well known and little known hardy plants, how to grow them to the best advantage and where they may be obtained. It also aims to ensure that all worthy hardy plants remain in cultivation and have the widest possible distribution.

## REGIONAL AND LOCAL GROUPS

Members may join any of the growing number of local groups organising many events in their own area including plant sales, garden visits, demonstrations and lectures. Most groups issue their own newsletter. The Groups form a basis for friendly exchange of information and plants and are an invaluable way of meeting other keen plantsmen locally. There is also a Correspondents Group for those not able to get out and about.

## GENUS AND SPECIAL GROUPS

Members may also join any of the specialised groups within the Society which will put them in touch with other members having similar interests. At present there are five such groups covering 'Variegated plants', 'Hardy Geraniums', 'Paeony', 'Pulmonarias' and 'Half Hardy Plants'.

## PUBLICATIONS AND SLIDE LIBRARY

The Society's Journal, *The Hardy Plant*, is currently issued twice a year containing major illustrated articles on a wide variety of plants and gardens. Regular newsletters keep members informed of current events. A central collection of slides is available for loan to members wishing to compile illustrated lectures.

## SEED DISTRIBUTION

Each year members are encouraged to collect seed from plants in their gardens for the Seed Distribution which produces a printed list of all available seed, much of which comes from overseas. This currently lists over 2,500 varieties of seed, the majority of which is not available from commercial sources and, for a nominal sum, members may select a number of packets from this.

## PLANT SALES AND SHOWS

At organised meetings, both national and local, members bring interesting and unusual plants which are sold to aid the Society's funds. The Society puts on displays at the Royal Horticultural Society and other shows around the country and members can be involved by helping with the stands or by supplying plants to be shown.

## CONSERVATION

The Society is most concerned about the conservation of garden plants. Countless fine plants have totally disappeared from cultivation and remain but a memory. In close cooperation with the National Council for the Conservation of Plants and Gardens, the Society is making efforts to ensure that all worthy plants are kept in cultivation.

For further information please contact:
**The Administrator**
**Mrs Pam Adams**
**Little Orchard**
**Great Comberton**
**Pershore**
**Worcs WR10 3DP**

Tel No 01386 710317     Fax No 01386 710117

*Please see overleaf for the application form*

# THE HARDY PLANT SOCIETY

## MEMBERSHIP APPLICATION FOR 1999

The Annual Subscriptions are as follows:

Single Membership **£10.00**
Joint Membership (any two members living at the same address) **£12.00**

- Subscriptions are renewable annually on **1 January**.
- Subscriptions of members joining after 1 October are valid until the end of the following year.
- Overseas members are requested to remit by International Money Order in Sterling or by Credit Card (Visa/Master Card/Eurocard).

**I/We wish to apply for membership for 1999**

NAME/S ........................................................................................................

ADDRESS ....................................................................................................

..................................................................................................................

.......................................................... POST CODE ....................................

TELEPHONE NUMBER .................................................................

and would like to apply for the following type of membership

| | | |
|---|---|---|
| SINGLE | £10.00 | ............... |
| JOINT (2 members at one address) | £12.00 | ............... |
| Airmail postage (outside Europe) | £6.00 | ............... |
| | TOTAL | |

I enclose a cheque in Pounds Sterling payable to **THE HARDY PLANT SOCIETY**
(Please **DO NOT** send cheques in Foreign Currency)

**OR**
Please debit my Visa / Master Card / Eurocard

CARD NUMBER ☐☐☐☐ ☐☐☐☐ ☐☐☐☐ ☐☐☐☐

EXPIRY DATE ☐☐☐☐

Your name as on Card ........................................................................

Signature ........................................................ Date ...............................

*Please print your name and address clearly, tear out the page and send it to*
*The Administrator at the address overleaf*

# Get the best out of your gardening year with the help of the Royal Horticultural Society

**M**embership of the RHS, Britain's premier gardening organisation, brings many exclusive benefits to help you get the best out of your gardening year. This includes a free subscription to *The Garden* magazine (worth £33 alone), which is delivered to your door every month. Practical advice and tips, features on various plants and gardens, design ideas and RHS news and events combine to make this an entertaining and informative read for all garden lovers. With beautiful colour photographs and articles by award-winning writers, it's easy to see why *The Garden* has long been recognised as Britain's leading monthly gardening magazine.

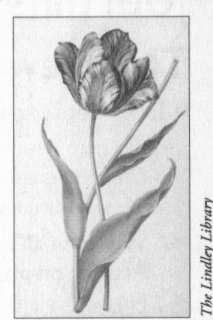

*The Lindley Library*

## Outstanding benefits for gardeners

Join today and you will also enjoy:

- FREE entry for you **and** a guest to RHS Gardens Wisley, Rosemoor and Hyde Hall
- FREE entry to a further 23 beautiful gardens nationwide
- Privileged tickets and Members' only days to the Chelsea and Hampton Court Palace Flower Shows
- FREE entry to regular RHS Westminster Flower Shows
- Privileged admission to the new RHS Flower Show at Tatton Park in Cheshire, BBC Gardeners' World Live, The Spring Gardening Show in Malvern, Scotland's National Gardening Show and the Malvern Autumn Show
- Discounted tickets to RHS talks, workshops and demonstrations at nurseries, gardens and horticultural colleges across Britain
- FREE gardening advice from RHS experts

## Save £5 on RHS Membership

Membership normally costs £34 for 12 months, which includes a one-off joining fee of £7, but join today and you can take advantage of a special introductory saving of £5 – pay just £29.

## Join now by calling the credit card hotline ☎ 0171 821 3000

Please quote code 1380. Lines open 9am to 5.30pm, Monday to Friday

- - - - - - - - - - - - - - - - - - - - - - - - - - - - - - - - - - - - - - - - - - - - - - - - - - - ✂

# If you have a passion for plants then these RHS journals are for you

THE ROYAL
HORTICULTURAL
SOCIETY

## The New Plantsman

A fresh approach to plantsmanship

Specially commissioned photography and illustrations combined with definitive editorial make this publication a must for gardeners, horticulturists and botanists everywhere.

- ❧ Studies of all aspects of garden plants old and new
- ❧ Articles on plant hunting and garden history
- ❧ News of plant introductions
- ❧ Developments in nomenclature and plant registration

An annual subscription to this quarterly publication is just £25. Each volume begins in March.*

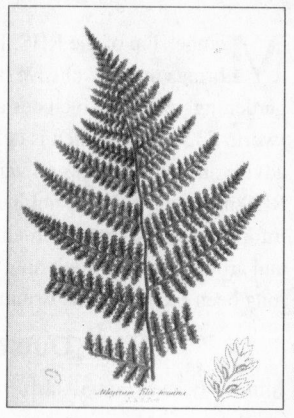

*The Lindley Library*

## The Orchid Review

The world's oldest and most eminent orchid journal

Whether you are a beginner with a few window-sill orchids, a botanist or a professional grower, this journal is essential reading.

- ❧ Basic cultural advice
- ❧ Articles on rare and unusual orchids
- ❧ Latest hybrid news and RHS awards
- ❧ Impressive photography and illustrations

You will receive six issues a year for just £24.95. Each volume begins in January.*

For more information about these journals, visit the RHS website on www.rhs.org.uk

*If you subscribe to these journals during the year you will be sent back issues of the current volume.

---

Please enrol me as a subscriber to ❑ The New Plantsman at £25    ❑ The Orchid Review at £24.95

| Title | Surname | | Initials |
|---|---|---|---|
| Address | | | |
| | | | |
| | | | |
| Postcode | | Daytime Tel. No. | |

❑ I enclose a cheque made payable to The Royal Horticultural Society

❑ Please debit my RHS Mastercard / Mastercard / Visa / Diners / AmEx

Card No. ☐☐☐☐ ☐☐☐☐ ☐☐☐☐ ☐☐☐☐

Expiry ____ / ____    Signature _____

Code PF99

Please return this form to The RHS Subscription Service, P.O.Box 38, Ashford, Kent, TN25 6PR
☎ 01303 813803   Fax: 01303 813737

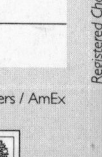

THE ROYAL
HORTICULTURAL
SOCIETY

Registered Charity No 222879